volume 4

# reviews in NUMBER THEORY

as printed in
MATHEMATICAL REVIEWS
1940 through 1972
volumes 1—44 inclusive

edited by

**WILLIAM J. LeVEQUE**

AMERICAN MATHEMATICAL SOCIETY · PROVIDENCE · RHODE ISLAND · 1974

**Reviews reprinted from**
**MATHEMATICAL REVIEWS**
**volumes 1—44 published during 1940—1972**

*AMS (MOS) classification numbers* (1970).
Primary 10 – XX, 12 – XX; Secondary 00 – XX, 01 – XX.

**Library of Congress Cataloging in Publication Data** CIP

LeVeque, William Judson, comp.
Reviews in number theory.

1. Numbers, Theory of–Abstracts. I. Mathematical reviews. II. Title.
QA241.L577 512'.7'08 74-11335
ISBN 0-8218-0206-2 (v. 4)

# SERIES CONTENTS

## volume 1



## volume 2



## volume 3



## volume 4



## volume 5



## volume 6

# CONTENTS

# L. EXPONENTIAL AND CHARACTER SUMS

Papers for which estimates for these sums are (obtained and) applied to other number-theoretic questions are listed in the field of application. Such a paper is cross-referenced here only if the review indicates that a significant new estimate of reasonably general interest has been obtained.

For Ramanujan sums, see **A36**.

See also Sections D80, K05, K10, K15, K20, K25, K30, K35, K40, R50, T25.

## L02 BOOKS AND SURVEYS

See also reviews L05-14, L15-29, P02-4.

**L02-1** **(10, 17e)**

**Segal, B. I. Trigonometric sums and some of their applications in the theory of numbers.** Uspehi Matem. Nauk (N.S.) **1**, no. 3–4(13–14), 147–193 (1946). (Russian)

This is a connected account of the estimation of trigonometric sums with applications to the distribution of primitive roots, indices and residues of powers, and to Waring's problem. The author's aim is to provide an introduction to the analytical theory of numbers for a wide circle of readers, rather than to carry the specialist to the frontiers of knowledge. He accordingly regards Vinogradov's methods as lying beyond his scope. He follows Hardy and Littlewood in basing his treatment of Waring's problem on Weyl's estimations, but he also includes an account of the complement supplied by Hua in 1938, so that his ultimate objective is the inequality $G(k)\leqq 2^k+1$, with the corresponding asymptotic formula. The exposition is full and clear, and the reader with a moderate knowledge of analysis and arithmetic is led by easy stages from the most elementary applications to the intricacies of Waring's problem.

*A. E. Ingham* (Cambridge, England).

**L02-2** **(10, 599a)**

**Vinogradov, I. M. The method of trigonometrical sums in the theory of numbers.** Trav. Inst. Math. Stekloff **23**, 109 pp. (1947). (Russian)

The present book is largely a revision of the author's earlier work [same Trav. **10** (1937)]. However, a number of sharper results are obtained in the present work. Chapter I [16 pp.] deals with general lemmas which are required for the development of the succeeding chapters. In chapter II [8 pp.], the singular series for Waring's problem is studied. In chapter III [4 pp.], there is obtained an asymptotic formula for an integral connected with Waring's problem. In chapter IV [5 pp.], there is obtained an estimate which implies the slightly weaker $G(n)<n(3\log n+11)$ for $n>2$. The best previous result, for large $n$, was $G(n)<n(4\log n+8\log\log n+12)$ [Vinogradov, Trav. Inst. Math. Tbilissi [Trudy Tbiliss. Mat. Inst.] **5**, 153–180 (1938)]. Since $G(n)>n$, there is still a gap in our knowledge of the behavior of $G(n)$. Chapter V [6 pp.] deals with approximation by fractional parts of polynomials. The result is the same as that given in 1937.

In chapter VI [15 pp.], an advance is made in the estimation of the Weyl sum $S=\sum_{x=1}^{P}\exp\{2\pi imF(x)\}$, where $m$ and $P$ are integers, $F(x)=a_{n+1}x^{n+1}+\cdots+a_1x$, and $a_{n+1},\cdots,a_1$ are real. As is well known, sums of this type are basic in many problems of number theory; e.g., estimations of $S$ are needed for estimating $\zeta(\sigma+it)$ in the neighborhood of $\sigma=1$, for estimating the error term in $\pi(x)\sim\mathrm{li}\,x$, determining the range of convergence of the singular series for Waring's problem, etc. This result, simplified in accordance with a footnote of the paper reviewed below, is: let $n>10$, let $s$ be one of the integers $2,\cdots,n+1$, $|a_s-a/q|\leqq 1/q^2$, $(a,q)=1$, let $\tau$ be a constant such that $0<\tau\leqq 1$ and $0<c_1P^\tau\leqq q\leqq c_2P^{s-\tau}$; then there exists an absolute constant $c(n)$ such that $|S|<c(n)P^{1-\rho t}m^{2\rho/\tau}$, where $t=1+(30n)^{-1}$ and $\rho^{-1}=(3n^2/\tau)\log\{12n(n+1)/\tau\}$. The previous result differed from his, in its most essential part, by having $n^3$ in place of $n^2$ in the expression for $\rho^{-1}$. Consequently the gain is quite substantial. Two other results, estimating sums of the form $\sum_{x=N+1}^{N+P}\phi(x)\exp\{2\pi if(x)\}$ for monotonic $\phi(x)$ and real-valued $f(x)$ whose $(n+1)$th derivative satisfies certain order conditions, are also given.

In chapter VII [4 pp.], the Hardy-Littlewood asymptotic formula for the number of representations of $N$ as the sum of $r$ positive $n$th powers (Waring's problem) is shown to be valid for $r\geqq[10n^2\log n]$ if $n>11$. This, too, improves Vinogradov's earlier result by a factor of about $n$. Chapter VIII [3 pp.] deals with the distribution of the fractional parts of polynomials where a similar improvement is obtained. In chapter IX [18 pp.] are given estimates of trigonometric (i.e., exponential) sums in which the summation variable runs over the prime numbers in a certain interval. The Goldbach-Vinogradov theorem, that every sufficiently large odd number is the sum of three primes, is proved in chapter X [9 pp.]. The proof takes for granted the work of Page and Siegel on the error term in the asymptotic formula $\pi(N,q,l)\sim(\mathrm{li}\,N)/\varphi(q)$. In chapter XI [2 pp.] a result is given on the distribution of the fractional parts of the function $\alpha p$, where $p$ is a prime.

In addition to the errata listed in the book, nineteen others were noted. The least obvious of these are: on page 48, third line, $2n+1$ should be replaced by $4n$; on page 73, five lines from the bottom, $2\pi if(x)$ should be replaced by $2\pi i\alpha f(x)$; page 102, line 2, $\sqrt{2}$ should be $\sqrt{r}$; the correct title for reference no. 17 in the bibliography is "On Waring's problem."

This book is a worthwhile addition to the too few books on analytic number theory and to the practically nonexistent expositions of the work on exponential sums of the Russian school. Together with the recent book of Hua in the same series [see the preceding review], there is now made available a connected treatment of a substantial part of the techniques and results which have been obtained since Landau's Vorlesungen and Fortschritte.

*L. Schoenfeld* (Urbana, Ill.).

Referred to in D52-140, E24-41, J04-26, K30-12, K30-13, L02-3, L15-14, L20-11, L20-12, L20-13, L20-15, L20-19, L20-20, L20-23, L25-5, N04-17, N12-9, P08-11, P08-16, P08-20, P08-33, P08-45, P12-14, P40-27, P44-16, R44-5, R46-22, Z25-9.

**L02-3** **(15, 941b)**

**Vinogradov, I. M. The method of trigonometrical sums in the theory of numbers.** Translated, revised and annotated by K. F. Roth and Anne Davenport. Interscience Publishers, London and New York. x+180 pp. $5.00.

A translation, with expansions and modifications of the text as well as annotations, of the author's monograph in Trudy Mat. Inst. Steklov. **23** (1947) [these Rev. **10**, 599].

Citations: MR 10, 599a = L02-2.

Referred to in J04-26, K30-13, K40-72, L20-15, L20-19, L20-23, N12-9, P08-45, P12-14, P48-19, R44-5, R46-22.

**L02-4** **(18, 286d)**

**Teghem, J. Sur des applications de certaines estimations de sommes trigonométriques.** Colloque sur la Théorie des Nombres, Bruxelles, 1955, pp. 183–204. Georges Thone, Liège; Masson and Cie, Paris, 1956.

Dans cet exposé l'auteur étudie les améliorations qui peuvent résulter de l'application des résultats d'estimation de $|\sum_{x=P+1}^{P+X} \exp\{2\pi i f(x)\}|$ obtenus dans les vingt dernières années par Vinogradow, van der Corput, Hua, Titchmarch, Tchudakoff et autres. Dans les sommes trigonométriques $\sum_{x=P+1}^{P+X} \exp\{2\pi i f(x)\}$, $f(x)$ est un polynôme à coefficients réels de degré $k$, ou une function réelle proche dans un certain sens, d'un polynôme de degré $k$. Les limitations supérieures non triviales de $|\sum_{x=P+1}^{P+X}|$ s'obtiennent sous la forme $c(k)X^{1-\Lambda(k)}$. Les auteurs susdits, tout comme Vinogradow lui-même dans ses premiers recherches, ont porté tous leurs efforts sur l'accroissement, dans toute la mesure possible, du nombre $\Lambda(k)$, sans se préoccuper de $c(k)$. Or, si l'ordre de grandeur de $c(k)$ ne présente effectivement aucun intérêt dans les problèmes de la théorie des nombres, où $k$ est fixe lorsque $X\to\infty$ (p.e. le problème de Waring; systèmes d'un nombre fixé d'inéquations diophantiennes), il joue au contraire un très grand rôle dans les problèmes où $k$ tend vers l'infini avec $X$ (p.e. dans les reccherches sur l'estimation de l'ordre de grandeur de $\zeta(s)$ dans le voisinage de $\sigma=1$). Il faut même alors que l'ordre de grandeur de $c(k)$ ne compromette pas l'amélioration apportée à $\Lambda(k)$. Les estimations récentes les plus exactes de $c(k)$ sont de la forme $c(k)=c\exp\{ak\log^2 k\}$ ($c$=constante positive, $a=32$ (Titchmarch), $a=18$ (Flett)). L'auteur exprime l'opinion que l'abaissement de l'ordre de grandeur de $c(k)$ constitue un problème difficile. Par rapport à la limitation supérieure de $\pi(x)-\operatorname{li} x$ l'auteur montre que le résultat de Tchudakoff

$$\pi(x)-\operatorname{li} x=O(x\exp\{-A(\log x)^{5/9-\varepsilon}\})$$

[C. R. (Dokl.) Acad. Sci. URSS (N.S.) **21** (1938), 421–422] n'est nullement amélioré en applicant les derniers résultats de Vinogradow. Il remarque enfin qu'un abaissement de l'ordre de grandeur de $c(k)$ à $k^c$ donnerait lieu au résultat amélioré

$$\pi(x)-\operatorname{li} x=O(x\exp\{-A(\log x)^{3/5-\varepsilon}\}).$$

Vinogradow a annoncé à deux reprises en 1942 et 1945 la démonstration par Tchudakoff d'un tel résultat. Mais aucune démonstration n'a paru, à la connaissance de l'auteur. Le résultat annoncé par Vinogradow est encore très éloigné du résultat $\pi(x)-\operatorname{li} x=O(\exp\{-A\log x\})$, valables si l'hypothèse de Riemann est vraie. Il est plus près du résultat de de la Vallée Poussin $\pi(x)-\operatorname{li} x=O(x\exp\{-A(\log x)^{\frac{1}{2}}\})$ [Mém. Couronnés Autres Mém. Acad. Roy. Sci. Lett. Beaux-Arts Belg. Coll. in 8° **59** (1899), no. 1].

*S. C. van Veen.*

**L02-5** **(24# A94)**

**Hua, Loo-Keng**

**Die Abschätzung von Exponentialsummen und ihre Anwendung in der Zahlentheorie.**

Enzyklopädie der mathematischen Wissenschaften: Mit Einschluss ihrer Anwendungen, Bd. I, 2, Heft 13, Teil I.

*B. G. Teubner Verlagsgesellschaft, Leipzig,* 1959. 123 *pp.* *DM* 13.00.

Das vorliegende Heft gibt nicht nur im Rahmen der Enzyklopädie einen bedeutsamen Beitrag, sondern stellt auch für sich allein genommen eine wesentliche Bereicherung der mathematischen Literatur dar, und dies um so mehr, als hier der Stoff von einem ausgesprochenen Kenner dargelegt wird, der selbst mit zahlreichen eigenen Arbeiten am Aufbau dieses mathematischen Zweiges beteiligt ist. — Die Abschätzung von Exponentialsummen (trigonometrischen Summen) stellt heute einen integrierenden Bestandteil bei der Untersuchung des Goldbachschen und Waringschen Problems dar. — Inhaltsübersicht: A. Elementare Methoden. Behandelt werden u.a. der Linniksche Beweis des Waringproblems, die Siebmethode und der Schnirelmannsche Beitrag zum Goldbachproblem, der elementare Beweis des Primzahlsatzes (A. Selberg). — B. Abschätzung von Exponentialsummen. Beginnend mit den Methoden von Weyl und van der Corput nimmt der Vinogradovsche Mittelwertsatz eine zentrale Stellung ein. Es werden Folgerungen aus diesem Satz gezogen; die Diskussion der Exponentialsummen wird weitergeführt. — C. Primzahlverteilung. Hier werden die analytischen Methoden der Primzahltheorie besprochen: über zahlreiche Einzelergebnisse wird berichtet. — D. Das Waringsche Problem. Es wird die analytische Behandlungsweise dargelegt; die Abschätzungen der beiden Basisordnungen $g(k)$ und $G(k)$ werden besprochen sowie einige Verallgemeinerungen des Waringproblems angegeben. Schließlich wird noch der Tarry-Escottsche Fragenkreis angeschnitten. — E. Das Goldbachsche Problem. In diesem Kapitel werden der Vinogradovsche Satz nebst Verallgemeinerungen, das klassische Goldbachproblem bezüglich der geraden Zahlen, das Goldbach-Waring-Problem und eine Übertragung des Tarry-Escott-Problems behandelt. — F. Gleichverteilung und G. Weitere zahlentheoretische Funktionen bilden den Inhalt der letzten beiden Kapitel. Am Schluß findet sich in Tabellenform eine Übersicht über die behandelten Probleme mit Angabe der neuesten Ergebnisse. *H. Ostmann* (Zbl **83**, 36)

Referred to in L02-6, R48-28, R48-31.

**L02-6** **(31# 4768)**

**Hua Lo-gen [Хуа Ло-ген] [Hua Lo-keng]**

**Method of trigonometric sums and its application in number theory [Метод тригонометрических сумм и его применения в теории чисел].**

Translated from the German by A. M. Polosnev.

*Izdat. "Mir", Moscow,* 1964. 188 *pp.* 0.60 *r.*

This is a translation of the original German edition published in 1959 by Teubner, Leipzig [MR **24** #A94].

Citations: MR 24# A94 = L02-5.

**L02-7** **(24# A721)**

**Postnikov, A. G.**

**Über kurze rationale trigonometrische Summen. (Russian. Bulgarian and German summaries)**

*Bŭlgar. Akad. Nauk Izv. Mat. Inst.* **4**, *no.* 1, 81–87 (1959).

This is an expository article on modern methods of estimating trigonometric sums. *H. Halberstam* (London)

**L02-8** **(36# 3737)**

**Walfisz, Arnold [Val'fiš, A. Z.]**

**Weylsche Exponentialsummen in der neueren Zahlentheorie.**

Mathematische Forschungsberichte, XV.

*VEB Deutscher Verlag der Wissenschaften, Berlin*, 1963. 231 *pp.* *MDN* 36.00.

This book contains a very detailed exposition of exponential sum estimates of N. M. Korobov [Uspehi Mat. Nauk **13** (1958), no. 4 (82), 185–192; MR **21** #4939] and I. M. Vinogradov [Izv. Akad. Nauk SSSR Ser. Mat. **22** (1958), 161–164; MR **21** #2624], and of the application of these estimates to obtain sharp results in the analytic theory of numbers. In the first, preliminary, chapter, the author expounds Weyl's method for the estimation of exponential sums, and some lemmas of Hua which are needed for Chapter II. Chapter II contains the main result, proved in two different ways, one due to Korobov and one due to Vinogradov; this is a pair of exponential estimates a trifle stronger than the following: Let $r$, $M$, $N$ be integers with $r\geqq 95$, $N\leqq M$; suppose that $w$, $t$ are real numbers such that $0\leqq w\leqq 1$, $1\leqq t\leqq M^r\leqq t^{21/10}$; write $\theta=(266{,}000r^2)^{-1}$; then there are absolute constants $B_1$, $B_2$ such that $|\sum_M{}^{M+N}\exp[it\log(m+w)]|<B_1M^{1-\theta}$, and $|\sum_M{}^{M+N}\exp[2\pi it/(m+w)]|<B_2M^{1-\theta}$. In the later chapters, these theorems are applied to classical problems. Let $\sigma(n)=\sum_{d|n}d$ be the divisor function; in Chapter III, it is proved that $\sum_{n\leqq x}\sigma(n)=\pi^2x^2/12+O(x\log^{2/3}x)$. Let $\phi(n)$ be Euler's function; in Chapter IV it is proved that $\sum_{n\leqq x}\phi(n)=3\pi^{-2}x^2+O(x\log^{2/3}x(\log\log x)^{4/3})$. In Chapter V are the most interesting applications, to the zeta function and to the distribution of primes; for instance, $\zeta(1+it)=O(\log^{2/3}t)$, and

$$\pi(x)-li(x) = O\{x\exp[-A\log^{3/5}x(\log\log x)^{-1/5}]\};$$

there is a similar result for primes in arithmetic progressions. The author acknowledges help from Richert in several places; in particular, Korobov and Vinogradov had asserted the existence of a zero-free region of the zeta function larger than could apparently be justified by their methods (so they gave an estimate for $\pi(x)-li(x)$ omitting the $(\log\log x)^{-1/5}$); the modification given here is apparently due to Richert. *B. J. Birch* (Manchester)

Citations: MR 21# 2624 = M15-19; MR 21# 4939 = L15-21.

Referred to in L99-11, N02-6, N02-12, N20-71, N24-72, N36-75, N48-32.

# L05 GAUSS AND KLOOSTERMAN SUMS, GENERALIZATIONS

See also Sections R50, T25.

See also reviews A14-8, A14-58, A14-62, D72-19, D80-4, D80-13, D80-16, D80-37, D80-38, D80-43, D80-46, D80-51, E08-17, E12-1, E44-12, E44-13, E76-30, F10-45, F30-30, F30-49, F70-2, F70-3, L10-18, L99-1, M05-1, M05-52, N72-22, P02-22, P44-17, P68-4, P72-1, R16-16, R18-43, T05-3, T20-32, T20-36, T25-5, T25-12, T25-13, T25-16, T25-24, T25-30, T25-32, T25-35, T35-37.

**L05-1** **(2, 40d)**

**Hua, Loo-Keng. Sur une somme exponentielle.** C. R. Acad. Sci. Paris **210**, 520–523 (1940).

Let $f(x)=a_kx^k+\cdots+a_1x+a_0$, $(q, a_1, \cdots, a_k)=1$,

$$S_q=\sum_{x=1}^{q}\exp(2\pi if(x)/q).$$

A neat proof is sketched that $S_q<Cq^{1+\epsilon-1/k}$, where $C=C(k,\epsilon)$. Mordell [Quart. J. Math. **3**, 161–167 (1932)] proved $S_q=O(q^{1-1/k})$ when $q$ is a prime. Hua treated this problem earlier [J. London Math. Soc. **13**, 54–61 (1938)]. This result fills a lacuna in an article by Vinogradow [Rec. Math. [Mat. Sbornik] N.S. **3** (**45**), 453 (1938)] and has applications to the theory of uniform distributions of the fractional part of $\alpha f(x)$, and to the Waring problem for polynomials [cf. the author's paper; these Rev. **2**, 35]. *G. Pall.*

Citations: MR 2, 35f = P04-6.

Referred to in L05-2, P04-6, T25-2.

**L05-2** **(2, 347h)**

**Hua, Loo-keng. On an exponential sum.** J. Chinese Math. Soc. **2**, 301–312 (1940).

Let $f(x)=a_kx^k+\cdots+a_1x$, $(a_1, \cdots, a_k, q)=1$,

$$S_q=\sum_{x=1}^{q}\exp(2\pi if(x)/q).$$

Then $|S_q|<C_{k,\epsilon}q^{1+\epsilon-1/k}$. The proof amplifies slightly and corrects (notably in the case $\operatorname{ind} f(x)=\operatorname{ind} f(px)$) that in C. R. Acad. Sci. Paris **210**, 520–523 (1940) [these Rev. **2**, 40]. However he should on p. 303 make the subdivision $l\leqq$ and $l>2t+1$, and not $t+1$. He proves next

$$\sum_{x=1}^{m}\exp(2\pi if(x)/q)=(m/q)S_q+O(q^{1+\epsilon-1/k}).$$

Also, let $f(x)$ be any integral-valued polynomial, $d$ be the least common denominator of the coefficients of $f$, $\bar q=(q, d)$, $\alpha=(a/q)+\beta$, $q=O(P^{1-\epsilon})$, $|\beta|=O(q^{-1}P^{-k+1-\epsilon})$; then

$$\sum_{x=0}^{P}e^{2\pi i\alpha f(x)}=(1/\bar q)\Big(\sum_{x=1}^{q}e^{2\pi iaf(x)/q}\Big)\int_0^P e^{2\pi if(x)\beta}dx+O(\bar q^{1+\epsilon-1/k}).$$

*G. Pall* (Montreal, Que.).

Citations: MR 2, 40d = L05-1.

Referred to in D52-130, L05-17, N36-5, P02-5, R50-2, T25-2.

**L05-3** **(6, 259f)**

**Whiteman, Albert Leon. A note on Kloosterman sums.** Bull. Amer. Math. Soc. **51**, 373–377 (1945).

This note is concerned with the important exponential sum

$$(1)\qquad A_k(n)=\sum\exp\{2\pi in(h+\bar h)/k\},\quad h\bar h\equiv 1 \pmod k,$$

summed over all integers $h\leqq k$ and prime to $k$. The problem of obtaining a more explicit formula for $A_k(n)$ is not completely solved. The sum is a "multiplicative function" of $k$, so that we may restrict $k$ to the case of a power of a prime, $p^\alpha$. For $\alpha=1$ no essentially simpler formula than (1) is known for $A_k(n)$. For $\alpha>1$, Salié [Math. Z. **34**, 91–109 (1931)] gave formulas for $A_{p^\alpha}(n)$ expressing it as a single term. The present paper gives a new derivation of these results. The proof is direct rather than by induction over $\alpha$. The proof fails for $\alpha=1$. The author's method applies also to certain character sums considered by Salié and the reviewer. *D. H. Lehmer* (Aberdeen Proving Ground, Md.).

Referred to in L05-38, L05-53.

**L05-4** **(7, 244g)**

**Guinand, A. P. Gauss sums and primitive characters.** Quart. J. Math., Oxford Ser. **16**, 59–63 (1945).

By means of an extension of the Poisson summation formula to sums involving primitive characters, due to Mordell [Proc. Cambridge Philos. Soc. **24**, 585–596 (1928)], the author derives formulae which are analogous to the reciprocity formula for Gauss sums. Thus he shows that

$$\sum_{n=1}^{q^k} \chi(n) \exp(n^2\pi ip/qk)$$
$$= e^{\frac{1}{4}\pi i}(q/pk)^{\frac{1}{2}}\tau(\chi)\sum_{n=1}^{p^k} \bar{\chi}(n) \exp(-n^2\pi iq/pk),$$

where $\chi(n)$ is a primitive character modulo $k$, $\chi(-1)=1$, and $\tau(\chi)=\sum_{n=1}^{k}\chi(n)e^{2\pi in/k}$. A similar but more complicated result (with $\chi(n)$ replaced by $n\chi(n)$) holds for a primitive character $\chi(n)$ for which $\chi(-1)=-1$. Some elementary properties of the sums concerned are also given.

*R. A. Rankin* (Cambridge, England).

## L05-5 (7, 414h)

**Estermann, T. On the sign of the Gaussian sum.** J. London Math. Soc. **20**, 66–67 (1945).

This paper gives a simple determination, by means of an elementary estimate, of the sign in the formula for the Gaussian sum $S=\sum_{n=0}^{k-1}e^{2\pi in^2/k}$ ($k$ an odd integer greater than 1).

*H. W. Brinkmann* (Swarthmore, Pa.).

## L05-6 (10, 14e)

**Bambah, R. P., and Chowla, S. On the sign of the Gaussian sum.** Proc. Nat. Inst. Sci. India **13**, 175–176 (1947).

The sign of the Gaussian sum $S=\sum_{n=0}^{n=k-1}e^{2\pi in^2/k}$ ($k$ an odd integer greater than 1) is determined by making use of a result, due to van der Corput, whereby it is possible to estimate the difference between a sum of the form $\sum_a^b e^{2\pi if(n)}$ and the corresponding integral $\int_a^b e^{2\pi if(x)}dx$ [Math. Ann. **84**, 53–79 (1921)]. It is thus possible to make an estimate of $S$ by means of the corresponding integral, which is in turn estimated by the second mean value theorem. As a result the sign of $S$ is readily determined for $k>49$. The idea of this determination of the sign of $S$ is somewhat similar to, but simpler than, the one used by van der Corput himself, in the paper referred to above.

*H. W. Brinkmann.*

## L05-7 (13, 823d)

**Cohen, Eckford. Rings of arithmetic functions.** Duke Math. J. **19**, 115–129 (1952).

Given a field $F$ of characteristic 0 containing the $r$th roots of unity for a positive integer $r$. Then a single-valued function $f(a)$ in $F$ is called $(r, F)$ arithmetic if $f(a)=f(a')$ for $a\equiv a' \pmod r$. It is proved that any $(r, F)$ arithmetic function $f(a)$ can be expressed in the form $\sum_{z=0}^{r-1}a_z\epsilon_z(a)$ with $\epsilon_z(a)=e^{2\pi iza/r}$ and $a_z$ in $F$. Thus the $(r, F)$ arithmetic functions are generalizations of common Gauss sums. Some algebraic properties of the set of $(r, F)$ arithmetic functions are given.

*H. Bergström* (Göteborg).

Referred to in A36-19, D80-15, D80-16, D80-33.

## L05-8 (13, 823e)

**Cohen, Eckford. Sur les fonctions arithmétiques relatives aux corps algébriques.** C. R. Acad. Sci. Paris **234**, 787–788 (1952).

The definitions and theorems in the paper reviewed above are here generalized from rational fields to algebraic fields.

*H. Bergström* (Göteborg).

Referred to in D80-15.

## L05-9 (13, 823f)

**Bochner, S. Remarks on Gaussian sums and Tauberian theorems.** J. Indian Math. Soc. (N.S.) **15** (1951), 97–104 (1952).

The author points out that Kronecker's derivation of the reciprocity formula for certain Gaussian sums from the modular relation

$$\tfrac{1}{2}+\sum_{n=1}^{\infty}e^{-\pi n^2/x}=x^{1/2}\left\{\tfrac{1}{2}+\sum_{n=1}^{\infty}e^{-\pi n^2x}\right\}$$

is fundamentally an Abelian-Tauberian argument. In the present paper this argument is reproduced in a general set-up, although the author remarks that he has no specific instances to offer other than those well known.

*A. L. Whiteman* (Los Angeles, Calif.).

## L05-10 (13, 913g)

**Kesava Menon, P. On Gauss's sums.** J. Indian Math. Soc. (N.S.) **16**, 31–36 (1952).

For integral values of $a$, $x$, $M$ the function $F(a, x, M)$ is defined by the relation

$$F(a, x, M)=\sum_{m \pmod M} \exp\frac{2\pi i}{M}(am^2+xm),$$

where $\sum_{m \pmod M}$ indicates summation over a complete set of residues modulo $M$. Two properties of this function are established. The simpler is that if $N=aA^2+bB^2$ is prime to $M$, then

$$F(a, x, M)F(b, y, M)$$
$$=F(N, Ax+By, M)F(Nab, aAy-bBx, M).$$

*W. H. Gage* (Vancouver, B. C.).

## L05-11 (14, 1126d)

**von Neumann, J., and Goldstine, H. H. A numerical study of a conjecture of Kummer.** Math. Tables and Other Aids to Computation **7**, 133–134 (1953).

Kummer [J. Reine Angew. Math. **32**, 341–359 (1846)] studied the theory of the periods in cyclotomy and was led to consider the counterpart of the Gauss sum in the cubic case, namely

$$(1) \qquad x=1+2\sum_{\nu=1}^{(p-1)/2}\cos(2\pi\nu^3/p)$$

where $p$ is a prime of the form $6n+1$. This sum and the two others which extend over the two kinds of cubic non-residues modulo $p$ are the three roots of the equation

$$(2) \qquad x^3-3px-pA=0,$$

where $4p=A^2+27B^2$, $A\equiv1 \pmod 3$. An unsolved problem is that of deciding in advance for a given $p$ whether the root (1) is the largest, middle or smallest root of (2). Kummer classified the primes $p$ into three classes accordingly and conjectured that the frequencies of these classes are 1/2, 1/3 and 1/6 respectively. His calculations based on the first 45 primes $p=6n+1$ gave densities of .5333, .3111 and .1556.

The present note extends Kummer's calculations to the primes less that 10,000; in all, 611 primes. The results do not bear out Kummer's conjecture. The densities obtained are .4452, .3290 and .2258. These "seem to indicate a trend toward randomness". On the other hand there is room for the conjecture that the ultimate densities are 4/9, 3/9 and 2/9. The calculation was made on the IAS Computer and required about 15 million multiplications.

*D. H. Lehmer* (Los Angeles, Calif.).

Referred to in L05-12, L05-16.

## L05-12 (16, 114c)

**Beyer, Gudrun. Über eine Klasseneinteilung aller kubischen Restcharaktere.** Abh. Math. Sem. Univ. Hamburg **19**, no. 1–2, 115–116 (1954).

In a recent note [Math. Tables and Other Aids to Computation **7**, 133–134 (1953); these Rev. **14**, 1126] von Neumann and Goldstine reported the results of extensive numerical investigation into the so-called Kummer conjecture.

Kummer classified all primes $p=6n+1$ into three classes and conjectured that their densities are 1/2, 1/3 and 1/6 from observations on the first 45 primes. The work of von Neumann and Goldstine extended to the 611 primes $p$ under 10000 and gave densities .4452, .3290, .2258 which do not differ much from 4/9, 3/9 and 2/9. The author points out that the problem may be generalized to the case in which $p$ is no longer a prime by multiplying the appropriate Gauss sums together. By considering 1115 cases, both prime and composite, under 7057 the author comes up with densities .4458, .3318, .2224. Unfortunately the author does not specify which composite cases were considered so that the reader is a little uncertain of the new rules of the game. The author has investigated similarly 619 cases less than 1000 of the biquadratic Gauss sums but he feels that he has insufficient evidence upon which to base a conjecture. Hence no results are given. *D. H. Lehmer* (Berkeley, Calif.).

Citations: MR 14, 1126d = L05-11.

**L05-13** **(15, 289j)**

**Carlitz, L. Applications of some basic identities.** Quart. J. Math., Oxford Ser. (2) **4**, 173–177 (1953).

As is well known, Gauss [Werke, vol. 2, Ges. Wiss. Göttingen, 1876, pp. 11–45] employed a polynomial identity to deduce the formula

$$\sum_{s=0}^{n-1}\epsilon^{s^2}=\prod_{r=1}^{\frac{1}{2}(n-1)}(\epsilon^{2r-1}-\epsilon^{-(2r-1)}),$$

where $n$ is odd and $\epsilon$ denotes a primitive $n$th root of unity. The present author derives similar formulas from known basic identities. A typical result is the formula

$$\prod_{r=1}^{m-1}(1+\alpha^r x)=\sum_{r=0}^{m-1}\frac{(1+\alpha)\cdots(1+\alpha^r)}{(1-\alpha)\cdots(1-\alpha^r)}x^r,$$

where $\alpha$ is a primitive $2m$th root of unity.

*A. L. Whiteman* (Princeton, N. J.).

**L05-14** **(17, 127d)**

**van der Blij, F. Gaussian sums.** Euclides, Groningen **30** (1954/55), 293–298. (Dutch)

**L05-15** **(18, 286a)**

**Carlitz, L. A note on Gauss' sum.** Proc. Amer. Math. Soc. **7** (1956), 910–911.

A simple algebraic evaluation of the Gaussian sum $S=\sum_{r=0}^{p-1}\exp(2\pi i r^2/p)$, for the case of an odd prime $p$, is given. This is accomplished by considering the determinant $D=|\varepsilon^{g^{r-s}}|$, where $\varepsilon=\exp(2\pi i/p)$, $g=$ a primitive root, modulo $p$, and $r, s=0, 1, \cdots, p-2$. The value of this determinant is known. On the other hand $D$ is a circulant and can be written as a product of factors one of which is $S$, another is trivial, and the rest are paired off in such a way that the products of each pair are known. Equating the two results gives the value of $S$.

*H. W. Brinkmann* (Swarthmore, Pa.).

**L05-16** **(19, 123a)**

**Lehmer, Emma. On the location of Gauss sums.** Math. Tables Aids Comput. **10** (1956), 194–202.

The generalized Gauss sum of order $k$,

$$S_k=\sum_{m=0}^{p-1}\exp(2\pi i m^k/p),$$

$p=kf+1$, $p$ prime, satisfies $|S_k|\leqq(k-1)\sqrt{p}$ and its distribution in this interval is subject to conjecture. The various hypotheses are examined in detail for $k=3,4,5,7$ using numerical evidence obtained from the SWAC. The earlier computation of $S_3$ [von Neumann and Goldstine, same journal **7** (1953), 133–134; MR **14**, 1126] is extended to the 1000th prime of the form $6n+1$. For $k=4$ and 5 the results extend to $p<10{,}000$ and for $k=7$, $p<5000$. All the conjectures concerning non-uniform distribution are suspected to be false, and the author looks with favor upon the hypothesis that for odd $k$, $|S_k|$ is equally distributed in the intervals $(0, \sqrt{p})$, $(\sqrt{p}, \sqrt{(kp)})$, and $(\sqrt{(kp)}, (k-1)\sqrt{p})$.

*J. L. Selfridge* (Los Angeles, Calif.).

Citations: MR 14, 1126d = L05-11.

**L05-17** **(20# 22)**

**Hua, Loo-keng. On exponential sums.** Sci. Record (N.S.) **1** (1957), 1–4.

Let $k$ be an integer $\geqq 2$ and let $(h, q)=1$. The exponential sum investigated in this paper is defined by $S_q=\sum_{x=1}^{q}\exp(2\pi i h x^k/q)$. The main theorem proved states that if $\varepsilon>0$ is fixed, then

$$\sum_{x=1}^{m}\exp(2\pi i h x^k/q)=\frac{m}{q}S_q+O(q^{\frac{1}{2}+\varepsilon}),$$

where the constant implied by the $O$ symbol depends only on $k$ and $\varepsilon$. This result improves substantially previous results by the author [J. Chinese Math. Soc. **2** (1940), 301–312; MR **2**, 347] and by I. M. Vinogradov [Selected works, Izdat. Akad. Nauk SSSR, Moscow, 1952; MR **14**, 610; pp. 291–295]. The author's principal tool is A. Weil's celebrated general theorem on exponential sums [Proc. Nat. Acad. Sci. U.S.A. **34** (1948), 204–207; MR **10**, 234], which may be formulated as follows: Let $p$ be a prime and $f(x)=a_kx^k+\cdots+a_1x+a_0$, $p\nmid(a_k, \cdots, a_1)$. Then

$$\left|\sum_{x=1}^{p}\exp(2\pi i f(x)/p)\right|\leqq kp^{\frac{1}{2}}.$$

*A. L. Whiteman* (Los Angeles, Calif.)

Citations: MR 2, 347h = L05-2; MR 10, 234e = T25-5; MR 14, 610i = Z25-9.

Referred to in L15-33, P08-27.

**L05-18** **(22# 6773)**

**Lehmer, D. H.; Lehmer, Emma. On the cubes of Kloosterman sums.** Acta Arith. **6** (1960), 15–22.

Let $p$ be a prime $>3$ and let $\chi(s)$ be the quadratic character of $s$ modulo $p$. The $p$ Kloosterman sums

$$S(\lambda, p)=S(\lambda)=\sum_{h=1}^{p-1}\varepsilon^{h+\lambda\bar{h}}\quad(\lambda=0, 1, \cdots, p-1),$$

where $\varepsilon=\exp(2\pi i/p)$ and $h\bar{h}\equiv 1 \pmod p$ are of two main types according as $\chi(\lambda)=+1$ or $-1$. Put $f(\varepsilon)=S(1)$, $g(\varepsilon)=S(N_0)$, where $\chi(N_0)=-1$, and write

$$\sum_{v=0}^{p-1}\{f(\varepsilon^v)\}^n=\sigma_n,\quad \sum_{v=0}^{p-1}\{g(\varepsilon^v)\}^n=\sigma_n'.$$

The authors deduce the formulas

$$\sigma_3=\begin{cases}p^2\{2\chi(-1)-1\}+2p & \text{if } p=6n-1,\\ p^2+2p\{1+2\chi(-1)A^2\} & \text{if } p=6n+1=A^2+3B^2,\end{cases}$$

$$\sigma_3'=\begin{cases}-p^2\{1+2\chi(-1)\}+2p & \text{if } p=6n-1,\\ p^2+2p\{1-2\chi(-1)A^2\} & \text{if } p=6n+1=A^2+3B^2,\end{cases}$$

from the identity

$$\sum_{x=1}^{p-1}\sum_{y=1}^{p-1}\chi(x+\bar{y}+1)\chi(\bar{x}+y+1)=\begin{cases}2p & \text{if } p=6n-1,\\ 4A^2 & \text{if } p=6n+1=A^2+3B^2.\end{cases}$$

The proof of the identity makes use of an ingenious transformation formula.

*A. L. Whiteman* (Princeton, N.J.)

Referred to in L05-23.

**L05-19** **(23# A2388)**

**Carlitz, L.**

**A note on exponential sums.**

*Acta Sci. Math. Szeged* **21** (1960), 135–143.

Let $p$ be an odd prime and let $\zeta$ denote a primitive $p$th root of 1. Put $B=\sum_{s=1}^{p-1} c_s\zeta^s$, where the coefficients $c_s$ independently take on the values $\pm 1$. Also put $B_r=\sum_{s=1}^{r} c_s\zeta^{k_s}$, where $r\leqq p-1$ and $1\leqq k_1<k_2<\cdots<k_r\leqq p-1$. Rédei [Acta Math. **79** (1947), 273–290; MR **9**, 271] has proved the following results. Theorem A: The sum $B$ satisfies $(1-\zeta)^{(p-1)/2}|B$ if and only if $B=\pm\sum_{s=1}^{p-1}(s|p)\zeta^s$; that is, if and only if $B$ is a Gauss sum. Otherwise $B$ is divisible by at most $(1-\zeta)^{(p-1)/4}$; this will occur if and only if $p=4m+1$ and $B=\pm(\eta_0-\eta_2)\pm(\eta_1-\eta_3)$, where $g$ is a primitive root $(\text{mod } p)$ and $\eta_j=\sum_{s=0}^{m-1}\zeta^{g^{4s+j}}$ $(j=0, 1, 2, 3)$. Theorem B: If $B_r$ satisfies $(1-\zeta)^e|B_r$, then $e\leqq\frac{1}{2}r$. The present author uses algebraic number theory to derive alternative proofs of Rédei's theorems. He also establishes some related results. For example, he proves that the sum $B$ satisfies the congruence $|B|^2\equiv 0 \pmod p$ if and only if $B$ is a Gauss sum.

*A. L. Whiteman* (Los Angeles, Calif.)

Citations: MR 9, 271g = T05-3.

**L05-20** **(23# A2391)**

**Malyšev, A. V.**

**A generalization of Kloosterman sums and their estimates. (Russian. English summary)**

*Vestnik Leningrad. Univ.* **15** (1960), no. 13, 59–75.

The author considers the following generalization of Kloosterman sums:

$$(1)\qquad K_r(u, v; q) = \sum_{x \bmod q}\left(\frac{x}{r}\right)e^{2\pi i(ux+vx')/q},$$

where $q$ is a positive integer; $r$ is an odd positive integer all prime divisors of which divide $q$; $u, v$ are integers; $x$ runs through the reduced set of residues mod $q$; $\left(\frac{x}{r}\right)$ denotes the Legendre symbol; and $x'$ is defined by $xx'\equiv 1 \pmod q$. He shows that estimations of sums (1) can be reduced to those of the ordinary Kloosterman sums (i.e., with $r=1$). Using the (deep) estimate of A. Weil

$$|K_1(1, v; p)| \leqq 2p^{1/2}$$

($p$ an odd prime, $(v, p)=1$), he concludes

$$|K_r(u, v; q)| \leqq \rho(q)2^\nu q^{1/2}\min\{(u, q)^{1/2}, (v, q)^{1/2}\},$$

where $\nu$ is the number of different prime factors of $q$ and

$$\rho(q) = 1 \text{ if } q \text{ is odd}, \quad = 2^{1/2} \text{ otherwise}.$$

{$2^{1/2}$ in formula (4.6) must be replaced by $q^{1/2}$.} More general sums are also considered. *S. Knapowski* (Poznań)

Referred to in F30-45, F30-54, L05-39.

**L05-21** **(23# A3715)**

**Malyšev, A. V.**

**Gauss and Kloosterman sums.**

*Dokl. Akad. Nauk SSSR* **133** (1960), 1017–1020 (*Russian*); *translated as Soviet Math. Dokl.* **1** (1961), 928–932.

The sum

$$S(f, l; q) = \sum_{x_1,\cdots,x_n}\exp[2\pi i(f(x_1, \cdots, x_n)+l(x_1, \cdots, x_n))/q],$$

where $f$ is an integral symmetric quadratic form, $l$ is an integral linear form, and each $x_i$ runs through a complete residue system modulo $q$, is called a nonhomogeneous multiple Gauss sum. Special cases have been studied by H. Weber [J. Reine Angew. Math. **74** (1872), 14–56] and H. D. Kloosterman [Acta Math. **49** (1926), 407–464]. The author introduces further integral parameters $g, b_1, \cdots, b_n$ and states (without proof) a number of properties of the sum $S_{g;b_1,\cdots,b_n}(f, l; q)$ given by

$$\frac{1}{g_n}\sum_{x_1,\cdots,x_n}\exp[2\pi i(f(gx_1+b_1, \cdots, gx_n+b_n) + l(gx_1+b_1, \cdots, gx_n+b_n))/q].$$

These properties can be used to calculate these sums in their most general form. The principal results are too lengthy to state here. *T. M. Apostol* (Pasadena, Calif.)

**L05-22** **(23# A3716)**

**Estermann, T.**

**On Kloosterman's sum.**

*Mathematika* **8** (1961), 83–86.

Let $m, q$ denote positive integers, $p$ a prime, and $r, s, u, v$ integers. If $(r, q)=1$, let $[r, q]$ be the integer $s$ for which $0<s\leqq q$ and $rs\equiv 1 \pmod q$. Then Kloosterman's sum is defined by

$$S(u, v, q) = \sum_{r=1}^{q}\exp\{2\pi i(ur+v[r, q])/q\},$$

where the sum is restricted to values of $r$ that are relatively prime to $q$. It was proved by Weil [Proc. Nat. Acad. Sci. U.S.A. **34** (1948), 204–207; MR **10**, 234] that $|S(u, v, p)|\leqq 2p^{1/2}(p>2, p\nmid uv)$, and by Salié [Math. Z. **34** (1931), 91–109] that $|S(u, v, p^m)|\leqq Cp^{m/2}$ $(p\nmid uv, m>1)$, where $C$ is an absolute constant. Weil's inequality is very deep, but Salié's is elementary. Both results together imply that

$$(*)\qquad S(u, v, q) = O\{q^{1/2+\varepsilon}(u, q)^{1/2}\},$$

for any $\varepsilon>0$. The present author gives a simple proof of Salié's inequality and obtains a slight refinement of (*), namely,

$$|S(u, v, q)| \leqq d(q)q^{1/2}(u, v, q)^{1/2},$$

where $d(q)$ is the number of positive divisors of $q$.

*A. L. Whiteman* (Los Angeles, Calif.)

Citations: MR 10, 234e = T25-5.

**L05-23** **(23# A3717)**

**Mordell, L. J.**

**On Lehmer's congruence associated with cubes of Kloosterman's sums.**

*J. London Math. Soc.* **36** (1961), 335–339.

Let $p$ be a prime greater than 3 and write $\zeta=\exp(2\pi i/p)$. Let $x$ be any integer $\not\equiv 0 \pmod p$, and let $\bar{x}$ be defined by $x\bar{x}\equiv 1 \pmod p$. Then the Kloosterman sum is defined for any integer $\lambda$ by $K(\lambda, \zeta)=\sum_{x=1}^{p-1}\zeta^{x+\lambda\bar{x}}$. Recently D. H. and E. Lehmer [Acta Arith. **6** (1960), 15–22; MR **22** #6773] evaluated the sum $\sum_{r=0}^{p-1}K^3(\lambda, \zeta^r)$. This required the number $N(\lambda)$ of solutions of the congruence

$$f_\lambda(x, y, z) = x+y+z+\lambda(\bar{x}+\bar{y}+\bar{z}) \equiv 0 \pmod p,$$

or, equivalently, the value of the sum

$$S = \sum_{x=1}^{p-1}\sum_{y=1}^{p-1}\chi(x+\bar{y}+1)\chi(\bar{x}+y+1),$$

where $\chi(k)$ is the quadratic character of $k$ modulo $p$. Employing an ingenious transformation formula the Lehmers showed that if (*) $p\equiv -1 \pmod 3$, $S=2p$, and if $p\equiv 1 \pmod 3$, $S=4A^2$, where $p=A^2+3B^2$ and $A, B$ are integers. In the present paper the author gives a very simple symmetrical proof of (*) which dispenses with troublesome details and makes the work more obvious.

*A. L. Whiteman* (Los Angeles, Calif.)

Citations: MR 22# 6773 = L05-18.

**L05-24** **(25# 2024)**

**Mordell, L. J.**

**The sign of the Gaussian sum.**

*Illinois J. Math.* **6** (1962), 177–180.

Another proof of the well-known theorem that if $p$ is an odd prime, then $\sum_{s=0}^{p-1} e^{2\pi i s^2/p} = \sqrt{p}$ for $p \equiv 1 \pmod 4$ and $= i\sqrt{p}$ for $p \equiv 3 \pmod 4$. The proof is not very dissimilar from one given by Hasse [*Vorlesungen über Zahlentheorie*, pp. 449–452, Springer, Berlin, 1950; MR **14**, 534], but a little simpler. In an addendum the author shows algebraically that $\sin(2n\pi/p) > 0$, $n = 1, 2, \cdots, (p-1)/2$, and frees the proof from analysis. *T. Hayashida* (Yokohama)

Citations: MR 14, 534b = Z02-23.

**L05-25** **(25# 2043)**

**Chowla, S.**

**On the signs of certain generalized Bernoulli numbers.**

*Norske Vid. Selsk. Forh. Trondheim* **34** (1961), 102–104.

Let the numbers $c_n$ be defined by the identity

$$\sum_{n=0}^{\infty} \frac{c_n x^n}{n!} = \frac{1}{e^{kx}-1} \sum_{m=1}^{k} X(m) e^{mx},$$

where $X(m)$ is a real primitive character (mod $k$), $k > 1$. It is trivial that if $X(-1) = +1$, then $c_n = 0$ for $n$ even. The author investigates the function $L(s) = \sum_{n=1}^{\infty} X(n)/n^s$ $(s = \sigma + it,\ \sigma > 0)$ and its analytic continuation over the whole $s$-plane. From the functional equation of $L(s)$ for $X(-1) = +1$ he deduces the relation $(-1)\, c_r = L(-r)$ for $r \geqq 0$ and the inequality $(-1)^{(n-1)/2} c_n > 0$ for $n$ odd. The inequality is completely equivalent to the result that $\sum_{n=1}^{k} X(n) \exp(2\pi i n/k) = +k^{1/2}$ when $X(-1) = +1$, i.e., to the positiveness of the Gaussian sum.

*A. L. Whiteman* (Los Angeles, Calif.)

**L05-26** **(25# 2044)**

**Chowla, S.**

**On some formulae resembling the Euler-Maclaurin sum formula.**

*Norske Vid. Selsk. Forh. Trondheim* **34** (1961), 107–109.

This paper is related to the paper reviewed above [#2043] and the same notation is used. Let $f(x)$ be a positive decreasing function of $x$, having derivatives of all orders, and tending to 0 as $x \to \infty$. The author states that the formula

$$\sum_{n=1}^{\infty} X(n) f(x+n) = \sum_{m=0}^{\infty} \frac{f^{(m)}(x) L(-m)}{m!}$$

is easily proved heuristically. He confirms the formula in the cases $k = 4$ and $f(x) = 1/x$.

*A. L. Whiteman* (Los Angeles, Calif.)

**L05-27** **(26# 2403)**

**Davenport, H.; Lewis, D. J.**

**Exponential sums in many variables.**

*Amer. J. Math.* **84** (1962), 649–665.

This paper is concerned with sums of the type

$$S(F) = \sum_{x_1} \cdots \sum_{x_n} \exp(2\pi i F(x_1, \cdots, x_n)/p),$$

where $p$ is a prime, $F(x_1, \cdots, x_n)$ is a polynomial with coefficients in a finite field $[p]$ of $p$ elements, and each variable of the summation runs through a complete set of residues modulo $p$. The particular case when $F$ is a cubic polynomial, $F = C + Q + L$, where $C$ is a cubic form, $Q$ a quadratic form, and $L$ a linear form in $x_1, \cdots, x_n$ is principally studied. The main result is expressed in terms of an invariant $h = h(C)$ defined to be the least number for which $C(\mathbf{x})$ is representable identically as $L_1 Q_1 + \cdots + L_h Q_h$, where $L_1, \cdots$ and $Q_1, \cdots$ are linear and quadratic forms, respectively, with coefficients in $[p]$. Theorem 1: For a cubic polynomial $F(\mathbf{x})$, expressed as above, we have $|S(F)| \ll p^{n-h/4}$, where $h = h(C)$. The proof is based on a recent method of Davenport ["Cubic forms in 16 variables", submitted to Proc. Roy. Soc. Ser. A] adapted for the present purpose. For $n = 2, 3$, Theorem 1 is supplemented by the following more precise results. Theorem 2: Suppose $F$ is not degenerate, that is, $F$ is not expressible under any non-singular linear transformation of $x_1, \cdots, x_n$ with coefficients in $[p]$ as a polynomial in fewer than $n$ variables. Then for $n = 2$ we have $|S(F)| \ll p^{5/4}$, and for $n = 3$ we have $|S(F)| \ll p^2$. Two immediate applications of Theorem 1 are the following. Theorem 3: Let $F = C + Q + L + c$ (where $c$ is a constant) be a cubic polynomial over $[p]$. Then the number of solutions of $F = 0$ in $[p]$ is $p^{n-1} + O(p^{n-h/4})$, where $h = h(C)$. Theorem 4: Let $\chi$ be any non-principal character (mod $p$). Then, with the notation of Theorem 3,

$$\sum_{x_1, \cdots, x_n} \chi(F(x_1, \cdots, x_n)) = O(p^{n-h/4+1/2}).$$

If $C$ is degenerate but $F$ is not the following supplement of Theorem 1 holds. Theorem 5: Let $F(x_1, \cdots, x_n)$ be a cubic polynomial over $[p]$, which is non-degenerate, and suppose that $C(x_1, \cdots, x_n)$ is equivalent to a form in $n_1 < n$ variables. Then $|S(F)| \ll p^{n-(n-n_1)/2-h/4}$, where $h = h(C)$. *A. L. Whiteman* (Los Angeles, Calif.)

Referred to in D72-37, T25-24.

**L05-28** **(26# 2404)**

**Anderson, D. R.; Stiffler, J. J.**

**Lower bounds for the maximum moduli of certain classes of trigonometric sums.**

*Duke Math. J.* **30** (1963), 171–176.

Put

$$S(k_1, \cdots, k_n; p) = \sum_{u=0}^{p-1} \exp\left[\frac{2\pi i}{p}(k_1 u + \cdots + k_n u^n)\right],$$

where the $k_j$ and $n$ are arbitrary positive integers and $p$ is a prime. Carlitz and Uchiyama [same J. **24** (1957), 37–41; MR **18**, 563] proved that

$$|S(k_1, \cdots, k_n; p)| < (n-1)p^{1/2}.$$

The present paper establishes a lower bound for the maximum absolute value of the $S(k_1, \cdots, k_n; p)$. It is proved that if $1 \leqq n < p-1$, then

$$\max |S(k_1, \cdots, k_n; p)| > \left[(n!)^2 \binom{p}{n} - p^n\right]^{1/2n},$$

where the maximum is taken over all $(k_1, \cdots, k_n) \neq (0, \cdots, 0)$. The proof is elementary and makes use of an estimate for the number of solutions of the system of congruences

$$\sum_{r=1}^{n} x_r^s \equiv \sum_{r=1}^{n} y_r^s \pmod p \qquad (s = 1, \cdots, n).$$

*L. Carlitz* (Durham, N.C.)

Citations: MR 18, 563c = T25-12.

**L05-29** **(26# 2405)**

**Mordell, L. J.**

**On a cyclotomic resolvent.**

*Arch. Math.* **13** (1962), 486–487.

Let $p$ be an odd prime and $\chi(n)$ a non-principal character (mod $p$). If $\zeta = e^{2\pi i/p}$, it is familiar that

$$\sum_{n=1}^{p-1} \chi(n)\zeta^n = p^{1/2}\varepsilon(\chi), \qquad |\varepsilon(\chi)| = 1.$$

The following result (conjectured by S. Chowla) is proved in the present paper: $\varepsilon(\chi)$ is a root of unity if and only if $\chi(n) = (n/p)$, the Legendre symbol. The proof makes use of some known properties of the field $K(\zeta, \omega)$, where $K$ is the

rational field and $\omega$ is some $(p-1)$th root of unity, $\omega \neq 1$.
*L. Carlitz* (Durham, N.C.)

## L05-30 (26# 4968)

**Muskat, Joseph**

**On certain prime power congruences.**

*Abh. Math. Sem. Univ. Hamburg* **26** (1963), 102–110. (16 *plates*)

Let $p$ and $r$ be primes, $r \geqq 3$, $p \equiv 1 \pmod r$. Let $\chi$ be a primitive $r$th power character modulo $p$. Let $\zeta_r$ and $\zeta_p$ be primitive $r$th and $p$th roots of unity, respectively. It is known that if $\tau(\chi)$ denotes the Gaussian sum $\sum_{n=1}^{p-1} \chi(n)\zeta_p{}^n$, then $\tau(\chi)^r = p \sum_{j=1}^{r-1} a_j \zeta_r{}^j$, where the $a_j$ are rational integers. These integers $a_j$ were studied by Ankeny, who studied their connection with $r$th power reciprocity laws [Pacific J. Math. **10** (1960), 1115–1124; MR **22** #9479]. In the present paper some of Ankeny's results are refined, and various congruences involving the integers $a_j$ are established. For $1 \leqq j \leqq r-1$ it is shown that $a_j \equiv 1 \pmod r$ and $p(a_j + a_{r-j}) \equiv 2 \pmod{r^2}$. Moreover, $p \sum_{j=1}^{r-1} a_j \equiv r - 1 - \frac{1}{2}r(p-1) \pmod{r^3}$. Finally, relationships between $\chi(r)$ and the integers $a_j$ are discussed.
*W. H. Mills* (New Haven, Conn.)

Citations: MR 22# 9479 = A14-47.

## L05-31 (27# 115)

**Chowla, S.**

**On Gaussian sums.**

*Norske Vid. Selsk. Forh.* (*Trondheim*) **35** (1962), 66–67.

Let $\chi$ denote a non-principal character (mod $p$), where $p$ is an odd prime. Let $k$ be the least positive integer such that $\chi^k$ is equal to the principal character $\chi_0$. Put $\tau(\chi) = \sum_{n=1}^{p-1} \chi(n) \exp(2n\pi i/p)$. It is known that $\tau(\chi) = p^{1/2}\varepsilon(\chi)$, where $|\varepsilon(\chi)| = 1$ [cf. Hasse, *Vorlesungen über Zahlentheorie*, § 20, Springer, Berlin, 1950; MR **14**, 534]. From the fact that $\tau^k(\chi)$ lies in the field $R(\omega)$, $\omega = \exp(2\pi ib/k)$, $(b, k) = 1$, the author deduces the following theorem. If $\chi \neq \chi_0$, then $\varepsilon(\chi)$ is not a root of unity unless $\chi^2 = \chi_0$.
*A. L. Whiteman* (Los Angeles, Calif.)

Citations: MR 14, 534b = Z02-23.

## L05-32 (27# 4800)

**Mordell, L. J.**

**On a cubic exponential sum in three variables.**

*Amer. J. Math.* **85** (1963), 49–52.

The sum in the title is defined by

$$S = \sum_{x,y,z=0}^{p-1} \exp(2\pi i f(x, y, z)/p),$$

where $p$ is a prime, and $f(x, y, z)$ is a cubic polynomial with integer coefficients which is not a function of less than three variables. An obvious conjecture for general $f(x, y, z)$ is $S = O(p^{3/2})$, where the constant implied in $O$ is independent of the coefficients of $f(x, y, z)$. For the special case when

$$f(x, y, z) = ax^3 + by^3 + cz^3 + dxyz, \qquad abcd \not\equiv 0,$$

the author proves $S = O(p^2)$ or $S = O(p^{3/2})$ according as $d^3 \equiv -27abc$ or not. The proof is elementary except at one point where an appeal is made to a deep result of A. Weil [Proc. Nat. Acad. Sci. U.S.A. **34** (1948), 204–207; MR **10**, 234].
*A. L. Whiteman* (Los Angeles, Calif.)

Citations: MR 10, 234e = T25-5.

## L05-33 (28# 2094)

**Cavior, Stephan R.**

**Exponential sums related to polynomials over the GF($p$).**

*Proc. Amer. Math. Soc.* **15** (1964), 175–178.

Let $f(x) = a_0 + a_1x + \cdots + a_rx^r$, where the $a_j$ are in the finite field $GF(p)$ and put $M(f) = \sum_{a \pmod p} e^{2\pi i f(a)/p}$. It has been proved by the reviewer and S. Uchiyama [Duke Math. J. **24** (1957), 37–41; MR **18**, 563] that $|M(f)| \leqq (r-1)p^{1/2}$. The object of the present paper is to determine which polynomial functions satisfy $|M(f)| = p^{1/2}$. The following results are proved.

(1) Let $\alpha$ be an integer in the cyclotomic field $R(\zeta)$, where $\zeta = e^{2\pi i/p}$ and $p$ is an odd prime. Then $|\alpha| = p^{1/2}$ if and only if

$$\alpha = \pm\zeta^s \sum_{r \pmod p} \zeta r^2 \qquad (0 \leqq s \leqq p-1).$$

(2) The total number of polynomials $f$ over $GF(p)$ such that $|M(f)| = p^{1/2}$ is given by $T = 2p \cdot p!/2^{(p-1)/2}$.
*L. Carlitz* (Durham, N.C.)

Citations: MR 18, 563c = T25-12.

## L05-34 (29# 3456)

**Chowla, S.**

**On Gaussian sums.**

*Proc. Nat. Acad. Sci. U.S.A.* **48** (1962), 1127–1128.

The author proves the following theorem. Let

$$\sum_{n=1}^{p-1} \chi(n) e^{2\pi i n/p} = \varepsilon(x)\sqrt{p};$$

then $\varepsilon(x)$ is a root of unity only for the case of a quadratic character $\chi^2 = \chi_0$.
*A. Vinogradov* (RŽMat **1963** #3 A98)

Referred to in R18-43.

## L05-35 (31# 2214)

**Akuliničev, N. M.**

**Bounds for rational trigonometric sums of a special type. (Russian)**

*Dokl. Akad. Nauk SSSR* **161** (1965), 743–745.

Let $f(x) = a_nx^n + \cdots + a_0$ be a polynomial with integer coefficients and $a_n \not\equiv 0 \pmod p$. By well-known work of A. Weil it is known that

$$\text{(1)} \qquad \left|\sum_{x=0}^{p-1} e^{2k i f(x)/p}\right| \leqq (n-1)\sqrt{p},$$

where $p$ is a prime. Denoting the exponential sum which occurs on the left side of (1) by $S_f(p)$, the author obtains sharper forms of (1) in various special cases (useful only if $p$ is "small" compared to $n$).

Theorem: Let $p$ be a prime $\geqq 3$; $A$, $B$, $n$ natural numbers, $p \geqq n$; $\delta = (n, p-1)$; $(A, p) = (B, p) = 1$. Then if $f = Ax^n + Bx$, one has (2) $|S_f(p)| \leqq p/\sqrt{\delta}$. This is sharper than (1) in the case when $\delta = n$ and $p \leqq (n-1)^2 n$. From (1) and (2) one also immediately obtains the following corollary. Suppose $p$ is a prime $\equiv 1 \pmod n$ and $(A, p) = (B, p) = 1$. Then if $f = Ax^n + Bx$, one has $|S_f(p)| \leqq p^{5/6}$. Define $B(T)$ as the number of solutions of $Ax^n + Bx \equiv y \pmod p$ for $0 \leqq x \leqq p-1$, $0 \leqq y < T$. The author proves Theorem 2: If $(A, p) = (B, p) = 1$ and $p$ (prime) $\equiv 1 \pmod n$, then $B(T) = T + \theta p^{5/6} \log p$ $(|\theta| \leqq 1)$. Theorem 3 contains an estimate for $S_f(p)$ when $f(x) = Ax^n + Bx^k$.

{This article has appeared in English translation [Soviet Math. Dokl. **6** (1965), 480–482].}
*S. Chowla* (University Park, Pa.)

## L05-36 (32# 2390)

**Yamamoto, Koichi**

**On Gaussian sums with biquadratic residue characters.**

*J. Reine Angew. Math.* **219** (1965), 200–213.

The object of this paper is to obtain an algebraic expression for the biquadratic Gaussian sum.

Let $Q$ be the field of rationals and let $p$ be a prime, $p \equiv 1 \pmod 4$. Let $\varepsilon = \frac{1}{2}(t + u\sqrt{p})$ be the fundamental unit of $Q(\sqrt{p})$. Write $p = a^2 + b^2$, where $a$ and $b$ are positive integers, $a$ odd. Set $\pi = a + bi$ and let $\chi$ denote the biquadratic character given by $\chi(x) \equiv x^{(p-1)/4} \pmod{\pi}$. The biquadratic Gaussian sum $\tau(\chi)$ is given by $\tau(\chi) = \sum_1^{p-1} \chi(x)\zeta^x$, where $\zeta$ is a primitive $p$th root of unity. Set $\omega = \frac{1}{2}(-1+\sqrt{p})$. Let $l$ be the length of a primitive recurring cycle of the continued fraction expansion of $\omega + [\omega] + 1$, and let $p_n/q_n$ be the $n$th convergent of this expansion. It is known that $l$ is odd, say $l = 2\lambda + 1$. Set $\eta = q_{\lambda+1} + iq_\lambda$ and $\bar{\eta} = q_{\lambda+1} - iq_\lambda$. Then $\beta = \frac{1}{2}(\pi\bar{\eta} - \eta\sqrt{p})$ is a prime element of the field $Q(\sqrt{p}, i)$. The main result of the paper is $\tau(\chi) = \xi\beta\sqrt{(\varepsilon\sqrt{p})}$, where $\xi^4 = 1$ and $\xi$ is given explicitly. This result is used to determine the octant to which $\tau(\chi)$ belongs. This octant was determined by numerical computation on an electronic computer for all $p < 4000$. This calculation suggests certain general rules, but the author has been unable to prove any of them.

*W. H. Mills* (Princeton, N.J.)

## L05-37 (32# 4092 )

**Carlitz, L.**

**A note on multiple exponential sums.**

*Pacific J. Math.* **15** (1965), 757–765.

Let $p$ be a (large) prime; put $e_p(x) = \exp(2\pi ix/p)$, $S(a, b, c) = \sum \sum_{1 \leq x,y < p} e_p(ax + by + cx'y')$, where $xx' \equiv yy' \equiv 1 \bmod p$. For $ab \not\equiv 0 \bmod p$, one has $S(a, b, c) = S(1, 1, c^*) = S(c^*)$, where $c^* = abc$. Mordell conjectured $S(c) = O(p)$. The author's aim is an estimation of $S(c)$.

Elementary arguments give $\sum_{c \bmod p} |S(c)|^2 = p^3 - p^2 - p$; consequently one has $S(c) = O(p^{3/2})$.

Using results of S. Lang and A. Weil [Amer. J. Math. **76** (1953), 819–827; MR **16**, 398] [respectively, Weil's well-known estimate

$$\sum_{u \bmod p} \left(\frac{f(u)}{p}\right) = O(p^{1/2})$$

for the estimation of the number of solutions of a system of congruences (mod $p$)], the author deduces

$$\sum_{c \bmod p} |S(c)|^4 = O(p^{11/2})$$

[respectively, $\sum \sum \sum_{a,b,c \bmod p} |S(a, b, c)|^4 = p^8 + O(p^7)$]; as a consequence the author proves $S(c) = O(p^{11/8})$ [$S(c) = O(p^{5/4})$].

Finally, an explicit evaluation of $\sum_{c \bmod p} S^3(c)$ is given.

*W. Schwarz* (Freiburg)

Citations: MR 16, 398d = G25-2.

Referred to in T20-36.

## L05-38 (34# 2532 )

**Carlitz, L.**

**A note on multiple Kloosterman sums.**

*J. Indian Math. Soc.* (*N.S.*) **29** (1965), 197–200.

The Kloosterman sum

$$S_1(a, b; q) = \sum_{x=1}^{q-1} \exp\{2\pi i(ax + bx')/q\},$$

where $xx' \equiv 1 \pmod q$, has been evaluated explicitly by H. Salié [Math. Z. **34** (1931), 91–109] when $q = p^m$, where $p$ is an odd prime and $m \geq 2$. (See also A. L. Whiteman [Bull. Amer. Math. Soc. **51** (1945), 373–377; MR **6**, 259].) The author extends Salié's method to the double sum $S_2(a, b; q) = \sum_{x,y=1}^{q-1} \exp\{2\pi i(ax + ay + bx'y')/q\}$, where $xx' \equiv yy' \equiv 1 \pmod q$, $q = p^m$, $p > 3$, $m \geq 2$. First he shows that the sum vanishes unless $ab^{-1}$ is a cubic residue mod $p$. In the latter case he reduces the problem to the case $a = b$ and obtains the formula

$$S_2(a, a; p^m) = p^{2r} \sum_{x,y} \exp\{2\pi ia(x + y + x'y')/p^m\},$$

where $r$ is any integer $\leq m/2$ and the last sum is extended over all $x, y$ satisfying $1 \leq x$, $y < p^{m-r}$, $x, y \not\equiv 0 \pmod p$, $x \equiv y$, $x^3 \equiv 1 \pmod{p^r}$. If $r = [m/2]$, there is only one term in this sum when $p \equiv 2 \pmod 3$. If $p \equiv 1 \pmod 3$ the sum contains three terms when $m = 2r$; when $m = 2r + 1$ it becomes $S_2(a, a; p^{2r+1}) = (-3/p) \sum_z \exp(6\pi iaz/p^{2r+1})$, where $z$ runs through the solutions of $z^3 \equiv 1 \pmod{p^r}$, $1 \leq z < p^r$.

*T. M. Apostol* (Pasadena, Calif.)

Citations: MR 6, 259f = L05-3.

## L05-39 (34# 5764 )

**Andruhaev, H. M.**

**A sum of Kloosterman type.** (Russian)

*Certain Problems in the Theory of Fields* (*Russian*), *pp.* 60–66. *Izdat. Saratov. Univ.*, *Saratov*, 1964.

Let $u, v, q$ be integers, $q > 0$, and set $d = (u, v, q)$. Suppose $r$ is a positive integer such that $r^2 | (q/d)$, and $\chi$ is a character (mod $r$). For any integer $x$ with $(x, q) = 1$, put $f(x) = \chi(x) \exp\{2\pi i(ux + vx')/q\}$, where $x'$ is the solution of the congruence $xx' \equiv 1 \pmod q$. Let $K_\chi(u, v; q) = \sum_{x \in R} f(x)$, where $R$ is a reduced residue system (mod $q$). The author proves that $|K_\chi(u, v; q)| \leq \tau(q)\sqrt{(dq)}$, where $\tau(q)$ is the number of divisors of $q$. Next, suppose that $l$ and $L$ are integers with $L > 0$, $L | q$. Let $K_\chi(u, v; l, L; q) = \sum_{x \in R \cap S} f(x)$, where $S = \{x : x \equiv l \pmod L\}$. It is stated that for any $\varepsilon > 0$, $|K_\chi(u, v; l, L; q)| \leq C_\varepsilon q^{1/2+\varepsilon}\sqrt{d}$, where $C_\varepsilon$ is a constant depending only on $\varepsilon$. Finally, let $q_1$ be a positive integer with $L | q_1 | q$, and suppose $Q_1, Q_2$ are integers such that $0 \leq Q_1 < Q_2 < q$. Put $T = \{x : Q_1 \leq x \leq Q_2 \pmod{q_1}\}$, $U = \{x : Q_1 \leq x' \leq Q_2 \pmod{q_1}\}$, where the notation $Q_1 \leq y \leq Q_2 \pmod{q_1}$ means that there exists a $z$ with $Q_1 \leq z \leq Q_2$ and $y \equiv z \pmod{q_1}$. The estimates $|\sum_{x \in R \cap S \cap T} f(x)| \leq C_\varepsilon q^{1/2+\varepsilon} \times \sqrt{((v, q)d)}$ and $|\sum_{x \in R \cap S \cap U} f(x)| \leq C_\varepsilon q^{1/2+\varepsilon}\sqrt{((u, q)d)}$ (for any $\varepsilon > 0$) are stated. The proofs are said to resemble those of A. V. Malyšev [Vestnik Leningrad. Univ. **15** (1960), no. 13, 59–75; MR **23** #A2391] for estimates of related sums.

*B. Gordon* (Los Angeles, Calif.)

Citations: MR 23# A2391 = L05-20.

## L05-40 (34# 5766 )

**Karacuba, A. A.**

**Estimates of complete trigonometric sums.** (Russian)

*Mat. Zametki* **1** (1967), 199–208.

Es werden für verschiedene spezielle Funktionen $f(x)$ Abschätzungen von $S = \sum_{x=1}^{p} \exp 2\pi if(x)/p$, $p$ eine Primzahl $\geq 3$, bewiesen. Beispielsweise folgt aus einer Betrachtung der bei $|S|^4$ entstehenden Kongruenzen bei $f(x) = ax + bx^n$, $p \nmid ab$, $2 \leq n \leq p-1$, $|S| \leq (n-1)^{1/4}p^{3/4}$. Dies ist nicht in jedem Falle eine Konsequenz der Weilschen Abschätzung $|S| \leq (n-1)\sqrt{p}$.

*H.-E. Richert* (Marburg)

## L05-41 (34# 7481 )

**Vinogradov, A. I.**

**On the cubic Gaussian sum.** (Russian)

*Izv. Akad. Nauk SSSR Ser. Mat.* **31** (1967), 123–148.

Let $p$ be a prime $\equiv 1 \pmod 3$. The author considers two cubic non-principal characters $\chi$ and $\bar{\chi}$ mod $p$; of these two, $\chi$ is the one with the property that the argument of $\tau(\chi)$, the cubic Gaussian sum, lies in the first, third or fifth sextant (symbolically, $\arg \tau(\chi) \in (j)$, where $j = 1, 3, 5$). Denoting by $\pi_j(x)$ the number of primes $p \equiv 1 \pmod 3$, $p \leq x$, for which $\arg \tau(\chi) \in (j)$, the author proves the asymptotic formula $\pi_j(x) = (\frac{1}{3} + \theta/(\log x)^{1/6-\varepsilon})\pi(x, 3, 1)$, where $j = 1, 3, 5$, $\varepsilon > 0$ is arbitrary, $\theta = O(1)$ and $\pi(x, 3, 1) =$ number of $p \leq x$, $p \equiv 1 \pmod 3$. The formula disproves the conjecture of Kummer, according to which

$$\pi_1(x) : \pi_5(x) : \pi_3(x) \sim 3:2:1$$

(see, e.g., H. Hasse [*Vorlesungen über Zahlentheorie*,

second revised edition, pp. 478–489, Springer, Berlin, 1964; MR **32** #5569; first edition, 1950; MR **14**, 534]).

*S. Knapowski* (Coral Gables, Fla.)

The author has communicated to the editors that a serious error appears in his article, due to different branches of the logarithm being used in formulas (4.12) and (4.13). According to the author, the work in its present form is incorrect.

Citations: MR 14, 534b = Z02-23; MR 32# 5569 = Z02-25.

Referred to in L05-42.

## L05-42 (40# 4219)

**Vinogradov, A. I.**

**Letter to the editor.** **(Russian)**

*Izv. Akad. Nauk SSSR Ser. Mat.* **33** (1969), 455.

This erratum to the author's paper in same Izv. **31** (1967), 123–148 [MR **34** #7481] has been previously noted [MR **37**, p. 1469].

Citations: MR 34# 7481 = L05-41.

## L05-43 (35# 4175)

**Yamamoto, Koichi**

**On a conjecture of Hasse concerning multiplicative relations of Gaussian sums.**

*J. Combinatorial Theory* **1** (1966), 476–489.

Denote the rational field by $Q$ and a primitive $n$th root of unity by $\xi_n$. Let $e$ be a fixed integer $>1$ and let $p$ be a prime such that $p\equiv 1 \pmod e$. Denote the group of $e$th power residue characters of $p$ by $X$ and the principal character by $I$. Assume $\chi(0)=0$ and denote the quadratic character by $\Psi$. The Gauss sum $\tau(\chi)$ is defined by $\tau(\chi)=-\sum_{x=1}^{p-1}\chi(x)\xi_p{}^x$. Then $\tau(I)=1$ and (*) $\tau(\chi)\overline{\tau(\chi)}=p$ for $\chi\neq I$.

The Jacobi sum $\pi(\chi_1,\chi_2)$ is defined by $\pi(\chi_1,\chi_2)=-\sum_{x+y\equiv 1}\chi_1(x)\chi_2(y)$; it belongs to the field $L=Q(\xi_e)$ of $e$th roots of unity. H. Davenport and H. Hasse [J. Reine Angew. Math. **172** (1934), 151–182] have proved the formula (**) $\prod_{\vartheta^l=I;\,\vartheta\neq I}\pi(\chi,\vartheta)=\chi(l^l)\tau(\chi)^l/\tau(\chi^l)$, where $l$ is a divisor of $e$ and $\chi^l\neq I$.

H. Hasse [*Vorlesungen über Zahlentheorie*, second edition, p. 465, Springer, Berlin, 1964; MR **32** #5569] has conjectured that (*) and (**) are essentially the only relations connecting the Gauss sums $\tau(\chi)$ for the $e$th power residue characters. The present paper contains a proof of Hasse's conjecture when the Gauss sums are considered as ideals. Considered as numbers, however, there are additional relations; an example is indicated for $e=12$.

The proof of Hasse's conjecture makes use of the analogy between (**) and the multiplication formula for the gamma function. It is shown in particular that if $e$ is even and $\geqq 4$, then the number of multiplicatively independent Gaussian sums is $\frac{1}{2}\phi(e)+1$, where $\phi(e)$ is the Euler function.

*L. Carlitz* (Durham, N.C.)

Citations: MR 32# 5569 = Z02-25.

## L05-44 (36# 1401)

**Krätzel, Ekkehard**

**Kubische und biquadratische Gaußsche Summen.**

*J. Reine Angew. Math.* **228** (1967), 159–165.

The author shows that the simple method used by L. J. Mordell [Messenger Math. **48** (1918), 54–56] for the summation of ordinary Gaussian sums yields also information on cubic and biquadratic Gaussian sums; namely, he obtains for them asymptotic expressions involving Bessel functions as the modulus tends to infinity.

*O. H. Körner* (Marburg)

## L05-45 (37# 4032)

**Chowla, S.**

**On Kloostermann's sum.**

*Norske Vid. Selsk. Forh.* (*Trondheim*) **40** (1967), 70–72.

The author proves that $|\sum_{x=1}^{p-1}\chi(x)e^{2\pi i(ax+\bar{x})/p}|\leqq 2\sqrt{p}$, where $p$ is a prime with $(a,p)=1$ and $\chi$ is a character (mod $p$) which is not the Legendre symbol. He does this by connecting the sum in the above theorem with the sum in the theorem $|\sum_{x=0}^{p-1}e^{2\pi ibx/p}\chi(x^2-c)|\leqq 2\sqrt{p}$ proved by A. Weil [Proc. Nat. Acad. Sci. U.S.A. **34** (1948), 204–207; MR **10**, 234]. The connection is made through the well-known character sum $\sum_{m=1}^{p-1}\chi(m)e^{2\pi imn/p}=(\sqrt{p})\varepsilon(\chi)\bar{\chi}(n)$ which holds for all $n$ whenever $\chi$ is not the principal character.

*W. Connor* (University Park, Pa.)

Citations: MR 10, 234e = T25-5.

## L05-46 (39# 1398)

**Carlitz, L.**

**A note on Gauss's sum.**

*Matematiche* (*Catania*) **23** (1968), 147–150.

Verfasser gibt einen kurzen Beweis des folgenden bekannten Satzes. Es seien $p$ eine ungerade Primzahl, $\zeta=\exp\left(\frac{2\pi i}{p}\right)$, $\left(\frac{k}{p}\right)$ das Legendresche Restsymbol, $S=\sum_{k=0}^{p-1}\left(\frac{k}{p}\right)\zeta^k$. Dann ist $S=\sqrt{p}$ für $p\equiv 1 \pmod 4$, $S=i\sqrt{p}$ für $p\equiv 3 \pmod 4$. Der Beweis beruht auf einer geschickten Umformung von $S$ und der Heranziehung geeigneter Kongruenzen mod$(\zeta-1)^{(p+1)/2}$.

{In Formel (3) scheint ein Druckfehler vorzuliegen.}

*H. J. Kanold* (Braunschweig)

## L05-47 (39# 5490)

**Carlitz, L.**

**Some formulas related to Gauss's sum.**

*Rend. Sem. Mat. Univ. Padova* **41** (1968), 222–226.

The reviewer [Tôhoku Math. J. **32** (1929/30), 352–353] proved that (1) $\sum_{s=0}^{m-1}(-1)^s e^{\pi in(2s+1)^2/(4m)}=e^{\pi i/4}(mn)^{-1/2}\times\sum_{s=1}^{mn}e^{-\pi is^2/(mn)}\sec(\pi s/m)$, where $m,n$ are arbitrary odd positive integers. The author gives a simple elementary proof of (1). Indeed he proves the "slightly more general formula" (2) $e^{-\pi ia'/m}\sum_{s=1}^{mn}e^{\pi ias^2/mn}=(-1/(mn))^{(a'-1)/2}\times(a/(mn))\sqrt{(mn)}\sum_{k=0}^{m-1}(-1)^k\exp\{-\pi i(2k+1)^2a'n/(4m)\}$, where $m,n$ are odd, $(a,2mn)=1$, $aa'\equiv 1 \pmod{2mn}$ and $(a/(mn))$ is the Legendre-Jacobi symbol. For $a=a'=-1$, (2) reduces to (1).

*S. Chowla* (University Park, Pa.)

## L05-48 (40# 5553)

**Mordell, L. J.**

**Some exponential sums in several variables.**

*Monatsh. Math.* **73** (1969), 348–353.

Let $p$ be a prime and write $e(x)=e(2\pi ix/p)$. Further, let $f(x)=f(x_1,x_2,\cdots,x_n)$ be a polynomial of degree $r$ with integral coefficients which when taken mod $p$ does not reduce to a function of less than $n$ variables. Then, if $S=\sum_{x=0}^{p-1}e(f(x))$, there is the conjecture that for general $f(x)$, $S=O(p^{n/2})$. The conjecture is proved in the following special cases. (i) $f(x)=(a_1x_1+\cdots+a_nx_n)g(x)$, where $g(x)=x_1{}^{l_1}\cdots x_n{}^{l_n}$, $1+l_1+l_2+\cdots+l_n\not\equiv 0 \bmod (p-1)$, (ii) $f(x)=g(x^2)$, where $g(x)$ is a quadratic polynomial in $x$ not a function of one variable mod $p$.

*K. Thanigasalam* (University Park, Pa.)

## L05-49 (41# 1661)

**Apostol, Tom M.**

**Euler's $\phi$-function and separable Gauss sums.**

*Proc. Amer. Math. Soc.* **24** (1970), 482–485.

Let $\chi$ be a character modulo $k$, and consider the Gauss sum

$G(r,\chi)=\sum_{h \bmod k}\chi(h)\exp(2\pi irh/k)$. It is well known that if $\chi$ is primitive, then its Gauss sum is separable for every $r$. In this paper the author establishes the converse of this theorem. The proof depends on a principle of decomposition of a reduced residue system first discovered by T. Nagell [Skr. Norske Vid. Akad. Oslo I **13** (1924), 23–25]. The author gives a new proof of this, using group-theoretic methods. *D. Rearick* (Boulder, Colo.)

## L05-50 (42# 3031)

**Rešetuha, I. V.**
**A certain question in the theory of cubic remainders. (Russian)**
*Mat. Zametki* **7** (1970), 469–476.

Let $\chi$ and $\bar\chi$ be complex conjugated cubic characters, $\zeta=e^{2\pi i/p}$, $p$ a simple odd number, $\tau(\chi,\zeta^c)=\sum_{x=1}^{p-1}\chi(x)\zeta^{cx}$ a cubic Gaussian sum and $\tau=\sum_{x=1}^{p-1}(x/p)\zeta^{cx}$ an ordinary Gaussian sum.

In studying quadratic remainders together with Gaussian sum $\tau$, a product (1) $\prod_{x=1}^{p-1}(\zeta^{cx}-\zeta^{-cx})$ is also used.

In the paper the author builds a cubic analogue of the product (1) and examines some arithmetical relations between the new product and the cubic Gaussian sum.

A computing method for investigating these relations is also suggested.

{This article has appeared in English translation [Math. Notes **7** (1970), 284–288].} *L. A. Kogan* (Tashkent)

## L05-51 (42# 4480)

**Waterhouse, William C.**
**The sign of the Gaussian sum.**
*J. Number Theory* **2** (1970), 363.

Let $p$ be an odd prime, and let $\zeta=\exp(2\pi i/p)$. Denote the matrix $(\zeta^{xy})$ $(m\leqq x,y\leqq p-1)$ by $A_m$. Schur's proof [see Z. I. Borevič and I. R. Šafarevič, *Number theory*, English translation, Academic Press, New York, 1966; MR **33** #4001; French translation, Gauthier-Villars, Paris, 1967; MR **34** #5734] of the sign of the Gaussian sum $\sum\chi(n)\zeta^n$ involves the evaluation of the determinant and the characteristic roots of $A_0$. In the present paper the determinant of $A_1$ is evaluated by considering $A_1$ as the matrix of the linear map from characters to characteristic functions as bases of the space of complex functions over the group of non-zero residues modulo $p$. The use of this result avoids some of the detailed consideration of congruences in Schur's proof. *H. J. Godwin* (London)

Citations: MR 33# 4001 = Z02-46; MR 34# 5734 = Z02-47.

## L05-52 (44# 1635)

**Williams, Kenneth S.**
**Note on Salié's sum.**
*Proc. Amer. Math. Soc.* **30** (1971), 393–394.

Let $S=\sum'(x/p)\exp\{2\pi i(ax+b\bar x)/p\}$ be Salié's modified Kloosterman sum for an odd prime $p$, where $x$ runs through a reduced set of residues modulo $p$, $x\bar x\equiv 1 \pmod p$ and $(x/p)$ denotes the Legendre symbol. The author uses the identity $\sum_{x+\bar x\equiv y}(x/p)=((y-2)/p)+((y+2)/p)$ to give a two-line evaluation of $S$ as a sum of two Gaussian sums. *R. A. Smith* (Toronto, Ont.)

## L05-53 (44# 2719)

**Williams, Kenneth S.**
**Note on the Kloosterman sum.**
*Proc. Amer. Math. Soc.* **30** (1971), 61–62.

The author gives a very short direct evaluation of the Kloosterman sum $\sum_{0\leq x\leq q,(x,q)=1}e^{2\pi in(x+\bar x)/q}$, $x\bar x\equiv 1 \bmod q$, where $q=p^\alpha$, $p$ an odd prime and $\alpha\geqq 2$. The literature contains two other evaluations of this sum, one by H. Salié [Math. Z. **34** (1931), 91–109] and one by A. L. Whiteman [Bull. Amer. Math. Soc. **51** (1945), 373–377; MR **6**, 259]. *R. A. Smith* (Toronto, Ont.)

Citations: MR 6, 259f = L05-3.

## L05-54 (44# 3951)

**Williams, Kenneth S.**
**On Salié's sum.**
*J. Number Theory* **3** (1971), 316–317.

Let $F(x)$ be a periodic function with period $p$, where $p$ is an odd prime. It is known that

$$\sum_{x=1}^{p-1}F(x)+\sum_{x=1}^{p-1}\left(\frac{x}{p}\right)F(x)=\sum_{x=1}^{p-1}F(x^2)$$

and

$$\sum_{x=0}^{p-1}F(x)+\sum_{x=0}^{p-1}\left(\frac{x^2-4a}{p}\right)F(x)=\sum_{x=1}^{p-1}F(x-a\bar x),$$

where $a\not\equiv 0 \pmod p$, $\left(\frac{x}{p}\right)$ is the Legendre symbol and $\bar x$ is the unique integer between zero and $p$ such that $x\bar x\equiv 1 \pmod p$. The author obtains a similar result, namely $\sum_{x=0}^{p-1}\left(\frac{x-2}{p}\right)F(x)+\sum_{x=0}^{p-1}\left(\frac{x+2}{p}\right)F(x)=\sum_{x=0}^{p-1}\left(\frac{x}{p}\right)F(x+\bar x)$.
The value of Salié's sum $\sum_{x=1}^{p-1}\left(\frac{x}{p}\right)e^{2\pi ik(x+\bar x)/p}$ can easily be deduced from this. *M. S. Cheema* (Tucson, Ariz.)

## L05-55 (44# 6618)

**McGettrick, Andrew D.**
**On the biquadratic Gauss sum.**
*Proc. Cambridge Philos. Soc.* **71** (1972), 79–83.

The most interesting statement in this paper is a conjecture concerning biquadratic Gauss sums. Let $p\equiv 1 \pmod 4$ and $\tau_4=\sum_{r=1}^{p-1}\chi(r)\zeta^r$, where $\zeta$ is a $p$th root of unity and let $\chi$ be the unique unit in $\mathbf{Z}[i]$ such that $\chi(r)\equiv r^{(1/4)(p-1)} \pmod{\tilde\omega}$; here $\tilde\omega$ is a prime factor of $p$ in $\mathbf{Z}[i]$. Further, let $J$ be defined by $J=\vartheta^{-1}\prod_{r\in M}\operatorname{sn}(2-2i)\gamma r\tilde\omega^{-1}$, where $\vartheta=\prod_{r\in M}r \pmod{\tilde\omega}$, $\vartheta^2=-1$ and $M$ is a half-set of residues mod $\tilde\omega$.

The conjecture says that $\tau_4 J\chi(2)=\tilde\omega p^{1/4}\delta^{-1}$, where $\delta$ is defined in a rather complicated way, depending on $\tilde\omega$. This study is closely connected with a paper of T. Kubota's [J. Reine Angew. Math. **214/215** (1964), 141–145; MR **29** #2240], in which he gives some arithmetical applications of the function sn, which leads up to a simple proof of the biquadratic reciprocity law. The conjecture is checked for all $p<5700$, by means of some results of the author and computer methods. *F. van der Blij* (Bilthoven)

Citations: MR 29# 2240 = R40-18.

# L10 COMPLETE CHARACTER SUMS (JACOBSTHAL, BREWER, ETC.)

There are close connections between this section and **N68-N76**.

See also Sections R50, T25.

See also reviews C20-25, D80-18, E28-7, E28-35, L05-20, L05-23, L05-27, L05-39, L05-43, L05-45, M20-12, N68-17, N68-19, R58-40, T15-55, T20-32, T25-5, T40-7, T40-11, T40-13, T45-1, Z02-48, Z30-28.

**L10-1** **(3, 271h)**

**Segal, B. Character sums and their application.** Bull. Acad. Sci. URSS. Sér. Math. [Izvestia Akad. Nauk SSSR] **5**, 401–410 (1941). (Russian. English summary)

Let $\chi_1, \cdots, \chi_r$ be nonprincipal multiplicative characters mod $p$ ($\geqq 5$); let $f_1(x), \cdots, f_r(x)$ be different normalized polynomials of degrees $k_1, \cdots, k_r$, each irreducible mod $p$. Set $k_1+\cdots+k_r=k$. H. Davenport proved [Acta Math. **71**, 99–121 (1939); these Rev. **1**, 41] that

$$\left|\sum_{x=0}^{p-1} \chi_1(f_1(x))\cdots\chi_r(f_r(x))\right| \leqq (k-1)p^{1-\theta_k},$$

where $\theta_2=\frac{1}{2}$, $\theta_3=\frac{1}{4}$, $\theta_k=3/(2k+8)$ if $k\geqq 4$; and $\theta_k$ can be replaced by $\theta_{k-1}$ if $\chi_1^{k_1}\cdots\chi_r^{k_r}=\chi_0$. Let $1\leqq q<p-1$, $\rho_k=3/(8k+16)$. Segal treats the partial sum in which $x$ runs only from 0 to $q$, and proves it is numerically less than $2(r^2-r+2k)^{\frac{1}{2}}p^{1-\rho_k}\log p$. Applications of both Davenport's and Segal's results follow. (i) Let $\chi_1, \cdots, \chi_n$ be any nonprincipal characters mod $p$, $\epsilon_1, \cdots, \epsilon_n$ be any set of $n$ roots of unity, $\epsilon_i$ being an $l_i$th root of unity. Let $E(\epsilon_1, \cdots, \epsilon_n)$ denote the number of sequences $x+1, x+2, \cdots, x+n$ out of $1, 2, \cdots, p-1$ for which $\chi_1(x+1)=\epsilon_1, \cdots, \chi_n(x+n)=\epsilon_n$; and $E_q(\epsilon_1, \cdots, \epsilon_n)$ the number of such sequences out of $1, \cdots, q$. By Davenport, $E=p/(l_1\cdots l_n)+\Theta n(p^{1-\theta_n}+1)$; by Segal, $E_q=q/(l_1\cdots l_n)+\Theta\cdot 2(n+1)p^{1-\rho_n}\log p$; $\Theta$ denotes some number between $-1$ and $+1$. (ii) The number of sequences out of $1, \cdots, p-1$ such that all of $x+1, \cdots, x+n$ are primitive roots mod $p$ is

$$p(p-1)^{-n}(\varphi(p-1))^n+\Theta 2^{n\sigma}n(p^{1-\theta_n}+1),$$

$\sigma$ denoting the number of distinct primes dividing $p-1$; hence, for any $n$, large primes have $n$ successive primitive roots. The number of such sequences out of $1, \cdots, q$ is

$$q(p-1)^{-n}(\varphi(p-1))^n+\Theta(n+1)2^{n\sigma+1}p^{1-\rho_n}\log p.$$

(iii) The number of sequences out of $1, \cdots, p-1$ for which $1\leqq \operatorname{ind}(x+1)\leqq Q_1, \cdots, 1\leqq \operatorname{ind}(x+n)\leqq Q_n$, where $Q_1, \cdots, Q_n$ are given positive integers not greater than $p-1$, is given by

$$Q_1\cdots Q_n(p-1)^{1-n}+\Theta n2^n(p^{1-\theta_n}+2)\log^n(p-1);$$

similarly for sequences out of $1, \cdots, q$. (iv) If $f(x)$ is a polynomial with integer coefficients, and if $f(x)\not\equiv(g_1(x))^2g_2(x)$ mod $p$ for any nonconstant $g_1(x)$, then an estimate is found for the number of values of $f(x)$, for $x=0, \cdots, p-1$, or for $x=0, \cdots, q$, such that $f(x)$ is a primitive root mod $p$, or such that $\chi(f(x))$ has a given value. *G. Pall.*

Citations: MR 1, 41e = T25-1.

**L10-2** **(10, 592f)**

**Chowla, S. The last entry in Gauss's diary.** Proc. Nat. Acad. Sci. U. S. A. **35**, 244–246 (1949).

The author proves the following two theorems by elementary methods: (I) $\sum_{x=1}^{p-1}((x^4-1)/p)=2\theta-2$, where $p$ denotes a prime of the form $4n+1$, $(m/p)$ is the Legendre symbol, $\theta$ is defined by $p=\theta^2+\phi^2$, and $\theta\equiv 1$ or 3 (mod 4), according as $p\equiv 5$ or 1 (mod 8); (II) $\sum_{x=1}^{p-1}((x^6-1)/p)=-4\theta-2$, where $p$ denotes a prime of the form $12n+1$, $\theta$ is defined by $p=\theta^2+3\phi^2$, and $\theta\equiv 1$ (mod 3). Theorem I implies a theorem stated as a conjecture by Gauss in the last entry of his Tagebuch [Werke, vol. $X_1$, p. 571]. [Note by the reviewer. A. Weil has pointed out, in the paper* reviewed above, that the first proof of Gauss's conjecture is due to Gauss himself, Werke, vol. II, p. 89.]

*A. L. Whiteman* (Los Angeles, Calif.).

Citations: MR 10, 592e = T50-8.
Referred to in D80-18, E28-35.

**L10-3** **(11, 230b)**

**Whiteman, Albert Leon. Theorems analogous to Jacobstahl's theorem.** Duke Math. J. **16**, 619–626 (1949).

The sums $\phi_q(s)=\sum_{m=1}^{p-1}(m/p)((m^q+s)/p)$, where $(m/p)$ denotes the quadratic character of $m$ mod $p$, were introduced by E. Jacobsthal [J. Reine Angew. Math. **132**, 238–245 (1907)], and the solutions $a, b$ of $a^2+b^2=p$ were expressed in terms of these sums for $p=4f+1$. This was extended by von Schrutka [J. Reine Angew. Math. **140**, 252–265 (1911)], and by Chowla [Proc. Lahore Philos. Soc. **7**, 2 pp. (1945); these Rev. **7**, 243] to the equation $a^2+3b^2=p$, $p=3f+1$. The present paper obtains these results, and in addition expresses the solutions of $a^2+50b^2+50c^2+125d^2=16p$, $p=5f+1$ and $a^2+2b^2=p$, $p=8f+1$ in terms of the Jacobsthal sums. For example, in the latter case $a=\frac{1}{4}\phi_4(r)$, where $r$ is any biquadratic residue of $p$. The proofs are based on a result relating the Jacobsthal sums and cyclotomic numbers.

*I. Niven* (Eugene, Ore.).

Citations: MR 7, 243g = E28-7.
Referred to in E28-12.

**L10-4** **(13, 626j)**

**Whiteman, Albert Leon. Cyclotomy and Jacobsthal sums.** Amer. J. Math. **74**, 89–99 (1952).

The Jacobsthal sum $\phi_e(n)$ is defined by

$$\phi_e(n)=\sum_{k=1}^{r-1}\left(\frac{h}{p}\right)\left(\frac{h^e+n}{p}\right),$$

where $\left(\frac{h}{p}\right)$ denotes the quadratic character of $h$ with respect to $p$. E. Jacobsthal and others have shown that there is a connection between these sums and a partition of $p$ into quadratic summands. Here the author gives summation formulas for the $\phi_e(n)$, from which the mentioned connection can be concluded more precisely. *H. Bergström.*

Referred to in T40-7.

**L10-5** **(22# 10959 )**

**Brewer, B. W. On certain character sums.** Trans. Amer. Math. Soc. **99** (1961), 241–245.

Let $p$ denote an odd prime and $\chi(f(x))$ the quadratic character of $f(x)$ with respect to $p$. The sum $\phi_k(Q)=\sum_{x=0}^{p-1}\chi(x(x^k+Q))$ has been studied by Jacobsthal [J. Reine Angew. Math. **132** (1907), 238–245]. Jacobsthal showed that if $p$ is of the form $a^2+b^2$ ($b$ even) and $Q$ is a quadratic nonresidue of $p$, then $\phi_2(Q)=\pm 2b$. In the first half of this paper the author determines the sign of $\phi_2(-3)$ if $p=12k+5$. Specifically, he shows that $\phi_2(-3)=2b$, where $a\equiv 1$ (mod 4) and $b\equiv a$ (mod 3). Moreover, he derives the congruence $\binom{6k+2}{k}\equiv 2b \pmod{p}$.

It is well known that $p$ can be expressed in the form $c^2+2d^2$ if and only if $p=8k+1$ or $8k+3$. Using cyclotomy the author proves in the second half of the paper that

$$\sum_{x=0}^{p-1}\chi((x+2)(x^2-2)) = 0 \quad \text{if} \quad p\neq c^2+2d^2,$$
$$= 2c \quad \text{if} \quad p = c^2+2d^2,$$

where $c\equiv(-1)^{k+1}$ (mod 4). He also indicates similar results for primes of the form $u^2+5v^2$.

*A. L. Whiteman* (Los Angeles, Calif.)

Referred to in L10-8, L10-9, L10-10, L10-16, L10-21.

**L10-6** **(26# 82 )**

**Chowla, S.**

**On a formula of Jacobsthal.**

*Norske Vid. Selsk. Forh.* (*Trondheim*) **34** (1961), 105–106.

By combining Jacobsthal's theorem with Hecke's result that there are infinitely many Gaussian primes in every sector containing the real axis, one sees that, given $\varepsilon>0$, there is an integer $c$ for which there are infinitely many primes $p$ with

$$|\Phi(c)| = \left|\sum_{x=1}^{p}\left(\frac{x}{p}\right)\left(\frac{x^2+c}{p}\right)\right| > (2-\varepsilon)\sqrt{p}.$$

This is one of several ways of seeing that the inequality $|\Phi(c)| \leqq 2\sqrt{p}$ is best possible.

*B. J. Birch* (Cambridge, England)

## L10-7 (26# 1276)

**Gordeev, N. V.**

**On the mean value of quadratic residues for a prime modulus. (Russian. English summary)**

*Vestnik Leningrad. Univ.* **17** (1962), *no.* 19, 137–140.

Let $\left(\frac{x}{p}\right)$ denote Legendre's symbol of quadratic reciprocity for an odd prime $p$ as modulus. Consider the expression

$$(1) \qquad R = \frac{p}{2} + \frac{1}{(p-1)} \sum_{x=1}^{p-1} \left(\frac{x}{p}\right) x.$$

This is transformed by elementary transformations (partial summations, etc.) to

$$(2) \qquad R = \frac{p}{2} - \left(\frac{1}{2} - \frac{1}{p-1}\right) \sum_{x=1}^{(p-1)/2} \left(\frac{x}{p}\right).$$

This is true for primes $p \equiv 1$ (4), but says little since then, obviously,

$$\sum_{1}^{(p-1)/2} \left(\frac{x}{p}\right) = \sum_{x=1}^{p-1} \left(\frac{x}{p}\right) x = 0.$$

For primes $p \equiv 3$ (4), the correct result is, for $p > 3$,

$$\sum_{1}^{p-1} \left(\frac{x}{p}\right) x = -p\varepsilon \sum_{x=1}^{(p-1)/2} \left(\frac{x}{p}\right)$$

$$(\varepsilon = \tfrac{1}{3} \text{ if } p \equiv 3 \ (8),\ \varepsilon = 1 \text{ if } p \equiv 7 \ (8)),$$

which does not agree with the result of comparing (1) and (2).

*S. Chowla* (Boulder, Colo.)

## L10-8 (27# 4801)

**Whiteman, Albert Leon**

**A theorem of Brewer on character sums.**

*Duke Math. J.* **30** (1963), 545–552.

Let

$$B = \sum_{u=0}^{p-1} \chi((u+2)(u^2-2)),$$

where $p$ is an odd prime and $\chi(u)$ is the Legendre symbol. Brewer [Trans. Amer. Math. Soc. **99** (1961), 241–245; MR **22** #10959] has proved that

$$(*) \qquad B = 0 \qquad (p \neq c^2+2d^2),$$
$$= 2c \qquad (p = c^2+2d^2),$$

the sign of $c$ being determined by $c \equiv (-1)^{k+1}$ (mod 4) when $p = 8k+1$ or $8k+3$. The proof makes use of the congruences

$$(**) \qquad 2c \equiv -\binom{4k}{k} \pmod p \qquad (p = 8k+1),$$
$$\equiv \binom{4k+1}{k} \pmod p \qquad (p = 8k+3),$$

due to Stern and Eisenstein, respectively. The present paper contains a direct proof of (*) from which (**) follows as a corollary.

*L. Carlitz* (Durham, N.C.)

Citations: MR 22# 10959 = L10-5.

## L10-9 (31# 137)

**Whiteman, Albert Leon**

**Theorems on Brewer and Jacobsthal sums. I.**

*Proc. Sympos. Pure Math., Vol. VIII, pp.* 44–55. *Amer. Math. Soc., Providence, R.I.*, 1965.

Let $V_n(x)$ be the polynomial defined by $V_{n+2}(x) = xV_{n+1}(x) - V_n(x)$, $n = 1, 2, \cdots$, $V_1(x) = x$, $V_2(x) = x^2 - 2$. Suppose that $\Lambda_n = \sum_{s=0}^{p-1} \chi(V_n(s))$, where $\chi(s) = (s/p)$ is the Legendre symbol. The author calls these Brewer sums [B. W. Brewer, Trans. Amer. Math. Soc. **99** (1961), 241–245; MR **22** #10959]. Brewer evaluated $\Lambda_3, \Lambda_4, \Lambda_5$ ($\Lambda_1 = 0$, $\Lambda_2 = -1$ trivially). The object of this paper is to evaluate $\Lambda_5$ by a method different from that used by Brewer. Only certain cases are considered here; the remaining cases will appear in another paper. The methods are based on a lemma of Brewer as well as the general theory of cyclotomy, certain cases reducing to an evaluation of Hurwitz-Dickson and Jacobsthal sums, these being based on the author's previous work in cyclotomy.

*R. Ayoub* (University Park, Pa.)

Citations: MR 22# 10959 = L10-5.

Referred to in L10-16.

## L10-10 (32# 5610)

**Brewer, B. W.**

**On primes of the form $u^2+5v^2$.**

*Proc. Amer. Math. Soc.* **17** (1966), 502–509.

Let $p$ be an odd prime and let $f(x)$ be a polynomial of degree $> 3$. There is a remote possibility that the sum of Legendre's symbols

$$\sum_{x=0}^{p-1} \left(\frac{f(x)}{p}\right)$$

can be evaluated in closed form. The author succeeds in doing this for the parametrized Chebyshev quintic $f(x) = x^5 - 5Qx^3 + 5Q^2x$, in which case the above sum is denoted by $\Lambda_5(Q)$. This paper generalizes the author's previous results for $Q = 1$ [Trans. Amer. Math. Soc. **99** (1961), 241–245; MR **22** #10959].

In almost all cases, $\Lambda_5(Q) = 0$. Otherwise, $\Lambda_5(Q) = \pm 4u$, where $p = u^2 + 5v^2$. More precisely, $\Lambda_5(Q)$ vanishes when $p \equiv 3, 5, 7, 11, 13, 17, 19$ (mod 20). In the remaining two cases ($p \equiv 1, 9$ (mod 20)), $p = a^2 + b^2 = u^2 + 5v^2$ with $a \equiv 1$ (mod 4).

If $Q$ is a quadratic residue of $p$, say $Q \equiv m^2$ (mod $p$), then $\Lambda_5(Q) = 0$ if $a \equiv 0$ (mod 5). Otherwise let the sign of $u$ be chosen so that $u \equiv pa$ (mod 5). Then $\Lambda_5(Q) = -4(m/p)u$.

If $Q$ is a nonresidue of $p$, then $\Lambda_5(Q) = 0$ if $a \not\equiv 0$ (mod 5). Otherwise choose $b \equiv aQ^{(p-1)/4}$ (mod $p$) and $u \equiv pb$ (mod 5). Then $\Lambda_5(Q) = -4u$.

Two corollaries are given for the cases in which either 2 or $-3$ is a nonresidue of $p$. These follow from the fact that $\Lambda_5(Qm^2) = (m/p)\Lambda_5(Q)$.

*D. H. Lehmer* (Berkeley, Calif.)

Citations: MR 22# 10959 = L10-5.

## L10-11 (32# 7521)

**Walum, H.**

**Some averages of character sums.**

*Pacific J. Math.* **16** (1966), 189–192.

Let $\chi$ and $\psi$ be nonprincipal characters mod $p$; let $f$ be a polynomial mod $p$ and let $a_1, \cdots, a_p$ be complex constants. Define $a_n$ for all $n$ by making $a_j = a_k$ for $j \equiv k$ (mod $p$) and set

$$S = \sum_r a_r \chi(f(r)), \qquad J_n(c) = \sum_r \psi(r)\chi(r^n - c),$$

where $r$ runs through a complete system of residues mod $p$. Exact formulas are found for $\sum_{a=1}^{p-1} |J_n(a)|^2$ and, in certain cases, for (*) $\sum |S|^2$, where the latter sum is taken over the coefficients mod $p$ of certain fixed powers of the variable in $f$. In fact, let $f(r) = yr^{m_1} + xr^{m_2} + g(r)$ and assume $(m_2 - m_1, p-1) = 1$; the sum in (*) is then taken over all $x$ and $y$ mod $p$, and is proved to be equal to

$$p(p-1) \sum_{r=1}^{p-1} |a_r|^2 + p^2 |a_0|^2$$

in case $g$ has a nonzero constant term and neither $m_1$ nor $m_2$ is zero. In the excepted cases the second term in the above expression is lacking.

*H. W. Brinkmann* (Swarthmore, Pa.)

## L10-12 (33# 108 )

**Tuškina, T. A.**

**A numerical experiment on the calculation of the Hasse invariant for certain curves. (Russian)**

*Izv. Akad. Nauk SSSR Ser. Mat.* **29** (1965), 1203–1204.

The values of $p \leqq 10007$ are given for which the sum

$$S_p = \sum_{x=0}^{p-1} \left(\frac{x^3+ax^2+bx+c}{p}\right)$$

vanishes, for four specific cubics. On the basis of this and a count of the values of $p$ for which $S_p/p^{1/2}$ lies in $[-2+k/5, -2+(k+1)/5]$, $k=0, \cdots, 19$, the author conjectures that the number of $p \leqq N$ for which $S_p=0$ has the order of magnitude $\pi(N)/N^{1/2}$.

*W. J. LeVeque* (Ann Arbor, Mich.)

Referred to in Z10-43.

## L10-13 (33# 4026 )

**Rosenberg, I.**

**Sums of Legendre symbols. I, II. (Czech. Russian and German summaries)**

*Sb. Vysoké. Učení Tech. Brno* **1962**, *no.* 1–2, 183–190; *ibid.* **1962**, *no.* 3–4, 311–314.

The author carries out elementary computations with sums of the type $\sum_{m=1}^{p}\left(\frac{f(m)}{p}\right)$, where $p$ is an odd prime, $\left(\frac{a}{p}\right)$ is the Legendre symbol, and $f$ is an integer-valued polynomial of a rather simple kind. It is not clear whether there is a major objective, but the author does prove, for example, that (Theorem 2) if $p=2dk+1$, $d$ even, then $p$ is the sum of $d$ squares, $p=a_0^2+\cdots+a_{d-1}^2$, where the $a_i$ are values taken by $\alpha^{-1}\sum_m\left(\frac{m(m^d+a)}{p}\right)$ (shown always to be an integer) at a well-defined set of values of $a$. This generalises the well-known constructive proof of Euler's result (the case $d=2$).

*H. Halberstam* (Nottingham)

## L10-14 (34# 4224 )

**Ayoub, R.; Chowla, S.; Walum, H.**

**On sums involving quadratic characters.**

*J. London Math. Soc.* **42** (1967), 152–154.

Let $S(k)=\sum_{n=1}^{p-1} n^k(n/p)$, where $p$ is a prime of the form $4j+3$ and $(n/p)$ is Legendre's symbol; then $S(k)<0$ for $k=1$, 2 and for $k \geqq p-2$.

Using a deep theorem of P. T. Bateman, the second author and P. Erdős [Publ. Math. Debrecen **1** (1950), 165–182; MR **12**, 244], the authors show that there exist infinitely many primes $p$ for which $S(3)>0$, and infinitely many for which $S(3)<0$. They ask whether there exists a $k_0$ such that $S(k)<0$ for all $k>k_0$ and all primes $p\equiv 3 \pmod 4$.

*H. Gupta* (Allahabad)

Citations: MR 12, 244b = M20-13.

Referred to in L10-20.

## L10-15 (35# 1558 )

**Perel'muter, G. I.**

**The problem of estimation of certain arithmetic sums. (Russian)**

*Certain Problems in the Theory of Fields (Russian), pp.* 6–15. *Izdat. Saratov. Univ., Saratov*, 1964.

The author studies the sums

$$S_1 = \sum_{\xi_1=0}^{q-1}\cdots\sum_{\xi_n=0}^{q-1}\exp((2\pi i/q)f(\xi_1, \cdots, \xi_n)),$$

$S_2=\sum_{\xi_1=0}^{q-1}\cdots\sum_{\xi_n=0}^{q-1}\chi(f(\xi_1, \cdots, \xi_n))$, where $q$ is a prime and $\chi$ is a non-principal character mod $q$. When $n=1$ such sums were estimated sharply by A. Weil (following earlier estimates by Mordell and others). The author proves that $S_2=\sum_j\beta_j^{-1}-\sum_i\alpha_i^{-1}$, where $\alpha$ and $\beta$ run over zeros and poles of a certain $L$-function $L(t)$. (See A. Weil [Proc. Nat. Acad. Sci. U.S.A. **34** (1948), 204–207; MR **10**, 234; Bull. Amer. Math. Soc. **55** (1949), 497–508; MR **10**, 592], B. Dwork [Amer. J. Math. **82** (1960), 631–648; MR **25** #3914] and S. Lang [Bull. Soc. Math. France **84** (1956), 385–407; MR **19**, 578; Ann. of Math. (2) **64** (1956), 285–325; MR **18**, 672].) *S. Chowla* (University Park, Pa.)

Citations: MR 10, 234e = T25-5; MR 10, 592e = T50-8; MR 18, 672b = G25-4; MR 19, 578c = G25-8; MR 25# 3914 = G25-20.

## L10-16 (36# 132 )

**Whiteman, Albert Leon**

**Theorems on Brewer and Jacobsthal sums. II.**

*Michigan Math. J.* **12** (1965), 65–80.

This paper continues the study begun in Part I [Proc. Sympos. Pure Math., Vol. VIII, pp. 44–55, Amer. Math. Soc., Providence, R.I., 1965; MR **31** #137]. Let $V_n(x)$ be the polynomial determined by the recurrence relation $V_{n+2}(x)=xV_{n+1}(x)-V_n(x)$ $(n=1, 2, \cdots)$, with $V_1(x)=x$, $V_2(x)=x^2-2$.

B. W. Brewer [Trans. Amer. Math. Soc. **99** (1961), 241–245; MR **22** #10959] has defined $\Lambda_n=\sum_{s=0}^{p-1}\chi(V_n(s))$, where $\chi(s)$ is Legendre's symbol and $p$ is a prime. The principal object of this paper is the evaluation of $\Lambda_5$ together with some applications. The method of proof is based on a theory of cyclotomy modulo a prime $p=E(2f+1)-1$ and upon certain Eisenstein sums. We quote a result. Let $p=20f+9=u^2+5v^2=x^2+4y^2$ with $x\equiv 1$ (4). If $5\nmid x$ let $u$ be uniquely determined by $u\equiv x$ (mod 5); then $\Lambda_5=0$ if $5|x$, and $\Lambda_5=4u$ if $5\nmid x$.

*R. Ayoub* (University Park, Pa.)

Citations: MR 22# 10959 = L10-5; MR 31# 137 = L10-9.

## L10-17 (37# 2706 )

**Robinson, S. F.**

**Theorems on Brewer sums.**

*Pacific J. Math.* **25** (1968), 587–596.

Let $p$ be an odd prime and let $m$ be an integer. If we define the polynomial $V_m(x, Q)$ by

$$V_m(x, Q) = 2Q^{m/2}\cos\{m \arccos(\tfrac{1}{2}xQ^{-1/2})\},$$

then the Brewer sum $\Lambda_m(Q)$ is given by $\Lambda_m(Q)=\sum_{x=0}^{p-1}\chi(V_m(x, Q))$, where $\chi(k)=\left(\frac{k}{p}\right)$ is Legendre's symbol. The main result of the paper is the duplication formula $\Lambda_{2n}(Q)=\Lambda_n(Q^2)+\frac{1}{2}\sum_{x=0}^{p-1}\chi(1+x^{2d})$, where $n$ is odd and $d=(n, p-1)$. The sum here is the so-called Jacobsthal sum.

*D. H. Lehmer* (Berkeley, Calif.)

## L10-18 (37# 5164 )

**Chowla, S.**

**Observation on a theorem of Stark.**

*Norske Vid. Selsk. Forh. (Trondheim)* **40** (1967), 34–36.

The object of this note is to prove that an exponential sum appearing in Stark's solution of the 10th discriminant problem [H. M. Stark, Michigan Math. J. **14** (1967), 1–27; MR **36** #5102] can be expressed in terms of Kloostermann sums.

Let $Q(x, y)=ax^2+bxy+cy^2$, $d=b^2-4ac<0$, $a>0$, $\chi$ a real nonprincipal character mod $k$. The sum in question is $T=\sum_{l=0}^{k-1}\chi(Q(l, y))\,e^{2\pi inl/(yk)}e^{\pi inb/(ak)}$, $n$ an integer $\geqq 1$. The details are carried out in case $k$ is a prime and $Q(x, y)$ is the special form $x^2+y^2$. The generalization to an arbitrary form $Q$ and $k$ a prime is easily carried out.

*R. Ayoub* (University Park, Pa.)

Citations: MR 36# 5102 = R14-62.

## L10-19 (38# 109)

**Chowla, S.**

**On some character sums.**

*Norske Vid. Selsk. Forh. (Trondheim)* **40** (1967), 62–66.

The author determines exactly the value of the sum

$$S(Q, m_1, m_2) = \sum_{0\leq\alpha,\beta<k} \chi(Q(\alpha, \beta))e((m_1\alpha+m_2\beta)/k),$$

where $e(x)=e^{2\pi ix}$, $Q(x, y)=ax^2+bxy+cy^2$ is a quadratic form with $ac\neq 0$, and $\chi$ is a character modulo $k$. The case when $k=p$ is prime and $Q(x, y)=gx^2+y^2$ is investigated, using the classical sign determination of the Gauss sum.

Application of this result will be given in another paper of the author. *T. Kubota* (Nagoya)

## L10-20 (40# 4214)

**Fine, N. J.**

**On a question of Ayoub, Chowla and Walum concerning character sums.**

*Illinois J. Math.* **14** (1970), 88–90.

Let $p$ be a prime $\equiv 3 \pmod 4$ and let $S(k)=\sum_{n=1}^{p-1}(n/p)n^k$, where $(n/p)$ is the Legendre symbol. R. Ayoub, S. Chowla and H. Walum [J. London Math. Soc. **42** (1967), 152–154; MR **34** #4224] have noted that $S(0)=0$, $S(1)<0$, $S(2)<0$. They have also proved that for $k=3$ there are infinitely many $p\equiv 3 \pmod 4$ for which $S(k)>0$ and infinitely many for which $S(k)<0$. Using methods similar to theirs, the author proves that this is true for each real $k>2$. *K. S. Williams* (Ottawa, Ont.)

Citations: MR 34# 4224 = L10-14.

## L10-21 (40# 5574)

**Chowla, Paromita**

**A new proof and generalization of some theorems of Brewer.**

*Norske Vid. Selsk. Forh. (Trondheim)* **41** (1968), 1–3.

Let $k$ be a prime $>3$ and let $p$ be an odd prime such that $p\not\equiv \pm 1 \pmod k$. Put

$$g(2m) = (m+\sqrt{(m^2-a)})^k+(m-\sqrt{(m^2-a)})^k,$$

so that $g(m)$ is a polynomial in $m$ of degree $k$. The author proves that if $\chi$ is any non-principal character $(\bmod p)$, then $\sum_{m=1}^{p}\chi(g(m))=0$. This result was previously proved by B. W. Brewer [Trans. Amer. Math. Soc. **99** (1961), 241–245; MR **22** #10959] in the special case where $k=5$, $a=1$ and $\chi(t)$ is the Legendre symbol. The author derives her result as an immediate consequence of the following theorem. If $p$ is an odd prime not $\equiv\pm 1 \pmod k$, then $g(m)$ is a substitution polynomial $(\bmod p)$, that is, a polynomial such that $g(x)\equiv g(y) \pmod p$ implies $x\equiv y \pmod p$. *A. L. Whiteman* (Los Angeles, Calif.)

Citations: MR 22# 10959 = L10-5.

## L10-22 (43# 220)

**Korobov, N. M.**

**An estimate of the sum of the Legendre symbols. (Russian)**

*Dokl. Akad. Nauk SSSR* **196** (1971), 764–767.

Let $n\geq 3$ be an odd integer and let $p$ be a prime. Put $f(x)=\sum_{i\leq n}a_ix^i$, where $a_i$ are integers and $(a_n, p)=1$. From results of Hasse and Weil, it is known that

$$|S| = \sum_{x\leq p}(f(x)/p) \leq (n-1)p^{1/2}.$$

In the present note, communicated through A. N. Kolmogorov, it is shown that in certain cases an improved upper bound for $|S|$ can be obtained. Specifically, if $(n^2+9)/2\leq p$ then $|S|\leq(n-1)(p-(n-3)(n-4)/4)^{1/2}$. The linchpin for the proof consists in establishing two difficult polynomial incongruences mod $p$.

{This article has appeared in English translation [Soviet Math. Dokl. **12** (1971), 241–245].}

*A. A. Mullin* (Long Binh)

## L10-23 (43# 1932)

**Williams, Kenneth S.**

**A class of character sums.**

*J. London Math. Soc.* (2) **3** (1971), 67–72.

Let $p$ denote an odd prime, $\chi$ a multiplicative character $(\bmod p)$, $e(t)=\exp(2\pi it/p)$ ($t$ real), and $r_1(x)$ and $r_2(x)$ rational functions of $x$ with integral coefficients. G. I. Perel'muter [Uspehi Mat. Nauk **18** (1963), no. 2 (110), 145–149; MR **26** #6137] has given conditions under which the sum $\sum^*{}_{x=0}^{p-1}\chi(r_1(x))e(r_2(x))=O(p^{1/2})$ (the asterisk indicates that the singularities of $r_1$ and $r_2$ are excluded). The present paper is concerned with the character sum $S_p(k, r_1, r_2, \chi)=\sum^*{}_{x=0}^{p-1}x^k\chi(r_1(x))e(r_2(x))$ $(k=1, 2, 3, \cdots)$. Put $S_p(r_1, r_2, \chi)=\sum^*{}_{x=1}^{p-1}\chi(r_1(x))e(r_2(x))$, for any integer $m$ define $\bar{m}(x)=mx$ and put

$$\Phi_p = \Phi_p(r_1, r_2, \chi) = \max_{0\leq m<p}|S_p(r_1, r_2+\bar{m}, \chi)|.$$

If $r_1$ and $r_2+\bar{m}$ $(0\leq m<p)$ satisfy Perel'muter's conditions then $\Phi_p=O(p^{1/2})$. The author's main result is that $S_p(k, r_1, r_2, \chi)=O(\Phi_p p^k \log p)$.

As an application he proves that $\sum_{x=1}^{p-1}x^k(x/p)=O(p^{k+1/2}\log p)$ $(k=1, 2, 3, \cdots)$.

*L. Carlitz* (Durham, N.C.)

## L10-24 (44# 3974)

**Pulatova, M. I.**

**The construction of periodic functions that have a generalized theorem of multiplication. (Russian. Uzbek summary)**

*Izv. Akad. Nauk UzSSR Ser. Fiz.-Mat. Nauk* **15** (1971), no. 2, 17–20.

Let $f(x)$ have period 1. If for a certain multiplicative function $\omega$ the equality $\omega(N)\cdot f(Nx)=\sum_{n=0}^{N-1}f(x+n/N)$ is valid and $F(x)=\sum_{d|N}\mu(d)\cdot\omega(d)\cdot f(xd)$ then the sum $\sum_{n=0}^{N-1}\chi(n)\cdot F(x+n/N)$ for the principal character $\chi=\chi_0 \pmod N$ is equal to $\chi_0(N)\cdot\omega(N)\cdot F(Nx)$, and for non-principal $\chi$ it is invariant under the substitution $F\to f$.

*A. I. Vinogradov* (Leningrad)

Citations: MR 26# 6137 = T25-17.

## L10-25 (44# 3987)

**Yamauchi, Masatoshi**

**Some identities on the character sum containing $x(x-1)(x-\lambda)$.**

*Nagoya Math. J.* **42** (1971), 109–113.

There are exactly $\frac{1}{2}(p-1)$ values $\lambda$ for which the corresponding elliptic curve $y^2=x(x-1)(x-\lambda)$ in characteristic $p\neq 2$ is hyperelliptic; one can ask how many of these values for $\lambda$ are already in the prime field $\mathbf{F}_p$. The answer is 0 if $p\equiv 1 \pmod 4$, and $3h(-p)$ if $p=3 \pmod 4$, where $h(-p)=$ class number of $Q(\sqrt{-p})$. This result is one of the corollaries that the author derives from interesting relations between sums of powers of elements of the form $\sum_{x\in\mathbf{F}_p}(x(x-1)(x-\lambda)/p)$ (Legendre symbol used), and eigenvalues of certain Hecke operators.

*F. Oort* (Amsterdam)

# L15 WEYL SUMS

See also Sections D72, K05, K10, K15, P04, P08.

See also reviews K05-1, K05-4, K10-26, L02-4, L05-2, L05-17, L20-1, L20-16, M15-18, M15-20, N02-6, N04-24, P02-5, P04-50, P08-2, P08-11.

## L15-1 (1, 66d)

**van der Corput, J. G. Sur un lemme de M. Vinogradow.** Nederl. Akad. Wetensch., Proc. **42**, 867–871 (1939).

The author considers the sum

$$S_m = \sum_{x,y} \psi(x)\omega(y)e(mf(xy)), \qquad e(u)=e^{2\pi i u},$$

where $m$ is a positive integer, $f(u)=\frac{1}{2}\alpha u^2+\beta u$ ($\alpha$, $\beta$ real),

$$\left|\alpha-\frac{a}{q}\right| \leqq \frac{\tau}{q^2}, \quad a, q \text{ integers}; q>0; (a, q)=1; \tau \geqq 1,$$

and the summation is over a certain set $E$ of lattice points $(x, y)$. It is proved that, if $\psi(x)$ and $\omega(y)$ are defined for $|x|\leqq A$, $|y|\leqq B$ ($A, B\geqq 2$) and satisfy

$$\sum_{|x|\leqq A} |\psi(x)|^2 \leqq A\Psi^2, \qquad \sum_{|y|\leqq B} |\omega(y)|^2 \leqq B\Omega^2,$$

and if $E$ lies in the rectangle $|x|\leqq A$, $|y|\leqq B$ and is such that for each $x$ the range of $y$ is a set of consecutive integers, then

$$|S_m| \leqq c_1 AB\Psi\Omega\left(\frac{1}{A^{1/4}}+(\log AB)^{(3l-1)/4l}\xi_m^{(l-1)/4l}\right),$$

where $l$ is any integer not less than 2, $c_1$ depends only on $l$, and

$$\xi_m = \left(m\tau+\frac{q}{B}\right)\left(\frac{1}{q}+\frac{1}{A^2B}\right).$$

Vinogradow considered the case in which $\psi(x)=1$, $\tau=1$, and $E$ is defined by $Y_0<y\leqq Y_1$, $0<xy\leqq N$ ($1\leqq Y_0<Y_1\leqq N$, $N\geqq 3$). The proof is similar in principle in the general case, and amounts in effect to estimating the "maximum" of a bilinear form by the inequality

$$\left|\sum_{x,y} a_{x,y}u_xv_y\right|^4 \leqq \left(\sum_x |u_x|^2\right)^2\left(\sum_y |v_y|^2\right)^2 \sum_{x,x',y,y'} a_{x,y}\bar{a}_{x',y}\bar{a}_{x,y'}a_{x',y'},$$

where $x$ and $y$ range over the intervals $|x|\leqq A$ and $|y|\leqq B$, $u_x=\psi(x)$, $v_y=\omega(y)$, and $a_{x,y}$ is $e(mf(xy))$, when $(x, y)$ belongs to $E$, and zero otherwise. The last sum is estimated by summing first for $y$, $y'$, and using the conditions on $E$.

*A. E. Ingham* (Berkeley, Calif.).

## L15-2 (2, 150b)

**Hua, Loo-Keng. On a lemma due to Vinogradow.** C. R. (Doklady) Acad. Sci. URSS (N.S.) **24**, 419–420 (1939).

Set

$$\phi = \left|\sum_{x=1}^{P} \exp(2\pi i(\alpha_n x^n+\cdots+\alpha_1 x))\right|,$$

$$I_r = \int_0^1 \cdots \int_0^1 \phi^r d\alpha_1\cdots d\alpha_n.$$

Vinogradow proved [Rec. Math. [Mat. Sbornik] N.S. **3** (45), 435–470 (1938)] that $I_r \ll P^{r-\frac{1}{2}n(n+1)}$, where $r$ is the greatest even integer less than $Ln(n+1)(n+2)\log n$, and $L_2=4.81, \cdots, L_{13}=4.12$, $L_n=4.10$ if $n\geqq 14$. Hua states an improvement for $n\leqq 10$, namely $I_s<KP^{s-\frac{1}{2}n(n+1)+\epsilon}$, where $s=2n+2^tu+2^{t+1}(t+2)+\cdots+2^{n-1}n$, and $t$ is the least integer such that $u=\frac{1}{2}(t+1)(t+2)-n\geqq 0$, and the constant $K$ depends only on $n$ and $\epsilon$. He proves that for $2t>\frac{1}{2}n(n+1)$, $I_{2t}\gg P^{2t-\frac{1}{2}n(n+1)}$.

*G. Pall* (Princeton, N. J.).

## L15-3 (2, 150c)

**Hua, Loo-Keng. On a theorem due to Vinogradow.** Quart. J. Math., Oxford Ser. **11**, 161–176 (1940).

Proof is given of results for $2\leqq n\leqq 10$ slightly better than those announced in the paper reviewed above. *G. Pall.*

Referred to in P02-5.

## L15-4 (2, 249g)

**Mardjanichvili, C. et Segal, B. Sur une estimation des sommes de Weyl.** C. R. (Doklady) Acad. Sci. URSS (N.S.) **26**, 731–734 (1940).

Let $n\geqq 2$; $\alpha, \alpha_1, \cdots, \alpha_n$ be real numbers, $f(x)=\alpha x^n+\alpha_1 x^{n-1}+\cdots+\alpha_n$; $Q$ and $P$ ($\geqq 3$) be integers. J. G. van der Corput [Nederl. Akad. Wetensch., Proc. **42**, 461–467 (1939)] obtained an excellent upper bound for the Weyl sum $S=|\sum e^{2\pi i f(x)}|$ (summed over $x=Q+1, \cdots, Q+P$), involving an undetermined constant $c=c(n, \epsilon)$. A similar result is here derived, with an explicit $c$; it is proved that

$$|S|^{2^{n-1}} < 11(l-1)(4P)^{2^{n-1}}\mu^{\sigma}((\Lambda+q/P)(1/q+1/P^{n-1}))^{1-\epsilon},$$

where $\alpha=a/q+\lambda/q^2$, $q>0$, $(a, q)=1$, $|\lambda|\leqq\Lambda$, $\Lambda\geqq 1$; $0<\epsilon\leqq\frac{1}{2}$; $l$ is the least integer not less than $1/\epsilon$, $\mu=\log P^{n-1}+(n-1)^l-1$, and $l\sigma=(n-1)^l-1$. If $n\geqq 3$, the factor $11(l-1)$ can be replaced by 8; if $f(x)$ is replaced by $mf(x)$, where $m$ is an integer not less than 1, $\Lambda$ is replaced in the right member by $\Lambda m$. Use is made of an upper bound due to Mardjanichvili [same C. R. **22**, 387–389 (1939)], for $\tau_k{}^l(1)+\cdots+\tau_k{}^l(n)$, where $\tau_k{}^l(h)$ is the number of solutions of $x_1x_2\cdots x_k=h$.

*G. Pall* (Princeton, N. J.).

## L15-5 (4, 211e)

**Vinogradow, I. M. On the estimation of trigonometrical sums.** C. R. (Doklady) Acad. Sci. URSS (N.S.) **34**, 182–183 (1942).

Several improvements are stated of results in Vinogradow's book [A New Method in the Analytical Theory of Numbers, Trav. Inst. Math. Stekloff, vol. 10, 1937]: (i) on an upper bound to $\sum \exp(2\pi i F(x))$ ($x=Q+1, \cdots, Q+P$), where $f(x)=a_nx^n+\cdots+a_1x$, $a_n=a/q+\theta/q^2$, etc.; (ii) and (iii) Hardy and Littlewood's asymptotic formula for the number of representations by $x_1{}^n+\cdots+x_r{}^n$ ($n>10$) and Vinogradow's similar formula for $p_1{}^n+\cdots+p_r{}^n$ both hold for $r\geqq 20n^2\log n$; (iv) the remainder in the formula for $\pi(N)$ does not exceed $N\cdot\exp(-(\log N)^{0.6+\epsilon})$. Finally, lemma 6 of Vinogradow [Rec. Math. [Mat. Sbornik] N.S. **3**(45), 435–470 (1938)] can be improved, it is stated, to yield $T<40p^{r-\frac{1}{2}n(n+1)}$.

*G. Pall* (Montreal, Que.).

Referred to in P02-5.

## L15-6 (4, 211f)

**Vinogradow, I. An improvement of the estimation of trigonometrical sums.** Bull. Acad. Sci. URSS. Sér. Math. [Izvestia Akad. Nauk SSSR] **6**, 33–40 (1942). (Russian. English summary)

The proof of a result similar to that in (i) of the preceding review is given. As an application an improved estimate is obtained of the number of integers $x$ between 1 and $P$ for which the fractional part of $f(x)$ does not exceed a given number $r$.

*G. Pall* (Montreal, Que.).

## L15-7 (4, 211g)

**Linnik, U. V. On Weyl's sums.** C. R. (Doklady) Acad. Sci. URSS (N.S.) **34**, 184–186 (1942).

A proof is outlined that $|S|\leqq P^{1-s}$, $s=1/(22400n^2\ln n)$, where $S=\sum_{x=1}^{P}\exp 2\pi i\alpha f(x)$, $\alpha=a/q+\theta/q^2$, $(a, q)=1$, $|\theta|\leqq 1$, $f(x)=a_0x^n+\cdots+a_n$, $P\leqq q\leqq P^{n-1}$. The proof is based on an upper bound $p^{v-\frac{1}{2}n(n+1)+1/n^{50}}$ to the number of solutions $x_j$ of the system of Diophantine equations

$x_1^i + \cdots + x_v^i = M_i$ $(i=1, \cdots, n)$, where the $x_j$ assume certain sets of prime values. *G. Pall* (Montreal, Que.).

Referred to in D52-140.

## L15-8 (4, 211h)

**Linnik, U. New estimations of Weyl's sums by the method due to Vinogradow.** Bull. Acad. Sci. URSS. Sér. Math. [Izvestia Akad. Nauk SSSR] **6**, 41–70 (1942). (Russian. English summary)

Results are proved similar to that stated in the preceding review, but having $n^{14/5}$ in place of $n^2$. *G. Pall.*

## L15-9 (5, 142f)

**Linnik, U. V. New estimations of Weyl's sums by I. M. Vinogradow's method.** C. R. (Doklady) Acad. Sci. URSS (N.S.) **32**, 531–533 (1941).

This note contains a theorem which is an improvement on the results of Vinogradow concerning exponential sums. It reads as follows. Let $F(z) = Az^{n+1} + A_0 z^n + \cdots + A_{n+1}$, where the $A_i$ are real numbers and $A = a/q + \theta/q\tau$, $(a, q) = 1$, $|\theta| \leqq 1$, $q \leqq \tau$; $S = \sum_{z=1}^{P} e^{2\pi i F(z)}$. Then for $n > 2$ and every $\epsilon > 0$ we have

$$S = O\{P[P^{-1} p^{t+\epsilon}(1 + p^{-n} q \log q)]^{bk/2} + p\},$$

where $p > 0$ is an auxiliary variable,

$$t = \{1 - [n^{1/5}]/n\}^k \{n(n+1)/2\},$$

and $k$ is an arbitrary positive integer. There is a brief account of the method of proof but few details are given. From this theorem it follows that the Hardy-Littlewood asymptotic formula for the number of solutions of $N = x_1^n + \cdots + x_s^n$ holds when $s > c_1 n^{14/5} \log n$, where $c_1$ is a constant. *R. D. James* (Vancouver, B. C.).

## L15-10 (5, 200a)

**Linnik, U. V. On Weyl's sums.** Rec. Math. [Mat. Sbornik] N.S. **12**(54), 28–39 (1943). (English. Russian summary)

A modification of Vinogradow's method for Weyl sums is expounded to prove that, if $S = \sum_{x=1}^{P} \exp 2\pi i \alpha f(x)$, where $f(x) = a_0 x^n + \cdots + a_n$ (the $a_i$ integers), $\alpha = a/q + \theta/q^2$, $(a, q) = 1$, $|\theta| < 1$, $P \leqq q < P^{n-1}$, then $|S| \ll P^{1-1/(22400 n^2 \log n)}$. The fundamental lemma, whose proof is given at length, gives an estimate $p^{v - \frac{1}{2}n(n+1) + 1/n^{50}}$ to the number of solutions of the system $x_1^i + \cdots + x_v^i = M_i$ $(i = 1, \cdots, n)$, where the $x_i$ run over certain products $(< p)$ of primes, and $v = 32n[100 n \log n]$. *G. Pall* (Montreal, Que.).

## L15-11 (6, 170i)

**Vinogradoff, I. M. General theorems on the estimations of trigonometric sums.** C. R. (Doklady) Acad. Sci. URSS (N.S.) **43**, 47–48 (1944).

New improvements in the author's well-known estimations of trigonometrical sums are announced. The main theorem is as follows. Let $m$, $Q$, $P$ be integers, $m > 0$, $P > 0$,

$$F(x) = a_{n+1} x^{n+1} + \cdots + a_1 x, \qquad n \geqq 11,$$

$a_{n+1}, \cdots, a_1$ real numbers, one of which, $a_s$, satisfies

$$a_s = a q^{-1} + \theta q^{-2}, \qquad (a, q) = 1; \ |\theta| \leqq 1.$$

Then

$$\left| \sum_{x=Q+1}^{Q+P} e^{2\pi i m F(x)} \right| \leqq C P^{1-\rho_\nu} m^{2\rho_\nu},$$

where $C$ is an absolute constant and $\rho_1 = \tau/3n^2 \log(5n\tau^{-\frac{1}{2}})$ if $1 < q \leqq P$, $q = P^\tau$, $\rho_2 = 1/3n^2 \log(5n)$ if $P \leqq q \leqq P^s$, $\rho_3 = \tau/3n^2 \log(5n\tau^{-\frac{1}{2}})$if $P^s \leqq q \leqq P^{s+1}$, $q = P^{s+1-\tau}$. Proofs are to be published in a forthcoming book. *E. C. Titchmarsh.*

Referred to in K35-4.

## L15-12 (11, 646d)

**Teghem, J. Sommes de Weyl. Sur la méthode de Vinogradow–van der Corput.** Acad. Roy. Belgique. Cl. Sci. Mém. Coll. in 8°. (2) **23**, no. 5, 50 pp. (1949).

This paper is devoted to the detailed proof of three theorems on the so-called Weyl sums $S = \sum_{x=Q+1}^{Q+X} \exp\{2\pi i f(x)\}$. Here $f(x)$ is a real polynomial of degree $k \geqq 2$ or, more generally, a real function on the integers whose $(k+1)$th difference is small, $X$ is an integer not less than $k+2$, and $Q$ is any integer whatever. The theorems give improved estimates of $S$, the statements of which are too long to quote here. The work follows the lines of van der Corput's form of the method of Vinogradov [cf. Mathematica, Zutphen. B. **5**, 1–30 (1936)]. The author has already indicated the applications of the results of the present memoir [C. R. Congrès Sci. Math. Liége, 1939, pp. 84–88; Bull. Soc. Roy. Sci. Liége **11**, 4–6 (1942); Acad. Roy. Belgique. Bull. Cl. Sci. (5) **34**, 593–603 (1948); these Rev. **7**, 146; **10**, 354]. *P. T. Bateman* (Urbana, Ill.).

Citations: MR 7, 146a = K05-4; MR 10, 354j = J24-9.

## L15-13 (12, 161a)

**Vinogradov, I. M. The upper bound of the modulus of a trigonometric sum.** Izvestiya Akad. Nauk SSSR. Ser. Mat. **14**, 199–214 (1950). (Russian)

The author gives a detailed, self-contained proof of the following theorem. Suppose $f(x) = a_{n+1} x^{n+1} + \cdots + a_1 x$ is a polynomial with real coefficients of degree $n+1 \geqq 12$, $m$ and $p$ are positive integers, and $S = \sum_{x=1}^{p} \exp\{2\pi i m f(x)\}$. Let $r$ be one of the numbers $2, 3, \cdots, n+1$ and suppose that $a_r = a/q + \theta/q^2$, where $a$ and $q$ are integers, $1 < q < p^r$, $(a, q) = 1$ and $|\theta| \leqq 1$. Put $\tau = (\log q)/(\log p)$ if $1 < q < p$, $\tau = 1$ if $p \leqq q \leqq p^{r-1}$, and $\tau = r - (\log q)/(\log p)$ if $p^{r-1} < q < p^r$. Then $|S| < 8 n^{\frac{1}{2}nl} m^{2\rho/\tau} p^{1-\rho}$, where $l = \ln\{12n(n+1)/\tau\}$ and $\rho = \pi/(3n^2 l)$. Previous papers of the author and others have considered only the case $r = n+1$. *P. T. Bateman.*

Referred to in D80-49, L15-14, L15-15, P08-16, Z10-51.

## L15-14 (13, 328e)

**Vinogradov, I. M. General theorems on the upper bound of the modulus of a trigonometric sum.** Izvestiya Akad. Nauk SSSR. Ser. Mat. **15**, 109–130 (1951). (Russian)

This paper is devoted to the determination of upper bounds for sums and integrals of the form

$$S = \sum_{x=1}^{P} \exp[2\pi i\{\alpha_{n+1} x^{n+1} + f(x)\} m],$$

$$H = \int_0^1 \cdots \int_0^1 |S|^\tau d\alpha_n \cdots d\alpha_1$$

when $f(x) = \alpha_n x^n + \cdots + \alpha_1 x$ and $m = 1$. Particular attention is paid to the determination of the parameters involved in the $O$-estimates for $S$ and $H$. Such explicit determinations of the parameters are needed, for example, in the estimation of $\zeta(s)$ near the line $\sigma = 1$ and a number of such results have been given by Hua [Quart. J. Math., Oxford Ser. (1) **20**, 48–61 (1949); these Rev. **10**, 597] and Flett [Quart. J. Math., Oxford Ser. (2) **2**, 26–52 (1951); these Rev. **13**, 209].

Lemmas 3 and 7 of this paper estimate $H$ explicitly, thereby providing mean-value theorems which may be compared with a related $O$-estimate on p. 73 of Vinogradov's book [Trudy Mat. Inst. Steklov **23** (1947); these Rev. **10**, 599], with the $O$-estimate on p. 49 of Hua's book [Trudy Mat. Inst. Steklov **22** (1947); these Rev. **10**, 597] and the explicit estimate of Theorem 1 of Hua's paper.

Theorem 1a explicitly estimates $S$ when $\alpha_{n+1} = 0$, $m = 1$, and suitable upper and lower bounds for $|f^{(n+1)}(x)|$ are known; this result is to be compared with the $O$-estimate on p. 68 of Vinogradov's book and with Flett's Theorem B which has a wider range of applicability. Theorems 2–5 deal with the explicit estimation of $S$ when $f(x)=\alpha_n x^n+\cdots+\alpha_1 x$ and diophantine inequalities are known for the real coefficients $\alpha_k$; the number $m$ is generally unrestricted (because of possible application to questions of uniform distribution and related problems). More specifically, Theorems 2 and 4 treat the case in which for some $s$ between 2 and $n+1$ it is known that $|\alpha_s-a/q|\leqq 1/q^2$ with $(a, q)=1$ and $1<q<P^s$; the results are similar to the $O$-estimate on p. 63 of Vinogradov's book and may be compared with the $O$-estimates on pp. 65 and 68 of Hua's book. A novel feature is introduced in Theorems 3 and 5 in which it is assumed that $|\alpha_s-a_s/q_s|\leqq 1/(Pq_s)$ with $(a_s, q_s)=1$, $0<q_s\leqq P$ for each $s=2, \cdots, n+1$; the explicit estimate is now given in terms of $Q$, the least common multiple of $q_2, \cdots, q_{n+1}$ provided $m\leqq P^{.05\tau/n}$ where $\tau=1$ if $Q\geqq P$ and $\tau=\log Q/\log P$ otherwise. Under the above assumptions, Theorem 3 gives the result $|S|\leqq(8n)^{.5nl}P^{1-\rho}$ where $\rho=\tau\{3n(n+1)l\}^{-1}$ and $l=\log\{12(n+1)^2/\tau\}$. The proofs depend in some measure on a previous paper of the author [Izvestiya Akad. Nauk SSSR. Ser. Mat. **14**, 199–214 (1950); these Rev. **12**, 161] and follow methods used previously by the author.

*L. Schoenfeld* (Urbana, Ill.).

Citations: MR 10, 597d = P08-11; MR 10, 597e = P02-5; MR 10, 599a = L02-2; MR 12, 161a = L15-13; MR 13, 209b = R42-7.

Referred to in D52-120, L15-15, M15-19, M15-20, M35-11, P44-17, Z10-51.

## L15-15 (16, 1089e)

**Vinogradov, I. M. Part I. Improvement of the remainder term of some asymptotic formulas. Part II. An upper bound of the modulus of a trigonometric sum. Part III. General theorems on the upper bound of the modulus of a trigonometric sum.** Amer. Math. Soc. Translation no. **94**, 66 pp. (1953).

Translated from Izv. Akad. Nauk SSSR **13**, 97–110 (1949); **14**, 199–214 (1950); **15**, 109–130 (1951); MR **11**, 233; **12**, 161; **13**, 328.

Citations: MR 11, 233d = E16-12; MR 12, 161a = L15-13; MR 13, 328e = L15-14.

Referred to in M35-11, Z10-51.

## L15-16 (19, 839b)

**Vinogradov, I. M. Trigonometric sums involving values of a polynomial.** Izv. Akad. Nauk SSSR. Ser. Mat. **21** (1957), 145–170. (Russian)

Let $f(x)=A_nx^n+\cdots+A_1x$ be a real polynomial of degree $n$ without constant term. Let $P$ and $k$ be positive integers. In the present paper the author improves his previous estimates [same Izv. **20** (1956), 289–302; MR **18**, 381] of trigonometric sums

$$S=\sum \exp\{2\pi ikf(x)\},$$

where $x$ runs through all integers, or else through all primes, from 1 to $P$. (The case $n=1$ was a key step in his attack on the Goldbach conjecture.) Each theorem exhibits two different estimates, depending on whether the coefficients $A_n, \cdots, A_1$ of $f$ are of the "first class" or not. For instance, Theorem 2 (in which the sum $S$ is taken over primes, and which the author designates as the principal theorem of the paper) puts $A_n, \cdots, A_1$ in the first class when they can be approximated by irreducible fractions $a_n/q_n, \cdots, a_1/q_1$ with the l.c.m. $Q$ of $q_1, \cdots, q_n$ not exceeding $P^{1/n}$ and with each $|A_s-a_s/q_s|\leqq P^{1/n}/P^s$. In this case, letting $r=1/(62^2\ln 12n^2)$, and keeping $k\leqq P^{2r}$, he proves $S=O(P^{1-r})$. On the other hand, when $A_n, \cdots, A_1$ cannot be so approximated he imposes the weaker restriction $k\leqq Q^{1/r}$ and proves $S=O(P^{1+\varepsilon}((k, Q)/Q)^{1/2n})$, for each positive $\varepsilon$. The author also states that a substantial further improvement of the estimate for $S$ is possible when $A_n, \cdots, A_1$ belong to the first class. *H. Mirkil.*

Citations: MR 18, 381f = L20-16.

Referred to in L20-18.

## L15-17 (20# 5264)

**Vinogradov, I. M. A multiple integral.** Izv. Akad. Nauk SSSR. Ser. Mat. **22** (1958), 577–584. (Russian)

An improved estimate is given for the integral

$$\int_0^1\cdots\int_0^1 |T_0|^{2b}d\alpha_n\cdots d\alpha_1,$$

where

$$T_0=\sum_{0<x\leq p_0}\exp 2\pi i(\alpha_nx^n+\cdots+\alpha_1x).$$

*Author's summary*

Referred to in L20-19.

## L15-18 (20# 6393)

**Korobov, N. M. Estimation of rational trigonometrical sums.** Dokl. Akad. Nauk SSSR (N.S.) **118** (1958), 231–232. (Russian)

The author announces a new estimate for exponential sums of the form

$$S=\sum_{x=1}^{P} e((a_{n+1}x^{n+1}+\cdots+a_1x)/q),\quad e(\theta)=e^{2\pi i\theta},$$

where $a_{n+1}, \cdots, a_1, q$ are integers and $(a_{n+1}, q)=1$. The improvement relates to the dependence on $n$, which is important for certain applications (see next review). Put $P=q^{1/r}$, and suppose $1<r<n+1$. Suppose also that the least prime divisor of $q$ is greater than $n+1$. Then the new estimate is

$$|S|\leqq CP^{1-\rho},\quad \rho=\frac{\alpha r(n+1-r)}{n^4l^2},$$

where $C$ and $\alpha$ are absolute constants and $l=\log(2n/(n+1-r))$. The proof is said to make essential use of the fact that the polynomial has rational coefficients, and to depend on the following auxiliary result. Let $n, r, k, \tau, q, P$ be integers satisfying

$$1\leqq r\leqq n,\quad \tau\geqq 1,\quad k>n(n+\tau),\quad q>2k,$$

$$\left(\frac{q}{2k}\right)^{1/(r+1)}<P\leqq\left(\frac{q}{2k}\right)^{1/r}.$$

Then the number of solutions of the $n$ simultaneous congruences

$$x_1^s+\cdots+x_k^s\equiv y_1^s+\cdots+y_k^s \pmod q,\quad 1\leqq s\leqq n,$$

with $x_1, \cdots, y_k$ between 1 and $P$, is less than

$$\exp(c(n+\tau)k\log k)P^{2k-\nu},$$

$$\nu=\tfrac{1}{2}r(2n+1-r)-\tfrac{1}{2}r(n+1)(1-1/n)^\tau.$$

This is said to be proved by the methods of Vinogradov. The estimate is nearly best possible if $\tau$ is large.

*H. Davenport* (Cambridge, England)

Referred to in D52-119, L15-21.

## L15-19 (20# 6394)

**Korobov, N. M. On zeros of the $\zeta(s)$ function.** Dokl. Akad. Nauk SSSR (N.S.) **118** (1958), 431–432. (Russian)

The author announces a further improvement in his estimate for exponential sums containing a polynomial with rational coefficients. With the notation of the preceding review, and with the same assumption about the least prime factor of $q$, suppose now that $n+\varepsilon\leqq r\leqq n+1-\varepsilon$, where $\varepsilon>0$. Then there exist an absolute constant $C$ and a constant $\alpha$ depending only on $\varepsilon$, such that

$$|S|\leqq CP^{1-\sigma},\quad \sigma=\frac{\alpha}{(n\log n)^{5/2}}.$$

This estimate is said to lead to the result

$$\zeta(1+it)=O(\log t)^{5/7+\varepsilon}$$

as $t\to\infty$, and (as a straightforward consequence)

$$\pi(x)=\operatorname{li} x+O(x\exp(-a(\log x)^{7/12-\varepsilon})),$$

where $a$ depends only on $\varepsilon$. The details will be awaited with interest. *H. Davenport* (Cambridge, England)

Referred to in L15-20, L15-21.

## L15-20 (20# 6395 )

**Korobov, N. M. New number-theoretic estimates.** Dokl. Akad. Nauk SSSR (N.S.) **119** (1958), 433–434. (Russian)

In a companion paper [#6394 above] the author proved the following theorem: For $n>1$, let $f(x)=\alpha_1x+\cdots+\alpha_{n+1}x^{n+1}$, where each $\alpha_\nu$ is real. Let $P$ and $Q$ be positive integers, $P>1$, and define $r$ by the equation $P^r=|\alpha_{n+1}^{-1}|$. If for every fixed $\delta$ satisfying $0<\delta<\frac{1}{2}$ we have $n+\delta\leqq r\leqq n+1-\delta$, then there exist an absolute constant $C$ and another constant $\alpha=\alpha(\delta)$ such that

$$\left|\sum_{x=Q+1}^{Q+P} e^{2\pi i f(x)}\right|<CP^{1-\alpha/(n\log n)^{5/2}}.$$

This is an improvement of similar estimates due to Vinogradov and Hua, and leads to corresponding improvements of estimates in various problems of analytic number theory. Improved results for $\zeta(1+it)$ and $\pi(x)-\operatorname{li}(x)$ are discussed in the paper above. In this paper he describes other improvements, for example

$$\sum_{n\leq x}\sigma(n)=\frac{\pi^2}{12}x^2+O(x\{\log x\}^{5/7+\varepsilon})$$

$$\sum_{n\leq x}\phi(n)=\frac{3}{\pi^2}x^2+O(x\{\log x\}^{5/7+\varepsilon}).$$

*T. M. Apostol* (Pasadena, Calif.)

Citations: MR 20# 6394 = L15-19.

Referred to in L15-21.

## L15-21 (21# 4939 )

**Korobov, N. M. Estimates of trigonometric sums and their applications.** Uspehi Mat. Nauk **13** (1958), no. 4 (82), 185–192. (Russian)

Let $f(x)=\alpha_1x+\alpha_2x^2+\cdots+\alpha_{n+1}x^{n+1}$ be a polynomial with real coefficients. For $\nu=s+2,\ s+3,\ \cdots,\ 3s$, where $1\leqq s\leqq(n+1)/3$, the coefficients $\alpha_\nu$ are assumed to be rational and $\alpha_\nu=a_\nu/q$, where $a_\nu$ and $q$ are integers. The $s$-rowed determinant

$$\left|\binom{s+i+j}{j}a_{s+i+j}\right| \quad (i,j = 1, 2, \cdots, s)$$

is denoted by $\Delta_s$. Let $\delta$ be a fixed positive number less than 1/3 and suppose that $n\delta\leqq s\leqq(n+1)/3$, $s+1\leqq r\leqq 2s(1-\delta)$, $q=P^r$ and $(\Delta_s, q)=1$, where $P$ and $r$ are integers. The author proves that there exist positive constants $C=C(\delta)$ and $\gamma=\gamma(\delta)$ such that

$$\left|\sum_{x=1}^{P} e^{2\pi i f(x)}\right| < CP^{1-\gamma/n^2}.$$

This represents an improvement of results announced by him in three earlier papers [Dokl. Akad. Nauk SSSR **118** (1958), 231–232, 431–432; **119** (1958), 433–434; MR **20** #6393, #6394, #6395]. The improvement consists mainly in the fact that only some of the coefficients need be rational. This enables him to approximate to $(1+x/Q)^{it}$ by a logarithmic series only some of whose coefficients are rational and have denominator $q$ satisfying $(\Delta_s, q)=1$. In this way he obtains the new estimate

$$\zeta(1+it) = O(\log^{2/3}|t|),$$

a result which he states has been obtained independently by I. M. Vinogradov, but not yet published by him.

Corresponding improvements can be obtained in other number-theoretic problems. Thus he obtains the estimates

$$\pi(x) = \operatorname{li} x+O\{x\exp(-a\log^{3/5}x)\}$$

and

$$\sum_{n\leq x}\sigma(n) = \frac{\pi^2}{12}x^2+O\{x(\log x)^{2/3+\varepsilon}\},$$

where $\sigma(n)$ is the sum of the divisors of $n$.

The proof of the estimate for the trigonometric sum depends on three lemmas which are too complicated to quote here; one of them is an application of a mean-value theorem of Vinogradov. *R. A. Rankin* (Glasgow)

Citations: MR 20# 6393 = L15-18; MR 20# 6394 = L15-19; MR 20# 6395 = L15-20.

Referred to in L02-8, L15-22, N48-10.

## L15-22 (21# 5610 )

**Korobov, N. M. Partially rational trigonometric sums.** Dokl. Akad. Nauk SSSR **125** (1959), 1193–1195. (Russian)

Let $f(x)=\alpha_1x+\cdots+\alpha_{n+1}x^{n+1}$ be a polynomial such that $\alpha_i$ is real for $1\leqq i\leqq s$ and $q\alpha_i$ is an integer for $s<i\leqq n+1$. Here $q$ is a prime and $(q, q\alpha_{n+1})=1$. By using estimations due to Weyl, Vinogradov and himself [see, in particular, Korobov, Uspehi Mat. Nauk **13** (1958), no. 4 (82), 185–192; MR **21** #4939], the author proves that

$$\left|\sum_{P<x\leqq P+q} e^{2\pi i f(x)}\right| \leqq q^{1-\gamma/(s^2\log 2s)}\exp\left\{\beta\left(\frac{\log n}{s^2\log 2s}+s\log^2 2s\right)\right\},$$

where $\beta$ and $\gamma$ are positive absolute constants, and $P$ is an arbitrary integer. Various improvements are mentioned. *R. A. Rankin* (Glasgow)

Citations: MR 21# 4939 = L15-21.

Referred to in L15-36.

## L15-23 (25# 1132 )

**Birch, B. J.; Davenport, H.**

**Note on Weyl's inequality.**

*Acta Arith.* 7 (1961/62), 273–277.

The following result is proved. Let $f(x_1, \cdots, x_n)$ be any form of degree $d$ in $n$ variables with integral coefficients which is expressible as a sum of $n$ $d$th powers of linear forms with real or complex coefficients and non-zero coefficients. Let $\Phi(x_1, \cdots, x_n)$ be any real polynomial of degree less than $d$. Let

$$S_n = \sum_{x_1=1}^{P_1}\cdots\sum_{x_n=1}^{P_n} e[af(x_1,\cdots,x_n)+\Phi(x_1, \cdots, x_n)],$$

where $e(z)=e^{2\pi iz}$, $0<P_j\leqq P$, $|a-h/q|<q^{-2}$, $(h, q)=1$, and $P\leqq q\leqq P^{d-1}$. Then

$$|S_n|^K \ll P^\varepsilon(P^{K-1}+P^Kq^{-1}+P^{K-d}q)^n,$$

where $\varepsilon>0$ and $K=2^{d-1}$. *L. Carlitz* (Durham, N.C.)

## L15-24 (26# 4980 )

**Lebedev, S. S.**

**Estimation of a trigonometric sum. (Russian. English summary)**

*Vestnik Moskov. Univ. Ser. I Mat. Meh.* **1961**, *no.* 3, 22–28.

The author obtains an estimate for the sum

$$\sum_{m=1}^{N}\exp\{2\pi i f(m)p_1^{-k_1}\cdots p_l^{-k_l}\},$$

where $f$ is a polynomial with integer coefficients and degree $n\geqq 43$, $p_1, \cdots, p_l$ are primes greater than $n$, $k_1, \cdots, k_l$

are positive integers, and $N=[(p_1^{k_1}\cdots p_l^{k_l})^\alpha]+1$ with $\{(\log n)/n\}^{1/2}\leqq\alpha\leqq 1$. It is assumed that the coefficients of $f$ are coprime with $p_1\cdots p_l$, and also that if $k_i=n^{\beta_i}$ $(i=1,2,\cdots,l)$, then $\beta_i\geqq 2$ and $(\beta_1+\beta_2+\cdots+\beta_l)l^{-1}\geqq 2.5+10(\log n)^{-1}$. The author states that his method is similar to that used by I. M. Koborov [Trudy 3-ego Vsesojuznogo Mat. S"ezda (Moscow, 1956), Tom II, pp. 6–7, Izdat. Akad. Nauk SSSR, Moscow, 1956; MR **20** #6973b] in some related estimations.

*H. Halberstam* (Dublin)

## L15-25 (28# 5044)

**Rodosskiĭ, K. A.**

**On some trigonometric sums. (Russian)**

*Mat. Sb. (N.S.)* **60 (102)** (1963), 219–234.

Let $f(x)=a_1x+\cdots+a_kx^k$ be a polynomial of degree $\geqq 2$ with real coefficients. The author is concerned with the sum $\Sigma_k=\sum_{x=1}^P e^{2\pi i f(x)}$ treated, for example, by I. M. Vinogradoff and L. K. Hua [see the latter's book, *Additive Primzahltheorie*, Teubner, Leipzig, 1959; MR **23** #A1620]. Restricting himself to the case $2\leqq k\leqq 11$ and supposing that $|a_r-a/q|\leqq 1/q^2$, $(a,q)=1$, $1\leqq q\leqq P^r$, where $2\leqq r\leqq k$, he obtains the estimate

$$|\Sigma_k| \leqq c(k,\varepsilon)\gamma(q)P^{1-1/\sigma_k+\varepsilon}$$

for arbitrary $\varepsilon>0$, $c(k,\varepsilon)$ is a constant depending only on $k$ and $\varepsilon$, and

$$\gamma(q) = (Pq^{-1})^{1/\sigma_k} \quad \text{for } 1\leqq q\leqq P,$$
$$= 1 \quad \text{for } P\leqq q\leqq P^{r-1},$$
$$= (qP^{1-r})^{1/\sigma_k} \quad \text{for } P^{r-1}\leqq q\leqq P^r,$$

and $\sigma_k$ is given by the table

| $k$ | 2 | 3 | 4 | 5 | 6 | 7 | 8 | 9 | 10 | 11 |
|---|---|---|---|---|---|---|---|---|---|---|
| $\sigma_k$ | 4 | 9 | 20 | 51 | 116 | 247 | 422 | 681 | 1090 | 1781 |

*S. Chowla* (University Park, Pa.)

Citations: MR 23# A1620 = P02-7.

Referred to in L15-28.

## L15-26 (31# 5843)

**Vinogradov, I. M.**

**On the estimation of trigonometric sums. (Russian)**

*Izv. Akad. Nauk SSSR Ser. Mat.* **29** (1965), 493–504.

The author gives an upper estimate of the "measure" of points $(\alpha_1,\alpha_2,\cdots,\alpha_n)$ for which

$$\sum_{0\leqq x\leqq p}\exp\{2\pi i(\alpha_n x^n+\cdots+\alpha_1 x)\}$$

is absolutely bigger than $p^{1-\varepsilon}$. As an application, he deduces an improved bound for $S=\sum_{a<k\leqq a_1}k^{-it}$, where $a<a_1\leqq 2a$, $t=a^{n-\theta}$, $n\geqq 20$, $0<\theta<1$. The result is $|S|<2a^{1-\rho}$, $\rho=(16500n^2)^{-1}$. *S. Knapowski* (Gainesville, Fla.)

## L15-27 (33# 5572)

**Karacuba, A. A.**

**Asymptotic formulae for a certain class of trigonometric sums. (Russian)**

*Dokl. Akad. Nauk SSSR* **169** (1966), 9–11.

Notation: $a$, $t$, $n$ denote positive integers with $t\geqq n\geqq 20$; $\delta_n(x)=1$ or 0 according as $x\equiv 0$ or $\not\equiv 0 \pmod n$; $p$ is a prime such that $(a,p)=1$; $P$ is a large positive integer restricted by the condition that if $P=p^{t/r}$, then $1\leqq r\leqq .1n$. The positive integers $s$, $a_0$ are defined by $a_0p^s\leqq P<(a_0+1)p^s\leqq p^{s+1}$.

Using a lemma proved in a previous paper [Izv. Akad. Nauk SSSR Ser. Mat. **28** (1964), 237–248; MR **28** #3010], the author sketches a proof of the theorem that there is a positive absolute constant $\gamma$ such that

$$\sum_{x=1}^{P}\exp 2\pi i a x^n p^{-t} = a_0p^{s-\alpha}(A+p^\beta)+O(P^{1-\gamma r^{-2}}),$$

where $\alpha=1+[t/n]$, $\beta=\delta_n(t)$,

$$A = \delta_n(t-1)\sum_{1}^{p-1}\exp 2\pi i a x^n p^{-1}.$$

{This article has appeared in English translation [Soviet Math. Dokl. **7** (1966), 845–848].} *S. Verblunsky* (Belfast)

Citations: MR 28# 3010 = M25-55.

Referred to in T50-26.

## L15-28 (34# 7464)

**Kamilov, M. H.**

**Double trigonometric sums. (Russian. Tajiki summary)**

*Dokl. Akad. Nauk Tadžik. SSR* **9** (1966), *no.* 10, 6–8.

Die trigonometrische Doppelsumme $\sum\sum_{(n,m)\in D}e^{2\pi i f(n,m)}$ wird unter verhältnismäßig allgemeinen Voraussetzungen abgeschätzt. Vorbilder zur Beweismethode sind Arbeiten von I. M. Vinogradov [*Selected works* (Russian), Izdat. Akad. Nauk SSSR, Moscow, 1952; MR **14**, 610], Hua Lo-keng [*The additive prime number theory* (Russian), Trudy Mat. Inst. Steklov. **22** (1947); MR **10**, 597; erratum, MR **11**, p. 870; Chinese translation, Acad. Sinica, Peking, 1953; MR **16**, 337; German translation, Teubner, Leipzig, 1959; MR **23** #A1620; English translation, Amer. Math. Soc., Providence, R.I., 1965; MR **33** #2614] und K. A. Rodosskiĭ [Mat. Sb. (N.S.) **60** (**102**) (1963), 219–234; MR **28** #5044]. *H.-E. Richert* (Marburg)

Citations: MR 10, 597e = P02-5; MR 14, 610i = Z25-9; MR 16, 337d = P02-6; MR 23# A1620 = P02-7; MR 28# 5044 = L15-25; MR 33# 2614 = P02-9.

## L15-29 (36# 2570)

**Korobov, N. M.**

**Weyl sum estimates and their applications. (Russian)**

*Proc. Fourth All-Union Math. Congr. (Leningrad, 1961) (Russian), Vol. II, pp.* 112–116. *Izdat. "Nauka", Leningrad,* 1964.

The article is devoted to a survey of a series of works dealing with estimates of trigonometric sums. In essence, these works belong to the author, and are well known. A series of new estimates of partially rational trigonometric sums is formulated, by means of which the author obtains a whole sequence of new estimates for well-known sum-theoretic problems. *O. Fomenko* (RŽMat **1964** #10 A92)

## L15-30 (36# 6360)

**Kamilov, M. H.**

**The estimation of double trigonometric sums. (Russian)**

*Leninabad. Gos. Ped. Inst. Učen. Zap. Vyp.* 24 (1967), 28–39.

In dieser Arbeit wird die I. M. Vinogradovsche Methode zur Abschätzung von trigonometrischen Summen auf Doppelsummen $\sum\sum_{(n,m)\in D}\exp\{2\pi i f(n,m)\}$ übertragen. Das Hauptresultat behandelt Funktionen der speziellen Gestalt $f(n,m)=\varphi(n)+\varphi(m)$, es kann wegen seines Umfanges hier nicht wiedergegeben werden. *H.-E. Richert* (Marburg)

## L15-31 (40# 4216)

**Kamilov, M. H.**

**Estimation of the constant in a certain theorem on the mean value of a trigonometric sum. (Russian. Tajiki summary)**

*Dokl. Akad. Nauk Tadžik. SSR* **12** (1969), *no.* 4, 11–14.

By considering the solutions of the Diophantine equations

$\sum_{\nu=1}^{3} x_\nu^h = \sum_{\nu=1}^{3} y_\nu^h$ $(1 \leqq h \leqq 2,\ 1 \leqq x_\nu,\ y_\nu \leqq P)$ in various cases, the author proves that, for $P \geqq e^{10}$,

$$\int_0^1 \int_0^1 |\sum_{x=1}^{P} e^{2\pi i(\alpha_2 x^2 + \alpha_1 x)}|^6 d\alpha_1 d\alpha_2 \leqq 74P^3 \log^3 P.$$

*R. A. Rankin* (Glasgow)

## L15-32 (40# 4995)

**Sprindžuk, V. G.**

**Gauss's error law in the distribution of the values of "short" Weyl sums. (Russian)**

*Dokl. Akad. Nauk BSSR* **13** (1969), 873–875.

L'auteur démontre le théorème suivant: Soit $S_M = \sum_{a \in M} f((a, \alpha))$, où $M$ est un ensemble de $m$ vecteurs entiers de $R^n$, $f$ une fonction réelle mesurable de période 1, et $(a, \alpha)$ le produit scalaire des vecteurs $a \in M$, $\alpha \in E^n$ ($E^n$ est le cube unité de $R^n$). Alors $S_M$ a la même distribution de probabilité que la somme $\sum_{j=1}^{m} f(\xi_j)$, les $\xi_j$ étant $m$ variables aléatoires indépendantes uniformément réparties sur $[0, 1]$.

Dans le cas particulier où $f(u) = \exp(2i\pi u)$ et où $a = (x, x^2, \cdots, x^n)$, on obtient un résultat sur les sommes de Weyl. *R. Cuppens* (Toulouse)

## L15-33 (41# 161)

**Karacuba, A. A.**

**Trigonometric sums. (Russian)**

*Dokl. Akad. Nauk SSSR* **189** (1969), 31–34.

The author proves subject to certain conditions asymptotic formulas for incomplete trigonometrical sums for the form $\sum_{1 \leq x \leq P} \exp(2\pi i a x^n/q)$. In some cases an improvement of Hua's result [L.-k. Hua, Sci. Record (N.S.) **1** (1957), 1–4; MR **20** #22] is obtained.

{This article has appeared in English translation [Soviet Math. Dokl. **10** (1969), 1334–1337].}

*H.-E. Richert* (Marburg)

Citations: MR 20# 22 = L05-17.

## L15-34 (42# 3041)

**Korobov, N. M.**

**Double trigonometric sums and their applications to the estimation of rational sums. (Russian)**

*Mat. Zametki* **6** (1969), 25–34.

Let $f(x, y) = \sum_{r=0}^{n} \sum_{s=0}^{m} \alpha_{rs} x^r y^s$ be a polynomial with real coefficients, and put $S(P_1, P_2) = \sum_{x=1}^{P_1} \sum_{y=1}^{P_2} e^{2\pi i f(x,y)}$. In this paper the author obtains an estimate of $S(P_1, P_2)$, which is then applied to estimate trigonometric sums with rational coefficients. To state the results obtained, let $N_{k,n}(P)$ be the number of integral solutions of the system $\sum_{i=1}^{k} x_i^\nu = \sum_{i=1}^{k} y_i^\nu$ $(\nu = 1, 2, \cdots, n)$ such that $1 \leq x_i, y_i \leq P$. For fixed integers $\lambda_1, \cdots, \lambda_n$, put $\beta_s = \sum_{r=0}^{n} \alpha_{rs} \lambda_r$. The main result is that for any natural numbers $k_1$ and $k_2$,

$$|S(P_1, P_2)|^{4k_1k_2} \leqq (2k_2)^m P_1^{2k_1(2k_2-1)} P_2^{2k_2(2k_1-1)} N_{k_1,n}(P_1) N_{k_2,m}(P_2) V,$$

where $V = \sum_{\lambda_1, \cdots, \lambda_n, |\lambda_\nu| < k_1 P_1^\nu} \prod_{s=1}^{m} \min(P_2^s, 1/\langle\langle \beta_s \rangle\rangle)$, and where $\langle\langle \beta_s \rangle\rangle$ is the distance from $\beta_s$ to the nearest integer. As an example of the applications, suppose that $n \geqq 300$, $\alpha \geqq n+1$, $f(x) = a_0 + \cdots + a_{n+1} x^{n+1}$ is a polynomial with integer coefficients, $p$ is a prime $> n^2$, $r$ is defined by $P^r = p^\alpha$, and $\alpha \log p > 10^8 rn \log n$. Then if $1 \leq r \leq n/300$, and if no coefficient $a_\nu$ $(27r \leq \nu \leq n+1)$ is divisible by $p^{[\alpha/11]}$, one has $|\sum_{x=1}^{P} e^{2\pi i f(x)/p^\alpha}| \leqslant 2n^2 P^{1-\rho}$, where $\rho = \gamma \min(r/n, 1/r^2)$ and $\gamma$ is a positive constant.

{This article has appeared in English translation [Math. Notes **6** (1969), 472–478].}

*B. Gordon* (Los Angeles, Calif.)

## L15-35 (43# 4777)

**Kamilov, M. H.**

**A certain estimate of the number of solutions of Diophantine equations and its application to the estimation of trigonometric sums. (Russian. Tajiki summary)**

*Dokl. Akad. Nauk Tadžik. SSR* **12** (1969), *no.* 11, 3–5.

The author finds improved estimates for the trigonometric sums $c_k = \sum_{x=1}^{P} \exp(2\pi i(\alpha_k x^k + \cdots + \alpha_1 x))$ by estimating $N_k(P)$, the number of solutions of $\sum_{\nu=1}^{k+1} x_\nu^h = \sum_{\nu=1}^{k+1} y_\nu^h$ $(1 \leqq h \leqq k)$, where $1 \leqq x_\nu, y_\nu \leqq P$. He finds that $N_K(P) \leqq (k+1)! P^{k+1} + (2^{k+1} \cdot k/k!) P(P-1)^k [k \log(P-1) + 2k - 1]^{2k-1}$. Analogous results are obtained for

$$c_k' = \sum_{x=1}^{P} \exp(2\pi i(\alpha_k x^k + \alpha_{k-2} x^{k-2} + \cdots + \alpha, x)).$$

*R. Spira* (E. Lansing, Mich.)

## L15-36 (44# 1634)

**Kocarev, B. G.**

**Partially rational trigonometric sums with polynomials. (Russian)**

*Mat. Zametki* **8** (1970), 529–540.

Let $f(x) = a_1 x + \cdots + a_n x^n + (a_{n+1} x^{n+1} + \cdots + a_{n+l} x^{n+l})/d$, where the coefficients $a_r$ $(1 \leqq r \leqq n)$ are arbitrary real numbers and where $a_{n+1}, \cdots, a_{n+l}$ and $d$ are integers with $(a_{n+1}, \cdots, a_{n+l}, d) = 1$. An upper bound is obtained for $S_n(d) = \sum_{x=1}^{P} \exp\{2\pi i m f(x)\}$, where $m$ is an integer and $1 \leqq d \leqq P$. It is assumed that $s$ of the numbers $a_r$ $(1 \leqq r \leqq n)$ are such that $a_r d = c_r/q_r + \theta_r/q_r^2$, where $(c_r, q_r) = 1$ and $|\theta_r| \leqq 1$. The upper bound for $|S_n(d)|$, which is too complicated to state here, depends on $d$, $m$, $n$, $P$, $s$ and on the $s$ denominators $q_r$, but not on $l$. This generalizes work of N. M. Korobov [Dokl. Akad. Nauk SSSR **125** (1959), 1193–1195; MR **21** #5610] and others.

{This article has appeared in English translation [Math. Notes **8** (1970), 765–771].} *R. A. Rankin* (Glasgow)

Citations: MR 21# 5610 = L15-22.

## L15-37 (44# 6617)

**Kamilov, M. H.**

**On the question of the estimation of double trigonometric sums. (Russian. Tajiki summary)**

*Dokl. Akad. Nauk Tadžik. SSR* **14** (1971), *no.* 1, 8–10.

The author obtains an estimate of a trigonometric sum in which the exponent is a quadratic polynomial of two variables with irrational coefficients, the sum being taken over a convex region. The method used is the standard one due to I. M. Vinogradov [*Selected works* (Russian), Izdat. Akad. Nauk SSSR, Moscow, 1952; MR **14**, 610].

*A. I. Vinogradov* (Leningrad)

Citations: MR 14, 610i = Z25-9.

# L20 SUMS OVER PRIMES

See also Section P32.

See also reviews K30-1, K30-2, K30-3, L15-16, L25-3, L25-15, L25-30, M02-3, M05-5, M25-59, M25-89, M55-70, N16-2, N16-7, N68-46, P16-28, P48-23.

## L20-1 (1, 293c)

**Vinogradow, I. Simplest trigonometrical sums with primes.** C. R. (Doklady) Acad. Sci. URSS (N.S.) **23**, 615–617 (1939).

For the sum

$$S=\sum_{N-A<p\leqq N} e^{2\pi i(a/q)p^n},\quad q>0;\ (a,q)=1;\ n \text{ a positive integer,}$$

the author states the following estimates ("near to the best possible ones"), in which $N>2$, $r=\log N$, and $c, \sigma, \alpha, \epsilon, \eta, h$ are positive constants, of which $\epsilon, \eta, h$ are arbitrarily small:

$$S=O(Ar^{3\epsilon-1}q^{\eta-\frac{1}{2}}) \quad \text{if } cNe^{-r^{1-2\epsilon}}\leqq A\leqq N,\quad 0<q\leqq e^{r^{\epsilon}},$$

$$S=O(Aq^{\eta-\frac{1}{3}}) \quad \text{if} \quad N^{1-\alpha}\leqq A\leqq N,\ e^{r^{\epsilon}}<q\leqq N^{\sigma},$$

$$4\alpha+6\sigma=\frac{1}{1+h},$$

$$S=O(Aq^{\eta-\frac{1}{3}}) \quad \text{if} \quad N^{1-\alpha}\leqq A\leqq N,\ N^{\epsilon}<q\leqq N^{\sigma},$$

$$3\alpha+5\sigma=\frac{1}{1+h}.$$

It is asserted that, when $n=1$, the second and third results hold under wider conditions. The author also announces improved forms of his previous estimates of

$$\sum_{x=Q+1}^{Q+P} e^{2\pi imf(x)} \quad \text{and} \quad \sum_{z=Q+1}^{Q+P} e^{2\pi iF(z)},$$

where $m$ is a positive integer, $f(x)$ a real polynomial and $F(z)$ a real function whose $n$th and $(n+1)$th derivatives satisfy certain inequalities. *A. E. Ingham.*

## L20-2 (2, 40b)

**Vinogradow, I. On the estimations of some simplest trigonometrical sums involving prime numbers.** Bull. Acad. Sci. URSS. Sér. Math. [Izvestia Akad. Nauk SSSR] **1939**, 371–398 (1939). (Russian. English summary)

Let $e(x)=e^x$. Let $p$ range over the primes in the interval $N-A<p\leqq N$; $n$ and $k$ denote fixed positive integers; $\epsilon, \eta, h$ given positive numbers; $a/q$ a rational fraction in lowest terms, $q>0$; a real $\lambda$ written $=a/q+\theta/q^2$, $|\theta|\leqq 1$; $N>2$, $r=\log N$; $1\leqq A\leqq N$. Five theorems are proved, Theorem 1 and a modified Theorem 2 having been previously announced [cf. these Rev. **1**, 293]. Theorem 1: let $\eta<\epsilon\leqq\frac{1}{3}$; $A\gg Ne(-r^{1-2\epsilon})$, $q\leqq e(r^{\epsilon})$; then $\sum_p e(2\pi ip^na/q)\ll A/(r^{1-3\epsilon}q^{\frac{1}{2}-\eta})$. Theorem 2: let $\epsilon, \eta, h<1$; $q>e(r^{\epsilon})$, $A\geqq N^{h+2/3}q^{3/2}$; then $\sum_p e(2\pi ip^na/q)\ll Aq^{\eta-\frac{1}{3}}$. Theorem 3: let $h\leqq 1/6$, $q\leqq N$; set $\tau=6+(\log r)/(\log \overline{1+h})$, $L=kN^{(2+h)/3}A^{-1}+NqA^{-2}+kq^{-1}+k^4q^{-2}$; then $\sum_p e(2\pi i\lambda kp)\ll Ar^{\tau}L^{1/2}$. Write $\{x\}=x-[x]$. Theorem 4: let $\epsilon$, $h\leqq 1/6$, $0<\delta\leqq 1$, $N\geqq N_0$, $N_0$ sufficiently large; $q\leqq N$; let $T$ denote the total number of values of $p$, and $T_1$ the number with $0\leqq\{\lambda p\}\leqq\delta$; then $T_1=\delta T+O(A\Delta)$, where $\Delta=e(r^{\epsilon})K^{1/2}$, $K=N^{h+2/3}A^{-1}+N^{1+h}q^{1-h}A^{-2}+q^{h-1}$. Theorem 5: let $\eta<1$, $1\leqq Q\leqq N$, $0\leqq\delta\leqq 1$; let $T_2$ denote the number of values $p$ for which the residue $P$ of $p$ (mod $Q$) lies in $0\leqq P\leqq\delta Q$; then $T_2=\delta T+O(A\Delta)$, where $\Delta=N^{\eta}H^{1/2}$, $H=N^{2/3}A^{-1}+NQA^{-2}+Q^{-1}$. Corrections are given on p. 396 to the author's paper on estimation of trigonometric sums [same journal **1938**, no. 5–6]: the limits for $k$ should be $k<1+R/(-\log \overline{1-\nu})$, with $R=\log U$ in Lemma 5, $R=\log 2Z$ in Lemma 6; the limit to $K$ in Lemma 6 should be $2^{bn/6}p_1^{bk}(p_1\cdots p_k)^{-b}$; $1/\rho$ in Theorem 2 should be $(n+1)^3\log 2(n+1)$. *G. Pall* (Princeton, N. J.).

Citations: MR 1, 293a = N24-1.
Referred to in N28-1.

## L20-3 (3, 165d)

**Vinogradoff, I. M. Two theorems relating to the theory of distribution of prime numbers.** C. R. (Doklady) Acad. Sci. URSS (N.S.) **30**, 287–288 (1941).

Estimates are stated for

$$S=\sum_{N_1<p\leqq N_2} \exp(2\pi if(p)),$$

where $f$ need not be an integral polynomial. The case $f(x)=kx^{\alpha}$, $0<\alpha<1$, was treated earlier [Rec. Math. [Mat. Sbornik] N.S. **7** (**49**), 365–372 (1940); these Rev. **2**, 40]. Let $N\geqq 8$, $\frac{1}{2}N<N_1<N_2\leqq N$. Theorem 1: Given $0<\eta\leqq 1/6$, $A>0$ and $f$ with property $H_1$ (namely, $f''(z)$ and $f'''(z)$ continuous in the interval $\frac{1}{2}N\leqq z\leqq N$, and satisfying $A^{-1}\ll|f''(z)|\ll A^{-1}$, $A^{-1}\ll|zf'''(z)+2f''(z)|\ll A^{-1}$); then $S\ll N^{1+\eta}(A^{-1}N+AN^{-2})^{1/4}$. Theorem 1*: With the same hypotheses, $\epsilon<2\eta$ and $0<\sigma\leqq 1$, then the number of primes $p\leqq N$ such that $0\leqq f(p)-[f(p)]<\sigma$ is $\sigma\pi(N)+O(N^{1+\epsilon}\Delta)$, $\Delta=(A^{-1}N+AN^{-2})^{1/5}$. Theorem 2: Given $0<\epsilon<0.01$, $k\geqq 12$, $n=[2k+2]$ and $f$ with property $H_2$ (namely, in the interval $\frac{1}{2}N\leqq z\leqq N$ and for $s=[k+2], [k+3], \cdots, n$, $f^{(s)}(z)$ continuous and satisfying $N^{k-s-0.01}\ll|f^{(s)}(z)|\ll N^{k-s+\epsilon}$, $N^{k-s-0.01}\ll|sf^{(s)}(z)+zf^{(s+1)}(z)|\ll N^{k-s+\epsilon}$); then $S\ll N^{1-0.133\rho}$, $\rho=(n^3\log 4n)^{-1}$. *G. Pall* (Montreal, Que.).

Citations: MR 2, 40a = K30-1.

## L20-4 (3, 165e)

**Vinogradoff, I. M. Some general property of distribution of products of prime numbers.** C. R. (Doklady) Acad. Sci. URSS (N.S.) **30**, 681–682 (1941).

Results are announced pertaining to the distribution not of primes $p$ as in earlier articles, but of numbers $P$ running over one of the ranges: (a) quadratfrei numbers, (b) numbers with a fixed number $h(>1)$ of prime factors, (c) numbers with an even (or odd) number of prime factors. Theorem 1: $N>2$, $\alpha=a/q+\theta/q^2$, $(a,q)=1$, $0<q<N$; then

$$\sum_{P\leqq N} e^{2\pi i\alpha P}\ll N^{\epsilon}K^{\frac{1}{2}},$$

where $K=N^{-\frac{1}{2}}+q/N+k/q+k^4/q^2$. Theorems 2, 3 and 6 are immediate extensions with $P$ in place of $p$, of Theorems 1, 2 and 1* of the preceding review. Theorem 4: If $0<\sigma\leqq 1$, $N\geqq 8$, $q$ an integer, $0<q<N$, then the number of values of $P$, not exceeding $N$, which fall into intervals of the form $cq<P\leqq(c+\sigma)q$ for integers $c$, is given by $\sigma T(1)+O(N^{1+\epsilon}\Delta)$, $\Delta^2=N^{-\frac{1}{2}}+q/N+1/q$. Theorem 5: Under the conditions of Theorem 4, if $M(\sigma)=\sum\mu(n)$, where the summation extends over all $n$'s not exceeding $N$ and falling into intervals of the form $cq<n\leqq(c+\sigma)q$, then $M(\sigma)=\sigma M(1)+O(N^{1+\epsilon}\Delta)$. The case $q=1$ seems to need some correction. *G. Pall* (Montreal, Que.).

Referred to in L20-12.

## L20-5 (4, 240d)

**Sambasiva Rao, K. and Nagabhushanam, K. A note on Vinogradow-numbers.** Proc. Indian Acad. Sci., Sect. A. **17**, 71–74 (1943).

Let $S(\alpha, N)=\sum e(\alpha p)$, where the summation is over all primes $p\leqq N$. The authors define a Vinogradow number as follows: a number $\alpha$ such that $0<\alpha\leqq 1$ is a Vinogradow number if for every $h>1$ there is a $c=c(h)$ for which $|S(\alpha,N)|<cN(\log N)^{-h}$ for all $N$. They prove, among other results, that the set of Vinogradow numbers has measure 1. *R. D. James* (Saskatoon, Sask.).

## L20-6 (5, 143a)

**Vinogradow, I. M. An improvement of the estimation of sums with primes.** Bull. Acad. Sci. URSS. Sér. Math. [Izvestia Akad. Nauk SSSR] **7**, 17–34 (1943). (Russian. English summary)

By improving his earlier methods the author obtains more exact estimates of the sums

$$S=\sum_{p\leqq N}\chi(p+k),\quad S'=\sum_{p\leqq N}\chi(p(p+k)),$$

where $\chi$ is a nonprincipal character mod $q$, $q$ is an odd prime, $(k,q)=1$ and $N>1$, namely, $S\ll N^{1+\epsilon}G$, $S'\ll N^{1+\epsilon}G$, $G=(1/q+q/N)^{\frac{1}{2}}+N^{-1/6}$. He also obtains a modification of the case $K=1$ of the result in the following review. *G. Pall* (Montreal, Que.).

Referred to in L25-3, N76-5.

**L20-7** **(5, 143b)**

**Vinogradoff, I. M. Improvement of some theorems in the theory of primes.** C. R. (Doklady) Acad. Sci. URSS (N.S.) **37**, 115–117 (1942).

The improvement over his 1937–38 methods is illustrated by proving that

$$S_0 = \sum_{0<k\leqq K} \sum_{p\leqq N} e^{2\pi i\alpha kp} \ll KNH,$$

where $K$ is an integer, $\alpha = a/q+\theta/q^2$, $(a,q)=1$, $|\theta|\leqq 1$ and $H = N^{\epsilon}((1/q+q/N)^{1/2}+N^{-1/5})$. As an application, if $0\leqq\sigma_1<\sigma_2<1$, the number $T$ of primes $p\leqq N$ such that $\sigma_1\leqq\{\alpha p\}<\sigma_2$ satisfies

$$T-(\sigma_1-\sigma_2)\pi(N)\ll NH.$$

This remains true if $p$ ranges over certain products of primes.

*G. Pall* (Montreal, Que.).

**L20-8** **(7, 146i)**

**Linnik, U. V. On the characters of primes. I.** Rec. Math. [Mat. Sbornik] N.S. **16(58)**, 101–120 (1945). (English. Russian summary)

This paper contains estimates for the sum $\sum_{p\leqq N}\chi(p)$, where $\chi(n)$ is either a complex primitive character (mod $D$) or $\chi(n)=(-D/n)$, where $-D<0$ is a fundamental discriminant. The fundamental lemma of the paper asserts that, if $\rho_k=\beta_k+it_k$ $(k=1,2,\cdots)$ are the zeros of $L(s,\chi)$ in the critical strip, then there exists an absolute constant $C$ such that

$$\sum m_k|\rho_k|^{-2}\exp(-C(1-\beta_k)\log D)$$

is bounded, where $m_k$ is the multiplicity of the zero $\rho_k$. This paper precedes logically the author's papers on the least prime in an arithmetic progression [same Rec. N.S. **15(57)**, 139–178, 347–368 (1944); these Rev. **6**, 260], where a knowledge of it is assumed. *H. Davenport* (London).

Citations: MR 6, 260c = N16-6.
Referred to in M02-3.

**L20-9** **(9, 333c)**

**Čudakov, N. G. On certain trigonometric sums containing prime numbers.** Doklady Akad. Nauk SSSR (N.S.) **58**, 1291–1294 (1947). (Russian)

The author estimates certain trigonometrical sums involving primes by relating them to the zeros $(\rho=\beta+i\gamma)$ of $\zeta(s)$, in contrast to the method of Vinogradov, which avoids all reference to the $\zeta$-function and the $L$-functions. The general result is as follows. Suppose $a, b\approx N$ $(0<a<b)$; $f(x)$ real in $[a,b]$; $f'(x)\approx A$, $f''(x)\neq 0$, $(xf'(x))'\approx B$, $(xf'(x))''\neq 0$, for $a\leqq x\leqq b$, $x\geqq x_0$, where $A, B>0$ and $N^{-1}\ll A\ll N^{-3/4}$, $B\ll 1$. Then

$$(1)\qquad S=\sum_{a\leqq p\leqq b} e^{if(p)}\ll((N/A)^{1/2}+(N/B)^{1/2})\log N$$

[$X\ll Y$ means $|X|\leqq c|Y|$ $(c>0$, constant); $X\approx Y$ (not the author's notation) means $X\ll Y\ll X$]. A typical example is as follows. Suppose $b>a\geqq e^2$; $a, b\approx N$; $\frac{1}{4}\leqq\mu\leqq 2$, $\mu\neq 1$; $1\ll t\ll N^{1/2}(\log N)^{-1}$. Then

$$\sum_{a\leqq p\leqq b} e^{it(\log p)^{\mu}}\ll N(\log N)^{11/8}t^{-1/2}|\mu-1|^{-1/2}.$$

It is not claimed that this method applies to Vinogradov's sums generally. Thus it fails (as it stands) when $f(x)=\alpha x$, a case of the first importance in connection with Goldbach's problem.

Sketch of proof of (1). For $3\leqq T\leqq a\leqq x$,

$$\psi(x)\equiv\sum_{n\leqq x}\Lambda(n)=x-\sum_{|\gamma|\leqq T}x^{\rho}/\rho+R_x,\qquad R_x\ll T^{-1}x\log^2 x$$

[Landau, Acta Math. **35**, 271–294 (1912), Satz 1]; whence

$$(2)\quad \sum_{a\leqq n\leqq b}\frac{\Lambda(n)}{\log n}F(n)=\sum_{a\leqq n\leqq b}\frac{F(n)}{\log n}-\sum_{|\gamma|\leqq T}\sum_{a\leqq n\leqq b}\frac{n^{\rho}-(n-1)^{\rho}}{\rho\log n}F(n)+\sum_{a\leqq n\leqq b}\frac{R_n-R_{n-1}}{\log n}F(n),$$

where $F(x)=e^{if(x)}$. The left hand side is $S+O(N^{1/2})$. On the right hand side the last sum is $O(T^{-1}N^2A\log N)$, by partial summation. The first is $O(A^{-1})$, by a theorem of van der Corput [Landau, Vorlesungen über Zahlentheorie, v. 1, Leipzig, 1927, Satz 352 (and Abel's lemma)]. In the second (double) sum $n^{\rho}-(n-1)^{\rho}$ is replaced by $\rho n^{\rho-1}$, with a total error $O(T^2\log T)$; $\sum_n$ is then estimated, again by van der Corput's theorem (but less directly), and the (modified) double sum found to be

$$\ll\sum_{|\gamma|\leqq T}\frac{N^{\beta-1}}{\log N}\left\{\frac{N}{B}\right\}^{1/2}\leqq\frac{4}{\sqrt{B}}\left(\frac{N(\frac{1}{2},T)}{\log N}+\int_{1/2}^{1}N(\sigma,T)N^{\sigma-1/2}d\sigma\right),$$

where $N(\sigma,T)$ is the number of $\rho$ with $\beta\geqq\sigma$, $0<\gamma\leqq T$. Finally, $N(\sigma,T)\ll T^{\lambda(1-\sigma)}$, $\lambda=8/3$; and (1) follows on taking $T=(NA)^{1/2}$. The last steps are based on an idea of Hoheisel [cf. Ingham, Quart. J. Math., Oxford Ser. **8**, 255–266 (1937)].

[Notes by the reviewer. (i) The inequality for $N(\sigma,T)$, attributed to the reviewer, was proved by him [loc. cit., theorem 3] only in the form $N(\sigma,T)\ll T^{\lambda(1-\sigma)}\log^5 T$. But this is true with $\lambda<8/3$; and this, with Čudakov's theorem that $N(\sigma,T)=0$ for $\sigma>1-(\log T)^{-\alpha}$, $T>T_0$, where $0<\alpha<1$, implies the result stated. (ii) The proof of (1) would seem to admit of simplification. Thus (2) may be replaced by

$$\sum_{a<n\leqq b}\frac{\Lambda(n)}{\log n}F(n)=\int_a^b\frac{F(x)}{\log x}d\psi(x)$$

$$=\int_a^b\frac{F(x)}{\log x}dx-\sum_{|\gamma|\leqq T}\int_a^b\frac{F(x)}{\log x}x^{\rho-1}dx+\int_a^b\frac{F(x)}{\log x}dR_x.$$

The last integral on the right may be estimated by partial integration, and the others reduced to integral analogues of van der Corput's sums (more easily estimated than the sums).] *A. E. Ingham* (Cambridge, England).

Referred to in M02-3.

**L20-10** **(9, 498l)**

**Turán, Paul. On certain exponential sums.** Nederl. Akad. Wetensch., Proc. **51**, 343–352 = Indagationes Math. **10**, 132–141 (1948).

The main result is as follows. If $-\frac{1}{2}\leqq\gamma\leqq 1$ $(\gamma\neq 0)$, $c\leqq t^{10}\leqq\frac{1}{2}N\leqq N'<N''\leqq N$, $t>0$, then

$$(*)\qquad\left|\sum_{N'\leqq p\leqq N''}e^{it\log^{1+\gamma}p}\right|<C\left(\frac{N\log^8 N}{(|\gamma|t)^{1/2}}+\frac{N\log^8 N}{|\gamma|t}\right),$$

where $p$ runs through primes, and $c$, $C$ are numerical constants. The author has discussed elsewhere the relation of the sum on the left, with $\gamma=0$, to the "quasi-Riemannian hypothesis" (the existence of a $\vartheta<1$ such that $\zeta(s)$ has at most a finite number of zeros in $\sigma>\vartheta$), and has shown how an estimate of this sum, with $\gamma\neq 0$, may be obtained by Vinogradov's method without reference to the zeta-function [Bull. Acad. Sci. URSS. Sér. Math. [Izvestia Akad. Nauk SSSR] **11**, 197–262 (1947); these Rev. **9**, 80]. This estimate is now obtained (in the slightly improved form (*)) from the theory of $\zeta(s)$ and the known facts about the distribution of its zeros, with the help of ideas introduced by Hoheisel in his study of $\pi(x+h)-\pi(x)$. [Cf. Čudakov, Doklady Akad. Nauk SSSR (N.S.) **58**, 1291–1294 (1947); these Rev. **9**, 333, and the reviewer's note on the possibility of simplification by the use of integrals instead of sums.]

*A. E. Ingham* (Cambridge, England).

## L20-11 (10, 599b)

**Vinogradov, I. M. On an estimate of trigonometric sums with prime numbers.** Izvestiya Akad. Nauk SSSR. Ser. Mat. **12**, 225–248 (1948). (Russian)

The main theorems in this paper are the analogues of those of chapters VI and VIII of the author's book reviewed above.* The main result is the following. Let $0<\kappa\leqq 1$, $l>0$ and integral, $n>9$, $p$ a prime, $f(p)=a_np^n+\cdots+a_1p$, where $a_n,\cdots,a_1$ are real, and for a certain $s$, which is one of the integers $2,\cdots,n$, we have $|a_s-a/q|\leqq 1/q\tau$, $(a,q)=1$, $d>0$ a constant, $dP^\kappa\leqq q\leqq\tau=P^{s/2}$; further, let $\rho=.041/n^2(2+\log n)$ and $\rho_0=(.416/.041)\rho$ if $q>P^{1/2}$, while $\rho=.37\kappa/n^2(4+\log n^2/\kappa)$ and $\rho_0=(.375/.37)\rho$ if $q\leqq P^{1/2}$. If $l\leqq P^{2\rho_0}$ we then have $|\sum_{p\leqq P}\exp\{2\pi ilf(p)\}|<kP^{1-\rho}$ for some $k(n)$. Similar results are obtained when $f(p)$ is not a polynomial and when $p$ has the range $P_1<p<P_2$. Finally, the estimate $\gamma\{\pi(P_2)-\pi(P_1)\}+O(P^{1-\rho'})$ is given for the number of primes $p$ such that $P_1<p<P_2$ and $0\leqq f(p)-[f(p)]<\gamma$; here $\rho'=.044/n^2(\log n+2)$. *L. Schoenfeld* (Urbana, Ill.).

*See MR **10**, 599A = L02-2

Citations: MR 10, 599a = L02-2.
Referred to in K40-72, L20-16.

## L20-12 (10, 599c)

**Vinogradov, I. M. On the distribution of products of prime numbers and the numerical function of Möbius.** Izvestiya Akad. Nauk SSSR. Ser. Mat. **12**, 341–350 (1948). (Russian)

This paper contains proofs of results previously announced without proof [C. R. (Doklady) Acad. Sci. URSS (N.S.) **30**, 681–682 (1941); these Rev. **3**, 165]. The main theorem is as follows. Let $m$, $a$, $q$ be integers, $m>0$, $q>0$, $(a,q)=1$; let $\epsilon_0>0$, $r=\log N$, $|\theta|\leqq 1$, $N^{1/2}\leqq\tau\leqq N\exp(-r^{\epsilon_0})$, $\alpha=a/q+\theta/q\tau$, $\exp(r^{\epsilon_0})\leqq q\leqq\tau$, $\Delta=(1/q+q/N)^{1/2}$, $f=\Delta^{-1}$. Then, for $K<f^2$,

$$\sum_{k=1}^{K}\left|\sum_{w\leqq N}e^{2\pi i\alpha kw}\right|\ll KN(\Delta^{1-\epsilon}+N^{-0.2+\epsilon}),$$

where $w$ runs through all numbers which are products of $m$ distinct prime factors. This theorem is a generalization of theorem 3 in chapter 9 of the author's book [see the second preceding review]*and the proof is analogous to the proof in the book. Applications are given to sums of the type $\sum_{n=1}^N\mu(n)$, where $\mu(n)$ denotes the Möbius function. A typical theorem is the following. Let $n$, $q$ be positive integers and $n'$ the least nonnegative residue of $n$ mod $q$. Let $0<\beta\leqq 1$, $r=\log N$, $\exp(r^{\epsilon_0})\leqq q\leqq N\exp(-r^{\epsilon_0})$. Put $M(\beta)=\sum\mu(n)$, where $n$ runs through all positive integers $n$ not exceeding $N$ such that $n'<\beta q$. Then

$$M(\beta)=\beta M(1)+O(N\Delta_2),\quad \Delta_2=(1/q+q/N)^{0.5-\epsilon}+N^{-0.2+\epsilon}.$$

The author states that "further attempts to refine these results by means of my method have met with considerable difficulty." *A. L. Whiteman* (Los Angeles, Calif.).

*i.e. MR **10**, 599A = L02-2

Citations: MR 3, 165e = L20-4; MR 10, 599a = L02-2.

## L20-13 (14, 22b)

**Vinogradov, I. M. New approach to the estimation of a sum of values of $\chi(p+k)$.** Izvestiya Akad. Nauk SSSR. Ser. Mat. **16**, 197–210 (1952). (Russian)

Let $q$ be a prime, let $\chi$ be a non-principal character (mod $q$), and let $k$ be a fixed integer $\not\equiv 0$ (mod $q$). The sum under consideration is $S=\sum_{p\leqq N}\chi(p+k)$, where $p$ runs through primes. The main result proved is that $S=O(N^{1+\epsilon}(q^{3/4}N^{-1})^{1/4})$ for any fixed $\epsilon>0$, provided $q$ is large and $N$ lies between fixed multiples of $q^{3/4}$ and $q^{5/4}$. This result is an improved form of that announced, with an indication of the method of proof, in a previous note [Doklady Akad. Nauk SSSR **73**, 635–638 (1950); these Rev. **12**, 161]. The proof, now given in detail, differs somewhat from that outlined earlier. One of the main ideas is still that of exhausting the hyperbolic region of summation of a double sum by rectangular regions. But the proof also uses (1) an argument similar to that used in the proof of Theorem 3 of Chapter 9 of the author's monograph [Trudy Mat. Inst. Steklov. **23** (1947); these Rev. **10**, 599], based on Lemma 5 of the same chapter; (2) a special case of A. Weil's general theorem on exponential sums [Proc. Nat. Acad. Sci. U. S. A. **34**, 204–207 (1948); these Rev. **10**, 234], namely the estimate $O(q^{1/2})$ for the generalized Kloosterman sum

$$\sum_{x=0}^{q-1}\chi\left(\frac{x+a}{x+b}\right)e^{2\pi imx/q}.$$

*H. Davenport* (London).

Citations: MR 10, 234e = T25-5; MR 10, 599a = L02-2; MR 12, 161b = L25-3.
Referred to in L20-14.

## L20-14 (15, 855g)

**Vinogradov, I. M. Improvement of an estimate for the sum of the values $\chi(p+k)$.** Izvestiya Akad. Nauk SSSR. Ser. Mat. **17**, 285–290 (1953). (Russian)

The author improves his previous estimate [same Izvestiya **16**, 197–210 (1952); these Rev. **14**, 22] for the sum $\sum_{p\leqq N}\chi(p+k)$ where $\chi$ is a nonprincipal character modulo $q$ and $p$ is prime. If $cq^{3/4}\leqq N\leqq c'q^{5/4}$, then the sum has an estimate of the form

$$N^{1+\epsilon}(q^{1/4}N^{-1/3}+N^{-1/10})$$

in place of the earlier inferior estimate of $N^{1+\epsilon}q^{3/16}N^{-1/4}$. The method now used is very similar to that used in the earlier paper and still depends on Weil's estimate of the Kloosterman sum. However, a more elaborate argument enables the author to obtain the sharper estimate. *L. Schoenfeld.*

Citations: MR 14, 22b = L20-13.

## L20-15 (16, 798c)

**Prachar, K. Über die Summe $\sum_{p\leqq N}e(\alpha p)$.** Monatsh. Math. **59**, 43–44 (1955).

Let $a$, $q$, $N$ be positive integers, $1<q<N$, $(a,q)=1$, and let the real number $\alpha$ satisfy $|\alpha-aq^{-1}|\leqq q^{-2}$. Vinogradov [Trudy Mat. Inst. Steklov. **23** (1947); MR **10**, 599; **15**, 941] proved that

$$1)\quad \Big|\sum_{p\leqq N}\exp(2\pi i\alpha p)\Big|<CN(\log N)^{9/2}\{(q^{-1}+qN^{-1})^{1/2}+H^{-1}\},$$

where $p$ runs through the primes $\leqq N$, and

$$H=\exp\{\tfrac12(\log N)^{1/2}\}.$$

The author shows that the result can be refined if a certain part of Vinogradov's proof is replaced by an argument based on an inequality of the reviewer, concerning the number of integers composed of small primes only [Nederl. Akad. Wetensch. Proc. Ser. A. **54**, 50–60 (1951); MR **13**, 724]. The result is that in (1) $H$ can be replaced by

$$H_1=\exp\{(\tfrac12-\epsilon)(\log N\log\log N)^{1/2}\}.$$

*N. G. de Bruijn* (Amsterdam).

Citations: MR 10, 599a = L02-2; MR 13, 724e = N28-28; MR 15, 941b = L02-3.

## L20-16 (18, 381f)

**Vinogradov, I. M. Special cases of estimations of trigonometric sums.** Izv. Akad. Nauk SSSR. Ser. Mat. **20** (1956), 289–302. (Russian)

This paper assumes a knowledge of both the results and the methods of proof of two earlier papers [same Izv.

**12** (1948), 225–248; **15** (1951), 109–130; MR **10**, 599; **15**, 328]. Because of the complexity of the subject, the reviewer is unable to do more than state the results. Let $f(x)=A_nx^n+\cdots+A_1x$ be a real polynomial of fixed degree $n\geqq 12$, and let $m$ be an integer. Let

$$S_m=\sum_{x=1}^{P}\exp\{2\pi i\, m\, f(x)\},\quad T_m=\sum_{p\leqq P}\exp\{2\pi i\, m\, f(p)\},$$

where $p$ runs through the primes. Let $\nu=1/n$.

Theorem 1. Let $\tau_1=P^{1/3}$, $\tau_s=P^{s-(1-\nu)/3}$ for $s=2,\cdots,n$. Approximate to $A_n,\cdots,A_1$ by $|A_s-a_s/q_s|<(q_s\tau_s)^{-1}$, $0<q_s\leqq\tau_s$, $(a_s,q_s)=1$. Let $Q=\mathrm{LCM}(q_n,\cdots,q_2)$ and $Q_1=\mathrm{LCM}(q_n,\cdots,q_1)$. Then (a) if $Q\geqq P^{(1-\nu)/3}$ and $0<m\leqq P^{\nu(1-\nu)/60}$ we have $S_m=O(P^{1-\rho})$, where $\rho^{-1}=10n^2\log 40n^2$; (b) if $Q<P^{(1-\nu)/3}$ but $Q_1>Q$ we have $S_1=O(P^{(2-\nu)/3})$; (c) if $Q<P^{(1-\nu)/3}$ but $Q_1=Q$, and if

$$\mu_0=\max(1,P^n|A_n-a_n/q_n|,\cdots,P|A_1-a_1/q_1|),$$

we have $S_1=O(PQ^{-\nu+\varepsilon}\mu_0^{-\nu})$ for any fixed $\varepsilon>0$.

Theorem 2. Approximate to $A_n,\cdots,A_2$ as above but with $\tau_s=P^{s/2}$ for $s=2,\cdots,n$. Suppose that some of $q_n,\cdots,q_2$ do not exceed $P^{1/4}$ and let $Q$ denote the LCM of any selection from them. Define $\kappa$ by $\kappa=\frac{1}{4}$ if $Q>P^{1/4}$ and by $Q=P^\kappa$ otherwise; define $\rho_0$ by

$$\rho_0=\kappa/\{6.7n^2\log 12n^2\}.$$

Then if $0<m\leqq P^{2\rho_0}$ we have $T_m=O(P^{1-\rho_0+\varepsilon})$.

Theorem 3. Approximate to $A_n,\cdots,A_1$ as above with $\tau_s=P^{s/2}$ for $s=1,\cdots,n$. Define $Q$ and $Q_1$ in the same way as in Theorem 1 and suppose that $Q\leqq P^{1/9}$. Define $\kappa_1$ by $Q_1=P^{\kappa_1}$ and define $\rho_1$ by

$$\rho_1=\min\left(\frac{\kappa_1}{6.75n^2\log 12n^2},\ \frac{1}{27n^2\log 108n^2}\right).$$

Then if $0<m\leqq P^{2\rho_1}$ we have $T_m^*=O(P^{-1\rho_1+\varepsilon})$.

*H. Davenport* (London).

Citations: MR 10, 599b = L20-11.
Referred to in L15-16.

## L20-17 (20# 3831)

**Heilbronn, H. On the averages of some arithmetical functions of two variables.** Mathematika **5** (1958), 1–7.

It is shown that

$$\sum_{p\leq x}\sum_{q\leq x}\left(\frac{p}{q}\right)=O(x^{7/4}(\log x)^{-5/4}),$$

where $p$ and $q$ are restricted to odd primes and $\left(\frac{p}{q}\right)$ denotes the Legendre symbol. A similar estimate is obtained for the more general sum, $\sum_{n=1}^N\sum_{p\leq x}\chi_n(p)$, where $\chi_1,\cdots,\chi_N$ are distinct Dirichlet characters. This latter result is generalized to algebraic number fields and then used to prove the following theorem: If $k$ and $l$ are two natural numbers, then the number of pairs of primes $p$ and $q$ not exceeding $x$ which satisfy $p\equiv 1\pmod k$, $q\equiv 1 \pmod l$ and for which the congruences $y^k\equiv q\pmod p$, $z^l\equiv p\pmod q$ are solvable in rational integers $y$ and $z$, equals

$$(kl\varphi(k)\varphi(l))^{-1}v\left\{\int_e^x(\log u)^{-1}du\right\}^2+O(x^2)\exp(-\alpha(\log x)^{\frac{1}{2}}),$$

where $v=1$ if $(2,k,l)=1$, $v=3/2$ if $k\equiv l\equiv 2\pmod 4$, $v=2$ otherwise, and $\alpha$ and the constant implied by the symbol $O$ depend on $k$ and $l$ only.

*W. H. Mills* (New Haven, Conn.)

## L20-18 (20# 5168)

**Vinogradov, I. M. A special case of estimation of trigonometric sums involving prime numbers.** Izv. Akad. Nauk SSSR. Ser. Mat. **22** (1958), 3–14. (Russian)

This is a continuation of the author's previous paper [same Izv. **21** (1957), 145–170; MR **19**, 839]. As there, let $f(x)=A_nx^n+\cdots+A_1x$, and suppose that $n\geqq 12$. Let $S=\sum_{p\leq P}\exp(2\pi ikf(p))$, where $p$ runs through primes and $k>0$ is an integer. Let $a_1/q_1,\cdots,a_n/q_n$ be irreducible fractions which approximate to $A_1,\cdots,A_n$ in the sense that $A_s-a_s/q_s=P^{-s}\delta_s$, where $|\delta_s|\leqq P^{1/n}$, for $s=1,\cdots,n$. Let $Q=$l.c.m. of $q_1,\cdots,q_n$. The present paper is concerned with the case $Q\leqq P^{1/n}$. Theorem 1 states that if $k\leqq P^{3/n^2}$, then $S=O(P\exp\{19(\log\log P)^2\}(k,Q)^{1/(2n)}Q^{\varepsilon-1/(2n)}$ for any fixed $\varepsilon>0$. Moreover, if there is a value $s'$ of $s$ for which $|\delta_{s'}|\geqq 1$, then the factor $(k,Q)^{1/(2n)}$ in the above estimate can be replaced by $|\delta_{s'}|^{-1/(2n)}$. Theorem 2 relates to the case when $Q$ is still smaller, namely $Q\leqq\exp(\log P)^{\frac{1}{3}}$; but the author's final remark indicates that the sum $S$ can then be estimated more effectively by using the theory of primes in arithmetic progressions.

*H. Davenport* (Cambridge, England)

Citations: MR 19, 839b = L15-16.

## L20-19 (21# 5611)

**Vinogradov, I. M. Estimate of a prime-number trigonometric sum.** Izv. Akad. Nauk SSSR. Ser. Mat. **23** (1959), 157–164. (Russian)

This paper contains an estimate for sums of the type

$$S=\sum_{p\leqq P}\exp(2\pi iAp^\alpha),$$

where $p$ runs through primes. Let $\alpha$ be a constant $\geqq 6$, and suppose that $\alpha$ differs from the nearest integer by at least $3^{-\alpha}$. Suppose that $1\leqq A\leqq P^\alpha$. Then $|S|\ll P^{1-\rho}$, where $\rho=(34{,}000{,}000\alpha^2)^{-1}$. The proof is complicated but highly ingenious, and involves a combination of ideas from the author's recent work on trigonometric sums [Izv. Akad. Nauk SSSR. Ser. Mat. **22** (1958), 161–164, 577–584; MR **21** #2624; **20** #5264] and from his earlier work on sums extended over primes [Chapter IX of Trudy Mat. Inst. Steklov **23** (1947); English transl. by Roth and Davenport, Interscience, New York, 1954; MR **10**, 599; **15**, 941]. The condition that $\alpha$ is not near an integer is used to ensure that the coefficients in the Taylor expansion of $A(x_0+x)^\alpha$ are not too small. *H. Davenport* (Cambridge, England)

Citations: MR 10, 599a = L02-2; MR 15, 941b = L02-3; MR 20# 5264 = L15-17; MR 21# 2624 = M15-19.

## L20-20 (22# 7986)

**Lavrik, A. F. Estimation of certain integrals connected with additive problems.** Vestnik Leningrad. Univ. **14** (1959), no. 19, 5–12. (Russian. English summary)

Let $p$ denote a prime and let $\gamma$, $\delta$ be a pair of non-negative numbers satisfying $0<\delta-\gamma\leqq 1$. Define

$$S(\vartheta,N)=\sum_{p\leqq N}\exp(2\pi i\vartheta p),$$

$$S_1(\vartheta,N)=\sum_{n=1}^{\infty}\Lambda(n)\exp\left(-\frac{n}{N}+2\pi i\vartheta n\right),$$

$$T(\vartheta,N)=\sum_{1\leqq n^2\leqq N}\exp(2\pi i\vartheta n^2);$$

as usual, $\Lambda(n)$ denotes von Mangoldt's function. The author proves that

$$\int_\gamma^\delta|S(\vartheta,N)|^2\,d\vartheta=(\delta-\gamma)(N/\log N)+O(N(\log\log N/\log N)^2),$$

$$\int_\gamma^\delta|S_1(\vartheta,N)|^2\,d\vartheta=\tfrac{1}{2}(\delta-\gamma)N\log N+O(N(\log\log N)^2),$$

$$\int_\gamma^\delta|T(\vartheta,N)|^2\,d\vartheta=(\delta-\gamma)N^{1/2}+O((\log N)^2).$$

Such results are of interest in the application of the circle method to additive problems in which the minor arcs

cannot be dealt with by the usual method of estimating trigonometric sums [see Yu. V. Linnik, Mat. Sb. (N.S.) **32 (74)** (1953), 3–60; MR **15**, 602]. The author uses Fourier series to pick out the interval $(\gamma, \delta)$ from $(0, 1)$, in the manner described in Lemma 12 of I. M. Vinogradov's book on trigonometric sums [*The method of trigonometrical sums in the theory of numbers*, Trav. Inst. Math. Stekloff **23** (1947); MR **10**, 599], and the Viggo Brun method.
*H. Halberstam* (London)

Citations: MR 10, 599a = L02-2; MR 15, 602j = P36-8.

## L20-21 (24# A1888 )

**Fomenko, O. M.**
**Estimates for certain trigonometrical sums.** **(Russian. English summary)**
*Bull. Acad. Polon. Sci. Sér. Sci. Math. Astronom. Phys.* **9** (1961), 757–759.

Author's summary: "The object of this note is to prove the following theorem. Let $\varepsilon > 0$ be any given number, $N > 2$; $r = \ln N$; $1 < H \leqq e^{r^\varepsilon}$; $\tau = NH^{-1}$; $\alpha = a/q + z$; $(a, q) = 1$; $0 < q \leqq e^{r^{0,5\varepsilon}}$, $|z| \leqq 1/q\tau$; $0 < u_1 < u_2 < \cdots < u_{m-1}$, even integers:

$$S = \sum_{\substack{p \leqq N \\ p + u_1 = p^{(1)} \\ \cdots\cdots\cdots\cdots \\ p + u_{m-1} = p^{(m-1)}}} e^{2\pi i \alpha p},$$

where $p, p^{(1)}, \cdots, p^{(m-1)}$ denote primes, then

$$S \ll \frac{N(rq)^{(2m+3)\varepsilon}}{r^m \sqrt{q}}$$

(the constant implied by the symbol $\ll$ is dependent on $u_1, u_2, \cdots, u_{m-1}, m, \varepsilon$)."

## L20-22 (25# 2040 )

**Perel'muter, G. I.**
**A bound for a sum with primes.** **(Russian)**
*Dokl. Akad. Nauk SSSR* **144** (1962), 48–51.

Let $\chi$ denote a non-principal character (mod $q$). Vinogradov has obtained estimates for the sum $\sum_{p \leqq N} \chi(f(p))$, where $f(x)$ is a polynomial in $x$, and $p$ denotes a typical prime. The author makes an application of the deep results of A. Weil [Proc. Nat. Acad. Sci. U.S.A. **27** (1941), 345–347; MR **2**, 345] to the problem of the estimation of the more general exponential sums:

$$\sum_{p \leqq N} \chi(R_1(p)) \exp\left(\frac{2\pi i}{q} R_2(p)\right),$$

where $R_1$, $R_2$ are rational functions (mod $q$).
*S. Chowla* (Boulder, Colo.)

Citations: MR 2, 345b = G20-3.

## L20-23 (32# 4093 )

**Chen Jing-run [Ch'en Ching-jun]**
**Estimates for trigonometric sums.**
*Acta Math. Sinica* **14** (1964), 765–768 (*Chinese*); *translated as Chinese Math.—Acta* **6** (1965), 163–167.

Using a method of Vinogradov [*The method of trigonometrical sums in the theory of numbers* (Russian), Trav. Inst. Math. Stekloff **23** (1948); MR **10**, 599; English translation, Chapter 9, Interscience, New York, 1954; MR **15**, 941] the author estimates the trigonometric sum with primes

$$\sum_{p \leqq P} \exp\left(\frac{2\pi i a p^k}{q}\right) = O(P^{1-\alpha/3+\varepsilon}),$$

where $(a, q) = 1$, $0 < \alpha \leqq \frac{3}{8}$, $P = q^{1/(1-\alpha)}$. {In the statement of the theorem the $\varepsilon$ is omitted.}
*W. Schwarz* (Freiburg)

Citations: MR 10, 599a = L02-2; MR 15, 941b = L02-3.

## L20-24 (33# 2608 )

**Vinogradov, I. M.**
**An estimate for a certain sum extended over the primes of an arithmetic progression.** **(Russian)**
*Izv. Akad. Nauk SSSR Ser. Mat.* **30** (1966), 481–496.

Let $\chi$ denote a non-principal character (mod $q$), where $q$ is a large prime; $k$, a number prime to $q$; $p$, a typical prime which is the variable in the following sum: $S = \sum_{p \leqq N} \chi(p+k)$. The author obtains the sharp estimate

$$S \ll \frac{Nq^\varepsilon}{a}\left(\frac{q^{1/4}}{N^{1/3}} a + \frac{a^{1/2}}{N^{1/10}}\right).$$

This is a deep result, whose proof is neatly developed in a series of lemmas. {Reviewer's remark: Applications are not indicated in this paper, but are probably forthcoming in a later publication.} *S. Chowla* (University Park, Pa.)

Referred to in L20-25, L25-30.

## L20-25 (42# 5923 )

**Karacuba, A. A.**
**Sums of characters with prime numbers.** **(Russian)**
*Izv. Akad. Nauk SSSR Ser. Mat.* **34** (1970), 299–321.

Main theorem: If $q$ is a sufficiently large prime number, $\chi$ is a non-principal character mod $q$, $0 < \omega \leqq \frac{1}{4}$ and $q^{(1/2)+\omega} \leqq N < q$, then $\sum_{p \leqq N} \chi(p+k) \ll Nq^{-\omega^2/1024}$. Here $k$ is any integer prime to $q$ and the constant in $\ll$ depends only on $\omega$. This is an improvement of the result of I. M. Vinogradov [same Izv. **30** (1966), 481–496; MR **33** #2608]. From this theorem it follows that for $N, q, \omega, k$ satisfying the above conditions, the number of quadratic residues (and of quadratic nonresidues) mod $q$ of the form $p+k$, where $p \leqq N$, is equal to $\frac{1}{2}\pi(N) + O(Nq^{-\omega^2/1024})$.
*J. Browkin* (Warsaw)

Citations: MR 33# 2608 = L20-24.
Referred to in N68-46, P48-23.

## L20-26 (42# 5926 )

**Alter, Ronald; Villarino, Mark**
**A remark on primes in arithmetic progressions.**
*Bull. Austral. Math. Soc.* **3** (1970), 185–192.

Let $\pi(x, \chi) = \sum_{p \leqq x} \chi(p)$. The authors establish that if $\chi$ is the quadratic character mod 5, then (1) $\liminf \pi(x, \chi) = -\infty$. In the course of their proof the authors use the known fact that if $\chi$ is the quadratic character mod 5, then (2) $L(s, \chi) \neq 0$ $(\frac{1}{2} \leqq s \leqq 1)$. The demonstration which the authors provide is more laborious than necessary [see S. Chowla, Acta Arith. **1** (1935), 113–114]. The authors seem to be unaware that E. Landau [Math. Z. **1** (1918), 1–24] showed that (1) holds for any quadratic character, regardless of whether (2) holds. It may also be remarked that it follows from the work of Littlewood [see Landau, Math. Z. **2** (1918), 52–154] that the deeper relation $\limsup \pi(x, \chi) = +\infty$ also holds, where $\chi$ is any quadratic character for which (2) is valid. The paper is flawed by verbal and notational ambiguities.
*H. L. Montgomery* (Princeton, N.J.)

# L25 CHARACTER SUMS OVER ARBITRARY INTERVALS

See also reviews E16-88, L15-1, L20-6, L30-9, M25-46, M25-50, M25-51, M55-43, N12-1, N12-27, N12-29, N68-28, N68-44, N72-1,

N72-14, N76-1, N76-9, N76-10, N76-12, Q15-11, R14-73, Z10-47.

**L25-1** **(5, 255h)**

**Hua, Loo-Keng. On character sums.** Acad. Sinica Science Record **1**, 21–23 (1942).

The following lemma is established and indications given of applications [cf. Bull. Amer. Math. Soc. **48**, 726–730 (1942); these Rev. **4**, 130]. Let $k$ be an integer greater than 1. For each nonprincipal character $\chi(n)$ mod $k$,

$$\left|\sum_{a=0}^{A}\sum_{n=-a}^{a}\chi(n)\right|\leqq(A^*+1)\sqrt{k},$$

where $A^*$ is the least positive integer satisfying $A^*\equiv A \bmod k$. *G. Pall* (Montreal, Que.).

Citations: MR 4, 130d = N76-1.

**L25-2** **(9, 228b)**

**Ren′i, A. A. On some new applications of the method of Academician I. M. Vinogradov.** Doklady Akad. Nauk SSSR (N.S.) **56**, 675–678 (1947). (Russian)

Let $\chi(n)$ be a nonprincipal primitive character mod $D$; let $\alpha$ and $\beta$ be irrationals whose continued fractions are $\alpha=1/a_1+1/a_2+\cdots$, $\beta=1/b_1+1/b_2+\cdots$, where

$$a_n\leqq(\log D)^t n^\rho,\quad b_n\leqq(\log D)^t n^\rho,$$

$t>0$ and $\rho\geqq 0$ being constants. The author proves

$$\sum_{\alpha D<n<\beta D}\chi(n)=O(1+t+\rho)(\log\log D)^2D^{\frac{1}{2}}.$$

If $\chi(-1)=1$, the result is also true for $\alpha=0$. The proof proceeds as follows. It follows from the classical theory of $L$-series that it suffices to prove

$$\sum_{n=1}^{D}\bar{\chi}(n)n^{-1}e^{2\pi in\alpha}=O(1+t+\rho)(\log\log D)^2.$$

The author writes $n=pm$, where $p$ is the greatest prime dividing $n$. If the summation is only extended over those values of $n$ for which either $p\leqq(\log D)^{5+t+\rho}$ or $m\leqq(\log D)^{5+t+\rho}$, the result is straightforward. For the other values of $n$, the author uses Vinogradov's argument

$$\Big|\sum_n\Big|^2=\Big|\sum_p\sum_m\Big|^2\leqq\sum_p p^{-2}\sum_p\Big|\sum_m\chi(m)m^{-1}e^{2\pi ip m\alpha}\Big|^2,$$

from which the result follows by a routine calculation. *H. Heilbronn* (Bristol).

**L25-3** **(12, 161b)**

**Vinogradov, I. M. A new improvement of the method of estimation of double sums.** Doklady Akad. Nauk SSSR (N.S.) **73**, 635–638 (1950). (Russian)

This paper is concerned with two separate questions, and the only common feature is that in both cases the method involves "exhausting" the region of summation of a double sum. The first result is as follows. Let $\chi$ be a nonprincipal character (mod $q$), and let $k$ be a fixed integer, positive or negative (but not zero). Then

$$(1)\qquad \sum_{p\leqq N}\chi(p+k)=O(Nq^\epsilon(N^{-1}q^{5/6})^{1/4}),$$

provided that $q^{5/6}<N<q^{7/6}$, the summation being over primes $p$. An earlier result [Bull. Acad. Sci. URSS. Sér. Math. [Izvestiya Akad. Nauk SSSR] **7**, 17–34 (1943); these Rev. **5**, 143] gave an estimate which was effective for $q>N^{1+\delta}$ $(\delta>0)$. The proof is given only in outline, and the reviewer has not been able to fill in the details in the proofs of lemmas 2 and 3 or of the main result (1). The second result relates to the straightforward character sum $\sum_{N+1}^{N+Q}\chi(x)$. Let (2) $U(M,P)=\sum_{x=M+1}^{M+P}\sum_{z=0}^{P-1}\chi(x+z)$. Let $M_1,\cdots,M_m$ be integers such that the intervals $M_i\leqq t\leqq M_i+P$ are nonoverlapping and are contained in $M_1\leqq t\leqq M_1+q$. Then it is easily proved, using Cauchy's inequality, that (3) $\sum_{i=1}^{M}|U(M_i,P)|<P(mq)^{\frac{1}{2}}$. The sum $U(M,P)$ can be regarded as the sum of $\chi(x)$ over all points $(x,y)$ of the parallelogram whose vertices are $(M,0)$, $(M+P,0)$, $(M+P,P)$, $(M+2P,P)$; and (3) estimates the sum over a series of such parallelograms, subject to the condition that their lower sides do not overlap and have a total length not more than $q$. Now put $Q=hq^{\frac{1}{2}}$, $\tau=[\log h/\log 3]$, $Q_0=2\cdot 3^\tau[3^{-\tau}Q/2]$, and suppose for simplicity that $\tau\geqq 1$. Let $S_0=\sum_{N+1}^{N+Q_0}\chi(x)$. Then $Q_0S_0$ is $\sum\chi(x)$ summed over the square $N<x\leqq N+Q_0$, $0<y\leqq Q_0$. This square is approximated to by parallelograms. The first parallelogram is $N-\frac{1}{2}Q_0<x-y\leqq N+\frac{1}{2}Q_0$, $0<y\leqq Q_0$. Next there are four parallelograms near the corners of the square, similar to $N-\frac{1}{2}Q_0<x-y\leqq N-\frac{1}{6}Q_0$, $0<y\leqq\frac{1}{3}Q_0$. Generally there are $4\cdot 3^{s-1}$ parallelograms of side $3^{-s}Q_0$. The sums of $\chi(x)$ over these are to be taken with appropriate + and − signs. The sum over a single parallelogram is equivalent to one of the type (2), and the sum over a group of parallelograms can be estimated by (3). The final result is that (4) $|\sum_{N+1}^{N+Q}\chi(x)|<q^{\frac{1}{2}}(a\log h+b)$, where $a=2/\log 27$ and $b=5/2$. But this result is less interesting than the ingenious and elementary method of proof. *H. Davenport.*

Citations: MR 5, 143a = L20-6.

Referred to in L20-13, N76-5.

**L25-4** **(12, 393f)**

**Cudakov, N. G., and Rodosskiĭ, K. A. On generalized characters.** Doklady Akad. Nauk SSSR (N.S.) **73**, 1137–1139 (1950). (Russian)

The authors define a generalized character as a complex-valued function $h(n)$ on the positive integers such that $h(mn)=h(m)h(n)$, $|h(n)|$ is 0 or 1 for any $n$, and $\sum_{n=1}^{x}h(n)$ is bounded for all positive integers $x$. The nonprincipal residue-characters of Dirichlet [cf. E. Landau, Vorlesungen über Zahlentheorie, Hirzel, Leipzig, 1927, vol. 1, pp. 83–87] obviously satisfy these requirements. By considering the sum $\sum_{n=1}^{m}(m-n)^2\sum_{d|n}h(d)$ with a suitable $m$, the authors prove that if $h(n)$ is a real generalized character and if $M$ is the maximum of $|\sum_{n=1}^{x}h(n)|$ for all positive integers $x$, then $\sum_{n=1}^{\infty}h(n)n^{-1}>(14M)^{-1}$. They also remark that the lemma used by Estermann [J. London Math. Soc. **23**, 275–279 (1948); these Rev. **10**, 356] in his proof of Siegel's theorem is valid for real generalized characters. *P. T. Bateman* (Urbana, Ill.).

Citations: MR 10, 356c = M20-7.

Referred to in L25-9, L25-11, M20-22.

**L25-5** **(12, 393g)**

**Čudakov, N. G., and Linnik, Yu. V. On a class of completely multiplicative functions.** Doklady Akad. Nauk SSSR (N.S.) **74**, 193–196 (1950). (Russian)

A generalized character $h(n)$ in the sense of the paper reviewed above is completely determined by the values of $h(p)$, where $p$ runs over the primes. The set of primes $p$ for which $h(p)\neq 0$ is called the basis of $h(n)$. It is easy to construct generalized characters for which the basis consists of exactly one prime. This paper is devoted to proving that there are no generalized characters with a finite basis consisting of more than one prime. The proof uses quantitative work of Vinogradov on uniform distribution [cf. Trav. Inst. Math. Stekloff **23** (1947); these Rev. **10**, 599] and work of Gelfond [Bull. Acad. Sci. URSS. Sér. Math. [Izvestiya Akad. Nauk SSSR] **1939**, 509–518; these Rev. **1**, 295] on the rational approximations to $\log\alpha/\log\beta$, where $\alpha$ and $\beta$ are positive algebraic numbers such that $\log\alpha/\log\beta$ is irrational (and thus transcendental). It is unknown whether or not there exist any generalized characters with an infinite

basis other than the nonprincipal Dirichlet characters.
*P. T. Bateman* (Urbana, Ill.).

Citations: MR 1, 295c = J80-1; MR 10, 599a = L02-2.
Referred to in L25-7, L25-9.

## L25-6 (13, 113d)

**Bateman, P. T., and Chowla, S. Averages of character sums.** Proc. Amer. Math. Soc. **1**, 781–787 (1950).

The authors consider the arithmetic means of the sums $S(n)=\sum_{m=1}^{n}\psi(m)$, where $\psi$ is a primitive residue character modulo $k$. Employing an argument involving Fourier series they derive a stronger form of Paley's $\Omega$-result [J. London Math. Soc. **7**, 28–32 (1932)] that $M(\psi)=\Omega(k^{\frac{1}{2}}\log\log k)$, where $M(\psi)$ is the maximum of $|S(0)|, \cdots, |S(k-1)|$. In the case $\psi(-1)=-1$, $\alpha k\leqq n\leqq k$, where $\alpha$ is a number between 0 and 1, they obtain an estimate for the arithmetic mean of $S(0), \cdots, S(n-1)$, which is valuable for $n$ not too small relative to $k$. Davenport [ibid. **6**, 198–202 (1931)] has proved that if $s$ is a fixed complex number with $0<\sigma=\Re(s)<1$, then for any primitive $\psi$ we have $|L(s,\psi)|\leqq Ck^{(1-\sigma)/2}$, where $L(s,\psi)$ is Dirichlet's function and $C$ is a constant depending on $s$. The authors give a very simple proof of this result in the case $\psi(-1)=1$, with a specific value of the constant. Unfortunately their method does not give Davenport's result for the case $\psi(-1)=-1$.
*A. L. Whiteman* (Los Angeles, Calif.).

## L25-7 (15, 105c)

**Čudakov, N. G., and Pavlyučuk, A. K. On summation functions of characters of numerical groups with a finite basis.** Trudy Mat. Inst. Steklov., v. 38, pp. 366–381. Izdat. Akad. Nauk SSSR, Moscow, 1951. (Russian) 20 rubles.

Suppose $\mathfrak{G}$ is a multiplicative group of positive algebraic numbers with a finite basis $\omega_1, \omega_2, \cdots, \omega_p$, where we assume $\omega_k>1$ for $k=1, 2, \cdots, p$. Let $\mathfrak{S}$ be the semigroup generated by $\omega_1, \omega_2, \cdots, \omega_p$. Suppose $\chi$ is a (not necessarily bounded) character of $\mathfrak{G}$, that is a homomorphism of $\mathfrak{G}$ into the multiplicative group of non-zero complex numbers. Let $H$ be the function defined on the non-negative real numbers by the formula $H(x)=\sum_{\alpha\in\mathfrak{S},\alpha\leqq\exp x}\chi(\alpha)$. Suppose $\sigma_0=\max_{1\leqq k\leqq p}(\log|\chi(\omega_k)|)/(\log\omega_k)$ and $q$ is the number of values of $k$ for which $\sigma_0=(\log|\chi(\omega_k)|)/(\log\omega_k)$. Then the authors prove the following assertions about the behavior of $H(x)$ as $x\rightarrow\infty$. (1) If $\sigma_0<0$, then $H(x)$ is bounded. (2) If $\sigma_0=0$, $q=1$, and $\chi(\omega_k)\neq1$ for all $k$, then $H(x)$ is bounded. (3) If $\sigma_0=0$ and $\chi(\omega_k)=1$ for some $k$, then $H(x)=\Omega(x)$. (4) If $\sigma_0=0$ and $q\geqq2$, then $H(x)=\Omega((\log\log\log x)^{\frac{1}{2}})$. (5) If $\sigma_0>0$, then $H(x)=\Omega(x^{-1}e^{\sigma_0 x})$. Although (1) and (2) are almost trivial, the proofs of (3), (4), and (5) require delicate methods from analytic number theory due to Vinogradov, Gelfond, and Linnik. A particular case of the above is a result of Čudakov and Linnik [Doklady Akad. Nauk SSSR (N.S.) **74**, 193–196 (1950); these Rev. **12**, 393] to the effect that if $\mathfrak{G}$ is a multiplicative subgroup of the positive rationals generated by a finite set $\mathfrak{P}$ of prime numbers and if $\chi$ is a bounded character of $\mathfrak{G}$, then $H(x)$ is bounded if and only if $\mathfrak{P}$ contains exactly one prime number and $\chi$ is not the principal character of $\mathfrak{G}$. *P. T. Bateman.*

Citations: MR 12, 393g = L25-5.
Referred to in L25-10.

## L25-8 (15, 105d)

**Bredihin, B. M. On characters of numerical semigroups with a sufficiently sparse base.** Doklady Akad. Nauk SSSR (N.S.) **90**, 707–710 (1953). (Russian)

Suppose $\mathfrak{G}$ is a multiplicative group of positive real numbers with a denumerable basis $\omega_1, \omega_2, \cdots$, where we assume that $\omega_k>1$ for all $k$ and that for any positive number $x$ there is only a finite number $\pi(x)$ of positive integers $k$ such that $\omega_k\leqq\exp x$. Suppose $\chi$ is a bounded character of $\mathfrak{G}$, that is, a homomorphism of $\mathfrak{G}$ into the multiplicative group of complex numbers of absolute value 1. Let $\mathfrak{S}$ be the semigroup generated by $\omega_1, \omega_2, \cdots$, put $H(x)=\sum_{\alpha\in\mathfrak{S},\alpha\leqq\exp x}\chi(\alpha)$, and let $\exp_m$ and $\log_m$ denote the $m$th iterates of the exponential and logarithmic functions respectively. Then the author proves the following assertions about the behavior of $H(x)$ as $x\rightarrow\infty$. (1) If $\pi(x)<\eta\log x$ for large $x$, where $\eta$ is a positive constant $<(\log 2)^{-1}$, and if $\chi(\omega_k)=1$ for some $k$, then $H(x)=\Omega(x^{1-\eta\log 2})$. (2) If $\pi(x)<\delta\log_{m+1}x$ for large $x$, where $\delta$ is a positive constant $<(\log 4)^{-1}$, if $\chi(\omega_k)\neq1$ for all $k$, and if there exists a pair of basis elements $\omega_k$ and $\omega_l$ such that the continued fraction of $(\log\omega_k)/(\log\omega_l)$ has the properties $a_\nu=O(\exp_m c\nu)$ and $q_{\nu+1}=O(\exp q_\nu{}^\rho)$, where $a_\nu$ is the $\nu$th partial quotient, $q_\nu$ is the denominator of the $\nu$th convergent, $c$ is a positive constant, and $\rho$ is a positive constant $<1$, then $H(x)=\Omega((\log_m x)^{\frac{1}{2}-\delta\log 2})$. The proof of (1) is easy, but the proof of (2) is like the proofs of the latter parts of the theorem of the paper reviewed above. *P. T. Bateman.*

Referred to in L25-10.

## L25-9 (15, 289k)

**Čudakov, N. G. On a class of completely multiplicative functions.** Uspehi Matem. Nauk (N.S.) **8**, no. 3(55), 149–150 (1953). (Russian)

Suppose $t$ is a non-zero real number and $\chi$ is a non-principal residue-character, and let $h$ be the function defined on the positive integers by the equality $h(n)=\chi(n)n^{ti}$. The author proves that $h$ is not a residue-character but nevertheless shares with residue-characters the property that $\sum_{n\leqq x}h(n)$ is bounded. In the terminology of earlier papers [Čudakov and Rodosskiĭ, Doklady Akad. Nauk. SSSR (N.S.) **73**, 1137–1139 (1950); these Rev. **12**, 393; Čudakov and Linnik, ibid. **74**, 193–196 (1950); these Rev. **12**, 393; Kubilyus and Linnik, Trudy Mat. Inst. Steklov. **38**, 170–172 (1951); these Rev. **15**, 103], this shows that the function $h$ is a generalized character which is not a residue-character and which has an infinite basis. It is unknown whether or not there exist other generalized characters with these two properties. *P. T. Bateman* (Urbana, Ill.).

Citations: MR 12, 393f = L25-4; MR 12, 393g = L25-5; MR 15, 103b = E24-41.
Referred to in L25-11.

## L25-10 (15, 940c)

**Bredihin, B. M. On sum functions of characters of numerical semigroups.** Doklady Akad. Nauk SSSR (N.S.) **94**, 609–612 (1954). (Russian)

Suppose $G$ is a multiplicative group of positive real numbers with a finite basis $\omega_1, \omega_2, \cdots, \omega_N$, where it is assumed that $\omega_k>1$ for $k=1, 2, \cdots, N$, and let $S$ be the semigroup generated by $\omega_1, \omega_2, \cdots, \omega_N$. The author proves a conjecture of A. O. Gel'fond to the effect that if $\chi$ is any (bounded) character of $G$ and $H(x)=\sum_{\alpha\in S,\alpha\leqq\exp x}\chi(\alpha)$, then $H(x)$ is unbounded. More specifically, he proves that if $M_{k,l}(x)$ is the number of convergents of the continued fraction for $\log\omega_l/\log\omega_k$ $(k\neq l)$ which have denominators in the interval $[0, x]$, then

$$\max_{t\in[0,x]}|H(t)|\geqq c[\max_{k\neq l}M_{k,l}(x^{1/2}\log^{-3/2}x)]^{1/2},$$

where $c$ is a suitable positive number. The proof belongs essentially to the domain of analytic number theory and uses ideas and methods from an earlier note of the author [same Doklady (N.S.) **90**, 707–710 (1953); these Rev. **15**, 105] and a paper of Čudakov and Pavlyučuk [Trudy Mat.

Inst. Steklov. **38**, 366–381 (1951); these Rev. **15**, 105].
*P. T. Bateman* (Urbana, Ill.).

Citations: MR 15, 105c = L25-7; MR 15, 105d = L25-8.

## L25-11 (16, 448d)

**Bronšteĭn, B. S. Unboundedness of the sum function of a generalized character.** Moskov. Gos. Univ. Uč. Zap. **165**, Mat. **7**, 212–220 (1954). (Russian)

The author defines a generalized character as a multiplicative function on the positive integers which takes on only values of absolute value 0 or 1. [This differs somewhat from the definition of Čudakov and Rodosskiĭ, Dokl. Akad. Nauk SSSR (N.S.) **73**, 1137–1139 (1950); MR **12**, 393.] Suppose $h$ is a generalized character which is not a residue-character (in the sense of Dirichlet), but for which there exists a residue-character $\chi$ such that $h(p)\neq\chi(p)$ for only finitely many primes $p$. Then the author shows that $\sum_{n=1}^{x} h(n)$ is unbounded. The proof requires nothing beyond the elementary facts about residue-characters. On the other hand, if $h$ is a generalized character which differs from any residue-character on infinitely many primes, it is possible for $\sum_{n=1}^{x} h(n)$ to be either bounded or unbounded [Čudakov, Uspehi Mat. Nauk (N.S.) **8**, no. 3(55), 149–150 (1953); MR **15**, 289]. *P. T. Bateman* (Urbana, Ill.).

Citations: MR 12, 393f = L25-4; MR 15, 289k = L25-9.
Referred to in L25-27.

## L25-12 (16, 905f)

**Postnikov, A. G. On the sum of characters with respect to a modulus equal to a power of a prime number.** Izv. Akad. Nauk SSSR. Ser. Mat. **19**, 11–16 (1955). (Russian)

The author proves the following lemma: Let $p$ be a prime greater than 2 and $n$ a positive integer not of the form $\alpha p^f-\nu$ for any $f>0$, $0\leqq\nu<f$, $(\alpha, p)=1$. Then there exists a polynomial $f(u)=u+a_2u^2+\cdots+a_{n-1}u^{n-1}$ with integral coefficients such that

$$\frac{\operatorname{ind}_g(1+pu)}{p-1}\equiv\Lambda f(u) \pmod{p^{n-1}},$$

for all integers $u$, where $g$ is any given primitive root modulo $p^n$. Here $(\Lambda, p)=1$ and $\Lambda$ is defined by

$$\frac{\operatorname{ind}_g(1+p)}{p-1}\equiv\Lambda f(1) \pmod{p^{n-1}}.$$

The coefficients $a_k$ are defined as follows: Let $k=p^\tau k'$ where $(k', p)=1$; then

$$a_k=(-1)^{k+1}p^{k-\tau-1}\kappa_k,$$

where $\kappa_k$ is a root of the congruence

$$k'\kappa_k\equiv 1 \pmod{p^{n-k+\tau}}.$$

In proving this result the fact that $1+p$ generates the subgroup of residues modulo $p^n$ of the form $1+pu$ is used.

Since a character $\chi(k)$ modulo $p^n$ and of degree not less than $p^{n-1}$ can be expressed as

$$\chi(k)=\exp\{2\pi imp^{1-n}\operatorname{ind}_g k/(p-1)\},$$

where $(m, p)=1$, the lemma can be used to replace character sums by exponential sums involving the polynomial $f(u)$ in their exponents. By using estimates of Vinogradov for such sums with polynomial exponents, the author proves that if $n$ is not of the form $\alpha p^f-\nu$, as in the lemma, then

$$\left|\sum_{k=1}^{l}\chi(k)\right|\leqq\{8(n-2)\}^{(n-2)\lambda/2}p^\mu l^{1-\mu},$$

where $\lambda=\log\{12(n-2)(n-1)/\tau\}$, $\mu^{-1}\tau=3(n-1)^2\lambda$, and $\tau=1$ if $p^{1+1/(n-2)}\leqq l\leqq p^2$, $p=(l/p)^\tau$ if $p^2\leqq l$. A similar result can be proved for $n$ of the form $\alpha p^f-\nu$. These estimates are applied to show that the associated Dirichlet $L$-function $L(s,\chi)$ is free of zeros in a certain region.
*R. A. Rankin* (Glasgow).

Referred to in M25-51.

## L25-13 (18, 719e)

**Tchudakoff, N. G. Theory of the characters of number semigroups.** J. Indian Math. Soc. (N.S.) **20** (1956), 11–15.

This paper was communicated by title to the International Colloquium on Zeta-functions held at Bombay, 1956. It seems to contain a brief report on the results obtained by the author and others in several Russian papers (for the latter, some seven titles are given). Since the present paper is somewhat condensed, the reviewer was not able to extract from it an exact statement of all of its results. However, it may be helpful to the reader of these reviews if one of the theorems is reproduced here, in order that he will get an idea of what kind of result the author has proved: Let $\mathfrak{G}$ be some semigroup of entire ideals of the algebraic number field of degree $n$; let $\chi(\mathfrak{a})$ be a character of an ideal $\mathfrak{a}$ with $|\chi(\mathfrak{a})|=1$. If $\mathfrak{G}$ has a basis consisting of $N$ prime ideals, where $n<N$, then

$$\sum_{1\leqq N(\mathfrak{a})\leqq e^x}\chi(\mathfrak{a})=\Omega(\sqrt{\lg_3 x}).$$

If $\mathfrak{G}$ has a basis consisting of an infinity of prime ideals and the number of prime ideals $\mathfrak{p}\in\mathfrak{G}$ with $N(\mathfrak{p})\leqq x$ is equal to $\pi(x)=O(\lg_4 x)$, then

$$\sum_{1\leqq N(\mathfrak{a})\leqq e^x}\chi(\mathfrak{a})=\Omega((\lg_3 x)^\mu\ (0<\mu<\tfrac{1}{2}).$$

*P. Roquette* (Hamburg).

## L25-14 (20# 5760)

**Čudakov, N. G.; and Bredihin, B. M. Application of Parseval's equality for the estimation of sum functions of characters of numerical semigroups.** Ukrain. Mat. Ž. **8** (1956), 347–360. (Russian)

The article deals with generalized characters, i.e., multiplicative functions defined on a multiplicative semigroup of real numbers. In connection with each character $\chi$ there is considered a summation function of the character

$$H(x)=\sum_{\alpha\leqq e^x}\chi(\alpha) \text{ and } \sum\chi(\alpha)\alpha^{-s},$$

namely, the $L$-function of the character.

The author obtains various estimates from below ($\Omega$-estimates) for summation functions of characters on the basis of the Parseval equality:

$$\frac{1}{2\pi}\int_{-\infty}^{\infty}\left|\frac{L(\sigma+it)}{\sigma+it}\right|^2 dt=\int_0^\infty|H(x)|^2e^{-2\sigma x}dx.$$

*N. I. Romanov* (RŽMat **1958** #1788)

Referred to in L25-25, L25-27.

## L25-15 (23# A2392)

**Fomenko, O. M.**

**On the sum of the values of a character.** (**Russian. English summary**)

*Bull. Acad. Polon. Sci. Sér. Sci. Math. Astronom. Phys.* **9** (1961), 29–31.

Author's summary: "Let $\varepsilon$ be an arbitrary small positive number. Let $q$ be a prime number, $q\geqq c_0$, where $c_0$ is sufficiently large. $l$ will denote a positive integer; $w$ runs over all products of $l$ different prime factors. Let $k$ be a fixed integer, $(k, q)=1$, $0<|k|<c_0$. The symbol $\chi(a)$ will denote the character with respect to the modulus $q$ which is different from the main character. Then we have

$$\sum_{w\leqq N}\chi(w+k)\ll N^{1+\varepsilon}\left(\left(\frac{q^{3/4}}{N}\right)^{1/3}+N^{-0,1}\right),$$

where $q^{3/4} \ll N \ll q^{5/4}$ (for $B>0$ the symbol $A \ll B$ will denote that $|A|/B \ll \text{const.}$)."

## L25-16 (24# A2569)

**Burgess, D. A.**
**On character sums and primitive roots.**
*Proc. London Math. Soc.* (3) **12** (1962), 179–192.

Let $\chi$ denote a non-principal character (mod $p$), $p$ prime, and put $S_H(N)=\sum_{m=N+1}^{N+H}\chi(m)$. It was proved independently by Pólya and Vinogradov in 1918 that

$$S_H(N) = O(p^{1/2}\log p).$$

The principal result of the present paper is contained in the following Theorem 1: If $H$ and $r$ are arbitrary positive integers, then

$$|S_H(N)| < AH^{1-1/(r+1)}p^{r/4}\log p$$

for every integer $N$, where $A$ is an absolute constant.

The proof of the theorem makes use of Weil's result on the analogue of the Riemann hypothesis for the zeta function of an algebraic function field over a finite field [*Sur les courbes algébriques et les variétés qui s'en déduisent*, Deuxième Partie, § IV, Actualités Sci. Ind., No. 1041, Hermann, Paris, 1945; MR **10**, 262].

For the application the following corollary of Theorem 1 is used. For $\varepsilon>0$ there exists a positive number $\delta$ such that if $p$ is sufficiently large and $H$ satisfies $H>p^{1/4+\varepsilon}$, then $|S_H(N)|<Hp^{-\delta}$ for all $N$.

The author also proves the following two theorems which greatly improve previously known results. Theorem 2: The maximum number of consecutive quadratic residues or non-residues (mod $p$) is $O(p^{1/4}(\log p)^{3/2})$. Theorem 3: For each $\varepsilon>0$ and every prime $p$, every interval of length $H \supset p^{1/4+\varepsilon}$ contains

$$(\phi(p-1)/(p-1))H(1+O(p^{-\delta}))$$

primitive roots (mod $p$), where $\delta>0$ depends only on $\varepsilon$. In particular, it follows that the least primitive root $g$ satisfies $g=O(p^{1/4+\varepsilon})$. *L. Carlitz* (Durham, N.C.)

Citations: MR 10, 262c = G20-8.
Referred to in L25-19, L25-20, M15-25, N72-36, N72-40, N72-42, N76-20, T25-20, T25-26, T25-27.

## L25-17 (24# A2570)

**Burgess, D. A.**
**On character sums and $L$-series.**
*Proc. London Math. Soc.* (3) **12** (1962), 193–206.

Let $\chi$ denote a non-principal character (mod $k$). It was proved by Davenport [J. London Math. Soc. **6** (1931), 198–202] that $|L_\chi(\frac12+it)| \ll k^{1/4}$. In the present paper it is shown in particular that

$$(*)\qquad |L_\chi(\tfrac12+it)| \ll k^{7/32+\varepsilon}.$$

As pointed out by the author, the principal difficulty is that of obtaining a suitable estimate for

$$\sum_{x=1}^{k}|\sum_{y=1}^{h}\chi(x+y)|^{2r}$$

when $k$ is composite, since Weil's estimate for $\sum_1^p \chi(f(x))$, $p$ prime, which was used in the author's earlier paper [#A2569 above] does not generalize to the case $k$ composite. The main result is contained in the following.

Theorem 1: Let $\chi$ belong properly to $k$. Let $\varepsilon>0$ and let $r$ be a fixed positive integer. If either $k$ is square-free or $r=2$, then for every pair of integers $N, H$ ($H>0$) we have

$$|\sum_{m=N+1}^{N+H}\chi(m)| \ll H^{1-1/(r+1)}k^{(1/4r)+\varepsilon},$$

the implied constant depending only on $\varepsilon$ and $r$.

($\chi$ belongs properly to $k$ if it is impossible to write $\chi=\chi_1\chi_2$, where $k=k_1k_2$, $k_1\supset 1$, $k_2\supset 1$, $\chi_1$ is a character (mod $k_1$) and $\chi_2$ is the principal character (mod $k_2$).)

Corollary: Let $K$ be a fixed integer and let $k$ be any integer such that if $p^\alpha$ ($\alpha \geqq 2$) divides $k$ then $p^\alpha$ also divides $K$. Then

$$|\sum_{m=N+1}^{N+H}\chi(m)| \ll H^{1-1/(r+1)}k^{(1/4r)+\varepsilon},$$

where the implied constant now depends on $K$, $r$ and $\varepsilon$. In particular, this inequality holds for every proper real character with an implied constant depending on $r$ and $\varepsilon$.

Theorem 2: Let $\chi$ be proper (mod $k$) and let $0<\sigma<1$. Then

$$(**)\qquad |L_\chi(\sigma+it)| \ll k^{1/2-(9/16)\sigma+\varepsilon} \quad (0<\sigma\leqq \tfrac23),$$
$$\ll k^{3/8(1-\sigma)+\varepsilon} \quad (\tfrac23 \leqq \sigma < 1).$$

In particular (*) holds.

Corollary: If $\chi$ is any non-principal character (mod $k$), then (**) holds. *L. Carlitz* (Durham, N.C.)

Referred to in E20-88, L25-19, L25-23, L25-24, L25-31, M15-30, M20-31, N72-40.

## L25-18 (26# 1288)

**Usol'cev, L. P.**
**Estimates of large deviations in certain problems on an incomplete system of residues. (Russian)**
*Dokl. Akad. Nauk SSSR* **143** (1962), 539–542.

Sei $p$ eine Primzahl $\geqq 3$, $h$ (ganz) $\geqq 5$, $h^h \leqq p^{1/2-\varepsilon}$, $0<\varepsilon<\frac12$, $\lambda=\lambda(h)\leqq\sqrt{h}$, $\lim_{h\to\infty}\lambda(h)=\infty$. Für die Anzahl $M_p(\lambda)$ der ganzen Zahlen $a$, $0\leqq a\leqq p-1$, für die

$$h^{-1/2}\sum_{x=1}^{h}((a+x)/p) > \lambda$$

($(m/p)$—Legendresymbol) ist, beweist der Verfasser $p^{-1}M_p(\lambda)\leqq 32\exp(-\lambda^2/4)$ ($p\geqq 2^{1/\varepsilon}$). Bei festem $\lambda$ und $p\to\infty$ wurde das Verhalten von $N_p(\lambda)$, der Anzahl der $a$, für die jener Ausdruck $<\lambda$ ausfällt, von Davenport und Erdős [Publ. Math. Debrecen **2** (1952), 252–265; MR **14**, 1063] untersucht. Der Beweis beruht auf der Abschätzung von Charaktersummen nach A. Weil. Ein entsprechendes Resultat wird zu einem Satz von A. G. Postnikov [Dokl. Akad. Nauk SSSR **133** (1960), 1298–1299; MR **24** #A105] gewonnen. *H.-E. Richert* (Syracuse, N.Y.)

Citations: MR 14, 1063h = N72-6; MR 24# A105 = L99-7.

## L25-19 (26# 6133)

**Burgess, D. A.**
**On character sums and $L$-series. II.**
*Proc. London Math. Soc.* (3) **13** (1963), 524–536.

Part I appeared in Proc. London Math. Soc. (3) **12** (1962), 193–206 [MR **24** #A2570].

Put $S_H(N)=\sum_{n=N+1}^{N+H}\chi(n)$, where $\chi(n)$ is a non-principal character (mod $p$), $p$ prime. Refining results of a previous paper [ibid. **12** (1962), 179–192; MR **24** #A2569], the author proves the following results. (I) If $H$ and $r$ are arbitrary positive integers, then

$$|S_H(N)| \ll H^{1-1/r}p^{(r+1)/(4r^2)}\log p$$

for any $N$, where $A\ll B$ means $|A|<cB$ for some absolute constant $c$. (II) Let $\chi$ be a non-principal character (mod $k$),

$\varepsilon > 0$, $r$ a fixed positive integer. Then, if either $k$ is cube-free or $r=2$, we have

$$|S_H(N)| \ll H^{1-1/r}k^{(r+1)/(4r^2)+\varepsilon} \quad (H > 0).$$

Applying (II), with $r=2$, the author obtains the following. (III) Let $0<\sigma<1$, $\varepsilon>0$. Then the Dirichlet $L$-function $L_\chi(\sigma+ti)$ satisfies

$$|L_\chi(\sigma+ti)| \ll k^{(4-5\sigma+\varepsilon)/8} \quad (0 < \sigma \leqq \tfrac{1}{2}),$$
$$\ll k^{(3-3\sigma+\varepsilon)/8} \quad (\tfrac{1}{2} \leqq \sigma < 1),$$

and in particular $|L_\chi(\frac{1}{2}+ti)| \ll k^{(3/16)+\varepsilon}$.

*L. Carlitz* (Durham, N.C.)

Citations: MR 24# A2569 = L25-16; MR 24# A2570 = L25-17.

Referred to in M05-41, M15-31, M25-68, N68-36, N72-40, N72-44, P32-77, R14-57.

## L25-20 (26# 6135)

**Burgess, D. A.**

**A note on the distribution of residues and non-residues.**

*J. London Math. Soc.* **38** (1963), 253–256.

The author in his important paper [Proc. London Math. Soc. (3) **12** (1962), 179–192; MR **24** #A2569] has shown that if $\chi$ is any non-principal character to the prime modulus $p$ and $\chi(N+1)=\cdots=\chi(N+H)$, then $H<kp^{1/4}(\log p)^{3/2}$ for some constant $k$. He now improves this result by showing that $H<kp^{1/4}\log p$. The proof consists of a number of small refinements of arguments used in the original paper. *D. J. Lewis* (Ann Arbor, Mich.)

Citations: MR 24# A2569 = L25-16.

Referred to in N72-38, N72-55.

## L25-21 (26# 6136)

**Vinogradov, A. I.**

**Double sums related to the zeros of the Dirichlet $L$-series. (Russian. English summary)**

*Vestnik Leningrad. Univ. Ser. Mat. Meh. Astronom.* **18** (1963), *no.* 1, 59–63.

This is a sketch of a study by the author of certain double sums, which are "character-sums" whose coefficients involve the zeros of Dirichlet's $L$-series. A fuller account of his deep analysis and its applications will, no doubt, be published later. The sums arise in connection with I. M. Vinogradoff's study of Goldbach's problem.

*S. Chowla* (Boulder, Colo.)

## L25-22 (29# 3449)

**Glazkov, V. V.**

**On a class of finite homomorphisms. (Russian)**

*Dokl. Akad. Nauk SSSR* **158** (1964), 33–36.

Let $h(n)$, $n=1, 2, \cdots$, be a generalized principal character, i.e., a completely multiplicative function of $n$, not identically zero, taking only a finite number of (complex) values and satisfying $\sum_{n\leq x} h(n)=ax+O(1)$, $a\neq 0$. The author shows in a basically elementary way that every such character is a Dirichlet character.

*S. Knapowski* (Marburg)

## L25-23 (31# 136)

**Vinogradov, A. I.**

**On the symmetry property for sums with Dirichlet characters. (Russian. Uzbek summary)**

*Izv. Akad. Nauk UzSSR Ser. Fiz.-Mat. Nauk* **1965**, *no.* 1, 21–27.

Verfasser benutzt die Periodizität von Dirichletschen Charakteren mod $D$, um mit Hilfe eines Lemmas über eine gewisse Fourierreihe von I. M. Vinogradov [Ž. Fiz. Mat. Permsk. Univ. **1** (1918), 94–96] die Abschätzung der Summe (1) $S_\chi(x)=\sum_{n\leq x}\chi(n)e^{2\pi i v n/D}$ auf eine solche von $S_{\bar\chi}(D/x)$ zurückzuführen. Er erhält für natürliches $r$ unter Benutzung der Abschätzung von Burgess [Proc. London Math. Soc. (3) **12** (1962), 193–206; MR **24** #A2570]

$$S_\chi(x) \ll \sqrt{D}\left(\frac{D^{3/4-1/4r-\varepsilon}}{x}\right)^{-1/r}.$$

Hierdurch wird die Verbesserung von Burgess der Pólya-I. M. Vinogradovschen Abschätzung $S_\chi(x)\ll\sqrt{D}\log D$ auf das Intervall $D^{1/4+\varepsilon}<x<D^{3/4-\varepsilon}$ ausgedehnt.

*H.-E. Richert* (Marburg)

Citations: MR 24# A2570 = L25-17.

## L25-24 (32# 97)

**Bhaskaran, M.; Schinzel, A.**

**A new elementary estimation for the sum of real characters.**

*Prace Mat.* **8** (1963/64), 99–102.

The authors give an elementary proof of the following result: For every $\varepsilon>0$ there is a constant $C$ such that if $0\leqq a<b$, $b^2-a^2\leqq m$ and $\chi$ is a real non-principal character mod $m$, then

$$\left|\sum_{a<k\leq b}\chi(k)\right| < \left(\varphi(m)-\left(\frac{12}{\pi^2}-1\right)\left(\frac{\varphi(m)}{m}\right)^2(b-a)^2\right)^{1/2}+C$$

Non-elementary methods yield a better estimation [D. A. Burgess, Proc. London Math. Soc. (3) **12** (1962), 193–206; MR **24** #A2570]. The latter paper, quoted by the authors, improved an earlier result of Landau.

*J. Mycielski* (Wroclaw)

Citations: MR 24# A2570 = L25-17.

Referred to in L25-31.

## L25-25 (35# 6637)

**Glazkov, V. V.**

**Generalized characters. (Russian)**

*Certain Problems in the Theory of Fields (Russian)*, *pp.* 67–78. *Izdat. Saratov. Univ., Saratov*, 1964.

The author proves several theorems, among them the following. Theorem 4: Let $h(n)$ be a completely multiplicative function whose absolute value is always 0 or 1. Let $S(x)\doteq\sum_{n\leq x}h(n)$. Suppose that there exist a number $\alpha\neq 0$ and a positive constant $c$ such that $S(x)=\alpha x+O(1)$, and for all primes $p$ with $h(p)\neq 0, 1$, one has $|h(p)-1|>c$; then $h(n)$ is a principal character of Dirichlet. This theorem is related to work of N. G. Čudakov, B. M. Bredihin and Ju. V. Linnik [see N. G. Čudakov and B. M. Bredihin, Ukrain. Mat. Ž. **8** (1956), 347–360; MR **20** #5760].

*S. Chowla* (University Park, Pa.)

Citations: MR 20# 5760 = L25-14.

## L25-26 (37# 4010)

**Burgess, D. A.**

**A note on character sums of binary quadratic forms.**

*J. London Math. Soc.* **43** (1968), 271–274.

Let $f(x_1, x_2)=x_1^2+ax_1x_2+bx_2^2$ be a binary quadratic form reducible mod $p$ ($p$ an odd prime) but not congruent to a perfect square (mod $p$). Let $\chi$ be a non-principal character (mod $p$) and let $B$ be the set of points $(x_1, x_2)$ such that $N_i\leqq x_i\leqq N_i+H$ $(i=1, 2)$. The author shows that for each $\varepsilon>0$ there exists a $\delta>0$ such that

$$S = \sum_B \chi\{f(x_1, x_2)\} = O(H^2p^{-\delta})$$

for all $H>p^{1/3+\varepsilon}$. The corresponding result for irreducible forms was established by the author [same J. **42** (1967), 73–80; MR **34** #5765], using results of H. Davenport and D. J. Lewis [Rend. Circ. Mat. Palermo (2) **12** (1963), 129–136; MR **29** #4755].

A similar conclusion holds if $f$ is a form of degree $n$ in $n$ variables that factors (mod $p$) into a product of $n$ linearly independent linear factors. *J. B. Kelly* (Tempe, Ariz.)

Citations: MR 29# 4755 = T25-20; MR 34# 5765 = N68-35.

## L25-27 (38# 4427)

**Glazkov, V. V.**

**Characters of the multiplicative semigroup of natural numbers. (Russian)**

*Studies in Number Theory, No. 2 (Russian)*, pp. 3–49. *Izdat. Saratov. Univ., Saratov*, 1968.

Der Verfasser versteht unter einem Charakter einen nichttrivialen Homomorphismus $h$ der natürlichen Zahlen in die komplexen Zahlen, wobei $|h(n)|$ nur Null oder Eins sein kann; speziell heißt der Charakter $h$ verallgemeinerter $D$-Charakter, wenn (für $x\to\infty$) $\sum_{n\leqq x} h(n)=\alpha_h x+O(1)$ gilt.

Der Verfasser verschärft Ergebnisse von B. S. Bronšteĭn [Moskov. Gos. Univ. Učen. Zap. **165** Matematika vyp. **7** (1954), 212–220; MR **16**, 448] und von N. G. Čudakov und B. M. Bredihin [Ukrain. Mat. Ž. **8** (1956), 347–360; MR **20** #5760] und erhält: Ist $\chi$ ein Dirichlet-Charakter und $h$ ein Charakter (aber kein Dirichlet-Charakter), der sich von $\chi$ nur auf einer "dünnen" Menge von Primzahlen unterscheidet (d.h. $\sum_{p:\chi(p)\neq h(p)} p^{-1}$ konvergiert), so ist $h$ kein verallgemeinerter $D$-Charakter. Ein verallgemeinerter $D$-Charakter $h$ mit $\alpha_h\neq 0$, der nur endlich viele Werte annimmt, ist ein Dirichlet-Charakter. Weiter zeigt er: Ist $h$ ein Charakter, der den Wert 0 nicht annimmt, so hat für jedes $\varepsilon>0$ die Ungleichung $|h(n+1)-h(n)|<\varepsilon$ unendlich viele Lösungen $n$; als Folgerung ergibt sich: Ist $\Omega(n)$ die Anzahl der Primteiler von $n$ (mit Vielfachheit gezählt), so hat für jedes $m$ die Kongruenz $\Omega(n)\equiv\Omega(n+1)$ mod $m$ unendlich viele Lösungen $n$.

*W. Schwarz* (Freiburg)

Citations: MR 16, 448d = L25-11; MR 20# 5760 = L25-14.

Referred to in L25-32.

## L25-28 (39# 4107)

**Elliott, P. D. T. A.**

**A conjecture of Erdős concerning character sums.**

*Nederl. Akad. Wetensch. Proc. Ser. A* **72** = *Indag. Math.* **31** (1969), 164–171.

For each prime $p$ let $f(\varepsilon, p)$ denote the least positive integer $t$ with the property that for any integer $m>t$, $\sum_{n=1}^{m}(n/p)<\varepsilon m$ ($(n/p)$ is the Legendre symbol). The reviewer conjectured that

(1) $$\lim_{x\to\infty}(1/\pi(x))\sum_{p\leqq x} f(\varepsilon, p) = c_\varepsilon.$$

The author defines $g(\varepsilon, p)$ as the least integer for which, for every $m>g(\varepsilon, p)$, $|\sum_{n=1}^{m}(n/p)|<\varepsilon m$. The author proves $\lim_{x\to\infty}(1/\pi(x))\sum_{p\leqq x} g(\varepsilon, p)=c_\varepsilon$ and states that a simple modification of his proof gives (1). (See also the reviewer [Mat. Lapok **12** (1961), 10–17; MR **26** #2410] and the author [Acta Arith. **13** (1967/68), 131–149; MR **36** #3741; ibid. **14** (1967/68), 43; MR **37** #4031].)

*P. Erdős* (Budapest)

Citations: MR 26# 2410 = N68-31; MR 36# 3741 = N72-33; MR 37# 4031 = N72-34.

## L25-29 (40# 1350)

**Lavrik, A. F.**

**Double sums with quadratic character. (Russian)**

*Dokl. Akad. Nauk SSSR* **186** (1969), 19–21.

Let $\chi(m, n)$ be a quadratic character, let $a_n$ and $b_m$ be any complex numbers. Let $Y$, $Z$, $M$, $N$ be any numbers exceeding 1. The author states the estimation

$$\sum_{Y\leqq n\leqq Z}\sum_{M\leqq m\leqq N} a_n b_m \chi(m, n) = \sum_{Y\leqq n^2\leqq Z,(n,\gamma)=1} a_{n^2}\sum_{M\leqq m\leqq N,(m,n)=1} b_m + O(A\min(T_1, T_2, T_3)),$$

where $\gamma=2$ if $\chi(m, n)=\chi_n(m)$ and $\gamma=1$ if $\chi(m, n)=\chi_m(n)$, $T_1=N^{3/2}Y^{-1/2}B_1+N^{1/4}B_2$, $T_2=(NY^{-1/4}+N^{1/2}Z^{1/4})B_3$, ${T_3}^2=\sum_{Y\leqq n\leqq Z}\sum_{l=1,(l,n)=1}^{n}|\sum_{M\leqq m\leqq N, M\equiv l \bmod n} b_m - F|^2$, $F$ is any number not depending on $l$,

$$A^2 = \ln^2 ZN \sum_{Y\leqq n\leqq Z} n|a_n|^2,$$

${B_1}^2=\sum_{M\leqq m\leqq N} m^{-1}|b_m|^2$, ${B_2}^2=\sum_{M\leqq m\leqq N} m^{-1/2}|b_m|^2$, ${B_3}^8=\sum_{M\leqq m\leqq N} m^{-1}|b_m|^8$.

Three further theorems are proved, each giving more exact estimations for sums of the above type in case the sequences $a_n$ and $b_m$ satisfy supplementary conditions.

The proof is only sketched. It is based on well-known estimations for character sums and the method of "large" sieve.

{This article has appeared in English translation [Soviet Math. Dokl. **10** (1969), 534–537].} *J. Kubilius* (Vilnius)

Referred to in M20-38.

## L25-30 (41# 5284)

**Karacuba, A. A.**

**Sums of characters with prime numbers. (Russian)**

*Dokl. Akad. Nauk SSSR* **190** (1970), 517–518.

Using I. M. Vinogradov's method [Izv. Akad. Nauk SSSR Ser. Mat. **30** (1966), 481–496; MR **33** #2608], the author sketches a proof of the following result: Let $q$ be a prime, let $\chi(\neq\chi_0)$ be a character mod $q$. Then for any $\omega$, $N$ and $k$, satisfying $0<\omega\leqq\frac{1}{4}$, $q^{1/2+\omega}\leqq N\leqq q$, $(k, q)=1$, we have $\sum_{p\leqq N}\chi(p+k)\ll N_q^{-\gamma\omega^2}$; here $\gamma$ denotes a positive constant, and $p$ runs through prime numbers. Furthermore, two applications of this result are stated.

{This article has appeared in English translation [Soviet Math. Dokl. **11** (1970), 135–137].}

*H.-E. Richert* (Marburg)

Citations: MR 33# 2608 = L20-24.

## L25-31 (41# 5286)

**Whyburn, Clifton T.**

**An elementary note on character sums.**

*Duke Math. J.* **37** (1970), 307–310.

Let $\varepsilon>0$, $0\leqq a<b$, $b^2-a^2\leqq m$, and let $\chi$ be a real non-principal character mod $m$. A. Schinzel and M. Bhaskaran [Prace Mat. **8** (1963/64), 99–102; MR **32** #97] established by elementary arguments that (*) $|\sum_{k=a+1}^{b}\chi(k)|<(\varphi(m)-(12/\pi^2-1)(\varphi(m)/m)^2(b-a)^2)^{1/2}+O(m^\varepsilon)$. (See D. A. Burgess [Proc. London Math. Soc. (3) **12** (1962), 193–206; MR **24** #A2570] for a better estimate via non-elementary arguments.) The author combines the methods of the first mentioned work with those he developed in Acta Arith. **14** (1967/68), 113–116 [MR **37** #139] to prove an estimate similar to (*), without the requirement that $\chi$ be real. This gives better estimates than (*) in certain cases, and generalizes the result in the author's work mentioned above. *O. P. Stackelberg* (Durham, N.C.)

Citations: MR 24# A2570 = L25-17; MR 32# 97 = L25-24; MR 37# 139 = N72-35.

## L25-32 (42# 4501)

**Glazkov, V. V.**

**Estimates of summatory functions of a certain class of characters. (Russian)**

*Studies in Number Theory, No. 3 (Russian)*, pp. 17–31. *Izdat. Saratov. Univ., Saratov*, 1969.

Der Verfasser betrachtet Charaktere $h$ (d.h. nichttriviale Homomorphismen $h\colon \mathbf{N}\to\mathbf{C}$ mit $|h(n)|\in\{0, 1\}$), die sich von geeigneten Dirichlet-Charakteren $\chi$ nur auf einer "dünnen" Menge von Primzahlen unterscheiden (d.h.

es ist $\sum_{p,h(p)\neq\chi(p)} p^{-1} < \infty$). In einer früheren Arbeit [*Studies in number theory, No. 2* (Russian), pp. 3–49 Izdat. Saratov. Univ., Saratov, 1968; MR **38** #4427] zeigte der Autor, daß $\sum_{n\leq x} h(n) = \alpha x + O(1)$ nur möglich ist, wenn $h$ ein Dirichlet-Charakter ist. Ist $h(p)=0$ für unendlich viele Primzahlen $p$, so verschärft der Verfasser dieses Ergebnis zu der $\Omega$-Abschätzung $\sum_{n\leq x} h(n) = \alpha x + \Omega(\min\{\pi_0(\frac{1}{2}\log\log x)^{1-\varepsilon}, (\int_{\frac{1}{2}\log\log x}^{\infty} \pi_1(t)t^{-2}\,dt)^{-1}\})$, wobei $\pi_0(x)$ die Anzahl der Primzahlen $p\leq x$ mit $h(p)=0$ und $\pi_1(x)$ die Anzahl der Primzahlen $p\leqq x$ mit $h(p)\neq\chi(p)$ bezeichnet. Ähnliche Sätze gelten, wenn $h(p)=0$ höchstens für endlich viele Primzahlen $p$ ist.

*W. Schwarz* (Frankfurt a.M.)

Citations: MR 38# 4427 = L25-27.

# L30 REAL TRIGONOMETRIC INEQUALITIES

See also reviews C15-24, M25-92, M30-7.

## L30-1 (1, 225a)

**Tschakaloff, Ljubomir. Trigonometrische Polynome mit einer Minimumeigenschaft.** Ann. Scuola Norm. Super. Pisa (2) 9, 13–26 (1940).

The classical proof of the prime number theorem [see, for example, Landau, Handbuch der Lehre von der Verteilung der Primzahlen, vol. I, pp. 245–258, and vol. II, pp. 891–893] suggests the following problem. Let $g(\varphi)=a_0+a_1\cos\varphi+\cdots+a_n\cos n\varphi$ denote a trigonometrical cosine polynomial of order not greater than $n$, where $a_0\geqq0$, $a_1\geqq0$, $\cdots$, $a_n\geqq0$; $a_1>a_0$. What is the minimum $P_n$ of the expression $g(0)/(a_1-a_0)$? Landau [Ann. Scuola Norm. Super. Pisa 2, 209–210 (1933); 5, 141 (1936)] showed that $P_2=7$, $P_3=P_4=P_5=6$. These results had previously been established by Tschakaloff [Yearbook of the University of Sofia, **19** (1923) in Bulgarian], who had also found the values of $P_6$, $P_7$, $P_8$, $P_9$. The proof of the latter results is reproduced in the reviewed paper: $P_6=5.9298\cdots$, $P_7=P_8=P_9=5.9052\cdots$.

*A. Zygmund* (Cambridge, Mass.).

In the fifth line from above, insert the word "positive" before "trigonometric cosine polynomial."

Referred to in L30-2.

## L30-2 (11, 655d)

**van der Waerden, B. L. Über Landau's Beweis des Primzahlsatzes.** Math. Z. 52, 649–653 (1950).

Let $g(\varphi)=a_0+a_1\cos\varphi+\cdots+a_n\cos n\varphi\geqq0$, with $a_k\geqq0$ and $a_0<a_1$. Landau's problem was to choose $g(\varphi)$ to minimize $P_n=g(0)/(a_1-a_0)$. By a result of Tschakaloff [Ann. Scuola Norm. Super. Pisa (2) 9, 13–26 (1940); these Rev. **1**, 225, 400], $U=\inf P_n\leqq P_9<5.903$. The author shows that $U>5.864$.

*R. P. Boas, Jr.* (Evanston, Ill.).

Citations: MR 1, 225a = L30-1.

## L30-3 (17, 31e)

**Salem, R. On a problem of Littlewood.** Amer. J. Math. 77, 535–540 (1955).

Raffinement des méthodes déjà utilisées par l'auteur [Duke Math. J. 8, 269–272 (1941); MR 3, 108] pour démontrer le théorème de Menchoff sur la convergence presque-partout des séries orthogonales. Entre autres applications, une solution partielle est donnée à un probleme de Littlewood: si $\{m_n\}$ est une suite croissante d'entiers, avec $\log m_n=O(\log n)$, on a

$$\limsup\,(\log n)^{-\frac{1}{2}}\int_0^{2\pi}|\cos m_1x+\cdots+\cos m_nx|\,dx>0.$$

*J. P. Kahane* (Montpellier).

Referred to in L30-10, L30-11.

## L30-4 (17, 1079g)

**Izumi, Shin-ichi. Some trigonometrical series. XX.** Proc. Japan Acad. 32 (1956), 93–96.

Let $K>0$, and let $M=\{m_i\}$ be a collection of distinct integers, such that (*) the number of solutions of $m_i+m_j=m_k$, $i<j<k\leqq n$ is $o(n^2)$. Then there exists an integer $N(K)$ such that if $n\geqq N(K)$

$$\min_{0=x<2\pi}\sum_{i=1}^{n}\cos m_ix<-K.$$

This is a partial answer to a problem posed by Chowla [Bull. Amer. Math. Soc. **58** (1952), 287–305; MR **13**, 915] of whether the same result holds with no condition such as (*).

*P. Civin* (Eugene, Ore.).

Citations: MR 13, 915c = M02-5.

## L30-5 (23# A870 )

**Uchiyama, née Katayama, Miyoko; Uchiyama, Saburô**
**On the cosine problem.**
*Proc. Japan Acad.* **36** (1960), 475–479.

In connection with a problem concerning zeta functions, N. C. Ankeny and the reviewer [in S. Chowla, Bull. Amer. Math. Soc. **58** (1952), 287–305; MR **13**, 915] conjectured the following theorem. Let $K$ be an arbitrary positive number. Then there exists a natural number $n_0=n_0(K)$ such that for any $n\geqq n_0$ and any set of $n$ distinct positive integers $m_1,\cdots,m_n$, we have

$$\min_{0\leqq x<2\pi}(\cos m_1x+\cos m_2x+\cdots+\cos m_nx)<-K.$$

The authors prove this conjecture, in fact, with

$$n_0(K)=\max(2^{48},[8K^2]^{3[256K^4]}).$$

The above theorem is also a special case of an unproved conjecture of Littlewood:

$$\int_0^{2\pi}|\cos m_1x+\cos m_2x+\cdots+\cos m_nx|\,dx>c\log n,$$

where $c$ is an absolute positive constant, weaker forms of which have recently been proved by P. J. Cohen and H. Davenport. In every case, the method used is that of P. J. Cohen [Amer. J. Math. **82** (1960), 191–212].

*S. Chowla* (Boulder, Colo.)

Citations: MR 13, 915c = M02-5.

## L30-6 (23# A1992 )

**Davenport, H.**
**On a theorem of P. J. Cohen.**
*Mathematika* **7** (1960), 93–97.

The author gives a simplified account of P. J. Cohen's method of obtaining a lower bound for $\int_0^1|\sum_{j=1}^N e^{2\pi in_jx}|\,dx$ [Amer. J. Math. **82** (1960), 191–212] and is able to improve the lower bound to $\frac{1}{8}\{(\log N)/\log\log N\}^{1/4}$.

*R. P. Boas, Jr.* (Evanston, Ill.)

Referred to in L30-7, L30-9, L30-11.

## L30-7 (24# A3231 )

**Cohen, Paul J.**
**On a conjecture of Littlewood and idempotent measures.**
*Amer. J. Math.* **82** (1960), 191–212.

Part I. Let $G$ be a compact connected Abelian group with normalized Haar measure $\lambda$, let $\{\chi_k\}_{k=1}^{\infty}$ be a sequence of distinct continuous characters of $G$, and let $\{c_k\}_{k=1}^{\infty}$ be a sequence of complex numbers all of absolute value at least 1. Then there is a universal constant $K$ such that

$$\int_G\Big|\sum_{k=1}^{N}c_k\chi_k(x)\Big|\,d\lambda(x)>K\left[\frac{\log N}{\log\log N}\right]^{1/8}$$

for all $N\geqq3$. H. Davenport has improved this result for the circle group, replacing the number $\frac{1}{8}$ by $\frac{1}{4}$ in the exponent, and showing that $K=\frac{1}{8}$ for sufficiently large $N$ [Mathematika **7** (1960), 93–97; MR **23** #A1992]. Davenport's result, barring the estimate on $K$, holds also for every compact connected Abelian group.

Part II. The basic idea of Part I is used to identify all idempotent measures in the measure algebra $\mathbf{M}(G)$ for an arbitrary locally compact Abelian group $G$. Let $H$ be a compact subgroup of $G$, let $\chi$ be normalized Haar measure on $H$, let $\chi_1, \cdots, \chi_m$ be distinct continuous characters on $H$, and let $\mu \in \mathbf{M}(G)$ be defined by $d\mu=(\chi_1+\cdots+\chi_m)d\lambda$. It is obvious that $\mu$ is idempotent; let $\mathbf{P}$ be the set of all measures of this class. Let $\varepsilon$ be the unit measure concentrated at the identity of $G$. Then every idempotent in $\mathbf{M}(G)$ is obtained from $\mathbf{P}$ by carrying out a finite number of operations $\mu_1 * \mu_2$, $\varepsilon-\mu$, and $\mu_1+\mu_2-\mu_1 * \mu_2$.

*E. Hewitt* (Seattle, Wash.)

Citations: MR 23# A1992 = L30-6.
Referred to in L30-9, L30-11.

## L30-8 (25# 3318 )

**Chowla, S.; Magnus, P.**
**On certain trigonometric sums.**
*Norske Vid. Selsk. Forh. (Trondheim)* **33** (1960), 66–73.

Let $a_i$ $(1 \leqq i \leqq s)$ be different positive integers. It is known that

$$\min_{0\leq x<2\pi} \left(\sum_{i=1}^{s} \cos a_i x\right) \to -\infty$$

as $s\to\infty$. The authors show that there exists a sequence of integers $a_i$ $(1\leqq i\leqq s)$ and an absolute constant $K$, independent of $s$, such that

$$\min_{0\leq x<2\pi} \left(\sum_{i=1}^{s} \cos a_i x\right) > -K\sqrt{s}$$

for infinitely many $s$. The proof involves a consideration of the trigonometric sum

$$A_r(x) = \sum_{k=1}^{r}\sum_{j=0}^{k-1} (\cos(4^k-4^j)x+\cos(4^k+4^j)x).$$

Most of the paper is devoted to a demonstration of the deeper fact that there exists a real number $y_r$ such that $A_r(y_r)<-r/2$.

*J. B. Kelly* (Tempe, Ariz.)

## L30-9 (27# 4890 )

**Hewitt, Edwin; Zuckerman, Herbert S.**
**On a theorem of P. J. Cohen and H. Davenport.**
*Proc. Amer. Math. Soc.* **14** (1963), 847–855.

Let $G$ be a compact Abelian group with character group $X$. The following generalizes a theorem that was first proved by P. J. Cohen [Amer. J. Math. **82** (1960), 191–212; MR **24** #A3231] and improved by Davenport [Mathematika **7** (1960), 93–97; MR **23** #A1992]. Theorem A: Suppose that the torsion subgroup of $X$ is finite and has $f$ elements. For each $\chi\in X$, let $\alpha_\chi$ be a complex number such that $|\alpha_\chi|\geqq 1$. Let Y be a finite set of $N$ distinct elements of $X$. Then for every number $K<(1-e^{-2})6^{-1/2}$, there is an integer $N_0$, depending only on $K$ and $f$, such that

$$\int_G \left|\sum_{\chi\in Y} \alpha_\chi\chi(x)\right| dx > K\left(\frac{\log N}{\log\log N}\right)^{1/4}$$

for $N>N_0$. For example, if $K=3/10$ and $f\leqq 6$, $N_0$ can be taken as $e^{310}$. Theorem B: If $\Gamma$ is a finite subgroup of $X$, then

$$\int_G \left|\sum_{\chi\in\Gamma} \chi(x)\right| dx = 1.$$

This shows that $N_0$ increases with $f$ in Theorem A and that Theorem A is not valid if the torsion subgroup of $X$ is infinite.

*K. A. Ross* (Rochester, N.Y.)

Citations: MR 23# A1992 = L30-6; MR 24# A3231 = L30-7.

## L30-10 (30# 3070 )

**Chowla, S.**
**Some applications of a method of A. Selberg.**
*J. Reine Angew. Math.* **217** (1965), 128–132.

Let $\alpha\in(0,1)$ satisfy $\int_0^{3\pi/2} x^{-\alpha}\cos x\,dx=0$ $(\alpha=0.308\ldots)$ and let $\beta$ be any fixed number $<\alpha$. It is proved that if $b_n\geqq 0$ and $\sum_{0\leqq n\leqq t} b_n\cos nx\geqq 0$ (for all $t\geqq 0$ and all $x$), then $\sum_{m\geqq 1} m^{\beta-1}b_m$ is a convergent series. (According to the author, the theorem and the proof are due to A. Selberg.) Using this theorem and supposing that $a_m$ $(m=1,2,\cdots)$ are different natural integers satisfying $a_m=O(m^{1+\varepsilon})$ (for any $\varepsilon>0$) and writing $M(s)=\min(\cos a_1x+\cdots+\cos a_sx)$, the author proves that whenever $\gamma<\alpha$, we have $\limsup_{s\to\infty} -M(s)/s^\gamma>0$. (In the case of $\log a_m=O(\log m)$, a weaker result was proved by R. Salem [Amer. J. Math. **77** (1955), 535–540; MR **17**, 31].) An analogous result holds (but with $\gamma<\alpha_0=2-\sqrt{3}=0.26\ldots$) if the system of functions $\cos mx$ is replaced by the system $g(mx)$, where $g(x)=(\{x\}-\frac{1}{2})^2-\frac{1}{12}$ and $\{x\}$ denotes the fractional part of $x$.

*E. Fogels* (Riga)

Citations: MR 17, 31e = L30-3.
Referred to in L30-11.

## L30-11 (31# 3387 )

**Uchiyama, Saburô**
**À propos d'un problème de M. J. E. Littlewood.**
*C. R. Acad. Sci. Paris* **260** (1965), 2675–2678.

If the $m$'s are an increasing sequence $M$ of positive integers, Littlewood conjectured that

$$I_n(M) = \int_0^1 \left|\sum_{k=1}^{n} e(m_kx)\right| dx > C\log n, \qquad (e(x)=e^{2\pi ix}),$$

where $C$ is a universal positive constant. The first positive result in this direction is due to P. J. Cohen [Amer. J. Math. **82** (1960), 191–212; MR **24** #A3231], and this was sharpened by H. Davenport [Mathematika **7** (1960), 93–97; MR **23** #A1992] to

$$I_n(M) > C\left(\frac{\log n}{\log\log n}\right)^{1/4} \qquad (n\geqq 3).$$

Further, R. Salem [Amer. J. Math. **77** (1955), 535–540; MR **17**, 31] proved $\limsup_{n\to\infty} I_n(M)/\sqrt{\log n}>0$ if $\log m_k=O(\log k)$ as $k\to\infty$.

Denote by $A(n)=A_M(n)$ the number of solutions of the equation $m_i+m_j=m_k+m_l$ $(1\leqq i,j,k,l\leqq n)$. The author notes several interesting results "pour des diverses suites particulières $M$". (0) $I_n(M)\geqq\sqrt{(n^3/A(n))}$ $(n\geqq 1)$. Other special cases are (4) $I_n(M)>C\sqrt{(n/\log n)}$ $(n>1)$, if $M=M^{(2)}=(k^2)$ is the sequence of perfect squares (this follows from (0) when one uses the well-known estimate $A(n)<Cn^2\log n$); (5) if $M=M^{(p)}=(k^p)$ is the sequence of $p$th powers ($p$ an odd prime) of the integers $>0$, $I_n(M)>C\sqrt{n}$. This follows from (0) and Hooley's result [Math. Z. **82** (1963), 259–266; MR **27** #5742] that $A(n)<Cn^2$.

For a study of the minimum of the sum $\sum_{k=1}^{n} e(m_kx)$, see a paper by the reviewer in J. Reine Angew. Math. **217** (1965), 128–132 [MR **30** #3070].

*S. Chowla* (University Park, Pa.)

Citations: MR 17, 31e = L30-3; MR 23# A1992 = L30-6; MR 24# A3231 = L30-7; MR 27# 5742 = P04-51; MR 30# 3070 = L30-10.

**L30-12** **(35# 5404)**

**French, Steven H.**

**Trigonometric polynomials in prime number theory.**
*Illinois J. Math.* **10** (1966), 240–248.

Let $g(\phi)=\sum_{k=0}^{n} a_k \cos \nu\phi$, and let $C_n$ denote the set of all polynomials $g$ such that $g(\phi)\geqq 0$, $a_1>a_0>0$, $a_k\geqq 0$, $k=2,\cdots,n$. The author deals with g.l.b.$_{g\in C_n} R(g)$, $R_n$ say, where $R(g)=\sum_{k=1}^{n} a_k/2(\sqrt{a_1}-\sqrt{a_0})^2$. This problem originated in one of Landau's proofs of the prime number theorem. Landau used a polynomial $\in C_3$ with $R(g)<18.53$; it is shown here that always $R_n>16.25$.

*H.-E. Richert* (Marburg)

Referred to in L30-13.

**L30-13** **(41# 8355)**

**Stečkin, S. B.**

**Certain extremal properties of positive trigonometric polynomials. (Russian)**
*Mat. Zametki* **7** (1970), 411–422.

Consider the class $P_n$ of all $n$th degree cosine polynomials $t_n(\varphi)=a_0+a_1\cos\varphi+\cdots+a_n\cos n\varphi$ which are such that $t_n(\varphi)\geqq 0$ for all real $\varphi$, $a_k\geqq 0$ for all $k$, and $a_1>a_0$. The author considers the associated quantity $V(t_n)\equiv(a_1+\cdots+a_n)/(\sqrt{a_1}-\sqrt{a_0})^2\equiv 2R(t_n)$. Such numbers $R=R(t_n)$ arise in prime number theory. Thus, J. B. Rosser and the reviewer [Illinois J. Math. **6** (1962), 64–94; MR **25** #1139] have essentially shown that for $t>t_0$, $\zeta(s)$ has no zeros in $\sigma>1-1/(R\log t)$, and that for $x>x_0$, the inequality $|\vartheta(x)-x|<\sqrt{(\log x)}\exp(-\sqrt{((\log x)/R)})$ holds.

The problem of minimizing $R$ was previously treated by S. H. French [ibid. **10** (1966), 240–248; MR **35** #5404] in a paper which appears to be unknown to the author. On the whole, French's results are stronger. However, the author's lower bounds for $\min_{t_n\in P_n} R(t_n)$ are better than French's for $3\leqq n\leqq 7$. Also, the author gives the polynomial $(9+10\cos\varphi)^2(3+10\cos\varphi)^2$ in $P_4$ for which $R=17.45415\ldots$ and thereby improves an earlier polynomial of Rosser and the reviewer which had $R=17.51631\ldots.$

{This article has appeared in English translation [Math. Notes **7** (1970), 248–255].}

*Lowell Schoenfeld* (Grand Island, N.Y.)

Citations: MR 25# 1139 = N04-37; MR 35# 5404 = L30-12.

# L99 NONE OF THE ABOVE, BUT IN THIS CHAPTER

Estimates for many exponential sums, needed for the application of Weyl's criterion for uniform distribution (mod 1), are to be found in section **K10-K30**.

See also reviews B44-12, D80-51, E12-123, K15-96, K15-98, K45-26, M55-45, M55-67, N52-13, T20-6.

**L99-1** **(12, 482b)**

**Karamata, J., et Tomić, M. Sur une inégalité de Kusmin-Landau relative aux sommes trigonométriques et son application à la somme de Gauss.** Acad. Serbe Sci. Publ. Inst. Math. **3**, 207–218 (1950).

The authors prove by geometric reasoning that if $\alpha_\nu$ are $n$ positive numbers satisfying

$$0<\vartheta\leqq\alpha_2-\alpha_1\leqq\cdots\leqq\alpha_n-\alpha_{n-1}\leqq\theta<1,$$

then $S_n=\sum_{\nu=1}^{n}\exp(2\pi\alpha_\nu i)$ is in the circle of radius $\frac{1}{2}\{\cot\vartheta\pi+\tan\frac{1}{2}\theta\pi\}$ and center $\frac{1}{2}i\exp(-\vartheta\pi i+2\pi\alpha_1 i)\csc\vartheta\pi$, and hence $|S_n|\leqq\frac{1}{2}\{\cot\frac{1}{2}\vartheta\pi+\tan\frac{1}{2}\theta\pi\}$; the latter inequality is the Kusmin-Landau inequality [see Landau, Nachr. Ges. Wiss. Göttingen. Math. Phys. Kl. **1928**, 21–24]. Still more precisely

$$|\tfrac{1}{2}\exp(2\pi\alpha_1 i)+\textstyle\sum_{\nu=2}^{n}\exp(2\pi\alpha_\nu i)|\leqq\cot\vartheta\pi+\tfrac{1}{2}\tan\tfrac{1}{2}\theta\pi,$$

and finally if $\alpha_1=\theta$ we have $\sum_{\nu=1}^{n}\sin 2\pi\alpha_\nu\geqq-\frac{1}{2}\tan\frac{1}{2}\theta\pi$. As a consequence the authors get a short determination of the sign of the Gauss sum $\sum_{\nu=0}^{n-1}\exp(2\pi i\nu^2/n)$.

*R. P. Boas, Jr.* (Evanston, Ill.).

Referred to in L99-2, L99-5.

**L99-2** **(12, 805a)**

**Karamata, J., and Tomić, M. On an inequality of Kuzmin-Landau concerning trigonometric sums and its application to the Gauss sum.** Glas Srpske Akad. Nauka. Od. Prirod.-Mat. Nauka **198**, 163–174 (1950). (Serbo-Croatian)

See Acad. Serbe Sci. Publ. Inst. Math. **3**, 207–218 (1950); these Rev. **12**, 482.

Citations: MR 12, 482b = L99-1.

**L99-3** **(13, 457d)**

**Postnikov, A. On some trigonometric inequalities.** Doklady Akad. Nauk SSSR (N.S.) **81**, 501–504 (1951). (Russian)

Let $S=\sum_{x=1}^{N}e^{2\pi if(x)}$, where $f(x)$ is real. It is well known that, if $\Delta f(x)\equiv f(x+1)-f(x)$ is monotonic and

$$0<\theta<\Delta f(x)<1-\theta,$$

then $|S|\leqq 1/\theta$. This paper develops a number of extensions with the monotonic condition relaxed. Thus (Theorem 3), if $\Delta f(1),\cdots,\Delta f(N-1)$ contains a monotonic subsequence of length $l$, and $\epsilon=\max|\Delta f(x)-\Delta f(y)|$, then

$$|S|\leqq\{1+\pi\epsilon(N-l-1)\}/\theta;$$

and (Theorem 4), if $\varphi(x)$ is monotonic, $0<\varphi(x)<1-\theta$, and $|\Delta f(x)-\varphi(x)|<\epsilon$, then $|S|\leqq\{1+\pi\epsilon(N-1)\}/\theta$. The proofs are by an adaptation of the analytical counterpart of Kuz'min's geometrical proof of the original inequality. There are numerous misprints.

*A. E. Ingham.*

**L99-4** **(17, 240a)**

**Rankin, R. A. Van der Corput's method and the theory of exponent pairs.** Quart. J. Math. Oxford Ser. (2) **6** (1955), 147–153.

Let $S_0$ be the set of all exponent pairs $(k,l)$ in the sense of van der Corput which can be obtained from $(0,1)$ by a finite number of applications of the two processes of Phillips [same J. **4** (1933), 209–225] and the obvious convexity process. The author announces without proof that the greatest lower bound of $k+l-\frac{1}{2}$ for all $(k,l)$ in $S_0$ is $0.32902\,13568\cdots$. This shows then that no combination of the processes mentioned can give as good results as Titchmarsh's two-dimensional method in the circle problem, the divisor problem, or the problem of the order of $\zeta(\frac{1}{2}+it)$. On the other hand, this calculation does make it possible to improve the known estimates for the difference between consecutive squarefree numbers, the error term in the formula for $\sum_{mnr\leqq x}1$, and the error term in the formula for the number of abelian groups of order not exceeding $x$.

*P. T. Bateman* (Urbana, Ill.).

Referred to in N24-30, N40-36, N40-41, P28-71.

**L99-5** **(20# 2303)**

**Mordell, L. J. On the Kusmin-Landau inequality for exponential sums.** Acta Arith. **4** (1958), 3–9.

Soient $a_\nu$ réels, $e^{ix}=e(x)$, $S=\sum_1^n e(2a_\nu)$, $\Delta a_{\nu-1}=a_\nu-a_{\nu-1}$, $0<\theta\leqq\Delta a_1\leqq\Delta a_2\leqq\cdots\leqq\Delta a_{n-1}\leqq\varphi<\pi$. Les estimations pour $|S|$ ont été données par van der Corput, Kusmin et Landau dans les cas $\varphi=\pi-\theta$ [J. F. Koksma, Diophantische

Approximationen, Springer, Berlin, (1936); p. 115]. J. Karamata et le rapporteur ont donné des estimations analogues, en supposant seulement $\varphi<\pi$ [Acad. Serbe Sci. Publ. Inst. Math. **3** (1950), 207–218; MR **12**, 482]. La plupart de ces résultats on obtient par des considérations géométriques élémentaires. L'auteur montre que toutes ces estimations résultent déjà de la transformation du type d'Abel $\sum_1^n \lambda_\nu(\mu_\nu-\mu_{\nu+1})=\sum_1^n \mu_\nu(\lambda_\nu-\lambda_{\nu-1})$, avec $\lambda_0=\mu_{n+1}=0$. En plus, on obtient ainsi des résultats plus précis, par exemple, de $\varphi\leqq\pi/2$, $S'=\frac{1}{2}e(2a_1)+\sum_2^{n-1} e(2a_\nu)+\frac{1}{2}e(2a_n)$ il vient $|S'|\leqq\cot\theta$. L'auteur déduit, dans le même ordre d'idées, le résultat suivant dû à I. Popken [Koksma, loc. cit., p. 115]: de $0<\theta\leqq\Delta a_r\leqq\pi/4$ $(r=1, 2, \cdots, n-1)$, $\Delta^2a_r=\Delta(\Delta a_r)\geqq 0$ $(r=1, 2, \cdots, n-2)$, $\Delta^3a_r=\Delta(\Delta^2a_r)$ $(r=1, 2, \cdots, n-3)$, résulte $|S|\leqq 1/\sin\theta$.

*M. Tomić* (Belgrade)

Citations: MR 12, 482b = L99-1.

## L99-6 (22# 7978 )

**Mineev, M. P. A metric theorem on trigonometric sums with rapidly increasing functions.** Uspehi Mat. Nauk **14** (1959), no. 3 (87), 169–171. (Russian)

Let $g_0, g_1, \cdots$ be a sequence of natural numbers with $g_0=1$, and $g_j>1$ $(j>1)$. For natural numbers $x$, $p$ write $F(x)=g_0g_1\cdots g_x$ and $S(\alpha, p)=\sum_{x=0}^{p-1} e^{2\pi i\alpha F(x)}$. Then the author shows that for any real $C>0$ the measure of the set of $\alpha$ in $0\leqq\alpha\leqq 1$ for which $|S(\alpha, p)|\leqq Cp^{1/2}$ tends to $1-e^{-C^2}$ as $p\to\infty$. In the proof the author first estimates the moments

$$\int_0^1 |S(\alpha, p)|^{2n}\, d\alpha,$$

using his earlier work on Tarry's problem [Mat. Sb. (N.S.) **46 (88)** (1958), 451–454; MR **21** #2632], and then uses the general theory of the determination of probability distributions by moments.

*J. W. S. Cassels* (Cambridge, England)

Citations: MR 21# 2632 = D99-14.

## L99-7 (24# A105 )

**Postnikov, A. G.**

**On a very short exponential rational trigonometric sum.** *Dokl. Akad. Nauk SSSR* **133** (1960), 1298–1299 (*Russian); translated as Soviet Math. Dokl.* **1** (1961), 979–980.

The author applies Markov's method of moments to prove the following theorem. Let $g$ be an integer $\geqq 2$, $p$ a prime and $\lambda$ a positive number. Let $h$ be an unbounded, positive-integer-valued function on the primes satisfying $h(p)\leqq \log p/(2\log g)$. Let $N_p(\lambda)$ denote the number of integers $a$ between 0 and $p-1$, inclusive, for which

$$\left|\sum_{x=0}^{h(p)} \exp(2\pi iag^x/p)\right| < \lambda\sqrt{h(p)}.$$

Then $\lim_{p\to\infty} N_p(\lambda)/p=1-e^{-\lambda^2}$.

*A. Sklar* (Chicago, Ill.)

Referred to in L25-18, L99-8.

## L99-8 (28# 2102 )

**Usol'cev, L. P.**

**On an exponential rational trigonometric sum of special type. (Russian)**

*Dokl. Akad. Nauk SSSR* **151** (1963), 62–64.

Let $N_p(\lambda)$ denote the number of integers $a$, with $0\leqq a<p$, for which

$$\text{(A)}\qquad \left|\sum_{x=0}^{h-1} \exp(2\pi iag^x/p)\right| < \lambda\sqrt{h},$$

where $g$ is an integer, $g\geqq 2$, $p$ is a prime, $\lambda$ is a positive real number, and $h\to\infty$ as $p\to\infty$. A. G. Postnikov [same Dokl. **133** (1960), 1298–1299; MR **24** #A105] proved that, as $p\to\infty$,

$$\text{(B)}\qquad N_p(\lambda)/p \to 1-e^{-\lambda^2},$$

subject to the condition that $h\leqq(\log p)/(2\log g)$. The author dispenses with this latter condition in the case when $p$ is a prime of the special form $p=g^\tau-1$ ($\tau$ an integer, $\tau\geqq 2$) and proves that (B) holds if $\lambda\sqrt{h}$ in (A) is replaced by $\lambda\sqrt{\{(2c-1)h-c(c-1)\tau\}}$, where $(c-1)\tau<h\leqq c\tau$ and $c\tau\to\infty$. He uses the method of moments as developed by Postnikov to obtain an estimate of the number $A_n(h)$ of solutions of the congruence

$$g^{x_1}+\cdots+g^{x_n} \equiv g^{y_1}+\cdots+g^{y_n} \pmod p,$$

where $0\leqq x_i, y_i<h$. It is shown in Theorem 2 that

$$A_n(h) = n![(2c-1)h-c(c-1)\tau]^n+O(c^nh^{n-1}).$$

*R. A. Rankin* (Bloomington, Ind.)

Citations: MR 24# A105 = L99-7.

## L99-9 (31# 135 )

**Rodosskiĭ, K. A.**

**On some aspects of the method of I. M. Vinogradov. (Russian)**

*Izv. Vysš. Učebn. Zaved. Matematika* **1965**, *no.* 1 (44), 123–132.

The author estimates $\sum_{n=a+1}^{a+P} \exp(2\pi if(n))$ under an assumption of the type $h_k\lambda_k\leqq f^{(k)}(x)\leqq\lambda_k$, with $5\leqq k\leqq 11$. He uses Vinogradov's method. *S. Knapowski* (Marburg)

## L99-10 (37# 170 )

**Kamilov, M. H.**

**The mean value of a double sum. (Russian. Tajiki summary)**

*Dokl. Akad. Nauk Tadžik. SSR* **11** (1968), *no.* 2, 3–6.

Author's summary: "In this paper the integral $J=\int_0^1\cdots\int_0^1 |\sum_{x=1}^{P}\sum_{y=1}^{q} \exp(2\pi i\sum_{i+j=1}^{k} \alpha_{ij}x^iy^j)|^4\, d\alpha_{10}\cdots d\alpha_{0k}$ is evaluated. Our problem differs from Vinogradov's classical problem on the mean values of trigonometric sums in that our mean value is interesting by virtue of the fact that it can be evaluated explicitly. Theorem: For $k\geqq 2$, $J=pq(2pq-1)$." *G. Halász* (Budapest)

## L99-11 (38# 4423 )

**van Hamme, L.**

**Généralisation d'un théorème de Walfisz.**

*Acad. Roy. Belg. Bull. Cl. Sci.* (5) **54** (1968), 498–511.

Let $k$, $M$, $M'$ be natural integers, and $t$ be a real number, such that $t\geqq 1$, $k\geqq 21$, $M\leqq M'\leqq 2M$, $t^{k-1}\leqq M\leqq t^{(k-1)^{-1}}$ and set $R(k)=(58{,}000\,k^2)^{-1}$; for $M\leqq x\leqq 2M$, let $f(x)=\sum_{j=0}^{\infty} A_j(x-x_0)^j$ be a real valued, $2k+1$ times differentiable function, such that for $M<x_0<M'$ and $0<j\leqq 2k+1$, one has the inequalities $(c_1j)^{-1}(ax_0)^{-j}<|A_j(x_0)|<c_2x_0^{-j}$ and, for $0<x-x_0<M^{1/2}$, also $|f(x)-\sum_{j=0}^{2k} A_j(x-x_0)^j|\leqq c_0|A_{2k+1}(x-x_0)^{2k+1}|$, with $c_2$ an absolute constant, $a$, $c_0$ and $c_1$ positive constants, depending on $k$ only. Under these conditions the author shows that $\sum_{x=M}^{M'} e^{2\pi itf(x)}=O(a^\alpha c_1^{\beta}M^{1-R(k)})+(c_0M^{1/2})$, with $\alpha=2\cdot 10^{-7}$, $\beta=62\cdot 10^{-9}$. This theorem generalizes two similar ones of A. Z. Val'fiš, valid for the particular cases $f(x)=\log(x+w)$ and $f(x)=(x+w)^{-1}$ $(0\leqq w<1)$, respectively. The method of proof is essentially the same as that of Val'fiš [see Math. Z. **72** (1959/60), 259–278; MR **22** #4702; *Weylsche Exponentialsummen in der neueren Zahlentheorie*, VEB Deutsch. Verlag Wissensch., Berlin, 1963; MR **36** #3737].

*E. Grosswald* (Philadelphia, Pa.)

Citations: MR 22# 4702 = P24-9; MR 36# 3737 = L02-8.

**L99-12** **(40# 102 )**

**Potockiĭ, V. V.**

**A sharpening of the estimate of a certain trigonometric sum.** **(Russian)**

*Izv. Vysš. Učebn. Zaved. Matematika* **1969**, *no.* 3 (82), 42–51.

The author investigates the sum

$$Q(N) = \sum_1^N r(n)\cdot\exp(2\pi i\sqrt{(x\cdot n)}),$$

where $x > \varepsilon_0 > 0$ is a real parameter and $r(n)$ is the number of representations of the integer $n$ as a sum of two squares. He obtains the estimate: $Q(N) \leqq c(x)\cdot\sqrt{(N)}\cdot\ln N$, with $c(x) \ll x$.

*A. I. Vinogradov* (Leningrad)

# M. ZETA FUNCTIONS AND $L$-FUNCTIONS; ANALYSIS RELATED TO MULTIPLICATIVE AND ADDITIVE NUMBER THEORY

See also Sections E44, F65, R42, S40.

## M02 BOOKS AND SURVEYS

General texts which include standard material on $\zeta(s)$ and $L(s, \chi)$ are listed in **Z01** and **Z02** and are not cross-referenced here.

See also Section N02.

See also reviews L02-2, L02-8, M25-21, M40-10, M40-16, M45-34, M45-37, M50-2, M50-10, M50-39, M55-10, M55-11, M55-48, M55-62, M55-77, N02-16, Q15-4, Z02-4, Z02-48, Z02-53, Z02-55, Z02-75.

**M02-1** **(11, 234b)**

**Čudakov, N. G. Vvedenie v Teoriyu $L$-Funkciĭ Dirihle. [Introduction to the Theory of Dirichlet's $L$-Functions].** OGIZ, Moscow-Leningrad, 1947. 203 pp.

This book, assuming only the elements of number theory and complex variable, deals with characters, Dirichlet $L$-functions and their zeros, primes in progressions and culminates in the three-prime theorem of Goldbach and Vinogradov. The theorems on the zeros of the $L$-functions are those of Page and Siegel; the proof of Siegel's theorem is based on the work of Heilbronn. For the most part, the proofs given are those which have been published previously by other authors. *L. Schoenfeld* (Urbana, Ill.).

Referred to in F30-46, P32-33.

**M02-2** **(13, 741c)**

**Titchmarsh, E. C. The Theory of the Riemann Zeta-Function.** Oxford, at the Clarendon Press, 1951. vi+346 pp.

This book is an enlargement and revision of the author's Cambridge tract of 1930. Some new material, based on recent research, is added although the author does not pretend to cover the field exhaustively. As in his previous book, the $\zeta$-function alone is treated with only one incidental reference to the more general Dirichlet $L$-functions being made; and, although the prime number theorem is proved, the error term is not sharpened by using the finer results on the $\zeta$-function here proved. Indeed, number theory, which gave rise to the study of $\zeta(s)$, is highly subordinated. Nevertheless, the book is well written and the author is to be thanked both for making this material so readily available and for including more than one proof of a number of results. A description of the contents follows.

Chapter I, "The function $\zeta(s)$ and the Dirichlet series related to it," deals with identities connecting $\zeta(s)$ with number-theoretic functions. Chapter II, "The analytic character of $\zeta(s)$, and the functional equation," gives seven proofs of the functional equation relating $\zeta(1-s)$ to $\zeta(s)$. Chapter III, "The theorem of Hadamard and de la Vallée Poussin, and its consequences," gives these mathematicians' proofs that $\zeta(1+it)\neq 0$ and a proof of the prime number theorem. In addition, general theorems relating the order of $\zeta(s)$ in a region near $\sigma=1$ to the zeros of $\zeta(s)$ and the orders of $\zeta'(s)/\zeta(s)$, $1/\zeta(s)$ near $\sigma=1$ are given. Finally, the series for $1/\zeta(s)$, $\zeta'(s)/\zeta(s)$, $\log \zeta(s)$ and the Euler product for $\zeta(s)$ are investigated on the line $\sigma=1$.

Chapter IV, "Approximate formulae," is concerned with the van der Corput estimation of integrals of the form $\int_a^b G(x)e^{iF(x)}dx$ and sums of the form $\sum_{a<n\leqq b} g(n)e^{2\pi i f(n)}$. Also, several approximate functional equations for $\zeta(s)$ are given with that for $\zeta^2(s)$ being mentioned but not proved. Chapter V, "The order of $\zeta(s)$ in the critical strip," uses the exponential sum methods of Weyl and of van der Corput to estimate $\zeta(s)$ on various vertical lines, and it is shown that the latter's estimates are sharper. In particular, several estimates of $\zeta(\frac{1}{2}+it)$ are given but not the best result that is known. Chapter VI, "Vinogradoff's methods," deals with the exponential sum $\sum e^{2\pi i f(n)}$ and derives the (essentially) best published results on the zero-free region of $\zeta(s)$, namely, $\sigma>1-A/(\log t \log\log t)^{3/4}$. This chapter has no counterpart in the earlier tract. Chapter VII, "Mean-value theorems," deals with estimates and asymptotic expressions for the closely related integrals $\int_0^T|\zeta(\sigma+it)|^{2k}dt$ and $\int_0^\infty|\zeta(\sigma+it)|^{2k}e^{-\delta t}dt$. In the case $\sigma=\frac{1}{2}$, a lower bound for the second of these integrals is given and asymptotic estimates are given for both integrals when $k=1, 2$. In addition, certain convexity theorems are proved.

Chapter VIII, "$\Omega$ theorems," uses the Dirichlet and Kronecker Diophantine approximation theorems and is more extensive than the corresponding part of the Cambridge tract. Among other things the following $\Omega$ result is proved: for fixed $\alpha$ and $\sigma$ satisfying $0<\alpha<1-\sigma\leqq\frac{1}{2}$, it is false that $\zeta(s)=o(\exp \log^\alpha t)$. In chapter IX, "The general distribution of the zeros," various estimates of the function $N(\sigma, T)$ and $N(T)=N(1, T)$ are derived. The familiar estimate for $N(T)$ as $aT\log T+bT+7/8+S(T)+O(1/T)$ is obtained as are estimates for $\int_0^T S(t)dt$. It is also proved that for arbitrary positive $h$ and large $T$, $N(T+h)-N(T)>K(h)\log T$. Here, again, the author is content to state certain results without proof. Chapter X, "The zeros on the critical line," gives lower bounds for the number $N_0(T)$ of such zeros with ordinate not exceeding $T$. Hardy's result that $N_0(T)\to\infty$ as $T\to\infty$ is proved as is A. Selberg's result that $N_0(T)>cT\log T$ for some positive $c$. Finally, a function having a functional equation similar to that for $\zeta(s)$ and possessing a number of other properties analogous to those of $\zeta(s)$ is constructed; this function has no Euler product and the Riemann hypothesis for it is false. Chapter XI, "The general distribution of the values of $\zeta(s)$," deals with the values taken on by $\zeta'(s)/\zeta(s)$ and $\log \zeta(s)$ on lines $\sigma=\sigma_0$ and for $s$ in certain regions. The following result, together with others proved in the book, shows the exceptional nature of the zeros: for fixed $a\neq 0$, $\alpha>\frac{1}{2}$ and $\beta<1$, the number of points in the rectangle $\alpha<\sigma<\beta$, $0<t<T$ at which $\zeta(s)=a$ is greater that $fT$ for some positive $f$.

Chapter XII, "Divisor problems," is concerned with the error $\Delta_k(x)$ in the formula $\sum_{n\leqq x} d_k(x)=xP_k(\log x)+\Delta_k(x)$ where $d_k(n)$ is the number of ways of expressing $n$ as a product of $k$ factors and $P_k(y)$ is a polynomial in $y$ of degree $k-1$. Estimates for $\Delta_k(x)$ and $\int_0^x\Delta_k^2(y)dy$ are given. None of this material appeared in the earlier tract. Chapter XIII, "The Lindelöf hypothesis," is concerned with necessary or sufficient conditions for the validity of this hypothesis that $\zeta(\frac{1}{2}+it)=O(t^\epsilon)$ for each positive $\epsilon$. One necessary and sufficient condition is that $N(\sigma, T+1)-N(\sigma, T)=o(\log T)$ for each $\sigma>\frac{1}{2}$; other conditions are connected with the behavior of $\Delta_k(x)$. Chapter XIV, "Consequences of the Riemann hypothesis," derives bounds for $\zeta'(s)/\zeta(s)$, $\log\zeta(s)$, $\zeta(1+it)$, $\zeta(\frac{1}{2}+it)$, $1/\zeta(1+it)$ and some $\Omega$ results under this hypothesis. Also, some results on $\sum_{n\leq x}\mu(n)$ are obtained both with and without this hypothesis. The concluding chapter, "Calculations relating to the zeros," provides a brief description of our numerical knowledge about the zeros. A fourteen page bibliography including references given in the Cambridge tract but not in Landau's Handbuch is appended. There is no index. The typography is excellent. *L. Schoenfeld.*

Referred to in A30-26, M05-27, M05-33, M05-43, M05-46, M10-16, M15-29, M25-40, M25-68, M30-52, M35-15, M40-30, M50-2, M99-3, N04-17, N20-71, N40-27, N40-28, R42-39.

## M02-3 (13, 824b)

**Čudakov, N. G., and Rodosskiĭ, K. A. New methods in the theory of Dirichlet's $L$-functions.** Uspehi Matem. Nauk (N.S.) 4, no. 2(30), 22–56 (1949). (Russian)

This is an expository paper mainly devoted to the method of "density of zeros". This is the name attached by the Russian number-theorists to the application in prime-number theory of estimates of $N(\sigma, T)$, the number of zeros of an $L$-function in the rectangle $\sigma\leq\Re(z)\leq 1$, $-T\leq\Im(z)\leq T$, where $\sigma>\frac{1}{2}$ and $T\geq 1$. The authors take these estimates of $N(\sigma, T)$ for granted and discuss only how they are applied. The paper consists of four sections.

In the first section the authors give a very complete proof of a result on trigonometric sums involving prime numbers which was announced earlier by Čudakov [Doklady Akad. Nauk SSSR (N.S.) **58**, 1291–1294 (1947); these Rev. **9**, 333]. Actually in this part of the paper the authors go much further in the direction of completeness than seems necessary, for they give detailed proofs of a number of preliminary theorems which are either immediate corollaries or obvious generalizations of well-known results. Thus Lemma 1 is a straightforward application of integration by parts, Lemma 2 is a direct corollary of the second mean-value theorem, Lemma 3 is a variant of the Fourier summation formula, and Theorem 1 is a rather routine generalization of a well-known theorem of van der Corput [Landau, Vorlesungen über Zahlentheorie, v. 1, Hirzel, Leipzig, 1927, Satz 352].

The second section is mainly devoted to Čudakov's proof of the Goldbach-Vinogradov theorem [Ann. of Math. (2) **48**, 515–545 (1947); these Rev. **9**, 11], starting from the relevant theorem on $N(\sigma, T)$ [op. cit., Theorem 2]. The authors sketch the proof of the essential approximation formula for $f(x)=\sum_{p>2}(\ln p)x^p$ [op. cit., Theorem 3] and the deduction therefrom of the asymptotic formula for the coefficients of $f^3(x)$. In addition they show in detail how the approximation formula for $f(x)$ leads to the theorem that almost all even natural numbers are sums of two odd primes. This latter proof is not found in Čudakov's paper and is attributed by the authors to V. Arhangel'skiĭ; it is similar to but slightly neater than the Hardy-Littlewood treatment [Proc. London Math. Soc. (2) **22**, 46–56 (1923)]. The section concludes with a brief resume of a paper of Čudakov [Izvestiya Akad. Nauk SSSR. Ser. Mat. **12**, 31–46 (1948); these Rev. **9**, 499] on the finite differences of $\psi(x, k, l)$, where $\psi(x, k, l)$ has its usual meaning in prime-number theory.

In the third section the authors sketch Linnik's proof that if $k>1$ and $(l, k)=1$, then there exists a prime number $p$ such that $p\equiv l \pmod{k}$ and $p<k^c$, where $c$ is an absolute constant [Mat. Sbornik N.S. **15**(**57**), 3–12, 139–178, 347–368 (1944); **16**(**58**), 101–120 (1945); these Rev. **6**, 260; **7**, 146]. The reviewer regrets that the authors did not treat the material of this section with the completeness of detail which characterizes the first section, for even after this exposition Linnik's proof will remain an enigma to many number-theorists.

The last section has no direct connection with the method of density of zeros and was actually written by Linnik. In it he shows that the Lindelöf hypothesis is equivalent to asserting that as $T\to\infty$ the relation

$$\sum_{n=1}^{\infty}\tau(n)n^{iT}\exp\left\{-\tfrac{1}{4}\ln^2\frac{T}{2\pi en}\right\}=O(T^{\frac{1}{2}+\epsilon})$$

holds for any positive $\epsilon$, where $\tau(n)$ denotes the number of divisors of $n$.

Although this paper is disappointing in some ways (mainly in the conciseness of its third section), it still is a very welcome addition to the literature of expository papers in analytic number theory. *P. T. Bateman.*

Citations: MR 6, 260a = N16-4; MR 6, 260b = N16-5; MR 7, 146i = L20-8; MR 9, 11d = P32-10; MR 9, 333c = L20-9; MR 9, 499b = N16-9.
Referred to in M02-4, Z10-51.

## M02-4 (14, 249a)

**Čudakov, N. G., and Rodosskiĭ, K. A. New methods in the theory of Dirichlet's $L$-functions.** Amer. Math. Soc. Translation no. **73**, 44 pp. (1952).

Translated from Uspehi Matem. Nauk (N.S.) **4**, no. 2(30), 22–56 (1949); these Rev. **13**, 824.

Citations: MR 13, 824b = M02-3.
Referred to in Z10-51.

## M02-5 (13, 915c)

**Chowla, Sarvadaman. The Riemann zeta and allied functions.** Bull. Amer. Math. Soc. **58**, 287–305 (1952).

This address, delivered to the American Mathematical Society, Dec. 28, 1949, gives a general review of the theory of the Riemann zeta-function, the prime-number problem, Dirichlet's $L$-functions, zeta-functions of an algebraic number-field, and $L$-functions of the type considered by A. Weil. A list of related unsolved problems is also given. *E. C. Titchmarsh* (Oxford).

Referred to in L30-4, L30-5, T10-15.

## M02-6 (15, 105e)

**Suetuna, Zyoiti. Kaisekiteki seisûron. [Analytical theory of numbers.]** Iwanami Shoten, Tokyo, 1950. iii+ii +295+ii pp. 450 yen.

The book under review was originally published some fifteen years ago in the form of lecture notes; the present revised one incorporates recent developments of the theory. The manuscript was, however, in the printer's hand when various elementary proofs were published of the Prime Number theorem and Dirichlet's theorem, thus necessitating their omissions. This book, based mainly on the Riemann $\zeta$-functions and $L$-functions, is a unique exposition of the analytical theory of numbers in a modern sense as can be seen from the chapter headings: I) Riemann's $\zeta$-functions; II) Hecke's $L$-functions; III) Dirichlet's $L$-functions; and IV) Artin's $L$-series. In order to indicate the importance of $L$-functions the book concludes with an appendix entitled "A general divisor problem," which was treated by H. Hasse and Z. Suetuna [J. Fac. Sci. Imp. Univ. Tokyo. Sect. I. **2**, 133–154 (1931)]. *S. Ikehara* (Tokyo).

**M02-7** **(30# 4736)**

**Turán, Paul**

**Untersuchungen über Dirichlet-Polynome.**

*Bericht von der Dirichlet-Tagung, pp.* 71–80. *Akademie-Verlag, Berlin,* 1963.

An expository lecture presented in 1959.

**M02-8** **(41# 8349)**

**Linnik, Ju. V.**

**On Hilbert's eighth problem.** (Russian)

*Hilbert's Problems (Russian), pp.* 128–130. *Izdat. "Nauka", Moscow,* 1969.

In this expository note the Riemann hypothesis (both for the ordinary ζ-function and for the congruence ζ-functions) and Goldbach's problem are stated, and some of the progress made toward proving them is briefly described.

*B. Gordon* (Los Angeles, Calif.)

## M05 REPRESENTATIONS AND FUNCTIONAL PROPERTIES OF $\zeta(s)$ AND $L(s,\chi)$

See also Sections F65, M40.

See also reviews E44-39, L05-26, M10-20, M20-34, M25-4, M25-19, M25-26, M25-30, M25-70, M25-71, M25-72, M30-44, M30-45, M35-13, M40-39, M40-53, M40-57, M40-60, M99-6, N40-62, N40-64, Q10-3, Q10-7, Q10-12, R14-79, R42-8, R42-14, R42-22.

**M05-1** **(1, 70b)**

**Speiser, Andreas. Die Funktionalgleichung der Dirichletschen $L$-Funktionen.** Monatsh. Math. Phys. **48**, 240–244 (1939).

The author first proves certain facts concerning a determinant involving the representations of finite Abelian groups. This is a generalization, from the case of cyclic groups, of the results used by I. Schur [Nachr. Ges. Wiss. Göttingen **1921**, 147–153] in his evaluation of the Gaussian sums. These results enable the author to prove the functional equation for the Dirichlet $L$-functions with the use of a relatively small amount of analysis.

*H. S. Zuckerman* (Seattle, Wash.).

**M05-2** **(2, 96a)**

**Košljakov, N. S. Some formulae for the functions $\zeta(s)$ and $\zeta_\Omega(s)$.** C. R. (Doklady) Acad. Sci. URSS (N.S.) **25**, 567–569 (1939).

The author proves:

$$\zeta(s)=\sum_{n=1}^{\infty}\frac{n^{-s}}{1+(n/x)^2}-\frac{\pi x^{1-s}}{2\sin(\pi(1-s)/2)}$$
$$+2x^{1-s}\int_0^{\infty}\left\{\sum_{n=1}^{\infty}\frac{n^{s-1}}{1+(n/x)^2}-\frac{\pi y^s}{2\sin(\pi s/2)}\right\}\frac{\cos 2\pi xy}{y^s}dy,$$
$$x>0;\ 0<\Re(s)<1.$$

Analogous formulae are obtained for other functions associated with Dirichlet's series. [Cf. A. P. Guinand, J. London Math. Soc. **14**, 97–100 (1939).]

*S. Ikehara* (Osaka).

**M05-3** **(5, 173a)**

**Turing, A. M. A method for the calculation of the zeta-function.** Proc. London Math. Soc. (2) **48**, 180–197 (1943).

Let $L_\mu$ denote the straight line $z=\mu-\epsilon r$, where $\mu$ is a given positive real number, $\epsilon=e^{\pi i/4}$ and $r$ runs through real values from $-\infty$ to $+\infty$; define

$$h(z)=\frac{e^{\pi i z^2}z^{-s}}{e^{\pi i z}-e^{-\pi i z}},$$

$J(s)=\int_{L_\mu}h(z)dz$, $0<\mu<1$, $f(s)=\pi^{-s/2}\Gamma(s/2)J(s)$. Riemann found the formula $\pi^{-s/2}\Gamma(s/2)\zeta(s)=f(s)+\bar f(1-\bar s)$ and obtained an asymptotic series for the zeta-function by using saddle-point integration. However, the estimation of the remainder terms is rather complicated unless the imaginary part $t$ of $s$ is sufficiently large. The author describes a method of calculation of $\zeta(s)$ which is applicable for all values of $s$. Let $m$ be a positive integer, $\kappa$ a positive real parameter, $m<\mu<m+1$, $g_1(z)=h(z)(1-e^{-2\pi\kappa\epsilon(z-\mu)})^{-1}$, $g_2(z)=h(z)-g_1(z)$. Then, by Cauchy's theorem,

$$J(s)-\sum_{n=1}^{m}n^{-s}=\int_{L_\mu}h(z)dz=R+\int_{C_1}g_1(z)dz+\int_{C_2}g_2(z)dz,$$

where $C_1$ and $C_2$ are certain curves of integration and $R$ is a sum of residues. If $\mu$, $\kappa$, $C_1$, $C_2$ are suitably chosen, depending upon $s$, then the two integrals on the right-hand side represent only small terms; their estimation is explicitly given. It is stated that this method is practical for the computation of $\zeta(s)$ in the strip $30<t<1000$.

*C. L. Siegel* (Princeton, N. J.).

**M05-4** **(6, 45e)**

**Szász, Otto. Introduction to the Theory of Divergent Series.** Department of Mathematics, Graduate School of Arts and Sciences, University of Cincinnati, Cincinnati, Ohio, 1944. v+72 pp. $1.25.

Lithoprinted lectures given by Szász in an introductory course in summability and transcribed by J. Barlaz. A novel feature of the course is that the simple regular transformation $Y$ defined by $\sigma_n=\frac{1}{2}(s_{n-1}+s_n)$ is systematically used to illustrate points in the theory. This transformation was previously used by W. A. Hurwitz [Bull. Amer. Math. Soc. **32**, 77–82 (1926)] to illustrate Tauberian theorems. The following result, which the reviewer has not seen elsewhere, is obtained. The series $1-2^{-s}+3^{-s}-\cdots$, which converges to $(1-2^{1-s})\zeta(s)$ when $\Re(s)>0$, is summable $Y$ when $\Re(s)>-1$, and, moreover, for each integer $r>0$, the series is summable $Y^r$ when $\Re(s)>-r$. It is an interesting fact that methods of summability so simple as $Y$ and its powers can furnish the analytic continuation of $\zeta(s)$ from the region of convergence of $\sum n^{-s}$ to the entire complex plane except $s=1$.

*R. P. Agnew* (Ithaca, N. Y.).

**M05-5** **(9, 228c)**

**Linnik, Yu. V. On the expression of $L$-series by means of $\zeta$-functions.** Doklady Akad. Nauk SSSR (N.S.) **57**, 435–437 (1947). (Russian)

The author proves the identity

$$\sum_{n=1}^{\infty}\chi(n)a_n n^{-s}e^{-n/N}=\epsilon(\chi)D^{-\frac{1}{2}}(2\pi i)^{-1}$$
$$\times\int A(w+s)\Gamma(w)\sum_{m=0}^{D-1}\bar\chi(-m)(N^{-1}+2\pi i m D^{-1})^{-w}dw,$$

where $\chi(n)$ is a primitive character mod $D$, $|\epsilon(\chi)|=1$, $N>0$ and the integral is extended over a vertical line in the half-plane of convergence of the Dirichlet series $A(s)=\sum a_n n^{-s}$. The proof is based on Mellin's formula and the fact that the residue classes $n$ (mod $D$) form a multiplicative group with characters $\chi(n)$ and an additive group with characters $e^{2\pi imn/D}$. As an example the author gives the formula

$$\sum_{n=2}^{\infty}\chi(n)\Lambda(n)e^{-n/N}=-\epsilon(\chi)D^{-\frac{1}{2}}\sum_{\rho}\Gamma(\rho)$$
$$\times\sum_{m=0}^{D-1}\bar{\chi}(-m)(N^{-1}+2\pi imD^{-1})^{-\rho}+O(\log^2 N),$$

where $\rho$ runs through those nontrivial zeros of $\zeta(s)$ whose imaginary parts are in absolute value less than $N\log^2 N$. Finally, the author states without proof that if $\xi(s)\neq 0$ for $\sigma>1-\eta$, $0\leqq\eta<\frac{1}{4}$, $\delta>0$, then

$$\sum_{p}e^{2\pi ip^{1/m}}e^{-(p/N)^{1/m}}=O(N^{1-1/(2m)-\eta/m+\delta}).$$

*H. Heilbronn* (Bristol).

## M05-6 (9, 508a)

**Atkinson, F. V. The Abel summation of certain Dirichlet series.** Quart. J. Math., Oxford Ser. **19**, 59–64 (1948).

Using contour integration, the author obtains the following formula: $\sum_1^\infty n^{-s}e^{-n\delta}-\Gamma(1-s)\delta^{s-1}\rightarrow\zeta(s)$ as $\delta\downarrow 0$, when $s$ is not a positive integer. He also gives a result of similar type, too long to quote here, relating to the (everywhere divergent) series $\sum p(n)(n-1/24)^{-s}$, where $p(n)$ denotes the number of unrestricted partitions of $n$. *A. Dvoretzky.*

## M05-7 (10, 104e)

**Brun, Viggo, Jacobsthal, Ernst, Selberg, Atle, and Siegel, Carl. Correspondence about a polynomial which is related to Riemann's zeta function.** Norsk Mat. Tidsskr. **28**, 65–71 (1946). (Norwegian and German)

The Euler-Maclaurin sum formula applied to the series $\sum n^{-s}$ gives (formally) the divergent expansion

$$(s-1)\zeta(s)=\sum_{n=0}^{\infty}B_n(s-1)s(s+1)\cdots(s+n-2)/n!=\sum_{n=0}^{\infty}P_n(s),$$

where $B_0, B_1, B_2, \cdots$ are the Bernoulli numbers, except $B_1$ which is $+\frac{1}{2}$. The first author observes that, if $Q_n(s)=\sum_0^n P_k(s)$, we may write

$$(2m)!Q_{2m}(s)=B_{2m}(s+2)(s+4)\cdots(s+2m)(s+2m+1)q_{2m}(s),$$

where $q_{2m}(s)=s^{m-1}+\cdots$ is a polynomial, so that $Q_{2m}(s)$ has $m$ real zeros in common with $\zeta(s)$; and he then asks whether the $m-1$ zeros of $q_{2m}(s)$ have anything to do with zeros of $\zeta(s)$. The second and third authors note that the observation about real zeros is a simple deduction from the formula for the remainder $R_n(s)=(s-1)\zeta(s)-Q_n(s)$ given by Stieltjes, and are sceptical about any deeper connection involving complex zeros. The fourth author substantiates this view by showing, with the aid of Rouché's theorem, that the $2m$ zeros of $Q_{2m}(s)$ all lie inside a set of circles of radius 11 about the points $s=-1, -2, \cdots, 2-2m$; and states that, by a more accurate estimation of $P_k/P_{2m}$, it can be shown that, when $m$ is large, the zeros of $Q_{2m}(s)$ are real and approximate to those of $P_{2m}(s)$, with the possible exception of a bounded number, which in any case lie inside a circle of fixed radius about $s=-2m$. *A. E. Ingham.*

## M05-8 (11, 162b)

**Atkinson, F. V. The Riemann zeta-function.** Duke Math. J. **17**, 63–68 (1950).

Let $\sum_1^\infty a_n\approx t$ denote that the infinite series $\sum_1^\infty a_n$ possesses the property that $\lim_{\delta\to 0}\{\sum_1^\infty a_ne^{-n\delta}-\psi(\delta)\}=t$, where $\psi(\delta)$ is a finite combination of powers of $\delta$ and $\log\delta$. The author shows that, for $u\neq 0, \pm 1, \pm 2, \cdots$,

$$\Gamma(1-u)2^{u-\frac{1}{2}}\pi^u\sum_{n=1}^{\infty}\sigma_{1-2u}(n)(-1)^{n+1}n^{u-\frac{1}{2}}Y_{u-\frac{1}{2}}(n)$$
$$\approx\zeta^2(u)-\zeta(2u)-2\zeta(2u-1)\Gamma(1-u)\Gamma(2u-1)/\Gamma(u).$$

*R. Bellman* (Stanford University, Calif.).

## M05-9 (11, 162e)

**Davenport, H. On the series for $L(1)$.** J. London Math. Soc. **24**, 229–233 (1949).

Let $k>1$ and $\chi$ be a real primitive character modulo $k$. Let $L(s, \chi)=\sum_{n=1}^\infty\chi(n)/n^s$ and $S_\nu(s, \chi)=\sum_{n=\nu k+1}^{(\nu+1)k}\chi(n)/n^s$ for a nonnegative integer $\nu$. It is known that $L(1, \chi)>0$. The author proves the following theorem concerning the portions $S_\nu(1, \chi)$ of the series for $L(1, \chi)$. If $\chi(-1)=1$, then $S_\nu(1, \chi)>0$ for all $\nu$ and $\chi$. If $\chi(-1)=-1$, then $S_0(1, \chi)>0$ and $S_\nu(1, \chi)>0$ for all $\nu>\nu_0(k)$, but to each integer $r>0$ there exists a $\chi$ such that $S_\nu(1, \chi)<0$ for $\nu=1, \cdots, r$. The proof is not very difficult. *L. Schoenfeld* (Urbana, Ill.).

## M05-10 (11, 420c)

**Bellman, Richard. An analog of an identity due to Wilton.** Duke Math. J. **16**, 539–545 (1949).

The author proves the following theorem. For $\sigma>\frac{1}{4}$, $\sigma'>\frac{1}{4}$, $\sigma+\sigma'>1$,

$$\zeta^2(s)\zeta^2(s')-\zeta'(s+s'-1)\{(s-1)^{-1}+(s'-1)^{-1}\}$$
$$+\zeta^2(s+s'-1)\{(s-1)^{-2}+(s'-1)^{-2}+2C(s-1)^{-1}$$
$$+2C(s'-1)^{-1}\}=2\sum_{r=1}^{\infty}\sum_{nk=r}d(k)d(n)n^{-s-s'+1}$$
$$\times\int_1^\infty M_0(4\pi r^{\frac{1}{2}}u)(u^{-2s+1}+u^{-2s'+1})du,$$

where $\zeta(s)$ is the Riemann $\zeta$-function, $C$ Euler's constant, $d(n)$ the number of divisors of $n$, and $M_0(u)=-Y_0(u)+2\pi^{-1}K_0(u)$ in the notation normally used for Bessel functions. This theorem is a generalization of a result by Wilton [Proc. London Math. Soc. (2) **31**, 11–17 (1930)], who proved a similar identity for $\zeta(s)\zeta'(s)$. The proof, based on Voronoi's summation formula, is complicated by considerations of convergence. The result is best possible in so far as the infinite series diverges for $\sigma=\sigma'=\frac{1}{2}$. *H. A. Heilbronn.*

## M05-11 (12, 600a)

**Denjoy, Arnaud. Une expression de la fonction $\zeta(s)$ de Riemann.** C. R. Acad. Sci. Paris **232**, 905–908 (1951).

The author develops the representation

$$\zeta(s)=2^s\lim_{p\to\infty}\int_0^\infty y^{-s}[\tfrac{1}{2}-\lambda_p(y)]dy$$

of the Riemann zeta-function in the region $0<\Re[s]<1$, where

$$\lambda_p(y)=\frac{\rho^p}{2\sin\frac{1}{2}y}\sin(p\theta-\tfrac{1}{2}y),$$

$$\rho\cos\theta+i\rho\sin\theta=1-\frac{\sin y}{y}+i\frac{1-\cos y}{y}.$$

*P. R. Garabedian* (Stanford University, Calif.).

## M05-12 (12, 690g)

**Beurling, Arne. An extremal property of the Riemann zeta-function.** Ark. Mat. **1**, 295–300 (1951).

For $k>0$ consider the class $C_k$ of all Dirichlet's series $\varphi(s)=\sum\lambda_n^{-s}$ with $0<\lambda_n\leqq\lambda_{n+1}$ such that the series converges for $\sigma>1$ and $\varphi(s)$ has the properties ($\alpha$) $\varphi(s)-(s-1)^{-1}$ is entire, ($\beta$) $\varphi(-2n)=0$, $n=1, 2, 3, \cdots$,

$$(\gamma) \qquad \max|\varphi(re^{i\theta})|<C\Gamma(r)(2\pi k)^{-r}$$

for $r>2$. Let $D_k=\bigcap_{\epsilon\geq 0}C_{k-\epsilon}$. Then for $0<k\leqq\frac{1}{2}$ each class $D_k$ contains infinitely many elements while all classes $D_k$ with $k>\frac{1}{2}$ are vacuous except for $D_1$ which consists of two elements $\zeta(s)$ and $(2^s-1)\zeta(s)$. The proof is based on the Phragmén-Lindelöf principle which yields two lemmas. (I) $\varphi(s)\varepsilon D_k$ if and only if the entire function $f(z)=\prod_1^\infty(1+z^2\lambda_n^{-2})$ satisfies $f(x)=a|x|^pe^{\pi|x|}+O[e^{\pi(1+\epsilon-2k)|x|}]$ for fixed $a$ and $p$, $a>0$, $p$ real, and all large real $x$. (II) If $f(z)$ is entire, $f(0)=1$, and $f(x)=a|x|^pe^{\pi|x|}+O[e^{-\delta|x|}]$ and if $f(z)$ is of order one and normal type, then $f(z)$ is either cosh $\pi z$ or sinh $\pi z/(\pi z)$.

*E. Hille* (New Haven, Conn.).

Referred to in M40-9.

## M05-13 (14, 248f)

**Wiebelitz, Rudolf. Über approximative Funktionalgleichungen der Potenzen der Riemannschen Zetafunktion.** Math. Nachr. **6**, 263–270 (1952).

The author generalizes the Hardy-Littlewood approximate functional equations for $\zeta(s)$ and $\zeta^2(s)$ to $\zeta^k(s)$ where $k>2$ is an integer. Modifying the author's notation, let $\chi(s)=\zeta(s)/\zeta(1-s)$, let $\zeta(\frac{1}{2}+it)=O(t^c)$ where $0<c\leqq 1/6$, let $\beta=3/2$ if $k=3$ but $\beta=k/\{4(1+kc-4c)\}$ if $k>3$, let $a_{p,k}$ be the coefficient of $(s-1)^p$ in the Laurent expansion of $\zeta^k(s)$ about $s=1$, and let

$$r_{p,\nu}=\frac{1}{\nu!}\sum_{\mu=0}^{p-\nu-1}(-1)^\mu\binom{k+\mu-1}{\mu}\binom{k-1}{p-\mu-\nu-1}.$$

Further, let $d_k(n)$ be the number of representations of $n$ as the product of $k$ positive integers and

$$Q_x(s)=\sum_{n\leq x}d_k(n)n^{-s}-x^{1-s}\sum_{\nu=0}^{k-1}\log^\nu x\sum_{\nu+1\leq p<\nu+\beta}a_{-p,k}r_{p,\nu}(1-s)^{\nu-p}.$$

Finally, let $xy=(|t|/2\pi)^k$. The main theorem is that if $x>A>0$ and $y>A$, then

$$\zeta^k(s)=Q_x(s)+\chi^k(s)Q_y(1-s)$$
$$+O(U_1)+O(U_2)+O(U_3)+O(U_4),$$

where the $U$'s are certain error terms given explicitly. Using the best known value of $c=15/92+\epsilon$ due to Min, the author shows that for $k=3$ the four error terms reduce to $O(x^{1/2-\sigma}|t|^{15/92+\epsilon})$.

Paralleling the proof given by Hardy and Littlewood, the author begins by considering

$$2\pi i\sum_{n\leq x}d_k(n)n^{-s}\log^{k-1}x/n=(k-1)!\int_{2-\sigma-i\infty}^{2-\sigma+i\infty}\zeta^k(s+z)x^zz^{-k}dz.$$

The path of integration is moved to $\Re(z)=-\gamma$ where $\gamma>0$ is suitably chosen. By evaluating the residues of the integrand at $z=0$ and $z=1-s$ and by a suitable treatment of the new integral along $\Re(z)=-\gamma$, the author obtains the stated result. He then states the mean-value theorem that for $k>2$ and $T>A$:

$$\int_1^T|\zeta(\sigma+it)|^{2k}dt=T\sum_{n=1}^\infty d_k^2(n)\cdot n^{-2\sigma}$$
$$+O(T^{1/2+k(1-\sigma)/2}\log^{k-1/2}T)$$
$$+O(T^{1/2}\log^{k-1/2}T)+O(T^{k(1-\sigma)}\log^{2k}T).$$

He says that this holds uniformly for $1-k\leqq\sigma\leqq 3/2$ but this is probably a misprint for $1-1/k\leqq\sigma\leqq 3/2$ since the series diverges if $\sigma\leqq 1/2$.

*L. Schoenfeld* (Urbana, Ill.).

## M05-14 (15, 11e)

**Kober, H. A remark on zeta functions.** Proc. Amer. Math. Soc. **4**, 588–590 (1953).

In section 1, the author obtains the following expression for Riemann's $\xi$-function:

$$(1) \quad \xi(s)=F_s(w)+F_{1-s}(1/w) \quad (w=u+iv,\ u\geqq 0,\ w\neq 0)$$

where $F_s(w)=\int_0^\infty\omega(x+w)(x+w)^{\frac{1}{2}s-1}dx-w^{\frac{1}{2}(s-1)}/(1-s)$, and $\omega(x)=\sum_{n=1}^\infty\exp(-n^2\pi x)$, thus generalizing the classic formula $\xi(s)=\int_0^\infty\omega(x)x^{\frac{1}{2}s-1}dx$. Formula (1) is then used to obtain two necessary and sufficient conditions for the nontrivial vanishing of the Riemann zeta function.

In section 2, the author considers the generalized zeta function $\zeta(s, a, b)$ defined by analytic continuation of the series $\sum_{n>-a}e^{2\pi inb}(n+a)^{-s}$ ($a$, $b$ arbitrary real numbers), and sketches a proof of the functional equation

$$\frac{(2\pi)^s}{\Gamma(s)}e^{2\pi iab}\zeta(1-s, a, b)=e^{\frac{1}{2}\pi is}\zeta(s, b, -a)+e^{-\frac{1}{2}\pi is}\zeta(s, -b, a).$$

For $0<a\leqq 1$, $0<b<1$, the result is equivalent to a transformation formula of Lerch [see Acta Math. **11**, 19–24 (1887)].

*T. M. Apostol* (Pasadena, Calif.).

## M05-15 (15, 606f)

**Denjoy, Arnaud. L'équation fonctionnelle de $\zeta(s)$.** C. R. Acad. Sci. Paris **238**, 533–536 (1954).

Still another proof of the functional equation for the Riemann zeta-function. The usual formula $\zeta(s)=\sum_1^\infty m^{-s}$ ($\sigma>1$) leads to

$$\zeta(s)=\lim_{n\to\infty}\left\{\sum_1^n m^{-s}+(n+\tfrac{1}{2})^{1-s}/(s-1)\right\} \quad (\sigma>-1).$$

The result follows from this and transformations of the formula

$$\Gamma(s)\zeta(s)=\int_0^\infty\frac{x^{s-1}}{e^x-1}dx.$$

*E. C. Titchmarsh* (Oxford).

Referred to in M05-17.

## M05-16 (15, 685c)

**Apostol, T. M. Some series involving the Riemann zeta function.** Proc. Amer. Math. Soc. **5**, 239–243 (1954).

Proof of formulae such as

$$\zeta(s)(1-k^{1-s})=\sum_{n=1}^\infty\frac{P_n(s)\zeta(n+s)}{k^{n+s}}\frac{B_{n+1}(k)-B_{n+1}}{n+1},$$

where $k$ is an integer greater than 1,

$$P_n(s)=\frac{s(s+1)\cdots(s+n-1)}{n!},$$

$B_n(x)$ is the $n$th Bernoulli polynomial, and $B_n$ is the $n$th Bernoulli number.

*T. Estermann* (London).

## M05-17 (15, 948d)

**Denjoy, Arnaud. Une démonstration de l'identité fondamentale de la fonction $\zeta(s)$ de Riemann.** J. Analyse Math. **3**, 197–206 (1954).

The author gives a more detailed version of his proof of the functional equation of the Riemann zeta-function [see C. R. Acad. Sci. Paris **238**, 533–536 (1954); these Rev. **15**, 606].

*E. C. Titchmarsh* (Oxford).

Citations: MR 15, 606f = M05-15.

**M05-18** **(16, 16c)**

**Tatuzawa, Tikao. The approximate functional equation for Dirichlet's *L*-series.** Jap. J. Math. **22** (1952), 19–25 (1953).

The main result is Theorem 2: If $0<\sigma<1$, $x \geqq \sqrt{k}$, $y \geqq \sqrt{k}$, $2\pi xy=kt$ $(s=\sigma+it)$, and $\chi(n)$ is a Dirichlet character mod $k$, then

$$L(s,\chi)=\sum_{n\leqq x}\chi(n)n^{-s}$$
$$+2(2\pi)^{s-1}k^{-s}\Gamma(1-s)\sum_{n\leqq y}\left(C(n)\sin\frac{\pi s}{2}+S(n)\cos\frac{\pi s}{2}\right)n^{s-1}$$
$$+O(kx^{-\sigma})+O(ky^{\sigma-1}(kt)^{\frac{1}{2}-\sigma}),$$

where

$$C(n)=\sum_{l=1}^{k}\chi(l)\cos\frac{2\pi ln}{k},\quad S(n)=\sum_{l=1}^{k}\chi(l)\frac{\sin 2\pi ln}{k},$$

and $O$ implies an absolute constant and an inequality valid for all stated values of the variables. The emphasis is on uniformity in $k$. Tchudakoff [Ann. of Math. (2) **48**, 515–545 (1947); these Rev. **9**, 11] had already obtained a result of this nature for primitive $\chi$, when the second sum takes a simpler form in terms of a partial sum of the Dirichlet series for $L(1-s,\bar{\chi})$. The argument here follows the lines of the Hardy-Littlewood 'real variable' proof of the approximate functional equation for $\zeta(s)$ [Proc. London Math. Soc. (2) **29**, 81–97 (1929)]. It is stated that, when $\chi$ is primitive, the first factor $k$ in the error terms may be reduced 'by a slight careful estimation' to $k^{\frac{1}{2}}\log(k+1)$. There are a few minor errors and some troublesome obscurities. Thus Lemma 4 is quoted from Hardy and Littlewood in an extended form, but without comment on the extension (particularly the extension from $\frac{1}{2}\leqq\sigma\leqq\frac{3}{2}$ to $0<\sigma<2$). Theorem 1 involves an infinite series, but the enunciation contains no reference to convergence or range of validity. The theorem is first proved for $-1<\sigma<0$ (the reader being left to supply his own justification of term-by-term limit operation), and could be extended at once by analytic continuation to $\sigma<0$ (the half-plane of absolute convergence). If something more than this is meant, the only clue is the cryptic sentence, 'By a slight modification we can deduce this functional equation for an arbitrary half plane'. However, Theorem 1 is not used in the sequel; it serves merely to prepare the reader for the form of the second sum in Theorem 2.

*A. E. Ingham* (Cambridge, England).

Citations: MR 9, 11d = P32-10.

**M05-19** **(16, 999f)**

**Briggs, W. E., and Chowla, S. The power series coefficients of $\zeta(s)$.** Amer. Math. Monthly **62**, 323–325 (1955).

Let $\zeta(s)=(s-1)^{-1}+\sum_{n=0}^{\infty}A_n(s-1)^n$. It is shown in two ways that $A_n=(-1)^n\gamma_n/n!$ where

$$\sum_{n=1}^{x}\frac{\log^k n}{n}=\frac{\log^{k+1}x}{k+1}+\gamma_k+o(1).$$

*H. S. Zuckerman* (Seattle, Wash.).

Referred to in M05-28, M05-31, M40-25.

**M05-20** **(17, 16a)**

**Guinand, A. P. Some rapidly convergent series for the Riemann $\xi$-function.** Quart. J. Math. Oxford Ser. (2) **6**, 156–160 (1955).

The author derives the following identity, valid for Re $z>0$ and for all $s$ except 0 or $\pm 1$,

$$\sum_{n=1}^{\infty}n^{-\frac{1}{2}s}\sigma_s(n)K_{\frac{1}{2}s}(2\pi nz)-z^{-1}\sum_{n=1}^{\infty}n^{-\frac{1}{2}s}\sigma_s(n)K_{\frac{1}{2}s}(2\pi n/z)$$
$$=\frac{\xi(s)}{2s(s-1)}(z^{\frac{1}{2}s-1}-z^{-\frac{1}{2}s})+\frac{\xi(-s)}{2s(s+1)}(z^{-\frac{1}{2}s-1}-z^{\frac{1}{2}s}),$$

where $\xi(s)=\frac{1}{2}s(s-1)\pi^{-\frac{1}{2}s}\Gamma(\frac{1}{2}s)\zeta(s)$, $\sigma_s(n)=\sum_{d|n}d^s$, and $K_\mu$ is a Bessel function. Repeated differentiation of this formula leads to the following formula, valid for $s\neq 0$:

$$\xi(s)=4\pi(1-s)\sum_{n=1}^{\infty}n^{1-\frac{1}{2}s}\sigma_s(n)K_{1+\frac{1}{2}s}(2n\pi)+$$
$$16\pi^3s^{-1}\sum_{n=1}^{\infty}n^{3-\frac{1}{2}s}\sigma_s(n)\{(s-7)K_{1+\frac{1}{2}s}(2n\pi)+(s+7)K_{1-\frac{1}{2}s}(2n\pi)\}.$$

The series on the right converges very rapidly and hence is particularly useful for computing $\xi(s)$.

The author also obtains rapidly convergent series for $\zeta(2p-1)$ ($p$=integer$>1$) as a consequence of a transformation formula for the Lambert series

$$\sum_{n=1}^{\infty}n^{1-2p}(e^{2\pi nz}-1)^{-1}$$

which he derived in an earlier paper [same J. **15**, 11–23 (1944); MR **5**, 263]. The last term in formula (9) should contain $z^{2p-2}$ instead of $z^{2p-1}$. *T. M. Apostol.*

Citations: MR 5, 263b = F65-2.

**M05-21** **(17, 828e)**

**Bochner, S. Gamma factors in functional equations.** Proc. Nat. Acad. Sci. U.S.A. **42** (1956), 86–89.

The gamma factors in the functional equation for a zeta function usually arise from an expression of the form

$$(1)\qquad \eta(x)\mu(x)^s\int_P e^{-(x,t)}R(t)^s d\Omega(t).$$

Here $P$ is an open set in real Euclidean $k$-space, $\Omega$ is a positive set function, $R(t)$ is a polynomial in $t_1,\cdots,t_k$, $R(t)$ is positive on $P$; $(x,t)$ denotes the inner product $x_1t_1+\cdots+x_kt_k$; $\eta(x)$ and $\mu(x)$ are positive functions of $x_1,\cdots,x_k$, defined and infinitely differentiable over an open set $G$. It is assumed that the integral converges absolutely, if $x\in G$, Re $s>\sigma_0$. Assuming, moreover, that the value $\Delta(s)$ of (1) does not depend on $x$ (if $x\in G$), the author shows that $\Delta(s)$ has the form $Ae^{as}\prod_{m=1}^{n}\Gamma(s-a_m)$, where $A>0$, $a$ real, $a_1,\cdots,a_n$ complex.

*N. G. de Bruijn* (Amsterdam).

**M05-22** **(17, 955c)**

**Briggs, William E. Some constants associated with the Riemann zeta-function.** Michigan Math. J. **3** (1955–56), 117–121.

The constants are the $\gamma_n$ in the expansion

$$\zeta(s)=\frac{1}{s-1}+\sum_{n=0}^{\infty}\frac{(-1)^n\gamma_n}{n!}(s-1)^n.$$

It is shown that infinitely many of the $\gamma_n$ satisfy each of the inequalities $\gamma_n>0$, $\gamma_n<0$, $n^{-\varepsilon n}<|\gamma_n|<n^{\varepsilon n}$, where $\varepsilon>0$ is arbitrary. It is also shown that $|\gamma_n|<(n/2e)^n$ for all $\gamma_n$. *H. S. Zuckerman* (Seattle, Wash.).

Referred to in M05-31, M20-34.

**M05-23** **(20# 24)**

**Mikolás, Miklós. A simple proof of the functional equation for the Riemann zeta-function and a formula of Hurwitz.** Acta Sci. Math. Szeged **18** (1957), 261–263.

The functional equation of the Riemann zeta-function

or, more generally, the Hurwitz formula for

$$\zeta(s, \mu) = \sum_{n=0}^{\infty} (\mu+n)^{-s} \quad (0<\mu\leqq 1,\ \Re(s)>1)$$

is deduced by expanding $\zeta(s, \mu)$ in a Fourier series $\sum_{-\infty}^{\infty} c_n e^{2\pi i n\mu}$ for $0<\Re(s)<1$, by means of the equation

$$\zeta(s, \mu) = \lim_{N\to\infty} \left[\sum_{n=0}^{N} (\mu+n)^{-s} - \frac{N^{1-s}}{1-s}\right] \quad (\Re(s)>0).$$

*H. Kober* (Birmingham)

## M05-24 (22# 7981 )

**Gel'fond, A. O. Some functional equations implied by equations of Riemann type.** Izv. Akad. Nauk SSSR. Ser. Mat. **24** (1960), 469–474. (Russian)

Verfasser beweist approximative Funktionalgleichungen für solche Dirichletreihen, die ein Potenzprodukt von $\zeta(s)$ und Dirichletschen $L$-Reihen sind. Die approximativen Formeln sind vom Riemann-Siegelschen Typus, d.h., durch Hinzunahme weiterer Terme kann die Genauigkeit beliebig weit getrieben werden. Speziell: Es sei $p\geqq 1$, $\mu\geqq 0$, $q>p/6+\mu+1$ ($p$, $\mu$, $q$ ganze Zahlen), $s=1/2+i\tau$, $1\geqq\alpha>\tau^{-1/2}$, $u(s)=[2(2\pi)^{-s}\Gamma(s)\cos\frac{1}{2}\pi s]^p$, $m=\frac{1}{2}u'(s)/u(s)$. Dann gilt

$$\zeta^p(s) = \sum_{n\leqq \exp(m-\alpha q)} \left[\nu_p(n)n^{-s} + \frac{\nu_p(n)}{u(s)} n^{s-1}\right]$$

$$+ \sum_{\exp(m-\alpha q)<n\leqq \exp(m+\alpha q)} \left[\nu_p(n)n^{-s} + \frac{\nu_p(n)}{u(s)} n^{s-1}\right]\psi_q\left(\frac{m-\ln n}{\alpha}\right)$$

$$+ \sum_{\exp(m-\alpha q)<n\leqq \exp(m+\alpha q)} \frac{1}{n^s} \sum^{\mu} \frac{c_k}{\alpha^k \tau^{k/2}} \psi_q^{(k)}\left(\frac{m-\ln n}{\alpha}\right)$$

$$+O((\alpha\sqrt{\tau})^{-\mu-1}\tau^{p/6}).$$

Hierbei sind $\nu_p(n)$ die Lösungsanzahlen von $x_1\cdots x_p=n$ in ganzen Zahlen $x_k$,

$$\psi_q(x) = \frac{1}{2\pi i}\int_{\sigma(>0)} \left(\frac{e^z-e^{-z}}{2z}\right)^q e^{xz}\frac{dz}{z}$$

und $c_k$ gewisse Zahlen, die gleichmäßig in $\alpha$ beschränkt sind. Das entsprechende Restglied bei Dirichletschen $L$-Reihen wird gleichmäßig bezüglich des Moduls abgeschätzt. Druckfehler! *H.-E. Richert* (Göttingen)

Referred to in M40-39.

## M05-25 (23# A1612 )

**Prowse, Ebenezer**

**On the analytic continuation of the ζ-function.**

*Canad. Math. Bull.* **3** (1960), 289–292.

Der Verfasser beweist die Formel

$$\zeta(s)-1 = \frac{1}{s-1}+\frac{B_1}{1!}+\frac{B_2}{2!}s+\frac{B_3}{3!}s(s+1)+\cdots+\frac{B_{k-1}}{(k-1)!}$$

$$\times s(s+1)\cdots(s+k-3)-s(s+1)\cdots(s+k-1)$$

$$\times\sum_{1}^{\infty} n\int_0^1 \frac{P_k(x)}{(n+x)^{s+k}}\,dx,$$

wo $B_n$ die Bernoullischen Zahlen, $P_k(x)$ das $k$-te Bernoullischen Polynom bezeichnen. Der letzte Term konvergiert für $\mathrm{Re}\, s>1-k$. *H.-E. Richert* (Syracuse, N.Y.)

## M05-26 (23# A3969 )

**Knobloch, Hans-Wilhelm**

**Eine Summenformel für Laplace-Transformierte und ihre Anwendung auf Dirichlet-Reihen.**

*Arch. Math.* **11** (1960), 441–453.

Der Verfasser untersucht

$$(1) \qquad \int_{\mathrm{Re}\,\zeta=\beta} \varphi(\zeta)\,d\zeta - 2\pi i \sum_{\mathrm{Re}\,\zeta\leqq\beta} \mathrm{Res}\,\varphi(\zeta)$$

für in $\mathrm{Re}\,\zeta\leqq\beta$ meromorphe Funktionen

$$\varphi(\zeta) = \exp(\zeta^2-h\zeta)f(\zeta)g(\zeta).$$

Hierin ist $f$ eine für $\mathrm{Re}\,\zeta\leqq\beta$ absolut konvergente Laplace-Transformierte einer Funktion $F(t)$, $g(\zeta)$ gehört zu einer gewissen Klasse meromorpher Funktionen und $h$ ist eine Konstante. (1) wird durch eine Faltung

$$\int_0^{\infty} F(t)G(h-t)\,dt$$

ausgedrückt, wo $G$ durch $g$ bestimmt ist [vgl. Mordell, Acta Math. **61** (1933), 323–360]. Als Anwendung ergibt sich eine Verallgemeinerung der Riemann-Siegelschen Integraldarstellungen von $\zeta(s)$ und $L(s, \chi)$ [Siegel, Quell. Stud. Gesch. Math. B **2** (1932), 45–80; Ann. of Math. (2) **44** (1943), 143–172; MR **4**, 189] auf die Funktionen

$$\zeta(s, \tau, \kappa, r) = \sum_{\mu+\tau>0} \exp\{2\pi i(r\mu^2+\kappa\mu)\}(\mu+\tau)^{-s}$$

($\tau$, $\kappa$ reell, $r$ rational),

und für $\zeta(s, \tau, \kappa, r)$ wird eine approximative Funktionalgleichung aufgestellt. *H.-E. Richert* (Syracuse, N.Y.)

Citations: MR 4, 189c = M25-4.

## M05-27 (26# 85 )

**Kesava Menon, P.**

**Some series involving the zeta function.**

*Math. Student* **29** (1961), 77–80 (1962).

Two formulas involving the zeta function, due respectively to Landau and Ramaswami, are given in Titchmarsh [*The theory of the Riemann zeta-function*, Sect. 2.14, Clarendon, Oxford, 1951; MR **13**, 741]. The author remarks that their proofs are simpler when based on the integral representation $\Gamma(s)\zeta(s)=\int_0^\infty \{x^{s-1}/(e^x-1)\}dx$, $\mathrm{Re}\,s>1$, of $\zeta(s)$, and that this method of proof leads to generalizations. He proves the following theorem. For all values of $s$, we have

$$\sum_{d|n}\frac{f(d)}{d^s} - \Gamma(s)\zeta(s) = \sum_{r=0}^{\infty}\frac{f_r(n)}{r!n^{r+s}}\Gamma(r+s)\zeta(r+s),$$

where $f_r(n)=\sum_{m=0}^{n-1}\sum_{d|(m,n)}f(d)m^r$ and $f_0(n)=\sum_{m=0}^{n-1}\sum_{d|n}f(d)$.

*R. D. James* (Vancouver, B.C.)

Citations: MR 13, 741c = M02-2.

## M05-28 (26# 2408 )

**Ferguson, Rolfe P.**

**An application of Stieltjes integration to the power series coefficients of the Riemann zeta function.**

*Amer. Math. Monthly* **70** (1963), 60–61.

The author proves the following theorem. If

$$\zeta(s) = \frac{1}{s-1}+\sum_{k=0}^{\infty} A_k(s-1)^k,$$

then

$$A_k = \frac{(-1)^k}{k!}\lim_{N\to\infty}\left\{\sum_{n=1}^{N}\frac{\log^k n}{n} - \frac{\log^{k+1} N}{k+1}\right\}$$

[see W. E. Briggs and the reviewer, same Monthly **62** (1955), 323–325; MR **16**, 999]. This result has been noticed independently by numerous authors.

*S. Chowla* (Boulder, Colo.)

Citations: MR 16, 999f = M05-19.

**M05-29** **(28# 2099)**

**Gould, H. W.**

**A general Turán expression for the zeta function.**

*Canad. Math. Bull.* **6** (1963), 359–366.

The general Turán functional operator $T$ is defined by

$$T(f) = f(x+a)f(x+b) - f(x)f(x+a+b).$$

The principal results of this paper are that if $\zeta(x)$ is the Riemann zeta function, then, for $x>1$, $x+a>1$, $x+b>1$, and $x+a+b>1$,

$$(1)\quad T(\zeta) = -\sum_{n=1}^{\infty} \frac{1}{n^{x+a+b}} \sum_{\substack{d|n \\ d<\sqrt{n}}} \left[\left(\frac{n}{d}\right)^b - d^b\right]\left[\left(\frac{n}{d}\right)^a - d^a\right],$$

$$(2)\quad T(1/\zeta) = -\sum_{n=1}^{\infty} \frac{1}{n^{x+a+b}} \sum_{\substack{d|n \\ d<n}} \mu(d)\mu\left(\frac{n}{d}\right)\left[\left(\frac{n}{d}\right)^a - d^a\right]\left[\left(\frac{n}{d}\right)^b - d^b\right],$$

where $\mu$ is the Möbius function.

*A. E. Danese* (Buffalo, N.Y.)

**M05-30** **(28# 5046)**

**Verma, D. P.**

**Laurent's expansion of Riemann's zeta-function.**

*Indian J. Math.* **5** (1963), 13–16.

If

$$A_{k,n} = \frac{(\log n)^{k+1}}{k+1} - \sum_{r=1}^{n} \frac{(\log r)^k}{r} \quad (k = 0, 1, 2, \cdots; n = 1, 2, \cdots),$$

then $\lim A_{k,n} = A_k$ $(n \to \infty)$ exists, and

$$\zeta(s) = \frac{1}{s-1} - \sum_{0}^{\infty} (-1)^k A_k (s-1)^k,$$

where the series is shown to converge for $|s-1|<1$. This expansion of $\zeta(s)$, however, holds on the whole finite plane: the author overlooks the basic fact that $\zeta(s) - 1/(s-1)$ is an entire function of $s$ and, therefore, of $s-1$ also.

Again a method of numerical calculation of the $A_k$ is indicated.

*H. Kober* (Birmingham)

**M05-31** **(29# 2232)**

**Mitrović, Dragiša**

**The signs of some constants associated with the Riemann zeta-function.**

*Michigan Math. J.* **9** (1962), 395–397.

Briggs and Chowla have proved the following theorem. If $\zeta(s) = (s-1)^{-1} + \sum_{n=0}^{\infty} a_n(s-1)^n$, then $a_n = (-1)^n \gamma_n / n!$, where

$$\gamma_n = \lim_{N\to\infty} \left[\sum_{k=1}^{N} \frac{\log^n k}{k} - \frac{\log^{n+1} N}{n+1}\right]$$

[Amer. Math. Monthly **62** (1955), 323–325; MR **16**, 999]. {Remark of the reviewer: This result was discovered by Stieltjes (1885) and it has been discussed thoroughly by Stieltjes and Hermite [cf. *Correspondance d'Hermite et de Stieltjes*, Tome I, pp. 153, 155, 158, lettre 75, Gauthier-Villars, Paris, 1905]. In *Correspondance*, II, p. 451, it is stated by Gram that this result has been rediscovered by Jensen.} Briggs has established that infinitely many $\gamma_n$ are positive and infinitely many are negative [Michigan Math. J. **3** (1955/56), 117–121; MR **17**, 955].

This result has been completed by the author in the present paper as follows: Each of the inequalities $a_{2n}>0$, $a_{2n}<0$, $a_{2n-1}<0$, $a_{2n-1}>0$ holds for infinitely many $n$; each of the inequalities $\gamma_{2n}<0$, $\gamma_{2n}>0$, $\gamma_{2n-1}<0$, $\gamma_{2n-1}>0$ holds for infinitely many $n$.

The method of the proofs rests on the supposition that the cardinal numbers of the sets of the first category, as well as those of the last category $<\aleph_0$, will lead to a contradiction.

*S. C. van Veen* (Delft)

Citations: MR 16, 999f = M05-19; MR 17, 955c = M05-22.

**M05-32** **(30# 74)**

**Ayoub, Raymond**

**On *L*-series with real characters.**

*Illinois J. Math.* **8** (1964), 550–555.

Let $d$ be the discriminant of an imaginary quadratic field. Let $\chi_d = \chi_d(n) = (d/n)$ be the Kronecker symbol and suppose that

$$L(s, \chi_d) = \sum_{n=1}^{\infty} \frac{\chi_d(n)}{n^s}.$$

The author proves the following interesting theorem. If $d$ is a fundamental discriminant and $\chi_d(n)$ the associated Kronecker symbol, then for $\frac{1}{2}<s\leq 1$, we have

$$\sum_{0<-d\leq N} L(s, \chi_d) = N\frac{\zeta(2s)}{\zeta(2)} \prod_p \left\{1 - \frac{1}{(p+1)p^{2s}}\right\} + O\left(\frac{N^{2(2-s)/3}\log N}{2s-1}\right),$$

where the summation is over fundamental discriminants and the constant implied by $O$ is absolute. The proof of the theorem "is based on a lemma which in its essential features is due to C. L. Siegel", who investigated the average measure of quadratic forms with given determinant and signature [Ann. of Math. (2) **45** (1944), 667–685; MR **7**, 51].

*S. Chowla* (University Park, Pa.)

Citations: MR 7, 51a = E12-20.

**M05-33** **(30# 3565)**

**Davies, D.**

**An approximate functional equation for Dirichlet *L*-functions.**

*Proc. Roy. Soc. Ser. A* **284** (1965), 224–236.

In 1951 Titchmarsh [*The theory of the Riemann zeta-function*, Clarendon Press, Oxford, 1951; MR **13**, 741] gave a development of the remainder of the Riemann-Siegel formula for $\zeta(s)$. This was modified in 1956 by the reviewer so as to provide a practical tool for computing $\zeta(\sigma+it)$ for very large values of $t$ [see Acta Math. **95** (1956), 291–298; MR **19**, 121; Mathematika **3** (1956), 102–108; MR **19**, 121; Erratum, MR **19**, p. 1431; Haselgrove and Miller, *Tables of the Riemann zeta function*, Cambridge Univ. Press, New York, 1960; MR **22** #8679].

In the present paper the author makes corresponding progress for the Dirichlet $L$-function $L(s) = L(s, \chi) = \sum \chi(n)n^{-s}$, where $\chi(n)$ is a character modulo $k$, and gives appropriate numerical coefficients for $k=3$ and 4. The formula calls for a combination of the first $(kt/2\pi)^{1/2}$ terms of the series for $L(s)$ and $L(1-s)$, and there is an expansion of the remainder too elaborate to quote here. This results in an effective machine program some 35 times faster than the classical Euler-Maclaurin formula for $L(s)$. A table of zeros for $k=3$, 4 up to $t=2500$ has been placed in the Royal Society Unpublished Mathematical Tables Depository (no. 83).

*D. H. Lehmer* (Berkeley, Calif.)

Citations: MR 13, 741c = M02-2; MR 19, 121a = M25-44; MR 19, 121b = M25-44; MR 22# 8679 = M15-23.

## M05-34 (30# 4735)

**Brödel, Walter**

**Entwicklungen der Riemannschen ζ-Funktion nach Dirichletschen Polynomen.**

*Jber. Deutsch. Math.-Verein.* **67** (1964/65), *Abt.* 1, 49–57.

Let $m$ be any non-negative integer, and let $g_m(s)$ be the "Dirichlet polynomial"

$$g_m(s) = \sum_{k=0}^{m} (-1)^k \binom{m}{k} (k+1)^{-s} \qquad (s = \sigma + it),$$

i.e., let its Dirichlet series have a finite number of terms only, while $g_{-m}(s) = \sum_{k=0}^{\infty} \binom{m+k-1}{m-1}(k+1)^{-s}$. Then

$$g_0(s) \equiv 1, \quad g_1(s) = 1-2^{-s}, \quad g_2(s) = 1-2\cdot 2^{-s}+3^{-s}, \cdots,$$
$$g_{-1}(s) = \zeta(s), \quad g_{-2}(s) = \zeta(s-1),$$
$$g_{-m}(s) = \frac{1}{(m-1)!}\sum_{\mu=0}^{m-2} \zeta(s+1+\mu-m)\sigma_\mu \qquad (m \geqq 2),$$

where $\sigma_\mu$ is the $\mu$th elementary symmetric function of $1, 2, \cdots, m-2$, $\sigma_0 = 1$. Again, the polynomials $f_n(s)$, of degree $n$, are defined by $f_0(s) \equiv 1$, $f_n(0) = 0$ for $n \geqq 1$, $f_n(1) = (n+1)^{-1}$, $f_n(s+1) = \sum_{k=0}^{n} f_{n-k}(s)/(k+1)$. With the aid of contour integrals, the author obtains basic properties of the $f_n$'s, and, incidentally, the formula $\Gamma(s) = \sum_0^\infty f_n(s-1)/(n+s)$ for the gamma-function; then he deduces the following representations of $\zeta(s)$:

$$\zeta(s) = \frac{1}{(s-1)\Gamma(s)} - \sum_{k=1}^{\infty} f_k(1-s) g_{k-1}(s)$$
$$= \frac{1}{(s-1)(s-2)\cdots(s-n)} \sum_{k=0}^{\infty} f_k(n) g_{k+n-1}(s-n)$$
$$= \frac{g_{n-1}(s-n)}{(s-1)(s-2)\cdots(s-n)} - \sum_{k=1}^{\infty} f_k(-n) g_{k-1}(s).$$

For $n=1$, the last two representations reduce to the forms

$$\zeta(s) = \frac{1}{s-1}\sum_0^\infty \frac{g_k(s-1)}{k+1}, \quad \zeta(s) = \frac{1}{s-1} - \sum_1^\infty f_k(-1) g_{k-1}(s).$$

*H. Kober* (Birmingham)

## M05-35 (30# 5460)

**Shanks, Daniel**

**Polylogarithms, Dirichlet series, and certain constants.**

*Math. Comp.* **18** (1964), 322–324.

In this paper certain Dirichlet series

$$L_a(s) = \sum_{\substack{n \text{ odd} \\ n>0}}^{\infty} \left(\frac{-a}{n}\right) n^{-s},$$

where $(-a/n)$ is the Jacobi symbol, are expressed in terms of appropriate polylogarithms

$$R_s(\alpha) + iI_s(\alpha) = F_s(e^{i\pi\alpha/2}),$$

where

$$F_s(z) = \sum_{m=1}^{\infty} z^m m^{-s}.$$

The results extend those of the author and J. W. Wrench, Jr. [Math. Comp. **17** (1963), 136–154; MR **28** #3012].

The particular cases considered are for $a = \pm 5, \pm 10$ ($10\alpha$ is then always an integer) and published tables of polylogarithms are used to give $L_a(s)$ for $s = 1(1)10$, to 10 decimals.

The results, with further calculations for $a = \pm 7$ (not given) are combined with earlier results [the author, ibid. **14** (1960), 320–332; MR **22** #10960; ibid. **17** (1963), 188–193; MR **28** #3013] to yield an 8-decimal table for the Hardy-Littlewood constants $h_n$, $n = -10(1)10$.

*J. C. P. Miller* (Cambridge, England)

Citations: MR 22# 10960 = N32-25; MR 28# 3012 = M10-20; MR 28# 3013 = N32-34.

## M05-36 (31# 134)

**Verma, D. P.**

**A note on the Riemann's zeta function.**

*Math. Student* **31** (1963), 89–94 (1964).

In this note the author obtains a "continuation" of the Riemann zeta function $\zeta(s)$ for real $s>0$. The function

$$\varphi(n, s) = \sum_{r=1}^{n} \frac{1}{r^s} - \frac{n^{1-s}}{1-s}, \qquad s \neq 0,$$

is a monotone decreasing function for $s>0$. Hence, $\lim \varphi(n, s) = \varphi(s)$ exists for $s>0$. But $\varphi(s) = \zeta(s)$ for $s>1$. If $\theta(s) = \zeta(s) - 1$, he proves that

$$\frac{1}{s-1} = \sum_{r=0}^{\infty} \frac{s(s+1)\cdots(s+r-1)}{(r+1)!}\theta(s+r),$$

and derives some consequences.

*R. Ayoub* (University Park, Pa.)

## M05-37 (31# 2219)

**Siegel, Carl Ludwig**

**Beweis einer Formel für die Riemannsche Zetafunktion.**

*Math. Scand.* **14** (1964), 193–196.

The author proves the validity in the entire complex plane of a series expansion proposed by Viggo Brun for $(s-1)\zeta(s)$. The terms involve Bernoulli numbers and the values $\zeta(s+k)$.

*S. Knapowski* (Gainesville, Fla.)

## M05-38 (32# 5609)

**Lavrik, A. F.**

**The abbreviated functional equation for the $L$-function of Dirichlet.** **(Russian. Uzbek summary)**

*Izv. Akad. Nauk UzSSR Ser. Fiz.-Mat. Nauk* **9** (1965), *no.* 4, 17–22.

Let $\chi$ be a primitive character mod $D$, $D>1$, $a = \frac{1}{2}(1-\chi(-1))$. Dirichlet's $L$-functions satisfy the functional equation $\xi(\omega, \chi) = \varepsilon(\chi)\xi(1-\omega, \bar\chi)$ with $\xi(\omega, \chi) = (D/\pi)^{\omega/2}\Gamma(\frac{1}{2}(\omega+a))L(\omega, \chi)$. Denote the incomplete $\Gamma$-function by $\Gamma(\alpha, u) = \int_u^\infty e^{-z}z^{\alpha-1}\,dz$. The author proves (for $0 < \operatorname{Re} s < 1$, $0 \leqq \varphi \leqq \frac{1}{2}$)

$$\Gamma(\tfrac{1}{2}(s+a))L(s,\chi) = \sum_1^\infty \chi(n)n^{-s}\Gamma\left(\tfrac{1}{2}(s+a), \frac{e^{i\varphi}\pi n^2}{D}\right)$$
$$+\varepsilon(\chi)\left(\frac{D}{\pi}\right)^{1/2-s}\sum_1^\infty \bar\chi(n)n^{s-1}\Gamma\left(\tfrac{1}{2}(1-s+a), \frac{e^{-i\varphi}\pi n^2}{D}\right).$$

From this theorem an approximate functional equation for $L$-functions is deducible [compare Suetuna, Japan. J. Math. **9** (1932), 111–116; Čudakov, Ann. of Math. (2) **48** (1947), 515–545; MR **9**, 11; Chandrasekharan and Narasimhan, Math. Ann. **152** (1963), 30–64; MR **27** #3605].

*W. Schwarz* (Freiburg)

Citations: MR 9, 11d = P32-10; MR 27# 3605 = M40-33.

Referred to in M05-48, M40-39.

## M05-39 (33# 5577)

**Ayoub, Raymond**

**A note on the Riemann zeta function.**

*Proc. Amer. Math. Soc.* **17** (1966), 1215-1217.

The author proves for all $s = \sigma + it$, $\sigma > -2M$, $s$ not an integer, the formula

$$\pi\cdot\zeta(s)/s\sin\pi s = \sum_{-2M\leq k<\infty;\, k\neq 0,1}(-1)^k\zeta(k)/k(s-k) + (1-\gamma)(s-1)^{-1}-(s-1)^{-2} + \zeta(0)\cdot s^{-2}+\zeta'(0)s^{-1}+g_M(s),$$

where

$$g_M(s) = \int_1^\infty H_M(z)z^{-s-1}\,dz$$

and $|H_M(z)|\leq C(M)\cdot|z|^{-2M-1}$ ($\zeta(0)=-\frac{1}{2}$, $\zeta'(0)=-\frac{1}{2}\log 2\pi$, $\zeta(-2k)=0$ for $k=1, 2, \cdots$). {The formulation of the theorem contains several misprints.}

Obviously such formulae are suggested by the decomposition of the meromorphic function $\pi\zeta(s)/s\sin\pi s$ into partial fractions, and the same formula (with $g_M(s)$ in different form) could be more easily derived from the integral $(1/2\pi i)\int_{a-i\infty}^{a+i\infty}(\pi\zeta(z)/((z\sin\pi z)(z-s)))\,dz$, $a=-2M-\frac{1}{2}$, Re $s>a$, $s$ not an integer, by the theorem of residues.

*W. Schwarz* (Freiburg)

## M05-40 (34# 1285)

**Turán, P.**

**On a characterization of Dirichlet's $L$-functions.**

*Ann. Univ. Sci. Budapest. Eötvös Sect. Math.* **8** (1965), 65–69.

Since Hamburger's first solution of the problem, all results concerning a characterization of the Riemann $\zeta$-function employed a more or less general form of Riemann's functional equation. In 1959 the author [Acta Math. Acad. Sci. Hungar. **10** (1959), 277–298; MR **22** #6774] found a surprisingly simple characterization of $\zeta(s)$ depending on a monotonicity of the coefficients in its Dirichlet series and an Euler-product representation. In the present paper the author generalizes his theorem to Dirichlet's $L$-series. He proves that if in a certain half-plane a function $f(s)$ can be represented both by a convergent Dirichlet series $\sum_1^\infty a_n\chi(n)n^{-s}$ with monotonic coefficients $a_n>0$ and by an absolutely convergent Euler-product $\prod_p(1-\varepsilon_p\chi(p)/p^s)^{-1}$ with numbers $\varepsilon_p>0$, then, for some real $c$, $f(s)=L(s+c, \chi)$. The proof is based on the result that $\psi(n)=c\log n$ is the only monotonic solution of $\psi(mn)=\psi(m)+\psi(n)$. For this, a very short proof due to Vera Sós is given.

*H.-E. Richert* (Marburg)

Citations: MR 22# 6774 = M30-30.

## M05-41 (34# 4223)

**Lavrik, A. F.**

**The functional equation for Dirichlet $L$-functions and the problem of divisors in arithmetic progressions. (Russian)**

*Izv. Akad. Nauk SSSR Ser. Mat.* **30** (1966), 433–448.

The author proves (Theorem 1): Let $\chi$ be a primitive character mod $d$, $d>1$; let $z\neq 0$, $|\arg z|\leq\pi/2$. Then

$$\Gamma\left(\frac{s+a}{2}\right)L(s,\chi) = \sum_{n=1}^\infty\frac{\chi(n)}{n^s}\Gamma\left(\frac{s+a}{2},\frac{\pi n^2 z}{d}\right) + \varepsilon(\chi)\left(\frac{d}{\pi}\right)^{1/2-s}\sum_{n=1}^\infty\frac{\bar\chi(n)}{n^{1-s}}\Gamma\left(\frac{1-s+a}{2},\frac{\pi n^2}{dz}\right),$$

where $s$ is a complex variable, $a=\frac{1}{2}[1-\chi(-1)]$, $\varepsilon(\chi)$ is defined by the well-known functional equation for $L(s,\chi)$, and $\Gamma(\alpha, u)=\int_u^{\infty\arg u}e^{-\xi}\xi^{\alpha-1}\,d\xi$.

From this he deduces four theorems, of which we mention only the third for reasons of space. Theorem 4: Define $\tau_k(n)$ as the coefficient of $n^{-s}$ in $\zeta^k(s)$, where $\zeta(s)$ is Riemann's zeta-function. Let the integer $k$ be $\geq 4$ and $4\leq 2m\leq k$; let $l$ and $d$ be mutually prime with $0<l\leq d$. Then we have

$$\sum_{n\leq x;\, n\equiv l \bmod d}\tau_k(n) = \frac{x}{\varphi(d)}\sum_{\delta|d^k}\sum_{\delta=\delta_1\cdots\delta_k}\frac{\mu(\delta_1)\cdots\mu(\delta_k)}{\delta}P_k\left(\ln\frac{x}{\delta}\right)+R,$$

where $\varphi$ is Euler's function, $\mu$ is the Möbius function, $P_k$ is a polynomial of degree $k-1$ defined by

$$P_k\left(\ln\frac{x}{\delta}\right) = \frac{\delta}{(k-1)!x}\lim_{s\to 1}\frac{\partial^{k-1}}{\partial s^{k-1}}\left\{\frac{\zeta^k(s)(s-1)^k}{s}\left(\frac{x}{\delta}\right)^s\right\}$$

and $R\ll(1/\varphi(d))x^{1-1/2^\nu m}d^{(3k+2m)/(2^\nu+3m)+\varepsilon_0}\ln^b x$. Here $\nu$ is an integer $\geq(2k-3m)/m$; $\varepsilon_0=0$ if $2m=k$, $\varepsilon_0$ is arbitrarily small if $2m<k$; $b$ is a positive constant depending only on $k$.

The results are deep, using, amongst other tools, the recent results of D. A. Burgess [Proc. London Math. Soc. **13** (1963), 524–536; MR **26** #6133].

*S. Chowla* (University Park, Pa.)

Citations: MR 26# 6133 = L25-19.

Referred to in M05-48, M40-41, R42-48.

## M05-42 (34# 4464)

**Lavrik, A. F.**

**Functional equations of the Dirichlet functions. (Russian)**

*Dokl. Akad. Nauk SSSR* **171** (1966), 278–280.

As first explicitly stated by R. O. Kuzmin [Izv. Akad. Nauk Otdel. Mat. Estestven. Nauk **1934**, 1471–1492], the functional equations for Dirichlet's $L$-functions lead to identities between certain associated series. The author announces several corresponding results for a wider class of Dirichlet series satisfying a more general functional equation.

{This article has appeared in English translation [Soviet Math. Dokl. **7** (1966), 1471–1473].}

*H.-E. Richert* (Syracuse, N.Y.)

Referred to in M05-48, R42-38.

## M05-43 (34# 7479)

**Mustafy, Ashoke Kumar**

**A new representation of Riemann's zeta function and some of its consequences.**

*Norske Vid. Selsk. Forh.* (*Trondheim*) **39** (1966), 96–100 (1967).

The author's new representation of Riemann's zeta function $\zeta(s)$ resembles somewhat one due to Siegel [cf. E. C. Titchmarsh, *The theory of the Riemann zeta-function*, p. 27, Clarendon Press, Oxford, 1951; MR **13**, 741]. His result is given by

$$\Gamma(s)2^{-s}(1-2^s)(1-2^{1-s})\zeta(s) = -\int_0^\infty[(\tfrac{1}{2}\pi)^{s-1}\Gamma(s)\sin(\tfrac{1}{2}\pi s)x^{-s}+x^{s-1}](\sin^2(x^2/2\pi)/\sinh x)\,dx,$$

and is valid in the region $-3<\text{Re } s<4$. The proof skillfully combines several well-known definite integral formulas. With his representation the author proposes to investigate many of the properties of zeros of the zeta function in a direct manner. In the present paper he deduces a formula for calculating the distribution of zeros whose real part is equal to $\sigma=\frac{1}{2}$. In particular, he obtains a condition on $\eta$ so that $s=\frac{1}{2}+i\eta$ can be a zero of $\zeta(s)$.

*A. L. Whiteman* (Los Angeles, Calif.)

Citations: MR 13, 741c = M02-2.

**M05-44** **(35# 5401 )**

**Ayoub, Raymond**

**On $L$-functions.**

*Monatsh. Math.* **71** (1967), 193–202.

Let $\chi$ be a primitive character mod $k$, $k \geqq 3$, and let $g(z, \chi) = \sum_{n=1}^{\infty} \chi(n) z^n$, where $|z| < 1$. From the periodicity of $\chi$ it follows that (1) $g(z, \chi) = (\sum_{r=0}^{k-1} \chi(r) z^r)(1 - z^k)^{-1}$. Partial-fraction decomposition leads to the formula (2) $g(z, \chi) = -(G(\chi)/k) \sum_{r=1}^{k-1} \bar{\chi}(r) \rho^r/(z - \rho^r)$, where $\rho = e^{2\pi i/k}$ and $G(\chi) = \sum_{n=0}^{k-1} \chi(n) \rho^n$ is a Gauss sum.

The author deduces a number of consequences from these two representations for $g(z, \chi)$. For example, some formulas for Dirichlet $L$-series are obtained by taking $z = e^{-t}$ and equating coefficients in the two power series in $t$ resulting from (1) and (2). The two formulas also show that $g(e^{-t}, \chi)$ is a self-reciprocal Fourier transform. This leads to an alternate proof of the functional equation for Dirichlet $L$-series. *T. M. Apostol* (Pasadena, Calif.)

**M05-45** **(36# 6359 )**

**Burlačenko, V. P.**

**The analytic continuation of the Riemann zeta-function by means of double series. (Ukrainian. Russian and English summaries)**

*Dopovīdī Akad. Nauk Ukraïn. RSR Ser. A* **1967**, 1005–1008.

The author derives the formula

$$(1-2^{1-s})\zeta(s) = 1 - \tfrac{1}{2}s - 2^{-1-s} + \tfrac{1}{2}s\zeta(s+1)(1-2^{-s}) + \tfrac{1}{2}\sum_{m,k=1}^{\infty}(-1)^{m+k}\frac{s(s+1)\cdots(s+k)}{(k+1)!(m+1)^{s+k+1}}$$

valid for $\operatorname{Re} s > -1$. *J. G. Krzyż* (Lublin)

**M05-46** **(37# 388 )**

**Burlačenko, V. P.**

**A method for the analytic continuation of the Riemann zeta-function. (Russian)**

*Ukrain. Mat. Ž.* **20** (1968), 238–243.

E. C. Titchmarsh [*The theory of the Riemann zeta-function*, Clarendon, Oxford, 1951; MR **13**, 741; Russian translation, Izdat. Inostran. Lit., Moscow, 1953] established several methods in order to obtain an analytic continuation of the $\zeta$-function of Riemann on the half-plane $\operatorname{Re} s < 1$ (where $s = \sigma + it$). The author gives a new method using double series, and finds an explicit expression for $\zeta(s)$ in the whole complex plane except $s = 1$. *F. Caraman* (Iași)

Citations: MR 13, 741c = M02-2.

**M05-47** **(37# 2704 )**

**Anfert'eva, E. A.**

**A generalized Riemann equation in the theory of Dirichlet series. (Russian)**

*Dokl. Akad. Nauk SSSR* **176** (1967), 1215–1216.

The author's theorem (stated without proof in this note) is too long to quote here. As an example of this theorem, the author notes a representation of the function $L(s, \chi)/L_1(s, \chi_1)$, where numerator and denominator are Dirichlet $L$-series, by an infinite series containing in each term an incomplete $\Gamma$-function (i.e., an integral $\int_0^w e^{-x} x^{\alpha-1}\, dx$), and two other infinite series.

{This article has appeared in English translation [Soviet Math. Dokl. **8** (1967), 1277–1279].}

*S. Chowla* (University Park, Pa.)

**M05-48** **(37# 2705 )**

**Lavrik, A. F.**

**Functional and approximate functional equations for Dirichlet functions. (Russian)**

*Mat. Zametki* **3** (1968), 613–622.

A résumé of the author's doctoral dissertation [Steklov Mathematical Institute, Moscow, 1967]. The contents of the dissertation were published in nine articles by the author [Dokl. Akad. Nauk SSSR **154** (1964), 34–37; MR **28** #68; Izv. Akad. Nauk UzSSR Ser. Fiz.-Mat. Nauk **9** (1965), no. 4, 17–22; MR **32** #5609; Dokl. Akad. Nauk SSSR **164** (1965), 1232–1234; MR **34** #5778; Litovsk. Mat. Sb. **6** (1966), 128–129; Izv. Akad. Nauk SSSR Ser. Mat. **30** (1966), 433–438; MR **34** #4223; Dokl. Akad. Nauk SSSR **171** (1966), 278–280; MR **34** #4464; "The approximate functional equation of Dirichlet $L$-functions", Trudy Moskov. Mat. Obšč. **18** MR **38** #4424; Izv. Akad. Nauk SSSR Ser. Mat. **31** (1967), 431–442; MR **35** #4174; Mat. Zametki **2** (1967), 475–482; MR **36** #2571].

Citations: MR 28# 68 = M15-28; MR 32# 5609 = M05-38; MR 34# 4223 = M05-41; MR 34# 4464 = M05-42; MR 34# 5778 = N40-64; MR 35# 4174 = M40-39; MR 36# 2571 = R42-38; MR 38# 4424 = M05-49.

**M05-49** **(38# 4424 )**

**Lavrik, A. F.**

**The approximate functional equation for Dirichlet $L$-functions. (Russian)**

*Trudy Moskov. Mat. Obšč.* **18** (1968), 91–104.

Der Verfasser beweist für $L$-Reihen mit primitivem $D$-Charakter $\chi$ mod $d$ im Streifen $0 < \sigma < 1$ eine abgekürzte Funktionalgleichung der Gestalt $L(s, \chi) = \sum_{n \leq x} \chi(n) n^{-s} + \varepsilon(\chi)(d/\pi)^{1/2-s} \cdot G(s, \chi) \sum_{n \leq y} \bar{\chi}(n) n^{s-1} + R_{xy}$, wobei $x = \Delta(d \cdot t/2\pi)^{1/2}$, $y = \Delta^{-1}(d \cdot t/2\pi)^{1/2}$ mit beliebigem $\Delta \geqq 1$ ist und $G(s, \chi) = \Gamma(\frac{1}{2}(1-s+a))/\Gamma(\frac{1}{2}(s+a))$ mit $a = \frac{1}{2}(1-\chi(-1))$ gesetzt wurde. Das Restglied $R_{xy}$ wird bis auf ein Fehlerglied $O((d \cdot t)^{-M})$ ($M > 0$, beliebig) durch zwei Summen der Gestalt $\sum_{n \leq y \log^{\gamma} dt} \chi(n) F(\frac{1}{2}(s+a), n^2 z/d)$ approximiert; hierbei hängt $z$ von $\Delta$, $t$ und $\operatorname{Im} s$ ab; $\gamma > \frac{1}{2}$ ist beliebig. Für die Funktion $F$ wird eine asymptotische Formel und eine in allen Argumenten gleichmäßige Abschätzung hergeleitet. In drei Korollaren werden verschiedene spezielle Abschätzungen des Restgliedes $R_{xy}$ gegeben, zum Beispiel $R = O(x^{-\sigma} d^{1/2} \log 2t)$ für $\Delta = 1$.

*W. Schwarz* (Freiburg)

Referred to in M05-48.

**M05-50** **(39# 4367 )**

**Zmorovič, V. A.; Burlačenko, V. P.**

**The connection of integral representations of the Riemann zeta-function with double series, and integral representations of this function in any part of the complex plane. (Ukrainian. Russian and English summaries)**

*Dopovīdī Akad. Nauk Ukraïn. RSR Ser. A* **1968**, 989–992.

Authors' summary: "A connection is established between integral representations of the Riemann $\zeta$-function $\zeta(s)$ in $\operatorname{Re} s > 0$ and $\operatorname{Re} s > -1$, and double series. An integral representation of $\zeta(s)$ in any part of the complex plane is deduced." *K. W. Lucas* (Aberystwyth)

**M05-51** **(39# 5489)**

**Burlačenko, V. P.**
**The analytic representation of the Riemann zeta-function in any part of the complex plane. (Ukrainian. Russian and English summaries)**
*Dopovīdī Akad. Nauk Ukraïn. RSR Ser. A* **1968**, 963–965.

Let $\zeta(s)$ denote the Riemann zeta function, defined in $\operatorname{Re} s > 1$ by the Dirichlet series $\zeta(s) = \sum_{m=1}^{\infty} 1/m^s$.

The author quotes (see the bibliography of the article under review) a double series representation of $\zeta(s)$ in $\operatorname{Re} s > 0$, uses it to continue $\zeta(s)$ throughout $\operatorname{Re} s > -1$, and by repeating the process, obtains explicit representations in $\operatorname{Re} s > -(l+1)$, $l = 1, 2, \cdots$.

*K. W. Lucas* (Aberystwyth)

**M05-52** **(41# 3412)**

**Apostol, Tom M.**
**Dirichlet $L$-functions and character power sums.**
*J. Number Theory* **2** (1970), 223–234.

For any character $\chi$ modulo $k$, let $G(\chi) = \sum_{h=1}^{k-1} \chi(h) e^{2\pi i h/k}$. The author obtains the following representation theorem for the $L$-functions modulo $k$. Theorem: If $\chi$ is a primitive character modulo $k$, then for complex $s$, $G(\bar{\chi})L(s, \chi) = \sum_{h=1}^{k-1} \bar{\chi}(h) F(h/k, s)$, where $F(x, s)$ is defined for real $x$ and $R(s) > 1$ by the series $\sum_{n=1}^{\infty} e^{2n\pi i x}/n^s$. Also, a new proof of the functional equation for the $L$-functions is given.

*K. Thanigasalam* (University Park, Pa.)

**M05-53** **(44# 164)**

**Spira, Robert**
**The integral representation for the Riemann $\Xi$-function.**
*J. Number Theory* **3** (1971), 498–501.

Riemann's $\Xi$ function has a representation of the form $\Xi(t) = 2\int_0^{\infty} \Phi(u) \cos ut\, du$. The function $\Phi(u)$ is shown to have a negative derivative for $u > 0$, and an application is made to show that the only real zero of the function $\Psi(t) = 2\int_0^{\infty} \Phi(u) \sin ut\, du$ is $t = 0$.

{Author's note: An earlier proof of the theorem was given by A. Wintner [J. London Math. Soc. **10** (1935), 82–83].}

*T. M. Apostol* (Pasadena, Calif.)

**M05-54** **(44# 2717)**

**Apostol, Tom M.**
**Dirichlet $L$-functions and primitive characters.**
*Proc. Amer. Math. Soc.* **31** (1972), 384–386.

Author's summary: "It is well known that a Dirichlet $L$-function $L(s, \chi)$ has a functional equation if the character $\chi$ is primitive. This note proves the converse result. That is, if $L(s, \chi)$ satisfies the usual functional equation then $\chi$ is primitive."

*K. Thanigasalam* (Monaca, Pa.)

# M10 $\zeta(s)$ AND $L(s, \chi)$ FOR $\sigma > 1$

See also reviews E24-34, M05-35, M15-33, M40-36, M40-44, R42-2.

**M10-1** **(1, 293e)**

**Brun, Viggo. Deux transformations élémentaires de la fonction zeta de Riemann.** Revista Ci., Lima **41**, 517–525 (1939).

The author establishes the formula

$$\zeta(s) = 1 + \frac{1}{s-1} - \beta(s), \qquad s \text{ real, } s > 1,$$

where $\zeta(s)$ is the Riemann zeta-function and

$$\beta(s) = \sum_{m=1}^{\infty} \frac{1}{2^m} \sum_{n=1}^{\infty} (-1)^{n-1} \left( \frac{2^m}{2^m+n} \right)^s.$$

The function $\beta(s)$ may be written in other forms, one of these being a double series which converges also for $s = -1, -2, \cdots$. The proof uses identities of which the following is an example:

$$\sum_{n=1}^{2r} (-1)^{n-1} n^{-s} = \sum_{n=1}^{2r} n^{-s} - 2^{1-s} \sum_{n=1}^{2^{r-1}} n^{-s}.$$

*R. D. James* (Saskatoon, Sask.).

**M10-2** **(2, 249d)**

**Selberg, Sigmund. Bemerkung zu einer Arbeit von Viggo Brun über die Riemannsche Zetafunktion.** Norske Vid. Selsk. Forh. **13**, 17–19 (1940).

The author proves the formula

$$\zeta(s) = \frac{1}{s-1} + \sum_{m=2}^{\infty} (-1)^m \frac{2^{s-1} + 4^{s-1} + \cdots + 2^{k(s-1)}}{m^s},$$

where $2^k \leqq m < 2^{k+1}$, which has been announced by Viggo Brun [9. Congr. Math. Scand., Helsingfors, 1938, pp. 101–104].

*H. S. Zuckerman* (Seattle, Wash.).

**M10-3** **(7, 48h)**

**Haviland, E. K. On the asymptotic behavior of the Riemann $\xi$-function.** Amer. J. Math. **67**, 411–416 (1945).

If $\zeta(s)$ is the Riemann zeta-function,

$$\xi(s) = \tfrac{1}{2} s(s-1) \pi^{-\frac{1}{2}s} \Gamma(\tfrac{1}{2}s) \zeta(s),$$

and $M(r)$ is the maximum of $|\xi(\frac{1}{2} + is)|$ on the circle $|s| = r$, then

$$M(r) \sim (\tfrac{1}{2}\pi)^{\frac{1}{4}} (2\pi e)^{-\frac{1}{2}r} r^{\frac{1}{2}r + 7/4}$$

as $r \to \infty$. This is the first term of an infinite asymptotic series.

*E. C. Titchmarsh* (Oxford).

**M10-4** **(9, 234d)**

**Estermann, T. Elementary evaluation of $\zeta(2k)$.** J. London Math. Soc. **22**, 10–13 (1947).

The author gives an evaluation of $\zeta(2k)$ $(k = 1, 2, 3, \cdots)$ independent of the theory of (real or complex) functions. The result $\zeta(2) = \frac{1}{6}\pi^2$ is derived from $1 - \frac{1}{3} + \frac{1}{5} - \cdots = \frac{1}{4}\pi$ without even using double series. Using only absolutely convergent double series, a reduction formula expressing $\zeta(2k+2)$ in terms of $\zeta(2), \zeta(4), \cdots, \zeta(2k)$ is proved. In an addendum it is pointed out that an elementary proof of a similar reduction formula was given by Titchmarsh [Proc. London Math. Soc. (2) **26**, 1–11 (1926)].

*N. G. de Bruijn* (Delft).

Referred to in M10-9.

**M10-5** **(10, 104f)**

**Kössler, M. Asymptotic expansions for the functions $\zeta(s)$ and $\zeta(a, s)$.** Rozpravy II. Třídy České Akad. **51**, no. 32, 10 pp. (1941). (Czech)

The author gives asymptotic expansions for

$$\zeta(2v+1) = \sum_{n=1}^{\infty} n^{-2v-1}, \quad S(2v) = \sum_{n=0}^{\infty} (-1)^n (2n+1)^{-2v}$$

($v$ a positive integer). They are based on asymptotic expansions for $\zeta(s)$ and $\zeta(a, s)$. For example, let $N > 0$, $K \geqq 0$ be integers, $\Re(s) < 2K+3$. Then

$$2(2\pi)^{-s}(1-2^s)\Gamma(s) \cos \tfrac{1}{2}\pi s\, \zeta(s) = \sum_{k=1}^{N} (-1)^{k+1} k^{s-1} + \sum_{k=0}^{K} (-1)^{k+N} E_k 2^{-2k-1} \binom{s-1}{2k} (N + \tfrac{1}{2})^{s-1-2k} + R(N, K),$$

where

$$2^{2K+3}(2K+2)!\Gamma(1-s)R(N, K) = (-1)^{N+K+1}E_{K+1}\int_0^\infty e^{-(N+\frac{1}{2})z}z^{2K+2-s}\theta(z)dz$$

($0<\theta(z)\leqq 1$; $E_i$, Euler's numbers). For $s=2v+1$ the left side is zero and it is necessary to calculate the derivative in order to obtain $\zeta(2v+1)$. Some of the asymptotic formulae also lead to exact formulae (for $N\to\infty$) which are analogous to Wallis's and Stirling's formulae, e.g.,

$$\frac{1}{4\pi^2}\zeta(3) = \lim_{n\to\infty} \log \frac{(1, 2)(2, 2)\cdots(n-1, 2)}{\exp\{\frac{1}{6}n(n-1)(2n-1)\log n+\frac{1}{12}n\}},$$

where $(k, s)=k^{k^s}$, $\exp x = e^x$. *V. Jarník* (Prague).

## M10-6 (10, 683d)

**Kuo, Huan-Ting. A recurrence formula for $\zeta(2n)$.** Bull. Amer. Math. Soc. **55**, 573–574 (1949).

The author derives a recurrence relation for $\zeta(4n)$ which requires only the values $\zeta(2), \zeta(4), \cdots, \zeta(2n)$, at the expense of being quadratic rather than linear. The idea is to use the identity $(\pi-x)/2=\sum_{k=1}^\infty k^{-1}\sin kx$, integrate $2n-1$ times between 0 and $x$ and then apply Parseval's formula to the resulting equation. *R. Bellman.*

Referred to in M10-19.

## M10-7 (11, 421b)

**Petersson, Hans. Über die Werte der Riemannschen Zetafunktion für positive ungerade Argumente.** Abh. Math. Sem. Univ. Hamburg 16, nos. 3–4, 72–100 (1949).

Denote by $C(q)$ ($q\geqq 2$, a prime) the linear set of all cusp forms (entire modular forms vanishing at all parabolic vertices of the fundamental region) of dimension $-r$ belonging to the group consisting of all modular substitutions $\tau\to(\alpha\tau+\beta)(\gamma\tau+\delta)^{-1}$ with $\gamma\equiv 0 \pmod q$. The author proves that two entire modular forms of dimension $-r$ ($r\geqq 4$, even) which [in the sense of the metric introduced by the author in Math. Ann. **117**, 453–537 (1940); these Rev. **2**, 87] are orthogonal to all forms of $C(q)$ and which possess a scalar product $\omega$ (i.e., if their product is a cusp form) must, except for numerical factors, be identical with the two functions $E_1=\sum_1(m_1\tau+m_2)^{-r}$, $E_2=\sum_2(m_1\tau+m_2)^{-r}$ where $\sum_1$ and $\sum_2$ denote summations over all pairs of rational integers satisfying (1) $m_1\equiv 0 \pmod q$, $(m_2, q)=1$ and (2) $(m_1, q)=1$, respectively. The scalar product $\omega=(E_1, E_2)$ of $E_1$ and $E_2$ is determined from theorem 6 in a previous paper by the author [Comment. Math. Helv. **22**, 168–199 (1949); these Rev. **10**, 445], which gives a relation $\zeta(r-1)=\pi^{r-1}\rho\omega$, where $\zeta$ denotes the Riemann zeta function and $\rho$ is a certain rational number. Thus the set of numbers $\pi^{-k}\zeta(k)$ ($k=3, 5, 7, \cdots$) is completely characterized by certain properties of modular forms. A special case of the relation mentioned represents $7\pi^{-3}\zeta(3)$ as a scalar product $(\vartheta_{00}^8, \vartheta_{01}^4\vartheta_{10}^4)$, where

$$\vartheta_{00}(\tau)=\sum \exp \pi i m^2\tau, \quad \vartheta_{01}(\tau)=\sum(-1)^m \exp \pi i m^2\tau,$$
$$\vartheta_{10}(\tau)=\sum \exp \pi i(m+\tfrac{1}{2})^2\tau$$

(summation over all rational integers $m$).

*H. D. Kloosterman* (Leiden).

Citations: MR 2, 87e = F10-3; MR 10, 445b = F25-5.

## M10-8 (13, 742b)

**Nanjundiah, T. S. Certain summations due to Ramanujan, and their generalisations.** Proc. Indian Acad. Sci., Sect. A. **34**, 215–228 (1951).

The author establishes certain identities which are generalizations of formulae due to Ramanujan, of which the following is typical:

$$\sum_{n=1}^\infty \frac{(-1)^{n-1}}{n^{2q-1}}\left[a^{2q-2}\operatorname{cosech}\frac{n\pi b}{a}+(-1)^q b^{2q-2}\operatorname{cosech}\frac{n\pi a}{b}\right]$$
$$=\frac{2}{\pi ab}\sum_{k=0}^{q}(-1)^k(1-2^{1-2k})\zeta(2k)(1-2^{1-2q+2k})\zeta(2q-2k)a^{2q-2k}b^{2k},$$

where $a>0$, $b>0$, and $q=1, 2, 3, \cdots$, $\zeta$ being the Riemann $\zeta$-function. The proofs make use of the partial fraction expansions of the hyperbolic functions plus elementary manipulations of series. In two places modular identities (ascribed by the author to Ramanujan) are used. These are actually the transformation equations ($\tau\to-1/\tau$) of the modular functions $\eta(\tau)$ and $\eta^2(2\tau)/\eta(\tau)\eta(4\tau)$, where $\eta$ is the Dedekind function. *J. Lehner* (Philadelphia, Pa.).

## M10-9 (14, 248e)

**Day, J. W. R. A theorem on Bernoulli numbers and the zeta function.** J. London Math. Soc. **27**, 502–504 (1952).

Proof of the well-known formula $\zeta(2k)=\frac{1}{2}(2\pi)^{2k}B_k/(2k)!$, depending on a recursion formula given by Estermann [same J. **22**, 10–13 (1947); these Rev. **9**, 234].

*N. G. de Bruijn* (Amsterdam)

Citations: MR 9, 234d = M10-4.

## M10-10 (14, 536j)

**Williams, G. T. A new method of evaluating $\zeta(2n)$.** Amer. Math. Monthly **60**, 19–25 (1953).

The formula

$$\zeta(2)\zeta(2n-2)+\zeta(4)\zeta(2n-4)+\cdots+\zeta(2n-2)\zeta(2) = (n+\tfrac{1}{2})\zeta(2n)$$

is proved by an elementary method. It seems to have some relation to the more complicated formulae obtained by the reviewer [Proc. London Math. Soc. (2) **26**, 1–11 (1926)].

Another result is

$$2\sum_{\nu=1}^\infty \frac{1}{\nu^n}\left(1+\tfrac{1}{2}+\cdots+\frac{1}{\nu-1}\right)=n\zeta(n+1)$$
$$-\{\zeta(2)\zeta(n-1)+\zeta(3)\zeta(n-2)+\cdots+\zeta(n-1)\zeta(2)\}.$$

*E. C. Titchmarsh* (Oxford).

## M10-11 (16, 1014d)

**Briggs, W. E., Chowla, S., Kempner, A. J., and Mientka, W. E. On some infinite series.** Scripta Math. **21**, 28–30 (1955).

The following two formulas are proved:

$$2\zeta(3)=\sum_1^\infty \frac{1}{n^2}\left(1+\tfrac{1}{2}+\cdots+\frac{1}{n}\right),$$

$$\zeta(3)=\sum_1^\infty \frac{1}{n}\left\{\frac{1}{(n+1)^2}+\frac{1}{(n+2)^2}+\cdots\right\}.$$

[These formulas, the second in a slightly different form, had been stated as problems by M. S. Klamkin, Amer. Math. Monthly **59**, 471 (1952).] *L. Carlitz.*

## M10-12 (19, 393a)

**Mitrović, Dragiša. Sur la fonction ζ de Riemann.** C. R. Acad. Sci. Paris **244** (1957), 1602–1604.

A number of theorems on the $k$th derivatives of $\zeta(s)$ in the half-plane $s=\sigma+it$, $\sigma>1$, are stated without proof. For example,

$$|\zeta^{(k)}(s)|<\frac{k!}{(\sigma-1)^{k+1}}, \quad \left|\left(\frac{1}{\zeta(s)}\right)^{(k)}\right|<\frac{k!}{(\sigma-1)^{k+1}}$$

hold for $\sigma>1$, all $t$, and $k=1, 2, \cdots$. Finally, all the odd derivatives of $\zeta(s)-1/(s-1)$ are completely monotone in the interval $1<s<\infty$.

*E. C. Titchmarsh* (Oxford).

Referred to in M10-13.

## M10-13 (19, 839a)

**Mitrović, Dragiša. Sur la fonction $\zeta$ de Riemann.** C. R. Acad. Sci. Paris **245** (1957), 885–886.

In this note bounds for the derivatives of $\zeta(s)$ and $1/\zeta(s)$ in the half-plane $\sigma>1$ are obtained, and results are stated about the signs of the coefficients in the Laurent series for $\zeta(s)$ in powers of $s-1$. These correct in certain respects the results stated in a previous note [same C. R. **244** (1957), 1602–1604; MR **19**, 393]. *E. C. Titchmarsh.*

Citations: MR 19, 393a = M10-12.

## M10-14 (20# 5172)

**Mikolás, Miklós. Sur l'expression fermée des séries**

$$\sum_{k=1}^{\infty} k^{-(2\nu+1)} \quad (\nu=1, 2, \cdots)$$

**et le rapport $\zeta(s, u)/\zeta(s)$.** Mat. Lapok **8** (1957), 100–107. (Hungarian. French and Russian summaries)

The principal result of this paper is the integral relation

$$\int_0^1 [\zeta(1-s, u)-\zeta(1-s)] \cot \pi u \, du = 2(2\pi)^{-s}\Gamma(s) \sin \frac{\pi s}{2} \zeta(s),$$

where $\zeta(s)$ is Riemann's zeta function, $\zeta(s, u)$ is Hurwitz' zeta function, and Re $s>1$. One of the consequences is

$$\int_0^1 \left[\frac{\zeta(s, u)}{\zeta(s)}-1\right] \cot \pi u \, du = \cot \frac{\pi s}{2},$$

valid for Re $s<0$, $s\neq -2, -4, \cdots$.

*A. Erdélyi* (Pasadena, Calif.)

## M10-15 (21# 5612)

**Mitrović, Dragiša. Le théorème $\Omega$ relatif aux dérivées de la fonction $\zeta$ de Riemann.** Glasnik Mat.-Fiz. Astr. Društvo Mat. Fiz. Hrvatske. Ser. II **14** (1959), 13–18. (Serbo-Croatian summary)

It is proved, for example, that if $\sigma>1$, $k=0, 1, 2, \cdots$,

$$|\zeta^{(k)}(\sigma+it)| \geq (1-\varepsilon)\zeta^{(k)}(\sigma)$$

for some arbitrarily large values of $t$. The results seem to be immediate consequences of well-known ideas due to H. Bohr.

*E. C. Titchmarsh* (Oxford)

## M10-16 (22# 29)

**Mitrović, Dragiša. Le théorème $\Omega$ relatif aux dérivées de la fonction $1/\zeta$ de Riemann.** Glasnik Mat.-Fiz. Astr. Društvo Mat. Fiz. Hrvatske. Ser. II **14** (1959), 115–119. (Serbo-Croatian summary)

It was proved by H. Bohr [see Titchmarsh, *The theory of the Riemann zeta-function*, Clarendon, Oxford, 1951; MR **13**, 741; Theorem 8.7] that for every $\sigma>1$ we have

$$\sup_{-\infty<t<\infty} |1/\zeta(\sigma+it)| = \zeta(\sigma)/\zeta(2\sigma).$$

This means that for $N\geq 1$, $\varepsilon>0$, we can choose $t$ such that $||\mu(n)n^{-it}-|\mu(n)|| < \varepsilon$ for $n=1, \cdots, N$. It follows that for the $k$th derivative ($k=1, 2, \cdots$) we have

$$\sup_{-\infty<t<\infty} |(1/\zeta(\sigma+it))^{(k)}| = |(\zeta(\sigma)/\zeta(2\sigma))^{(k)}|.$$

*N. G. de Bruijn* (Amsterdam)

Citations: MR 13, 741c = M02-2.

## M10-17 (22# 10957)

**Buschman, R. G. Some infinite series for $\zeta(n+1)$.** Amer. Math. Monthly **67** (1960), 260–263.

The author obtains some transformations of infinite series. Example:

$$\zeta(n+1) = \sum_{m=1}^{\infty} \left( \sum_{k=1}^{m} \frac{k^{n-1}+m^{n-1}}{(mk)^n} - \zeta(n) \right),$$

where $n(\geq 2)$ is a positive integer, and $\zeta(s)$ is Riemann's zeta function.

*S. Chowla* (Boulder, Colo.)

## M10-18 (24# A100)

**Lotockiĭ, A. V.**

**Expressions for $\zeta(2)$, $\zeta(3)$ in series by means of the coefficients of interpolation polynomials. (Russian)**

*Dokl. Akad. Nauk SSSR* **126** (1959), 19–21.

## M10-19 (24# A3140)

**Carlitz, L.**

**A recurrence formula for $\zeta(2n)$.**

*Proc. Amer. Math. Soc.* **12** (1961), 991–992.

In an earlier paper (with the same title as the present one) Kuo [Bull. Amer. Math. Soc. **55** (1949), 573–574; MR **10**, 683] proved a recursion formula for $C_{2n}$, where $C_0=-\frac{1}{2}$, $C_{2n}=\zeta(2n)$, $n\geq 1$. The author points out that since $\zeta(2n)$ can be expressed in terms of $B_{2n}$, a Bernoulli number in even suffix notation, the recursion formula is really a complicated one for the Bernoulli numbers. He points out that there is a simpler formula of this kind, namely,

$$\sum_{j=0}^{m} \sum_{k=0}^{n} \binom{m}{j}\binom{n}{k} \frac{B_j B_k}{m+n-j-k+1} = (-1)^{m-1} \frac{m!n!B_{m+n}}{(m+n)!},$$

where $m+n$ is even and $mn>0$.

*R. D. James* (Vancouver, B.C.)

Citations: MR 10, 683d = M10-6.

## M10-20 (28# 3012)

**Shanks, Daniel; Wrench, John W., Jr.**

**The calculation of certain Dirichlet series.**

*Math. Comp.* **17** (1963), 136–154.

The Dirichlet series under consideration are $L_a(s)=\sum(-a/n)n^{-s}$ summed over all positive odd integers $n$. The symbol is that of Jacobi. The first part of the paper discusses the known methods available for expressing $L_a(s)$ in closed form or as a Fourier series. The cases considered are $a=\pm q$, where $q$ is a square-free integer $<16$. The fact that in some cases $L_a(1)$ can be computed from the class number formula is brought out. There is a discussion of the exact evaluation of $L_a(s)$, where $s$ is an integer $<1$. Finally, a table of $L_a(s)$ to $30D$ for $s=1(1)10$ and for $a$ equal to the positive and negative divisors of 18. These tables suffice to present the Dirichlet $L(\chi, s)$ series for all the characters $\chi$ mod $k$, for $k=8$, 12 and 24.

*D. H. Lehmer* (Berkeley, Calif.)

Referred to in M05-35, M10-21.

## M10-21 (37# 2414)

**Lal, Mohan; Shanks, Daniel; Wrench, John W., Jr.**

**Corrigenda to: "The calculation of certain Dirichlet series".**

*Math. Comp.* **22** (1968), 699.

The authors point out misprints in an article by the last two authors [Math. Comp. **17** (1963), 136–154; MR **28** #3012].

Citations: MR 28# 3012 = M10-20.

## M10-22 (42# 7606)

**Grosswald, Emil**

**Die Werte der Riemannschen Zetafunktion an ungeraden Argumentstellen.**

*Nachr. Akad. Wiss. Göttingen Math.-Phys. Kl. II* **1970**, 9–13.

A formula for the value $\zeta(a)$ of the Riemann zeta function at an odd integer $a=2n+1$ $(n\geqq 1)$ is given. Let $\delta(a)=1+(-1)^n$, and let $r(a)=-\sum_{m=1}^{\infty} a_m$ with $a_m=2(\pi m)^{-a}(e^{2\pi m}-1)^{-1}[1+2\delta(a)(a-1)^{-1}\pi m e^{2\pi m}(e^{2\pi m}-1)^{-1}]$. Then, $\zeta(a)=\pi^a(A(a)+r(a))$, where $A(a)$ is a certain polynomial of Bernoulli numbers with rational coefficients. As the author notes, some part of this result has been mentioned in Ramanujan's work without proof.

*T. Kubota* (College Park, Md.)

# M15 $\zeta(s)$ AND $L(s, \chi)$ FOR $0 < \sigma \leq 1$

See also reviews L15-19, L25-6, L25-17, L25-19, L99-4, M25-4, M25-9, M25-16, M25-23, M25-28, M25-50, M25-52, M25-70, M25-73, M25-76, M25-78, M30-2, M30-6, M30-41, M35-11, M40-20, M40-62, M45-10, M55-52, N04-24, N12-16, N40-33, N40-64, P20-12, P20-19, P20-22, P20-31, P20-33, P32-17, P48-6, R18-68, R20-57.

## M15-1 (3, 69g)

**Wintner, Aurel. On the asymptotic behavior of the Riemann zeta-function on the line $\sigma=1$.** Amer. J. Math. **63**, 575–580 (1941).

The author denotes by $\tau_r(T)$ the measure of the set of points $t$ of the interval $-T\leqq t\leqq T$ at which $|\zeta(1+it)|\leqq r$, and defines $\psi(r)$, the asymptotic distribution function of $r=|\zeta(1+it)|$, to be the limit of $\tau_r(T)/(2T)$ as $T\to\infty$. B. Jessen and A. Wintner [Trans. Amer. Math. Soc. **38**, 48–88 (1935)] found that $\psi(r)=O\exp(-\lambda\log^2 r)$ as $r\to 0$ for every fixed $\lambda>0$; the author here improves this estimate, and shows that $\psi(r)=O\exp(-\lambda/r)$ as $r\to 0$ (for every fixed $\lambda>0$). The reasoning is based on the author's result that $1/\zeta(1+it)$ is almost periodic $(B^2)$ and

$$(1)\qquad 1/\zeta(1+it)\sim\sum_{n=1}^{\infty}\mu(n)n^{-1}\exp(-it\log n).$$

H. R. Pitt's extension of the Hausdorff-Young theorem applied to $\sum_{n=m}^{\infty}\mu(n)n^{-1}\exp(-it\log n)=S_m$, say, yields for every positive integral $k$ a function $f_{2k}^{(m)}\sim S_m$, and an inequality for the mean of $|f_{2k}^{(m)}|$, from which (using results of the paper cited above) the author concludes that

$$(2)\qquad \left[\int_0^{\infty} r^{2k}d\phi(r)\right]^{1/2k}=o(k)$$

as $k\to\infty$, where $\phi$ is the asymptotic distribution function of $1/|\zeta(1+it)|$. (2) is equivalent to the above estimation for $\psi(r)$.

*D. C. Spencer* (Cambridge, Mass.).

## M15-2 (3, 70a)

**Atkinson, F. V. The mean value of the zeta-function on the critical line.** Proc. London Math. Soc. (2) **47**, 174–200 (1941).

This paper consists of a proof of the asymptotic formula

$$\int_0^{\infty}|\zeta(\tfrac{1}{2}+it)|^4 e^{-\delta t}dt=\delta^{-1}(A\log^4 1/\delta+B\log^3 1/\delta+C\log^2 1/\delta+D\log 1/\delta+E)+O((1/\delta)^{13/14+\epsilon}),$$

as $\delta\to 0$, for $\epsilon>0$. Here $A=(2\pi^2)^{-1}$ and $B$, $C$, $D$, $E$ are other constants. The value of $B$ is given in the paper and the other constants could also be found by tracing them through the proof. The formula is an improvement on the formula

$$\int_0^{\infty}|\zeta(\tfrac{1}{2}+it)|^4 e^{-\delta t}dt\sim(2\pi^2\delta)^{-1}\log^4 1/\delta,$$

as $\delta\to 0$, which is due to Titchmarsh; and this is equivalent to

$$\int_0^{T}|\zeta(\tfrac{1}{2}+it)|^4 dt\sim(2\pi^2)^{-1}T\log^4 T,$$

as $T\to\infty$, which was proved by Ingham. The proof makes use of a result of Estermann's concerning sums of the type $\sum_{m=1}^{n}d(m)d(m+k)$, and this depends on estimates for Kloosterman sums. It is pointed out by the author that the error term $O((1/\delta)^{13/14+\epsilon})$ can be replaced by $O((1/\delta)^{8/9+\epsilon})$ if better estimates for Kloosterman sums are used.

*H. S. Zuckerman* (Seattle, Wash.).

## M15-3 (4, 131b)

**Titchmarsh, E. C. On the order of $\zeta(\frac{1}{2}+it)$.** Quart. J. Math., Oxford Ser. **13**, 11–17 (1942).

A proof of the formula $\zeta(\frac{1}{2}+it)=O(t^{19/116}\log^{1/58}t)$ is given. This proof follows van der Corput's method and makes use of a number of the author's previous results as well as one new lemma concerning the integral $\int\int e^{2\pi i f(x,y)}dxdy$. Too few details are given to make the proof easily read. Apparently the estimate for $|f''(x)|$ in §3 should read $|f''(x)|>AtRa^{-3}$, considerably complicating the following partial summations.

*H. S. Zuckerman* (Seattle, Wash.).

Referred to in M15-8, M15-29, N16-9.

## M15-4 (5, 4d)

**Wintner, Aurel. The behavior of Euler's product on the boundary of convergence.** Duke Math. J. **10**, 429–440 (1943).

The almost periodicity $(B^2)$ of a function $g(t)$ implies, in particular, the existence of the mean value $M(|g(t)|^2)$. Conversely, for boundary values of analytic almost periodic functions (Bohr), the existence of the mean value is in many cases strongly suggestive (even in matters of proof) of full almost periodicity $(B^2)$. In a previous paper [Duke Math. J. **2**, 443–446 (1936)] the author discussed almost periodicity $(B^2)$ of $1/\zeta(1+it)$; however, the existence of the mean value had been anticipated by Landau and Schnee. In the present paper the author extends his treatment to the functions $\zeta'/\zeta(1+it)$ and $\log\zeta(1+it)$ for which the existence of the mean value had not been known before.

*S. Bochner* (Princeton, N. J.).

## M15-5 (8, 567g)

**Wang, F. T. A mean-value theorem of the Riemann zeta function.** Quart. J. Math., Oxford Ser. **18**, 1–3 (1947).

In this note the author states that

$$T^{-1}\int_0^{T}|\zeta(\sigma+it)|^2\log|\zeta(\sigma+it)|dt\sim\zeta(2\sigma)\log\zeta(2\sigma),\qquad \sigma>\tfrac{1}{2}.$$

For the case $\sigma=\frac{1}{2}$, the author is not able to obtain by his method an asymptotic result, analogous to

$$\int_0^{T}|\zeta(\tfrac{1}{2}+it)|^2 dt\sim T\log T$$

[Titchmarsh, The Zeta-Function of Riemann, Cambridge University Press, 1930, p. 34]. He only states without proof the order-result

$$\int_0^{T}|\zeta(\tfrac{1}{2}+it)|^2\log|\zeta(\tfrac{1}{2}+it)|dt=O(T\log T\log\log T).$$

Moreover he states without proof the generalization of the first result,

$$\int_0^{T}|\zeta(\sigma+it)|^{2k}\log|\zeta(\sigma+it)|dt\sim TC_{2k}(2\sigma)\sum_p\frac{\sum_{\nu=1}^{\infty}\binom{\nu+k-1}{\nu}E(\nu)p^{-2\nu\sigma}}{\sum_{\nu=0}^{\infty}\binom{\nu+k-1}{\nu}^2p^{-2\nu\sigma}}$$

for $0<k\leqq 2$, $\sigma>\frac{1}{2}$; here

$$C_k(\sigma)=\prod_p\left\{\sum_{\nu=0}^{\infty}\binom{\nu+k-1}{\nu}^2 p^{-2\sigma\nu}\right\},\quad E(\nu)=\sum_{\mu=1}^{\nu}\frac{\mu+k-1}{\mu^2}.$$

[Reviewer's remark: The last result seems to be inconsistent with the first for $k=1$. Should not $C_{2k}(2\sigma)$ in the second member be $C_k(\sigma)$?] *S. C. van Veen* (Delft).

## M15-6 (10, 104d)

**Wintner, Aurel. On an oscillatory property of the Riemann Ξ-function.** Math. Notae 7, 177–178 (1947).

The author deals with properties of

$$\Xi(t)=\tfrac{1}{2}s(s-1)\pi^{-s/2}\Gamma(s/2)\zeta(s),$$

where $s=\frac{1}{2}+it$ and $\zeta(s)$ is the Riemann $\zeta$-function. He proves that $\int_0^t\Xi(u)du$ and the "conjugate" of $\Xi(t)$ are both positive for $0<t<\infty$, deducing this from the known fact [Hurwitz-Wintner] that $\phi(x)$, the Fourier cosine transform of $(2/\pi)^{\frac{1}{2}}\Xi(t)$, is positive and decreasing for $0\leqq x<\infty$.

*H. Kober* (Birmingham).

## M15-7 (10, 356b)

**Borchsenius, Vibeke, and Jessen, Børge. Mean motions and values of the Riemann zeta function.** Acta Math. 80, 97–166 (1948).

The authors employ the notion of generalized almost periodic functions in a half-strip in studying the functions $\log\zeta(s)-x$ and $\zeta(s)-x$ in the half-plane $\sigma>\frac{1}{2}$. These functions are shown to have mean motions and twice differentiable Jensen functions. Very complete relationships are found between the Jensen functions, mean motions, asymptotic distributions and relative frequency of zeros for these functions. *R. H. Cameron* (Minneapolis, Minn.).

## M15-8 (11, 84c)

**Min, Szu-Hoa. On the order of $\zeta(1/2+it)$.** Trans. Amer. Math. Soc. 65, 448–472 (1949).

The author proves that $\zeta(\frac{1}{2}+ti)=O(|t|^{\theta})$ for $\theta>15/92$. Previously the best proved result was

$$\zeta(\tfrac{1}{2}+ti)=O(|t|^{19/116}\log^{1/58}|t|)$$

[Titchmarsh, Quart. J. Math., Oxford Ser. 13, 11–17 (1942); these Rev. 4, 131]. The author's proof is a refinement of Titchmarsh's proof, the details of which are too complicated to be explained shortly. *H. Heilbronn.*

Citations: MR 4, 131b = M15-3.

Referred to in M15-29, M15-34, N40-22, N40-41.

## M15-9 (11, 162c)

**Haselgrove, C. B. A connection between the zeros and the mean values of $\zeta(s)$.** J. London Math. Soc. 24, 215–222 (1949).

For fixed $\sigma$ with $\frac{1}{2}<\sigma<1$ write $k(\sigma)$ for the upper bound of numbers $k$, not necessarily integral, for which

$$\lim_{T\to\infty} T^{-1}\int_1^T|\zeta(\sigma+it)|^{2k}dt=\sum_{n=1}^{\infty}d_k^2(n)n^{-2\sigma}.$$

The author proves

$$(2\mu(\sigma))^{-1}\geqq k(\sigma)\geqq(1-\nu^*(\sigma))(2\mu(\sigma))^{-1},$$

the lower bound being new. Here $\mu(\sigma)$ is the lower bound of $\xi$ such that $\zeta(\sigma+it)=O(t^{\xi})$, $\nu(\beta)$ the lower bound of $\eta$ such that the number of zeros of $\zeta(\sigma+it)$ with $\sigma>\beta$, $0<t<T$ is $O(T^{\eta})$, and $\nu^*(\sigma)=\lim_{\beta\to\sigma-0}\nu(\beta)$. The proof is based on order-results for $\zeta(s)$ and $\zeta^k(s)-\sum_1^{\infty}d_k(n)n^{-s}e^{-n\delta}$, which hold in $s$-regions free from zeros of $\zeta(s)$.

Explicit lower bounds for $k(\sigma)$ are derived from the inequalities $\nu^*(\sigma)\leqq(4c+2)(1-\sigma)$, where $\zeta(\frac{1}{2}+it)=O(t^c)$, so that $c\leqq\frac{1}{6}$, and $\mu(1-2^{1-q})\leqq(q+1)^{-1}2^{1-q}$, where $q\geqq 2$, together with the convexity property of $\mu(\sigma)$. For $k>13$ the resulting range of values of $\sigma$ is shown to be wider than that of H. Davenport [J. London Math. Soc. 10, 136–138 (1935)]. Methods for sharpening the results are indicated. Conditions are stated for the investigation to apply to the general Dirichlet series $\sum_1^{\infty}a_n n^{-s}$. *F. V. Atkinson.*

## M15-10 (11, 234c)

**Bellman, Richard. Wigert's approximate functional equation and the Riemann zeta-function.** Duke Math. J. 16, 547–552 (1949).

Writing $V_k(z)$ for the Mellin transform of $\Gamma(s)^k$ and $W_k(z)=\sum_{n=1}^{\infty}d_{2k}(n)V_k(nz)$, the author proves an approximate functional relation connecting $W_k(z)$ and $W_k((2\pi)^{2k}/z)$. For $k=1$ this reduces to Wigert's approximate functional equation for the Lambert series [Acta Math. 41, 197–218 (1917)]. This leads to a certain advance in the mean-value problem when the exponent is a multiple of 4, and gives a variant of existing proofs in the case of $|\zeta(\frac{1}{2}+it)|^4$. The above result combined with Plancherel's theorem reduces the mean-value problem for $|\zeta(\frac{1}{2}+it)|^{4k}$ to the consideration of

$$\int_{(2\pi)^k}^{\infty}|W_k(ue^{-i(\frac{1}{2}k\pi-\delta)})|^2du,$$

which seems somewhat more tractable than the integral originally derived by Titchmarsh [The Zeta-Function of Riemann, Cambridge University Press, 1930, § 2.53]. It is remarked that this provides a reformulation of the Lindelöf hypothesis. *F. V. Atkinson* (Ibadan).

## M15-11 (11, 234e)

**Atkinson, F. V. The mean-value of the Riemann zeta function.** Acta Math. 81, 353–376 (1949).

Hardy and Littlewood first showed that $\zeta(\frac{1}{2}+it)$ possesses an asymptotic mean-value, $\int_0^T|\zeta(\frac{1}{2}+it)|^2dt=T\log T+R(T)$, $R(T)=o(T\log T)$, as $T\to\infty$. Since then, the order of magnitude of the remainder term has been investigated successively by Littlewood, Ingham and Titchmarsh. The last-named showed that $R(T)=-T(1+\log 2\pi-2C)+O(T^{5/12})$. The problem has much in common with the Dirichlet divisor problem, as far as methods and results are concerned [see Atkinson, Quart. J. Math., Oxford Ser. 10, 122–128 (1939)]. This analogy is carried a step further by the author when he shows that the $O(T^{5/12})$ term possesses an expansion in terms of oscillating functions quite similar to that obtained by applying Voronoi's summation formula to $\sum_{n\leqq x}d(n)$.

*R. Bellman* (Stanford University, Calif.).

## M15-12 (11, 420d)

**Flett, T. M. On the function**

$$\sum_{n=1}^{\infty}\frac{1}{n}\sin\frac{t}{n}.$$

J. London Math. Soc. 25, 5–19 (1950).

Let $Q(t)=\sum_{n=1}^{\infty}n^{-1}\sin(t/n)$, $P(t)=\sum_{n<t}n^{-1}\cos(t/n)$. Hardy and Littlewood proved that both $P(t)$ and $Q(t)$ are unbounded. The author proves that both $Q(t)$ and $P(t)$ are $O[(\log t)^{\frac{2}{3}}(\log\log t)^{\frac{1}{3}+\epsilon}]$. In the proof the author uses results of van der Corput and Tchudakoff. The author also improves the $O$ results for $\xi(1+it)$. *P. Erdös.*

## M15-13 (14, 451a)

**Rodosskiĭ, K. A. On the theory of the $\zeta$-function.** Doklady Akad. Nauk SSSR (N.S.) **86**, 1069–1070 (1952). (Russian)

The author sketches a proof of the following result. Let $T$ be a large integer; let

$$\tfrac{1}{2}\leqq\Delta\leqq 1-(\log\log T)^2/\log T,\quad \delta=(1-\Delta)/(2-3\Delta+2\Delta^2).$$

Then the number of rectangles $R^{(n)}$, $T+n-1\leqq t<T+n$, $\Delta\leqq\sigma\leqq 1$ $(n=1,\cdots,T)$, containing at least one point $\xi_0^{(n)}$ such that $|\zeta(\xi_0^{(n)})|\leqq(6T^{(2\Delta-1)\delta})^{-1}$ does not exceed $T^{(2\Delta+1)\delta}e^{c(\log\log T)^2}$. In the proof, there is used the approximate functional equation for the zeta function as well as methods used in a paper of Čudakov [Ann. of Math. (2) **48**, 515–545 (1947); these Rev. **9**, 11] and in a previous (unavailable) paper of the author [Ukrain. Mat. Žurnal **3**, 339–403 (1951)]. The author states that the result can be significantly improved when $\Delta$ is in the neighborhood of 1 by using estimates of exponential sums. *L. Schoenfeld.*

Citations: MR 9, 11d = P32-10.

Referred to in M15-15.

## M15-14 (15, 402c)

**Turán, Paul. On an application of the typical means in the theory of the zeta-function of Riemann.** Comm. Sém. Math. Univ. Lund [Medd. Lunds Univ. Mat. Sem.] Tome Supplémentaire, 239–251 (1952).

The following result is proved under the assumptions that $\frac{1}{2}\leqq\alpha<1$ and $0<\epsilon<(1-\alpha)/10$. There exists a sequence $s_n=\sigma_n+it_n$ such that $t_n\to\infty$ as $n\to\infty$, $\alpha+\epsilon\leqq\sigma_n<1$ and $|\zeta(s_n)|\leqq\exp\{-(\log t_n)^{\frac{1}{2}(1-\alpha-4\epsilon)}\}$. Since the result is clearly trivial if there are an infinity of zeros in $\Re(s)\geqq\alpha+\epsilon$, only the contrary case is considered; and for this case the author shows that the above is true with all $\sigma_n=\alpha+2\epsilon$.

The point of departure is the following modified form of the Perron-Hadamard formula, where $f(w)=\sum_{n=1}^{\infty}a_n e^{-\lambda_n w}$,

$$\sum_{n\leqq N}a_n(\lambda_N-\lambda_n)e^{-\lambda_n s}=\frac{1}{2\pi i}\int_{\beta-i\infty}^{\beta+i\infty}\left\{\frac{2}{w-s}\sinh\left(\frac{w-s}{2}\lambda_n\right)\right\}^2 f(w)\,dw.$$

The author applies this result to $f(w)=\log 1/\zeta(w)$, $\lambda_n=\log n$ and $s=\alpha+2\epsilon+it$. The line of integration is moved to the left so that for $|\Im(w)|\geqq\frac{1}{2}t$ the path is along $\Re(w)=\alpha+2\epsilon$; the remainder of the new integration path is along $\Re(w)=1$ except for a small detour to the right of $w=1$ and two horizontal paths. The real parts of both sides are taken and the integrals along all paths, except that part of $\Re(w)=\alpha+2\epsilon$ in the upper half-plane, are easily estimated. At this stage the result is

$$-\sum_{p^k\leqq N}\frac{\cos(kt\log p)}{kp^{k(\alpha+2\epsilon)}}\log\frac{N}{p^k}\leqq\frac{1}{2\pi}\int_{\frac{1}{2}t}^{\infty}\Re f(\alpha+2\epsilon+iv)\left\{\frac{2}{v-t}\sin\left(\frac{v-t}{2}\log N\right)\right\}^2 dv$$
$$+c_1(\epsilon)N^{1-\alpha-2\epsilon}\log\log N\cdot(\log t)/t.$$

That part of the integral having $v\geqq 4t$ is easily estimated and is absorbed in the other error term. If $L=\max_{t/2\leqq v\leqq 4t}\log 1/|\zeta(\alpha+2\epsilon+iv)|$ the rest of the integral has the estimate

$$\frac{1}{2\pi}L\int_{\frac{1}{2}t}^{4t}\left\{\frac{2}{v-t}\sin\left(\frac{v-t}{2}\log N\right)\right\}^2 dv\leqq c_2 L\log N,$$

and the sum of all the terms on the left for which $k\geqq 2$ has the easily obtained estimate $c_3(\epsilon)\log N$. (Correction: both sums in (6.1) of the paper should be restricted by the condition $k\geqq 2$.) Consequently, after division by $\log N$ one obtains

$$-\sum_{p\leqq N}\frac{\cos(t\log p)}{p^{\alpha+2\epsilon}}\left(1-\frac{\log p}{\log N}\right)\leqq c_2 L$$
$$+c_4(\epsilon)\{1+N^{1-\alpha-2\epsilon}(\log t)/t\}.$$

At this point the author extends a theorem of Bohr and Landau used for a similar purpose in the half plane $\Re(s)>1$. The new result is that to each $N>c_5$ there corresponds a $\tau_N$ such that

$$\exp(2N^3)\leqq\tau_N\leqq 2\exp(2N^3)\quad\text{and}\quad\cos(\tau_N\log p)\leqq-\tfrac{1}{2}$$

for all primes $p\leqq N$. Taking $t=\tau_N$ in the above result, the left side is greater than or equal to

$$\frac{1}{2}\sum_{p\leqq\frac{1}{2}N}p^{-\alpha-2\epsilon}\left(1-\frac{\log p}{\log N}\right)\geqq\frac{1}{2}\left(1-\frac{\log\frac{1}{2}N}{\log N}\right)\sum_{p\leqq\frac{1}{2}N}p^{-\alpha-2\epsilon}$$
$$\geqq c_6(\epsilon)N^{1-\alpha-2\epsilon}/\log^2 N.$$

The proof is now easily completed. *L. Schoenfeld.*

## M15-15 (16, 906a)

**Rodosskiĭ, K. A. On the distribution of small values of the modulus of the $\zeta$-function.** Izv. Akad. Nauk SSSR. Ser. Mat. **19**, 97–102 (1955). (Russian)

The author proves a theorem on the absolute value of a segment of an ordinary Dirichlet series and uses it to prove the following result on the Riemann zeta-function. Suppose $T\geqq 3$ and $\{\ln(8c\ln T)\}^{1/2}/\{\ln T\}^{1/2}+\frac{1}{2}\leqq\Delta\leqq 1$, where $c$ is a certain positive constant. For $n=0,1,\cdots,[\frac{1}{2}T]$ let $R_n$ be the rectangle in the plane of the complex variable $s$ defined by $\Delta\leqq\mathrm{Re}(s)\leqq 1$, $\frac{1}{2}T+n\leqq\mathrm{Im}(s)<\frac{1}{2}T+n+1$. Then the number of rectangles $R_n$ for which

$$\min_{s\in R_n}|\zeta(s)|<5\{\ln T\cdot T^{(2\Delta-1)(1-\Delta)/(2-3\Delta+2\Delta^2)}\}^{-1}$$

does not exceed

$$c\ln^{12}T\cdot T^{(2\Delta+1)(1-\Delta)/(2-3\Delta+2\Delta^2)}.$$

A cruder form of this result was given earlier [Dokl. Akad. Nauk SSSR (N.S.) **86**, 1069–1070 (1952); MR **14**, 451]. *P. T. Bateman* (Urbana, Ill.).

Citations: MR 14, 451a = M15-13.

## M15-16 (18, 286c)

**Grosswald, Emil. The order of the zeta function in the critical strip.** Duke Math. J. **23** (1956), 621–622.

In addition to correcting an oversight in the author's previous paper [Duke Math. J. **23** (1956) 41–44; MR **17**, 588], an inequality for the order $\mu(\sigma)$ of $\zeta(\sigma+it)$ is given. A special case of this is: (*) $\mu(1-l/(2^l-2))\leqq a/(2^l-2)$, $a=1.0276$, if $l\geqq 4$ is a real number (rather than an integer). If $l$ is not too large, the author's result is superior to an earlier result of van der Corput and Koksma [Ann. Fac. Sci. Univ. Toulouse (3) **22** (1930), 1–39]. Both the latter and the former are obtained from a still earlier result of van der Corput [Math. Z. **29** (1928), 397–426] of the same form (*), but with $a=1$, by using the convexity of $\mu(\sigma)$. *L. Schoenfeld* (East Pittsburgh, Pa.).

Citations: MR 17, 588f = N48-5.

## M15-17 (20# 5171)

**Vinogradov, I. M. On the $\zeta(s)$ function.** Dokl. Akad. Nauk SSSR (N.S.) **118** (1958), 631. (Russian)

The author announces the estimate

$$\zeta(1+it)=O((\log t\log\log t)^{\frac{2}{3}})$$

as $t\to\infty$. This result and others like it lead to a reduction in the estimate for the remainder in the asymptotic formula for $\pi(x)$. Also it follows that $\zeta(s)$ has no zero $\sigma+it$ in the region $\sigma\geqq 1-C(\log t \log\log t)^{-\frac{3}{4}}$ for some constant $C$.

A detailed account of these results is promised.

*D. H. Lehmer* (Berkeley, Calif.)

## M15-18 (21# 2623)

**Walfisz, A. Über die Wirksamkeit einiger Abschätzungen trigonometrischer Summen.** Acta Arith. **4** (1958), 108–180.

The author first restates various estimates for exponential sums, all obtained by methods due to Vinogradov, given by Tchudakov, Hua, Flett, Walfisz, Tatuzawa, and Vinogradov himself. The relations between these estimates are discussed, and they are applied (in combination with Weyl's estimate) to four well-known asymptotic problems. These are: (1) the estimation of $\zeta(1+it)$, (2) the error term in the prime number theorem, (3) the error term in the formula for the number of integer points in a large (rational) ellipsoid, (4) the error term for $\sum_{n\leqq x}\varphi(n)$. In (1), for example, the result in every case is of the form $O((\log t)^{3/4}(\log\log t)^{\alpha})$, with some particular constant $\alpha$. Since results with exponents less then $\frac{3}{4}$ have now been announced [see the following review], the paper may soon be mainly of historical interest.

*H. Davenport* (Cambridge, England)

Referred to in N48-10.

## M15-19 (21# 2624)

**Vinogradov, I. M. A new estimate of the function $\zeta(1+it)$.** Izv. Akad. Nauk SSSR. Ser. Mat. **22** (1958), 161–164. (Russian)

This paper outlines a proof that

(1) $$\zeta(1+it) = O((\log t)^{2/3})$$

as $t\to\infty$, this being a better estimate than was previously known. It follows, by arguments that are now well known, that

(2) $$\pi(x) = \mathrm{li}\, x+O\{x\exp(-C(\log x)^{3/5})\},$$

where $C$ is a positive constant. The result (1) is a consequence of the following estimate for the sum

$$S = \sum_{m=a}^{a_1} m^{-it}, \quad \text{where } a < a_1 \leqq 2a.$$

If $a\geqq \exp(320000\, n^2)$ and $a^{n-1}\leqq t<a^n$, then $|S|<1.04a^{1-\rho}$, where $\rho=(41792000\, n^2)^{-1}$. The special merit of this (and similar recent results) lies in the fact that the constants in it are absolute. The proof is based on an improved form of the author's mean-value theorem [Izv. Akad. Nauk SSSR. Ser. Mat. **15** (1951), 109–130; MR **13**, 328; see also L. K. Hua, Quart. J. Math. **20** (1949), 48–61; MR **10**, 597]. This is stated without proof. [See also the review which follows.] *H. Davenport* (Cambridge, England)

Citations: MR 10, 597d = P08-11; MR 13, 328e = L15-14.

Referred to in A32-93, D52-120, L02-8, L20-19, N02-12, N24-54.

## M15-20 (21# 2625)

**Korobov, N. M. Weyl's estimates of sums and the distribution of primes.** Dokl. Akad. Nauk SSSR **123** (1958), 28–31. (Russian)

The author outlines his own proof, obtained independently, of (1) and (2) of the preceding review. He proves (in reasonable detail) the following estimate for the exponential sum

$$S = \sum_{x=1}^{P} e(\alpha_1 x+\alpha_2 x^2+\cdots+\alpha_{n+1}x^{n+1}),$$

where $e(t)=\exp 2\pi it$. Suppose $\alpha_1, \cdots, \alpha_{n+1}$ are real, and

$$|\alpha_{n+1}-a/q| \leqq q^{-2}, \quad (a, q) = 1,$$

and $q=P^r$, where $n^{1/2}\log n<r<n-n^{1/2}\log n$. Then

$$|S| < CP^{1-\gamma/(n^2\log n)},$$

where $C$ and $\gamma$ are positive absolute constants. The only essential result quoted is Vinogradov's mean value theorem [references in preceding review]. The above is theorem 1; in theorem 2 it is observed that the estimate can be improved, by the omission of $\log n$, if $r$ is restricted to the narrower range $\varepsilon n<r<(1-\varepsilon)n$, for fixed $\varepsilon>0$. Theorem 3 states a similar result for exponential sums in which several consecutive coefficients $\alpha_{s+2}, \cdots, \alpha_{3s}$ are rational. The proof is said to depend on an improved form of Vinogradov's mean-value theorem. It is from theorem 3 that the results (1) and (2) are stated to follow.

*H. Davenport* (Cambridge, England)

Citations: MR 10, 597d = P08-11; MR 13, 328e = L15-14.

## M15-21 (22# 7980)

**Putnam, C. R. On averages of the Riemann Zeta-Function.** Arch. Math. **11** (1960), 346–349.

Let $A(t)$ and $B(t)$ denote, respectively, the real and imaginary parts of Riemann's zeta-function $\zeta(s)$, where $s=\sigma+it$. For $q=\text{const}>0$, define $A_n=A(nq)$ and $B_n=B(nq)$ for $n=0, 1, 2, \cdots$. Write $S_n=n^{-1}\sum_{k=1}^{n}B_k$, $T_n=n^{-1}\sum_{k=1}^{n}S_k$. The author obtains several results concerning $B_n, S_n, T_n$. We quote the following: (I) $\lim_{n\to\infty}B_n$ does not exist; (III) $\lim_{n\to\infty}T_n=0$. It was previously shown by the author [Amer. J. Math. **76** (1954), 97–99; MR **15**, 412] that the sequence $B_1, B_2, \cdots$ does not have the limit 0.

*S. Chowla* (Boulder, Colo.)

Citations: MR 15, 412e = M25-36.

## M15-22 (22# 7982)

**Rademacher, Hans. On the Phragmén-Lindelöf theorem and some applications.** Math. Z. **72** (1959/60), 192–204.

In analytic number theory the Phragmén-Lindelöf theorem is usually applied to a half-strip, which is often less successful in cases where an infinity of functions is considered simultaneously, for then we need uniform estimates on the horizontal parts of the boundary of the (vertical) half-strip. The author presents theorems of Phragmén-Lindelöf type for the whole strip. The main result is as follows: Let $-Q<a<b$, put $s=\sigma+it$; let $f(s)$ be regular analytic in the strip $a\leqq\sigma\leqq b$, with $|f(s)|<C\exp(|t|^c)$ for suitable constants $c$ and $C$; assume $|f(a+it)|\leqq A|Q+a+it|^{\alpha}$, $|f(b+it)|\leqq B|Q+b+it|^{\beta}$, where $A, B, \alpha, \beta$ are real constants, with $\alpha\geqq\beta$; then we have

$$|f(s)| \leqq (A|Q+s|^{\alpha})^{\lambda}(B|Q+s|^{\beta})^{\mu}$$

throughout the strip, with

$$\lambda = (b-\sigma)/(b-a), \quad \mu = (\sigma-a)/(b-a).$$

There are applications to the gamma function, e.g., that for $Q\geqq 0$, $-\frac{1}{2}\leqq\sigma\leqq\frac{1}{2}$ we have

$$|\Gamma(\tfrac{1}{2}(Q+1-s))/\Gamma(\tfrac{1}{2}(Q+s))| \leqq (\tfrac{1}{2}|Q+1+s|)^{\frac{1}{2}-\sigma}.$$

{The reviewer remarks that in the right-hand side $Q+1$ can be replaced by $Q'=\max(Q, 1-Q)$, an improvement indicated by the author for $Q\geqq\frac{1}{2}$ only.}

A further application concerns an estimate for all

Dirichlet $L$-functions $L(s, \chi)$ with primitive character $\chi$ mod $k$, uniformly with respect to $k$: If $0<\eta \leqq \frac{1}{2}$, $-\eta \leqq \sigma \leqq 1+\eta$, $k>1$ we have

$$|L(s, \chi)| \leqq (k|1+s|/2\pi)^{\frac{1}{2}(1+\eta-\sigma)}\zeta(1+\eta);$$

this is obtained from estimates on the line $\sigma=-\eta$, produced by the functional equation.

In a similar way the author derives estimates for the Dedekind $\zeta$-function $\zeta_K$. The result is somewhat simpler if $K$ is normal over the rational field. In that case it reads: If $0<\eta \leqq \frac{1}{2}$, $-\eta \leqq \sigma \leqq 1+\eta$ we have

$$|\zeta_K(s)| \leqq |\zeta(s)|(|d|(2\pi)^{1-n}|1+s|^{n-1})^{\frac{1}{2}(1+\eta-\sigma)}(\zeta(1+\eta))^{n-1},$$

where $d$ is the discriminant and $n$ is the degree of $K$.

There is a similar, but somewhat more complicated result for the Hecke functions $\zeta(s, \lambda)$ with "Grössencharacter" $\lambda$. *N. G. de Bruijn* (Eindhoven)

## M15-23 (22# 8679)

**Haselgrove, C. B.; Miller, J. C. P. Tables of the Riemann zeta function.** Royal Society Mathematical Tables, Vol. 6. Cambridge University Press, New York, 1960. xxiii+80 pp. $9.50.

This volume gives the first tabulation of the Riemann function $\zeta(s)=\sum_{n=1}^{\infty} n^{-s}$ in the complex plane, although only for $\mathrm{Re}(s)=\frac{1}{2}$ and 1. There are five separate tables.

Table I gives 6D values of the real and imaginary parts of $\zeta(\frac{1}{2}+it)$ and $\zeta(1+it)$ together with $Z(t)$ and $\theta(t)$ where $Z(t)e^{-i\pi\theta(t)}=\zeta(\frac{1}{2}+it)$ and $\pi\theta(t)=\mathrm{ph}\{\Gamma(\frac{1}{4}+\frac{1}{2}it)/\pi^{it/2}\}$ for $t=0(.1)100$.

Table II gives only the "signed modulus" $Z(t)$, for $t=100(.1)1000$, to 6D. This is the function used for computing the zeros of $\zeta(\frac{1}{2}+it)$.

Table III is concerned with the zeros $\gamma_n$ of $Z(t)$. The first 1600 zeros are given to 6D together with the absolute values of $\zeta'(\frac{1}{2}+\gamma_n)$ to 5D. For the first 650 zeros the quantities $g_{n-1}$ and $\phi_n$ where $\theta(g_n)=n\pi$, $\pi\phi_n=\mathrm{ph}\zeta'(\frac{1}{2}+i\gamma_n)$ are given to 6D. The 1600th zero is given as 2090.036207.

Table IV deals with special ranges of $t$ on the critical line, namely, $t=7000+u$, $17120+u$, $100{,}000+u$ and $250{,}000+u$ for $u=0(.1)25$ where the function $Z(t)$ is given to 6D. The zeros $\gamma$ of $Z(t)$ in these ranges and $|Z'(\gamma)|$ are also given. The first two ranges were chosen because of the close pairs of zeros:

| | |
|---|---|
| 7005.062866 | 17143.786536 |
| 7005.100565 | 17143.821844. |

The largest value of $|\zeta(\frac{1}{2}+it)|$ so far computed occurs near $t=17123$ and is 19.0.

Table V is an auxiliary table of $\pi^{-1}\mathrm{ph}\Gamma(\frac{1}{2}+it)$ for $t=0(.1)50(1)600(2)1000$. Pages xxi and xxii of the introduction give 10 to 20 D values of the coefficients in the power series expansions of certain functions $\phi_r$ used in the reviewer's form of the Riemann-Siegel formula for $\zeta(\frac{1}{2}+it)$ and of the corresponding functions $\psi_r$ for dealing with $\zeta(1+it)$.

This is the first table of the Royal Society to be produced automatically by electronic computers. Any other method would not have been feasible. A great many terms of the Euler-Maclaurin or Riemann-Siegel series were used to calculate each entry. For some cases 15 figure logarithms were needed as input data to obtain barely 6 decimal accuracy. The large zeros of Table IV required inverse interpolation involving 14th differences.

The tables will be very helpful in future exploration of inequalities involving certain numerical functions. Haselgrove had already used the first 600 zeros of $\zeta(s)$ to disprove Pólya's conjecture that there are always at least as many numbers $\leqq x$ having an odd number of prime factors as those having an even number of prime factors [Mathematika **5** (1958), 141–145; MR **21** #3391.]

*D. H. Lehmer* (Berkeley, Calif.)

Citations: MR 21# 3391 = N44-20.

Referred to in M05-33.

## M15-24 (23# A869)

**Linnik, Ju. V.**

**The sixth moment for the $L$-series and an asymptotic formula in a problem of Hardy-Littlewood.**

*Dokl. Akad. Nauk SSSR* **133** (1960), 1015–1016 (*Russian*); *translated as Soviet Math. Dokl.* **1** (1961), 927–928.

The author's proof of the Hardy-Littlewood conjecture—an asymptotic formula for the number of representations of a large number as a sum of two squares and a prime—depends on the following estimate for the sixth (non-normalized) moment for the $L$-series:

$$\sum_{D_1 \leqq D \leqq D_1+D_2} \sum_{\chi_D} |L(\tfrac{1}{2}+it, \chi_D)|^6 = BD_2D_1(|t|+1)^{l_0}\exp(\ln D_1)^{\varepsilon_0},$$

where $B$ is a bounded constant, $l_0>0$ is a constant, $\varepsilon_0>0$ is an arbitrarily small constant. Further, $D_2 \geqq D_1(\ln D_1)^{-k}$, where $k>0$ is some constant and $\chi_D$ runs through all Dirichlet characters (mod $D$); $L(s, \chi_D)$ are Dirichlet's $L$-series, in standard notation.

*S. Chowla* (Boulder, Colo.)

Referred to in R14-57.

## M15-25 (24# A1889)

**Fomenko, O. M.**

**On Dirichlet $L$-functions.** (Russian)

*Dokl. Akad. Nauk SSSR* **142** (1962), 554–555.

The author uses an estimate for character sums due to D. A. Burgess [Mathematika **4** (1957), 106–112; MR **20** #28] and a formula for $L(s, x)$, Dirichlet's $L$-function formed with a character $\chi$ [Wang Yuan, Acta Math. Sinica **9** (1959), 432–441, p. 433; MR **22** #4] to obtain the theorem: Suppose $|t| \leqq 1$ and $\frac{2}{3}<\omega<1$; if $\chi(n)$ is a non-principal character (mod $p$), then

$$L(\tfrac{1}{2}+it, \chi) = O(p^{(42+\omega)/4(46+\omega)}).$$

The weaker (non-trivial) theorem with $\frac{1}{4}$ for the exponent of $p$ is due to Davenport [J. London Math. Soc. **6** (1931), 198–202]. It is to be noted that Burgess has also announced improvements in the order of $L(\frac{1}{2}+it, \chi)$ for large $p$ ($t$ fixed) [Proc. London Math. Soc. (3) **12** (1962), 179–192; p. 181; MR **24** #A2569].

*S. Chowla* (Boulder, Colo.)

Citations: MR 20# 28 = N68-28; MR 24# A2569 = L25-16.

## M15-26 (24# A1893)

**Staś, W.**

**Über das Verhalten der Riemannschen $\zeta$-Funktion und einiger verwandter Funktionen, in der Nähe der Geraden $\sigma=1$.**

*Acta Arith.* **7** (1961/62), 217–224.

Sharpening a theorem of L. Schoenfeld [Duke Math. J. **24** (1957), 601–609; MR **19**, 1162] the author proves Theorem 1: If $1-2^{-13} \leqq \sigma \leqq 1$, $t \geqq 3$, then $|\zeta(\sigma+it)| \leqq c_4 t^{2^{15}(1-\sigma)^{3/2}} \log^{5/2} t$, where $c_4$ is a numerical constant. The author obtains a similar result for the Dedekind zeta function of a quadratic field, and hence for Dirichlet's $L$-functions. *S. Chowla* (Boulder, Colo.)

Citations: MR 19, 1162a = M35-11.

## M15-27 (25# 1138 )

**Turán, P.**
**On Lindelöf's conjecture concerning the Riemann zeta-function.**
*Illinois J. Math.* **6** (1962), 95–97.
The conjecture of Lindelöf asserts that (with $s=\sigma+it$) for $\sigma \geqq 1/2$, $|s-1| \geqq 1/10$, with an arbitrary small $\varepsilon>0$, the inequality $|\zeta(s)| \leqq d_1(2+|t|)^\varepsilon$ holds, where $\zeta(s)$ stands for the Riemann zeta function and $d_1$ depends only upon $\varepsilon$. The author shows that for the truth of Lindelöf's conjecture the truth of the inequality

$$\left|\sum_{n \leqq N}(-1)^n e^{-it \log n}\right| < d_2 N^{1/2+\varepsilon}(2+|t|)^\varepsilon$$

with an arbitrary small $\varepsilon>0$ ($d_2$ depending on $\varepsilon$) is necessary and sufficient. *B. K. Ghosh* (Calcutta)

## M15-28 (28# 68 )

**Lavrik, A. F.**
**The sum over the characters of powers of the modulus of the Dirichlet $L$-function in the critical strip. (Russian)**
*Dokl. Akad. Nauk SSSR* **154** (1964), 34–37.
The author states Theorem 1: Let $D>1$, $\chi$ a character (mod $D$), $L(s, \chi)$ the corresponding Dirichlet $L$-series. Then for $k \geqq 1$,

$$\sum_{\chi \bmod D}\left|L\left(1-\frac{1}{k}+ti, \chi\right)\right|^{2k} = B\varphi(D)(|t|+1)\ln^b D(|t|+1),$$

where $\varphi(D)$ is Euler's totient function, $b$ a certain constant depending on $k$.

Applications to sums of the type $\sum_{n \leqq x, n \equiv l \bmod D} d_{2k}(n)$ [where $D \leqq x^\gamma \exp(-\ln^{4\delta} \ln x)$, $\gamma \leqq 1/k$, $\delta>1$, and $d_{2k}(n)$ is equal to the number of ways $n$ can be expressed as a product $m_1 m_2 \cdots m_{2k}$ where $m_i \geqq 1$] are also stated. The methods used are closely related to work of Linnik. *S. Chowla* (University Park, Pa.)

Referred to in M05-48, M15-31.

## M15-29 (28# 1179

**Haneke, W.**
**Verschärfung der Abschätzung von $\zeta(1/2+it)$.**
*Acta Arith.* **8** (1962/63), 357–430.
In this paper the author obtains a new upper bound for the Riemann zeta function $\zeta(s)$ on the "critical line" $s=\frac{1}{2}+it$.

The ideas used go back to Weyl and van der Corput [see Titchmarsh, *The theory of the Riemann zeta function*, Ch. 5, pp. 81–101, Clarendon, Oxford, 1951; MR **13**, 741] and are based on a study of "one-dimensional" exponential sums. However, Titchmarsh opened the way to sharper results by introducing "two-dimensional" exponential sums [see his papers, Proc. London Math. Soc. (2) **36** (1934), 485–500; Quart. J. Math. Oxford Ser. **13** (1942), 11–17; MR **4**, 131]. The two-dimensional method was sharpened by Min [Trans. Amer. Math. Soc. **65** (1949), 448–472; MR **11**, 84]. Min obtained (as $t \rightarrow \infty$)

$$\text{(A)} \qquad \zeta(\tfrac{1}{2}+it) = O(t^{15/92+\varepsilon}).$$

The author obtains

$$\text{(B)} \qquad \zeta(\tfrac{1}{2}+it) = O(t^{6/37} \log t)$$

which improves (A) since $6/37=12/74<15/92$.

He works with a new type of exponential sum, namely with

$$\sum_{\substack{m,n \\ a<m \leqq b \\ B(m)<n+p(m) \leqq r''}} e^{2\pi i f(m, n+p(m))},$$

where $f(w, z)$ is defined in a region of the form $\{(w, z)$: $w, z$ complex, $|w-\frac{3}{2}r'|<Cr'$, $|z|<r\}$ with $r>r''>0$, $1 \leqq a \leqq b \leqq 2r'$, $C>\frac{1}{2}$ and is holomorphic therein; $f(w, z)$ is real for real arguments $(w, z)$, $p(x)$ is a real function and $B(x)$ denotes a real differentiable function. The three-fold application of his "Weyl-step" (his Theorem 1) involves six parameters. The theorems are too long to quote, but the result is certainly an achievement. One may ask: If the proof for the exponent 6/37 needs 74 pages, how many pages will be required to achieve the exponent $\varepsilon$ of Lindelöf? *S. Chowla* (University Park, Pa.)

Citations: MR 4, 131b = M15-3; MR 11, 84c = M15-8; MR 13, 741c = M02-2.

Referred to in M15-34, M25-80, P40-24.

## M15-30 (28# 3973 )

**Burgess, D. A.**
**A note on $L$-functions.**
*J. London Math. Soc.* **39** (1964), 103–108.
The author [Proc. London Math. Soc. (3) **12** (1962), 193–206; MR **24** #A2570] has shown that if $L_\chi(s)$ is the Dirichlet $L$-function belonging to the non-principal character $\chi$ (mod $p$), $t$ is a fixed real number and $\varepsilon$ is an arbitrary fixed positive real number, then $L_\chi(\frac{1}{2}+it) \ll k^{3/16+\varepsilon}$. In this paper the author shows that when $k$ is a prime, then $k^\varepsilon$ may be replaced by $\log k$. The proof relies on further refinements of the author's estimates on the size of exponential sums. *D. J. Lewis* (Ann Arbor, Mich.)

Citations: MR 24# A2570 = L25-17.

## M15-31 (30# 1101 )

**Saparnijazov, O.**
**A character sum of powers of the modulus of the Dirichlet $L$-functions in the critical strip. (Russian. Uzbek summary)**
*Izv. Akad. Nauk UzSSR Ser. Fiz.-Mat. Nauk* **1964**, no. 4, 13–19.
Using Linnik's method [Mat. Sb. (N.S.) **53 (95)** (1961), 3–38; MR **22** #10964], Lavrik proved [Dokl. Akad. Nauk SSSR **154** (1964), 34–37; MR **28** #68] that for any integer $k \geqq 1$ we have, uniformly in $D$ and $t$,

$$\text{(1)} \qquad \sum_{\chi \bmod D}|L(\sigma_k+it, \chi)|^{2k} \ll \varphi(D)(|t|+1)^b \log^c D(|t|+2),$$

where $\sigma_k=1-1/k$, $b=1$, and $c$ is a positive constant which depends merely on $k$. The author of the present note follows the same method, but he uses the estimate for the character sums due to Burgess [Proc. London Math. Soc. (3) **13** (1963), 524–536, Theorem 2; MR **26** #6133] and proves (1) with $\sigma_k=1-\{k(3/4+2/k+\varepsilon)\}^{-1}$ ($\varepsilon$ any fixed positive constant) and $b<6$. The proof is merely outlined. On the right-hand side of (1) the author actually writes $\varphi(D)t^b \log^c D(|t|+1)$, which is wrong at least for $t=0$. (1) is used to prove an asymptotic estimate for the sum of the functions $\tau_{2k}(m)$, $m \equiv l$ (mod $D$), where $\tau_n(m)$ denotes the number of solutions of the equation $x_1 x_2 \cdots x_n=m$ in positive integers. *E. Fogels* (Riga)

Citations: MR 22# 10964 = P36-25; MR 26# 6133 = L25-19; MR 28# 68 = M15-28.

**M15-32** **(30# 3075 )**

**Urazbaev, B. M.**

**Some asymptotic bounds and their applications to the problem of the distribution of absolute Abelian fields. (Russian. Kazak summary)**

*Izv. Akad. Nauk Kazah. SSR Ser. Fiz.-Mat. Nauk* **1964**, *no.* 2, 16–21.

Let $L(s, \chi)$ be the Dirichlet function with a character $\chi \bmod l$ with $l \ll 1$, and let $s=\sigma+it$. The author proves that in the region $t>t_0$, $\sigma \geqq 1-c_1/\log t$ $(0<c_1<10^{-3})$ we have $|L(s,\chi)|^{-1} \leqq \log^c t$ and $|\log L(s,\chi)|<c_2 \log^2 t$. By means of these inequalities he gets an estimate for the modulus of the derivative (with respect to $\tau$) of the function

$$f(s, \tau) = \prod_{p \equiv 1 \pmod l} \left(1+\frac{\tau(l-1)}{p^s}\right), \ \tau \in (0, 1], \ p \text{ and } l \text{ primes,}$$

used in his previous paper [Izv. Akad. Nauk Kazah. SSR Ser. Mat. Meh. **1959**, no. 8 (12), 70–87]. This leads to an asymptotic estimate (given without proof) for the number of absolute Abelian fields of a certain type.

*E. Fogels* (Riga)

**M15-33** **(31# 5849 )**

**Spira, Robert**

**Zero-free regions of $\zeta^{(k)}(s)$.**

*J. London Math. Soc.* **40** (1965), 677–682.

The author gives some bounds for regions free of zeros of $\zeta^{(k)}(s)$ in the right- and left-half planes. Also, a table of zeros of $\zeta'$ and $\zeta''$ in the region $-1 \leqq \sigma \leqq 5$, $0 \leqq t \leqq 100$ is provided.

*S. Knapowski* (Gainesville, Fla.)

**M15-34** **(32# 5608 )**

**Chen Jing-run [Ch'en Ching-jun]**

**On the order of $\zeta(\frac{1}{2}+it)$.**

*Acta Math. Sinica* **15** (1965), 159–173 (*Chinese*); *translated as Chinese Math.—Acta* **6** (1965), 463–478.

For the Riemann-zeta function, the author proves that $\zeta(\frac{1}{2}+it)=O(t^{6/37})$. Apparently he did not know of W. Haneke's paper [Acta Arith. **8** (1962/63), 357–430; MR **28** #1179], published two years earlier, where essentially the same result, namely, $\zeta(\frac{1}{2}+it)=O(t^{6/37}\log t)$, was obtained. Like Szu-hoa Min [Trans. Amer. Math. Soc. **65** (1949), 448–472; MR **11**, 84] and Haneke, he uses the two-dimensional method of estimating trigonometrical sums, based on ideas of Weyl, van der Corput and Titchmarsh. Then, as in Haneke's proof, the resulting Hessians are more carefully estimated than was done by Szu-hoa Min.

*O. H. Körner* (Marburg)

Citations: MR 11, 84c = M15-8; MR 28# 1179 = M15-29.

Referred to in M15-35.

**M15-35** **(34# 5773 )**

**Chen, Jing-run [Ch'en Ching-jun]**

**On the order of $\zeta(\frac{1}{2}+it)$.**

*Sci. Sinica* **14** (1965), 522–538.

This article is identical to one which has already been reviewed [Acta Math. Sinica **15** (1965), 159–173; translated as Chinese Math.—Acta **6** (1965), 463–478; MR **32** #5608].

Citations: MR 32# 5608 = M15-34.

**M15-36** **(32# 7517 )**

**Dixon, R. D.; Schoenfeld, Lowell**

**The size of the Riemann zeta-function at places symmetric with respect to the point $\frac{1}{2}$.**

*Duke Math. J.* **33** (1966), 291–292.

R. Spira [same J. **32** (1965), 247–250; MR **31** #1232] recently proved that the Riemann zeta-function satisfies $|\zeta(1-s)|>|\zeta(s)|$ for all $s$ with $\zeta(s)\neq 0$, $t \geqq 10$, and $\frac{1}{2}<\sigma<1$. The authors give a simpler proof for this inequality and extend its validity to $|t| \geqq 6.8$.

*O. H. Körner* (Marburg)

Citations: MR 31# 1232 = M30-41.

Referred to in M15-42.

**M15-37** **(33# 4025 )**

**Urazbaev, B. M.**

**On the behavior of the function $1/L(s, \chi)$ in the critical strip. (Russian)**

*Proc. First Kazakh Interuniv. Sci. Conf. on Math. Mech.* (*October* 17–22, 1963) (*Russian*), *pp.* 138–139. *Izdat. "Nauka" Kazah. SSR, Alma-Ata,* 1965.

The author formulates three theorems about the behavior of the function $1/\mathscr{L}(s, x)$ in the critical strip ($x$ being Dirichlet characters for a fixed modulus $k \geqq 2$). Instead of proofs, he gives outlines from which one can construct the demonstrations of these theorems. Here is the first one. Theorem I: Let $\mathscr{L}(s, x)$ be a Dirichlet function with fixed modulus $k \geqq 2$, and let $t \geqq t_0$, $\sigma \geqq 1-\eta(\lg t)^{-10/11-\varepsilon}$ be a Čudakov region, in which $\mathscr{L}(s,x)\neq 0$. Then one has the estimate $1/|\mathscr{L}(s,x)| \leqq e^{c(\lg t)^{1/11-\varepsilon}}$ $(s=\sigma+it)$ for $t \geqq t_0$, $\sigma \geqq 1-\eta_1(\lg t)^{-10/11-\varepsilon}$ ($\eta_1$ $(<\eta)$ and $\varepsilon$ $(>0)$ are arbitrary numbers, $c$ an absolute constant $(>0)$).

*C. Karanikolov* (Sofia)

**M15-38** **(34# 5779 )**

**Richert, H.-E.**

**Zur Abschätzung der Riemannschen Zetafunktion in der Nähe der Vertikalen $\sigma=1$.**

*Math. Ann.* **169** (1967), 97–101.

This elegantly written note expounds the inequality $|\zeta(\sigma+it)|<ct^{100(1-\sigma)^{3/2}}\log^{2/3} t$ $(\frac{1}{2} \leqq \sigma \leqq 1,\ t \geqq 2,\ c$ numerical$)$, with a similar result for the Hurwitz $\zeta(s, w)$-function. A combination of van der Corput's and Vinogradov's methods is used throughout.

*S. Knapowski* (Coral Gables, Fla.)

**M15-39** **(35# 4173 )**

**Deuring, Max**

**Asymptotische Entwicklungen der Dirichletschen $L$-Reihen.**

*Math. Ann.* **168** (1967), 1–30.

In his edition of Riemann's manuscripts, C. L. Siegel published in 1932 an asymptotic expansion of Riemann's zeta-function $\zeta(\sigma+it)$ for $t\to\infty$ [Quellen und Studien Geschichte Math.-Astronom. Phys. **2** (1932), 45–80; reprinted in C. L. Siegel, *Gesammelte Abhandlungen*, Vol. I, pp. 275–310, Springer, Berlin, 1966; see MR **33** #5441]. Later, Siegel generalized these ideas to expansions of Dirichlet's $L$-series [Ann. of Math. **44** (1943), 143–172*; reprinted in C. L. Siegel, *Gesammelte Abhandlungen*, Vol. II, pp. 360–389, Springer, Berlin, 1966; see MR **33** #5441] using a simplification due to R. O. Kuz'min [Dokl. Akad. Nauk SSSR **2** (1934), 398–400; Izv. Akad. Nauk SSSR Ser. Mat. **7** (1934), 1470–1491]. The present author generalizes the expansions of Dirichlet's $L$-series to the modulus $n$, $L(s, \chi)$, by introducing a parameter $m$, where $m$ is an integer and $1 \leqq m \leqq n$. His asymptotic expansion of $L(\sigma+it, \chi)$ for $t\to\infty$ holds for any character $\chi$ modulo $n$, i.e., the characters are not restricted to primitive characters modulo $n$. The proofs are given for both $m$ and $n$ odd.

For complex variables $u$, $\tau$ with $R\tau>0$, define $\phi(u,\tau)=\int_{\nearrow 0}(e^z-1)^{-1}\exp(i\tau z^2/4\pi^2+uz)\,dz$, the path of integration being the straight line $z=x\cdot\exp(\pi i/4)+i\beta$, $-\infty<x<\infty$, $\beta$ a constant with $0<\beta<2\pi$. In § 1 the author

*MR 4, 189C = M25-4.

computes the value of the integral $\phi(u, m/n)$, $m, n = 1, 2, \cdots$ (formula (5)). The law of reciprocity for Gaussian sums is derived from this result by choosing special values for $u$.

For complex variables $s$, $\alpha$ and positive integers $m, n$, let $F(s; m, n, \alpha) = \int_{\nearrow 0} (e^z-1)^{-1}z^{s-1} \exp(imz^2/4\pi n + \alpha z)\, dz$. In § 2 the author uses formula (5) for odd $m$ and $n$ to give a representation of $L(s, \chi)$, $\chi$ modulo $n$, in terms of a certain sum of the integrals $F(1-s; m, n, r/2n)$ and $F(1-s; m, n, 1-r/2n)$, where $r$ runs over a system of odd residues modulo $n$ (formulas (21), (30)). Here $m \geqq 1$ is an arbitrary odd integer and the system of odd residues $r$ modulo $n$ can be chosen at will, too. Applications of formula (21) to the representation of $\zeta(s)$ are given.

In the last section, the saddle point method is applied to derive an asymptotic expansion of the integral $F(\sigma+it; m, n, \alpha)$ for $t \to \infty$ under the restrictions $m \leqq n$, $0 \leqq \alpha \leqq 1$; for convenience $0 \leqq \sigma \leqq 1$ and $t \geqq 2\pi \cdot 100$ are assumed. The sums and integrals occurring are carefully estimated; formula (5) is used to express the $j$th partial derivative with respect to $u$ of $\phi(u, 2m/n)$ in appropriate terms.

{Reviewer's remarks: The elimination of $\zeta(s, 1-\nu/n)$, $\nu = 0, \cdots, n-1$, from equation (12) is not correct as it stands because (14) holds only for $(\nu, n) = 1$. However, the author has communicated another proof of the final result (formula (21)) to the reviewer, as follows. Denote the bracket $\{\cdots\}$ in (21) by $Q(s; m, n, r) \cdot \exp(-\pi i s/2)$; then (21) becomes

$$n\Gamma(s)g(s, \chi)L(s, \chi) = \sum_{r \pmod n;\, r \text{ odd}} a(\chi, r)Q(s; m, n, r), \qquad n \text{ odd}.$$

Formula (12) can be written as

$$Q(s; m, n, r) = \Gamma(s) \sum_{\nu=0}^{n-1} \exp(-\pi i m\nu^2/n) \times \left[\exp\left(-\pi i\left(\frac{r\nu}{n} - \frac{s}{2}\right)\right) + \exp\left(\pi i\left(\frac{r\nu}{n} - \frac{s}{2}\right)\right)\right] n^{-s}\zeta\left(s, 1-\frac{\nu}{n}\right),$$

where $r$ runs through a system of odd residues modulo $n$. Thus one has a system of $n$ linear equations for the $n$ unknowns $\zeta(s, 1-\nu/n)$. Solving this system for the $\zeta(s, 1-\nu/n)$, $L(s, \chi)$ can be obtained by using the well-known formula $L(s, \chi) = n^{-s} \sum_{l=0}^{n-1} \chi(l)\zeta(s, l/n)$, $n > 1$.

{There is an error on page 9, second line from the bottom; so formula (30) holds only when $\chi$ is a primitive character. For the general case, the second term of the sum of (30) must be replaced by

$$(2\pi)^s n^{-s}\Gamma(s)^{-1}g(s, \chi)^{-1} \sum_{l=1}^{M} \tau(\chi_n|\zeta_n^l)l^{s-1},$$

where $\tau(\chi_n|\zeta_n^l)$ is the Gaussian sum in Hasse's notation [see H. Hasse, *Vorlesungen über Zahlentheorie*, 422–430, Springer, Berlin, 1950; MR **14**, 534; second revised edition, 1964; MR **32** #5569; Russian translation of first edition, Izdat. Inostran. Lit., Moscow, 1953; MR **16**, 569]. The constant 21/20 in formula (38) should be replaced by 95/81; otherwise $t$ must be chosen larger than in formula (34).} *Werner G. H. Schaal* (Marburg)

Citations: MR 4, 189c = M25-4; MR 14, 534b = Z02-23; MR 16, 569a = Z02-24; MR 32# 5569 = Z02-25; MR 33# 5441 = Z25-23.

### M15-40 (36# 1400)

**Götze, Friedhelm**

**Mittelwerteigenschaften der Riemannschen Zeta-Funktion.**

*J. Math. Soc. Japan* **19** (1967), 426–436.

The author proves the following generalization of the mean value theorem of G. H. Hardy and J. E. Littlewood [Acta Math. **41** (1917), 119–196, 151] and F. V. Atkinson [Quart. J. Math. Oxford Ser. **10** (1939), 122–128]. Let $K(n, x, t)$ be the hypergeometric kernel $K(n, x, t) =$

$$(e^{\pi t}F(\tfrac{1}{2}+it, n, 1; x) + e^{-\pi t}F(\tfrac{1}{2}-it, n, 1; x))/(e^{\pi t}+e^{-\pi t})$$

and $\operatorname{Re}(n) < \frac{1}{2}$, $-3\pi/2 < \operatorname{arc} x/i < \pi/2$. Then

$$\lim_{\delta\to+0}(\delta^{1-n}/\log \delta) \int_0^\infty |\zeta(\tfrac{1}{2}+it)|^2 K(n, x, t)e^{-\delta t}\, dt = -(i/x)^n,$$

where $\zeta(s)$ denotes the Riemann zeta function. The earlier mean value theorem is obtained for $n = 0$.

*O. H. Körner* (Marburg)

### M15-41 (37# 1324)

**Berlowitz, B.**

**Extensions of a theorem of Hardy.**

*Acta Arith.* **14** (1967/68), 203–207.

Let $f(s) = \pi^{-s/2}\Gamma(s/2)\zeta(s)$, where $\zeta(s)$ is the Riemann zeta function. G. H. Hardy [C. R. Acad. Sci. Paris **158** (1914), 1012–1014] has shown that $f(\frac{1}{2}+it)$ vanishes infinitely often as $t \to \infty$. By simple extensions of ideas of Hardy and Ramanujan, the author shows that for any real $\lambda$, $0 < \lambda < 1$, the real part of $f(\lambda+it)$ vanishes infinitely often and also the imaginary part of $f(\lambda+it)$ vanishes infinitely often as $t \to \infty$. As the author remarks, this is very far from determining whether or not $f(\lambda+it)$ itself vanishes for some $\lambda \neq \frac{1}{2}$. *T. M. Apostol* (Pasadena, Calif.)

Referred to in M25-76.

### M15-42 (41# 5308)

**Spira, Robert**

**On the Riemann zeta function.**

*J. London Math. Soc.* **44** (1969), 325–328.

This paper describes the results of some exploratory calculation of $|\zeta(s)|$ and its derivative and logarithmic derivative with respect to the variable $\sigma = \operatorname{Re}(s) < \frac{1}{2}$.

A theorem due to L. Schoenfeld and based on R. D. Dixon and Schoenfeld [Duke Math. J. **33** (1966), 291–292; MR **32** #7517] is sketched. This states that

$$|\operatorname{Re}\{\zeta'(\tfrac{1}{2}+it)/\zeta(\tfrac{1}{2}+it)\} + \tfrac{1}{2}\log|t| - \tfrac{1}{2}\log 2\pi - (1/48)t^{-2} < (1/32)t^{-4}|$$

holds when $|t| > 3.8$ and when $\zeta(\frac{1}{2}+t) \neq 0$.

It follows that on the critical line, $\zeta'(s)$ can vanish only because $s$ is a double root of $\zeta(s)$.

*D. H. Lehmer* (Berkeley, Calif.)

Citations: MR 32# 7517 = M15-36.

## M20 REAL ZEROS OF $L(s, \chi)$; RESULTS ON $L(1, \chi)$

See also Section R14.

See also reviews D99-23, E16-2, E16-5, E16-11, E16-18, E16-30, E16-56, E44-25, L25-4, M05-9, M10-20, M25-5, M25-79, M55-40, N04-58, N68-37, N68-39, R12-37, R14-21, R14-104, R18-79, R26-19.

### M20-1 (5, 142e)

**Linnik, U. V. On a conditional theorem by J. E. Littlewood.** C. R. (Doklady) Acad. Sci. URSS (N.S.) **37**, 122–124 (1942).

Let $L(s, -\Delta) = \sum(-\Delta|n)n^{-s}$, where $-\Delta$ is a fundamental negative discriminant. J. E. Littlewood [Proc. London Math. Soc. (2) **27**, 358–372 (1927)] has proved, on the condition that $L(s, -\Delta)$ has no zeros with real part greater than $\frac{1}{2}$, that there exist infinitely many $\Delta_i$ such that $L(1, -\Delta)<c_1/\ln\ln\Delta$, where $c_1$ is a constant. It is now proved without this condition that such a sequence exists satisfying $L(1, -\Delta)<c_2/(\ln\ln\Delta)^{\frac{1}{2}}$. The proof starts with a demonstration that, if $P_k$ is a product of $k$ consecutive primes $q$ ($>17$) satisfying $(5|q)=-1$ and if $N_k=aP_k$, where $a$ ($=7$, 11, 13 or 17) is chosen so that $N_k\equiv 3 \pmod 8$, then the number $r(N_k)$ of representations of $N_k$ in $x^2+y^2+z^2+5t^2$ does not exceed $c_3N_k/(\ln\ln N_k)^{\frac{1}{2}}$. By counting the number of solutions $t$ of $80t^2\equiv N \pmod{m^2}$ in the interval $I=[N_k^{\frac{1}{2}}/20,\ N_k^{\frac{1}{2}}/10]$, it is seen that there are at least $s(>c_4N^{\frac{1}{2}})$ numbers $M_{1k}, \cdots, M_{sk}$ of the form $N_k-80t^2$ with $t$ in $I$, which are not divisible by any square $r^2$ with $r>10^6$, if $N_k>10^{10}$. Then, if $r_3(M)$ is the number of representations of $M$ as a sum of three squares,

$$r(N_k)\geqq c_5\sum_{j=1}^{s} r_3(M_{jk})\geqq c_6\sum_{j=1}^{s} h(-M_{jk}),$$

while, as shown by Dirichlet, if $-\Delta_j$ is squarefree, $h(-\Delta_j)=(\sqrt{\Delta_j}/\pi)L(1, -\Delta_j)$. The result follows.

*G. Pall* (Montreal, Que.).

Referred to in M20-4.

## M20-2 (7, 243k)

**Chowla, S. On the $K$-analogue of a result in the theory of the Riemann zeta function.** Proc. Benares Math. Soc. **5**, 23–27 (1943) = Proc. Lahore Philos. Soc. **6**, no. 1, 9–12 (1944).

The author proves that for any $\epsilon>0$ there exists a real primitive character $\chi \pmod k$, for some $k$, such that $L_\chi(1)<\epsilon$. Much more precise results were proved by Littlewood [Proc. London Math. Soc. (2) **27**, 358–372 (1928)] on the assumption of the generalised Riemann hypothesis. Let $p_1, \cdots, p_g$ be the first $g$ odd primes, $a=4p_1\cdots p_g$, $b$ any integer with $(b/p_1)=\cdots=(b/p_g)=-1$, $b\equiv 1 \pmod 4$. Let

$$S(x)=\sum_{n=1}^{x}\sum_{m=1}^{\infty}\frac{1}{m}\left(\frac{m}{4an+b}\right),$$

where the symbol is the Jacobi symbol if $m$ is odd and prime to $4an+b$, otherwise 0. The author proves that $\limsup_{x\to\infty} S(x)/x<\epsilon(g)$, where $\epsilon(g)\to 0$ as $g\to\infty$. He deduces his result from this by considering the values of $n$ for which $4an+b$ is quadratfrei, so that the Jacobi symbol is a primitive character mod $2(4an+b)$. There are several misprints.

*H. Davenport* (London).

Referred to in M20-4.

## M20-3 (7, 416a)

**Wintner, Aurel. The fundamental lemma in Dirichlet's theory of the arithmetical progressions.** Amer. J. Math. **68**, 285–292 (1946).

Let $\chi(n)$ be any multiplicative function (that is, $\chi(mn)=\chi(m)\chi(n)$ for all positive integers $m$ and $n$) which satisfies the restriction (*) $\chi(p)\geqq -1$ for every prime $p$. Suppose also that the Dirichlet series $J(s)=\sum_{n=1}^{n=\infty}\chi^2(n)n^{-s}$ is convergent for $s>1$. Then so, clearly, is $L(s)=\sum_{n=1}^{n=\infty}\chi(n)n^{-s}$. The author proves that, if $L(s)$ admits across the point $s=1$ an analytic continuation which is regular for $\frac{1}{2}\leqq s\leqq 1$, then $L(1)\neq 0$. This result is a generalisation of Dirichlet's well-known result for a real nonprincipal character $\chi(n)$, and also of a more general result due to Ingham in which (in the case when $\chi$ is real) $\chi(p)$ is restricted to the values 0, $\pm 1$, this restriction being essential to the method of proof [A. E. Ingham, J. London Math. Soc. **5**, 107–112 (1930)]. Landau's theorem on the singularities of a Dirichlet series with positive coefficients occupies a central position in the author's proof, as also in the work of Ingham and earlier writers, and is applied to the function

$$\sum_{n=1}^{\infty}\beta(n)n^{-s}=\zeta(s)L(s)/J(2s),$$

whose coefficients $\beta(n)$ are nonnegative because of (*). If $L(1)=0$, it can be concluded that this series is convergent for $s>\frac{1}{2}$, and this, combined with the assumption regarding the behaviour of $L(s)$ in the neighbourhood of $s=\frac{1}{2}$, eventually produces a contradiction. The author's result raises the interesting question whether the inequality (*) is the best possible. Whether this is so is not known, although the manner in which (*) arises in the proof leaves little doubt that it is.

*R. A. Rankin* (Cambridge, England).

Referred to in M20-8.

## M20-4 (10, 285d)

**Chowla, S. Improvement of a theorem of Linnik and Walfisz.** Proc. London Math. Soc. (2) **50**, 423–429 (1949).

If $\chi$ is a real primitive character modulo $k$ and $L(s,\chi)=\sum_{n=1}^{\infty}\chi(n)n^{-s}$, then it is known [cf. Siegel, Acta Arith. **1**, 83–86 (1935)] that for any positive $\epsilon$ we have $Ak^{-\epsilon}<L(1,\chi)<B\log k$, where $A$ is a positive number depending only on $\epsilon$ and $B$ is an absolute constant. Linnik [C. R. (Doklady) Acad. Sci. URSS (N.S.) **37**, 122–124 (1942); these Rev. **5**, 142] and Walfisz [Trav. Inst. Math. Tbilissi [Trudy Tbiliss. Mat. Inst.] **11**, 57–71 (1942); these Rev. **5**, 254] have both proved that there is a positive constant $C$ such that for infinitely many $k$ we have $L(1,\chi)<C(\log\log k)^{-\frac{1}{2}}$ if $\chi$ is a real primitive character modulo $k$. In the present paper the author proves that there are infinitely many $k$ such that $L(1,\chi)<\{1+o(1)\}\pi^2/(6e^\gamma\log\log k)$ for $\chi$ a real primitive character modulo $k$, $\gamma$ being Euler's constant. The proof is rather simple; it is a sharpening of the method used earlier by the author [Proc. Benares Math. Soc. **5**, 23–27 (1943) = Proc. Lahore Philos. Soc. **6**, no. 1, 9–12 (1944); these Rev. **7**, 243] to prove a result weaker than the Linnik-Walfisz theorem. The sharpening consists of choosing the number $g$ of the earlier paper as $[\log x/(\log\log x)^2]$. [Correction: the inequality signs should be reversed in (21), in (iii) of theorem 1, and in theorem 2.]

*P. T. Bateman.*

Citations: MR 5, 142e = M20-1; MR 5, 254i = E16-5; MR 7, 243k = M20-2.

Referred to in M20-6, M20-13, M55-40.

## M20-5 (10, 285e)

**Chowla, S. On the class-number of the corpus $P(\sqrt{-k})$.** Proc. Nat. Inst. Sci. India **13**, 197–200 (1947).

This paper contains a result similar to that of the paper reviewed above, but in the opposite direction. The author has proved earlier [Math. Z. **38**, 483–487 (1934)] that there is a positive constant $D$ such that for infinitely many $k$ the inequality $L(1,\chi)>D\log\log k$ holds if $\chi$ is a real primitive character modulo $k$. Walfisz [Trav. Inst. Math. Tbilissi [Trudy Tbiliss. Mat. Inst.] **11**, 57–71 (1942); these Rev. **5**, 254] improved this result slightly by showing that for infinitely many $k$ (*) $L(1,\chi)>\{1+o(1)\}e^\gamma\log\log k$ if $\chi$ is a real primitive character modulo $k$, $\gamma$ being Euler's constant. In the present paper the author gives a simpler proof of (*); the method is very much like that used in the paper above.

Corrections. The theorem that $\sum_{n=u}^{v}\chi(n)=O(k^{\frac{1}{2}}\log k)$ for any non-principal character $\chi$ modulo $k$ is erroneously attributed to Davenport. Actually this theorem seems to have been first proved generally by Landau [Nachr. Ges. Wiss. Göttingen. Math.-Phys. Kl. **1918**, 79–97, pp. 85–86]; the basic case of a primitive $\chi$ was first given by Pólya [ibid. 21–29]. Also $\chi$ is consistently written as $x$ (which is also used otherwise) and "$m$ odd" is consistently written as "mod $d$." *P. T. Bateman* (Princeton, N. J.).

Citations: MR 5, 254i = E16-5.

## M20-6 (11, 162f)

**Chowla, S. An improvement of a theorem of Linnik and Walfisz.** Proc. Nat. Inst. Sci. India **15**, 81–84 (1949).

This is a briefer version of the paper by the author in Proc. London Math. Soc. (2) **50**, 423–429 (1949) [these Rev. **10**, 285]. *L. Schoenfeld* (Urbana, Ill.).

Citations: MR 10, 285d = M20-4.

## M20-7 (10, 356c)

**Estermann, T. On Dirichlet's $L$ functions.** J. London Math. Soc. **23**, 275–279 (1948).

Here there is given a complete proof of Siegel's theorem that, if $\chi$ is a real primitive character mod $k$, then, corresponding to each $\epsilon>0$, there is an $A(\epsilon)>0$ such that $L(1,\chi)>A(\epsilon)/k^{\epsilon}$. This proof demands less previous knowledge than both the original proof of Siegel [Acta Arith. **1**, 83–86 (1935)] and a later proof of Heilbronn [Quart. J. Math., Oxford Ser. **9**, 194–195 (1938)]. The only special knowledge required is the product representation of $L(s,\chi)$, the fact that $L(s,\chi)$ is regular for $\sigma>0$ if $\chi$ is a real primitive character mod $k$, $k>1$, $\sum_{n=1}^{k}\chi(n)=0$ for the same type of $\chi$, $L(1,\chi)\neq 0$, and that $\zeta(s)-1/(s-1)$ is regular for $\sigma>0$. In addition, Cauchy's inequality for the coefficients of a Taylor expansion is used. *L. Schoenfeld* (Urbana, Ill.).

Referred to in L25-4, M20-11, P02-5.

## M20-8 (11, 13c)

**Shapiro, George. On the non-vanishing at $s=1$ of certain Dirichlet series.** Amer. J. Math. **71**, 621–626 (1949).

Suppose (i) $f(n)$ is a completely multiplicative function, (ii) $|f(n)|=0$ or 1 for each $n$, so that

$$L(s)\equiv\sum_{1}^{\infty}f(n)n^{-s}=\prod_{p}(1-f(p)p^{-s})^{-1}\quad(\sigma=\Re s>1),$$

(iii) $L(s)$ (regular in $\sigma>1$) admits a regular analytical continuation along the real segment $\frac{1}{2}\leqq s\leqq 1$. Then $L(1)\neq 0$. [For this result, which includes all cases of the fundamental theorem on the nonvanishing of Dirichlet's functions $L(s,\chi)$ on the line $\sigma=1$, see Ingham, J. London Math. Soc. **5**, 107–112 (1930).] For real $f(n)$ Wintner generalised (ii) to (ii'): $f(p)\geqq -1$ for each prime $p$, and $\sum f^2(n)n^{-s}$ is convergent for $\sigma>1$ [same J. **68**, 285–292 (1946); these Rev. **7**, 416]. The aim of the present paper is to relax (ii) without restricting $f(n)$ to be real. Thus theorem I asserts that (ii) may be replaced by (ii''): $f(n)$ is bounded (which means, with (i), that $|f(n)|\leqq 1$). The attempt to extend the discussion to unbounded (complex) $f(n)$ does not lead to a direct generalisation of Wintner's theorem, but yields a somewhat different type of result (theorem II) in which (iii) is relaxed at the cost of more elaborate forms of restriction in (ii). *A. E. Ingham* (Cambridge, England).

Citations: MR 7, 416a = M20-3.

## M20-9 (11, 332c)

**Rosser, J. Barkley. Real roots of Dirichlet $L$-series.** Bull. Amer. Math. Soc. **55**, 906–913 (1949).

Let $\chi$ be a real non-principal character modulo $k$. It is shewn that, for $2\leqq k\leqq 67$, $L(s,\chi)$ has no positive real zeros. For these values of $k$, therefore, the error terms in the asymptotic formulae for $\pi(k,l;x)$ can be improved considerably since they depend upon the abscissae of real zeros of such functions $L(s,\chi)$ [see A. Page, Proc. London Math. Soc. (2) **39**, 116–141 (1935)]. The author expresses $L(s,\chi)$ as a sum

$$\sum_{M=1}^{\infty}f(s,k,M)\Sigma_M$$

where, for $s>0$, $f(s,k,M)$ is positive and

$$\Sigma_M=\sum_{n=1}^{[\frac{1}{2}k]}\chi(n)(k-2n)^M.$$

When considering the positive zeros of $L(s,\chi)$ attention may be confined to primitive characters. It is stated that for all such characters $\chi(n)$ with $k\leqq 67$, except $k=43$ and $k=67$, it is possible to shew, by grouping terms suitably, that $\Sigma_M\geqq 0$; hence $L(s,\chi)\neq 0$ for $s>0$. See also the work of S. Chowla [Acta Arith. **1**, 113–114 (1935)]. For $k=43$ or 67, $\Sigma_3<0$ but it can be shewn that the initial positive terms in the infinite series outweigh the negative terms. This is demonstrated in detail for $k=67$; it is stated that the proof for $k=43$ is similar and easier. The author also states that his method has been tried on all $k\leqq 227$ and that it has been ascertained that, except for the cases $k=148$ and $k=163$, $L(s,\chi)$ has no positive real zeros for $2\leqq k\leqq 227$. The cases $k=148$ and $k=163$ are now being studied. *R. A. Rankin* (Cambridge, England).

Referred to in M20-10.

## M20-10 (12, 804i)

**Rosser, J. Barkley. Real roots of real Dirichlet $L$-series.** J. Research Nat. Bur. Standards **45**, 505–514 (1950).

It is surprisingly hard to prove for an individual discriminant $d$ that $\sum_{n=1}^{\infty}(d/n)n^{-s}>0$ for $s>0$. The author has previously proved this for all $|d|\leqq 227$ except $d=-163$ [Bull. Amer. Math. Soc. **55**, 906–913 (1949); these Rev. **11**, 332]. In this paper the result is also proved for $d=-163$ by first showing numerically that the series is positive for $s=\frac{1}{2}$ and then proving that the series can have at most one zero in $\frac{1}{2}\leqq s<1$. The author also discusses a different method due to Chowla and Selberg [Proc. Nat. Acad. Sci. U. S. A. **35**, 371–374 (1949); these Rev. **11**, 84]. *H. Heilbronn.*

Citations: MR 11, 84d = E44-5; MR 11, 332c = M20-9.

## M20-11 (11, 420e)

**Chowla, S. A new proof of a theorem of Siegel.** Ann. of Math. (2) **51**, 120–122 (1950).

The author gives a slightly simplified proof of Siegel's theorem [Acta Arith. **1**, 83–86 (1935)] that $L(1,\chi)>C(\epsilon)k^{-\epsilon}$, where $\chi$ is a real character mod $k$. See also Estermann [J. London Math. Soc. **23**, 275–279 (1948); these Rev. **10**, 356]. *H. A. Heilbronn* (Bristol).

Citations: MR 10, 356c = M20-7.

Referred to in M20-19, M20-21, Z02-48.

## M20-12 (11, 420f)

**Stoll, W. Eine Bemerkung über die Dirichletschen $L$-Reihen.** Math. Z. **52**, 307–309 (1949).

The author proves a relation which is essentially the identity ($p\equiv 3 \pmod 4$ a prime)

$$\pi^{-1}p^{\frac{1}{2}}\sum_{n=1}^{\infty}(n/p)n^{-1}=-\sum_{n=1}^{p-1}n(n/p).$$

Since the finite sum is odd, the infinite series is different from zero. All this was known to Dirichlet [J. Reine Angew. Math. **21**, 134–155 (1840)]. *H. A. Heilbronn* (Bristol).

## M20-13 (12, 244b)

**Bateman, P. T., Chowla, S., and Erdös, P. Remarks on the size of $L(1,\chi)$.** Publ. Math. Debrecen **1**, 165–182 (1950).

Let $(d/n)$ denote the Kronecker symbol,

$$L_d(1) = \sum_{n=1}^{\infty} n^{-1}(d/n),$$

$A = \limsup L_d(1) (\log\log d)^{-1}$ and $a = \liminf L_d(1) \log\log d$ for prime $d$ as $d \to \infty$; $B$ and $b$ are defined similarly as $d \to -\infty$. The authors prove that $A \geqslant (18)^{-1}e^{\gamma}$, $B \geqslant (18)^{-1}e^{\gamma}$, $a \leqslant 3\pi^2 e^{-\gamma}$, $b \leqq 3\pi^2 e^{-\gamma}$, and announce without proof the stronger results $A \geqslant \frac{1}{4}e^{\gamma}$, $B \geqslant \frac{1}{4}e^{\gamma}$, $a \leqslant \frac{2}{3}\pi^2 e^{-\gamma}$, $b \leqslant \frac{2}{3}\pi^2 e^{-\gamma}$. Similar results were obtained by Chowla [Proc. London Math. Soc. (2) **50**, 423–429 (1949); these Rev. **10**, 285]. The proof is based on the sieve method of Linnik and Rényi [J. Math. Pures Appl. (9) **28**, 137–149 (1949); these Rev. **11**, 161]. The authors also give a slight numerical improvement of the classical inequality $L(1, \chi) < \log k$, where $\chi$ is any non-principal character mod $k$. The following misprints were communicated by one of the authors: p. 167, line 12, replace 5/4 by 7/4; p. 167, second line from bottom, replace $\sum_{m=1}^{m}$ by $\sum_{n=1}^{m}$; p. 171, fifth line from bottom, replace $\log(\frac{1}{2}\log\log x - \log\log\log x)$ by

$$\log(\tfrac{1}{2}\log\log x - 2\log\log\log x);$$

p. 174, line 7, replace $p\varepsilon\mathfrak{S}$ by $q\varepsilon\mathfrak{S}$; p. 176, line 6, replace $b\varepsilon\mathfrak{S}$ by $q\varepsilon\mathfrak{S}$; p. 177, last line, replace $\frac{1}{2}b(\log x)1+\delta$ by $\frac{1}{2}b(\log x)^{1+\delta}$; Chowla [3] in the references, replace Proc. Nat. Acad. Sci. India by Proc. Nat. Inst. Sci. India.

*H. Heilbronn* (Bristol).

Citations: MR 10, 285d = M20-4; MR 11, 161c = M55-6.

Referred to in L10-14, Z02-53.

## M20-14 (12, 482a)

**Linnik, Yu. V. An elementary proof of Siegel's theorem based on the method of I. M. Vinogradov. (With an appendix of a short analytical proof.)** Izvestiya Akad. Nauk SSSR. Ser. Mat. **14**, 327–342 (1950). (Russian)

The author gives two proofs of Siegel's inequality [Acta Arith. **1**, 83–86 (1935)] that $L_d(1) > \gamma(\epsilon)|d|^{-\epsilon}$ for every positive $\epsilon$, and positive $\gamma$ depending on $\epsilon$ only, where $L_d(s)$ is the Dirichlet series whose coefficients are the Kronecker symbol $(d/n)$. The proofs are not very illuminating, though the first one is elementary in the technical sense.

*H. Heilbronn* (Bristol).

Referred to in E16-14.

## M20-15 (13, 439a)

**Chowla, S., and Erdös, P. A theorem on the distribution of the values of $L$-functions.** J. Indian Math. Soc. (N.S.) **15**, 11–18 (1951).

Let $(d/n)$ be the Kronecker symbol and

$$L_d(s) = \sum_{n=1}^{\infty} n^{-s}(d/n)$$

for real $s > 0$. For fixed $s > 0$, let $g(a, x)$ be the number of integers $d$ such that $1 \leqq d \leqq x$, $d$ is congruent to 0 or 1 (mod 4), $d$ is not a square and $L_d(s) < a$. The authors prove that if $s$ is a fixed number greater than $\frac{3}{4}$, then $\lim_{x\to\infty} 2g(a, x)/x = g(a)$ exists; further, $g(0) = 0$, $g(\infty) = 1$ and $g(a)$ is continuous and strictly increasing. One consequence of this result is that $L_d(s) > 0$ for "almost all" $d$. The proof depends on Polya's estimate for character sums as well as special properties of the sub-series $\sum n^{-s}(d/n)$ in which the summation is extended over all positive integers $n$ whose greatest prime factor does not exceed a given number $t$. *L. Schoenfeld.*

Referred to in R14-104.

## M20-16 (14, 728b)

**Rodosskiĭ, K. A. On some estimates of the quantities $L(1, \chi)$.** Doklady Akad. Nauk SSSR (N.S.) **86**, 889–891 (1952). (Russian)

**Let $D$ be a positive integer, $4\log\log D/\log D < \eta < 1/10$. The author shows that there are only $O(D^{8\eta}\log^8 D)$ $L$-series formed by characters mod $D$, which do not satisfy the inequality**

$$\bigl|\log|L(1, \chi)|\bigr| < O(1) + \log \eta^{-1}.$$

**For the proof the author refers to a previous paper [Ukrain. Mat. Žurnal 3, 399–403 (1951)] (not accessible to the reviewer). The author also gives the following inequalities**

$$L(1, \chi_D^{(2)})L(1, \chi_{dD}^{(2)}) = O(\log d \log(dD)),$$
$$L(1, \chi_d^{(4)}\chi_D^{(2)}) = O(\log^{\frac{1}{2}} d \log^{\frac{1}{2}}(dD)),$$
$$1 = O(\log D)(L(1, \chi_D^{(2)}) + L(1, \chi_{dD}^{(2)})),$$

**where $\chi^{(2)}$ and $\chi^{(4)}$ denote quadratic and quartic characters and where in the last inequality**

$$(d, D) = 1, \quad \log d < \log D/\log\log D.$$

***H. Heilbronn* (Bristol).**

## M20-17 (15, 402a)

**Gel'fond, A. O. On an elementary approach to some problems from the field of distribution of prime numbers.** Vestnik Moskov. Univ. Ser. Fiz.-Mat. Estest. Nauk **8**, no. 2, 21–26 (1953). (Russian)

Let $\chi$ be a real non-principal character modulo $m$ and $q = \max_{k\geq 1} |\sum_{n=1}^{k} \chi(n)|$. The author gives an elementary proof that $|L(1, \chi)| > c/q \log q$ if $q > q_0$. The proof is based on the identity

$$\sum_{n=1}^{\infty} \chi(n)x^n/(1-x^n) = \sum_{n=1}^{\infty} x^n \prod_{p^s || n} \{1 + \chi(p) + \cdots + \chi^s(p)\}.$$

A lower bound is obtained for the right side by dropping all terms except those for which $n$ is a square; the product is then at least 1. The left side is estimated by a number of partial summations and the identity

$$\frac{\chi(n)}{1-x^n} = \frac{1}{1-x}\frac{\chi(n)}{n} + \frac{1}{1-x}\chi(n)\left\{\frac{1-x}{1-x^n} - \frac{1}{n}\right\}.$$

By taking $x = 1 - c'/(q \log q)^2$, the result is obtained. When Pólya's result that $q \leqq m^{\frac{1}{2}} \log m$ is used the author's result yields the estimate $|L(1, \chi)| > c''/m^{\frac{1}{2}} \log^2 m$ which is inferior to both Siegel's lower bound of $c(\epsilon)/m^{\epsilon}$ and the earlier bound of $C/m^{\frac{1}{2}}$.

A second result, proved in a similar manner, is that if $\Theta(n)$ is a completely multiplicative function taking only the values 0, 1, $-1$ and if $\limsup_{n\to\infty} n^{-\frac{1}{2}} |\sum_{k=1}^{n} \Theta(k)| < 1/12$, then $\sum_{n=1}^{\infty} \Theta(n)/n \neq 0$. By taking $\Theta(k)$ to be Liouville's function $\lambda(k)$, the author shows that the exponent $\frac{1}{2}$ cannot be increased, if the Riemann hypothesis holds.

*L. Schoenfeld* (Urbana, Ill.).

Referred to in M20-23.

## M20-18 (15, 402b)

**Tatuzawa, Tikao. On the product of $L(1, \chi)$.** Nagoya Math. J. **5**, 105–111 (1953).

Let $k$ be a positive integer, let $\omega(k)$ be the number of distinct prime factors of $k$ and let $\lambda_k$ be the product of $L(1, \chi)$ extended over all characters $\chi$ modulo $k$ with the exception of $\chi_0$. Then for each $\epsilon > 0$

$$c(\epsilon)k^{-\epsilon} < \lambda_k < \exp[c\{\log\log k + \omega(k)\}].$$

A similar result is obtained when the product $\lambda_k$ is restricted to the characters for which $\chi(-1)=-1$. From the first result the author obtains upper and lower bounds for the product of the regulator and the class number of the cyclotomic field $P(e^{2\pi i/p})$ for an odd prime $p$; this result is sharper than a general result of R. Brauer [Amer. J. Math. **72**, 739–746 (1950); these Rev. **12**, 482]. From the second result, the author obtains upper and lower bounds for the first factor of the class number of $P(e^{2\pi i/p})$ these bounds being sharper than those of Ankeny and S. Chowla [Proc. Nat. Acad. Sci. U. S. A. **35**, 529–532 (1949); these Rev. **11**, 230]. *L. Schoenfeld* (Urbana, Ill.).

Citations: MR 11, 230d = R18-8; MR 12, 482g = R42-6.

Referred to in R18-50, R18-68, R18-72.

## M20-19 (18, 563e)

**Rodosskiĭ, K. A. On the exceptional zero.** Izv. Akad. Nauk SSSR. Ser. Mat. **20** (1956), 667–672. (Russian)

The author considers the real zeros of $L$-functions formed with real primitive residue characters modulo $D>100$. For fixed $\varepsilon \in (0; 0.025]$ it is shown that there is at most one zero $\beta$ of one exceptional $L$-function of this class which fails to satisfy

$$1-\beta \geqq \min\{\varepsilon;\ 0{\cdot}015 \ln^{-5} D\cdot D^{-26\varepsilon}\}.$$

A consequence is that, without exception,

$$1-\beta \geqq C(\varepsilon)\cdot D^{-30\varepsilon},$$

effectively a result due to Siegel [see, e.g., S. Chowla, Ann. of Math. (2) **51** (1950), 120–122; MR **11**, 420].

*F. V. Atkinson* (Canberra).

Citations: MR 11, 420e = M20-11.

## M20-20 (22# 10972)

**Chowla, S.; Mordell, L. J. Note on the nonvanishing of $L(1)$.** Proc. Amer. Math. Soc. **12** (1961), 283–284.

The authors give a simple proof of the fact that

$$\sum_{m=1}^{\infty}\left(\frac{m}{p}\right)\frac{1}{m} \neq 0$$

where $p$ is any odd prime, and $\left(\frac{m}{p}\right)$ is the Legendre symbol. The novelty of the proof consists in an ingenious use of the Gaussian product

$$P = \prod_{n \text{ non-res.}}\left(1-e\left(\frac{n}{p}\right)\right)\Big/\prod_{r \text{ residue}}\left(1-e\left(\frac{r}{p}\right)\right).$$

*D. J. Newman* (New York)

## M20-21 (23# A127)

**Turán, P.**

**A note on the real zeros of Dirichlet's $L$-functions.**

*Acta Arith.* **5** (1959), 309–314.

For $s=\sigma+it$, the $L$-functions are defined for $\sigma>1$ by

$$L(s,\chi) = \sum_{n=1}^{\infty}\frac{\chi(n)}{n^s},$$

where $\chi(n)$ is a character (mod $k$). In connection with the well-known phenomenon of a possible real "exceptional zero" of the $L$-functions [see, e.g., Page, Proc. London Math. Soc. (2) **39** (1935), 116–142], the author proves the following theorem, in which $\gamma=\gamma(\chi)$ denotes the greatest real zero of any $L(s,\chi)$ belonging to the modulus $k$: with $P=\exp\{(\log k \log\log k)^2\}$, we have, for $k>c$,

$$(\tfrac{1}{2}\leqq)\ \ \gamma(\chi) \leqq \frac{2\log\log\log k}{\log\log k} + \frac{1}{\log P}\max_{1\leqq X\leqq P}\log\Big|\sum_{n\leqq X}\Lambda(n)\chi(n)\Big|$$

for each $\chi\neq\chi_0$ (mod $k$) (if there are any real zeros of $L(s,\chi)$). Here $\Lambda(n)$ is the well-known "Dirichlet symbol" in the theory of primes. The reference to the reviewer on p. 310, footnote 3, is to his paper, Ann. of Math. (2) **51** (1950), 120–122 [MR **11**, 420].

*S. Chowla* (Boulder, Colo.)

Citations: MR 11, 420e = M20-11.

Referred to in N04-58.

## M20-22 (23# A1613)

**Bateman, Paul T.**

**Theorems implying the non-vanishing of $\sum\chi(m)m^{-1}$ for real residue-characters.**

*J. Indian Math. Soc. (N.S.)* **23** (1959), 101–115 (1961).

Let $h$ be a given real-valued function on the positive integers, and let the functions $S$ and $f$ on the positive integers be defined in terms of $h$ by:

$$S(n) = \sum_{m=1}^{n} h(m), \quad f(n) = \sum_{m|n} h(m).$$

The author gives elementary proofs of the following theorems. Theorem A: If $S(n)\geqq -K$ $(K\geqq 0)$ for all $n$, if $f(n)\geqq 0$ for all $n$, and if $\sum_{n=1}^{\infty} f(n) > \frac{1}{2}K$, then

$$\liminf_{n\to\infty}\sum_{m=1}^{n} h(m)/m > 0.$$

Theorem B: If $S(n)\geqq -K$ $(K\geqq 0)$ for all $n$, if $f(n)\geqq 0$ for all $n$, and if $f(n)\geqq 1$ whenever $n$ is a square, then

$$\liminf_{n\to\infty}\sum_{m=1}^{n} h(m)/m \geqq 32/(75K+150).$$

Theorem B is an improvement of a result of Čudakov and Rodosskiĭ [Dokl. Akad. Nauk SSSR **73** (1950), 1137–1139; MR **12**, 393] on generalized characters. Since the hypotheses of both Theorems A and B are satisfied when $h$ is a real non-principal character $\chi$ [see, e.g., LeVeque, *Topics in number theory, Vol. 2*, Addison-Wesley, Reading, Mass., 1956; Theorems 6-6 and 6-16; MR **18**, 283], an immediate corollary of either theorem is the non-vanishing of the Dirichlet $L$-series $\sum_{m=1}^{\infty}\chi(m)/m^s$ at $s=1$. This result in turn is crucial in Dirichlet's celebrated proof of the existence of infinitely many primes in arithmetic progressions with relatively prime first term and common difference. The author also discusses and proves theorems in which the conditions on $f(n)$ in Theorems A and B are replaced by conditions on the Riesz means $\sum_{n\leqq x}(1-n/x)^r f(n)$.

*A. Sklar* (Chicago, Ill.)

Citations: MR 12, 393f = L25-4; MR 18, 283b = Z01-38.

Referred to in M20-24, M20-30.

## M20-23 (23# A3725)

**Bombieri, Enrico**

**Limitazioni riguardanti somme di caratteri reali e somme di funzioni completamente moltiplicative. (English summary)**

*Ist. Lombardo Accad. Sci. Lett. Rend. A* **94** (1960), 642–649.

Let $\theta(n)$ be a (totally) multiplicative function, taking only the values 0, $\pm 1$, and let $\chi(n)$ be a real, non-principal character mod $k$. The author proves the following. Theorem 1: If $q=\max_{m>1}(-\sum_{n=1}^{m}\chi(n))$, then $L(1,\chi)>(\pi/16)(q+1)^{-1}$. Theorem 2: The conditions $\sum_{n=1}^{\infty}\theta(n)n^{-1}<\infty$ and $\liminf_{m\to\infty} m^{-1/2}\sum_{n=1}^{m}\theta(n)>-|\zeta(\frac{1}{2})|^{-1}$ imply that $\sum_{n=1}^{\infty}\theta(n)n^{-1}>0$. The proof uses the identity (already used by Gel'fond [Vestnik Mosk. Univ. Ser. Fiz.-Mat. Estest. Nauk **8** (1953), 21–26; MR **15**, 402] in the proof of similar theorems)

$$\sum_{n=1}^{\infty}\theta(n)x^n(1-x^n)^{-1} = \sum_{n=1}^{\infty}x^n\prod_{p^s\|n}(1+\theta(p)+\cdots+\theta^s(p))$$

(here $p^s$ is the highest power of $p$ that divides $n$) and also $\sum_{n=1}^{\infty}x^{n^2}\sim\frac{1}{2}\pi^{1/2}(1-x)^{-1/2}$ for $x\to 1^-$. Comparing these results with Gel'fond's theorems, it is of interest to observe that here the hypotheses involve only one-sided inequalities. *E. Grosswald* (Philadelphia, Pa.)

Citations: MR 15, 402a = M20-17.
Referred to in M20-29, M20-30.

## M20-24 (24# A2571)

**Wilf, H. S.**

**On the monotonicity of certain Riesz means.**

*J. London Math. Soc.* **37** (1962), 121–122.

In attempting to simplify the proof of Dirichlet's theorem on primes in an arithmetic progression, Bateman ["Theorems implying the non-vanishing of $\sum\chi(m)m^{-1}$ for real residue characters $\chi$", J. Indian Math. Soc. (to appear)*] has made use of properties of the function

$$D_r(x) = \int_0^x\left(1-\frac{y}{x}\right)^r dy - \sum_{m\le x}\left(1-\frac{m}{x}\right)^r,$$

where $r>0$ is not necessarily an integer. In the present paper the following result is proved. $D_r(x)$ is monotone [respectively, of bounded variation] on $(0,\infty)$ if and only if $r\ge 2$ [respectively, $r\ge 1$]. Also the complete asymptotic expansion of $D_r(x)$ is obtained for large $x$.

*L. Carlitz* (Durham, N.C.)

*MR 23 #A1613 = M20-22.

Citations: MR 23# A1613 = M20-22.

## M20-25 (25# 2060)

**Bateman, Paul T.; Grosswald, Emil**

**Imaginary quadratic fields with unique factorization.**

*Illinois J. Math.* **6** (1962), 187–192.

The authors prove the following theorem. If $p>163$ and if the ring of integers of the imaginary quadratic field with discriminant $-p$ has unique factorization, then

$$L_p(s) = \sum_1^{\infty}\left(\frac{n}{p}\right)\frac{1}{n^s}\quad (s>0)$$

has a real zero greater than

$$1-\frac{6}{\pi\sqrt{p}}\left(1+\frac{6\log(p/4)}{\pi\sqrt{p}}\right).$$

It is interesting to compare this with an unpublished result of Rosser that there are no zeros of $L_p(s)$ greater than $1-6/\pi\sqrt{p}$ [see also the reviewer and A. Selberg, Proc. Nat. Acad. Sci. U.S.A. **35** (1949), 371–374; MR **11**, 84; the reviewer, Quart. J. Math. Oxford Ser. **5** (1934), 302–303].

*S. Chowla* (Boulder, Colo.)

Citations: MR 11, 84d = E44-5.

## M20-26 (29# 4741)

**Fluch, Wolfgang**

**Zur Abschätzung von $L(1,\chi)$.**

*Nachr. Akad. Wiss. Göttingen Math.-Phys. Kl. II* **1964**, 101–102.

The author shows that there exists an absolute constant $c$ with the following property: For every integer $k\ge 2$ and for every real non-principal character mod $k$, we have either $L'(1,\chi)>1$ or $L(1,\chi)\ge c/(\log k)$ (or both).

*N. G. de Bruijn* (Eindhoven)

## M20-27 (30# 1986)

**Chowla, S.**

**A special infinite series.**

*Norske Vid. Selsk. Forh.* (*Trondheim*) **37** (1964), 85–87.

Reproduction of a portion of a letter from C. L. Siegel to Chowla, giving an elegant proof of the following theorem: If $f$ is an integer-valued number-theoretic function, not identically zero, such that for some fixed integer $m$, $f$ is periodic of period $m$, $f(n)=0$ if $(n,m)>1$, and $f(-n)=-f(n)$, then $\sum_1^{\infty}f(n)/n\ne 0$.

*W. J. LeVeque* (Ann Arbor, Mich.)

Referred to in R14-49.

## M20-28 (32# 4104)

**Livingston, Arthur E.**

**The series $\sum_1^{\infty}f(n)/n$ for periodic $f$.**

*Canad. Math. Bull.* **8** (1965), 413–432.

The author is concerned with the problem of deciding when $\sum_1^{\infty}f(n)/n\ne 0$, given that $f$ is periodic and the series convergent.

Erdős communicated to the author the following conjecture: If $p$ is a positive integer and $f$ is a number-theoretic function with period $p$ for which $f(n)\in\{-1,1\}$ when $n=1,2,\cdots,p-1$ and $f(p)=0$, then $\sum_1^{\infty}f(n)/n\ne 0$ whenever the series is convergent.

The author proves that this is true if the numbers

$$\pi,\ \log\left(2\sin\frac{\pi}{p}\right),\ \log\left(2\sin\frac{2\pi}{p}\right),\ \cdots,\ \log\left(2\sin\frac{(p-1)\pi}{p}\right)$$

are linearly independent over the algebraic numbers when $p$ is odd; he has a similar result when $p$ is even.

*S. Chowla* (University Park, Pa.)

## M20-29 (32# 7518)

**Goldsmith, Donald L.**

**On a result of E. Bombieri concerning Dirichlet's $L$-functions.**

*Ist. Lombardo Accad. Sci. Lett. Rend. A* **99** (1965), 662–668.

Let $h(m)$ be a real-valued function on the positive integers, $r$ a positive integer, and set $S(n)=\sum_{m=1}^{n}h(m)$, $f_j(n)=\sum_{m^j|n}h(m)$, $L(r)=\liminf_{n\to\infty}\sum_{m=1}^{n}m^{-r}h(m)$. Then it is shown that the assumptions (i) $h(n)=O(1)$, (ii) $S(n)\ge -K$, (iii) $\liminf_{n\to\infty}\sum_{\nu=1}^{n}f_r(\nu)=B$, and (iv) $B>K$ imply the conclusion $L(r)\ge B$. This generalizes a similar result of Bombieri [same Rend. **94** (1960), 642–649; MR **23** #A3725] and, like Bombieri's result, contains Dirichlet's theorem $L(1,\chi)\ne 0$ ($\chi$ a real residue character) as a corollary. The previous conclusion holds also if conditions (ii), (iii), (iv) are replaced by (ii') $\liminf_{n\to\infty}n^{-1/2}S(n)>-|\zeta(1/2r)|^{-1}$; (iii') $f_1(n)\ge 0$; (iv') $f_1(n^2)\ge 1$. Finally, conditions (i), (ii), (iii'), (iv') and $K\ge K_0(\varepsilon)$ ($\varepsilon>0$) imply the stronger result

$$L(r)\ge\left\{\left(1-\frac{1}{2r}\right)^{2r-1}(2r)^{-1}\Gamma^{2r}\left(1+\frac{1}{2r}\right)-\varepsilon\right\}K^{1-2r}.$$

{In a more recent paper P. T. Bateman [J. Math. Anal. Appl. **15** (1966), 2–20] shows that, for $r\ge 2$ (and $f_1$ not identically zero), $L(r)>0$ follows already from (iii'), while (iii') and (iv') imply $L(r)\ge\zeta(2r)/\zeta(r)$.}

*E. Grosswald* (Philadelphia, Pa.)

Citations: MR 23# A3725 = M20-23; MR 33# 7313 = M20-30.

**M20-30** **(33# 7313)**

**Bateman, Paul T.**
**Lower bounds for $\sum h(m)/m$ for arithmetical functions $h$ similar to real residue-characters.**
*J. Math. Anal. Appl.* **15** (1966), 2–20.

The author proves the following theorem. Suppose $h$ is a real-valued function on the positive integers and $S(n)=\sum_{m=1}^{n} h(m)$, $f(n)=\sum_{m\mid n} h(m)$. If (a) $f(n)\geqq 0$ for all positive integers $n$, (b) $f(n)\geqq 1$ when $n$ is a perfect square and (c) $S(n)\geqq -Hn^{1/2}-K$ for all positive integers $n$, where $0\leqq H<|\zeta(\frac{1}{2})|^{-1}$, $K\geqq 0$, then $\liminf_{n\to+\infty}\sum_{m=1}^{n} h(m)/m\geqq (16/75)\{1+H\zeta(\frac{1}{2})\}^2/(1+K/2)$. This theorem improves a result given by E. Bombieri [Ist. Lombardo Accad. Sci. Lett. Rend. A **94** (1960), 642–649; MR **23** #A3725], who proved, under the additional assumption $h(n)=O(1)$, that $\liminf_{n\to+\infty}\sum_{m=1}^{n} h(m)/m>0$. The proof of the theorem is carried out by applying a method which was developed earlier by the author [J. Indian Math. Soc. (N.S.) **23** (1959), 101–115 (1961); MR **23** #A1613].

In the second part of the paper, the author discusses a set $F$ of functions $\rho(u)$ which can be used to derive explicit lower bounds for $\liminf_{n\to+\infty}\sum_{m=1}^{n} h(m)/m$. These investigations give rise to the conjecture that the function $\rho_2(u)=\{\max(1-u,0)\}^2$, used by the author in the above theorem, furnishes the best lower bound of all the functions $\rho(u)\in F$. *Werner G. H. Schaal* (Marburg)

Citations: MR 23# A1613 = M20-22; MR 23# A3725 = M20-23.
Referred to in M20-29.

**M20-31** **(35# 5403)**

**Burgess, D. A.**
**Estimating $L_x(1)$.**
*Norske Vid. Selsk. Forh. (Trondheim)* **39** (1966), 101–108 (1967).

S. Chowla [same Forh. **37** (1964), 88–90; MR **30** #1987] proved that $0<\sum_{n=1}^{\infty}(n/p)n^{-1}<(\frac{1}{4}+\varepsilon)\log p$ for $p>p_0(\varepsilon)$, where $(n/p)$ is the Legendre symbol. The author improves the right member of this inequality to $.2456\log p$ for $p>p_0$. This is established by use of the author's character sum estimate proved earlier [Proc. London Math. Soc. (3) **12** (1962), 193–206; MR **24** #A2570] and the following result. If $f$ is a real multiplicative function defined over the positive integers and satisfying $|f(x)|\leqq 1$ and $f(q)=\pm 1$ for all primes $q$, then

$$\sum_{m\leqq H} m^{-1}f(m)<\{.9823+.09H^{-1}|\sum_{m\leqq H}f(m)|\}\log H+O(1).$$

This is proved by adaptation of a method of I. M. Vinogradov [Trans. Amer. Math. Soc. **29** (1927), 209–217]. *I. Niven* (Eugene, Ore.)

Citations: MR 24# A2570 = L25-17; MR 30# 1987 = R14-49.
Referred to in R14-101.

**M20-32** **(36# 120)**

**Davenport, H.**
**Eine Bemerkung über Dirichlets $L$-Funktionen.**
*Nachr. Akad. Wiss. Göttingen Math.-Phys. Kl. II* **1966**, 203–212.

Let $L(s,\chi)$ be Dirichlet's $L$-Function corresponding to a real proper character $\chi$ modulo $q\geqq 3$. The author proves: $L(s,\chi)$ does not vanish for $s>1-cq^{-1/2}(\log\log q)^{-1}$ if $\chi(-1)=-1$ and for $s>1-cq^{-1/2}\log q(\log\log q)^{-1}$ if $\chi(-1)=1$. The factor $(\log\log q)^{-1}$ can even be omitted if $q$ is a prime. $c$ denotes a positive constant. The proof starts with the relation between $L(1,\chi)$ and the class number of the associated quadratic number field. Then it uses estimates of character sums. The author's result can be considered as a step toward the explicit computation of the constant $c(\varepsilon)$ occurring in the well-known theorem of C. L. Siegel [Acta Arith. **1** (1936), 83–86] stating that $L(s,\chi)\neq 0$ for $s>1-c(\varepsilon)q^{-\varepsilon}$ with arbitrary positive $\varepsilon$. *O. H. Körner* (Marburg)

**M20-33** **(37# 4034)**

**Knapowski, S.**
**On Siegel's theorem.**
*Acta Arith.* **14** (1967/68), 417–424.

The author obtains by Turan's method [P. Turán, *Eine neue Methode in der Analysis und deren Anwendungen*, Akadémi Kiadó, Budapest, 1953; MR **15**, 688; Hungarian edition; MR **15**, 688] the following slight improvement of a well known consequence of Siegel's theorem on the zeros of Dirichlet's $L$-series $L(s,X)$: If $X_1$ is an arbitrary real or complex character mod $k_1$ and if $L(s,X_1)$ has a zero at $b_1+ig_1$ with $1-d<b_1<1$, then the real zeros of all $L(s,X)$ for characters $X$ mod $k$ with $k>c(d,k_1,g_1)$ are less than $1-k^{-dc_1}$ for an absolute constant $c_1$. *O. H. Körner* (Marburg)

Citations: MR 15, 688b = M50-2; MR 15, 688c = M50-3.

**M20-34** **(38# 4425)**

**Low, M. E.**
**Real zeros of the Dedekind zeta function of an imaginary quadratic field.**
*Acta Arith.* **14** (1967/68), 117–140.

This paper combines number theory and computer results. For $d>4$, let $L_{-d}(s)=\sum_{n=1}^{\infty}(-d|n)n^{-s}$ (Re $s>0$), where $(-d|n)$ is the Kronecker symbol. Define $b_n$, $\beta_n$ by $b_n=(2^n-1)\zeta(n)n^{-1}+2^n\beta_n$ with

$$\log((s-1)\zeta(s)) = \sum_{n=1}^{\infty}(-1)^n\beta_n(s-1)^n$$

($|s|<3$), where $\zeta$ denotes the Riemann zeta function. Theorem 1: $b_n>0$ ($n\geqq 2$). The proof goes about as follows. Write $\zeta(s)$ as a Laplace integral; after $k$ partial integrations the Bernoulli function $B_k$ appears. Elementary estimates for $B_k$ ($k=2,3$) and an estimate for $\beta_k$ by Cauchy's theorem give $b_n>0$ ($n\geqq 6$). Using Euler's sum formula and an IBM 1920, the cases $2\leqq n\leqq 5$ are settled. (Here the author points out that his results do not agree with those of W. E. Briggs [Michigan Math. J. **3** (1955/56), 117–121; MR **17**, 955].) Theorem 2 says that a certain hypothesis would imply $L_{-d}(s)>0$ for $s>0$. An IBM 7094 is put to work to check this hypothesis for given $d$. This gives Theorem 5: If $-d$ is a fundamental discriminant and $d<593000$, then $L_{-d}(s)\neq 0$ for $s>0$ with the possible exception of $L_{-115147}(s)$. A description of the computer program is given. We also read: "Our value of .000071 compares favorably with his [N. Hamilton's] value of .000067."

{The reviewer feels that not enough is said about error estimates.} *G. J. Rieger* (Buffalo, N.Y.)

Citations: MR 17, 955c = M05-22.

**M20-35** **(39# 142)**

**Miech, R. J.**
**A number-theoretic constant.**
*Acta Arith.* **15** (1968/69), 119–137.

Let $\mathfrak{L}(s)$ be the product of all the $L$-series modulo $k$. Then it is well known that there is a positive constant $c$ independent of $k$ such that $\mathfrak{L}(s)$ has at most one zero in the region $1-c/\log k(2+|t|)\leqq\sigma\leqq 1$. Previously various estimates have been found for the size of $c$. The author obtains the following improvement in this direction. For sufficiently large $k$, $\mathfrak{L}(s)$ has at most one zero in the region $1-1/20\log k(1+|t|)\leqq\sigma\leqq 1$. Also, such a zero is necessarily real and is a zero of an $L$-series associated with a real character modulo $k$.

This result can be applied to obtain a more precise estimate for the smallest prime in the arithmetic progression $kn+l$ $((k, l)=1)$.

*K. Thanigasalam* (University Park, Pa.)

Referred to in M25-88.

## M20-36 (40# 2619)

**Elliott, P. D. T. A.**

**On the size of $L(1, \chi)$.**

*J. Reine Angew. Math.* **236** (1969), 26–36.

Employing only the large sieve and the Siegel-Walfisz theorem, the author proves Theorem 1: Let $\varepsilon>0$ be given. Then there are constants $c_3(\varepsilon)$, $c_4(\varepsilon)$ and for each $x\geqq 2$, a set $S(x)$ such that for all primes $p\leqq x$, $p\notin S(x)$, we have $c_3(\log\log p)^{-1}\leqq |L(1, \chi)|\leqq c_4 \log\log p$ for all non-principal characters $\chi$ mod $p$. The set $S(x)$ has cardinality at most $O(x^{\varepsilon})$.

Moreover, the author outlines a method to prove the following Theorem 2: Let $\varepsilon, F>0$ be given. For each $x\geqq 3$ there is a set $S(x)$ such that for each prime $p\leqq x$, $p\notin S(x)$, and each $l$ with $p\nmid l$,

$$\pi(x, p, l) = (\mathrm{li}(x)/\Phi(p))\{1+O((\log x)^{-F})\}$$

holds uniformly for $x\geqq p^{3+\varepsilon}$. There is a constant $G(\varepsilon, F)$ such that the cardinality of $S(x)$ is at most $O((\log x)^G)$.

As an application of Theorem 2, a result about the number $N(H, p)$ is proved, where $N(H, p)$ is the number of primes $q\leqq H$ which are primitive roots mod $p$.

*W. G. H. Schaal* (Marburg)

## M20-37 (40# 4215)

**Joshi, Padmini Tryambak**

**The size of $L(1, \chi)$ for real nonprincipal residue characters $\chi$ with prime modulus.**

*J. Number Theory* **2** (1970), 58–73.

The paper considers the series (*) $\sum_{n=1}^{\infty}(n/q)n^{-1}$, where $q$ is an odd prime and $(n/q)$ the Legendre symbol. It is shown that the sum of (*) oscillates "strongly" if $q$ runs over primes $\equiv 1$ and $\equiv -1$ (mod 4). More precisely, we have $\limsup(1/\log\log q)\sum(n/q)n^{-1}\geqq e^{\gamma}$ ($\gamma$ is the Euler constant) and $\liminf \log\log q \sum (n/q)n^{-1}\leqq \pi^2/(6e^{\gamma})$ as $q\to\infty$ over primes $\equiv 1$ (mod 4) and over primes $\equiv -1$ (mod 4). An analogous result is proved if $q$ runs over primes of a given arithmetic progression; then the constants $e^{\gamma}$, respectively, $\pi^2/(6e^{\gamma})$ are multiplied by numbers depending only on the arithmetic progression.

The proofs are based on the prime-number theorem and on the large sieve.

*P. Szüsz* (Stony Brook, N.Y.)

## M20-38 (41# 8352)

**Lavrik, A. F.**

**$L(1, \chi)$ with real Dirichlet character on sparse sets of values of the modulus of the character.** (Russian)

*Dokl. Akad. Nauk SSSR* **190** (1970), 1286–1288.

Using the method of his earlier paper [same Dokl. **186** (1969), 19–21; MR **40** #1350], the author considers the values of the Dirichlet $L(s, \chi_D)$ functions at $s=1$, $\chi_D$ being a real non-principal character mod $D$.

Theorem 2: Let $d$ be the product of primes not exceeding $q\geqq 2$; then for any positive integer $k$,

$$\sum_{m=1}^{N}\mu(dm+l)L^k(1, \chi_{dm+l}) = N\prod_{p\mid d}(1-\chi_p(l)p^{-1})^{-k}[1+O(q^{-1}\ln^2 q)]$$

uniformly in $N$, $d\leqq N^{1/9}$, $1\leqq l\leqq d$, $(l, d)=1$.

Hence it follows that for $\varepsilon>0$ and for all of the numbers $m\leqq N$, except those $\leqq N\ln^{1-\varepsilon}N$, satisfying $\mu^2(dm+l)=1$, the equality

$$L(1, \chi_{dm+l}) = \prod_{p\mid d}(1-\chi_p(l)p^{-1})^{-1}[1+O(1/\ln\ln 2d)]$$

holds.

{This article has appeared in English translation [Soviet Math. Dokl. **11** (1970), 288–291].} *J. Kubilius* (Vilnius)

Citations: MR 40# 1350 = L25-29.

# M25 THE NONREAL ZEROS OF $\zeta(s)$ AND $L(s, \chi)$

See also reviews E20-55, L10-15, L20-8, L20-9, L25-12, M05-33, M05-43, M15-9, M15-13, M15-14, M15-15, M15-17, M15-23, M15-37, M15-41, M15-42, M40-10, M40-23, M40-28, M40-38, M40-45, M40-51, M40-56, M50-2, M55-43, N02-8, N04-40, N04-45, N04-51, N04-56, N12-2, N12-16, N12-27, N12-51, N16-3, N16-9, N16-11, N16-14, N16-16, N16-29, N36-32, N44-4, N44-40, N44-42, N72-8, P32-11, P32-17, P32-66, P40-24, R42-19, Z10-33.

## M25-1 (2, 41b)

**Levinson, Norman. On Hardy's theorem on the zeros of the zeta function.** J. Math. Phys. Mass. Inst. Tech. **19**, 159–160 (1940).

The author deduces from Riemann's formula

$$z^{\frac{1}{4}}\frac{d}{dz}\{z^{\frac{1}{4}}\theta'(z)\}=\frac{1}{4\pi}\int_{-\infty}^{\infty}\Xi(2t)z^{-it}dt,\qquad \Re z>0,$$

$$\theta(z)=\sum_{-\infty}^{\infty}e^{-n^2\pi z},\quad \Xi(t)=-\tfrac{1}{2}(\tfrac{1}{4}+t^2)\pi^{-\frac{1}{4}-\frac{1}{2}it}\Gamma(\tfrac{1}{4}+\tfrac{1}{2}it)\zeta(\tfrac{1}{2}+it),$$

and the known behavior of $\theta(z)$ near $z=i$ and $z=2i$ that

$$\int_{-\infty}^{\infty}\Xi(2t)e^{\frac{1}{2}(\pi-\epsilon)t}dt\to 0,\qquad \left|\int_{-\infty}^{\infty}\Xi(2t)2^{-it}e^{\frac{1}{2}(\pi-\epsilon)t}dt\right|\to\infty,$$

when $\epsilon\to+0$. But this is obviously impossible if $\Xi(2t)$ (which is even, continuous and real for real $t$) has only a finite number of changes of sign in $(-\infty, \infty)$.

*A. E. Ingham* (Cambridge, England).

## M25-2 (2, 151e)

**Scott, S. A. Some applications of the generalised Poisson-Jensen formula.** Proc. Edinburgh Math. Soc. (2) **6**, 151–156 (1940).

The formula in question is

$$-2\pi\sum_{\mu}g(a_\mu)+2\pi\sum_{\nu}g(b_\nu)=\iint_G \log|f(s)|\Delta g(s)d\Sigma + \int_\Gamma\left\{\log|f(s)|\frac{\partial g(s)}{\partial n}-g(s)\frac{\partial \log|f(s)|}{\partial n}\right\}du,$$

where $f(s)$ is meromorphic with zeros $a_\mu$ and poles $b_\nu$ in the domain $G$ with boundary $\Gamma$; $g(s)=g(\sigma+ti)$ is a real function of $\sigma$ and $t$ with continuous partial derivatives up to the second order, and $\partial/\partial n$ is taken along the inside normal of $\Gamma$. In all applications the function $f(s)$ is taken as $\zeta(s)$, and by different specializations of $g(s)$ the author obtains formulae containing the non-trivial zeros of $\zeta(s)$, as, for example, the Riemann-von Mangoldt formula for $N(T)$. The following formula seems to be new:

$$(*)\quad \sum_{\beta_\mu \geqq \frac{1}{2}} \log |\chi(\rho_\mu)| = -2 \int_2 \log |\zeta(\tfrac{1}{2}+ti)| \Re\left\{\frac{\zeta'}{\zeta}(\tfrac{1}{2}+ti)\right\} dt + O(\log^2 T),$$

where the sum is taken over all zeros $\rho_\mu = \beta_\mu + i\gamma_\mu$ of $\zeta(s)$ with $2 < \gamma_\mu < T$, $\chi(s)$ being

$$\zeta(1-s)/\zeta(s) = 2(2\pi)^{-s} \cos \frac{\pi s}{2} \Gamma(s).$$

The left-hand member of (*) can be replaced by

$$\sum_{\beta_\mu \geqq \frac{1}{2}} (\beta_\mu - \tfrac{1}{2}) \log (\gamma_\mu / 2\pi).$$

*H. Rademacher* (Philadelphia, Pa.).

## M25-3 (2, 249e)

**Ingham, A. E. On the estimation of $N(\sigma, T)$.** Quart. J. Math., Oxford Ser. **11**, 291–292 (1940).

Let $N(\sigma, T)$ be the number of zeros $\rho = \beta + \gamma i$ of the Riemann zeta-function for which $\beta \geqq \sigma$, $0 < \gamma \leqq T$. It is proved that $N(\sigma, T) = O(T^{\lambda(\sigma)(1-\sigma)} \log^5 T)$ uniformly for $\frac{1}{2} \leqq \sigma \leqq 1$ as $T \to \infty$ with (A) $\lambda(\sigma) = 3/(2-\sigma)$. The author has previously shown [Quart. J. Math., Oxford Ser. **8**, 255–266 (1937)] that the estimate is valid with (B) $\lambda(\sigma) = 1 + 2\sigma$ and with (C) $\lambda(\sigma) = 2 + 4c$, where $c$ is a constant for which $\zeta(\frac{1}{2}+ti) = O(t^c)$. (A) is an improvement on (B) for $\frac{1}{2} \leqq \sigma \leqq 1$, while (C) is the best near $\sigma = 1$. The estimate of the difference between consecutive primes is not changed because it depends on the maximum of $\lambda(\sigma)$ for $\frac{1}{2} \leqq \sigma \leqq 1$ and this is still given by (C). The proof of (A) is so similar to that of (B) and (C) that the author merely notes the necessary changes. *H. S. Zuckerman* (Seattle, Wash.).

## M25-4 (4, 189c)

**Siegel, Carl Ludwig. Contributions to the theory of the Dirichlet $L$-series and the Epstein zeta-functions.** Ann. of Math. (2) **44**, 143–172 (1943).

In the first part of this paper the author improves, generalizes and simplifies previous results of Hardy and Littlewood, of Kusmin and of his own. The author proves an asymptotic formula for $L(s)$ which is a generalization of the recently discovered formula of Riemann for $\zeta(\frac{1}{2}+it)$. The formula is proved by using a representation of $L(s)$, due to Kusmin but proved here in a different way, as the sum of two integrals.

Using some of the results obtained in the proof of this asymptotic formula, the author then deals with the zeros of $L(s)$. Let $N(\Delta t)$ denote the number of different zeros of odd order of $L(\frac{1}{2}+i\tau)$ in the interval $t - \Delta t < \tau < t$. Let $\Delta t$ be a function of $t$ such that, as $t \to \infty$, $t^{\frac{1}{2}} \log t/\Delta t \to 0$. Then the author proves that

$$\liminf_{t\to\infty} \frac{N(\Delta t)}{\Delta t} \geqq \frac{m}{\pi e \phi(m)},$$

where $m$ is the modulus of the characters of $L(s)$ and $\phi(m)$ is Euler's function. The author also obtains refined results for the number $B(\Delta t, \epsilon)$ of zeros of $L(s)$, $s = \sigma + i\tau$, in the rectangle $t - \Delta t < \tau < t$, $\frac{1}{2} - \epsilon < \sigma < \frac{1}{2} + \epsilon$, where $\Delta t$ satisfies the same requirement as above, and $\epsilon = o(\log \log t/\log t)$. He proves

$$\liminf_{t\to\infty} \frac{B(\Delta t, \epsilon)}{t^\epsilon \Delta t} \geqq \frac{1}{4} \frac{m}{\pi e \phi(m)}.$$

In the second part of the paper similar problems are considered for certain Epstein zeta-functions. However, as the author indicates, the methods used are quite different. The Epstein zeta-functions considered are those associated with positive quadratic forms of variables. The matrix of the quadratic form is denoted by $\mathfrak{S}$ and the zeta-function by $\zeta(s; \mathfrak{S})$. If $\mathfrak{S}$ is unimodular then the line $\sigma = \frac{1}{4}k$ corresponds in certain respects to the critical line $\sigma = \frac{1}{2}$ for the ordinary zeta-function. Let $\mathfrak{E}_k$ denote the unit matrix of $k$ rows and let $\mathfrak{S}$ belong to the genus of $\mathfrak{E}_k$. Then the author's results indicate that, for $k \geqq 12$, the zeros of $\zeta(s; \mathfrak{S})$, $s = \sigma + i\tau$, in the strip $2 \leqq \sigma \leqq \frac{1}{2}k - 2$, $0 < \tau < t$ number $t \log 2/\pi + O(1)$. Moreover, all except at most a finite number of these lie on the line $\sigma = \frac{1}{4}k$. The cases $k = 4$ and $k = 8$ are completely known from certain identities and the remaining cases $3 < k < 12$ can be discussed but require some numerical computation. For the case $k = 3$ the method gives no results. *N. Levinson* (Cambridge, Mass.).

Referred to in M05-26, M15-39.

## M25-5 (6, 39c)

**Linnik, U. V. The zeros of $L$-series, power non-residues and the class number of $k(\sqrt{-D})$.** C. R. (Doklady) Acad. Sci. URSS (N.S.) **39**, 123–124 (1943).

A statement is given of results obtained by using the "analogy property" of $L$-series [C. R. (Doklady) Acad. Sci. URSS (N.S.) **38**, 107–109 (1943); these Rev. **5**, 142]. Let $\chi(n)$ be a nonprincipal character mod $D$, $N_0$ the least positive integer for which $\chi(n) \neq 1$; if $N > D^\eta$, then the number of zeros of $L(s)$ in the square $1 - (\ln D)^{-\alpha} \leqq \sigma \leqq 1$, $|t| \leqq \frac{1}{2}(\ln D)^{-\alpha}$ exceeds $c_2 r \cdot \ln D/(\ln \ln D)^2$. A connection is stated between the least cubic nonresidue mod $p$ and the magnitude of the class number $h(-p)$. *G. Pall* (Montreal, Ont.).

Citations: MR 5, 142d = R14-4.

## M25-6 (6, 39f)

**Popov, A. I. Several series containing primes and roots of $\zeta(s)$.** C. R. (Doklady) Acad. Sci. URSS (N.S.) **41**, 362–363 (1943).

Results are announced of formulas involving certain series connected with the roots of $\zeta(s)$. A typical result is

$$\sum_{n>x} \Lambda(n) \frac{\{n/x\} - \{n/x\}^2}{n^2} = \frac{2 - \lg 2\pi}{x} + \sum_\rho \frac{x^{\rho-2}}{\rho(\rho-1)} + \sum \frac{k+1-2k\zeta(2k+1)}{2k(k+1)(2k+1)x^{2k+2}},$$

where $\Lambda(n)$ has the customary meaning in analytic number theory; $\{t\}$ is the fractional part of $t$; the first summation on the right side extends over all complex roots $\rho$ of $\zeta(s)$; the series on the left extends over all integers $n$ greater than the continuous variable $x$, $x \geqq 1$. It is stated that other formulas can be derived from these determining the numerical values of certain series whose terms are functions of primes, and that the proofs are based on the theory of Dirichlet series. *I. Niven* (Lafayette, Ind.).

## M25-7 (6, 58a)

**Selberg, Atle. On the zeros of Riemann's zeta-function.** Skr. Norske Vid. Akad. Oslo. I. no. **10**, 59 pp. (1942).

Let $N_0(T)$ be the number of zeros of $\zeta(\sigma+it)$ with $\sigma = \frac{1}{2}$, $0 < t < T$; $N(\sigma', T)$ the number with $\sigma > \sigma'$, $0 < t < T$. If $a > \frac{1}{2}$, $U \geqq T^a$, the principal results are (I) $N_0(T+U) - N_0(T) > AU \log T$ for $T > T_0$ and (II) $N(\sigma, T+U) - N(\sigma, T) = O(U/(\sigma - \frac{1}{2}))$ uniformly for $\frac{1}{2} < \sigma \leqq 1$. These represent considerable improvements over known results and consequently yield improvements in certain corollaries. Thus from (I) there follows $N_0(T) > AT \log T$ for $T > T_0$ and that, if $\Phi(t)$ is a positive function, increasing to infinity, then for almost all $t>0$ there is a zero of $\zeta(\frac{1}{2}+it)$ between $t$ and $t+\Phi(t)/\log t$. Analogous corollaries are deduced from (II). The lower bound for $N_0(T)$ combined with a well-known upper bound shows that $N_0(T)$ is of order $T \log T$. The method of proof depends on the usual arguments applied not to $\zeta(s)$ but to $\zeta(s)$ multiplied by a function that tends to smooth out the peculiarities of $\zeta(s)$.

*H. S. Zuckerman* (Seattle, Wash.).

Referred to in M25-24.

## M25-8 (6, 58b)

**Linnik, U. On the connexion of extended Riemann hypothesis with I. M. Vinogradow's method in the theory of primes.** C. R. (Doklady) Acad. Sci. URSS (N.S.) **41**, 145–146 (1943).

The author announces a theorem on Dirichlet's $L$-series, which gives an upper bound for the number of those $L$-series (mod $D$) possessing zeros in a rectangle $1-\theta \leqq \sigma \leqq 1$, $|t|<D^{\eta/2}$. He mentions some deductions from this in the theory of primes. The paper is too condensed to be completely intelligible. *H. Davenport* (Bangor).

Referred to in N16-4, P32-8.

## M25-9 (6, 118g)

**Wang, Fu Traing. A formula on Riemann zeta function.** Ann. of Math. (2) **46**, 88–92 (1945).

Put

$$\Phi(z)=\prod_{\nu=1}^{\infty}(1-z^2/\rho_\nu^2),$$

where $\rho_\nu=\gamma_\nu+i\beta_\nu$ are the nontrivial zeros of $\zeta(s)$; let $N(T)$ be the number of zeros in the rectangle $0\leqq\sigma\leqq 1$, $1\leqq t\leqq T$, and let $\lambda_\nu=|\rho_\nu|$, $\alpha_\nu=|\beta_\nu|/\lambda_\nu$; then the author proves

$$\int_0^T x^{-5/2}\log|\Phi(x)|dx$$
$$=(4\pi/3)\sum_{\nu=1}^{\infty}\lambda_\nu^{-\frac{3}{2}}(2\alpha_\nu-1)(1+2\nu)^{\frac{1}{2}}+O(T^{-\frac{1}{2}}\log T).$$

A more general formula is stated at the end of the paper.

*L. Carlitz* (Durham, N. C.).

## M25-10 (7, 48f)

**Selberg, Atle. On the zeros of Riemann's zeta-function on the critical line.** Arch. Math. Naturvid. **45**, no. 9, 101–114 (1942).

The result $N_0(2T)-N_0(T)>KT\log\log\log T$ is proved, where $N_0(T)$ is the number of zeros of $\zeta(s)$ with $\sigma=\frac{1}{2}$, $0<t<T$. The factor $\log\log\log T$ represents an improvement over the result of Hardy and Littlewood. Certain other possible improvements are mentioned without proofs.

*H. S. Zuckerman* (Seattle, Wash.).

Referred to in M25-11.

## M25-11 (8, 446h)

**Selberg, Atle. On the zeros of the zeta-function of Riemann.** Norske Vid. Selsk. Forh., Trondhjem **15**, no. 16, 59–62 (1942).

Announcement of results which have already been reviewed. Cf. Arch. Math. Naturvid. **45**, no. 9, 101–114 (1942); these Rev. **7**, 48.

Citations: MR 7, 48f = M25-10.

## M25-12 (7, 48g)

**Taylor, P. R. On the Riemann zeta function.** Quart. J. Math., Oxford Ser. **16**, 1–21 (1945).

A number of disconnected results collected by J. E. Reese and E. C. Titchmarsh from the author's work. One result is that if $\xi_1(s)=\pi^{-\frac{1}{2}s}\Gamma(\frac{1}{2}s)\zeta(s)$ then $\xi_1(s+\frac{1}{2})-\xi_1(s-\frac{1}{2})$ has all its complex zeros on $\sigma=\frac{1}{2}$. Some of the other results are attempts to supplement this with the proof of Riemann's hypothesis in view. *H. S. Zuckerman* (Seattle, Wash.).

## M25-13 (7, 146j)

**Siegel, Carl Ludwig. On the zeros of the Dirichlet $L$-functions.** Ann. of Math. (2) **46**, 409–422 (1945).

The author considers the number of zeros of Dirichlet's function $L(s,\chi)$, where $\chi$ is a character with modulus $m$, in rectangles $\frac{1}{2}+\delta<\sigma<1$, $-T_0<t<T_0$, or $0<\sigma<1$, $0\leqq t\leqq T_0$ ($T_0$ fixed). The number of zeros in the former is

$$O\{\phi(m)\delta^{-1}\log^{-2\delta}m\}$$

if $\delta>1/\log\log m$, and the number in the latter is

$$(T/2\pi)\phi(m)\log m+O\{\phi(m)\log^{\frac{3}{4}}m\};$$

here $\phi(m)$ denotes the number of characters $\chi$. Various consequences are noted, for example, that every point of the line $\sigma=\frac{1}{2}$ is a limit point for the set of the zeros of $L(s,\chi)$, with variable $m$ and $\chi$. On the Riemann hypothesis this was proved by the reviewer [Proc. London Math. Soc. (2) **32**, 488–500 (1931)]. *E. C. Titchmarsh.*

## M25-14 (7, 285g)

**Tsuji, Masatsugu. On the zeros of the Riemann zeta-function.** Proc. Imp. Acad. Tokyo **18**, 631–634 (1942).

Another proof of Littlewood's theorem that $\zeta(s)$ $(s=\sigma+it)$ has a zero in every strip $|t-T|<A/\log\log\log T$ $(T\geqq T_0)$, depending on Doetsch's three-lines theorem [Math. Z. **8**, 237–240 (1920)]. *E. C. Titchmarsh* (Oxford).

## M25-15 (7, 415i)

**Turán, P. Über die Verteilung der Primzahlen. I.** Acta Univ. Szeged. Sect. Sci. Math. **10**, 81–104 (1941).

It was proved by Hoheisel [S.-B. Preuss. Akad. Wiss. Phys.-Math. kl. **1930**, 580–588] that $\pi(x+x^\theta)-\pi(x)\sim x^\theta/\log x$ as $x\to\infty$, where $\pi(x)$ is the number of primes not exceeding $x$ and $\theta=32999/33000$. Heilbronn, Tchudakoff, and Ingham in turn reduced the value of $\theta$. Ingham's main result [Quart. J. Math., Oxford Ser. **8**, 255–266 (1937)] is that if $\zeta(\frac{1}{2}+it)=O(t^c)$ as $t\to\infty$ then $N(\sigma,T)=O(T^{2(1+2c)(1-\sigma)}\log^5 T)$ for $\frac{1}{2}<\sigma\leqq 1$ as $T\to\infty$. Here $N(\sigma,T)$ is the number of zeros $\beta+i\gamma$ of $\zeta(s)$ with $\beta\geqq\sigma$, $0<\gamma\leqq T$. His value of $\theta$ is then $(1+4c)/(2+4c)+\epsilon$ for every $\epsilon>0$. In the present paper the author proves, subject to a certain hypothesis, that

$$N(\sigma,T)\leqq T^{2(1-\sigma)}\exp(13\log^{0.18}T),$$

uniformly for $\frac{1}{2}\leqq\sigma\leqq 1$, $T\geqq C$ and

$$\pi(x+\sqrt{x}\exp(\log^{0.996}x))-\pi(x)\sim\sqrt{x}\exp(\log^{0.996}x)/\log x,$$

which are improvements on Ingham's results. The point of the paper is that the new conjecture, unlike the Riemann or Lindelöf hypotheses, has apparently no direct connection with the prime numbers. The author's hypothesis reads as follows: if $n\geqq C$ and $z_1=1$, $|z_2|\leqq 1,\cdots,|z_n|\leqq 1$, then the maximum value of $|z_1^\nu+z_2^\nu+\cdots+z_n^\nu|$ for $n^{1.5}-n^{1.08}\leqq\nu\leqq n^{1.5}$ is greater than $\exp(-n^{0.09})$. It is used to approximate a sum which arises in connection with the integral

$$J=\int_{T/2}^{T}|g_\nu(s)|^2dt,$$

where $s=\sigma_0+it$ and $g_\nu(s)$ is the $(\nu+1)$th derivative of $\log\zeta(s)$. The study of the integral is suggested by the following considerations: (a) with suitable restrictions on $s_0=\sigma_0+it_0$ the function $\zeta(s)$ has no zeros in the circle

$$|s-s_0|=\lim\inf[|g_\nu(s_0)|/\nu!]^{-1/\nu}=R;$$

(b) an inequality $|g_\nu(s)|\leqq T^{\sigma-1}\sqrt{J}$ holds for $T/2\leqq t<T$ with the exception of a set of intervals of total length less than $c(\epsilon)T^{2(1-\sigma)+\epsilon}$. In contrast to classical methods the

author works with functional values away from the critical strip. *R. D. James* (Vancouver, B. C.).

## M25-16 (7, 417a)

**Wang, Fu Traing. A note on the Riemann zeta-function.** Bull. Amer. Math. Soc. **52**, 319–321 (1946).

Let $\rho_\nu=\beta_\nu+i\gamma_\nu$ be the zeros of $\zeta(\frac{1}{2}+z)$, with $\beta_\nu\geqq 0$, $\gamma_\nu>0$. It is proved by means of contour integration of $z^{-2}\log\zeta(\frac{1}{2}+z)$ [cf. Titchmarsh, The Zeta-Function of Riemann, Cambridge University Press, 1930, p. 53] that

$$(1)\quad \int_1^T t^{-2}\log|\zeta(\tfrac{1}{2}+it)|dt=2\pi\sum_1^\infty\beta_\nu|\rho_\nu|^{-2}+A+O(T^{-1}\log T),$$

where

$$A=\int_0^{\pi/2}\Re\{e^{-i\theta}\log\zeta(\tfrac{1}{2}+e^{i\theta})\}d\theta.$$

Consequently, a necessary and sufficient condition for the truth of the Riemann hypothesis is that

$$\int_1^\infty t^{-2}\log|\zeta(\tfrac{1}{2}+it)|dt=A.$$

[The $O$-term in (1) can be replaced by $O(T^{-1}\log\log T)$.]
*N. G. de Bruijn* (Eindhoven).

## M25-17 (7, 417b)

**Selberg, Atle. On the remainder in the formula for $N(T)$, the number of zeros of $\zeta(s)$ in the strip $0<t<T$.** Avh. Norske Vid. Akad. Oslo. I. **1944**, no. 1, 27 pp. (1944).

The formula considered is

$$N(T)=(1/2\pi)T\log(T/2\pi e)+\tfrac{7}{8}+S(T)+O(1/T)$$

and it is a question of proving theorems about the term $S(T)$. The main result is that, on the Riemann hypothesis, for every fixed positive integer $k$

$$\int_0^T|S(t)|^{2k}dt=\frac{(2k)!}{k!(2\pi)^{2k}}T(\log\log T)^k+O\{T(\log\log T)^{k-1}\}.$$

There are similar results with integrals over $(T, T+H)$, and also when $S(t)$ is replaced by its integral of any order. Applications are made to questions of changes of sign of $S(t)$.
*E. C. Titchmarsh* (Oxford).

## M25-18 (7, 507c)

**Turán, P. Über die Wurzeln der Dirichletschen $L$-Funktionen.** Acta Univ. Szeged. Sect. Sci. Math. **10**, 188–201 (1943).

The author proves that the total number $N_k(\alpha)$ of zeros of all the $L$-functions (mod $k$) in the rectangle $\alpha\leqq\sigma\leqq 2$, $|t|\leqq 5$ satisfies

$$N_k(\alpha)=O(k^{4(1-\alpha^2)}\log^{11/2}k)$$

for $\sqrt{2}-\frac{1}{2}\leqq\alpha\leqq 1-2(\log k)^{-1}$ and satisfies

$$N_k(\alpha)=O(k^{\frac{1}{2}+2\alpha-2\alpha^2}\log k)$$

for $\frac{1}{2}+5(\log\log k)^{-\frac{1}{2}}\leqq\alpha\leqq\sqrt{2}-\frac{1}{2}$. It follows that "almost all" the $L$-functions (mod $k$) have no zeros in the region $\sigma\geqq\frac{1}{2}+5(\log\log k)^{-\frac{1}{2}}$, $|t|\leqq 5$. An important part in the proof is played by estimates for $\sum_\chi|f(s,\chi)-1|^2$, where

$$f(s,\chi)=L(s,\chi)\sum_{n\leqq x}\chi(n)\mu(n)n^{-s},$$

with a modification when $\chi$ is the principal character, and $x$ is a certain function of $k$. *H. Davenport* (London).

## M25-19 (8, 11g)

**Linnik, U. V. On the density of the zeros of $L$-series.** Bull. Acad. Sci. URSS. Sér. Math. [Izvestia Akad. Nauk SSSR] **10**, 35–46 (1946). (Russian. English summary)

The author proves the approximate functional equation for Dirichlet $L$-series: if $c>0$ is a suitable constant, $\chi(n)$ a primitive character mod $q$, $0\leqq\sigma\leqq 1$, $|t|>c$, $x>cq$, $y>c$, $2\pi xy=q|t|$, then

$$L(s,\chi)=\sum_{n<x}\chi(n)n^{-s}+\alpha(s,\chi)\sum_{n<y}\bar{\chi}(n)n^{s-1}$$
$$+O(q^2(x^{-\sigma}+y^{\sigma-1}t^{\frac{1}{2}-\sigma})\log t),$$

where $\alpha(s,\chi)$ is defined by the functional equation $L(s,\chi)=\alpha(s,\chi)L(s-1,\bar{\chi})$. The author proves this uniformly in $\sigma$, $t$, $q$ and $\chi$. For fixed values of $q$, the result is contained in a theorem by Suetuna [Jap. J. Math. **9**, 111–116 (1932)].

Following a method applied to the $\zeta$-function by Titchmarsh [Proc. London Math. Soc. (2) **30**, 319–321 (1929)], the author then proves that for $0<\nu<\frac{1}{2}$, $T\geqq q^{50}$ there are at most $O(q^{2\nu}T^{1-\nu/(1-\nu)}\log^{10}T+q^{30})$ zeros of $L(s,\chi)$ in the rectangle $\frac{1}{2}+\nu\leqq\sigma\leqq 1$, $|t|\leqq T$; this holds uniformly in $\nu$, $T$, $q$ and $\chi$. This result has already been applied by the author in a previous paper on Goldbach's problem [C. R. (Doklady) Acad. Sci. URSS (N.S.) **49**, 3–7 (1945); these Rev. **7**, 507].
*H. A. Heilbronn* (Bristol).

Citations: MR 7, 507b = P32-8.
Referred to in P32-9, P32-10.

## M25-20 (8, 197f)

**Tchudakoff, N. On zeros of Dirichlet's $L$-functions.** Rec. Math. [Mat. Sbornik] N.S. **19**(61), 47–56 (1946). (Russian. English summary)

The main results are the following two theorems. (1) Dirichlet's function $L(s,\chi)$, where $\chi$ is a character mod $k$ ($\geqq 3$), has no zeros in the part of the $s$-plane defined by

$$0<|t|\leqq t_0,\quad \sigma\geqq 1-c(\log k)^{-1};$$
$$|t|\geqq t_0,\quad \sigma\geqq 1-c(\log|t|)^{-\gamma},$$

where $s=\sigma+it$, $c$ and $\gamma$ are positive absolute constants, $\gamma<1$, and $\log t_0=(\log k)^{1/\gamma}$. [The need for the condition $|t|>0$ arises from the possibility that (so far as is known at present) one $L$-function belonging to a given $k$, say $L(s,\chi_1)$, may have one real simple zero $\beta_1$ between 1 and $1-c(\log k)^{-1}$.]

(2) Let $\pi(x,k,l)$ be the number of primes $p$ for which $p\leqq x$, $p\equiv l$ (mod $k$), where $(l,k)=1$. Then, if $1\leqq k\leqq\exp(\log x)^{\mu\gamma}$,

$$\pi(x,k,l)=h^{-1}\sum_{n=2}^x\frac{1}{\log n}-Eh^{-1}\bar{\chi}_1(l)\sum_{n=2}^x\frac{n^{\beta_1-1}}{\log n}+O(xe^{-c'(\log x)^\mu}),$$

where $h=\varphi(k)$, $\gamma$ has the same meaning as in (1), $\mu=(1+\gamma)^{-1}>\frac{1}{2}$, $c'$ is a positive absolute constant, $E=1$ or 0 according as the special zero $\beta_1$ does or does not exist (in the position stated), and $O$ implies an absolute constant. [In the English summary the restriction on $k$ is omitted.]

The essential novelty lies in a combination of the precision afforded by Vinogradov's estimations of trigonometrical sums with an explicit specification of the dependence on $k$ based on earlier work of Landau, Titchmarsh and Page. With the help of the researches of Heilbronn and Siegel [C. L. Siegel, Acta Arith. **1**, 83–86 (1935)] it is shown that the terms involving $\beta_1$ in (2) can certainly be omitted if $k\leqq(\log x)^A$, provided that the constant of the $O$ is now understood to depend on the constant $A$.

The task of following out the intricacies of the argument is made needlessly difficult by a number of inaccuracies of detail. Obvious "misprints" will be easily detected, and the missing error terms in the integral formula for $S(n)$ on page 54 can be supplied by reference to Landau's paper. But lemma 1 is more puzzling. This is quoted as a known result of Vinogradov, but is not easy to identify from the references given, and is plainly false as stated. There is in any case no direct reference to lemma 1 in the course of the paper. The appeal to the relevant result of Vinogradov comes in lemma 4, through a paper by Tchudakoff. The reference to that paper should, however, be completed by an appeal to lemma 3 as well as to lemmas 1 and 2.

*A. E. Ingham* (Cambridge, England).

Referred to in R44-2.

## M25-21 (8, 446i)

**Selberg, Atle. The zeta-function and the Riemann hypothesis.** C. R. Dixième Congrès Math. Scandinaves 1946, pp. 187–200. Jul. Gjellerups Forlag, Copenhagen, 1947.

"The object of the following lecture is . . . to give an outline of some recent investigations in the distribution of the zeros of the zeta-function in relation to the critical line. Particular stress is laid upon explaining the main ideas underlying the methods." It is of interest that, in spite of the author's advance in proving the zeros on the critical line to be within a multiplicative constant of the total number in the critical strip, the author is suspicious of the Riemann hypothesis. He presents considerable evidence for being suspicious. A selected list of papers published since Titchmarsh's tract [The Zeta-function of Riemann, Cambridge University Press, 1930] is appended.

*N. Levinson* (Cambridge, Mass.).

## M25-22 (8, 447a)

**Guinand, A. P. Some Fourier transforms in prime-number theory.** Quart. J. Math., Oxford Ser. **18**, 53–64 (1947).

Assuming the truth of the Riemann hypothesis, the author constructs two pairs of Fourier cosine-transforms illustrating the relationship between the nontrivial zeros $\frac{1}{2}+i\gamma_n$ of $\zeta(s)$ and the logarithms of the powers of the primes. [Cf. Wintner, Duke Math. J. **10**, 99–105 (1943); these Rev. **4**, 217.] In one of the examples, one function involves $\sum_{0<\gamma_n\leqq x} 1/\gamma_n$ and elementary functions, while its transform involves $\sum_{m \log p\leqq x} \log p/p^{\frac{1}{2}m}$ and elementary functions.

*P. Hartman* (Baltimore, Md.).

Citations: MR 4, 217e = M30-3.

## M25-23 (8, 567e)

**Selberg, Atle. Contributions to the theory of the Riemann zeta-function.** Arch. Math. Naturvid. **48**, no. 5, 89–155 (1946).

It is first proved that, if $N(\sigma, T)$ is the number of zeros $\beta+iy$ of $\zeta(s)$ with $\beta>\sigma$ and $0<y<T$, then $N(\sigma, T)=O(T^{1-\frac{1}{4}(\sigma-\frac{1}{2})}\log T)$ uniformly for $\frac{1}{2}\leqq\sigma\leqq 1$. For values of $\sigma$ near to $\frac{1}{2}$ this is an improvement on a result of Ingham, which contained a factor $\log^5 T$. The remainder of the paper is devoted to the study of $S(t)=\pi^{-1}\arg\zeta(\frac{1}{2}+it)$ and $S_1(T)=\int_0^t S(t)dt$. The most remarkable results are

$$S(t)=\Omega_{\pm}\{(\log t)^{\frac{1}{3}}(\log\log t)^{-\frac{1}{3}}\},$$
$$S_1(t)=\Omega_{\pm}\{(\log t)^{\frac{1}{3}}(\log\log t)^{-10/3}\},$$
$$S_1(t)=\Omega_{+}\{(\log t)^{\frac{1}{2}}(\log\log t)^{-4}\}.$$

The last result approaches what was previously known only on the assumption of the Riemann hypothesis.

*E. C. Titchmarsh* (Oxford).

## M25-24 (8, 567f)

**Titchmarsh, E. C. On the zeros of the Riemann zeta function.** Quart. J. Math., Oxford Ser. **18**, 4–16 (1947).

The author gives a shorter proof for Selberg's inequality $N_0(T)>AT\log T$ [Skr. Norske Vid. Akad. Oslo. I. **1942**, no. 10; these Rev. **6**, 58] for the zeros of the zeta function in the interval $(0, T)$ of the critical line. "This is done by using a Fourier transform method similar to that which I used in my Cambridge tract to prove" $N_0(T)>AT$.

*N. Levinson* (Cambridge, Mass.).

Citations: MR 6, 58a = M25-7.

## M25-25 (9, 250e)

**van der Pol, Balth. An electro-mechanical investigation of the Riemann zeta function in the critical strip.** Bull. Amer. Math. Soc. **53**, 976–981 (1 plate) (1947).

Starting with the infinite integral for $\zeta(s)$, where $\Re(s)>1$ [Whittaker and Watson, A Course of Modern Analysis, 4th ed., Cambridge University Press, 1927, p. 266] the author obtains several relations for $\zeta(s)$ including the integral

$$\zeta(s)/s=\int_0^\infty([u]-u)u^{-s-1}du, \quad 0<\Re(s)<1. \tag{1}$$

[Compare van der Pol, Philos. Mag. (7) **26**, 921–940 (1938).] Setting $u=e^x$ and $s=a+it$ in (1) gives a Fourier transform representation.

This result was applied to investigate the zeros in the critical strip by taking $a=\frac{1}{2}$ and approximating the moduli of more than 600 harmonics of the Fourier series for the portion of the function $e^{x/2}-e^{-x/2}[e^x]$ between $x=-9$ and $x=+9$. This was accomplished by means of an electro-mechanical harmonic analyzer of heterodyne type in which the function to be analyzed was introduced by optical means [for such instruments see H. H. Hall, J. Acoust. Soc. Amer. **8**, 257–262 (1937)]. The investigation so far has been confined to the line $\Re(s)=\frac{1}{2}$ so as to test the experimental technique. The results are in good agreement with what is known of the zeros on this line as far as $t=210$.

*R. Church* (Annapolis, Md.).

## M25-26 (9, 271i)

**Selberg, Atle. Contributions to the theory of Dirichlet's *L*-functions.** Skr. Norske Vid. Akad. Oslo. I. **1946**, no. 3, 62 pp. (1946).

The author gives further examples of the well-known analogy between the behaviour of $\zeta(s)$ as a function of $t$ and the behaviour of the Dirichlet $L$-series $L(s, \chi)=\sum_{n=1}^{\infty}\chi(n)n^{-s}$ ($\chi(n)$ a primitive character mod $k$) as a function of $k$. To avoid tedious arithmetical complications, he limits himself to the case $k$ prime. His first result (theorems 1 and 2) is an asymptotic formula for the sum $\sum_\chi L(s, \chi)L(s', \bar{\chi})\chi(\mu_1)\bar{\chi}(\pm\mu_2)$, where $\chi$ runs through all primitive characters mod $k$, $s$ and $s'$ lie inside the critical strip and $\mu_1$ and $\mu_2$ are positive integers prime to each other.

He next proves theorem 3. Let $|t_1|\leqq K^{\frac{1}{4}-\epsilon}$ and

$$(\log k)^{-1}<H<(\log k)^{-\frac{1}{2}};$$

then there is an $A=A(\epsilon)>0$ and a $k_0=k_0(\epsilon)$ such that for $k>k_0$ at least $k(1-A(H\log k)^{-\frac{1}{2}})$ of the functions $L(s, \chi)$ have zeros on the line $\sigma=\frac{1}{2}$ in the interval $t_1<t<t_1+H$. This implies that for $|t|\leqq k^{\frac{1}{4}-\epsilon}$ more than "$\gamma$ percent" of the zeros of $\prod_\chi L(s, \chi)$ lie on the line $\sigma=\frac{1}{2}$, $\gamma$ being an absolute constant.

The next step is to prove theorem 4. Let $0<\epsilon<\frac{1}{4}$, $-k^{\frac{1}{4}-\epsilon}<t_1<t_2<k^{\frac{1}{4}-\epsilon}$, $t_2-t_1\geqq\log^{-1}k$, $\sigma\geqq\frac{1}{2}+\log^{-1}k$, and let $N_\chi(\sigma; t_1, t_2)$ be the number of zeros $\beta+\gamma i$ of $L(s, \chi)$ in the rectangle $\sigma\leqq\beta<1$, $t_1\leqq t\leqq t_2$. Then

$$\sum_\chi N_\chi(\sigma; t_1, t_2)=O(k^{1-\frac{1}{4}(\sigma-\frac{1}{2})\epsilon}(t_2-t_1)\log k).$$

Expressed roughly this means that "almost all" zeros of the functions $L(s, \chi)$ are near the line $\sigma=\frac{1}{2}$.

Finally the author gives inequalities for $S(t, \chi)$, the principal value of the argument of $L(s, \chi)$ at the point $s=\frac{1}{2}+ti$. The function $S(t, \chi)$ is important because it gives the dominant error term in von Mangoldt's formula for the number of zeros of $L(s, \chi)$ in the critical strip. The most striking results are as follows. If $L(s, \chi)\neq 0$ for $\sigma>\frac{1}{2}$, then

$$S(t, \chi)=O\left(\frac{\log (k(1+|t|))}{\log\log (k(3+|t|))}\right).$$

If $|t|\leqq k^{\frac{1}{4}-\epsilon}$, then $\sum_\chi S(t, \chi)=O(k)$. If $|t|<k^{\frac{1}{4}-\epsilon}$ and if $r$ is a fixed positive integer, then

$$\sum_\chi |S(t, \chi)|^{2r}=(2r)!(r!)^{-1}(2\pi)^{-r}k((\log\log k)^r+O(\log\log k)^{r-\frac{1}{2}}).$$

*H. Heilbronn* (Bristol).

## M25-27 (9, 413d)

**Rodosskiĭ, K. A. On the complex zeros of Dirichlet's $L$-functions.** Izvestiya Akad. Nauk SSSR. Ser. Mat. **12**, 47–56 (1948). (Russian)

This paper is devoted to a generalization of a theorem of Linnik [Rec. Math. (Mat. Sbornik) N.S. **15**(57), 3–12 (1944); these Rev. **6**, 260] on the number of the Dirichlet $L(s, \chi)$ functions having zeros near the line $R(s)=1$. The author's theorem is as follows. Let $\lambda$ be an arbitrary number between 0 and 1, $\psi(D)$ a number satisfying the inequalities $\frac{1}{3}\log D\geqq\psi(D)\geqq(\log D)^\lambda$, and $T_1$ a real number such that $|T_1|=T\geqq\log^4 D$; then the number of $L$-functions (mod $D$) which have zeros in the rectangle $1-(\psi(D)/\log DT)\leqq\sigma\leqq 1$, $|t-T_1|\leqq\log^4 DT$, does not exceed $\exp\{A(\lambda)\psi(D)+28\log\log DT\}$, where $A(\lambda)$ is a constant depending only on $\lambda$. This differs from Linnik's theorem in the presence of the parameter $T_1$. The proof follows very closely the method used by Linnik in the paper referred to. Each of Linnik's eight lemmas is extended to apply to the broader situation. The present paper is actually somewhat less difficult to read than Linnik's, since more of the details of proof are given.

The result stated has the following consequence, important for the study of primes in arithmetic progressions. If $\epsilon$ is a fixed number between 0 and $\frac{1}{3}$ and $T_1$ is any real number such that $|T_1|\leqq D^{\epsilon^{-1}-1}$, then there is an absolute constant $A$ such that for sufficiently large $D$ at most $D^{A\epsilon}$ of the $L$-functions (mod $D$) have zeros in the rectangle $1\geqq\sigma\geqq 1-\epsilon$, $|t-T_1|\leqq\log^4 D$. Linnik's theorem itself gives only the weaker form of this result in which the condition $|T_1|\leqq D^{\epsilon^{-1}-1}$ is replaced by the condition $T_1=O(\log^c D)$ for some $c$. *P. T. Bateman* (Princeton, N. J.).

Citations: MR 6, 260a = N16-4.
Referred to in M25-29, N16-8, N16-11.

## M25-28 (10, 182d)

**Atkinson, F. V. A mean value property of the Riemann zeta-function.** J. London Math. Soc. **23**, 128–135 (1948).

Let $\chi(s)=2^{1-s}\pi^{-s}\Gamma(s)\cos\frac{1}{2}\pi s$, the real function $\theta(t)$ be defined by $e^{2i\theta(t)}=\chi(\frac{1}{2}+it)$, and the real function $f(t)$ be defined by $f(t)=e^{i\theta(t)}\zeta(\frac{1}{2}+it)$. The author proves the following result. Let $t'$ be defined as a function of $t$ by the relation $\theta(t')-\theta(t)=\alpha$, $\alpha$ fixed and positive. Then

$$\int_0^T f(t)f(t')dt\sim(T\log T)\alpha^{-1}\sin\alpha$$

as $T\to\infty$. The proof uses the approximate functional equation for $\zeta(s)$. Then it is shown that the number of zeros of $\zeta(\frac{1}{2}+it)$, $T/2\leqq t\leqq T$, is greater than $AT/\log T$. The theorem above is analogous to a result obtained by Titchmarsh for a corresponding sum [Quart. J. Math., Oxford Ser. **5**, 98–105 (1934)]. *R. Bellman.*

## M25-29 (11, 84e)

**Rodosskiĭ, K. A. On the zeros of Dirichlet's $L$-functions.** Izvestiya Akad. Nauk SSSR. Ser. Mat. **13**, 315–328 (1949). (Russian)

The author proves that if $\log\log D\leqq\Psi(D)\leqq\frac{1}{4}\log D$, then the number of $L$-series formed with characters mod $D$ which have at least one zero in the rectangle

$$1-\Psi(D)/\log (D(|T|+2))\leqq\sigma\leqq 1,$$
$$|t-T|\leqq K\log^2 (D(|T|+2))$$

does not exceed $Be^{A\Psi(D)}\log^5 (D(|T|+2))$, where $A$, $B$, $K$ are absolute constants. This is a slight improvement on a previous result by the author [same Izvestiya Ser. Mat. **12**, 47–56 (1948); these Rev. **9**, 413]. From this he derives the theorem about the distribution of primes in an arithmetical progression in the following form (using the conventional notation):

$$\varphi(D)\psi(x; D, l)=x-E\chi(\rho)x^\beta\beta^{-1}+xO(\exp(-A_3\log x/\log D))$$

uniformly in $D$ and $l$ for $A_1\log D\log\log D\leqq\log x\leqq A_2\log^2 D$. Here $\beta$ is the largest positive zero of all the $L(s, \chi)$, $\chi$ the corresponding character mod $D$, and $E=1$ or 0 if such a zero exists or does not exist. This again is a slight improvement on a previous result by the author [same Izvestiya Ser. Mat. **12**, 123–128 (1948); these Rev. **9**, 499].

*H. Heilbronn* (Bristol).

Citations: MR 9, 413d = M25-27; MR 9, 499a = N16-8.
Referred to in N16-11.

## M25-30 (11, 162d)

**Guinand, A. P. Fourier reciprocities and the Riemann zeta-function.** Proc. London Math. Soc. (2) **51**, 401–414 (1949).

The function $V(w)=\sum e^{\rho w}$, $\Im(w)>0$, where $\rho=\frac{1}{2}+i\gamma$, $\gamma>0$, runs through the nontrivial zeros of the zeta function, was introduced by H. Cramér [Math. Z. **4**, 104–130 (1919)]. There exists a sort of reciprocity between $V(w)$ and $\zeta'(s)/\zeta(s)$, which shows itself in the poles and residues of the functions and the coefficients and exponents of their Dirichlet series. Moreover, the functions

$$F(x)=\left\{\frac{\zeta'(\frac{1}{2}+x)}{\zeta(\frac{1}{2}+x)}+\frac{1}{x-\frac{1}{2}}\right\}+\frac{1}{2}\left\{\frac{\Gamma'(\frac{5}{4}+\frac{1}{2}x)}{\Gamma(\frac{5}{4}+\frac{1}{2}x)}-\log\frac{1}{2}x\right\},$$

$$G(x)=(2\pi)^{\frac{1}{2}}\{e^{-\frac{1}{2}ix}V(ix)+(2\pi x)^{-1}(C+\log 2\pi x)\}$$

are Fourier sine transforms of each other for real positive $x$. In analogy to the functional equation for $\zeta'(s)/\zeta(s)$ we have further for the function $U(z)=e^{-\frac{1}{2}iz}V(iz)+\frac{1}{4}\pi^{-1}\log z\operatorname{cosec}\frac{1}{2}z$, which possesses a single-valued continuation over the $z$-plane, the functional equation $U(z)+U(-z)=2\cos\frac{1}{2}z-\frac{1}{4}\sec\frac{1}{2}z$. These results are then generalized in two further theorems to a Dirichlet series

$$f(z)=(2\pi)^{\frac{1}{2}}\{\tfrac{1}{2}a_0+\sum_{n=1}^{\infty}a_n\exp(-\alpha_n z)\}$$

which converges absolutely for $\Re(z)>\delta>0$, has a single-valued continuation whose only singularities in $-\delta\leqq\Re(z)\leqq\delta$ are poles, and which satisfies a functional equation $f(z)+f(-z)=0$. *H. Rademacher* (Philadelphia, Pa.).

## M25-31 (13, 742a)

**Turán, P. On Carlson's theorem in the theory of the zeta-function of Riemann.** Acta Math. Acad. Sci. Hungar. **2**, 39–73 (1951). (English. Russian summary)

Estimates of the number $N(\sigma_0, T)$ of zeros of the Riemann zeta-function in the domain $\sigma_0\leqq\sigma<1$, $0<t\leqq T$, play an important part in questions of prime-number theory, and have been given by Carlson and several later writers. The result obtained in this paper is

$$N(\sigma, T)=o(T^{2(1-\sigma)+600(1-\sigma)^{101/100}}\log^6 T),$$

valid if $1-B\leqq\sigma\leqq 1$, where $B$ is sufficiently small. The proof, which is rather intricate, depends essentially on the lemma: for $m\geqq n$, $\nu$ an integer, $1=|z_1|\geqq|z_2|\geqq\cdots\geqq|z_n|$, we have

$$\max_{m\leq\nu\leq m+n}|d_1z_1^\nu+\cdots+d_nz_n^\nu|\geqq\left(\frac{n}{e^8m}\right)^n\min_{j=1,\cdots,n}|d_1+\cdots+d_j|.$$

Further results depending on the Lindelöf hypothesis are also stated.

*E. C. Titchmarsh* (Oxford).

Referred to in M25-40, M50-2, N04-17.

## M25-32 (13, 928a)

**Miyatake, Osamu. On the distribution of zero points of a function which is related to Riemann's $\xi$-function.** J. Inst. Polytech. Osaka City Univ. Ser. A. Math. **2**, 39–59 (1951).

Verf. untersucht die Nullstellen der ganzen Funktionen

$$\text{(A)}\qquad \xi_i(z)=2\int_0^\infty\psi_i(t)\cos zt\,dt,\quad i=1,2,3,$$

mit

$$\psi_1=\sum_{n=1}^\infty n^4\exp\left(-n^2\pi(e^t+e^{-t})\right)$$

$$\psi_2=\sum{}'n^4\exp\left(-n^2\pi(e^{+t}+e^{-t})\right)$$

$$\psi_3=\sum_{n=1}^\infty n^3\exp\left(-n^2\pi(e^t+e^{-t})\right),$$

wo $\sum'$ über alle $n$ erstreckt wird, die keinen Primfaktor $>N$ enthalten. Die $\xi_i$ stehen mit der Riemannschen $\xi$-Funktion in gewisser Verwandtschaft [vgl. hiefür auch G. Pólya, Acta Math. **48**, 305–317 (1926)]. Für $\xi_1$ wurde kein Resultat erzielt, während bei $\xi_2$ und $\xi_3$ die Nullstellen mit genügend grossem Betrag alle auf der reellen Achse liegen und für deren Anzahl im Streifen $0\leqq x\leqq T$ die asymptotische Formel

$$N(T)=\frac{T}{2\pi}\log\frac{T}{2\pi}-\frac{T}{2\pi}+O(1)$$

besteht. *A. Pfluger* (Zürich).

## M25-33 (13, 928b)

**Miyatake, Osamu. Note on Riemann's $\xi$-function.** J. Inst. Polytech. Osaka City Univ. Ser. A. Math. **2**, 61–70 (1951).

Verf. betrachtet die ganze Funktion $\xi_4(z)$ (vgl. den Ausdruck (A) im vorangehenden Referat) mit

$$\psi_4=\sum{}'(e^{t/4}+e^{-t/4})\exp\left(-n^2\pi(e^t+e^{-t})\right)-\tfrac{1}{2}(e^{t/4}+e^{-t/4})^{-1}$$

wo $\sum'$ wie bei $\psi_2$ im vorangehenden Referat zu verstehen ist. Die Nullstellen genügend grosser Beträge sind alle reell und für ihre Anzahl im Streifen $0\leqq x\leqq T$ gilt

$$N(T)=\frac{T}{\pi}\log\frac{T}{\pi}+O(T).$$

*A. Pfluger* (Zürich).

## M25-34 (14, 249c)

**Rodosskiĭ, K. A. On the number of zeros of all $L$-functions with characters of given modulus.** Doklady Akad. Nauk SSSR (N.S.) **84**, 669–671 (1952). (Russian)

An outline of the proof of the following result is indicated. Let $.9\leqq\Delta<1$ and $T\geqq D^{8/3}$. Then for suitable absolute constants $D_0$ and $c$ the number of zeros $\sigma+it$ of all $L$-functions, with characters $\chi$ modulo $D$, such that $\Delta\leqq\sigma\leqq 1$ and $|t|\leqq T$ does not exceed $c(DT)^{9(1-\Delta)/(2\Delta)}\log^{12}DT$ provided $D\geqq D_0$. The proof depends on previous results of the author [Ukrain. Mat. Žurnal **3**, p. 399 ff. (1951)], not available to the reviewer, and the approximate functional equation for $L(s,\chi)$ in the form due to Čudakov [Ann. of Math. (2) **48**, 515–545 (1947); these Rev. **9**, 11]. This result should be compared with a related estimate of Tatuzawa in the paper reviewed above* which depends on an order estimate for $L(s,\chi)$ on the line $\sigma=1/2$. *L. Schoenfeld* (Urbana, Ill.).

*MR 14, 249B = N16-11.

Citations: MR 9, 11d = P32-10; MR 14, 249b = N16-11.

## M25-35 (14, 1126e)

**Turing, A. M. Some calculations of the Riemann zeta-function.** Proc. London Math. Soc. (3) **3**, 99–117 (1953).

The paper gives an account of two investigations of the zeros of the Riemann Zeta-function in the critical strip. The principal investigation of $\zeta(\sigma+it)$ was for $63^2<t/2\pi<64^2$, that is $24938<t<25736$. This region is at a great distance from the previous calculations of Titchmarsh, which were for $0<t<1468$. A second investigation covered the range $1413<t<1540$. For each of these regions all the zeros of $\zeta(\sigma+it)$ are simple and have $\sigma=1/2$. The larger region contains about 1070 of these zeros. No reason is given for selecting this region. The calculation was performed in 1950 on the Manchester University Mark 1 Computer.

The paper is in two parts. The first part is devoted to the formulation and analysis of the problem along the lines laid down by Titchmarsh [Proc. Roy. Soc. London. Ser. A. **151**, 234–255 (1935)] but with simplifications and certain modifications for machine application. The second part describes the actual calculations as performed on the Manchester machine. The time required to calculate one value of the function in the large interval was about 14 seconds.

Although the author tends to belittle the actual results obtained in a few hours of machine time, the paper shows that a great deal of careful work has been done in preparing the calculation for the machine and this work will be of value to future computers. Since 1950 there has been a large increase in the number and reliability of large scale computers. No doubt further results on this problem will appear in due course. *D. H. Lehmer*.

Referred to in M25-44, M25-83.

## M25-36 (15, 412e)

**Putnam, C. R. On the non-periodicity of the zeros of the Riemann zeta-function.** Amer. J. Math. **76**, 97–99 (1954).

It is proved that the sequence of the consecutive positive zeros of $\zeta(\frac{1}{2}+it)$ does not contain any periodic subsequence.

*E. C. Titchmarsh* (Oxford).

Referred to in M15-21.

## M25-37 (15, 855h; 15, 855i)

**Klimov, A. I. On an estimate of a bound for the zeros of $L$-functions.** Doklady Akad. Nauk SSSR (N.S.) **89**, 205–208 (1953). (Russian)

**Klimov, A. I. Improved estimate of a bound for the zeros of $L$-functions.** Ukrain. Mat. Žurnal **5**, 171–184 (1953). (Russian)

The first paper is a summary of the second. The main result is that for a character $\chi$ modulo $k$, the Dirichlet series $L(s,\chi)$ has no zeros in the region $|t|\geqq 1$,

$$\sigma\geqq 1-c/\{\log(k+3)+(\log\gamma\log\log\gamma)^{3/4}\},$$

where $\gamma=|t|+8$ and $c=.0005$. However, (for unspecified $c$) this was proved earlier by Tatuzawa [Jap. J. Math. **21**,

93–111 (1952); these Rev. **15**, 202]. The details are by now familiar, depending as they do on exponential sums.

*L. Schoenfeld* (Princeton, N. J.).

Citations: MR 15, 202d = N12-7.

## M25-38 (16, 346g)

**Putnam, C. R. Remarks on periodic sequences and the Riemann zeta-function.** Amer. J. Math. **76**, 828–830 (1954).

A theorem is proved of which the gist is that the imaginary part of $\zeta(\sigma+it)$, on any fixed line $\sigma=$const. $>0$, does not tend to zero as $t=t_n\to\infty$, if the sequence $t_1, t_2, \cdots$ approximates closely enough to a periodic sequence $d, 2d, 3d, \cdots$. In particular, the sequence of the consecutive zeros, of $\zeta(\frac{1}{2}+it)$ does not contain any periodic subsequence.

*E. C. Titchmarsh* (Oxford).

## M25-39 (16, 449b)

**Turán, Pal. On the roots of the Riemann zeta function.** Magyar Tud. Akad. Mat. Fiz. Oszt. Közl. **4**, 357–368 (1954). (Hungarian)

After a historical survey, without bibliographical details, the author proves the following for $N(\alpha, T)$, the number of roots of $\zeta(\sigma+it)$ with $\sigma\geqq\alpha$, $0<t\leqq T$. Let there be a $\vartheta$ with $\frac{1}{2}<\vartheta<1$ such that for $\sigma\geqq\vartheta$, $t\geqq1$ and for some sufficiently small $\eta>0$ there holds

$$|\zeta(\sigma+it)|\leqq c_{10}(\eta)t^{\eta^{1000}}.$$

Then for $\vartheta+4\eta\leqq\sigma_1\leqq1$, $T>c_{11}(\eta)$, there holds

$$N(\sigma_1, T)<c_{12}(\eta)T^{2(1+3\eta)(1-\sigma_1)}\log^5 T.$$

*F. V. Atkinson* (Ibadan).

Referred to in M25-40.

## M25-40 (16, 999g)

**Turán, P. On Lindelöf's conjecture.** Acta Math. Acad. Sci. Hungar. **5**, 145–163 (1954). (Russian summary)

$N(\alpha, T)$ denotes, as usual, the number of zeros $\sigma+it$ of the Riemann zeta function in the rectangle $\alpha\leqq\sigma\leqq1$, $0<t\leqq T$. Various estimates of $N(\alpha, T)$ are known, for which we refer to Titchmarsh [The theory of the Riemann zeta-function, 2nd ed., Oxford, 1951, p. 196–211; MR **13**, 741]. We quote A. E. Ingham's result [Quart. J. Math. Oxford Ser. **8**, 255–266 (1937)] that $N(\alpha, T)<CT^{(2+\epsilon)(1-\alpha)}\log^5 T$ $(\frac{1}{2}\leqq\alpha\leqq1, T>2)$, assuming the Lindelöf hypothesis

$$\zeta(\tfrac{1}{2}+it)=O(t^{\epsilon'}).$$

The present author gives a method by which results on $N(\alpha, T)$ can be obtained from information on the order of $\zeta(s)$ on vertical lines to the right of the critical line, without assuming anything about $\zeta(\frac{1}{2}+it)$. His theorem is as follows. Let $\frac{1}{2}<\vartheta<1$. Then there is a positive number $\eta_0(\vartheta)$ such that for $0<\eta<\eta_0(\vartheta)$ the following theorem holds: If

(1) $|\zeta(\sigma+it)|\leqq c_1(\eta)\exp(\eta^{1000}\log t)$ $(\sigma\geqq\vartheta, t\geqq1)$,

then we have

(2) $N(\sigma, T)<c_2(\eta)T^{(2+6\eta)(1-\sigma)}\log^5 T$ $(\sigma\geqq\vartheta+4\eta, T>c_3(\eta))$.

In the proof the author applies his power-sum method [Eine neue Methode in der Analysis und deren Anwendungen, Akad. Kiadó, Budapest, 1953; MR **15**, 688] to the sum $g_k(s)=\sum_{n\geqq\xi}\Lambda(n)n^{-s}\log^k(n/\xi)$ with values of $s$ far in the half-plane $\sigma>1$; $k$ large, $\xi=e^{k+1}$. This is similar to a previous application [Acta Math. Acad. Sci. Hungar. **2**, 39–73 (1951); MR **13**, 742; also Th. 38 in his book just cited], which dealt with the case that $\sigma$ is close to 1, and which is an auxiliary result in the present paper.

The reviewer remarks that $\log^5 T$ in (2) is an error for $\log^6 T$; this factor comes in from the case "$\sigma$ close to 1". On the other hand, the $\log T$ factors can easily be disposed of entirely, by remarking that $N(\sigma, T)=O(1)$ if

$$\sigma>1-(\log T)^{-7/8}$$

[see Titchmarsh, loc. cit., p. 114]. A somewhat abbreviated exposition of these results also appears in Hungarian [Magyar Tud. Akad. Mat. Fiz. Oszt. Közl. **4**, 357–368 (1954); MR **16**, 449]. *N. G. de Bruijn* (Amsterdam).

Citations: MR 13, 741c = M02-2; MR 13, 742a = M25-31; MR 15, 688b = M50-2; MR 16, 449b = M25-39.

## M25-41 (18, 792e)

**Turan, Paul. On the zeros of the zeta-function of Riemann.** J. Indian Math. Soc. (N.S.) **20** (1956), 17–36.

Denote by $N(\alpha, T)$ the number of roots of $\zeta(s)=0$ in the parallelogram $\alpha\leqq\sigma\leqq1$, $0<t\leqq T$. Carlson and Hoheisel proved that

$$N(\alpha, T)<c_1T^{4\alpha(1-\alpha)}(\log T)^{c_2},$$

and Ingham proved this with 8/3 instead of 4. The author discusses the so called density hypothesis

(1) $N(\alpha,T)<c_1T^{2\alpha(1-\alpha)}(\log T)^{c_2}$

or its slightly weaker form

(2) $N(\alpha, T)<c_1T^{(2+\varepsilon)\alpha(1-\alpha)}$.

(It is known that (1) and (2) would imply $p_{n+1}-p_n<p_n^{\frac{1}{2}+\varepsilon}$.) Ingham proved that Lindelöf's hypothesis $|\zeta(\frac{1}{2}+it)|=o(t^{\varepsilon})$ implies (2), and the author found a different proof by his well-known method; further he proved (2) "near" to the line $\sigma=1$. More precisely, he proved that for a certain (small) $c_3$ and $T>c_4$, $N(\alpha, T)<T^{2\alpha(1-\alpha)+(1-\alpha)^{1.4}}$ $(1<c_{21}<\alpha<1)$. The author finally discusses several conjectures which seem weaker than Lindelöf's hypothesis and which imply (2). Here I want to state only one of them: There exists a $g(x)$, $\lim_{x=0}g(x)=0$, $g(x)$ monotone increasing and positive for $x>0$, which has the following property. Assume that for some $\alpha_4$ $(\frac{1}{2}<\alpha_4<1)$, $\zeta(s)$ does not vanish in the parallelogram $\alpha_4\leqq\sigma\leqq1$, $|t-\tau|\leqq\log\tau$ with a $\tau\geqq3$. Then we have for $0<\delta<1/10$, $\tau>c_{28}(\delta)$, in the parallelogram $a_4-2\delta\leqq\sigma\leqq a_4$, $|t-\tau|\leqq\delta$, the inequality $|\zeta(s)|\leqq\tau^{g(\delta)(c_4-\sigma)}$. The author proves (2) using this conjecture and discusses possible methods which might lead to the proof of this conjecture. *P. Erdös* (Haifa).

Referred to in M25-42, R42-30.

## M25-42 (19, 1039f)

**Turán, Paul. Über eine Anwendung einer neuen Methode auf die Theorie der Riemannschen Zetafunktion.** Wiss. Z. Humboldt-Univ. Berlin. Math.-Nat. Reihe **5** (1955/56), 281–285. (Russian, English and French summaries)

In this lecture the author derives the "density hypothesis" from assumptions which are essentially weaker than Lindelöf's hypothesis. A more complete account of almost the same result was given in a later lecture, a report of which has appeared [J. Indian Math. Soc. (N.S.) **20** (1956), 17–36; MR **18**, 792]. *N. G. de Bruijn.*

Citations: MR 18, 792e = M25-41.

## M25-43 (18, 793a)

**Postnikov, A. G. On Dirichlet $L$-series with the character modulus equal to the power of a prime number.** J. Indian Math. Soc. (N.S.) **20** (1956), 217–226.

The author considers Dirichlet $L$-series $L(s, \chi)$, where $\chi$ is a primitive character mod $p^n$, and $p$ is a prime $>2$. Both $p$ and $n$ are large, and submitted to $n^Q\geqq\log p\geqq C_1n^4(\log n)^3$ ($C_1, C_2, C_3, Q$ are arbitrary positive constants, $Q>4$). It is shown that $L(s, \chi)$ has no zeros in the region $|t|>C_2$, $\sigma>1-C_5(\log p^n)^{-Q/(Q+1)}(\log\log p^n)^{-1}$, provided that $n$ is large enough.

The proof uses summation of $\chi(1+pu)$ with respect to $u$. It is shown that $\chi(1+pu)$ can be written as $\exp(2\pi i f(u))$, where $f(u)$ is a polynomial, so that Vinogradov's estimates on trigonometric sums can be applied.

There are several minor errors and many misprints.

*N. G. de Bruijn* (Amsterdam).

Referred to in N12-29.

## M25-44 (19, 121a; 19, 121b)

**Lehmer, D. H. On the roots of the Riemann zeta-function.** Acta Math. **95** (1956), 291–298.
**Lehmer, D. H. Extended computation of the Riemann zeta-function.** Mathematika **3** (1956), 102–108.

These two papers describe numerical calculations which establish the result that the first 25,000 zeros of $\zeta(s)$ lie on $\sigma=\frac{1}{2}$, thereby verifying the Riemann hypothesis for $|t|\leqq 21,943$. Earlier computations by Titchmarsh [Proc. Roy. Soc. London. Ser. A. **151** (1935), 234–255; **157** (1936), 261–263] have established a corresponding result for $|t|\leqq 1468$, while Turing [Proc. London Math. Soc. (3) **3** (1953), 99–117; MR **14**, 1126] carried the result to 1540. Some flaws in the argument are noted below.

The analytic basis for the computation may be described as follows. Let

$$\vartheta(t)=-\frac{1}{2}t\log\pi+\Im\log\Gamma\left(\frac{1}{4}+\frac{1}{2}it\right)$$

$$=\frac{1}{2}t\log\frac{t}{2\pi}-\frac{t}{2}-\frac{\pi}{8}+O\left(\frac{1}{t}\right),$$

$$F(t)=e^{i\vartheta(t)}\zeta(\tfrac{1}{2}+it).$$

Then $F(t)$ is real for real $t$. We let $N(t)$ be the number of zeros $\rho$ of $\zeta(s)$ such that $0\leqq\Re\rho\leqq 1$ and $0\leqq\Im\rho\leqq t$. As shown by Titchmarsh, if $k$ is the integer nearest to $\vartheta(t)/\pi$ and if $\Re\zeta(\sigma+it)\neq 0$ for $\frac{1}{2}\leqq\sigma\leqq 2$, then $N(t)=k+1$. Further, we define the Gram point $\tau_n$ for real $n\geqq -9/8$ as the unique solution of $\tau\log\tau-\tau=n+\frac{1}{8}$ satisfying $\tau\geqq 1$. As $n\to\infty$, one then has $\tau_{n+1}-\tau_n\sim 1/\log n$ and $\tau_n\sim n/\log n$. Gram's law, which is not strictly true, asserts that $\zeta(\frac{1}{2}+it)$, and hence $F(t)$, has exactly one zero between $2\pi\tau_n$ and $2\pi\tau_{n+1}$. If $\Re\zeta(\sigma+2\pi i\tau_n)\neq 0$, $\frac{1}{2}\leqq\sigma\leqq 2$, then $N(2\pi\tau_n)=n+1$. One then examines the signs of $F(2\pi\tau_k)$ for $k=-1, 0, \cdots, n$. If these alternate, one is then assured of at least $n+1$ zeros for $\zeta(s)$ up to $2\pi\tau_n$ and these all lie on $\sigma=\frac{1}{2}$; the equation $N(2\pi\tau_n)=n+1$ now establishes that $\zeta(s)$ has no other zeros up to $2\pi\tau_n$ but those on $\sigma=\frac{1}{2}$. This, in principle, is the basis for all such calculations. In practice, a number of difficulties have to be surmounted. First, an efficient method for determining the sign of $F(t)$ must be devised. Second, Gram's law does not hold universally, so that the numbers $F(2\pi\tau_k)$ do not always alternate in sign; hence, in numerous cases, one must choose other points than $2\pi\tau_k$ at which to test the sign of $F(t)$.

With regard to the calculation of $F(t)$, there are two methods which are used in the present work. The major portion of the computation was based on the Riemann-Siegel asymptotic formula; the error committed by taking only the first term has been numerically bounded by Titchmarsh, who gave usable estimates for almost all cases. It might be mentioned that Titchmarsh's bound is not quite correct and the present author does not indicate whether he used a corrected form of the bound. The author, however, gives three additional terms of the asymptotic expansion together with a fourth term which is written (with a slight change of notation) as $O(t^{-2})$ It is not entirely clear whether this extension has been used in the calculation, but there is evidence that it was. If so, we must express regret that the author did not replace the term $O(t^{-2})$ by a bound $ct^{-2}$ with an explicit value for $c$; without such a value for $c$, one can not be entirely certain that the contribution of this term is not large enough to alter the sign of $F(t)$. In at least two cases where Titchmarsh's estimate was not strong enough to establish the sign of $F(t)$ recourse was made to an earlier method, based on the Euler-Maclaurin sum formula. This method has associated with it a smaller error term but suffers from the defect of requiring that a large number of terms (1500 and 2000) be taken in a sum approximating $F(t)$. We also note that the author makes no mention of the values $t$ for which he has established that $\Re\zeta(\sigma+it)\neq 0$ for $\frac{1}{2}\leqq\sigma\leqq 2$ and, as a result, it is not clear for which values of $t$ the quantity $N(t)$ was precisely determined.

The author gives statistics concerning the failures of Gram's law. In the last 15,000 intervals $(2\pi\tau_n, 2\pi\tau_{n+1})$, about 10% fail to contain a zero of $\zeta(\frac{1}{2}+it)$. However, all but about 1% of the intervals $(2\pi\tau_{n-1/4}, 2\pi\tau_{n+5/4})$ contain a zero. The total calculation took only a few hours of time on the computing machine known as SWAC.

*L. Schoenfeld* (East Pittsburgh, Pa.).

Citations: MR 14, 1126e = M25-35.
Referred to in M05-33.

## M25-45 (20# 2304)

**Turán, P. On the so-called density-hypothesis in the theory of the zeta-function of Riemann.** Acta Arith. **4** (1958), 31–56.

Let $N(T)$ be the number of zeros $\rho=\beta+i\gamma$ of $\zeta(s)=\zeta(\sigma+it)$ with $0<\gamma\leqq T$, and $N(\alpha, T)$ the number of these with $\beta\geqq\alpha$. The density hypothesis (DH) may be stated with various degrees of refinement. The roughest form is

$$N(\alpha, T)<AT^{(2+\varepsilon)(1-\alpha)}\log^B T\ (\tfrac{1}{2}\leqq\alpha\leqq 1, T\geqq C),$$

where $A$, $B$ are absolute constants, $\varepsilon$ is an arbitrarily small positive number, and $C=C(\varepsilon)$. (In this review $\varepsilon$ and $C$ will always be used thus, and may have different values at different occurrences.) With $B=5$ this was shown by the reviewer to follow from the Lindelöf hypothesis (LH) that $\zeta(\frac{1}{2}+it)=O(t^\varepsilon)$ as $t\to\infty$ [Quart. J. Math. Oxford Ser. **8** (1937), 255–266]. The object of this paper is to deduce this hypothesis, with $A=1$, $B=0$, from the weaker conjecture (B): If (i) $\frac{1}{2}<\frac{1}{2}+10\delta\leqq\kappa\leqq\alpha<1$, and (ii) the rectangle $\alpha\leqq\sigma\leqq 1$, $|t-\tau|\leqq[\log\frac{1}{2}\tau]$ contains no zero of $\zeta(s)$, then, for $\tau>\tau_0(\kappa, \delta)$, the square $\alpha-\delta\leqq\sigma\leqq\alpha$, $|t-\tau|\leqq\frac{1}{2}\delta$, contains at most $\delta g(\delta)\log\frac{1}{2}\tau$ zeros, where $g(\delta)\downarrow 0$ as $\delta\downarrow 0$. This is, in fact, weaker, since LH implies, even without (ii), that the number of zeros in the square is $o(\log\tau)$ uniformly in $\alpha$ as $\tau\to\infty$. An intermediate conjecture (A) is B without the restriction (ii).

The starting point is an identity

$$\sum_\rho f(\rho-s)=\sum_n\Lambda(n)F(n)n^{-s}+R(s),$$

proved by contour integration. Here, $f$ is defined by

$$f\left(\frac{z}{\lambda}\right)=\left(e^z\frac{\sinh\varepsilon z}{\varepsilon z}\right)^k\quad (k \text{ a positive integer}),$$

with $\lambda=\lambda(\varepsilon)>0$ and $\varepsilon\lambda$ large; the corresponding $F(n)$ is 0 outside a finite interval; and $R(s)$ is relatively unimportant. Consideration of the mean value of $|\sum_n|^2$ (and so of $|\sum_\rho|^2$) over $T\leqq t\leqq 2T$, for $\frac{1}{2}<\sigma<1$, leads to a dissection of the strip $T\leqq t\leqq 2T$ into two sets of horizontal strips $I=I(T, \alpha)$, $J=J(T, \alpha)$, relative to an arbitrary $\alpha$ in $\frac{1}{2}+\varepsilon\leqq\alpha\leqq 1-\varepsilon$. The set $I$ is relatively small (in total width and in the number of strips comprising it) and contains only $o(T^{2(1-\alpha)})$ zeros altogether. The set $J$ is such that $|\sum_\rho|<CT^{\alpha-\sigma+\varepsilon}$ when $k$ belongs to a certain interval $K(T)$ and $s$ belongs to $J$ and to a certain discrete subset $S(T)$ of the strip $\frac{1}{2}<\sigma<1$. If the inequality for $\sum_\rho$ could be transferred to the individual terms, it would follow that any $\rho$ in $J$

must have $\beta<\alpha+\varepsilon$. The author seeks to approximate to this situation, for a suitable $k$, by first restricting $\sum_\rho$ to a set of $\rho$ near $s$, and by then applying his general method based on sums of powers of complex numbers [P. Turán, Eine neue Methode in der Analysis und deren Anwendungen, Akadémiai Kiadó, Budapest, 1953; MR **15**, 688]. This, however, is not completely effective; but, by an elaborate analysis of the possible distribution of zeros in $J$, the difficulty is reduced to one that can be resolved by the assumption of conjecture B with a suitable $\delta=\delta(\varepsilon)$. The result is an inequality for $N(\alpha+\varepsilon, 2T)-N(\alpha+\varepsilon, T)$, from which DH is deduced. For $\alpha$ near 1, however, the deduction involves another deep theorem of the author (Satz XXXVIII of the book quoted above). {It is not clear how the refinement $A=1$, $B=0$ is obtained by the method of p. 52, which seems to ignore the factor $\log^6 T$ in (1.1.10); it can, however, be obtained with the help of deep theorems on the non-existence of zeros in regions of the type $1-\eta(t)\leqq\sigma\leqq 1$.}

In support of his contention that B is essentially weaker than LH or A, the author proves in an appendix the corresponding statement with $g(\delta)$ replaced by 0.71, and remarks that a similar (or more drastic) modification of A seems almost as difficult as LH itself.

*A. E. Ingham* (Cambridge, England)

Citations: MR 15, 688b = M50-2.

## M25-46 (22# 4680)

**Rozin, S. M. On null Dirichlet *L*-series.** Izv. Akad. Nauk SSSR. Ser. Mat. **23** (1959), 503–508. (Russian)

Soit $p>2$ un nombre premier, $n>0$ entier, $D=p^n$, $\chi$ le caractère primitif mod $D$; $c_i>0$ sont des constantes. Soit $(n_1/(\log n_1)^3)^{1/4}\geqq 13$. Pour tout $n>n_1$, on a lorsque $l>p^{2(n\log n)^{3/4}}$: $\sum_{z=N}^{N+l-1}\chi(x)<l\cdot p^{-(n\log n)^{1/4}}$. Application: Pour $p$ constant, $n\to\infty$, $\varepsilon>0$ arbitraire, $L(s,\chi)$ ne s'annule pas dans $|t|<c_1$, $\sigma>1-c_2/(\log^{3/4+\varepsilon}D\cdot\log\log D)$.

*S. Mandelbrojt* (Paris)

Referred to in N12-29, N16-28.

## M25-47 (22# 10958)

**Staś, W. Über die Dichte der Nullstellen der Dirichletschen *L*-Funktionen.** Acta Arith. **6** (1960/61), 313–323.

Denote by $N(\vartheta, T)$ the number of zeros of all $\phi(k)$ $L$-functions (mod $k$) where $k\geqq 1$ in the region: $\sigma\geqq\vartheta$, $\frac12\leqq\vartheta<1$, $0<t\leqq T$ (multiplicity taken into account). Generalizing a result of P. Turán in his well-known book *Eine neue Methode in der Analysis und deren Anwendungen* [Akadémiai Kiadó, Budapest, 1953; MR **15**, 688], the author proves the following theorem: There exist positive constants $b$, $c_1$, $c_2$ such that

(1) $$N(\vartheta, T)<c_2k^6T^{2(1-\vartheta)+(1-\vartheta)^{1.08}}\log^8(kT)$$

holds for

(2) $$1-\min(b, k^{-40})\leqq\vartheta\leqq 1$$

and

(3) $$T>\max(c_1, \exp\exp k^3).$$

The proof uses the interesting Satz X of Turán's book as well as results of Tatuzawa [Proc. Japan Acad. **26** (1950), no. 9, 1–13; MR **14**, 249] and Hua [Quart. J. Math. Oxford Ser. (2) **20** (1949), 48–61; MR **10**, 597].

*S. Chowla* (Boulder, Colo.)

Citations: MR 10, 597d = P08-11; MR 14, 249b = N16-11; MR 15, 688b = M50-2.

## M25-48 (23# A1611)

**Rodosskiĭ, K. A.**

**A new application of some results of I. M. Vinogradov to Riemann zeta-function theory.**

*Dokl. Akad. Nauk SSSR* **134** (1960), 1303–1304 (*Russian); translated as Soviet Math. Dokl.* **1** (1961), 1215–1216.

Let $N(\Delta, T)$ be the number of zeros of the function $\zeta(s)$, $s=\sigma+it$, in $\Delta\leqslant\sigma<1$, $0\leqslant t\leqslant T$. It was known previously (A. E Ingham) that

$$N(\Delta, T)=O(T^{\lambda(\Delta)(1-\Delta)}\log^{c_1}\Delta),$$

with

$$\lambda(\Delta)\leqq\min(3/(2-\Delta), 2(1+2c_2)),$$

$c_2$ being such that $\zeta(\frac12+it)=O(t^{c_2}\log^{c_3}t)$, and later (P. Turán) that

$$\lambda(\Delta)\leqq 2+(1-\Delta)^{0.14}$$

for $\Delta$ sufficiently close to 1. The present author improves the latter inequality, using a certain trigonometric-sum result of Vinogradov, to

$$\lambda(\Delta)\leqq 2+c_4(1-\Delta)^{1/3}$$

for $\Delta$ sufficiently close to 1. *S. Knapowski* (Poznań)

Referred to in M25-62.

## M25-49 (23# A2397)

**Turán, Paul**

**Zur Theorie der Dirichletschen Reihen. (Russian summary)**

*Sammelband zu Ehren des* 250. *Geburtstages Leonhard Eulers, pp.* 322–336. *Akademie-Verlag, Berlin,* 1959.

Let $\mathfrak{A}$ be the class of functions $f(s)$ $(s=\sigma+it)$ with the following properties, in which the $c$'s are positive constants depending only on the parameters (if any) shown explicitly: (a) $f(s)=\sum_1^\infty a_nn^{-s}$ $(\sigma>1)$ with $a_1=1$, and $|f(s)|\geqq c_1(\varepsilon)$ for $\sigma\geqq 1+\varepsilon>1$; (b) $f(s)$ is meromorphic for $\sigma\geqq\frac12$ and satisfies

$$|f(s)|\leqq c_2(1+|t|^{c_3(1-\sigma)})\log^{10}|t|\quad(\sigma\geqq\tfrac12;\ |t|\geqq 3);$$

(c) $\varphi(s)\equiv f'(s)/f(s)=\sum_2^\infty b_nn^{-s}$ $(\sigma>1)$ with $|b_n|\leqq c_4\log n$. Let $\mathfrak{B}$ be the subclass of $\mathfrak{A}$ for which: (d) $|f(s)|\leqq|t|^\eta$ $(\sigma\geqq\frac12+\varepsilon$, $|t|\geqq c_5(\varepsilon))$, where $\eta=\eta(\varepsilon)\to 0$ as $\varepsilon\to 0$. For $f\in\mathfrak{A}$, let $\sigma_w$ be the lower bound of numbers $\theta\geqq\frac12$ such that $f(s)$ has at most a finite number of zeros in $\sigma>\theta$; and let $S=S(f)$ be the set of pairs of positive numbers $(\alpha,\beta)$ such that

(1) $$\left|\sum_{N_1}^{N_2}\frac{b_n}{n^{it}}\right|\leqq c_6\frac{N\log^{100}N}{|t|^\beta}$$
$$(|t|>c_7;\ |t|^\alpha\leqq\tfrac12N\leqq N_1<N_2\leqq N).$$

The author recalls his theorem, essentially Satz XXXI of his book *Eine neue Methode in der Analysis und deren Anwendungen* [Akadémiai Kiadó, Budapest, 1953; MR **15**, 688], that, if $f\in\mathfrak{B}$, then $\sigma_w=1-L$, where $L$ is the upper limit (equivalent in this context to the upper bound) of $\beta/\alpha$ when $(\alpha,\beta)$ runs through the subset $S_0$ of $S$ for which $0<\beta\leqq 1$, $\alpha>2\beta$. He notes, however, that this theorem is not at present applicable to the Riemann zeta-function $\zeta(s)$, since (d) is equivalent in this case to the unproved Lindelöf hypothesis. He therefore introduces another subclass $\mathfrak{C}$ of $\mathfrak{A}$ defined by the properties (a), (b), (c), and: (e) For arbitrarily small positive $\gamma$, $\delta$, the number of zeros of $f(s)$ in the square

$$(\tfrac12+\gamma\leqq)\kappa-\delta\leqq\sigma\leqq\kappa\ (\leqq 1),\quad |t-\tau|\leqq\tfrac12\delta,$$

is less than $g(\delta)\log\tau$ where $g(\delta)/\delta\to 0$ as $\delta\to 0$, whenever $\tau > c_8(\gamma,\delta)$ and the adjoining half-strip $\sigma\geqq\kappa$, $|t-\tau|\leqq\log\tau$ contains no zeros of $f(s)$. The author proves (in outline) his theorem for the class $\mathfrak{C}$ in place of $\mathfrak{B}$, and gives reasons for believing that a proof of (e) for $\zeta(s)$, as opposed to the Lindelöf hypothesis (d), is not entirely hopeless in our present state of knowledge.

The proof that $\sigma_w\leqq 1-L$ is by reductio ad absurdum. If this is false, we can find a fixed $(\alpha,\beta)$ in $S_0$ such that, for sufficiently small $\varepsilon>0$, the half-plane $\sigma>1-(\beta/\alpha)+\varepsilon$ contains an infinity of zeros of $f(s)$. From these an infinite subset of zeros $\rho^*=\sigma^*+it^*$ is chosen so that each has associated with it a zero-free half-strip $G(\rho^*)$ of the type mentioned in (e) lying symmetrically about $t=t^*$ and a little to the right of $\sigma=\sigma^*$. The author then considers in two ways the expression

$$J = -\frac{1}{2\pi i}\int_{(2)}\left(e^{aw}\frac{e^{bw}-e^{-bw}}{2bw}\right)^k\varphi(\rho^*+w)\,dw,$$

where $a=\varepsilon^{-2}$, $b=\varepsilon^{-1}$, and $k$ is a positive integer. Firstly, $J$ is expressed in terms of the $b_n$ and an upper estimate of $|J|$ is obtained from (1). Secondly, an application of calculus of residues gives an expression for $J$ in which the most significant part is a sum $\Sigma$ over zeros $\rho$ lying in a small square surrounding $\rho^*$ and abutting on $G(\rho^*)$. The condition (e) provides an upper estimate of the number of terms in $\Sigma$ and enables the author to apply the algebraical lemmas that form the basis of his method and so to obtain a lower estimate of $|\Sigma|$ for a suitable $k$. Combination of the two estimates leads to an upper estimate of $\sigma^*$ which contradicts $\sigma^*>1-(\beta/\alpha)+\varepsilon$ when $|t^*|$ is taken arbitrarily large and $\varepsilon$ arbitrarily small. The proof that $\sigma_w\geqq 1-L$ is by a contour integration argument in which the sum on the left of (1) is treated as a sum of coefficients in the expansion of $\varphi(w+it)$ as a Dirichlet series in $w$. Nothing essentially new is involved here, and the author merely refers to Anhang IV of his book.

*A. E. Ingham* (Cambridge, England)

Citations: MR 15, 688b = M50-2.

## M25-50 (23# A3123)

**Kaširskiĭ, Ju. V.**

**On the problem of the distribution of zeros of Dirichlet *L*-series. (Russian)**

*Dokl. Akad. Nauk SSSR* **138** (1961), 279–282.

The author proves the following results. Theorem 1: Set

$$S = \sum_{k=T+1}^{T+N}\chi_D(k),$$

where $\chi_D(k)$ is a primitive character to the modulus $D=p_1^{\alpha_1}\cdots p_l^{\alpha_l}$ and $\min(p_1,\cdots,p_l)>2$. Further suppose $\alpha_\nu=\min(\alpha_1,\cdots,\alpha_l)$ and $(\alpha_\nu/\log^3\alpha_\nu)^{1/4}\geqq 13$ and $\prod_{i=1}^l p_i^{3\alpha_i(\log^3\alpha_\nu/\alpha_\nu)^{1/4}}<N$. Then

$$|S| < N\prod_{i=1}^l p_i^{-(\alpha_i/\alpha_\nu)(\alpha_\nu\log\alpha_\nu)^{1/4}}.$$

This leads to the interesting Theorem 2: Let $Q$ be a constant $>3$, $\log D\leqq(\alpha_\nu/\log^3\alpha_\nu)^{(Q+1)/4}$; $D=p_1^{\alpha_1}\cdots p_l^{\alpha_l}$; $s=\sigma+it$; $|s|<C_1$; $\sigma\geqq 1-1/(\log D)^{Q/(Q+1)}$; $\chi_D(k)$, a primitive character to the modulus $D$. Then

$$|L(s,x)| < C(\log D)^{Q/(Q+1)}.$$

Finally the author states the following consequence. Theorem 3: If $\chi_D(k)$ is defined as in the above theorems and $\log D\leqq(\alpha_\nu/\log^3\alpha_\nu)^{(Q+1)/4}$, $Q>3$, $(\alpha_\nu/\log^3\alpha_\nu)^{1/4}\geqq 13$, then $L(s,x)$ does not vanish if

$$\sigma > 1-\frac{c}{\log^{Q/(Q+1)}D\cdot\log\log D}.$$

{It seems to the reviewer that the condition $|s|<C_1$ (which occurs in Theorem 2) has been omitted by an oversight in the author's statement of Theorem 3.}

*S. Chowla* (Boulder, Colo.)

## M25-51 (24# A1891)

**Karacuba, A. A.**

**Estimates of trigonometric sums of a special form, and their applications. (Russian)**

*Dokl. Akad. Nauk SSSR* **137** (1961), 513–514.

Let

$$S = \sum_{x=1}^N \exp\left[2\pi i\left\{\frac{a_1x}{p^n}+\frac{a_2x^2}{p^{n-1}}+\cdots+\frac{a_nx^n}{p}\right\}\right],$$

where $(a_\nu,p)=1$ $(\nu=1,2,\cdots,n)$. The author states, without proof, the result that, if $p\leqq N\leqq p^n$ and $\log p\gg n^2\log^3 n$, then $|S|\leqq c_1N^{1-c_2/n^2}$, where $c_1$ and $c_2$ are positive constants. A number of consequences are stated. Thus, if $n^2\log^3 n\ll\log p\leqq n^\theta$ and $\chi(k)$ is a primitive character modulo $D=p^n$, where $p$ is an odd prime, then the Dirichlet $L$-series $L(s,\chi)$ has no zeros in the region

$$|s| < c_5,\ \sigma > 1-(\log D)^{-\theta/(\theta+1)}.$$

In particular, if $n^2\log^3 n\ll\log p\leqq n^{2+\varepsilon}$ $(\varepsilon>0)$, then $L(s,\chi)$ has no zeros in the region

$$|s| < c_5,\ \sigma > 1-(\log D)^{-2/3-\varepsilon}.$$

These results improve estimates of A. G. Postnikov [Izv. Akad. Nauk SSSR Ser. Mat. **19** (1955), 11–16; MR **16**, 905].

*R. A. Rankin* (Glasgow)

Citations: MR 16, 905f = L25-12.

## M25-52 (24# B2091)

**Davies, D.; Haselgrove, C. B.**

**The evaluation of Dirichlet *L*-functions.**

*Proc. Roy. Soc. Ser. A* **264** (1961), 122–132.

Methods are described for calculating the values and the zeros of the $L$-function $L(\frac{1}{2}+it,\chi)=\sum_{n=1}^\infty\chi(n)n^{-1/2+it}$ for both real and complex characters $\chi$. Results for various ranges of $t$ have been obtained for many character moduli, including 163. These constitute No. 25 of the Royal Soc. Depository for Unpublished Tables. No exception to the extended Riemann Hypothesis was discovered. A few specimen results are published.

As with the Riemann zeta-function, for the zeros of $L$ one studies the real-valued function

$$Z(t,\chi) = \eta(t,\chi)L(\tfrac{1}{2}+it,\chi),$$

where $\eta$ is a continuously turning unit vector. The formulas used are of the Euler-Maclaurin type. These are more than adequate for the limited range $t\leqq 105$ considered. Zeros of $L$ were obtained by inverse interpolation of the values of $Z$. Page 129 gives the first 50 zeros of $L$ for the characters with moduli 43, 67, and 163, as well as the first derivatives of $Z$ at these zeros.

*D. H. Lehmer* (Berkeley, Calif.)

## M25-53 (26# 3681)

**Turán, P.**

**On a density theorem of Yu. V. Linnik. (Russian summary)**

*Magyar Tud. Akad. Mat. Kutató Int. Közl.* **6** (1961), 165–179.

In the course of his proof that the least prime $p\equiv l\ (\mathrm{mod}\ \Delta)$ is smaller than $\Delta^{c_1}$, Ju. V. Linnik used the following theorem. If $2\leqq\lambda\leqq 10^{-1}\log\Delta$ and $N(\lambda,\Delta)$ stands for the number of zeros of all $L$-functions (mod $\Delta$) in the domain $1-\lambda(\log\Delta)^{-1}\leqq\sigma\leqq 1$, $|t|\leqq e^\lambda(\log\Delta)^{-1}$, then for $\Delta>c_2$ the inequality $N(\lambda,\Delta)\leqq e^{c_3\lambda}$ holds. (For a simplified version of Linnik's proof, see K. Prachar [*Primzahlverteilung*, Springer, Berlin, 1957; MR **19**, 393].) In the present note a new and simpler proof is given for a rather more general theorem: If $N(\lambda, \Delta, t_0)$ denotes the number of zeros of all $L$-functions (mod $\Delta$) in the domain $1-\lambda(\log \Delta)^{-1} \leqq \sigma \leqq 1$, $|t-t_0| \leqq e^{\lambda}(\log \Delta)^{-1}$, then for $|t_0| \leqq \Delta^{1/2}$ and suitable $c_4, c_6, c_7$, we have for $0 \leqq \lambda \leqq c_4 \log \Delta$ and $\Delta > c_5$ the inequality $N(\lambda, \Delta, t_0) \leqq c_6 e^{c_7 \lambda}$. The proof depends on the author's "second main theorem" as expounded in his book, *Eine neue Methode in der Analysis und deren Anwendungen*, Akad. Kiadó, Budapest, 1953 [MR **15**, 688]. *W. J. LeVeque* (Ann Arbor, Mich.)

Citations: MR 15, 688b = M50-2; MR 19, 393b = N02-7.

Referred to in M25-54, M25-58, M25-59, M25-90.

## M25-54 (26# 6131)

**Knapowski, S.**

**On Linnik's theorem concerning exceptional $L$-zeros.**

*Publ. Math. Debrecen* **9** (1962), 168–178.

Let $p(l, k)$ denote the least prime in the arithmetic progression $l, l+k, l+2k, \cdots$, where $0<l<k$, $(l, k)=1$, $k \geqq 3$. Linnik [Mat. Sb. (N.S.) **15 (57)** (1944), 139–178; MR **6**, 260; ibid. **15 (57)** (1944), 347–368; MR **6**, 260] has proved that

$$(*) \qquad p(l, k) < k^C,$$

where $C$ is a constant. The proof depends upon the following two deep results. (I) Let $k \geqq 3$, $0 \leqq \lambda \leqq \log k$. Let $N_0 = N(\lambda, k)$ be the number of zeros of $\prod_\chi L(s, \chi)$ in the rectangle $\sigma \geqq 1-\lambda/\log k$, $|t| \leqq e^{\lambda}/\log k$. Then $N_0 \leqq e^{c_1}$. (II) There exist constants $c_2, c_3$ such that if $\beta_1$ is a zero of $L(s, \chi_1)$ such that $1-c_2/\log k \leqq \beta_1 < 1$, then $\prod_\chi L(s, \chi) \neq 0$ for $s \neq \beta_1$ in the domain

$$\sigma \geqq 1 - \frac{c_3}{\log k(|t|+1)} \log \frac{c_2 e}{\delta_1 \log k(|t|+1)},$$

$$\delta_1 \log k(|t|+1) \leqq c_2 \qquad (\delta_1 = 1-\beta_1).$$

Rodosskiĭ [ibid. **34 (76)** (1954), 331–356; MR **15**, 935] simplified the proof of (*) but still made use of (I) and (II).

Turán [Magyar Tud. Akad. Mat. Kutató Int. Közl. **6** (1961), 165–179; MR **26** #3681] has given a much simpler proof of (I). In the present paper the author gives a proof of (II) similar to Turán's proof of (I). The author makes use of the estimate $\delta_1 > c_5 k^{-1}$ (which is a weakened form of a theorem of Page [Proc. London Math. Soc. (2) **39** (1935), 116–141]) and in addition an improved form of a theorem of Turán [Sós and Turán, Acta Math. Acad. Sci. Hungar. **6** (1955), 241–255; MR **17**, 1061]. *L. Carlitz* (Durham, N.C.)

Citations: MR 6, 260b = N16-5; MR 6, 260c = N16-6; MR 15, 935e = N16-16; MR 17, 1061b = M50-6; MR 26# 3681 = M25-53.

Referred to in M25-90.

## M25-55 (28# 3010)

**Karacuba, A. A.**

**Trigonometric sums of a special type and their applications. (Russian)**

*Izv. Akad. Nauk SSSR Ser. Mat.* **28** (1964), 237–248.

The author proves that if $\chi$ is a primitive character modulo $D$, where $D=p^n$ and (for $0<\theta<1$) $c_1 n^{1+2/\theta} \geqq \log p \geqq c_2 n^{\theta}$, then the Dirichlet $L$-series $\sum_1^\infty \chi(n)/n^s$ does not vanish in the region

$$|s| < c_3, \qquad \sigma > 1 - \frac{1}{\log^{\theta/(\theta+1)} D},$$

where $c_1, c_2, c_3$ are certain positive absolute constants.

The argument is based on I. M. Vinogradov's estimates of exponential sums. *S. Chowla* (University Park, Pa.)

Referred to in L15-27.

## M25-56 (29# 82)

**Pan, Cheng-dong [Pan, Cheng-Tung]**

**A note on the large sieve method and its applications.**

*Acta Math. Sinica* **13** (1963), 262–268 (*Chinese*); *translated as Chinese Math.* **4** (1963), 283–290.

The author proves the following. Theorem 1: Suppose $q$ is square-free, and let $k = \log q/\log A + 1$. If $k \leqq \log^3 A$, then for all primes $p$ such that $(p, q)=1$ and $A<p \leqq 2A$, except for at most $A^{1-\varepsilon}$ $(\varepsilon>0)$ $L$-functions belonging to the modulus $D=pq$, when $\chi_D(n)$ is primitive with respect to $p$, $L(s, \chi_D)$ is not zero in the following region:

$$\sigma > 1 - \frac{\frac{2}{9}-\varepsilon}{k} \frac{\log D}{4 \log D + 2\log(|t|+1)}, \qquad |t| \leqq T.$$

With regard to this result the author says: "The important difference between the results we have here obtained and those of A. Rényi is that here $T$ may be arbitrarily large and is not limited to $|T| \leqq \log^3 D$. This point is useful in the theory of the distribution of primes" [see A. Rényi, Izv. Akad. Nauk SSSR Ser. Mat. **12** (1948), 57–78; MR **9**, 413; Amer. Math. Soc. Transl. (2) **19** (1962), 299–321; MR **24** #A1264]. From Theorem 1 he can deduce Theorem 2: Let $N_{\min}(p, k)$ represent the smallest positive non-residue of order $k$ (mod $p$), where $A<p \leqq 2A$; then with the exception of at most $A^{1-\varepsilon}$ exceptional primes $p$, we always have

$$N_{\min}(p, k) < C_1(\log A)^{18+\varepsilon}.$$

{A sharper form of Theorem 2 when $k=p-1$ is due to N. C. Ankeny, however, under the assumption of the "extended Riemann hypothesis".} *S. Chowla* (University Park, Pa.)

Citations: MR 9, 413g = P32-12; MR 24# A1264 = P32-13.

Referred to in M55-43.

## M25-57 (30# 68)

**Vinogradov, A. I.**

**On the density hypothesis and the quasi-Riemann hypothesis. (Russian)**

*Dokl. Akad. Nauk SSSR* **158** (1964), 1014–1017.

Consider the zeros $\rho_\nu$ of the Riemann zeta function $\zeta(s)$, which for $\nu = 0, 1, 2, \cdots, r \leqq \log T$ lie in the classes $C_0, C_1, \cdots, C_r$, where $\rho_\nu \in C_\nu$ if $\operatorname{Re} \rho_\nu < 1-\eta_\nu$, where $\eta_\nu = c_0 \varepsilon_\nu^3$, $\varepsilon_\nu = \nu/\log T$, and $\operatorname{Re} \rho_\nu \geqq \sigma$. Then the total number of such zeros with ordinates $\leqq T$ $(T>1)$, which we call $N_\nu(\sigma, T)$, satisfies

$$(1) \qquad N_\nu(\sigma, T) \ll T^{2(1+\varepsilon_\nu)(1-\sigma)} \log^5 T.$$

The author also sketches the proof of (in Littlewood's language) "mod $k$ analogues" of (1) for Dirichlet $L$-series formed by characters (mod $k$). These use the recent work of D. A. Burgess. *S. Chowla* (University Park, Pa.)

## M25-58 (30# 4737)

**Fogels, È. K. [Fogels, E.]**

**On the zeros of $L$-functions. (Russian. Latvian and English summaries)**

*Latvijas PSR Zinātņu Akad. Vēstis Fiz. Tehn. Zinātņu Sēr.* **1964**, *no.* 5, 31–35.

The author sketches a proof of the following theorem: The number of zeros of $\prod_\chi L(s, \chi)$, $\chi \bmod D$, in $1-\lambda/(\log T) < \sigma < 1$, $|t| \leqq T$, where $T \geqq D$, $0<\lambda \leqq \log T$, does not exceed $e^{c\lambda}$ ($c$ a constant). For $T=D$, this theorem was essentially proved by Ju. V. Linnik [Mat. Sb. (N.S.) **15 (57)** (1944), 139–178, 347–368; MR **6**, 260] and later by P. Turán [Magyar Tud. Akad. Mat. Kutató

Int. Közl. **6** (1961), 165–179; MR **26** #3681] by another method. The present author uses Turán's method.

*S. Knapowski* (Marburg)

Citations: MR 6, 260b = N16-5; MR 26# 3681 = M25-53.

## M25-59 (31# 1230)

**Fogels, E.**

**On the zeros of $L$-functions.**

*Acta Arith.* **11** (1965), 67–96.

The author proves the following main theorem: Let $0 \leqq \lambda \leqq \log T$, where $T \geqq D$; the number of zeros of $\prod_{\chi \bmod D} L(s, \chi)$ in $1-\lambda/\log T \leqq \sigma \leqq 1$, $|t| \leqq T$, $s = \sigma + it$, does not exceed $e^{c\lambda}$ ($c$ a constant). Moreover, it is pointed out (with an outline of the proof) that a similar theorem holds for the product $\prod_\chi \zeta(s, \chi)$ of Hecke's $L$-functions over an arbitrary algebraic field. As an arithmetic application, the author deduces an estimate of $\sum_{p \leq x} \chi(p)$, where $p$ runs through primes, $\chi$ is a complex character mod $D$ and $x$ is comparatively small. The main theorem is essentially due to Ju. V. Linnik in case $T = D$ [see Rec. Math. [Mat. Sb.] (N.S.) **15 (57)** (1944), 139–178; MR **6**, 260]; however, it was established for a rectangle of smaller height than $D$ so that even in this case the author's result is much stronger. An alternative proof of Linnik's theorem has been offered by P. Turán [see Magyar Tud. Akad. Mat. Kutató Int. Közl. **6** (1961), 165–179; MR **26** #3681]. The present author combines Turán's method with some ideas of an earlier paper by Linnik.

*S. Knapowski* (Gainesville, Fla.)

Citations: MR 6, 260b = N16-5; MR 26# 3681 = M25-53.

Referred to in M25-60, M25-91.

## M25-60 (37# 4033)

**Fogels, E.**

**Corrigendum: "On the zeros of $L$-functions".**

*Acta Arith.* **14** (1967/68), 435.

The original article appeared in same Acta **11** (1965), 67–96 [MR **31** #1230].

Citations: MR 31# 1230 = M25-59.

## M25-61 (31# 5848)

**Grosswald, Émile [Grosswald, Emil]**

**Sur une propriété des racines complexes des fonctions $L(s, \chi)$.**

*C. R. Acad. Sci. Paris* **260** (1965), 4299–4302.

It is proved that the function

$$\sum_{\chi \bmod k} (\chi(b) - \chi(b')) \frac{L'}{L}(s, \chi),$$

where $b \not\equiv b' \pmod k$ and $(b, k) = (b', k) = 1$, has infinitely many poles that are not real.

*S. Knapowski* (Gainesville, Fla.)

Referred to in M25-86.

## M25-62 (32# 1175)

**Pan Cheng-tung [P'an Ch'eng-tung]**

**On the zeroes of the zeta function of Riemann.**

*Sci. Sinica* **14** (1965), 303–305.

Let $N(r, T)$ be the number of zeros of $\zeta(s)$ in the rectangle $\sigma \geqq r$, $1 \leqq t \leqq T$, where $r \geqq \frac{1}{2}$. The author proves that

$$N(r, T) = O(T^{A(r)(1-r)} \log^c T),$$

with $A(r) \leqq (2+2/(k+1))/(1-(2^{k-1}-2)(1-r))$ for $r \geqq 1-1/2^{k-1}$ and any integer $k \geqq 2$, and $A(r) \leqq 2+2^{18}(1-r)^{1/3}$ for $r \geqq 1-1/2^{18}$. This result may be regarded as an almost immediate consequence of well-known estimates of $\zeta(s)$ in the critical strip obtained by Hardy and Ingham [Ingham, Quart. J. Math. Oxford Ser. **8** (1937), 255–266] and Rodosskiĭ [Dokl. Akad. Nauk SSSR **134** (1960), 1303–1304; translated as Soviet Math. Dokl. **1** (1961), 1215–1216; MR **23** #A1611]; in fact, the author derives it from these estimates by the usual convexity argument for integrals.

*O. H. Körner* (Marburg)

Citations: MR 23# A1611 = M25-48.

## M25-63 (33# 106)

**Čudakov, N. G.**

**On zeros of Dirichlet's $L$-function for moduli equal to powers of an odd prime. (Russian. English summary)**

*Vestnik Leningrad. Univ.* **21** (1966), *no.* 1, 91–98.

Let $L(s, \chi) = \sum_1^\infty (\chi(n)/n^s)$, where $\chi(n)$ is a non-principal character mod $D$. The series is convergent for $\sigma > 0$. Although it has been conjectured that $L(s, \chi) \neq 0$ for $\sigma > \frac{1}{2}$, one is still very far from approaching this hypothesis. Using deep estimates of exponential sums due to I. M. Vinogradov [*Selected works* (Russian), Izdat. Akad. Nauk SSSR, Moscow, 1952; MR **14**, 610; Proc. Third All-Union Math. Congress, Vol. III (Russian), pp. 3–13, Izdat. Akad. Nauk SSSR, Moscow, 1956], the author proves the following. Let $p$ be an odd prime, $n$ a positive integer, and $D = p^n$. Then $L(s, \chi) \neq 0$ provided $|t| \leqq \exp(b_1 \log\log^2 D)$, $\sigma \geqq 1 - b_2(\log D \log\log D)^{-3/4}$, where $b_1$, $b_2$ are parameters depending only on $p$. This result gives no information for $n = 1$ (since $b_1$, $b_2$ depend on $p$), but it gives deep information (surpassing previous results) when we regard $p$ as fixed and allow $n$ to tend to $\infty$.

{In the summary there is a misprint; for

$$\sigma \geqq 1 - b_2(\log D \log\log D)^{3/4}$$

read

$$\sigma \geqq 1 - b_2(\log D \log\log D)^{-3/4}.\}$$

*S. Chowla* (University Park, Pa.)

Citations: MR 14, 610i = Z25-9.

## M25-64 (34# 2542)

**Grosswald, Émile [Grosswald, Emil]**

**Sur une propriété des racines complexes des fonctions $L(s, \chi)$.**

*C. R. Acad. Sci. Paris Sér. A-B* **263** (1966), A447–A450.

The author proves that the function

$$\sum_{\chi \bmod k} \{\bar\chi(a) - \bar\chi(b)\}(L'/L)(s, \chi),$$

where $a \not\equiv b \pmod k$ and $(a, k) = (b, k) = 1$, has infinitely many poles in the half-plane $\sigma \geqq \frac{1}{2}$.

*S. Knapowski* (Coral Gables, Fla.)

## M25-65 (34# 2543)

**Rubel, L. A.; Straus, E. G.**

**Special trigonometric series and the Riemann hypothesis.**

*Math. Scand.* **18** (1966), 35–44.

A series of the form $\sum_n \lambda_n^{-1} \sin(\lambda_n x)$, where $0 < \lambda_0 \leqq \lambda_1 \leqq \cdots$, $\lambda_n \to \infty$, is said to be a special trigonometric series. Letting $\rho = \beta + i\gamma$ ($\beta \geqq \frac{1}{2}$, $\gamma > 0$) run through the zeros of the Riemann $\xi$-function, the authors show that the series $\sum \gamma^{-1} \sin(\gamma x)$ has jump discontinuities at the logarithms of prime powers, as soon as $\sum \gamma^{-1}(\beta - \frac{1}{2})^2 < \infty$. This improves on a previous result by H. Rademacher ["Report of the Institute in the Theory of Numbers" (University of Colorado, Boulder, Colo., 1959), pp. 31–37, sponsored by the Amer. Math. Soc., mimeographed report], who worked under the assumption of the Riemann hypothesis. The authors also construct a special trigonometric series having any preassigned jumps, with the only restriction that the places where the jumps are to occur have no finite limit point.

*S. Knapowski* (Coral Gables, Fla.)

## M25-66 (34# 3756)

**Lehman, R. Sherman**

**Separation of zeros of the Riemann zeta-function.**

*Math. Comp.* **20** (1966), 523–541.

From the author's introduction: "In this paper we describe computations which establish that there are exactly 250000 zeros of $\zeta(\sigma+it)$ for which $0<t<170571.35$, all of which lie on the line $\sigma=\frac{1}{2}$ and are simple."

Referred to in M25-82.

## M25-67 (34# 3757)

**Spira, Robert**

**Zeros of sections of the zeta function. I.**

*Math. Comp.* **20** (1966), 542–550.

From the author's introduction: "In this paper, theorems on zero-free regions of $\zeta_M(s)=\sum_{n=1}^{M} n^{-s}$ are derived, the methods used for calculating the zeros are given, and the locations of the zeros are described."

Referred to in M25-71.

## M25-68 (34# 5776)

**Iglina, G. S.**

**On the density of zeros of the Riemann $\zeta$-function and the Dirichlet $L$-functions near the straight line $\sigma=1$. (Russian)**

*Izv. Vysš. Učebn. Zaved. Matematika* **1966**, *no.* 6 (55), 64–73.

Let $N(\Delta, T)$ be the number of zeros $\rho$ of $\zeta(s)$ $(s=\sigma+it)$ in the rectangle $R(\Delta\leqq\sigma<1,\ |t|\leqq T)$, and let $A$, $B$ denote positive absolute constants (not necessarily the same in different statements). Various estimates of the type (1) $N(\Delta, T)\leqq AT^{\kappa(\Delta)(1-\Delta)}\ln^B T$ $(\frac{1}{2}\leqq\Delta<1,\ T\geqq 2)$ are known. The "density hypothesis" asserts (in one of its forms) that this holds with $\kappa(\Delta)=2$. This has not been proved, but approximations to it for $\Delta$ near to 1 have been obtained by a number of writers. To these the present author adds Theorem 1: If $3\leqq k\leqq 11$ ($k$ an integer), $T>T_0$, and $0<1-\Delta<1/(2^k k+2)-\varepsilon$,

$$(3\ln\ln T)/\ln T \;<\; \varepsilon \;<\; 6/((\ln T)^{1/3}\ln\ln T),$$

then (1) holds with $\kappa(\Delta)\leqq 2+2^k\,(2^{k-1}(k-1)+1)^{-1}$; with a somewhat smaller lower bound for $\Delta$ if $k=10$ or 11. The argument is based on estimates of trigonometric sums combined with a method of K. A. Rodosskiĭ for the study of small values of $|\zeta(s)|$. Somewhat similar results are obtained for the $\kappa_1(\Delta)$ occurring in the estimate (2) $N(\Delta, T, D)\leqq AD^{\kappa_1(\Delta)(1-\Delta)}T^{\kappa_2(\Delta)(1-\Delta)}\ln^B(DT)$ for the number of zeros in $R$ of all $L$-functions $L(s,\chi)$ formed with characters $\chi$ of modulus $D$. These are based on estimates of character sums by D. A. Burgess [Proc. London Math. Soc. (3) **13** (1963), 524–536; MR **26** #6133], and are subject to similar restrictions: $D$ prime (Theorem 2) or cube-free (Theorem 3). The results are too elaborate to quote in detail, but their general effect is to indicate that $\kappa_1(\Delta)$ is not much greater than 5/2, for $T$ fixed, $D$ large, and $\Delta$ near to 1. Within their limits, they correspond to the known fact that, in the analogue of (2) for the number $N(\Delta, T, \chi)$ of zeros in $R$ of a single $L(s,\chi)$, we may take $\kappa_1(\Delta)=2$.

{Omissions and obscurities make some of the arguments difficult to follow. Lemma 1 involves $t$ and $T$ with no statement of any relationship between them. The context suggests $|t|\leqq T$, or $\frac{1}{2}T\leqq t\leqq T$. On p. 69 a sum over an interval $(z/n, T]$ is split into sums over intervals $(a, b]$ $(b\leqq 2a)$, to each of which a certain estimate (Lemma 2) is applied; but the statement that $z/n$ lies in the interval $[L_l, L_{l-1})$ does not imply that the same holds for each $a$, as the wording seems to suggest. Any $a$ does, however, lie in some $[L_h, L_{h-1})$ with $h=h(a)\leqq l$; which seems to suffice (in essentials) if it is assumed that $\frac{1}{2}T\leqq t\leqq T$ and that the detailed argument is to be supplied by the reader (though the origin and significance of the second inequality for $\varepsilon$ are not clear to the reviewer). The task of reconstructing accurate details from the author's account is not greatly facilitated by the references to the Russian translation [Izdat. Inostran. Lit., Moscow, 1953] of E. C. Titchmarsh's book *The theory of the Riemann zeta-function*, Clarendon, Oxford, 1951 [MR **13**, 741]; for these take the form of references to whole chapters, or (as in Lemma 1) to numbered paragraphs that may not fit the English original.} *A. E. Ingham* (Cambridge, England)

Citations: MR 13, 741c = M02-2; MR 26# 6133 = L25-19.

## M25-69 (35# 5402)

**Barban, M. B.**

**Density hypothesis of E. Bombieri. (Russian)**

*Dokl. Akad. Nauk SSSR* **172** (1967), 999–1000.

Let $N(\alpha, T, \chi)$ denote the number of zeros of $L(s,\chi)$ in the rectangle $\alpha\leqq\sigma\leqq 1$, $|t|\leqq T$. E. Bombieri's density theorem (as formulated in Chapter 24 of H. Davenport's *Multiplicative number theory*, Markham, Chicago, 1967 [MR **36** #117]; see also the last displayed formula of Bombieri [Mathematika **12** (1965), 201–225; MR **33** #5590]) asserts that

$$(*)\qquad \textstyle\sum_{q\leq X}\sum_{\chi}^{*} N(\alpha, T, \chi) \ll X^{\theta(\alpha)}T^{c}(\log X)^{10}$$

if $1\leqq T\leqq X$, uniformly in $X$ and $\alpha$ $(\frac{1}{2}\leqq\alpha\leqq 1)$, where $\sum_{\chi}^{*}$ denotes summation over primitive characters only, and the exponent pairs $\theta$, $c$ satisfy (i) $\theta(\alpha)=8(1-\alpha)/(3-2\alpha)$, $c=1$, and (ii) $\theta(\alpha)=5(1-\alpha)$, $c=2$. Bombieri conjectured that (*) holds with $\theta(\alpha)=4(1-\alpha)$, $c=1+\varepsilon$. It would seem that existing methods allow for some compensation between $\theta$ and $c$, whereby $\theta$ can be diminished at the expense of increasing $c$. The author states that if $c$ is allowed to be large, possible forms of $\theta(\alpha)$ are $10(1-\alpha)/(3-\alpha)$ and $19(1-\alpha)/4$. He relates the origin of his proofs to existing literature, but gives no details. An immediate consequence of (*), as the author points out, is that, given a small $\gamma>0$, all $L$-functions formed with primitive characters $\chi \bmod q$ for all except possibly $X^{1-\varepsilon}$ values of $q\leqq X$, have $\sigma\geqq\alpha$, $|t|\leqq X^{\gamma}$ as a zero-free region. Bombieri's second value of $\theta(\alpha)$ would allow us to take $\alpha=4/5+\delta$, whereas the author's first value permits $\alpha=7/9+\delta$ $(\delta>0,\ \varepsilon=\varepsilon(\gamma,\delta))$. It is clear that in this context having $c$ small is not important. As companion to Bombieri's conjecture, the author proposes $\theta(\alpha)=2(1-\alpha)$, $c$ unspecified.

{This article has appeared in English translation [Soviet Math. Dokl. **8** (1967), 202–204].}

*H. Halberstam* (Nottingham)

Citations: MR 33# 5590 = M55-43; MR 36# 117 = N02-13.

## M25-70 (36# 5090)

**Lammel, Ernst**

**Ein Beweis, dass die Riemannsche Zetafunktion $\zeta(s)$ in $|s-1|\leqq 1$ keine Nullstelle besitzt.**

*Univ. Nac. Tucumán Rev. Ser. A* **16** (1966), 209–217.

The power-series expansion

$$(s-1)\zeta(s) \;=\; 1+\textstyle\sum_{\nu=0}^{\infty}\gamma_\nu(s-1)^{\nu+1}$$

implies $|(s-1)\zeta(s)|\geqq 1-\sum_{\nu=0}^{\infty}|\gamma_\nu|$ in the region $|s-1|\leqq 1$. Therefore, the nonvanishing of $\zeta(s)$ in this region is a consequence of the inequality $\sum_{\nu=0}^{\infty}|\gamma_\nu|<1$. The author proves this inequality by applying Euler's summation formula to the equation $\gamma_\nu=$

$$((-1)^\nu/\nu!)\lim_{m\to\infty}(\textstyle\sum_{n=1}^{m} n^{-1}\log^\nu n-(\nu+1)^{-1}\log^{\nu+1}m).$$

*T. M. Apostol* (Pasadena, Calif.)

**M25-71** **(37# 4036 )**

**Spira, Robert**

**Zeros of sections of the zeta function. II.**

*Math. Comp.* **22** (1968), 163–173.

Continuing earlier work [Math. Comp. **20** (1966), 542–550; MR **34** #3757] on the zeros of Dirichlet polynomials $\zeta_N(s)=\sum_{n=1}^{N} n^{-s}$ $(s=\sigma+it)$, the author determines g.l.b. $|\zeta_N(s)|$ for $\sigma\geqq 1$ and $N\leqq 5$. He also describes machine proofs that $\zeta_N(s)$ has no zeros with $\sigma\geqq 1$ for $N\leqq 9$, and proofs of the existence of such zeros for a variety of small $N$ starting with $N=19$. *T. M. Apostol* (Pasadena, Calif.)

Citations: MR 34# 3757 = M25-67.

**M25-72** **(38# 2945 )**

**Spira, Robert**

**Zeros of approximate functional approximations.**

*Math. Comp.* **21** (1967), 41–48.

Let $g_N(s)=\sum_{n=1}^{N} n^{-s}+\chi(s)\sum_{n=1}^{N} n^{s-1}$, where $s$ is complex, $s=\sigma+it$, and $(1/\chi(s))=2(2\pi)^{-s}\cdot\cos\frac{1}{2}\pi s\cdot\Gamma(s)$. By the approximate functional equation for Riemann's zeta-function, the $g_N(s)$ can be looked upon as approximations to it. The author showed in a previous paper [Proc. Amer. Math. Soc. **17** (1966), 314–317; MR **33** #7312] that for $t$ sufficiently large, $g_1(s)$ and $g_2(s)$ have their zeros on the line $\sigma=\frac{1}{2}$. Here he presents calculations which suggest that for $N\geqq 3$ an infinity of zeros may be off the line $\sigma=\frac{1}{2}$.

*K. Chandrasekharan* (Zürich)

Citations: MR 33# 7312 = M30-45.

**M25-73** **(38# 3238 )**

**Pospeev, V. E.**

**On the "density" of the zeros of Dirichlet *L*-functions. (Russian. Uzbek summary)**

*Izv. Akad. Nauk UzSSR Ser. Fiz.-Mat. Nauk* **12** (1968), *no.* 4, 22–26.

In Theorem 1, from a hypothesis on the averaged estimate of arbitrary moments of $L$-series of fixed modulus $D$, the author deduces a new density theorem on the number of zeros of all $L$-series of a given modulus $D$. In Theorem 2 this general fact is made concrete for the fourth moment (unconditional result): $N_D(\sigma,T)<<D^{3(1-\sigma)/(3-2\sigma)+\varepsilon}\cdot T^c$.

*A. I. Vinogradov* (Leningrad)

**M25-74** **(38# 4422 )**

**Halász, G.; Turán, P.**

**On the distribution of roots of Riemann zeta and allied functions. I.**

*J. Number Theory* **1** (1969), 121–137.

For $\alpha\geqq\frac{1}{2}$, let $N(\alpha,T)$ denote the number of zeros of the Riemann zeta function $\zeta(\sigma+it)$ in the rectangle $\alpha\leqq\sigma\leqq 1$, $0<t\leqq T$. The authors prove that if $T>c$ for some $c>0$ and if $1-A\leqq\alpha\leqq 1$ for some sufficiently small $A>0$, then $N(\alpha,T)<T^{e(\alpha)}$, where $e(\alpha)=(1-\alpha)^{3/2}\log^3(1-\alpha)^{-1}$. They also prove that the Lindelöf hypothesis implies the estimate $N(\alpha,T)=O(T^\varepsilon)$ for $\alpha\geqq\frac{3}{4}+\delta$, where $\varepsilon$ and $\delta$ are arbitrarily small. *T. M. Apostol* (Pasadena, Calif.)

Referred to in M25-87.

**M25-75** **(39# 1418 )**

**Levinson, N.**

**Zeros of the Riemann zeta-function near the 1-line.**

*J. Math. Anal. Appl.* **25** (1969), 250–253.

Under an isolation hypothesis the width of the zero free region of the zeta function is estimated. For some $\delta>0$ and some large $T_0$ it is assumed that, of the non-trivial zeros $\rho=\beta+i\gamma$ of $\zeta(s)$, those which lie in $\beta>1-\delta$, $|\gamma|>T_0$, are all isolated (not necessarily simple) in the sense that there is no zero other than $\beta+i\gamma$ in the rectangle $1-\delta<\sigma<1$, $|t-\gamma|<2\delta$ on the $s=\sigma+it$-plane. It is then shown that there are no zeros in the region $\sigma>1-A/\log\log t$, $|t|>T_0$ for some $A>0$. *Y. Komatu* (Tokyo)

**M25-76** **(39# 4104 )**

**Berndt, Bruce C.**

**On the zeros of the Riemann zeta-function.**

*Proc. Amer. Math. Soc.* **22** (1969), 183–188.

Let $R(s)=\pi^{-s/2}\Gamma(s/2)\zeta(s)$ and let $N_R(\lambda,T)$ and $N_I(\lambda,T)$ denote, respectively, the number of zeros of the real and imaginary parts of $R(\lambda+it)$ in the interval $0<t<T$. B. Berlowitz [Acta Arith. **14** (1967/68), 203–207; MR **37** #1324] has shown that for $0<\lambda<1$ both $N_R(\lambda,T)\to\infty$ and $N_I(\lambda,T)\to\infty$ as $T\to\infty$. The author improves this result by showing that $N_R(\lambda,T)>AT$ and $N_I(\lambda,T)>AT$, where $A$ is a positive constant depending on $\lambda$. The method is that used by Hardy and Littlewood in treating the case $\lambda=\frac{1}{2}$. *T. M. Apostol* (Pasadena, Calif.)

Citations: MR 37# 1324 = M15-41.

Referred to in M25-77.

**M25-77** **(40# 5552 )**

**Berndt, B. C.**

**Erratum: "On the zeros of the Riemann zeta-function".**

*Proc. Amer. Math. Soc.* **24** (1970), 839.

The author corrects an error in his paper [same Proc. **22** (1969), 183–188; MR **39** #4104]. The conclusions remain unchanged.

Citations: MR 39# 4104 = M25-76.

**M25-78** **(40# 1004a; 40# 1004b)**

**Spira, Robert**

**Calculation of Dirichlet *L*-functions.**

*Math. Comp.* **23** (1969), 489–497.

**Spira, Robert**

**Tables and programs for Dirichlet *L*-series.**

*Math. Comp.* **23** (1969), *no.* 107, *loose microfiche suppl.*

Author's summary: "A method for calculating Dirichlet $L$-series is presented along with the theory of residue class characters and their automatic generation. Tables are given of zeros of $L$-series for moduli $\leqq 24$."

**M25-79** **(40# 2618 )**

**Narasimhan, Raghavan**

**Une remarque sur $\zeta(1+it)$.**

*Enseignement Math.* (2) **14** (1968), 189–191 (1969).

This article contains a variant of Ingham's proof [A. E. Ingham, *The distribution of prime numbers*, Cambridge Univ. Press, London, 1932; reprinting, Stechert-Hafner, New York, 1964; MR **32** #2391] that $\zeta(1+ia)\neq 0$ for real $a\neq 0$. Ingham avoided the inequality $3+4\cos\theta+\cos 2\theta\geqq 0$, which was used in the classical proof by Hadamard and Mertens, and used instead Landau's theorem that the real point of the line of convergence of a Dirichlet series, with positive coefficients and a finite abscissa of convergence, is a singularity of the function represented by the series. He works with the function

$$\zeta^2(s)\zeta(s+ia)\zeta(s-ia)/\zeta(2s)$$

and its Dirichlet series. The author uses instead the simpler function $\zeta^2(s)\zeta(s+ia)\zeta(s-ia)$. This seems the more appropriate if one thinks of the function $\zeta(s)<(s,x_0)<L(s,\chi)L(s,\chi\chi_0)$, where $\chi_0$ and $\chi$ are real, non-principal characters, used in the proof of Siegel's theorem on the real zeros of Dirichlet's $L$-functions [C. L. Siegel, Acta Arith. **1** (1935), 83–86; T. Estermann, *Introduction to*

*modern prime number theory*, Cambridge Univ. Press, Cambridge, 1952; MR **13**, 915].

*K. Chandrasekharan* (Zürich)

Citations: MR 13, 915b = P02-12; MR 32# 2391 = N02-11.

## M25-80 (40# 2620)

**Montgomery, H. L.**

**Zeros of $L$-functions.**

*Invent. Math.* **8** (1969), 346–354.

Let $\chi$ denote a character modulo $q$ and $N_\chi(\sigma, T)$ with $\sigma \geqq \frac{1}{2}$, $T \geqq 1$ denote the number of zeros $\rho$ of $L(s, \chi)$, where $\mathrm{Re}\,\rho \geqq \sigma$, $|\mathrm{Im}\,\rho| \leqq T$. Also, denote the corresponding expression for the $\zeta$-function (with $q=1$) by $N(\sigma, T)$. E. Bombieri in his exposition of the large sieve [Mathematika **12** (1965), 201–225; MR **33** #5590], obtained estimates for $\sum_{q\leq Q} \sum_\chi^* N_\chi(\sigma, T)$, where $T$ is made to depend on $Q$ (the * signifying that the summation is over all primitive characters mod $q$). Using some results in a previous paper of his [Invent. Math. **8** (1969), 334–345], the author obtains the following estimate for the above function without assuming the dependence of $T$ on $Q$. Theorem 1: For $Q \geqq 1$, $T \geqq 2$, $\sum_{q\leqq Q} \sum_\chi^* N_\chi(\sigma, T) \ll (Q^2T)^{3(1-\sigma)/(2-\sigma)}(\log QT)^{13}$ $[(Q^2T)^{2(1-\sigma)/\sigma}(\log QT)^{13}]$ for $\frac{1}{2} \leqq \sigma \leqq 4/5$ [for $4/5 \leqq \sigma \leqq 1$]. For $4/5 < \sigma \leqq 1$, this theorem (with $Q=1$) is more effective than A. E. Ingham's estimate $N(\sigma, T) \ll T^{3(1-\sigma)/(2-\sigma)}(\log T)^5$. Also combining the results of the theorem, one gets $N(\sigma, T) \ll T^{5(1-\sigma)/2}(\log T)^{13}$. Using this estimate and a method of Ingham, the author deduces that for every $\varepsilon > 0$ and sufficiently large $x$, there is a prime between $x$ and $x + x^{3/5+\epsilon}$. Similar results were proved by Ingham in 1937 [Quart. J. Math. Oxford Ser. **8** (1937), 255–266] and W. Haneke in 1963 [Acta Arith. **8** (1962/63), 357–430; MR **28** #1179] with 5/8 and 61/98 instead of 3/5, so that the author's result is a substantial improvement in this direction.

Writing $M(T) = \max_{2\leq t\leq T, \alpha \geq 1/2} |\zeta(\alpha + it)|$ for $T \geqq 2$, the following theorem is also proved. Theorem 2: For $\frac{3}{4} \leqq \sigma \leqq 1$, $N(\sigma, T) \ll \{M(5T)(\log T)^6\}^{8(1-\sigma)(3\sigma-2)/((4\sigma-3)(2\sigma-1))}(\log T)^{11}$. Using van der Corput's estimate for $M(T)$, namely, $M(T) \ll T^{1/6} \log T$, and Theorem 2, it is deduced that $N(\sigma, T) \ll T^{2(1-\sigma)}(\log T)^{11}$ (for $9/10 \leqq \sigma \leqq 1$).

*K. Thanigasalam* (University Park, Pa.)

Citations: MR 28# 1179 = M15-29; MR 33# 5590 = M55-43.

Referred to in M25-91.

## M25-81 (40# 4211)

**Allison, D.**

**On obtaining zero-free regions for the zeta-function from estimates of $M(x)$.**

*Proc. Cambridge Philos. Soc.* **67** (1970), 333–337.

It is classical that from the non-vanishing of the Riemann zeta function $\zeta(s)$ for (Re $s=$) $\sigma \geqq 1$, one can prove the prime number theorem (PNT) without error term in any one of a number of equivalent formulations, such as $\psi(x) \sim x$ or $M(x) = o(x)$ (where $\psi(x) = \sum_{p^n \leq x} \log p$ and $M(x) = \sum_{n\leq x} \mu(n)$, with $\mu(n)$ the Möbius function). Conversely, using any of these formulations, one may show that $\zeta(s) \neq 0$ for $\sigma \geqq 1$. Similarly, using the stronger statement of the existence of a zero-free region for $\zeta(s)$ in $\sigma < 1$, one can prove versions of the PNT with error terms; that is, from $\zeta(s) \neq 0$ for $\sigma \geqq 1 - \eta(|t|)$ ($t = \mathrm{Im}\, s$) follows $\psi(x) - x = O(xe^{-\varphi(x)})$, and $M(x) = O(xe^{-\varphi(x)})$ for $x \to \infty$. Conversely, from a knowledge of $\varphi(x)$ in $\psi(x) - x = O(xe^{-\varphi(x)})$, it has been shown [see W. Staś, Acta Arith. **6** (1960/61), 435–446; MR **26** #3679] that one can infer the existence of a region in $\sigma < 1$, free of zeros of $\zeta(s)$. The purpose of the present paper is to show that $M(x) = O(xe^{-\varphi(x)})$ with known $\varphi(x)$ implies the existence of a region in $\sigma < 1$ where $\zeta(s) \neq 0$. Actually, the author proves the following, more general theorem: Let $\chi(s)$ be regular for $\sigma \geqq \frac{1}{2}$, $t \geqq 1$ and regular and non-zero for $\sigma > 1$ and all $t$. Suppose also that $|\chi(s)| < Kt^{1/2}$ ($\frac{1}{2} \leqq \sigma \leqq 4$, $t \geqq 1$) and $\chi^{-1}(s) = \sum_{n=1}^\infty b_n n^{-s}$ ($\sigma > 1$), with real $b_n$ and $B(x) = \sum_{n\leq x} b_n$ satisfying $|B(x)| < C_1 x$ ($x > 0$), and $|B(x)| < C_2 xe^{-\varphi(x)}$ ($x > x_0$) ($\varphi(x)$ has to satisfy also six mild but complicated conditions). Then $\chi(s) \neq 0$ for $t > t_0$ and $1 - \eta(t) \leqq \sigma \leqq 1$, with $\eta(t) = (\log t)/(\log X)$, where $X = X(t)$ is defined by $\varphi(X) = 20 \log t$. The proof uses Hadamard's three circles theorem. The desired statement for $\zeta(s)$ now follows by taking $b_n = \mu(n)$.

*E. Grosswald* (Philadelphia, Pa.)

Citations: MR 26# 3679 = N04-40.

## M25-82 (41# 2892)

**Rosser, J. Barkley; Yohe, J. M.; Schoenfeld, Lowell**

**Rigorous computation and the zeros of the Riemann zeta-function. (With discussion)**

*Information Processing 68 (Proc. IFIP Congress, Edinburgh, 1968), Vol. 1: Mathematics, Software, pp.* 70–76. *North-Holland, Amsterdam,* 1969.

Authors' summary: "We discuss the problems of rigorous computation and illustrate these from our experience in programming and running a large-scale computation which showed, among other things, that the first 3,500,000 zeros of $\zeta(s)$ lie on the critical line. This extends work, carried out in a similar spirit, by R. S. Lehman [Math. Comp. **20** (1966), 523–541; MR **34** #3756], who stopped after 250,000 zeros. Our paper discusses the handling of the round-off errors in the floating-point arithmetic that was used and the errors that were introduced by the FORTRAN compiler and the operating system; additional difficulties were caused by the tape units, but the main frame was extremely reliable. Also discussed are the various checks which were used and the question of what reliance may be placed on the final results."

Citations: MR 34# 3756 = M25-66.

Referred to in M25-83.

## M25-83 (41# 3414)

**Lehman, R. Sherman**

**On the distribution of zeros of the Riemann zeta-function.**

*Proc. London Math. Soc.* (3) **20** (1970), 303–320.

Let $S(t) = \arg \zeta(\frac{1}{2} + it)/\pi$, where the argument is obtained by continuous variation from $\infty + it$ to $\frac{1}{2} + it$ starting with the value zero when there is no zero of $\zeta(s)$ on $s = \frac{1}{2} + it$ and when there is a zero, $S(t)$ is defined so as to be right continuous. Let $S_1(t) = \int_0^t S(u)\, du$. The main result of the paper is the proof of the inequality (Theorem 1) that if $t_2 > t_1 > 168\pi$, then $|S_1(t_2) - S_1(t_1)| \leqq 1.91 + 0.114 \log(t_2/2\pi)$. The same inequality with larger constants was proved and used by A. M. Turing [Proc. London Math. Soc. (3) **3** (1953), 99–117; MR **14**, 1126] for calculating the complex zeros of the Riemann zeta function. The author closely follows Turing's proof, correcting the errors in the latter, and obtains the above improved result. The rest of the paper is devoted to a discussion of the properties of $S(t)$ in relation to what is known as Gram's law. Define $k(t) = -\frac{1}{2}t \log \pi + \mathrm{Log}[\Gamma(\frac{1}{2} + it)/\Gamma(\frac{1}{2} - it)]/4\pi i$ and $Z(t) = e^{2\pi i k(t)}\zeta(\frac{1}{2} + 2\pi i t)$. The equations $2k(t) = n$, $n = -1, 0, \cdots, n, \cdots$ have unique positive solutions $t = t_n$. The intervals $(t_n, t_{n+1}]$ are known as Gram intervals, the $t_n$'s being the Gram points. Gram's law (hypothesis) says that the $(n+2)$nd zero of $Z(t)$ for $\mathrm{Re}(t) > 0$ is a real number in the $n$th Gram interval and that there are no other zeros in $t_n < \operatorname{Re}(t) \leqq t_{n+1}$. This has been verified for such values of $n$ for which computations have been completed (in particular, when $n < 127$). Similarly, a Gram block $(t_n, t_{n+1}]$ is an interval of length 1 such that $(-1)^j Z(t_j) > 0$ for $j = n, n+1$ while it is $\leqq 0$ for $n < j < n+1$. The modified Gram law says that every Gram block contains exactly 1 zero of $Z(t)$. This too has been verified for several cases but the author shows that it is not universally true. Finally, the author describes the notion of approximate Gram blocks and obtains lower and upper bounds for $N(t)$, the number of zeros of the Zeta function $\zeta(s)$ in $0 < \operatorname{Im}(s) \leqq t$ in such intervals. The Gram law is due to J. P. Gram [Skr. København (8) **9** (1925), 311–325] and the modified Gram law to J. B. Rosser, L. Schoenfeld and J. M. Yohe [*Information processing 68* (Proc. IFIP Congress, Edinburgh, 1968), *Vol. I: Mathematics, Software*, pp. 70–76, North-Holland, Amsterdam, 1969; MR **41** #2892].

*V Ganapathy Iyer* (Annamalainagar)

Citations: MR 14, 1126e = M25-35; MR 41# 2892 = M25-82.

## M25-84 (41# 8354)

**Spira, Robert**

**Another zero-free region for $\zeta^{(k)}(s)$.**

*Proc. Amer. Math. Soc.* **26** (1970), 246–247.

Let $\zeta^{(k)}(s)$ denote the $k$th derivative of the Riemann zeta function, with $s = \sigma + it$. It is shown that for $k \geqq 0$, there exists an $\alpha_k$ such that $\zeta^{(k)}(s)$ has only real zeros for $\sigma \leqq \alpha_k$, and exactly one real zero in each open interval $(-1-2n, 1-2n)$ with $1-2n \leqq \alpha_k$.

*K. Thanigasalam* (Bronx, N.Y.)

## M25-85 (42# 1776)

**Berndt, Bruce C.**

**The number of zeros for $\zeta^{(k)}(s)$.**

*J. London Math. Soc.* (2) **2** (1970), 577–580.

Let $N_k(T)$, $k \geqq 1$, denote the number of zeros $\alpha + i\beta$ of the $k$th derivative of the Riemann zeta function such that $0 < \beta < T$. The author shows $N_k(T) = (2\pi)^{-1} T \log T - ((1 + \log 4\pi)/(2\pi))T + O(\log T)$ as $T$ tends to $\infty$. This implies that $N(T) = N_k(T) + (T \log 2)/(2\pi) + O(\log T)$, where $N(T)$ gives the corresponding number of zeros of $\zeta(s)$.

*R. Spira* (E. Lansing, Mich.)

## M25-86 (42# 1778)

**Turán, P.**

**On a problem concerning the zeros of Dirichlet's $L$-functions.**

*Publ. Ramanujan Inst. No.* 1 (1968/69), 95–100.

The singularities of the function $F(s) = F_{a,b}(s) = (\phi(k))^{-1} \sum_{\chi \bmod k} (\bar\chi(b) - \bar\chi(a))(L'/L)(s, \chi)$ play an important role in studying the discrepancies of the distribution of primes in residue classes $a$ and $b$ mod $k$. A zero $\rho = \beta + i\gamma$ of $L(s, \chi)$ of multiplicity $m_\chi(\rho)$ is a singular point of $F(s)$ if and only if $\mu(\rho) = (\varphi(k))^{-1} \sum_{\chi \bmod k} (\bar\chi(a) - \bar\chi(b)) m_\chi(\rho) \neq 0$. E. Grosswald [C. R. Acad. Sci. Paris **260** (1965), 4299–4302; MR **31** #5848] proved the existence of infinitely many $\rho$ with $\mu(\rho) \neq 0$. The present paper strengthens this result by showing that the number $f(y)$ of zeros $\rho$ with $\mu(\rho) \neq 0$ and $0 < \gamma < y$ satisfies $f(y) > c_1 \exp(\log^{1/5} y)$ if $y > \psi_1(k)$, where $c_1$ is a positive explicitly calculable constant and $\psi_1(k)$ is an explicit function of $k$, independent of $a$ and $b$. Moreover, if the Riemann-Piltz conjecture holds, then $f(y) > c_2 y^{1/2}$ for $y > \psi_2(k)$.

*T. M. Apostol* (Pasadena, Calif.)

Citations: MR 31# 5848 = M25-61.

## M25-87 (42# 3035)

**Halász, G.; Turán, P.**

**On the distribution of roots of Riemann zeta and allied functions. II.**

*Acta Math. Acad. Sci. Hungar.* **21** (1970), 403–419.

Let $N(\alpha, T, k, \chi)$ be the number of zeros of the Dirichlet $L$-function $L(\sigma + it, k, \chi)$ in the rectangle $\alpha \leqq \sigma \leqq 1$, $0 < t \leqq T$, where $\frac{1}{2} \leqq \alpha \leqq 1$, $T \geqq 2$, and let

$$S(\alpha, T, X) = \sum_{k \leq X} \sum\nolimits^*_{\chi \bmod k} N(\alpha, T, k, \chi),$$

where $\Sigma^*$ is over primitive characters mod $k$. E. Bombieri [Mathematika **12** (1965), 201–225; MR **33** #5590] proved that $S(\alpha, T, X) \ll T(X^2 + XT)^{4(1-\alpha)/(3-2\alpha)} \log^{10}(X + T)$ and conjectured that for every $\varepsilon > 0$ there is a positive constant $c(\varepsilon)$ such that $S(\alpha, T, X) < c(\varepsilon) X^{4(1-\alpha)+\varepsilon} T^{1+\varepsilon}$. The authors ask whether such results can be deduced from an extension of the Lindelöf hypothesis which they state in the form $|L(\sigma + it, k, \chi)| < c_1(T, \lambda) k^{\lambda^2}$ for arbitrarily small $\lambda > 0$, uniformly for $\sigma \geqq \frac{1}{2}$, $|t| \leqq T$. They prove that this extended Lindelöf hypothesis is equivalent to an inequality of the form $S(\alpha, T, X) < c_2(\varepsilon, T) X^{4(1-\alpha)+\varepsilon}$ for $\frac{1}{2} \leqq \alpha \leqq 1$, $T \geqq 2$, and also to the stronger inequality $S(\frac{3}{4} + \delta, T, X) < X^\varepsilon$ for $T \geqq 2$ and arbitrarily small positive $\varepsilon$, $\delta$ for $X > c(\delta, \varepsilon, T)$.

{Part I appeared in J. Number Theory **1** (1969), 121–137 [MR **38** #4422].}

*T. M. Apostol* (Pasadena, Calif.)

Citations: MR 33# 5590 = M55-43; MR 38# 4422 = M25-74.

## M25-88 (42# 3036)

**Metsänkylä, Tauno**

**Zero-free regions of Dirichlet's $L$-functions near the point 1.**

*Ann. Univ. Turku. Ser. A I No.* 139 (1970), 11 *pp.*

Theorems of the type: If $\chi$ is a complex character mod $k$, $k \geqq 8$, then $L(s, \chi)$ has no zeros in the rectangle $1 - b/\log k \leqq \sigma \leqq 1$, $|t| < c/\log k$ with explicit values of $b$ and $c$, are proved.

Similar results for real non-principal characters are also proved.

The method used gives better results the smaller $t$ is, and so is adapted to proving results for "low regions" of the type described, in contrast to that used by R. J. Miech [Acta Arith. **15** (1968/69), 119–137; MR **39** #142] to discuss similar questions for infinite vertical strips.

*S. L. Segal* (Rochester, N.Y.)

Citations: MR 39# 142 = M20-35.

## M25-89 (42# 5925)

**Turán, P.**

**Zeta roots and prime numbers.**

*Number Theory* (*Colloq., János Bolyai Math. Soc., Debrecen,* 1968), *pp.* 205–216. *North-Holland, Amsterdam,* 1970.

The author proves two theorems connecting zero-free rectangles of the Riemann zeta function $\zeta(s)$ and estimates of trigonometric sums over prime numbers $p$ taken from certain intervals. In the theorems, $c_1(\beta)$, $c_2$, $c_3$ and $c_4$ are positive constants. Theorem I: Let $0 < \beta < (107)^{-4}$ and $T > c_1(\beta)$. If for all $N$, $N_1$, $N_2$, $\tau$ satisfying $T^2 \leqq \frac{1}{2}N \leqq N_1 < N_2 \leqq N \leqq T^8$, $T \leqq \tau \leqq 2T$, $|\sum_{N_1 \leq p \leq N_2} e^{i\tau \log p}| \leqq c_2 N(\log^3 N)/\tau^\beta$, then $\zeta(\sigma + it) \neq 0$ for $\sigma \geqq 1 - \beta^2$, $T \leqq t \leqq 2T$. Theorem II: If $\zeta(\sigma + it) \neq 0$ for $\sigma \geqq \theta$ $(\geqq \frac{1}{2})$, $T > c_3$, $T \leqq t \leqq 2T$ and $T^2 \leqq \frac{1}{2}N = N_1 < N_2 \leqq N \leqq e^T$, $5T/4 \leqq \tau \leqq 7T/4$, then

$$\left|\sum_{N_1 < p < N_2} e^{-i\tau \log p}\right| \leqq c_4 N(\log^3 N)/\tau^{2(1-\theta)}.$$

*R. Spira* (E. Lansing, Mich.)

**M25-90** **(43# 1930)**

**Jutila, Matti**

**On two theorems of Linnik concerning the zeros of Dirichlet's $L$-functions.**

*Ann. Acad. Sci. Fenn. Ser. A I No.* 458 (1969), 32 *pp.*

From the author's introduction: "In 1944 Ju. V. Linnik [Mat. Sb. (N.S.) **15** (**57**) (1944), 139–178; MR **6**, 260; ibid. **15** (**57**) (1944), 347–368; MR **6**, 260] proved that the least prime in an arithmetical progression $\{Dn+l\}$ with $(D, l)=1$ is $\ll D^L$, where $L$ is an absolute constant. The proof was based on two new results on the distribution of the zeros of Dirichlet's $L$-functions near the point $s=1$. ... Linnik's very complicated proofs of these main results were simplified by K. A. Rodosskiĭ [see K. Prachar, *Primzahlverteilung*, pp. 331–364, Springer, Berlin, 1957; MR **19**, 393]. New and still much simpler proofs, based on the method of P. Turán, were given at the beginning of this decade by Turán [Magyar Tud. Akad. Mat. Kutató Int. Közl. **6** (1961), 165–179; MR **26** #3681] and S. Knapowski [Publ. Math. Debrecen **9** (1962), 168–178; MR **26** #6131]. ... In this paper, we refine the method of Turán in some respects and work out the main theorems in a numerical form." *O. H. Körner* (Ulm)

Citations: MR 6, 260b = N16-5; MR 6, 260c = N16-6; MR 19, 393b = N02-7; MR 26# 3681 = M25-53; MR 26# 6131 = M25-54.

**M25-91** **(43# 4775)**

**Gallagher, P. X.**

**A large sieve density estimate near $\sigma=1$.**

*Invent. Math.* **11** (1970), 329–339.

Recent work on the distribution of primes in arithmetic progressions is related to density estimates on the zeros of Dirichlet $L$-functions $L(s, \chi)$, $s=\sigma+it$. Let $N_\chi(\alpha, T)$ denote the number of zeros of $L(s, \chi)$ in the rectangle $\alpha \leqq \sigma \leqq 1$, $|t| \leqq T$. E. Fogels [Acta Arith. **11** (1965), 67–96; MR **31** #1230] has shown that (1) $\sum_{\chi \bmod q} N_\chi(\alpha, T) \ll T^{c(1-\alpha)}$ $(T \geqq q)$, where $c$ is a positive constant. H. L. Montgomery [Invent. Math. **8** (1969), 346–354; MR **40** #2620] and M. Jutila [Acta Arith. **16** (1969/70), 207–216; MR **40** #5557] obtained hybrid density theorems of the form

(2) $\sum_{q \leqq Q} \sum_\chi^* N_\chi(\alpha, T) \ll (Q^2T)^{c(1-\alpha)} \log^b(QT)$,

where $\sum^*$ is extended over primitive characters. This paper gives a common basis for Fogels' method and the hybrid mean estimates of Montgomery and Jutila. By using a general mean value estimate for exponential sums, a large sieve estimate due to Bombieri and Davenport for character sums with prime argument, and Turan's power sum lemma, the author obtains the following generalization of (1): $\sum_{q \leqq T} \sum_\chi^* N_\chi(\alpha, T) \ll T^{c(1-\alpha)}$ $(T \geqq 1)$. He applies this to obtain the estimate $\sum_{1<q\leqq Q} \sum_\chi^* |\sum_x^{x+h} \chi(p) \log p| \ll h \exp(-a \log x/\log Q)$ provided $x/Q \leqq h \leqq x$ and $\exp(\log^{1/2} x) \leqq Q \leqq x^b$. Here $a$ and $b$ are positive constants, and it is further assumed that there is no Siegel zero. If a Siegel zero exists, a modified estimate holds.

*T. M. Apostol* (Pasadena, Calif.)

Citations: MR 31# 1230 = M25-59; MR 40# 2620 = M25-80; MR 40# 5557 = P40-24.

**M25-92** **(43# 6168)**

**Stečkin, S. B.**

**The zeros of the Riemann zeta-function.** **(Russian)**

*Mat. Zametki* **8** (1970), 419–429.

Let $P_n$ $(n \geqq 2)$ be the class of even trigonometric polynomials $p_n(\varphi)=\sum_{k=0}^n a_k \cos(k\varphi)$, where $p_n(\varphi) \geqq 0$ for all $\varphi$, $a_k \geqq 0$ $(k=0, 1, 2, \cdots, n)$ and $a_0 < a_1$. Put $V(p_n)=(a_1+\cdots+a_n)/(\sqrt{a_1}-\sqrt{a_0})^2$ and $V=\lim_{n\to\infty} \inf_{p_n \in P_n} V(p_n)$. Developing ideas due to C. J. de la Vallée Poussin [Mém. Acad. Roy. Sci. Belg. **59** (1899), no. 8], the author proves two theorems on zeros of the Riemann zeta-function $\zeta(\sigma+it)$: (1) for any $\varepsilon>0$, $\zeta(\sigma+it)$ has no zeros in the domain $\sigma \geqq 1-1/(R \ln t)$ $(t \geqq T)$, where $R=((5-\sqrt{5})/10)V+\varepsilon$ and $T=T(\varepsilon)$; (2) $\zeta(\sigma+it)$ has no zeros in the domain $\sigma \geqq 1-1/(R \ln t)$ $(t \geqq T)$, where $R=9.65$ and $T=12$.

{This article has appeared in English translation [Math. Notes **8** (1970), 706–711].} *C. Tanaka* (Tokyo)

# M30 RIEMANN AND OTHER HYPOTHESES FOR $\zeta(s)$ AND $L(s, \chi)$

It is intended that all papers are listed here in which the Riemann hypothesis or one of its variants over **Q** or an algebraic number field is assumed or implied.

See also Section N44.

See also reviews E20-55, E20-59, E24-37, F25-25, F65-1, K15-92, L20-10, M15-27, M25-8, M25-16, M25-17, M25-21, M25-22, M25-26, M25-35, M25-44, M25-65, M25-66, M25-67, M25-69, M25-71, M25-72, M25-74, M25-87, M40-60, M50-2, M55-33, M99-3, N02-2, N04-3, N04-6, N04-13, N04-28, N04-48, N08-4, N08-44, N12-23, N12-26, N12-33, N12-34, N12-36, N12-46, N12-47, N16-1, N24-27, N24-66, N24-72, N40-23, N48-24, N52-28, N52-39, N52-48, N52-50, N56-36, N68-13, N68-37, N72-38, N76-10, N76-18, N80-3, P32-16, P32-19, P32-20, P32-33, P32-38, P32-45, P32-50, P32-66, P32-72, P32-76, P32-77, P36-15, P36-17, P52-9, R14-39, R18-9, R42-10, R42-23, R44-14, Z10-34, Z30-28.

**M30-1** **(1, 214b)**

**Miyatake, Osamu. On Riemann's $\xi$-function.** Tôhoku Math. J. 46, 160–172 (1939).

Der Verfasser formuliert Seite 169 eine Annahme; diese betrifft die absolute Konvergenz einer Reihe, welche in Zusammenhang mit einer in der Riemann'schen Integraldarstellung der $\xi$-Funktion auftretenden Funktion steht. Aus dieser Annahme zieht der Verfasser durch Überlegungen, die allerdings stellenweise schon im sprachlichen Ausdruck etwas dunkel sind, eine Folgerung über die Nullstellen von $\xi(s)$, also über die nichttrivialen Nullstellen von $\zeta(s)$, welche ein neues, einschneidendes Resultat in der Richtung der Riemann'schen Vermutung wäre. Allerdings zieht der Verfasser schon vorgängig aus derselber Annahme einen Schluss, einen Grenzwert betreffend [Seite 169, $\psi(z)\to 0$], woraus insbesondere sofort folgen würde, dass $\zeta(s)$, in einer gewissen Halbebene, entlang jeder Parallelen zur imaginären Achse für $s\to\infty$ den Grenzwert 1 hat. Da dies jedoch bekanntlich nicht zutrifft, ist entweder die Annahme falsch, oder ist daraus der erwähnte Schluss falsch gezogen worden.

*G. Pólya* (Zürich).

**M30-2** **(1, 294a)**

**Wintner, Aurel. Riemann's hypothesis and almost periodic behavior.** Revista Ci., Lima 41, 575–585 (1939).

The author gives the following necessary and sufficient conditions that the Riemannian hypothesis be true; namely, that the reciprocal of the zeta function be a Besicovitch almost periodic function of infinite order ($B^\infty$) on every vertical line in the right hand half of the critical strip (when $\sigma>\frac{1}{2}$). An equivalent condition is that every negative integral power of the zeta function be of class $B^2$ when $\sigma>\frac{1}{2}$. He also shows that the corresponding condition for positive integral powers of the zeta function is equivalent to the Lindelöf hypothesis. *R. H. Cameron.*

## M30-3 (4, 217e)

**Wintner, Aurel. Riemann's hypothesis and harmonic analysis.** Duke Math. J. **10**, 99–105 (1943).

Let $f(t)$ be defined in $0\leqq t<\infty$ and $L$-integrable in every bounded subinterval; $f(t)$ is said to have a Fourier expansion if

$$M(f_\lambda)=\lim_{T\to\infty} T^{-1}\int_0^T f(t)e^{i\lambda t}dt$$

exists for every $\lambda$ and is 0 except for an enumerable set of $\lambda$'s. It is not known whether a function $f(t)$ exists such that $M(f_\lambda)$ exists for every $\lambda$ and is different from 0 for a non-enumerable set of $\lambda$'s. A function possessing a Fourier development need not be almost periodic. Put

$$S(t)=\pi^{-1}\arg\zeta(\tfrac{1}{2}+it).$$

Then $S(t)$ has the following Fourier expansion:

$$2\pi\varphi(t)\sim\sum_{n=2}^{\infty}\frac{-\Lambda(n)}{n^{\frac{1}{2}}\log(n^{\frac{1}{2}})}\sin(t\log n),$$

where $\Lambda(n)=\log n$ for $n=p^k$ and $\Lambda(n)=0$ for $n\neq p^k$, but $S(t)$ is not almost periodic ($B$). Write $\varphi_1(t)=\int_0^t\varphi(u)du$. Then

$$\varphi_1(t)\sim\frac{1}{\pi}\sum_{n=2}^{\infty}\frac{\Lambda(n)}{n^{\frac{1}{2}}\log^2 n}\cos(t\log n).$$

$S(t)$ is almost periodic ($B^2$). *P. Erdös.*

Referred to in M25-22.

## M30-4 (4, 265h)

**Titchmarsh, E. C. Some properties of the Riemann zeta-function.** Quart. J. Math., Oxford Ser. **14**, 16–26 (1943).

The author considers the effect of the Riemann hypothesis on some asymptotic formulas concerning $\zeta(s)$, $M(x)=\sum_{n\leqq x}\mu(n)$ and the zeros of $\zeta(s)$. He also considers the related hypothesis $\int_1^X(M(x)/x)^2dx=O(\log X)$, showing that it implies the Riemann hypothesis, that all the complex zeros of $\zeta(s)$ are simple and a number of other results. This hypothesis, which is less than $M(x)=O(x^{\frac{1}{2}})$, arises by analogy with a similar formula involving $\psi(x)-x$.

*H. S. Zuckerman* (Seattle, Wash.).

## M30-5 (5, 255c)

**Wintner, Aurel. Random factorizations and Riemann's hypothesis.** Duke Math. J. **11**, 267–275 (1944).

If $x$ is a random sequence of signs ($\pm,\pm,\pm,\cdots$) and if in the product

$$1/\zeta_x(s)=\prod_p(1\pm p^{-s})$$

the prime numbers are arranged in ascending order, then, for almost all $x$, this product and the corresponding series

$$1/\zeta_x(s)=\sum_{n=1}^{\infty}\mu_x(n)n^{-s}$$

are convergent for $\sigma>\frac{1}{2}$ but are not continuable anywhere beyond the line $\sigma=\frac{1}{2}$. *S. Bochner* (Princeton, N. J.).

## M30-6 (5, 255e)

**Wintner, Aurel. The singularities in a family of zeta-functions.** Duke Math. J. **11**, 287–291 (1944).

The author discusses the function

$$\zeta_\alpha(s)=\prod_p(1-\alpha p^{-s})^{-1}$$

for real parameters $\alpha$. In particular, he shows that $(\zeta-1)^\alpha\zeta_\alpha(s)$ is regular and nonvanishing on the line $\sigma=1$ and that the Riemann hypothesis for the classical series $\zeta_1(s)$ implies the same hypothesis for the other series.

*S. Bochner* (Princeton, N. J.).

## M30-7 (9, 80d)

**Turán, P. On a theorem of Littlewood.** J. London Math. Soc. **21** (1946), 268–275 (1947).

The basic result is (essentially): If $G(y)=\sum_{j=1}^n b_jz_j^y$, where $|z_j|\geqq 1$ $(j=1,\cdots,n)$, then every interval $m-n\leqq\nu\leqq m$ $(m>n)$ contains an integer $\nu$ such that $|G(\nu)|\geqq|G(0)|(n/Am)^n$, where $A$ is a numerical constant (for which $A=33$ is a possible value). A simple algebraical proof is given. An easy deduction is that, if $\xi>1$, $\lambda_j>0$, then

$$(*)\qquad \max_{\xi-1\leqq x\leqq\xi}\left|b_0+\sum_{j=1}^N b_j\cos\lambda_jx\right|\geqq(A\xi)^{-2N-1}\left|\sum_{j=0}^N b_j\right|.$$

The factor $(A\xi)^{-2N-1}$ cannot be replaced by anything greater than $(\pi/2\xi)^{2N}$. This is an extension and simplification of Littlewood's "inequality for a sum of cosines" [see the same J. **12**, 217–221 (1937)]. It is pointed out (since there was a slip in Littlewood's statement of what he actually proved) that there is no one-sided (algebraic) version of (*), even if the $b_j$ are positive. The object of these and similar inequalities is to show that certain sums arising in the analytical theory of primes do not become too small through mutual interference of their terms. [For the author's application to the "quasi-Riemannian hypothesis," briefly noted here, see the following review.] *A. E. Ingham.*

Referred to in M50-2, N04-16.

## M30-8 (9, 80e)

**Turan, Paul. On Riemann's hypothesis.** Bull. Acad. Sci. URSS. Sér. Math. [Izvestia Akad. Nauk SSSR] **11**, 197–262 (1947). (English. Russian summary)

The following statements are shown (in theorem II) to be equivalent. (i) There is a $\vartheta<1$ such that $\zeta(s)$ has at most a finite number of zeros in the half-plane $\sigma>\vartheta$; (ii) there are numbers $\alpha,\beta$ $(\alpha\geqq 2,\ 0<\beta\leqq 1)$ such that

$$\left|\sum_{N'\leqq p\leqq N''}e^{it\log p}\right|<ANe^{23(\log\log N)^2}/|t|^\beta$$

($p$ prime) whenever $a\leqq|t|^\alpha\leqq\frac{1}{2}N\leqq N'<N''\leqq N$, where $A$ and $a$ are appropriate constants. The assumption (i) (with a "numerically given" $\vartheta$) is called, after Kalmár, the "quasi-Riemannian hypothesis." It implies, of course, (i′): there is a $\vartheta'<1$ such that $\zeta(s)$ has no zeros in $\sigma>\vartheta'$. But $\vartheta$ seems to be more directly related than $\vartheta'$ to $\alpha$ and $\beta$ (though no final form of connection is attempted in either case). The separate implications (i)→(ii) and (ii)→(i) are refined in various ways. Of special interest are theorems VI and VII, which relate the assertion (ii) for finite ranges of $t$ to the nonexistence of zeros in half-strips $\sigma>\vartheta$, $t_1<t<t_2$, thus localising to some extent the connection between primes and zeros.

The proof that (ii)→(i) (the more difficult implication) is based on an identity equivalent to

$$\frac{1}{(\nu-1)!}\sum_{n>\xi}\frac{\Lambda(n)}{n^s}\log^{\nu-1}n/\xi=\frac{\xi^{1-s}}{(s-1)^\nu}-\sum_\rho\frac{\xi^{\rho-s}}{(s-\rho)^\nu}-\sum_{n=1}^{\infty}\frac{\xi^{-2n-s}}{(s+2n)^\nu},$$

$(\sigma>1,\ \xi\geqq 1,\ \nu=2,3,\cdots)$. The idea is to estimate the left hand side by (ii), and to show that, if $\zeta(s)$ had a zero $\rho^*$ too near $\sigma=1$, the contribution of the term $\rho=\rho^*$ to the right hand side could be made too large by taking $s$ near $\rho^*$ (subject to $\sigma>1$), $\nu$ large (of order $\log t$), and $\xi=e^\nu$. The danger of interference from other terms $\rho$ near $s$ is met by a series of algebraical lemmas (of independent interest) designed to show that $\nu$ can be so chosen (within the permitted range) that this interference is not too great. A typical example is lemma XII: if $\max(|z_1|, \cdots, |z_n|)=1$, $m\geqq 28n$, then

$$\max_{m\leqq\nu\leqq m+n} |z_1^\nu+z_2^\nu+\cdots+z_n^\nu|>n^{-2}(e^{-26}n/m)^n.$$

The condition (ii) is of a novel type among necessary and sufficient conditions for (i) or (i′) in that the sum involved can in principle be estimated by known methods independent of the theory of $\zeta(s)$. An appendix is devoted to the study by Vinogradov's method of various modifications of this sum. If, for example, $\log p$ is replaced by $(\log p)^c$ $(\frac{1}{4}\leqq c\leqq 2)$, the direct attack fails when $c=1$, but the author shows how we may argue from a smaller $c$ to a larger $c'$ (theorem X is the case $c=\frac{1}{2}$, $c'=1$), and hazards a conjecture for the case $c<1$ that would carry with it (ii) and therefore (i). *A. E. Ingham* (Cambridge, England).

Referred to in M50-2, N04-16, P44-16.

## M30-9 (10, 286b)

**Turán, Paul. On some approximative Dirichlet-polynomials in the theory of the zeta-function of Riemann.** Danske Vid. Selsk. Mat.-Fys. Medd. **24**, no. 17, 36 pp. (1948).

(I) If the partial sums $U_n(s)=\sum_1^n \nu^{-s}$ of the series for $\zeta(s)$ $(s=\sigma+it)$ have no zeros in $\sigma>1$ $(n>n_0)$, then $\zeta(s)$ has no zeros in $\sigma>\frac{1}{2}$ (i.e., the Riemann hypothesis is true). Proof. By a theorem of Bohr (based on the linear independence of the numbers $\log p$) the hypothesis $U_n(s)\neq 0$ $(\sigma>1, n>n_0)$ is equivalent to $W_n(s)\equiv\sum_1^n\lambda(\nu)\nu^{-s}\neq 0$ $(\sigma>1, n>n_0)$, and so implies $W_n(\sigma)\geqq 0$ $(\sigma\geqq 1, n>n_0)$, where $\lambda(n)$ is Liouville's function; and this implies, by a theorem of Landau, that the function on the right of the identity

$$\int_1^\infty x^{-s}W_{[x]}(1)dx=\frac{\zeta(2s)}{(s-1)\zeta(s)}, \qquad \sigma>1,$$

being regular along the stretch $s>\frac{1}{2}$ of the real axis, is regular in the half-plane $\sigma>\frac{1}{2}$. Among refinements and extensions the following may be mentioned. (IV) If, for $n>n_0$, $U_n(s)$ omits in $\sigma>1+Kn^{\vartheta-1}$ a real value $c_n$ with $-K_1n^{\vartheta-1}\leqq c_n\leqq K_1n^{\vartheta-1}$, then $\zeta(s)\neq 0$ for $\sigma>\vartheta$ $(\frac{1}{2}\leqq\vartheta<1)$. (X) If, for some character $\chi(n)$ mod $k$, $\sum_1^n\chi(\nu)\nu^{-s}\neq 0$ for $\sigma>1$, then $\zeta(s)\neq 0$ for $\sigma>\frac{1}{2}$. No implication in the opposite direction is suggested. The hypothesis $U_n(s)\neq 0$ $(\sigma>1)$ is tested in various ways. (1) A possible threat from Knopp's theorem, that every point of $\sigma=1$ is a cluster point of zeros of $\{U_n(s)\}$, is countered by a proof (VI) that the clustering is wholly from the left, at any rate if $|t|\geqq\tau_0$. (2) The inequality $W_n(1)>0$ has been verified up to $n=1000$ by a group of Danish mathematicians.

[Note by the reviewer. The plausibility of the hypothesis $U_n(s)\neq 0$ $(\sigma>1)$ (or the weaker hypothesis of (IV) with $\vartheta=\frac{1}{2}$) is somewhat diminished by the observation that it implies, by way of $W_n(1)\geqq 0$ (or $W_n(1)>-K_2n^{-\frac{1}{2}}$), not merely that the complex zeros of $\zeta(s)$ are of the form $\frac{1}{2}\pm i\gamma_n$ $(\gamma_n>0$ and distinct), but also that the $\gamma_n$ are linearly dependent. For the parallel discussion of Pólya's hypothesis $W_n(0)\leqq 0$ $(n\geqq 2)$ see Ingham, Amer. J. Math. **64**, 313–319 (1942); these Rev. **3**, 271.] *A. E. Ingham.*

Citations: MR 3, 271c = N44-4.
Referred to in M30-19, M30-30, N44-12, N44-16.

## M30-10 (10, 433e)

**Mikolás, Miklós. Sur l'hypothèse de Riemann.** C. R. Acad. Sci. Paris **228**, 633–636 (1949).

Let $\rho_\nu$ be the $\nu$th fraction of the Farey series of order $[x]$ and let $\Phi(x)$ be the number of fractions in the series. The author shows that, if $|\lambda|<2\{5/\zeta(3)\}^{\frac{1}{2}}=4.078\cdots$ and $\lambda\neq 0$, then the Riemann hypothesis is equivalent to

$$\sum_{\nu=1}^{\Phi(x)} e^{\lambda\rho_\nu}-\frac{e^\lambda-1}{\lambda}\Phi(x)=o(x^{\frac{1}{2}+\epsilon}),$$

where $\epsilon$ is an arbitrary positive number. This is deduced from the well-known result that the Riemann hypothesis is equivalent to $\sum_{n\leqq x}\mu(n)=o(x^{\frac{1}{2}+\epsilon})$. Criteria of a similar form employing the functions $\cos\lambda\rho$, $\sin\lambda\rho$, $\rho^2$ and $\rho^3$ in place of $e^{\lambda\rho}$ are stated without proof. There are numerous misprints. *R. A. Rankin* (Cambridge, England).

Referred to in M30-11, M30-25.

## M30-11 (11, 645a)

**Mikolás, Miklós. Farey series and their connection with the prime number problem. I.** Acta Univ. Szeged. Sect. Sci. Math. **13**, 93–117 (1949).

Let $\rho_\nu$ be the $\nu$th fraction of the Farey series of order $[x]$ and let $\Phi(x)$ be the number of fractions in the series. The author considers the asymptotic behavior (for $x\to\infty$) of sums of the type $\sum_{\nu=1}^{\Phi(x)}f(\rho_\nu)$, where $f(t)$ is a function defined on the interval $0<t\leqq 1$ (or at least on the rational points thereof). He proves the following theorems. (1) If $f(t)$ is (properly) Riemann-integrable in the interval $0\leqq t\leqq 1$, then $\sum_{\nu=1}^{\Phi(x)}f(\rho_\nu)\sim\Phi(x)\int_0^1 f(t)dt$. [This is problem 189 of section II of Pólya and Szegö, Aufgaben und Lehrsätze aus der Analysis, v. 1, Springer, Berlin, 1925.] More generally, if $\lim_{n\to\infty}\{n^{-1}\sum_{k=1}^n f(k/n)\}$ exists and has the value $A$, then $\sum_{\nu=1}^{\Phi(x)}f(\rho_\nu)\sim A\Phi(x)\sim 3\pi^{-2}Ax^2$.(2) If $f(t)$ has a bounded derivative in the interval $0\leqq t\leqq 1$, then

$$\sum_{\nu=1}^{\Phi(x)} f(\rho_\nu)=\Phi(x)\int_0^1 f(t)dt+O(x\exp\{-c(\log x)^\gamma\}),$$

where $c$ is a positive constant and $\gamma$ is the same exponent that appears in the error term of the prime number theorem. With the same condition on $f(t)$ the Riemann hypothesis implies (*) $\sum_{\nu=1}^{\Phi(x)}f(\rho_\nu)=\Phi(x)\int_0^1 f(t)dt+O(x^{\frac{1}{2}+\epsilon})$. (3) Under various more stringent restrictions on the function $f(t)$, the relation (*) implies the Riemann hypothesis [cf. an earlier paper of the author, C. R. Acad. Sci. Paris **228**, 633–636 (1949); these Rev. **10**, 433]. *P. T. Bateman.*

Citations: MR 10, 433e = M30-10.
Referred to in K20-8, M30-15, M30-18, M30-25.

## M30-12 (11, 645b; 11, 645c)

**Mikolás, Miklós. On a theorem of J. Franel.** Norske Vid. Selsk. Forh., Trondheim **21**, no. 24, 98–101 (1949).
**Mikolás, Miklós. Un théorème d'équivalence et ses applications.** Norske Vid. Selsk. Forh., Trondheim **22**, no. 28, 128–131 (1950).

Let $\rho_\nu(x)$ be the $\nu$th term of the Farey series $F_x$ of order $x$ when arranged in increasing order. Let $\Phi(x)=\sum_{n=1}^{[x]}\varphi(n)$ be the number of terms in $F_x$, let $\delta_\nu(x)=\rho_\nu(x)-\nu/\Phi(x)$ and let $\Delta(x)=\sum_{\nu=1}^{\Phi(x)}\delta_\nu^2(x)$. The significance of $\Delta(x)$ arises from the fact that the Riemann hypothesis is true if and only if $\Delta(x)=O(x^{-1+\epsilon})$ for each positive $\epsilon$ as $x\to\infty$. Let $M(x)=\sum_{n=1}^{[x]}\mu(n)$ and $Q(x; c, \gamma)=\exp\{-c(\log x)^\gamma\}$. Using a result of Tchudakov on the zeros of $\zeta(s)$ which implies that $\pi(x)=\mathrm{li}\,x+O(xQ(x; c', \gamma))$ for each $\gamma<11/21$, the author indicates that $M(x)=O(xQ(x; c, \gamma))$ in the first paper. From this he proves that $\Delta(x)=O(Q(x; c, \gamma))$.

In the second paper, the latter result is generalized as follows. Let $q(x)>0$, let there exist $q'(x)\geqq 0$ for all $x\geqq 1$

and let there be a positive constant $\eta$ such that for all sufficiently large $x$, $q(x)x^{-\frac{1}{2}+\eta}$ decreases monotonely. Then $M(x)=O(x/q(x))$ and $\Delta(x)=O(1/q^2(x))$ are equivalent to one another with a similar result holding when $O$ is replaced by $o$. In the first paper, $q(x)=1/Q(x; c, \gamma)$ and the conclusion was weaker.

It may be remarked that Tchudakov improved the result $\gamma<11/21$ to $\gamma<4/7$ in a later paper [C. R. (Doklady) Acad. Sci. URSS (N.S.) **21**, 421–422 (1938)]. In the first paper under review, the proof is incorrect in its final stages but can be fixed; the corresponding details of the second paper are likewise incorrect. By replacing the lim sup by a least upper bound, it can be shown that $\eta$ can be taken to be zero in the $O$-statement and it can be taken to be zero in the $o$-statement if it is further assumed that $q(x)x^{-\frac{1}{2}}=o(1)$.

*L. Schoenfeld* (Urbana, Ill.).

Referred to in M30-18.

## M30-13 (12, 250a)

**de Bruijn, N. G. The roots of trigonometric integrals.** Duke Math. J. **17**, 197–226 (1950).

It is not possible to give a complete account of the many results contained in this paper. The main results are the following. (1) Let $f(t)$ be an even nonconstant entire function of $t$, $f(t)\geqq 0$ for real $t$, and such that $f'(t)$ can be approximated, uniformly in every bounded domain, by polynomials all of whose zeros are purely imaginary. (In other words, $f'(t)=\exp(\gamma t^2)g(t)$, where $\gamma\geqq 0$ and $g(t)$ is an entire function of genus $\leqq 1$ with purely imaginary zeros only.) Then $\Psi(z)=\int_{-\infty}^{\infty}\exp\{-f(t)\}e^{izt}dt$ has real zeros only. This result contains several results of Pólya as special cases [see, for example, J. Reine Angew. Math. **158**, 6–18 (1927)]. (2) Let $P(t)=\sum_{-N}^{N}p_n e^{nt}$, where $\Re p_N>0$, $p_{-n}=\bar{p}_n$ for $n=0, 1, \cdots$; let $q(x)$ be regular in the closed sector $-\frac{1}{2}\pi-\arg p_N\leqq N\arg x\leqq\frac{1}{2}\pi-\arg p_N$ except possibly at 0 and at $\infty$, where $q(x)$ may have poles, and let $q(x)$ be real on the part of $|x|=1$ in the sector. Set $q(e^t)=Q(t)$. Then all but a finite number of the zeros of $\Phi(z)=\int_{-\infty}^{\infty}\exp\{-P(t)\}Q(t)e^{izt}dt$ are real.

In order to arrive at a proof of (2), the asymptotic behavior of $\Phi(z)$ for large $|z|$ is studied in some detail. The author concludes that $\Phi(z)$ has only a finite number of zeros outside any strip $|\Im z|\leqq\epsilon$ $(\epsilon>0)$. Together with an auxiliary result this is sufficient to show that $\Phi(z)$ has only a finite number of nonreal zeros. A proof of (1) is now obtained as follows. By (2), the zeros of $\Phi(z)=\int_{-\infty}^{\infty}\exp\{-P(t)\}e^{izt}dt$ lie in some strip $|\Im z|\leqq\Delta$. Now let $P'(t)$ have purely imaginary zeros only. If $\Delta>0$, by an auxiliary result, the zeros of $\Phi_1(z)=\int_{-\infty}^{\infty}\exp\{-P(t)\}P'(t)e^{izt}dt$ lie in a narrower strip $|\Im z|\leqq\Delta_1<\Delta$. However, $\Phi_1(z)=iz\Phi(z)$, so that the zeros of $\Phi(z)$ must be real. By letting $P'(t)\to f'(t)$, $P(t)\to f(t)$, uniformly in every bounded domain, (1) follows. Several miscellaneous results give information on the zeros of trigonometric integrals which are similar to the integrals (*) and (**) connected with the Riemann and Ramanujan zeta-functions, $\zeta(s)$ and $F(s)=\sum\tau(n)n^{-s}$: (*) $\Xi(2z)=\int_{-\infty}^{\infty}\varphi(t)e^{izt}dt$, where

$$\Xi\{i(\tfrac{1}{2}-s)\}=\xi(s)=\tfrac{1}{2}s(s-1)\Gamma(\tfrac{1}{2}s)\pi^{-\frac{1}{2}s}\zeta(s),$$

$$\varphi(t)=\sum_{n=1}^{\infty}(2n^4\pi^2e^{9t/4}-3n^2\pi e^{5t/4})\exp(-n^2\pi e^t);$$

and (**) $\Xi^{\sim}(z)=\int_{-\infty}^{\infty}\varphi^{\sim}(t)e^{izt}dt$, where

$$\Xi^{\sim}(is)=(2\pi)^{-s-6}\Gamma(s+6)F(s+6),$$

$$\varphi^{\sim}(t)=\exp(-2\pi\cosh t)$$

$$\times\prod_{\nu=1}^{\infty}[\{1-\exp(-2\pi\nu e^t)\}\{1-\exp(-2\pi\nu e^{-t})\}]^{12}.$$

The Riemann hypothesis is that all the zeros of (*) are real; there exists a corresponding hypothesis about the zeros of (**). The following results of the author in this connection are characteristic. (3) If $\lambda>0$, $\mu\geqq 0$, $k=1$ or 2, then $\int_{-\infty}^{\infty}\exp(-\lambda\cosh t)(\mu+\cosh^k t)e^{izt}dt$ has real zeros only. (4) If $\lambda>0$, $0<\delta<\frac{1}{2}\pi$, $n$ a positive integer, then there exists a number $\Delta=\Delta(\lambda, \delta, n)>0$ such that the zeros of $\int_{-\infty}^{\infty}\exp(-\lambda\cosh t)f(\cosh t)e^{izt}dt$ lie in the strip $|\Im z|\leqq\Delta$ for any real polynomial $f(y)$ of degree $n$ whose zeros lie in the sector $\frac{1}{2}\pi+\delta\leqq\arg y\leqq\frac{3}{2}\pi-\delta$. (5) If $\lambda>0$ and if $f(y)=\prod_{\mu=1}^{\infty}(1+c_\mu y)$, $c_\mu\geqq 0$, $\sum c_\mu(1+c_\mu)^{-1}\leqq 2\lambda$, then

$$\int_{-\infty}^{\infty}\exp(-\lambda\cosh^2 t)f(\cosh t)e^{izt}dt$$

has real zeros only. *J. Korevaar* (Lafayette, Ind.).

## M30-14 (13, 113a)

**Mikolás, Miklós. An equivalence theorem concerning Farey series.** Mat. Lapok **2**, 46–53 (1951). (Hungarian. Russian and English summaries)

Let $u(n)$ be the Moebius function, $\varphi(n)$ Euler's function, $M(x)=\sum_{n=1}^{x}u(n)$, $\Phi(x)=\sum_{n=1}^{x}\varphi(n)$, $\rho_\nu$ the $\nu$th Farey fraction of order $\nu$. Littlewood proved that $M(x)=o(x^{\frac{1}{2}+\epsilon})$ is equivalent to the Riemann hypothesis and Franel proved that

$$N(x)=\sum_{\nu=1}^{\Phi(x)}\left(\rho_\nu-\frac{\nu}{\Phi(x)}\right)^2=o(x^{-1+\epsilon})$$

is equivalent to the Riemann hypothesis. The author connects these theorems by the following result: Let $g(x)$ satisfy the following conditions: $g(x)>0$, $g'(x)>0$; further, there exists an $\eta>0$ so that $g(x)/x^{\frac{1}{2}-\eta}$ decreases for $x$ sufficiently large. Then

$$M(x)=O(x/g(x)) \quad\text{and}\quad N(x)=O(1/(g(x))^2)$$

are equivalent. Also $M(x)=o(x/g(x))$ and $N(x)=o(1/(g(x))^2)$ are equivalent. As a corollary the author obtains that $N(x)=o(1)$ is equivalent to the prime number theorem.

*P. Erdös* (Aberdeen).

## M30-15 (13, 627b)

**Mikolás, Miklós. Farey series and their connection with the prime number problem. II.** Acta Sci. Math. Szeged **14**, 5–21 (1951).

Let $\rho_\nu$ be the $\nu$th (positive) fraction in the Farey series of order $x$ and let $\Phi(x)$ be the number of fractions (not exceeding unity) in the series. Continuing the work of an earlier paper [Acta Univ. Szeged. Sect. Sci. Math. **13**, 93–117 (1949); these Rev. **11**, 645] the author proves the following theorems. (1) If $\psi(x)$ denotes the logarithm of the least common multiple of the positive integers not exceeding $x$, then $\sum_{\nu=1}^{\Phi(x)}\log\rho_\nu=-\Phi(x)+\frac{1}{2}\psi(x)+O(x\exp\{-c(\log x)^\gamma\})$, where $c$ is a positive constant and $\gamma$ is the same exponent that appears in the error term of the prime number theorem. (2) The Riemann hypothesis is true if and only if the relation $\sum_{\nu=1}^{\Phi(x)}\log\rho_\nu+\Phi(x)-\frac{1}{2}\psi(x)=O(x^{\frac{1}{2}+\epsilon})$ holds for any positive value of $\epsilon$. [The author claims that this statement is still correct if $\psi(x)$ is replaced by $x$, but the reviewer does not understand how the Riemann hypothesis would follow from the validity of the relation $\sum_{\nu=1}^{\Phi(x)}\log\rho_\nu+\Phi(x)-\frac{1}{2}x=O(x^{\frac{1}{2}+\epsilon})$ for every positive $\epsilon$]. (3) Asymptotic formulas exist for $\sum_{\nu=1}^{\Phi(x)}\rho_\nu^{-\lambda}$ as $x\to\infty$, $\lambda$ being any fixed positive number. (4) If $\lambda>1$, $B>0$, and $f(t)$ is a non-negative decreasing function defined for $0<t\leqq 1$, then $\sum_{\nu=1}^{\Phi(x)}f(\rho_\nu)\sim Bx^{\lambda+1}$ as $x\to\infty$ if and only if $f(t)\sim B\{(\lambda+1)\zeta(\lambda+1)/\zeta(\lambda)\}t^{-\lambda}$ as $t\to 0$.

*P. T. Bateman* (Urbana, Ill.).

Citations: MR 11, 645a = M30-11.
Referred to in M30-18, M30-25.

## M30-16 (13, 122c)

**Mironov, V. T. On the zeros of Riemann's zeta-function.** Izvestiya Akad. Nauk SSSR. Ser. Mat. **15**, 91–94 (1951). (Russian)

The author uses results of R. Lagrange [Acta Math. **64**, 1–80 (1935)] on interpolation series for analytic functions to establish the following result (corrected for a misprint by the reviewer): Let $u>1$,

$$I_n=\sum_{k=1}^{n+1}(-1)^{k-1}(n+k)!/\{k!^2(n-k+1)!(ku)^q\zeta(ku)\},$$

and $\lambda(q)=\frac{1}{2}u\{1+\limsup_{n\to\infty}(\log|I_n|)/\log n\}$. Then a necessary and sufficient condition for the Riemann hypothesis is that $\lim_{q\to\infty}\lambda(q)=\frac{1}{2}$. *L. Schoenfeld* (Urbana, Ill.).

Referred to in M30-29.

## M30-17 (14, 727a)

**Salem, Raphaël. Sur une proposition équivalente à l'hypothèse de Riemann.** C. R. Acad. Sci. Paris **236**, 1127–1128 (1953).

A necessary and sufficient condition for the Riemann hypothesis, derived from a theorem of Wiener on Fourier transforms, is that the integral equation

$$\int_{-\infty}^{\infty}\frac{e^{-\sigma y}\phi(y)dy}{e^{e^{x-y}}+1}=0$$

should have no bounded solution $\phi(y)$ other than the trivial solution $\phi(y)=0$, for $\frac{1}{2}<\sigma<1$. *E. C. Titchmarsh.*

## M30-18 (14, 950j)

**Mikolás, Miklós. Über summatorische Funktionen von Möbiusschem Charakter.** C. R. Acad. Bulgare Sci. **4** (1951), no. 2–3, 9–12 (1953). (Russian summary)

It is well known that the Möbius $\mu$ function satisfies $M(x)=\sum_{k=1}^{x}\mu(k)=o(x)$, and $M(x)=o(x^{\frac{1}{2}+\epsilon})$ is equivalent to the Riemann hypothesis. The author says that $g(n)$ has Möbius characteristics if $\sum_{k=1}^{x}g(k)=o(x)$ and $\sum_{k=1}^{x}g(k)=o(x^{\frac{1}{2}+\epsilon})$ implies the Riemann hypothesis. In several recent papers the author investigated this property [these Rev. **11**, 645; **13**, 627]. In the present note he proves that if $h(n)=\sum_{d|n}g(d)$ is strongly multiplicative and $h(n)=O(n^{-\frac{1}{2}})$, then $g(n)$ has Möbius characteristics. *P. Erdös* (South Bend, Ind.).

Citations: MR 11, 645a = M30-11; MR 11, 645b = M30-12; MR 11, 645c = M30-12; MR 11, 645d = C15-9; MR 13, 627b = M30-15.

## M30-19 (15, 939c)

**Bateman, P. T., and Chowla, S. The equivalence of two conjectures in the theory of numbers.** J. Indian Math. Soc. (N.S.) **17** (1953), 177–181 (1954).

Let $\lambda(n)$ be Liouville's function (i.e. the purely multiplicative function for which $\lambda(p)=-1$ for $p$ a prime). Define $L_1(x)=\sum_{\nu\leq x}\lambda(\nu)\nu^{-1}$, and $\xi(\chi,x)=\sum_{\nu\leq x}\chi(\nu)\nu^{-1}$, where $\chi$ is a real character function. Turán conjectured [Danske Vid. Selsk. Mat.-Fys. Medd. **24**, no. 17 (1948); these Rev. **10**, 286] that $L_1(x)>0$ for every $x$, and observed that this implies the Riemann hypothesis. The SWAC has shown that $L_1(x)>0$ for $x<100000$. The second conjecture,

$$\xi(\chi,x)>0 \text{ for every } x \text{ and every } \chi,$$

is shown by the authors to be equivalent to the first. The only difficulty is in showing that the first implies the second. This theorem, communicated to the authors by A. B. Showalter, is proved by double induction for a more general class of functions $\chi$ satisfying the following conditions: $\chi(mn)=\chi(m)\chi(n)$, $\chi(1)=1$, $\chi(p)=-1$ or $\chi(p)\geqq 0$ ($p$ a prime). The authors point out that for a fixed character $\chi$ (mod $D$), say $\xi(\chi,x)>0$ for all sufficiently large $x$ since $\xi(\chi,\infty)$ is proportional to the class number of $D$. It is shown that (*) $\xi(\chi,x)>0$ for all $x>1.75D\log D$ and that, provided $D>D_0$, (*) holds for all $x>D^{\frac{1}{2}+\epsilon}$. *D. H. Lehmer.*

Citations: MR 10, 286b = M30-9.

Referred to in M30-27.

## M30-20 (16, 465f)

**Korevaar, Jacob. The Riemann hypothesis and numerical Tauberian theorems for Lambert series.** Nederl. Akad. Wetensch. Proc. Ser. A. **57** = Indag. Math. **16**, 564–571 (1954).

It is shown that the following unproved Tauberian proposition on Lambert series is equivalent to the Riemann hypothesis on the zeros of the zeta function. Let the Lambert series

$$\sum_{n=1}^{\infty}a_n\frac{nx}{e^{nx}-1}$$

converge when $x>0$ to a function $f(x)$ which is the restriction of a function analytic at $x=0$. Let $f(x)\to s$ as $x\to 0+$. If the numbers $a_n$ are real, let there correspond to each $\delta>0$ a number $A_1(\delta)$ such that

$$a_n\geqq -A_1(\delta)n^{-1+\delta} \quad (n=1,2,3,\cdots),$$

and in case of nonreal $a_n$, let Re $a_n$ and Im $a_n$ satisfy similar conditions. Then to each $\epsilon>0$ corresponds a constant $K_1(\epsilon)$ such that

$$\left|\sum_{k=1}^{n}s_k-s\right|\leqq K_1(\epsilon)n^{-\frac{1}{2}+\epsilon} \quad (n=1,2,3,\cdots).$$

Numerous related theorems and remarks are given. *R. P. Agnew* (Ithaca, N. Y.).

## M30-21 (17, 15a)

**Beurling, Arne. A closure problem related to the Riemann zeta-function.** Proc. Nat. Acad. Sci. U.S.A. **41**, 312–314 (1955).

Let $\varrho(x)$ be the fractional part of $x$ and let $C$ be the set of functions $f(x)=\sum_1^n c_\nu\varrho(\theta_\nu x^{-1})$, where $0<\theta_\nu\leq 1$, $\sum_1^n c_\nu\theta_\nu=0$. Let $C_p$ be the closure of $C$ in $L_p(0,1)$, $1<p<\infty$. Here $C_p=L_p$ if and only if the function $f(x)\equiv 1$, $0<x<1$, is in $C_p$. It is shown that the Riemann zeta-function has no zeros in $\Re(s)>1/p$ if and only if $C_p=L_p$. The sufficiency follows from the relation $s\int_0^1 x^{s-1}f(x)dx=-\zeta(s)\sum_1^n c_\nu\theta_\nu^s$ valid for any $f(x)\in C$. The necessity is concluded by observing that if $C_p\neq L_p$, then among the functions of $L_q$, $1/p+1/q=1$, which are orthogonal to $C$, there is also a power $x^\lambda$, $\Re(\lambda)>-1/q$ and if $s_0=\lambda+1$, then $\zeta(s_0)=0$ where $\Re(s_0)>1/p$. Here $x^\lambda$ is a character of the semi-group of positive reals $\leq 1$ under multiplication and the set $C$ is mapped into itself by the operators $\{T_a; 0\leq a\leq 1\}$ which take $f(x)$ into $f(x/a)$ where $f(x)=0$ for $x>1$. *E. Hille* (New Haven, Conn.).

## M30-22 (17, 15b)

**Kopřiva, Jiří. On a relation of the Farey series to the Riemann hypothesis on the zeros of the $\xi$ function.** Časopis Pěst. Mat. **78**, 49–55 (1953). (Czech)

It is proved that each of the estimates

$$\sum_{0<r<\frac{1}{2}}(r-\tfrac{1}{4})\ll q^{\frac{1}{2}+\varepsilon},\quad \sum_{0<r<1}(r^2-\tfrac{1}{3})\ll q^{\frac{1}{2}+\varepsilon},\quad \sum_{0<r<1}(r^3-\tfrac{1}{4})\ll q^{\frac{1}{2}+\varepsilon},$$

where $\varepsilon>0$ is arbitrarily small and the sums extend over all Farey fractions $r$ lying in the indicated intervals with denominators $\leq q$, are equivalent to the relation

$$\sum_{n\leq q}\mu(n)\ll q^{\frac{1}{2}+\varepsilon}$$

(the sign $\ll$ of I. M. Vinogradov is taken, as usual, in

the sense $O$). Here $\mu(n)$ is the Möbius function. By a known theorem of Littlewood [C. R. Acad. Sci. Paris **154**, 263–266 (1912)] follows the equivalence of these estimates to the Riemann hypothesis.

These results are analogous to known results of Franel [Landau, Vorlesungen über Zahlentheorie, Bd. 2, Hirzel, Leipzig, 1927, pp. 167–177].

*I. P. Kubilyus* (RŽMat **1955,** no. 595).

## M30-23 (17, 15c)

**Kopřiva, Jiří. Contribution to the relation of the Farey series to the Riemann hypothesis.** Časopis Pěst. Mat. **79,** 77–82 (1954). (Czech)

Let $M(x)$ denote the sum $\sum_{m<x}\mu(m)$, where $\mu$ is the Möbius function. The statement (1) $M(x)=O(x^{\frac{1}{2}+\epsilon})$ is known to be equivalent to the Riemann Hypothesis. The author is interested in obtaining transformations of this statement (1). In the present paper he introduces the function $H(q)=\sum_{m=1}^{q}m^{-k}M(q/m)$, where $k$ is an integer parameter and shows that (1) is equivalent to the statement $H(q)=O(q^{\frac{1}{2}+\epsilon})$, and that this is equivalent to the statement

$$\sum_{\varrho}(\varrho^{n-1}-n^{-1})=O(q^{\frac{1}{2}+\epsilon})\quad (n=2,3,\cdots),$$

where the sum extends over all Farey fractions whose denominators do not exceed $q$. This last statement for $n=2, 3$ was given in the paper (unavailable to the reviewer) reviewed above. *D. H. Lehmer.*

## M30-24 (17, 588d)

**Voelker, Dietrich. Sufficient conditions for the validity of the Riemann hypothesis.** Univ. Nac. Tucumán. Rev. Ser. A. **10** (1954), 141–149 (1955). (Spanish. German summary)

The author translates the Riemann hypothesis into an equivalent condition concerning the abscissa of convergence of some particular Laplace transforms.

*R. Bellman* (Santa Monica, Calif.).

## M30-25 (18, 382a)

**Kopřiva, Jiří. Remark on the significance of the Farey series in number theory.** Publ. Fac. Sci. Univ. Masaryk **1955,** 267–279. (Czech. Russian summary)

M. Mikolás [C. R. Acad. Sci. Paris **228** (1949), 633–636; Acta Sci. Math. Szeged **13** (1949), 93–117; **14** (1951), 5–21; MR **10,** 433; **11,** 645; **13,** 627, 1138] has shown that Riemann's hypothesis about the zeros of $\zeta(s)$ is equivalent to the truth of the relation

$$\text{(A)}\qquad \sum_{\nu=1}^{P(x)} f(\rho_\nu)-P(x)\int_0^1 f(x)dx=O(x^{\frac{1}{2}+\varepsilon})$$

for every $\varepsilon>0$; here $\rho_\nu$ runs through the Farey fractions of order $[x]$ which lie in the interval $(0, 1)$, $P(x)$ is the number of such Farey fractions, and $f(\xi)$ may be $\sin\lambda\xi$, $\cos\lambda\xi$ $(0<|\lambda|<2\{(\zeta(3)+5\pi^{-2})/5\}^{-\frac{1}{2}}, |\lambda|\neq\pi)$, a quadratic polynomial, or a cubic polynomial $a_0\xi^3+a_1\xi^2+a_2\xi+a_3$ $(a_1\neq 3a_0/2)$. The function $f$ may take other forms, but those are not considered in the present paper. Supposing $f$ to be any one of the four types mentioned above, the author shows that if from the sum on the left of (A) are omitted those terms which correspond to Farey fractions of type $a/2^n$ and $P(x)$ is reduced accordingly, relation (A), thus altered, is still equivalent to Riemann's hypothesis. He proves a similar result in which the excluded Farey fractions are of type $b/m^2$, and he asks how far one may carry on this process of exclusion without disturbing the equivalence between the corresponding relations derived from (A), and Riemann's hypothesis.

*H. Halberstam* (Exeter).

Citations: MR 10, 433e = M30-10; MR 11, 645a = M30-11; MR 13, 627b = M30-15.

## M30-26 (18, 468b)

**Levinson, Norman. On closure problems and the zeros of the Riemann zeta function.** Proc. Amer. Math. Soc. **7** (1956), 838–845.

This paper is concerned with conditions that the Riemann zeta-function $\zeta(s)$ should have no zeros in certain regions of the $s$-plane. The main result is that if $\lambda_n$ is a positive increasing sequence such that $\sum\lambda_n^{-1}$ is divergent, a necessary and sufficient condition that $\zeta(s)$ should have no zeros in the strip $\sigma_1<\operatorname{re}s<\sigma_2$, where $\frac{1}{2}\leqq\sigma_1<\sigma_2\leqq 1$, is that given any $\varepsilon>0$ and $\alpha$ and $\beta$ such that $\sigma_1<\alpha<\beta<\sigma_2$, there exists an integer $N$ and numbers $a_n$, $n=1, \cdots N$, (depending on $\varepsilon$, $\alpha$ and $\beta$) such that

$$\int_0^\infty\left(\sum_1^N a_n\frac{e^{-\lambda_n x}}{1+e^{-\lambda_n x}}-e^{-x}\right)^2\left(x^{2\alpha-1}+x^{2\beta-1}\right)dx<\varepsilon.$$

*E. C. Titchmarsh* (Oxford).

## M30-27 (20# 5759)

**Wiener, Norbert; and Wintner, Aurel. Notes on Pólya's and Turán's hypotheses concerning Liouville's factor.** Rend. Circ. Mat. Palermo (2) **6** (1957), 240–248.

Pólya pointed out that if

$$\text{(P)}\qquad \sum_1^x\lambda(n)\leqq 0\quad (x>1),$$

where $\lambda(n)$ is Liouville's function, then the Riemann hypothesis (R.H.) is true {however, Haselgrove has informed the reviewer that he has disproved Hypothesis (P)}. Turán has observed that if

$$\text{(T}_1\text{)}\qquad \sum_1^x\frac{\lambda(n)}{n}\geqq 0\quad (x>x_0),$$

then the R. H. is true, and also that the R. H. is true if

$$\text{(T}_2\text{)}\qquad \sum_1^x n^{-s}\neq 0\quad (\Re(s)>1)\text{ for } x>x_0.$$

The authors prove the following result related to $(T_2)$: If there exists a positive $\varepsilon<1$ for which

$$\text{(W)}\qquad \sum_1^\infty\frac{r^n}{n^s}\neq 0\quad (\Re(s)>1,\ 1-\varepsilon<r<1),$$

then the R. H. is true. The authors also observe that in view of a result of Showalter [in Bateman and Chowla, J. Indian Math. Soc. (N.S.) **17** (1953), 177–181; MR **15,** 939] the hypothesis:

$$\text{(H)}\qquad \text{For all } x, \sum_1^x\frac{\chi(n)}{n}\geqq 0\quad (x\geqq 1)$$

for all real characters $\chi$, would also imply the R. H.

*S. Chowla* (Boulder, Colo.)

Citations: MR 15, 939c = M30-19.

## M30-28 (20# 6396)

**Meller, N. A. Computations connected with the check of Riemann's hypothesis.** Dokl. Akad. Nauk SSSR **123** (1958), 246–248. (Russian)

## M30-29 (21# 4940)

**Mironov, V. T. On the zeros of the Riemann zeta function.** Mat. Sb. N.S. **45(87)** (1958), 397–400. (Russian)

The author finds a precise upper bound for the real parts of the zeros, resembling his criterion for the truth of the Riemann hypothesis [Izv. Akad. Nauk SSSR Ser. Mat. **15** (1951), 91–94; MR **13,** 122]. The other result proved is that for any $\varepsilon>0$, there is a $T>0$ such that if $\zeta(z)$ has no zeros in the rectangle $h\leqq\Re z\leqq 1$, $0\leqq\Im z\leqq T$, where $\frac{1}{2}<h<1$, then it has no zeros in the half-plane $\Re z>h+\varepsilon$. While the existence of such a $T(\varepsilon)$ appears trivial, his argument could no doubt be used to obtain a suitable $T(\varepsilon)$ explicitly. *F. V. Atkinson* (Canberra)

Citations: MR 13, 122c = M30-16.

## M30-30 (22# 6774)

**Turán, P. Nachtrag zu meiner Abhandlung "On some approximative Dirichlet polynomials in the theory of zeta-function of Riemann".** Acta Math. Acad. Sci. Hungar. **10** (1959), 277–298. (Russian summary, unbound insert)

The author writes

$$U_n(s) = \sum_{\nu \leqq n} \frac{1}{\nu^s}, \quad G_n(s) = \sum_{\nu \leqq n} \frac{\lambda(\nu)}{\nu^s}, \quad H(x) = G_{[x]}(1),$$

where $s=\sigma+it$ and $\lambda(\nu)$ is Liouville's function; and he pursues his investigation into the logical relation between the existence of zeros of $\zeta(s)$ and of $U_n(s)$ in portions of the half-planes $\sigma>\frac{1}{2}$ and $\sigma \geqq 1$, respectively, [Danske Vid. Selsk. Mat.-Fys. Medd. **24** (1948), no. 17; MR **10**, 286; quoted as (i)]. Denote by $R$ the Riemann hypothesis (that $\times\,\zeta(s)$ has no zeros in $\sigma>\frac{1}{2}$) and by $\{\delta_n;a_n,b_n\}$ the statement that $U_n(s)$ has no zeros in the half-strip $\sigma\geqq 1+\delta_n$, $a_n \leqq t \leqq b_n$. Let $c_1, c_2, \cdots$ denote positive numerical constants, and $c_1(\cdots), \cdots$ positive numbers depending only on the parameters shown. The main results take the forms: (I) $\{\delta_n;\gamma_n,\gamma_n+T_n\}$ (some $\gamma_n \geqq 0$; all $n>c_1$) $\Rightarrow R$; (II) $R \Rightarrow \{0;c_2,T_n'\}$ (all $n>c_1$); with explicit $\delta_n$, $T_n$, $T_n'$. The author's values are

$$\delta_n = n^{-1/2}\log^3 n,$$
$$T_n = e_1(n^3),$$
$$T_n' = e_2(c_3\sqrt{(\log n \log\log n)}),$$

where $e_1(x)=e^x$, $e_2(x)=e_1(e^x)$; but he indicates possibilities of improvement. He also states (sometimes with a sketch of proof) analogous results for other Dirichlet polynomials in place of $U_n(s)$, such as its first Cesàro mean.

As in (i), the proof of (I) is in two stages. By a combination of Kronecker's theorem on diophantine approximation and Rouché's theorem on zeros of analytic functions (after the manner of H. Bohr) a connection is first established between zeros of $U_n(s)$ and $G_n(s)$; from this and the hypothesis of (I) it is then deduced that $H(x) \geqq -x^{-1/2+\varepsilon}$ (any $\varepsilon>0$; $x>c_1(\varepsilon)$), and the conclusion that $\zeta(2s)/\{(s-1)\zeta(s)\}$ is regular for $\sigma>\frac{1}{2}+\varepsilon$ follows by an application of Landau's theorem on singularities of functions represented by Dirichlet integrals. [In (9.4) the first term on the right-hand side should have a factor $(s-1)$ in the denominator; the corresponding formula (14.1) of (i) is correct.] The main novelty in the proof is the use of a localized form of Kronecker's theorem when the linearly independent numbers occurring in it are logarithms of distinct primes; this is based on an idea of Bohr and Landau. The author notes, as in (i), that the conclusion of (I) still holds even if the hypothesis fails for an infinity of $n$'s, provided that the number of exceptional $n \leqq x$ is $o(\log x)$ as $x \to \infty$; this comes by an application of a theorem of Pólya in place of Landau's theorem.

Implications in the direction (II) are new. The proof is by two applications of contour integration. In the first, an estimate of $\log\zeta(s)$ and thus of $\zeta(s)$ is deduced from the hypothesis $R$ by the use of a formula for $\zeta'(s)/\zeta(s)$ due to Littlewood. In the second, this estimate is applied to the study of $U_n(s)$ regarded as a coefficient sum in the expansion of $\zeta(s+z)$ as a Dirichlet series in $z$.

*A. E. Ingham* (Cambridge, England)

Citations: MR 10, 286b = M30-9.
Referred to in M05-40, M30-35, M30-40.

## M30-31 (23# A126)

**Kosambi, D. D.**

**An application of stochastic convergence.**

*J. Indian Soc. Agric. Statist.* **11** (1959), 58–72.

The author claims to have proved that

$$\lim_{x\to\infty} \Big( \sum_{n \leqq x} n^{-\sigma} - \sum_{p \leqq x} p^{-\sigma}\log p\Big)$$

exists and is finite for real $\sigma>\frac{1}{2}$, a result which easily implies the Riemann hypothesis. The idea of the proof is to find a large set of series approximating to the given one (the different approximations arising from random grouping of terms, roughly speaking), and then to attach a measure to this set of approximations and show that on a set of positive measure, both the approximation and the difference between the approximation and the given series are well behaved for $\sigma>\frac{1}{2}$.

Of the two proofs given for the crucial Lemma 1.2, the reviewer does not understand the first, which seems to involve more 'hand-waving' than is customarily accepted even in proofs of theorems less significant than the present one. The second proof appears to be erroneous, in that it invokes a sieve theorem under inappropriate conditions. Specifically, the theorem used is that the number of primes $p \leqq N$ for which $p+b_1, \cdots, p+b_r$ are also prime is less than $cMN/\log^{r+1} N$, where $M$ depends on $p$, $b_1, \cdots, b_r$. [Cf. K. Prachar, *Primzahlverteilung*, Springer, Berlin, 1957; Kap. 2, Satz 4.7; MR **19**, 393]. The error lies in failing to note that although $c$ is independent of the $b$'s, it is not in general independent of $r$, while it is treated on p. 65 of the present paper as if it were.

Aside from the sieve theorem, the only properties of primes which are used are these: the prime number theorem, Mertens' estimate for $\prod_{p\leqq x}(1-p^{-1})$, Landau's estimate for $\pi_k(x)$, and Selberg's theorem that for almost all $x$ and $h>cx^{1/4}$, $\pi(x+h)-\pi(x)\sim h(\log h)^{-1}$. No properties of the $\zeta$-function are used. The probability theory invoked consists essentially of Kolmogoroff's 3-series theorem and standard 'tails' estimates for the central limit theorem.

The reviewer is unable either to accept this proof or to refute it conclusively. The author must replace verbal descriptions, qualitative comparisons and intuition by precise definitions, equations and inequalities, and rigorous reasoning, if he is to claim to have proved a theorem of the magnitude of the Riemann hypothesis.

*W. J. LeVeque* (Ann Arbor, Mich.)

Citations: MR 19, 393b = N02-7.

## M30-32 (23# A867)

**Gavrilov, N. I.**

**The foundation of the Riemann hypothesis concerning the zeros of the zeta-function.** (Russian)

*Odess. Gos. Univ. Nauč. Ežegodnik* **1961**, *no.* 2, 7–40.

An erroneous work. The author uses essentially only such properties of $\zeta(s)$ which belong also to a wide class of Dirichlet's series with the functional equation, which have infinitely many zeros inside the critical strip but not on $\sigma=\frac{1}{2}$. The principal error is on p. 35 where the increase of the argument is incorrectly evaluated.

*A. I. Vinogradov* (Moscow)

Referred to in M30-33, M30-34.

## M30-33 (28# 3015)

**Gel'fond, A. O.; Linnik, Ju. V.; Čudakov, N. G.; Jakubovič, V. A.**

**Letter to the editor: On an erroneous paper of N. I. Gavrilov.** (Russian)

*Uspehi Mat. Nauk* **17** (1962), *no.* 1 (103), 265–267.

The paper in question appeared in Odess. Gos. Univ. Naučn. Ežegodnik **1961**, no. 2, 7–40, and was reviewed earlier [MR **23** #A867]. Gavrilov has since published an extended version of the paper (see #3016 below).

Citations: MR 23# A867 = M30-32.

## M30-34 (28# 3016 )

**Gavrilov, N. I. [Гаврилов, Н. И.]**

**An asymptotic law for the distribution of prime numbers [Асимптотический закон распределения простых чисел].**

*Odess. Gosudarstv. Univ., Odessa,* 1962. 79 *pp.* 0.75 *r.*

This brochure consists of two chapters. In the first, the author expounds some elements of the theory of the Riemann zeta-function (the analytic continuation, the functional equation, the theorems of Hadamard and de la Vallée Poussin) and gives a routine proof of the prime number theorem. At the very end of this Chapter I (p. 34), the author is incorrect when saying that the Riemann hypothesis would imply the relation $\pi(x)-x\log^{-1}x=O(x^{1/2})$. In fact, it is known without any hypothesis that $\liminf_{x\to\infty}|\pi(x)-x\log^{-1}x|x^{-1}\log^2 x>0$. The second chapter contains an alleged proof of the Riemann hypothesis. Its material coincides, except for some slight developments, with the author's previous work published in 1961 [Odess. Gos. Univ. Naučn. Ežegodnik **1961**, no. 2, 7–40; MR **23** #A867]. He supposes that the Riemann hypothesis breaks down, i.e., that there exists a zero $\alpha+i\theta_0$ ($\alpha>0$, $\theta_0>0$) of the Riemann $\Xi$-function, and on this conjecture he investigates two differential equations bound up with $\Xi(s)$ and $\theta_0$. He studies their solutions and derives a number of facts which eventually lead him to a contradiction. The author's arguments are rather disorganized but it is fairly obvious that he never makes any serious use of his main assumption: $\theta_0>0$. Hence, his method cannot be correct, because otherwise it should also function (with $\theta_0=0$) in a proof that $\zeta(\sigma+it)$ does not vanish in $0<\sigma<1$, $-\infty<t<+\infty$, except at a few numerical zeros used in the computations in § 2.

*S. Knapowski* (Poznań)

Citations: MR 23# A867 = M30-32.

## M30-35 (23# A3115 )

**Turán, P.**

**A theorem on diophantine approximation with application to Riemann zeta-function.**

*Acta Sci. Math. Szeged* **21** (1960), 311–318.

In a previous paper [Acta Math. Acad. Sci. Hungar. **10** (1959), 277–298; MR **22** #6774] the author proved (among other things) a theorem of the following type: If the Dirichlet polynomial $U_n(s)=\sum_{\nu\leq n}\nu^{-s}$ $(s=\sigma+it)$ has no zeros in the half-strip $\sigma\geqq 1+\delta_n$, $\gamma_n\leqq t\leqq\gamma_n+T_n$ for some real $\gamma_n$ and all $n>n_0$, then the Riemann hypothesis, that $\zeta(s)$ has no zeros in the half-plane $\sigma>\frac{1}{2}$, is true; and the conclusion remains valid even if the hypothesis on $U_n(s)$ fails for an infinity of $n$, provided that the number of exceptional $n\leqq x$ is $o(\log x)$ as $x\to\infty$. The author proved this with $\delta_n=n^{-1/2}\log^3 n$, $T_n=\exp(n^3)$; he now reduces the value of $T_n$ to $\exp(n^{3/2})$, and suggests that a further reduction to $\exp(cn)$ ($c$ a positive numerical constant) might be possible. The improvement is achieved by a further development of the localized form of Kronecker's theorem for logarithms of primes that formed the basis of the author's earlier work.

*A. E. Ingham* (Bombay)

Citations: MR 22# 6774 = M30-30.

## M30-36 (24# A3139 )

**Klambauer, Gabriel**

**A note on Nyman's function system.**

*Proc. Amer. Math. Soc.* **13** (1962), 312–314.

B. Nyman [Thesis, Univ. of Uppsala, 1950; MR **12**, 108] has proved that the Riemann hypothesis is true if and only if the set $\{[\alpha/x]-\alpha[1/x]\}$ $(0<\alpha\leqq 1)$ is fundamental in $L^2(0,1)$. In the present paper the writer shows that if $P(x)$ is a polynomial with real coefficients such that $\int_0^1 P(x)f_\alpha(x)dx=0$ for all $0<\alpha\leqq 1$, then $P(x)\equiv 0$.

*L. Carlitz* (Durham, N.C.)

## M30-37 (29# 5799 )

**Grosswald, E.**

**Considerations concerning the complex roots of Riemann's zeta-function.**

*Publ. Math. Debrecen* **10** (1963), 157–170.

The results are too elaborate to quote in detail, but the general idea is to connect the upper bound $\theta$ of the real parts of the zeros of $\zeta(s)$ with the behaviour of functions such as

$$F(x)=\sum_{n=1}^{\infty}\frac{(-x)^n}{\zeta(2n)\varphi(n)},\qquad \Psi(u)=\sum_{n=3}^{\infty}\frac{u^{n-2}}{\zeta(\frac{1}{2}n)\varphi(\frac{1}{2}n)}.$$

M. Riesz proved that, when $\varphi(s)=\Gamma(s)$, a necessary and sufficient condition for the Riemann hypothesis $(\theta=\frac{1}{2})$ is that $F(x)=O(x^\alpha)$ as $x\to\infty$, for every fixed $\alpha>\frac{1}{4}$. Theorem 1 extends results of this type to general classes $\Phi$ and $\Phi_1$ of functions $\varphi(s)$: and Theorem 2 transforms the results into a different shape. Theorem 4 asserts that, if, for some $\varphi$ in $\Phi$, the integral function $\Psi(u)$ is of order $<\frac{1}{2}$ (or of order $\frac{1}{2}$ and minimal type), then $\theta=1$. Another type of result gives analogues, for various arithmetical functions $R_i(x)$, of the theorem that $R(x)=\psi(x)-x$ is $O(x^\alpha)$ if $\alpha>\theta$ but not if $\alpha<\theta$. (This seems to be the intention of Theorem 3 and the succeeding remarks, though the italicized statement of the theorem appears to be nothing more than a list of definitions.) [The basic assumptions about $\varphi(s)$ are stated in a form that does not seem to accord with what is assumed in proofs. Thus, on p. 158, the hypothesis (I) is stated only for fixed $\sigma$ and varying $t$, and (II) for fixed $t$ and varying $\sigma$; but any normal application of Cauchy's theorem, such as the one on p. 162, presumes uniform estimates of the integrand. There are other inaccuracies of presentation.]

*A. E. Ingham* (Cambridge, England)

## M30-38 (30# 1989 )

**Wilf, Herbert S.**

**On the zeros of Riesz' function in the analytic theory of numbers.**

*Illinois J. Math.* **8** (1964), 639–641.

Write

$$F(z)=\sum_{n=1}^{\infty}\frac{(-1)^{n+1}z^n}{(n-1)!\zeta(2n)}.$$

This is an entire function. M. Riesz [Acta Math. **40** (1915/16), 185–190] showed that a necessary and sufficient condition for the validity of the Riemann hypothesis is that, for each $\varepsilon>0$, $F(x)=O(x^{1/4+\varepsilon})$. Let $\{r_n e^{i\theta_n}\}$ denote some arrangement of the set of zeros of $F(z)$; let $x_1, x_2, \cdots$ denote the positive real zeros of $F(z)$, and let $h(r,\delta)$ denote the number of zeros in the sector

$$|z| \leqq r, \quad |\arg z| \leqq \tfrac{1}{2}\pi - \delta \qquad (\delta > 0).$$

The author proves that

$$(1) \qquad r_n \sim n\pi,$$

$$(2) \qquad h(r, \delta) = o(r),$$

$$(3) \qquad \sum_{n=1}^{\infty} x_n^{-1} < \infty,$$

$$(4) \qquad \sum_{\substack{n \\ x_n < x}} 1 = \Omega(\log x),$$

where $\Omega$ is used in the sense of Hardy and Littlewood.

*S. Chowla* (University Park, Pa.)

Referred to in M30-50.

## M30-39 (31# 133)

**Denjoy, Arnaud**

**Probabilités confirmant l'hypothèse de Riemann sur les zéros de $\zeta(s)$.**

*C. R. Acad. Sci. Paris* **259** (1964), 3143–3145.

Let $\zeta(s)$ be the Riemann $\zeta$-function. Then for Re $s > 1$,

$$\zeta(2s)/\zeta(s) = \sum_{n=1}^{\infty} \mu(n)n^{-s},$$

where $\mu(n)$ is the Liouville function defined as follows: $\mu(n) = 1$ or $-1$ according as the representation of $n$ as a product of primes contains an even or odd number of prime factors, counting multiplicities. The density of those positive integers $n$ for which $\mu(n)$ has a given sign is $\frac{1}{2}$. The Riemann hypothesis is equivalent to the assertion that $\zeta(2s)/\zeta(s)$ is regular for Re $s > \frac{1}{2}$. Instead of the function $\zeta(2s)/\zeta(s)$, the author considers the function $g(s) = \sum_{n=1}^{\infty} \nu(n)n^{-s}$, where $\nu(n)$ $(n = 1, 2, \cdots)$ are independent random variables which take the values 1 and $-1$ with the probabilities $\frac{1}{2}$. By simple arguments he proves that the function $g(s)$ is regular in the half-plane Re $s > \frac{1}{2}$ with probability 1. *J. Kubilius* (Vilnius)

## M30-40 (31# 1229)

**Apostol, Tom M.**

**Sets of values taken by Dirichlet's $L$-series.**

*Proc. Sympos. Pure Math., Vol. VIII, pp.* 133–137. *Amer. Math. Soc., Providence, R.I.*, 1965.

The author remarks that H. Bohr's well-known theorem on the values taken by an absolute convergent Dirichlet series [Math. Ann. **79** (1919), 136–156] can be used to show the following: if $\sigma_1 \geqq 1$, $k > 1$, and $\chi_1, \cdots, \chi_{\varphi(k)}$ are the characters mod $k$, then the set of values taken by $L(s, \chi_i)$ in the open half-plane Re $s > \sigma_1$ does not depend on $i$.

The same idea is used in order to show that a sufficient condition for the Riemann hypothesis for the zeta-function is that, for some $\chi$, the partial sums of $L(s, \chi)$ have no zeros in certain half-planes. By Bohr's theorem this is equivalent to the same statement for the principal character, and for that case it is implied in P. Turán's work [Acta Math. Acad. Sci. Hungar. **10** (1959), 277–298; MR **22** #6774; errata, MR **22**, p. 2546]. {There is a minor error in the proof of Theorem 2, where the author applies Bohr's theorem to closed half-planes instead of open ones.}

*N. G. de Bruijn* (Eindhoven)

Citations: MR 22# 6774 = M30-30.

## M30-41 (31# 1232)

**Spira, Robert**

**An inequality for the Riemann zeta function.**

*Duke Math. J.* **32** (1965), 247–250.

Let $g(s)$ be the function involved with the functional equation of $\zeta(s)$: $\zeta(1-s) = g(s)\zeta(s)$. The author shows that $|g(s)| > 1$ for $t \geqq 10$, $\frac{1}{2} < \sigma < 1$. As an immediate corollary he obtains the following: The Riemann hypothesis is true if and only if $|\zeta(1-s)| > |\zeta(s)|$ in $\frac{1}{2} < \sigma < 1$, $t \geqq 10$.

*S. Knapowski* (Gainesville, Fla.)

Referred to in M15-36, M30-42.

## M30-42 (32# 96)

**Spira, Robert**

**Erratum: An inequality for the Riemann zeta function.**

*Duke Math. J.* **32** (1965), 765.

The original article, in which a misprint is corrected, appeared in same J. **32** (1965), 247–250 [MR **31** #1232].

Citations: MR 31# 1232 = M30-41.

## M30-43 (31# 2215)

**Staś, W.**

**Some remarks on a series of Ramanujan.**

*Acta Arith.* **10** (1964/65), 359–368.

Consider the series of Ramanujan

$$S(\beta) = \sum_{n=1}^{\infty} \frac{\mu(n)}{n} e^{-\beta^2/n^2},$$

where $\beta$ is real and $\mu$ is the Möbius function. Hardy and Littlewood proved that $S(\beta) = O(\beta^{-1/2})$, $\beta \to \infty$, is equivalent to the Riemann hypothesis. The author proves the following theorem. Suppose Riemann's conjecture; then for $T > C$,

$$\max_{T^{1-o(1)} \leqq \beta \leqq T} |S(\beta)| \geqq T^{-1/2-o(1)}.$$

This is sharper than his previous result [same Acta **8** (1962/63), 261–271; MR **27** #5737]. The proof uses the method of Turán, recently used with great success by Knapowski and Turán [see, e.g., ibid. **10** (1964), 293–313; MR **30** #4739] and the author [e.g., ibid. **7** (1961/62), 409–416; MR **27** #3607].

*S. Chowla* (University Park, Pa.)

Citations: MR 27# 3607 = N44-25; MR 27# 5737 = N44-28; MR 30# 4739 = N12-33.

Referred to in M30-46.

## M30-44 (32# 4252)

**Grosswald, E.**

**Generalization of a formula of Hayman and its application to the study of Riemann's zeta function.**

*Illinois J. Math.* **10** (1966), 9–23.

Suppose that $f(z) = \sum_0^{\infty} a_n z^n$ is regular in $|z| < R$, where $0 < R \leqq \infty$, and that $f(z)$ is real on the real axis and $f(x) \to +\infty$, as $x \to R^-$. Set $a_\nu(x) = (x\,d/dx)^\nu \log f(x)$ and let $r = r(n)$ be defined by the equation $a_1(r) = n$. Then the author obtains, under suitable hypotheses, the asymptotic series

$$(1) \quad a_n = f(r)r^{-n}[2\pi a_2(r)]^{-1/2} \times \{1 + \pi^{-1/2} \sum_{\nu=2}^{3m} (2a_2^{-1}(r))^\nu \Gamma(\nu + \tfrac{1}{2}) A_{2\nu}(r) + O[\phi_m(r, \delta, n)]\}$$

as $n \to \infty$ for any fixed $m$, where $A_{2\nu}(r)$ is a polynomial in $a_1(r), \cdots, a_{2\nu}(r)$ and $\phi_m(r, \delta, n)$ is a smaller error term. The case $m = 0$ is due to the reviewer [J. Reine Angew. Math. **196** (1956), 67–95; MR **18**, 293]. In the case of the exponential function, for instance, this leads to the (known) formula

$$\frac{1}{n!} = \left(\frac{e}{n}\right)^n (2\pi n)^{-1/2} \left\{1 + \sum_{j=1}^{m-1} \frac{C_j}{n^j} + O(n^{-m})\right\},$$

where the $C_j$ are constants.

In the second part the author applies his series to

Riemann's function $\Xi(t)=\sum_{m=0}^{\infty}(-1)^m\alpha_m t^{2m}$. If one writes $f(z)=\sum_0^{\infty}\alpha_n z^n$, the Riemann hypothesis is equivalent to the statement that all the zeros of $f(z)$ are real and negative. This would imply, in particular, that

$$(2) \qquad D_n = n\alpha_n^2-(n+1)\alpha_{n-1}\alpha_{n+1} > 0$$

for all $n$. The question of whether (2) holds has been raised by Pólya [Mat.-Fys. Medd. Danske Vid. Selsk. **7** (1927), 1–33]. By means of (1), the author proves that

$$\alpha_n = r^{-n}[2\pi a_2(r)]^{-1/2}f(r)\left[1-\frac{24}{n}+O(n\log n)^{-1}\right],$$

which yields (2) for all sufficiently large $n$.

*W. K. Hayman* (London)

Referred to in M30-48.

## M30-45 (33# 7312 )

**Spira, Robert**

**Approximate functional approximations and the Riemann hypothesis.**

*Proc. Amer. Math. Soc.* **17** (1966), 314–317.

Starting from Siegel's formula for Riemann's zeta-function $\zeta$, given by $\zeta(s)=g_m(s)+e^{i\pi s}\Gamma(1-s)(2\pi i)^{-1}\times\int_C w^{s-1}e^{-mw}(e_w-1)^{-1}\,dw$, where $g_m(s)=\sum_{n=1}^{m}n^{-s}+\chi(s)\sum_{n=1}^{m}n^{s-1}$, the author considers the zeros of $g_m(s)$ on the critical line. He shows that for $m=1$ and 2, and for large $t$, $g_m(s)$ has all its non-real zeros on the line $\sigma=\frac{1}{2}$, where $\sigma=\operatorname{Re}s$. For $m\geqq 3$, the author is collecting computational data in support of a conjecture, which he promises to report later on. *K. Chandrasekharan* (Zürich)

Referred to in M25-72.

## M30-46 (34# 4214 )

**Kátai, I.**

**An estimate of type $\Omega$ for the Ramanujan function. (Russian)**

*Ann. Univ. Sci. Budapest. Eötvös Sect. Math.* **9** (1966), 95–102.

Write $S(\beta)=\sum_{n=1}^{\infty}(\mu(n)/n)e^{-(\beta/n)^2}$, where $\beta>0$. The author shows that under the Riemann hypothesis there exist positive numerical $\delta$, $c_1$, $c_2$ such that for $T>c_1$, one has $\max_{T\leq\beta\leq T_1}\beta^{1/2}S(\beta)>\delta$, $\min_{T\leq\beta\leq T_1}\beta^{1/2}S(\beta)<-\delta$, where $T_1=T\exp\{c_2(\log\log T\cdot\log\log\log T/\log T)^{1/2}\}$. This localization improves on a previous result of W. Staś [Acta Arith. **10** (1964/65), 359–368; MR **31** #2215].

*S. Knapowski* (Coral Gables, Fla.)

Citations: MR 31# 2215 = M30-43.
Referred to in N44-39.

## M30-47 (36# 119 )

**Kosambi, D. D.**

**Statistical methods in number theory.**

*J. Indian Soc. Agric. Statist.* **16** (1964), 126–135.

The late author tried in the last 10 years of his life to prove the Riemann hypothesis by probabilistic methods. Though he did not succeed in this, he has formulated the following highly interesting conjecture on prime numbers. Put $\operatorname{li}(x,a)=\int_a^x(1/\log t)\,dt$ for $x\geqq a$, $2\leqq a<3$. Let $p_1<p_2<\cdots<p_n<\cdots$ denote the sequence of odd primes and consider the numbers $q_n(a)=\operatorname{li}(p_n,a)$ $(n=1,2,\cdots)$. Clearly $q_n(a)\sim n$ by the prime number theorem. Let $\pi_n(u,a)$ $(n=1,2,\cdots)$ denote the number of points $q_r(a)$ $(r=1,2,\cdots)$ lying in the interval $[(n-1)u,nu)$, where $u>0$. Let $V_k(N,u,a)$ denote the number of those values of $n\leqq N$ for which $\pi_n(u)=k$. The author's conjecture states that one can choose the values of $a$ and $u$ in such a way that $\lim_{N\to\infty}V_k(N,u,a)/N=u^k e^{-u}/k!$ $(k=0,1,\cdots)$. In other words, his conjecture states that the points $q_n(a)$ are distributed as the points in a typical realization of a homogeneous Poisson process with density 1.

Neither in this paper nor in his previous paper [Proc. Nat. Acad. Sci. U.S.A. **49** (1963), 20–23; MR **26** #3690] did the author succeed in proving his hypothesis, nor in deducing from it the Riemann hypothesis.

The reviewer thinks that at the present moment one does not have enough knowledge of the fine structure of the distribution of primes to prove or disprove the author's conjecture. The problem seems to be even more difficult than the problem of the validity of the Riemann hypothesis. As a matter of fact, no obvious method exists to prove the author's hypothesis even under the assumption of the Riemann hypothesis. Nevertheless, the conjecture is worthy of study in its own right, and the reviewer proposes to call it "the Kosambi hypothesis" in commemoration of the enthusiastic efforts of the late author.

*A. Rényi* (Budapest)

Citations: MR 26# 3690 = N08-34.

## M30-48 (36# 1399 )

**Alter, Ronald**

**On a necessary condition for the validity of the Riemann hypothesis for functions that generalize the Riemann zeta function.**

*Trans. Amer. Math. Soc.* **130** (1968), 55–74.

For many functions representable in a half-plane by Dirichlet series, one can formulate conjectures concerning their zeros that parallel Riemann's conjecture for the $\zeta$-function. By simple changes of variables, this conjecture (and its extensions) can be formulated as a statement that all zeros of a certain entire function are real. Necessary and sufficient conditions for this to be the case are known [J. Grommer, J. Reine Angew. Math. **144** (1914), 114–165], but no way has been devised yet to verify whether these (infinitely many) conditions hold or not, even in the case of the Riemann zeta function. Using W. K. Hayman's generalization of the Stirling formula [ibid. **196** (1956), 67–95; MR **18**, 293] in the reviewer's version [Illinois J. Math. **10** (1966), 9–23; MR **32** #4252], it is possible to verify that the first of these conditions holds. This has been done by the reviewer for the Riemann zeta function [loc. cit.] and is done in the present paper for several generalizations of $\zeta(s)$ ($L$-functions of real, primitive characters, Ramanujan's function $\sum_{n=1}^{\infty}\tau(n)n^{-s}$ and Dedekind's zeta function $\sum_{\mathfrak{a}\subset K}(N\mathfrak{a})^{-s}$, $K$ an algebraic number field). The Epstein zeta function is exhibited as an example that the first condition of Grommer, while necessary, is not sufficient, and some examples are given to show that the condition itself is not trivially satisfied by all functions of the class to which the Hayman theorem (in the present version) is applicable. The method used is that of the cited papers of Hayman and the reviewer; some of the proofs are only sketched and others are difficult to follow in detail (some misprints do not help either). Also, some correct statements are formulated in a rather startling fashion and require careful interpretation (e.g., on p. 56, lines 8–9(b): "For a proof that the Riemann hypothesis is false see [3], . . ."). {Remark: The printed proof of the reviewer's theorem is incomplete; the needed correction has been submitted to the Illinois J. Math.; the results needed for the present paper follow also from a paper by Harris and Schoenfeld, to appear shortly ibid.}

*E. Grosswald* (Philadelphia, Pa.)

Citations: MR 32# 4252 = M30-44.

## M30-49 (38# 128 )

**Kátai, Imre**

**On the Möbius $\mu$-function. (Hungarian)**

*Magyar Tud. Akad. Mat. Fiz. Oszt. Közl.* **15** (1965), 9–13.

Let $\mu(n)$ be the Möbius function; the series $S(\beta)=\sum_{n=1}^{\infty} n^{-1}\mu(n)l^{-(\beta/n)^2}$ is the so-called Ramanujan sum. The author gives a localized $\Omega_{\pm}$-estimate for the function $S(\beta)$ and, under the assumption that the Riemann hypothesis holds, shows that, for suitable $\delta$ and positive constants $c_1$ and $c_2$, the inequalities $\max_{M_1\leqq\beta\leqq N_1}\beta^{1/2}S(\beta)\geqq\delta$, $\min_{M_1\leqq\beta\leqq N_1}\beta^{1/2}S(\beta)\leqq-\delta$ hold in all intervals of the type $M_1>c_1$ and $N_1=\exp((\log M_1)^{c_2\log_3 M_1})$. Hitherto only an $\Omega$-estimate on the assumption that the Riemann hypothesis holds has been known in the literature. The above problem is of interest since the relation $S(\beta)=O(\beta^{1/2+\varepsilon})$ is equivalent to the Riemann hypothesis.

*K. Korradi* [*K. Corrádi*] (RŽMat **1966** #1 A109)

Referred to in N44-39.

## M30-50 (38# 1061)

**Grosswald, E.**
**On some properties of the Riesz function.**
*Rev. Roumaine Math. Pures Appl.* **12** (1967), 1263–1270.

The function $F(z)$ in question is an entire function of order 1, type 1, which has the power series representation $F(z)=\sum_{n=1}^{\infty}(-1)^n z^n\Gamma(n)^{-1}/\zeta(2n)$. M. Riesz [Acta Math. **40** (1915/16), 185–190] proved that the Riemann hypothesis is true if and only if $F(x)=O(x^{1/4+\varepsilon})$ for every $\varepsilon>0$ as $x\to+\infty$ through positive values. H. S. Wilf [Illinois J. Math. **8** (1964), 639–641; MR **30** #1989] has shown that $F(z)$ has infinitely many real zeros. In this paper the author studies further properties of the zeros of $F(z)$ and represents $F$ by an infinite series extended over the nontrivial zeros of the Riemann zeta function.

*T. M. Apostol* (Pasadena, Calif.)

Citations: MR 30# 1989 = M30-38.

## M30-51 (39# 1416)

**Good, I. J.; Churchhouse, R. F.**
**The Riemann hypothesis and pseudorandom features of the Möbius sequence.**
*Math. Comp.* **22** (1968), 857–861.

One aim of this note is to suggest a "reason" for believing Riemann's hypothesis, namely, that the "complex zeros" all occur where $R(s)=\frac{1}{2}$. This is in contrast to a remark of Littlewood in 1962: "In the spirit of this anthology of partly baked ideas I should also record my feeling that there is no imaginable reason why the Riemann hypothesis should be true."

The Möbius function is defined by $\mu(n)=(-)^k$ if the positive integer $n$ is the product of $k$ different primes, $\mu(1)=1$, and $\mu(n)=0$ if $n$ has any repeated factor. The authors compute a multitude of values to strengthen the following new conjectures: (A) The sums of $\mu(n)$ in blocks of length $N$, where $N$ is large, have asymptotically a normal distribution with mean zero and variance $6N/\pi^2$. (B) lim sup$[M(x)(x\log\log x)^{-1/2}]=\sqrt{(12)}/\pi$. (C) For large $N$, the standard deviation of $\nu_0$ is $O(\sqrt{N})$. (D) The variance of $\nu_0$ for large $N$ is a constant.

*E. Karst* (Tucson, Ariz.)

## M30-52 (42# 1777)

**Гаврилов, Н. И. [Gavrilov, N. I.] [Gavrilov, M. Ī.]**
**Проблема Римана о распределении корней дзета-функции. (Russian) [The Riemann problem on the distribution of the roots of the zeta function]**
*Izdat. L'vov. Univ., Lvov*, 1970. 172 *pp.* 0.90 *r.*

The book consists of a preface and five chapters: (1) General analytic properties of the Riemann $\zeta$-function; (2) The asymptotic prime number law; (3) On the zeros of the $\zeta$-function on the line $\sigma=\frac{1}{2}$; (4) Proof of the Riemann hypothesis on the zeros of the $\zeta$-function; (5) On the absence of real roots of Dirichlet's $L$-functions in the critical strip. The first three chapters contain standard material taken from the well known book of E. C. Titchmarsh [*The theory of the Riemann zeta-function*, Clarendon, Oxford, 1951; MR **13**, 741; Russian translation, Izdat. Inostran. Lit., Moscow, 1953].

In the fourth chapter the author attempts to prove the Riemann hypothesis by studying a differential equation involving the $\zeta$-function in a formal way. His arguments are, however, completely invalidated by the errors on pp. 145–148 in computing the increase of an argument. Moreover, there is an error on p. 130. A counter-example can be constructed showing that the author's arguments can give no information on the zeros of the $\zeta$-function. Chapter 5 is invalidated by the same errors.

*Ju. V. Linnik* (Leningrad)

Citations: MR 13, 741c = M02-2.

## M30-53 (42# 7608)

**Saffari, Bahman**
**Sur l'hypothèse de Riemann et sur certains problèmes de diviseurs.**
*C. R. Acad. Sci. Paris Sér. A-B* **272** (1971), A197–A198.

Author's summary: "Équivalence de l'hypothèse de Riemann à la véracité en moyenne quadratique de 'l'hypothèse de Hardy-Landau' pour le problème des diviseurs de Mertens."

# M35 HURWITZ AND LERCH ZETA-FUNCTIONS

See also reviews E44-40, K20-8, M05-14, M05-23, M05-26, M10-5, M10-14, M15-38, M40-9, M40-20, M40-43, Q99-3.

## M35-1 (13, 220f)

**Fine, N. J. Note on the Hurwitz zeta-function.** Proc. Amer. Math. Soc. **2**, 361–364 (1951).

The Hurwitz zeta-function is defined for $\Re(s)>1$ and $0<a<1$ by $\zeta(s,a)=\sum_{n=0}^{\infty}(n+a)^{-s}$. Its continuation to the entire $s$-plane with the exception of a simple pole at $s=1$, and its functional equation are here obtained by using the transformation equation for the theta-function $\vartheta(\pi a, ix)$.

*W. H. Simons* (Vancouver, B. C.).

## M35-2 (13, 328a)

**Apostol, T. M. Remark on the Hurwitz zeta function.** Proc. Amer. Math. Soc. **2**, 690–693 (1951).

The author uses the functional equation for the function $\phi(x,a,s)=\sum_{n=0}^{\infty}e^{2\pi nix}(a+n)^{-s}$ [Lerch, Acta Math. **11**, 19–24 (1887)] in order to prove the formula

$$\zeta(1-s,a)=2\Gamma(s)(2\pi)^{-s}\sum_{1}^{\infty}n^{-s}\cos\left(\tfrac{1}{2}\pi s-2\pi an\right)\qquad(0<a\leqq1,\ \Re s>1)$$

[see Whittaker and Watson, A course of modern analysis . . . , Macmillan, New York, 1943, p. 269]. Here $\zeta(s,a)$ represents the Hurwitz zeta function, defined by $\zeta(s,a)=\sum_{0}^{\infty}(a+n)^{-s}$ $(0<a\leqq1, \Re s>1)$.

*N. G. de Bruijn* (Delft).

## M35-3 (13, 328b)

**Apostol, T. M. On the Lerch zeta function.** Pacific J. Math. **1**, 161–167 (1951).

The author gives a new proof of Lerch's functional equation [see Acta Math. **11**, 19–24 (1887)] for the function

$\phi(x, a, s)$, defined by analytic continuation of the series $\sum_0^\infty e^{2\pi nix}(a+n)^{-s}$. His proof depends on the use of the transformation formula for $\vartheta_3(y|\tau)$ and of the differential-difference equations satisfied by $\phi$. The values of $\phi$ for $s=0, -1, -2, \cdots$ are studied in detail. If

$$\beta_n(a, \alpha) = -n\phi(x, a, 1-n) \quad (\alpha=e^{2\pi ix}; n=1, 2, \cdots),$$

then $(\alpha-1)^n\beta_n(a, \alpha)$ turns out to be a polynomial in $a$ and $\alpha$. A number of properties of $\beta_n(a, \alpha)$ are derived, most of which are generalizations of properties of the Bernoulli numbers $B_n(\alpha)=\beta_n(0, \alpha)$. *N. G. de Bruijn* (Delft).

Referred to in M35-4.

## M35-4 (13, 725b)

**Apostol, T. M. Addendum to 'On the Lerch zeta function.'** Pacific J. Math. **2**, 10 (1952).

This note refers to a paper in Pacific J. Math. **1**, 161–167 (1951) [these Rev. **13**, 328]. Additional references are given, and a misprint is corrected. *N. G. de Bruijn* (Delft).

Citations: MR 13, 328b = M35-3.

## M35-5 (13, 781b)

**Powell, E. O. A table of the generalized Riemann zeta function in a particular case.** Quart. J. Mech. Appl. Math. **5**, 116–123 (1952).

The Hurwitz zeta function, defined by

$$\zeta(s, a) = \sum_{n=0}^{\infty} (n+a)^{-s}$$

when $\Re(s)>1$ and $\Re(a)>0$, occurs in various connections; for $\Re(a)>0$, the function, aside from a simple pole at $s=1$, has an analytic continuation over the whole $s$-plane. It reduces to the Riemann zeta function when $a=1$, and $\zeta(2, a)=\{\Gamma'(a)/\Gamma(a)\}'$; furthermore, it occurs in number theory because of its relation to the Dirichlet $L$-function: $\sum_{n=1}^\infty \chi(n)n^{-s}=k^{-s}\sum_{r=1}^k \chi(r)\zeta(s, r/k)$ where $\chi$ is a character modulo $k$. The author's interest in the function $\zeta(\frac{1}{2}, a)$ stems from the fact that it is a solution of the difference equation $f(a+1)-f(a)+a^{1/2}=0$. The author provides a 10-decimal place table of $\zeta(\frac{1}{2}, a)$ for $a=1.00(.01)2.00(.02)5.00(.05)10.00$ together with modified second central differences; he also makes reference to unpublished 5-decimal tables of $\zeta(s, a)$ for $s=-10.0(.1).0$, $a=.0(.1)2.0$ and of $(s-1)\zeta(s, a)$ for $s=.0(.1)1.0$, $a=.0(.1)2.0$. *L. Schoenfeld* (Urbana, Ill.).

## M35-6 (15, 402d)

**Koksma, J. F., and Lekkerkerker, C. G. A mean-value theorem for $\zeta(s, w)$.** Nederl. Akad. Wetensch. Proc. Ser. A. **55** = Indagationes Math. **14**, 446–452 (1952).

For $\Re(s)>1$ and $0\leqq w\leqq 1$ let

$$\zeta^*(s, w) = \sum_{n=1}^{\infty} (n+w)^{-s} = \zeta(s, w) - w^{-s}$$

and let the function be defined for other values of $s$ by analytic continuation. The authors give a straightforward proof of the following results for the mean value, taken with respect to $w$,

$$f(s) = \int_0^1 |\zeta^*(s, w)|^2 dw.$$

If $|t|\geqq 3$ then $f(\frac{1}{2}+it)<64 \log |t|$. Their second result may be phrased as follows: if $|t|\geqq 3$ and $\frac{1}{2}<\sigma\leqq 1$ then

$$|f(\sigma+it)-(2\sigma-1)^{-1}| \leqq |t|^{1-2\sigma}(32 \log |t| + (2\sigma-1)^{-1});$$

hence, if $\frac{1}{2}+(2A \log |t|)^{-1}\leqq\sigma\leqq 1$ and $A\geqq 32$, then the right side may be replaced by $2A|t|^{1-2\sigma} \log |t|$. The proof is carried out with the aid of a weak form of the approximate functional equation for $\zeta^*(s, w)$; for a stronger form of such an equation, see Čudakov [Ann. of Math. (2) **48**, 515–545 (1947); these Rev. **9**, 11]. *L. Schoenfeld* (Urbana, Ill.).

Citations: MR 9, 11d = P32-10.

## M35-7 (16, 798d)

**Parodi, Maurice. Fonction $\zeta$ de Riemann et nombres de Bernoulli.** C. R. Acad. Sci. Paris **240**, 1395–1396 (1955).

The following formula is obtained:

$$\zeta(2, s+1) = \sum_{k=1}^{\infty} \frac{1}{k} \frac{(k-1)!}{(s+1)\cdots(s+k)} \quad (s>0).$$

[cf. K. Knopp, Theorie und Anwendungen der unendlichen Reihen, 3rd ed., Springer, Berlin, 1931, p. 274].
*L. Carlitz* (Durham, N. C.).

## M35-8 (17, 1188c)

**Oberhettinger, F. Note on the Lerch zeta function.** Pacific J. Math. **6** (1956), 117–120.

The author gives a new proof of the functional equation for the Lerch zeta function $\Phi(z, s, v)$ defined by analytic continuation of the series $\sum_{m=0}^\infty z^m(v+m)^{-s}$. This is done by a simple and direct application of Poisson's summation formula. The convergence difficulties which arise in applying Poisson's formula to the special cases of the Riemann zeta function $\zeta(s)=\Phi(1, s, 1)$ and the Hurwitz zeta $\zeta(s, v)=\Phi(1, s, v)$ do not arise in this more general situation.

By using an appropriate integral representation for $\Phi(z, s, v)$ the author also shows how to derive Hurwitz's formula

$$\zeta(s, v)=2(2\pi)^{s-1}\Gamma(1-s) \sum_{n=1}^{\infty} n^{s-1} \sin(2\pi nv+\pi s/2)$$

as a limiting case of the functional equation for $\Phi$.
*T. M. Apostol* (Pasadena, Calif.).

## M35-9 (19, 731e)

**Mikolás, Miklós. Mellinsche Transformation und Orthogonalität bei $\zeta(s, u)$. Verallgemeinerung der Riemannschen Funktionalgleichung von $\zeta(s)$.** Acta Sci. Math. Szeged **17** (1956), 143–164.

Hurwitz's function $\zeta(s, u)=\sum_{n=0}^\infty (u+n)^{-s}$ ($\Re(s)>1$, $u>0$) can be continued into the whole $s$-plane as a meromorphic function with one simple pole at $s=1$. Put $\zeta(s, u)=\zeta(s, v)$, where $v\equiv u \pmod 1$, $0<v\leqq 1$. The Mellin transform

$$\mathfrak{M}(s, z)=\int_0^\infty u^{z-1}\zeta(s, u)du, \quad \max(0, \Re(s))<\Re(z)<1,$$

is proved to satisfy the relation

$$\mathfrak{M}(1-s, z)=\mathfrak{M}(1-z, s)=$$
$$=2(2\pi)^{-s-z}\Gamma(s)\Gamma(z) \cos\frac{\pi(s-z)}{2} \zeta(s+z),$$

which for $\Re(s)\geqq 1$, $z\to+0$, becomes the functional equation of the Riemann $\zeta$-function. In the opposite direction,

$$\zeta(1-s, u)-u^{s-1}=$$
$$\frac{1}{2\pi i}\int_{\alpha-\infty i}^{\alpha+\infty i} u^{-z}\cdot 2(2\pi)^{-s-z}\Gamma(s)\Gamma(z) \cos\frac{\pi(s-z)}{2} \zeta(s+z)dz$$

if $0<u<1$, $0<\Re(s)<1$, $0<\alpha<\max(\Re(s), 1-\Re(s))$. The author proves further integral formulae; e.g.,

$$\int_0^1 \zeta(s, u)\zeta(z, u)du=$$
$$(2\pi)^{s+z-2}\Gamma(1-s)\Gamma(1-z) \cos\frac{\pi(s-z)}{2} \zeta(2-s-z)$$

if $\max(0, \Re(s))+\max(0, \Re(z))<1$,

$$\int_0^1 |\zeta(s, u)|^2 du=2(2\pi)^{2(\sigma-1)} \cosh \pi\tau\cdot|\Gamma(1-s)|^2\zeta(2-2\sigma) \quad (s=\sigma+\tau i,\ \sigma<\tfrac{1}{2});$$

and he announces more general identities which appear in the paper reviewed below. *K. Mahler* (Manchester).

## M35-10 (19, 731f)

**Mikolás, Miklós. Integral formulae of arithmetical characteristics relating to the zeta-function of Hurwitz.** Publ. Math. Debrecen **5** (1957), 44–53.

The Hurwitz zeta function satisfies the formula

$$\zeta(1-s, x)=\frac{2\Gamma(s)}{(2\pi)^s}\left(\cos\frac{\pi s}{2}\sum_{m=1}^{\infty}\frac{\cos 2\pi mx}{m^s}+\sin\frac{\pi s}{2}\sum_{m=1}^{\infty}\frac{\sin 2\pi mx}{m^s}\right)$$

if $s=\sigma+i\tau$, $\sigma>0$, $0<x<1$. The author shows that $\zeta(1-s, x)\in L^2(0, 1)$ if $\sigma>\frac{1}{2}$. Considering the above as a Fourier expansion, he uses the Parseval formula to derive the identity

$$\int_0^1 \zeta(1-s, \{au\})\zeta(1-s, \{bu\})du=2\Gamma(s)^2\frac{\zeta(2s)}{(2\pi)^{2s}}\frac{(a, b)^2}{[a, b]^2},$$

where $a$, $b$ are positive integers, $(a, b)$ their g.c.d., $[a, b]$ their l.c.m., and $\{x\}=x-[x]$ is the fractional part of $x$. A similar formula is derived with the factor $\zeta(1-s, \{bu\})$ replaced by its complex conjugate. The hypothesis $\sigma>\frac{1}{2}$ is essential because the integrals do not exist when $\sigma\leqq\frac{1}{2}$.
*T. M. Apostol* (Pasadena, Calif.).

Referred to in Q99-2.

## M35-11 (19, 1162a)

**Schoenfeld, Lowell. The order of the zeta function near the line $\sigma=1$.** Duke Math. J. **24** (1957), 601–609.

Let $\zeta(s, w)$ stand for the Hurwitz zeta-function, and denote by $\mu(\sigma, w)$ the order of $\zeta(s, w)$, i.e., the greatest lower bound of the numbers $\mu_1$, such that $|\zeta(s, w)|\leqq\beta t^{\mu_1}$, where $\beta=\beta(\sigma)$. The following estimates [van der Corput and Koksma, Ann. Fac. Sci. Univ. Toulouse (3) **22** (1930), 1–39] are classical: If $Q=2^q$ and $\sigma=1-q/(Q-2)$, then, for integral $q\geqq3$, $\mu(\sigma, w)\leqq1/(Q-2)$; for $\frac{1}{2}\leqq\sigma\leqq1$,

$$(*)\qquad \mu(\sigma, w)\leqq\frac{(1-\sigma)\log 2}{\log(1-\sigma)^{-1}}.$$

The author uses an estimate due to Vinogradov [Izv. Akad. Nauk SSSR. Ser. Mat. **15** (1951), 109–130; MR **13**, 328; **16**, 1089] of $|\sum_{P<n<P'}(n+w)^{-s}|$, $1\leqq P\leqq P'<2P$, in conjunction with classical theorems on $\zeta(s, w)$, and proves: There exists a function $C(\omega)$, defined for every $\omega>\log 120\sqrt{2}$ and such that if $C(\omega)<\sigma<1$, then

$$(**)\quad \mu(\sigma, w)<\frac{\sqrt{2}}{3}(1-\sigma)^{3/2}\log^{\frac{1}{2}}(1-\sigma)^{-1} \times\left\{1-\frac{1}{2}\frac{\log\log(1-\sigma)^{-1}}{\log(1-\sigma)^{-1}}+\frac{\omega}{\log(1-\sigma)^{-1}}\right\}.$$

For $\omega=6$, in particular, the expression in braces may be replaced by 1. Clearly, (**) represents an improvementover (*), for values of $\sigma$ close to $\sigma=1$. Assuming a certain generalization (to the best of the reviewer's knowledge, so far unproven) of Vinogradov's result, an estimate of the form $\mu(\sigma, w)\leqq C(a)(1-\sigma)^{1+1/a}$ follows, which is still better than (**), provided that one may use it with some $a\leqq2$. Under certain conditions, the order of the Dirichlet series $L(s, \chi)$ is shown to admit the same bound as $\mu(\sigma, w)$. Finally, a simple proof is given of the fact that, for $1-\sigma$ sufficiently small, (*) may be improved by multiplying the second member by

$$\left\{1-\frac{\log\log(1-\sigma)^{-1}}{\log(1-\sigma)^{-1}}+\frac{\omega}{\log(1-\sigma)^{-1}}\right\}$$

for any $\omega>(\log 4)/e$. *E. Grosswald.*

Citations: MR 13, 328e = L15-14; MR 16, 1089e = L15-15.

Referred to in M15-26.

## M35-12 (20# 7121)

**Franklin, J. N. An enveloping series for the zeta function.** Nederl. Akad. Wetensch. Proc. Ser A. **61** = Indag. Math. **20** (1958), 505-507.

Let $\zeta(s, a)$ denote the generalized zeta function [E. T. Whittacker and G. N. Watson, *A course of modern analysis*, 4th ed., University Press, Cambridge, 1952; p. 265] and let $B_n$ denote the $n$th Bernoulli number. The author shows that

$$\sum_{n=1}^{\infty}(-1)^{n-1}[(2n)!]^{-1}B_n s(s+1)\cdots(s+2n-2)a^{1-s-2n}$$

is an enveloping series [J. G. van der Corput, *Asymptotic expansions, II*, Dept. of Math., Univ. of California, Berkeley, California, 1955; MR **17**, 1201] for the function $\zeta(s, a)-(s-1)^{-1}a^{1-s}-\frac{1}{2}a^{-s}$, valid for positive integers $a$ and Re $s>-1$. Modified results are also obtained for different complex values of $s$.
*C. A. Swanson* (Vancouver, B.C.)

## M35-13 (21# 1953)

**Mikolás, Miklós. Über die Charakterisierung der Hurwitzschen Zetafunktion mittels Funktionalgleichungen.** Acta Sci. Math. Szeged **19** (1958), 247–250.

Let $f(s)$ and $g(s)$ $(s=\sigma+it)$ both be representable as Dirichlet series which converge absolutely for $\sigma>1$, let $f(s)$ satisfy a certain condition concerning analytic continuation over the whole plane, and let

$$g(s)\Gamma\left(\frac{s}{2}\right)\pi^{-s/2}=f(1-s)\Gamma\left(\frac{1-s}{2}\right)\pi^{(s-1)/2}.$$

Then $f(s)=g(s)=c\zeta(s)$ ($c$ a constant) [H. Hamburger, e.g. Math. Z. **10** (1921), 240–254]. Here a similar problem is dealt with, but from a different point of view, for the Hurwitz zetafunction

$$\zeta(s, u)=\sum_{n>-u}^{\infty}(u+n)^{-s}\quad(\sigma>1,\ u \text{ real}).$$

Clearly $\zeta(s, u+1)=\zeta(s, u)$. The author proves: if $\Phi(s, u)$ is an entire function of $s$ and a periodic and differentiable function of the real variable $u$, and belongs to $\mathrm{Lip}_K\,1$ with respect to $s$ $(s>1)$ for any real $u$; if furthermore

$$(\partial/\partial u)\Phi(s+1, u)=\Phi(s, u),$$

$$\int_0^1\Phi(s_1, v)\Phi(s_2, u-v)dv=\Phi(s_1+s_2, u)\quad(1<s, s_1, s_2<2),$$

and $c_1(s)\neq0$, $|\arg c_n(s)|<\pi$, where $1<s<2$, $n=1, 2, \cdots$, $c_n(s)=\int_0^1\Phi(s, v)e^{-2\pi inv}dv$; then $\Phi(s, u)\Gamma(s)=\zeta(1-s, u)$. Finally the analogy of this result to a known property of the Bernoulli polynomials is indicated.
*H. Kober* (Birmingham)

## M35-14 (23# A3726)

**Apostol, T. M.; Chowla, S.**
**On the non-existence of certain Euler products.**
*Norske Vid. Selsk. Forh. Trondheim* **32** (1959), 65–67.

The authors show that the series $\sum_{n=0}^{\infty}(kn+h)^{-s}$ $(1 \leqq h \leqq k,\ (h,k)=1)$ does not have an Euler product decomposition if $k>2$. {The reviewer remarks that there is a simpler proof, resulting from the following fact: if $k>2$, $(h,k)=1$, then we can find $m_1$ and $m_2$ such that $m_1 \not\equiv h \pmod{k}$, $m_1 m_2 \equiv h \pmod{k}$, $(m_1, m_2)=1$.}

*N. G. de Bruijn* (Eindhoven)

## M35-15 (24# A2567)

**Fomenko, O. M.**

**Series containing the Hurwitz function.**

*Ann. Polon. Math.* **10** (1961), 207–208.

The Hurwitz function $\vartheta(s,a)$ is defined for $\operatorname{Re} s>1$, $0<a\leqq 1$, by the series $\sum_{n=0}^{\infty}(n+a)^{-s}$. Let $R(s,a,i)=\sum_{n=i+1}^{\infty}(n+a)^{-s}$. By justifying the inversion of the order of summation, the author establishes the formula

$$R(s,a,i)-(a-\tfrac{1}{2}(\omega-1)+i)^{s-1}(s-1)^{-1} = -\sum_{j=0}^{\infty}\omega^{j+1}\frac{s(s+1)\cdots(s+j)}{(j+2)!}R(s+j+1,a,i),$$

$i=0,1,\cdots$, for all $s$ and for the two cases $\omega=1$ and $\omega=-1$. The result is analagous to a series involving the zeta-function due to Landau and reduces to it when $\omega=1$, $i=0$, $a=1$ [see, e.g., E. C. Titchmarsh, *The theory of the Riemann zeta-function*, Sect. 2.14, Clarendon, Oxford, 1951; MR **13**, 741]. There is a similar result for the Lerch function $\varphi(x,b,s)=\sum_{n=0}^{\infty}e^{2\pi ixn}(n+b)^{-s}$, which is analagous to another series involving the zeta-function due to Ramaswami [Tirchmarsh, loc. cit.].

*R. D. James* (Vancouver, B.C.)

Citations: MR 13, 741c = M02-2.

## M35-16 (26# 3881)

**Cassels, J. W. S.**

**Footnote to a note of Davenport and Heilbronn.**

*J. London Math. Soc.* **36** (1961), 177–184.

Nach Davenport und Heilbronn [dasselbe J. **11** (1936), 181–185; ibid. **11** (1936), 307–312] gilt für jedes rationale oder transzendente $\sigma$ mit $0<\sigma<1$ und $\sigma\neq\frac{1}{2}$ die folgende Aussage (*): Für jedes $\delta>0$ liegen im Streifen $1<\Re s<1+\delta$ noch Nullstellen von $\zeta(s,\sigma):=\sum_{n=0}^{\infty}(n+\sigma)^{-s}$.

Der Autor beweist, dass (*) auch für irrationales algebraisches $\sigma$ mit $0<\sigma<1$ gilt. Der Beweis benutzt neben dem Rouchéschen Satz noch folgenden Hilfssatz: Es sei $K$ der von $\sigma$ erzeugte algebraische Zahlkörper über dem Körper der rationalen Zahlen; $\sigma$ habe in $K$ den Idealnenner $\mathfrak{a}$; dann gibt es eine nur von $\sigma$ abhängige Konstante $c>10^6$ derart, dass es für $N>c$ und $M:=[10^{-6}N]$ mindestens $51M/100$ natürliche Zahlen $n$ mit $N<n\leqq N+M$ gibt, für die $(n+\sigma)\mathfrak{a}$ durch ein Primideal $\mathfrak{p}_n$ aus $K$ mit $\mathfrak{p}_n\nmid\prod_{m\leqq N+M, m\neq n}(m+\sigma)\mathfrak{a}$ teilbar ist.

*G. J. Rieger* (Munich)

Referred to in R46-34.

## M35-17 (26# 4978)

**Hansen, Eldon R.; Patrick, Merrell L.**

**Some relations and values for the generalized Riemann zeta function.**

*Math. Comp.* **16** (1962), 265–274.

Put

$$\zeta(s,a)=\sum_{n=0}^{\infty}\frac{1}{(n+a)^s},$$

where $a$ is not zero or a negative integer. It is familiar that if $\zeta(s,a)$ is known for $0<a\leqq 1$, then it can be determined readily for all $a$. The authors point out that it is sufficient to take $\frac{1}{2}<a\leqq 1$. This follows from the case $q=2$ of

$$\sum_{r=1}^{q}\zeta(s,\frac{r}{q}-b)=q^s\zeta(s,1-bq)\quad(q=1,2,3,\cdots).$$

Various relations involving $\zeta(s,a)$ are obtained, in particular, the formula

$$\zeta\left(1-s,\frac{p}{q}\right)=\frac{2\Gamma(s)}{(2\pi q)^s}\sum_{r=1}^{q}\cos\pi\left(\frac{s}{2}-\frac{2rp}{q}\right)\zeta\left(s,\frac{r}{q}\right)$$

which follows from a formula of Hurwitz [Whittaker and Watson, *A course of modern analysis*, 4th ed. (reprinted), p. 269, Cambridge Univ. Press, New York, 1962], may be cited.

The paper includes two tables. Table 1 gives $\zeta(s,a)$ to seventeen decimal places for $a=1/4$ and $3/4$ and for $s=-(61/3)\,(1/3)\,(64/3)$. Table 2 gives $\zeta(s)$ to seventeen places for $s=0\,(1/3)\,(64/3)$.

*L. Carlitz* (Durham, N.C.)

## M35-18 (29# 79)

**Kesava Menon, P.**

**On a function of Ramanujan.**

*J. Indian Math. Soc. (N.S.)* **25** (1961), 109–119 (1962).

Ramanujan [*Collected papers*, Cambridge Univ. Press, London, 1927] obtained a formula for

$$(1)\quad \Phi(2s+1,x)=\sum_{n=0}^{\infty}\{(x+n+1)^{1/2}-(x+n)^{1/2}\}^{2s+1}=\sum_{n=0}^{\infty}\{(x+n+1)^{1/2}+(x+n)^{1/2}\}^{-(2s+1)}\quad(s=1,2,3,\cdots)$$

in terms of the generalised zeta-function $\zeta(s,a)=\sum_{n=0}^{\infty}1/(a+n)^s$ $(\operatorname{Re} s>1)$. He proved by induction that

$$(2)\quad \Phi(2s+1,x)+\tfrac{1}{2}[\{x^{1/2}+(x-1)^{1/2}\}^{2s+1}+\{x^{1/2}-(x-1)^{1/2}\}^{2s+1}]+(2s+1)\sum_{m=0}^{[(s-1)/2]}\frac{2^{2(s-2m-1)}}{s-m}\times\binom{2s-2m}{2m+1}\zeta(2m+\tfrac{1}{2}-s,x)=0.$$

The author claims to give a direct proof of this result. He starts from a formula (which he calls "known") which ought to be, as it seems,

$$(3)\quad \frac{1}{2s+1}(\sqrt{y}-\sqrt{(y+1)})^{2s+1}=\sum_{m=0}^{s}\frac{2^{2(s-m)}}{2s-m+1}\binom{2s-m+1}{m}\{y^{s-m+1/2}-(-1)^m(y+1)^{s-m+1/2}\}.$$

He attains his aim indeed by a method which seems to be sound, but his development is quite unintelligible, as it is mutilated by an enormous quantity of grave errors and misprints (e.g., (1), (2) and (3) contain already six serious errors). Ramanujan's result (2) is expressed in a different form by means of Hurwitz's well-known formula for $\zeta(s,a)$ if $\operatorname{Re} s<0$ (cf. Whittaker and Watson, *A course in modern analysis*, 4th ed., 13.15, Cambridge Univ. Press, Cambridge, 1927). By differentiation of (2) the author obtains Ramanujan's evaluation of

$$\Psi(2s+1,x)=\sum_{n=0}^{\infty}\frac{\{(x+n)^{1/2}+(x+n+1)^{1/2}\}^{-(2s+1)}}{\{(x+n)(x+n+1)\}^{1/2}}\quad(s=1,2,3,\cdots).$$

From his result the author tries to find simple transformations for certain sums, e.g.,

$$\sum_{n=0}^{\infty}\frac{(-1)^n}{\{(x+n)^{1/2}+(x+n+1)^{1/2}\}^{2s+1}}.$$

He states as an example

$$\sum_{n=0}^{\infty}\frac{(-1)^n}{(\sqrt{n}+\sqrt{(n+1)})^3}=\frac{2\sqrt{2}}{3\pi}\sum_{n=0}^{\infty}\frac{1}{(2n+1)^{3/2}},$$

but an easy verification gives for the sum in the left-hand member a number between 0.93 and 0.96, but for the right-hand member gives $0.51\cdots$.

*S. C. van Veen* (Delft)

**M35-19** **(34# 2959)**

**Glaeske, Hans-Jürgen**

**Über eine Charakterisierung der Hurwitzschen Zetafunktion.**

*Publ. Math. Debrecen* **13** (1966), 139–144.

W. Maier [Math. Ann. **113** (1936), 363–379] gave an integro-functional equation for the Hurwitz zeta function, more precisely, for $\Gamma(s)\zeta(s, \alpha)$. This equation involves under the sign of integration, besides elementary powers, also three sets of products $\varphi(u, \beta)\varphi(s-u, \beta)$ for different values of $\beta$. The author assumes $\varphi(u, \alpha)$ to be the Mellin transform of a function $p(z, \alpha)$ and finds for $p(z, \alpha)$ a quadratic functional equation involving seven functions $p$ with different arguments. If now $p$ is an entire function of $z$ and $\alpha$ and $p\not\equiv 0$, then $p(z, \alpha) = -\exp[c(1-\alpha)z]$, $\varphi(u, \alpha) = -\Gamma(u)[(\alpha-1)c]^{-u}$, $\Re[(\alpha-1)c] > 0$. Next, if $p$ is entire in $z$ and meromorphic in $\alpha$, then

$$\varphi(u, \alpha) = \Gamma(u)\zeta(u, 1-(1-\alpha)\mu/\lambda)\lambda^{-u},$$

$\Re[(1-\alpha)\mu/\lambda] > 0$. The Hurwitz case corresponds to $\lambda = \mu = 1$ and may be singled out by prescribing the residues of $\varphi(u, \alpha)$ at $u=0$ and 1. *E. Hille* (Canberra)

**M35-20** **(44# 6622)**

**Berndt, Bruce C.**

**On the Hurwitz zeta-function.**

*Rocky Mountain J. Math.* **2** (1972), *no.* 1, 151–157.

Earlier authors have calculated the coefficients of the Laurent expansion of the Riemann zeta-function $\zeta(s)$ about $s=1$. Also, by estimating these coefficients, they proved that $\zeta(s)$ has no zeros on $|s-1| \leq 1$. The author obtains corresponding results for the coefficients of the Laurent expansion of the Hurwitz zeta-function $\zeta(s, a)$, $0 < a \leq 1$ about $s=1$. *K. Thanigasalam* (Monaca, Pa.)

# M40 OTHER DIRICHLET SERIES AND EULER PRODUCTS

See also Sections E44, F65.

See also reviews A26-75, A28-4, A30-22, A30-26, A34-14, A34-16, A34-30, A34-32, A36-19, B68-42, E44-18, E44-35, E44-38, E44-39, F30-18, F35-43, M05-12, M05-35, M05-40, M05-42, M05-47, M05-48, M15-9, M20-3, M20-8, M20-17, M20-22, M20-23, M20-27, M20-28, M20-29, M20-30, M20-31, M25-30, M25-49, M25-84, M25-85, M30-5, M30-6, M45-11, M50-2, M99-6, N04-1, N36-12, N36-13, N36-14, N36-21, N36-24, N36-25, N36-26, N36-27, N36-32, N36-36, N36-46, N36-50, N36-58, N36-86, N40-62, N52-30, N80-5, P28-72, P48-2, Q10-1, Q10-4, Q10-6, Q10-7, Q10-10, Q20-25, Q20-27, Q20-43, R42-3, R42-8, R42-20, R42-32, Z02-4, Z10-33.

**M40-1** **(1, 294b)**

**Crum, M. M. On some Dirichlet series.** J. London Math. Soc. **15**, 10–15 (1940).

The author discusses formal properties of some Dirichlet series $\sum f(n)n^{-s}$ for which he either proves or assumes that they are expressible as products and quotients of the zeta-function with arguments $\alpha s+\beta$. In several cases $f(n)$ is constructed with the function $\sigma_\lambda^{(\mu)}(n)$ which is the sum of the $\lambda$th powers of those divisors of $n$ which are $\mu$th powers of integers. *S. Bochner* (Princeton, N. J.).

Referred to in A30-22.

**M40-2** **(2, 347f)**

**Anfertieva, E. A. Sur les formules sommatoires et les identités analytiques, liées à une classe de fonctions arithmétiques.** C. R. (Doklady) Acad. Sci. URSS (N.S.) **30**, 391–393 (1941).

The author considers the Dirichlet series

$$\zeta(\rho-\nu)\zeta(\rho+\nu)+\sum_{n=1}^{\infty} a_\nu(n)/n^\rho,$$

where

$$a_\nu(n) = \sum_{d\delta=n} d^{2\nu}/n^\nu,$$

and obtains identities for this function. The detailed proofs will be given in a subsequent paper. *P. Erdös.*

Referred to in M40-30.

**M40-3** **(5, 255d)**

**Wintner, Aurel. Eulerian products and analytic continuation.** Duke Math. J. **11**, 277–285 (1944).

The author exhibits a multiplicative function $g(n)$ for which the Euler product

$$\prod_p \left(1+\sum_{k=1}^{\infty} g(p^k)/p^{ks}\right)$$

converges in a larger half-plane than the corresponding series

$$\sum_{n=1}^{\infty} g(n)/n^s,$$

thus controverting the classical cases in which the series invariably converges at least as far as the Euler product. *S. Bochner* (Princeton, N. J.).

Referred to in Z02-4.

**M40-4** **(9, 571b)**

**Anfert'eva, E. A. On the representation of certain special Dirichlet series by definite integrals.** Izvestiya Akad. Nauk SSSR. Ser. Mat. **12**, 79–96 (1948). (Russian)

The author studies the functions $\varphi_\nu(s) = \zeta(s+\nu)\zeta(s-\nu)$, where $\zeta(s)$ is the Riemann zeta function. Generalizations are obtained of results which are well known for $\zeta(s)$ [C. L. Siegel, Quellen u. Studien z. Geschichte der Math. **2**, 45–80 (1932)]. The author proves three formulas involving $\varphi_\nu(s)$. Two of these (which are typical) are as follows. (1) Let

$$a_\nu(n) = \sum_{d|n} d^{2\nu}/n^\nu, \qquad \nu\neq 0, \ -\tfrac{1}{2}<\nu<\tfrac{1}{2},$$

$$\psi(x) = \sum_{n=1}^{\infty} a_\nu(n)K_\nu(2\pi n x),$$

$$\xi(s) = \Gamma(\tfrac{1}{2}(s+\nu))\Gamma(\tfrac{1}{2}(s-\nu))\,(s^2-\nu^2)[(1-s)^2-\nu^2]\pi^s\varphi_\nu(s),$$

$$w(t) = \xi(\tfrac{1}{2}+it).$$

Then

$$w(t)=\frac{\pi}{\sin \pi\nu}\left[-\frac{\zeta(2\nu)\pi^{-\nu}(1-2\nu)}{\Gamma(1-\nu)}\{(\tfrac{1}{2}+\nu)^2+t^2\}+\frac{\zeta(-2\nu)\pi^{\nu}(1+2\nu)}{\Gamma(1+\nu)}\{(\tfrac{1}{2}-\nu)^2+t^2\}\right]$$
$$+8\{(\tfrac{1}{2}-\nu)^2+t^2\}\{(\tfrac{1}{2}+\nu)^2+t^2\}\times\int_1^\infty x^{-\frac{1}{2}}\psi(x)\cos(t\ln x)dx.$$

(2) Let $\epsilon=e^{\pi i/4}$, $\bar{\epsilon}=e^{-\pi i/4}$,

$$N(2\pi\bar{\epsilon}x, 2\pi\epsilon n)=2\pi\epsilon nK_{\nu+1}(2\pi\epsilon n)J_\nu(2\pi\bar{\epsilon}x)-2\pi\bar{\epsilon}xJ_{\nu+1}(2\pi\bar{\epsilon}x)K_\nu(2\pi\epsilon n)$$

and

$$\omega(\bar{\epsilon}, x)=\frac{1}{2\pi i}\left\{-\frac{\Gamma(\nu)\zeta(2\nu)}{\pi^\nu}\bar{\epsilon}^{1+3\nu}\pi J_{1-\nu}(2\pi\bar{\epsilon}x)-\frac{\Gamma(-\nu)\zeta(-2\nu)}{\pi^{-\nu}}\bar{\epsilon}^{1-3\nu}\pi J_{1+\nu}(2\pi\bar{\epsilon}x)+2x\epsilon^{2\nu}\sum_{n=1}^\infty a_\nu(n)\frac{N(2\pi\bar{\epsilon}x, 2\pi\epsilon n)}{x^2-n^2}\right\}.$$

Then

$$\pi^{-s}\Gamma(\tfrac{1}{2}(s+\nu))\Gamma(\tfrac{1}{2}(s-\nu))\varphi_\nu(s)=\Gamma(\tfrac{1}{2}(s+\nu))\Gamma(\tfrac{1}{2}(s-\nu))\pi^{-s}\times\int\omega(\bar{\epsilon}, x)x^{-s}dx+\Gamma(\tfrac{1}{2}(1-s+\nu))\Gamma(\tfrac{1}{2}(1-s-\nu))\pi^{s-1}\times\int\omega(\epsilon, x)x^{s-1}dx,$$

where the last two integrals are taken along the path $x=(y-i\xi)e^{i\pi/4}$ (for some fixed $\xi$, $0<\xi<2^{-\frac{1}{2}}$), with $y$ going from $\infty$ to $-\infty$. The third formula is even more complicated and we omit it here.

The paper is marred by a tremendous number of misprints which render portions of it almost unreadable. Also, the author seems to have overlooked a previous paper on the same question in which many of the results were given [N. Koschliakov, C. R. (Doklady) Acad. Sci. URSS. **2**, 342–345 (1934)]. *H. N. Shapiro* (New York, N. Y.).

## M40-5 (12, 319a)

**Anfert'eva, E. A. Summation formulas containing special numerical functions.** Mat. Sbornik N.S. **27(69)**, 69–84 (1950). (Russian)

Various summation formulae are obtained by utilizing the functional equation for $\varphi_\nu(s)=\zeta(s+\nu)\zeta(s-\nu)$ (obtained from that of the $\zeta$ function). The method used is that given by Ferrar [Compositio Math. **4**, 394–405 (1937)] for obtaining such summation formulae from a rather general class of functions possessing a functional equation.

*H. N. Shapiro* (New York, N. Y.).

## M40-6 (13, 15c)

**Apostol, T. M. Identities involving the coefficients of certain Dirichlet series.** Duke Math. J. **18**, 517–525 (1951).

The author proves a general theorem concerning certain Dirichlet series. Suppose that $\lambda>0$, $\kappa>0$, $\gamma=\pm1$, and let $\varphi(s)=\varphi(\sigma+it)$ satisfy the following conditions: (i) $\varphi(s)=\sum_{n=1}^\infty a(n)n^{-s}$ converges absolutely for $\sigma>\kappa$, (ii) $(2\pi/\lambda)^{-s}\Gamma(s)\varphi(s)=\gamma(2\pi/\lambda)^{s-\kappa}\Gamma(\kappa-s)\varphi(\kappa-s)$, (iii) $(s-\kappa)\varphi(s)$ is an integral function of finite genus. Then, if $\rho$ is the residue of $\varphi(s)$ at $s=\kappa$,

$$\frac{1}{q!}\sum_{n=0}^{x}a(n)(x-n)^q=\rho\frac{\Gamma(\kappa)x^{\kappa+q}}{\Gamma(\kappa+q+1)}+\gamma\left(\frac{\lambda}{2\pi}\right)^q x^{\frac{1}{2}(\kappa+q)}\sum_{n=1}^\infty\frac{a(n)}{n^{\frac{1}{2}(\kappa+q)}}J_{\kappa+q}\left(\frac{4\pi}{\lambda}(nx)^{\frac{1}{2}}\right),$$

where $x>0$, $q$ is a positive integer, $J_\nu(z)$ is the ordinary Bessel function of order $\nu$, and $a(0)$ is defined to be $-\varphi(0)$. The series of Bessel functions is absolutely convergent if $q>\kappa-\frac{1}{2}$. The author has not observed that this identity is a particular case of equation (47) (p. 225) of a famous paper by E. Landau [Nachr. Ges. Wiss. Göttingen. Math.-Phys. Kl. **1915**, 209–243], Landau's function $L(x)$ reducing to a Bessel function in the author's case. The three conditions VI, VIII and IX of Landau's theorem, which is of such generality that its enunciation occupies three and a half pages, are not needed by the author, nor are they used by Landau until the second stage of his proof after (47) has been proved. A result of the same type given by A. Oppenheim [Proc. London Math. Soc. (2) **26**, 295–350 (1927)] for the sum $\sum_{n=1}^{x}(x^p-n^p)\sum_{d|n}d^{-p}$ $(0<p<\frac{1}{2})$ is proved by similar methods; here the appropriate Dirichlet series is the function $\zeta(ps)\zeta(ps+p)$. *R. A. Rankin.*

Referred to in M40-18.

## M40-7 (13, 920b)

**Bochner, S. Some properties of modular relations.** Ann. of Math. (2) **53**, 332–363 (1951).

A modular relation is a relation resembling an identity where

(1) $\Phi(x)=x^{-\delta}\Psi(1/x)$ (Re $(x)>0$)

where $\Phi(x)=\sum_0^\infty a_m e^{-\lambda_m x}$, $\Psi(x)=\sum_0^\infty b_n e^{-\mu_n x}$, $\delta>0$, $\lambda_m\geqq0$, $\mu_n\geqq0$, sometimes $0<\lambda_1<\lambda_2\cdots\to\infty$, $0<\mu_1<\mu_2\cdots\to\infty$. In classical results $\lambda_m=m\lambda^*$, $\mu_n=n\mu^*$. In this case the relation (1) is equivalent to the functional equation

(2) $\Gamma(\delta-s)\psi(\delta-s)=\Gamma(\delta)\varphi(s)=\chi(s)$,

where $\varphi(s)=\sum_1^\infty a_m/\lambda_m^s$, $\psi(s)=\sum_1^\infty b_n/\mu_n^s$. In section I (Functional Equations) the main result is a generalisation of (2). Theorem 4: For general $\lambda_m$ and $\mu_n$, (2) implies

(3) $\sum_1^\infty a_m e^{-\lambda_m x}-x^{-\delta}\sum_1^\infty b_n \exp(-\lambda_m/x)=P(x)$,

where $P(x)$ is a "residual" function $(2\pi i)^{-1}\int_C\chi(s)x^{-s}ds$, the integral taken over a bounded curve or curves $C$, encircling all unramified singularities of $\chi(s)$. And conversely, any relation (3) with any residual function $P(x)$ leads back to an equation (2). By introducing Laplace-Stieltjes integrals, (3) is to be replaced by

(4) $\int_0^\infty e^{-\lambda x}dA(\lambda)=x^{-\delta}\int_0^\infty \exp(-\mu/x)dB(\mu)=P(x)$

where $A_\lambda=\sum_{\lambda_m<\lambda}|a_m|$, $B(\mu)=\sum_{\mu_n<\mu}b_n$. Usually the function $\chi(s)$ will have only a finite number of unramified singularities. In this case, by introducing the indefinite integrals

$$U(\lambda)=\frac{1}{2\pi i}\int_0^\lambda d\lambda\int_{C_1}\varphi(s)\lambda^{s-1}ds;\quad V(\mu)=\int_0^\mu d\mu\int_{C_2}\psi(s)\mu^{\delta-s-1}ds$$

($C_1$ enclosing the singularities of $\chi(s)$ in the half plane $\sigma>0$, and $C_2$ those in the left-hand plane $\sigma<\delta$) and putting $R(\lambda)=A(\lambda)+U(\lambda)$; $S(\mu)=B(\mu)+V(\mu)$, the relation (4) assumes the "unified" appearance

$$\int_0^\infty e^{-\lambda x} dR(\lambda) = x^{-\delta} \int_0^\infty \exp(-\mu/x) dS(\mu)$$

in which the residual part $P(x)$ has been assimilated to the modular part proper.

In Section II (Summation Formulas) the author shows that under general conditions the "summation" formula

$$\int_0^\infty f(\lambda) dR(\lambda) = \int_0^\infty g(\mu) dS(\mu)$$

holds. Here $f(\lambda)$ is an arbitrary function in $0 \leqq \lambda < \infty$ and $g(\mu)$ is the Hankel transform

$$g(\mu) = \mu^{-\frac{1}{2}(\delta-1)} \int_0^\infty J_{\delta-1}\{2(\mu\lambda)^{\frac{1}{2}}\} \lambda^{\frac{1}{2}(\delta-1)} f(\lambda) d\lambda.$$

For instance, the Riesz kernel

$$f(\lambda) = \begin{cases} (1-\lambda)^\gamma & 0 < \lambda < 1 \\ 0 & 1 \leqq \lambda < \infty \end{cases}$$

falls under these conditions for $\gamma \geqq 2\beta - \delta - \frac{1}{2}$ and $\gamma > 0$ simultaneously, where $\beta > 0$ is a constant such that $\int_1^\infty \mu^{-\beta} |dS(\mu)| < \infty$. Then

$$\frac{1}{\Gamma(\gamma+1)} \int_0^x (x-\lambda)^\gamma dR(\lambda)$$
$$= \int_0^\infty (x/\mu)^{\frac{1}{2}(\delta+\gamma)} J_{\delta+\gamma}\{2(x\mu)^{\frac{1}{2}}\} dS(\mu), \quad 0 < x < \infty.$$

In section III some supplementary remarks are made. In section IV (Modular Exponential Sums) many general results are obtained. We mention in particular, in the case of the modular relation (1) and under general assumptions: The series

$$\sum_1^\infty a_m \lambda_m^l e^{-2it\lambda^{\frac{1}{2}}}, \quad l \lesseqgtr 0$$

and

$$\sum_0^\infty a_m (t^2/\lambda_m)^{\frac{1}{2}(\delta+\gamma)} J_{\delta+\gamma}(2t\lambda^{\frac{1}{2}}), \quad \gamma \lesseqgtr 0$$

are Abel summable for $t^2 > 0$, if $t^2 \neq \mu_k$ $(k = 1, 2, \cdots)$. In an addendum the author shows how the non-arithmetical part of Hecke's reasoning in regard to the functional equation for zeta functions in algebraic fields can be formalized and technically generalized. *S. C. van Veen* (Delft).

Referred to in F10-86, M40-14, M40-22, N36-25, P28-29.

## M40-8 (14, 151d)

**Dahlquist, Germund. On the analytic continuation of Eulerian products.** Ark. Mat. **1**, 533–554 (1952).

Let $h(z)$ be analytic in $|z| \leqq 1$, except for isolated singularities, and $h(0) = 1$. Construct the "Euler product" $f(s) = \prod_p h(p^{-s})$, where $p$ runs over the primes. The author first shows that $f(s)$ is analytic in $\sigma > 0$ $(s = \sigma + i\tau)$ except on an isolated point set. His main result is Theorem I: The imaginary axis is a natural boundary of $f(s)$, except when $h(z)$ is of the form $\prod_{\nu=1}^k (1-z^\nu)^{-\beta_\nu}$; in the exceptional case $f(s) = \prod_{\nu=1}^k \zeta(\nu s)^{\beta_\nu}$ and is analytic in the whole plane except for isolated points. The author makes the proof by uniquely factorizing $h(z)$: $h(z) = \prod_{\nu=1}^\infty (1-z^\nu)^{-\beta_\nu}$, $|z| < a$, which leads easily to the representation (not unique)

$$f(s) = \prod_{p \leqq q} h(p^{-s}) \prod_{\nu=1}^\infty \zeta_q(\nu s)^{\beta_\nu}, \quad \text{where} \quad \zeta_q(s) = \zeta(s) \prod_{p \leqq q} (1 - p^{-s}),$$

$q$ satisfies $q > a^{-1/\sigma}$, and $a$ is the smaller of the numbers 1 and the modulus of the smallest zero or singularity of $h(z)$. Thus he can use known results on the distribution of the zeros of $\zeta(s)$. The proof depends crucially on Lemma 3.2, a general theorem on sequences of positive integers. In the last part of the paper the author extends his results to the class

$$f(s) = \prod_p h(\chi(p) p^{-s}),$$

$h$ satisfying the same conditions as before, and $\chi$ a group character to a fixed modulus. *J. Lehner.*

## M40-9 (16, 231h)

**Dyson, F. J. The rate of growth of functions defined by Dirichlet series.** Ann. of Math. (2) **60**, 437–446 (1954).

Let $E$ denote the class of analytic functions $\phi(s)$ having the following properties: (i) $\phi(s) = \sum \lambda_n^{-s}$ for $\sigma > 0$ with $0 < \lambda_n \leqq \lambda_{n+1}$, (ii) $\phi(s) - (s-1)^{-1}$ is entire, and

(iii) $\quad |\phi(s)| < A\Gamma(r)(2\pi k)^{-r}$ for $|s| = r \geqq 2$.

The author answers in this paper a question raised by Beurling [Ark. Mat. **1**, 295–300 (1951); these Rev. **12**, 690] showing that the functions $\zeta_\alpha(s) = \sum_0^\infty (n+\alpha)^{-s}$ possess some minimal growth properties in the class $E$. Of the two results proved we cite the second: Let $1/4 \leqq \alpha \leqq 3/4$ and suppose that $|\phi(-m)| \leqq |\zeta_\alpha(-m)|$ for $m = 0, 1, 2, \cdots$, then either $\phi(s) = \zeta_\alpha(s)$ or $\phi(s) = \zeta_{1-\alpha}(s)$. It is pointed out that in contrast with the results of Beurling (who assumed that in addition the functions $\phi(s)$ satisfy $\phi(-2n) = 0$) the Riemann zeta-function has no distinguished role among the class of minimal functions $\zeta_\alpha(s)$. *S. Agmon* (Jerusalem).

Citations: MR 12, 690g = M05-12.

## M40-10 (16, 1010c)

**Lekkerkerker, C. G. On the zeros of a class of Dirichlet series.** Van Gorcum & Comp. N.V., Assen, 1955. v+65 pp. 6.90 florins.

This dissertation extends known facts concerning the distribution of the zeros of the Riemann zeta faction to a class of Dirichlet series which includes the $(\lambda, \kappa, \gamma)$-functions of Hecke. A class of functions $\varphi(s)$ has the property $P$ if (1) there exists an allied function $\varphi^*(s)$ such that $\varphi(s)$ and $\varphi^*(s)$ are represented by convergent Dirichlet series $\sum a_n n^{-s}$ and $\sum a_n^* n^{-s}$ in some right half-plane and are holomorphic outside of some rectangle; (2) there exists real $\beta$, $h$ and a positive $\mu$ such that $R(s) = R^*(2h-s)$ outside the rectangle where $R(s) = e^{-\beta s}\Gamma(\mu s)\varphi(s)$, $R^*(s) = e^{-\beta s}\Gamma(\mu s)\varphi^*(s)$; and (3) $\log|\varphi(s)| = O(|s|^K)$ for all large $|s|$ and some fixed $K > 0$. Such a function $\varphi(s)$ has trivial negative real zeros, the distance between consecutive zeros being $1/\mu$, all other zeros lie in some vertical strip and the number of zeros in the strip $0 < t < T$ (and in $-T < t < 0$) is

$$N(T) = \frac{1}{\pi}\mu T \log T - \frac{1}{\pi}[\tfrac{1}{2}\log cd + \beta + \mu - \mu\log\mu]T + O(\log T),$$

where $c$ and $d$ are the subscripts of the first non-vanishing coefficients $a_n$ and $a_n^*$ respectively. For a $(\lambda, \kappa, \gamma)$-function $\mu = 1$ and the bracket equals $1 + \log(2\pi c/\lambda)$. If $\varphi(s)$ is an entire $(1, \kappa, \gamma)$-function and $\chi = \chi(n)$ is a character modulo $q$, similar formulas hold for the functions $\varphi(s, \chi) = \sum a_n \chi(n) n^{-s}$. If now (i) $\varphi(s)$ is holomorphic and of finite order for $\sigma \geqq h$, (ii) $R(s) \equiv ae^{-bs}\Gamma(s)\varphi(s)$ is real on $\sigma = h$, and

(iii) $\quad |f(x+iy)| = O(x^{-h})$

as $x \to 0+$ where $f(z) = \sum a_n e^{-nz}$, then the number of zeros $N_0(T)$ on $\sigma = h$, $0 < t < T$ (or $-T < t < 0$), exceeds a constant multiple of $T$. It is shown that if $\varphi(s)$ satisfies (i) then it can satisfy (ii) if and only if property $P$ holds with $\mu = 1$ and

$a_n^* = \gamma \bar{a}_n$. In particular, $N_0(T) > AT$ for every entire $(\lambda, \kappa, \gamma)$-function with real coefficients and $0 < \lambda < 2$. Here $h = \frac{1}{2}\kappa$. *E. Hille* (New Haven, Conn.).

## M40-11 (17, 462b)

**Min, Szu-Hoa. On a way of generalization of the Riemann $\zeta$ function. I. The analytic continuation of $Z_{n,k}(s)$ to the whole plane.** Acta Math. Sinica **5** (1955), 285–294. (Chinese. English summary)

Let $n$ be even, $\nu = 1/n$, $s = \sigma + it$, and

$$Z_{n,k}(s) \sum_{x_1, \cdots, x_k = -\infty}^{+\infty}{}' (x_1^n + \cdots + x_k^n)^{-s}$$

(the dash means that there is no term $x_1 = \cdots = x_k = 0$). The author proves that $Z_{n,k}(s)$ is meromorphic, with one simple pole of residue $2^k \Gamma^k(1+\nu)/\Gamma(k\nu)$ at $s = k\nu$, by showing that

$$Z_{n,k}(s) = \frac{1}{\Gamma(s)} \Big\{ \frac{2^k \Gamma^k(1+\nu)}{s - k\nu} - \frac{1}{s}$$

$$+ \int_1^\infty \omega^{s-1} \Big( \Big( \sum_{x=-\infty}^{+\infty} e^{-x^n \omega} \Big)^k - 1 \Big) d\omega + \int_0^1 2^k \omega^{s-k\nu-1} \Big[ \Big( \Gamma(1+\nu)$$

$$+ 2\omega^{2h\nu} \sum_{y=1}^\infty \frac{(-1)^h}{(2\pi y)^{2h}} \int_1^\infty \frac{d^{2h} e^{-x^n}}{dx^{2h}} \cos \frac{2\pi y x}{\omega^\nu} dx \Big)^k$$

$$- \Gamma^k(1+\nu) \Big] d\omega \Big\}.$$

Here $h$ can be any positive integer; a slightly different development holds when $h = 0$. A much more general theorem was already obtained by Hj. Mellin [Acta Soc. Sci. Fenn. **29** (1902), no. 4]. *K. Mahler.*

Referred to in M40-19.

## M40-12 (18, 112d)

**Min, Szu-Hoa. A generalization of the Riemann $\zeta$ function. II. The order of $Z_{n,k}(s)$.** Acta Math. Sinica **6** (1956), 1–11. (Chinese. English summary)

In this paper it is proved that for $A_1 \leqq \sigma \leqq A_2$ we can find a constant $A$ depending on $A_1$ and $A_2$ such that

$$Z_{n,k}(s) = O(t^A)$$

as $t \to \infty$. *Author's summary.*

Referred to in M40-19.

## M40-13 (18, 19a)

**Bochner, S.; and Chandrasekharan, K. On Riemann's functional equation.** Ann. of Math. (2) **63** (1956), 336–360.

The authors consider solutions $\{\varphi(s), \psi(s)\}$ of the functional equation (1) $\pi^{-s/2}\Gamma(s/2)\varphi(s) = \pi^{-\frac{1}{2}(\delta-s)}\Gamma(½(\delta - s))$ $\psi(\delta - s)$ such that there are Dirichlet series for $\varphi$ and $\psi$:

$$\varphi(s) = \sum_1^\infty a_n \lambda_n^{-s}, \ \psi(s) = \sum_1^\infty b_n \mu_n^{-s} \ (s = \sigma + i\tau)$$

converging absolutely for $\sigma > \alpha > 0$, $\sigma > \beta > 0$ respectively. Here $\delta > 0$ as well as the increasing sequences $\lambda_n \to \infty$, $\mu_n \to \infty$ are supposed to be given. They further suppose the existence of a bounded closed set $S$ in the $s$-plane, symmetric relative to the line $\sigma = \delta/2$, $-\infty < \tau < +\infty$ and the existence of a holomorphic function $\chi(s)$ in the exterior $R$ of $S$ which in a right half-plane coincides with the left hand side of (1) and in a left half-plane with the right hand side of (1) and such that

$$\lim_{|\tau| \to \infty} \chi(\sigma + i\tau) = 0,$$

uniformly in every bounded interval $\sigma_1 \leqq \sigma \leqq \sigma_2$, $-\infty < \sigma_1 < \sigma_2 < +\infty$. They obtain an upper bound for the number of linearly independent solutions which depends on the distribution of the sequences $\{\lambda_n\}$ and $\{\mu_n\}$. After introducing certain further restrictions the only solutions that can occur are $\zeta(s)$, $(2^s - 1)\zeta(s)$, $(2^{1-s} - 1)\zeta(s)$, $2^{s-1}L(s-1)$. The method used is essentially that of Siegel for the proof of Hamburger's well-known theorem on the solution of Riemann's functional equation for $\zeta(s)$.

*H. D. Kloosterman* (Leiden).

Referred to in M40-21, M40-22, M40-27, M40-32.

## M40-14 (18, 19b)

**Chandrasekharan, Komaravolu; et Mandelbrojt, Szolem. Sur l'équation fonctionnelle de Riemann.** C. R. Acad. Sci. Paris 242 (1956), 2793–2796.

The authors announce a most interesting proposition in a topic recently initiated, more or less, by this reviewer [Ann. of Math. (2) **53** (1951), 332–363; MR **13**, 920 and very recently continued in the paper reviewed above. Take two Dirichlet series

$$\varphi(s) = \sum a_n \lambda_n^{-s}, \ \psi(s) = \sum b_n \mu_n^{-s} \ (s = \sigma + i\tau)$$

each absolutely convergent somewhere, $\lambda_n > 0$, $\mu_n > 0$, $\lambda_n \uparrow \infty$, $\mu_n \uparrow \infty$, and for some $\delta > 0$ they shall satisfy a functional equation

$$(*) \qquad \pi^{-s/2}\Gamma(\tfrac{1}{2}s)\varphi(s) = \pi^{-\frac{1}{2}(\delta-s)}\Gamma(\tfrac{1}{2}(\delta - s))\psi(\delta - s)$$

in the sense that there exists, in a domain $|s| > R$, a holomorphic function $\chi(s)$ which in some right half-plane coincides with the left side of (*) and in some left half-plane with its right side, and for which $\lim_{|\tau| \to \infty} \chi(\sigma + i\tau) = 0$ uniformly in every bounded interval $\sigma_1 \leqq \sigma \leqq \sigma_2$.

The authors deal only with the parameters $\delta = 1$ and $= 3$ which "correspond" to the classical cases $\varphi(s) = \psi(s) = \zeta(s)$ and $L(s)$, in substance, and their statement is as follows. If only the exponents in one of the Dirichlet series are spaced apart, say $\liminf_{n \to \infty} (\mu_{n+1} - \mu_n) < \infty$, than those in the other are only one step from being equidistant: there exists an $l > 0$ such that for any $c \geqq 0$ if one denotes the exponents $\{\lambda_m\}$ in $c < \lambda \leqq c + l$ by $\lambda_q \lambda_{q+1}, \cdots, \lambda_{q+r}$, then any other $\lambda_n$ is a linear combination $p_0^{(n)}\lambda_q + p_1^{(n)}\lambda_{q+1} + \cdots + p_k^{(n)}\lambda_{q+r}$ with integer coefficients $p_k^{(n)}$.

Furthermore, the function $\sum b_n e^{-2\pi\mu_n s}$, $\sigma > 0$, of which it was known that it has a univalent continuation into $\sigma < 0$ (except for poles at $\pm i\lambda_n$ and perhaps also at 0), is such that in $\sigma < 0$ it has an expansion $\sum_0^\infty \gamma_n e^{2\pi\mu_{-n} s}$, $0 < \mu_{-n} \uparrow \infty$, likewise. *S. Bochner* (Princeton, N.J.).

Citations: MR 13, 920b = M40-7.

Referred to in M40-15, M40-24.

## M40-15 (19, 635i)

**Chandrasekharan, K.; and Mandelbrojt, S. On Riemann's functional equation.** Ann. of Math. (2) **66** (1957), 285–296.

The paper gives proofs to a preceding note already reviewed [C. R. Acad. Sci. Paris **242** (1956), 2793–2796; MR **18**, 19]. A general lemma (generalizing a theorem of S. Agmon) which is used in the proof of the main result is as follows. Take a Dirichlet series $F(s) = \sum c_n \exp(-2\pi\mu_n s)$, with $h_\mu \equiv \liminf_{n \to \infty} (\mu_{n+1} - \mu_n) > 0$, which is convergent in a half-plane $\sigma > \sigma_F$. On a boundary segment $\sigma = \sigma_F$, $a \leqq \tau \leqq b$, with $b - a > \limsup_{n \to \infty} (n/\mu_n) + h_\mu^{-1}$, let $F(s)$ have a finite number of simple poles at $\sigma_F + i\alpha_q$ $(q = 1, \cdots, k)$ and no other singularities there, and let it be continuable into the half-strip $\sigma < \sigma_F$, $a \leqq \tau \leqq b$, boundedly in $\sigma < \sigma_F - 1$. Then $F(s)$ has a continuation into the entire half-plane $\sigma < \sigma_F$, $-\infty < \tau < \infty$ with an expansion $\sum d_n' \exp(2\pi\mu_n' s)$, with $\mu_{n+1}' - \mu_n' \geqq h_\mu$, and also $\mu_{n+1} - \mu_n \geqq h_\mu$. Furthermore, the largest analytic continuation of $F(s)$ is on a schlicht domain, and each of its isolated singularities is a simple pole at $\sigma_F+i(m_1\alpha_1+\cdots+m_k\alpha_k)$, for some integers $m_1, \cdots, m_k$. *S. Bochner.*

Citations: MR 18, 19b = M40-14.
Referred to in M40-21, M40-22, M40-26, M40-27, M40-32.

## M40-16 (18, 123h)

**Richert, Hans-Egon. Beiträge zur Summierbarkeit Dirichletscher Reihen mit Anwendungen auf die Zahlentheorie.** Nachr. Akad. Wiss. Göttingen. Math.-Phys. Kl. IIa. 1956, 77–125.

The paper is devoted to the problem of obtaining information about the convergence or Riesz summability of a Dirichlet series from the function-theoretic behaviour of its sum, in particular from its order of growth on vertical lines. The author derives a large number of new results, and compares their strength to existing results. Owing to the large number of results quoted, the paper can also be used as a literature report, though it was not written for that purpose. The main feature of the paper is that old theorems dealing with the Lindelöf function $\mu(\sigma)$ are replaced by the stronger theorems involving the Carlson function $\mu_1(\sigma)$ (see below), whereas new results involving $\mu_2(\sigma)$ are obtained by introduction of a new type of strong summability. Moreover, some results are strengthened by admitting a finite number of poles.

Let $Z(s)=Z(\sigma+it)$ be analytic in a half-plane $\sigma>E$ apart from a finite number of poles in a strip $E<\sigma\leqq S$. Assume that $Z(\sigma+it)=O(|t|^C)$ $(\sigma>E, |t|>T_0)$ for some constant $C$. Further, it is assumed that $Z(s)$ is the sum of the Dirichlet series $\sum_1^\infty a_n n^{-s}$ if $\sigma$ is sufficiently large. $\sigma^*$ denotes the inf of the set of all $\xi$ such that $a_n=O(n^\xi)$. If $\kappa\geqq0$, then $\sigma_\kappa$ is the inf of the set of all $\xi$ such that the series is summable by Riesz means $(R, \log n, \kappa)$ at $s=\xi$, and similarly $\bar\sigma_\kappa$ refers to absolute summability by these means (so $\sigma$ and $\bar\sigma_0$ denote the abscissae of convergence and of absolute convergence, respectively). If $\sigma>E$, Carlson's function $\mu_k(\sigma)$ is defined as the inf of all numbers $\xi$ satisfying $\int_{T_0<|t|<T}|Z(\sigma+it)|^k dt=O(T^{\xi+1})$ (where $T_0$ is suitably chosen in order to avoid the possible poles). The author proves that (1) $\sigma^*\leqq\eta+\mu_1(\eta)$ $(\eta>E)$.

$$(2)\sigma_\kappa\leqq\sigma^*+1-(\kappa+1)(\sigma^*+1-\eta)/(1+M)\leqq\eta+M-\kappa(\eta>S)$$

where $M=\max(\mu_1(\eta), \kappa)$, and related results involving residues if $\eta>E$. (3) $\bar\sigma_0\leqq\eta+\frac12\mu_2(\eta)+\frac12$ $(\eta>E)$.

Next the author develops a theory about strong summability $|R, \log n, \kappa|^2$: the series $\sum_\infty^1 c_n$ is summable to $c$ by this method if

$$\int_1^x|C_\kappa(u)-c\log^\kappa u|^2u^{-1}du=o(\log^{2\kappa+1}x),$$

where $C_\kappa(x)=\sum_{n\leqq x} c_n$. If $\kappa'>\kappa\geqq0$ it is shown that summability $(R, \log n, \kappa)$ implies summability $|R, \log n, \kappa|^2$, and summability $|R, \log n, \kappa|^2$ implies summability $|R, \log n, \kappa'|^2$. If a Dirichlet series is summable $|R, \log n, \kappa|^2$ at a point $s=\sigma'+it'$, then the same thing applies to any point $\sigma+it$ $(\sigma>\sigma')$. Therefore it is possible to define the abscissa $\tilde\sigma_\kappa$ of summability $|R, \log n, \kappa|^2$. It is shown that $\bar\sigma_{\kappa+1}\leqq\tilde\sigma_\kappa\leqq\frac12(\bar\sigma_{\kappa+1}+\sigma_\kappa)\leqq\sigma_\kappa$. There is also a product theorem: If $\kappa\geqq0$, $\lambda\geqq0$, and if the series $Z_1(s)$ and $Z_2(s)$ are summable $|R, \log n, \kappa|^2$ and $|R, \log n, \lambda|^2$, respectively, at $s=0$, then the product series $Z_1(s)Z_2(s)$ is summable $(R, \log n, \kappa+\lambda+1)$ at $s=0$.

Bohr showed in his dissertation [Collected mathematical works, København, 1952, v. I, Dansk Matematisk Forening, København, 1952; MR 15, 276] that the abscissa $\sigma_0$ of ordinary convergence is not uniquely determined by the Lindelöf $\mu$-function. It is now shown, however, that there is a complete correspondence between $\mu_2$ and $\tilde\sigma_\kappa$: If $\kappa\geqq0$, then $\tilde\sigma_\kappa$ is the point where $\mu_2(\tilde\sigma_\kappa)=2\kappa+1$, as long as this point lies to the right of $S$. (In particular $\mu_2(\tilde\sigma_0)=1$, and in this connection it may be remarked that in special cases a proof of the stronger statement $\mu_2(\sigma_0)=1$ would imply some well-known conjectures like the one concerning the exponent $\frac14+\varepsilon$ in the problem of lattice points inside a circle.) The author extends the function $\tilde\sigma_\kappa$ to the interval $\kappa\geqq-\frac12$ by the equation $\mu_2(\tilde\sigma_\kappa)=2\kappa+1$. He shows that (1) $\sigma_\kappa\leqq\tilde\sigma_{\kappa-\frac12}\leqq\bar\sigma_\kappa(\kappa\leqq0)$; (2) $\bar\sigma_{\kappa+1}\leqq\tilde\sigma_\kappa$ $(\kappa\geqq-\frac12)$; (3) $\tilde\sigma_\kappa$ is a concave function of $\kappa$ $(\kappa\geqq-\frac12)$; (4) $\sigma_\kappa\leqq\tilde\sigma_\kappa+\frac12\leqq\sigma_{k+1}+1$ $(\kappa\geqq0)$. (5) $\bar\sigma_\kappa\leqq\tilde\sigma_{\kappa-\frac12}+\frac12\leqq\sigma_\kappa+1$ $(\kappa\geqq0)$.

The results of the paper are applied in a detailed discussion of the generalized Piltz divisor problem about the error term in the asymptotic formula of

$$f(x)=\sum_{n_1\cdots n_k\leqq x}\chi_1(n_1)\cdots\chi_k(n_k),$$

whose main term equals the residue of

$$s^{-1}x^sL(s, \chi_1)\cdots L(s, \chi_k)$$

at $s=1$. Further applications concern Hecke series related to cusp forms.

*N. G. de Bruijn* (Amsterdam).

Citations: MR 15, 276i = Z25-10.
Referred to in N36-26, N36-27, N56-15.

## M40-17 (19, 943d)

**Bochner, S. On Riemann's functional equation with multiple Gamma factors.** Ann. of Math. (2) **67** (1958), 29–41.

The functional equation

$$\pi^{-\frac12 s}\Gamma(\tfrac12 s)\phi(s)=\pi^{-\frac12+\frac12 s}\Gamma(\tfrac12-\tfrac12 s)\psi(1-s)$$

is satisfied by $\phi(s)=\psi(s)=\zeta(s)$, and it is known from the work of Hamburger and others that, if $\phi(s)$ and $\psi(s)$ are Dirichlet series of a certain type, there is no other solution. Here, the more general functional equation

$$(2P\pi)^{-\frac12 s}\Delta_1(s)\phi(s)=(2P\pi)^{\frac12 s}\Delta_2(-s)\psi(-s),$$

where $\Delta_1$ and $\Delta_2$ are products of $\Gamma$-functions, is considered. It is shown that, according to what is assumed about $\phi(s)$ and $\psi(-s)$, this has either no solutions, or at most a finite number of solutions. *E. C. Titchmarsh.*

Referred to in M40-21.

## M40-18 (20 # 838)

**Apostol, T. M.; and Sklar, Abe. The approximate functional equation of Hecke's Dirichlet series.** Trans. Amer. Math. Soc. **86** (1957), 446–462.

Die approximative Funktionalgleichung der Riemannschen Zetafunktion von Hardy und Littlewood [Proc. London Math. Soc. (2) **21** (1922), 39–74] ist von verschiedenen Autoren auf Klassen weiterer spezieller Dirichletreihen ausgedehnt worden. Die Verfasser untersuchen dieses Problem für Heckes Dirichletreihen $\phi(s)$ der Signatur $(\lambda, \kappa, \gamma)$. Ausgehend von einer Formel von Apostol [Duke Math. J. **18** (1951), 517–525; MR **13**, 15] wird eine Identität hergeleitet, aus der dann mittels Hilfssätzen von Hardy und Littlewood eine einfachste und dann die allgemeine Form einer approximativen Funktionalgleichung für diese Dirichletreihen bewiesen werden. Der Spezialfall $\phi(s)=\zeta(2s)$ mit der Signatur $(2, \frac12, 1)$ ergibt die erste Hardy-Littlewoodsche Form [Math. Z. **10** (1921), 283–317], d.h. einen zusätzlichen Logarithmusfaktor im Fehlerglied. Als Anwendung wird gezeigt, daß für die Abszisse $\sigma_a$ der absoluten Konvergenz der Reihe von $\phi(s)$ stets $\sigma_a\leqq\frac12\kappa+\frac14$ gilt [vgl. A. Z. Val'fiš, Soobšč. Akad. Nauk Gruzin. SSR. **16** (1955), 497–502; MR **17**, 349].

*H.-E. Richert* (Göttingen)

Citations: MR 13, 15c = M40-6; MR 17, 349a = F30-19.
Referred to in M40-47.

**M40-19** **(20# 4527)**

**Min, Szu-Hoa. A generalization of the Riemann $\zeta$-function. III. The mean-value theorems for $Z_{n,k}(s)$.** Acta Math. Sinica **6** (1956), 347–362. (Chinese. English summary)

[For Parts I and II, see Acta Math. Sinica **5** (1955), 285–294; **6** (1956), 1–11; MR **17**, 462; **18**, 112]. Let $\delta > k\nu$ and

$$z_{n,k}(s) = \sum_{x_1=-\infty}^{+\infty} \cdots \sum_{x_k=-\infty}^{+\infty}{}' (x_1^n + \cdots + x_k^n)^{-s},$$

where the term with $x_1 = \cdots = x_k = 0$ is excluded; further $\nu = 1/n$. The author continues his work of parts I and II and proves the following two mean value theorems. (A) Let $0 < a < k\nu - \nu$ and let $an$ not be an integer. Then, as $\delta \to 0+$,

$$\int_0^\infty t^{2a-1} |z_{n,k}(a+it)|^2 e^{-2\delta t} dt$$
$$= c_1 \delta^{-2(n-1)(k\nu-\nu-a)-1}(1+o(1)) + O(\delta^{-2a}) + O(\delta^{-4-\varepsilon}),$$

where $\varepsilon > 0$ and

$$c_1 = k^2 (2\pi)^{\frac{1}{2}} (2\pi\nu)^{-2(k-na-1)-\frac{1}{2}} (2\Gamma(1+\nu))^{2k-2}$$
$$\times \Gamma(2(1-\nu)(k-na-1)+1)\zeta(2(k-na)).$$

(B) Let $an > 0$ not be an integer, and let $2(n-1)(k\nu-\nu-a) + 1 > \max(2a, 4)$. Then, as $T \to +\infty$,

$$\int_0^T |z_{n,k}(a+it)|^2 dt \backsim c_3 T^{2(n-1)(k\nu-\nu-a)-2a+2},$$

where

$$c_3 = 2^{-2(k\nu-\nu)+\frac{1}{2}} [2(n-1)(k\nu-\nu-a) - 2a + 2]^{-1}$$
$$\times \pi^{-2(k-na)+3/2} k^2 \nu^{2na} \Gamma(\nu)^2 \zeta(2(k-na)).$$

*K. Mahler* (Manchester)

Citations: MR 17, 462b = M40-11; MR 18, 112d = M40-12.

**M40-20** **(20# 5758)**

**Maier, Wilhelm. Über einige Lambertsche Reihen.** Arch. Math. **9** (1958), 186–190.

For $\mathrm{Im}(\omega) > 0$, $\log i = \pi i/2$, put

$$H(\omega) = \frac{(-2\pi i)^s}{\Gamma(s)} \sum_{n=1}^\infty \frac{n^{s-1}}{e^{-2n\pi i\omega} - 1},$$

an analytic function of $\omega$ and $s$. Then

$$H(\omega) = \sum_{h=-\infty}^\infty \sum_{k=1}^\infty (h+k\omega)^{-s},$$

and for $\mathrm{Re}(s) > 2$, $|\mathrm{arc}(\omega/i)| < \pi/2$,

$$H(\omega) = -\frac{(-2\pi i)^s}{\Gamma(s)} \int_{(s+\varepsilon)} \frac{\Gamma(t)\zeta(t)\zeta(t+1-s)}{(-2\pi i\omega)^s} dt.$$

It is shown that for $\omega = p/q + iy$, where $(p, q) = 1$,

$$(*) \quad H(\omega) = \frac{\zeta(s)}{(q\omega-p)^s} + \frac{\zeta(2-s)}{q\omega-p} \frac{(-2\pi iq)^{s-1}}{2\Gamma(s)}$$
$$- \frac{\zeta(1-s)(-2\pi i)^s}{2\Gamma(s)} \sum_{r=1}^{q-1} \zeta\left(1-s, \frac{r}{q}\right) \cot \frac{r\pi p}{q} + O(q\omega - p),$$

where $\zeta(s, a)$ is the Hurwitz zeta-function. From (*) the author derives

$$\lim_{\delta=0} \frac{-\delta}{\log \delta} \int_0^\infty e^{-\delta t} |\zeta(\tfrac{1}{2}+it)|^2 \cos\left(t \log \frac{p}{q}\right) = (pq)^{-\frac{1}{2}}$$

for $(p, q) = 1$, which reduces to a formula of Hardy for $p = 1$. Making use of the representation

$$(-2\pi i)^{-s}\Gamma(s)H(\omega, s) = \sum_{k=1}^\infty e^{2\pi i\omega k} k^{s-1} \sigma_{1-s}(k), \quad \sigma_{1-s}(k) = \sum_{d|k} d^{1-s},$$

the author obtains the integral equation

$$\binom{a+b}{a} \sum_{n=1}^\infty q_{a,b}(n) H(n\omega, a+b-1) =$$
$$\frac{1}{2\pi i} \int_\delta^{\delta+1} H(t, a+1) H(\omega-t, b+1) dt,$$

where $0 < \mathrm{Im}(\delta) < \mathrm{Im}(\omega)$ and

$$\frac{\zeta(s-a)\zeta(s-b)}{\zeta(2s-a-b)} = \sum_{n=1}^\infty n^{-s} q_{a,b}(n).$$

*L. Carlitz* (Durham, N.C.)

Referred to in F65-17.

**M40-21** **(21# 4941)**

**Bochner, S. Theorems on analytic continuation which occur in the study of Riemann's functional equation.** J. Indian Math. Soc. (N.S.) **21** (1957), 127–147.

Given the sequences $0 < \lambda_n \uparrow \infty$, $0 < \mu_n \uparrow \infty$, and a real number $\delta > 0$, the problem of determining the maximum number of linearly independent solutions $(\varphi, \psi)$, where $\varphi(s) = \sum a_n \lambda_n^{-s}$ and $\psi(s) = \sum b_n \mu_n^{-s}$, of the functional equation

$$\pi^{-1/2s}\Gamma(\tfrac{1}{2}s)\varphi(s) = \pi^{-1/2(\delta-s)}\Gamma\{\tfrac{1}{2}(\delta-s)\}\psi(\delta-s),$$

has recently been studied by S. Bochner and K. Chandrasekharan [*] [Ann. of Math (2) **63** (1956), 336–360; MR **18**, 19] and K. Chandrasekharan and S. Mandelbrojt [**] [ibid. **66** (1957), 285–296; MR **19**, 635]. Bochner and Chandrasekharan applied a theorem of Polya [S.-B. Preuss. Akad. Wiss. **22** (1923), 45–50] on the location of singularities of an analytic function defined by a Dirichlet series $\sum a_n e^{-2\pi\lambda_n s}$ on its axis of convergence. The theorem requires two assumptions: (a) $\lim n\lambda_n^{-1} = D < \infty$; (b) $\liminf (\lambda_{n+1} - \lambda_n) > 0$. Some of the results of [*] likewise required both the assumptions. However, it was later shown in [**] that the application of Polya's theorem could be avoided, and an inequality of Mandelbrojt [*Séries adhérentes, régularisation des suites, applications*, Gauthier-Villars, Paris, 1952; MR **14**, 542; Theorem 3.7, I] used instead. This made it possible to remove the restriction (b) on $\lambda_n$ in the results of [*]. Subsequently, Bochner studied [Ann. of Math. (2) **67** (1958), 29–41; MR **19**, 943] functional equations with products of gamma factors in place of the single gamma factors $\Gamma(\frac{1}{2}s)$, $\Gamma(\frac{1}{2}(\delta-s))$—the products being subject to some arithmetical restrictions, still using the theorem of Polya [loc. cit.]. Here he shows that by the use of Mandelbrojt's theorem [loc. cit.] it is possible to relax restriction (b) on $\lambda_n$, even in the case of multiple gamma factors. He incidentally gives a variation on the theorem of Mandelbrojt, and discusses some lemmas on the analytic continuation of certain families of power series.

*K. Chandrasekharan* (Bombay)

Citations: MR 18, 19a = M40-13; MR 19, 635i = M40-15; MR 19, 943d = M40-17.

**M40-22** **(21# 4942)**

**Kahane, J. P.; et Mandelbrojt, S. Sur l'équation fonctionnelle de Riemann et la formule sommatoire de Poisson.** Ann. Sci. École Norm. Sup. (3) **75** (1958), 57–80.

[* and ** below indicate the references in #4941.]

Pursuing a line of investigation initiated by Hamburger [Math. Z. **10** (1921), 240–254; **11** (1922), 224–245; **13** (1922), 283–311; Math. Ann. **85** (1922), 129–140] and continued, in a more general setting, by Bochner [Ann. of Math. (2) **53** (1951), 332–363; MR **13**, 920], Bochner and Chandrasekharan [*] and Chandrasekharan and Mandelbrojt [C. R. Acad. Sci. Paris **242** (1956), 2793–2796; MR **18**, 195 and **], the authors study functional equations modelled on, but more general than, the functional equation of Riemann's Zeta-function.

Let $\{\lambda_n\}$, $\{\mu_n\}$ $(n \geqq 1)$ be two sequences of positive numbers increasing to infinity, and let $\delta > 0$. Let $s$ be a complex variable, $s = \sigma + i\tau$. Let the triplet $\{\delta, \lambda_n, \mu_n\}$ be called a 'label'. One speaks of a solution of the functional equation

$$(1) \qquad \pi^{-1/2s}\Gamma(\tfrac{1}{2}s)\varphi(s) = \pi^{-1/2(\delta-s)}\Gamma\{\tfrac{1}{2}(\delta-s)\}\psi(\delta-s)$$

with the label $\{\delta, \lambda_n, \mu_n\}$, if there exist two Dirichlet series $\varphi(s) = \sum a_n\lambda_n^{-s}$, $\psi(s) = \sum b_n\mu_n^{-s}$, and a function $\chi(s)$ which is holomorphic and uniform in a domain $|s| > R$, such that $\lim_{|\tau|\to\infty} \chi(\sigma + i\tau) = 0$ uniformly in every segment $\sigma_1 \leqq \sigma \leqq \sigma_2$, and such that for some pair of real numbers $\alpha$, $\beta$, we have $\chi(s) = \pi^{-1/2s}\Gamma(\frac{1}{2}s)\varphi(s)$ for $\sigma > \alpha$, and $\chi(s) = \pi^{-1/2(\delta-s)}\Gamma\{\frac{1}{2}(\delta-s)\}\psi(\delta-s)$ for $\sigma < \beta$. The authors study the relationship between such a functional equation and a summation formula of the type

$$(2) \qquad \sum_{-\infty}^{\infty} a_n f(-\lambda_n) = \sum_{-\infty}^{\infty} b_n F(\mu_n),$$

where $f \in L_1(-\infty, \infty)$, and $F$ is the Fourier transform of $f$. They refine a theorem of Hamburger [Math. Ann. **85** (1922), 129–140] by proving that with suitable restrictions on the label and on the class of functions $f$, one can pass from (1) to (2) or from (2) to (1). An interesting by-product is the result that under very light restrictions on the gap $(\lambda_{n+1} - \lambda_n)$, equation (1) has no solution if $\delta$ is an odd number greater than 3. The method of proof, which is both novel and elegant, combines the technique of almost-periodic (Schwartz) distributions with a formula first established in [*] (Th. 2.1), and since simplified by the reviewer, which exhibits the $\{\mu_n\}$ as the exponents of a Dirichlet series, and the $\{\lambda_n\}$ as the singularities of its sum-function on the axis of convergence. The authors also refine some of the results previously obtained in [*] and [**], on the maximum number of linearly independent solutions of (1), by replacing the notion of upper or lower density of the sequence $(\lambda_n)$ by the notion of upper or lower density of repartition [J. P. Kahane, Ann. Inst. Fourier, Grenoble **7** (1957), 293–314; MR **21** #1489]. Finally they obtain a generalization of a theorem proved earlier in [**] (Th. 3),—with the aid of an interesting result of S. Agmon [Bull. Res. Council Israel **3** (1954), 385–389; MR **16**, 28]—by showing that if the upper and lower densities of repartition of the sequences $(\lambda_n)$, $(\mu_n)$ exist, and equation (1) is satisfied with $\delta$ odd, then each of the sequences admits a finite base. They also obtain several properties of the sequences $(\lambda_n \pm \lambda_m)$ and $(\mu_n \pm \mu_m)$. *K. Chandrasekharan* (Bombay)

Citations: MR 13, 920b = M40-7; MR 18, 19a = M40-13; MR 19, 635i = M40-15.

## M40-23 (22# 1556 )

**Knapowski, S. On the zeros of certain Dirichlet polynomials.** Nederl. Akad. Wetensch. Proc. Ser. A **63** = Indag. Math. **22** (1960), 54–58.

The author considers a Dirichlet series $f(s) = \sum_1^\infty a_n n^{-s}$ with some of the properties of the Riemann zeta function, viz.: (1) $a_1 = 1$, $a_n = O(1)$; (2) $f(s)$ is regular and $\neq 0$ on the line $s = 1 + it$, save at $s = 1$ where it has either a pole or a zero; (3) $(f(s))^{-1} = \sum_1^\infty b_n n^{-s}$, $f'(s)/f(s) = \sum_1^\infty r_n n^{-s}$ with $b_n = O(1)$, $r_n = O(\log n)$; (4) either $r_n \leqq 0$ for all $n$ or $r_n \geqq 0$ for all $n$. He proves that, if $N$ is sufficiently large, the partial sum $\sum_1^N a_n n^{-s}$ has at least one zero in a small rectangle around the point $s = 1$, viz., the rectangle described by

$$|\sigma - 1| \leqq 2 \log\log N/\log N, \quad |t| \leqq 3 \log\log N(\log N)^{-1/2}.$$

{The author's statement that the theorem applies to the Dedekind zeta functions is incorrect, for there the $a_n$ are not always bounded.} *N. G. de Bruijn* (Eindhoven)

## M40-24 (22# 2589 )

**Chandrasekharan, K.; Mandelbrojt, S. On solutions of Riemann's functional equation.** Bull. Amer. Math. Soc. **65** (1959), 358–362.

Let $\lambda_n$, $\mu_n$ $(n \geqq 1)$ be positive increasing sequences, and consider solutions of

$$\pi^{-s/2}\Gamma(\tfrac{1}{2}s)\phi(s) = \pi^{-(\delta-s)/2}\Gamma\{\tfrac{1}{2}(\delta-s)\}\psi(\delta-s)$$

with $\varphi(s) = \sum a_n\lambda_n^{-s}$, $\psi(s) = \sum b_n\mu_n^{-s}$. One result is that if a solution exists when $\delta$ is a positive odd integer, and the infima $h_\lambda$, $h_\mu$ of $\lambda_{n+1} - \lambda_n$, $\mu_{n+1} - \mu_n$ satisfy $h_\lambda \cdot h_\mu = 1$, then $\lambda_{n+1} - \lambda_n = h_\lambda$, $\mu_{n+1} - \mu_n = h_\mu$ for all $n$. Two other results give conditions under which the existence of a solution implies that $\delta = 1$. One result requires that $h_\mu > 0$ and that $b_n = O(1)$, while the other considers solutions with $\psi(s)$ having the three forms $\sum b_n\mu_n^{-s}$, $\sum d_n\mu_n^{-s}$, $\sum b_n d_n\mu_n^{-s}$ corresponding to three $\lambda$-sequences $\{\lambda_n\}$, $\{\lambda_n'\}$, $\{\lambda_n''\}$. The proofs depend on the function $\sum b_n \exp(-2\pi\mu_n s)$. For previous work see, for example, the same authors' paper, C. R. Acad. Sci. Paris **242** (1956), 2793–2796 [MR **18**, 19—where another relevant review appears]. *F. V. Atkinson* (Toronto)

Citations: MR 18, 19b = M40-14.

## M40-25 (22# 10956 )

**Briggs, W. E.; Buschman, R. G. The power series coefficients of functions defined by Dirichlet series.** Illinois J. Math. **5** (1961), 43–44.

Let the Dirichlet series $f(s) = \sum_{n=1}^\infty h(n)n^{-s}$ have abscissa of convergence $\mathrm{Re}\, s = a$ and a simple pole at the point $s = a$. Then it possesses a Laurent expansion about $s = a$ of the form

$$f(s) = \frac{C}{s-a} + \sum_{r=0}^{\infty} \frac{(-1)^r C_r}{r!}(s-a)^r.$$

The purpose of the present note is to exhibit the coefficients $C_r$ in terms of summatory functions involving $h(n)$. It is shown, in fact, that

$$C_r = \lim_{x\to\infty} \left\{ \sum_{n \leqq x} n^{-a}h(n)(\log n)^r - \frac{C}{r+1}(\log x)^{r+1} \right\}.$$

The special case of this result corresponding to $h(n) = 1$ had been obtained previously by W. E. Briggs and S. Chowla [Amer. Math. Monthly **62** (1955), 323–325; MR **16**, 999]. *L. Mirsky* (Sheffield)

Citations: MR 16, 999f = M05-19.

## M40-26 (23# A297 )

**Bronšteĭn, B. S.**

**Singularities of a class of Dirichlet series.**

*Dokl. Akad. Nauk SSSR* **131** (1960), 996–999 (*Russian*); *translated as Soviet Math. Dokl.* **1**, 354–357.

The reviewer and S. Mandelbrojt [Ann. of Math. (2) **66** (1957), 285–296; MR **19**, 635] made use of a theorem of S. Agmon [Bull. Res. Council Israel **3** (1954), 385–389; MR **16**, 28] in their study of the solutions, in Dirichlet series, of a general functional equation similar to that satisfied by Riemann's zeta-function. The author here considers a variant of Agmon's theorem in a similar context. Let $f(s) = \sum_{n=0}^\infty a_n e^{-\lambda_n s}$, and $\liminf (\lambda_{n+1} - \lambda_n) \geqq h > 0$. Let the sequence $\{\lambda_n\}$ have an "almost regular part of dimension 1". Suppose that the only singularities of $f(s)$ on a segment $L$, of the line of convergence of the series, of length $|L| > 2\pi h^{-1}$, are simple poles at the points $i\alpha_1$, $i\alpha_2, \cdots, i\alpha_k$. Let $i\alpha$ be any simple pole of $f(s)$ on the line of convergence. Then we have $\alpha = \alpha_q + 2\pi d N_\alpha$, where $N_\alpha$ is an integer, $d$ is a positive number, and $\alpha_q$ is one of the numbers $\alpha_1, \cdots, \alpha_k$. *K. Chandrasekharan* (Bombay)

Citations: MR 19, 635i = M40-15.

**M40-27** **(23# A298)**

**Bronštein, B. S.**

**On the solution of equations of Riemann type in a class of Dirichlet series.**

*Dokl. Akad. Nauk SSSR* **130** (1960), 719–722 (*Russian*); *translated as Soviet Math. Dokl.* **1**, 82–84.

The reviewer in collaboration first with S. Bochner [Ann. of Math. (2) **63** (1956), 336–360; MR **18**, 19] and later with S. Mandelbrojt [ibid. **66** (1957), 285–296; MR **19**, 635] considered the functional equation

$$\pi^{-s/2}\Gamma\left(\frac{s}{2}\right)f(s) = \pi^{-(\delta-s)/2}\Gamma\left(\frac{\delta-s}{2}\right)g(\delta-s), \quad \delta>0,$$

and the maximum number of linearly independent solutions of the form $f(s)=\sum a_n\lambda_n^{-s}$, $g(s)=\sum b_n\mu_n^{-s}$. The author here considers the case $\delta=1$ with an additional polynomial on either side, namely,

$$\pi^{s/2}\Gamma\left(\frac{s}{2}\right)P(s)f(s) = \pi^{-(1-s)/2}\Gamma\left(\frac{1-s}{2}\right)Q(s)g(1-s),$$

and announces results similar to those in the papers cited. In particular, his equation has a solution if and only if $P(s)=s(s+1)(s+2)\cdots(s+2k-1)$, with $Q$ constant; or $Q(s)=(s-1)(s-2)\cdots(s-2k)$, with $P$ constant, where $k$ is a positive integer. In these cases the solutions are constant multiples of a translate of Riemann's zeta-function, namely, $c\zeta(s+2k)$ or $c\zeta(s-2k)$.

*K. Chandrasekharan* (Bombay)

Citations: MR 18, 19a = M40-13; MR 19, 635i = M40-15.

**M40-28** **(23# A2514)**

**Staś, W.**

**Über eine Klasse der Dirichletschen Reihen.**

*Zeszyty Nauk. Uniw. Mickiewicza No.* 25 (1960), 27–32.

Der Verfasser betrachtet die Klasse der in $\sigma>1$ absolut konvergenten Dirichletreihen $f(s)=1+\sum_{n=2}^{\infty} a_n/n^s$, $s=\sigma+it$, mit den Eigenschaften: $f(s)$ ist für $\sigma\geqq 0$ regulär mit Ausnahme eines einfachen Poles bei $s=1$; mit passenden Konstanten $K_n$ sei für $\sigma=2$ $|f(s)|>K_1>0$, für $0\leqq\sigma\leqq 4$ und alle $t$ sei $|(s-1)f(s)|\leqq K_2(|t|+1)^{K_3}$, und $|r_n|\leqq K_4\log^2 n$, wo $-(f'/f)(s)=\sum_{n=1}^{\infty} r_n/n^s$, sowie $f(s)\neq 0$ für $\sigma>1$. Es beweist das folgende (in Spezialfällen wohlbekannte) Resultat für diese Klasse: Sei

$$\Theta = \sup\{\beta: f(\beta+i\gamma) = 0,\ 0<\beta\leqq 1\}$$

und

$$\Theta' = \inf\{a: \sum_{n\leqq x} r_n - x = O(x^a)\}.$$

Dann ist $\Theta=\Theta'$. Dies verallgemeinert einen Satz von Turán [Acta. Math. Acad. Sci. Hungar. **1** (1950), 48–63; MR **13**, 208] und sein eigenes Ergebnis [Acta Arith. **5** (1959), 179–195; MR **21** #6355].

*H.-E. Richert* (Syracuse, N.Y.)

Citations: MR 13, 208f = N04-16; MR 21# 6355 = R44-13.

**M40-29** **(24# A718)**

**Mitrović, Dragiša**

**Une application de certaines inégalités de Turán. (Serbo-Croatian summary)**

*Glasnik Mat.-Fiz. Astronom. Društvo Mat. Fiz. Hrvatske Ser. II* **14** (1959), 241–246.

[Bounds for derivatives of a Dirichlet series in terms of the coefficients and exponents of the series. Ed.]

**M40-30** **(24# A1890)**

**Anfert'eva, E. A.**

**An integral similar to the classical Legendre integral. (Russian. English summary)**

*Vestnik. Leningrad. Univ.* **15** (1960), *no.* 13, 76–80.

One proof of the functional equation of Riemann's zeta function $\xi(s)$ can be made to depend on the fact that the function $f(x)=(e^{2\pi x}-1)^{-1}-(2\pi x)^{-1}$ is self-reciprocal for the Fourier sine transform, in the sense that

$$2\int_0^\infty f(x)\sin 2\pi ax\,dx = f(a)$$

(see E. C. Titchmarsh, *The theory of the Riemann zeta-function*, Ch. II, § 2.7, Clarendon, Oxford, 1951; MR **13**, 741]. The author proves here that if $g(x)=\pi^{-1}x^{\nu-1}\phi_\nu(\nu)+\sigma_\nu(x)$, where

$$\phi_\nu(s) = \xi(s+\nu)\xi(s-\nu) = \sum_{n=1}^{\infty} n^{-s-\nu}\Big(\sum_{d|n} d^{2\nu}\Big)$$

and $\sigma_\nu(x)$ is a certain related function involving modified Bessel functions of the second kind, discussed by the author in an earlier paper [Dokl. Akad. Nauk SSSR **30** (1941), 391–393; MR **2**, 347], then $g(x)$ is self-reciprocal for Hankel transforms; that is, for $a>0$,

$$\int_0^\infty J_{2\nu}(4\pi(ax)^{1/2})g(x)\,dx = (2\pi)^{-1}g(a).$$

*H. Halberstam* (London)

Citations: MR 2, 347f = M40-2; MR 13, 741c = M02-2.

**M40-31** **(25# 2045)**

**Nadler, Horst**

**Über einige Dirichletsche Reihen.**

*Math. Nachr.* **23** (1961), 265–270.

Put

$$\rho_a(n) = n^{-a/2}\sigma_a(n) = n^{-a/2}\sum_{d|n} d^a.$$

The author obtains such identities as

$$\sum_{n=1}^{\infty} \rho_a(n^k)n^{-s} = \zeta\left(s+\frac{ak}{2}\right)\zeta\left(s-\frac{ak}{2}\right)\prod_p [1+\rho_a(p^{k-2})p^{-s}],$$

$$\sum_{n=1}^{\infty} \rho_a(n^2)n^{-s} = \frac{\zeta(s)\zeta(s+a)\zeta(s-a)}{\zeta(2s)},$$

$$\sum_{n=1}^{\infty} \bar\rho_a(n)n^{-s} = \zeta\left(s+\frac{ak}{2}\right)\zeta\left(s-\frac{ak}{2}\right)\prod_p [1-\bar\rho_a(p^{k-2})p^{-s}],$$

where $\bar\rho_a(n)=\rho_{2a}(n)/\rho_a(n)$ and $k$ is an integer $\geqq 2$. He also obtains a sufficient condition such that $\sum_{n=1}^{\infty}\rho_a(n^k)n^{-s}=0$. Similar results are obtained which are related to $\eta(s)=\sum_{n=0}^{\infty}(-1)^n(2n+1)^{-s}$.

*L. Carlitz* (Durham, N.C.)

Referred to in A30-22.

**M40-32** **(26# 86)**

**Bronšteĭn, B. S.**

**The solution of equations of Riemann type in a class of Dirichlet series. (Russian)**

*Mat. Sb.* (*N.S.*) **54 (96)** (1961), 425–452.

L'auteur considère l'équation de la forme

$$f(s)P(s)\pi^{-s/2}\Gamma\left(\frac{s}{2}\right) = g(1-s)Q(s)\pi^{-(1-s)/2}\Gamma\left(\frac{1-s}{2}\right),$$

où $f(s)=\sum a_n/\lambda_n^s$, $g(s)=\sum b_n/\mu_n^s$, chacune de ces séries admettant une abscisse de convergence absolue finie. Il obtient pour ces équations des résultats semblables à ceux obtenus dans les travaux de Bochner et Chandrasekharan

[Ann. of Math. (2) **63** (1956), 336–360; MR **18**, 19] et Chandrasekharan et le rapporteur [ibid. **66** (1957), 285–296; MR **19**, 635]. *S. Mandelbrojt* (Paris)

Citations: MR 18, 19a = M40-13; MR 19, 635i = M40-15.

## M40-33 (27# 3605)

**Chandrasekharan, K.; Narasimhan, Raghavan**
**The approximate functional equation for a class of zeta-functions.**
*Math. Ann.* **152** (1963), 30–64.

The authors have significantly generalized the well-known "approximate functional equation" for the Riemann zeta function, due to Hardy and Littlewood. In particular, they have solved the difficult question of obtaining an approximate functional equation for the Dedekind zeta function $\zeta_K(s)$ of an algebraic number-field $K$.

Let $\{a_n\}$, $\{b_n\}$ be two sequences of complex numbers, not all of the terms of which are zero. Let $\{\lambda_n\}$, $\{\mu_n\}$ be two sequences of real numbers such that

$$0 < \lambda_1 < \lambda_2 < \cdots < \lambda_n \to \infty,$$
$$0 < \mu_1 < \mu_2 < \cdots < \mu_n \to \infty.$$

Let $\delta$ be a real number, $s$ a complex number with $s = \sigma + it$. Let

$$\Delta(s) = \prod_{\nu=1}^{N} \Gamma(\alpha_\nu s + \beta_\nu),$$

where $N \geqq 1$, $\beta_\nu$ is an arbitrary complex number and $\alpha_\nu > 0$. Let $A \equiv \sum_1^N \alpha_\nu$. We say that the functional equation

$$(1) \qquad \Delta(s)\phi(s) = \Delta(\delta - s)\psi(\delta - s)$$

is satisfied if $\phi$ and $\psi$ can be represented by the Dirichlet series $\phi(s) = \sum_{n=1}^\infty a_n\lambda_n^{-s}$, $\psi(s) = \sum_{n=1}^\infty b_n\mu_n^{-s}$, each of which converges absolutely in some half-plane, and there exists in the $s$-plane a domain $D$ which is the exterior of a bounded closed set $S$, in which there exists a holomorphic function $\chi$ with the property $\lim_{|t|\to\infty} \chi(\sigma + it) = 0$ uniformly in every interval $-\infty < \sigma_1 \leqq \sigma \leqq \sigma_2 < +\infty$ and

$$\chi(s) = \Delta(s)\phi(s), \qquad \text{for } \sigma > c_1,$$
$$= \Delta(\delta - s)\psi(\delta - s), \qquad \text{for } \sigma < c_2,$$

where $c_1$, $c_2$ are certain constants.

The authors then prove the following. Theorem 1: If the functional equation (1) holds, and if $\rho$ is the smallest integer satisfying $\rho > 2A\alpha - A\delta - \frac{1}{2}$, where $\alpha$ is the abscissa of absolute convergence of $\sum_{n=1}^\infty b_n\mu_n^{-s}$, and $\sigma \geqq \delta/2 - \rho/2A$, and

$$B(u) \equiv \sum_{\mu_n \leqq u} |b_n| = c_1 u^\alpha (\log u)^p + O(u^{\alpha - q}(\log u)^p), \quad q \geqq \frac{1}{2A},$$

then we have the approximate functional equation given by

$$\phi(s) - \sum_{\lambda_n \leqq x} a_n\lambda_n^{-s} = \frac{1}{2\pi i}\int \frac{\phi(z)}{s - z} x^{z-s}\,dz$$
$$- x^{-s} \sum_{r=0}^{\rho-1} \frac{\Gamma(s+r)}{\Gamma(s)} x^{-r}[A_\lambda{}^r(x) - S_r(x)]$$
$$+ \frac{\Delta(\delta - s)}{\Delta(s)}\left[1 + O\left(\frac{1}{|s|^{m+1}}\right)\right] \sum_{\mu_n \leqq y} b_n\mu^{s-\delta}$$
$$+ O\left[x^{\delta/2 - \sigma - 1/4A} y^{\alpha - \delta/2 - 1/4A} \log^p y \left\{\log y + \left(\frac{x}{y}\right)^{1/4A}\right\}\right]$$
$$+ O(y^{\rho/2A} x^{-K}).$$

where $K$ is an arbitrary positive number, $x > M > 1$, $y > M > 1$, and $xy = (2A/h)^{2A}|t|^{2A}$. The $O$'s are uniform in $\sigma$ for $\delta/2 - \rho/2A \leqq \sigma \leqq H$, $H$ being any positive constant.

When applied to $\zeta_K(s)$, one gets the estimate

$$(1) \qquad \zeta_K(s) = O(t^{n(1-\sigma)/2})$$

uniformly in $0 < \varepsilon \leqq \sigma \leqq 1 - \varepsilon < 1$. Also $\zeta_K(1 + it) = O(\log |t|)$.
*S. Chowla* (University Park, Pa.)

Referred to in M05-38, M40-41, M40-47, N36-36, R42-51, R42-53.

## M40-34 (28# 2100)

**de Bruijn, N. G.; van Lint, J. H.**
**On the asymptotic behaviour of some Dirichlet series with a complicated singularity.**
*Nieuw Arch. Wisk.* (3) **11** (1963), 68–75.

For $n$ a positive integer, let $\alpha(n)$ be the product of all the different primes dividing $n$. Say that $n$ is $\lambda$-full if $n$ is divisible by at least the $\lambda$th power of each prime which divides it. Put

$$f_\lambda(s) = \sum^{(\lambda)} (\alpha(n))^{-1} n^{-s} \quad \text{and} \quad S_\lambda(x) = \sum_{n \leqq x}^{(\lambda)} (\alpha(n))^{-1},$$

where the summations are over the $\lambda$-full positive integers. Finally, put $g(s) = \sum_{n=1}^\infty n^{-1}\varphi(n)(\alpha(n))^{-1}n^{-s}$. The authors obtain asymptotic results concerning the $f_\lambda(s)$ and $g(s)$ as $s \to 0$, and $S_\lambda(x)$ as $x \to \infty$. Typical results are:

$$(1) \qquad g(s)/f_1(s) \sim e^{-\gamma}/\log(1/s) \quad \text{as} \quad s \to 0+;$$
$$(2) \qquad f_\lambda(s)/f_{\lambda+1}(s) \sim \lambda^{-1}e^{-\gamma}(-s\log s)^{-1} \quad \text{as} \quad s \to 0+;$$
$$(3) \qquad \log S_\lambda(e^t) \sim (8t/\log t)^{1/2} \quad \text{as} \quad t \to \infty.$$

*D. G. Cantor* (Seattle, Wash.)

## M40-35 (30# 1988)

**Chandrasekharan, K.; Narasimhan, Raghavan**
**Hecke's functional equation and arithmetical identities.**
*Ann. of Math.* (2) **74** (1961), 1–23.

The authors prove that the functional equations

$$(1) \qquad (2\pi)^{-s}\Gamma(s)\varphi(s) = (2\pi)^{s-\delta}\Gamma(\delta - s)\psi(\delta - s),$$

$$(2) \qquad \sum_{n=1}^\infty a_n e^{-\lambda_n x} = P(x) + \left(\frac{2\pi}{x}\right)^\delta \sum_{n=1}^\infty b_n \exp(-4\pi^2\mu_n/x)$$

are equivalent to the identities

$$(3) \qquad \frac{1}{\Gamma(\rho+1)} \sum_{\lambda_n \leqq x}' a_n(x - \lambda_n)^\rho = \left(\frac{1}{2\pi}\right)^\rho \sum_{n=1}^\infty \left(\frac{x}{\mu_n}\right)^{(\delta+\rho)/2} \times b_n J_{\delta+\rho}(4\pi\sqrt{(\mu_n x)}) + Q_\rho(x),$$

$$(4) \qquad \left(-\frac{1}{s}\frac{d}{ds}\right)^\rho \left[\frac{1}{s}\sum_{n=1}^\infty a_n e^{-s\sqrt{\lambda_n}}\right] = 2^{3\delta+\rho}\Gamma(\delta+\rho+\tfrac{1}{2})\pi^{\delta-1/2} \sum_{n=1}^\infty \frac{b_n}{(s^2 + 16\pi^2\mu_n)^{\delta+\rho+1/2}} + R_\rho(s)$$

if

$$\varphi(s) = \sum_{n=1}^\infty a_n\lambda_n^{-s}, \qquad \psi(s) = \sum_{n=1}^\infty b_n\mu_n^{-s},$$

where $\delta$ is a real number,

$$P(x) = \frac{1}{2\pi i}\int_C \Gamma(s)\varphi(s)x^{-s}\,ds$$

$$\sum_{n=1} |b_n|\mu_n^{-\infty} < \infty,$$

$$\rho \geqq 2\beta - \delta - \tfrac{1}{2},$$

$$Q_\rho(x) = \frac{1}{2\pi i}\int_C \frac{\Gamma(s)\varphi(s)x^{s+\rho}}{\Gamma(\rho+1+s)}\,ds,$$

$$R_\rho(s) = \frac{1}{2\pi i}\int_C \frac{\Gamma(z)\varphi(z)\Gamma(2z+2\rho+1)2^{-\rho}}{\Gamma(z+\rho+1)} s^{-2z-2\rho-1}\,dz,$$

and where $J_{\delta+\rho}(4\pi\sqrt{(\mu_n x)})$ is a Bessel function. They also establish (3) in the case $\rho=0$ for certain classes of Dirichlet series. As examples they consider identities of the type (3) and (4) for the Ramanujan function $\tau(n)$; $\sigma_k(n)=\sum_{d|n} d^k$; $r_k(n)$, the number of representations of $n$ as a sum of $k$ squares; $r(Q,n)$, the number of representations of $n$ as a positive definite quadratic form in $k$ variables, and for $\mu(S,t)$, the "measure of representability" of the number $t$ by an indefinite quadratic form in $k\geqq 4$ variables $x_1,\cdots,x_k$ with rational coefficients.

{Reviewer's remark: Part of the results related to identities of the type (3) overlap with results of A. A. Val'fiš [Soobšč. Akad. Nauk Gruzin. SSR **26** (1961), 9–16; MR **26** #83].} *B. V. Levin* (RŽMat **1962** #7 A96)

Citations: MR 26# 83 = P28-55.
Referred to in M40-43, M40-46, M40-49, M40-59.

## M40-36 (32# 5606)

**Götze, Friedhelm**
**Ein Analogon zu einer Identität von Titchmarsh.**
*Math. Nachr.* **30** (1965), 203–207.

The author proves for Re $s>1$ the identity

$$\sum_{n=1}^{\infty} d^k(n)n^{-s} = \zeta^2(s)\prod_p R_{k-1}((1+p^{-s})(1-p^{-s})^{-1}),\qquad k=1,2,\cdots,$$

where $d(n)$ denotes the number of divisors of $n$ and $\zeta(s)$ the Riemann $\zeta$-function; the $R_k(z)$ are certain polynomials (of degree $k$ in $z$), for which a recursion formula and a generating function are given.

As a by-product, the author obtains $d_3{}^2(n)=\sum_{t|n} d^3(t)$. *W. Schwarz* (Freiburg)

Referred to in M40-44.

## M40-37 (33# 4022)

**Emersleben, Otto**
**Erweiterung des Konvergenzbereichs einer Potenzreihe durch Herausnahme von Singularitäten, insbesondere zur Berechnung einer Zetafunktion zweiter Ordnung.**
*Math. Nachr.* **31** (1966), 195–220.

P. Epstein [Math. Ann. **56** (1903), 615–644] defined a generalized zeta function of order $p$:

$$^{(p)}Z\begin{vmatrix} g_1, g_2, \cdots, g_p \\ h_1, h_2, \cdots, h_p\end{vmatrix}(s)_\phi,$$

where $\phi$ denotes a quadratic form. The present paper is concerned mainly with the special case $s=p=2, \phi=u^2+v^2$:

$$Z\begin{vmatrix} 0 & 0 \\ x & y\end{vmatrix}(2) = \sum_{n=1}^{\infty}\frac{1}{n}\sum_{k^2+l^2=n}\cos 2\pi(kx+ly);$$

it is assumed that $x$ and $y$ are not both rational integers. The function can be evaluated explicitly in certain special cases; for example,

$$Z\begin{vmatrix} 0 & 0 \\ \frac14 & \frac14\end{vmatrix}(2) = -\frac{\pi}{4}\log 2,\qquad Z\begin{vmatrix} 0 & 0 \\ \frac12 & \frac12\end{vmatrix}(2) = -\pi\log 2.$$

The author showed in his dissertation [Göttingen, 1922] that

$$Z\begin{vmatrix} 0 & 0 \\ x & y\end{vmatrix}(2) = -\pi\log(x^2+y^2)+c_0 +\pi^2(x^2+y^2)+\sum_{n=1}^{\infty} c_{4n}R(x+yi)^{4n}.$$

The formula $c_0=-2\pi\{\log 2-\pi/6+2\sum_{n=1}^{\infty}\log(1-e^{-2\pi n})\}$ is due to C. L. Siegel. Also, it is known that all $c_{4n}>0$. The author shows that $c_{4n}\sim 2\pi/n$. Put $\wp(z;g_2,0)=1/z^2+\sum_{n=1}^{\infty} a_n g_2{}^n z^{4n-2}$, where the left member is the Weierstrass $\wp$-function in the case $g_3=0$. Then $a_1=1/20$ and $a_n=(3/(2n-3)(4n+1))\sum_{k=1}^{n-1} a_k a_{n-k}$ $(n\geqq 2)$; moreover, $a_n=2^{2n}E_n/4n(4n-2)!$, where the $E_n$ are the coefficients introduced by A. Hurwitz [Math. Ann. **51** (1898/99), 196–226]. The $c_{4n}$ are related to $a_n$ by means of $c_{4n}=(\pi/2n(4n-1))a_n g_2{}^n$; $g_2$ is a certain numerical constant.

The author employs the above formulas for the computation of $a_n$, $c_{4n}$ as well as certain related sequences; $a_n$ is computed to 25 places and $c_{4n}$ to 24 places for $n\leqq 15$. *L. Carlitz* (Durham, N.C.)

## M40-38 (33# 7311)

**Sokolovskiĭ, A. V.**
**Density theorems for a class of zeta functions.** (Russian. Uzbek summary)
*Izv. Akad. Nauk UzSSR Ser. Fiz.-Mat. Nauk* **10** (1966), *no.* 3, 33–40.

Verfasser überträgt die bei der Riemannschen Zetafunktion entwickelten Beweise für Abschätzungen der Anzahl $N(\alpha,T)$ der Nullstellen in $\alpha\leqq\sigma\leqq 1$, $|t|\leqq T$, auf eine allgemeinere Klasse von Dirichletreihen. $Z(s)$ sei mit höchstens der Ausnahme eines Pols bei $s=1$ analytisch für $\sigma\geqq\frac12$. Für $\sigma>1$ besitzen $Z(s)$ und $1/Z(s)$ Dirichletreihen für deren Koeffizienten je eine Abschätzung der Form $\sum_{n\leqq x}|c_n|^2\ll x\log^{2k}x$ bestehe. Falls dann $|Z(1/2+it)|\ll|t|^c\log^{c_1}(|t|+2)$ für $\alpha\geqq\frac12+1/\log T$ gilt, so beweist Verfasser $N(\alpha,T)\ll T^{2(1+2c)(1-\alpha)}(\log T)^{4c_1(1-\alpha)+2k+5}$. *H.-E. Richert* (Marburg)

Referred to in R44-40.

## M40-39 (35# 4174)

**Lavrik, A. F.**
**Functional equations of the Dirichlet functions.** (Russian)
*Izv. Akad. Nauk SSSR Ser. Mat.* **31** (1967), 431–442.

Sei $\Gamma_k(s)=\prod_{1\leqq\kappa\leqq k}\Gamma(\alpha_\kappa s+\beta_\kappa)$ ein Produkt von Gammafunktionen; $\varphi(s)=\sum a_n n^{-s}$ und $\psi(s)=\sum b_n n^{-s}$ seien für Re $s>\delta$ absolut konvergent. Der Autor folgert aus dem Bestehen der Funktionalgleichung $A^s\Gamma_k(s)\varphi(s)=\lambda B^{\delta-s}\times\Gamma_k(\delta-s)\psi(\delta-s)$ die Beziehung

$$(*)\quad \sum a_n\int_{(\sigma)}\Gamma_k(z)(A/n)^z\phi(z-s)\,dz -\lambda\sum b_n\int_{(\delta-\gamma)}\Gamma_k(z)(B/n)^z\phi(-z+\delta-s)\,dz = 2\pi i\sum_{z\in\Omega}\operatorname{res}\{A^z\Gamma_k(z)\varphi(z)\phi(z-s)\}$$

für alle in $\Omega=\{z:\gamma\leqq\text{Re } z\leqq\sigma\}$ analytischen Funktionen $\phi$ (mit höchstens endlich vielen Polen in $\Omega$) von "nicht zu starkem Wachstum", die so beschaffen sind, daß $\sum$ und $\int$ in (*) vertauschbar sind. Weitere Sätze ersetzen die letzte Bedingung durch eine weitere Wachstumsbedingung für $\phi$ ($\phi$ ist vom Exponentialtyp, Typ $<\frac12\pi\sum\alpha_\kappa$) und geben einige Spezialfälle.

Der Autor illustriert die Tragweite des Satzes am Beispiel der Dirichletschen $L$-Funktionen (mit $\phi(w)=w^{-1}\exp(yw)$); insbesondere kann die approximative Funktionalgleichung erhalten werden.

Die Sätze des Autors verallgemeinern Ergebnisse von A. O. Gel'fond [dieselben Izv. **24** (1960), 469–474; MR **22** #7981] und eigene Ergebnisse [der Autor, Izv. Akad. Nauk UzSSR Ser. Fiz.-Mat. Nauk **9** (1965), no. 4, 17–22; MR **32** #5609]. *W. Schwarz* (Freiburg)

Citations: MR 22# 7981 = M05-24; MR 32# 5609 = M05-38.
Referred to in M05-48, M40-41.

## M40-40 (36# 5089)

**Anfert'eva, E. A.**

**Cauchy type integrals representing Dirichlet series. (Russian)**

*Izv. Vysš. Učebn. Zaved. Matematika* **1968**, *no.* 2 (69), 3–15.

The author obtains some interesting identities for some general functions which satisfy functional equations similar to those satisfied by Riemann's zeta function and Dirichlet's $L$-series. The general results are too long to quote here. We mention one of the striking simple cases:

$$\pi^{-s/2}\Gamma(\tfrac{1}{2}s)\zeta(s) = 1/(s-1)+\pi^{-s/2}\sum_{n=1}^{\infty} n^{-s}\Gamma(\tfrac{1}{2}s,\pi n^2) + \pi^{-(1-s)/2}\sum_{n=1}^{\infty} n^{s-1}\Gamma(\tfrac{1}{2}(1-s),\pi n^2),$$

where $\zeta(s)$ is Riemann's zeta function and $\Gamma(\alpha,u)=\int_u^\infty e^{-x}x^{\alpha-1}\,dx$ (Re $\alpha>0$). This is Formula (2.26) of the author's paper. *S. Chowla* (University Park, Pa.)

## M40-41 (36# 6361)

**Lavrik, A. F.**

**Approximate functional equations of Dirichlet functions. (Russian)**

*Izv. Akad. Nauk SSSR Ser. Mat.* **32** (1968), 134–185.

Die durch die Dirichletreihe $\varphi(s)=\sum a_n\lambda_n^{-s}$ definierte Funktion $\varphi$ genüge einer Funktionalgleichung der Gestalt

$$A^s\prod_{1\le\kappa\le k}\Gamma(\alpha_\kappa s+\beta_\kappa)\cdot\varphi(s) = \lambda B^{\delta-s}\prod_{1\le\kappa\le k}\Gamma(\alpha_\kappa(\delta-s)+\beta_\kappa)\cdot\psi(\delta-s)$$

(mit $\psi(s)=\sum b_n\xi_n^{-s}$; $A$, $B$, $\alpha_\kappa>0$; $\lambda$ und $\beta_\kappa$ komplex).

In der vorliegenden langen und technisch schwierigen Arbeit (die als Fortsetzung der Arbeit des Verfassers in denselben Izv. **31** (1967), 431–442 [MR **35** #4174] betrachtet werden kann) beweist der Verfasser für $\varphi$ eine abgekürzte Funktionalgleichung. Eine solche Funktionalgleichung haben auch K. Chandrasekharan und R. Narasimhan [Math. Ann. **152** (1963), 30–64; MR **27** #3605] bewiesen; die abgekürzte Funktionalgleichung des Verfassers unterscheidet sich von dieser dadurch, daß sie in einer ganzen Reihe von Parametern gleichmäßig ist. Dabei geht allerdings die vertraute Gestalt der abgekürzten Funktionalgleichung verloren; $\varphi(s)$ wird nicht mehr durch Summen der Gestalt $\sum_{n<x} a_n\lambda_n^{-s}$ und $\sum_{n<y} b_n\xi_n^{\delta-s}\times$ (Produkt von Gamma-Funktionen) approximiert; vielmehr geht in diese beiden Summen ein zusätzlicher Faktor $F(s,\lambda_n,A)$ bzw. $F(\delta-s,\xi_n,B)$ ein. Für diesen Faktor $F$ wird eine Darstellung durch Hauptglied und Restglied gegeben, aus der man ersehen kann, daß die übliche Gestalt der abgekürzten Funktionalgleichung in der des Verfassers enthalten ist.

Spezialfälle des Ergebnisses finden sich in früheren Arbeiten des Verfassers [Izv. Akad. Nauk SSSR Ser. Mat. **30** (1966), 433–448; MR **34** #4223; Mat. Zametki **2** (1967), 475–482; MR **36** #2571]. *W. Schwarz* (Freiburg)

Citations: MR 27# 3605 = M40-33; MR 34# 4223 = M05-41; MR 35# 4174 = M40-39; MR 36# 2571 = R42-38.

## M40-42 (37# 167)

**Israilov, M. I.**

**Certain Dirichlet series with multiplicative coefficients. (Russian)**

*Voprosy Vyčisl. Mat. Tehn. Vyp.* 1 (1964), 11–17.

The author proves that if $a_n$ is completely multiplicative, then in the half plane of absolute convergence,

$$\sum a_n n^{-s} = \sum a_n\mu^2(n)/\varphi_{s,a}(n) = (p^s/\varphi_{s,a}(p))\sum_{(n,p)=1} a_n\mu^2(n)/\varphi_{s,a}(n),$$

where $\varphi_{s,a}(n)=n^s\prod_1^k(1-a_{p_i}/p_i^s)$ and $p_1,\cdots,p_k$ are the primes dividing $n$. {Reviewer's remarks: The identity (3) is false with counterexample $a_n=(1+(-1)^{n+1})/2$, the proof failing between pages 14 and 15. The proof of identity (4) fails on line 6 of page 15. Identities (7), (9), (12) and (13) are also false or not proved.}

*R. Spira* (E. Lansing, Mich.)

## M40-43 (37# 1325)

**Berndt, Bruce C.**

**Generalised Dirichlet series and Hecke's functional equation.**

*Proc. Edinburgh Math. Soc.* (2) **15** (1966/67), 309–313.

In a generalisation of Hecke's functional equation due to K. Chandrasekharan and R. Narasimhan [Ann. of Math. (2) **74** (1961), 1–23; MR **30** #1988], functions $\phi(s)=\sum a(n)\lambda_n^{-s}$ and $\psi(s)=\sum b(n)\mu_n^{-s}$ satisfy $\Gamma(s)\phi(s)=\Gamma(r-s)\psi(r-s)$ if both sides of the equation are equal to the same analytic function $\chi(s)$ in appropriate regions. In these circumstances the author defines $\phi(s,a)=\sum a(n)(a+\lambda_n)^{-s}$ $(a>0)$ and establishes the relation $\Gamma(s)a^s\times\phi(s,a)=2a^{(r+s)/2}\sum b(n)\mu_n^{(r-s)/2}K_{r-s}(2(a\mu_n)^{1/2})+(1/2\pi i)\times\int_C\Gamma(s-z)\chi(z)a^z\,dz$, $K_p$ being a Bessel function, for a suitable $C$ in an appropriate $s$-region.

*M. E. Noble* (Canterbury)

Citations: MR 30# 1988 = M40-35.

Referred to in M40-59.

## M40-44 (37# 2708)

**Carlitz, L.**

**Note on a paper of Götze.**

*Math. Nachr.* **35** (1967), 289–293.

Define $d_r(n)$ by $\zeta^r(s)=\sum d_r(n)\cdot n^{-s}$ $(r=2,3,\cdots)$. Generalizing a result of F. Götze's [same Nachr. **30** (1965), 203–207; MR **32** #5606] the author derives the identity

$$\sum_1^\infty\{d_{r+1}(n)\}^k\cdot n^{-s} = \zeta^{r+1}(s)\cdot\prod_p\{\textstyle\sum_{j=0}^{(k-1)r}S_r(k,j)\cdot p^{-sj}(1-p^{-s})^{-j}\},$$

with explicitly given coefficients $S_r(k,j)$.

*W. Schwarz* (Freiburg)

Citations: MR 32# 5606 = M40-36.

## M40-45 (38# 4421)

**Fröberg, Carl-Erik**

**On the prime zeta function.**

*Nordisk Tidskr. Informationsbehandling* (*BIT*) **8** (1968), 187–202.

The function in the title is defined by the Dirichlet series $P(s)=\sum p^{-s}$, $s=\sigma+it$, $\sigma>1$, where the sum runs over all primes $p$. The author tabulates $P(s)$ for various values of $s$. Table I lists four roots of the equation $P(s)=0$, one root of $P(s)=-1$, and one (real) root of $P(s)=1$. Table II lists $P(s)$ for $\sigma=0.05(0.01)1.1(0.1)10$ and $t=0$, while Table III gives $P(s)$ for $\sigma=0.2(0.2)2.0$ and $t=1(1)20$. The author also considers the related Dirichlet series defined by $(1+P(s))\sum a_n n^{-s}=1$ and $(1-P(s))\sum A_n n^{-s}=1$ and gives properties of the partial sums $\sum_{r=1}^n a_r$, $\sum_{r=1}^n a_r/r$, $\sum_{r=1}^n A_r$, and $\sum_{r=1}^n A_r/r$. *T. M. Apostol* (Pasadena, Calif.)

## M40-46 (38# 4656)

**Berndt, Bruce C.**

**Identities involving the coefficients of a class of Dirichlet series. I, II.**

*Trans. Amer. Math. Soc.* **137** (1969), 345–359; *ibid.* **137** (1969), 361–374.

Es seien $\varphi(s)=\sum a(n)\lambda_n^{-s}$, $\psi(s)=\sum b(n)\mu_n^{-s}$ mit $\lambda_n\to\infty$, $\mu_n\to\infty$ Dirichletreihen, die einer Funktionalgleichung $\Gamma^m(s)\varphi(s)=\Gamma^m(r-s)\psi(r-s)$ genügen. Z.B. sei $f(s)=\sum\tau(n)n^{-s}$ und $(2\pi)^{-s}\Gamma(s)f(s)=(2\pi)^{-(12-s)}\Gamma(12-s)f(12-s)$, d.h. $\varphi(s)=\psi(s)=\sum\tau(n)(2\pi n)^{-s}$, $m=1$, $r=12$. Bekanntlich ist diese Funktionalgleichung mit jeder der folgenden beiden Gleichungen für die Ramanujanschen $\tau(n)$ äquivalent: $\sum\tau(n)e^{-ny}=(2\pi/y)^{12}\sum\tau(n)e^{-4\pi^2n/y}$ und

(1) $(1/\Gamma(q+1))\sum_{n\le x}\tau(n)(x-n)^q=$

$$(2\pi)^{-q}\sum\tau(n)(x/n)^{6+q/12}\mathfrak{J}_{12+q}(4\pi\sqrt{(nx)}).$$

Dabei bedeuten die $\mathfrak{J}_r(z)$ Besselfunktionen. Im Unterschied zu K. Chandrasekharan und R. Narasimhan [Ann. of Math. (2) **74** (1961), 1–23; MR **30** #1988], die entsprechende Äquivalenzsätze für sehr allgemeine $\varphi$ und $\psi$, jedoch nur für den Fall $m=1$ herleiten, behandelt Verfasser den Fall $m=$natürliche Zahl und erhält wiederum die Äquivalenz der entsprechenden 3 Typen von Funktionalgleichungen. Die Gültigkeit der Funktionalgleichungen vom Typ (1) wird besonders für kleine $q$ behandelt. Beweise, im wesentlichen, nach Heckeschem Vorbild mit Mellintransformation. Als Beispiele werden behandelt: das Quadrat $f^2(s)$ der oben eingeführten Funktion $f(s)$, das Quadrat $\zeta^2(2s)$ der Riemannschen $\zeta$-Funktion und die Dedekindsche $\zeta$-Funktion $\zeta_K(s)$ eines algebraischen Zahlkörpers $K$ vom Grad $r_1+2r_2$, wobei entweder $r_1=0$ oder $r_2=0$ sein muß ($r_1$, $r_2$ Anzahl der reellen bzw. imaginären Konjugierten). Im 2. Teil der Abhandlung wird die Gleichung des Typs (1) durch einen anderen Gleichungstyp ersetzt, bei dem die linke Seite $\sum_{\lambda_n\le x}^{1} a(n)\log^q(x/\lambda_n)$ lautet. Für $q=0$ ergibt sich das gleiche wie in Teil 1. Als Beispiel werden behandelt: Die Riemannsche $\zeta$-Funktion. Etwa im Falle $q=1$ erhält man für $\sum_{n\le x}\log(x/n)$ eine Reihe, in der die Bernoullischen Polynome auftreten. Ferner: $\zeta^2(2s)$, Epstein's $\zeta$-Funktion und weitere Dirichletreihen, die wie $f(s)$ mit $\Delta(z)$ zusammenhängen. *W. Maak* (Göttingen)

Citations: MR 30# 1988 = M40-35.
Referred to in M40-50, M40-59.

## M40-47 (38# 6036)

**Berndt, B. C.**

**An identity for certain Dirichlet series.**

*Glasgow Math. J.* **9** (1968), 79–82.

Bei der Herleitung der approximativen Funktionalgleichung für gewisse Dirichletreihen wird zuerst eine Identität bewiesen, in der die Partialsumme der Dirichletreihe auftritt [T. M. Apostol and A. Sklar, Trans. Amer. Math. Soc. **86** (1957), 446–462; MR **20** #838; K. Chandrasekharan and R. Narasimhan, Math. Ann. **152** (1963), 30–64; MR **27** #3605]. Für diese Identität gibt Verfasser einen (kurzen) Beweis, der allerdings nur für den Fall Heckescher Dirichletreihen explizit vorgeführt wird.

*W. Maak* (Göttingen)

Citations: MR 20# 838 = M40-18; MR 27# 3605 = M40-33.

## M40-48 (40# 105)

**Halász, G.**

**Über die Konvergenz multiplikativer zahlentheoretischer Funktionen.**

*Studia Sci. Math. Hungar.* **4** (1969), 171–178.

The author proves that if $g(n)$ is a completely multiplicative function, with $|g(n)|\le 1$, then the partial sums of the Dirichlet series $G(s)=\sum_{n=1}^{\infty} g(n)/n^s$ ($s=\sigma+it$) are bounded almost everywhere on $\sigma=1$. Furthermore, if in fact the series converges at a single point of $\sigma=1$, it converges almost everywhere on $\sigma=1$.

The proof of the first statement proceeds in two steps: (i) It is first shown that if $g$ satisfies the above conditions and also $G(s)=O(|s-1|/(\sigma-1))$ uniformly in $\sigma>1$, then $\sum_{n\le x} g(n)/n=O(1)$; (ii) then, that for $g$ as above, for almost all real $a$, $G(s)=O(|s-1-ia|/(\sigma-1))$ uniformly for $\sigma>1$.

The proof of (i) depends on showing that $f(n)=\sum_{d|n} g(d)$ satisfies the conditions of an earlier theorem of the author concerning mean values of multiplicative functions [Acta Math. Acad. Sci. Hungar. **19** (1968), 365–403; MR **37** #6254].

The proof of (ii) depends upon an appropriate use of Parseval's theorem and Fatou's theorem.

The statement about convergence is proved completely analogously and is carried out in footnotes where the necessary variations in proof are remarked.

*S. L. Segal* (Rochester, N.Y.)

Citations: MR 37# 6254 = N36-69.
Referred to in M40-62.

## M40-49 (40# 4212)

**Berndt, Bruce C.**

**Arithmetical identities and Hecke's functional equation.**

*Proc. Edinburgh Math. Soc.* (2) **16** (1968/69), 221–226.

Let $r(n)$ denote the number of representations of a positive integer as a sum of two squares. The well-known identity of Hardy and Landau gives an expansion of the function $\{\Gamma(\alpha+1)\}^{-1}\sum_{n\le x} r(n)(x-n)^\alpha$ in a series of Bessel functions, which converges in any closed interval in $x>0$, in which the function is continuous, provided that $\alpha\ge 0$. The reviewer and R. Narasimhan proved [Ann. of Math. (2) **74** (1961), 1–23; MR **30** #1988], by the application of the theory of formal multiplication and of equiconvergence of trigonometrical integrals, that this identity can, in fact, be upheld for $\alpha>-\frac{1}{2}$. The method is quite general, and applies to a wide class of arithmetical identities. In this paper the author works out the effect of this stronger result on some of the older formulae due to E. Landau [*Vorlesungen über Zahlentheorie*, Band II, Satz 523, Hirzel, Leipzig, 1927; reprinting, #4076 above].

*K. Chandrasekharan* (Zürich)

Citations: MR 30# 1988 = M40-35; MR 40# 4076 = Z02-71.

## M40-50 (40# 5551)

**Berndt, Bruce C.**

**Identities involving the coefficients of a class of Dirichlet series. III.**

*Trans. Amer. Math. Soc.* **146** (1969), 323–348.

Es seien, wie in den vorangegangenen Teilen I und II dieser Arbeit [dieselben Trans. **137** (1969), 345–359; ibid. **137** (1969), 361–374; MR **38** #4656] (dort ein Druckfehler: statt Riemannsche $\varphi$-Funktion, lies Riemannsche $\zeta$-Funktion), $\varphi(s)=\sum a(n)\lambda_n^{-s}$, $\psi(s)=\sum b(n)\mu_n^{-s}$ mit $\lambda_n\to\infty$, $\mu_n\to\infty$ Dirichletreihen, die einer Funktionalgleichung $\Delta(s)\varphi(s)=\Delta(r-s)\psi(r-s)$ genügen; jedoch sei der $\Gamma$-Faktor $\Delta(s)$ allgemeiner, nämlich $\Delta(s)=\prod_{k=1}^{N}\Gamma(\alpha_k s+\beta_k)$. Ferner braucht $\Delta(s)\varphi(s)$ nur außerhalb eines Kompaktums $K$ holomorph zu sein. Es werden die Fälle $\Delta(s)=\Gamma(s+m)$ mit natürlichem $m$ und beliebigem $r$, $\Delta(s)=\Gamma^2((s+1)/2)$ mit $r=1$, $\Delta(s)=\Gamma(s/2)\Gamma((s-p)/2)$ mit $r=p+1$ und $p$ ganz behandelt. In allen Fällen werden für die Funktionen $A_q(x)=\Gamma(q+1)^{-1}\sum_{\lambda_n\le x} q(n)(x-\lambda_n)^q$ und $S(x,q)=\Gamma(q+1)^{-1}\sum_{\lambda_n\le x} q(n)\log^q(x/\lambda_n)$ andere Reihenetwicklungen angegeben, in denen statt der $a(n)$ die $b(n)$ und eine von $K$ abhängige "residual function" auftreten. Die Herleitungsmethode ist ähnlich der in den Teilen I und II: Anwendung geeigneter Integraltransformationen (wie die von Mellin) und Verschieben einer Integrationsgeraden. Mit dieser auf Hecke zurückgehenden Methode kann man aus der Heckeschen Funktionalgleichung ($\Delta(s)=\Gamma(s)$) eine entsprechende Funktionalgleichung für die Funktionen $\phi(x)=\sum a(n)E_i(-\lambda_n x)$, $\psi(x)=\sum b(n)E_i(-\mu_n x)$ herleiten. Hierin ist $E_i(x)=-\int_x^\infty t^{-1}e^{-t}\,dt$. Es wird eine Anzahl weiterer Beispiele gebracht, in denen u.a. auch Besselfunktionen und Laguerrepolynome eine Rolle spielen.

*W. Maak* (Göttingen)

Citations: MR 38# 4656 = M40-46.
Referred to in M40-53, M40-59.

## M40-51 (41# 3413)

**Chakravarty, I. C.**
**The secondary zeta-functions.**
*J. Math. Anal. Appl.* **30** (1970), 280–294.

Let $\Lambda(n)=\log p$ if $n=p^m$, $p$ a prime, and $=0$ otherwise, as usual, and let $\frac{1}{2}+i\gamma$ denote the complex zeros of the Riemann zeta-function $\zeta(s)$ (so if the Riemann hypothesis should be false, some $\gamma$ will be complex). Using this notation and assuming no hypothesis, the author proves the following functional relations. Let $\theta_p(z)=\sum_{n=1}^\infty(\Lambda(n)/\sqrt{n})e^{-1/2z(\log n)^2}$ and

$$\theta_\gamma(z)=\sqrt{(2\pi)}\sum_{\mathrm{Re}(\gamma)>0}e^{-\gamma^2z/2};$$

then

$$\theta_p(z)=-\sqrt{z^{-1/2}}\theta_\gamma(1/z)-\tfrac{1}{4}(C+\log(8\pi^2/z))+\sqrt{(2\pi/z)}e^{1/8z}+\tfrac{1}{2}\int_0^\infty e^{-zu^2/8}(1/u-e^{3u/4}/(e^u-1))\,du.$$

Define, for $\mathrm{Re}(s)>0$,

$$\zeta_p(s)=\lim_{h\to+0}\{\sum_{n=1}^\infty(\Lambda(n)/\sqrt{n})(\log n)^{-s}e^{-2h(\log n)^2/2}-\sqrt{(2\pi)}f(s,h)/(2^{s/2}\Gamma(\tfrac{1}{2}s))\},$$

where

$$f(s,h)=h^{(s-1)/2}e^{1/8h}\Gamma(\tfrac{1}{2}-\tfrac{1}{2}s)\Gamma(\tfrac{1}{2}s)F_1(\tfrac{1}{2}s,\tfrac{1}{2};-\tfrac{1}{8}h)/\sqrt{\pi};$$

and

$$\zeta_\gamma(s)=\lim_{h\to+0}\{\sum_{\mathrm{Re}(\gamma)>0}\gamma^{-s}e^{-\gamma^2h/2}-I(s,h)/(\sqrt{(2\pi)}2^{s/2}\Gamma(\tfrac{1}{2}s))\},$$

where

$$I(s,h)=\Gamma(\tfrac{1}{2}s)\Gamma(\tfrac{1}{2}-\tfrac{1}{2}s)h^{(s-1)/2}((\Gamma'/\Gamma)(\tfrac{1}{2}-\tfrac{1}{2}s)-\log 2\pi^2h)/(4\sqrt{\pi});$$

then the analytic continuations of $\zeta_p(s)$ and $\zeta_\gamma(s)$ satisfy

$$\zeta_p(s)+\Gamma(1-s)\{2^{-s}\eta(1-s)+(2^{-s}-\tfrac{1}{2})\zeta(1-s)\}=-2\Gamma(1-s)\sin\tfrac{1}{2}s\pi\zeta_\gamma(1-s),$$

where $\eta(s)$ is defined by $\eta(s)=\sum_{n=0}^\infty(-1)^n(2n+1)^{-s}=1^{-s}-3^{-s}+5^{-s}-\cdots$ for $\mathrm{Re}(s)>1$ and by its analytic continuation elsewhere.

*S. L. Segal* (Rochester, N.Y.)

## M40-52 (41# 3720)

**Halász, G.**
**On the average order of magnitude of Dirichlet series.**
*Acta Math. Acad. Sci. Hungar.* **21** (1970), 227–233.

This paper is concerned with analytic functions $F(s)$ defined in $\sigma=\mathrm{Re}\,s>1$ by an ordinary Dirichlet series $\sum_{n=1}^\infty a_nn^{-s}$ with bounded coefficients and assumed continuable into a half plane $\sigma\geqq\alpha$ $(0<\alpha<1)$. The object is to show that information about the growth of the Riemann $\zeta$-function on lines $\sigma=\mathrm{const}$ can be applied to yield information about the more general $F(s)$. If $F(\sigma+it)=O(|t|^\lambda)$ for some $\lambda$ uniformly for $\sigma\geqq\alpha$, the author defines the average order $\mu_p(\sigma)=\inf\nu$ taken over all $\nu$ such that $\{(2T)^{-1}\int_{-T}^T|F(\sigma+it)|^p\,dt\}^{1/p}=O(T^\nu)$. Assuming Lindelöf's hypothesis, it is shown that if $F(\sigma+it)=O(|t|^\mu)$ uniformly for $\sigma\geqq\alpha$, then, for $\sigma\geqq\mathrm{Max}(\alpha,\frac{3}{4})$,

$$\mu_p(\sigma)\leqq\max\{0,\mu(1-\sigma)/(1-\alpha)-1/p,\ \mu(1-\sigma)/(1-\alpha)-\tfrac{1}{2}(\sigma-\alpha)/(1-\alpha)\}.$$

*M. E. Noble* (Canterbury)

## M40-53 (41# 5309)

**Berndt, Bruce C.**
**Identities involving the coefficients of a class of Dirichlet series. IV.**
*Trans. Amer. Math. Soc.* **149** (1970), 179–185.

Es seien $\varphi(s)=\sum a(n)\lambda_n^{-s}$, $\psi(s)=\sum b(n)\mu_n^{-s}$ zwei irgendwo absolut konvergente Dirichletreihen, die einer Funktionalgleichung $\Delta(s)\varphi(s)=\Delta(r-s)\psi(r-s)$ genügen. Dabei ist $r$ reell und $\Delta(s)=\prod_{k=1}^N\Gamma(\alpha_ks+\beta_k)$ mit $\alpha_k>0$, $\beta_k$ komplex. Außerdem sei $\varphi$ eine in der ganzen Ebene meromorphe Funktion mit nur endlich vielen Polstellen. Im ersten Teil der Arbeit zeigt der Autor, daß dann die verallgemeinerte Dirichletreihe $\varphi(s,a)=\sum a(n)(\lambda_n+a)^{-s}$ (mit $a>0$) ebenfalls eine in der ganzen Ebene meromorphe Funktion ist, und er gewinnt eine Darstellung von $\varphi(s,a)$ aus $\varphi$, $b(n)$, $\mu_n$. Ist $\varphi$ ganz, so ist auch $\varphi(s,a)$ ganz. Als Beispiele werden Dedekindsche $\zeta$-Funktionen und Dirichletsche $L$-Reihen angeführt.

Im zweiten Teil der Arbeit wird $\Delta=\Gamma$ vorausgesetzt, d.h. $\varphi$, $\psi$ genügen der Heckeschen Funktionalgleichung. Außerdem möge $\Gamma(s)\varphi(s)$ nur einfache Pole besitzen. Setzt man $\tilde\varphi(s,\delta)=\sum a(n)\lambda_n^{-s}\exp(-\lambda_n\delta)$ und zieht hiervon eine geeignete (von $\delta$ und den Residuen von $\Gamma(s)\varphi(s)$ abhängende) Kombination der $\Gamma$-Funktion mit Exponentialfunktionen ab, so strebt dies für $\delta\to0$ gegen $\varphi(s)$. Auf diese Weise bekommt man eine Fortsetzung für $\varphi$. Ist beispielsweise $f(s)=\sum\tau(n)n^{-s}$, wobei $\tau(n)$ die Ramanujanschen Koeffizienten bedeuten, so gilt für alle komplexen $s$ die Darstellung $f(s)=\lim_{\delta\to0}\sum\tau(n)n^{-s}e^{-n\delta}$.

{Part III appeared in same Trans. **146** (1969), 323–348; MR **40** #5551.}

*H. S. Holdgrün* (Göttingen)

Citations: MR 40# 5551 = M40-50.
Referred to in M40-59.

## M40-54 (41# 8353)

**Romanov, N. P.; Jagudaev, B. Ja.**
**Operator Dirichlet series connected with Liouville's operator. (Russian. Uzbek summary)**
*Dokl. Akad. Nauk UzSSR* **1966**, *no.* 4, 9–11.

The authors pose the question of the analytic continuation of the operator zeta-function $\sum(a_n/n^s)f(x)=\zeta(s,G)f(x)$, where $G_uf(x)=(\Gamma(1+i\ln u))^{-1}\int_0^x(x-t)^{-i\ln u}f'(t)\,dt$ and $f$ is in the space $F$ consisting of all differentiable functions on $(0,1)$ that satisfy the condition $f(0)=f'(0)=0$.

*A. Vinogradov* (RŽMat **1967** #3 A87)

## M40-55 (42# 3261)

**Berndt, Bruce C.**
**On the zeros of a class of Dirichlet series. I.**
*Illinois J. Math.* **14** (1970), 244–258.

From the author's introduction: "The purpose of this paper is to show that many theorems concerning the distribution of zeros for the Riemann zeta-function $\zeta(s)$ can be generalized to a large class of Dirichlet series. For the most part our results are concerned with the distribution of zeros in a certain vertical strip. The proofs are similar to those that have been given for $\zeta(s)$."

*K. Chandrasekharan* (Zürich)

Referred to in M40-56.

**M40-56** **(42# 3034 )**

**Berndt, Bruce C.**

**On the zeros of a class of Dirichlet series. II.**

*Illinois J. Math.* **14** (1970), 678–691.

From the author's introduction: "In Part I [same J. **14** (1970), 244–258; MR **42** #3261] we considered the distribution of zeros for a large class of Dirichlet series. One of our theorems concerned the number of zeros on the critical line, but the remainder were concerned with the distribution in a vertical strip. In this paper our theorems pertain to the number of zeros on the critical line."

*K. Chandrasekharan* (Zürich)

Citations: MR 42# 3261 = M40-55.

**M40-57** **(42# 5922 )**

**Gesztelyi, E.**

**The application of the operational calculus in the theory of numbers.**

*Number Theory (Colloq., János Bolyai Math. Soc., Debrecen,* 1968), *pp.* 51–104. *North-Holland, Amster-*

Die als Instrument der analytischen Zahlentheorie benutzten Dirichletschen Reihen werden so verallgemeinert, daß die Beschränkung auf konvergente Reihen wegfällt. Dies geschieht durch Einführung eines Operatorenkalküls, der vermittels der Abbildung $t = \log x$ isomorph zu dem von Mikusiński, aber den Dirichletschen Reihen besonders angepaßt ist. Die Rolle des Produkts spielt dabei die "multiplikative Faltung" $f(x) * g(x) = \int_0^\infty f(x/v)g(v)v^{-1}\,dv$, die bei der Multiplikation von Mellin-Transformierten auftritt. Es sei $C_\xi(0, \infty)$ die Klasse der in $0 < x < \infty$ stetigen Funktionen $f(x)$ mit $f(x) = 0$ für $0 < x \leqq \xi$ und $C_+(0, \infty) = \bigcup_{0<\xi<\infty} C_\xi(0, \infty)$. Mit der multiplikativen Faltung als Produkt ist $C_+(0, \infty)$ ein Ring, dessen Elemente mit $\{f(x)\}$ bezeichnet werden. Er läßt sich zu einem Quotientenkörper $\mathfrak{M}_l$ erweitern, dessen Elemente $\{f\}/\{g\}$ multiplikative Operatoren genannt werden. Eine Folge $f_n \in C_+(0, \infty)$ heißt konvergent in $C_+(0, \infty)$ gegen $f \in C_\xi(0, \infty)$, wenn $f_n \in C_\xi(0, \infty)$ und die Folge $f_n$ gegen $f$ konvergiert, gleichmäßig in jedem Teilintervall $[\xi, \eta]$ von $[\xi, \infty)$, geschrieben $f_n \rightrightarrows f$. Eine Folge von Elementen $a_n \in \mathfrak{M}_l$ heißt konvergent in $\mathfrak{M}_l$ gegen $a \in \mathfrak{M}_l$, wenn Repräsentanten $f_n/g_n = a_n$, $f/g = a$ ($f_n, g_n, f, g \in C_+(0, \infty)$) existieren mit $f_n \rightrightarrows f$, $g_n \rightrightarrows g$ in $C_+(0, \infty)$. Es sei $H_\lambda(x) = 0$ für $0 < x < \lambda$, $= 1$ für $\lambda \leqq x < \infty$. $l = \{H_1(x)\}$ heißt der Integrationsoperator in Bezug auf $\log x$, weil $l\{f(x)\} = \{\int_0^x f(t)t^{-1}\,dt\} = \{\int_0^x f(t)d\log t\}$. Der inverse Operator $1/l$ wird mit $s$ bezeichnet. Für jedes $\lambda > 0$ heißt $h(\lambda) = s\{H_\lambda(x)\}$ ein Translationsoperator von $\mathfrak{M}_l$. Es ist $h(\lambda)\{f(x)\} = \{f(x/\lambda)\}$. Die Funktion $\lambda^s$ ($\lambda > 0$) wird definiert durch $\lambda^s = h(1/\lambda)$. Diese Funktion hat dieselben Eigenschaften wie die aus der Analysis bekannte. Die Reihe $\sum_{n=1}^\infty f(n)/n^s$ im Sinne eines Limes in $\mathfrak{M}_l$ ($f(n)$ eine beliebige komplexe Folge) heißt eine $D$-Reihe. Sie konvergiert immer in $\mathfrak{M}_l$, ihre Summe heißt ein $D$-Operator. Die Menge $\mathfrak{D}$ aller $D$-Operatoren bildet einen kommutativen Ring ohne Nullteiler. Die Elemente $\{f(x)\}$ des Körpers $\mathfrak{M}_l$ werden auch als verallgemeinerte Funktionen betrachtet, für die eine Anzahl von Operationen ähnlich wie in der Distributionstheorie definiert wird. Zu einer verallgemeinerten Funktion läßt sich die Mellin-Transformierte definieren, die zu den $D$-Reihen in derselben Beziehung steht, wie die klassische Mellin-Transformierte zu den Dirichletschen Reihen. Zum Schluß werden, ausgehend von einer beliebigen, in $0 \leqq x \leqq 1$ integrablen Funktion $\varphi(x)$, verallgemeinerte Bernoullische Polynome $B_n(x)$ aufgestellt, die für $\varphi \equiv 1$ mit den klassischen Polynomen übereinstimmen und ähnliche Eigenschaften wie diese haben. Für die Riemannsche Funktion $\zeta(z)$ wird die Formel abgeleitet: $\zeta(z) = z/(z-1) + B_1 + \sum_{k=2}^n (B_k/k!) \times \prod_{j=0}^{k-2}(z+j) - \prod_{j=0}^{n-1}(z+j)\int_1^\infty (F_n(t)/t^{z+n})\,dt$, wo die $B_k$ die aus den Polynomen abgeleiteten Bernoullischen Zahlen und die $F_n(t)$ die periodischen Fortsetzungen der verallgemeinerten Bernoullischen Polynome sind.

*G. Doetsch* (Freiburg)

**M40-58** **(43# 5009 )**

**Lewittes, Joseph**

**Analytic continuation of the series $\sum (m+nz)^{-s}$.**

*Trans. Amer. Math. Soc.* **159** (1971), 505–509.

This is an informally written paper in which the author develops some properties of the function $G(z, s) = \sum_{m,n} (m+nz)^{-s}$, where the summation is taken over all pairs of integers $m, n$ except $m = n = 0$. $G$ is an analytic function of two complex variables on $\{z: \operatorname{Im} z > 0\} \times \{s: \operatorname{Re}(s) > 2\}$ and it is shown that $G$ satisfies the functional equation $G(z, s)(1 + e^{\pi i s})^{-1} = \zeta(s) + ((-2\pi i)^s/\Gamma(s))A(z, s)$, where $\zeta(s)$ is the Riemann zeta function and $A(z, s)$ is a certain infinite series that is absolutely and uniformly convergent on any compact subset of $\{z: \operatorname{Im} z > 0\} \times \mathbf{C}$. This equation gives the analytic continuation of $G(z, s)$ for all values of $s$.

Other results are given including the behavior of $G$ under the transformation $z \to -1/z$.

*J. P. King* (Bethlehem, Pa.)

**M40-59** **(43# 6412 )**

**Berndt, Bruce C.**

**Identities involving the coefficients of a class of Dirichlet series. V, VI.**

*Trans. Amer. Math. Soc.* **160** (1971), 139–156; *ibid.* **160** (1971), 157–167.

Es seien $\varphi(s) = \sum a(n)\lambda_n^{-s}$, $\psi(s) = \sum b(n)\mu_n^{-s}$ Dirichletreihen mit positiven monoton gegen $\infty$ wachsenden Folgen $(\lambda_n)$, $(\mu_n)$, die irgendwo absolut konvergieren. Wie in den vorangehenden Arbeiten gleichen Titels [dieselben Trans. **137** (1969), 345–359; MR **38** #4656; ibid. **137** (1969), 361–374; MR **38** #4656; ibid. **146** (1969), 323–348; MR **40** #5551; ibid. **149** (1970), 179–185; MR **41** #5309] betrachtet der Verfasser Dirichletreihen dieser Art, die einer Funktionalgleichung $\Delta(s)\varphi(s) = \Delta(r-s)\psi(r-s)$ genügen, d.h. beide Seiten dieser Gleichung lassen sich zur selben in der ganzen Ebene meromorphen Funktion mit den üblichen Wachstums- und Regularitätsbedingungen fortsetzen. Dabei ist $\Delta$ die Gammafunktion $\Gamma$ oder aus zwei Gammafunktionen zusammengesetzt und $r$ geeignet reell.

Im fünften Teil der Arbeit gibt der Verfasser explizit zwei analytische Funktionen $Q_0'$ und $I_{-1}$ an, die sich aus $\Gamma$, $\varphi$ und Besselfunktionen zusammensetzen, so daß für alle auf $0 < a \leqq x \leqq b < \infty$ einmal stetig differenzierbaren Funktionen $f$ die Beziehung (1) $\sum'_{a \leqq \lambda_n \leqq b} a(n)f(\lambda_n) = \int_a^b Q_0'(x)f(x)\,dx + \sum_{n=1}^\infty b(n)\mu_n^{1-r}\int_a^b I_{-1}(\mu_n x)f(x)\,dx$ gilt. (Der Strich am Summenzeichen deutet an, daß in den Fällen $a = \lambda_n$ und $\lambda_n = b$ der Summand zu halbieren ist; die Koeffizientenfolge $(b(n))$ muß einer geeigneten Wachstumsbedingung genügen.) Unter geeigneten Nebenbedingungen ist (1) auch in den Fällen $a = 0$ oder $b = \infty$ richtig. Beim Beweis werden Gleichungen benutzt, die K. Chandrasekharan und R. Narasimhan [Ann. of Math. (2) **74** (1961), 1–23; MR **30** #1988] aus der obigen Funktionalgleichung für Dirichletreihen abgeleitet haben. Der Verfasser gibt weiter eine Verallgemeinerung von (1) für Funktionen $f$ mit beschränkter Schwankung an. Im Falle $a(n) = b(n) = 1$, $\lambda_n = \mu_n = n$ erhält man aus (1) die Poissonsche Summationsformel. Andere Spezialisierungen liefern auf Voronoï zurückgehende Summationsformeln. Hinweise auf weitere Resultate werden gegeben, beispielsweise für Fälle, in denen (1) für $L^2$-Funktionen gilt.

S. Chowla und A. Selberg gaben 1949 [Proc. Nat. Acad.

Sci. U.S.A. **35** (1949), 371–374; MR **11**, 84; siehe auch J. Reine Angew. Math. **227** (1967), 86–110; MR **35** #6632] eine Formel an, die die zur positiv definiten quadratischen Form $Q(m, n) = am^2 + bmn + cn^2$ mit reellen $a$, $b$, $c$ gebildete Epsteinsche Zetafunktion $Z(s, Q) = \sum' Q(m, n)^{-s}$ mit einer Reihe über Besselfunktionen in Beziehung setzt, und die eine gewisse Bedeutung für die Zahlentheorie besitzt. Aus dieser Formel läßt sich unter Anderem ein einfacher Beweis der ersten Kroneckerschen Grenzformel gewinnen. Der Verfasser verallgemeinert die Formel von Chowla und Selberg im sechsten Teil der Arbeit auf allgemeinere Zetafunktionen, beispielsweise von der Art $Z(s, Q; g_1, g_2, h_1, h_2) = \sum'_{m,n} \exp(2\pi i(h_1 m + h_2 n))Q(m+g_1, n+g_2)^{-s}$ mit reellen $g_1, g_2, h_1, h_2$, ebenso für höherdimensionale quadratische Formen. Hieraus leitet er einen einfachen Beweis der zweiten Kroneckerschen Grenzformel ab. Während frühere Beweise der Chowla-Selbergschen Formel Fourierreihen, die Poissonsche Summationsformel oder Funktionalgleichungen für Thetafunktionen heranziehen, benutzt der Verfasser ein von ihm in einer vorangehenden Arbeit [Proc. Edinburgh Math. Soc. (2) **15** (1966/67), 309–313; MR **37** #1325] abgeleitetes Resultat über Dirichletreihen, die der oben angegebenen Funktionalgleichung genügen. Aus der Chowla-Selbergschen Formel wird schließlich die Funktionalgleichung für Epsteinsche Zetafunktionen gewonnen. *H. S. Holdgrün* (Göttingen)

Citations: MR 11, 84d = E44-5; MR 30# 1988 = M40-35; MR 35# 6632 = E44-25; MR 37# 1325 = M40-43; MR 38# 4656 = M40-46; MR 40# 5551 = M40-50; MR 41# 5309 = M40-53.

**M40-60** **(44# 413 )**

**Lavrik, A. F.**
**On zeros of periodic Dirichlet functions.**
*Dokl. Akad. Nauk SSSR* **192** (1970), 1214–1216 (*Russian*); *translated as Soviet Math. Dokl.* **11** (1970), 802–805.

Der Verfasser betrachtet durch Dirichletreihen $\sum_0^\infty a_n \lambda_n^{-s}$ (mit reellen Koeffizienten $a_n$) darstellbare meromorphe Funktionen $Z(s)$, die an der Stelle $s=1$ einen einfachen Pol besitzen, periodisch mit der Periode $2\pi i/\log q$ (für ein geeignetes $q>1$) sind und der Funktionalgleichung (*) $q^s Z(s) = q^{1-s} Z(1-s)$ genügen. Ohne Beweis wird ein umfangreicher Satz gegeben, der die Verteilung der Nullstellen von $Z(s)$ in der Halbebene $\operatorname{Re} s \geqq \frac{1}{2}$ in Abhängigkeit von $q, a_0, a_1, a_2$ charakterisiert.

Ist zum Beispiel $|A-B| \leqq 4\sqrt{q}$, $|A+B| \leqq 4\sqrt{q}$ und $C \geqq 0$ [mit $A = q+1-a_1/a_0$, $C = A^2 - 4(a_2/a_0 - q - (q+1)a_1/a_0)$, $B = \sqrt{|C|}$], so liegen alle Nullstellen von $Z(s)$ (in $\operatorname{Re} s \geqq \frac{1}{2}$) auf der Geraden $\operatorname{Re} s = \frac{1}{2}$.

Umgekehrt wird aus der Verteilung der Nullstellen auf Relationen zwischen $q, a_0, a_1, a_2$ geschlossen. Ähnliche Ergebnisse werden für Funktionen angegebenen, die an Stelle von (*) der Funktionalgleichung $Z^*(s) = Z^*(1-s)$ genügen. *W. Schwarz* (Frankfurt a.M.)

**M40-61** **(44# 6619 )**

**Shintani, Takuro**
**On Dirichlet series whose coefficients are class numbers of integral binary cubic forms.**
*J. Math. Soc. Japan* **24** (1972), 132–188.

Let $h(m)$ be the number of equivalence classes (under integral unimodular substitution) of integral binary cubic forms $ax^3 + bx^2y + cxy^2 + dy^3$ with discriminant $m$. Let $\hat{h}(m)$ be the number of classes of such forms with $b \equiv c \equiv 0 \pmod 3$. The author defines four Dirichlet series as follows:

$$\xi_1(L, s) = \sum_{n=1}^\infty h(n)/n^s - \tfrac{1}{3} \sum'{}_{x,y=-\infty}^{\infty} 1/(9x^2+3xy+y^2)^{2s},$$
$$\xi_2(L, s) = \sum_{n=1}^\infty h(-n)/n^s,$$
$$\xi_1(\hat{L}, s) = \sum_{n=1}^\infty \hat{h}(n)/n^s - (1/3^{1+4s}) \times \sum'{}_{x,y=-\infty}^{\infty} 1/(x^2+xy+y^2)^{2s},$$
$$\xi_2(\hat{L}, s) = \sum_{n=1}^\infty \hat{h}(-n)/n^s,$$

where the prime on a summation sign indicates omission of the term with $x=y=0$. It is shown that these series converge absolutely for $\operatorname{Re} s>1$, and can be continued analytically to the entire plane except for simple poles at $s=1$ and $s=5/6$. Furthermore, they satisfy the functional equations

$$\xi_i(L, 1-s) = \Gamma(s-1/6)\Gamma(s)^2\Gamma(s+1/6)2^{-1}3^{6s-3+i}\pi^{-4s} \times \sin \pi s \sin 2\pi s \xi_i(\hat{L}, s) \quad (i=1, 2).$$

The author also computes the residues of $\xi_i(L, s)$ and $\xi_i(\hat{L}, s)$ at their poles. *B. Gordon* (Los Angeles, Calif.)

**M40-62** **(44# 6628 )**

**Warlimont, Richard**
**Über die Summierbarkeit von Dirichletreihen mit multiplikativen Koeffizienten.**
*J. Reine Angew. Math.* **252** (1972), 107–111.

Let $g(n)$ be a complex-valued multiplicative function satisfying $|g(n)| \leqq 1$. G. Halász [Studia Sci. Math. Hungar. **4** (1969), 171–178; MR **40** #105] showed that partial sums of (*) $\sum_{n=1}^\infty g(n)n^{-1-it}$ are bounded for almost all $t$. The present author shows the series (*) to be almost everywhere summable in the sense $(R; \log n, \kappa)$, $\kappa > 0$. This means that there exists an $a$ such that $\sum_{n \leq x} a_n(\log(x/n))^\kappa = a(\log x)^\kappa + O((\log x)^\kappa)$, $x \to \infty$.

*R. Spira* (E. Lansing, Mich.)

Citations: MR 40# 105 = M40-48.

# M45 TAUBERIAN THEOREMS

See also reviews B16-22, K05-9, L05-9, M30-20, N04-4, N04-52, N08-41, N12-50, N20-8, N20-10, N20-39, N20-42, N20-71, N36-1, N36-16, N36-18, N36-41, N36-83, N40-24, N60-58, P72-28, R44-31, Z02-4, Z10-30.

**M45-1** **(1, 51b)**

**Sundaram, S. Minakshi. On generalised Tauberian theorems.** Math. Z. **45**, 495–506 (1939).

The author deals with relations between the behavior of

$$F(\sigma) = \sigma \int_0^\infty \varphi(\sigma t) s(t) dt$$

as $\sigma \to 0$ and that of $s(t)$ as $t \to \infty$. Here $\varphi(t)$ is positive, differentiable, ultimately monotone, and the following integrals exist:

$$\int_0^\infty \varphi(t)dt = 1, \qquad \int_0 [1-\psi(t)]t^{-1}dt, \qquad \int^\infty \psi(t)t^{-1}dt,$$

where $\psi(t)=\int_t^\infty \varphi(u)du$. Assuming, for instance, that $s(t)$ is differentiable and $\liminf_{t\to\infty} ts'(t)\geqq 0$, while $F(\sigma)=O(1)$ as $\sigma\to 0$, he shows that $\text{osc}_{\sigma\to 0} F(\sigma)=\text{osc}_{t\to\infty} s(t)$. Applications to Dirichlet series. *E. Hille* (New Haven, Conn.).

## M45-2 (2, 92b)

**Pitt, H. R. General Tauberian theorems. II.** J. London Math. Soc. **15**, 97–112 (1940).

The following extension of Wiener's general Tauberian theorem was proved in recent papers by the author [Amer. J. Math. **60**, 532–534 (1938); Proc. London Math. Soc. (2) **45**, 243–288 (1938)]. Theorem 1. Hypothesis. (I) $k_1(x)$, $k_2(x)$ are measurable and absolutely integrable in $(-\infty, \infty)$; (II) $K_1(u)=\int_{-\infty}^\infty e^{-iux}k_1(x)dx\neq 0$ $(-\infty<u<\infty)$; (III) $|f(x)|\leqq M$, (IV) $g_1(x)=\int_{-\infty}^\infty k_1(x-y)f(y)dy$, $g_2(x)=\int_{-\infty}^\infty k_2(x-y)f(y)dy$. Conclusion. (A) $G_2\leqq\Psi(G_1)$, where, if $g_1$ is bounded, we write $G_1=\overline{\lim}_{x\to\infty} g_1(x)$, and similarly for the other letters, and where $\Psi(\xi)$ depends only on $k_1(x)$, $k_2(x)$ and $M$, and $\Psi(0)=\Psi(+0)=0$. (B) If we have the further condition (V) $\overline{\lim}_{x\to\infty} |f(x+\epsilon)-f(x)|=\delta(\epsilon)$, $\lim_{\epsilon\to 0}\delta(\epsilon)=0$, then $F\leqq\Phi(G_1)$, where $\Phi(\xi)$ depends only on $k_1(x)$ and $\delta(\epsilon)$ (not on $M$), and $\Phi(0)=\Phi(+0)=0$.

Previously only case (B) was stated, but the author now shows that (A) follows from it very easily. The object of this paper is to show that, even if $K_1(u)$ vanishes for certain values of $u$, Theorem 1 remains true if we have extra conditions on $f(x)$ and $k_2(x)$. Main results are generalizations of Theorem 1 in which the extra condition, instead of on $k_2(x)$, is on $f(x)$. When $K_1(u)\neq 0$ except at $\alpha$, the kind of condition which is required to make Theorem 1 remain true is one which excludes functions $f(x)$ behaving in any way like $e^{i\alpha x}$, that is, which make the harmonic component of $f(x)$ with frequency near to $\alpha$ small. The most natural way of stating this condition is in terms of the harmonic representation of $f(x)$ defined by Wiener [Acta Math. **55**, 117–258 (1930)], and extended by the author [Proc. London Math. Soc. (2) **46**, 1–18 (1939); these Rev. **1**, 139].

*S. Ikehara* (Osaka).

## M45-3 (6, 127e)

**Haviland, E. K. A note on the Lambert transform.** Amer. J. Math. **66**, 523–530 (1944).

Let $\alpha(x)$ be of bounded variation in every finite interval $(0, b)$, and constant near $x=0$, and write

$$A(s)=\int_0^\infty e^{-sx}d\alpha(x),\quad L(s)=\int_0^\infty (xe^{-sx}/(1-e^{-sx}))d\alpha(x).$$

The author proves that the integrals converge or diverge together, and that, if $sL(s)\to 0$ as $s\to 0+$, then $A(s)\to 0$ as $s\to 0+$. This is the integral analogue of a theorem of Hardy and Littlewood [Proc. London Math. Soc. (2) **19**, 21–29 (1921)] for power series; because the integrals may fail to converge absolutely or uniformly, the original proof requires considerable modification. However, the prime number theorem is applied in the same way as in the work of Hardy and Littlewood. *R. P. Boas, Jr.* (Cambridge, Mass.).

## M45-4 (7, 61f)

**Beurling, Arne. Un théorème sur les fonctions bornées et uniformément continues sur l'axe réel.** Acta Math. **77**, 127–136 (1945).

Let functions $\varphi_n(x)$, $\psi(x)$ be defined on $(-\infty, \infty)$. The author calls $\{\varphi_n\}$ strictly convergent to $\psi$ if $\varphi_n(x)\to\psi(x)$ uniformly on every finite interval and

$$\sup_{-\infty<x<\infty}|\varphi_n(x)|\to\sup_{-\infty<x<\infty}|\psi(x)|<\infty.$$

Now let $\varphi(x)$ be bounded and uniformly continuous and consider the closed linear manifold $T$ (in the topology of strict convergence) determined by the translations $\varphi(x+t)$, $-\infty<t<\infty$. Then, unless $\varphi\equiv 0$, $T$ contains at least one function $e^{i\lambda x}$, $\lambda$ real; at least two such functions unless $\varphi(x)\equiv e^{i\lambda x}$; and so on. This leads in a very simple way to Wiener's general Tauberian theorems. Another application is that if $\mu(x)$ is of bounded variation on $(-\infty, \infty)$ and if $\int_{-\infty}^\infty \varphi(x-t)d\mu(t)=0$ has a bounded uniformly continuous solution, not identically zero, then the Fourier-Stieltjes transform of $\mu(x)$ has at least one real zero.

*R. P. Boas, Jr.* (Providence, R. I.).

Referred to in M45-5, M45-36.

## M45-5 (8, 14d)

**Godement, Roger. Extension à un groupe abélien quelconque des théorèmes taubériens de N. Wiener et d'un théorème de A. Beurling.** C. R. Acad. Sci. Paris **223**, 16–18 (1946).

Two theorems are stated and the proofs are sketched. The first asserts that a closed ideal in the group algebra $A$ of a locally compact Abelian group (that is, the algebra of complex-valued functions on the group which are integrable relative to Haar measure, multiplication being defined as convolution) coincides with $A$ provided it has the property that for each point in the (topological) character group there is an element of the ideal whose Fourier transform is not zero at the point. In the special case that the group is the additive group of the reals, the theorem is essentially identical with one of the two theorems known collectively as the general Tauberian theorem of Wiener [The Fourier Integral and Certain of its Applications, Cambridge University Press, 1933, p. 37, theorem 4]. The second theorem, which is indicated to follow readily from the first, has as a corresponding special case a theorem of A. Beurling [Acta Math. **77**, 127–136 (1945); these Rev. **7**, 61]. The first theorem is a fairly easy consequence of a theorem of the reviewer [Proc. Nat. Acad. Sci. U. S. A. **27**, 348–352 (1941), theorem 2; these Rev. **3**, 36]. *I. E. Segal.*

Citations: MR 7, 61f = M45-4.

## M45-6 (8, 147i)

**Ingham, A. E. Some Tauberian theorems connected with the prime number theorem.** J. London Math. Soc. **20**, 171–180 (1945).

The author uses Wiener's general Tauberian theorem to prove the following special Tauberian theorems. (I) Suppose that (i) $f(x)$ is positive and increasing for $x\geqq 1$;

(ii) $$F(x)=\sum_{n\leqq x} f(x/n)=ax\log x+bx+o(x)$$

when $x\to\infty$, where $a$ and $b$ are constants. Then (a) $f(x)\sim ax$ when $x\to\infty$; (b) $\int_1^\infty x^{-2}\{f(x)-ax\}dx$ converges to $b-a\gamma$, where $\gamma$ is Euler's constant. (II) Suppose that (i) $a_n>-K/n$, where $K$ is a positive constant and $n=1, 2, \cdots$; (ii) $\sum_{n\leqq x} a_n(n/x)[x/n]\to A$ when $x\to\infty$. Then $\sum_{n=1}^\infty a_n$ converges to sum $A$.

Theorem (II) is deduced from (I) by putting

$$f(x)=\sum_{n\leqq x} na_n+K[x].$$

The prime number theorem, together with the group of theorems equivalent to it, follows in a particularly simple and direct way from (I(a)) with $f(x)=\psi(x)$ in the usual notation. When the Tauberian condition (i) is dropped in theorem (I), the conclusion (b) remains true and the analogous conclusion that $\sum_{n=1}^\infty a_n+A$ $(C, 1)$ is also true when the Tauberian condition (i) is dropped in theorem (II).

The author remarks, finally, that the method of summation defined by theorem (II(ii)) is intermediate in strength between $(C, -\delta)$ and $(C, \delta)$ for any positive $\delta$, but is not directly comparable with ordinary convergence.

*H. R. Pitt* (Belfast).

Referred to in M45-34, M45-48, M45-49, M45-50, N04-44, N04-52.

## M45-7 (8, 375e)

**Wintner, Aurel. On the Tauberian nature of Ikehara's theorem.** Amer. J. Math. **69**, 99–103 (1947).

Ikehara's theorem for ordinary Dirichlet series may be stated as follows. If (i) $f(s)=\sum a_n n^{-s}$ $(s=\sigma+it)$, where the series is absolutely convergent in the half-plane $\sigma>1$ and the function $f(s)$ is continuous for $\sigma\geqq 1$, (ii) $a_n=O_L(1)$, then $\sum_1^x a_n=o(x)$. It is shown by an example that the hypothesis (ii) cannot be omitted. This is contrasted with the situation that arises with the Tauberian theorem for Lambert summability. If (i′) $\sum c_n$ is $(L)$-summable, (ii′) $c_n=O_L(1/n)$ [the author's (2 bis) is presumably a slip for this], then $\sum c_n$ is convergent. Here it is known that we may omit the Tauberian condition (ii′) at the expense of replacing the conclusion by "$\sum c_n$ is $(A)$-summable"; so that we have a pure Abelian inference from $(L)$- to $(A)$-summability. It is apparently inferred from the example cited above that Ikehara's theorem cannot be deprived of its Tauberian character in a similar manner. [The comparison seems, however, imperfect, in that there is no proposal to balance the omission of the hypothesis (ii) by a corresponding weakening of the conclusion.] *A. E. Ingham.*

Referred to in M45-25.

## M45-8 (8, 457b)

**Delange, Hubert. Sur la réciproque du théorème d'Abel sur les séries entières.** C. R. Acad. Sci. Paris **224**, 436–438 (1947).

Suppose that $s(t)$ is a complex function of the real variable $t$ for $t\geqq 0$, that $s(0)=0$ and that $s(t)$ is of bounded variation in every finite interval $(0, L)$. Let

$$w(\lambda)=\limsup_{t\to\infty}\ \{\ \text{u.b.}_{t\leqq t'<\lambda t}\ |s(t')-s(t)|\ \}.$$

The author states the following result. If $w(\lambda)<\infty$ for some $\lambda>1$, $z_n=r_n e^{i\theta_n}$, $\lim_{n\to\infty} r_n=0$, $\lim_{n\to\infty} r_{n+1}/r_n=1$, $\limsup_{n\to\infty}|\theta_n|<\pi/2$, and if

$$\lim_{n\to\infty}\int_0^\infty e^{-z_n t}ds(t)=S,$$

then $\limsup_{n\to\infty}|s(t)-S|\leqq\lim_{\lambda\to 1} w(\lambda)$. More generally, for any sequence $t_n$ tending to $+\infty$,

$$\limsup_{n\to\infty}|s(t_n)-S|\leqq\lim_{\lambda\to 1} w[(t_n), \lambda],$$

where

$$w[(t_n), \lambda]=\limsup_{n\to\infty}\ \{\ \text{u.b.}_{t_n\leqq t'<\lambda t_n}\ |s(t')-s(t_n)|\ \}.$$

This result generalizes the theorem of Littlewood to the effect that, if $0<\lambda_1<\lambda_2<\cdots$, $\lambda_k\to\infty$, if $\lim_{k\to\infty}\lambda_{k+1}/\lambda_k=1$, if $\sum_{k=1}^\infty a_k e^{-\lambda_k z}=f(z)$ converges for $\Re(z)>0$, and if $f(z)\to S$ when $z\to 0$ through positive real values, then $\sum_1^\infty a_k$ converges to sum $S$ provided that $|a_k|\leqq(\lambda_k-\lambda_{k-1})M/\lambda_k$ and $M$ is constant. The author states the "one-sided" extension of his theorem which is analogous to the Hardy-Littlewood theorem in which the condition on $a_k$ above is replaced by the weaker condition $a_k\geqq-(\lambda_k-\lambda_{k-1})M/\lambda_k$ when $a_k$ is real.

*H. R. Pitt* (Belfast).

## M45-9 (9, 279f)

**Wintner, Aurel. The sum formula of Euler-Maclaurin and the inversions of Fourier and Möbius.** Amer. J. Math. **69**, 685–708 (1947).

The author investigates the approximation of improper integrals by equidistant Riemann sums. The most striking of the results is the following, which is deeper than the prime number theorem, and in fact contains the theorem that Lambert summability implies Abel summability. If $f(x)$ is continuous on $0<x\leqq 1$ and the limit

$$\lim_{\epsilon\to 0}\epsilon\sum_{n\epsilon\leqq 1} f(n\epsilon)$$

exists, then $\int_{0+}^1 f(x)dx$ exists and has the same value. This is closely related to the inversions mentioned in the title, and to Poisson's summation formula in the theory of Fourier transforms. The exact connections are carefully examined.

As a consequence of his results the author obtains a formula for the stable distribution corresponding to the function $e^{-|x|^\lambda}$, $0<\lambda<1$. *H. Pollard* (Ithaca, N. Y.).

## M45-10 (9, 279g)

**Guinand, A. P. Some formulae for the Riemann zeta-function.** J. London Math. Soc. **22**, 14–18 (1947).

The author shows that if $\phi(x)$ is absolutely continuous on every finite interval on $x>0$, tends to 0 at $\infty$, and $x\phi'(x)$ is of class $L^2(0, \infty)$, then for $x>0$ the limits

$$f(x)=\lim_{N\to\infty}\left\{\sum_{n=1}^N\phi(n/x)-\int_0^N\phi(t/x)dt\right\}/x,$$

$$g(x)=\lim_{N\to\infty}\left\{\sum_{n=1}^N\phi(x/n)/n-\int^N\phi(x/t)dt\right\}$$

exist and are a pair of Fourier transforms of class $L^2(0, \infty)$ with respect to the kernel $2\cos 2\pi x$. It is of interest to compare this result with those of Duffin [Bull. Amer. Math. Soc. **51**, 447–455 (1945); these Rev. **6**, 266] and of Wintner [see the paper reviewed above, pp. 695 ff.]. If $\phi(x)$ has the additional property that $f, g$ are so smooth (locally) as to allow the application of the Fourier integral formula, there result formulae involving the Riemann zeta function.

*P. Hartman* (Baltimore, Md.).

## M45-11 (9, 345b)

**Wintner, Aurel. On Riemann's reduction of Dirichlet series to power series.** Amer. J. Math. **69**, 769–789 (1947).

The author attaches a number of observations of a Tauberian nature to the classical formula

$$\Gamma(s)f(s)=\int_0^\infty x^{s-1}F(e^{-x})dx,$$

where $f(s)=\sum_1^\infty a_n n^{-s}$, $F(r)=\sum_1^\infty a_n r^n$. If the Dirichlet series converges for $\sigma>1$ and if the coefficients $\{a_n\}$ have an Abel mean so that (1) $\lim_{r\to 1}(1-r)F(r)=l$, then they also have a Dirichlet mean (2) $\lim_{\epsilon\to 0}\epsilon f(1+\epsilon)=l$. Since (2) does not imply (1), the author raises the question of when (1) may be concluded from properties of $f(s)$ and $F(r)$. The main result is the following. Suppose that (i) the Dirichlet series converges for $\sigma>1$ and there exists an $l$ such that $f^*(s)=f(s)-l\zeta(s)$ has boundary values on $\sigma=1$ in the sense that $f^*(\sigma+it)$, when $\sigma\to 1$, converges in the mean of order one on each finite interval $-T<t<T$, and (ii) $F(r)$ is a monotone function of $r$ as $r\to 1$. Then (1) holds. Here (ii) may be replaced by conditions of the form $\sum_{n<x}a_n=O(x)$ or $\sum_{n<x}na_n=O_L(x^2)$, while (i) is implied by integrability conditions on $F^*(r)=F(r)-lr(1-r)^{-1}$ of the form $\int_0^1(1-r)^{p-1}|F^*(r)|^p dr<\infty$ for some $p\geqq 1$. *E. Hille.*

## M45-12 (9, 577c)

**Bowen, N. A. A function-theory proof of Tauberian theorems on integral functions.** Quart. J. Math., Oxford Ser. **19**, 90–100 (1948).

The principal theorem in question concerns an entire function $f(z)$ of order $\rho$, $0<\rho<1$, with negative real zeros; $n(r)$ denotes the number of zeros of absolute value not exceeding $r$; then if $\log f(x) \sim \pi x^\rho \csc \pi\rho$ as $x \to +\infty$, it follows that $n(r) \sim r^\rho$. This was proved by Valiron [Ann. Fac. Sci. Univ. Toulouse (3) **5**, 117–257 (1914), pp. 237–243] by a lengthy Tauberian argument; by Titchmarsh [Proc. London Math. Soc. (2) **26**, 185–200 (1927)] by showing it equivalent to a Tauberian theorem of Hardy and Littlewood; and by Paley and Wiener [Fourier Transforms in the Complex Domain, Amer. Math. Soc. Colloquium Publ., v. 19, New York, 1934, p. 79] by using Wiener's general Tauberian theorem. The author gives a much more elementary proof. The same line of argument is shown to apply to more general situations when the zeros only approach the negative real axis, when proximate orders are used or when the order of $f(z)$ is greater than 1 and not integral; these results were known. Finally, the theorem is extended to cases when the behavior of $f(z)$ is prescribed only along a sufficiently dense discrete set of points. [For a substantially equivalent "function-theory" proof see M. Heins, Ann. of Math. (2) **49**, 200–213 (1948), pp. 210–212; these Rev. **9**, 341]. *R. P. Boas, Jr.* (Providence, R. I.).

## M45-13 (12, 405a)

**Delange, Hubert. Sur le théorème taubérien de Ikéhara.** C. R. Acad. Sci. Paris **232**, 465–467 (1951).

Theorem: Let $G(s)=\int_0^{+\infty} e^{-st}\beta(t)\,dt$, where $\beta(t)$ is a real function defined for $t\geqq 0$, measurable and bounded over any finite interval, and where the integral is convergent for $\Re(s)>0$. Let there exist an integer $p\geqq 0$, and a real continuous and nondecreasing function $\gamma(t)$ such that (1) the integral $\int_0^{+\infty} e^{-tu}\gamma(u)\,du$ be convergent for $t>0$, and (2) $1/\beta(t) \sim t^{p+1}\int_0^{+\infty} e^{-tu}\gamma(u)\,du$ as $t\to\infty$. In case $\gamma(0)=0$, let further the integral $\int_0 \log[1/\gamma(t)]\,dt$ be convergent. This being the case, let (1) $\alpha(t)$ be real and nondecreasing for $t\geqq 0$; (2) the integral $\int_0^{+\infty} e^{-st}\alpha(t)\,dt$ converge for $\Re(s)>a$ $(a>0)$; (3) for each real $y$, there exist a positive function $\varphi_y(t)$ defined for sufficiently small and nonincreasing positive $t$ such that the integral $\int_0 \varphi_y(t)\,dt$ and $\int_0 \varphi_y(t)\log[1/\gamma(t)]\,dt$ be convergent, and that when $s$ tends to zero in the half-plane $\Re(s)>0$, $F^{(p)}(a+iy+s)=O(\varphi_y(r)/\gamma(r))$, where $r=|s|$ and $F(s)=\int_0^{+\infty} e^{-st}\alpha(t)\,dt-AG(s-a)$, $A>0$, $a>0$. Then we have $\alpha(t)\sim Ae^{at}\beta(t)$ as $t\to\infty$.

When we take $\gamma(u)=1$, $p=0$, $\beta(t)=1$, this theorem reduces to the Wiener-Ikehara theorem. The author states two corollaries of the above theorem susceptible of arithmetical applications. *S. Ikehara* (Cambridge, Mass.).

Referred to in M45-24, M45-28, N24-28, N28-23.

## M45-14 (12, 497d)

**Delange, Hubert. Nouveaux théorèmes pour l'intégrale de Laplace.** C. R. Acad. Sci. Paris **232**, 589–591 (1951).

The author announces two very general Tauberian theorems for the Laplace-Stieltjes transform. These extend results obtained by M. Riesz [Acta Litt. Sci. Szeged, Sect. Sci. Math. **2**, 18–31 (1924)], A. E. Ingham [Proc. London Math. Soc. (2) **38**, 458–480 (1935)], and J. Karamata [Math. Z. **38**, 701–708 (1934)]. It is not possible to reproduce the statements of these results because of their complexity. *I. I. Hirschman, Jr.* (St. Louis, Mo.).

Referred to in M45-28, M45-39, N24-28, N28-23, N60-11.

## M45-15 (12, 604f)

**Karamata, J. Sur le théorème tauberien de N. Wiener.** Acad. Serbe Sci. Publ. Inst. Math. **3**, 201–206 (1950).

In this note, dated May 1939, the author outlines a brief proof of Wiener's Tauberian theorem in three steps, assuming the oscillation of the function $s(x)$ to be suitably restricted and that $tK(t)\varepsilon L(-\infty,\infty)$. In one variant $K(t)$ is supposed to be positive. The first step consists in proving that $s(x)$ is bounded under the given assumptions, the second involves passing from the given kernel $K(t)$ to the kernel $\lambda[\sin\lambda t/\lambda t]^4$ of H. R. Pitt. For the final step, the passage from the existence of Pitt's limit to that of $s(x)$, he refers to an earlier paper [J. Reine Angew. Math. **178**, 29–33 (1937)].

*E. Hille* (New Haven, Conn.).

## M45-16 (12, 820e)

**Postnikov, A. G. The remainder term in the Tauberian theorem of Hardy and Littlewood.** Doklady Akad. Nauk SSSR (N.S.) **77**, 193–196 (1951). (Russian)

It is proved that, if $\sum_1^\infty a_n e^{-\lambda_n\sigma}=\sigma^{-1}+O(1)$ as $\sigma\to+0$, and if $a_n\geqq 0$, then $\sum_{\lambda_n\leqq P} a_n = P+O[P/\sqrt{(\log P)}]$ as $P\to\infty$. The idea is to consider $\sum a_n e^{-\lambda_n\sigma} f(e^{-\lambda_n\sigma})$ with a suitable $f(x)$ and to approximate to $f(x)$ in $[0,1]$ by a polynomial $P_N(x)=\sum_0^N b_i x^i$, as in Karamata's method. But $P_N(x)$ is now chosen in a special way, namely as the best approximation to $f(x)$ in the sense of minimizing $E_N=\max_{0\leqq x\leqq 1}|f(x)-P_N(x)|$ (for a given continuous $f(x)$ and given $N$). With this choice, the terms of $\sum|b_i|$ (and so the sum itself) do not exceed the corresponding expressions for the polynomial $2M\cos\{N\arccos(2x-1)\}$, where $M=\max_{0\leqq x\leqq 1}|f(x)|$; while $E_N<12\omega(1/2N)$, where $\omega(\delta)$ is the modulus of continuity of $f(x)$. This leads to

$$\sigma\sum_1^\infty a_n e^{-\lambda_n\sigma} f(e^{-\lambda_n\sigma}) = \int_0^1 f(x)dx + O(M6^N\sigma)+O(\omega(1/2N)).$$

The stated result is obtained by taking $f(x)$ to be 0 in $[0,e^{-\alpha}]$, $1/x$ in $[e^{-\beta},1]$, linear in $[e^{-\alpha},e^{-\beta}]$, and choosing $\sigma=1/P$, $N=[c\log P]$ $(0<c<1/\log 6)$, $\alpha-\beta=1/\sqrt{(\log P)}$, $\beta$ or $\alpha=1$ (to obtain alternative inequalities for $\sum_{\lambda_n\leqq P} a_n$).

*A. E. Ingham* (Cambridge, England).

Referred to in M45-27, M45-42.

## M45-17 (13, 22c)

**Eggleston, H. G. A Tauberian lemma.** Proc. London Math. Soc. (3) **1**, 28–45 (1951).

Using elementary methods (Taylor's expansion and Cauchy's inequality) the author gives theorems describing the behaviour of a bounded analytic function (or that of its derivatives) at a boundary point $z_0$ of its domain of definition $D$. If $L$ is an arc in $D$ with an endpoint $z_0$, if $f(z)\to 0$ for $z\to z_0$ along $L$, and if $d(z)$ denotes the distance from $z$ to the boundary of $D$, then (a) $f^{(p)}(z)d(z)^p\to 0$, $p=1,2,\cdots$, along $L$; (b) for any $0<\chi<1$, $f(z_1)\to 0$ as $z_1\to z_0$ in such a way that there are points $z\varepsilon L$ with $|z_1-z|<\chi d(z)$. In other theorems $D$ is a strip or an angle, $L$ a straight line and $f(z)$ approaches 0 when $z\to z_0$ along a set on $L$ of "positive $h$-density"; the conclusion is then changed accordingly. There are applications to almost periodic functions which are analytic in a strip. Finally, theorem (a) is shown to lead in a natural way to a new proof of Littlewood's Tauberian theorem for general Dirichlet series.

*G. G. Lorentz* (Toronto, Ont.).

## M45-18 (14, 361a)

**Freud, Géza. Restglied eines Tauberschen Satzes. I.** Acta Math. Acad. Sci. Hungar. **2**, 299–308 (1951). (Russian summary)

Let $v(t)$ be monotone increasing over $0\leqq t<\infty$. Let $f(t)$ be non-negative and such that $F(s)=\int_0^\infty f(t)e^{-st}dv(t)$ exists, as a Lebesgue-Stieltjes integral, for $s>0$. If $\alpha$, $c_0$, and $\epsilon$ are positive constants and $F(s)=S\Gamma(\alpha+1)s^{-\alpha}[1+r(s)]$ where

$|r(s)| < c_0 s^\epsilon$ when $s > 0$, then there is a constant $c_1$ such that

$$\int_0^x f(t)dv(t) = Sx^\alpha[1+\beta(x)]$$

where $|\beta(x)| < c_1/\log x$ when $x > 2$. The proof employs the Karamata method of polynomial approximation.

*R. P. Agnew* (Ithaca, N. Y.).

Referred to in M45-20, M45-26, M45-27, M45-38.

**M45-19** **(14, 634g)**

**Delange, Hubert. Encore une nouvelle démonstration du théorème taubérien de Littlewood.** Bull. Sci. Math. (2) 76, 179–189 (1952).

Let $\sum a_n e^{-\lambda_n s}$ converge when $\text{Re}(s) > 0$ to a function $f(s)$. The author gives new proofs of theorems saying that if $f(s) \to S$ as $s \to 0$ over an appropriate set, and if $\sum a_n$ satisfies the Tauberian condition $|a_n| < M(\lambda_n - \lambda_{n-1})/\lambda_n$ or a more general Tauberian condition of Schmidt type, then $\sum a_n$ converges to $S$. The proof depends upon a Tauberian theorem for Laplace integrals. Proof of the latter theorem depends upon a theorem of Montel on the behavior of functions analytic in a sector of the complex plane.

*R. P. Agnew* (Ithaca, N. Y.).

**M45-20** **(14, 958a)**

**Freud, Géza. Restglied eines Tauberschen Satzes. II.** Acta Math. Acad. Sci. Hungar. 3 (1952), 299–307 (1953). (Russian summary)

In paper I, the author [same Acta 2, 299–308 (1951); these Rev. 14, 361] made appropriate hypotheses on the Laplace transform $\int_0^\infty f(t)e^{-st}d\tau(t)$ and obtained an estimate of the function $\int_0^x t^\beta f(t)d\tau(t)$. Under the same hypotheses, the present paper gives an estimate of the $m$-fold integral of the latter function, $m$ being a positive integer.

*R. P. Agnew* (Ithaca, N. Y.).

Citations: MR 14, 361a = M45-18.
Referred to in M45-21, M45-26, M45-27, M45-38.

**M45-21** **(15, 698c)**

**Korevaar, Jacob. A very general form of Littlewood's theorem.** Nederl. Akad. Wetensch. Proc. Ser. A. 57 = Indagationes Math. 16, 36–45 (1954).

The author proves a Tauberian theorem which we give with omission of some details. Let $\phi(t) = t^\alpha L(t)$, where $L(t)$ is slowly oscillating. Let $\omega(u)$ be a bounded positive function which converges monotonely to 0 as $u \to 0+$. Let $\sum a_n$ be a real series for which $a_n > -\phi(n)$ and

(1) $$\left|\sum_{n=0}^{\infty} a_n e^{-nu} - s\right| < \omega(u)$$

when $u > 0$. Then, when $n > 0$, $|\sum_{k=0}^n a_k - s| < \rho(n)$, where

$$\rho(n) = \min_{p \leq K_1} \left\{ K_2 \frac{n\phi(n)}{p} + K_3^p \omega\left(\frac{p}{n}\right) \right\}$$

if $\liminf_{u\to 0} u \log \omega(u) > -\infty$ and $\rho(n) = 0$ otherwise. The proof depends upon lemmas on polynomial approximation, principally one due to Freud [Acta Math. Acad. Sci. Hungar. 2, 299–307 (1953); these Rev. 14, 958], of which independent proofs are given. There are numerous examples.

*R. P. Agnew* (Ithaca, N. Y.).

Citations: MR 14, 958a = M45-20.
Referred to in M45-27, M45-38.

**M45-22** **(15, 950c)**

**Korevaar, Jacob. Numerical Tauberian theorems for Dirichlet and Lambert series.** Nederl. Akad. Wetensch. Proc. Ser. A. 57 = Indagationes Math. 16, 152–160 (1954).

L'auteur a prouvé [mêmes Proc. 57, 46–56 (1954); ces Rev. 15, 698] le résultat suivant: Soit $f(x) = \sum_1^\infty a_n e^{-nx}$, convergente pour $x > 0$, et $\liminf na_n > -\infty$. Si existent $s$ et $\alpha$ positif tels que $f(x) - s = O(1)$ si $x > 1$, $= O(x^\alpha)$, si $0 < n < 1$, alors $\sum_1^n a_p = O(\log n)$, cet ordre de grandeur étant le meilleur. Ce résultat est équivalent au suivant. On suppose $|a_n| = O(n^k)$ $(k > 0)$ et $\liminf na_n > -\infty$. Soit $F(z) = \sum_1^\infty a_n n^{-z}$ $(z = u + iv)$. Si pour $u \geqq -a$ $(a > 0)$, $F(z)$ est régulière et $|F(z)| = O(\exp\{k'|v|\})$ $(k' > 0)$, alors $\sum_1^n a_k - F(0) = O(\log n)$, cet ordre de grandeur étant le meilleur. Résultat analogue en considérant, au lieu de la série de Dirichlet, la série de Lambert $\sum a_n nx/(e^{nx}-1)$.

*M. Zamansky* (Paris).

Referred to in M45-27.

**M45-23** **(16, 31b)**

**Rajagopal, C. T., and Jakimovski (Amir), Amnon. Applications of a theorem of O. Szász for the product of Cesàro and Laplace transforms.** Proc. Amer. Math. Soc. 5, 370–384 (1954).

O. Szász has used the device of integrating an absolutely convergent Laplace integral under the integral sign with respect to the parameter, and the first author has used the same idea for integration of fractional order [Szász, Trans. Amer. Math. Soc. 39, 117–130 (1936); Rajagopal, Amer. J. Math. 69, 371–378, 851–852 (1947); these Rev. 9, 26, 278; see also Szász, Proc. Amer. Math. Soc. 3, 257–263 (1952); these Rev. 13, 835]. Here the authors exploit the idea in the form: (1) if

$$\frac{s^{\alpha+1}}{\Gamma(\alpha+1)} \int_0^\infty e^{-su} s(u) u^\alpha du \to C$$

as $s \to +0$, where $\alpha > 0$, then the same holds with $\alpha = 0$.

They prove some Tauberian theorems of the Hardy-Littlewood type for Laplace integrals which supplement known results. In particular, (2) if

$$\int_0^\infty e^{-su} s(u) du \sim Cs^{-\alpha-1} \quad \text{as} \quad s \to +0,$$

and

(*) $$s(x) - \frac{\alpha+1}{x} \int_0^x s(u) du \geqq -Kx^\alpha,$$

then

$$\int_0^x s(u) du \sim Cx^{\alpha+1}/\Gamma(\alpha+2) \quad \text{as} \quad x \to +\infty.$$

[the case $\alpha = 0$ was proved by Szász, loc. cit., 1936]. They observe that the Hardy-Littlewood "positive" theorem (for integrals), in which the Tauberian condition $s(x) \geqq -Kx^\alpha$ takes the place of (*), may be deduced from (2).

In view of the fact that the "positive" theorem is usually regarded as the fundamental one in this field it is perhaps relevant to remark that (a) in proving (2) the authors use the case $\alpha = 0$ of the "positive" theorem [this case was formulated for integrals by G. Doetsch, Math. Ann. 82, 68–82 (1920)], (b) the general form of the "positive" theorem, with $\alpha > 0$, may be deduced directly from the case $\alpha = 0$ by means of (1).

*L. S. Bosanquet* (London).

**M45-24** **(16, 921e)**

**Delange, Hubert. Généralisation du théorème de Ikehara.** Ann. Sci. Ecole Norm. Sup. (3) 71, 213–242 (1954).

The theorem of the title reads: If $\alpha(t)$ is a non-negative, non-decreasing function in $(0 \leqq t < \infty)$ such that the integral $f(s) = \int_0^\infty e^{-st}\alpha(t)dt$ $(s = \sigma + it)$ converges for $\sigma > a > 0$, and if for some constant $A$ and some function $g(\tau)$,

$$\lim_{\sigma \to a+} f(s) - A(s-a)^{-1} = g(\tau)$$

uniformly in every finite interval $(-b \leqq \tau \leqq b)$, then

$$\lim_{t\to\infty} \alpha(t)e^{-at} = A.$$

The author generalizes this theorem as follows: Let $\beta(t)$ be a real function defined for $t \geqq 0$, measurable and bounded on every finite interval, and suppose that the integral $\int_0^\infty e^{-st}\beta(t)dt$ is convergent for $\Re s > 0$ and equal to $G(s)$. Suppose, besides, that there exists an integer $p$, positive or null, and a real function $\gamma(u)$, continuous and non-decreasing on an interval, $[0, l]$ and positive for $0 < u \leqq l$ such that 1) the integral $\int_0^l \log(1/\gamma(u))du$ is convergent, 2) the product $t^{p+1}\beta(t)\int_0^l e^{-tu}\gamma(u)du$ tends to 1 when $t \to \infty$.

Let us suppose, furthermore, that there exists a positive number $A$ such that the function $F(s) = f(s) - AG(s)$ has the following properties: 1) For each real $y$ different from zero, $F^{(p)}(s)$ tends to a finite limit when $s$ tends to $a+iy$ in the half-plane $\Re s > a$, 2) when $s$ tends to 0 in the half-plane $\Re s > 0$, we have $F^{(p)}(a+s) = O\{\psi(r)/\gamma(r)\}$ $(r = |s|)$. Here $\psi(t)$ is a real, positive and non-increasing function defined for sufficiently small positive $t$ such that $\int_0 \psi(t)dt$ and $\int_0 \psi(t)\log(1/\gamma(t))dt$ are convergent. Then when $t \to \infty$, we have $\alpha(t) \sim Ae^{at}\beta(t)$.

When we put $\beta(t) = 1$, $p = 0$ and $\gamma(u) = 1$ $(l > 0)$, this theorem reduces to the reviewer's theorem. A theorem with stronger assumptions on the behavior of $F^{(p)}(s)$ was previously stated [C. R. Acad. Sci. Paris **232**, 465–467 (1951); MR **12**, 405], the detailed proof of which is now given with two related theorems applicable to arithmetical problems [ibid. **232**, 1392–1393 (1951); MR **12**, 677]. *S. Ikehara.*

Citations: MR 12, 405a = M45-13; MR 12, 677d = N28-23.

Referred to in M45-28, M45-29, N24-28, N36-18, N60-22, N64-48.

## M45-25 (17, 255c)

**Chen, Kien-Kwong. Ikehara's theorem and absolute summability *C*.** Acta Math. Sinica 3 (1953), 8–11. (Chinese. English summary)

In a study of a theorem of Ikehara, Wintner [Amer. J. Math. **69** (1947), 99–103; MR **8**, 375] constructed a series $a_1 + a_2 + \cdots$ for which (i) the Dirichlet series $\sum a_n n^{-(\sigma+it)}$ converges absolutely when $\sigma > 1$; (ii) the power series $\sum a_n x^n$ converges over $0 < x < 1$ to a function $f(x)$ for which $\int_0^1 |f(x)|dx < \infty$; and (iii) the series $\sum a_n$ is not evaluable $C_1$ to 0, i.e. $n^{-1}\sum_{k=1}^n a_k \neq o(1)$. Using the fact that there exists a divergent series $\sum c_n$ absolutely evaluable $C_\alpha$ for each $\alpha > 0$, the author constructs a series $\sum a_n$ for which (i) and (iii) hold and, in addition to (ii), the function $f(x)$ in (ii) has bounded variation over $0 < x < 1$.

*R. P. Agnew* (Ithaca, N.Y.).

Citations: MR 8, 375e = M45-7.

## M45-26 (17, 260c)

**Freud, G. Restglied eines Tauberschen Satzes. III.** Acta Math. Acad. Sci. Hungar. 5 (1954), 275–289.

[For parts I and II see same Acta **2** (1951), 299–308; **3** (1952), 299–307; MR **14**, 361, 958.] The main theorem deduces asymptotic appraisals of Riesz-Stieltjes transforms of nonnegative integer orders from a given asymptotic appraisal of a Laplace-Stieltjes transform and a Tauberian hypothesis. Let $\tau^*(t)$ have bounded variation over each finite interval $0 \leqq t \leqq t_0$, and let

$$F^*(s) = \int_0^\infty e^{-st}d\tau^*(t)$$

exist when $s > 0$. Let, as $s \to 0+$,

$$F^*(s) = A + O\{R(s)\}$$

where $R(s)$ is increasing over $s \geqq 0$, $R(0+) = 0$, and $R(ks) < e^{c_1 k}R(s)$ when $s > 0$ and $k = 2, 3, 4, \cdots$. Let $\beta_2(t)$ be a monotone increasing function and let $L$ be a positive constant such that, as $s \to 0+$,

$$\int_0^\infty e^{-st}d\beta_2(t) = \frac{1}{s}[1 + O\{R(s)\}]$$

and the function $\gamma_2(t)$ defined by

$$\gamma_2(t) = L\beta_2(t) + \int_0^t u\,d\tau^*(u)$$

is a monotone increasing function of $t$. Then, for each $m = 0, 1, 2, \cdots$,

$$\int_0^x (x-t)^m d\tau^*(t) = A\frac{x^m}{m!}\left[1 + O\left\{\left(\log\frac{1}{R(1/x)}\right)^{-m-1}\right\}\right]$$

as $x \to \infty$. Related theorems and applications to Dirichlet series and power series are given. *R. P. Agnew.*

Citations: MR 14, 361a = M45-18; MR 14, 958a = M45-20.

Referred to in M45-27.

## M45-27 (17, 609e)

**Ganelius, Tord. Un théorème taubérien pour la transformation de Laplace.** C. R. Acad. Sci. Paris **242** (1956), 719–721.

Recently several authors have obtained estimates of the remainder in Tauberian theorems for power series, Dirichlet series and Laplace transforms. Estimates based on behavior of the transforms on the real axis were obtained by A. G. Postnikov [Dokl. Akad. Nauk SSSR (N.S.) **77** (1951), 193–196; MR **12**, 820], G. Freud [Acta Math. Acad. Sci. Hungar. **2** (1951), 299–308; **3** (1952), 299–307; **5** (1954) 275–289; MR **14**, 361, 958, **17**, 260; Acta Sci. Math. Szeged **16** (1955), 12–28; MR **17**, 30] and the reviewer [Duke Math. J. **18** (1951), 723–734; Nederl. Akad. Wetensch. Proc. Ser. A. **56** (1953), 281–293; **57** (1954), 36–45, 46–56, 152–160, 432–443, 444–455; MR **13**, 227; **15**, 119, 698, 950; **16**, 239]. The most notable advance in these estimates came when Freud and the reviewer independently replaced the customary uniform approximation in the Karamata-Wielandt proof by approximation in the sense of $L_1$. The present author uses similar methods. However, by introducing Schmidt's Tauberian condition into the Tauberian theorems with remainder he is able to announce more elegant results. The following special case is typical. As $\omega \to \infty$ let $Q(\omega)/\omega \uparrow \infty$, let

$$\int_0^\infty e^{-\lambda/\omega}d\alpha(\lambda) = O\{\omega^{\varrho+1}\exp(-2Q(\omega)/\omega)\}$$

and let $\alpha(\Omega) - \alpha(\omega) \leqq C\omega^\varrho q(\omega)$ for $\omega \leqq \Omega \leqq \omega + q(\omega)$, where $q$ is the inverse function of $Q$. Then $\alpha(\omega) = \alpha(0) + O\{\omega^\varrho q(\omega)\}$ as $\omega \to \infty$. The special case $Q(\omega) = \omega^r$ $(1 < r \leqq 2)$ of this result was considered earlier by V. Vučković [Srpska Akad. Nauka. Zb. Rad. **35**. Mat. Inst. **3** (1953), 255–288; MR **15**, 869]. Vučković derived his result from the known estimates of the remainder which are based on the behavior of transforms in the complex plane.

*J. Korevaar* (Madison, Wis.).

Citations: MR 12, 820e = M45-16; MR 14, 361a = M45-18; MR 14, 958a = M45-20; MR 15, 698c = M45-21; MR 15, 950c = M45-22; MR 17, 260c = M45-26.

## M45-28 (17, 965c)

**Delange, Hubert. Théorèmes taubériens' et applications arithmétiques.** Mém. Soc. Roy. Sci. Liège (4) **16** (1955), no. 1–2, 87 pp.

This memoir consists of four lectures; the first two deal essentially with the theorems called "inverse theorems of the summation process", which are examplified by Karamata in "Sur les théorèmes inverses des procédés de sommabilité" [Hermann, Paris, 1937], and which are closely related to Wiener's Tauberian theorems [Ann. of Math. (2) **33** (1932), 1–100] together with the author's work [Ann. Sci. Ecole Norm. Sup. (3) **67** (1950), 99–160, 199–242; MR **12**, 253]. In this category we find Lambert summability which the author applies to several known arithmetical problems besides the prime-number theorem.

The last two lectures are concerned with the Tauberian theorems for the Laplace-Stieltjes integral which the author has been generalizing in a series of papers [C. R. Acad. Sci. Paris **232** (1951), 465–467, 589–591, 1176–1178, 1392–1393; MR **12**, 405, 497, 605, 677]. From his generalized Tauberian theorems [Ann. Sci. Ecole Norm. Sup. (3) **71** (1954), 213–242; MR **16**, 921] are deduced several corollaries in a form susceptible of arithmetical applications. For example, let $q>1$ and $r$ be integers, and let $\omega(n)$ denote the number of distinct prime factors in the positive integer $n$; then the number of numbers not exceeding $x$, which are "quadratfrei" and such that $\omega(n)\equiv r \pmod q$ will tend to $6\pi^{-2}x/q$ as $x\to\infty$. A particular case for $q=2$ is given in Landau, Handbuch der Primzahlen [Bd. 2, 2nd ed., Chelsea, New York, 1953, p. 606; MR **16**, 904]. Applications to many other problems are now unified by his generalized theorems. *S. Ikehara.*

Citations: MR 12, 405a = M45-13; MR 12, 497d = M45-14; MR 12, 677c = R36-22; MR 16, 904d = N02-3; MR 16, 921e = M45-24.
Referred to in N24-28.

## M45-29 (17, 965d)

**Delange, Hubert. Quelques théorèmes taubériens relatifs à l'intégrale de Laplace et leurs applications arithmétiques.** Univ. e Politec. Torino. Rend. Sem. Mat. **14** (1954–55), 87–103.

The author gives various arithmetical applications of his generalized Tauberian theorems published in a series of papers [in particular, Ann. Sci. Ecole Norm. Sup. (3) **71** (1954), 213–242; MR **16**, 921]. The present paper is essentially a resumé of the paper reviewed above.

*S. Ikehara.*

Citations: MR 16, 921e = M45-24.
Referred to in N24-28.

## M45-30 (18, 478e)

**Erdös, P.; et Karamata, J. Sur la majorabilité $C$ des suites de nombres réels.** Acad. Serbe Sci. Publ. Inst. Math. **10** (1956), 37–52.

With $C$ representing the arithmetic mean transformation $C_1$, a real sequence $a_1, a_2, \cdots$ is said to be majorable $C$ with the majorability constant $A<\infty$ if there exists a sequence $A_1, A_2, \cdots$ such that $a_k\leqq A_k$ for each $k$ and

$$\lim_{n\to\infty} n^{-1}\sum_{k=1}^{n} A_k=A.$$

The following and two similar theorems are given. In order that $a_1, a_2, \cdots$ be majorable $C$, it is necessary and sufficient that (i) as $n\to\infty$, $\sum_{j=n+1}^{n+k} a_j<o(n)$ when $k=o(n)$ and (ii) $W(\varepsilon)=O(\varepsilon)$ where

$$W(\varepsilon)=\limsup_{n\to\infty}\max_{n<n'\leqq(1+\varepsilon)n}\left\{\frac{1}{n}\sum_{j=n+1}^{n'} a_j\right\};$$

moreover if (i) and (ii) hold, then, as $\varepsilon\to 0+$, $\varepsilon^{-1}W(\varepsilon)=o(1)+A^*$, where $A^*$ is the least majorability constant. It is shown how that concept of majorable $C$ and these theorems are related to quadrature theorems, to Tauberian theorems, and to the prime number theorem.

*R. P. Agnew* (Ithaca, N.Y.).

## M45-31 (19, 647b)

**Wintner, Aurel. On arithmetical summation processes.** Amer. J. Math. **79** (1957), 559–574.

In Part I the author pursues the study of the logical relationship of the summation methods $(C,p)$, $(A)$, $(L)$, (E) (Cesàro, Abel, Lambert, Eratosthenes), the (E)-sum of $\sum_1^\infty a_n$ being defined as the limit as $n\to\infty$ (when it exists and is finite) of

$$E_n=E_n(a)=\sum_{k=1}^{n}\{n/k\}a_n,\quad \{x\}=[x]/x.$$

Let $(K)$ denote convergence. It is known (i) that

(†) $\qquad (E)\to(C,1)\to(L)\to(A);$

(ii) that the statements involving (E) or $(L)$ as hypothesis are connected with the prime number theorem; (iii) that the implications $(K)\to$(E), (E)$\to(K)$, and the converses of (†) are all false, but that some of them become true under suitable Tauberian conditions. The author adds a further Tauberian theorem, and replaces some of (†) by oscillation theorems, of which a typical example (corresponding to the first arrow) is: osc $S_n\leqq\alpha$ osc $E_n$, where $S_n=S_n(a)$ is the $(C,1)$-mean, $\alpha$ is a universal constant, and osc $B_n$ denotes the upper limit of $|B_n-B_m|$ when $n>m\to\infty$. Some of these results are based on the observation that (E) and $(L)$ for the given series $\sum a_n$ are equivalent, respectively, to $(C,1)$ and $(A)$ for $\sum(b_n-b_{n-1})$, where $b_n=\sum_{d|n} a_d d$ {the corrected version of the author's (2)} for $n\geqq 1$ and $b_0=0$.

Part II is devoted to some observations on Axer's theorem. An appendix gives a simplified proof of Ananda Rau's theorem $\|A\|\to(L)$, and comments on a related theorem of Hardy and Littlewood. Here $\|A\|$-summability of $\sum a_n$ means integrability of $\varphi(x)$ over $(0,\infty)$, where $\varphi(x)$ is the upper bound for $y\geqq x$ of $|f'(y)|$, and $f(y)=\sum a_n e^{-ny}$. In these parts of the paper, the author's main theme is the unification of existing techniques by systematic use of the relation

$$h\sum_{n=1}^{\infty} F(nh)\to\int_0^\infty F(x)dx \text{ as } h\to+0.$$

This is known to be valid if $F(x)$ is monotonic and has a finite (improper) integral over $(0,\infty)$. The author uses this, and also the generalization in which $|F(x)|\leqq\varphi(x)$, where $\varphi(x)$ satisfies these conditions while $F(x)$ itself has a (proper) Riemann integral over every interval $[\lambda,\mu]$ $(0<\lambda<\mu<\infty)$.

The paper contains a number of inaccuracies of detail, and some statements that the reviewer has not been able to verify from the indications given.

{The reviewer much regrets that, when writing in 1945 about the method (E) and its relation to the prime number theorem, he overlooked the discussion of these topics in the author's book "Eratosthenian averages" [Baltimore, 1943; MR **7**, 366]; and that through a similar oversight, this method is wrongly ascribed to the reviewer in Hardy's "Divergent series", Appendix IV [Oxford, 1949; MR **11**, 25]. It may be added that the account of Axer's theorem in this Appendix, by aiming at the utmost simplicity of proof for the applications in view (on lines indicated by the reviewer) and omitting detailed references to Landau, presents an imperfect picture of the known developments of this theorem. Landau's general version [Rend. Circ. Mat. Palermo **34** (1912), 121–131, Satz 5] includes Wintner's statement (*) on p. 567, and also Theorem 267 of Hardy's book, and indeed under wider conditions, namely (35) instead of (25) in Wintner's account, and $(c2)$ $(d1)$ instead of the alternatives in

Hardy's account. The only change required in the proof in Hardy is to write $|S_1| \leqq H \sum_{n \leqq \delta x} |a_n|(x/n)^\alpha$ and to estimate by partial summation from $(d1)$ rather than by the simpler (but rougher) methods on p. 379.} *A. E. Ingham.*

Citations: MR 7, 366a = Z02-4.

## M45-32 (20# 2556)

**Gopalakrishna, J.; and Ramamohana Rao, C. Some generalized Tauberian type theorems.** J. London Math. Soc. **33** (1958), 147–156.

For a monotonic increasing function $g$, define a transformation $F \to F^*$ by $F^*(x) = (1/g(x)) \int_0^x F(t) dg(t)$. Regarding this as a summation method, the authors are interested in relationships between the limits of oscillation of $F$, and those of $F^*$; denoting lim inf $F(x)$ and lim sup $F(x)$ by $l$ and $L$, and for $F^*$, $l^*$ and $L^*$, one has $l \leqq l^* \leqq L^* \leqq L$. When $f(x) = g(x)F(x)$ is restricted, one can expect inequalities acting in the opposite direction. Extending a theorem of the reviewer [J. Indian Math. Soc. (N.S.) **16** (1952), 147–149; MR **14**, 631], Lakshminarasimhan [ibid. **17** (1953), 55–58; MR **15**, 114] showed that there were functions $A$ and $B$ such that $L^* \geqq A(l, L)$ and $l^* \leqq B(l, L)$, provided $f$ was non-decreasing and $g(x)$ behaved essentially like $x^c$. The present authors remove the restrictions on $g$, and allow $f$ to be slowly oscillating, relative to $g$; they obtain mutual restrictions on the possible values of the four numbers $l$, $L$, $l^*$ and $L^*$. As an application, they obtain an interesting theorem for "generalized" primes. Let $\{n_j\}$ increase, and define two functions $\vartheta$ and $\psi$ by: $\vartheta(x) = \sum_{n_k \leqq x} a(n_k)$, $\psi(x) = \sum_{n_k \leqq x} a(n_k)/f(n_k)$ where $a(t)$ and $f(t)$ are positive, and $f(t) \to \infty$ as $t \to \infty$. Then, if $\psi(x) = \log f(x) + O(1)$, it follows that for some positive $b$ and $B$, $0 < b \leqq \liminf \vartheta(x)/f(x) \leqq 1 \leqq \limsup \vartheta(x)/f(x) \leqq B < \infty$. In the special case $a(t) = \log t$, $f(t) = t$, this is an analogue for Chebysheff's inequalities. {In this case, however, the result can be established directly without resort to the authors' Tauberian theorem.} *R. C. Buck* (Stanford, Calif.)

## M45-33 (20# 7173)

**Karamata, J. Sur les procédés de sommation intervenant dans la théorie des nombres.** Colloque sur la théorie des suites, tenu à Bruxelles du 18 au 20 décembre 1957, pp. 12–31. Centre Belge de Recherches Mathématiques. Librairie Gauthier-Villars, Paris; Établissements Ceuterick, Louvain; 1958. 167 pp. 220 fr. belges.

The author discusses various Tauberian theorems which are of importance in prime number theory. Put

(1) $$G(x) = \sum_{n \leq x} f(n)[x/n] = Ax \log x + Bx + P(x).$$

If we only assume $P(x) = o(x)$ then if $f(n) \geqq -M$ $(1 \leqq n < \infty)$ it is shown that

(2) $$\sum_{n \leq x} f(n) = Ax + o(x).$$

The proof utilises $\sum_{n=1}^{x} \mu(n) = O(x/(\log x)^2)$ ($\mu(n)$ is the Möbius symbol). If in (1) we assume $\rho(x) = o(g(x))$, $g(x)$ monotone increasing, where $\int_1^\infty g(x)/x^2 < \infty$, then (2) follows without the condition $f(n) > -M$.

If $\sum_{n \leq x} f(n)[x/n] = O(x)$, then $\int_1^x F(t)/t = O(x)$, where $F(n) = \sum_{k=1}^n f(k)$. All these results are connected with the prime number theorem.

Several further results are discussed and there is an extensive bibliography. *P. Erdős* (Birmingham)

## M45-34 (21# 5109)

**Pitt, H. R. Tauberian theorems.** Tata Institute of Fundamental Research, Monographs on Mathematics and Physics, 2. Oxford University Press, London, 1958. xi+174 pp. $6.00; 22.50 rs.

This is the first book exclusively devoted to the study of tauberian theorems, which have been associated with the names of Hardy, Littlewood, and Wiener among others. The author has succeeded in giving a brief introduction to some of the more important tauberian theorems, including mercerian theorems as limiting cases, and the methods which have been developed to prove them. Because of the size of the book, he omits, except for occasional relevant references, the theory of ideals in normed rings, which Gelfand and others have used to relate Wiener's general tauberian theorems to general algebraic properties of these structures [e.g., L. H. Loomis, *An introduction to abstract harmonic analysis*, van Nostrand, Toronto-New York-London, 1953; MR **14**, 883].

Chapter I states the definitions and plan of the book, which deals essentially with relations of the form (1) $g(u) = \int k(u, v)s(v)dv$ (integrals without limits hereafter are over $(-\infty, \infty)$) between the functions $g(u)$, $s(v)$ and the kernel $k(u, v)$. Under certain conditions on $k(u, v)$ it is natural to expect that the boundedness or convergence as $u \to \infty$ of $g(u)$ will follow from the same properties of $s(v)$. Theorems of this kind are called abelian theorems after the theorem of Abel to the effect that the convergence to $A$ of the series $\sum a_n$ implies that (2) $A(r) = \sum a_n r^n \to A$ as $r \to 1-0$. The converse is not true, and it is this fact which forms the basis of the modern theory of summation of divergent series. If we put $g(u) = A(e^{-1/u})$, $s(v) = \sum_{n \leqq v} a_n$, $k(u, v) = u^{-1}e^{-(v/u)}$, then the transformation from $\sum a_n$ to $A(r)$ assumes the form (1).

Theorems in which conclusions about the behavior of $s(v)$ in (1) are derived from the assumptions about that of $g(u)$ are generally much deeper than the corresponding abelian theorems. And this tract is mainly concerned with the convergence or other order properties of $s(v)$ and $g(u)$ as $u \to \infty$. Theorems of this kind are called tauberian theorems after the theorem of Tauber [Monatsh. Math. **8** (1897), 273–277], which states that the converse of Abel's limit theorem is true in the sense that (2) implies the convergence of $\sum a_n$, provided that the tauberian condition $a_n = o(n^{-1})$ is satisfied.

Chapters II and III give some account of the results which can be obtained by elementary methods. These include all "$o$" theorems and the classical "$O$" theorems, the first one of which was proved by G. H. Hardy [Proc. London Math. Soc. (2) **8** (1910), 301–320] and then by J. E. Littlewood [ibid. **9** (1910), 434–448]. There are also theorems in which only the boundedness, and not the convergence of $s(v)$, is deduced from that of $g(u)$ and an "$O$" tauberian condition. These latter results are of some intrinsic interest and importance in that they are substantially best possible and establish the boundedness of $s(v)$, which appears as a hypothesis in Wiener's theory (chapter IV), and which is the first step in the classical tauberian theorems.

Chapter IV deals with Wiener's theory [Ann. of Math. (2) **33** (1932), 1–100], which transformed the whole subject into a simple form, as may be seen from one of the two forms of his general tauberian theorems:

Suppose that $k_1(x)$, $k_2(x)$ belong to $L$, and

$$\int \exp(-itx)k_1(x)dx \neq 0$$

for real $t$, that $s(x)$ is bounded and that

$$\lim_{x\to\infty} \int k_1(x-y)s(y)dy = A \int k_1(x)dx;$$

then

$$\lim_{x\to\infty} \int k_2(x-y)s(y)dy = A \int k_2(x)dx.$$

All the special theorems then known may be expressed in the form above. Wiener's theorems and their extensions are applied to special tauberian theorems such as summation by the methods of Cesáro, Riesz, Lambert, Riemann, Hausdorff, Euler, and Borel, and Abel's summation with a curved path.

Chapter V is occupied with mercerian theorems, after the theorem proved by J. Mercer [Proc. London Math. Soc. (2) **5** (1907), 206–224]. Its integral analogue reads: if $R(\alpha)>0$ and

$$g(x) = \alpha s(x)+\frac{(1-\alpha)}{x}\int_0^x s(y)dy \to 0 \quad \text{as } x\to\infty,$$

then $s(x)\to 0$. By exponential transformations we have

$$g(e^x) = \alpha s(e^x)+(1-\alpha)\int_0^x s(e^y)e^{-(x-y)}dy = \int_0^x s(e^{x-y})dk(y),$$

where $k(+0)-k(0)=\alpha$, $k'(y)=(1-\alpha)e^{-y}$ for $y>0$. This belongs to the transformation (1), which may be generalized to the form $g(u)=\int s(v)dh_v(u,v)$ with the "Stieltjes kernel" $h(u,v)$. Under certain conditions on $h(u,v)$ the convergence of $g(u)$ is found to imply that of $s(v)$ even without a tauberian condition and, in some cases, with no condition whatever on $s(v)$. The generalization of theorems of this type and their relationship to linear integro-differential equations are mainly due to the author [Proc. Cambridge Philos. Soc. **40** (1944), 199–211; **43** (1947), 155–163; MR **6**, 273; **9**, 40].

Chapter VI. Tauberian theorems are appropriate in the analytical theory of numbers, which is concerned with the behavior of assemblages of whole numbers as the size of these assemblages increases. One of the most celebrated theorems in this field is the prime number theorem of Hadamard and de la Vallée Poussin [Landau, *Primzahlen*, 2nd. ed., ed. by P. T. Bateman, Chelsea, New York, 1953; MR **16**, 904], which asserts that if $\pi(x)$ is the number of primes not exceeding $x$, then $\pi(x)\log x\sim x$ as $x\to\infty$. In any attempt to prove the theorem, it is at once apparent that the only easily accessible formulae for $\pi(x)$ all involve its means, and that the deduction of the theorem is essentially tauberian in character. The aim of this final chapter is to set out and compare arguments which have been used to prove the prime number theorem. After giving the classical proofs of the prime number theorem, the author discusses the proofs by the Landau-Ikehara theorem [Landau, loc. cit. pp. 917–924], the Lambert tauberian theorem [Wiener, J. Math. Phys. **7** (1928), 161–184], Ingham's method [J. London Math. Soc. **20** (1945), 171–180; MR **8**, 147] and Selberg's method [Ann. of Math. (2) **50** (1949), 305–313; MR **10**, 595; P. Erdös, Proc. Nat. Acad. Sci. U.S.A. **35** (1949), 374–384; MR **10**, 595].

*S. Ikehara* (Tokyo)

Citations: MR 8, 147i = M45-6; MR 10, 595b = N20-3; MR 10, 595c = N20-3; MR 16, 904d = N02-3.
Referred to in B16-17, M45-42, N20-57, R44-31.

## M45-35 (21# 5847)

**De Bruijn, N. G. Pairs of slowly oscillating functions occurring in asymptotic problems concerning the Laplace transform.** Nieuw Arch. Wisk. (3) **7** (1959), 20–26.

A measurable function $L(x)$, $x>0$, is called a slowly oscillating function (=s.o.f.) if $L(x)>0$ and if, for every $p>0$, $L(px)/L(x)\to 1$ as $x\to\infty$. The author discusses some properties of such functions and proves in particular that to every s.o.f. $L(x)$ there corresponds another such function, $L^*(x)$, so that $L(x)L^*(xL(x))\to 1$ and $L^*(x)L(xL^*(x))\to 1$ as $x\to\infty$. The function $L^*$ is determined uniquely up to asymptotic equivalence, and the relation between $L$ and $L^*$ is symmetric. $L$ and $L^*$ are called a pair of conjugate s.o. functions (c.s.o.f.). The two principal results of the paper are as follows.

Theorem 2: Let $A$, $B$, $\beta$ be real constants, $(1-\beta)A>0$, $\beta(1-\beta)B>0$. Let $P(u)$ be a real function, $\in L(0,R)$ for every $R>0$, and such that $f(s)=s\int_0^\infty P(u)e^{-Asu}du$ converges for every $s>0$. Let $L$, $L^*$ be c.s.o.f. Then

$$(1)\qquad \log P(u) \sim Bu^\beta[L(u^\beta)]^{(\beta-1)/\beta} \quad \text{as } u^\beta\to\infty$$

implies

$$(2)\quad \log f(s) \sim (1-\beta)B\left(\frac{As}{B\beta}\right)^{\beta/(\beta-1)}[L^*(s^{\beta/(\beta-1)})]^{1/\beta} \quad \text{as } s^{\beta/(\beta-1)}\to\infty;$$

and if $P(u)$ is monotonic, then (2) implies (1).

Theorem 3: Let $a$, $\alpha$ be positive constants, and let $f(t)$ be a positive measurable function for $0<t\leqq a$. Assume that $\inf[f(t): \delta\leqq t\leqq a]>0$ for each $\delta>0$, and put $F(x)=\int_0^a e^{-xf(t)}dt$ for $x>0$. Let $L$, $L^*$ be c.s.o.f. Then (3) $f(t)\sim t^\alpha[L(t^{-\alpha})]^{-1}$ as $t\downarrow 0$ implies (4) $F(x)\sim\Gamma(1+\alpha^{-1})[xL^*(x)]^{-1/\alpha}$ as $x\to\infty$; and if $f(t)$ is non-decreasing then (4) implies (3).

These theorems are extensions of results of Kohlbecker [Trans. Amer. Math. Soc. **88** (1958), 346–365; MR **20** #2309] and Békéssy [Magyar Tud. Akad. Mat. Kutató Int. Közl. **2** (1957), 105–120; MR **20** #4134].

*A. Erdélyi* (Pasadena, Calif.)

Citations: MR 20# 2309 = P72-36.
Referred to in P72-41.

## M45-36 (22# 11247)

**König, Heinz. Neuer Beweis eines klassischen Tauber-Satzes.** Arch. Math. **11** (1960), 278–279.

Es handelt sich um einen neuen Beweis des klassischen Tauber-Satzes: Ist $\varphi(t)$ für $t\geqq 0$ monoton wachsend und existiert $f(x)=\int_0^\infty e^{-xt}d\varphi(t)$ für $x>0$, aus $f(x)\sim A/x^\lambda$, $x\to 0+$, $\lambda>0$ folgt dann $\varphi(t)\sim At^\lambda/\Gamma(\lambda+1)$, $t\to\infty$.

Der Gedankengang ist der folgende: Aus der Monotonie von $\varphi(t)$ schliesst man elementar (für $\alpha\geqq 1$)

$$0\leqq \varphi(\alpha t)/\alpha^\lambda \leqq M \quad \text{für } 0\leqq t\leqq 1,$$
$$\leqq Mt^\lambda \quad \text{für } 1\leqq t.$$

Nach dem Auswahlsatz von Helly gibt es dann eine Folge $\alpha_j\nearrow\infty$ für die $C=\lim_{j\to\infty}\varphi(\alpha_j)/\alpha_j^\lambda$ existiert. Durch sukzessive Anwendung des Hellyschen Satzes beweist man jetzt $C=A/\Gamma(\lambda+1)$. Monotonie von $\varphi(t)$ ergibt dann die Behauptung.

Der Verfasser betont dass ähnliche Ansätze schon in der berühmten Thesis von R. Schmidt [Math. Z. **22** (1925), 89–152], und bei A. Beurling [Acta Math. **77** (1945), 127–136; MR **7**, 61] zu finden sind.

*V. Vučković* (Belgrade)

Citations: MR 7, 61f = M45-4.

**M45-37** (27# 511)

**Ganelius, Tord**

**The remainder in Wiener's tauberian theorem.**

Mathematica Gothoburgensia, 1.

*Acta Universitatis Gothoburgensis, Göteborg*, 1962. 13 pp. Kr. 5.00.

Suppose that $\Phi(y)$ is bounded, $K(x)$ integrable in $(-\infty, \infty)$ with Fourier transform $\hat{K}(\xi)$ and that $s>0$ and $\int K(x-y)\Phi(y)dy=O(\exp(-sx))$ as $x\to\infty$. Then if $[\hat{K}(\xi)]^{-1}=g(\xi)$ and $g(\zeta)=g(\xi+i\eta)$ is analytic and $|g(\zeta)|<M\exp(m|\zeta|)$ for $|\eta|<b$ and constants $m$, $M$, and if $\Phi(x)$ satisfies the tauberian condition that $\Phi(x)+Cx$ increases for some constant $C$, it is shown that $\Phi(x)=O(x^{-1})$. The result is related to one of Beurling [C. R. 9ième Congr. Math. Scand. (Helsingfors, 1938), pp. 345–366, Akad. Bokhandeln, Helsinki, 1939] in which the condition on $\hat{K}(\xi)$ is that $[\hat{K}(\xi)]^{-1}=\lim_{\eta\to+0}f(\xi+i\eta)$ and $f(\zeta)$ is analytic and $|f'(\zeta)|<C(1+|\zeta|^{p-1})$ in $0<\eta<a$ and $a>s$, $p>\frac{1}{2}$. Then if $\Phi(y)$ satisfies the tauberian condition $\Phi(y)-\Phi(x)\geqq -C\exp(-sx/(p+1))$ for $x_0<x<y<x+\exp(-sx/(p+1))$, it follows that $\Phi(x)=O(\exp(-sx/(p+1)))$.

The special case in which the kernel can be expressed in the Bessel function form $J_{2q+4}(e^{-x})e^{(q+2)x}$ can be used to improve an estimate of Bureau [J. Math. Anal. Appl. **1** (1960), 423–483; ibid. **4** (1962), 181–192] for the spectral function of a second-order self-adjoint elliptic operator with analytic coefficients.

*H. R. Pitt* (New Haven, Conn.)

**M45-38** (27# 1747)

**Lindberg, Magnus**

**On two Tauberian remainder theorems.**

*Pacific J. Math.* **12** (1962), 607–615.

Following T. Ganelius, the author gives sharper estimates on two Tauberian problem remainders than those recently found by Avakumović and Korevaar based on Freud [V. Avakumović, Math. Z. **53** (1950), 53–58; MR **12**, 254; Acad. Serbe Sci. Publ. Inst. Math. **6** (1954), 47–56; MR **16**, 239; J. Korevaar, Nederl. Akad. Wetensch. Proc. Ser. A **57** (1954), 36–45; MR **15**, 698; G. Freud, Acta Math. Acad. Sci. Hungar. **2** (1951), 299–308; MR **14**, 361; ibid. **3** (1952), 299–307; MR **14**, 958]. For the first problem, arising from the work on number theory of Erdős, the author shows that if the non-decreasing, real-valued function $F$ on $[0, +\infty)$ has $\int_0^x F(x-t)dF(t)=\frac{1}{2}x^2+O(x^q)$ over $x\in(1,+\infty)$ with real $q\in[0,2)$, then the remainder $w(x)=F(x)-x$ satisfies there $w(x)=O(x^{(q+1)/3})$. The second result proves a sharpened version of the conjecture of the reviewer stated as a research problem [Bull. Amer. Math. Soc. **66** (1960), 275–276], and a little long to restate here. In this connection, there is a typographical error in the exponent in the author's condition (1.4), which should read $|g(s)|<M_1|s|^{1-2\gamma+\eta}+M_2$ over $R[s]>0$, as is also clear from the later correct statement of Theorem 2. The reviewer wishes to add here that, despite this affirmative solution of his research problem, he has not been able to utilize this according to his expressed hope to include the next lower degree boundary length term in the asymptotic formula for polygonal membrane eigenvalues, since he cannot verify the previously expected estimate [see J. Math. Anal. Appl. **4** (1962), 212–239; MR **26** #2748].

*F. H. Brownell* (Seattle, Wash.)

Citations: MR 14, 361a = M45-18; MR 14, 958a = M45-20; MR 15, 698c = M45-21.

**M45-39** (28# 3277)

**Delange, Hubert**

**Théorèmes taubériens relatifs à l'intégrale de Laplace.**

*J. Math. Pures Appl.* (9) **42** (1963), 253–309.

The function $V(t)$ is positive for $t>0$ and, for some real $\rho$, $V(t)=t^\rho L(t)$, where $L(\lambda t)/L(t)\to 1$ as $t\to\infty$, for every $\lambda>0$. The real or complex function $\alpha(t)$ is bounded in every finite part of $t\geqq 0$, $\int_0^\infty e^{-st}\alpha(t)dt$ converges to $f(s)$ in $\operatorname{Re} s>0$, and $\alpha(t)$ satisfies the Tauberian condition

$$\limsup_{t\to\infty}\,[V(t)]^{-1}\Big\{\sup_{t\leqq t'\leqq t+h}|\alpha(t')-\alpha(t)|\Big\} = \bar{\omega}(h) < \infty,$$

or a related but more complicated "one-sided" condition. It is then proved that $\alpha(t)=O[V(t)]$ when, for some integer $p\geqq\max[0,-\rho]$, $f^{(p)}(s)=O\{r^{-p}V(r^{-1})\phi(r)\}$ as $r=|s|\to 0$ in $\operatorname{Re} s>0$, provided that $\phi(t)$ is positive and decreasing,

$$\int_0^1 \phi(t)\,dt, \qquad \int_0^1 \phi(t)\log[t^{-p}V(t^{-1})]\,dt$$

both converge, and (in the case $p+\rho=0$) that $t^pV(t)$ increases for large enough $t$.

The conclusion can be strengthened to $\alpha(t)=o[V(t)]$ if $\bar{\omega}(h)=0$. The more explicit conclusion

$$\limsup|\alpha(t)/V(t)| \leqq W(+0)$$

(with analogous results in the "one-sided" case) follows if it is assumed that, for every real $y$, either $f^{(p)}(s)$ is bounded as $s\to iy$ in $\operatorname{Re} s>0$ or $f^{(p)}(iy+s)=O\{r^{-p}V(r^{-1})\phi_y(r)\}$ with conditions on $\phi_y$ similar to those above.

The results were first announced in an earlier paper [C. R. Acad. Sci. Paris **232** (1951), 589–591; MR **12**, 497] and are used here in the special case $V(t)=t^{\omega-2}$ ($\omega$ real) to derive closer estimates for $\alpha(t)$ when $f(s)$ takes the form $\sum a_j(s)s^{-\omega_j}+h(s)$ with $h(s)$, $a_j(s)$ regular near 0. Using the fact that the zeta function has no zero in $\operatorname{Re} s\geqq 1$, it is also possible to derive an expression $\sum_{j=0}^q C_j(\log\log x)^{q-j}+o[(\log\log x)^{q-1}(\log x)^{-1}]$ for the sum of the reciprocals of the positive integers up to $x$ which are products of $q$ distinct primes, thus sharpening a result of S. Selberg [Skr. Norske Vid.-Akad. Oslo I **1942**, no. 5; MR **6**, 57].

*H. R. Pitt* (Nottingham)

Citations: MR 6, 57h = N28-9; MR 12, 497d = M45-14.

**M45-40** (30# 387)

**Skof, Fulvia**

**Effetto dell'attenuazione delle condizioni tauberiane per le serie di potenze.**

*Ann. Mat. Pura Appl.* (4) **65** (1964), 329–340.

Let $\mathscr{C}$ be the class of functions $f(z)$ regular in $|z|<1$ and continuous in $|z|\leqq 1$. Let

$$f(z) = \sum_{n=0}^\infty a_n z^n \quad (|z|<1), \qquad s_n = \sum_{\nu=0}^n a_\nu.$$

By specialized forms of known theorems we have the propositions (for $f\in\mathscr{C}$ and $n\to\infty$): (1) if $a_n=O(1/n)$, then $s_n\to f(1)$; (2) if $s_q-s_p>-\sigma$ for $p_0\leqq p<q\leqq p+\omega p$ (any $\sigma>0$, some $p_0=p_0(\sigma)>0$, $\omega=\omega(\sigma)>0$), then $s_n\to f(1)$; (3) $s_n=o(\log n)$. The object of this paper is to establish the "best possible" nature of these results in specially precise senses. Thus, with reference to (1) and (3), it is proved in Theorem A that, given $\psi(t)$, $\varepsilon(t)>0$ such that $\varepsilon(t)\to 0$, $\psi(t)\nearrow\infty$, $\psi(t)/t\searrow 0$ as $t\uparrow\infty$, we can construct $f(z)\in\mathscr{C}$ such that (a) $|a_n|\leqq\psi(n)/n$ $(n\geqq 1)$, (d) $|a_n|=\psi(n)/n$, $|s_n|>\varepsilon(n)\log\psi(n)$ for an infinity of $n$. Theorem B shows, with reference to (2) and (3), that given $\chi(t)$ with $\chi(t)\nearrow\infty$, $\chi(t)/t\searrow 0$, we can satisfy (b), the hypothesis of (2) with

$\omega p$ replaced by $\chi(p)$, and (d)′ $|s_n| > \varepsilon(n) \log(n/\chi(n))$ for an infinity of $n$. Theorem C shows that we can satisfy (a), (b), (d) simultaneously, if $\psi, \chi$ have the further property that $\chi(t)\psi(t)/t \searrow 0$. The constructions are based on the polynomials

$$G(z; k, n, m) = z^k \sum_{r=m}^{n} \frac{z^{n-r} - z^{n+r}}{r},$$

a generalization by Turán [Mat. Lapok **10** (1959), 278–283; MR **23** #A2511] of the classical Fejér polynomials $g(z; k, n) = G(z; k, n, 1)$. {Following a current fashion, the author seeks (p. 333) to prove a series $\sum_{h=1}^{\infty} u_h(z)$ uniformly convergent for $z = x + iy \in R$ by saying, in effect: $\sum_{h=1}^{\infty} |u_h(z)| \leqq \sum_{h=1}^{\infty} M_h$ $(z \in R)$, the last series is convergent with terms independent of $z$, so the original series is uniformly convergent in $R$. This is incorrect. Counter-example: $u_h(z) = ze^{-hz}$, $M_h = 2^{1-h}$, $R = \{z : |y| \leqq x\}$. Inequalities should, of course, be stated for the individual terms $|u_h(z)|$, not for the sum as a whole. (Such inequalities are in fact satisfied, and the author's argument is basically correct but wrongly expressed.)}

*A. E. Ingham* (Cambridge, England)

Referred to in Z02-57.

## M45-41 (31# 1228)

**Erdős, P.; Ingham, A. E.**

**Arithmetical Tauberian theorems.**

*Acta Arith.* **9** (1964), 341–356.

Let $a_1, a_2, \cdots$ be real numbers with $1 < a_1 \leqq a_2 \leqq \cdots$, and suppose $A = \sum a_n^{-1} < \infty$. Let $f(x)$ be a function defined for real $x$, bounded in every bounded interval, with $f(x) = 0$ for $x < 1$. It is shown that if $A < 1$, and if (1) $f(x) + \sum f(x/a_n) = (1 + A)x + o(x)$ as $x \to \infty$, then (2) $f(x) = x + o(x)$. If $A = 1$, then (1) implies that $\limsup\,[\inf] f(x)/x = 1 + c\ [1 - c]$, where $0 \leqq c \leqq \infty$. If $A = 1$ and $f(x)$ is non-decreasing, then (1) implies (2) unless $a_n = a^{r_n}$ for some fixed $a > 1$ and odd integers $r_n$. The proofs use elementary methods.

When $A > 1$, these methods only work if special relations exist among the $a_n$. For example, suppose that for a fixed $\lambda > 1$ and some subset $S$ of $\{a_n\}$, the numbers $\lambda$ and $\lambda a_n$ $(a_n \in S)$ form a subset $T$ of $\{a_n\}$, and suppose $\sum_{T'} a_n^{-1} + \lambda^{-1} \sum_{S'} a_n^{-1} < 1$, where $S'$, $T'$ are the complements of $S$, $T$ in $\{a_n\}$. Then (1) implies (2).

To deal with the general case, let $Z(s) = 1 + \sum a_n^{-s}$, where $s = \sigma + it$ is a complex variable. In order that (1) imply (2) for all non-decreasing functions $f(x)$ it is necessary and sufficient that $Z(s) \neq 0$ on the line $\sigma = 1$. The relation of this result to the previous theorems, and the possibility of weakening the hypotheses, is discussed. An example shows that when $A = 1$, the monotone condition on $f(x)$ is needed to deduce (2) from (1), even if the $a_n$ are integers. The authors ask for an example where the $a_n$ are integers and $Z(s)$ has a zero on $\sigma = 1$.

*B. Gordon* (Los Angeles, Calif.)

## M45-42 (32# 1483)

**Ingham, A. E.**

**On Tauberian theorems.**

*Proc. London Math. Soc.* (3) **14a** (1965), 157–173.

It is J. E. Littlewood who has raised Tauberian theorems to their present status of importance [same Proc. (2) **9** (1911), 434–448]. This was achieved via a theorem on Dirichlet series $\sum a_n e^{-s\lambda_n}$, which reads, in the power series form $(\lambda_n = n,\ e^{-s} = x)$, that if $a_n = O(1/n)$ as $n \to \infty$, so that $f(x) = \sum a_n x^n$ is convergent for $|x| < 1$, and if $f(x)$ tends to a finite limit $A$ when $x \to 1-$, then $\sum a_n$ is convergent to the sum $A$.

The powerful method invented by Littlewood for the proof of this theorem is based on the use of a "peak function". The function whose properties are required, say $A(u)$, occurs in a sum or an integral, along with an elementary factor such as $e^{-su}$. The general idea is to convert this factor by a suitable operation on the sum or integral into one that has a sharp peak at some point $u = u_0$, thus emphasizing the values of $A(u)$ near this point. For this purpose Littlewood introduced the method of repeated differentiations, which raised, however, other difficulties besides those associated with the "peak" idea [see Hardy, *Divergent series*, § 7.12, Clarendon Press, Oxford, 1949; MR **11**, 25], but these were surmounted to achieve a successful conclusion.

Since Littlewood's original proof, Tauberian theory has been developed by many, in particular, Hardy and Littlewood, while N. Wiener has produced a general theory to include special theories into a unified scheme [H. R. Pitt, *Tauberian theorems*, Oxford Univ. Press, London, 1962; MR **21** #5109]. In 1930, Karamata introduced his method of polynomial approximation [Hardy, loc. cit., §§ 7.6, 7.11], where the factor $e^{-su}$ is first converted into a polynomial in $e^{-su}$, and this is then used as an approximation to a more general function of $e^{-su}$, designed to isolate values of $A(u)$ over a selected range of $u$. Karamata's method may be made self-contained by the inclusion of Weierstrass's theorem on the approximation of continuous functions by polynomials, in which a peak function is more than likely to make its appearance. The author has pointed out that this situation may be replaced by one in which the peak function is used directly in the Tauberian argument, without the intervention of approximation theory [Quart. J. Math. Oxford Ser. **8** (1937), 1–7]. He has carried out this program in detail for the "high-indices theorem" of Hardy and Littlewood, but only indicated it for other Tauberian theorems. In this paper, the author makes full use of the "peak function" for Tauberian theorems deducible from Theorem 108 of Hardy's book, and also for "numerical" Tauberian theorems due to A. G. Postnikov [Dokl. Akad. Nauk SSSR **77** (1951), 193–196; MR **12**, 820], J. Korevaar [Nederl. Akad. Wetensch. Proc. Ser. A **57** (1954), 432–455; MR **16**, 239], and others. Finally, relative efficiency of different peak functions and examples are discussed.

*S. Ikehara* (Tokyo)

Citations: MR 12, 820e = M45-16; MR 21# 5109 = M45-34.

## M45-43 (32# 1484)

**Mandelbrojt, S.**

**Les taubériens généraux de Norbert Wiener.**

*Bull. Amer. Math. Soc.* **72** (1966), *no.* 1, *pt.* 2, 48–51.

## M45-44 (32# 2788)

**Kac, M.**

**A remark on Wiener's Tauberian theorem.**

*Proc. Amer. Math. Soc.* **16** (1965), 1155–1157.

One version of Wiener's Tauberian theorem reads: Let $K(x) \in L(-\infty, \infty)$ and let its Fourier transform $k(\xi) \neq 0$ $(-\infty < \xi < \infty)$. If $m(y)$ is a bounded measurable function such that for almost all $x$, $\int_{-\infty}^{\infty} K(x-y)m(y)\,dy = 0$, then $m(y) = 0$ almost everywhere. The author obtains a weaker version of the Tauberian theorem by adding an extra requirement on the function $K(x)$, namely, that $x^2 K(x) \in L(-\infty, \infty)$. It is pointed out that this theorem is strong enough to establish the prime number theorem by following the proof given by Levinson [same Proc. **15** (1964), 480–485; MR **29** #81].

*S. Ikehara* (Tokyo)

Citations: MR 29# 81 = N04-44.

## M45-45 (33# 3003 )

**Wagner, Eberhard**

**Taubersche Sätze reeller Art für die Laplace-transformation.**

*Math. Nachr.* **31** (1966), 153–168.

Suppose that $f(s)=\int_0^\infty e^{-st}F(t)\,dt$ $(s>0)$. The aim of the paper is to derive estimates or asymptotic formulae for $\log F(t)$ or $F(t)$ from assumptions about the behaviour of $f(s)$ as $s\to 0+$ together with Tauberian conditions on $F(t)$. The results are too complicated to quote in detail, but the paper works in the general region where $f(s)$ is of higher order than any power of $1/s$ when $s\to 0+$. It is well known that, in this region, an asymptotic formula for $F(t)$ itself cannot be derived from a plain asymptotic assumption $f(s)\sim f_0(s)$ $(s\to 0+)$ with a suitably restricted comparison function $f_0(s)$, together with the standard Tauberian condition "$F(t)$ positive and increasing". Known theorems in this field make stronger assumptions about $f(s)$ (possibly involving complex values of $s$), or impose heavier Tauberian conditions on $F(t)$. The author's Satz 5 is of the latter type.

*A. E. Ingham* (Cambridge, England)

Referred to in P72-50.

## M45-46 (36# 566 )

**Hoischen, L.**

**An inclusion theorem for Abel and Lambert summability.**

*J. London Math. Soc.* **42** (1967), 591–594.

$\sum_1^\infty a_n$ is said to be $A$-summable to $a$ if

$$\sum_1^\infty a_n \exp(-sn)\to a \text{ as } s\to 0+,$$

and $L$-summable to $a$ if

$$\sum_1^\infty a_n sne^{-sn}(1-e^{-sn})^{-1}\to a \text{ as } s\to 0+.$$

The inclusion $L\subseteq A$ was proved by G. H. Hardy and J. E. Littlewood [Proc. London Math. Soc. (2) **19** (1919), 21–29]. The proof makes use of the fact that (*) $\sum_1^\infty n^{-1}|N(n)|<\infty$, where $N(n)=\sum_1^n \mu(k)k^{-1}$ and $\mu(k)$ is the Möbius function. As is known, (*) is more than the prime number theorem, which is equivalent to the convergence of $\sum_1^\infty n^{-1}N(n)$. Here, without using deeper results of the theory of numbers, the following is proved: $L\subseteq A$ implies $\sum_1^\infty n^{-1}|N(n)|<\infty$.

*A. Meir* (Edmonton, Alta.)

## M45-47 (38# 1434 )

**Glasser, M. L.**

**A note on the Littlewood-Tauber theorem.**

*Proc. Amer. Math. Soc.* **20** (1969), 39–40.

Ausgehend von einem Hilfssatz, der auf Wiener zurückgeht, wird auf wenigen Zeilen der Satz bewiesen: Konvergiert $\sum a_n x^n$ gegen $f(x)$ in $-1<x<1$ und gilt $f(x)\to s<\infty$ für $x\to 1$, gilt weiter die Tauber-Bedingung $a_n=O(n^{-1})$, so folgt $\sum a_n=s$.

*W. Biegert* (Stuttgart)

## M45-48 (38# 4854 )

**Segal, S. L.**

**A Tauberian relative of the Landau-Ingham Tauberian theorem.**

*Proc. Amer. Math. Soc.* **20** (1969), 287–294.

The author proves the following Tauberian theorem: Let $a_n\geqq 0$ and let $F(x)=\sum_{n\leqq x}a_n$. If (*) $\sum_{d\leqq x}F(x/d)=ax\log\log x+bx+cx/\log x+o(x/\log x)$, where $a$, $b$ and $c$ are real constants, then $F(x)=\sum_{n\leqq x}a_n=ax/\log x(1+o(1))$. This type of Tauberian theorem is originally due to E. Landau [*Handbuch der Lehre von der Verteilung der Primzahlen*, 2 Bände, second edition, Vol. 2, p. 599, Chelsea, New York, 1953; MR **16**, 904; S.-B. Akad. Wiss. Wien Math.-Natur. Kl. **120** (1911), 973–988, especially p. 979, § 2]. A more general result than Landau's was subsequently obtained by A. Ingham [J. London Math. Soc. **20** (1945), 171–180; MR **8**, 147], with (*) replaced by the condition $\int_1^x F(t)/t^2\,dt=A\log x+(B-A\gamma)+o(1)$, where $\gamma$ is Euler's constant.

The proof depends on an appropriate use of Ingham's theorem, as well as an additional Tauberian argument [e.g., E. Grosswald, Amer. Math. Monthly **71** (1964), 736–743; MR **29** #4742]. The author concludes the paper with a discussion of the hypotheses.

*S. Ikehara* (Tokyo)

Citations: MR 8, 147i = M45-6; MR 29# 4742 = N04-46.

Referred to in M45-50.

## M45-49 (39# 143 )

**Segal, S. L.**

**A Tauberian theorem for Dirichlet convolutions.**

*Illinois J. Math.* **13** (1969), 316–320.

Using Wiener's Tauberian theory, A. E. Ingham [J. London Math. Soc. **20** (1945), 171–180; MR **8**, 147] had shown that from $\sum_{d\leqq x}f(x/d)=ax\log x+bx+o(x)$, for a positive nondecreasing $f(x)$, it follows that $f(x)\sim ax$, by appealing only to the fact that the Riemann zeta-function has no zeros with real part 1, thus providing a new proof of the prime number theorem. The author modifies Ingham's procedure so that it yields a Tauberian theorem for the more general convolution $\sum_{d\leqq x}f(x/d)k(d)=ax\sum_{d\leqq x}k(d)/d+bx+o(x)$. The hypotheses of this theorem are too complicated to be stated here.

*O. H. Körner* (Marburg)

Citations: MR 8, 147i = M45-6.

## M45-50 (40# 2624 )

**Segal, Sanford L.**

**A general Tauberian theorem of Landau-Ingham type.**

*Math. Z.* **111** (1969), 159–167.

The author proves the following two Tauberian theorems. (A) Let $f(x)$ be a positive non-decreasing function satisfying (1) $\sum_{\nu\leqq x}f(x/\nu)=xg(x)+o(x^2g'(x))$, where $g(x)$ is a positive twice continuously differentiable function defined in $[1,\infty)$ such that (i) $g'(x)>0$ for $x\in(1,\infty)$, (ii) $xg'(x)$ is non-increasing from some point on, (iii) for some positive integer $k$, $x(\log x)^k g'(x)=h(x)$ is non-decreasing from some point on and $\liminf_{x\to\infty}h(x)=\infty$. Then $f(x)\sim x^2g'(x)$ as $x\to\infty$.

(B) With $g(x)$ as in A, if $f(x)$ is any function bounded and integrable in every finite sub-interval of $[1,\infty)$ which satisfies (1), then

$$\int_1^x (f(t)/t^2)\,dt = g(x)-\gamma\sum_{\nu\leqq x}(\mu(\nu)/\nu)g(x/\nu)+o(xg'(x))$$

as $x\to\infty$, where $\gamma$ is Euler's constant and $\mu(\nu)$ is the Möbius function. The proofs require the estimate

$$\sum_{1\leqq\nu\leqq x}\mu(\nu)/\nu = o(1/(\log x)^k)$$

for every $k>0$. These theorems generalize earlier work by A. E. Ingham [J. London Math. Soc. **20** (1945), 171–180; MR **8**, 147] and the author [Proc. Amer. Math. Soc. **20** (1969), 287–294; MR **38** #4854], where $g(x)$ is taken, respectively, as $a\log x$ and as $a\log\log(x+2)+b+c/\log(x+2)$.

*R. A. MacLeod* (Victoria, B.C.)

Citations: MR 8, 147i = M45-6; MR 38# 4854 = M45-48.

# M50 POWER-SUM THEOREMS OF THE TURÁN TYPE

See also reviews A40-28, M20-33, M25-15, M25-31, M25-40, M25-45, M25-47, M25-49, M25-53, M25-54, M25-58, M25-90, M30-7, M40-29, N04-16, N04-27, N04-28, N04-32, N04-36, N04-40, N04-42, N12-21, N12-23, N12-25, N12-26, N12-33, N12-37, N12-39.

**M50-1** **(12, 490b)**

**Turán, Pál. On a new method in the analysis with applications.** Časopis Pěst. Mat. Fys. **74** (1949), 123–131 (1950). (English. Czech summary)

In this lecture the author states two estimates for sums of the form $\sum_{\nu=1}^{n} b_\nu z_\nu^{\nu}$, where $z_\nu$ are complex numbers and $y$ is an integer, and indicates how they apply to gap theorems, quasi-analytic functions, zeros of trigonometric sums, and the Riemann zeta function. *R. P. Boas, Jr.*

Referred to in M50-2.

**M50-2** **(15, 688b)**

**Turán, Paul. Eine neue Methode in der Analysis und deren Anwendungen.** Akadémiai Kiadó, Budapest, 1953. 196 pp. 80.00 Ft.

As the author says in his introduction, the method to which this book is devoted is not entirely new; H. Bohr seems to have been the first one who applied the theory of Diophantine approximations to problems in function theory and analytical theory of numbers. During the last 10 years, however, Turán sharpened the analytical tools and widened the range of applications. Most of the material in the book has been published before (see the quotations below), but apart from an expository lecture [Časopis Pěst. Mat. Fys. **74**, 123–131 (1950); these Rev. **12**, 490] this is the first systematic account.

The book consists of two parts: Part I ("Über einige neuere Aufgaben der Theorie der diophantischen Approximationen") deals with the method, Part II ("Anwendungen") with its applications. There are 6 appendices, where the author treats auxiliary theorems which are used in Part II but which are not an essential part of the main method.

Part I. The author compares the Kronecker and Dirichlet approximation theorems with their analytical equivalents. Roughly equivalent to Dirichlet's theorem is the following one (essentially used by Bohr and Landau [see Titchmarsh, The theory of the Riemann zeta-function, Oxford, 1951, Ch. 8; these Rev. **13**, 741] in order to prove that $\zeta(\sigma+it)$ is not $O(\log\log t)$ in the region $\sigma>1$, $t>4$): If $a_1, \cdots, a_k$ are complex, $0<\lambda_1<\cdots<\lambda_k$, $\omega>4$, then

$$\text{(i)}\quad \max_{1\leq t\leq \omega^k}\left|1+\sum_{j=1}^{k} a_j \exp(2\pi i\lambda_j t)\right| > \left\{1+\sum_{j=1}^{k}|a_j|\right\}\cos 2\pi/\omega.$$

The author remarks that, for most applications, it is important to reduce rigorously the range for $t$ rather than clinging to the best possible estimate on the right hand side of (i). Further, he considers complex values of $\lambda$ also, and writes $\exp(2\pi i\lambda_j)=z_j$. Put $\sum_{j=1}^{k} a_j z_j^{\,t}=f(t)$, $\max_{1\leq j\leq k}|z_j|=U$, $\min_{1\leq j\leq k}|z_j|=u$. The "first problem" consists of finding lower estimates for $f(t)u^{-t}$; the more difficult "second problem" deals with $f(t)U^{-t}$. Typical results are as follows. If $m\geqq 0$, then (ii) there is an integer $\nu$ $(m\leqq\nu\leqq m+k)$ such that

$$|f(\nu)|u^{-\nu}\geqq k^k(2e(m+k))^{-k}|a_1+\cdots+a_k|;$$

and (iii) if, moreover, $U=|z_1|\geqq\cdots\geqq|z_k|$ then there is also a $\nu$ $(m\leqq\nu\leqq m+k)$ such that

$$|f(\nu)|U^{-\nu}\geqq k^k(24e^2(m+2k))^{-k}\min_{1\leqq j\leqq k}|a_1+\cdots+a_j|.$$

Part II. §1 and §2. Generalization of inequalities of Littlewood [see Turán, J. London Math. Soc. **21**, 268–275 (1947); these Rev. **9**, 80] and S. Bernstein on trigonometric polynomials. §3. The real roots of almost periodic trigonometric polynomials with positive coefficients [Publ. Math. Debrecen **1**, 38–41 (1949); these Rev. **11**, 512]. §4. Gap theorems for Dirichlet series [Hungarica Acta Math. **1**, 21–29 (1947); Acta Sci. Math. Szeged **14**, 209–218 (1952); these Rev. **9**, 276; **14**, 738]. §5. Quasianalytic functions [C. R. Acad. Sci. Paris **224**, 1750–1752 (1947); these Rev. **9**, 16]. §6. Approximations of analytic functions in $|z|\leqq R$ by finite sums $\sum b_j h(z\tau_j)$, where $h(z)$ is an integral function [cf. Gelfond, Mat. Sbornik N.S. **4**(46), 149–156 (1938)]. §7. The asymptotic behaviour of the solutions of systems of linear differential equations. §8. Approximative solutions of differential equations. §9 and §13. Remainder term in the Prime Number Theorem [Acta Math. Acad. Sci. Hungar. **1**, 48–63, 155–166 (1950); these Rev. **13**, 208; **14**, 137]. §10. The author proves for a general class of Dirichlet series a result analogous to his main theorem on the Quasi Riemann Hypothesis, assuming, however, an analogue of the Lindelöf hypothesis. §11 and §12. The Quasi Riemann Hypothesis [Izvestiya Akad. Nauk SSSR. Ser. Mat. **11**, 197–262 (1947); these Rev. **9**, 80]. §14. Carlson's theorem on the roots of the zeta function [Acta Math. Acad. Sci. Hungar. **2**, 39–73 (1951); these Rev. **13**, 742]. §15. The author suggests a method which may lead to a simplified proof of Linnik's theorem on the smallest prime in an arithmetic progression [see Linnik, Mat. Sbornik N.S. **15**(57), 139–178 (1944); these Rev. **6**, 260].

The book can be read completely without knowledge of the literature cited. The presentation is clear and the printing is excellent. *N. G. de Bruijn* (Amsterdam).

Citations: MR 6, 260b = N16-5; MR 9, 80d = M30-7; MR 9, 80e = M30-8; MR 12, 490b = M50-1; MR 13, 208f = N04-16; MR 13, 741c = M02-2; MR 13, 742a = M25-31; MR 14, 137e = N04-17.

Referred to in M20-33, M25-40, M25-45, M25-47, M25-49, M25-53, M50-4, M50-5, M50-6, M50-7, M50-10, M50-13, M50-14, M50-15, M50-17, M50-19, M50-20, M50-24, M50-26, M50-27, M50-31, M50-36, M50-37, M50-39, M50-40, N04-25, N04-27, N04-40, N04-42, N12-18, N12-23, N44-17, N44-25, R04-26, R44-13, R44-15, R44-18.

**M50-3** **(15, 688c)**

**Turán, Pál. Az analízis egy új módszeréről és annak egyes alkalmazásairól. [On a new method in analysis and on some of its applications.]** Akadémiai Kiadó, Budapest, 1953. 197 pp. 60.00 Ft.

Hungarian version of the book reviewed above.

Referred to in M20-33, M50-5.

**M50-4** **(21# 2638 )**

**Turán, Paul. Eine neue Methode in der Analysis und deren Anwendungen.** Advancement in Math. **2** (1956), 312–565. (Chinese)

A Chinese version of the original German [Akadémiai Kiado, Budapest, 1953; MR **15**, 688].

Citations: MR 15, 688b = M50-2.

Referred to in M50-5.

**M50-5** **(23# A113)**

**Turán, Paul**

**Eine neue Methode in der Analysis und deren Anwendungen. (Chinese)**

*Advancement in Math.* **2** (1956), 312–565.

[Previously listed as MR **21** #2638; originally published in German and Hungarian by Akad. Kiadó, Budapest, 1953; MR **15**, 688.]

As the author states in the introduction, this new edition differs much from the old one. The former appendices have been worked into the main text; the order of chapters and theorems has been altered; estimates have been improved; and an attempt has been made to change the "method" of the first edition into something like a "theory" by explaining how to apply the (now three) basic theorems under different circumstances. A number of unsolved problems have been collected in § 11, and some further possible applications are discussed in § 28.

*K. Mahler* (Manchester)

Citations: MR 15, 688b = M50-2; MR 15, 688c = M50-3; MR 21# 2638 = M50-4.

Referred to in M50-36, M50-39, M50-40.

**M50-6** **(17, 1061b)**

**Sós, Vera T.; and Turán, P. On some new theorems in the theory of Diophantine approximations.** Acta Math. Acad. Sci. Hungar. **6** (1955), 241–255. (Russian summary)

The principal result of this paper is the following improvement of the fundamental Theorem II of the author's recent book, Über eine neue Methode in der Analysis und deren Anwendungen [Akad. Kiadó, Budapest, 1953; MR **15**, 688]. Let $m$ be a non-negative integer, and suppose that the $b_j$'s and $z_j$'s are complex numbers with $|z_1|\geqq\cdots\geqq|z_n|$. Let $A_1$ be the infimum of the positive real numbers $\alpha$ such that there exists an integer $\nu$ with $m+1\leqq\nu\leqq m+n$ for which

$$(*)\qquad |b_1z_1^\nu+\cdots+b_nz_n^\nu|\geqq |z_1|^\nu\left(\frac{n}{\alpha(n+n)}\right)^n\cdot\min_{1\leqq j\leqq n}(|b_1+\cdots+b_j|).$$

Then $1.321<A_1<2e^{1+4/e}$ $(<24)$ if $b_1=\cdots=b_n=1$. A similar proof shows that the inequality (*) holds for some $\nu$ in the specified range and for arbitrary $b_1,\cdots,b_n$, if $\alpha=2e^{1+4/e}$. (The earlier value of $\alpha$ was $24e^2\approx177$.) In the latter part of the paper special systems $z_1,\cdots,z_n$ are considered, for which $s_3=s_4=\cdots=s_{n+1}=0$, where $s_\nu=z_1^\nu+\cdots+z_n^\nu$. It is shown that all such systems are given by the sets of zeros of the polynomials

$$f_n(z,a,\lambda)=z^n+\frac{H_1(\lambda)}{1!}az^{n-1}+\cdots+\frac{H_n(\lambda)}{n!}a^n,$$

where $H_\nu$ is the $\nu$th Hermite polynomial, $\lambda$ is any zero of $H_{n+1}$ and $a$ is an arbitrary complex number.

*W. J. LeVeque* (Ann Arbor, Mich.).

Citations: MR 15, 688b = M50-2.

Referred to in M25-54, M50-9, M50-15, M50-25, M50-29.

**M50-7** **(19, 397a)**

**Cassels, J. W. S. On the sums of powers of complex numbers.** Acta Math. Acad. Sci. Hungar. **7** (1956), 283–289. (Russian summary)

Let $b_1,\cdots,b_k$ be positive numbers, let $z_1,\cdots,z_k$ be complex, and put $s_\nu=b_1z_1^\nu+\cdots+b_kz_k^\nu$. In the case $b_1=\cdots=b_k=1$, it is shown that if $\max_{1\leq j\leq k}|z_j|\geqq1$, then

$$(*)\qquad \max_{1\leq\nu\leq 2k-1}|s_\nu|\geqq1.$$

Equality holds in (*) if $z_1=1$, $z_2=\cdots=z_k=0$, and it is shown that the range of the max in (*) cannot be decreased to $1\leqq\nu\leqq2k-2$. [This was known earlier; see P. Turán, Eine neue Methode in der Analysis und deren Anwendungen, Akad. Kiadó, Budapest, 1953; MR **15**, 688.] In the general case, it is shown that always Re $s_\nu\geqq0$ for some $\nu$ with $1\leqq\nu\leqq4^k-1$, but that, for suitable $b_j$ and $z_j$, Re $s_\nu<0$ for all $\nu$ with $1\leqq\nu\leqq3^k-1$. Finally, an analytic proof is given of a weakened version of Dirichlet's theorem: if $q>q_0(n)$ and if $\vartheta_1,\cdots,\vartheta_n$ are any real numbers, then there is an integer $\nu$ with $1\leqq\nu\leqq q^n$ such that, for suitable integers $e_j$, $|\vartheta_j\nu-e_j|\leqq c(\log q)^{1/2}/q$ $(j=1,\cdots,n)$, where $c$ depends only on $n$. The fact that Fejér's kernel

$$\tfrac12+\sum_{\nu=1}^N\left(1-\frac{\nu}{N+1}\right)\mathrm{Re}\,z^\nu$$

is non-negative for all positive integers $N$ and all complex $z$ with $|z|\geqq1$ plays an important role in the proofs.

*W. J. LeVeque* (Ann Arbor, Mich.).

Citations: MR 15, 688b = M50-2.

Referred to in M50-28.

**M50-8** **(19, 636d)**

**Erdös, P.; and Rényi, A. A probabilistic approach to problems of Diophantine approximation.** Illinois J. Math. **1** (1957), 303–315.

Let $z_1,\cdots,z_n$ be complex numbers, $|z_1|=\cdots=|z_n|=1$, and put $S_k=z_1^k+\cdots+z_n^k$. Using a simple probability argument, the authors show that, for every $c$ $(0<c<1)$,, it is possible to choose $z_1,\cdots,z_n$ such that $|S_k|<cn$ $(1\leqq k<T)$, where $T=[\frac14\exp(\frac12nc^2)]$, and, more generally, the inequalities $|S_{k_1}|<cn,\cdots,|S_{k_T}|<cn$ can be simultaneously satisfied if $\{k_1,\cdots,k_T\}$ is a set of $T$ distinct integers. Moreover, it is possible to choose $z_1,\cdots,z_n$ such that $|S_k|<\{6n\log(k+1)\}^{\frac12}$ for all integers $k\geqq1$. Essentially better results are obtained if $c$ is close to 1. The authors also consider the case that $k$ is a continuous variable.

Furthermore, it is shown that there is, for every $n$, a set $z_1,\cdots,z_n$ of unimodular complex numbers such that for every not too large value $k$ the set $\{z_1^k,\cdots,z_n^k\}$ is more or less equidistributed. There is an absolute constant $c$ such that, for every $\delta$ $(0<\delta<1)$ and for every $n\geqq1$, the numbers $z_1,\cdots,z_n$ can be found on the unit circle such that, for every pair $\alpha,\beta$ $(0\leqq\alpha<\beta<2\pi)$ and for every integer $k$ $(1<k\leqq e^{\delta n}-2)$, the number $N_n^{(k)}(\alpha,\beta)$ of those among $z_1^k,\cdots,z_n^k$ which lie in the arc $(\alpha,\beta)$ of the unit circle satisfies

$$|n^{-1}N_n^{(k)}(\alpha,\beta)-(\beta-\alpha)/2\pi|<c\delta^{\frac12}(\log e/\delta)^{3/2}.$$

There are also some results in another direction, e.g., for every set of unimodular numbers $z_1,\cdots,z_n$, and for every $c$ $(2\leqq c\leqq n-1)$, there is an integer $k$ $(1\leqq k\leqq 2n\cdot(4\pi(c+2)^{\frac12}n)^{c+2})$ with $|S_k|\geqq c$. *N. G. de Bruijn.*

**M50-9** **(19, 736b)**

**Uchiyama, Saburô. Complex numbers with vanishing power sums.** Proc. Japan Acad. **33** (1957), 10–12.

Recently, Sós and Turán [Acta Math. Acad. Sci. Hungar. **6** (1955), 241–255; MR **17**, 1061] were led to the problem of determining the set $\mathfrak{Z}_{m,n}$ of systems of $n$ complex numbers $z_1,z_2,\cdots,z_n$ for which $s_\nu=\sum_{j=1}^n z_j^\nu=0$ $(\nu=m+1,\cdots,m+n-1)$ ($m$ a non-negative integer). In the present paper, for general $m$ and $n$, a characterization is given of the systems in $\mathfrak{Z}_{m,n}$. *C. G. Lekkerkerker.*

Citations: MR 17, 1061b = M50-6.

Referred to in M50-12.

**M50-10** **(19, 1039e)**

**Turán, Paul. Über eine neue Methode der Analysis.** Wiss. Z. Humboldt-Univ. Berlin. Math.-Nat. Reihe **5** (1955/56), 275–280. (Russian, English and French summaries)

In this expository lecture the author formulates four fundamental extremal problems which are in some respects more general than those of his book [Eine neue Methode in der Analysis und deren Anwendungen, Akad. Kiadó, Budapest, 1953; MR **15**, 688]. Some refinements found after publication of this book are announced without proof. Part of this material will be published in a forthcoming joint paper with Vera T. Sós.

*N. G. de Bruijn* (Amsterdam).

Citations: MR 15, 688b = M50-2.

**M50-11** **(20# 860 )**

**Uchiyama, S. Sur un problème posé par M. Paul Turán.** Acta Arith. **4** (1958), 240–246.

Let $Z(m, n)$ denote the number of sets $(Z_1, \cdots, Z_n)$ of complex numbers satisfying the system

$$S_{m+1}=S_{m+2}=\cdots=S_{m+n-1}=0,$$

where $S_k=Z_1^k+\cdots+Z_n^k$ and $m$ is an integer $\geqq 0$. Two sets $(Z_1, \cdots, Z_n)$ and $(Z_1', \cdots, Z_n')$ are equivalent in $Z(m, n)$ if there exists a complex number $\lambda\neq 0$ such that

$$f(x; Z_1, \cdots, Z_n)=f(x; \lambda Z_1', \cdots, \lambda Z_n'),$$

where

$$f(x; Z_1, \cdots, Z_n)=\prod_{j=1}^{n} (x-Z_j).$$

Let $B(m,n)$ denote the number of classes of non-trivial sets in $Z(m, n)$ relative to this equivalence relation. The object of the paper is to determine the number $B(m, n)$. The following theorems are proved.

(I) $$\sum_{d\mid(m,n)} a(d)B\left(\frac{m}{d}, \frac{n}{d}\right)=\frac{(m+n-1)!}{m!n!},$$

where $a(1)=1$ and $a(d)=d^{-1}\prod_{p\mid d} (1-p)$.

(II) $$B(m, n)=B(n, m).$$

Clearly, II is an immediate consequence of I.

*L. Carlitz* (Durham, N.C.)

Referred to in M50-12, M50-18.

**M50-12** **(20# 6513 )**

**Uchiyama, Saburô. Systems of $n$ complex numbers with vanishing power sums.** J. Fac. Sci. Hokkaido Univ. Ser. I **14** (1958), 29–36.

Let $B(m, n)$ be the number of essentially different systems of $n$ complex numbers $z_1, z_2, \cdots, z_n$ with

$$\sum z_i^\nu=0 \quad (\nu=m+1, m+2, \cdots, m+n-1).$$

The author evaluates $B(m, n)$ directly in the cases $m=2$, 3; $n=2$, 3. He does not note, however, that these values follow immediately from a general recurrence formula for $B(m, n)$ published by him elsewhere [Proc. Japan Acad. **33** (1957), 10–12; Acta Arith. **4** (1958), 240–246; MR **19**, 736; **20** #860].

*C. G. Lekkerkerker* (Amsterdam)

Citations: MR 19, 736b = M50-9; MR 20# 860 = M50-11.

**M50-13** **(21# 668 )**

**Dancs, I. On an extremal problem.** Acta Math. Acad. Sci. Hungar. **9** (1958), 309–313.

A new proof is given of a result of E. Makai [same Acta **9** (1958), 105–110, MR **20** #1757]. As an application, an improvement is given of one of Turán's main theorems [*Eine neue Methode in der Analysis und deren Anwendungen*, Akadémiai Kiadó, Budapest, 1953; MR **15**, 688], which reads: If $z_1, \cdots, z_n, b_1, \cdots, b_n$ are complex numbers, and if $m$ is an integer $\geqq -1$, then there exists an integer $\nu$ with $m+1\leqq\nu\leqq m+n$ and

$$|b_1z_1^\nu+\cdots+b_nz_n^\nu| \geqq |b_1+\cdots+b_n|\left(\frac{n}{2e(m+n)}\right)^n \min_{1\leqq j\leqq n} |z_j|^\nu.$$

The author replaces $(n/2e(m+n))^n$ by $(2e)^{-1}(n/2e(n+m))^{n-1}$.

*N. G. de Bruijn* (Amsterdam)

Citations: MR 15, 688b = M50-2.

Referred to in M50-19.

**M50-14** **(21# 669 )**

**Uchiyama, S. Sur les sommes de puissances des nombres complexes.** Acta Math. Acad. Sci. Hungar. **9** (1958), 275–278.

If $z_1, \cdots, z_n$ are complex numbers, we put

$$K(z_1, \cdots, z_n) = \max_{1\leqq\nu\leqq n} |z_1^\nu+\cdots+z_n^\nu|,$$

and let $M_n$ denote the minimum of $K(z_1, \cdots, z_n)$ under the condition that $\max_{1\leqq j\leqq n}|z_j|=1$. It was shown by P. Turán [*Eine neue Methode in der Analysis und deren Anwendungen*, Akadémiai Kiadó, Budapest, 1953; MR **15**, 688] that $M_n>C_1(\log n)^{-1}$ with a positive constant $C_1$, and this was improved by the reviewer [see the Chinese edition of Turán's book, Peking, 1956], who showed that $M_n>C_2$ $(\log\log n)/(\log n)$ with a positive constant $C_2$. The present author shows that $M_n \exp (M_n \sum_1^n \nu^{-1})>2\cdot 3^{\frac{1}{2}}/\pi$, which implies that for all $\varepsilon>0$ we have $M_n>(1-\varepsilon)(\log\log n)/(\log n)$ for all $n>n_0(\varepsilon)$. An application is given to the Bernoulli-Graeffe method for approximation of the roots of algebraic equations.

*N. G. de Bruijn* (Amsterdam)

Citations: MR 15, 688b = M50-2.

Referred to in M50-20.

**M50-15** **(21# 1293 )**

**Makai, E. An estimation in the theory of diophantine approximations.** Acta Math. Acad. Sci. Hungar. **9** (1958), 299–307.

Let $z_1, \cdots, z_n$ be $n$ complex numbers with $1=z_1\geqq|z_2|\geqq \cdots\geqq|z_n|$, and put $s_\nu=b_1z_1^\nu+\cdots+b_nz_n^\nu$. P. Turán [*On a new method in analysis*, Budapest, Akad. Kiadó, 1953; MR **15**, 688] has shown that there is an absolute constant $A>0$ such that

$$\operatorname*{Max}_{m+1\leqq\nu\leqq m+n} |s_\nu| \geqq \left(\frac{n}{A(m+n)}\right)^n \min_{1\geqq j\geqq n} |b_1+\cdots+b_j|$$

for all integers $m\geqq 0$, $n>0$. Turán and Vera T. Sós [same Acta **6** (1955), 241–255; MR **17**, 1061] showed that

$$24 \approx 2 \exp (1+4/e) \geqq A \geqq 1.321,$$

the second inequality holding even under the restriction $b_1=\cdots=b_n=1$. By further development of another idea of that paper, the present author shows that $A\geqq 1.473$, also in the restricted case. The proof depends on an asymptotic estimate for the least of the moduli of the zeros of the $n$th section of the power series expansion of $\exp(-z^2+2\lambda z)$, where $\lambda$ is a zero of the Hermite polynomial $H_{n+1}(z)$.

*W. J. LeVeque* (Ann Arbor, Mich.)

Citations: MR 15, 688b = M50-2; MR 17, 1061b = M50-6.

Referred to in M50-19.

**M50-16** **(21# 1294 )**

**Uchiyama, S. A note on the second main theorem of P. Turán.** Acta Math. Acad. Sci. Hungar. **9** (1958), 379–380.

In the notation of the preceding review, it is shown that $A \geqq e$. In the proof, which is simple and constructive, not all the $b_j$ are unity. It is also asserted that the upper bound $2 \exp(1+4/e)$ for $A$ can be replaced by $8e \approx 21.75$, using the argument of Turán and Sós.

*W. J. LeVeque* (Ann Arbor, Mich.)

Referred to in M50-25, M50-29.

## M50-17 (21# 1965)

**Turán, P. Über die Potenzsummen komplexer Zahlen.** Arch. Math. **9** (1958), 59–64.

The author has considered in his book [*Eine neue Methode in der Analysis und deren Anwendungen*, Akadémiai Kiadó, Budapest, 1953; MR **15**, 688] and in other papers, the quantity

$$M_n = \min \max_{1 \leqq \nu \leqq n} |s_\nu| = \min \max_{1 \leqq \nu \leqq n} |z_1{}^\nu + \cdots + z_n{}^\nu|,$$

where the minimum is extended over all the sets of complex numbers $z_1, \cdots, z_n$ with $z_n = 1$. It has been conjectured that $M_n > c > 0$, but all that is known is that $M_n > (1-\varepsilon) \log \log n / \log n$. In the present paper the related quantity

$$m_n = \min_{z_n=1} \sum_{j=1}^{n} \frac{|s_j|^2}{j}$$

is considered. It is shown that $m_n \leqq e^4$. Moreover, if $\xi_1, \cdots, \xi_{n-1}, 1$ is a set of nonzero values of $z_1, \cdots, z_n$ for which the above sum is minimal, it is shown that the polynomial $\psi(z) = (1-\bar{\xi}_1 z) \cdots (1-\bar{\xi}_{n-1} z)(1-z)$ satisfies the differential-functional equation

$$\lambda\psi'(z) - \bar{\lambda} z^{2n-1} \bar{\psi}'(z^{-1}) = z^n (1-z)^{-1} \psi(z) \bar{\psi}(z^{-1}),$$

with $\psi(1) = 0$ and suitable constant $\lambda = \lambda(n)$.

*W. J. LeVeque* (Ann Arbor, Mich.)

Citations: MR 15, 688b = M50-2.

## M50-18 (22# 694)

**Carlitz, L. Note on a theorem of S. Uchiyama.** Acta Arith. **5**, 289–292 (1959).

Let $Z(m, n)$ denote the number of systems of complex numbers $(z_1, \cdots, z_n)$ satisfying the system of equations $s_{m+1} = s_{m+2} = \cdots = s_{m+n-1} = 0$, where $s_k = \sum_{i=1}^n z_i^k$ and $m$ is an integer $\geqq 0$. Two systems $(z_1, \cdots, z_n)$ and $(z_1', \cdots, z_n')$ are equivalent in $Z(m, n)$ if there exists a complex number $\lambda \neq 0$ such that $f(x; z_1, \cdots, z_n) = f(x; \lambda z_1', \cdots, \lambda z_n')$, where $f(x; z_1, \cdots, z_n) = \prod_{j=1}^n (x - z_j)$. Let $B(m, n)$ denote the number of classes of non-trivial sets relative to this equivalence relation. Recently Uchiyama [Acta Arith. **4** (1958), 240–246; MR **20** #860] proved that

$$(1) \qquad \sum_{d|(m,n)} a(d) B\left(\frac{m}{d}, \frac{n}{d}\right) = \frac{(m+n-1)!}{m!n!},$$

where $a(1) = 1$ and $a(n) = n^{-1} \prod_{p|n} (1-p)$. The present author proves that (1) implies the explicit result

$$(2) \qquad B(m, n) = \sum_{d|(m,n)} \frac{\phi(d)}{d} C\left(\frac{m}{d}, \frac{n}{d}\right),$$

where $\phi(d)$ is the Euler $\phi$-function and $C(m, n) = (m+n-1)!/m!n!$. He also shows directly that the right member of (2) is integral.

*A. L. Whiteman* (Princeton, N.J.)

Citations: MR 20# 860 = M50-11.

## M50-19 (22# 3715)

**Makai, E. The first main theorem of P. Turán.** Acta Math. Acad. Sci. Hungar. **10** (1959), 405–411. (Russian summary, unbound insert)

P. Turán's first main theorem [*Eine neue Methode in der Analysis und deren Anwendungen*, Akadémiai Kiadó, Budapest, 1953; MR **15**, 688] deals with

$$Q = \max_{m+1 \leqq \nu \leqq m+n} \frac{|b_1 z_1{}^\nu + \cdots + b_n z_n{}^\nu|}{|b_1 + \cdots + b_n| \min_{1 \leqq j \leqq n} |z_j|^\nu}.$$

He proved that, for all values of the $b_1, \cdots, b_n, z_1, \cdots, z_n$, we have $Q \geqq \{n/2e(n+m)\}^n$. This was improved by I. Dancs [same Acta **9** (1958), 309–313; MR **21** #668] who proved that $Q \geqq (2e)^{-1}\{n/2e(m+n)\}^{n-1}$. The present author obtains the best possible result, viz.,

$$Q \geqq \left[\sum_{k=0}^{n-1} 2^k \binom{m+k}{k}\right]^{-1}.$$

In an appendix an improvement is given of Turán's second main theorem. In a previous paper [ibid. **9** (1958), 299–307; MR **21** #1293] the author showed that the absolute constant $A$ occurring in that theorem satisfies $2e \leqq A \leqq 8e$. He now shows that $A \geqq 2e/\log 2$.

*N. G. de Bruijn* (Eindhoven)

Citations: MR 15, 688b = M50-2; MR 21# 668 = M50-13; MR 21# 1293 = M50-15.

Referred to in M50-23, M50-29, M50-38.

## M50-20 (23# A3714)

**Atkinson, F. V.**
**On sums of powers of complex numbers. (Russian summary, unbound insert)**
*Acta Math. Acad. Sci. Hungar.* **12** (1961), 185–188.

Let $z_1, \cdots, z_n$ be complex numbers satisfying $1 = |z_1| \geqq |z_2| \geqq \cdots \geqq |z_n|$. The author shows that there is an integer $k$ in the range $1 \leqq k \leqq n$ such that $|\sum_{m=1}^n z_m{}^k| > \frac{1}{6}$. Apart from the fact that the constant $\frac{1}{6}$ might be improved a little, this gives the ultimate answer to a question proposed by Turán [*Eine neue Methode in der Analysis und deren Anwendungen*, Akad. Kiadó, Budapest, 1953; MR **15**, 688; see also S. Uchiyama, Acta Math. Acad. Sci. Hungar. **9** (1958), 275–278; MR **21** #669].

*N. G. de Bruijn* (Eindhoven)

Citations: MR 15, 688b = M50-2; MR 21# 669 = M50-14.

## M50-21 (23# A3958)

**Ławrynowicz, Julian**
**Calculation of a minimum maximorum of complex numbers.**
*Bull. Soc. Sci. Lettres Łódź* **11** (1960), *no.* 2, 9 *pp.*

Let $n$ be a positive integer. Let $z_1, z_2, \cdots, z_{n-1}$ be arbitrary complex numbers, and $\zeta_1, \zeta_2, \cdots, \zeta_{n-1}$ arbitrary complex numbers of modulus 1. The author proves that the two expressions

$$M_n = \inf_{z_i} \max_{1 \leqq r \leqq n} |1 + z_1{}^r + \cdots + z_{n-1}^r|,$$

$$m_n = \min_{\zeta_i} \max_{1 \leqq r \leqq n} |1 + z_1{}^r + \cdots + z_{n-1}^r|$$

are equal.

*M. Newman* (Washington, D.C.)

## M50-22 (23# A3959)

**Ławrvnowicz, Julian**
**Remark on a problem of P. Turán.**
*Bull. Soc. Sci. Lettres Łódź* **11** (1960), *no.* 1, 4 *pp.*

Let $n$ be a positive integer. Let $z_1, z_2, \cdots, z_{n-1}$ be arbitrary complex numbers. The author has proved [see #A3958 above] that the minimum of

$$\max_{1 \leqq r \leqq n} |1 + z_1{}^r + \cdots + z_{n-0}^r| = \max_{1 \leqq r \leqq n} s_r$$

is assumed for some set of complex numbers $z_i$ of modulus 1. In this paper the author proves that minimizing systems $z_i$ exist such that $s_1 = s_2 = \cdots = s_n$, and conjectures that this holds for every minimizing system.

*M. Newman* (Washington, D.C.)

## M50-23 (24# A88 )

**de Bruijn, N. G.**

**On Turán's first main theorem. (Russian summary, unbound insert)**

*Acta Math. Acad. Sci. Hungar.* **11** (1960), 213–216.

The paper is concerned with the first main theorem of P. Turán, in particular, with determining the best possible constant occurring in it (which was previously done by E. Makai [same Acta. **10** (1959), 405–411; MR **22** #3715] and independently, though somewhat later, by the author), and presents an elegant and self-contained account of the whole matter. By use of a generating function, the proof of Makai's theorem has been reduced to a few lines. Also, a new proof of the fact that the constant is best possible has been supplied. *S. Knapowski* (Poznań)

Citations: MR 22# 3715 = M50-19.

Referred to in M50-36.

## M50-24 (24# A1881 )

**Turán, P.**

**On an improvement of some new one-sided theorems of the theory of diophantine approximations. (Russian summary, unbound insert)**

*Acta Math. Acad. Sci. Hungar.* **11** (1960), 299–316.

In his paper in J. Indian Math. Soc. (N.S.) **24** (1960), 563–574, the author gives one-sided versions of the first two main theorems of his book, *Eine neue Methode in der Analysis und deren Anwendungen* [Akadémiaí Kiadó, Budapest, 1953; MR **15**, 688]. The present paper sharpens these results. There are two theorems. In both it is assumed that $n$ $(n > 2)$ and $m$ $(m > 0)$ are integers, that $\kappa$ satisfies $0 < \kappa < \frac{1}{2}\pi$, that $z_1, \cdots, z_n$ are complex numbers outside the angle $|\mathrm{arc}\, z| < \kappa$. The interval $m+1 \leqq \nu \leqq m + n(3 + \pi\kappa^{-1})$ is denoted by $S$. Theorem I: If $b_1, \cdots, b_n$ are complex numbers with $\mathrm{Re}(b_1 + \cdots + b_n) > 0$, and $|z_1| \geqq |z_2| \geqq \cdots \geqq |z_n| = 1$, then there exists an integer $\nu \in S$ such that

$$5n^{1-2n}(27(m+n))^{2n}\,\mathrm{Re}\,(b_1 z_1^\nu + \cdots + b_n z_n^\nu)/\mathrm{Re}\,(b_1 + \cdots + b_n)$$

is $\geqq 1$, and there exists an integer $\nu \in S$ such that the same expression is $\leqq -1$. Theorem II: If $|z_1| \leqq |z_2| \leqq \cdots \leqq |z_n| = 1$, $\lambda = 2n^3(3 + \pi\kappa^{-1})$, then there exists an integer $\nu \in S$ such that $(81(m+n))^\lambda\,\mathrm{Re}\,(z_1^\nu + \cdots + z_n^\nu)$ is $\geqq 1$, and there exists an integer $\nu \in S$ such that this expression is $\leqq -1$. *N. G. de Bruijn* (Eindhoven)

Citations: MR 15, 688b = M50-2.

Referred to in M50-27, M50-32, P40-19.

## M50-25 (24# A2006 )

**Makai, E.**

**On a minimum problem.**

*Ann. Univ. Sci. Budapest. Eötvös Sect. Math.* **3–4** (1960/61), 177–182.

Given the complex numbers $z_0 = 1$ and $z_1, \cdots, z_n$, none of which is equal to 1, the author investigates the infimum of

$$\max_{r=m,\cdots,m+n} |b_0 z_0^r + b_1 z_1^r + \cdots + b_n z_n^r|,$$

where $b_0 = 1$ and $b_1, \cdots, b_n$ are arbitrary complex numbers. It is proved that this infimum is not less than

$$(*) \qquad \frac{|(z_1-1)(z_2-1)\cdots(z_n-1)|}{1+|S_1|+\cdots+|S_n|},$$

where the $S_j$ are elementary symmetric functions of $z_1, \cdots, z_n$. When $|z_j| \leqq 1$ for $j = 1, \cdots, n$, it follows from (*) that the infimum $> (1/2^n) \prod_{j=1}^n |z_j - 1|$.

In the second part of the paper the writer considers the inequality

$$(**) \qquad \max_{r=m+1,\cdots,m+n} \left|\sum_{j=1}^n b_j z_j^r\right| \geqq \left(\frac{n}{A(m+n)}\right)^n \min_{k=1,\cdots,n} |b_1 + \cdots + b_k|,$$

where $z_1 = 1$ and $|z_j| < 1$ for $j = 2, \cdots, n$. Soś and Turán [Acta Math. Acad. Sci. Hungar. **6** (1955), 241–255; MR **17**, 1061] proved that $A < 2\exp(1 + 4e^{-1})$, while Uchiyama [ibid. **9** (1958), 379–380; MR **21** #1294] showed that $A \leqq 8e$. In the present paper it is proved that the exponent $n$ in (**) can be replaced by $n-1$; moreover, this exponent is best possible, for there exist examples for which $\max|\sum b_j z_j|/\min|b_1 + \cdots + b_n| = O(m^{-n+1})$ with $n$ fixed and $m \to \infty$. *L. Carlitz* (Durham, N.C.)

Citations: MR 17, 1061b = M50-6; MR 21# 1294 = M50-16.

Referred to in M50-29, M50-31.

## M50-26 (24# A2565 )

**Turán, P.**

**On some further one-sided theorems of new type in the theory of Diophantine approximations. (Russian summary)**

*Acta Math. Acad. Sci. Hungar.* **12** (1961), 455–468.

The author proves the following theorem which combines the desirable features of several of those in his book *Eine neue Methode in der Analysis und deren Anwendungen* [Akadémiai Kiadó, Budapest, 1953; MR **15**, 688]. Applications to analytic number theory are promised in a subsequent paper. Theorem: Let $0 < \kappa \leqq \pi/2$, and let $z_1, \cdots, z_n$ be complex numbers such that $1 = |z_1| \geqq |z_2| \geqq \cdots \geqq |z_n|$, $|\arg z_j| > \kappa$ $(1 \leqq j \leqq n)$. Let $b_1, \cdots, b_n$ be complex numbers such that $B = \min_{1 \leqq \mu \leqq n} \mathrm{Re}(b_1 + \cdots + b_\mu) > 0$. Let $m$ be an integer $> 0$ and write

$$\mathfrak{B} = \frac{1}{2n+1}\left(\frac{n}{24e^3(m+n(3+\pi/\kappa))}\right)^{2n} B.$$

Then

$$\max_{m<\nu\leqq m+n(3+\pi/\kappa)} \mathrm{Re} \sum_{j=1}^n b_j z_j^\nu \geqq \mathfrak{B},$$

$$\min_{m<\nu\leqq m+n(3+\pi/\kappa)} \mathrm{Re} \sum_{j=1}^n b_j z_j^\nu \leqq -\mathfrak{B}$$

where $\nu$ runs through integral values.

*J. W. S. Cassels* (Cambridge, England)

Citations: MR 15, 688b = M50-2.

Referred to in N04-36, N12-23, N44-27.

## M50-27 (25# 5039 )

**Turán, Paul**

**On some one-sided theorems of the theory of Diophantine approximation.**

*J. Indian Math. Soc.* (*N.S.*) **24** (1960), 563–574 (1961).

With a view to possible new applications in analytic number theory the author poses the problem of giving positive lower bounds for expressions of the type

$$\max_{m+1\leqq\nu\leqq m'} \mathscr{R}(b_1 z_1^\nu + \cdots + b_n z_n^\nu)$$

instead of the expressions

$$\max_{m+1\leqq\nu\leqq m+n} |b_1 z_1^\nu + \cdots + b_n z_n^\nu|$$

which he dealt with in his book [*Eine neue Methode in der Analysis und deren Anwendungen*, Akad. Kiadó, Budapest, 1953; MR **15**, 688]. He proves the following theorem. If

$z_1, \cdots, z_n$ are complex numbers with $\max_{j=1,\cdots,n} |z_j| = 1$ and with $\alpha \leqq |\arc z_j| \leqq \pi$ $(j = 1, \cdots, n)$, where $0 < \alpha \leqq \pi/2$, then there exist integers $\nu_1$, $\nu_2$ with $m+1 \leqq \nu_1 \leqq m + 2n(1+\pi/\alpha)$, $m+1 \leqq \nu_2 \leqq m+3n(1+\pi/\alpha)$, such that

$$\mathscr{R}(z_1^{\nu_1} + \cdots + z_n^{\nu_1}) \geqq 16^{-n^2(m+2n(1+\pi/\alpha))},$$

$$\mathscr{R}(z_1^{\nu_2} + \cdots + z_n^{\nu_2}) \leqq -16^{-n^2(m+3n(1+\pi/\alpha))}.$$

Since the paper was written (in 1958), the author has improved this result considerably [Acta Math. Acad. Sci. Hungar. **11** (1960), 299–316; MR **24** #A1881]. Applications will be given in a forthcoming series, "The comparative theory of primes", written in collaboration with S. Knapowski. *C. G. Lekkerkerker* (Amsterdam)

Citations: MR 15, 688b = M50-2; MR 24# A1881 = M50-24.

## M50-28 (26# 2582 )

**Dancs, István**

**Power sums of complex numbers. (Hungarian. Russian and English summaries)**

*Mat. Lapok* **13** (1962), 108–114.

Author's summary: "J. W. S. Cassels proved [Acta Math. Acad. Sci. Hungar. **7** (1956), 283–289; MR **19**, 397] the following theorem.

"If $n \geqq 2$ and the complex numbers $z_1, \cdots, z_n$ have a certain property, then

$$\text{(1)} \qquad \min_{z_j} \max_{1 \leqq \nu \leqq 2n-1} |z_1^\nu + \cdots + z_n^\nu| = 1.$$

"He left open the question for which systems this minmax is attained (beside the trivial $(1, 0, \cdots, 0)$). We show in this paper that (1) is attained for infinitely many systems, and the same holds for

$$\min_{z_j} \max_{1 \leqq \nu \leqq 3n-4} |z_1^\nu + \cdots + z_n^\nu| = 1,$$

whereas

$$\min_{z} \max_{1 \leqq \nu \leqq 3n-3} |z_1^\nu + \cdots + z_n^\nu| = 1$$

is attained only for the trivial system. Cassels himself proved the last assertion only for

$$\min_{z_j} \max_{1 \leqq \nu \leqq 4n-3} |z_1^\nu + \cdots + z_n^\nu| = 1."$$

Citations: MR 19, 397a = M50-7.

## M50-29 (28# 3007 )

**Makai, E.**

**On a minimum problem. II.**

*Acta Math. Acad. Sci. Hungar.* **15** (1964), 63–66.

Let $z_0 = 1, z_1, z_2, \cdots, z_n$ be complex numbers with $|z_j| \leqq |z_k|$ for $j < k$, $m$ an arbitrary positive integer and $b_0, b_1, \cdots, b_n$ arbitrary complex numbers. V. T. Sós and P. Turán [same Acta **6** (1955), 241–255; MR **17**, 1061] proved the inequality

$$(*) \qquad \max_{\nu = m, m+1, \cdots, m+n} \left| \sum_{j=0}^{n} b_j z_j^\nu \right| \geqq \left(\frac{n}{8e(m+n)}\right)^{n+1} \min_{k=0,1,\cdots,n} \left| \sum_{j=0}^{k} b_j \right|.$$

The present author [Ann. Univ. Sci. Budapest. Eötvös Sect. Math. **3–4** (1960/61), 177–182; MR **24** #A2006] showed that the exponent $n+1$ can be replaced by $n$.

Let $A$ be the lim inf of those constants that can replace $8e$ in (*). Erdős (see first reference above) showed that $A > 1.32$; this result was improved by S. Uchiyama [Acta Math. Acad. Sci. Hungar. **9** (1958), 379–380; MR **21** #1294] and the author [ibid. **10** (1959), 405–411; MR **22** #3715]. In the present paper the author shows that $A \geqq 4e$. *L. Carlitz* (Durham, N.C.)

Citations: MR 17, 1061b = M50-6; MR 21# 1294 = M50-16; MR 22# 3715 = M50-19; MR 24# A2006 = M50-25.

Referred to in M50-38.

## M50-30 (30# 3217 )

**Dancs, S.; Turán, P.**

**On the distribution of values of a class of entire functions. I.**

*Publ. Math. Debrecen* **11** (1964), 257–265.

Let the complex variables $z_1, \cdots, z_n$ satisfy the conditions

$$\min_{\mu \neq \nu} |z_\mu - z_\nu| / \min_j |z_j| \geqq \delta, \quad \delta \leqq 1,$$

$$\max |z_j| / \min_j |z_j| \leqq D, \quad D \geqq 1.$$

Then it is shown that for all fixed complex $d_{\mu j}$, positive integers $m$ and $p$, the inequality

$$(*) \qquad \max_{\nu = m+1, \cdots, m+np} \frac{\left| \sum_{j=1}^{n} z_j^\nu \left\{ \sum_{\mu=0}^{p-1} d_{\mu j} \mu! \binom{\nu}{\mu} \right\} \right|}{\sum_{j=1}^{n} |z_j|^\nu \sum_{\mu=0}^{p-1} |d_{\mu j}| \mu! \binom{\nu}{\mu}} \geqq (m+np)^{-2p^2} \left(\frac{\delta}{8D}\right)^{2pn + p(p-1)/2}$$

holds. An analogous inequality was proved by Pólya [Math. Z. **12** (1922), 36–60]. This inequality (*) is utilised in Part II (#3218 below] to study the distribution of the zeros of entire functions of the form $\sum_{j=1}^{n} P_j(z) \exp(w_j z)$, where $P_j$ are polynomials. *S. M. Shah* (Lawrence, Kans.)

Referred to in J76-57, Q05-89.

## M50-31 (31# 127 )

**Dancs, I.**

**On generalized sums of powers of complex numbers.**

*Ann. Univ. Sci. Budapest. Eötvös Sect. Math.* **7** (1964), 113–121.

Let $z_1, \cdots, z_n, b_1, \cdots, b_n$ be complex numbers, and let $m$ be an integer. Assume $m \geqq 0$, $|z_1| \leqq 1, \cdots, |z_n| \leqq 1$, and $0 = |1 - z_1| \leqq |1 - z_2| \leqq \cdots \leqq |1 - z_n|$. The author proves that

$$\max_{m+1 \leqq \nu \leqq m+n} |b_1 z_1^\nu + \cdots + b_n z_n^\nu| \geqq \frac{1}{2n}\left(\frac{n-1}{8e(m+n)}\right)^{n-1} \min_{1 \leqq j \leqq n} |b_1 + \cdots + b_j|.$$

This slightly improves (with a new proof) the version by E. Makai [same Ann. **3–4** (1960/61), 177–182; MR **24** #A2006] of Turán's second main theorem [*Eine neue Methode in der Analysis und deren Anwendungen*, Akadémiai Kiadó, Budapest, 1953; MR **15**, 688].

The author also proves the following generalization: If, moreover, $k_1, \cdots, k_n$ are integers, with $0 \leqq k_i \leqq m+2$, and if $B_i(t)$ is a polynomial of degree $\leqq k_i$ $(1 \leqq i \leqq n)$, then

$$\max_{m+1 \leqq \nu \leqq m+n} |B_1(\nu) z_1^\nu + \cdots + B_n(\nu) z_n^\nu| \geqq \frac{1}{2k}\left(\frac{k}{8e(m+k)}\right)^{k-1} \min_{1 \leqq j \leqq n} |B_1(0) + \cdots + B_j(0)|,$$

where $k = n + k_1 + \cdots + k_n$.

{The author points out that the proof of Lemma 2.4 is unsatisfactory (it applies Lemma 2.3 for all $\mu$, whereas Lemma 2.3 should be restricted to $\mu \geqq 0$), but that a correct proof of Lemma 2.4 can be given with the aid of a modified Lemma 2.3.} *N. G. de Bruijn* (Eindhoven)

Citations: MR 15, 688b = M50-2; MR 24# A2006 = M50-25.

Referred to in M50-36.

**M50-32** **(31# 128 )**

**Dancs, I.**

**Remarks on a paper of P. Turán.**

*Ann. Univ. Sci. Budapest. Eötvös Sect. Math.* **7** (1964), 133–141.

The author gives a simpler proof (with a slightly better result) for a theorem by Turán [Acta Math. Acad. Sci. Hungar. **11** (1960), 299–316; MR **24** #A1881] on one-sided estimates for power sums. In the review of that paper, Turán's Theorem I was quoted with a factor $5n^{-n}\times(27(m+n))^{2n}$; this is an error made by the reviewer, for it should be $5n^{1-2n}(27(m+n))^{2n}$. The present author reduces it to $4n^{1-2n}(4e(m+n))^{2n}$.

The second part of the article concerns the following situation (which plays a rôle in one of Turán's lemmas). Let $n$ be a positive integer, and let $\alpha$ be a real number, $\pi/(n+2)\leqq\alpha\leqq\pi/(n+1)$. If a polynomial $\varphi(z)$ has the property that $\varphi(z)(1-2z\cos\alpha+z^2)$ is a polynomial with non-negative coefficients, then the degree of $\varphi$ is at least $n$. Moreover, the minimum is attained by the polynomial $\sum_{\nu=0}^{n} z^\nu(\sin(\nu+1)\alpha)/(\sin\alpha)$. The author now determines all polynomials $\varphi$ of degree $n$ which have the property just mentioned, constructing a set of $n$ special solutions of which all others are linear combinations with non-negative coefficients. *N. G. de Bruijn* (Eindhoven)

Citations: MR 24# A1881 = M50-24.

**M50-33** **(34# 2534 )**

**Komlós, János; Sárközy, András; Szemerédi, Endre**

**On sums of powers of complex numbers.** (Hungarian. Russian and English summaries)

*Mat. Lapok* **15** (1964), 337–347.

Authors' summary: "Let $z_1, z_2, \cdots, z_n$ be complex numbers and $s_\nu=\sum_{m=1}^{n} z_m^\nu$ and $s=\max_{\nu=1,2,\cdots,n}|s_\nu|$. Further, let $\inf s=f(n)$, where the inf sign refers to systems $z_1, z_2, \cdots, z_n$ with $1=|z_1|\geqq|z|\geqq\cdots\geqq|z_n|$. It was proved by P. Turán that $f(n)>(\log 2)/(\sum_{i=1}^{n} 1/i)$ holds for every natural number, and applied, e.g., to the approximate determination of eigenvalues of matrices. On the other hand, we have the trivial inequality $f(n)\leqq 1$, which was improved by Cassels to $f(n)\leqq 1-c/n^n$. The authors show that for arbitrary $\varepsilon>0$ there are infinitely many $n$ for which $f(n)<1-\frac{1}{2}(1-\varepsilon)\log n/n$ holds. Further, they prove that for sufficiently large $n$, $f(n)<1-1/(250n)$."

**M50-34** **(34# 5767 )**

**Tijdeman, R.**

**On a conjecture of Turán and Erdős.**

*Nederl. Akad. Wetensch. Proc. Ser. A* **69** = *Indag. Math.* **28** (1966), 374–383.

Suppose that $b_1, b_2, \cdots, b_n$ are $n$ non-zero complex numbers and that $z_1=1, z_2, \cdots, z_n$ are $n$ distinct non-zero complex numbers. Put $s_k=\sum_{j=1}^{n} b_j z_j^k$. The author proves that if there exist two integers $p$ and $q$ with $n-1\leqq p<q$ such that $s_{p-1}=s_{p-2}=\cdots=s_{p-n+1}=0$ and $s_{q-1}=s_{q-2}=\cdots=s_{q-n+1}=0$, then the $z_j$ are $(q-p)$th roots of unity. It follows that the sequence $s_k$ is periodic, say with period $A$. He next assumes in addition that the $b_j$ are real and $\sum_{j=1}^{n} b_j\neq 0$. With this assumption he shows that if $p\geqq n-1$ is minimal with respect to the property that $s_{p-1}=s_{p-2}=\cdots=s_{p-n+1}=0$, then $A+n=2p$. He then assumes in addition that all $b_j=1$ and proves that if $n$ is odd then $A=n$ and the $z_j$ are the $n$th roots of unity, while if $v$ is even then $n$ divides $A$ and the $z_j$ comprise the set $\{1, \alpha, \alpha^2, \cdots, \alpha^{m-1}, \beta, \alpha\beta, \alpha^2\beta, \cdots, \alpha^{m-1}\beta\}$, where $m=n/2$, $\alpha$ is a primitive $m$th root of unity and $\beta$ is a primitive $A$th root of unity. *D. G. Cantor* (Los Angeles, Calif.)

**M50-35** **(35# 4181 )**

**Clunie, J.**

**On a problem of Erdős.**

*J. London Math. Soc.* **42** (1967), 133–136.

Let $\{z_\nu\}$ be an infinite sequence of complex numbers with $|z_\nu|=1$. Put $A_\nu=\limsup_{n\to\infty}|\sum_{k=1}^{n} z_k^\nu|$. The author shows that there is a sequence such that for every $\nu$, $A_\nu\leqq\nu$, but for every sequence $\limsup_{\nu\to\infty} A_\nu/\sqrt{\nu}>0$. These results sharpen previous results of the reviewer [Israel J. Math. **3** (1965), 6–12; MR **32** #1181]. *P. Erdős* (Budapest)

Citations: MR 32# 1181 = A40-28.

**M50-36** **(39# 5491 )**

**Geysel, J. M.**

**On generalized sums of powers of complex numbers.**

*Math. Centrum Amsterdam Afd. Zuivere Wisk.* **1968**, ZW-013, 20 *pp.*

The following theorems are proved. Theorem 1: Let $z_1, \cdots, z_n$ be complex numbers $\neq 0$ and $m$ an integer, $m\geqq -1$. Let $B_j$ be polynomials with complex coefficients and of degree $k_j$ $(j=1, \cdots, n)$. Let $k=k_1+\cdots+k_n+n$. Then there exists an integer $\nu$ with $m+1\leqq\nu\leqq m+k$ such that

$$|B_1(\nu)z_1^\nu+\cdots+B_n(\nu)z_n^\nu|\geqq ((k-1)/(2e(m+k)))^{k-1}|B_1(0)+\cdots+B_n(0)|\min_j|z_j|^\nu.$$

Theorem 2: Let $z_1, \cdots, z_n$ be complex numbers $\neq 0$ with $|z_i|\leqq 1$ $(i=1, \cdots, n)$ and $0=|1-z_1|\leqq|1-z_2|\leqq\cdots\leqq|1-z_n|$. Let $m$, $B_j$ and $k$ be as in Theorem 1. Then there exists an integer $\nu$ with $m+1\leqq\nu\leqq m+k$ such that

$$|B_1(\nu)z_1^\nu+\cdots+B_n(\nu)z_n^\nu|\geqq \tfrac{1}{4}((k-1)/(8e(m+k)))^{k-1}\min_j|B_1(0)+\cdots+B_j(0)|.$$

Theorem 1 is a generalization of a theorem of P. Turán [*Eine neue Methode in der Analysis und deren Anwendungun*, Satz 8, Akadémiai Kiadó, Budapest, 1953; Hungarian translation; MR **15**, 688; Chinese translation, Advancement in Math. **2** (1956), 312–565; MR **23** #A113] and Theorem 2 is a refinement of a theorem of I. Dancs [Ann. Univ. Sci. Budapest. Eötvös Sect. Math. **7** (1964), 113–121; MR **31** #127]. The proofs are based on ideas of Dancs and N. de Bruijn [Acta Math. Acad. Sci. Hungar. **11** (1960), 213–216; MR **24** #A88]. *J. B. Kelly* (Tempe, Ariz.)

Citations: MR 15, 688b = M50-2; MR 23# A113 = M50-5; MR 24# A88 = M50-23; MR 31# 127 = M50-31.

**M50-37** **(41# 3717 )**

**Tijdeman, Robert**

**On the distribution of the values of certain functions.** (**Dutch foreword and summary**)

Doctoral dissertation, University of Amsterdam.

*Universiteit van Amsterdam, Amsterdam*, 1969.

x + 94 *pp.* (*loose insert*)

P. Turan, in his book *Eine neue Methode in der Analysis und deren Anwendungen* [Akadémiai Kiadó, Budapest, 1953; MR **15**, 688], gave lower bounds for $A_m=\max\{|\sum_{k=1}^{n} b_k\alpha_k^\nu|:\nu=m+1, m+2, \cdots, m+n\}$ with $\min|\alpha_k|=1$ or $\max|\alpha_k|=1$ for $k=1, 2, \cdots, n$.

In the present paper these bounds are given a new

derivation and extended to sums $\sum_{k=1}^{n} P_k(\nu)\alpha_k^{\nu}$, where $P_k(\nu)$ are polynomials of degree $m_k$. The new bounds are applied to the study of the value distribution and zeros of exponential sums $F(z)=\sum_{k=1}^{n} P_k(z)e^{\omega_k z}$. If $\Delta=\max\{|\omega_k|: k=1, 2, \cdots, n\}$, $\sigma=n+\sum_{k=1}^{n} m_k$ and $R\geqq 2\sigma/\Delta$, $\nu>5$, then there exists $R^*$ with $R\leqq R^*\leqq \nu R$ such that the number of zeros of $F$ for $|z|\leqq R^*$ does not exceed $R^*\Delta(1+5/\nu)+2(\sigma-1)\log\nu$. Applications are also made to $n$th order linear differential equations with constant coefficients. Each solution has a number of $c$-points in any disk of radius $R$ not exceeding $3n+4R\delta$, if all the eigenvalues of the differential equation lie in $|z|\leqq\delta$. This result is extended to certain linear differential equations with variable coefficients. *M. Marden* (Milwaukee, Wis.)

Citations: MR 15, 688b = M50-2.

## M50-38 (42# 217 )

**Van der Poorten, A. J.**

**Generalisations of Turán's main theorems on lower bounds for sums of powers.**

*Bull. Austral. Math. Soc.* **2** (1970), 15–37.

In his book, *Eine neue Methode in der Analysis und deren Anwendungen* [Akadémiai Kiadó, Budapest, 1953; MR **15**, 688], P. Turan proved a number of theorems giving lower bounds for sums of powers. The author generalizes Turan's main theorem to exponential sums with polynomial coefficients. He proves: Let $\alpha_1, \cdots, \alpha_m$ be complex numbers so arranged that $|\alpha_1|\geqq|\alpha_j|$ $(1\leqq j\leqq m)$, and $|\alpha_1-\alpha_j|\leqq|\alpha_1-\alpha_k|$ for $1\leqq j\leqq k\leqq m$. Let $F(z)=\sum_{k=1}^{m} p_k(z)\alpha_k^{z}$, where $p_k(z)$ are polynomials and $\sigma=\sum_{k=1}^{m}\text{degree}(p_k(z))$. Let $F_t(z)=\sum_{k=1}^{t} p_k(z)\alpha_k^{z}$ $(1\leqq t\leqq m)$. Then if $n, r$ are integers such that $n\geqq -1$, $1\leqq r<\sigma$, $\max_{n+1\leqq\mu\leqq n+\sigma}|F(\mu)|/|\alpha_1^{\mu}|\geqq 8^{-r}((\sigma-r)/8e(n+\sigma))^{\sigma-r}\min_{1\leqq t\leqq m}|F_t^{(r-1)}(0)|$. From this he can deduce the results of E. Makai (currently best avai'`ble) [Acta Math. Acad. Sci. Hungar. **10** (1959), 405–411; MR **22** #3715; ibid. **15** (1964), 63–66; MR **28** #3007], where the $p_k(z)$ are constants.

*D. J. Lewis* (Ann Arbor, Mich.)

Citations: MR 22# 3715 = M50-19; MR 28# 3007 = M50-29.

## M50-39 (43# 158 )

**Turán, Paul**

**Analysis and diophantine approximation.**

*Symposia Mathematica, Vol. IV (INDAM, Rome, 1968/69), pp.* 133–153. *Academic Press, London,* 1970.

This is a very interesting survey article on the application of certain "power sum" inequalities to various areas of analysis, namely, complex function theory, summability, ordinary differential equations, numerical analysis, and analytic number theory. The inequalities considered are lower bounds for sums of the type $\sum_{j=1}^{n} b_j z_j^{\nu}$, where the $b_j$, $z_j$ are complex numbers and $\nu$ ranges over some set of positive integers. These types of inequalities are intimately connected with the theorems of Dirichlet and Kronecker in Diophantine approximations. Unfortunately, no references are given to the many results quoted. He states that the results are to appear in a book to be published soon.

This book would be a new edition, in English, of his *Eine neue Methode in der Analysis und deren Anwendungen* [Akad. Kiadó, Budapest, 1953; MR **15**, 688; Chinese translation, Advancement in Math. **2** (1956), 312–565; MR **23** #A113]. *W. W. Adams* (College Park, Md.)

Citations: MR 15, 688b = M50-2; MR 23# A113 = M50-5.

## M50-40 (43# 164 )

**Van der Poorten, A. J.**

**A generalisation of Turán's main theorems to binomials and logarithms.**

*Bull. Austral. Math. Soc.* **2** (1970), 183–195.

Author's summary: "The main theorems of P. Turán's book *Eine neue Methode in der Analysis und deren Anwendungen* [Akademiai Kiadó, Budapest, 1953; MR **15**, 688; Hungarian edition; MR **15**, 688; Chinese translation, Advancement in Math. **2** (1956), 312–565; MR **23** #A113] concern only sums of powers but are easily generalised to exponential sums with polynomial coefficients. It does not appear to have been observed, however, that similar such theorems with analogous implication as to value distribution and arithmetical behaviour can be formulated for a wider class of functions. We prove a result for functions of the form $\sum p_{kq}(z)(1-z)^{\alpha_k}\log^{q-1}(1-z)$ subsuming identities which Mahler has shown to contain transcendence results on the exponential and logarithmic functions and diophantine results of the Thue-Siegel-Roth type."

The following theorem is proved. Let

$$F(z) = \sum_{h=1}^{m}\sum_{q=1}^{n(h)}\sum_{s=1}^{\rho(h,q)} \alpha_{hqs}z^{s-1}(1-z)^{\alpha_h}(\log(1-z))^{q-1} = \sum_{h=1}^{m}\sum_{q=1}^{n(h)} p_{hq}(z)(1-z)^{\alpha_h}(\log(1-z))^{q-1},$$

where the $\alpha$'s are complex constants, so that the $p_{hq}(z)$ are polynomials of degree at most $\rho(h, q)-1$. If $\rho(h, 1)\geqq\rho(h, 2)\geqq\cdots\geqq\rho\{h, n(h)\}$, $1\leqq h\leqq m$, and

$$A = \max_{1\leqq h\leqq m;\, 1\leqq q\leqq n(h);\, 1\leqq t\leqq\rho(h,q)}|t-1+\alpha_h|;$$

then for $u\neq 1$, $\max_{1\leqq\mu\leqq\sigma}|((\sigma-\mu)!/(\sigma-1)!)F^{(\mu-1)}(0)|\geqq|F(u)|\min\{|1-u|, |1-u|^{-1}\}^{A+1}/(\sigma+A)^{\sigma}$ where $\sigma=\sum\rho(h, q)$.

*K. Thanigasalam* (Bronx, N.Y.)

Citations: MR 15, 688b = M50-2; MR 23# A113 = M50-5.

# M55 SIEVES

Papers in which sieve methods are applied to other problems are, by and large, classified under the application. When they involve what appear to be new results or methodology (as of the time of publication) of sieves, they are cross-referenced here, but there are many other papers, not mentioned here, where a sieve argument was used.

See also reviews A22-107, B02-3, E20-4, L25-29, M20-13, M25-56, M25-73, M25-80, M25-91, N02-6, N02-13, N04-50, N08-43, N12-5, N12-6, N12-28, N12-31, N12-38, N12-40, N12-48, N12-49, N16-20, N16-31, N24-35, N24-45, N24-48, N24-52, N24-65, N24-68, N28-12, N28-15, N28-22, N28-27, N28-53, N28-79, N32-33, N32-37, N32-54, N36-84, N48-34, N56-18, N60-9, N60-37, N60-89, N76-23, P32-1, P32-6, P32-11, P32-30, P32-35, P32-39, P32-40, P32-44, P32-45, P32-50, P32-53, P32-55, P32-56, P32-57, P32-60, P32-62, P32-63, P32-66, P32-68, P32-70, P32-73, P32-74, P32-76, P36-37, P40-7, P40-16, P40-19, P40-21, P40-23,

P40-24, P48-8, P99-1, Q15-4, Q15-8, R44-9, R44-17, R44-38, R44-44, R46-12, R46-15, R46-24, R46-26, R46-28, R46-32, R48-34, T10-26, Z02-53, Z10-35.

## M55-1 (2, 349a)

**Linnik, U. V. "The large sieve."** C. R. (Doklady) Acad. Sci. URSS (N.S.) **30**, 292–294 (1941).

The Viggo Brun sieve method enables one to find bounds for the number of integers not greater than $X$ which do not belong to $k$ given residue classes modulo $p_i$, where the $p_i$ are the primes not exceeding $\sqrt{X}$. The method does not apply if the fixed number $k$ is replaced by $f(p_i)$, where $f(p_i)$ increases with $p_i$. A method of dealing with this case is discussed in the present paper. It involves the exponential sum

$$S(\alpha)=\sum_{j=1}^{Z} e^{2\pi i\alpha M_j}$$

and an estimation of the integral

$$\int_0^1 |S(\alpha)|^2 d\alpha = Z.$$

*R. D. James* (Saskatoon, Sask.).

Referred to in B08-12, N68-2, P32-12, P40-23, R46-15, Z02-53.

## M55-2 (4, 211d)

**Sispánov, S. The sieve of Eratosthenes and the logarithmic integral of Tchebysheff.** Bol. Mat. **15**, 105–116 (1942). (Spanish)

After eliminating multiples of the first $k$ primes, the sequence of the remaining positive integers $1, p_1, \cdots, p_k, p_{k+1}, \cdots, p_n, p_{k+1}^2, \cdots$ is said to have (approximate) density $\delta_k=\prod p_i/(p_i-1)$ $(i=1, \cdots, k)$. Consider now a graph having as ordinates the primes $p_n$ for abscissae $n=1, 2, \cdots$. This is approximated by a continuous differentiable curve with slopes at the points with $p=p_k^2$ determined by $dp/dn=\delta_k$. From this is obtained $dp/dn=\ln p$, whence $n=\int_2^p dx/\ln x$. The closeness of the approximation is not investigated. *G. Pall* (Montreal, Que.).

## M55-3 (6, 169b)

**Benckert, Curt Ragnar. A variant of the sieve of Eratosthenes.** Ark. Mat. Astr. Fys. **29B**, no. 13, 5 pp. (1943). (Swedish)

Write an infinite multiplication table in the form of a matrix with elements $a_{ik}=(i-1)(k-1)$. This matrix contains all positive integers except primes. In similar ways the author constructs tables containing all numbers of the form $4n-1$, $6n-1$, and $12n-1$. *W. Feller.*

## M55-4 (9, 271h)

**Selberg, Atle. On an elementary method in the theory of primes.** Norske Vid. Selsk. Forh., Trondhjem **19**, no. 18, 64–67 (1947).

Let $p_1, p_2, \cdots$ be an arbitrary set of primes. Denote by $N(n)$ the number of integers $m\leqq n$ which are not divisible by any of the $p$'s. The author obtains (and in fact improves) in a simple way the estimate for the upper bound of $N(n)$ which was previously obtained by Brun's method. His method seems to have great possibilities. *P. Erdös.*

Referred to in M55-12, N04-50, P40-2, R44-9.

## M55-5 (10, 104b)

**Behrend, F. A. Generalization of an inequality of Heilbronn and Rohrbach.** Bull. Amer. Math. Soc. **54**, 681–684 (1948).

Let

$$T(a_1, \cdots, a_m)=1-\sum_{1\leqq\mu\leqq m} 1/a_\mu+\sum_{1\leqq\mu<\nu\leqq m} 1/\{a_\mu, a_\nu\} -\cdots+(-1)^m 1/\{a_1, \cdots, a_m\},$$

where $\{u_1, \cdots, u_m\}$ denotes the least common multiple of the positive integers $u_1, \cdots, u_m$. Rohrbach [J. Reine Angew. Math. **177**, 193–196 (1937)] and the reviewer [Proc. Cambridge Philos. Soc. **33**, 207–209 (1937)] proved: $T(a_1, \cdots, a_m)\geqq(1-1/a_1)\cdots(1-1/a_m)$. The author proves the stronger inequality $T(a_1, \cdots, a_m, b_1, \cdots, b_n) \geqq T(a_1, \cdots, a_m)T(b_1, \cdots, b_n)$. His proof is based on the following lemma. If $(d, v_1)=\cdots=(d, v_l)=1$, then $T(du_1, \cdots, du_k, v_1, \cdots, v_l)=(1/d)T(u_1, \cdots, u_k, v_1, \cdots, v_l)+(1-1/d)T(v_1, \cdots, v_l)$.

Assuming that $a_\mu$ does not divide $a_\nu$ $(\mu\neq\nu)$, $b_\mu$ does not divide $b_\nu$ $(\mu\neq\nu)$, the author shows that

$$T(a_1, \cdots, a_m, b_1, \cdots, b_n)=T(a_1, \cdots, a_m)T(b_1, \cdots, b_n)$$

if and only if the products $a_1\cdots a_m$ and $b_1\cdots b_n$ are relatively prime. *H. Heilbronn* (Bristol).

Referred to in M55-16, M55-32.

## M55-6 (11, 161c)

**Rényi, Alfred. Un nouveau théorème concernant les fonctions indépendantes et ses applications à la théorie des nombres.** J. Math. Pures Appl. (9) **28**, 137–149 (1949).

Let $f_1(t), \cdots, f_n(t), \cdots$ be pairwise independent functions defined on the interval (0, 1). Let $V_m(x)$ be the distribution function of $f_m(t)$ and $V_m(x; E)$ the distribution function of $f_m(t)$ on the set $E\subset(0, 1)$, i.e.,

$$V_m(x; E)=\text{meas } \underset{t}{\mathrm{E}}\{f_m(t)\leqq x, t\varepsilon E\}/\text{meas } E.$$

For an interval $I=(a, b)$ define

$$V_m(I)=V_m(b)-V_m(a), \quad V_m^{(E)}(I)=V_m(b; E)-V_m(a; E).$$

The author first proves that

$$(*)\qquad \sum_{n=1}^{\infty}\int_{-\infty}^{\infty}(V_n^{(E)}(I)-V_n(I))^2/V_n(I)<1/|E|,$$

where the integrals are taken in the sense of Burkill. Next the author considers a sequence of functions $f_1(t), f_2(t), \cdots$ which are "almost pairwise independent" in the following sense: there exists a sequence $\{\delta_n\}$ of nonnegative constants such that $\delta^2=\sum_1^\infty\delta_n^2<1$ and such that for all indices $m\neq n$ and all real $a, b, c, d$ one has

$$\left|\frac{\text{meas } \mathrm{E}_t\{a<f_m(t)<b; c<f_n(t)<d\}}{\text{meas } \mathrm{E}_t\{a<f_m(t)<b\}\text{ meas } \mathrm{E}_t\{c<f_n(t)<d\}}-1\right|\leqq\delta_n\delta_m.$$

(It is, of course, understood that only such $a, b, c, d$ need be considered for which the denominator does not vanish.) The inequality (*) must now be modified to the extent that the right hand side is to be replaced by $(1-\delta^2)/|E|$.

This result is now applied to obtain a generalization of the "large sieve" of Linnik. Let $n_1\leqq n_2\leqq\cdots\leqq n_Z\leqq N$ be $Z$ integers and let $p_1, p_2, \cdots$ be primes. Let $f(p)$ and $Q(p)$ be arithmetical functions such that $0<f(p)\leqq p$, $Q(p)>1$. Set

$$\min_{p<\frac{1}{2}N^{\frac{1}{2}}} f(p)/p=\tau, \quad \max_{p<\frac{1}{2}N^{\frac{1}{2}}} Q(p)=Q$$

and denote by $Z(p, k)$ the number of integers from the sequence $n_j$ which are congruent to $k \pmod p$. The author shows that for all primes $p < \frac{1}{2}N^{\frac{1}{2}}$ except at most $9NQ^2/(Z\tau)$ and for all residues $k \pmod p$ except at most $f(p)$ one has the inequality

$$|Z(p, k) - Z/p| < Z/\{pQ(p)\}.$$

This result played an important part in the author's proof that every integer is a sum of a prime and a number whose number of prime factors is less than an absolute constant [Izvestiya Akad. Nauk SSSR. Ser. Mat. **12**, 57–78 (1948); these Rev. **9**, 413]. *M. Kac* (Ithaca, N. Y.).

Citations: MR 9, 413g = P32-12.

Referred to in M20-13, M55-7, M55-8, M55-23, M55-62, N12-5.

## M55-7 (11, 581g)

**Rényi, Alfred. On the large sieve of Ju V. Linnik.** Compositio Math. **8**, 68–75 (1950).

The results of this paper are essentially those reviewed previously [J. Math. Pures Appl. (9) **28**, 137–149 (1949); these Rev. **11**, 161]. The only difference is that in the former paper the "large sieve" is derived from a general probabilistic theorem whereas in the present paper a direct and self-contained approach is used. *M. Kac.*

Citations: MR 11, 161c = M55-6.

Referred to in M55-8, M55-23, N12-5, R46-12, R46-15, Z02-53.

## M55-8 (12, 161c)

**Rényi, Alfréd. Probability methods in number theory.** Publ. Math. Collectae Budapest **1**, no. 21, 9 pp. (1949).

This paper is the author's inaugural lecture at the University of Budapest. First a brief summary of some applications of probabilistic methods to number theory are given. These also include incorrect applications which the author analyzes and criticizes. The major part of the paper is devoted to the exposition of the author's approach to the "large sieve." The details of this approach have been published elsewhere [J. Math. Pures Appl. (9) **28**, 137–149 (1949); Compositio Math. **8**, 68–75 (1950); these Rev. **11**, 161, 581]. *M. Kac* (Ithaca, N. Y.).

Citations: MR 11, 161c = M55-6; MR 11, 581g = M55-7.

## M55-9 (12, 243b)

**Blanuša, D. Une interprétation géométrique du crible d'Ératosthène.** Hrvatsko Prirodoslovno Društvo. Glasnik Mat.-Fiz. Astr. Ser. II. **4**, 201–202 (1949). (Croatian. French summary)

En joignant les points $A_r(0, a/r)$, $r=1, 2, \cdots$, aux points $B_s(s, 0)$, $s=2, 3, \cdots$, on obtient sur la droite $y=-a$ les points d'intersection $C_k(k, -a)$ avec $k=(r+1)s$, $r=1, 2, \cdots$; $s=2, 3, \cdots$, c'est à dire les points dont les abscisses sont tous les nombres naturels à l'exception de l'unité et des nombres premiers. *Author's summary.*

## M55-10 (13, 438d)

**Selberg, Atle. The general sieve-method and its place in prime number theory.** Proceedings of the International Congress of Mathematicians, Cambridge, Mass., 1950, vol. 1, pp. 286–292. Amer. Math. Soc., Providence, R. I., 1952.

This is a clear exposition of the general sieve-method due to the author. The method includes Brun's method and the improvements of it as a special case. The formulation of the technique is not only considerably simpler than in the older methods, but it also leads to better results.

Let there be given a finite set of integers $n_i$ and a set of $r$ primes $p_i$. Let $N_r = N(p_1, p_2, \cdots, p_r)$ denote the number of $n$'s not divisible by any $p_i$. Then $N_r = \sum_n \sum_{d|n} \mu(d)$, where $\mu(d)$ is the Möbius-function, and each $d$ is composed only of primes $p_i$. The problem of the sieve-method is to find upper and lower bounds for $N_r$. To accomplish this the author introduces ingenious devices for replacing the expression $\sum_{d|n} \mu(d)$ with a similarly built expression which respectively majorizes or minorizes it, and at the same time diminishes the remainder term to a reasonable size. The analysis is reduced to the solution of two extremal problems which, in turn, may be employed to deduce information about the limitations of the method. There are several alternative procedures some of which require extensive numerical calculations.

The older sieve-methods are characterized by their broad generality which makes them yield results where the powerful analytic tools will not work. They lead, however, only to partial and incomplete results. A surprising feature of the present method is that in some special cases the results are the best possible. On the other hand, it is shown that several problems which have been attacked repeatedly by the sieve-method cannot be solved in this way. The author concludes that ". . . it seems that the sieve-method will be of little value for the further progress of these problems in prime number theory which it was originally designed to deal with. But it remains as an extremely general and versatile tool for establishing, for instance, upper bounds, and may perhaps, when in some way combined with an analytic approach, still play an important part in the future of these problems." *A. L. Whiteman* (Los Angeles, Calif.).

Referred to in P32-35.

## M55-11 (14, 726j)

**Selberg, Atle. On elementary methods in primenumber-theory and their limitations.** Den 11te Skandinaviske Matematikerkongress, Trondheim, 1949, pp. 13–22. Johan Grundt Tanums Forlag, Oslo, 1952. 27.50 kr.

This is a review of methods based on the general idea of the sieve of Eratosthenes. The well-known form given to it by Viggo Brun is developed into a more flexible instrument by the removal of certain restrictions. Some indications of the procedure are given, but in the main the lecture is a descriptive account without detailed proofs. The more general method leads to improvements in earlier results; thus it is stated that it can be proved that every sufficiently large even integer can be expressed as a sum of two positive integers each having at most three prime factors. The method is, however, subject to natural limitations, and the author develops the thesis that such methods alone cannot be expected to solve the deeper problems of the theory of primes. At the same time he discusses the possibility of going further by widening the concept of "sieve", and indicates how this idea led him to the asymptotic formula underlying elementary proofs of the prime number theorem. *A. E. Ingham* (Cambridge, England).

Referred to in P32-35, P44-31.

## M55-12 (15, 202e)

**Ožigova, E. P. Modification of the method of the "sieve of Eratosthenes" given by A. Selberg.** Uspehi Matem. Nauk (N.S.) **8**, no. 3(55), 119–124 (1953). (Russian)

The sieve method of A. Selberg [Norske Vid. Selsk. Forh., Trondhjem **19**, no. 18, 64–67 (1947); these Rev. **9**, 271] is presented with slightly more detail than in the original paper of Selberg. Several applications of the method are stated. *H. N. Shapiro* (New York, N. Y.).

Citations: MR 9, 271h = M55-4.

**M55-13** **(16, 676e)**

**Kuhn, P. Neue Abschätzungen auf Grund der Viggo Brunschen Siebmethode.** Tolfte Skandinaviska Matematikerkongressen, Lund, 1953, pp. 160–168 (1954). 25 Swedish crowns (may be ordered from Lunds Universitets Matematiska Institution).

The author presents an interesting method for sharpening results obtained by the sieve method. The idea is a simple one, but the results are surprising. It is based on the observation that if an integer has $v+w+1$ or more prime factors, then at least $w+1$ of them cannot be too large. The details are given for one example and the following theorem is proved. For sufficiently large $x$ there is always an integer between $x-x^{1/v}$ and $x$ that has at most $v+w$ prime factors. Here $v$ is any positive integer and $w$ is the least integer satisfying the inequality $\log(6v-w)\leqq 0.968(w+1)$. Two numerical examples are $v=3$, $w=2$ and $v=100$, $w=6$. The author indicates that from the work of Buchstab [C. R. (Dokl.) Acad. Sci. URSS (N.S.) **29**, 544–548 (1940); MR **2**, 348] and Tartakowski [ibid. **23**, 126–129 (1939)] it follows that the same result holds if $w$ is the least positive integer satisfying $\log 5(6v-w)-\log(w+6)\leqq 1.097(w+1)$. For example, $v=2$, $w=1$ and $v=100$, $w=5$. Other results which have been obtained by the sieve method may also be improved. For example, it can be shown that there are infinitely many integers of the form $x^2+1$ which have at most 3 prime factors. *R. D. James* (East Lansing, Mass.).

Citations: MR 2, 348d = P32-1.
Referred to in M55-15, M55-55.

**M55-14** **(17, 711b)**

**Gardiner, Verna; Lazarus, R.; Metropolis, N.; and Ulam, S. On certain sequences of integers defined by sieves.** Math. Mag. **29** (1956), 117–122.

The authors generate a sequence of numbers

$$1, 3, 7, 9, 13, 15, 21, 25, 31, 33, 37, 43, \cdots,$$

called lucky numbers, by the following variant of Eratosthenes' sieve for the primes. Beginning with the natural numbers we delete all those occupying positions divisible by 2, i.e. all even numbers. The remaining odd numbers are now attacked by deleting every third one, that is every term whose rank is a multiple of 3. The result is

$$1, 3, 7, 9, 13, 15, 19, 21, \cdots.$$

We now delete every seventh number (beginning with 19) and every ninth element of what remains etc. Lucky numbers are very much like primes in their distribution at least as far as 48600. They show roughly the same densities and the same frequencies of gaps. The number of luckies of the form $4n+1$ less than $x$ is nearly equal to the number of the form $4n+3$, the latter being more numerous up to about $x=27000$. Their distribution into residue classes modulo 5 is also fairly uniform. Every even number less than 100000 is the sum of two lukcy numbers. *D. H. Lehmer* (Berkeley, Calif.).

Referred to in M55-19, M55-38.

**M55-15** **(19, 533c)**

**Wang, Yuan. On sieve methods and some of their applications.** Sci. Record (N.S.) **1** (1957), no. 3, 1–5.

The method of P. Kuhn [Tolfte Skandinaviska Matematikerkongressen, Lund, 1953, pp. 160–168; MR **16**, 676] is further developed to give improved results as follows. For sufficiently large $x$ there exists a number $n$ in the interval $x-x^{\delta_i}<n\leqq x$ with at most $i$ prime factors, where $\delta_2=10/17$, $\delta_3=20/49$, $\delta_6=1/5$, $\delta_{103}=3/301$. For infinitely many integers $x$, $x^3+2$ has at most 4 prime factors. *D. H. Lehmer* (Berkeley, Calif.).

Citations: MR 16, 676e = M55-13.

**M55-16** **(20# 3811)**

**van der Corput, J. G. Inequalities involving least common multiple and other arithmetical functions.** Nederl. Akad. Wetensch. Proc. Ser. A **61** = Indag. Math. **20** (1958), 5–15.

Let $P_1, \cdots, P_n$ be distinct primes, $A=P_1\cdots P_n$, $\{u_1, \cdots, u_n\}$ the least common multiple of the positive integers $u_1, \cdots, u_n$, $\Lambda(u_1, \cdots, u_n)=\{u_1, \cdots, u_n\}^{-r}$ $(r\geqq 0)$. For each (positive) divisor $B$ of $A$ introduce a real number $\lambda(B)$ and put $\sigma(B)=\sum_{D|B}\lambda(D)$ and $\tau(B)=\sum_{D|B}\lambda(D)\Lambda(a_1^{\delta_1}, \cdots, a_n^{\delta_n})$, where $D=P_1^{\delta_1}\cdots P_n^{\delta_n}$ and $a_1, \cdots, a_n$ are positive integers. The main theorem is in eight parts, too lengthy to be given in full, but the following two are typical. (2) If $\sigma(D)\leqq\sigma(B)$ for each divisor $B$ of $A$ and each divisor $D$ of $B$, then $\tau(D)\leqq\tau(B)$ for each divisor $B$ of $A$, for each divisor $D$ of $B$ and for each choice of the positive integers $a_1, \cdots, a_n$. (3) If $\sigma(B)+\sigma(C)\leqq\sigma(BC)$ for any two positive integers $B$ and $C$ whose product divides $A$, then $\tau(B)+\tau(C)\leqq\tau(BC)$ for any $B$, $C$ whose product divides $A$ and for each choice of $a_1, \cdots, a_n$. A typical consequence is the inequality

$$\sum_{D|B}\mu(D)\{a_1^{\delta_1}, \cdots, a_n^{\delta_n}\}^{-r}\cdot\sum_{D|C}\mu(D)\{a_1^{\delta_1}, \cdots, a_n^{\delta_n}\}^{-r} \leqq\sum_{D|BC}\mu(D)\{a_1^{\delta_1}, \cdots, a_n^{\delta_n}\}^{-r},$$

where $B$, $C$ are relatively prime quadratfrei numbers and $\mu$ is the Möbius function. For $r=1$ this reduces to an inequality of the reviewer [Bull. Amer. Math. Soc. **54** (1948), 681–684; MR **10**, 104]. Further results are obtained for more general functions $\Lambda$ and for the case where $A$ is no longer quadratfrei. *F. A. Behrend* (Victoria)

Citations: MR 10, 104b = M55-5.

**M55-17** **(20# 5761)**

**Hawkins, David. The random sieve.** Math. Mag. **31** (1957/58), 1–3.

The author investigates the following sieve: Check the number 2, then with probability $\frac{1}{2}$ strike out each subsequent number. If $P_2$ is the first number not stricken out, check it and strike out each number thereafter with probability $1/P_2$. $P_3$ is the next number not stricken out, we check it and strike out each subsequent number with probability $1/P_3$, etc. Thus we obtain a random sequence $P_1=2<P_2<P_3<\cdots$. The author outlines a proof that with probability 1, $P_n/n\log n\to 1$ [further literature: Cramer, Acta Arith. 2 (1936), 23–46]. *P. Erdös* (Birmingham)

Referred to in M55-24.

**M55-18** **(21# 2627)**

**David, Yosef. On a sequence generated by a sieving process.** Riveon Lematematika **11** (1957), 26–31. (Hebrew. English summary)

An asymptotic expression is found for $e(n)$, the number of terms smaller than $n$ in the sequence obtained from the positive integers by crossing out every $k$th term in the $k$th successive sequence, with $k=2, 3, \cdots$. The same sieving process is considered in an article by Erdös and Jabotinsky [reviewed below]. *From the author's summary*

**M55-19** **(21# 2628)**

**Erdös, Paul; and Jabotinsky, Eri. On sequences of integers generated by a sieving process. I, II.** Nederl. Akad. Wetensch. Proc. Ser. A **61** = Indag. Math. **20** (1958), 115–128.

The authors' algorithms depend on an initial integer $\lambda$ and on an auxiliary sequence $B$ of integers $b_k$ $(k=1, 2, \cdots)$ with $b_k\geqq 2$. A family of intermediary sequences $A^{(i)}$ $(i=1, 2, \cdots)$ is formed. $A^{(i)}$ consists of the integers $a_k^{(i)}$

($k=1, 2, \cdots$). The sequence $A^{(1)}$ is defined by: $a_k^{(1)}=\lambda+k$. We obtain $A^{(i+1)}$ from $A^{(i)}$ by striking out all the terms of the form $a^{(i)}_{1+mb_i}$ ($m=0$, 1, $\cdots$) and then renaming the sequence of remaining terms $a_1^{(i+1)}$, $a_2^{(i+1)}$, $a_3^{(i+1)}$, $\cdots$. Finally, the sequence $A$ consisting of integers $a_k$ ($k=1, 2, \cdots$) is defined by $a_k=a_1^{(k)}$.

As an example, take $b_k=k+1$ and $\lambda=0$. Then the first nine $a$'s are 1, 2, 4, 6, 10, 12, 18, 22, 30. A second example is $b_k=a_k$ with $\lambda=1$. Then the first ten $a$'s are 2, 3, 5, 7, 11, 13, 17, 23, 25, 29.

We quote only two of the authors' results: I. For $b_k=k+1$ we have

$$a_k = \frac{k^2}{\pi}+O(k^{4/3});$$

II. For $b_k=a_k$ we have ($\gamma$ Euler's constant)

$$(1) \qquad a_k = k\log k+\tfrac{1}{2}k(\log\log k)^2 + (2-\gamma)k\log\log k+o(k\log\log k).$$

The dominant term here was also obtained independently by D. Hawkins and W. E. Briggs and, following these authors, the reviewer noted the second term in (1) [Hawkins learnt of these algorithms from S. Ulam. See the paper by V. Gardiner, R. Lazarus, N. Metropolis and S. Ulam in Math. Mag. **29** (1956), 117–122; MR **17**, 711].

*S. Chowla* (Boulder, Colo.)

Citations: MR 17, 711b = M55-14.
Referred to in M55-38.

## M55-20 (21# 2629)

**Hawkins, D.; and Briggs, W. E. The lucky number theorem.** Math. Mag. **31** (1957/58), 81–84.

The authors define a sequence of integers $a_1<a_2<\cdots$ by a sieve process as follows: Let $S_2$ be the sequence 2, 3, 5, 7, $\cdots$. Assume $S_n$ has been already defined and that the elements of $S_n$ are $t_{n,m}$, $1\leqq m<\infty$. $S_{n+1}$ is obtained from $S_n$ by crossing out every $t_{n,n}$-th element of $S_n$. {It seems to the reviewer that the authors' definition is inaccurate in going from $S_1$ to $S_2$.}

The authors prove by an elementary Tauberian argument that $a_k/(k\log k)\to 1$. This result is analogous to the prime number theorem. {Substantially the same result has been proved independently by Jabotinsky and the reviewer [preceding review].} *P. Erdös* (Birmingham)

Referred to in M55-26.

## M55-21 (21# 2630)

**Hawkins, D.; and Briggs, W. E. The lucky number theorem.** Math. Mag. **31** (1957/58), 277–280.

Identical with the article reviewed above.

Referred to in M55-26.

## M55-22 (22# 1937)

**Rényi, Alfréd. On the probabilistic generalization of the large sieve of Linnik.** Magyar Tud. Akad. Mat. Kutató Int. Közl. **3** (1958), 199–206. (Hungarian and Russian summaries)

Let $\eta$ be a random variable with finite variance and let $\{\xi_n\}$ be a sequence of discrete random variables. Denote by $z_{nk}$ ($k=1, 2, \cdots$) the possible values of $\xi_n$ and write $A_{nk}=\{\xi_n=z_{nk}\}$. Let $\varphi(\xi_n, \xi_m)$ be the mean square contingency of $\xi_n$ and $\xi_m$, i.e.,

$$\varphi^2(\xi_n, \xi_m) = \sum_k\sum_l\left\{\frac{[P(A_{nk}A_{ml})-P(A_{nk})P(A_{ml})]^2}{P(A_{nk})P(A_{ml})}\right\}$$

and $\theta_{\xi_n}(\eta)$, the correlation ratio of $\eta$ on $\xi_n$, i.e.,

$$\theta_{\xi_n}{}^2(\eta) = \frac{D^2\{E\{\eta|\xi_n\}\}}{D^2\{\eta\}}.$$

The author, generalizing his earlier result [Ann. Inst. Fourier Grenoble **1** (1949), 43–52; MR **14**, 886], proves that if

$$\Big|\sum_{n\neq m}\sum\varphi(\xi_n, \xi_m)x_nx_m\Big| \leqq B\sum_n x_n^2$$

provided that $\sum_n x_n^2<\infty$, then

$$\sum_{n=1}^{\infty}\theta_{\xi_n}{}^2(\eta) \leqq (1+B).$$

*L. Takács* (New York)

## M55-23 (22# 1938)

**Rényi, A. New version of the probabilistic generalization of the large sieve.** Acta Math. Acad. Sci. Hungar. **10** (1959), 217–226. (Russian summary, unbound insert)

Let $\eta$ and $\xi$ be two random variables. Denote by $R(\xi, \eta)$ their correlation coefficient, and by $\theta_\xi(\eta)$ the correlation ratio of $\eta$ on $\xi$. Following H. Gebelein [Z. Angew. Math. Mech. **21** (1941), 364–379; MR **4**, 104] the author defines the maximal correlation $S(\xi, \eta)$ as follows:

$$S(\xi, \eta) = \sup_{f,g} R(f(\xi), g(\eta))$$

where $f$ and $g$ run through all Borel measurable functions for which $R(f(\xi), g(\eta))$ is defined.

The author proves the following new version of the large sieve. Let $\xi_n$, $1\leqq n<\infty$, be an infinite sequence of random variables for which there exists a constant $C$ so that

$$\Big|\sum_{n=1}^{\infty}\sum_{m=1}^{\infty}S(\xi_n, \xi_m)x_nx_m\Big| < C\sum_{n=1}^{\infty}x_n^2.$$

Let $\eta$ be an arbitrary random variable for which $M(\eta^2)$ exists. Then we have

$$\sum_{n=1}^{\infty}\theta_{\xi_n}{}^2(\eta) \leqq C.$$

Loosely stated the theorem means that if we have a sequence of nearly independent variables $\xi_n$, then an arbitrary random variable $\eta$ can not depend too strongly on too many of them. This result contains all previous versions of the large sieve. [See A. Rényi, J. Math. Pures Appl. (9) **28** (1949), 137–149; Compositio Math. **8** (1950), 68–75; MR **11**, 161, 581; and #1937 above.]

The author also proves some theorems about various measures of dependence of random variables.

*P. Erdös* (Budapest)

Citations: MR 11, 161c = M55-6; MR 11, 581g = M55-7.

## M55-24 (23# A3132)

**Lachapelle, Benoît**

**L'espérance mathématique du nombre de nombres premiers aléatoires inférieurs ou égaux à $x$.** *Canad. Math. Bull.* **4** (1961), 139–142.

Let $p_1<p_2<\cdots$ be the sequence of random prime numbers of Hawkins [Math. Mag. **31** (1957/58), 1–3; MR **20** #5761], and denote by $\pi_a(x)$ the mathematical expectation of the number of random primes not exceeding $x$. The author proves that

$$\pi_a(x) = \frac{x}{\log x}+(1-B)\frac{x}{(\log x)^2}+\cdots + (n-1)!\left(1-B+\frac{B^2}{2!}-\cdots+(-1)^{n-1}B^{n-1}/(n-1)!\right) \times\frac{x}{(\log x)^n}+O\left(\frac{x}{(\log x)^{n+1}}\right).$$

*P. Erdös* (Budapest)

Citations: MR 20# 5761 = M55-17.

## M55-25 (25# 2051)

**Barban, M. B.**

**On a theorem of I. P. Kubiljus. (Russian. Uzbek summary)**

*Izv. Akad. Nauk UzSSR Ser. Fiz.-Mat. Nauk* **1961**, *no.* 5, 3–9.

The author proves two lemmas, whose importance justifies calling them "fundamental lemmas". Lemma 1: Let $\{b\}$ denote a sequence of natural numbers all of whose prime factors are $\leqq r$. Then

$$\sum_{\substack{m \\ m\equiv 0 (\mathrm{mod}\ b), \\ b\geqq u,\ m\leqq n}} 1 = O(ne^{-c\log u/\log r}),$$

where $c$ is an absolute positive constant. Lemma 2: Let $a_1, a_2, \cdots, a_N$ be a sequence of integers, and (B) $p_1, \cdots, p_s$ a sequence of primes with $p_1 < p_2 < \cdots < p_s \leqq r$. Let $L(m)$ denote the number of solutions of the congruence $a_n \equiv 0 \pmod m$. Let $I(N, r)$ denote the number of $a$'s not divisible by any prime of the sequence (B). Then

$$I(N, r) = \prod_{p|\pi_s} \{1-L(p)/p\}[1+O(e^{-c\log N/\log r})],$$

where $\pi_l = \prod_{j=1}^{l} p_j$ $(1 \leqq j \leqq s)$.

These lemmas are of interest in connection with (1) the sieve method of A. Selberg; (2) a theorem of I. P. Kubiljus on pages 113–120 of his book *Probability methods in number theory* (Russian) [Gosudarstv. Izdat. Polit. Naučn. Lit. Litovsk. SSR, Vilna, 1959; MR **23** #A134].

*S. Chowla* (Boulder, Colo.)

Citations: MR 23# A134 = N60-37.

Referred to in N28-53.

## M55-26 (26# 6145)

**Briggs, W. E.**

**Prime-like sequences generated by a sieve process.**

*Duke Math. J.* **30** (1963), 297–311.

Let $A^{(1)}$ be the sequence $\{a_k^{(1)}\}$, where $a_k^{(1)} = k+1$ $(k = 1, 2, 3, \cdots)$; $A^{(n+1)} = \{a_k^{(n+1)}\}$ is obtained recursively from the sequence $A^{(n)}$ by choosing an integer $r_n$ satisfying $1 \leqq r_n \leqq a_n = a_n^{(n)}$ and then eliminating from $A^{(n)}$ those elements of the form $a^{(n)}_{n+r_n+ma_n}$ for $m = 0, 1, 2, \cdots$; this process generates a sequence $A = \{a_n\}$. These sieves were studied by Ulam and others, e.g., by Hawkins and Briggs [Math. Mag. **31** (1957/58), 81–84; MR **21** #2629; ibid. **31** (1957/58), 277–280; MR **21** #2630] and by Erdős and Jabotinsky. Sharpening earlier results, the author proves

$$a_n = n\log n + \tfrac{1}{2}n(\log\log n)^2 + \{1+o(1)\}cn\log\log n$$

in the three cases $r_n = a_n - n$, $r_n = 1$, $r_n = n$ (with different $c$ in each case). *S. Chowla* (Boulder, Colo.)

Citations: MR 21# 2629 = M55-20; MR 21# 2630 = M55-21.

Referred to in M55-38, M55-47, M55-51.

## M55-27 (27# 1432)

**Uchiyama, Saburô**

**A note on the sieve method of A. Selberg.**

*J. Fac. Sci. Hokkaido Univ. Ser. I* **16**, 189–192 (1962).

Let $a_1, \cdots, a_N$, $N > 1$, be positive integers, not necessarily distinct. Let $S$ denote the number of $a_j$ which are not divisible by any prime $p \leqq z$, where $z \geqq 2$; and for $d$ a positive integer let $S_d$ denote the number of $a_j$ divisible by $d$. It is assumed that $S_d$ is of the form

$$S_d = \frac{\omega(d)}{d}N + R(d),$$

where $R(d)$ is an error term and $\omega(d)$ is a multiplicative arithmetic function of $d$. Put $f(d) = d/\omega(d)$ and assume that $f(d) > 1$ for $d > 1$; $f(d) = \infty$ only if $\omega(d) = 0$, and then $S_d = R(d)$. Define

$$f_1(m) = \sum_{n|m} \mu(n)f(m/n),$$

$$Z(d) = \sum_{\substack{r\leqq z/d \\ (r,d)=1}} \frac{\mu^2(r)}{f_1(r)}, \quad Z = Z(1),$$

$$\lambda(d) = \mu(d)\prod_{p|d}\left(1-\frac{1}{f(p)}\right)^{-1}\frac{Z(d)}{Z}.$$

Then Selberg's formula is

$$S \leqq \frac{N}{Z} + R,$$

where

$$R = \sum_{d_1, d_2 \leqq z} |\lambda(d_1)\lambda(d_2)R([d_1, d_2])|$$

and $[d_1, d_2]$ denotes the least common multiple of $d_1$ and $d_2$.

The author makes the additional assumptions that $|R(d)| \leqq \omega(d)$, $\omega([d_1, d_2]) \leqq \omega(d_1)\omega(d_2)$ and proves that $R$ now satisfies $R = O(z^2(\log\log z)^2)$. Furthermore, if $\omega(p) \leqq 1$ for all primes $p$, then $R = O(z^2/Z^2)$. Several applications are given which improve upon known results.

*M. Newman* (Washington, D.C.)

Referred to in M55-28.

## M55-28 (29# 1196)

**Uchiyama, Saburô**

**A further note on the sieve method of A. Selberg.**

*J. Fac. Sci. Hokkaido Univ. Ser. I* **17** (1963), 79–83.

The author continues the work originated in his paper [same J. **16** (1962), 189–192; MR **27** #1432]. Previously a universal upper bound for the remainder term in the "upper" sieve of A. Selberg was obtained under certain restrictions. Here the analogous problem is treated for the "lower" sieve, and similar results are obtained under similar restrictions. A full description is given in the review of the previous paper [MR **27** #1432].

*Morris Newman* (Washington, D.C.)

Citations: MR 27# 1432 = M55-27.

## M55-29 (28# 1166)

**Bauer, Jean-Pierre**

**Méthodes d'approximations successives en arithmétique élémentaire.**

*C. R. Acad. Sci. Paris* **250** (1960), 3098–3100.

Die Veränderlichen sind ganze nichtnegative Zahlen. Verfasser formuliert sein Problem so: Die durch keine der $\lambda$ gegebenen Zahlen $a, \cdots, l$ (durchwegs $>1$) teilbaren Zahlen $a_0, \cdots$ bilden, nach ihrer Größe geordnet, eine wachsende Zahlenfolge. $\alpha(s)$ bezeichne das Glied mit Rang $s$, und es sei $\alpha(1) = 1$. Analog sei $\beta_0, \cdots$ die Folge der durch mindestens eine der Zahlen $a, \cdots, l$ teilbaren Zahlen, wieder geordnet nach ihrer Größe, also $\beta(0) = 0$. $\beta(s)$ bezeichne die Zahl des Ranges $s$. Aufgabe des Verfassers ist die Berechnung von $\alpha(r)$ und $\beta(s)$. Er gibt dafür verschiedene Formeln, die sich aber ihrer Kompliziertheit wegen der Wiedergabe entziehen. Nur sei eine merkwürdige Bezeichnungsweise angeführt: Versteht man unter $\Gamma_{e,\cdots,j}$, das kleinste gemeinsame Vielfache der Zahlen $e, \cdots, j$, so schreibt Verfasser:

$$\sum F(\Gamma) = F(a) + \cdots + F(l) - F(\Gamma_{a,b}) - \cdots - F(\Gamma_{k,l}) + \cdots + (-1)^{\lambda+1}F(\Gamma_{a,\cdots,l}).$$

Er gibt dann verschiedene Methoden an, wie man die Rechnung abkürzen kann. *L. Holzer* (Zbl **93**, 46)

Referred to in M55-30, M55-31.

## M55-30 (30# 30a; 30# 30b)

**Bauer, Jean-Pierre**
**Méthodes d'approximations successives en arithmétique élémentaire.**
*C. R. Acad. Sci. Paris* **259** (1964), 15–18.

**Bauer, Jean-Pierre**
**Méthodes d'approximations successives en arithmétique élémentaire.**
*C. R. Acad. Sci. Paris* **259** (1964), 269–272.

Let $a_1, a_2, \cdots, a_\lambda$ be integers $>1$ and let $C=C(a_1, \cdots, a_\lambda)$ be the class of all positive integers divisible by none of the $a$'s. In a previous paper [same C. R. **250** (1960), 3098–3100; MR **28** #1166] the author considered the problem of determining for a given $s$ that member of $C$ which ranks $s$ in order of magnitude. This amounts to a recursive inversion of the cross-classification process. The author attempts to do this in a cumbersome symbolic manner much too complicated to set forth here. In these two papers he continues his consideration of the problem subject to two hypotheses about the vanishing of two complicated recursive functions.

{The problem solves itself as follows. For any $x \geqq 0$, define $\theta(x)=\theta(a_1, a_2, \cdots, a_\lambda; x)$ as the number of members of $C$ not exceeding $x$. By cross-classification

$$\theta(x) = [x]-\sum\left[\frac{x}{a_i}\right]+\sum\left[\frac{x}{[a_i, a_j]}\right]-\cdots,$$

where $[a_1, a_2, a_3]$ denotes the least common multiple of $a_1$, $a_2$, and $a_3$. Now define $n_0, n_1, \cdots$ recursively by

$$n_0 = s, \qquad n_{i+1} = s-\theta(n_0+n_1+\cdots+n_{i-1}).$$

Ultimately $n_k=0$. Then $n_0+n_1+\cdots+n_{k-1}$ is the $s$th member of $C$.} *D. H. Lehmer* (Berkeley, Calif.)

Citations: MR 28# 1166 = M55-29.

## M55-31 (41# 3364)

**Bauer, J. P.**
**Sur les multiples et les contremultiples d'un système d'entiers donnés.**
*Publ. Dép. Math. (Lyon)* **4** (1967), *fasc.* 4, 1–63.

The essential results of this paper are given in C. R. Acad. Sci. Paris **250** (1960), 3098–3100 [MR **28** #1166].
*W. G. H. Schaal* (Marburg)

Citations: MR 28# 1166 = M55-29.

## M55-32 (28# 1185)

**Rieger, G. J.**
**Verallgemeinerung eines Satzes von Romanov und anderes.**
*Math. Nachr.* **20** (1959), 107–122.

1. Für natürliche Zahlen $a_\kappa$ und reelle Zahlen $\xi_\kappa$ $(0 \leqq \xi_\kappa \leqq 1;$ $\kappa=1, 2, \cdots, k)$ sei

$$(*) \quad T(a_1, \cdots, a_k; \xi_1, \cdots, \xi_k) =$$
$$1-\sum_\kappa \frac{\xi_\kappa}{a_\kappa}+\sum_{\kappa<\mu}\frac{\xi_\kappa \xi_\mu}{[a_\kappa, a_\mu]}-\cdots+(-1)^k\frac{\xi_1\xi_2\cdots\xi_k}{[a_1, a_2, \cdots, a_k]}$$

$(k>0)$ bzw. $=1$ für $k=0$; dabei ist $[a_1, \cdots, a_\kappa]$ das kleinste gemeinsame Vielfache dieser Zahlen. Ungleichungen von Heilbronn [Proc. Cambridge Philos. Soc. **33** (1937), 207–209], Rohrbach [J. Reine Angew. Math. **177** (1937), 193–196] und Behrend [Bull. Amer. Math. Soc. **54** (1948), 681–684; MR **10**, 104] verallgemeinernd, beweist Verfasser mit weiteren natürlichen Zahlen $b_\lambda$ und reellen Zahlen $\eta_\lambda$ $(0 \leqq \eta_\lambda \leqq 1;\ \lambda=1, 2, \cdots, l)$ für $k \geqq 0$, $l \geqq 0$:

$$T(a_1, \cdots, a_k, b_1, \cdots, b_l; \xi_1, \cdots, \xi_k, \eta_1, \cdots, \eta_l) \geqq$$
$$T(a_1, \cdots, a_k; \xi_1, \cdots, \xi_k)T(b_1, \cdots, b_l; \eta_1, \cdots, \eta_l).$$

Diese Abschätzung wird dann wesentlich weiter verallgemeinert, indem $a_\kappa$ und $b_\lambda$ durch Ideale $\mathfrak{a}_\kappa$ bzw. $\mathfrak{b}_\lambda$ aus dem Ring der ganzen Zahlen eines algebraischen Zahlkörpers $\mathsf{K}$ ersetzt werden. Hierbei ist $[a_1, \cdots, a_r]$ in (*) durch $N[\mathfrak{a}_1, \cdots, \mathfrak{a}_r]$ zu ersetzen. 2. In Verallgemeinerung eines Satzes von Erdős und Turán [Mitt. Forsch.-Inst. Math. Mech. Univ. Tomsk **1** (1935), 101–103] der seinerseits einen Satz von Romanov verschärft, wird gezeigt: Ist $f(m)$ eine nicht abnehmende, positivwertige zahlentheoretische Funktion mit $\sum_{m=1}^{\infty}\{mf(m)\}^{-1}=c(f)<\infty$, so ist für jede natürliche Zahl $a>1$ $\sum'\{df(e(a, d))\}^{-1}<c_1 c(f)\log\log(a+2)$, wobei $c_1>0$ eine absolute Konstante, $e(a, d)$ den Exponenten von $a$ mod $d$ und $\sum'$ bedeutet, daß über alle zu $a$ teilerfremden, quadratfreien natürlichen Zahlen $d$ zu summieren ist. Auch dieser Satz wird, mit gewissen Modifikationen, auf Ideale von $\mathsf{K}$ übertragen. In beiden Fällen wird auch die Umkehrung bewiesen. 3. Ist $\mathfrak{a}$ Ideal aus $\mathsf{K}$, $E(\mathfrak{u})$ eine Funktion mit den Eigenschaften: $E(\mathfrak{u})$ ist für alle zu $\mathfrak{a}$ teilerfremden Ideale $\mathfrak{u}$ aus $\mathsf{K}$ erklärt, $E(\mathfrak{u})$ ist eine natürliche Zahl, $E(\mathfrak{u}\mathfrak{v})=[E(\mathfrak{u}), E(\mathfrak{v})]$ für $(\mathfrak{u}, \mathfrak{a})=(\mathfrak{v}, \mathfrak{a})=\mathfrak{o}$, so folgt aus

$$\sum_{(\mathfrak{m},\mathfrak{a})=\mathfrak{o}}\frac{|\mu(\mathfrak{m})|}{N\mathfrak{m}E(\mathfrak{m})} < \infty$$

stets

$$\sum_{(\mathfrak{m},\mathfrak{a})=\mathfrak{o}}\frac{|\mu(\mathfrak{m})|}{N\mathfrak{m}E(\mathfrak{m})} \geqq \prod_{\mathfrak{p}\nmid\mathfrak{a}}\left(1-\frac{1}{N\mathfrak{p}E(\mathfrak{p})}\right) > 0.$$

Durch passende Spezialisierung folgt hieraus ein Satz von Heilbronn [loc. cit.], sogar in verallgemeinerter Form. 4. Schließlich wird noch ein Satz von Behrend [J. London Math. Soc. **10** (1935), 42–44] zu

$$\sum_{N\mathfrak{a}_i \leqq x}(N\mathfrak{a}_i)^{-1} < c(\mathsf{K})\log x(\log\log x)^{-1/2}$$

verallgemeinert, wo $\mathfrak{a}_1, \mathfrak{a}_2, \cdots$ eine Folge von Idealen aus $\mathsf{K}$ ist mit $\mathfrak{a}_i \nmid \mathfrak{a}_j$ für $i \neq j$. *H. Rohrbach* (Zbl **100**, 275)

Citations: MR 10, 104b = M55-5.

## M55-33 (29# 4740)

**Ankeny, N. C.; Onishi, H.**
**The general sieve.**
*Acta Arith.* **10** (1964/65), 31–62.

The authors derive both upper and lower bounds for a large class of sieve problems, on the basis of Selberg's method. Let $T$ be an infinite set of primes, and let $T_Y$ denote the set of all $p \in T$ with $p \leqq Y$. For each $N$ let $S_N$ be a given set of positive integers. With a fixed $\lambda>0$, it is required to obtain upper and lower bounds for $M(S_N, T_{N^\lambda})$, i.e., the number of integers $m \in S_N$ which are not divisible by any $p \in T_{N^\lambda}$.

In the following, $\alpha, \beta, \delta, C_1, C_2$ are fixed positive numbers. It is assumed that for each $N$ there exists a positive multiplicative function $f_N$ such that, for every square-free $d$, the number of $m$ with $m \in S_N$, $m \equiv 0 \pmod d$, equals $N(f_N(d))^{-1}+R_d(N)$, where $(f_N(p))^{-1}<1-\delta$ for all $p \in T$, and

$$\sum_{d \leqq N^\beta}(6\delta^{-2})^{\nu(d)}|R_d| = O(N(\log N)^{-\alpha-2})$$

$(\nu(d)$ represents the number of prime divisors of $d)$. Moreover, it is assumed that

$$\sum_{p<X} p(f_N(p))^{-1} < C_1X(\log X)^{-1} \quad \text{for } X < \log N,$$

$$\sum_{p<X} (p(f_N(p))^{-1}-\alpha) < C_2X(\log X)^{-2} \text{ for } \log N < X < N^{\lambda}.$$

With the abbreviation

$$B_\alpha(N) = \Gamma(\alpha)\prod(1-(f(p))^{-1})(1-p^{-1})^{-\alpha},$$

where $p$ runs through $T_{N^\lambda}$, the main result is as follows.

The expression

$$M(S_N, T_{N^\lambda})(B_\alpha(N))^{-1}N^{-1}(\log N)^\alpha$$

lies between positive bounds depending on $\alpha, \beta, \lambda$ only. The bounds which are actually obtained contain $J_\alpha(\beta/2\lambda)$ and $G_\alpha(\beta/2\lambda)$, where $J_\alpha$ and $G_\alpha$ are related to special solutions of the differential-difference equation

$$\tau'(u) = -u^{-1}\{\alpha\tau(u-1)-(\alpha-1)\tau(u)\}.$$

Some applications are given. Let $d_1, \cdots, d_a$ be distinct integers which do not form a complete set of residues for any prime, and $K(\chi)=\prod_{i=1}^a(\chi+d_i)$. Then if $a$ is sufficiently large, there exist infinitely many $n$ for which $\nu(K(n))<a(\log a+2)$. Another application is that if we assume the extended Riemann hypothesis, then there exist infinitely many primes $q$ such that $q+2$ has at most three prime factors.

{The reviewer was unable to check as many details as he wished, because of many minor errors and omissions. For example, the very crucial Lemma 3.1 is obscure in several respects, and instead of a proof, there is a reference that seems to be irrelevant.} *N. G. de Bruijn* (Eindhoven)

Referred to in M55-34, M55-37, M55-66, N08-40.

## M55-34 (31# 141)

**Ankeny, N. C.**

**Applications of the sieve.**

*Proc. Sympos. Pure Math., Vol. VIII, pp.* 113–118. *Amer. Math. Soc., Providence, R.I.*, 1965.

This paper contains, without proof, various statements of a general form of Selberg's sieve method. A more detailed version by the author and Onishi has appeared in Acta Arith. **10** (1964/65), 31–62 [MR **29** #4740]. The main contribution is a determination of some functions occurring in the upper and lower estimates by a difference-differential equation. Apart from special cases, these functions have not been known to the previous authors dealing with this subject. As to the applications, reference should be made to Y. Wang's papers [e.g., Theorem 2: Sci. Sinica **11** (1962), 1033–1054; MR **27** #1424; Theorem 3: ibid. **8** (1959), 357–381; MR **21** #4944; Theorem 4: ibid. **11** (1962), 1607–1624; MR **26** #3685], where both more general and stronger results have been proved.

*H.-E. Richert* (Marburg)

Citations: MR 21# 4944 = P32-41; MR 26# 3685 = N24-36; MR 29# 4740 = M55-33.

## M55-35 (29# 5806)

**Roth, K. F.**

**Remark concerning integer sequences.**

*Acta Arith.* **9** (1964), 257–260.

Let $N$ be a positive integer, and let $\mathcal{N}$ be a set of distinct positive integers not exceeding $N$. For each integer $m$, $0<m\leqq N$, and each residue class $h \pmod q$, denote by $\Phi_{q,h}(\mathcal{N}; m)$ the number of elements of $\mathcal{N}$ not exceeding $m$ and in the residue class, and by $\Phi_{q,h}^*(\mathcal{N}; m)$ the corresponding "expectation",

$$\Phi_{q,h}^*(\mathcal{N}; m) = \eta\Phi_{q,h}(\mathcal{I}; m),$$

where $\mathcal{I}$ is the set $\{1, \cdots, N\}$ and

$$\eta = N^{-1}\sum_{\substack{n\leqq N\\ n\in\mathcal{N}}} 1.$$

For each $m$ and $q$, define

$$V_q(m) = \sum_{h=1}^{q}\{\Phi_{q,h}(\mathcal{N}; m)-\Phi_{q,h}^*(\mathcal{N}; m)\}^2.$$

It is shown that for every positive integer $Q$,

$$\sum_{q=1}^{Q} q^{-1}\sum_{m=1}^{N} V_q(m)+Q\sum_{q=1}^{Q} V_q(N) > c\eta(1-\eta)Q^2N,$$

where $c$ is an absolute constant. Qualitatively and crudely speaking, this theorem shows that unless a sequence of integers has density nearly 0 or 1, its elements cannot be too evenly distributed simultaneously among all residue classes. *W. J. LeVeque* (Ann Arbor, Mich.)

## M55-36 (30# 1994)

**van Lint, J. H.; Richert, H.-E.**

**Über die Summe** $\sum_{\substack{n\leqq x\\ p(n)<y}} \frac{\mu^2(n)}{\varphi(n)}$.

*Nederl. Akad. Wetensch. Proc. Ser. A* **67** = *Indag. Math.* **26** (1964), 582–587.

In the sum $S$ (say) specified in the title, $p(n)$ for $n>1$ denotes the largest prime divisor of $n$ and $p(1)=1$; $\mu$ and $\varphi$ denote, respectively, the functions of Möbius and Euler. Writing $u=\log x/\log y$ and introducing the function $d(u)=u$ $(0\leqq u\leqq 1)$, $\{u^{-1}d(u)\}'=u^{-2}d(u-1)$ (if $u\geqq 1$), the authors prove that $S=d(u)\log y+O(1)$. The proof rests on results of de Bruijn [same Proc. **54** (1951), 50–60; MR **13**, 724; J. Indian Math. Soc. (N.S.) **15** (1951), 25–32; MR **13**, 326] and Wang [Acta Math. Sinica **6** (1956), 565–582; MR **20** #4530]. The sum $S$ plays an important rôle in applications of the sieve method of A. Selberg. *E. Fogels* (Riga)

Citations: MR 13, 326f = N28-26; MR 13, 724e = N28-28; MR 20# 4530 = P32-38.

## M55-37 (31# 4774)

**Levin, B. V.**

**A one-dimensional sieve. (Russian)**

*Acta Arith.* **10** (1964/65), 387–397.

The author continues his investigations [see, e.g., Mat. Sb. (N.S.) **61 (103)** (1963), 389–407; MR **30** #1991] into the application of sieve methods to additive and related problems in prime number theory, and states many interesting theorems. As before, he combines the Selberg sieve (augmented by the Kuhn device) with Barban's elaboration of Linnik's large sieve [ibid. (N.S.) **61** (**103**), (1963), 418–425; MR **30** #1992]. All the results depend critically on this latter work of Barban, which does not appear to the reviewer to be available for checking. Actually, it follows from new work of E. Bombieri [to appear in Mathematika], and probably also from K. F. Roth's large sieve [Mathematika **12** (1965), 1–9], that

$$(*) \quad \sum_{d\leqq x^{1/2-\varepsilon}} \mu^2(d) \max_{\substack{l \pmod D\\ (l,D)=1}} \left| \sum_{\substack{n\leqq x\\ n\equiv l \pmod D}} \Lambda(n)-\frac{x}{\phi(D)}\right| = O\left(\frac{x}{(\log x)^A}\right)$$

for arbitrarily large $A$, and analogous results of the kind required by the author (e.g., formulae (1) and (3)) can be derived in the same way and in sharper form (so far as the size of $\alpha$ in these formulae is concerned). The result (*) is also claimed in a recent paper of A. I. Vinogradov [Izv. Akad. Nauk Ser. Mat. **29** (1965), 903–935], but appears again to depend on Barban's approach. For recent work on the sieve, see also Ankeny and Onishi [Acta Arith. **10** (1964/65), 31–62; MR **29** #4740] and Jurkat and Richert [ibid. **11** (1965), 217–240]. P'an Ch'eng-tung [Acta Math. Sinica **14** (1964), 597–606; MR **30** #3871] proves weaker results of type (*) and criticises Barban's work. However, the accuracy of P'an Ch'eng-tung's own work has been called in question. *H. Halberstam* (Nottingham)

Citations: MR 29# 4740 = M55-33; MR 30# 1991 = P32-62; MR 30# 1992 = P32-63; MR 30# 3871 = N12-31.

Referred to in N32-47.

## M55-38 (32# 5625)

**Wunderlich, M. C.**

**Sieve-generated sequences.**

*Canad. J. Math.* **18** (1966), 291–299.

The author generalises and completes previous work of Briggs [Duke Math. J. **30** (1963), 297–311; MR **26** #6145], the reviewer and Jabotinsky [Indag. Math. **20** (1958), 115–128; MR **21** #2628], and Gardiner, Lazarus, Metropolis and Ulam [Math. Mag. **29** (1956), 117–122; MR **17**, 711].

He defines a sieve-generated sequence as follows. Put $A^{(1)}=\{2, 3, \cdots\}$. Assume that $A^{(1)}, \cdots, A^{(n)}=\{a_1^{(n)}, \cdots\}$ have already been defined. Define $A^{(n+1)}$ as follows. For each integer $t\geqq 0$, choose an arbitrary element $a_l^{(n)}$ from the set $\{a^{(n)}_{n+ta_n+1}, a^{(n)}_{n+ta_n+2}, \cdots, a^{(n)}_{n+ta_n+a_n}\}$, where $a_n=a_n^{(n)}$. Delete the elements $a_l^{(n)}$ from $A^{(n)}$ to form $A^{(n+1)}$. The sequence $A=\{a_n\}$ is called sieve-generated.

The author obtains a necessary and sufficient condition for the truth of the limit relation $a_n=(1+o(1))n \log n$. He also proves some further theorems and raises some questions. *P. Erdős* (Budapest)

Citations: MR 17, 711b = M55-14; MR 21# 2628 = M55-19; MR 26# 6145 = M55-26.

Referred to in M55-47, M55-51, M55-59.

## M55-39 (32# 7534)

**Levin, B. V.**

**Comparison of A. Selberg's and V. Brun's sieves. (Russian)**

*Uspehi Mat. Nauk* **20** (1965), *no.* 5 (125), 214–220.

Für eine Folge $\{a_n\}$ sei $I_1(N, N^{1/\delta})$ die Anzahl der $a_n$, $n\leqq N$, mit der Eigenschaft, daß keine Primzahl $p\leqq N^{1/\delta}$ in $a_n$ aufgeht. Zur Abschätzung von $I_1(N, N^{1/\delta})$ nach oben und nach unten wird eine allgemeine Siebmethode beschrieben, die als Spezialfälle die Siebe von Eratosthenes, Brun und Selberg enthält.

Der Autor zeigt an Hand expliziter Abschätzungen, daß für kleine $\delta$ das Selberg'sche, für große $\delta$ hingegen das Brun'sche Sieb bessere Ergebnisse liefert; hierbei stützt er sich auf eigene frühere Arbeiten [Trudy Taškent. Gos. Univ. **228** (1963), 56–58; Mat. Sb. **61** (**103**) (1963), 389–407; MR **30** #1991]. Unter geeigneten Voraussetzungen wird schließlich (für $N\to\infty$) eine asymptotische Formel für $I_1(N, N^{1/\delta})$ gegeben, wenn $\delta=\delta(N)$ mit $N$ gegen $\infty$ strebt. *W. Schwarz* (Freiburg)

Citations: MR 30# 1991 = P32-62.

## M55-40 (33# 109)

**Barban, M. B.**

**On a theorem of P. Bateman, S. Chowla and P. Erdős. (Russian. English summary)**

*Magyar Tud. Akad. Mat. Kutató Int. Közl.* **9** (1964), 429–435 (1965).

The author gives a simple proof of the following "large sieve" inequality. Theorem: Let $\{a_n\}$ denote an increasing sequence of natural numbers, let $A(x)=\sum_{a_n\leqq x} 1$ and $A(x; p, l)=\sum_{a_n\leqq x, a_n\equiv l(p)} 1$, where $p$ denotes a prime number. Then for $1<M<x$ and $1<B<\min(M, x/M)$,

$$\sum_{p\leqq M} p \sum_{l=0}^{p-1}\left(A(x; p, l)-\frac{A(x)}{p}\right)^2 \leqq 2\pi A(x)\frac{M}{B}+A^2(x)\frac{B^2}{M}.$$

The author applies this inequality to give another proof of a result of Val'fiš [Trudy Tbiliss. Mat. Inst. **11** (1942), 57–71; MR **5**, 254; also S. Chowla, Proc. Nat. Inst. Sci. India **13** (1947), 197–200; MR **10**, 285] and of a result of S. Chowla [Proc. London Math. Soc. (2) **50** (1949), 423–429; MR **10**, 285], namely, $\lim\sup_{p\to\infty} L(1, \chi_p)/\log\log p\geqq e^\gamma$ and $\lim\inf_{p\to\infty} L(1, \chi_p)\log\log p\leqq \pi^2 e^{-\gamma}/6$, where $p$ denotes a prime number and $\chi_p$ is the quadratic character (mod $p$).

{The character $\chi_D$ on page 432 must be read as $\chi_q$.} *E. Bombieri* (Sardinia)

Citations: MR 5, 254i = E16-5; MR 10, 285d = M20-4.

## M55-41 (33# 2591)

**Bezborodnikov, M. F.**

**A multiple generalized sieve and certain of its applications. (Russian)**

*Volž. Mat. Sb. Vyp.* 1 (1963), 232–237.

The author describes an Eratosthenian-type-sieve for the determination of the primes $p\leqq x$, $p\equiv a_j \bmod b_j$ $(j=1, \cdots, s)$. An example is worked out (with $x=250$, $s=2$). The paper concludes with some heuristic remarks concerning, among other things, prime twins. *W. Schwarz* (Freiburg)

## M55-42 (33# 5589)

**Roth, K. F.**

**On the large sieves of Linnik and Rényi.**

*Mathematika* **12** (1965), 1–9.

Let $n_1, n_2, \cdots, n_Z$ be a non-empty set of integers in the interval $[1, N]$, and for any prime $p$, denote by $Z(p, h)$ the number of elements $n_i\equiv h \pmod p$. Let $D(p)=\sum_{h=0}^{p-1}(Z(p, h)-Z/p)^2$, so that $D(p)$ measures the regularity of distribution of the sequence $\{n_j\}$ among the residue classes mod $p$. Let $X\geqq 2$, and let $\mathscr{P}$ denote a set of distinct primes $p\leqq X$, containing $P$ elements. The author proves that there exists a positive absolute constant $c$ such that, for every number $R\geqq 2$, $\sum_{p\in\mathscr{P}} pD(p)\leqq c(ZN+ZX^2\log R+Z^2PR^{-2})$. In particular, if $N\geqq 2$ and $X\geqq (N/\log N)^{1/2}$, $\sum_{p\leqq X} pD(p)\ll ZX^2\log X$. This important theorem is the culmination of a sequence of "large sieves" initiated by Linnik and continued by Rényi. To indicate its accuracy, take $\{n_i\}$ to be the sequence of odd integers not exceeding $N$, and $\mathscr{P}$ the set of all primes $\leqq (N/\log N)^{1/2}$; the contribution from $p=2$ alone to the sum on the left is at least $\frac{1}{4}N^2$, whereas the right-hand side is of the order $N^2$. Thus the theorem of Roth is virtually best possible. Previously, a result of this quality (due to Rényi) had been available only for the shorter "sifting" set $p\leqq N^{1/3}$. A simple account of the Linnik-Rényi theory is given in Chapter IV of *Sequences*, Vol. I [Clarendon Press, Oxford, 1966] by the reviewer and the author. The theorem is of remarkable generality; it tells one (for a precise formulation see Corollary 2) that for all but a few exceptional primes $p\leqq N^{1/2}$, any sequence $\{n_j\}$ of integers in $[1, N]$ is well-distributed among all but a few residue classes $h$ (mod $p$). Apart from its intrinsic interest, the large sieve concept found powerful application in Rényi's proof of the quasi-Goldbach conjecture [Izv. Akad. Nauk SSSR Ser. Mat. **12** (1948), 57–78; MR **9**, 413; English translation, Amer. Math. Soc. Transl. (2) **19** (1962), 299–321; MR **24** #A1264] and has played a similar part in more recent attempts to sharpen Rényi's result. There have been other applications, and there will be many more.

Some important developments of the large sieve concept, with striking applications, have recently been discovered by E. Bombieri [#5590 below]. The basis of the author's method is the construction, by iteration, of a trigonometric function $\Psi(\alpha)=\sum_{m=-\infty}^{\infty} d_m e^{2\pi i\alpha m}$ ($d_m=d_{-m}$) which has the following properties: it is 0 unless $|\alpha|<\eta$ (mod 1), where $\eta=\frac{1}{2}X^{-2}$; $\sum |d_m|$ is convergent and $|d_m-1|<R^{-1}$ for $1\leqq m\leqq N$; and $\int_0^1 \Psi^2(\alpha)\,d\alpha \ll \eta^{-1}\log R+N$. With the help of $\Psi$, the author constructs an orthogonal sequence which leads, in the manner of Rényi's approach, to a Bessel inequality; this, in turn, translates into the inequality of the main result.

{See also #5592 below.} *H. Halberstam* (Nottingham)

Citations: MR 9, 413g = P32-12; MR 24# A1264 = P32-13; MR 33# 5592 = M55-45; MR 35# 1565 = B02-3.

Referred to in E16-82, M55-62.

## M55-43 (33# 5590)

**Bombieri, E.**

**On the large sieve.**

*Mathematika* **12** (1965), 201–225.

The grand, or generalized, Riemann hypothesis asserts that the real parts of all zeros of all Dirichlet $L$-functions $L(s,\chi)$ are at most $\frac{1}{2}$. If this were true, it would follow that, for $(a,q)=1$,

$$(1)\qquad E(x;q,a) = \sum_{\substack{n\leqq x\\ n\equiv a(\mathrm{mod}\, q)}} \Lambda(n)-\frac{x}{\phi(q)} = O(x^{1/2}(\log x)^2)$$

uniformly in $q$; but the best result known at the present time (uniform in $q$) is the Siegel-Walfisz theorem according to which, given any positive number $N$, there exists a constant $c=c(N)>0$ such that, if $q\leqq(\log x)^N$, then $E(x;q,a)=O(x\exp(-c(\log x)^{1/2}))$ uniformly in $q$. The Siegel-Walfisz theorem has proved to be adequate for some important applications, notably for Vinogradov's three primes theorem; but there are many problems in analytic number theory which depend in a natural way on $E(x;q,a)$ being small uniformly in $q$ for $q$ belonging to longer ranges of type $q\leqq x^\alpha$ $(0<\alpha<1)$. With such problems little progress was possible, except where the dependence on $E(x;q,a)$ was circumvented by the invention of new methods—Linnik's "dispersion method" is an outstanding example that springs to mind. One important area where the lack was felt especially keenly was the application of sieve methods to binary additive problems of Goldbach's type; and here it came to be realised [see, e.g., Wang Yuan, Sci. Sinica **11** (1962), 1033–1054, Appendix; MR **27** #1424] that substantial progress was possible on the basis of weaker mean value results of the type

$$(2)\qquad \sum_{q\leqq x^{\alpha-\varepsilon}} \max_{(a,q)=1} |E(x;q,a)| = O(x(\log x)^{-A}),$$

with $A>0$ free to be chosen as large as required. For example, Buhštab [Dokl. Akad. Nauk SSSR **162** (1965), 735–738; MR **31** #2226] has shown recently that if (2) holds with $\alpha=\frac{3}{8}$, then every sufficiently large even number is the sum of a prime and an integer having at most three prime factors (this paper appears to contain at least one serious misprint, and many important steps in the proof are omitted). A result (2) of this quality (with $\alpha=\frac{3}{8}$) has actually been claimed, by Barban [Mat. Sb. (N.S.) **61** (**103**) (1963), 418–425; MR **30** #1992] and P'an Ch'eng-tung [Acta Math. Sinica **13** (1963), 262–268; translated as Chinese Math.—Acta **4** (1963), 233–290; MR **29** #82; ibid. **14** (1964), 597–606; translated as Chinese Math.—Acta **5** (1964), 642–652; MR **30** #3871] but an account of this work that is even partially satisfactory does not appear (to this reviewer) to be available in print—a truly remarkable circumstance in view of its importance. Be that as it may, the author of this paper has made a notable contribution to analytic number theory by proving, in convincing detail, that (2) holds with $\alpha=\frac{1}{2}$. Actually, in his Theorem 4 the author proves the even better result that, for any given $A>0$, there exists a constant $B$ ($B=3A+23$ will do) such that, if $X\leqq x^{1/2}(\log x)^{-B}$,

$$(3)\qquad \sum_{q\leqq X} \max_{y\leqq x} \max_{(a,q)=1} |E(y;q,a)| = O(x(\log x)^{-A}).$$

Starting out from K. F. Roth's [#5589 above] recent far-reaching improvement of the Linnik-Rényi large sieve, the author first reproves Roth's result (in slightly sharper form, but the extent of this improvement is not relevant to the author's main purpose), and, in fact, generalises it to a form which leads to this remarkable inequality for averages of character sums: For any complex numbers $a_n$, and any finite set $Q$ of positive integers,

$$(4)\qquad \sum_{q\in Q} \frac{1}{\phi(q)} \sum_{\chi} |\tau(\chi)|^2 \left|\sum_{Y<n\leqq Z} \chi(n)a_n\right|^2 \leqq 7D\max(Z-Y, M^2) \sum_{Y<n\leqq Z} d(n)|a_n|^2,$$

where, in the inner sum, $\chi$ runs through all characters mod $q$, $\tau(\chi)=\sum_{a=1}^{q}\chi(a)\exp(2\pi ia/q)$, $M=\max_{q\in Q} q$, and $D=\max_{q\in Q} d(q)$, with $d(n)$ denoting, as usual, the divisor function.

This inequality, of considerable interest in itself, is the author's principal technical innovation in a method which, otherwise, uses with great skill and power the classical analytic techniques described in Prachar's *Primzahlverteilung* [Springer, Berlin, 1957; MR **19**, 393], especially those of Chapter IX. The main argument is directed towards what the author justly calls a new type of density theorem for zeros of $L$-functions (and the importance of (4) may be judged from the fact that (4) is used several times, in different contexts and with different coefficient sets $a_n$, in the course of the argument): If $N(\alpha,T;\chi)$ denotes the number of zeros of $L(s,\chi)$ in the rectangle $\alpha\leqq\sigma\leqq 1$, $|t|\leqq T$ ($\frac{1}{2}\leqq\alpha\leqq 1$, $T\geqq 2$), then

$$\sum_{q\in Q}\frac{1}{\phi(q)}\sum_{\chi}|\tau(\chi)|^2 N(\alpha,T;\chi) = O(DT(M^2+MT)^{4(1-\alpha)/(3-2\alpha)}\log^{10}(M+T))$$

uniformly with respect to $Q$. (The author conjectures that even $\sum_{q\leqq X}\sum_{\chi}{}^{*} N(\alpha,T;\chi)=O(X^{4(1-\alpha)+\varepsilon}T^{1+\varepsilon})$, uniformly in $\alpha$, $\frac{1}{2}\leqq\alpha\leqq 1$, where the asterisk indicates summation over primitive characters mod $q$.)

The step from the density theorem to (3) is carried out in Section 3, using the Siegel-Walfisz theorem (to deal with small $q$) and the classical explicit formula for $\sum_{n\leqq x}\chi(n)\Lambda(n)$ in terms of the zeros of $L(s,\chi)$. It should be noted that applying (1) to the left-hand side of (3) (with $X=x^{1/2}(\log x)^{-B}$) leads to the estimate $x(\log x)^{-B+2}$, a result, for all practical purposes, no better than (3). Thus Bombieri's theorem leads to a result as good on average as (1). Without a doubt, many important results will follow from his theorem; moreover, his density theorem and extension of the Linnik-Rényi-Roth large sieve

should both lead to interesting developments.
{See also #5591 and #5592 below.}

*H. Halberstam* (Nottingham)

Citations: MR 19, 393b = N02-7; MR 27# 1424 = P32-50; MR 29# 82 = M25-56; MR 30# 1992 = P32-63; MR 30# 3871 = N12-31; MR 31# 2226 = P40-17.

Referred to in D68-29, E16-77, E16-82, M25-69, M25-80, M25-87, M55-52, M55-53, M55-56, M55-62, M55-64, M55-70, N02-6, N02-13, N08-43, N12-48, N32-59, N52-40, P36-50, P40-25, P48-10, P48-16, P52-12, R44-41, R46-26, R46-32, Z10-34, Z10-41.

## M55-44 (33# 5591 )

**Bombieri, Enrico**

**On the large sieve.**

Collectanea Mathematica. Pubblicazioni dell'Istituto di Matematica dell'Università di Milano, N. 281.
*Tamburini Editore, Milan,* 1965. 29 *pp.*

A more complete version has been published [#5590 above].

## M55-45 (33# 5592 )

**Davenport, H.; Halberstam, H.**

**The values of a trigonometrical polynomial at well spaced points.**

*Mathematika* **13** (1966), 91–96.

Theorem 1: Let $a_{-N}, \cdots, a_N$ be any complex numbers and let $S(x)=\sum_{n=-N}^{N} a_n e(nx)$, where $e(\theta)=e^{2\pi i\theta}$. Let $x_1, x_2, \cdots, x_R$ $(R\geqq 2)$ be any real numbers and define $\delta=\min_{j\neq k}\|x_j-x_k\|$, where $\|\theta\|$ denotes the distance from $\theta$ to the nearest integer. Then

$$\sum_{r=1}^{R} |S(x_r)|^2 \leqq 2.2 \max(\delta^{-1}, 2N) \sum_{n=-N}^{N} |a_n|^2.$$

As the authors point out, they were led to Theorem 1 by a study of the papers of K. F. Roth [see #5589 above] and Bombieri [see #5590 above]. By means of Theorem 1 above they also obtain sharper versions of Bombieri's Theorems 2 and 3. *L. Carlitz* (Durham, N.C.)

Referred to in M55-42, M55-46, M55-56, M55-62, M55-67, M55-68, M55-70, M55-80, N02-13, N12-40, R46-28.

## M55-46 (36# 2569 )

**Davenport, H.; Halberstam, H.**

**Corrigendum and addendum: "The values of a trigonometrical polynomial at well spaced points".**

*Mathematika* **14** (1967), 229–232.

The authors note that the proof of Theorem 3 of their paper in Mathematika **13** (1966), 91–96 [MR **33** #5592] is incorrect. The present paper contains a proof of the following modified version of the theorem: For any character $\chi(\mathrm{mod}\ q)$ let $\tau(\chi)=\sum_{m=1}^{q}\chi(m)e(m/q)$ and let the $a_n$ be any complex numbers. Then

$$\sum_{q\leqq X} (1/\phi(q)) \sum_{\chi} |\tau(\chi)|^2 |\sum_{n=Y+1}^{Y+U} \chi(n)a_n| < 2.3(\log X)\max(U, X^2) \sum_{Y+1}^{Y+U} |a_n|^2,$$

provided $X$ is greater than some numerical constant.

*L. Carlitz* (Durham, N.C.)

Citations: MR 33# 5592 = M55-45.

Referred to in E16-82, M55-62, M55-67, M55-68, M55-70, N02-13, N12-41, R46-28.

## M55-47 (34# 153 )

**Wunderlich, M. C.; Briggs, W. E.**

**Second and third term approximations of sieve-generated sequences.**

*Illinois J. Math.* **10** (1966), 694–700.

Continuing earlier investigations [the second author, Duke Math. J. **30** (1963), 297–311; MR **26** #6145; the first author, Canad. J. Math. **18** (1966), 291–299; MR **32** #5625], the authors define a sieve process as follows. Put $A^{(1)}=\{2, 3, 4, \cdots\}$, and obtain $A^{(k+1)}$ from $A^{(k)}=\{a_n^{(k)}, n=1, 2, \cdots\}$ by omitting from each "block" $\{a_{k+1+ta_k}^{(k)}, \cdots, a_{k+a_k+ta_k}^{(k)}\}$, $t=0, 1, 2, \cdots$, one (freely chosen) element $\alpha_t^{(k)}$. Put $B=\{b_n: n=1, 2, \cdots\}=\bigcap_{k=1}^{\infty} A^{(k)}$, and $r_k=n-k$, where $a_n^{(k)}$ is the smallest element eliminated from $A^{(k)}$ in forming $A^{(k+1)}$. The authors are interested in asymptotic formulae for $b_n$, depending on certain assumptions on $r_n$. For instance, they prove: If $r_k=\beta k(1+\rho(k))$, where $\beta>0$, $\rho(k)=o(1)$ and $\rho(\alpha k)\sim\rho(k)$ for constant $\alpha$ and $k\to\infty$, then (for $n\to\infty$)

$$b_n = n\{\log n+(c_1(\beta)+o(1))\rho(n)\log n+ (c_2(\beta)+o(1))\textstyle\sum_{2\leqq k\leqq n}\rho(k)/k+O(\log\log n)^2\}.$$

*W. Schwarz* (Freiburg)

Citations: MR 26# 6145 = M55-26; MR 32# 5625 = M55-38.

Referred to in M55-51.

## M55-48 (34# 2540 )

**Jurkat, W. B.; Richert, H.-E.**

**An improvement of Selberg's sieve method. I.**

*Acta Arith.* **11** (1965), 217–240.

Let $M$ denote a finite set of natural numbers, and $M_d$ the set consisting of all multiples from $M$ of a positive integer $d$. Assume the existence of a real number $y>1$ such that, for any $d$ coprime with a certain integer $k$ (in practice, $k$ is a number characteristic of the structure of $M$), $(H_k)$ $\big||M_d|-y/d\big|\leqq 1$, where $|M_d|$ denotes the number of elements of $M_d$ (in practice, $y$ is close to $|M|$). The authors set out to sift $M$ by the "sieve" consisting of all primes less than $z$ that are not factors of $k$. Writing $A_k(M; z)$ for the number of elements of $M$ that are coprime with $P_k(z)=\prod_{p<z, p\nmid k} p$, the authors prove the following theorem (Theorem 5): If $z\leqq y$, there exists a positive constant $c$ such that

$$f(\log y/\log z)-c\log\log 3k/(\log y)^{1/14} \leqq y^{-1}\prod_{p<z, p\nmid k}(1-1/p)^{-1}\cdot A_k(M; z) \leqq F(\log y/\log z)+c\log\log 3k/(\log y)^{1/14},$$

where, if $\omega(u)$, $\rho(u)$ are the well-known functions arising as solutions of the differential-difference equations $(u\omega(u))'=\omega(u-1)$, $(u-1)\rho'(u)=-\rho(u-1)$ $(u\geqq 2)$; $\omega(u)=u^{-1}$, $\rho(u)=1$ $(0<u\leqq 2)$, then $F(u)=e^{\gamma}\{\omega(u)+\rho(u)/u\}$, $f(u)=e^{\gamma}\{\omega(u)-\rho(u)/u\}$ $(u>0)$.

By virtue of the condition $(H_k)$, the sieve problem considered is rather a special one, but for it the above theorem represents the sharpest solution known to date, as well as the simplest and most elegant. The authors give various applications displaying the accuracy of their method; for example, they show that for $\varepsilon>0$, $k\geqq k_0(\varepsilon)$, $(k, l)=1$, there exists an integer $n\equiv l \pmod k$, $1\leqq n\leqq k^{25/11+\varepsilon}$, having at most two prime factors. The exponent $25/11$ improves on the previous record $7/2$ [S. Uchiyama, J. Fac. Sci. Hokkaido Univ. Ser. I **18** (1964), 1–22; MR **30** #1108].

The authors' method may be said to be a synthesis of all existing sieve techniques—even the old method of Eratosthenes-Legendre has a place, serving as it does to "spark off" the sieving process (see beginnings of proofs of Theorems 3 and 5). The upper bound method of Selberg, of course, plays a central part (see Theorem 2); by means of it, and using also the Buhštab identity (for $z_0<z$) (1) $A_k(M; z)=A_k(M; z_0)-\sum_{z_0\leqq p<z; p\nmid k} A_k(M_p; p)$ as well as a non-trivial estimate for $\Psi(x, z)$, the number of integers $\leqq x$

made up of primes $<z$, the authors show (in Theorem 3) that (2): $y^{-1}\prod_{p<z;\,p\nmid k}(1-1/p)^{-1}\cdot A_k(M;z)$ is $\leqq 1+O(\exp(-\log y/\log z))$, $1\leqq \log z\leqq \log y$, and $=1+O(1/\log y)$, $\log z\leqq \log y/(2\log\log 3y)$. But then the authors return to the combinatorial approach of V. Brun and A. A. Buhštab, and, by iteration of (1), they derive the identity, valid for all positive integers $r$, $2\leqq z_1\leqq z\leqq \sqrt{y}$, (3) $A_k(M;z)-A_k(M;z_1)=\sum_{1\leqq i\leqq r-1}(-1)^i\sum^1 A_k(M_{p_1\cdots p_i};z_1)+(-1)^r\sum^1 A_k(M_{p_1\cdots p_r};p_r)+\sum_{1\leqq i\leqq r}(-1)^i\sum^2 A_k(M_{p_1\cdots p_i};p_i)$, where the summation conditions in $\sum^1$ are $z_1\leqq p_i<\cdots<p_1<z$; $p_j<\sqrt{y_j}$, $p_j\nmid k$ $(j=1,\cdots,i)$, and in $\sum^2$ are $z_1\leqq p_i<\cdots<p_1<z$; $p_j<\sqrt{y_j}$, $p_j\nmid k$ $(j=1,\cdots,i-1)$, $\sqrt{y_i}\leqq p_i<y_i$, $p_i\nmid k$ (we have used the notation $y_j=y/(p_1\cdots p_j)$). They match this identity by a relation between $f$, $F$ possessing a precisely similar structure (apart from an error term in the latter) and, on subtraction, arrive at an expression for

$$(-1)^\nu\{A_k(M;z)-y\prod_{p<z;\,p\nmid k}(1-1/p)\cdot g_\nu(\log y/\log z)\},$$

where $g_\nu$ is $F$ or $f$ according as $\nu$ is even or odd. The theorem follows on showing that the expression is sufficiently small. Now the expression is the sum of terms of the form

$$(4)\quad (-1)^{\nu+i}\{A_k(M_{p_1\cdots p_i};\theta)-y_i\prod_{p<p_i;\,p\nmid k}(1-1/p)\cdot g_{\nu+i}(\log y_i/\log\theta)\},$$

where $\theta=p_i$ or $z_1$ (cf. (3)), and the various parameters are so chosen that these terms arise only when $\log y_i/\log\theta$ is large or small. It turns out that (2) suffices for the estimation of all the terms (4), and that a special problem arising from the second sum on the right of (3) is settled by the important but simple Lemma 5.2. In this way, even though $r$ (in (3)) has to be chosen large, the authors succeed in arriving at their main theorem in a manner which, while hardly simple, is yet more accurate and at the same time much less involved than the calculations to which one has grown to be accustomed in this context.

Finally, when it comes to applications, the authors make use of the well-known Kuhn device. At this stage some numerical computation is inevitable, but the precision of the authors' analysis has kept this down to a minimum. A full bibliography is appended.

*H. Halberstam* (Nottingham)

Citations: MR 30# 1108 = N24-52.
Referred to in M55-55, M55-66, N24-65, N28-75.

## M55-49 (34# 4235)

**Roth, K. F.**
**Irregularities of sequences relative to arithmetic progressions.**
*Math. Ann.* **169** (1967), 1–25.

The following two theorems are proved. (i) Let $k$ be a natural number and suppose that the integer $N$ satisfies $N>(10k)^7$. Then, for every set $s_1,\cdots,s_N$ of real numbers, there exist integers $n$, $q$ satisfying (*) $1\leqq n<n+(k-1)q\leqq N$, such that $|\sum_{\nu=0}^{k-1}s_{n+\nu q}|\geqq\{k(10N)^{-1}\sum_{j=1}^N s_j^2\}^{1/2}$. (ii) Let $\Lambda\geqq 1$ and let $k$ be an integer satisfying $k>10^8\Lambda^4$. Then there exists a number $N_1$ such that the following statement is true: if $N>N_1$ and the set $s_1,\cdots,s_N$ of real numbers satisfies $1\leqq|s_j|\leqq\Lambda$ $(j=1,\cdots,N)$ and $\sum_{j=1}^N s_j=0$, then there exist integers $n$, $q$ satisfying (*) such that

$$\sum_{\nu=0}^{k-1}s_{n+\nu q}>\{10^{-4}\Lambda^{-2}\sum_{\nu=0}^{k-1}s_{n+\nu q}^2\}^{1/2}.$$

*G. Goes* (Chicago, Ill.)

Referred to in M55-50, M55-63.

## M55-50 (36# 134)

**Roth, K. F.**
**Irregularities of sequences relative to arithmetic progressions. II.**
*Math. Ann.* **174** (1967), 41–52.

This paper continues [for Part I, see the author, same Ann. **169** (1967), 1–25; MR **34** #4235] the investigation of the following conjecture A: If a strictly increasing sequence of natural numbers has positive asymptotic density then it contains arbitrarily long arithmetic progressions. The purpose of this paper is, in the author's words, "partly to discuss the relationship between conjecture A and the second theorem of Part I and partly to obtain a refinement relevant in this connection". This refinement contains this second theorem of Part I as a special case. It is also shown that conjecture A has an equivalent counterpart relating to finite sequences.

*G. Goes* (Chicago, Ill.)

Citations: MR 34# 4235 = M55-49.
Referred to in B24-31, M55-63.

## M55-51 (35# 2855)

**Buschman, R. G.; Wunderlich, M. C.**
**Sieve-generated sequences with translated intervals.**
*Canad. J. Math.* **19** (1967), 559–570.

The authors are interested in certain sieve processes, yielding subsequences $\{a_1,a_2,\cdots\}$ of the set of natural numbers which behave (asymptotically) like the sequence of primes. Sieve processes of this sort were given by W. E. Briggs [Duke Math. J. **30** (1963), 297–312; MR **26** #6145], the second author [Canad. J. Math. **18** (1966), 291–299; MR **32** #5625], and the second author and W. E. Briggs [Illinois J. Math. **10** (1966), 694–700; MR **34** #153]. The authors define a similar sieve, depending on a given function $\alpha_n$ of $n$; thereby the element $a_n$ of the resulting sequence $\{a_1,a_2,\cdots\}$ depends only on $\alpha_1,\cdots,\alpha_{n-1}$. First a "Tchebycheff-theorem" is proved: If $n^{-1}\alpha_n>1+\varepsilon$, $n^{-1}\alpha_n\nearrow$ and $\log\alpha_n<r\log n$, then $a_n(n\log n)^{-1}$ is bounded above and below by positive constants. If $\alpha_n=c(a_n)^a(\log a_n)^b-n$, $1<a<e$, $c>0$, then the asymptotic formula $a_n\sim n\log n$ is obtained.

Finally, the authors are interested in a second term of this asymptotic formula. They prove that if $\alpha_n\sim c(a_n)^a(\log a_n)^b$, and if $a_n-n\log n\sim An(\log\log n)^B$, $B>0$, then $B=1$.

*W. Schwarz* (Freiburg)

Citations: MR 26# 6145 = M55-26; MR 32# 5625 = M55-38; MR 34# 153 = M55-47.

## M55-52 (35# 5411)

**Gallagher, P. X.**
**The large sieve.**
*Mathematika* **14** (1967), 14–20.

Put $S(\alpha)=\sum_{M<n\leqq M+N}a_n\exp(2\pi in\alpha)$; the author gives a very simple proof of Bombieri's inequality [E. Bombieri, Mathematika **12** (1965), 201–225; MR **33** #5590] $\sum_{q\leqq Q}\sum_{1\leqq a\leqq q;(a,q)=1}|S(a/q)|^2\ll(Q^2+N)\sum_{M<n\leqq M+N}|a_n|^2$. This inequality leads immediately to Bombieri's version of the "large sieve". As an application, the author proves that in any interval of length $N$, the number of integers which are primitive roots for no primes $p\leqq N^{1/2}$ is $O(N^{1/2}\log N)$. {Reviewer's remark: Assuming Riemann's hypothesis for the zeta function of certain algebraic number fields, C. Hooley [J. Reine Angew. Math. **225** (1967), 209–220; MR **34** #7445] proved Artin's conjecture.}

Further, the author improves on H. Davenport and H. Halberstam's estimate [Michigan Math. J. **13** (1966), 485–489; MR **34** #156] for $\sum_{q\leqq Q}\sum_{(a,q)=1}(\psi(N;q,a)-N/\varphi(q))^2$; finally, he derives (for $|t|\leqq T$) an estimate for the fourth mean of $L$-functions: $\sum_{q\leq Q}\sum^*_{\chi \bmod q}|L(\frac{1}{2}+it;\chi)|^4 \ll Q^2\times T^2\log^4 QT$, where * means summation over primitive characters. *W. Schwarz* (Freiburg)

Citations: MR 33# 5590 = M55-43; MR 34# 156 = N12-40; MR 34# 7445 = N76-18.

Referred to in E16-82, M55-62, M55-64, M55-73, N02-13, N12-49, N16-36, N24-68, R46-32.

## M55-53 (36# 1413)

**Buhštab, A. A.**

**Combinatorial strengthening of the sieve of Eratosthenes method. (Russian)**

*Uspehi Mat. Nauk* **22** (1967), *no.* 3 (135), 199–226.

Let $P(x, q, y)$ denote the number of members of a given sequence of positive integers that do not exceed $x$, are divisible by $q$, and are not divisible by any prime less than $y$. Heuristic arguments give

$$(*)\quad E = 2e^{-C}\prod_{p\neq 2}(1-(p-1)^{-2}) \times (\alpha\,\mathrm{li}\,x/\phi(q)\log y)\prod_{p|q;\,p\neq 2}(p-1)/(p-2)$$

as an approximation to $P(x, q, y)$, where $C$ is Euler's constant, and $p$ always denotes a prime. The author defines by iterative processes two functions $\Lambda(\alpha)$ and $\lambda(\alpha)$ that are essentially upper and lower bounds for $\alpha P(x, q, y)/E$. For $\alpha\geqq 5$ these two functions take values very close to $\alpha$, but this ceases to hold for smaller values of $\alpha$; for $\alpha=2.5$, $\Lambda(\alpha)=3.58$ and $\lambda(\alpha)=1.42$.

By taking the sequence to consist of the numbers $p+2$, for odd primes $p$, the author proves that there exist infinitely many primes $p$ such that $p+2$ either has not more than two different prime factors or else has three prime factors one of which lies in the interval $(p^{1/19}, p^{2/15})$. In addition he shows that every sufficiently large even number $2N$ can be expressed in the form $2N=p+n$, where $p$ is prime and $n$ either has not more than two different prime factors or else has three prime factors one of which lies in the interval $(N^{1/19}, N^{2/15})$. In these results use is made of the estimates of

$$\sum_{D\leqq x^\nu}\mu^2(D)\max_{a(\bmod D);(a,D)=1}|\pi_a(x, D)-(\mathrm{li}\,x)/\phi(D)|$$

due to A. I. Vinogradov [Izv. Akad. Nauk SSSR Ser. Mat. **29** (1965), 903–934; MR **33** #5579; correction, ibid. **30** (1966), 719–720; MR **33** #2607] and A. Bombieri [Mathematika **12** (1965), 201–225; MR **33** #5590]. Here $0<\nu<1$, and $\pi_a(x, D)$ is the number of primes $p\leqq x$ for which $p\equiv a \pmod D$.

The author concludes by giving a theorem which he states can be proved by similar methods: Let $f$ be an irreducible primitive polynomial of degree $g$ with integral coefficients. Then the sequence $f(1), f(2), f(3), \cdots$ contains infinitely many members each of which has not more than $g$ prime factors. For $g\geqq 8$ this is a considerable improvement on the previously best known result due to B. V. Levin in which $g+1$ is replaced by $g+U(g)$, where $U(g)$ is a certain explicit function that tends to infinity as $g\to\infty$.

{This article has appeared in English translation [Russian Math. Surveys **22** (1967), 205–233].}

*R. A. Rankin* (Glasgow)

Citations: MR 33# 2607 = P32-67; MR 33# 5579 = P32-66; MR 33# 5590 = M55-43.

Referred to in M55-66.

## M55-54 (36# 2548)

**Brun, Viggo**

**Reflections on the sieve of Eratosthenes.**

*Norske Vid. Selsk. Skr. (Trondheim)* **1967**, *no.* 1, 9 *pp.*

It was a great achievement of the author when, fifty years ago, he applied the sieve of Eratosthenes to solve problems concerning the distribution of primes. The present paper (a fifteen minute lecture given at the International Congress of Mathematicians in Moscow in 1966) consists of reflections on the salient features of the method. Let $a$ be a positive integer and cancel all numbers $\leqq a$ divisible by the primes $2, 3, 5, \cdots, p_r$. Denote the number of uncancelled integers by $E(a, 2, 3, 5, \cdots, p_r)$. Thus

$$E(a, 2, 3, 5, \cdots, p(a^{1/2})) = \pi(a)-\pi(a^{1/2})+1,$$

where $p(a^{1/2})$ is the largest prime not exceeding $a^{1/2}$, and $\pi(a)$ is the number of primes not exceeding $a$. The author's observations stem from the important formula

$$E(a, 2, \cdots, p_{s-1}, \cdots, p_r) = E(a, 2, \cdots, p_{s-1}) - E(a/p_s, 2, \cdots, p_{s-1}) - E(a/p_{s+1}, 2, \cdots, p_{s-1}) - \cdots - E(a/p_r, 2, \cdots, p_{s-1}) + (r-s)(r-s-1)/2,$$

which is valid if $p_r\leqq a^{1/2}$ and $p_{s-1}\geqq a^{1/3}$. It is supposed that $p_s\leqq p_r$ so that $p_r\geqq p_{s-1}\geqq p_r^{2/3}$. In particular, the case wherein $p_s=p(x^{1/3})$ and $p_r=p(x^{1/2})$ yields the formula of Meissel. Two ways of constructing functions that approximate $E(a, 2, \cdots, p_r)$ are sketched. The author hopes that younger mathematicians will continue to explore the reasons for the subtle influence of the distribution of primes not exceeding $a^{1/2}$ on the distribution of primes between $a^{1/2}$ and $a$. *A. L. Whiteman* (Princeton, N.J.)

## M55-55 (36# 6374)

**Halberstam, Heini; Jurkat, Wolfgang; Richert, Hans-Egon**

**Un nouveau résultat de la méthode du crible.**

*C. R. Acad. Sci. Paris Sér. A-B* **264** (1967), A920–A923.

In dieser wichtigen Arbeit kündigen die Verfasser eine Verbesserung der Selberg'schen Siebmethode an und geben bemerkenswert scharfe Abschätzungen nach oben und nach unten.

Der erste Satz der Verfasser verbessert durch die Wahl hinreichend allgemeiner Voraussetzungen, die für Anwendungen gut geeignet sind, den Hauptsatz einer Arbeit vom zweiten und dritten Verfasser [Acta Arith. **11** (1965), 217–240; MR **34** #2540]. Ein Kunstgriff von P. Kuhn [Tolfte Skand. Mat. Kongress (Lund, 1953), pp. 160–168, Ohlssons, Lund, 1954; MR **16**, 676] führt zu einem weiteren Satz, aus dem etwa—unter Benützung einer Abschätzung von E. Bombieri [Mathematika **12** (1965), 201–225; MR **35** #5590]—folgendes Ergebnis hergeleitet werden kann: Jede genügend große gerade Zahl ist Summe einer Primzahl und einer Fastprimzahl mit höchstens drei Primteilern. Wie die Verfasser bemerken, wurde dieser Satz schon von A. A. Buhštab [Dokl. Akad. Nauk SSSR **162** (1965), 735–738; MR **31** #2226] ohne Beweis angekündigt.

Die Beweise der Verfasser sollen in einem Buch des ersten und dritten Verfassers über Siebmethoden veröffentlich werden; auf das Erscheinen dieses Buches darf man gespannt sein. *W. Schwarz* (Freiburg)

Citations: MR 16, 676e = M55-13; MR 31# 2226 = P40-17; MR 34# 2540 = M55-48.

Referred to in N76-23, P32-73.

## M55-56 (37# 184)

**Montgomery, H. L.**

**A note on the large sieve.**

*J. London Math. Soc.* **43** (1968), 93–98.

While in former versions of the large sieve [see, e.g., E. Bombieri, Mathematika **12** (1965), 201–225; MR **33** #5590; H. Davenport and H. Halberstam, ibid. **13** (1966), 91–96; MR **33** #5592] sums of the type $\sum_{q\leq X}\sum^q_{a=1;(a,q)=1}|S(a/q)|^2$ were estimated from above where the inner sum runs only over $a$'s relatively prime to $q$, the present author succeeds in transforming the inner sum in the following way: $\sum_{a=1;(a,q)=1}^{q} |S(a/q)|^2 = q\sum_{h=1}^{q} |\sum_{d/q}(\mu(d)/d)Z(q/d, h)|^2$, $S(x)$, $Z(q, h)$ having their usual meanings. Applying this identity, the author proves the following theorem (which is a special case of a more general result): Let $\mathfrak{N}$ be a set of $Z$ integers with $M+1 \leqq n_1 < \cdots < n_Z \leqq M+N$. Let $X \geqq 1$ and for prime $p \leqq X$, let $\omega(p)$ be the number of residue classes mod $p$ that contain no element of $\mathfrak{N}$. Then $Z \leqq (N^{1/2}+X)^2/Q$, $Q = \sum_{q \leq X} \mu^2(q) \prod_{p/q} \omega(p)/(p-\omega(p))$. This result is of great importance since it enables one to give upper bounds comparable to those given by Selberg's method. The above result furnishes another proof for Selberg's result: $\pi(M+N)-\pi(M) < (2N/\log N)\{1+[(2+\delta)\log\log N]/\log N\}$, $N \geqq N_0(\delta)$. *W. G. H. Schaal* (Marburg)

Citations: MR 33# 5590 = M55-43; MR 33# 5592 = M55-45.

Referred to in D68-29, M55-78.

## M55-57 (37# 1338)

**Levinson, N.**

**Summing certain number theoretic series arising in the sieve.**

*J. Math. Anal. Appl.* **22** (1968), 631–645.

Elementary proofs are given for asymptotical developments of certain functions arising in Selberg's sieve method. In many cases, a treatment of these functions represents the only non-elementary part in this method. For example, let

$$J_N(x) = \sum_{n \leq x;(n,N)=1} n^{-1}\mu^2(n) \prod_{p|n} (1+g(p)),$$

and $g(p) = O(p^{-a})$ for some $a > 0$ (in the proof it is further assumed that always $g(p) \neq 0$). Then, $J_N(x) = c_N \log x + I_N$, where $I_N = O(\log\log 3N)$. For $N=1$ a systematic approach to series of this type has been given by B. V. Levin and A. S. Faĭnleĭb [Uspehi Mat. Nauk **22** (1967), no. 3 (135), 119–197; MR **37** #5174]. *H.-E. Richert* (Marburg)

Citations: MR 37# 5174 = N36-68.

Referred to in M55-58.

## M55-58 (38# 5739)

**Levinson, N.**

**Correction and addendum to: "Summing certain number theoretic series arising in the sieve".**

*J. Math. Anal. Appl.* **25** (1969), 710–716.

The author corrects the theorems of his earlier paper [same J. **22** (1968), 631–645; MR **37** #1338] to the extent that in the error terms another term involving the divisor function is added. He also gives a more explicit asymptotic formula for the sum arising in estimations for the number of solutions of $2N = p+p'$ in primes $p$ and $p'$. {Reviewer's remark: The additional error terms are actually unnecessary, and the results are true as they were stated before.}
*H.-E. Richert* (Marburg)

Citations: MR 37# 1338 = M55-57.

## M55-59 (37# 1339)

**Wunderlich, M. C.**

**Sieve-generated sequences with a limiting distribution property.**

*J. London Math. Soc.* **43** (1968), 339–346.

Der Autor betrachtet folgendes Sieb-Verfahren: Sei $A_1$ die Folge der natürlichen Zahlen $>1$; sei $A_n = \{a_1^{(n)}, a_2^{(n)}, \cdots\}$ konstruiert; ist $b = a_n^{(n)}$ und $1 \leqq r_n \leqq b$, so bilde man $A_{n+1}$, indem man aus dem "Block" $(a_{n+1}^{(n)}, \cdots, a_{n+b}^{(n)})$ das $r_n$-te Element, aus allen folgenden Blöcken $(a_{n+tb+1}^{(n)}, \cdots, a_{n+(t+1)b}^{(n)})$, $t=1, 2, \cdots$, ein beliebiges Element streicht; sei $A = \bigcap_{n \geq 1} A_n = \{a_1, a_2, \cdots\}$ die übrigbleibende Folge.

In einer früheren Arbeit [Canad. J. Math. **18** (1966), 291–299, Theorem 5; MR **32** #5625] bewies der Verfasser: Existiert $\lim_{k\to\infty} k^{-1}r_k$, so gilt (*) $a_n \sim n \log n$, d.h. die Folge $\{a_n\}$ verhält sich asymptotisch wie die Folge der Primzahlen. Der Autor zeigt nun: Besitzt die Folge $k\cdot(r_k+k)^{-1}$ eine Verteilungsfunktion $\nu$ auf $[0, 1]$, die die Lipschitz-Bedingung $|\nu(y)-\nu(x)| < K|y-x|$ erfüllt, so gilt (*). *W. Schwarz* (Freiburg)

Citations: MR 32# 5625 = M55-38.

## M55-60 (38# 3242)

**Bombieri, Enrico**

**Nuovi metodi e nuovi risultati nella teoria dei numeri.**

*Boll. Un. Mat. Ital.* (4) **1** (1968), 96–106.

After briefly mentioning H. M. Stark's result on the class number of $\mathbf{Q}(\sqrt{-d})$ [Michigan Math. J. **14** (1967), 1–27; MR **36** #5102], W. M. Schmidt's generalization of Roth's theorem [Acta Math. **119** (1967), 27–50; MR **36** #6357], and A. Baker's extension of the Gel'fond-Schneider theorem [Mathematika **13** (1966), 204–216; ibid. **14** (1967), 102–107; ibid. **14** (1967), 220–228; MR **36** #3732], the author describes some of his recent work on Linnik's large sieve. Let $S(x) = \sum_{M+1}^{M+N} a_n e^{2\pi inx}$ be a trigonometric polynomial with complex coefficients $a_n$, and $\mu$ a measure on $\mathbf{R}/\mathbf{Z}$. The inequality of the large sieve is stated in the form $\int_0^1 |S(x)|^2\, d\mu \leqq \Delta(N, \delta)m_\delta \int_0^1 |S(x)|^2\, dx$, where $\Delta(N, \delta)$ can be taken to be either $(N^{1/2}+\delta^{-1/2})^2$ or $2\max(N, \delta^{-1})$, and where $m_\delta$ is the greatest $\mu$-measure of any interval of length $\delta$. As an application, let positive integers $n_j \leqq N$ be given $(j=1, \cdots, Z)$. For each prime $p$ and integer $h$, let $Z(p, h) = \#\{n_j | n_j \equiv h \pmod p\}$. Put

$$S_X = \sum_{p \leq X} p \sum_{h=0}^{p-1} [Z(p, h) - Z/p]^2.$$

The author proves that $S_X \leqq 2\max(N, X^2)Z$.

Next he states the inequality

$$\sum_{q \leq X} \sum_{\chi}{}^* \left|\sum_{M+1}^{M+N} a_n \chi(n)\right|^2 \leqq 2\max(N, X^2) \sum_{M+1}^{M+N} |a_n|^2,$$

where the sum $\sum_{\chi}^*$ is extended over the primitive characters (mod $q$). An indication is given of how this leads to his theorem that for any $A>0$, $\sum_{q \leq X} E^*(x; q) < C(A)x/(\log x)^A$, where

$$E^*(x; q) = \max_{y \leq x} \max_{(a,q)=1} \left|\sum_{n \leq y;\, n \equiv a (\mathrm{mod}\, q)} \Lambda(n) - y/\varphi(q)\right|$$

and $X = (\log x)^{-4A-40}$. In conclusion some other applications of the same methods are mentioned.
*B. Gordon* (Los Angeles, Calif.)

Citations: MR 36# 3732 = J80-26; MR 36# 5102 = R14-62; MR 36# 6357 = J68-56.

## M55-61 (38# 4410)

**Barban, M. B.; Vehov, P. P.**

**An extremal problem.** (Russian)

*Trudy Moskov. Mat. Obšč.* **18** (1968), 83–90.

The authors estimate the minimum of the quadratic form $S = \sum_{1 \leq n \leq x} (\sum_{d|n, d \leq y} \lambda_d)^2$ under the condition $\lambda_d = \mu(d)$ for $d \leqq z$, $z < \min(x, y)$. They prove that $\min S \ll x/\ln(y/z)$. This estimate was known for the case $x > y^2$.
*A. I. Vinogradov* (Leningrad)

## M55-62 (38# 5740)

**Roth, K. F.**

**The large sieve.**

Inaugural Lecture, 23 January, 1968.

*Imperial College of Science and Technology, London,* 1968. 9 *pp.* 3*s.*

This Inaugural Lecture gives a very clear survey on the development of Linnik's large sieve. The different methods of Ju. A. Linnik [cf. A. A. Rényi, Izv. Akad. Nauk SSSR Ser. Mat. **12** (1948), 57–78; MR **9**, 413], A. A. Rényi [J.

Math. Pures Appl. (9) **28** (1949), 137–149; MR **11**, 161] and the author [Mathematika **12** (1965), 1–9; MR **33** #5589], who first reached the "best possible" result, apart from a logarithmic factor, are sketched, as well as the subsequent improvements by E. Bombieri [ibid. **12** (1965), 201–235; MR **33** #5590], H. Davenport and H. Halberstam [ibid. **13** (1966), 91–96; MR **33** #5592; corrigendum, ibid. **14** (1967), 229–232; MR **36** #2569] and P. X. Gallagher [ibid. **14** (1967), 14–20; MR **35** #5411]. The paper closes with a few remarks on extensions and on some applications of the large sieve method.

*H.-E. Richert* (Marburg)

Citations: MR 9, 413g = P32-12; MR 11, 161c = M55-6; MR 33# 5589 = M55-42; MR 33# 5590 = M55-43; MR 33# 5592 = M55-45; MR 35# 5411 = M55-52; MR 36# 2569 = M55-46.

## M55-63 (39# 1421)

**Choi, S. L. G.**

**On a theorem of Roth.**

*Math. Ann.* **179** (1969), 319–328.

Let $k$ and $N$ be positive integers, $N \geqq k^{1/2}$. For any set of real numbers $s_1, \cdots, s_N$ it is proved that there exist integers $n, q$ satisfying $1 \leqq n < n+(k-1)q \leqq N$ such that $|\sum_{r=0}^{k-1} s_{n+rq}| \geqq \{(\frac{1}{2}-O(k^{-1}))kN^{-1}\sum_{j=1}^{N} s_j^2\}^{1/2}$. This is an improvement of a result of K. F. Roth [same Ann. **169** (1967), 1–25; MR **34** #4235] using a refinement of Roth's method. Related work can be found in another paper of Roth [ibid. **174** (1967), 41–52; MR **36** #134].

*I. Niven* (Eugene, Ore.)

Citations: MR 34# 4235 = M55-49; MR 36# 134 = M55-50.

## M55-64 (39# 2718)

**Erdős, P.; Rényi, A.**

**Some remarks on the large sieve of Yu. V. Linnik.**

*Ann. Univ. Sci. Budapest. Eötvös Sect. Math.* **11** (1968), 3–13.

Let $S_N$ be a sequence of $Z$ positive integers $\leqq N$. Let $Z(a, p)$ be the number of elements of $S_N$ that are $\equiv a$ (mod $p$). Define $\Delta^2(p) = p\sum_{a=0}^{p-1}(Z(a, p)-Z/p)^2$. E. Bombieri [Mathematika **12** (1965), 201–225; MR **33** #5590] has shown that $\sum_{p\leqq Q}\Delta^2(p) = O((Q^2+N)Z)$ and P. X. Gallagher [ibid. **14** (1967), 14–20; MR **35** #5411] more explicitly that if $Q \leqq \sqrt{N}$, then $\sum_{p\leqq Q}\Delta^2(p) \leqq (Q^2+\pi N)Z$, which for $Q=\sqrt{N}$ yields (A) $\sum_{p\leqq Q}\Delta^2(p) \leqq (1+\pi)NZ$.

The authors show via probability arguments that there are sequences for which inequality (A) does not hold when $Q \geqq C(\sqrt{N})\log N$ and show that the standard probabilistic arguments cannot obtain (A) for $\sqrt{N} \leqq Q \leqq C(\sqrt{N})\log N$. Whether or not inequality (A) holds for $Q$ in this range is unknown.

Suppose $Z = cN$ for $0<c<1$ and let $Y(\alpha, \varepsilon)$, $0<\varepsilon<1$, $\frac{1}{2} \leqq \alpha < 1$, denote the number of primes $p \leqq N^\alpha$ for which at least $p\varepsilon$ residue classes mod $p$ are void of elements of $S_N$. As a consequence of (A) it follows that $Y(\frac{1}{2}, \varepsilon) \leqq (\pi+1)/(\varepsilon c)$, and from the predecessor of (A) it follows that $Y(\alpha, \varepsilon) \leqq (N^{2\alpha-1}+\pi)/(\varepsilon c)$ for $\frac{1}{2}<\alpha<1$. The authors state that this inequality seems far from being the best possible and leave as an open problem for which, if any, of the values of $\alpha$, $\frac{1}{2}<\alpha<1$, $Y(\alpha, \varepsilon)$ is bounded.

Approached from another point, given $A_\varepsilon > 0$ such that for $A_\varepsilon < p < N^\alpha$, $0<\alpha\leqq 1$, there are $\varepsilon p$ residue classes mod $p$ void of elements of $S_N$, find the maximum $Z$, depending on $N$, $\varepsilon$ and $\alpha$, for which this can be true. For $\varepsilon < \frac{1}{2}$ the authors claim it is easy to show $Z \geqq [\sqrt{N}]$ for $\alpha = 1$, and exhibit a sequence for which it is true.

*J. H. Jordan* (Pullman, Wash.)

Citations: MR 33# 5590 = M55-43; MR 35# 5411 = M55-52.

Referred to in M55-71.

## M55-65 (39# 6852)

**Wunderlich, M. C.**

**A general class of sieve generated sequences.**

*Acta Arith.* **16** (1969/70), 41–56.

The author describes a sieve process in a very general context so that the prime number sieve as well as the lucky number type sieves can be described. Conditions are obtained which imply that the sequence generated is prime-like, that is, the sequence $\{a_n\}$ satisfies $a_n \sim n\log n$.

*I. Kátai* (Budapest)

## M55-66 (40# 119)

**Richert, H.-E.**

**Selberg's sieve with weights.**

*Mathematika* **16** (1969), 1–22.

The author combines the Brun-Selberg sieve method with very skilfully chosen weights and, thus, is in a position to strengthen results of his former paper [W. B. Jurkat and the author, Acta Arith. **11** (1965), 217–240; MR **34** #2540] and to give other applications. Before we can formulate the main theorem (Theorem A) we have to introduce several notations. Let $\mathscr{A}$ be a finite non-empty set of integers and $K$ a fixed natural number; define $P_K(z) = \prod'_{p<z} p$ for $z \geqq 2$, where the dash indicates that the primes $p$ are restricted to those with $p\nmid K$. Then $S_K(\mathscr{A}, z) = |a \in \mathscr{A};\ (a, P_K(z)) = 1|$. Furthermore, let $X > 1$ and let $\gamma(d)$ be a multiplicative function satisfying $0 \leqq \gamma(p) \leqq (1-A_1^{-1})p$ if $p \nmid K$ and $|\sum'_{z\leqq p<w} p^{-1}(\gamma(p)-1)\log p| \leqq A_2$ for $w \geqq z \geqq 2$ (all constants $A_i$ are $\geqq 1$). Put

$$\eta(X, d) = |\textstyle\sum_{a\in\mathscr{A}, a\equiv 0 (\mathrm{mod}\, d)} 1 - (\gamma(d)/d)X|$$

for $\mu^2(d) = 1$, $(d, K) = 1$, and let $\Gamma_K(z) = \prod'_{p<z}(1-\gamma(p)p^{-1})$. The main theorem, then, essentially states: For $\xi > B_2$, $z \ll \xi^{A_7}$,

$$S_K(\mathscr{A}, z) \leqq X\Gamma_K(z)\{F((\log \xi^2)/\log z) + B_3(\log\log 3K)/(\log \xi)^{1/14}\} + R,$$

$$S_K(\mathscr{A}, z) \geqq X\Gamma_K(z)\{f((\log \xi^2)/\log z) - B_3(\log\log 3K)/(\log \xi)^{1/14}\} - R,$$

$R = \sum_{n\leqq \xi^2, n|P_K(z)} 3^{\nu(n)}\eta(X, n)$, $\nu(n)$ the number of pairwise distinct primes of $n$. The functions $F(u), f(u)$ were defined in the paper mentioned. (The $B_i$'s are constants depending on the $A_i$'s and a real number $\alpha$ which is needed later.) The following restriction on $\eta(X, d)$ is required for the applications: There are reals $\alpha$, $B$ with $0<\alpha\leqq 1$, $B>0$ such that

$$(*)\quad \textstyle\sum_{d\leqq X^\alpha(\log X)^{-B}, (d,K)=1} \mu^2(d)3^{\nu(d)}\eta(X, d) \leqq A_3X(\log X)^{-15/14}.$$

Theorem 1 has to be considered as the essential part of the paper: The above mentioned conditions are supposed to hold for $\mathscr{A}$, $K$, $X$, $\gamma(p)$; moreover, the following conditions are required: $\sum_{a\in\mathscr{A}, a\equiv 0(\mathrm{mod}\, p^2)} 1 \leqq A_4(X\log X\cdot p^{-2}+1)$, $p\nmid K$ and $\log K \leqq A_5 \log z$. Define $W = W_K(\mathscr{A}, v, u, \lambda) = \sum\{1-\lambda\sum'_{X^{1/v}\leqq p<X^{1/u}, p|a}(1-u(\log p)/\log X)\}$, where the first sum runs over all $a \in \mathscr{A}$ satisfying $(a, P_K(X^{1/v})) = 1$, $a \neq 0$

(mod $p^2$) for $X^{1/v} \leqq p < X^{1/u}$, $p \nmid K$. If $\alpha^{-1} < u < v$, $0 \leqq \lambda \leqq A_6$, then

$$W \geqq X\Gamma_K(X^{1/v})\{f(\alpha v) - \lambda \int_u^v F(v(\alpha - t^{-1}))(1 - ut^{-1})t^{-1}\, dt - b(\log X)^{-1/15}\},$$

$b = b(u, v, A_i, \lambda)$. (The weights occurring in $W$ are extensions of weights used by N. C. Ankeny and H. Onishi [ibid. **10** (1964/65), 31–62, especially p. 56; MR **29** #4740].) We should like to mention a few applications of Theorem 1: Denote by $P_r$ an integer having at most $r$ prime divisors, multiple primes counted multiply. There are numbers $P_2$ with $x - x^{6/11} < P_2 \leqq x$ if $x \geqq x_2$ (cf. Theorem 4). For $(k, l) = 1$ there are $P_2$ with $P_2 \leqq k^{11/5}$, $P_2 \equiv l \pmod k$ if $k \geqq k_2$ (cf. Theorem 5). Weaker results of this form had been obtained in the earlier paper mentioned. Let $F(x) \in \mathbf{Z}[x]$ denote an irreducible polynomial of degree $g \geqq 1$ without fixed prime divisor; then there are infinitely many $n$ with $F(n) = P_{g+1}$ (cf. Theorem 6). (This result was first stated by A. A. Buhštab [Uspehi Mat. Nauk **22** (1967), no. 3 (135), 205–233; MR **36** #1413], but his proof is more complicated.) Imposing more restrictive conditions on $F(x)$ the author proves: There are infinitely many primes $p$ with $F(p) = P_{2g+1}$ (cf. Theorem 7); in particular, there are infinitely many primes $p$ with $p + 2 = P_3$. Bombieri's prime number theorem is applied to prove condition (*) for $\eta$ in Theorem 7. Finally, it should be mentioned that the paper is written very clearly; only a minimal amount of computation is needed to prove the explicit results of Theorems 2–8.

*W. G. H. Schaal* (Marburg)

Citations: MR 29# 4740 = M55-33; MR 34# 2540 = M55-48; MR 36# 1413 = M55-53.
Referred to in N24-65, N32-66.

## M55-67 (40# 2636)

**Bombieri, E.; Davenport, H.**
**Some inequalities involving trigonometrical polynomials.**
*Ann. Scuola Norm. Sup. Pisa* (3) **23** (1969), 223–241.

Let $N$ be a positive integer, let $a_{M+1}, \cdots, a_{M+N}$ be arbitrary complex numbers, and define $S(x) = \sum_{n=M+1}^{M+N} a_n \times \exp(2\pi inx)$. Let $x_1, \cdots, x_R$ be real numbers satisfying $\|x_r - x_s\| \geqq \delta$ for $r \neq s$, where $\|\theta\|$ denotes the distance from $\theta$ to the nearest integer, $0 < \delta \leqq \frac{1}{2}$. In a recent paper (*Abhandlungen aus Zahlentheorie und Analysis*, VEB Deutsch. Verlag Wissensch., Berlin, to appear) the authors proved the "large sieve" estimate, that $\sum_{r=1}^R |S(x_r)|^2 \leqq (N^{1/2} + \delta^{-1/2})^2 \sum_{n=M+1}^{M+N} |a_n|^2$, and also that the first factor on the right can be replaced by $2\max(N, \delta^{-1})$. These factors are of importance in arithmetical applications, and the above estimates improve former results by the second author and H. Halberstam [Mathematika **13** (1966), 91–96; MR **33** #5592; corrigendum, ibid. **14** (1967), 229–232; MR **36** #2569]. In the present paper the authors deal more deeply with the two cases in which $N\delta$ is either large or small. They prove that if $N\delta \geqq 1$ the factor in question can be replaced by $N(1 + 5(N\delta)^{-1})$, and that if $N\delta \leqq \frac{1}{4}$ one can use $\delta^{-1}(1 + 270(N\delta)^3)$; moreover, it is shown that the constants 5 and 270 cannot be replaced by arbitrarily small constants. The proofs are quite delicate; they start again from a general inequality due to Davenport and Halberstam [loc. cit.] but make use of a more suitable Fourier series as well as of a maximization argument which permits consideration of "maximal sets" of the coefficients only.

*H.-E. Richert* (Syracuse, N.Y.)

Citations: MR 33# 5592 = M55-45; MR 36# 2569 = M55-46.
Referred to in M55-70.

## M55-68 (40# 2637)

**Liu, Ming-chit**
**On a result of Davenport and Halberstam.**
*J. Number Theory* **1** (1969), 385–389.

Let $a_{-N}, a_{-N+1}, \cdots, a_N$ be any complex numbers, $x_1, x_2, \cdots, x_L$ $(L \geqq 2)$ any real numbers such that $\min_{j \neq k} \|x_j - x_k\| = \delta > 0$, where $\|\theta\|$ means the distance from $\theta$ to the nearest integer. Let $S(x_r) = \sum_{-N}^{N} a_n \exp(2\pi i x_r)$. H. Davenport and H. Halberstam [Mathematika **13** (1966), 91–96; MR **33** #5592; corrigendum, ibid. **14** (1967), 229–232; MR **36** #2569] proved that

$$\sum_1^L |S(x_r)|^2 \leqq 2.2 \max(\delta^{-1}, 2N) \sum_{n=-N}^{N} |a_n|^2.$$

The author replaces 2.2 by 2 (H. Stark proved [see Davenport and Halberstam, loc. cit.] that the constant cannot be replaced by a number less than $2 - 8\pi^{-2}$). The author states that this result was also found by H. Davenport and E. Bombieri (*Edmund Landau memorial volume*, MR **41** #5327).

*S. Chowla* (University Park, Pa.)

Citations: MR 33# 5592 = M55-45; MR 36# 2569 = M55-46; MR 41# 5327 = M55-70.

## M55-69 (41# 1679)

**Deshouillers, Jean-Marc**
**Crible de Selberg méthodes de la borne inférieure.**
*Séminaire Delange-Pisot-Poitou: 1968/69, Théorie des Nombres, Fasc. 2, Exp. 14, 7 pp. Secrétariat mathématique, Paris*, 1969.

This is a brief report on known methods which originated from Selberg's sieve. Methods for determining lower bounds are emphasized.

*O. H. Körner* (Marburg)

## M55-70 (41# 5327)

**Bombieri, E.; Davenport, H.**
**On the large sieve method.**
*Number Theory and Analysis (Papers in Honor of Edmund Landau), pp. 9–22. Plenum, New York*, 1969.

Es sei $S(x) = \sum_{M+1}^{M+N} a_n e^{2\pi ixn}$ mit beliebigen Zahlen $a_n$ und ganzen Zahlen $M$ und $N > 0$. Es seien ferner $x_1, \cdots, x_R$ reelle Zahlen mit $\|x_r - x_s\| \geqq \delta$, $0 < \delta \leqq \frac{1}{2}$, für $r \neq s$, wo $\|x\|$ den Abstand von $x$ zur nächsten ganzen Zahl bezeichnet; schließlich werde zur Abkürzung $\sum_{M+1}^{M+N} |a_n|^2 = Z$ gesetzt. Verfasser beweisen unter den genannten Voraussetzungen die Abschätzungen $\sum_{r=1}^R |S(x_r)|^2 \leqq (N^{1/2} + \delta^{-1/2})^2 Z$ und $\sum_{r=1}^R |S(x_r)|^2 \leqq 2\max(N, \delta^{-1})Z$ (nach einem Beispiel von B. Berndt ist die letzte Ungleichung bestmöglich). Diese für das große Sieb grundlegenden Ungleichungen verschärfen frühere Ergebnisse von dem erstgenannten Verfasser [Mathematika **12** (1965), 201–225; MR **33** #5590] und dem zweitgenannten Verfasser und H. Halberstam [ibid. **13** (1966), 91–96; MR **33** #5592; corrigendum, ibid. **14** (1967), 229–232; MR **36** #2569]. (Für weitere Ergebnisse vgl. die Verfasser [Ann. Scuola Norm. Sup. Pisa (3) **23** (1969), 223–241; MR **40** #2636].) Der Beweis beruht auf dem Ansatz von dem zweitgenannten Verfasser und Halberstam, benutzt jedoch eine andere Fourierreihe. Von den tiefliegenden, interessanten Anwendungen sie die folgende erwähnt: Sei $\pi(x, \chi) = \sum_{p \leqq x} \chi(p)$. Dann gilt für $N \geqq N_0$, $X = N^{1/2}/\log N$ und $M \geqq X$ die Ungleichung

$$\sum_{q \leqq X} \log(X/q) \sum_\chi{}^* |\pi(M+N, \chi) - \pi(M, \chi)|^2 \leqq (N^{1/2} + X)^2(\pi(M+N) - \pi(M)),$$

wobei $\sum^*$ Summation über die primitiven Charaktere modulo $q$ bezeichnet. Berücksichtigt man von den (nichtnegativen) Gliedern der linken Seite nur dasjenige mit

$q=1$, so ergibt sich immer noch ein Satz vom Brun-Titchmarshen Typ. *H.-E. Richert* (Marburg)

Citations: MR 33# 5590 = M55-43; MR 33# 5592 = M55-45; MR 36# 2569 = M55-46; MR 40# 2636 = M55-67.

Referred to in M55-68, M55-78, M55-80.

## M55-71 (41# 5328)

**Wolke, Dieter**

**Farey-Brüche mit primem Nenner und das große Sieb.**
*Math. Z.* **114** (1970), 145–158.

For any complex numbers $a_n$ $(M<n\leqq M+N)$, let $S(\alpha)=\sum_{M<n\leqq M+N} a_n e(\alpha n)$ $(e(\alpha)=e^{2\pi i\alpha})$. Linnik's large sieve can be interpreted in terms of upper estimates for the sum $\sum_{p\leqq Q}\sum_{b=1}^{p-1}|S(b/p)|^2$, but up to now all such estimates have been derived via the (obviously) larger sum

$$\sum_{m\leqq Q}\sum_{b=1,(b,m)=1}^{m}|S(b/m)|^2.$$

It is natural to ask whether there is not some resulting loss of precision; and, indeed, P. Erdős and A. Rényi [Ann. Univ. Sci. Budapest. Eötvös Sect. Math. **11** (1968), 3–13; MR **39** #2718] have shown, subject to $Q\leqq N^{1/2}$, that for almost all sequences $\{a_n\}$ of 0's and 1's, one can save a factor $\log Q$ by working directly with the sum over primes. On the other hand, P. D. T. A. Elliott has found (in an unpublished ms) coefficient sequences $\{a_n\}$ where, if $Q\leqq N^{1/2}$, both sums possess the same order of magnitude. The author proves that a factor $(\log Q)^{1-\varepsilon}$ can be saved provided that $N\leqq Q(\log Q)^A$ ($A$ being an arbitrarily large fixed constant), and that one can save even $\log Q$ if $Q\log Q\leqq N\leqq Q(\log Q)$ $(1<\delta<2)$. He applies the latter result to obtain a mean value theorem for the least primes $p_1(p,b)$ in arithmetic progressions $b \bmod p$, which implies, in particular, that the number of primes $p\leqq Q$, $1\leqq b\leqq p-1$ for which $p_1(p,b)\geqq Q(\log Q)f(Q)$ $(f(Q)\to\infty$ as $Q\to\infty)$ is $o(\pi(Q)Q)$, as $Q\to\infty$. *H. Halberstam* (Nottingham)

Citations: MR 39# 2718 = M55-64.

## M55-72 (41# 8360)

**Elliott, P. D. T. A.**

**The Turan-Kubilius inequality, and a limitation theorem for the large sieve.**
*Amer. J. Math.* **92** (1970), 293–300.

Let $f(m)$ be a complex-valued additive function, $A_n=\sum_{p^k\leqq n}p^{-k}f(p^k)$, $B_n{}^2=\sum_{p^k\leqq n}p^{-k}|f(p^k)|^2$. Applying an inequality of the large sieve, a new proof is given for the Turan-Kubilius inequality $\sum_{m\leqq n}|f(m)-A_n|^2\leqq c_1 nB_n{}^2$. A similar argument leads to the proof of the inequality $\sum_{m\leqq n}|f(m+1)-f(m)|^2\leqq c_2 nB_n{}^2$, $c_1$, $c_2$ positive constants. Combining the first inequality with a probabilistic argument, the author shows the following result: Write the large sieve inequality in the form

$$\sum_{q\leqq X}\sum_{a=1,(a,q)=1}^{q}\left|\sum_{l=1}^{n}b_l e(la/q)\right|^2\leqq\Delta(X,n)\cdot\sum_{l=1}^{n}|b_l|^2,$$

where $\Delta(X,n)$ denotes the greatest lower bound of all the possible numbers which can appear as first factors on the right-hand side independently of the $b_l$'s. Now, let $X\geqq 2$, $n\geqq 10^4$; then there is a positive constant $c_3$ such that $\Delta(X,n)\geqq n-c_3 n(\log_2 X)^{-1}\log_3 X$ if $X\leqq\exp(\sqrt{\log n})$, $\Delta(X,n)\geqq n-c_3 n(\log_2 n)^{-1}\log_3 n$ if $X>\exp(\sqrt{\log n})$. *W. G. H. Schaal* (Marburg)

## M55-73 (42# 224)

**Hlawka, E.**

**Bemerkungen zum großen Sieb von Linnik.**
*Österreich. Akad. Wiss. Math.-Natur. Kl. S.-B. II* **178** (1970), 13–18.

The author reproduces some remarks he made in a letter to A. Rényi. The author first gives an interesting derivation of P. X. Gallagher's [Mathematika **14** (1967), 14–20; MR **35** #5411] formulation of the Linnik-Rényi large sieve. This derivation is then extended to an $n$-dimensional situation; similar generalizations have also been given by A. G. Samandarov [Mat. Zametki **2** (1967), 673–680; MR **36** #6379], M. N. Huxley [Mathematika **15** (1968), 178–187; MR **38** #5737], R. J. Wilson [ibid. **16** (1969), 189–204; MR **41** #8374] and W. Schaal [J. Number Theory **2** (1970), 249–270]. An application to the distribution of integral lattice points modulo sub-lattices is given. The author concludes with the interesting remark that this multidimensional large sieve may be applied to the consideration of character sums in finite fields, after the manner of H. Davenport and D. J. Lewis [Rend. Circ. Mat. Palermo (2) **12** (1963), 129–136; MR **29** #4755]. *H. L. Montgomery* (Princeton, N.J.)

Citations: MR 29# 4755 = T25-20; MR 35# 5411 = M55-52; MR 36# 6379 = R46-26; MR 38# 5737 = R46-28; MR 41# 8374 = R46-32.

## M55-74 (42# 3029)

**Montgomery, H. L.**

**Mean and large values of Dirichlet polynomials.**
*Invent. Math.* **8** (1969), 334–345.

The paper is concerned with estimating double averages of sums of the form $|\sum_{n=1}\chi(n)a_n n^{-s}|$. Up until the present, there have been effective methods for treating sums such as $\sum_{n=1}^{N}a_n n^{-it}$ and $\sum_{n=M+1}^{M+N}\chi(n)a_n$, and the author combines techniques for each of these types of sums by means of an elegant device due to Halász. This device enables one to get rid of absolute value signs in a sum by writing $\sum_{k=1}^{n}|a_k|=\sum_{k=1}^{n}a_k\eta_k$, $\eta_k=e^{-i\arg a_k}$. For estimating multiple summands, this is effective when one wishes to interchange summations.

The author's first theorem is due to Davenport, which the author re-proves using the Halász method and an inequality of Gallagher. His second theorem states this: Let $N$ and $Q$ be given, $\chi$ a primitive character modulo $q$, $q\leqq Q$, $R_\chi$ given, and for $1<r<R_\chi$, $S_{\chi,r}=\sigma_{\chi,r}t_i t_{\chi,r}$ arbitrary complex numbers. Put $\delta=\min_{q,\chi,a\neq b}|t_{\chi,a}-t_{\chi,b}|$, $T=1+\max_{q,\chi,r}t_{\chi,r}-\min_{q,\chi,r}t_{\chi,r}$ and, finally, $\sigma=\min_{q,\chi,r}\sigma_{\chi,r}$. Then

$$\sum_{q\leqq Q}\sum_\chi{}^*\sum_{r=1}^{R}\left|\sum_{n=1}^{N}\chi(n)a_n n^{-s_{\chi,r}}\right|^2\ll(Q^2T+N)(1+(\log N)^2/q)(\log N)^4\sum_{n=1}^{N}|a_n|^2 n^{-2}.$$

He has two other theorems whose statements are fairly complicated, but whose proofs are similar to the proof of his second theorem. *B. Berlowitz* (Chicago, Ill.)

## M55-75 (42# 5944)

**Huxley, M. N.**

**The large sieve inequality for algebraic number fields. II. Means of moments of Hecke zeta-functions.**
*Proc. London Math. Soc.* (3) **21** (1970), 108–128.

The author's goal is to extend to algebraic number fields results of the following type: $(^+)$ $\sum_{q\leqq Q}\sum_{\chi \bmod q}^*|L(\tfrac12+it,\chi)|^4\ll Q^2(|t|+2)\log^8\{Q(|t|+2)\}$, where $L(s,\chi)$ denotes an $L$-function over the rationals belonging to a character $\chi \bmod q$; the asterisk indicates that the corresponding sum is restricted to primitive characters mod $q$. The above given estimate is due to Ju. V. Linnik [Mat. Sb. (N.S.) **53 (95)** (1961), 3–38; MR **22** #10964; translated in Amer. Math. Soc. Transl. (2) **37** (1964), 197–240; see MR **28** #3907].

The functions $L(s,\chi)$ are replaced by Hecke's zeta-functions $\zeta(s,\lambda,\chi)$ of the algebraic number field $K$, where $\lambda$ is a Hecke Grössencharakter and $\chi$ is a character of the group of narrow ideal-classes modulo a fixed ideal $\mathfrak{f}$ of the field $K$. The author generalizes an unpublished proof of Montgomery to number fields who observed that Paley's and Linnik's analytical techniques for proving results of type $(^+)$ can be combined with Gallagher's approach applying the large sieve to sums over characters.

An approximate functional equation for Hecke's zeta-functions is given in Theorem 2, which is too involved to quote here. Theorem 1 is a consequence of results concerning the large sieve in algebraic number fields which are due to the author [Mathematika **15** (1968), 178–187; MR **38** #5737]. These two theorems enable him to give estimates for the sums $\sum_{N\mathfrak{f}\le Q}(N\mathfrak{f}/\Phi(\mathfrak{f}))\sum_\chi^* |\zeta^{2l}(s,\lambda,\chi)|$, $l$ a positive integer. These estimates reduce in the rational field to $\sum_{q\le Q}\sum_{\chi \bmod q}^* |L(\frac{1}{2}+it,\chi)|^4 \ll \{Q^2+Q(|t|+2)\}\log^4\{Q(|t|+2)\}$, and this inequality contains results of Linnik and Gallagher. *W. G. H. Schaal* (Marburg)

Citations: MR 22# 10964 = P36-25; MR 38# 5737 = R46-28.

Referred to in R44-44.

## M55-76 (42# 5945)

**Pleasants, P. A. B.**

**A sum related to the distribution modulo 1 of sets of real numbers.**

*Quart. J. Math. Oxford Ser.* (2) **21** (1970), 321–336.

Let $x=(x_1,\cdots,x_R)$ and $\delta=(\delta_1,\cdots,\delta_R)$ be two sets of $R$ not necessarily distinct real numbers with $0<\delta_i\le\frac{1}{2}$ and $0\le x_i<1$ for $i=1,2,\cdots,R$. Denote by $\nu_r=\nu_r(x,\delta_r)$ the number of indices $s$ for which $\|x_r-x_s\|<\delta_r$, where $\|y\|$ is the distance of $y$ to the nearest integer. The author studies the sum $\Delta(x,\delta)=\sum_{r=1}^R\delta_r/\nu_r$. He shows by example that $\Delta$ need not be bounded as $R\to\infty$; in fact, for each positive integer $R$ there exist two sets of $R$ numbers $x$ and $\delta$ such that $\Delta(x,\delta)>\alpha\log R$, where $\alpha$ is the unique root in the range $(0,2]$ of the equation $\alpha(1-\log\alpha)=\frac{1}{2}$. Let $M_R$ be the least upper bound of $\Delta(x,\delta)$ as $x$ and $\delta$ vary over sets of $R$ numbers from the appropriate ranges. Then $M_R\le\log R/\log 4+\frac{3}{2}$ for all $R$. Moreover, $M_R/\log R$ tends towards a limit $L$ as $R\to\infty$, and $0.1866\ldots=\alpha\le L\le(\log 4)^{-1}=0.7213\ldots$. The author conjectures that $L=\alpha$. Finally, the estimates of $\Delta$ are used to get generalizations of certain large sieve inequalities due to H. Davenport and H. Halbertstam. Theorems 1A and 1B of Chapter 23 in *Multiplicative number theory* [Markham, Chicago, Ill., 1967; MR **36** #117] by Davenport are then special cases of these generalizations.

*O. P. Stackelberg* (Durham, N.C.)

Citations: MR 36# 117 = N02-13.

## M55-77 (42# 7625)

**Halberstam, H.**

**The large sieve.**

*Number Theory (Colloq., János Bolyai Math. Soc., Debrecen,* 1968), *pp.* 123–131. *North-Holland, Amsterdam,* 1970.

Der vorliegende Vortrag gibt einen kurzen, aber sehr gut verständlichen Überblick über die Theorie des großen Siebes und über die wesentlichsten Anwendungen der entsprechenden Sätze. Obwohl seit dem Zeitpunkt, zu dem dieser Vortrag gehalten wurde, eine Reihe von Arbeiten erschienen ist, die diese Theorie fortführen bzw. ihre Anwendungsmöglichkeit auf einige wichtige zahlentheoretische Probleme zeigen, ist der Vortrag für jemanden, der sich einen ersten Überblick über dieses Gebiet verschaffen möchte, nach wie vor gut geeignet, ihm diesen zu vermitteln. *W. G. H. Schaal* (Marburg)

## M55-78 (42# 7626)

**Schaal, Werner**

**On the large sieve method in algebraic number fields.**

*J. Number Theory* **2** (1970), 249–270.

E. Bombieri and H. Davenport [*Number theory and analysis (Papers in honor of Edmund Landau)*, pp. 9–22, Plenum, New York, 1969; MR **41** #5327] proved that if $\{x_1,x_2,\cdots,x_R\}$ are real numbers and if $\delta=\min_{j\ne k}\{|x_j-x_k|\}\le\frac{1}{2}$ but not 0, and if we let $M$ and $N$ be positive integers, and $\|x\|=\min\{|x-m|\}$, $m$ an integer, and $\alpha_m$ an arbitrary complex number associated with $m$ in the interval $M+1\le m\le M+N$, and if

$$S(x)=\sum_{M+1}^{M+N}\alpha_m\exp(2\pi imx),$$

then $\sum_{j=1}^R|S(x_j)|^2\le(\sqrt{N}+1/\sqrt{\delta})^2\sum_{M+1}^{M+N}|\alpha_m|^2$. M. N. Huxley [Mathematika **15** (1968), 178–187; MR **38** #5737] generalized Bombieri and Davenports' result to algebraic number fields of degree $n$ by replacing the domain of $n$ by an $n$-dimensional parallelepiped defined in terms of a basis for the number field.

This paper manages to generalize Huxley's result by replacing the parallelepiped by a bounded subset of $R^{r_1}\times C^{2r_2}$, $r_1+2r_2=n$.

The main theorem essentially states that if $H$ numbers $x_1,x_2,\cdots,x_H$ are selected from the bounded subset $U$, then the inequality

$$\sum_{j=1}^H|S(x_j)|^2(Zo/(N(\mathfrak{Z})|\sqrt{d}))((\sqrt{n})/\delta)^n\prod_{i=1}^n(1+(2U_l\delta)^{1/2})^2$$

holds, where (i) $Zo=\sum|\alpha_\nu|^2$, $\nu$ in $U$ and $\mathfrak{Z}|\nu$, with $\alpha_\nu$ arbitrary complex numbers, (ii) $\mathfrak{z}$ is the different and $N\mathfrak{z}=|d|$, (iii) $U_l$ is a constant defined by $U_l=\max\{|\nu^{(l)}|/\sqrt{n},\sqrt{2}|\mathrm{Re}\,\nu^{(l)}|/\sqrt{n},\sqrt{2}|\mathrm{Im}\,\nu^{(l)}|/\sqrt{n}\}$, $\nu\in U$ and $\mathfrak{Z}|\nu$, (iv) $\delta\le\|x_i-x_j\|$, $i\ne j$, and

(v) $$S(x)=\sum\alpha\nu\exp(2\pi iT(\nu x)),$$

with $\nu$ in the set $U$ and $\mathfrak{Z}|\nu$, where $T(\nu x)=\sum_{l=1}^n\nu^{(l)}x^{(l)}$, providing $U_l\ge 2/(\pi-2)^2\delta$. Applications of the theorem combined with modifications of a theorem of H. L. Montgomery [J. London Math. Soc. **43** (1968), 93–98; MR **37** #184] will yield estimates for the number of prime ideals in an "arithmetic progression" whose conjugates fall in a predesignated range.

*J. H. Jordan* (Pullman, Wash.)

Citations: MR 37# 184 = M55-56; MR 38# 5737 = R46-28; MR 41# 5327 = M55-70.

## M55-79 (43# 1943)

**Elliott, P. D. T. A.; Halberstam, H.**

**A conjecture in prime number theory.**

*Symposia Mathematica, Vol. IV (INDAM, Rome,* 1968/69), *pp.* 59–72. *Academic Press, London,* 1970.

The paper is essentially a survey of results that have been proved by sieve methods in prime number theory. The following results are known for any given $A>0$. If $\pi(x,q,h)$ denotes the number of primes not exceeding $x$ that are congruent to $h$ modulo $q$, then

(I) $$\sum_{q\le X}\phi(q)\max_{1\le h\le q,(h,q)=1}\{\pi(x,q,h)-(\mathrm{li}\,x)/\phi(q)\}^2\ll x^2/\log^A x$$

if $X\le x^{1/2}/\log^B x$, where $B=B(A)>0$, and

(II) $$\sum_{q\le X}\sum_{h=1,(h,q)=1}^{q}\{\pi(x,q,h)-(\mathrm{li}\,x)/\phi(q)\}^2\ll x^2/\log^A x$$

if $X<x/\log^{A+1}x$.

Knowing (I) and (II) or their analogues for other sequences, one can formulate a number of problems in such

a way that they can be solved. Some recent work of R. Orr in this direction for the sequence of square free integers, and some results of the first author [J. Number Theory **2** (1970), 22–55; MR **41** #3422] lead the authors to wonder whether analogues of (I) and (II) hold for more general sequences, and also whether there exists an $\alpha$, with $\frac{1}{2}<\alpha\leqq 1$, such that (I) holds for $X\leqq x^\alpha/\log^B x$, where $B=B(A)>0$.
Assuming the truth of (I) with $A\doteq 8$ for

$$X \leqq x\exp(-\log^{9/20} x),$$

they deduced that, as $x\to\infty$, $\sum_{p\leqq x} 3^{\nu(p-1)}\sim(3/\pi^2)x\log x$, where $\nu(n)$ denotes the number of distinct prime factors of $n$. *K. Thanigasalam* (Monaca, Pa.)

Citations: MR 41# 3422 = N60-85.

## M55-80 (43# 4791)

**Bombieri, Enrico**
**On a theorem of van Lint and Richert.**
*Symposia Mathematica, Vol. IV (INDAM, Rome, 1968/69), pp. 175–180. Academic Press, London, 1970.*

It was first noticed by the author (first published in a paper by H. Davenport and the author [*Abhandlungen aus Zahlentheorie und Analysis* (Zur Erinnerung an Edmund Landau), pp. 11–22, VEB Deutsch. Verlag Wissensch., Berlin, 1968; see MR **41** #3200a; English edition, pp. 9–22, Plenum, New York, 1969; MR **41** #5327] that in certain cases the upper estimate in Selberg's sieve can also be obtained by an application of the large sieve. In the present paper the author shows that the same holds true for an improved form of Selberg's upper bound given by J. H. van Lint and the reviewer [Acta Arith. **11** (1965), 209–216; MR **32** #5613] for theorems of the Brun-Titchmarsh type. The method consists of starting from the inequality of H. Davenport and H. Halberstam [Mathematika **13** (1966), 91–96; MR **33** #5592] and then making use of several results about the related Fourier series that was considered in the first paper mentioned above.
*H.-E. Richert* (Marburg)

Citations: MR 32# 5613 = N12-38; MR 33# 5592 = M55-45; MR 41# 3200a = Z10-60; MR 41# 5327 = M55-70.

## M55-81 (43# 4907)

**Frucht W., Roberto**
**A sieve method for calculating generators of cyclic groups. (Spanish)**
*Scientia (Valparaíso) No.* 137 (1969), 62.

This is a brief résumé of a lecture dealing with an elementary method similar to the sieve method of Eratosthenes for finding all generators of a finite cyclic group. The author has used the method for calculating primitive roots modulo a prime number and also generators of certain Galois fields. *B. H. Neumann* (Canberra)

## M55-82 (44# 3982)

**Bombieri, E.**
**A note on the large sieve.**
*Acta Arith.* **18** (1971), 401–404.

Let $x_1,\cdots,x_R$ denote distinct real numbers such that $\min_{i\neq j}\|x_i-x_j\|\geqq\delta>0$, where $\|x\|=\min_n|x-n|$, and $S(x)=\sum_{n=M+1}^{M+N} a_n e^{2\pi inx}$, $a_n\in\mathbf{C}$, $M$ an integer, $N$ a natural number. The author proves the following theorem: $\sum_{l=1}^R |S(x_l)|^2\leqq(N+2/\delta)\sum_{n=M+1}^{M+N}|a_n|^2$. The proof is very short and makes use of the following lemma: Let $H$ be a Hilbert space with inner product ( , ) and let $\varphi_1,\cdots,\varphi_R$, $f\in H$; then we have $\sum_{l=1}^R |(f,\varphi_l)|^2/\sum_{j=1}^R|(\varphi_l,\varphi_j)|\leqq\|f\|^2$. The Hilbert space of infinite sequences $\alpha=(\alpha_n)$, $-\infty<n<\infty$, with inner product $(\alpha,\beta)=\sum_{n=-\infty}^{+\infty}\alpha_n\bar\beta_n$ is used in the proof of the theorem. *W. G. H. Schaal* (Marburg)

## M55-83 (44# 3983)

**Elliott, P. D. T. A.**
**On inequalities of large sieve type.**
*Acta Arith.* **18** (1971), 405–422.

Let $P$ denote a set of primes not exceeding $Q$. Define $\Delta(N,Q)$ to be (for each pair $N,Q$) the least number for which the inequality

$$\sum_{p\in P}\sum_{b=1}^{p-1}|S(b/p)|^2\leqq\Delta(N,Q)\sum_{n=1}^N|a_n|^2$$

is satisfied for all complex numbers $a_1,\cdots,a_N$. Here, for real numbers $\alpha$, $S(\alpha)=\sum_{n=1}^N a_n e^{2\pi i\alpha n}$. The author proves several results concerning $\Delta(N,Q)$, e.g., the following theorem: (i) $\Delta(N,Q)\geqq\max(N,\sum_{p\in P}(p-1))$; (ii) $\Delta(N,Q)=\sum_{p\in P}p+O(N^2(\log N)^{-1})$; in fact (iii) $\sum_{p\in P}\sum_{b=1}^{p-1}|S(b/p)|^2=\{\sum_{p\in P}p+O(N|P|+N^2(\log N)^{-1})\}\sum_{n=1}^N|a_n|^2$. The proofs depend on the determination of the largest eigenvalue of the Hermitian matrix $B\bar B^T$, $B=(e^{2\pi i(b/p)m})$ rows $1\leqq m\leqq N$, columns $1\leqq b\leqq p-1$, $2\leqq p\leqq Q$, $p\in P$. In an analogous way the author proves results about the least number $\rho(N,T)$ with the property that $\int_{-T}^T|\sum_{n=1}^N a_n n^{-it}|^2\,dt\leqq\rho(N,T)\sum_{n=1}^N|a_n|^2$. *W. G. H. Schaal* (Marburg)

## M55-84 (44# 6626)

**Halberstam, H.; Richert, H.-E.**
**Mean value theorems for a class of arithmetic functions.**
*Acta Arith.* **18** (1971), 243–256.

For all squarefree $d$ define $g(d)=\prod_{p|d}\omega(p)/(p-\omega(p))$, where $0\leqq\omega(p)/p\leqq 1-A_1$ for all primes $p$ and some constant $A_1\geqq 1$. Put $W(z)=\prod_{p<z}(1-\omega(p)/p)$, $G(z)=\sum_{d<z}\mu^2(d)g(d)$ and $G(x,z)=\sum_{d<x,d|P(z)}g(d)$ where $P(z)=\prod_{p<z}p$, and assume there exist constants $\chi>0$ and $A_2\geqq 1$ and a number $L\geqq 1$ such that (*) $-L\leqq\sum_{w\leqq p<z}\omega(p)\log p/p-\chi\log(z/w)\leqq A_2$ if $2\leqq w\leqq z$. The sums $G(z)$ and $G(x,z)$ together with a condition like (*) occur naturally in Selberg sieve theory, where typically the number $L$ depends on other parameters. The following two theorems are proved: (1) $G(z)W(z)=e^{-\gamma\chi}/\Gamma(\chi+1)+O(\min(L,\log z)/\log z)$; (2) $G(x,z)W(z)=\sigma_\chi(2\tau)+O(L\tau^{2\chi+1}/\log z)$ if $z\leqq x$, where $\tau=\log x/\log z$ and $\sigma_\chi$ is the solution of a certain differential-difference problem. (A misprint in the statement of Theorem 2 has been corrected above.) *D. Rearick* (Boulder, Colo.)

# M99 NONE OF THE ABOVE, BUT IN THIS CHAPTER

See also review Z15-37.

## M99-1 (5, 255b)

**Hurwitz, S. On a class of functions suggested by the zeta of Riemann.** Ann. of Math. (2) **45**, 340–346 (1944).

Let $p$ denote a nonnegative integer. Put $\log_0 x=x$, $\log_{p+1}x=\log(\log_p x)$, and define

$$\zeta_p(s)=\sum_{n=V+1}^{\infty}\left\{\prod_0^{p-1}\log_i n\right\}^{-1}(\log_p n)^{-s},$$

where $V=[e_p(0)]$, $e_{p+1}(x)=\exp(e_p(x))$, $e_0(x)=x$. Thus $\zeta_0(s)=\zeta(s)$, the Riemann zeta-function. The writer proves that $\zeta_p(s)$ is regular everywhere except at $s=1$, where it has a simple pole with residue 1. Various integral formulas are obtained and it is proved that $\zeta_p(s)$ has an infinite number of negative zeros (exact values not determined). Finally some theorems on the asymptotic behavior of $\zeta_p(s)$ are proved. *L. Carlitz* (Durham, N. C.).

## M99-2 (12, 490a)

**Denjoy, Arnaud. Expressions sommatoires de séries appartenant à la classe de $\zeta(s)$.** C. R. Acad. Sci. Paris **232**, 365–368 (1951).

Given a function $u(n)$ of class $C^\infty$ with derivatives of alternating sign, the author obtains the formula

$$\sum_1^\infty u(n)=\sum_1^p(-1)^k C_p^k D_{k-1}[u^{(-k)}(1)] +(-1)^p\int_0^1\cdots\int_0^1(1-t_1)\cdots(1-t_p) \times\sum_{n\geq 1}u^{(p)}(n+t_1+\cdots+t_p)dt_1\cdots dt_p,$$

where the $C_p{}^k$ are the binomial coefficients, $u^{(-k)}$ is the $k$th successive indefinite integral of $u$, and

$$D_{k-1}[u^{(-k)}(1)]=\sum_0^{k-1}(-1)^j C^j_{k-1}u^{(-k)}(1+[k-1-j]).$$

This formula is applied in order to express

$$Z(s)=(\Gamma(s))^{-1}\int_0^\infty [x^{s-1}/(e^x-1)]\varphi(x)dx$$

as a series of meromorphic functions with the single pole $s=1$. *P. R. Garabedian* (Stanford University, Calif.).

## M99-3 (29# 77 )

**Chowla, S.; Hawkins, D.**

**Asymptotic expansions of some series involving the Riemann zeta function.**

*J. Indian Math. Soc.* (*N.S.*) **26** (1962), 115–124.

Hardy and Littlewood (stimulated by a conjecture of Ramanujan) proved that the truth of

$$\sum_{n=0}^\infty\frac{(-x)^n}{n!\zeta(2n+1)}=O(x^{-1/4+\varepsilon})$$

is a necessary and sufficient condition for the truth of the Riemann hypothesis. {Remark: Hardy and Littlewood have proved the equivalence with the Riemann hypothesis if $\varepsilon=0$ [cf. Hardy and Littlewood, Acta Math. **41** (1917), 119–196; Titchmarsh, *The theory of the Riemann zeta-function*, p. 328, Clarendon, Oxford, 1951; MR **13**, 741].} The authors of the present paper obtain the following result which has a superficial resemblance with the above, namely,

(A) $$\sum_{n=2}^\infty\frac{(-x)^n}{n!}\zeta(n)=x\log x+(2C-1)x+\tfrac12+O(e^{-c\sqrt{x}})$$

($x$ is large and positive; $c$ is a certain positive constant). It is presumed that the error term cannot be essentially sharpened, but the authors assert that they are unable to prove this. Furthermore, they obtain the similar result

(B) $$\sum_{n=2}^\infty(-1)^n\binom{x}{n}\zeta(n)=x\log x+(2C-1)x+o(1).$$

The proof of this formula is based upon the study of the ratio

$$g(x,s)=\frac{\sum_{n\leq x}(x-n)^s\left\{\frac{x}{n}-\left[\frac{x}{n}\right]\right\}}{\sum_{n\leq x}(x-n)^s}$$

for a fixed natural number $s$, as $x\to\infty$. It is shown that $\lim_{x\to\infty}g(x,s)=h(s)$ exists, and furthermore that $\lim_{s\to\infty}h(s)=\frac12$. The paper ends with the proof of an exact expansion of the term $O(\exp(-c\sqrt{x}))$ in (A), viz.,

$$O(\exp(-c\sqrt{x}))=\sum_{n=1}^\infty\frac{K(2\pi ny)}{n}$$

with

$$K(y)=\frac{1}{4\pi i}\int_{\sigma=1/2}\frac{\Gamma(s)}{\Gamma(-s)}\frac{y^{-s}}{\cos\frac12 s\pi}ds.$$

The authors end with the remark that it is not hard to show that $K(y)$ is expressible in terms of "almost" Bessel functions, but it is not quite clear which kind of functions they mean.

{Remark: A part of the proof is obscured by the fact that on pp. 116, 118 in the same formula the letter $m$ is used simultaneously as a variable index of summation, and as an arbitrary positive constant integer. It seems, however, that the results are right.}

*S. C. van Veen* (Delft)

Citations: MR 13, 741c = M02-2.

Referred to in M99-5.

## M99-4 (29# 78 )

**Chowla, S.; Hawkins, D.**

**Asymptotic expansions of some series involving the Riemann zeta function. I, II.**

*Norske Vid. Selsk. Forh.* (*Trondheim*) **35** (1962), 99–103; *ibid.* **35** (1962), 104–110.

The content of both these papers is identical with the preceding paper [#77]. *S. C. van Veen* (Delft)

## M99-5 (31# 2220 )

**Verma, D. P.**

**Asymptotic expansion of some series involving the Riemann zeta-function.**

*Indian J. Math.* **6** (1964), 121–127.

Using simpler methods, the author proves the following results obtained by D. Hawkins and the reviewer [J. Indian Math. Soc. (N.S.) **26** (1962), 115–124; MR **29** #77]:

$$\sum_2^\infty\frac{x^n}{n!}(-1)^n\zeta(n)=x\log x+(2\gamma-1)x+\tfrac12+O(x^{-1}),$$

$$\sum_2^\infty(-1)^m\zeta(m)\frac{x(x-1)\cdots(x-m+1)}{m!}= x\log x+(2\gamma-1)x+O(x^{-1}).$$

Here $\zeta(s)$ is Riemann's zeta-function. He also obtains other similar identities.

*S. Chowla* (University Park, Pa.)

Citations: MR 29# 77 = M99-3.

## M99-6 (43# 3221 )

**Oldham, Keith B.**

**On the evaluation of certain sums involving the natural numbers raised to an arbitrary power.**

*SIAM J. Math. Anal.* **1** (1970), 538–546.

The author studies sums of the form $\sum_{k=1}^l g(k)/k^r$ where $r$ is an arbitrary real number and $g$ is a periodic real-valued function with integral period. He obtains an asymptotic expansion for this sum that involves certain values of gamma functions, Bernoulli polynomials and the generalized zeta function $\zeta(r,q)=\sum_{n=0}^\infty(n+q)^{-r}$, but is too complicated to give here. Several special cases are:

(i) $\lim_{l\to\infty}\{1-2^{1/2}+3^{1/2}-\cdots\pm(l-1)^{1/2}\mp\frac12 l^{1/2}\}=(1-2^{3/2})\zeta(-\frac12,1),$

and

(ii) $1-3^{1/2}+5^{1/2}-\cdots\mp(L-2)^{1/2}\pm L^{1/2}= 4\zeta(-\frac12,\frac14)+(\sqrt2-1)\zeta(-\frac12,1) \pm\{L^{1/2}/2+L^{-1/2}/4-L^{-5/2}/16+O(L^{-9/2})\}.$

*R. L. Graham* (Murray Hill, N.J.)

# N. MULTIPLICATIVE NUMBER THEORY

For multiplicative properties of the set of "shifted primes" $p + a$ ($a$ a constant), see **P48**. See also Sections A38, B28, R44, R46.

## N02 BOOKS AND SURVEYS

General texts which include standard material on the prime number theorem, Dirichlet's theorem, estimates of sums etc., are listed in **Z01** and **Z02** and are not cross-referenced here.

See also Section M02.

See also reviews A02-4, A02-5, L02-1, L02-2, L02-5, L02-8, M02-3, M02-5, M02-6, M40-16, M55-79, N04-22, N04-41, N08-14, N20-4, N20-13, N20-67, N20-70, N36-10, N44-6, N60-10, N60-23, N60-33, N60-37, N60-96, N64-22, N72-43, N72-55, P02-12, Q15-4, R02-5, Z02-3, Z02-4, Z02-53, Z02-55, Z02-75, Z25-17, Z25-29.

**N02-1** **(11, 419a)**

**van der Corput, J. G. On the regularity of large numbers.** Handelingen van het XXXI$^e$ Nederlands Natuur- en Geneeskundig Congres, pp. 36–52, Haarlem, 1949. (Dutch)

Lecture on the distribution of primes and computation of series.

**N02-2** **(13, 759d)**

**Lévy, Paul. Arithmétique et calcul des probabilités.** Congrès International de Philosophie des Sciences, Paris, 1949. Vol. IV, Calcul des probabilités, pp. 125–133. Actualités Sci. Ind., no. 1146. Hermann & Cie., Paris, 1951. 860 francs.

Expository article reviewing some of the number-theoretic theorems which are suggested by probability arguments. These include the prime number theorem, the twin prime problem and the Riemann hypothesis, the last, if the heuristic approach is valid, even at the second approximation. It is remarkable that the more elementary results predicted by such arguments have mostly turned out to be true.

*K. L. Chung* (Ithaca, N. Y.).

**N02-3** **(16, 904d)**

**Landau, Edmund. Handbuch der Lehre von der Verteilung der Primzahlen. 2 Bände. 2d ed. with an appendix by Paul T. Bateman.** Chelsea Publishing Co., New York, 1953. xviii+pp. 1–564; ix+pp. 565–1001. $17.50.

The present edition of this classic work [Teubner, Leipzig-Berlin] of 1909 differs from the original principally by the addition of a preface and appendix (in English) by P. T. Bateman and by the inclusion of two papers of Landau himself. Also, a few minor misprints have been corrected.

The first appended paper of Landau [Math. Z. **20**, 98–104 (1924)] shows how the use of the functional equation for the zeta function can be avoided in deriving the error term of the type $O(x \exp \{-c\sqrt{\log x}\})$ for the prime number theorem. It might be remarked, however, that the newer method leads to a larger value of $c$ than the older one. The second paper [S.-B. Preuss. Akad. Wiss. **1932**, 514–521] gives Landau's version of Wiener's Tauberian proof of the prime number theorem.

In his slightly terse preface and appendix, occupying about 23 pages, Bateman surveys the place of the book in the history of the subject, points out the later major developments and improvements which have taken place in the material treated by Landau and gives many references to the literature. These references do not pretend to be on the extensive scale of the original; but they, and the accompanying comments, are nevertheless quite comprehensive and form a very useful guide to the more recent literature. Since the writing of the appendix another significant development has taken place with the appearance of a paper of A. Z. Val'fiš [Akad. Nauk Gruzin. SSR. Trudy Tbiliss. Mat. Inst. Razmadze **19**, 1–31 (1953); MR **16**, 338] in which an estimate, sharper than that in §152 of the book, is given for the error term in the asymptotic formula for $\sum_{n\leqq x} \phi(n)$.

*L. Schoenfeld* (Ithaca, N. Y.).

Citations: MR 16, 338d = N48-3.

Referred to in A26-68, A38-56, M45-28, M45-34, N04-47, N24-28, N28-58, N28-78, N32-54, N60-58, Z02-30.

**N02-4** **(17, 462a)**

**Dehn, Edgar. Prime numbers. A study of their distribution.** Rock Way House, Yonkers, N. Y., 1952. viii+48 pp.

The author sets out to discuss several well-known problems in prime number theory, such as Goldbach's conjecture and the estimation of gaps between consecutive primes, but his intentional neglect of all error terms and cavalier use of the equality sign render most of the arguments invalid, and, indeed, prevent him from preceiving the real difficulties in each problem. In particular, the key formulae on page 10, line 17, page 12, line 18 and page 13, line 5, are false. Some numerical evidence of a restricted nature is put forward in support of the author's conclusions.

The book ends with two letters on freedom of scientific thought.

*H. Halberstam* (Providence, R.I.).

**N02-5** **(19, 250f)**

**Specht, Wilhelm. Elementare Beweise der Primzahlsätze.** Hochschulbücher für Mathematik, Band 30. VEB Deutscher Verlag der Wissenschaften, Berlin, 1956. v+78 pp. DM 6.40.

Die vorliegende Monographie macht es sich zur Aufgabe, unter Voraussetzung „elementarer" Kenntnisse beim Leser eine ausführliche Darstellung der Beweise der beiden Primzahlsätze zu geben:

$$\lim_{x\to\infty} \frac{\pi(x) \log x}{x} = 1, \quad \lim_{x\to\infty} \frac{\pi(k, l; x)}{x} = \frac{1}{\phi(k)}.$$

Die Beweisführung stützt sich in ihren wesentlichen Teilen auf die Arbeiten von A. Selberg und H. N. Shapiro, kombiniert ihre Gedankengänge und vereinfacht in mancher

Beziehung den rechnerischen Apparat; zum Teil werden auch ältere Überlegungen von E. Landau herangezogen.
*Aus der Einleitung.*

## N02-6 (41# 8358)

**К. Прахар [Prahar, K.] [Prachar, Karl]**

**Распределение простых чисел.** (Russian) **[Distribution of prime numbers]**

Translated from the German by A. A. Karacuba. Edited by A. I. Vinogradov. With two supplements by M. B. Barban and A. I. Vinogradov, and N. M. Korobov. *Izdat. "Mir", Moscow*, 1967. 511 *pp.* 2.25 *r.*

The German original has been reviewed [Springer, Berlin, 1957; MR **19**, 393]. The first supplement (pp. 464–478), by M. B. Barban and A. I. Vinogradov, is on the large sieve and follows the treatment of E. Bombieri [Mathematika **12** (1965), 201–225; MR **33** #5590], while the second (pp. 479–499) is on the method of trigonometric sums and contains various of the author's, i.e., N. M. Korobov's, results on the subject, most of which can be found in the book of A. Z. Val′fiš [*Weylsche Exponentialsummen in der neueren Zahlentheorie*, VEB Deutsch. Verlag Wissensch., Berlin, 1963; MR **36** #3737].

Citations: MR 19, 393b = N02-7; MR 33# 5590 = M55-43; MR 36# 3737 = L02-8.
Referred to in N04-57.

## N02-7 (19, 393b)

**Prachar, Karl. Primzahlverteilung.** Springer-Verlag, Berlin-Göttingen-Heidelberg, 1957. x+415 pp. DM 55.00.

This is a comprehensive and up-to-date treatise covering most aspects of the theory of the distribution of primes. Its scope may be judged from the chapter headings. I. Elementary results; II. Sieve methods; III. The prime number theorem; IV. Primes in an arithmetical progression; V. Various applications; VI. The Goldbach problem; VII. Functiontheoretic properties of the $L$-functions. Explicit formulae and their applications; VIII. Trigonometric sums; IX. Theorems on the density of zeros of the $L$-functions and their application in prime number theory; X. The smallest prime in an arithmetical progression; Appendix; Literature; Index. Some remarks may be added by way of amplification. Chapter II is devoted to A. Selberg's modification of Brun's method, and deals only with upper bounds. Chapter III contains an analytical proof on classical lines, and a version of the elementary proof. Chapter VII includes a discussion of $\Omega$-theorems, leading to Littlewood's theorem that $\pi(x) > \operatorname{li} x$ for arbitrarily large $x$. Various aspects of the problem of the difference between consecutive primes are discussed in V and IX. Chapter VIII includes an account of Vinogradov's method, with applications to the $L$-functions. Chapter $X$ is devoted to the very difficult theorem of Linnik that the least prime in the arithmetical progression $kx+l$ $(0<l<k,\ (l, k)=1;\ x=0, 1, 2, \cdots)$ is less than $k^C$, where $C$ is an absolute constant. General theorems not specifically concerned with primes are collected (usually with proofs) in an Appendix. This is a convenient arrangement, but it sometimes has the effect of making proofs in the body of the text appear deceptively short, since most of the work is done in the Appendix. The main text is supplemented by useful collections of examples at the ends of the chapters. These contain statements of further results, or indications of alternative proofs of results established in the relevant chapter. There are copious references to original sources.

The presentation usually follows the recent literature, but in some cases the author has preferred older methods. The treatment is full and clear, and in general accurate, but there is a curious lapse on pp. 145–146, where it is stated that Deuring [Math. Z. **37** (1933), 405–415] proved that the absence of zeros of $\zeta(\sigma+it)$ in the half-plane $\sigma>\frac{1}{2}$ implies the truth of Gauss's conjecture that there is only a finite number of negative fundamental discriminants $d=-k$ for which $h(d)=1$, where $h(d)$ is the number of classes of positive definite binary quadratic forms of discriminant $d$. It was in fact the contrary hypothesis (the existence of a zero in $\sigma>\frac{1}{2}$) that was proved by Deuring to have the stated consequence. (This was an implication in the opposite direction to an earlier one of Hecke, and it was by bringing the two together and bridging the gap between them that Heilbronn proved Gauss's conjecture.)

This book is a most valuable addition to the literature of prime number theory. Workers in this field owe a great debt of gratitude to the author for making such a wealth of material readily accessible in the relatively small compass of a little over 400 pages. The chapters need not be read consecutively, for, as the author points out in his preface, the material is so arranged that the reader can exercise considerable freedom in varying the order and selecting particular topics for study. *A. E. Ingham.*

Referred to in M25-53, M25-90, M30-31, M55-43, N02-6, N02-16, N04-57, N08-32, N08-35, N12-27, N12-38, N12-40, N16-20, N16-21, N28-58, N28-67, N56-22, P32-63, P44-26, R42-25, R44-27, R44-28.

## N02-8 (28# 1180)

**Knapowski, S.**

**A survey of some problems in analytic number theory concerning the distribution of primes. (Polish)**

*Wiadom. Mat.* (2) **6**, 115–134 (1963).

Expository paper. Proofs of the prime number theorem, Littlewood's theorem about $\pi(x)-\operatorname{li} x$ and Hardy's theorem about the zeros of $\zeta(s)$ are outlined.
*A. Schinzel* (Warsaw)

## N02-9 (28# 3954)

**Ayoub, Raymond**

**An introduction to the analytic theory of numbers.**

Mathematical Surveys, No. 10.
*American Mathematical Society, Providence, R.I.*, 1963. xiv+379 *pp.* $10.20.

The scope of the book may be judged from the chapter headings: (I) Dirichlet's theorem on primes in an arithmetic progression; (II) Distribution of primes; (III) The theory of partitions; (IV) Waring's problem; (V) Dirichlet $L$-functions and the class number of quadratic fields; Appendix A (gamma function); Appendix B (functional equations).

Any book of modest size on such a vast subject as the analytic theory of numbers must be highly selective, and each reader will no doubt have his own view of the ideal selection within a given compass. No comment is offered here on the general plan, which must be largely arbitrary; but some questions may be raised on the organization of material within the chosen fields. The book is an "Introduction" and does not aim at reaching the frontiers of knowledge, but there is a certain unevenness in the balance between classical and more modern results in the various fields. Thus, the chapter on Waring's problem includes some of Vinogradov's work, but the chapter on distribution of primes does not include an elementary proof of the prime number theorem. This omission is naturally linked in the sophisticated reader's mind with the inclusion of several pages on "equivalences" between various theorems of prime number theory. Such equivalences were important and fascinating under the old classification of "elementary" and "transcendental", and may still serve as an unofficial guide to strategy in the selection and arrangement of proofs of the main theorems. But they lost most of their significance when the prime number theorem itself became "elementary"; and the reader for whom this book is indeed an introduction may wonder what logical meaning he is to attach to a formal statement that two theorems (involving no variable element) are equivalent, beyond the fact that both are true.

In order to cater for different classes of reader the author has adopted the policy of leading up to his final results by way of simpler ones. It may be thought that this has been carried too far in some places; but this is a matter of taste, and many readers will no doubt welcome the leisurely approach to the more comprehensive results, with the opportunity of breaking off before the end is reached.

At this point it must be stated, with regret, that the presentation is marred by some serious defects. There is a certain lack of economy, in that details are needlessly repeated in special cases when a general result might be quoted. Thus, on p. 19 and on p. 20, most of the calculation could be avoided by appeals to (I) Lemma 3.1. Again (pp. 102, 105) individual instances of Euler's identity are worked out without reference to the general result. This entails some bold expansions that really call for comment if they are written down at all; but they need not be written down if (I) Theorem 1.5 is quoted. But the main ground for criticism is the inordinately large number of inaccuracies of detail. These occur with depressing regularity throughout the book, and a comprehensive list is out of the question. But we note some typical instances. (Numbers refer to pages.)

4. Conditions for Euler's identity (Theorem 1.5) incorrectly stated. Counterexample: $f(n)$ multiplicative; $f(p)=-1$, $f(p^2)=1+p^{-2}$, $f(p^\nu)=0$ $(\nu \geqq 3)$. (Product $\prod(1+p^{-2})$ absolutely convergent, series $\sum f(n)$ not convergent.) Correct statement: identity holds if either side is convergent when every $f(.)$ in it is replaced by its modulus.

21. "there exists a region enclosing the real axis for $s>\sigma_0$ in which the series (23) converges uniformly." False unless the series converges at $s=\sigma_0$.

37. "$n$ is a prime if and only if $n!+1$ is divisible by $n$."

62–64, Theorems 4.6, 4.7, 4.8. Inequalities $\log T \geqq |t| > 1$ should presumably read $T \geqq |t| > 1$. (See application on pp. 68–9.)

92. "The requisite properties (and more) have already been established in Corollary 2 of Theorem 4.2." Since this theorem precedes any consideration of zeros, this might suggest that the Hardy-Littlewood proof of the prime number theorem is free from such considerations. Admittedly, this impression is corrected by the preceding remark about regularity of $-\zeta'(s)/\zeta(s)$ for $\sigma \geqq 1$, $s \neq 1$, but the sentence quoted is in itself misleading.

98. The possibility $L=\infty$ is ignored.

106, Theorem 7.6. Definitions and identities should be for all $x \geqq 1$. Equivalence does not extend to all real $x$ unless $f(x)$ and $g(x)$ are defined as 0 for $x<1$. (But the author is not the only delinquent here.)

129. Numerical values of $\pi(x)$ are taken from Gauss's works, and not from more recent (and presumably more accurate) sources.

153. "$H=\ldots=O(\sigma^{1/4})$." Apparently $O(..)$ must be (mis)read as meaning 'exactly of order..'; for the application requires an inequality $H>\ldots$.

218, 222, 237–8, etc. Back-handed technique for convergence proofs. It is scarcely logical to conduct such proofs in terms of symbols that are not known to be meaningful until after the required convergence has been established. Nor is absolute convergence correctly expressed by saying that the infinite series or integral in question is "$O(1)$". Such techniques are acceptable when summand or integrand is non-negative (so that there is always a 'value', finite or infinite), but this is not the case here.

237. Fallacy with (first) mean-value theorem when the factor retained in the integrand is not of fixed sign.

238. Argument of doubtful validity as it stands, since "absolute convergence" (lines 8–9) refers, not to the multiple integral, but to a special arrangement as a repeated integral.

241. Meaningless group of symbols of the form $\lim_{n\to\infty} f(n)=g(n)$.

256, Theorem 8.1. False for $p=2$, $r \geqq 3$ (and the reference on p. 257 only covers the case $r=1$).

296. $L(1,\chi)$ written as product over $p$ with no mention of convergence.

364. "the interchange of integration and summation being clearly justified." No mention of the condition $\sigma>1$; indeed it is (wrongly) stated later that the integral is "well behaved for $\sigma>0$".

365, (12). Variable $y$ retained after integration over $-1 \leqq y \leqq 1$.

There are also some systematic peculiarities of style, such as: (1) incomplete statement of conditions in enunciations (as in Waring's problem, where the text may have to be searched for the current restriction on $s$), or incorrect statement (as in (I) Lemma 3.2, where continuity is not enough to make sense of the enunciation); (2) omission of modulus signs in several places; (3) a tendency to ignore questions of regularity (as on pp. 81–2, where several statements may be false or meaningless under the restriction $\gamma \geqq 0$, or even $\gamma > 0$). The bibliography of 30 items, and the references scattered through the book, contain several mistakes in the spelling of authors' names and in the titles of books or papers.

In spite of its imperfections, however, the book has some positive merits. Complicated arguments are usually prefaced by clear and accurate explanations of the basic ideas, before ideas tend to become obscured by details. The subject matter includes topics not usually found in books in English, such as Hua's contribution to Waring's problem (which was overshadowed by Vinogradov's work but not rendered entirely obsolete), Rademacher's identity for the partition function in a self-contained treatment including proofs of the transformation formulae from first principles, and a connected account of various matters relating to the class number $h(d)$. The author does not always choose what might seem to be the simplest methods available, but it is clear from the problems and notes at the ends of the chapters that he is aware of the alternatives and has therefore made his choice deliberately. The generous collections of problems give the reader an opportunity of extending his knowledge and of picking up some interesting historical points.

{On p. 71, and again on p. 131, currency is given to the belief that the prime number theorem has been proved with error $O(xe^{-c\lambda(x)})$, where $\lambda(x)=(\log x)^{3/5}$. This result was claimed by I. M. Vinogradov and by N. M. Korobov in 1958, and has been widely quoted. So far as the reviewer is aware, however, no proof has been published, and various workers who have tried to reconstruct the details have had to be content with the less elegant result involving

$$\lambda_1(x) = (\log x)^{3/5}(\log\log x)^{-1/5}$$

in place of $\lambda(x)$. See the remarks on pp. 226–7 of A. Walfisz, *Weylsche Exponentialsummen in der neueren Zahlentheorie* [VEB Deutscher Verlag der Wiss., Berlin, 1963; author's reference 29, corrected]. It is highly desirable that the claim to the stronger and neater result should be substantiated or withdrawn without further delay.}

*A. E. Ingham* (Cambridge, England)

**N02-10** **(29# 4744 )**

**Maier, Wilhelm**

**Aus der analytischen Zahlentheorie.**

*S.-B. Sächs. Akad. Wiss. Leipzig Math.-Natur. Kl.* **105**, *no.* 4, 15 *pp.* (1963).

An expository article on the distribution of primes, and the analytic functions which have played an important role in research in that subject.

*W. J. LeVeque* (Ann Arbor, Mich.)

**N02-11** **(32# 2391 )**

**Ingham, A. E.**

**The distribution of prime numbers.**

Cambridge Tracts in Mathematics and Mathematical Physics, No. 30.

*Stechert-Hafner, Inc., New York,* 1964. v + 114 *pp.* $3.00.

This is a reprinting of the first edition, originally published in 1932 by Cambridge University Press.

Referred to in M25-79, N80-42.

**N02-12** **(35# 4176 )**

**Cugiani, Marco**

**Recenti progressi nello studio della distribuzione dei numeri primi.**

*Atti del Settimo Congresso dell'Unione Matematica Italiana (Genova,* 1963), *pp.* 214–237. *Edizioni Cremonese, Rome,* 1965.

In diesem Übersichtsartikel skizziert der Autor Ergebnisse über die Verteilung der Primzahlen, die teils klassisch, teils neueren Datums sind.

Nach numerischen Ergebnissen über Fermatsche und Mersennesche Primzahlen (im I. Teil) gibt der II. Teil Ergebnisse zum Primzahlsatz von Čebyšev (1850), Hadamard und de la Vallée-Poussin (1896), Littlewood (1922) und Vinogradov [Izv. Akad. Nauk SSSR Ser. Mat. **22** (1958), 161–164; MR **21** #2624], sowie den Taubersatz von Ikehara. {Bemerkung: In Formel (4) ist das Restglied $O(x\exp(-\alpha\log^{3/5}x))$ durch

$$O(x\exp(-\alpha\log^{3/5}x(\log\log x)^{1/5}))$$

zu ersetzen [vgl. A. Z. Valfiš, *Welysche Exponentialsummen in der neueren Zahlentheorie*, pp. 187, 226, VEB Deutsch. Verlag Wissensch., Berlin, 1963].} Im III. Teil werden Primzahlen in der arithmetischen Progression, Bruns Siebmethode, Primzahlzwillinge und Abschätzungen der Differenz aufeinanderfolgender Primzahlen nach oben und unten behandelt. Der IV. Teil kreist um den elementaren Beweis des Primzahlsatzes.

Ein guter Teil der neueren Fortschritte in der Primzahltheorie wird in der vorliegenden Arbeit nicht erwähnt, wie etwa die Abschätzung der kleinsten Primzahl einer arithmetischen Progression [Ju. V. Linnik, Mat. Sb. (N.S.) **15 (57)** (1944), 139–178; MR **6**, 260; ibid. **15 (57)** (1944), 347–368; MR **6**, 260], der Satz von Brun-Titchmarsh und dessen Verschärfungen [vgl. J. van Lint und H. Richert, Acta Arith. **11** (1965), 209–216; MR **32** #5613], Turáns Methode und ihre Anwendungen in der "comparative prime number theory" [Acta Math. Akad. Sci. Hungar. **13** (1962), 299–314; MR **26** #3682a; ibid. **13** (1962), 315–342; MR **26** #3682b; ibid. **13** (1962), 343–364; MR **26** #3682c und weitere Arbeiten von S. Knapowski und P. Turán], Fortschritte beim Goldbachproblem durch Abschätzungen nach unten bei der Siebmethode, die mit dem großen Sieb erzielten Abschätzungen [vgl. etwa die zusammenfassende Darstellung bei M. B. Barban, Uspehi Mat. Nauk **21** (1966), no. 1, 51–102; MR **33** #7320], sowie die Lösung eines Hardy-Littlewoodschen Problems durch C. Hooley [Acta Math. **97** (1957), 189–210; MR **19**, 532] und Ju. V. Linnik [*The dispersion method in binary additive problems* (Russian), Izdat. Leningrad. Univ., Leningrad, 1961; MR **25** #3920; English translation, Amer. Math. Soc., Providence, R.I., 1963; MR **29** #5804].

*W. Schwarz* (Freiburg)

Citations: MR 6, 260b = N16-5; MR 6, 260c = N16-6; MR 19, 532a = P36-17; MR 21# 2624 = M15-19; MR 25# 3920 = P02-18; MR 26# 3682a = N12-23; MR 26# 3682b = N12-23; MR 26# 3682c = N12-23; MR 29# 5804 = P02-19; MR 32# 5613 = N12-38; MR 33# 7320 = Z02-53; MR 36# 3737 = L02-8.

**N02-13** **(36# 117 )**

**Davenport, Harold**

**Multiplicative number theory.**

Lectures given at the University of Michigan, Winter Term, 1966. Lectures in Advanced Mathematics, No. 1.

*Markham Publishing Co., Chicago, Ill.,* 1967. vii + 189 *pp.*

The scope of this book is best characterized by the following passages taken from the author's preface: "My principal object in these lectures was to give a connected account of analytic number theory insofar as it relates to problems of a multiplicative character, with particular attention to the distribution of primes in arithmetic progressions. My secondary object was to prove, in the course of this account, all the results quoted from the literature in the recent paper of E. Bombieri [Mathematika **12** (1965), 201–225; MR **33** #5590] on the average distribution of primes in arithmetic progressions; and to end by giving an exposition of this work, which seems likely to play an important part in future researches. The choice of what was included in the main body of the lectures and what was omitted, has been greatly influenced by this consideration."

Accordingly, the first part of the book covers Dirichlet's theorem on primes in arithmetic progressions, Dirichlet's class number formula, the functional equation and the distribution of zeros of the $L$-functions, the explicit formula for $\psi(x,\chi)$, the prime number number theorem for arithmetic progressions and Siegel's theorem on the zeros of $L$-functions.

The second part starts with a discussion of the large sieve method of Linnik and Rényi in its classical form, and then leads to the most recent versions by Roth and Bombieri. The main theorem on estimates of exponential sums (Theorem 1) is taken from a joint paper by the author and H. Halberstam [ibid. **13** (1966), 91–96; MR **33** #5592], which provides a simpler proof and a more general result than Bombieri's original theorem. (Meanwhile, along the lines of this proof the result has been sharpened again; see a forthcoming paper by Bombieri and the author; also, as indicated in the addenda, another approach was given by P. X. Gallagher [ibid. **14** (1967), 14–20; MR **35** #5411].) This is followed by a series of results of a similar kind, in particular those involving character sums. (As was pointed out by L. Schoenfeld, there is an oversight in the proof of Theorem 4, corresponding in Theorem 4A in the original paper of the author and Halberstam [loc. cit.]; see Mathematika **14** (1967), 229–232; MR **36** #2569. However, the corollaries are correct, and it is only these corollaries which are used later on.)

The following sections provide a complete proof of Bombieri's prime number theorem: Let $\psi(x;q,a)=\sum_{n\leqq x;\, n\equiv a \bmod q}\Lambda(n)$. Then, for any positive $A$, there exists a positive constant $B$ such that

$$\sum_{q\leqq x^{1/2}(\log x)^{-B}} \max_{(a,q)=1} \max_{y\leqq x} |\psi(y;q,a)-y/\phi(q)| \ll x(\log x)^{-A}.$$

Here, following Bombieri's paper, the main tool is a density theorem on the zeros of $L$-functions which in turn is proved by one of the new versions of the large sieve. {Regarding this result the following paper should be mentioned: A. I. Vinogradov, Izv. Akad. Nauk SSSR Ser. Mat. **29** (1965), 903–934 [MR **33** #5579]; correction, ibid. **30** (1966), 719–720 [MR **33** #2607].}

The reader will of course find many points, both in choice of material and information which he has not seen in other expositions of this subject. However, most of all, one has to be very grateful to the author for making the important new work on the large sieve readily accessible so soon. Indeed, in the recent development of number theory there are very few methods with so great an influence on further investigations with respect to both the number and the depth of the results.

*H.-E. Richert* (Marburg)

Citations: MR 33# 2607 = P32-67; MR 33# 5579 = P32-66; MR 33# 5590 = M55-43; MR 33# 5592 = M55-45; MR 35# 5411 = M55-52; MR 36# 2569 = M55-46.

Referred to in M25-69, M55-76, N02-16, P40-23.

## N02-14 (36# 2572)

**Turán, Pál**

**On some problems in comparative prime number theory. (Hungarian)**

*Mat. Lapok* **17** (1966), 19–32.

In this expository paper the author discusses some of the results he and the late Knapowski obtained on the comparative theory of primes (i.e., the study of the irregularities of the distribution of primes in arithmetic progressions). They published so far more than ten papers on this subject [see, e.g., S. Knapowski and the author, Acta Arith. **12** (1966/67), 85–96; MR **34** #149]. Stated here are one of their results and one of their unsolved problems: For all sufficiently large $T$ there are consecutive primes $p_v$ and $p_{v+1}$ satisfying $\log\log\log T\leqq p_v<p_{v+1}<T$, $p_v\equiv p_{v+1}\equiv 1 \pmod 4$. For primes $\equiv 3 \pmod 4$ the corresponding limits are $(T\exp(-(\log T)^{1/2}), T)$. It is not known if there are infinitely many triples of consecutive primes $p_v\equiv p_{v+1}\equiv p_{v+2} \pmod 4$.

*P. Erdős* (Budapest)

Citations: MR 34# 149 = N12-39.

## N02-15 (39# 1420)

**Schwarz, Wolfgang**

**Der Primzahlsatz.**

B. I. Hochschultaschenbücher 161/161a.

*Überblicke Math.* **1** (1968), 35–61.

Expository paper. It is a good introduction to the prime number theorem (PNT) and contains a bibliography of 79 items (up to 1966), that could be useful to anybody who desires to learn about the distribution of primes. It consists of an introduction (tables of primes, statements of the PNT), elementary estimates, the PNT and the Riemann zeta function $\zeta(s)$, properties of $\zeta(s)$, the Riemann hypothesis (in this section are listed several heuristic reasons for and against the validity of the Riemann hypothesis), explicit formulae, Tauberian theorems, elementary proofs of the PNT, generalizations (e.g., the PNT for primes in arithmetic progression), applications (e.g., the Goldbach problem), unsolved problems, selective bibliography.

*E. Grosswald* (Philadelphia, Pa.)

## N02-16 (41# 8350)

**Schwarz, Wolfgang**

**Einführung in Methoden und Ergebnisse der Primzahltheorie.**

B·I-Hochschultaschenbücher, 278/278a*.

*Bibliographisches Institut, Mannheim-Vienna-Zürich,* 1969. 227 *pp.* *DM* 8.90.

This handy paperback volume constitutes a valuable compendium of analytic prime number theory. We shall attempt to convey the flavor of the book by alluding to the contents chapter by chapter.

Chapter 1. Introduction. Primes. The sieve of Eratosthenes. Fermat and Mersenne numbers. Arithmetic functions that represent primes (the formulas of W. H. Mills, E. M. Wright, W. Sierpiński, and C. P. Willans). Chapter 2. Elementary methods. The infinitude of primes. The number of primes not exceeding $x$. The methods of Tchebycheff. Bertrand's postulate. Chapter 3. Elementary proofs of the prime number theorem (PNT). The original elementary proof of Selberg and Erdős. The variations thereof due to V. Nevanlinna and to E. Wirsing and Th. Bang. Chapter 4. Analytic proofs of the PNT. Proof by means of the Riemann-Lebesgue lemma. Proof by means of Cauchy's integral theorem. The Riemann zeta-function. The order of $\zeta(s)$ in the neighborhood of $\sigma=1$. The PNT with an error term. The Riemann hypothesis. Consequences of the PNT. Sums involving the Möbius $\mu$-function. Chapter 5. Tauberian theorems. The Tauberian theorem of Landau and Ikehara. Proof of the PNT by means of Ikehara's Tauberian theorem. Proof of the PNT by means of Wiener's Tauberian theorem. The Tauberian theorem of Hardy-Littlewood-Karamata (the proof of H. König). Chapter 6. Distribution of primes in an arithmetic progression. Elementary results. Characters. Dirichlet's theorem. Application of Tauberian theorems. The theorem of Siegel. Estimation of $L$-series. The PNT with an error term for arithmetic progressions. Chapter 7. The theorem of Goldbach-Vinogradov. Vinogradov's estimate for exponential sums extending over primes. Every sufficiently large odd integer is the sum of three primes. Appendix. Ancillary theorems from number theory and analysis are provided in this supplement. There is also a useful list of references.

Because of the book's pocket size limitation many relevant topics have been excluded. Thus the reader will find nothing on the sieve methods of Brun and Selberg, on the "large sieves" of Linnik and Rényi, on the smallest prime in an arithmetic progression, and on the application of Turán's methods. For more extensive coverage the author cites the deeper texts of H. Halberstam and K. F. Roth [*Sequences*, Vol. I, Clarendon, Oxford, 1966; MR **35** #1565], H. Davenport [*Multiplicative number theory*, Markham, Chicago, Ill., 1967; MR **36** #117], and K. Prachar [*Primzahlverteilung*, Springer, Berlin, 1957; MR **19**, 393].

The author's style is penetrating and yet lucid. All in all, this should be a delightful text for a one year's course on elementary and analytic methods of prime number theory.

*A. L. Whiteman* (Los Angeles, Calif.)

Citations: MR 19, 393b = N02-7; MR 35# 1565 = B02-3; MR 36# 117 = N02-13.

# N04 DISTRIBUTION OF PRIMES: GLOBAL QUESTIONS ($\pi(x)$, ETC.)

See also Sections A38, N12, N20, N80, R44.

See also reviews A48-7, C05-9, L02-4, L15-5, L15-19, L15-21, M15-17, M15-18, M25-81, M30-3, M30-14, M40-28, M40-45, M45-6, M45-30, M45-31, M45-33, M45-39, M45-44, M50-2, N02-1, N02-6, N02-8, N12-14, N20-70, N32-10, N36-49, N36-77, N40-70, N48-19, N80-59, P02-12, P48-2, Q15-1, Q20-27, Z02-4, Z10-9, Z10-32, Z15-71, Z30-51.

## N04-1 (1, 41d)

**Kienast, Alfred. Über die asymptotische Darstellung der summatorischen Funktion von Dirichletreihen mit positiven Koeffizienten.** Math. Z. **45**, 554–558 (1939).

A general asymptotic formula, obtained in a previous paper by an adaptation of Wiener's method [Math. Z. **44**, 115–126 (1938)], is corrected by the addition of further terms in the case in which a certain parameter $\rho$ is non-integral. The correction does not affect (for example) the application to the estimation of the error in the prime number theorem, which is now derived in the Titchmarsh form $e^{-\omega}\psi(e^{\omega})=1+O(e^{-p\omega^q})$, $p>0$, $q=5/9-\epsilon$.

*A. E. Ingham* (Princeton, N. J.).

Referred to in N36-46.

## N04-2 (2, 150e)

**Rosser, Barkley. Explicit bounds for some functions of prime numbers.** Amer. J. Math. **63**, 211–232 (1941).

Denote by $\pi(x)$, $p(n)$ and $\theta(x)$, respectively, the number of primes not exceeding $x$, the $n$th prime and the logarithm of the product of all primes not exceeding $x$. It is known that for each positive constant $A$ there exists a constant $N$ for which the following statements are true:

$$\frac{x}{\log x-1+A}<\pi(x)<\frac{x}{\log x-1-A},\qquad x\geqq N,$$

$$n\log n+n\log\log n-n-An<p(n)$$
$$<n\log n+n\log\log n-n+An,\qquad n\geqq N,$$

$$\left(1-\frac{A}{\log x}\right)x<\theta(x)<\left(1+\frac{A}{\log x}\right)x,\qquad x\geqq N.$$

The author considers two problems: (i) that of determining the $N$ which goes with a particular $A$; (ii) that of determining how small $A$ can be without requiring that $N$ be large. Partial answers are given of which the following are sample results:

$$(1)\qquad \frac{x}{\log x}<\pi(x)<\frac{x}{\log x-2},\qquad 17\leqq x\leqq e^{100};\ x\geqq e^{2000},$$

$$(2)\qquad \frac{x}{\log x+2}<\pi(x)<\frac{x}{\log x-4},\qquad x\geqq 55.$$

It is to be noticed from (1) and (2) that there is a gap from $e^{100}$ to $e^{2000}$ for which we must be satisfied with $A=3$ instead of $A=1$. The author explains that this situation is apparently due to the insufficiency of our information about the zeros of the Riemann zeta function. For $x\leqq 10^6$ the proof is based on comparisons with Lehmer's "List of Prime Numbers" and the ingenious use of a computing machine. For $x\geqq 10^6$ analytical methods are used. These are based on methods discussed in Landau's "Handbuch der Lehre von der Verteilung der Primzahlen," with the later improvements of Backlund, Ingham, Titchmarsh and the author.

*R. D. James* (Saskatoon, Sask.).

Referred to in R12-5.

## N04-3 (2, 347d)

**Wintner, Aurel. On the distribution function of the remainder term of the prime number theorem.** Amer. J. Math. **63**, 233–248 (1941).

Let $\psi(x)=\sum_{p^m\leqq x}\log p$. Then a classical result of Littlewood states that for infinitely many $x$

$$\psi(x)-x>cx^{\frac{1}{2}}\log\log\log x$$

and

$$\psi(x)-x<-cx^{\frac{1}{2}}\log\log\log x.$$

The author proves the following theorem: Let us assume the Riemann hypothesis; then

$$h(t)=\psi(x)-x/x^{\frac{1}{2}},\qquad x=e^t,$$

has a distribution function, which has an unbounded spectrum and moments of arbitrarily high order. The proof depends on the fact proved a few years ago by the author [Amer. J. Math. **57**, 534–538 (1935)] that the trigonometric series occurring in the explicit formula of Riemann is actually the Fourier expansion of the function which it represents. (The Fourier character is meant in the sense ($B^2$) of the theory of almost periodic functions.) *P. Erdös.*

## N04-4 (3, 271a)

**Wintner, Aurel. On the prime number theorem.** Amer. J. Math. **64**, 320–326 (1942).

The author points out advantages of the Tauberian method for certain proofs and discussions in the analytic theory of numbers. He then states and proves a generalization of Ikehara's theorem and shows that it unifies and simplifies the proofs of several theorems, including the prime number theorem. *H. S. Zuckerman* (Seattle, Wash.).

Referred to in Z02-4.

## N04-5 (4, 35d)

**Wintner, Aurel. On an elementary analogue of the Riemann-Mangoldt formula.** Bull. Amer. Math. Soc. **48**, 759–762 (1942).

In connection with Ramanujan's attempt to obtain the prime number theorem, Hardy [Ramanujan, Cambridge University Press, Cambridge, England, 1940, chap. 2; these Rev. **3**, 71] gives an expansion for the function $\sum_{n=1}^{\infty}p^n x^{p^n}$ of the same type as the explicit formula of Riemann and von Mangoldt. The author shows that the expansion can be obtained in a simple way and that this approach was found by Dedekind, whose purpose was to show that the argument later used by Ramanujan is incorrect. The present proof of the expansion corrects two errors in the formula as it is given by Hardy. *H. S. Zuckerman.*

Citations: MR 3, 71d = Z20-4.

## N04-6 (4, 98d)

**Guinand, A. P. Summation formulae and self-reciprocal functions. III.** Quart. J. Math., Oxford Ser. **13**, 30–39 (1942).

[The two previous parts appeared in Quart. J. Math., Oxford Ser. **9**, 53–67 (1938) and **10**, 104–118 (1939)].

The author proves that the function

$$F(x)=x^{-1}\{\sum_{n\leqq x}{}'\Lambda(n)-x\}+\tfrac{1}{2}\sum_{\rho}(x^{\rho-1}/\rho)+A(x),$$

where

$$A(x)=\begin{cases}(4x)^{-1}\log((1+x)/(1-x)) & \text{for } x<1,\\ (2x)^{-1}\log(2\pi+j)+(4x)^{-1}\log(x^2-1) & \text{for } x>1,\end{cases}$$

satisfies the relation

$$F(x)=x^{-1}F(x^{-1})-x^{-1}\int_{x^{-1}}^{\infty}F(t)dt/t.$$

This leads to a general summation formula which the author does not substantiate in detail. He also shows that, for $0<\Re(\alpha)<\frac{1}{2}$, a function

$$F_\alpha(x)=x^{\alpha-1}\{\sum_{n\leq x}{}'\Lambda(n)n^{-\alpha}-x^{1-\alpha}/(1-\alpha)\}+\tfrac{1}{2}\sum_\rho(x^{\rho-1}/(\rho-\alpha))+A_\alpha(x)$$

satisfies the relation

$$F_\alpha(x)=x^{-1}F_\alpha(x^{-1})+(2\alpha-1)x^{\alpha-1}\int_{x-1}^{\infty}t^{\alpha-1}F_\alpha(t)dt.$$

However, this case presupposes the Riemann hypothesis.

*S. Bochner* (Princeton, N. J.).

**N04-7** **(6, 169a)**

**Terrill, H. M., and Sweeny, Lucile. Two constants connected with the theory of prime numbers.** J. Franklin Inst. **239**, 242–243 (1945).

The authors determine to 23 decimal places the value of the limit

$$\lim_{x\to\infty}(\sum_{p\leq x}p^{-1}-\log\log x)=C+\sum_p\{p^{-1}+\log(1-p^{-1})\}$$

$$=.26149\ 72128\ 47642\ 78375\ 543,$$

where $C$ is Euler's constant [see, for example, Hardy and Wright, Theory of Numbers, Oxford University Press, 1938, p. 350]. Two calculations were made of the last sum, first writing it as $-\sum_{k=2}^{\infty}k^{-1}\sum_p p^{-k}$ and then as $-\sum_{k=2}^{\infty}\mu(k)\zeta(k)$. Values of $\sum p^{-k}$ and $\zeta(k)$ were taken from H. T. Davis, Tables of the Higher Mathematical Functions, The Principia Press, Bloomington, Ind., 1935, v. 2, pp. 244, 249, 250.

*D. H. Lehmer* (Berkeley, Calif.).

**N04-8** **(6, 172f)**

**Wintner, Aurel. Gibbs' phenomenon and the prime number theorem.** Amer. J. Math. **67**, 167–172 (1945).

If $p$ denotes a prime and $S(x)=\int_0^x u^{-1}\sin u\,du$, then

$$\sum_{p\leq m}p^{-1}\sin(t\log p)-S(t\log m)$$

tends to a finite limit as $m\to\infty$, uniformly in every finite interval $|t|<T$. It should be noted that $S(x)$ is bounded.

*S. Bochner* (Princeton, N. J.).

**N04-9** **(7, 146h)**

**Linnik, U. V. On a theorem in the theory of primes.** C. R. (Doklady) Acad. Sci. URSS (N.S.) **47**, 7–9 (1945).

The formula

$$\sum_{x=1}^{N^{\frac{1}{2}}}[\psi\{(x+1)^2\}-2\psi\{(x+\tfrac{1}{2})^2\}+\psi(x^2)]=O(N^{63/64}),$$

where $\psi(x)$ is Chebyshev's function from the theory of prime numbers, is proved by means of results due to Hoheisel [S.-B. Preuss. Akad. Wiss. **1930**, 72–82 (1930)]; cf. Ingham [Quart. J. Math., Oxford Ser. **8**, 255–266 (1937)] and Segal [Trav. Inst. Math. Stekloff **4**, 37–48, 49–62 (1933)].

*H. D. Kloosterman* (Leiden).

**N04-10** **(8, 197e)**

**Brun, Viggo. The integral-logarithm as an expression for the number of prime numbers less than $x$.** Norsk Mat. Tidsskr. **26**, 41–50 (1944). (Norwegian)

**N04-11** **(8, 316g)**

**Selmer, Ernst S. A special summation method in the theory of prime numbers and its application to "Brun's sum."** Norsk Mat. Tidsskr. **24**, 74–81 (1942). (Norwegian)

The author discusses the "probable" order of magnitude of sums of the type $\sum_{p\leq x}F(p)$ extended over all primes not exceeding $x$; the hypotheses are compared with the results of numerical calculations.

*T. Nagell* (Uppsala).

**N04-12** **(8, 316i)**

**Selmer, Ernst S. Two series for the sum $\vartheta(x)=\sum_{p\leq x}\ln p$.** Norsk Mat. Tidsskr. **25**, 37–40 (1943). (Norwegian)

Discussion of the following asymptotic formula for the sum of the title:

$$\vartheta(x)\sim\sum_{s=2}^{\infty}(\log x)^s/\{s!\zeta(s)\}.$$

*T. Nagell* (Uppsala).

**N04-13** **(10, 104g)**

**Guinand, A. P. A summation formula in the theory of prime numbers.** Proc. London Math. Soc. (2) **50**, 107–119 (1948).

The Riemann hypothesis is assumed to be true. Let $N(t)$ denote the number of zeros $s=\frac{1}{2}+i\gamma$ of the Riemann zeta function $\zeta(s)$, satisfying $0<\gamma<t$; the Hankel transform $2\pi G(x)$ of order $\frac{3}{2}$ of the function

$$2\pi F(x)=1-\log(x/2\pi)+2\pi N(x)/x$$

is found explicitly in terms of $\sum p^{-\frac{1}{2}m}\log p$ (summed over $0<m\log p\leq x$) and elementary functions. For suitable functions $f(x)$, the functions $xf'(x)$ and $xg'(x)$ are a pair of Hankel transforms of order $\frac{3}{2}$, when $g(x)$ is the cosine transform of $f(x)$ [Guinand, Ann. of Math. (2) **42**, 591–603 (1941); these Rev. **3**, 109]. These two results, when combined with the Parseval relation $\int_0^\infty xf'(x)G(x)dx=\int_0^\infty xg'(x)F(x)dx$, lead to summation formulae involving $\sum p^{-\frac{1}{2}m}(\log p)f(m\log p)$ summed over $0<m\log p<x$ and $\sum g(\gamma)$ summed over $0<\gamma<x$.

*P. Hartman* (Baltimoı . Md.).

Referred to in N04-56.

**N04-14** **(10, 285f)**

**Romanov, N. P. Concerning the distribution of prime numbers.** Mat. Sbornik N.S. **23**(65), 259–278 (1948). (Russian)

Let $\Lambda(n)$, $\mu(n)$ and $\varphi(n)$ be the functions of von Mangoldt, Möbius and Euler, respectively, and let

$$Q_n(x)=-\mu(n)x+\sum_{d|n}\mu(n/d)\frac{dx^d}{1-x^d}=\sum_\rho\frac{\rho^2x^2}{1-\rho x},$$

where $\rho$ runs through the $\varphi(n)$ primitive $n$th roots of unity. In the course of the paper the following result of Hardy and Littlewood is applied several times:

(A) $$\lim_{r\to1-0}(1-r)\sum_{n=1}^{\infty}c_nr^n=A,\qquad c_n\geqq0,$$

implies $\lim_{N\to\infty}N^{-1}\sum_{n=1}^{N}c_n=A$. The author proves, by elementary methods, the formula

(B) $$\sum_{m=1}^{\infty}m^{-1}\varphi(m)\Lambda(m)x^m=\sum_{n=1}^{\infty}\{\mu(n)/\varphi(n)\}Q_n(x),\qquad |x|<1.$$

This is achieved by considering partial sums of the second

series which are shown to tend to the first series as the number of terms included is increased. The second series, when multiplied by $1-|x|$, is uniformly convergent for $x=re^{2\pi il/k}$, $(k,l)=1$, as $r\to 1-0$, and it is shown that the prime number theorem, and the corresponding result (C) $\pi(k,l;x)\sim x/\{\varphi(k)\log x\}$ for the number of primes in an arithmetic progression, can be deduced quite simply from this fact. However, the uniform convergence cannot be deduced from the elementary proof of (B) which is given, and the author has to make use of complex variable methods which are of the same depth as the prime number theorem, as proved by Hadamard and de la Vallée Poussin, in order to prove that the convergence is uniform. The analysis is complicated and an adequate account of the methods used cannot be given here.

Other applications of the same ideas are given, and (B) is generalised to sequences of exponents $n_1, n_2, \cdots$ in place of $1, 2, \cdots$. An alternative method of deducing (C) is sketched. This is based on the result

(D) $$\limsup_{x\to\exp(2\pi il/k)} (1-|x|)|F_s(x)-F(x)|\leqq A(s-1),$$

where $F(x)=\sum_{n=1}^{\infty}\Lambda(n)x^n$ and

$$F_s(x)=\sum_{n=1}^{\infty}\lambda(n,s)x^n=\zeta(s)\sum_{n=1}^{\infty}x^n\prod_{p|n}(1-p^{1-s}).$$

Here $\zeta(s)$ denotes the Riemann zeta-function and $\lambda(n,s)\to\Lambda(n)$ as $s\to 1$. It is shown that it is sufficient to prove that

(E) $$\sum_{n\leqq N}\frac{d}{ds}\lambda(n,s)=O(N) \qquad (n\equiv l(\mathrm{mod}\ k)),$$

uniformly for $1\leqq s\leqq 2$. Only the first part of the proof of (E) is given in full, so that it is not clear to the reviewer whether the complete proof uses complex variable methods or not. If it does not, the author has obtained an elementary proof of (C) and the full details would be of interest.

The application of the method to problems such as that of Goldbach for two primes is sketched. Here again everything hinges on the uniform convergence of the series obtained, and it is shown that, if this is assumed, the conjectured asymptotic formulae follow. The paper is a sequel to, but is largely independent of, a previous paper [Bull. Acad. Sci. URSS. Sér. Math. [Izvestia Akad. Nauk SSSR] **10**, 3–34 (1946); these Rev. **8**, 9]. *R. A. Rankin.*

Citations: MR 8, 9c = Q20-20.

## N04-15 (11, 419b)

**Rényi, Alfred. On a theorem of Erdös and Turán.** Proc. Amer. Math. Soc. **1**, 7–10 (1950).

The theorem referred to in the title states that, if $p_n$ denotes the $n$th prime, then the sequence $\log p_n$ is neither convex nor concave for all sufficiently large $n$, that is, the sequence $p_{n+1}p_{n-1}-p_n^2$ changes sign infinitely often [Erdös and Turan, Bull. Amer. Math. Soc. **54**, 371–378 (1948); these Rev. **9**, 498]. The present paper establishes the following more general result. The total curvature $G_N=\sum_{k=2}^{n-1}|\arg(z_{k+1}-z_k)/(z_k-z_{k-1})|$ of the polygonal line having vertices $z_k=k+i\log p_k$, $p_n\leqq N$, exceeds $c\log\log\log N$, where $c$ is a positive constant. It is clear that if the sequence $\log p_n$ were convex (or concave) for all sufficiently large $n$, the total curvature would be finite. The proof uses the prime number theorem in the form $\pi(n)\sim n/\log n$, and the result $p_{n+1}-p_n=O(p_n/\log^2 p_n)$. It is shown first of all that $G_N\geqq c_3\sum_{p_{n+1}\leqq N}(\Delta_n/p_n)-c_4$, where $\Delta_n=p_{n+1}-2p_n+p_{n-1}$ and $c_3$, $c_4$ are positive constants. A lower bound for the sum is then found by estimating the number of primes $p_{n+1}\leqq N$ for which $\Delta_n\neq 0$. This leads to the final result. The author remarks that whether there exist blocks of primes $p_{\nu_r}, p_{\nu_r+1}, \cdots, p_{\nu_r+k_r}$ with $\Delta_{\nu_r+\nu}=0$, $\nu=1,2,\cdots,k_r$, of any length $k_r$ and whether there exist infinitely many $k$ for which $\Delta_k=0$ are unsolved problems. *R. D. James.*

Citations: MR 9, 498k = N08-6.

## N04-16 (13, 208f)

**Turán, Paul. On the remainder-term of the prime-number formula. I.** Acta Math. Acad. Sci. Hungar. **1**, 48–63 (1950). (English. Russian summary)

Let $\Delta(x)=\psi(x)-x$ and $M(T)\doteq\max_{1\leqq x\leqq T}|\Delta(x)|$. E. Schmidt [Math. Ann. **57**, 195–204 (1903)] showed that $\Delta(T)=\Omega_\pm(T^{\frac12})$. In this paper the author gives an explicit lower bound for $M(T)$. A specialization of his result is that there are positive numerical constants $c$ and $d$ (which may be calculated) such that for all $T>c$ we have

$$M(T)>T^{\frac12}\exp(-d\log T\log\log\log T/\log\log T).$$

For integral $x$, $\Delta(x)=\sum_{n\leqq x}\{\Lambda(n)-1\}$. The author now defines $F(s)=\sum_{n=1}^{\infty}\{\Lambda(n)-1\}/n^s$ and

$$J=(2\pi i)^{-1}\int_{1+\eta-iU}^{1+\eta+iU}\xi^s s^{-k-1}F(s)ds,$$

where $\eta$, $U$, $\xi$, and $k$ are suitable functions of $T$. The author easily obtains an upper estimate for $J$ in terms of $M(T)$; but the determination of a lower estimate is more difficult and the author appeals to previous results of his [Izvestiya Akad. Nauk SSSR. Ser. Mat. **11**, 197–262 (1947); J. London Math. Soc. **21**, 268–275 (1947); these Rev. **9**, 80] which give a lower bound for $|\sum_{k=1}^{n}z_k^r|$ for $r$ in the interval $[m, m+N]$. These upper and lower estimates for $J$ yield the inequality for $M(T)$. *L. Schoenfeld* (Urbana, Ill.).

Citations: MR 9, 80d = M30-7; MR 9, 80e = M30-8.
Referred to in M40-28, M50-2, N04-36.

## N04-17 (14, 137e)

**Turán, P. On the remainder-term of the prime-number formula. II.** Acta Math. Acad. Sci. Hungar. **1**, 155–166 (1950). (English. Russian summary)

The usual derivations of estimates of $D(x)=\pi(x)-\mathrm{Li}(x)$ are based on the knowledge of zero-free regions for $\zeta(s)$. For example, it is known that if (i) $\zeta(s)\neq 0$ in $\sigma>1-c/\log^\beta|t|$, $|t|>c'$, then (ii) $D(x)=O\{x\exp(-c''(\log x)^{1/(1+\beta)})\}$, provided $0<\beta\leqq 1$. Here, the author proves the converse statement that if $0<\beta<1$, then (ii) implies (i). Consequently, it is not possible to improve (ii) (except possibly for the constant $c''$) unless (i) is improved.

The proof depends on obtaining upper and lower bounds for

$$S=\sum_{n\geqq\xi}\Lambda(n)n^{-s}\log^{k+1}n/\xi.$$

Beginning with $\sum\Lambda(n)n^{-it}$, the summation being over a subinterval of $(N, 2N)$, the author replaces $\Lambda(n)$ by $\psi(n)-\psi(n-1)$, uses partial summation, and applies hypothesis (ii) in the form that $\psi(x)-x$ has the same estimate as that given for $D(x)$. By using partial summation, $\sum\Lambda(n)n^{-s}$ is now estimated. Now the function $f_2(s,\eta)=\sum_{n>\eta}\Lambda(n)n^{-s}$ is estimated from above by breaking the range $n>\eta$ up into a number of sub-intervals of the form $(\eta 2^i, \eta 2^{i+1})$. Since $S/(k+1)=\int_\xi^\infty f_2(s,\eta)\eta^{-1}\log^k(\eta/\xi)d\eta$, an upper bound for $S$ is thereby obtained. $S$ is now expressed as the sum of three terms one of which is $S_1=-(k+1)!\sum_\rho\xi^{\rho-s}/(s-\rho)^{k+2}$. Under the assumption that there is a zero $\rho^*=\sigma^*+it^*$ for which $\sigma^*>1-d/\log^\beta t^*$, $t^*>d'$, the author readily gives upper bounds for the other two terms. There is also no trouble about estimating the contribution to $S_1$ of all those terms which fail to satisfy both the conditions: (iii) $|t_\rho-t^*|<6(\sigma_1-\sigma^*)$ and $\sigma_\rho\geqq 1-3(\sigma_1-\sigma^*)$, where $\sigma_1=1+10d/\log^\beta t^*$. Using all these upper bounds, the author concludes that

$$\Big|\sum_{(\mathrm{iii})}e^{(\rho-\rho^*)/(\sigma_1-1)}\{(s-\rho^*)/(s-\rho)\}^{k+2}\Big|<d''e^{k+2}(t^*)^{-7/8}$$

where $k$ is merely restricted by the condition

$$\log t^* \leqq k+2 \leqq (5/4) \log t^*.$$

At this point the author applies a previous result of his [same Acta **2**, 39–73 (1951); these Rev. **13**, 742] which gives a lower bound for sums of the form $|z_1^{k+2}+\cdots+z_n^{k+2}|$. This result enables the author to choose $k$ in such a fashion that he now finds that $\sigma^* < 1-4d/\log^\beta t^*$; this contradicts the earlier assumption that $\sigma^* > 1-d/\log^\beta t^*$.

The author remarks that routine calculations based on Vinogradov's book [Foundations of the theory of numbers, 5th ed., Moscow-Leningrad, 1949; these Rev. **10**, 599] establish that $\zeta(s)\neq 0$ when $\sigma > 1-f/(\log|t|\log\log|t|)^{2/3}$. Actually, the best published results [T. Flett, Quart. J. Math., Oxford Ser. (2) **2**, 26–52 (1951); these Rev. **13**, 209; E. Titchmarsh, The theory of the Riemann zeta function, Oxford, 1951; these Rev. **13**, 741] are based on Vinogradov's work and have the exponent 2/3 replaced by 3/4. The reviewer is inclined to doubt that 2/3 can be obtained by routine calculation. *L. Schoenfeld* (Urbana, Ill.).

In lines 9 and 10 from the end of the review read "Trav. Inst. Math. Stekloff **23** (1947)" instead of "Foundations of the theory of numbers, 5th ed., Moscow-Leningrad, 1949."

Citations: MR 10, 599a = L02-2; MR 13, 209b = R42-7; MR 13, 741c = M02-2; MR 13, 742a = M25-31.

Referred to in M50-2.

## N04-18 (14, 440g)

**Kreisel, G. On the interpretation of non-finitist proofs. II. Interpretation of number theory. Applications.** J. Symbolic Logic 17, 43–58 (1952).

The author continues the work of part I [same J. **16**, 241–267 (1951); these Rev. **14**, 122] giving a detailed demonstration of the "no-counter-example" interpretation for extensions of the number-theoretic system $Z$ of Hilbert-Bernays obtained by adding free function variables and verifiable free variable formulas as axioms. The complicated work depends upon the $\epsilon$-substitution method of Hilbert-Bernays and Ackermann's consistency proof [see Ackermann, Math. Ann. **117**, 162–194 (1940); these Rev. **1**, 322]. The author applies a method suggested by the general theory to a discussion of Littlewood's theorem that $\pi(n)-\mathrm{li}(n)$ changes sign infinitely often ($\pi(n)$ is the number of primes not exceeding $n$ and $\mathrm{li}(n)$ is the logarithmic integral). Contrary to earlier opinion that the theorem was non-constructive or that "new ideas" of proof would be required to establish it in a constructive way, the author shows that it admits of a constructive interpretation. He also presents a free-variable calculus conjectured to be adequate for the provability of the free-variable formulas of his interpretations. Erratum supplied by the author: p. 57 read "$a_n=\sum_{m=1}^{\infty}a(n,m)2^{-m}$" instead of "$a_n=\sum_{m=1}^{n}a(n,m)2^{-m}$". *D. Nelson* (Washington, D. C.).

Referred to in U99-2.

## N04-19 (16, 676b)

**Ritson, Max. De-gaussing Gauss.** Math. Gaz. 39, 45–46 (1955).

The author points out that a previous attempt by B. E. Lawrence [Math. Gaz. **37**, 280 (1953)] to improve Gauss' approximation $x/\log x$ to the number $\pi(x)$ of primes $\leqq x$ for small $x$ leads to a formula that is asymptotically incorrect. He offers as a substitute

$$\log \pi(x) = \frac{\pi}{10} x^f \{1-x\log(1+x^{-1})\},$$

where $f$ is a function of $x$ which "decreases slowly and steadily to a limit slightly less than 1". Without specifying this function or justifying the factor $\pi/10$ the author gives data to show that the fit is good for $x\leqq 100$ and for $x=1000$. *D. H. Lehmer* (Berkeley, Calif.).

## N04-20 (16, 676c)

**de la Vallée Poussin, Ch.-J. Sur la fonction $\xi(s)$ de Riemann et le nombre des nombres premiers inférieurs à une limite donnée.** Colloque sur la Théorie des Nombres, Bruxelles, 1955, pp. 9–66. Georges Thone, Liège; Masson and Cie, Paris, 1956.

Reprinted from Mémoires de l'Académie royale de Belgique, Classe des Sciences, 1898, tome LIX.

Referred to in N04-36, N04-51.

## N04-21 (18, 112b)

**Skewes, S. On the difference $\pi(x)-\mathrm{li}\,x$. II.** Proc. London Math. Soc. (3) 5, 48–70 (1955).

In Part I of this paper the author assumes hypothesis (H): Every complex zero $\rho=\beta+i\gamma$ of Riemann's zeta function $\zeta(s)$ satisfies

$$\beta-\tfrac{1}{2}\leqq X_1^{-3}\log^{-2}X_1 \quad \text{provided} \quad |\gamma|<X_1^3.$$

On this assumption he proves that $\pi(x)-\mathrm{li}\,x>0$ for some $x$ satisfying $2\leqq x<X_1=\exp\exp\exp(7.703)$.

In a previous paper [J. London Math. Soc. **8**, 277–283 (1933)] the author has obtained a larger value of $X_1$ (the so-called Skewes number) on the assumption of the Riemann hypothesis, whose truth would, of course, imply hypothesis (H). In Part II of the paper the author assumes (NH), the negation of (H). Assuming (NH) the author proves that $\pi(x)-\mathrm{li}\,x>0$ for some $x<X_2$ where

$$X_2=\exp_{10}\exp_{10}\exp_{10}\exp_{10}3.$$

The proofs are complete, except for the omission of certain computational details. *S. Chowla* (Boulder, Colo.).

## N04-22 (18, 112c)

**Errera, A. Sur le théorème fondamental des nombres premiers.** Colloque sur la Théorie des Nombres, Bruxelles, 1955, pp. 111–118. Georges Thone, Liège; Masson and Cie, Paris, 1956.

La démonstration apporte une simplification à celle de Landau (Sitzungsberichte der preussischen Akademie der Wissenschaften, phys.-math. Klasse, 1932) et semble être, a son tour, devenue la démonstration analytique la plus courte, à ce jour. *From the introduction.*

Referred to in N04-23.

## N04-23 (21# 1285)

**Errera, A. Une modification de la démonstration de Landau du théorème des nombres premiers.** Mathesis 67 (1958), 321–337.

The author gives a simplification of Landau's last proof of the prime number theorem [S.-B. Preuss. Akad. Wiss. H. **32/33** (1932), 514–521]. It is similar to the author's paper "Sur le théorème fondamental des nombres premiers" [Colloque sur la théorie des nombres, Bruxelles, 1955, pp. 111–118, Thone, Liège, Masson, Paris, 1956; MR **18**, 112], but now the proof is carried through in all details. It is clear and even accessible to a student who may never have heard of the Riemann $\zeta$-function before. The author shows in particular

$$\pi(x) = x/\log x + O(x/\log^2 x) \quad \text{if} \quad x\to\infty.$$

*J. Popken* (Minneapolis, Minn.)

Citations: MR 18, 112c = N04-22.

**N04-24** **(20# 5170)**

**Hua, Loo-keng; and Wu, Fang. An improvement of Vinogradov's mean value theorem and some applications.** Acta Math. Sinica 7 (1957), 574–589. (Chinese. English summary)

The authors prove the following improvement of Vinogradov's mean value theorem for trigonometrical sums: Let

$$f(x)=\alpha_k x^k+\alpha_{k-1}x^{k-1}+\cdots+\alpha_1 x,\quad C_k(P)=\sum_{n=1}^{P} e^{2\pi i f(x)}.$$

There exist two absolute constants $A$ and $B$ such that, if $t$ is a positive integer satisfying $\frac{1}{3}k(k+1)+lk\leqq t\leqq Ak^2\log k$, then

$$\int_0^1\cdots\int_0^1 |C_k(P)|^{2t}d\alpha_1\cdots d\alpha_k\leqq e^{Bk^3\log k}(\log P)^l P^{2t-\frac{1}{2}k(k+1)+\delta_l},$$

where $\delta_l=\frac{1}{2}k(k+1)(1-1/k)^l$. From this inequality, they deduce that

$$\pi(x)=lix+o(xe^{-A(\log x)^{4/7}(\log\log x)^{-1/7}})$$

and

$$\zeta(1+it)=o((\log t)^{\frac{3}{4}}(\log\log t)^{\frac{1}{4}}).$$

{Since the paper was written, Vinogradov announced further improvements of his method at the Edinburgh International Congress, 1958.} *K. Mahler* (Manchester)

**N04-25** **(21# 4139)**

**Knapowski, S. On new "explicit formulas" in prime number theory. I.** Acta Arith. 5 (1958), 1–14 (1959).

Let $\Lambda(n)=\log p$ if $n=p^m$, where $p$ is a prime, $m=1, 2, \cdots$, and let $\Lambda(n)=0$ otherwise. For $x>1$, let $\psi(x)=\sum_{n\leqq x}\Lambda(n)$. Let $\psi_0(x)=\frac{1}{2}[\psi(x-0)+\psi(x+0)]$, and $U_N(s)=\sum_{n\leqq N}n^{-s}$. The author proves the following result. For $2\leqq x\leqq N$, $N\geqq N_0$, we have

$$\psi_0(x) = N^{-1}(\log N!)-\sum_\rho (x^\rho/\rho),$$

with the understanding that $\rho=\beta+i\gamma$ stands for the zeros of $U_N(s)$, and $\sum_\rho (x^\rho/\rho)$ stands for $\lim_{T\to\infty}\sum_{|\gamma|\leqq T}(x^\rho/\rho)$. The use of the zeros of the "Dirichlet polynomial" $U_N(s)$ instead of the zeros of the zeta-function is suggested by the work of P. Turán [*Eine neue Methode in der Analysis und deren Anwendungen*, Akadémiai Kiadó, Budapest, 1953; MR 15, 688]. This result implies a new approximation for $\psi_0(x)-x$. *K. Chandrasekharan* (Bombay)

Citations: MR 15, 688b = M50-2.
Referred to in N04-26.

**N04-26** **(23# A128)**

**Knapowski, S.**
**On new "explicit formulas" in prime number theory. II.**
*Acta Arith.* 6 (1960), 23–35.

Let $\psi(x)\equiv\sum_{n\leqq x}\Lambda(n)\equiv\sum_{p^m\leqq x}\log p$, and $\psi_0(x)=\frac{1}{2}\{\psi(x-0)+\psi(x+0)\}$. In a previous paper [Acta Arith. 5 (1958), 1–14; MR 21 #4139] the author gave explicit formulae for $\psi_0(x)$ using the zeros of the "Dirichlet polynomial" $U_N(s)=\sum_{n\leqq N}n^{-s}$. In this paper he gives analogous formulae using the zeros of $R_N(s)=\sum_{n\leqq N}(1-(\log n/\log N))n^{-s}$.
*K. Chandrasekharan* (Bombay)

Citations: MR 21# 4139 = N04-25.

**N04-27** **(22# 1555)**

**Staś, W. Über eine Abschätzung des Restgliedes im Primzahlsatz.** Acta Arith. 5, 427–434 (1959).

Let $\psi(x)=\sum_{n\leqq x}\Lambda(n)=\sum_{p^m\leqq x}\log p$, $R(x)=\psi(x)-x$, where $n$ and $m$ run over positive integers, and $p$ over primes. Let $\zeta(s)$ be the Riemann zeta-function. The main result of this paper is: If $\zeta(\rho_0)=0$, $\rho_0=\beta_0+i\gamma_0$ $(\frac{1}{2}\leqq\beta_0<1)$, and $T>\max(c, \exp\exp(2|\rho_0|))$, where $c$ is an explicit numerical constant, then

$$\max_x |R(x)| > T^{\beta_0}\exp\left(-8\frac{\log T}{\log\log T}\right),$$

where the max relates to the range

$$T\exp\left(\frac{-\log T\log\log\log T}{(\log\log T)^2}\right)-1\leqq x\leqq T.$$

A result of this kind for the range $1\leqq x\leqq T$ had previously been obtained by Turán with the aid of his new method in analysis [*Eine neue Methode in der Analysis und deren Anwendungen*, Akadémiai Kiadó, Budapest, 1953; MR 15, 688; p. 113]. The main point of the new result is the closer localization of $x$. The proof is based on a study of the integral

$$I_k = \frac{1}{2\pi i}\int_{(2)}\left(e^{A\omega}\frac{e^{B\omega}-e^{-B\omega}}{2B\omega}\right)^k F(\omega)d\omega,$$

$$F(s) = -\zeta(s)-\frac{\zeta'}{\zeta}(s),$$

where $A=\log\log T$, $B=1/A$, $k$ is a positive integer (roughly of order $(\log T)/(\log\log T)$). By expressing $I_k$ in terms of $\Lambda(n)$ the author first obtains an upper estimate of $|I_k|$ in terms of $\max|R(x)|$ $(e^{(A-B)k}-1\leqq x\leqq e^{(A+B)k})$. A lower estimate is then obtained, for a suitable $k$, by expressing $I_k$ in terms of a sum over the complex zeros $\rho=\beta+i\gamma$ of $\zeta(s)$ and applying one of Turán's fundamental theorems to a finite part $|\gamma|<T_l$ of this sum, where $T_l$ is about $(\log T)/(\log\log T)^4$. Combination of the two estimates gives the desired result.
*A. E. Ingham* (Cambridge, England)

Citations: MR 15, 688b = M50-2.
Referred to in R44-18.

**N04-28** **(22# 2584)**

**Knapowski, S. On the mean values of certain functions in prime number theory.** Acta Math. Acad. Sci. Hungar. 10 (1959), 375–390. (Russian summary, unbound insert)

Let $\Delta(x)=\sum_{n\leqq x}\Lambda(n)-x$, where $\Lambda(n)=\log p$ if $n=p^m$ $(m=1, 2, \cdots)$ and zero otherwise. Let $M(x)=\sum_{n\leqq x}\mu(n)$, where $\mu$ is the Möbius function. The author gives lower estimates for the integrals $\int_1^T x^{-1}|\Delta(x)|dx$ and $\int_1^T x^{-1}|M(x)|dx$. The results are: (1) If $\rho_0=\beta_0+i\gamma_0$ $(\beta_0\geqq\frac{1}{2})$ is a zero of Riemann's Zeta-function, then

$$\int_1^T x^{-1}|\Delta(x)|dx > T^{\beta_0}\exp\left\{-\frac{14\log T}{(\log\log T)^{\frac{1}{2}}}\right\}$$

for $T\geqq\max\{c_1, \exp(\exp 60\log^2|\rho_0|)\}$, where $c_1$ is a numerical constant. (2) If $\int_1^T x^{-1}|M(x)|dx<aT^{1/2}$, for $T\geqq 1$, $a$ being independent of $T$, then

$$\int_1^T x^{-1}|M(x)|dx > T^{\frac{1}{2}}\exp\left\{-\frac{\log T}{(\log\log T)^{\frac{1}{2}}}\right\}$$

for $T>\max(c_2, e^a)$, where $c_2$ is a numerical constant.
*K. Chandrasekharan* (Bombay)

Referred to in N44-23.

**N04-29** **(23# A872)**

**de Visme, G. Hoffman**
**The density of prime numbers.**
*Math. Gaz.* 45 (1961), 13–14.

The author notes that $\prod_{p\leqq x}(1-p^{-1})$ is not the probability that a number near $x$ be a prime, since this does not fit the facts of the prime number theorem. He blames this on the lack of randomness in the distribution of the primes. By using the same approach, however, he derives the differential equation

$$2x\{z'(x)/z(x)\}+z(x^{1/2}) = 0,$$

where $z(x)$ is the density of primes in the neighborhood of $x$. This also does not quite fit the facts, since $z=1/\log x$ is not quite a solution. *D. H. Lehmer* (Berkeley, Calif.)

**N04-30** **(23# A873 )**

**Wright, E. M.**

**A functional equation in the heuristic theory of primes.**
*Math. Gaz.* **44** (1960), 15–16.

The equation mentioned in the title is essentially that displayed in the preceding review. The author makes the substitutions $\nu=\log\log x/\log 2$, $W(\nu)=z\log x-1$, and transforms the equation into the differential-difference equation

$$(1) \qquad W'(\nu)+(\log 2)W(\nu-1)\{1+W(\nu)\} = 0,$$

which he has studied in a previous paper [J. Reine Angew. Math. **194** (1955), 66–87; MR **17**, 272]. There he has shown that $W(\nu)\to 0$ as $\nu\to\infty$, so that $z\sim 1/\log x$. The equation (1) has been encountered recently by Kakutani and Markus [*Contributions to the theory of nonlinear oscillations, Vol. IV*, pp. 1–18, Princeton Univ. Press, Princeton, N.J., 1958; MR **21** #755] and by Cunningham [Proc. Nat. Acad. Sci. U.S.A. **40** (1954), 708–713; MR **16**, 714]. The equation of de Visme was also discovered by Lord Cherwell in some unpublished work. *D. H. Lehmer* (Berkeley, Calif.)

**N04-31** **(23# A1615 )**

**Karamata, J.**

**Sur un lemme de Mertens relatif aux nombres premiers.**
*C. R. Congr. Soc. Sav. Paris Dépts. Sect. Sci.* **1954**, 277–284.

The Prime Number Theorem

$$(1) \qquad \pi(x) = \sum_{p\leqq x} 1 \sim \frac{x}{\log_e x}$$

is shown to be a direct consequence of Landau's relation

$$(2) \qquad m(x) = \sum_{p\leqq x}\frac{\log p}{p} = \log_e x+E+o(1) \quad (x\to\infty).$$

Landau [Rend. Circ. Mat. Palermo **34** (1912), 121–131] deduced (2) in an elementary way from (1). The author proves several results of this type.
*S. Chowla* (Boulder, Colo.)

**N04-32** **(24# A1261 )**

**Knapowski, S.; Staś, W.**

**A note on a theorem of Hardy and Littlewood.**
*Acta Arith.* **7** (1961/62), 161–166.

Let $\Lambda(n)$ be the Mangoldt function of prime-number theory, and let $F(y)=\sum_{n=1}^{\infty}\{\Lambda(n)-1\}e^{-ny}$ for $y>0$. Assuming the Riemann hypothesis, Hardy and Littlewood [Acta Math. **41** (1917), 119–196] proved that, as $y\to 0+$, we have $F(y)=O(1/y^{1/2})$ and $F(y)=\Omega_{\pm}(1/y^{1/2})$. In this paper the authors dispense with the Riemann hypothesis and replace the $\Omega$-estimate by the following more explicit inequality:

$$\max_{\delta\leqq y\leqq 1}|F(y)| > \frac{1}{\delta^{1/2}}\exp\left(-4\frac{\log 1/\delta\log\log\log 1/\delta}{\log\log 1/\delta}\right),$$

valid for $0<\delta<c_1$, where $c_1$ is a positive numerically calculable constant. The use of Mellin transforms reduces the problem to that of obtaining a lower bound for a sum involving certain non-trivial zeros of the Riemann zeta function. This sum, in turn, is estimated by a modification of a theorem of P. Turán which gives a lower bound for sums of the form $|\sum_{i=1}^{N} b_i z_i^{\nu}|$.
*T. M. Apostol* (Pasadena, Calif.)

**N04-33** **(24# A1899 )**

**Fomenko, O. M.**

**Sur des formes équivalentes des lois asymptotiques de répartition de différents ensembles de nombres premiers. (Russian. Czech and French summaries)**
*Časopis Pěst. Mat.* **86** (1961), 195–199.

Let $M$ denote an arbitrary set of prime numbers $p$. The author introduces the functions

$$\pi_M(x) = \sum_{\substack{p\leqq x\\ p\in M}} 1, \quad \theta_M(x) = \sum_{\substack{p\leqq x\\ p\in M}} \ln p, \quad \psi_M(x) = \sum_{\substack{p^k\leqq x\\ p\in M}} \ln p.$$

He proves the following. Theorem: Let $F(x)$ be a positive function on $(0,\infty)$ and $F(x)=O(x^{\beta})$, $x^{\beta-\varepsilon}=O(F(x))$, where $\varepsilon$ is an arbitrary positive number, and $\beta$ a positive constant. Consider the ratios $\pi_M(x)/F(x)$, $\theta_M(x)/(\ln x)F(x)$, $\psi_M(x)/(\ln x)F(x)$. Let $N_1, N_2, N_3, n_1, n_2, n_3$ denote their lim sup and lim inf as $x\to\infty$. Then $N_2\leqq N_3\leqq N_1$, $n_2\leqq n_3\leqq n_1$, $N_2\geqq\beta N_1$, $n_2\geqq\beta n_1$. He applies his theorem to some problems on prime numbers.
*S. Chowla* (Boulder, Colo.)

**N04-34** **(24# A2566 )**

**Vinogradov, A. I.**

**On Mertens' theorem. (Russian)**
*Dokl. Akad. Nauk SSSR* **143** (1962), 1020–1021.

The author sketches a proof that

$$\prod_{p\leqq x}\left(1-\frac{1}{p}\right) = \frac{e^{-C}}{\log x}\{1+O(e^{-a(\log x)^{1/3}})\},$$

where $C$ is Euler's constant, and $a$ is a certain positive constant. *K. Mahler* (Manchester)

Referred to in N04-39.

**N04-35** **(24# A3142 )**

**Knapowski, S.**

**On sign-changes of the difference $\pi(x)-\mathrm{li}\,x$.**
*Acta Arith.* **7** (1961/62), 107–119.

Let $\nu(T)$ denote the number of sign-changes of the difference $\pi(x)-\mathrm{li}\,x$ for $2\leqq x\leqq T$. The aim of this paper is to estimate $\nu(T)$ explicitly from below.

$T$ is supposed to satisfy

$$(1) \qquad T \geqq \exp\exp\exp\exp\exp 35.$$

Write $X=(\log\log T)^{1/7}$ ($\geqq\exp\exp\exp 34$). Then from the conjecture (C) that every $\zeta$-zero $\rho=\beta+i\gamma$ with $0<\beta<1$, $|\gamma|\leqq X^3$, is such that $|\beta-\frac{1}{2}|<2/3X^3\log X$, the author establishes the inequality

$$\nu(X) \geqq e^{-32}\log\log X-1.$$

The author then assumes the negation of (C), namely, (NC) there exists a $\zeta$-zero $\rho_0=\beta_0+i\gamma_0$ such that

$$\beta_0-\tfrac{1}{2} \geqq 14/\{3(\log\log T)^{3/7}\log\log\log T\},$$
$$0 < \gamma_0 < (\log\log T)^{3/7}.$$

Assuming (NC) the author proves that

$$\nu(T) \geqq e^{-35}\log\log\log\log T$$

when $T$ satisfies (1). *B. K. Ghosh* (Calcutta)

Referred to in N04-51.

**N04-36** **(24# A3143)**

**Knapowski, S.**

**On sign-changes in the remainder-term in the prime-number formula.**

*J. London Math. Soc.* **36** (1961), 451–460.

In earlier papers, Skewes [same J. **8** (1933), 277–283; Proc. London Math. Soc. (3) **5** (1955), 48–70; MR **16**, 676] showed that $\pi(x) - \operatorname{li} x > 0$ for some $x$ satisfying $2 \leqq x < \exp\exp\exp\exp(7.705)$. Here $\pi(x)$ is the number of primes not exceeding $x$ and $\operatorname{li} x = \lim_{\varepsilon \to 0}\{\int_0^{1-\varepsilon} + \int_{1+\varepsilon}^{x} (du/\log u)\}$. The author of this paper points out that the results of Skewes would follow if it were possible to prove the following: Let $\rho_0 = \beta_0 + i\gamma_0$ be an arbitrary zero of the Riemann function $\zeta(s)$. Then for arbitrary $\varepsilon > 0$, we have $\max_{2 \leqq x \leqq T}\{\Pi(x) - \operatorname{li} x\} > T^{\beta_0 - \varepsilon}$ for $T > c(\rho_0, \varepsilon)$, the latter function being explicit, where $\Pi(x) = \sum_{p^m \leqq x} m^{-1}$. It is of importance to estimate $\max\{\Pi(x) - \operatorname{li} x\}$ from below and $\min\{\Pi(x) - \operatorname{li} x\}$ from above, with analogous estimates for the error term $\Delta(x)$ in $\psi(x) = x + \Delta(x)$, where $\psi(x) = \sum_{p^m \leqq x} \log p$.

Turán [Acta Math. Acad. Sci. Hungar. **1** (1950), 48–63; MR **13**, 208] found an explicit estimate for $|\Delta(x)|$ from below, based on the following result: Let $z_1, \cdots, z_M$ be complex numbers such that $|z_1| \geqq \cdots \geqq |z_M|$, $|z_1| \geqq 1$; then, if $m$ is positive and $N \geqq M$, we have

$$\max_{m \leqq \nu \leqq m+N} |z_1 + \cdots + z_M|^\nu \geqq \left(\frac{1}{48e^2} \cdot \frac{N}{2N+m}\right)^N,$$

where $\nu$ runs through the integers. What is required for the present paper is a one-sided analogue of this result, and the author quotes one communicated to him by Turán [ibid. **12** (1961), 455–468; MR **24** #A2565].

The author's main results include the following: Let $\rho_0 = \beta_0 + i\gamma_0$ ($\beta_0 \geqq \frac{1}{2}$, $\gamma_0 > 0$) be an arbitrary $\zeta$-zero; then for $T > \max(c_2, \exp\exp(\log^2 \gamma_0))$, we have

$$\max_{1 \leqq x \leqq T} \Delta(x) > T^{\beta_0} \exp\left(-15 \frac{\log T}{\sqrt{(\log\log T)}}\right)$$

and $\min \Delta(x)$ less than the negative of the above expression. There are similar results for $\Pi(x) - \operatorname{li} x$ and $\pi(x) - \operatorname{li} x$.

The estimates just given may be used to investigate the functions $W(n)$ and $V(n)$ which denote, respectively, the number of changes of sign in $\psi(j) - j$, $1 \leqq j \leqq n$ and $\pi(j) - j$, $2 \leqq j \leqq n$. Thus, it is shown that $W(n) > (\log\log n)/(\log 3) + O(1)$.

The proof of the main result depends on a lemma and the estimation of a sum using the Turán one-sided result mentioned above. The lemma in question reads as follows: Let $T > c_3$, and let $\rho = \beta + i\gamma$ run through the nontrivial zeros of $\zeta(s)$; then there exists an $\alpha_0 = \alpha_0(T)$, $10 \leqq \alpha_0 \leqq 12$, such that for all $\rho$ we have

$$\left|\arg\left(\frac{e^{i\gamma x_0}}{\beta + i\gamma}\right)\right| \geqq \frac{c_4}{|\gamma|^5 \log|\gamma|},$$

where

$$x_0 = \frac{\log T}{\alpha_0(\log T)/(\log\log T) + (\log T)^{4/5}}.$$

The sum is

$$S(T, \nu) = \sum_{|\gamma| \leqq 2\log^{1/10} T} \left(\frac{e^{(\rho - \beta_0)x_0}}{\rho/|\rho_0|}\right)^\nu,$$

where $\rho$ is a $\zeta$-zero, $\nu$ is an integer, and $\rho_0$ and $x_0$ are as defined above. *R. D. James* (Vancouver, B.C.)

Citations: MR 13, 208f = N04-16; MR 16, 676c = N04-20; MR 24# A2565 = M50-26.

**N04-37** **(25# 1139)**

**Rosser, J. Barkley; Schoenfeld, Lowell**

**Approximate formulas for some functions of prime numbers.**

*Illinois J. Math.* **6** (1962), 64–94.

The authors present approximate formulas for $\pi(x)$, $\vartheta(x)$, $\psi(x)$, $p_n$, $\phi(n)$, and other functions related to prime numbers, and they show how one can get even sharper (improved) results, especially by using modern computing machinery and by taking advantage of new information about the zeros of the zeta function. The various results are embodied in a large number of theorems. Some important tables are given at the end.

*B. K. Ghosh* (Calcutta)

Referred to in B64-60, C10-47, J80-20, L30-13, N44-35, N44-40.

**N04-38** **(25# 2047)**

**Rodosskiĭ, K. A.**

**On regularity in the distribution of primes. (Russian)**

*Uspehi Mat. Nauk* **17** (1962), *no.* 3 (105), 189–191.

Let $R(x) = \psi(x) - x$, where $\psi(x)$ is Chebyshev's function. A statement to the effect that an interval on which $|R(x)|$ is large cannot be very long may be regarded as a result about the regularity of distribution of primes. In the present paper the following result is established independently of any unproved hypothesis about the zeros of the zeta function. Let $c > 0$, $\frac{1}{2} \leqq \theta \leqq 1$, and suppose that $|R(x)| \leqq cx^\theta$ for all $x \geqq 1$. Then there exist positive constants $c_1, c_2, c_3$ depending on $c$ such that, if $y > c_1$, $c_2(\log y)^{-1/2} < \alpha < \theta - c_3(\log y)^{-1}$, then the interval $[y, y^\gamma]$, where $\gamma = (\theta + (\theta^2 - \alpha^2)^{1/2})/(\theta - (\theta^2 - \alpha^2)^{1/2})$ contains a value of $x$ for which $|R(x)| < x^\alpha$. The principal step in the argument is the proof of the relation

$$\frac{1}{2u}\int_1^\infty \frac{R(x)\log x}{x} \exp\left(-\frac{\log^2 x}{4u}\right) dx = O(1) \quad (u \to \infty),$$

which the author establishes by expressing the sum

$$\sum_{n=2}^{\infty} \Lambda(n) \exp\left(-\frac{\log^2 n}{4u}\right)$$

in the form of a complex integral.

*L. Mirsky* (Sheffield)

Referred to in N44-32.

**N04-39** **(26# 1292)**

**Vinogradov, A. I.**

**On the remainder in Merten's formula. (Russian)**

*Dokl. Akad. Nauk SSSR* **148** (1963), 262–263.

Merten's formula

$$\prod_{p \leqq x}\left(1 - \frac{1}{p}\right) = \frac{e^{-c}}{\log x}\{1 + O(e^{-a(\log x)^\alpha})\}$$

is now proved with $\alpha = 3/5$; previously, the author [same Dokl. **143** (1962), 1020–1021; MR **24** #A2566] showed that $\alpha = 1/3$. *V. Linis* (Ottawa)

Citations: MR 24# A2566 = N04-34.

Referred to in A32-93.

**N04-40** **(26# 3679)**

**Staś, W.**

**Über die Umkehrung eines Satzes von Ingham.**

*Acta Arith.* **6** (1960/61), 435–446.

A theorem of Ingham [*The distribution of prime numbers*, Cambridge, 1932] shows how any precise information about the extent of the region in the critical strip which is free of zeros of $\zeta(s)$ $(s=\sigma+it)$ leads to a correspondingly precise estimate of the error term $\Delta(x)=\sum_{n\leq x}\Lambda(n)-x$ in the prime number theorem. The author, using Turán's methods [*Eine neue Methode in der Analysis und deren Anwendungen*, Akad. Kiadó, Budapest, 1953; MR **15**, 688], obtains a partial converse of this theorem. The actual results are too complicated to state here, but the author illustrates their accuracy by showing that even if one takes $\Delta(x)=O(x(\log x)^{-1/10})$ (a result which one can prove by the elementary methods of Erdős and Selberg), one obtains the non-trivial result that $\zeta(s)\neq 0$ in the region $\sigma>1-(1/400)(\log t)t^{-20}$, $t>c$, where $c$ is a positive constant. *H. Halberstam* (Dublin)

Citations: MR 15, 688b = M50-2.
Referred to in M25-81.

## N04-41 (27# 1422)

**Gál, I. S.**
**The asymptotic distribution of primes.**
*Nederl. Akad. Wetensch. Proc. Ser. A* **66** = *Indag. Math.* **25** (1963), 282–294.

This paper contains proofs of the prime number theorem, the prime ideal theorem and the prime number theorem of arithmetic progressions. The author uses Wiener's Tauberian theorem and a similar one of Pitt. The prime number theorem is derived from the fact that $\alpha(s)=(2-2^{1-s}-3^{1-s})\zeta(s)$ is convergent for $\sigma>0$ $(s=\sigma+it$, $\sigma$ and $t$ real). The proofs are clear and nicely arranged.
*S. Chowla* (Boulder, Colo.)

Referred to in R44-24.

## N04-42 (27# 3608)

**Knapowski, S.; Staś, W.**
**Another note on Hardy-Littlewood's theorem.**
*Acta Arith.* **8** (1962/63), 205–212.

Let $F(y)=\sum_{n=1}^{\infty}\{\Lambda(n)-1\}e^{-ny}$ for $y>0$. Hardy and Littlewood [Acta Math. **41** (1917), 119–196] showed that on the Riemann hypothesis there is a constant $K>0$ such that each of the inequalities $F(y)>Ky^{-1/2}$, $F(y)<-Ky^{-1/2}$ is satisfied for infinitely many values of $y$ tending to zero. Here the authors obtain similar inequalities which, although somewhat weaker, are more explicit and do not rest on any hypothesis. The principal theorem states that if $0<\delta<c$, where $c$ is an absolute constant, we have $\max\{F(y);\,\delta\leq y\leq\delta^{1/3}\}>K(\delta)\delta^{-1/2}$ and $\min\{F(y);\,\delta\leq y\leq\delta^{1/3}\}<-K(\delta)\delta^{-1/2}$, where

$$K(\delta) = \exp\{-14\log(1/\delta)\log\log\log(1/\delta)/\log\log(1/\delta)\}.$$

A consequence is that, without any assumptions concerning the Riemann hypothesis, the Hardy-Littlewood inequalities hold with the exponent $\frac{1}{2}$ replaced by $\frac{1}{2}-\varepsilon$ for every $\varepsilon>0$ and infinitely many $y$ tending to zero. The proof makes use of Turán's method, as expounded in his book [*Eine neue Methode in der Analysis und deren Anwendungen*, Akad. Kiadó, Budapest, 1953; MR **15**, 688], particularly as adapted by Turán and Knapowski to the study of oscillatory questions in prime number theory [Acta Math. Acad. Sci. Hungar. **13** (1962), 343–364; MR **26** #3682c]. *T. M. Apostol* (Pasadena, Calif.)

Citations: MR 15, 688b = M50-2; MR 26# 3682c = N12-23.

## N04-43 (28# 3014)

**Rosser, J. Barkley**
**Unexpected dividends in the theory of prime numbers.**
*Proc. Sympos. Appl. Math., Vol. XV, pp.* 259–268. *Amer. Math. Soc., Providence, R.I.*, 1963.

This paper gives some account of numerical investigations of the distribution of primes $<10^8$. In spite of the results of Littlewood that show that $\pi(x)=\mathrm{li}(x)+O(\mathrm{li}(x^{1/2}))$ and $\theta(x)=x+O(x^{1/2})$ are both false, the author studies the functions

$$\mathrm{PI}(x) = x^{-1/2}(\mathrm{li}(x)-\pi(x))\log x,$$
$$\mathrm{TH}(x) = x^{-1/2}(x-\theta(x)),$$
$$\mathrm{TL}(x) = x^{2/3}\int_x^{\infty}(\mathrm{TH}(y)-1)y^{-3/2}\,dy.$$

This last function is remarkably constant for $x<10^8$, as is shown by a table of its maxima and minima in this range. In fact, the function lies between 1.33 and 2.04. The author considers the combination

$$(1)\quad x^{1/6}[\mathrm{PI}(x)-\mathrm{TH}(x)+1-\tfrac{1}{2}x^{-1/2}\,\mathrm{li}(x^{1/2})\log x]\log x = x^{-1/3}\log^2 x\int_c^x(\mathrm{TH}(y)-1)y^{-1/2}\log^{-2}y\,dy,$$

where $c=1.653$.

A table of its maxima and minima shows it also to be remarkably constant, fluctuating between 4.17 and 6.88. The author is puzzled by the fact that $\mathrm{TH}(y)-1$ should be approximately $y^{1/6}$, and when this average value is substituted on the right-hand side of (1), he gets a function that is "approximately constant, and equal to 3". The reviewer can explain some of this difficulty by pointing out that the approximate value 3 results from cancelling $\log^2 x$ against $\log^{-2}y$. If one avoids this simplification, one gets a larger nearly constant function which for $x=10^8$, for example, is equal to 4.97091.
*D. H. Lehmer* (Berkeley, Calif.)

## N04-44 (29# 81)

**Levinson, N.**
**The prime number theorem from $\log n!$.**
*Proc. Amer. Math. Soc.* **15** (1964), 480–485.

The author gives another proof of the prime number theorem, this time by applying the Wiener Tauberian theory with the kernel $K(s)=e^{-s}R(e^s)$, $s>0$; $K(s)=0$, $s<0$, where

$$R(x) = 1+2r(x)-\frac{4}{x}\int_1^x r(\xi)\,d\xi$$

and $r(x)=[x]-x+\frac{1}{2}$. Starting from the formula

$$\int_1^x\left[\frac{n}{y}\right]d\psi(y) = \log n! = n\log n-n+O(\log n),$$

where as usual

$$\psi(x) = \sum_{p^m\leq x}\log p = \sum_{p\leq x}\left[\frac{\log x}{\log p}\right]\log p,$$

he obtains the prime number theorem in the form $\psi(x)\sim x$ as $x\to\infty$.

In an addendum the author notes that an earlier proof based on $\log n!$ had been given by Ingham [J. London Math. Soc. **20** (1945), 171–180; MR **8**, 147]. It should be noted however that Ingham's proof is a corollary of more general Tauberian theorems of some interest (in fact, all the familiar equivalent forms of the prime number theorem follow easily and directly from Ingham's analysis), whereas the author confines himself to $\psi(x)\sim x$ alone.
*S. L. Segal* (Rochester, N.Y.)

Citations: MR 8, 147i = M45-6.
Referred to in M45-44.

## N04-45 (29# 3450)

**Katai, I. [Kátai, I.]**
**An asymptotic formula in the theory of numbers. (Russian)**

*Ann. Univ. Sci. Budapest. Eötvös Sect. Math.* **6** (1963), 83–87.

The following conditional result is proved. If for all $\sigma_0$, $\frac{1}{2} \leqq \sigma_0 \leqq 1$, $T > 2$, the number of zeros of Riemann's zeta-function $\zeta(\sigma+it)$ in the rectangle $\sigma_0 \leqq \sigma \leqq 1$, $|t| \leqq T$, is equal to $O(T^{2(1-\sigma_0)} \log^2 T)$, then

$$\sum_{n \leqq u} \left( \sum_{p<n} \frac{1}{n-p} \right)^2 = u + o(u),$$

where the inner sum is taken over all primes $p < n$.

*J. Kubilius* (Vilnius)

## N04-46 (29# 4742)

**Grosswald, E.**

**A proof of the prime number theorem.**

*Amer. Math. Monthly* **71** (1964), 736–743.

The proof uses the Riemann-Lebesgue theorem for an infinite interval. It is similar in principle to the one outlined (in small print) on pp. 34–35 of the reviewer's Cambridge Tract [*The distribution of prime numbers*, Cambridge Univ. Press, London, 1932], but works with $\Pi(x)$ and $\log \zeta(s)$ (in the notation of the Tract) instead of $\psi(x)$ and $-\zeta'(s)/\zeta(s)$. It is claimed that the proof, though not as short as some or as elementary as others, "seems to have the advantage of great clarity". Such judgments are highly personal; the reviewer merely records his inability to share this view of the proof as presented. Some observations of a more objective kind may, however, be offered. (1) It seems to be assumed (statement and proof of Lemma 1) that, if $f(t)$ is differentiable in a finite interval $[\varepsilon, T]$, then $|f'(t)|$ is integrable in $[\varepsilon, T]$. (2) On p. 740 the wording suggests (in two places) that uniform convergence is sufficient to justify term-by-term integration, even when the range of integration is infinite. (3) The second reference to the Euler-Maclaurin sum formula on p. 737 might well be amplified; it is not clear (to the reviewer) how this formula facilitates the passage from $\zeta(1+it) \neq 0$ to an explicit lower estimate of $|\zeta(1+it)|$ or a uniform upper estimate of $|\log \zeta(\sigma+it)|$ for $1 \leqq \sigma \leqq c$ (a need not explicitly recognized in the application of Cauchy's theorem at the bottom of p. 740). (4) The argument under (c) on pp. 741–742 is basically sound (though needlessly complicated), but contains statements that are incorrect or inadequate as they stand.

*A. E. Ingham* (Cambridge, England)

Referred to in M45-48.

## N04-47 (30# 3076)

**Kalecki, M.**

**On certain sums extended over primes or prime factors. (Polish. Russian and English summaries)**

*Prace Mat.* 8 (1963/64), 121–129.

Denote by $\pi(N)$ the number of primes $p \leqq N$, and by $S(N)$ their sum. The author generalizes a theorem by E. Landau [*Handbuch der Lehre von der Verteilung der Primzahlen*, Band 1, p. 226, Teubner, Leipzig, 1953; MR **16**, 904] that $S(N) = [(1+o(1))/2](N^2/\ln N)$. Theorem 1: Let $f(x)$ be a function defined for $x > 0$ and such that (a) $f(x) > 0$, (b) $f(x)$ is a non-decreasing function, (c) for each $u > 0$, $\varphi(u) = \lim_{x\to\infty} f(ux)/f(x)$ exists. Then

$$\sum_{p \leqq N} f(p) = [(1+o(1))/(s+1)]f(N)(N/\ln N),$$

where $s = \ln \varphi(e) \geqq 0$ ($e$ the base of the natural logarithm). Two more theorems are proven. Theorem 2:

$$\sum_{n=2}^{N} \sum_{p|n} p = [(\pi^2+o(1))/12](N^2/\ln N),$$

$$\sum_{n=2}^{N} \sum_{a=1}^{\infty} \sum_{p^a|n} p = [(\pi^2+o(1))/12](N^2/\ln N).$$

Theorem 3: Let $\delta(n)$ be the smallest prime factor of $n$, and $\delta(n, p_k) = 0$ if $\delta(n) > p_k$, $= \delta(n)$ if $\delta(n) \leqq p_k$. Then

$$\sum_{n \leqq N} \delta(n) = [(1+o(1))/2](N^2/\ln N),$$

$$\sum_{n \leqq N} \delta(n, p_k) = N(1+o(1))(1+\sum_{j=2}^{k} \prod_{i=1}^{j-1} (1-1/p_i))$$

if $k \leqq \ln N$.

*J. W. Andrushkiw* (S. Orange, N.J.)

Citations: MR 16, 904d = N02-3.

## N04-48 (31# 3397)

**Grosswald, Émile [Grosswald, Emil]**

**Sur l'ordre de grandeur des différences $\psi(x) - x$ et $\pi(x) - \text{li}\, x$.**

*C. R. Acad. Sci. Paris* **260** (1965), 3813–3816.

Let $\theta = \lim\sup \sigma$, where $\sigma \in \Sigma$, $\Sigma$ is the set of all $\sigma$ such that $\zeta(\sigma+it) = 0$, and let $\psi(x) = \sum_{m<x} \Lambda(m)$, where $\Lambda(m)$ has its usual definition ($\log p$ if $m$ is a power of a prime $p$, 0 otherwise) and $x$ is not an integer. Then $\frac{1}{2} \leqq \theta \leqq 1$, and it is known that $\psi(x) - x = O(x^\theta \log^2 x)$. It has been shown by Littlewood that if the Riemann hypothesis is true ($\theta = \frac{1}{2}$), then $\psi(x) - x = \Omega_\pm(x^{1/2} \log\log\log x)$. The author proves the following results: (1) If $\theta > \frac{1}{2}$, then $\psi(x) - x = O(x^\theta)$. (2) If $\theta > \frac{1}{2}$ and there are zeroes $s = \sigma + it$ of $\zeta(s)$ with $\sigma = \theta$, then $\psi(x) - x = \Omega_\pm(x^\theta)$. The proof uses a variant of a theorem of Landau's. Two corollaries concerning $\pi(x)$ are noted.

*Morris Newman* (Washington, D.C.)

Referred to in Z02-70.

## N04-49 (31# 3399)

**Ducray, S.**

**Probability and prime numbers.**

*Proc. Indian Acad. Sci. Sect. A* **60** (1964), 159–164.

Let the half-line $x \geqq x_0 \geqq 2$ be mapped onto $y \geqq 0$ by the transformation $y = \int_{x_0}^{x} dt/\log t$. Denote by $s_n = s_n(x_0, u)$ ($n = 1, 2, \cdots$) the number of primes whose images belong to the interval $I_n = [(n-1)u, nu)$. Consider the sequences $\{s_n\}$ obtained by displacement of the point $x_0$ continuously through an interval whose image is the interval $[0, u)$. There exists at least one $u > 0$ such that a subset of the sequences $\{s_n\}$ may be mapped in a one-to-one manner on $(0, 1]$. Make a probability space of $(0, 1]$, with Lebesgue measure as probability measure.

If the random variables $S_n$ were independent, then the law of the iterated logarithm would be applicable to the sum $s_1 + s_2 + \cdots + s_n$. Hence the estimate $\pi(x) = \text{Li}\, x + O(x \log\log x/\log x)^{1/2}$ would follow. The author tries to show this result without assuming independence of the $s_n$. The reviewer could not follow the proof of the cardinal Lemma 3.

*J. Kubilius* (Vilnius)

## N04-50 (33# 5581)

**Bellman, Richard**

**Dynamic programming and the quadratic form of Selberg.**

*J. Math. Anal. Appl.* **15** (1966), 30–32.

In this paper a dynamic programming formulation is given for a counting technique developed by A. Selberg [Norske Vid. Selsk. Forh. (Trondheim) **19** (1947), 64–67; MR **9**, 271] for obtaining useful bounds for the number of primes less than or equal to a given integer $N$. A recurrence relation is derived which, after some analytical simplifications, leads to a recurrence algorithm by which it is possible to actually compute this number of primes provided $N$ is not too large.

*H. F. Karreman* (Madison, Wis.)

Citations: MR 9, 271h = M55-4.

## N04-51 (34# 2546)

**Lehman, R. Sherman**

**On the difference $\pi(x) - \text{li}(x)$.**

*Acta Arith.* **11** (1966), 397–410.

In this paper $\pi(x)$ denotes, as usual, the number of primes not exceeding $x$, and li $x$ the integral logarithm. The author is concerned with the old question of determining an upper bound $X$ for the position of the first sign-change of $\pi(x)-\operatorname{li} x$, where $x \geqq 2$. He improves considerably on the previous result $X \leqq \exp\exp\exp\exp(7.705)$ due to S. Skewes [Proc. London Math. Soc. (3) **5** (1955), 48–70; MR **16**, 676] by showing that between $1.53\times 10^{1165}$ and $1.65\times 10^{1165}$ there are more than $10^{500}$ successive integers $n$ for which $\pi(n) > \operatorname{li} n$. The author arrives at this statement by first deriving an explicit formula for $ue^{-u/2}(\pi(e^u)-\operatorname{li}(e^u))$ averaged by a Gaussian kernel, and then computing numerically the main term of the resulting formula at some special values of the parameters. This main term appears to be a sum extended over $\xi$-zeros $\rho=\beta+i\gamma$, with $0<\gamma<12000$. The zeros in question have been computed to about seven decimal places on an IBM 7090 at the Computer Center of the University of California at Berkeley.

{Reviewer's remark: An explicit lower bound for the number of sign-changes of $\pi(x)-\operatorname{li} x$ in $2\leqq x\leqq T$, holding however only for $T\geqq \exp\exp\exp\exp\exp(35)$, had been given by the reviewer [Acta Arith. **7** (1961/62), 107–119; MR **24** #A3142].} *S. Knapowski* (Coral Gables, Fla.)

Citations: MR 16, 676c = N04-20; MR 24# A3142 = N04-35.
Referred to in N04-53.

## N04-52 (37# 168 )

**Davison, T. M. K.**

**A Tauberian theorem and analogues of the prime number theorem.**

*Canad. J. Math.* **20** (1968), 362–367.

A Tauberian theorem of A. E. Ingham [J. London Math. Soc. **20** (1945), 171–180; MR **8**, 147] states that if $f$ is a non-decreasing, non-negative function on $[1,\infty)$ and (*) $\sum_{n<x} f(xn^{-1}) = cx\log x + c'x + o(x)$ as $x\to\infty$, then $f(x)\sim cx$, where $c$ and $c'$ are constants. By modifying Ingham's proof to take account of suitable weighting functions $\alpha(n)$, the author deduces the "fine" behavior of a function $f$ if its "gross" behavior is known, and if $\sum_{n<x}\alpha(n)f(xn^{-1})$ has an estimate similar to the right side of (*). In the proof the author uses a modified zeta-function $\zeta_\alpha(s)$ which, for $\mathscr{R}(s)>1$, has the Dirichlet representation $\zeta_\alpha(s)=\sum_1^\infty \alpha(n)n^{-s}$.

By use of properties of the Dirichlet convolution $f*g(n)=\sum_{d\mid n} f(d)g(nd^{-1})$ of the arithmetic functions $f$ and $g$, the author introduces an arithmetical function $\alpha$ such that $\alpha(1)\neq 0$ to define $\mu_\alpha$ by $(\mu_\alpha * \alpha)(n)=\delta(n)$, where $\delta(1)=1$, $\delta(n)=0$ for all $n>1$. For all $x>0$, $M_\alpha$ is defined by $M_\alpha(x)=\sum_{n<x}\mu_\alpha(n)$ to deduce $M_\alpha(x)=o(x)$. This is an analogue of the prime number theorem without error term, $\sum_{n<x}\mu(n)=M(x)=o(x)$, where $\mu$ is the Moebius function. Another equivalent form of the prime number theorem is proved, and, finally, examples for the weighting functions $\alpha$ are given. *S. Ikehara* (Cambridge, Mass.)

Citations: MR 8, 147i = M45-6.

## N04-53 (38# 2102 )

**Cohen, A. M.; Mayhew, M. J. E.**

**On the difference $\pi(x)-\operatorname{li} x$.**

*Proc. London Math. Soc.* (3) **18** (1968), 691–713.

Let $\operatorname{li} x=\lim_{\eta\to 0^+}(\int_0^{1-\eta}+\int_{1+\eta}^x)(\log u)^{-1}\,du$. For $1.42<x<10^7$, $\pi(x)-\operatorname{li} x$ is negative. But J. E. Littlewood [C. R. Acad. Sci. Paris **158** (1914), 1869–1872] proved that $\pi(x)-\operatorname{li} x$ changes sign infinitely often. The authors show that $\pi(x)-\operatorname{li} x>0$ for some $x$, $2\leqq x\leqq 10^{10^{529.7}}$, without the Riemann hypothesis. The method is illustrated by considering the analogous problem of where $\theta(x)>x$. This reduces to finding $t$ such that $G(t)=-\sum_\rho e^{(\rho-t/2)}/\rho>1$ (summation over complex zeros of $\rho(s)$). One can argue back from the value of $I=\int_0^\infty G(t)f(t)\,dt$ to the inequality $G(t)>1$, where $f(t)$ is taken as $\{(\sin\beta t)/t\}^4\exp(-\frac{1}{2}\alpha^2t^2)$. The value of $t$ for which $I$ is sufficiently large and positive can be obtained by Diophantine approximation. R. S. Lehman [Acta Arith. **11** (1966), 397–410; MR **34** #2546] has shown the rather stronger result that there are more than $10^{500}$ successive integers $x$, in the range $1.53\times 10^{1165}<x<1.65\times 10^{1165}$, for which $\pi(x)>\operatorname{li} x$.
*R. A. MacLeod* (Victoria, B.C.)

Citations: MR 34# 2546 = N04-51.

## N04-54 (39# 2710 )

**Corrádi, K. A.**

**On an extension of the prime-number theorem.**

*Ann. Univ. Sci. Budapest. Eötvös Sect. Math.* **10** (1967), 103–111.

The well known theorem that the asymptotic relation $\sum_{n\leqq x}\lambda(n)=o(x)$ for Liouville's function $\lambda(n)$ is equivalent to the prime number theorem is generalized to the following: For an arbitrary integer-valued function $f$ defined on the set of natural numbers with the properties $f(ab)=f(a)f(b)$ and $|f(a)|\leqq 1$ for all natural $a$ and $b$, the relation $\sum_{n\leqq x} f(n)/n=O_r(1)$ always implies $\sum_{n\leqq x}f(n)=o(x)$. The technique used for the proof is essentially that by E. Wright [Proc. Roy. Soc. Edinburgh Sect. A **63** (1952), 257–267; MR **14**, 137]. *O. H. Körner* (Marburg)

Citations: MR 14, 137d = N20-16.

## N04-55 (41# 8357 )

**Pólya, G.**

**Über das Vorzeichen des Restgliedes im Primzahlsatz.**

*Number Theory and Analysis (Papers in Honor of Edmund Landau), pp.* 233–244. *Plenum, New York,* 1969.

This is a corrected reprint of a well known paper of the author [Nachr. Gesell. Wiss. Göttingen Math.-Phys. Kl. **1930**, 19–27]. The original proof contained a small gap, which, indeed, the author was able to rectify shortly after the paper appeared in print [see A. E. Ingham, Acta Arith. **1** (1936), 201–211, footnote 3]. Although the result of this paper has been frequently used and known to be correct during the intervening years, nevertheless no published version of the necessary correction appeared, though many knew of it. In this version, where the lacuna was, and how to fill it, are clearly indicated.

A corrected version of Pólya's proof has also been recently published by J. Steinig [Comment. Math. Helv. **44** (1969), 385–400; MR **41** #1658] in the course of further investigation of the changes of sign of arithmetical error terms. *S. L. Segal* (Rochester, N.Y.)

Citations: MR 41# 1658 = N36-77.

## N04-56 (42# 1779 )

**Chakravarty, I. C.**

**A proof of the prime number summation formula without assuming the Riemann hypothesis.**

*Aequationes Math.* **4** (1970), 384–394.

A. P. Guinand [Proc. London Math. Soc. (2) **50** (1948), 107–119; MR **10**, 104] obtained, under the Riemann hypothesis, a summation formula connecting the imaginary parts of the zeros of the Riemann zeta function and the logarithms of powers of primes. The formula involves a class of functions $\psi$ and their cosine transforms $\varphi$. By restricting the functions $\psi$ the author shows that a summation formula of the same type can be derived without assuming the Riemann hypothesis.

*T. M. Apostol* (Pasadena, Calif.)

Citations: MR 10, 104g = N04-13.

**N04-57** **(42# 1790)**

**Šalát, Tibor; Znám, Štefan**

**On sums of the prime powers.**

*Acta Fac. Rerum Natur. Univ. Comenian. Math. Publ.* 21 (1968), 21–24 (1969).

K. Prachar [*Primzahlverteilung*, Theorem 4.2, Springer, Berlin, 1957; MR **19**, 393; Russian translation, Izdat. "Mir", Moscow, 1967; MR **41** #8358] states that if $S_a(x)=\sum_{p\leq x}p^a$, then for $a>-1$, $c_1x^{1+a}/\log x<S_a(x)<c_2x^{1+a}/\log x$; the proof uses only the elementary Čebyčev estimates. In the present paper this is partially sharpened to $\lim_{x\to\infty}S_a(x)\log x/x^{1+a}=1/(1+a)$ for $a\geqq 0$; the proof uses the prime number theorem.

*I. Danicic* (Aberystwyth)

Citations: MR 19, 393b = N02-7; MR 41# 8358 = N02-6.

**N04-58** **(43# 4776)**

**Haneke, W.**

**Über eine Turánsche Ungleichung mit reellen Charakteren.**

*Acta Arith.* **16** (1969/70), 315–326.

Let $k$ be a natural number $\geqq 3$. Denote by $L(s,\chi_1)$ a Dirichlet $L$-function, with $\chi_1$ a real character (mod $k$), that has an "exceptional zero" $\beta$ satisfying $0<\delta=1-\beta<c_0/\log^2 k$ with sufficiently small $c_0$. Here $c_0$ (like $c_1$, $c_2$, etc.) denote positive "computable" constants. The same is true of the constants involved in the $\ll$ and $O$-symbols in this paper. P. Turán [same Acta **5** (1959), 309–314; MR **23** #A127] discussed the question of the connection between the position of $\beta$ and the distribution of primes $p$ with $p\leqq X$, with $\chi_1(p)=1$, for a given $X>k^{c_1}$.

The author's object is to get a further result in this direction, namely:

$$\sum_{p\leq X}(1+\chi_1(p)/p)\log^2 p \ll ((\log k)/\log(1/\delta))\log_2 k+\delta(\log^3 X+\log^3 k)$$

for $X>\exp(c_2[((\log k)/\log(1/\delta))\log_2 k]^2)$. {The reviewer remarks that one of the objects of such investigations would be a possible new solution of the "class-number $g$" problem (solved for $g=1$ independently by A. Baker and H. M. Stark [Ann. of Math. (2) **94** (1971), 190–199], Baker [ibid. (2) **94** (1971), 139–152] and Stark [ibid. (2) **94** (1971), 153–173], for $g=2$ jointly by these two authors).}

*S. Chowla* (Princeton, N.J.)

Citations: MR 23# A127 = M20-21.

# N08 DISTRIBUTION OF PRIMES: LOCAL QUESTIONS ($p_{n+1}-p_n$, ETC.)

See also Sections A38, R44, R46.

See also reviews A26-53, A32-105, A38-26, A38-47, A40-15, A40-31, A46-52, A46-63, K30-1, M02-1, M25-3, M25-15, M25-41, M25-80, M30-47, M30-49, M55-56, M55-66, N04-15, N04-38, N16-10, N24-8, N24-11, N24-35, N24-45, N24-48, N36-11, N44-3, N44-34, N44-37, N44-38, N44-39, P32-17, P32-20, R44-46.

**N08-1** **(1, 292h)**

**Erdös, P. The difference of consecutive primes.** Duke Math. J. 6, 438–441 (1940).

Let $p_n$ be the $n$th prime. Using the Riemann hypothesis, Hardy and Littlewood proved some years ago that

$$A=\liminf_{n\to\infty}\frac{p_{n+1}-p_n}{\log p_n}\leqq\frac{2}{3},$$

and Rankin recently proved, again by using the Riemann hypothesis, that $A\leqq 3/5$. Their proofs have not been published. The author proves, without the Riemann hypothesis, that $A<1-c$ for a certain $c>0$. Moreover, he conjectures the following theorem: Let $n$ be any integer and let $0<a_1<a_2<\cdots<a_{\varphi(n)}<n$ be the $\varphi(n)$ integers relatively prime to $n$, then

$$\sum_{\nu=1}^{\varphi(n)}(a_{\nu+1}-a_\nu)^2<k\frac{n^2}{\varphi(n)},$$

where $k$ is independent of $n$.

*A. Brauer.*

Referred to in N08-40, N08-43, N16-12.

**N08-2** **(1, 292i)**

**Rankin, R. A. The difference between consecutive prime numbers. II.** Proc. Cambridge Philos. Soc. **36**, 255–266 (1940).

In this paper the author proves the theorem: Let $\theta$ be the lower bound of all positive numbers $\sigma_0$ such that no Dirichlet $L$-function $L(s,\chi)$ has a zero at $s=\sigma+it$, $\sigma>\sigma_0$. Then for every $\epsilon>0$ there exists a positive number $N_0=N_0(\epsilon)$ such that for all $N\geqq N_0$ there is always a pair of primes $p$, $p'$ satisfying the relations

$$N<p'<p\leqq 2N,\quad p-p'<\left(\frac{1+4\theta}{5}+\epsilon\right)\log p.$$

The proof proceeds along the following lines. The integral

$$I(N,k)=\int_0^1|S(\alpha)\Psi(\alpha)|^2d\alpha,$$

where

$$S(\alpha)=\sum_{N<p\leqq 2N}e^{2\pi i\alpha p}\log p,\quad \Psi(\alpha)=\sum_{\nu=1}^{k}e^{2\pi i\nu\alpha},$$

involves the sum

$$\sum_{\nu=1}^{k-1}(k-\nu)w(\nu),$$

where $w(\nu)$ is the number of prime pairs $p$, $p'$ satisfying $N<p'<p\leqq 2N$ and $p-p'=\nu$. Since the integrand is positive, $I(N,k)$ obviously exceeds the integral taken over certain parts of the interval (0, 1) called major arcs. The assumption that $w(\nu)=0$ for $1\leqq\nu\leqq k-1$ then leads to a contradiction when

$$k=\left[\left(\frac{1+4\theta}{5}+\epsilon\right)\log N\right]+1.$$

*R. D. James* (Saskatoon, Sask.).

Referred to in N08-13.

**N08-3** **(1, 293d)**

**Fogels, E. On average values of arithmetical functions.** Acta Univ. Latviensis **3**, 285–313 (1940) = Publ. Sem. Math. Univ. Lettonie, no. 16 (1940). (English. Latvian summary)

For a given arithmetic function $a(n)$ the writer considers the problem of determining the least $h=h(x)$ such that

$\sum_{n\leqq x} a(n) \sim \psi(x)$ will imply

$$\sum_{x<n\leqq x+h} a(n) \sim \psi(x+h) - \psi(x).$$

Using methods of Heilbronn and Ingham he proves that

$$\sum_{x<n\leqq x+h} \Lambda(n) \sim h,$$

where $h = x^\Theta$, $\Theta = (1+4c/2+4c)+\epsilon$, and $c$ is such that $\zeta(\frac{1}{2}+it) = O(t^c)$; the best known value of $c = 19/116$ gives $\Theta = (48/77)+\epsilon$. From this result it follows that there is at least one prime in the interval $y^\vartheta$, $(y+1)^\vartheta$ $(y>y_0)$, where $\vartheta = 1/(1-\Theta)$ (we may take $\vartheta = (77/29)+\epsilon$). Similar results are derived for various other arithmetic functions.

*L. Carlitz* (Durham, N. C.).

## N08-4 (7, 48e)

**Selberg, Atle. On the normal density of primes in small intervals, and the difference between consecutive primes.** Arch. Math. Naturvid. **47**, no. 6, 87–105 (1943).

The relation

(1) $$\pi(x+\Phi(x)) - \pi(x) \sim \Phi(x)/\log x, \qquad x\to\infty,$$

where $\Phi(x)$ is a positive increasing function of $x$ such that $\Phi(x)/x$ is decreasing, was shown by A. E. Ingham [Quart. J. Math., Oxford Ser. **8**, 255–266 (1937)] to hold if

(2) $$\liminf_{x\to\infty} \frac{\log \Phi(x)}{\log x} > \frac{48}{77}.$$

On the Riemann hypothesis, (1) holds provided

(3) $$\Phi(x)/(x^{\frac{1}{2}} \log x) \to \infty, \qquad x\to\infty,$$

as may be deduced by arguments of H. Cramér [Ark. Mat. Astr. Fys. **15**, no. 5 (1921)].

The author shows that, on the Riemann hypothesis, (1) holds for almost all $x$ provided the weaker condition

(4) $$\Phi(x)/(\log x)^2 \to \infty, \qquad x\to\infty,$$

is satisfied by $\Phi(x)$. By "for almost all values of $x$" is meant: as $x\to\infty$ through any sequence of real numbers lying outside a certain set $S$ of mean density zero in $(0, \infty)$. This is near to a best possible result, since the conclusion becomes false on replacing (4) by any condition weaker than $\Phi(x)/\log x\to\infty$.

Further theorems improve on two results of H. Cramér [Acta Arith. **2**, 23–46 (1936)] concerning the gaps in the prime number sequence by showing, still on the Riemann hypothesis, that the sum of $p_n - p_{n-1}$ over the range $p_n \leqq x$, $p_n - p_{n-1} \geqq (H/x)p_n$, is $O((x/H)\log^2 x)$, where $H = x^\alpha \log^\beta x$, $0\leqq\alpha\leqq 1$, $\beta>0$, and that

$$\sum_{p_n\leqq x} (p_n - p_{n-1})^2/p_n = O(\log^3 x).$$

Finally, it is shown independently of the Riemann hypothesis that (1) holds for almost all $x$ when 48 is replaced by 19 in (2).

*E. H. Linfoot* (Bristol).

A later and stronger result had already been reviewed; cf. these Rev. **6**, 58.

*H. S. Zuckerman* (Seattle, Wash.).

Referred to in N08-41, N40-40, P32-72, P36-39.

## N08-5 (9, 498i)

**Rankin, R. A. The difference between consecutive prime numbers. III.** J. London Math. Soc. **22** (1947), 226–230 (1948).

Let $p_n$ denote the $n$th prime and let

$$l = \liminf_{n\to\infty} (p_{n+1} - p_n)/\log p_n.$$

It follows from the prime number theorem that $l\leqq 1$, and the author has shown [part II, Proc. Cambridge Philos. Soc. **36**, 255–266 (1940); these Rev. **1**, 292] that if $\theta$ is the lower bound of all positive numbers $\sigma_0$ such that no Dirichlet $L$-function $L(s, \chi)$ has a zero at $s = \sigma + it$, where $\sigma > \sigma_0$, then $l \leqq (1+4\theta)/5$. Erdös [Duke Math. J. **6**, 438–441 (1940); these Rev. **1**, 292] established the existence of a number $c<1$ such that $l\leqq c<1$. He made use of Brun's method. In this note the author points out that the improved results of Buchstab [Rec. Math. [Mat. Sbornik] N.S. (4) **46**, 375–387 (1938); C. R. (Doklady) Acad. Sci. URSS (N.S.) **29**, 544–548 (1940); these Rev. **2**, 348] may be used to show that $l\leqq 57/59$.

*R. D. James* (Vancouver, B. C.).

Referred to in N08-13.

## N08-6 (9, 498k)

**Erdös, P., and Turán, P. On some new questions on the distribution of prime numbers.** Bull. Amer. Math. Soc. **54**, 371–378 (1948).

For $a, b>0$ let $M_t(a, b) = ((a^t + b^t)/2)^{1/t}$ $(t\neq 0)$,

$$M_0(a, b) = \lim_{t\to 0} M_t(a, b) = (ab)^{\frac{1}{2}}.$$

Let $p_n$ be the $n$th prime. It is proved that, for fixed real $t$, each of the inequalities $M_t(p_{n-1}, p_{n+1}) > p_n$, $M_t(p_{n-1}, p_{n+1}) < p_n$ has an infinity of solutions. In particular $(t=0)$, $\log p_n$ is neither a convex nor a concave function of $n$ for all sufficiently large $n$. The proof is elementary. A transcendental method, based on the distribution of primes in arithmetical progressions, is also indicated, and it is suggested that this might possibly be used to attack some unsolved problems which naturally arise.

*A. E. Ingham.*

Referred to in N04-15, N08-7.

## N08-7 (10, 235b)

**Erdös, P. On the difference of consecutive primes.** Bull. Amer. Math. Soc. **54**, 885–889 (1948).

Let $p_k$ be the $k$th prime and $d_k = p_{k+1} - p_k$; also let $N(c, n)$ and $N'(c, n)$ be the numbers of integers $k\leqq n$ for which $d_{k+1} > (1+c)d_k$ and $d_{k+1} < (1-c)d_k$, respectively, and let $N_t(n)$ and $N_t'(n)$ be the numbers of integers $k\leqq n$ for which $\{\frac{1}{2}(p_{k+1}^t + p_{k-1}^t)\}^{1/t} > p_k$ and $\{\frac{1}{2}(p_{k+1}^t + p_{k-1}^t)\}^{1/t} < p_k$, respectively. The author proves that positive numbers $c_1$, $c_2$ $(c_1<1, c_2<1)$ exist for which both $N(c_1, n)$ and $N'(c_1, n)$ are greater than $c_2 n$. From this he deduces that, for fixed $t$ and sufficiently large $n$, $N_t(n)$ and $N_t'(n)$ are each greater than $\frac{1}{2}c_2 n$. This is an improvement on a result obtained by the author and P. Turán in an earlier paper [same vol., 371–378 (1948); these Rev. **9**, 498] in which it was shown that $N_t(n)$ and $N_t'(n)$ tend to infinity with $n$. The proofs, which employ Brun's method, are elementary; there are several minor misprints.

*R. A. Rankin* (Cambridge, England).

Citations: MR 9, 498k = N08-6.

## N08-8 (10, 431b)

**Sierpiński, W. Remarque sur la répartition des nombres premiers.** Colloquium Math. **1**, 193–194 (1948).

This note contains a proof of the following theorem: to each integer $n$ there corresponds a prime $p>n$ such that not one of the integers $p\pm j$, $j=1, 2, \cdots, n$, is a prime. The proof is simple, but uses the Dirichlet theorem about primes in an arithmetic progression. The author remarks that it would be interesting to discover an elementary proof of his result. Now that there are elementary proofs of the Dirichlet theorem his proof is technically elementary, but it would still be interesting to obtain a direct elementary proof.

*R. D. James* (Vancouver, B. C.).

Referred to in A40-12, N08-9, N08-25, N08-27, N16-10.

## N08-9 (11, 714g)

**Jarden, Dov. Remark to Sierpinski's theorem on isolated primes.** Riveon Lematematika **3**, 68–69 (1949). (Hebrew. English summary)

The reference is to W. Sierpiński, Colloquium Math. 1, 193–194 (1948) [these Rev. 10, 431]. *A. Dvoretzky.*

Citations: MR 10, 431b = N08-8.

## N08-10 (11, 84a)

**Erdös, P. Problems and results on the differences of consecutive primes.** Publ. Math. Debrecen 1, 33–37 (1949).

Let $m=\epsilon \log n$, where $n$ is a large integer and $\epsilon$ is a small but fixed number; let $f(m)$ be a function which tends to infinity with $m$ and such that $f(m)=o((\log m)^{\frac{1}{2}})$; let $N$ be the product of the primes not exceeding $m$. Employing the method of Chang [Schr. Math. Inst. u. Inst. Angew. Math. Univ. Berlin 4, 33–55 (1938)], the author demonstrates the existence of a residue class $x \pmod N$ such that $(x+1, N)=1$ and $(x+k, N)\neq 1$ for all $k$ for which $|k|\leqq mf(m)$, $k\neq 1$. Making use of the theorem of Linnik [Rec. Math. [Mat. Sbornik] N.S. 15(57), 139–178, 347–368 (1944); these Rev. 6, 260] on the least prime in an arithmetic progression, and a classical inequality of prime number theory, he deduces the following theorem. Let $d_n=p_{n+1}-p_n$ be the difference between two consecutive primes. Then

$$\limsup\, (\min\, (d_n, d_{n+1})/\log n)=\infty\,;$$

that is, corresponding to every positive constant $c$, there exist values of $n$ satisfying the inequalities $d_n>c\log n$, $d_{n+1}>c\log n$. A novel feature of the argument is that it does not employ the Brun method. *A. L. Whiteman.*

Citations: MR 6, 260b = N16-5; MR 6, 260c = N16-6.

## N08-11 (11, 644d)

**Erdös, P., and Rényi, A. Some problems and results on consecutive primes.** Simon Stevin 27, 115–125 (1950).

Let $p_n$ be the $n$th prime, $d_n=p_n-p_{n-1}$, $z_n=n+i\log p_n$ and

$$G_N=\sum_{k=2}^{N-1}\left|\arg\frac{z_{k+1}-z_k}{z_k-z_{k-1}}\right|,$$

where $p_{n+1}\leqq N<p_{n+2}$. If $G_N$ were bounded the sequence $\log p_n$ would be convex or concave from some point onwards. Rényi has proved in a forthcoming paper that $G_N\rightarrow\infty$ as $N\rightarrow\infty$, and the present authors prove that in fact positive constants $c_2$ and $c_3$ exist such that $c_2\log N<G_N<c_3\log N$. Brun's method, Chebyshev's estimates for $\pi(x)$ and $p_{n+1}<2p_n$ are all that is used. Other results proved are as follows. (a) The number of solutions of $p_n\leqq N$, $d_{n+1}=d_n+h$ does not exceed $c_{12}N(\log N)^{-\frac{3}{2}}$ [the reciprocal of this expression is given in error in the relation (25)]. (b) For any integer $N$ and any $r<c\sqrt{(\log N)}$ there is a prime $p_n\leqq N$ for which $d_{n+j}\geqq c_{15}(\log N)/r^2$ $(j=0, 1, \cdots, r-1)$. A table of $d_n$ for $n=2, 3, \cdots, 599$ is given. [Among misprints noted the following are the more important. (i) In (12) read $d_n$ for $du$. (ii) In (14) read $(d_{n+1}-d_n)/p_n$ for $(d_{n+1}-d_n)/p_n^2$. (iii) Third last line of § 3. Read $>$ for $<$. (iv) Bottom of p. 121. Read $\underline{\lim}$ for lim.]

*R. A. Rankin* (Cambridge, England).

Referred to in N08-12, N08-22, N08-37, N16-12.

## N08-12 (16, 221d)

**Prachar, K. Bemerkung zu einer Arbeit von Erdös und Rényi und Berichtigung.** Monatsh. Math. 58, 117 (1954).

A correction to a paper by Erdös and Rényi [Simon Stevin 27, 115–125 (1950); these Rev. 11, 644] pointing out that in the upper bound obtained for the number of solutions of $p_n-p_{n-1}=a$, $p_{n+1}-p_n=b$, $p_n\leqq N$, an extra factor $\prod_{p|b,\, p\nmid a}(1+1/p)$ is necessary. A similar but more complicated correcting factor is needed in the generalisation of this result given by the author [Monatsh. Math. 56, 307–312 (1952); these Rev. 14, 727]. *R. A. Rankin.*

Citations: MR 11, 644d = N08-11; MR 14, 727d = N16-12.

## N08-13 (11, 644e)

**Rankin, R. A. The difference between consecutive prime numbers. IV.** Proc. Amer. Math. Soc. 1, 143–150 (1950).

This paper deals with the problem of finding a lower bound for $l=\lim\inf_{n\to\infty}(p_{n+1}-p_n)/\log p_n$, where $p_n$ denotes the $n$th prime. It is shown that $l\leqq c(1+4\Theta)/5$, where $c<42/43$ and $\Theta$ is the lower bound of all positive numbers $\sigma_0$ such that no Dirichlet function $L(s,\chi)$ has a zero at $s=\sigma+it$, where $\sigma>\sigma_0$. The method is to consider the integral $\int_0^1|S(\theta)\Psi(\theta)|^2d\theta$, where $S(\theta)=\sum_{N<p\leqq 2N}\exp(2\pi i\theta p)\log p$ and $\Psi(\theta)$ is a suitably defined auxiliary function. A lower bound for the integral and other necessary estimates are found by the methods of two previous papers with the same title [part II, Proc. Cambridge Philos. Soc. 36, 255–266 (1940); part III, J. London Math. Soc. 22 (1947), 226–230 (1948); these Rev. 1, 292; 9, 498].

*R. D. James* (Vancouver, B. C.).

Citations: MR 1, 292i = N08-2; MR 9, 498i = N08-5.

Referred to in N08-36, N08-43.

## N08-14 (14, 727b)

**Ricci, Giovanni. La differenza di numeri primi consecutivi.** Univ. e Politecnico Torino. Rend. Sem. Mat. 11, 149–200 (1952).

The author reviews the history of the various problems concerned with the difference between consecutive primes, including the latest results on the values of $\alpha$ in the inequality $p_{n+1}-p_n<p_n{}^\alpha$. It is also shown, for example, that the inequality $p_{n+1}-p_n>(e^C-\epsilon)\log p_n$, where $\epsilon>0$ and $C$ is Euler's constant, holds for an infinity of $n$. Various data on the differences between successive primes $<1000$ are given in tabular and graphical form. *D. H. Lehmer.*

Referred to in N08-15, N08-20.

## N08-15 (15, 602i)

**Ricci, Giovanni. Errata corrige: La differenza di numeri primi consecutivi.** Univ. e Politecnico Torino. Rend Sem. Mat. 12, 315 (1953).

See same Rend. 11, 149–200 (1952); these Rev. 14, 727.

Citations: MR 14, 727b = N08-14.

## N08-16 (14, 727c)

**Prachar, K. Über Primzahldifferenzen.** Monatsh. Math. 56, 304–306 (1952).

The author proves, by using Brun's method, that the density of integers of the form $p_{k+1}-p_k$ ($p_k$ the sequence of primes) is positive. *P. Erdös* (Los Angeles, Calif.).

Referred to in N08-25, N08-37.

## N08-17 (15, 102d)

**Val'fiš, A. Z. Isolated prime numbers.** Doklady Akad. Nauk SSSR (N.S.) 90, 711–713 (1953). (Russian)

Sierpiński introduced the concept of isolated primes, which is to say primes which are sufficiently far from a neighboring prime. Walfisz shows that it is possible for arbitrary $k$ to find sequences of $k$ consecutive primes which are each isolated. *R. Bellman* (Santa Monica, Calif.).

The review should be amended as follows. "The author defines a prime $p$ to be strongly isolated, if logloglog $p>1$ and its distance from the nearest prime is greater than $\log p/(\text{logloglog}\, p)^2$. Using the well known result of Schnirelman on the number of solutions of $p-q=a$, the author proves that almost all primes are strongly isolated. This sharpens a previous result of Sierpiński [Colloquium Math. **1**, 193–194 (1948); these Rev. **10**, 431]."

*R. Bellman.*

Referred to in N08-19, N08-27.

**N08-18** **(15, 935d)**

**Cugiani, Marco. Sulle "catene" di numeri primi consecutivi a differenze limitata.** Ann. Mat. Pura Appl. (4) **36**, 121–132 (1954).

The author proves among others the following theorem: Let $n\to\infty$ and $c_1<f(n)<c_1^{-1}\log n$, where $c_1$ is a suitable constant, and let $\eta>0$ be an arbitrary positive constant. Then there exists a constant $c_2$ so that there are $c_2f(n)$ consecutive primes $p_k, p_{k+1}, \cdots$ in the interval $((1-\eta)n, n)$ for which $p_{k+r+1}-p_{k+r}>\log n/f(n)$. *P. Erdös.*

Referred to in N08-21.

**N08-19** **(16, 114d)**

**Prachar, K. Über ein Resultat von A. Walfisz.** Monatsh. Math. **58**, 114–116 (1954).

The author shows that almost all primes are "isolated" from their neighbouring primes. More precisely, let $f(x)$ be a function monotonic for large $x$ and such that $f(x)\to\infty$, $\log x/f(x)\to\infty$ as $x\to\infty$. Then the number $s(x)$ of primes $p\leqq x$, for which every $q$ with $0<|q-p|\leqq\log p/f(p)$ is composite, satisfies the relation $s(x)\sim x/\log x$. This result sharpens an earlier result of the same type due to A. Walfisz [Doklady Akad. Nauk SSSR (N.S.) **90**, 711–713 (1953); these Rev. **15**, 102]. The main tool used in the proof is the Brun-Schnirelmann upper estimate of the number $A(x, y)$ of primes $p\leqq x$ for which $p+y$ is also a prime.

*L. Mirsky* (Sheffield).

Citations: MR 15, 102d = N08-17.
Referred to in N08-25, N08-27, P36-42.

**N08-20** **(16, 675e)**

**Ricci, Giovanni. Sull'andamento della differenza di numeri primi consecutivi.** Riv. Mat. Univ. Parma **5**, 3–54 (1954).

The present memoir is in part a sequel to two earlier papers by the same author [Univ. e Politec. Torino. Rend. Sem. Mat. **11**, 149–200 (1952); Ann. Scuola Norm. Sup. Pisa (3) **7**, 133–151 (1953); MR **14**, 727; **15**, 202]. The author continues his extensive investigations of various problems concerned with the difference $p_{n+1}-p_n$ of two consecutive primes. Given the interval $(1-\delta)\xi<p_n\leqq\xi$ of length $\delta\xi$, he develops methods for estimating the number $N$ of those differences $p_{n+1}-p_n$ within the interval which do not exceed a specified value. He also studies how to select the bounds of the given interval so that $N$ lies within prescribed limits. In particular, he determines the bounds as a function of $p_n$ so that $N$ is of the same order of magnitude as $\delta\xi/\log\xi$. An interesting theorem states that for $\delta$ fixed, $0<\delta<1$, and $\xi$ sufficiently large, at least 55 out of a thousand of the differences $p_{n+1}-p_n$ within the interval $(1-\delta)\xi<p_n\leqq\xi$ satisfy the inequality $p_{n+1}-p_n<\log p_n$. Most of the results, however, are too complicated to be stated briefly. *A. L. Whiteman* (Los Angeles, Calif.).

Citations: MR 14, 727b = N08-14; MR 15, 202f = A46-12.
Referred to in N08-29, N08-32, N08-43.

**N08-21** **(17, 127k)**

**Cugiani, Marco. Nuovi risultati sulle "catene" di numeri primi.** Ann. Mat. Pura Appl. (4) **38** (1955), 309–320.

Extending the investigations of an earlier paper [same Ann. (4) **36** (1954), 121–132; MR **15**, 935] the author again considers "chains" consisting of consecutive primes whose differences satisfy given conditions. He is principally concerned with those chains in the interval $((1-\eta)\xi, \xi)$ for which the difference of two consecutive elements is always less (or those in which it is always not less) in absolute value than an expression of the form $\alpha\log\xi$, where $\alpha$ is a constant ($\alpha>1$ or $\alpha<1$). A number of inequalities are derived. These are related either to the extension of the maximal chain or to the total number of chains in the interval. *A. L. Whiteman.*

Citations: MR 15, 935d = N08-18.

**N08-22** **(17, 1057c)**

**Knödel, Walter. Primzahldifferenzen.** J. Reine Angew. Math. **195** (1955), 202–209 (1956).

Put $d_n=p_{n+1}-p_n$. The reviewer and Rényi proved [Simon Stevin **27** (1950), 115–125; MR **11**, 644] that

$$c_1\frac{x}{(\log x)^2}<\sum_{p_n<x}\frac{1}{d_n}<c_2\frac{x}{(\log x)^2}\log\log x.$$

In 1951 the author and Schmetterer observed (unpublished) that

$$c_3\frac{x}{(\log x)^2}<\sum_{p_n<x}\left|\frac{1}{d_n}-\frac{1}{d_{n+1}}\right|<c_4\frac{x}{(\log x)^2}.$$

Using Bruns method the author proves the following theorems:

$$c_5\sum_{p_n<x}\frac{1}{d_n}<\sum_{p_n<x}\left|\frac{1}{d_n}-\frac{1}{d_{n+1}}\right|<c_6\sum_{p_n<x}\frac{1}{d_n}$$

and

$$c_7\frac{x}{(\log x)^2}<\sum{}'\frac{1}{d_n}<c_8\frac{x}{(\log x)^2},$$

where the ′ indicates that $p_n<x$ and $d_n\geqq d_{n-1}$.

*P. Erdös* (Haifa).

In the last line of the review the dash should be replaced by a prime.

Citations: MR 11, 644d = N08-11.
Referred to in N08-37.

**N08-23** **(18, 112e)**

**Ricci, Giovanni. Recherches sur l'allure de la suite $\left\{\dfrac{p_{n+1}-p_n}{\log p_n}\right\}$.** Colloque sur la Théorie des Nombres, Bruxelles, 1955, pp. 93–106. Georges Thone, Liège; Masson and Cie, Paris, 1956.

Let $p_1<p_2<\cdots$ be the sequence of consecutive primes. Put $\varrho_n=(p_{n+1}-p_n)/\log p_n$. Denote by $D(x, a, b)$ the number of integers $k$ satisfying $p_k<x$ and $a<\varrho_k\leqq b$, $\omega(x, a, b)$ denotes

$$\frac{D(x, a, b)}{(b-a)x(\log x)^{-1}}.$$

The author calls $u$ a point of condensation from the right of the sequence $\varrho_n$ if there exist two numbers $\gamma>0$ and $h_0>0$ so that for each $0<h<h_0$ there exists a sequence $x_n\to\infty$ satisfying

$$(1)\qquad D(x_n, u, u+h)>\gamma h\frac{x_n}{\log x_n}.$$

Left and two sided points of condensation are defined analogously, $u$ is called point of condensation if

$$D(x_n, u-h, u+h)>\gamma h\frac{x_n}{\log x_n}.$$

$U$ denotes the set of points of condensation from the right, $V$ from the left, and $W$ denotes the points of condensation.

Clearly $UCWCX$ and $VCWCX$, where $X$ is the set of all limit points of $\varrho_n$.

Westrynthuis proved that $\lim\sup\varrho_n=\infty$ (or $\infty\in X$)

and the reviewer proved that $X$ has positive measure and that it contains numbers less than 1.

The author proves among other results that inf $U<1$, inf $<V1$ and that $U$ and $V$ both have positive measure (in fact, he proves that both $U$ and $V$ have measure greater than $\frac{1}{8}$).

He further defines

$$*\Lambda(a)=\liminf_{x=\infty}\frac{D(x,0,a)}{x(\log x)^{-1}},$$

$$\Lambda^*(a)=\limsup_{x=\infty}\frac{D(x,0,a)}{x(\log x)^{-1}}.$$

Clearly both $*\Lambda(a)$ and $\Lambda^*(a)$ are non-decreasing functions satisfying $0\leqq *\Lambda(a)\leqq 1$, $0\leqq \Lambda^*(a)\leqq 1$. $A^*$ and $\Omega^*$ are defined by $\Lambda^*(A^*)=0$, $\Lambda^*(A^*+\varepsilon)>0$, $\Lambda^*(\Omega^*)=1$, $\Lambda^*(\Omega^*-\varepsilon)<1$ for every $\varepsilon>0$. $*A$ and $*\Omega$ are defined analogously. The author obtains inequalities for $\Omega^*-A^*$ and $*\Omega-*A$. Many problems are posed, e.g. is $*A=A^*$ and $*\Omega=\Omega^*$? Is it true that $*A<\Omega^*$ and $*\Omega\geqq 1$?

In general one would expect that $*\Lambda(a)=\Lambda^*(a)$ for all $a$ and $*A=A^*=0$, $*\Omega=\Omega^*=\infty$. *P. Erdös.*

Referred to in N08-24.

## N08-24 (19, 16h)

**Ricci, Giovanni. Sull'insieme dei valori di condensazione del rapporto $(p_{n+1}-p_n)/\ln p_n$ $(n=1,2,3,\cdots)$.** Riv. Mat. Univ. Parma **6** (1955), 353–361.

This is essentially an Italian version of pp. 93–106 of Colloque sur la Théorie des Nombres, Bruxelles, 1955 [Thone, Liège, 1956; MR **18**, 112].

*P. Erdös* (Haifa).

Citations: MR 18, 112e = N08-23.

## N08-25 (19, 121c)

**Hornfeck, Bernhard. Verallgemeinerte Primzahlsätze.** Monatsh. Math. **60** (1956), 93–95.

For a positive integer $d$, the prime $p$ is called $d$-isolated if it is the only prime in the interval $[p-d, p+d]$. W. Sierpiński [Colloq. Math. **1** (1948), 193–194; MR **10**, 431] proved that, for any given $d$, there exist $d$-isolated primes; and K. Prachar [Monatsh. Math. **58** (1954), 114–116; MR **16**, 114] sharpened this result by showing that almost all primes are $d$-isolated. In the present paper the author states the following more general theorem. Let $\mathfrak{A}$ be a set of positive and pairwise coprime integers, and suppose that the number of $a\in\mathfrak{A}$, $a\leqq x$, exceeds $cx/\log x$ for some $c>0$. Let $a\in\mathfrak{A}$ be called $d$-isolated if it is the only element of $\mathfrak{A}$ in the interval $[a-d, a+d]$. Then, for any given $d$, almost all elements of $\mathfrak{A}$ are $d$-isolated. It is shown that this result depends on a generalization of Theorem 88 in E. Landau's tract "Über einige neuere Fortschritte der additiven Zahlentheorie" [Cambridge, 1937]; for the proof of this generalization the reader is referred to J. Reine Angew. Math. **196** (1956), 156–169 [MR **18**, 564]. The author also states a theorem concerning the density of the set of numbers $d$ for which the equation $d=a-a'$, $a\in\mathfrak{A}$, $a'\in\mathfrak{A}$ is soluble. This theorem generalizes an earlier result of Prachar [Monatsh. Math. **56** (1952), 304–306; MR **14**, 727.]

The factor $x^2$ in the equation (2) should be $x$.

*L. Mirsky* (Sheffield).

Citations: MR 10, 431b = N08-8; MR 14, 727c = N08-16; MR 16, 114d = N08-19; MR 18, 564c = P36-16.

## N08-26 (23# A871)

**Bombieri, Enrico**

**Un collegamento tra un teorema di K. Prachar e un teorema di G. Ricci sulle differenze di numeri primi consecutivi. (English summary)**

*Boll. Un. Mat. Ital.* (3) **15** (1960), 30–33.

Let $p_1, p_2, \cdots, p_n, \cdots$ be the succession of primes. Let $g(x)$ be a function that is monotone increasing to infinity with $x$. Then "almost all" differences $p_{n+1}-p_n$ satisfy

$$\frac{\log p_n}{g(p_n)}\leqq p_{n+1}-p_n\leqq g(p_n)\log p_n.$$

*W. H. Simons* (Vancouver, B.C.)

## N08-27 (24# A68)

**Klimov, N. I.**

**Isolated prime numbers in an interval. (Russian)**

*Izv. Vysš. Učebn. Zaved. Matematika* **1958**, *no.* 2 (3), 154–162.

A prime number $p$ is said to be $y$-isolated if $\min_{q\neq p}|p-q|$, where $q$ runs through primes, is $>y$. W Sierpiński [Colloq. Math. **1** (1948), 193–194; MR **10**, 431], A. Z. Walfisz [Dokl. Akad. Nauk SSSR **90** (1953), 711–713; MR **15**, 102, 1139]; K. Prachar [Monatsh. Math. **58** (1954), 114–116; MR **16**, 114] and others proved a number of results concerning isolated primes. The present author generalizes some of them in various ways, including questions relating to isolated primes in arithmetical progression with increasing difference, isolated primes in an interval $[x, x+H]$, $H\leqq x^{1/\theta}$, $\theta=48/77+\varepsilon$, $\varepsilon>0$, etc. *S. Knapowski* (Poznań)

Citations: MR 10, 431b = N08-8; MR 15, 102d = N08-17; MR 16, 114d = N08-19.

## N08-28 (24# A1867)

**Cugiani, Marco**

**Sulla massima estensione di particolari sequenze di numeri primi.**

*Atti Sem. Mat. Fis. Univ. Modena* **10** (1960/61), 78–91.

Author's summary: "Si danno informazioni circa la massima estensione di una successione di numeri primi consecutivi: $p_n, p_{n+1}, \cdots, p_{n+\rho}$, contenuti in un intervallo $((1-\delta)\xi, \xi)$ e tali che le differenze $p_{i+1}-p_i$ siano contenute in un intervallo del tipo $(\log\xi/\alpha(\xi), \alpha(\xi)\cdot\log\xi)$ dove $\alpha(\xi)$ è una funzione tendente monotonamente $a+\infty$ insieme alla funzione $\log\xi/\alpha(\xi)$. Il principale risultato ottenuto è del tipo: max $\rho>\alpha(\xi)/K$, dove $K$ è una costante $>9-1/16$ e $\xi$ si sceglierà abbastanza grande. È trattato anche un altro problema analogo."

Referred to in N08-29.

## N08-29 (31# 3396)

**Cugiani, Marco**

**Su alcune recenti ricerche intorno alle differenze fra numeri primi consecutivi.**

*Confer. Sem. Mat. Univ. Bari No.* 72 (1962), 20 *pp.*

Exposition of results obtained earlier by G. Ricci [Rivista Mat. Univ. Parma **5** (1954), 3–54; MR **16**, 675] and the author [Atti Sem. Mat. Fis. Univ. Modena **10** (1960/61), 78–91; MR **24** #A1867].

*C. G. Lekkerkerker* (Amsterdam)

Citations: MR 16, 675e = N08-20; MR 24# A1867 = N08-28.

## N08-30 (25# 3018)

**Segal, Sanford L.**

**On $\pi(x+y)\leqq\pi(x)+\pi(y)$.**

*Trans. Amer. Math. Soc.* **104** (1962), 523–527.

As usual, $P_i$ denotes the $i$th prime number and $\pi(x)$ the number of prime numbers $\leqq x$. The author considers the old conjecture (1) $\pi(x+y)\leqq\pi(x)+\pi(y)$ and proves the following two theorems. Theorem I: (1) is true for all integers $x, y\geqq 2$ if and only if for all integers $n\geqq 3$ and all integers $q$, $1\leqq q\leqq(n-1)/2$, (2) $P_n\geqq P_{n-q}+P_{q+1}-1$ is true. Theorem II: If (1) is false for some integer $x+y$, then the smallest such value of $x+y$ is the smallest value of $P_n$ for which (2) is false. The inequality (2) was found to hold for $P_n \leqq 101{,}081$ (by using a computer). The result of this paper supplements the results of Schinzel and Sierpiński. *B. K. Ghosh* (Calcutta)

**N08-31** **(25# 3901)**

**Erdős, P.; Prachar, K.**

**Sätze und Probleme über $p_k/k$.**

*Abh. Math. Sem. Univ. Hamburg* **25** (1961/62), 251–256.

Let $p_k$ denote the $k$th prime. The authors prove the following. Theorem 1: We have

$$(1) \qquad c_1 \log^2 x < \sum_{p_k \leqq x} \left| \frac{p_{k+1}}{k+1} - \frac{p_k}{k} \right| < c_2 \log^2 x,$$

where $c_1$, $c_2$ denote absolute positive constants. It follows that there cannot exist an integer $k_0$ such that $p_k/k$ is monotonic for $k > k_0$. Theorem 2: Let $p_{k_i}$ $(i = 1, 2, 3, \cdots)$ denote a sequence of primes for which $p_{k_i}/k_i < p_{k_i+1}/k_{i+1}$ $(i = 1, 2, 3, \cdots)$. Then the number of such $p_{k_i}$ with $p_{k_i} \leqq x$ is $o(x/\log_e x)$. *S. Chowla* (Boulder, Colo.)

Referred to in N08-39.

**N08-32** **(25# 3915)**

**Cugiani, Marco**

**Sulla densità delle differenze fra numeri primi consecutivi.**

*Riv. Mat. Univ. Parma* **10** (1959), 3–17.

Let $p_n$ be the $n$th prime $(n \geqq 1)$. It is known that the differences $p_{n+1} - p_n$ form a set of positive lower asymptotic density [Prachar, *Primzahlverteilung*, Satz 4.1, p. 154, Springer, Berlin, 1957; MR **19**, 393]. The present author shows that this density exceeds 0.00279 and derives a similar result for the differences $p_{n+1} - p_n$ with $(1-\delta)e^{(p_{n+1}-p_n)/2} < p_n < e^{32(p_{n+1}-p_n)}$, where $\delta$ is a fixed positive number. His proofs are based on methods and results of Ricci [Ann. Scuola Norm. Sup. Pisa (3) **7** (1953), 133–151; MR **15**, 202; Riv. Mat. Univ. Parma **5** (1954), 3–54; MR **16**, 675]. *C. G. Lekkerkerker* (Amsterdam)

Citations: MR 15, 202f = A46-12; MR 16, 675e = N08-20; MR 19, 393b = N02-7.

**N08-33** **(26# 3680)**

**Schönhage, Arnold**

**Eine Bemerkung zur Konstruktion grosser Primzahllücken.**

*Arch. Math.* **14** (1963), 29–30.

The author shows that for infinitely many $n$,

$$p_{n+1} - p_n > (\tfrac{1}{2}e^C - \varepsilon) \log p_n \frac{\log_2 p_n \log_4 p_n}{(\log_3 p_n)^2},$$

where $p_n$ is the $n$th prime, $C$ is Euler's constant and $\varepsilon$ is an arbitrary positive number. This is an improvement on a result of the reviewer [J. London Math. Soc. **13** (1938), 242–247], where the constant $\frac{1}{2}e^C$ was replaced by $\frac{1}{3}$. The proof follows similar lines; a different classification of the relevant prime moduli is used, and Chang's "sieve" process is applied to a larger set of them.

*R. A. Rankin* (Glasgow)

Referred to in N08-36.

**N08-34** **(26# 3690)**

**Kosambi, D. D.**

**The sampling distribution of primes.**

*Proc. Nat. Acad. Sci. U.S.A.* **49** (1963), 20–23.

Let the half-line $x \geqq x_0 \geqq 2$ be mapped onto $y \geqq 0$ by the transformation $y = \int_{x_0}^{x} dt/\log t$. The author's object is to show that, with all $x_0$ equally likely, the probability that exactly $r$ primes will lie in the $x$-image of $0 \leqq y < s$ is $e^{-s}s^r/r!$, the Poisson distribution with parameter $s$. The exposition is rather sketchy; in particular, the reviewer could not follow the proof of the crucial Lemma 4. The principal tools employed are the prime number theorem and an estimate of Erdős for the number of primes $p \leqq x$ for which $p + b_1, p + b_2, \cdots, p + b_r$, $0 < b_1 < b_2 < \cdots < b_r$ are also primes. *J. B. Kelly* (Tempe, Ariz.)

Referred to in M30-47.

**N08-35** **(27# 3594)**

**Rieger, G. J.**

**Über die Differenzen von drei aufeinanderfolgenden Primzahlen.**

*Math. Z.* **82** (1963), 59–62.

For any prime number $p$, let $p^+$ denote the least prime greater than $p$, and $p^-$ the greatest prime less than $p$. Knödel and Prachar [K. Prachar, *Primzahlverteilung*, pp. 154–155, Springer, Berlin, 1957; MR **19**, 393] had shown that there exist positive constants $C_1$, $C_2$, $C_3$ such that, for $x > C_1$, the number of positive integers $m < C_2 \log x$ of the form $m = p^+ - p$ with $p \leqq x$ is greater than $C_3 \log x$. Making use of Hoheisel's form of the prime number theorem [Prachar, op. cit., p. 323] and of Brun's sieve method, the author establishes the following sharper results. If $38/61 < \sigma \leqq 1$, then there exist constants $C_4(\sigma)$ and $C_5$ such that, for $x > C_4(\sigma)$, the number of positive integers $m < 3 \log x$ of the form $m = p^+ - p$ with $x - x^\sigma < p \leqq x$ is greater than $C_5 \log x$. He then goes on to discuss the analogous question relating to pairs of numbers $m$, $n$ of the form $m = p^+ - p$, $n = p - p^-$, and also the modified problems which result if only primes in a single class of residues are considered. *L. Mirsky* (Sheffield)

Citations: MR 19, 393b = N02-7.

**N08-36** **(28# 3978)**

**Rankin, R. A.**

**The difference between consecutive prime numbers. V.**

*Proc. Edinburgh Math. Soc.* (2) **13** (1962/63), 331–332.

Part IV appeared in Proc. Amer. Math. Soc. **1** (1950), 143–150 [MR **11**, 644]. Let $p_n$ denote the $n$th prime. In a previous paper [J. London Math. Soc. **13** (1938), 242–247] the author showed that

$$p_{n+1} - p_n > A \log p_n (\log_2 p_n)(\log_4 p_n)(\log_3 p_n)^{-2}$$

infinitely often, where $\log_2 = \log\log$, $\log_3 = \log\log_2$, $\log_4 = \log\log_3$, and $A$ is any positive constant $< \frac{1}{3}$. Recently A. Schönhage proved [Arch. Math. **14** (1963), 29–30; MR **26** #3680] that $A$ may be any constant $< \frac{1}{2}e^\gamma$ (where $\gamma$ is Euler's constant). The author shows now that $\frac{1}{2}e^\gamma$ can be replaced by $e^\gamma$. He uses estimates of the reviewer [Nederl. Akad. Wetensch. Proc. Ser. A **54** (1951), 50–60; MR **13**, 724] for the number of integers $\leqq x$ which are composed of primes $\leqq y$ only.

*N. G. de Bruijn* (Eindhoven)

Citations: MR 11, 644e = N08-13; MR 13, 724e = N28-28; MR 26# 3680 = N08-33.

Referred to in N08-45.

**N08-37** **(31# 4772)**

**Barner, K.**

**Zur Abschätzung von Reihen, deren Glieder von rationalen Funktionen einer festen Anzahl sukzessiver Primzahlen gebildet werden.**

*Monatsh. Math.* **68** (1964), 1–16.

Put $d_n = p_n - p_{n-1}$, where $p_n$ is the $n$th prime. Further, let $a_1, \cdots, a_r$ be real constants which do not all vanish.

The author proves that

$$(1)\quad \frac{c_1 x}{(\log x)^2} < \sum_{p_{N+r} \leq x} \left| \frac{a_1}{d_{N+1}} + \cdots + \frac{a_r}{d_{N+r}} \right| < c_2 \frac{x}{(\log x)^2} \log\log x.$$

(1) generalizes a result of the reviewer and Rényi [Simon Stevin **27** (1950), 115–125; MR **11**, 644] and of Knödel and Schmetterer [see Knödel, J. Reine Angew. Math. **195** (1955), 202–209 (1956); MR **17**, 1057; errata, MR **18**, p. 1118]. The author further generalizes a result of K. Prachar [Monatsh. Math. **56** (1952), 304–306; 307–312; MR **14**, 727]. *P. Erdős* (Budapest)

Citations: MR 11, 644d = N08-11; MR 14, 727c = N08-16; MR 17, 1057c = N08-22.

## N08-38 (32# 1177)

**Prachar, K.**

**Über die Differenzen aufeinanderfolgender Primzahlen.**

*Bull. Soc. Math. Phys. Serbie* **14** (1962), 165–168.

A lecture stating several solved and unsolved problems concerning the difference of consecutive primes. It also contains some new results of the author, along with sketchy proofs outlining the important points.

*S. Knapowski* (Gainesville, Fla.)

## N08-39 (32# 1178)

**Rieger, G. J.**

**Über $p_k/k$ und verwandte Folgen.**

*J. Reine Angew. Math.* **221** (1966), 14–19.

Let $p_k$ denote the $k$th prime, and let $k_j$ $(j=1, 2, 3, \cdots)$ be an increasing sequence of natural numbers with $p_{k_j}/k_j < p_{k_{j+1}}/k_{j+1}$ $(j=1, 2, 3, \cdots)$. If $N(x)$ denotes the number of $k_j$ with $p_{k_j} \leq x$, Erdős and Prachar [Abh. Math. Sem. Univ. Hamburg **25** (1961/62), 251–256; MR **25** #3901] have shown that $N(x)=o(x/\log x)$ and indicated a stronger estimate. The author here obtains the still stronger bound

$$N(x) < c \frac{x}{\log x} \left( \frac{\log\log x}{\log x} \right)^{1/3} \qquad (x > 4)$$

under the weaker hypothesis that $p_{k_j}/k_j < (p_{k_{j+1}}/k_{j+1}) \times (1+f(k_j))$, where $f(t)=(1/t)((\log\log 4t)/(\log 2t))^{2/3}$.

The author uses his method to obtain a similar result for the sequence $\{v_k\}$ of integers representable as a sum of two squares, and indicates how a general result may be formulated and proved. *E. S. Barnes* (Adelaide)

Citations: MR 25# 3901 = N08-31.

## N08-40 (32# 5617)

**Wang Yuan;**

**Xie Sheng-gang [Hsieh Sheng-kang];**

**Yu Kun-rui [Yu K'un-jui]**

**Remarks on the difference of consecutive primes.**

*Sci. Sinica* **14** (1965), 786–788.

Let $l=\liminf_{n\to\infty}(p_{n+1}-p_n)/\log p_n$, where $p_n$ is the $n$th prime. P. Erdős [Duke Math. J. **6** (1940), 438–441; MR **1**, 292] proved that $l<1$, and this has been improved by the reviewer and more recently by N. C. Ankeny and H. Onishi [Acta Arith. **10** (1964/65), 31–62; MR **29** #4740]. The present authors use a method similar to these authors, but with a weighted sum, to prove that $l \leq 29/32$.

*R. A. Rankin* (Glasgow)

Citations: MR 1, 292h = N08-1; MR 29# 4740 = M55-33.

## N08-41 (33# 1295)

**Katai, I. [Kátai, I.]**

**On differences between prime numbers.** (Russian)

*Ann. Univ. Sci. Budapest. Eötvös Sect. Math.* **8** (1965), 61–64.

Cramér and A. Selberg [Cramér, Acta Arith. **2** (1937), 23–46; Selberg, Arch. Math. Naturvid. **47** (1943), 87–105; MR **7**, 48], assuming the Riemann hypothesis, showed (roughly speaking) that large differences between consecutive primes are rare. Assuming the weaker density hypothesis (the number $N(\vartheta, T)$ of zeros $s=\sigma+it$, $\sigma\geq\vartheta$, $|t|\leq T$ of the Riemann $\zeta$-function is $O(T^{2(1-\vartheta)}\log^2 T)$), and using some results of Linnik [Izv. Akad. Nauk SSSR **16** (1952), 503–520; MR **14**, 847], the author proves an analogous result: Let $h(x)$ be monotone increasing, $1\leq h(x)=O(x^{1/4})$ and $K=[(\log x)^{7.5}h(x)]$; then the number of $n\leq x$ such that there is no prime between $n-K$ and $n$ is $O(x/h(x))$. *W. Schwarz* (Freiburg)

Citations: MR 7, 48e = N08-4; MR 14, 847b = P32-20. Referred to in N52-39.

## N08-42 (33# 2609)

**Baženova, T. M.**

**On improvement of a theorem of finite differences for the function $\pi(x)$.** (Russian)

*Kuĭbyšev. Gos. Ped. Inst. Učen. Zap. Vyp.* 29 (1959), 21–24.

Ingham [Quart. J. Math. Oxford Ser. **8** (1937), 255–266] proved that if (*) $\zeta(\frac{1}{2}+it)=O(t^c)$ as $t\to\infty$, and if $(1+4c)/(2+4c)<\phi<1$, then $\pi(x+x^\phi)-\pi(x)\sim x^\phi/\log_e x$. The author claims to have proved three theorems, of which we quote the first. Theorem: If $x^\phi\leq h(x)\leq xe^{-c(\log x)^{1/3}}$ where $\phi=(1+4c)/(2+4c)+\varepsilon$ with $c$ as in (*), then

$$\pi(x+h(x))-\pi(x) = \frac{h(x)}{\log_e x}+O(h(x)e^{-c(\log x)^{1/3}}).$$

*S. Chowla* (University Park, Pa.)

## N08-43 (33# 7314)

**Bombieri, E.; Davenport, H.**

**Small differences between prime numbers.**

*Proc. Roy. Soc. Ser. A* **293** (1966), 1–18.

Let $p_n$ denote the $n$th prime and write

$$E = \liminf_{n\to\infty} (p_{n+1}-p_n)/\log p_n.$$

It follows immediately from the prime number theorem that $E\leq 1$. In 1926, in their unpublished manuscript Partitio Numerorum VII, G. H. Hardy and J. E. Littlewood proved that $E\leq(1+2\Theta)/3$, where $\Theta$ is an upper bound for the real parts of the zeros of all Dirichlet $L$-functions, so that, if the extended Riemann hypothesis is true, $E\leq\frac{2}{3}$. In 1940, P. Erdős [Duke Math. J. **6** (1940), 438–441; MR **1**, 292] proved, unconditionally, that $E<1$. Until recently the best known estimate, due to G. Ricci [Riv. Mat. Univ. Parma **5** (1954), 3–54; MR **16**, 675], was $E\leq 15/16$, although the reviewer had shown earlier, by combining the methods of Hardy, Littlewood and Erdős, that $E<(42/43)(1+4\Theta)/5$ [Proc. Amer. Math. Soc. **1** (1950), 143–150; MR **11**, 644], which gives $E<0.58602\ldots$, if $\Theta=\frac{1}{2}$.

In the present paper, the authors obtain a substantial improvement of these earlier results by showing that, without any hypothesis, $E\leq(2+\sqrt{3})/8=0.46650\ldots$. Their starting-point is the same as that of Hardy and Littlewood, namely, the integral $I=\int_0^1 |S(\alpha)|^2 T(\alpha)\,d\alpha$, where $S(\alpha)=\sum_{p\leq N}(\log p)e(p\alpha)$ and $T(\alpha)=|\sum_{n=1}^k e(2n\alpha)|^2$. Here $p$ is a prime and $e(\alpha)=e^{2\pi i\alpha}$; the authors actually work with a more general non-negative trigonometrical polynomial than $T(\alpha)$, but, in their application, they use this particular polynomial. It is shown that (Theorem 1)

$$(1)\quad 4\sum_{n=1}^{k}(k-n)Z(N,2n)+(1+4\varepsilon)kN\log N > 8N\sum_{n=1}^{k}(k-n)H(n),$$

where $k<(\log N)^C$ for some fixed $C$ and $\varepsilon$ is any positive number, provided that $N$ is sufficiently large. Here $Z(N, 2n)=\sum(\log p)(\log p')$, where the summation is over all primes $p, p'$ for which $p\leqq N$, $p'\leqq N$ and $p'-p=2n$; also, $H(n)=H\prod_{p|n,p>2}(p-1)/(p-2)$ and $H=\prod_{p>2}\{1-(p-1)^{-2}\}$. The left-hand side of (1) is (essentially) equal to the integral $I$. Since the integrand is positive, $I\geqq I^*$, where in $I^*$ the integration is carried out over a subset of $[0, 1]$ consisting of arcs of fixed length centred at rational points $\alpha=a/q$ of small denominator $q$. The hardest step in the argument is to show that $I^*$ exceeds the right-hand side of (1) and this requires Theorem 4 of Bombieri's work on the large sieve [Mathematika **12** (1965), 201–225; MR **33** #5590], which states that, for any positive constant $A$ there exists a positive constant $B$ such that, if $X\leqq z^{1/2}(\log z)^{-B}$, then (2) $\sum_{q\leqq X}E^*(z;q)\ll z(\log z)^{-A}$. Here

$$E^*(n;q) = \max\left|\sum_{p\leqq n';\,p\equiv m(\mathrm{mod}\,q)}\log p-n'/\phi(q)\right|,$$

the maximum being taken over all $m$ prime to $q$ and all $n'\leqq n$. By taking $k\sim(\frac{1}{4}+3\varepsilon)\log N$ in (1) it is shown that $Z(N, 2n)>2\varepsilon N$ for some $n\leqq k$, and this leads to the estimate $E\leqq\frac{1}{2}$.

More information, however, can be extracted from (1) if a good upper bound for $Z(N, 2n)$ is known. By further use of (2) (in a modified form), and of Selberg-type sieve methods, it is proved that (Theorem 2), for any fixed $\delta>0$, $Z(N, 2n)<(8+\delta)H(n)N$ for all $n$, provided that $N$ is sufficiently large. This estimate is used for the larger values of $n$ on the right of (1), namely, for $l<n\leqq k$, where $k\sim\kappa\log N$ and $l\sim\lambda\log N$, the optimal choice of the constants $\kappa$ and $\lambda$ being $\kappa=(3+\sqrt{12})/24$ and $\lambda=(2+\sqrt{3})/16$. From this it follows that $E\leqq 2\lambda$.

The earlier argument is also extended to show that, for fixed $r\geqq 2$, $\liminf_{n\to\infty}(p_{n+r}-p_n)/\log p_n\leqq r-\frac{1}{2}$.

*R. A. Rankin* (Glasgow)

Citations: MR 1, 292h = N08-1; MR 11, 644e = N08-13; MR 16, 675e = N08-20; MR 33# 5590 = M55-43.

Referred to in N08-46, N32-55, P32-81, P36-64, R44-46.

## N08-44 (34# 7482)

**Wang Yuan; Hsieh Sheng-kang; Yu K'un-jui**

**Two results on the distribution of prime numbers. (Chinese)**

*J. China Univ. Sci. Techn.* **1** (1965), *no.* 1, 32–38.

If $p_1, p_2, p_3, \cdots$ are the successive primes, and if $l=\liminf_{n\to\infty}(p_{n+1}-p_n)/\log p_n$, the authors show that $l\leqq 29/32$. If further $(l,k)=1$, and $p(k, l)$ denotes the smallest prime $\equiv l \pmod k$, then it is proved, under the Riemann hypothesis, that $p(k,l)=O(\varphi(k)^2\log^2 k)$.

*K. Mahler* (Canberra)

## N08-45 (38# 110)

**Nicolas, Jean-Louis**

**Ordre maximal d'un élément du groupe des permutations et nombres très hautement abondants.**

*C. R. Acad. Sci. Paris Sér. A-B* **266** (1968), A513–A515.

The author states without proof a number of theorems. His first result is that if $\{b_n\}$ is an increasing sequence of positive numbers such that $\mathrm{Card}\{b_n: b_n\leqq x\}=O(x^\alpha)$ and $\mathrm{Card}\{b_n: x\leqq b_n\leqq x+x^b\}=O(\log x)$ as $x\to\infty$, where $\alpha<1$ and $b>0$, then for an infinity of values of $n$ and arbitrary positive $\varepsilon$,

$$(1)\quad a_{n+1}-a_n\geqq(\alpha e^\gamma-\varepsilon)\log a_n\log_2 a_n\log_4 a_n/\log_3{}^2 a_n,$$

where $\{a_n\}$ is the sequence obtained by arranging in increasing order the prime numbers and the numbers of the sequence $\{b_n\}$. This is deduced from the reviewer's similar result concerning the difference $p_{n+1}-p_n$ between consecutive primes [Proc. Edinburgh Math. Soc. (2) **13** (1962/63), 331–332; MR **28** #3978]. An immediate corollary is that, if $\{a_n\}$ is the ordered sequence of prime powers, then (1) holds with $\alpha=\frac{1}{2}$. The theorem is applied to the function $g(n)$, defined as the maximum order of any element of the symmetric group of degree $n$, to show that there are long intervals over which $g(n)$ remains constant. Other results concerning the distribution of abundant numbers of various kinds are stated.

*R. A. Rankin* (Glasgow)

Citations: MR 28# 3978 = N08-36.

## N08-46 (39# 5494)

**Huxley, M. N.**

**On the differences of primes in arithmetical progressions.**

*Acta Arith.* **15** (1968/69), 367–392.

Let $k$ and $l$ be relatively prime positive integers with $k$ even, let $p_n$ be the $n$th prime in the arithmetic progression with first term $l$ and common difference $k$, let $E_r=\liminf_{n\to\infty}(p_{n+r}-p_n)/(\varphi(k)\log p_n)$, and let $F_r=\liminf_{n\to\infty}\max_{1\leqq s\leqq r}(p_{n+s}-p_{n+s-1})/(\varphi(k)\log p_n)$. Upper bounds are obtained for $E_r$ and for $F_r$ for each positive integer $r$. For large $r$, $E_r\leqq r-5/8+o(1/r)$. The methods employed are similar to those of E. Bombieri and H. Davenport [Proc. Roy. Soc. Ser. A **293** (1966), 1–18; MR **33** #7314].

*B. Garrison* (San Diego, Calif.)

Citations: MR 33# 7314 = N08-43.

## N08-47 (40# 118)

**Ramachandra, K.**

**A note on numbers with a large prime factor.**

*J. London Math. Soc.* (2) **1** (1969), 303–306.

The author proves: "There is an $\alpha<\frac{1}{2}$ such that for all $x>X$ there is a natural number $n$ between $x$ and $x+x^\alpha$ such that there is a prime $p$ dividing $n$ with $p>n^{1/2+1/13}$."

An application of the result yields: "Between $m^2$ and $(m+1)^2$ there is an $n$ and a prime $p$ dividing $n$ and such that $p>n^{1/2+1/13}$."

The proof utilizes Selberg's sieve method and a theorem of van der Corput concerning an upper bound for the sum of real functions of period 1.

*J. H. Jordan* (Pullman, Wash.)

# N12 PRIMES IN PROGRESSIONS AND IN VARIOUS NONPOLYNOMIAL SEQUENCES: GLOBAL QUESTIONS

Elementary proofs of the full Dirichlet theorem are reviewed in **N20**; special cases occur in **A42**. For prime values of polynomials (which may sometimes be linear), see **N32**.

See also Section R44.

See also reviews A12-50, A40-32, A52-61, C05-22, E16-68, M20-9, M20-36, M25-20, M25-29, M50-2, M55-52, M55-79, N02-14, N04-14, N04-41, N04-58, N16-2, N16-26, N16-37, N20-38, N20-46, N20-54, N28-43, N32-27, N44-32, N48-16, N56-11, N76-5, N80-25, N80-38, P02-12, P32-63, P32-66, P36-50, R14-11, R24-18, T05-28, U99-3, Z02-73, Z02-74, Z10-10, Z30-37.

## N12-1 (6, 119a)

**Tchudakoff, N. On certain sums occurring in the analytic theory of numbers.** C. R. (Doklady) Acad. Sci. URSS (N.S.) **42**, 326–330 (1944).

Put

$$S_n = \sum_{m \leqq n} \chi_0(m)\Lambda(m)\rho^m,$$

where $\chi_0(m)$ is the principal character (mod $q$) and $\rho$ is a primitive $q$th root of unity. The author develops a new method for the evaluation of $S_n$ and similar sums connected with prime numbers. First $S_n$ is expressed in terms of integrals involving the logarithmic derivative of $L(S, \chi)$. Using results of A. Page [Proc. London Math. Soc. (2) **39**, 116–141 (1935)] and C. L. Siegel [Acta Arith. **1**, 83–86 (1935)], as well as some classical results on $L'/L$, an application of Cauchy's theorem finally leads to

$$S_n = n\mu(q)/\varphi(q) + O\{n \exp(-c_1(\log n)^{\frac{1}{2}})\}.$$

Applications to various prime number problems are indicated. *L. Carlitz* (Durham, N. C.).

Referred to in H20-7.

## N12-2 (8, 11h)

**Tchudakov, N. Sur les zéros des *L*-fonctions de Dirichlet.** C. R. (Doklady) Acad. Sci. URSS (N.S.) **49**, 89–91 (1945).

The author states an extension of his previous result [Rec. Math. [Mat. Sbornik] N.S. **1(43)**, 591–602 (1936)] on the zeros of Dirichlet's $L$-functions. It is that there exist positive absolute constants $C_1$, $\gamma$ $(\gamma<1)$ such that $L(s, \chi) \neq 0$ for $0<|t| \leqq t_0$, $\sigma \geqq 1-C_1(\log k)^{-1}$; $|t| \geqq t_0$, $\sigma \geqq 1-C_1(\log|t|)^{-\gamma}$, where $(\log t_0)^\gamma = \log k$. From this result it follows, by classical methods, that, if $k<(\log x)^A$ for any fixed $A$, then

$$\pi(x; k, l) = (\text{li } x)/\phi(k) + O\{x \exp(-C_2(\log x)^\mu)\},$$

where $\mu=(1+\gamma)^{-1}$. Finally, by generalising to the $L$-functions Ingham's estimate [Quart. J. Math., Oxford Ser. **8**, 255–266 (1937)] for the number of zeros of the zeta function, the author proves that

$$\pi(x+x^\theta; k, l) - \pi(x; k, l) \sim x^\theta/(\phi(k) \log x)$$

for $k<(\log x)^A$, where $\theta = \frac{3}{4}+\epsilon$. *H. Davenport* (London).

## N12-3 (8, 136g)

**Tietze, Heinrich. Einige Tabellen zur Verteilung der Primzahlen auf Untergruppen der teilerfremden Restklassen nach gegebenem Modul.** Abh. Bayer. Akad. Wiss. Math.-Nat. Abt. (N.F.) no. **55**, 31 pp. (1944).

The 26 tables of this paper give data (rather meager in all but three cases) on the distribution of primes belonging to certain residue classes modulo $m$ for $m=8$, 9, 10, 26, 30 and 262. In each case these residue classes form a group $\Gamma$ under multiplication, in fact, a subgroup of the full group $H$ of $\varphi(m)$ residue classes prime to $m$. Let $\varphi(m)=ih$, where $h$ is the order of $\Gamma$, and let $\pi_H(x)$ and $\pi_\Gamma(x)$ denote the number of primes not exceeding $x$ belonging to $H$ and $\Gamma$, respectively. Then by the prime number theorem,

$$\pi_H(x) \sim i\pi_\Gamma(x) \sim mx/\varphi(m) \log x$$

as $x \to \infty$. The tables of this paper give values of the difference $\Delta = \pi_H(x) - i\pi_\Gamma(x)$ for $x$ just before and just after each change in the step function $\pi_\Gamma(x)$. The most extensive tables are the last three for $x \leqq 300000$, $m=262$, $i=130$ in which primes of each of the forms $262y+1$, 17 and 259 are considered. The number 262 was chosen because 131 is the least prime having 3, 5, 7, 11, 13 as quadratic residues and 17 and 259 are the extreme primitive roots. The values of $\Delta$ show no definite trends except perhaps the case $p=262y+17$ where these primes seem to be more numerous than average. *D. H. Lehmer* (Berkeley, Calif.).

Referred to in A42-6, A42-7.

## N12-4 (11, 419d)

**Shapiro, Harold N. Some assertions equivalent to the prime number theorem for arithmetic progressions.** Comm. Pure Appl. Math. **2**, 293–308 (1949).

It is shewn that the prime number theorem for primes $p \equiv B \pmod{A}$, where $(A, B)=1$, may be stated in the following equivalent forms:

(1) $\pi(A, B, x) \sim x/\{\varphi(A) \log x\}$,

(2) $\theta(A, B, x) \sim x/\varphi(A)$,

(3) $\psi(A, B, x) \sim x/\varphi(A)$,

(4) $\sum_{n \equiv B \pmod{A}} \mu(n)/n$ converges,

(5) $M_B(x) = \sum_{n \leqq x;\, n \equiv B \pmod{A}} \mu(n) = o(x)$,

(6) $H_B(x) = \sum_{n \leqq x;\, n \equiv B \pmod{A}} \mu(n)n^{-1} \log n = o(\log x)$.

These results are the analogues of similar results for the ordinary prime number theorem derived by Landau [see, for example, Handbuch der Lehre von der Verteilung der Primzahlen, v. 2, Teubner, Leipzig-Berlin, 1909], the word "equivalent" bearing the same interpretation as that given by Landau; i.e., no use is made of complex variable theory or any other "transcendental" methods. That (1), (2) and (3) are equivalent is well known; the author proves that (3)➛(6)➛(4)➛(5)➛(3). The fact that $L(1, \chi) \neq 0$ is used. *R. A. Rankin* (Cambridge, England).

Referred to in N12-11, N12-50.

## N12-5 (12, 590j)

**Rényi, Alfred. On a theorem of the theory of probability and its application in number theory.** Časopis Pěst. Mat. Fys. **74** (1949), 167–175 (1950). (Russian. Czech summary)

The theorem of the theory of probability is the same as one given previously [J. Math. Pures Appl. (9) **28**, 137–149 (1949); Compositio Math. **8**, 68–75 (1950); these Rev. **11**, 161, 581]. It is applied here to prove the following result: Let $\Lambda(n)$ be the Mangoldt function and set $\psi(N) = \sum_{n=1}^{N} \Lambda(n)$, $\psi(N, p, r) = \sum_{n \leqq N,\, n \equiv r \pmod{p}} \Lambda(n)$. Let $\frac{1}{3} \leqq \alpha < \frac{1}{2}$ and $\beta, \gamma, \delta$ positive numbers subject to the condition $\beta+\gamma+\delta<\alpha^{-1}-2$. Then, for all primes $p<N^\alpha$, except at most $N^{\alpha(1-\delta)}$, and all $r=1, 2, \cdots, p-1$, except at most $p^{1-\gamma}$, one has $\psi(N, p, r) = \psi(N)/p + \theta\psi(N)/p^{1+\beta}$, where $|\theta| \leqq 1$. *M. Kac* (Ithaca, N. Y.).

Citations: MR 11, 161c = M55-6; MR 11, 581g = M55-7.

## N12-6 (13, 725g)

**Fogels, È. K. Analogue of the Brun-Titchmarsh theorem.** Latvijas PSR Zinātņu Akad. Fiz. Mat. Inst. Raksti. **2**, 46–58 (1950). (Russian. Latvian summary)

The theorem mentioned in the title is the result that the number of primes not exceeding $x$ in an arithmetic progression with difference $k\leqq x^a$, $0<a<1$, is $O(x/\{\varphi(k)\log x\})$. Here, the author proves a result formulated as follows. Let $f=au^2+buv+cv^2$ be a positive definite form with discriminant $-D=b^2-4ac$, let $h(-D)$ be the number of classes of forms with discriminant $-D$, and let $\pi(x, f)$ be the number of primes not exceeding $x$ which are represented by the form $f$. Then, corresponding to each $\epsilon>0$ there is a number $D_0(\epsilon)$ such that if $D>D_0(\epsilon)$ and if $D<x^{1/5}$ then $\pi(x, f)<\alpha x/\{h(-D)\log x\}$ where

$$\alpha=(1+\epsilon)(.5-2.1\log D/\log x-\log\log x/\log x)^{-1}.$$

The principal tool in the proof is a ready extension of A. Selberg's sieve method from the case of rational integers to the case of ideals in $K(\sqrt{-D})$. *L. Schoenfeld.*

## N12-7 (15, 202d)

**Tatuzawa, Tikao. On the number of the primes in an arithmetic progression.** Jap. J. Math. **21** (1951), 93–111 (1952).

The paper is concerned with the order of the remainder term in the asymptotic formula for $\pi(x, k, l)$ which denotes the number of primes $p\leqq x$ such that $p\equiv l \pmod k$, where $(k, l)=1$. The main result is that for $x\geqq\exp(c_1\log k\log\log k)$

$$\pi(x, k, l)=\frac{1}{\varphi(k)}\int_2^x\frac{du}{\log u}+O\left(\frac{x^\beta}{\varphi(k)\log x}\right)+O\left(\frac{1}{\varphi(k)}x^{1-c_2/\Delta}\right)$$

where $\Delta=\text{Max}\,\{\log k, (\log x\log\log x)^{3/7}\}$, and $\beta$, which depends on $k$, is the possible simple real zero, lying in the interval $1-c_3/\log k<\sigma<1$, of some one of the $L$ functions modulo $k$. Also, the $O$ estimates are uniform in $k$. This result is a slight improvement of known results, and yields for $\pi(x)=$ the number of primes $\leqq x$,

$$\pi(x)=\int_2^x\frac{du}{\log u}+O\left[x\exp\left(-c_4\frac{(\log x)^{4/7}}{(\log\log x)^{3/7}}\right)\right].$$

*H. N. Shapiro* (New York, N. Y.).

Referred to in M25-37, N24-54.

## N12-8 (15, 507e)

**Pyateckiĭ-Šapiro, I. I. On the distribution of prime numbers in sequences of the form [f(n)].** Mat. Sbornik N.S. **33**(75), 559–566 (1953). (Russian)

The principal result is that the number of primes in the sequence $[n^c]$ not exceeding $x$ is asymptotically $x^{1/c}/\log x$ for $1\leqq c<12/11$. The proof depends upon the estimation of trigonometric sums à la Vinogradoff. *R. Bellman.*

Referred to in N12-45.

## N12-9 (16, 338b)

**Vinogradov, I. M. Distribution according to a prime modulus of prime numbers with a given value of the Legendre symbol.** Izvestiya Akad. Nauk SSSR. Ser. Mat. **18**, 105–112 (1954). (Russian)

Let $\psi(z)$ be a periodic function of $z$ with period 1, defined to be $1-\sigma$ if $0\leqq z<\sigma$ and to be $-\sigma$ if $\sigma\leqq z<1$. Let $q$ be a sufficiently large prime. The paper is concerned with the distribution of the primes $p\leqq N$ (where $N$ is sufficiently large) for which the Legendre symbol $(p|q)$ has a given value. The main result is that, for the sum extended over these primes,

$$\sum\psi(ap/q)=O(N^\epsilon(N^{5/6}+Nq^{-1/2}+N^{1/2}q^{1/2}))$$

for any fixed $\epsilon>0$, where $a$ denotes any integer $\not\equiv 0 \pmod q$. The proof is arithmetical (i.e. without the use of exponential sums), and the method is an extension of that used by the author in a recent paper [same Izvestiya **17**, 3–12 (1953); these Rev. **15**, 855], from which two lemmas are quoted. An important part in the proof is played by another lemma, similar in its general nature to Lemma 5 of Chapter 9 of the author's paper, Trudy Mat. Inst. Steklov. **23** (1947) [these Rev. **10**, 599; see these Rev. **15**, 941 for an English translation]. *H. Davenport* (London).

Citations: MR 10, 599a = L02-2; MR 15, 855f = K30-12; MR 15, 941b = L02-3.

Referred to in N12-19.

## N12-10 (18, 642d)

**Leech, John. Note on the distribution of prime numbers.** J. London Math. Soc. **32** (1957), 56–58.

Let $\pi_j(x)$ be the number of primes $1<p\leqq x$ of the form $4n+j$. It is known that $\pi_3(x)-\pi_1(x)$ changes sign infinitely often for sufficiently large $x$. The author finds that $\pi_3(x)-\pi_1(x)$ is negative for $x=26{,}861$ and for certain values of $x$ between 616,000 and 634,000; the extreme value $-8$ occurs for $x=623{,}681$. The investigation was carried to $x=3{,}000{,}000$.

Let $\pi_i(x)$ be the number of Gaussian primes $a+bi$ with $a\geqq 1$, $b\geqq 0$, $1<a^2+b^2\leqq x$. Then

$$\pi_i(x)=2\pi_1(x)+\pi_3(\sqrt{x})+1\sim\text{li}(x).$$

Now $\pi(x)-\text{li}(x)$ is predominantly negative, and so is $\pi_i(x)-\text{li}(x)$, but the author has found values of $x$ between 615,000 and 626,000 for which $\pi_i(x)-\text{li}(x)>0$; the extreme value 19.5 occurs for $x=617{,}537$. The prime counts were done on the EDSAC (Cambridge) using tapes of differences between consecutive primes constructed by J. C. P. Miller. *J. L. Selfridge.*

## N12-11 (18, 874a)

**Glatfeld, Martin. Anwendungen der wienerschen Methode auf den Primzahlsatz für die arithmetische Progression.** J. London Math. Soc. **32** (1957), 67–73.

The author applies N. Wiener's general theory of Tauberian theorems to the proof of the prime number theorem for arithmetical progressions:

$$(1)\qquad \pi(x; k, l)\equiv\sum_{\substack{p\leqq x\\ p\equiv l(k)}}1=\frac{1}{\varphi(k)}\frac{x}{\log x}+o\left(\frac{x}{\log x}\right),$$

where $k$, $l$ are fixed integers, $k>0$, $(k, l)=1$. The fundamental theorem of Wiener's theory, in the form given to it by H. R. Pitt, is applied directly to the proof of asymptotic formulae for the sums

$$\sum_{n\leqq u}\frac{\chi(n)\mu(n)}{n},\qquad \sum_{n\leqq u}\chi(n)\mu(n),$$

where $\chi(n)$ is a character (mod $k$) and $\mu(n)$ is the Möbius function; and the truth of (1) is then inferred from equivalence theorems of H. N. Shapiro [Comm. Pure Appl. Math. **2** (1949), 293–308; MR **11**, 419]. [For a similar treatment of the case $k=1$ see G. H. Hardy, Divergent series, Oxford, 1949, pp. 303–304, 378–380; MR **11**, 25]. The formal relation of this proof to proofs based on Lambert's series is discussed. *A. E. Ingham.*

Citations: MR 11, 419d = N12-4.

Referred to in N12-50, R44-12.

## N12-12 (19, 391b)

**Duma, N. On a problem of Hua Lo-Ken.** Latvijas PSR Zinātņu Akad. Vēstis 1953, no. **1** (66), 159–162. (Russian. Latvian summary)

Some obvious conclusions are drawn from the theorem of Dirichlet on primes in an arithmetic progression. *Yu. V. Linnik* (RŽMat **1953**, no. 30).

**N12-13** **(20# 3105 )**

**Knapowski, S. On prime numbers in an arithmetical progression.** Acta Arith. **4** (1958), 57–70.

Denote by $\pi(x, k, l)$ the number of primes less than $x$ which are $\equiv l \pmod{k}$. If $(k, l)=1$, $\Delta(x, k, l)=\pi(x, k, l)-\varphi(k)^{-1}\int_2^x (\log u)^{-1}du$ ($\varphi(k)$ is the Euler $\varphi$ function), then by classical results $\Delta(x, k, l)=O(x \exp[-c_1 \sqrt{(\log x)}])$, with $c_1$ a constant and $k$ fixed. Furthermore, if there exists $\delta$, $\frac{1}{2}\leq\delta<1$, such that $\Delta(x, k, 1)=O(x^{\delta+\varepsilon_1})$ for any $\varepsilon_1>0$, $x\to\infty$, then $\Delta(x, k, l)=O(x^{\delta+\varepsilon_2})$ for any $\varepsilon_2>0$, $x\to\infty$.

The author replaces this last existence result by the fairly sharp inequality: If $T>\exp\{\exp[c_2(k \log k)^2]\}$, $c_2$ a constant, then

$$\max_{1\leq x\leq T} |\Delta(x, k, l)|\leq T^{\delta(T)} \exp\{(1+k^{-1})\log T(\log\log T)^{-\frac{1}{4}}\} \times(\max_{1\leq x\leq T} |\Delta(x, k, 1)|+\sqrt{T}),$$

where $\delta(T)\to 0$ as $T\to\infty$.

More explicitly, $\delta(T)$ can be defined as follows. Let $\varepsilon(T)$ be the largest real part of any zero of any $L$ function generated by a character (mod $k$). Clearly, $\varepsilon(T)<1$. Then $\delta(T)=\varepsilon(\sqrt{T})-\varepsilon(\exp[\sqrt{(\log\log T)}])$. On the generalized Riemann hypothesis, $\varepsilon(T)=\frac{1}{2}$, $\delta(T)=0$.

*N. C. Ankeny* (Cambridge, Mass.)

Referred to in N12-15.

**N12-14** **(21# 7186 )**

**Shanks, Daniel. Quadratic residues and the distribution of primes.** Math. Tables Aids Comput. **13** (1959), 272–284.

The author gives data and discussion about anomalous distribution phenomena of primes, mostly primes under 3 million.

One of these phenomena is the preponderance of the number of primes of the form $4n-1$ over those of the form $4n+1$ noticed by Chebyshev. Let $\Delta(x)$ denote the excess of the number of primes of the former form $\leq x$ over the latter so that

$$\Delta(x) = -\sum_{2<p\leq x} (-1)^{(p-1)/2}.$$

Although $\Delta(26861)=-1$ and $\Delta(x)$ is negative again just beyond 617000 a census to $x=3.10^6$ shows that 99.84 percent of the integers $n$ make $\Delta(n)>0$. The author believes that this preponderance is not a temporary phenomenon and makes the following conjecture. Let $\pi(x)$ denote the number of primes $\leq x$. Define $\tau(n)\equiv\Delta(n)n^{1/2}/\pi(n)$; then

$$\sum_{n\leq x} \tau(n) \sim x.$$

The closest result to this conjecture is the existence of a constant $K>0$ such that the above sum exceeds $Kx$ for all sufficiently large $x$. This follows from theorems of Hardy, Littlewood and Landau but involves the assumption that the associated $L$-series has no zero with real part greater than $\frac{1}{2}$. The overall deficiency of primes of the form $4m+1$ appears to be due to the scarcity of primes $8m+1$, the other three kinds of primes being roughly equally popular. Similarly primes $12m+1$ are scarce as compared to the equally numerous primes of the forms $12m+5,7,11$.

On the other hand the 4 classes of primes modulo 10 are equally distributed. These facts are explained by considering the multiplicative group of residue classes prime to $M$. For $M=8$ and 12 the group is the fours group whereas for $M=10$ it is the cyclic group. In general, primes of the form $Mk+r$ will be less numerous when $r$ is a quadratic residue of $M$.

The paper closes with some remarks about the analogous phenomenon $\pi(x) < \mathrm{Li}(x)$ which fails for infinitely many unknown values of $x$. The author defines $\rho(n)\equiv\{\mathrm{Li}(n)-\pi(n)\}n^{1/2}/\pi(n)$ and conjectures that

$$\sum_{n\leq x} \rho(n) \sim x.$$

*D. H. Lehmer* (Berkeley, Calif.)

Referred to in N24-60.

**N12-15** **(22# 2585 )**

**Knapowski, S. On an explicit lower estimate in prime number theory.** J. London Math. Soc. **34** (1959), 437–441.

Let $\psi(X, k, l)$ be the sum $\sum_n \Lambda(n)$ ($n\equiv l \pmod{k}$, $n\leq X$), where $k$ and $l$ are relatively prime positive integers. The following theorem is proved: there exists a positive constant $c_0$ such that, if $T\geqq\max(c_0, \exp(\exp(\log k)^3))$, then

$$\max_{1\leq X\leq T} |\psi(X, k, l)-\psi(X, k, 1)| > T^{\frac{1}{2}} \exp\left(-\frac{\log T}{(\log\log T)^{\frac{1}{2}}}\right).$$

The result and method of proof are similar to the author's previous paper, Acta Arith. **4** (1958), 57–70 [MR **20** #3105].

*N. C. Ankeny* (Cambridge, Mass.)

Citations: MR 20# 3105 = N12-13.

**N12-16** **(22# 4681 )**

**Gel'fond, A. O. On the arithmetic equivalent of analyticity of the Dirichlet $L$-series on the line $\operatorname{Re} s=1$.** Izv. Akad. Nauk SSSR. Ser. Mat. **20** (1956), 145–166. (Russian)

The paper consists of two parts. In the first is given an elementary proof of Dirichlet's theorem which reads

$$\sum_{\substack{n\equiv a \pmod{k}\\ n\leq x}} \frac{\Lambda(n)}{n} = \varphi^{-1}(k) \ln x+O(1).$$

In addition a generalized Dirichlet theorem is obtained for sequences $L$ obtained from systems of linear substitutions $L_k(x)=mx+qm+k$, $k=0, 1, \cdots, m-1$:

$$\sum_{\substack{p\equiv a \pmod{k}\\ p\in L, p\leq x}} \frac{\ln p}{p} = \frac{1}{\varphi(k)\ln m} \ln\left(1+\frac{m-1}{(r+q)m-r}\right) \ln x+o(\ln x).$$

In the second part it is shown that the absence of zeros of $\zeta(s)$ on the line $\operatorname{Re} s=1$ is a consequence of two relations for finite sums:

$$\zeta(1+i\tau) \sum_{n\leq x} \Lambda(n)n^{-(1+i\tau)} = O(\ln^2 \tau),$$

$$\zeta(1+i\tau) \sum_{n\leq x} \mu(n)n^{-1} \ln x = \ln x+\sum_{n<x} \Lambda(n)n^{-1}+O(\ln^3 \tau).$$

From them, with application of some further considerations, comes the estimate (1) $|\zeta(1+i\tau)|>\lambda/\ln^5 \tau$, $\lambda$ being a positive absolute constant. This result is generalized to arbitrary $L$-series. In addition, by using (1) the bound on the zeros may be moved to the left of the line $\operatorname{Re} s=1$, giving the law of distribution of primes with the remainder term $x \exp(-(\ln x)^{1/q})$.

*A. I. Vinogradov* (RŽMat **1957** #1103)

Referred to in N12-17.

**N12-17** **(24# A1262 )**

**Gel'fond, A. O.**

**On the arithmetic equivalent of analyticity of the Dirichlet $L$-series on the line $\operatorname{Re} s=1$.**

*Amer. Math. Soc. Transl.* (2) **19** (1962), 87–108.

The original Russian article appeared in Izv. Akad. Nauk SSSR Ser. Mat. **20** (1956), 145–166 [MR **22** #4681].

Citations: MR 22# 4681 = N12-16.

**N12-18** **(23# A3119)**

**Knapowski, S.**

**Contributions to the theory of the distribution of prime numbers in arithmetical progressions. I.**

*Acta Arith.* **6** (1960/61), 415–434.

Consider the arithmetic progression $l, l+k, l+2k, \cdots$, where $0<l<k$, $(l, k)=1$. Also write, as usual,

$$\psi(x, k, l) = \sum_{n\equiv l(\mathrm{mod}\, k);\, n\leqq x} \Lambda(n),$$

where $\Lambda(n)=\log p$ if $n=p^a$ ($p$ a prime), $\Lambda(n)=0$ if $n\neq p^a$. The author's Theorem 1 below is based on the following assumption: (A) In the rectangle $0<\sigma<1$, $|t|\leqq\max(c_3, k^7)$, $s=\sigma+it$, the $L$-functions (mod $k$) vanish only at points of the line $\sigma=\frac{1}{2}$ (here $c_3$ is supposed to be sufficiently large and capable of explicit calculation). Theorem 1: Let $k\geqq 3$, $0<l<k$, $(l, k)=1$. Suppose (A) is satisfied. Then we have

$$\int_X^T \left|\frac{\psi(x, k, l)}{x}-\frac{1}{\varphi(k)}\right| dx > T^{1/2}\exp\left(-\frac{2\log T}{\log\log T}\right)$$

with

$$X = T\exp(-(\log T)^{3/4})$$

and for $T\geqq\max(c_{15}, \exp(k^{40}))$ where $c_{15}$ is a calculable numerical constant.

The author's second result (Theorem 2, below) involves Linnik's constant $L_0$ defined by Linnik's theorem that there exists a prime number $D_1$ with $k<D_1\leqq k^{L_0}$. Theorem 2: Let $k\geqq 3$, $0<l<k$, $(l, k)=1$. We have

$$\int_X^T \left|\frac{\psi(x, k, l)}{x}-\frac{1}{\varphi(k)}\right| dx > T^{1/4}$$

with $X=T\exp(-(\log T)^{0.9})$ for $T\geqq\max(c_{22}, \exp k^{30L_0})$ where $L_0$ is Linnik's constant, and $c_{22}$ is numerically calculable.

The proofs of these interesting theorems are based on a well-known lemma of Turán [*Eine neue Methode in der Analysis und deren Anwendungen*, Akadémiai Kiadó, Budapest, 1953; MR **15**, 688]. *S. Chowla* (Boulder Colo.)

Citations: MR 15, 688b = M50-2.
Referred to in N12-21, N12-22.

**N12-19** **(25# 2042)**

**Fomenko, O. M.**

**Sur la répartition du module premier des nombres premiers à valeur du symbole de Legendre donnée. (Russian. French summary)**

*Czechoslovak Math. J.* **11 (86)** (1961), 143–149.

Author's summary: "Soient $p$ et $q$ deux nombres premiers, $\varepsilon, \varepsilon_0, \varepsilon'$ des nombres positifs aussi petits qu'on veut, $0<\beta\leqq 1$ une constante réelle fixée, et $|\vartheta|\leqq 1$; désignons par $(p/q)$ le symbole de Legendre. Soit ensuite $N$ un nombre positif suffisamment grand et $r=\ln N$, $s=1$ ou $-1$. Par $p^{(s)}$ nous désignons le nombre premier pour lequel $(p^{(s)}/q)=s$. Soit enfin $\pi_{s,\beta}(N)$ le nombre de nombres premiers $p^{(s)}$ ne dépassant pas $N$ et dont les plus petits restes non-négatifs mod $q$ sont plus petits que $\beta q$. Théorème 1. Soit $\sqrt{N}\leqq\tau\leqq Ne^{-r^{\varepsilon_0}}$, $\alpha=a/q+\vartheta/q\tau$, $(a, q)=1$, $e^{r^{\varepsilon_0}}\leqq q\leqq\tau$, $\Delta=\sqrt{(1/q+q/N)}$, $f=\Delta^{-1}$; soit ensuite $K$ un entier, $0<K\ll f^2$ et

$$S = \sum_{k=1}^{K}\Big|\sum_{p^{(s)}\leqq N} e^{2\pi i\alpha k p^{(s)}}\Big|.$$

Alors

(1) $$S \ll KN(\Delta^{1-\varepsilon'}+N^{-0,2+\varepsilon'}).$$

Théorème 2. Soit $\sqrt{N}\leqq\tau\leqq Ne^{-r^{\varepsilon_0}}$, soit $\alpha$ réel $\alpha=a/q+\vartheta/q\tau$, $(a, q)=1$, $e^{r^{\varepsilon_0}}\leqq q\leqq\tau$, $0<\beta\leqq 1$ soit enfin $H^{(s)}=\sum_{p^{(s)}\leqq N} 1$, $\{\alpha p^{(s)}\}<\beta$. Alors

(2) $$H^{(s)} = \beta\pi_{s,1}(N)+O(N\gamma),$$

où $\gamma=(1/q+q/N)^{1/2-\varepsilon}+N^{-1/5+\varepsilon}$. Théorème 3. Soit $q$ un nombre premier, $e^{r^{\varepsilon_0}}\leqq q\leqq Ne^{-r^{\varepsilon_0}}$. Alors

(3) $$\pi_{s,\beta}(N) = \beta\pi_{s,1}(N)+O(N\gamma),$$

où $\gamma=(1/q+q/N)^{1/2-\varepsilon}+N^{-1/5+\varepsilon}$.

"Les théorèmes 1 et 2 généralisent les résultats de I. M. Vinogradov qui a obtenu les mêmes relations (1) et (2) pour les sommes $S=\sum_{k=1}^{K}|\sum_{p\leqq N} e^{2\pi i\alpha k p}|$ où

$$H = \sum_{p\leqq N, \{\alpha p\}<\beta} 1,$$

resp. La relation (3) avec une estimation moins précise du reste, savoir

$$\pi_{s,\beta}(N) = \beta\pi_{s,1}(N)+O(N\gamma')$$

où $\gamma'=(1/q+q/N)^{1/2}N^{\varepsilon}+N^{-1/5+\varepsilon}$ a été également trouvée par Vinogradov dans son travail dans Izv. Akad. Nauk SSSR Ser. Mat. **18** (1954), 105–112 [MR **16**, 338]."

Citations: MR 16, 338b = N12-9.

**N12-20** **(25# 5043)**

**Kuhn, P.**

**Über ein Problem in der Theorie der Primzahlen.**

*Ark. Mat.* **4**, 1–14 (1960).

The author proves the following theorem. Given that $ky+l_1, \cdots, ky+l_\lambda$ are $\lambda$ different residue classes relatively prime to $k$, $\Theta(1)=1$, and, for $n>1$, $\Theta(n)=1$ or 0 according as all prime numbers of $n$ digits belong to the $\lambda$ classes or not. If $\phi(k)=h$ denotes Euler's function, then the limit

$$\lim_{x=\infty}\sum_{n\leqq x}\Theta(n)\cdot x^{-1}\log^{1-\lambda h^{-1}} x$$

exists and is $>0$. A less sharp result is

$$\lim_{x=\infty}\sum_{n\leqq x}\Theta(n)n^{-1}\cdot\log^{-\lambda h^{-1}} x = B_0,$$

where $B_0$ has a constant value $>0$.

*B. K. Ghosh* (Calcutta)

**N12-21** **(26# 89)**

**Knapowski, S.**

**Contributions to the theory of the distribution of prime numbers in arithmetical progressions. II.**

*Acta Arith.* **7** (1961/62), 325–335.

Part I appeared in same Acta **6** (1960/61), 415–434 [MR **23** #A3119]. Let

$$\psi(x, k, l) = \sum_{\substack{n\leqq x\\ n\equiv l\,(\mathrm{mod}\, k)}} \Lambda(n),$$

where $\Lambda(n)=\log p$ if $n=p^m$ ($p$ prime), 0 otherwise. Assume the following conjecture: (C) In the rectangle $0<\sigma<1$, $|t|\leqq\max(c_1, k^7)$, where $s=\sigma+it$, the $L$-functions (mod $k$) vanish only at points of the line $\sigma=\frac{1}{2}$.

If (C) is true the author proves the following. Let $k\geqq 3$, $0<l_1$, $l_2<k$, $l_1\neq l_2$, $(l_1, k)=(l_2, k)=1$; then

(1) $$\int_X^T \frac{|\psi(x, k, l_1)-\psi(x, k, l_2)|}{x} dx > T^{1/2}\exp\left(-\frac{2\log T}{\log\log T}\right)$$

with $X=T\exp(-(\log T)^{3/4})$ for $T\geqq\max(c_2, \exp(k^{40}))$, where $c_2$ is a calculable numerical constant.

He further proves a weaker form of (1), with $T^{1/4}$ on the right side of (1), with

$$X = T\exp(-(\log T)^{9/10}),$$

$$T \geqq \max(c_3, \exp(k^{30L_0})),$$

where $L_0$ is the so-called Linnik constant, and $c_3$ is numerically calculable. The proofs rest on a lemma which is a modification of Turán's "second main theorem" concerning inequalities for sums of the type $b_1 z_1^n + \cdots + b_N z_N^n$, where the $z_m$ are subject to $1 \geqq |z_1| \geqq |z_2| \geqq \cdots \geqq |z_N|$ and another condition. There are similar results with $\pi(x; k, l)$ replacing $\psi(x, k, l)$.

*S. Chowla* (Boulder, Colo.)

Citations: MR 23# A3119 = N12-18.

## N12-22 (26# 90 )

**Knapowski, S.**

**Contributions to the theory of the distribution of prime numbers in arithmetical progressions. III.**

*Acta Arith.* **8** (1962/63), 97–105.

Writing, as usual,

$$\pi(x, k, l) = \sum_{\substack{p \equiv l \,(\mathrm{mod}\, k) \\ p \leqq x}} 1,$$

where $p$ denotes a typical prime, the author assumes: (C) In the rectangle $0<\sigma<1$, $|t| \leqq \max(c_1, k^7)$, $s=\sigma+it$, all $L$-functions (mod $k$) vanish only at points of the line $\sigma=\frac{1}{2}$. He proves the following. Theorem: Let $k \geqq 3$, $0<l_1$, $l_2<k$, $l_1 \neq l_2$, $(l_1, k)=(l_2, k)=1$, and suppose (C) is true. Then

$$\int_X^T |\pi(x, k, l_1) - \pi(x, k, l_2)| \frac{dx}{x} > T^{1/2} \exp\left(-\frac{7 \log T}{\log\log T}\right),$$

with $X = T\exp\{-(\log T)^{3/4}\}$ for $T \geqq \max(c_2, e^{e^k})$. Here $c_1$ and $c_2$ are positive numerical constants. This work is a continuation of the author's previous work [same Acta **6** (1960/61), 415–434; MR **23** #A3119; and the preceding paper (#89)].

*S. Chowla* (Boulder, Colo.)

Citations: MR 23# A3119 = N12-18.

## N12-23 (26# 3682a; 26# 3682b; 26# 3682c)

**Knapowski, S.; Turán, P.**

**Comparative prime-number theory. I. Introduction.**

*Acta Math. Acad. Sci. Hungar.* **13** (1962), 299–314.

**Knapowski, S.; Turán, P.**

**Comparative prime-number theory. II. Comparison of the progressions $\equiv 1$ mod $k$ and $\equiv l$ mod $k$, $l \not\equiv 1$ mod $k$.**

*Acta Math. Acad. Sci. Hungar.* **13** (1962), 315–342.

**Knapowski, S.; Turán, P.**

**Comparative prime-number theory. III. Continuation of the study of comparison of the progressions $\equiv 1$ mod $k$ and $\equiv l$ mod $k$.**

*Acta Math. Acad. Sci. Hungar.* **13** (1962), 343–364.

These constitute the first three parts of an eight-part work on the irregularity of the distribution of primes in the various residue classes (mod $k$). Thus, if as usual $\pi(x, k, l)$ designates the number of primes $p \leqq x$ such that $p \equiv l$ (mod $k$), where $(k, l)=1$, a wide variety of questions can be raised about the comparative size of $\pi(x, k, l_1)$ and $\pi(x, k, l_2)$ for large $x$. In Part I, twelve such questions are posed, together with their analogues for the functions

$$\psi(x, k, l) = \sum_{\substack{n \leqq x \\ n \equiv l \bmod k}} \Lambda(n),$$

$$\Pi(x, k, l) = \sum_{\substack{n \leqq x \\ n \equiv l \bmod k}} \frac{\Lambda(n)}{\log n},$$

$$\sum_{p \equiv l \bmod k} e^{-pr},$$

the last of these being of interest as $r \to 0+$. A survey is also given in Part I of the results concerning these questions to be found, implicitly or explicitly, in the literature. The remainder of Part I is devoted to an outline of what is to follow. Certain of the results to be obtained are hypothetical, depending for example on the Riemann-Piltz conjecture that no $L$-function vanishes in the half-plane $\sigma > \frac{1}{2}$, or the Haselgrove condition that $L(s, \chi) \neq 0$ for $0<\sigma<1$ and $|t| \leqq A(k)$, where $0 < A(k) \leqq 1$. It is known that the Haselgrove condition is satisfied for $3 \leqq k \leqq 12$ and for $k=19$ and 24, so that in these cases this hypothesis is unnecessary.

Limitations of space preclude giving all the results of Parts II and III. As examples, we quote the following from II, in which $\log_k$ and $e_k$ denote the $k$-fold iterates of the logarithm and exponential functions. For the $k$'s listed above for which Haselgrove's condition holds, there is a calculable constant $c$ such that for $T>c$ and $l \neq 1$,

$$\max_{T^{1/3} \leqq x \leqq T} \{\psi(x, k, 1) - \psi(x, k, l)\} > T^{1/2} e_1\left(-41 \frac{\log T \log_3 T}{\log_2 T}\right),$$

$$\min_{T^{1/3} \leqq x \leqq T} \{\psi(x, k, 1) - \psi(x, k, l)\} < -T^{1/2} e_1\left(-41 \frac{\log T \log_3 T}{\log_2 T}\right).$$

Similarly, for such $k$ and $T>c$ (not necessarily the same $c$ as before),

(*)
$$\max_{e_1(\log_3^{1/130} T) \leqq x \leqq T} \frac{\pi(x, k, 1) - \pi(x, k, l)}{\dfrac{\sqrt{x}}{\log x}} > \frac{1}{100} \log_5 T,$$

$$\min_{e_1(\log_3^{1/130} T) \leqq x \leqq T} \frac{\pi(x, k, 1) - \pi(x, k, l)}{\dfrac{\sqrt{x}}{\log x}} < -\frac{1}{100} \log_5 T.$$

More generally, if Haselgrove's condition is satisfied and $T > \max(e_5(ck), e_2(A(k)^{-3}))$, then the inequalities (*) hold.

In Part III, comparison of the residue classes 1 and $l$ (mod $k$) is continued. It is shown that if the Haselgrove condition holds for $k$, then for $T > \max(e_4(k^c), e_2(2A(k)^{-3}))$, the number of sign changes of $\pi(x, k, 1) - \pi(x, k, l)$ for $0 < x \leqq T$ exceeds $k^{-c} \log_4 T$. Moreover, for such $k$, suppose that the congruences $x^2 \equiv 1$ and $x^2 \equiv l$ (mod $k$) have the same number of solutions, and that $\rho_0 = \beta_0 + i\gamma_0$, $\beta_0 \geqq \frac{1}{2}$, is a zero of $L(s, \chi_1)$ with $\chi_1(l) \neq 1$. Then for

$$T > \max(c, e_2(k), e_2(A(k)^{-3}), e_2(10|\rho_0|)),$$

the inequalities

$$\max_{T^{1/3} \leqq x \leqq T} \{\pi(x, k, 1) - \pi(x, k, l)\} > T^{\beta_0} e_1\left(-42 \frac{\log T \log_3 T}{\log_2 T}\right),$$

$$\min_{T^{1/3} \leqq x \leqq T} \{\pi(x, k, 1) - \pi(x, k, l)\} < -T^{\beta_0} e_1\left(-42 \frac{\log T \log_3 T}{\log_2 T}\right)$$

hold.

The proofs of all these theorems depend on Turán's method, as expounded in his book [*Eine neue Methode in der Analysis und deren Anwendungen*, Akad. Kiadó, Budapest, 1953; MR **15**, 688] and in particular on a theorem due to Turán giving one-sided bounds for certain power sums [Acta Math. Acad. Sci. Hungar. **12** (1961), 455–468; MR **24** #A2565]. They also depend on techniques developed by Ingham, Knapowski, Littlewood, and Skewes.

*W. J. LeVeque* (Ann Arbor, Mich.)

Citations: MR 15, 688b = M50-2; MR 24# A2565 = M50-26.

Referred to in N02-12, N04-42, N12-25, N12-26, N12-34, N12-52, P40-19.

**N12-24** **(26# 3683a; 26# 3683b; 26# 3683c)**

**Knapowski, S.; Turán, P.**
**Comparative prime-number theory. IV. Paradigma to the general case, $k=8$ and 5.**
*Acta Math. Acad. Sci. Hungar.* **14** (1963), 31–42.

**Knapowski, S.; Turán, P.**
**Comparative prime-number theory. V. Some theorems concerning the general case.**
*Acta Math. Acad. Sci. Hungar.* **14** (1963), 43–63.

**Knapowski, S.; Turán, P.**
**Comparative prime-number theory. VI. Continuation of the general case.**
*Acta Math. Acad. Sci. Hungar.* **14** (1963), 65–78.

For Parts I–III, see #3682 above; we preserve the notation introduced there. Comparison of the distribution of primes in the residue classes 1 and $l$ (mod $k$) (more briefly, the case $(1, l)_k$) was effected in II and III. In IV the authors consider in detail the case $(l_1, l_2)_8$, $l_1 \neq 1$, $l_2 \neq 1$, which they can treat with no reference to unproved hypotheses. It is shown that in this case, for $T$ sufficiently large,

$$\max_{T^{1/3} \leqq x \leqq T} \{\Pi(x, 8, l_1) - \Pi(x, 8, l_2)\} > T^{1/2} e_1\left(-23 \frac{\log T \log_3 T}{\log_2 T}\right),$$

and the same inequality holds when $\Pi$ is replaced by $\pi$ or $\psi$. It follows from this that in the case considered in this part, the number of changes in sign of each of the functions

$$f(x,k,l_1) - f(x,k,l_2) \qquad (f = \pi, \psi, \Pi)$$

for $0 < x \leqq T$ is greater than $c_2 \log_2 T$. (These three numbers of sign changes will henceforth be designated by $W_k(T, l_1, l_2)$, $U_k(T, l_1, l_2)$, $V_k(T, l_1, l_2)$, respectively.)

In V the authors turn to the general case $(l_1, l_2)_k$, and obtain results under what they call the finite Riemann-Piltz conjecture, that no $L(s, \chi)$ with $\chi \neq \chi_0$ vanishes for $\sigma > \frac{1}{2}$, $|t| \leqq C_1 k^{10}$, and $\sigma = \frac{1}{2}$, $|t| \leqq A(k)$. It is shown that if this holds for sufficiently large $c_1$, then for sufficiently large $c_2$ and

$$(*) \qquad T > \max\{e_2(c_2 k^{20}), e_1(2e_1(A(k)^{-3})) + c_2 k^{20}\},$$

the inequality

$$\max_{T^{1/3} \leqq x \leqq T} \{f(x, k, l_1) - f(x, k, l_2)\} > T^{1/2} e_1\left(-44 \frac{\log T \log_3 T}{\log_2 T}\right)$$

holds for $f = \psi$ and $\Pi$. This leads to the lower bound $(2 \log 3)^{-1} \log_2 T$ for $U_k(T, l_1, l_2)$ and $V_k(T, l_1, l_2)$ when

$$T > \max\{e_1(9e_1(2c_2 k^{20})), e_1(72e_1(2A(k)^{-3}) + 18c_2^2 k^{40}\}.$$

A result is also obtained on $\pi(x, k, l_1) - \pi(x, k, l_2)$ which is stronger than that given in IV but which depends on the conjecture above and the hypothesis that the congruences $x^2 \equiv l_1 \pmod{k}$, $x^2 \equiv l_2 \pmod{k}$ are unsolvable.

In VI it is shown that if the finite Riemann-Piltz conjecture holds for sufficiently large $c_1$, if the congruences $x^2 \equiv l_1 \pmod{k}$ and $x^2 \equiv l_2 \pmod{k}$ have the same number of solutions, and if (*) holds with sufficiently large $c_2$, then

$$\max_{T^{1/3} \leqq x \leqq T} \{\pi(x, k, l_1) - \pi(x, k, l_2)\} > T^{1/2} e_1\left(-44 \frac{\log T \log_3 T}{\log_2 T}\right).$$

*W. J. LeVeque* (Ann Arbor, Mich.)

Referred to in N12-25, N12-26, N12-34, N12-46, P40-19.

**N12-25** **(28# 70a; 28# 70b)**

**Knapowski, S.; Turán, P.**
**Comparative prime-number theory. VII. The problem of sign-changes in the general case.**
*Acta Math. Acad. Sci. Hungar.* **14** (1963), 241–250.

**Knapowski, S.; Turán, P.**
**Comparative prime-number theory. VIII. Chebyshev's problem for $k=8$.**
*Acta Math. Acad. Sci. Hungar.* **14** (1963), 251–268.

For Parts I–VI, see same Acta **13** (1962), 299–314 [MR **26** #3682a]; ibid. **13** (1962), 315–342 [MR **26** #3682b]; ibid. **13** (1962), 343–364 [MR **26** #3682c]; ibid. **14** (1963), 31–42 [MR **26** #3683a]; ibid. **14** (1963), 43–63 [MR **26** #3683b]; ibid. **14** (1963), 65–78 [MR **26** #3683c]. Part VII is devoted to the oscillatory behavior of $\psi(x, k, l_1) - \psi(x, k, l_2)$, where as usual $\psi(x, k, l) = \sum_n \Lambda(n)$, the summation being on $n$ with $n \leqq x$ and $n \equiv l \pmod{k}$. The authors prove the following theorem, which is more special than the principal result of V, but depends on a weaker hypothesis concerning the zeros of $L$-functions: There is a (large) constant $c$ such that if $k$ satisfies a Haselgrove condition, then all the functions $\psi(x, k, l_1) - \psi(x, k, l_2)$, for $l_1 \neq l_2$, change sign in every interval $\omega \leqq x \leqq e_1(2\sqrt{\omega})$ with $\omega \geqq \max(e_1(k^c), e_1(2A(k)^{-3}))$.

In the eighth and final part of the present sequence, the authors are chiefly concerned with the limiting behavior of

$$f_{l_1 l_2}(x) = \sum_{p \equiv l_1 \pmod 8} \log p \cdot e^{-px} - \sum_{p \equiv l_2 \pmod 8} \log p \cdot e^{-px}$$

as $x \to 0^+$. They show that if $0 < \delta < c_1$ and if 1, $l_1$ and $l_2$ are distinct (mod 8), then

$$\max_{\delta \leqq x \leqq \delta^{1/3}} f_{l_1 l_2}(x) > \delta^{-1/2} e_1\left(-22 \frac{\log \delta^{-1} \log_3 \delta^{-1}}{\log_2 \delta^{-1}}\right),$$

and by symmetry the negative of this lower bound provides an upper bound for the corresponding minimum. In particular, this shows that $f_{l_1 l_2}(x)$ oscillates in sign as $x \to 0^+$. On the other hand it is shown, using methods of Hardy-Littlewood and Landau, that if for some $l \not\equiv 1 \pmod 8$, $\lim_{x \to 0^+} f_{1l}(x) = -\infty$, then no $L$-function (mod 8) with $\chi(l) \neq 1$ can vanish for $\sigma > \frac{1}{2}$, and that if no $L$-function (mod 8) with $\chi \neq \chi_0$ vanishes for $\sigma > \frac{1}{2}$, then $\lim_{x \to 0^+} f_{1l}(x) = -\infty$ for $l \not\equiv 1 \pmod 8$. *W. J. LeVeque* (Boulder, Colo.)

Citations: MR 26# 3682a = N12-23; MR 26# 3682b = N12-23; MR 26# 3682c = N12-23; MR 26# 3683a = N12-24; MR 26# 3683b = N12-24; MR 26# 3683c = N12-24.

Referred to in N12-26, N12-33, N12-34, N12-35, N12-52, P40-19.

**N12-26** **(29# 75)**

**Knapowski, S.; Turán, P.**
**Further developments in the comparative prime-number theory. I.**
*Acta Arith.* **9** (1964), 23–40.

This is Part I of a new series on this subject, the earlier series of eight papers having appeared in Acta Math. Acad. Sci. Hungar. **13** (1962), 299–314 [MR **26** #3682a]; ibid. **13** (1962), 315–342 [MR **26** #3682b]; ibid. **13** (1962), 343–364 [MR **26** #3682c]; ibid. **14** (1963), 31–42 [MR **26** #3683a]; ibid. **14** (1963), 43–63 [MR **26** #3683b]; ibid. **14** (1963), 65–78 [MR **26** #3683c]; ibid. **14** (1963), 241–250 [MR **28** #70a]; ibid. **14** (1963), 251–268 [MR **28** #70b]. The present paper begins by posing 44 problems dealing with irregularities in the distribution of primes in the various residue classes modulo $k$; these are essentially amplifications of those posed in Part I of the first series. It is intended that the first few parts of the present series deal with what the authors call "accumulation problems". In this part the following theorem is proved: If $k$ is a modulus for which the so-called Haselgrove condition holds, then there exists $T_0(k)$ such that for $T > T_0$ and for all $(l, k) = 1$ there are suitable $U_1, U_2$ with $T \exp(-\log^{11/12} T) \leqq U_1 < U_2 \leqq T$ so that

$$\sum_{\substack{n \equiv 1(k) \\ U_1 \leqq n \leqq U_2}} \Lambda(n) - \sum_{\substack{n \equiv l(k) \\ U_1 \leqq n \leqq U_2}} \Lambda(n) > T^{1/2} \exp(-\log^{11/12} T)$$

holds; a symmetrical upper bound holds also, not necessarily for the same $U_i$. Here $\Lambda(n)$ has its usual meaning. The Haselgrove condition requires the explicit value of an $E = E(k)$ such that no $L(s, \chi)$ belonging to the modulus $k$ vanishes for $0 < \sigma < 1$, $|t| \leqq E$; it is to be noted that it is satisfied for $3 \leqq k \leqq 10$. The methods used in the proof are similar to those used in the first series.

*H. W. Brinkmann* (Swarthmore, Pa.)

Citations: MR 26# 3682a = N12-23; MR 26# 3682b = N12-23; MR 26# 3682c = N12-23; MR 26# 3683a = N12-24; MR 26# 3683b = N12-24; MR 26# 3683c = N12-24; MR 28# 70a = N12-25; MR 28# 70b = N12-25.

Referred to in N12-33.

## N12-27 (30# 1103)

**Barban, M. B.**

**On an analytic lemma of Ju. V. Linnik. (Russian. Uzbek summary)**

*Izv. Akad. Nauk UzSSR Ser. Fiz.-Mat. Nauk* **1964**, *no.* 4, 5–12.

Let $S(N) = \sum_{p \leqq N} \chi(p) \log p$, where $p$ runs through the primes and $\chi(n)$ is any non-principal character mod $D$. Supposing that the Dirichlet function $L(s, \chi)$ has a zero in the rectangle $\{1 - \lambda/\log D \leqq \sigma \leqq 1, |t| \leqq \log^A D\}$ (where $\log^{1/5} D < \lambda < \frac{1}{3} \log D$ and $A$ is any fixed constant), the author proves that there is a number

$$N_1 \in [D^{(\log\log D)/20\lambda}, D^{O(1)}]$$

such that $|S(N_1)| > N_1^{1-2\lambda/\log D} (\log D)^{-A-15}$. He follows closely the arguments of Linnik's paper [Mat. Sb. (N.S.) **15 (57)** (1944), 3–12, Lemma 6; MR **6**, 260], where a similar estimate has been proved for $A = 3$. The author says that he needs the result for a later paper.

{Reviewer's remark: In the proof on p. 9 it is necessary that the function $|\varphi(s)|$, defined by

$$(1) \qquad L'/L(s, \chi) = \sum_{\rho} \{(s-\rho)^{-1} + \rho^{-1}\} + \varphi(s)$$

(where $\rho$ runs through the zeros of $L(s, \chi)$ in $0 < \sigma < 1$), is not too large. Following Linnik, the author says that $\varphi(s) \ll \log D(|t| + 2)$ in $\sigma \geqq \frac{1}{4}$. However, if $L(s, \chi)$ has the real exceptional zero $\rho_1 = 1 - \delta$, then from the theorems on pp. 130, 207, 143, 218, 331 and 225 of Prachar's book, *Primzahlverteilung* [Springer, Berlin, 1957; MR **19**, 393] it follows that $\varphi(s) = -1/\delta + O(\log D(|t| + 2))$ and $1/\delta \leqq c(\varepsilon) D^{\varepsilon}$ (for any constant $\varepsilon > 0$). To save the proof in this case one has to separate the term with $\rho = \delta$ from the sum $\sum_\rho$ in (1) and add it to the function $\varphi(s)$.}

*E. Fogels* (Riga)

Citations: MR 6, 260a = N16-4; MR 19, 393b = N02-7.

## N12-28 (30# 1990)

**Barban, M. B.**

**New applications of the "great sieve" of Ju. V. Linnik. (Russian)**

*Akad. Nauk Uzbek. SSR Trudy Inst. Mat. No.* 22 (1961), 1–20.

Let $\pi(x, k, l)$ denote the number of primes $p \leqq x$, $p \equiv l \pmod k$, $\varphi(n)$ the Euler function, $\mu(n)$ the Möbius function, $\tau_k(n)$ the number of representations of $n$ as a product of $k$ primes. Furthermore, let $A$ be an arbitrarily large constant, $a_1$, $a_2$ positive constants depending upon $A$, $M \geqq a_1$, $\mu(q) \neq 0$, $\log q \leqq a_2 \log^4 M$.

By using the method of Ju. V. Linnik [Mat. Sb. (N.S.) **15 (57)** (1944), 3–12; MR **6**, 260] and a lemma of A. Rényi [Izv. Akad. Nauk SSSR Ser. Mat. **12** (1948), 57–78; MR **9**, 413], the author proves the bound

$$(1) \quad \pi(x, pq, l) = \pi(x, q, l)/\varphi(p) + O(x/(\varphi(pq) \log^A pq))$$

for all $p \in (M, 2M)$ with not more than $M^{3/4}$ exceptions, where $(p, q) = (pq, l) = 1$ and $pq \leqq x^{1/6-\varepsilon}$ (where $\varepsilon > 0$ is a fixed, sufficiently small number). By means of (1) the author proves that

$$\sum_{D \leqq x^{1/6-\varepsilon}} \mu^2(D) \max_{\substack{l \pmod D \\ (l,D)=1}} \left| \pi(x, D, l) - \frac{\operatorname{li} x}{\varphi(D)} \right| = O(x/\log^A x),$$

which is used to obtain upper and lower bounds for the sum $\sum_{p \leqq x} F(p-a)$, where $F$ is a multiplicative function subject to a certain restriction. As an application, for the sum $\sum_{p \leqq x} \tau_k{}^l(p-a)$ the author gives upper and lower estimates of the form $c(k, l)x(\log x)^b$ $(b = k^l - 2)$.

Citations: MR 6, 260a = N16-4; MR 9, 413g = P32-12.

Referred to in N12-30, N60-62, P32-63.

## N12-29 (30# 1993)

**Barban, M. B.; Linnik, Yu. V. [Linnik, Ju. V.]; Tshudakov, N. G. [Čudakov, N. G.]**

**On prime numbers in an arithmetic progression with a prime-power difference.**

*Acta Arith.* **9** (1964), 375–390.

Assuming the extended Riemann hypothesis, one can prove, for the number of primes $p \leqq x$, $p \equiv l \bmod D$, $(l, D) = 1$,

$$(1) \quad \pi(x, D, l) = (\operatorname{li} x/\varphi(D))(1 + O(\log^{-M} x)) \quad \text{for } x \geqq D^{2+\varepsilon}.$$

In particular, for the least prime $P(D, l)$ in the arithmetic progression $n \equiv l \bmod D$ one would obtain $P(D, l) < c(\varepsilon) D^{2+\varepsilon}$. Linnik [Mat. Sb. (N.S.) **15 (57)** (1944), 139–178; MR **6**, 260; ibid. **15 (57)** (1944), 347–368; MR **6**, 260] gave the first proof of the existence of a constant $c$ such that $P(D, l) < D^c$. Pan [Sci. Record (N.S.) **1** (1957), 311–313; MR **21** #4140], making use of this paper and a simplified proof given by Rodosskiĭ [Mat. Sb. (N.S.) **34 (76)** (1954), 331–356; MR **15**, 935], obtained the estimate $c \leqq 5448$.

In this paper, without assuming any unproved hypothesis, the authors succeed in showing the truth of (1) for a certain subsequence of the moduli $D$; actually, they prove it for $D = p^n$, where $p$ is any fixed prime $\geqq 3$, $n \geqq n_0$ and $x \geqq D^{8/3+\varepsilon}$, $M$ being arbitrarily large. Consequently, the following estimate is true: $P(D, l) < c_1(\varepsilon) D^{8/3+\varepsilon}$ for all $D = p^n$, where $p \geqq 3$ and $n \geqq n_0$. Also, there is an absolute constant $c_2$ such that $\pi(x, p^n, l) > 0$ for any prime $p \geqq 3$ and $n \geqq c_2 \exp(p^2)$.

The main tools in the proof are results concerning characters $\chi$ with respect to those moduli $D$ obtained by A. G. Postnikov [J. Indian Math. Soc. (N.S.) **20** (1956), 217–226; MR **18**, 793] and S. M. Rozin [Izv. Akad. Nauk SSSR Ser. Mat. **23** (1959), 503–508; MR **22** #4680]. Also $\sum_{\nu \leqq x} \chi(\nu) = O(\sqrt{x} D^{1/6} \log^{1/2} D)$ is used for $D^{1/3} \leqq x \leqq D^{2/3}$, the assumption $n \geqq n_0$ being important. From these one obtains estimates of the corresponding $L$-series, and a lemma of Barban [#1990 above] leads to the desired result for some logarithmic mean of the remainder term, while a Tauberian argument completes the proof. {Unfortunately, there are numerous misprints.}

*H.-E. Richert* (Marburg)

Citations: MR 6, 260b = N16-5; MR 6, 260c = N16-6; MR 15, 935e = N16-16; MR 18, 793a = M25-43; MR 21# 4140 = N16-19; MR 22# 4680 = M25-46.

**N12-30** **(33# 4037)**

**Barban, M. B.**

**A remark on the author's paper "New applications of the 'large sieve' of Ju. V. Linnik". (Russian)**

*Theory Probability Math. Statist. (Russian), pp.* 130–133. *Izdat. "Nauka" Uzbek. SSR, Tashkent,* 1964.

This is a correction of an error in the proof of the basic lemma on page 11 of the author's article in Akad. Nauk Uzbek. SSR Trudy Inst. Mat. No. 22 (1961), 1–20 [MR **30** #1990].

Citations: MR 30# 1990 = N12-28.

**N12-31** **(30# 3871)**

**Pan, Cheng-dong [Pan, Cheng-Tung]**

**A new application of the Ju. V. Linnik large sieve method.**

*Acta Math. Sinica* **14** (1964), 597–606 (*Chinese*); *translated as Chinese Math.—Acta* **5** (1964), 642–652.

Let, as usual, $\pi(x, D, l)$ be the number of primes $p \leqq x$ in the residue class $p \equiv l \pmod D$. The author proves the following main theorem.

$$\sum_{D \leqq x^{(1/3)-\varepsilon}} \mu^2(D) \max_{(l,D)=1} \left|\pi(x, D, l) - \frac{\operatorname{Li} x}{\varphi(D)}\right| = O\left(\frac{x}{\log^5 x}\right),$$

where $\varepsilon$ is any given positive number. This improves on an earlier result by A. Rényi [Izv. Akad. Nauk SSSR Ser. Mat. **12** (1948), 57–78; MR **9**, 413]. The theorem allows one to deduce the following two results. (1) Every sufficiently large even number is the sum of a prime and of a product of at most 4 primes [Yuan Wang, Sci. Sinica **11** (1962), 1033–1054; MR **27** #1424; the author, ibid. **12** (1963), 455–473; MR **28** #73]. (2) If $Z(x)$ denotes the number of primes $p \leqq x$ for which $p+2$ is also prime, then

$$Z(x) \leqq^{\bullet} (12+\varepsilon) \prod_{p>2} \left(1 - \frac{1}{(p-1)^2}\right) \frac{x}{\log^2 x} + O\left(\frac{x}{\log^3 x}\right)$$

(A. Selberg; see Yuan Wang [loc. cit.]).

*K. Mahler* (Canberra)

Citations: MR 9, 413g = P32-12; MR 27# 1424 = P32-50; MR 28# 73 = P32-56.

Referred to in M55-37, M55-43.

**N12-32** **(30# 3872)**

**P'ang, Ch'en-tung [Pan, Cheng-Tung]**

**New applications of the "large sieve" of Ju. V. Linnik. (Russian)**

*Sci. Sinica* **13** (1964), 1045–1053.

A Russian version of the preceding paper [#3871].

*K. Mahler* (Canberra)

**N12-33** **(30# 4739)**

**Knapowski, S.; Turán, P.**

**Further developments in the comparative prime-number theory. II. A modification of Chebyshev's assertion.**

*Acta Arith.* **10** (1964), 293–313.

Part I appeared in same Acta **9** (1964), 23–40 [MR **29** #75]. The main results of this paper are of the same general character as those of Part VIII of the first series [Acta Math. Acad. Sci. Hungar. **14** (1963), 251–268; MR **28** #70b], but extended to a general modulus $k$ in place of $k=8$. Numerical inequalities about zeros, applied as known facts in the special case, are now replaced by the hypothesis that the functions $L(s, \chi)$ $(s=\sigma+it)$ associated with the $k$ under consideration have no zeros in the rectangle $0<\sigma<1$, $|t| \leqq E(k)$, for some explicit $E(k)>0$. The authors conclude, however, that this hypothesis, named by them the Haselgrove-property because the late C. B. (not P. C.) Haselgrove had supplied numerical values of $E(k)$ for special $k$, cannot be used effectively with the Abel sums $\sum_p a_p e^{-p/x}$ that would occur in a direct generalization of Chebyshev's original assertion for $k=4$. They therefore replace these sums by sums of the type

$$\sum_p a_p \exp\left(-\frac{1}{r} \log^2 \frac{p}{x}\right) \qquad (p \text{ prime}),$$

where $(c \log k)/E^2(k) \leqq r \leqq \log x$, and $a_p$ is $\log p$ if $p \equiv l_1 \pmod k$, $-\log p$ if $p \equiv l_2 \pmod k$, and 0 otherwise. The results are connected with unproved hypotheses about the existence, or non-existence, of zeros of certain $L$-functions in the half-plane $\sigma > \frac{1}{2}$.

*A. E. Ingham* (Cambridge, England)

Citations: MR 28# 70b = N12-25; MR 29# 75 = N12-26.

Referred to in M30-43, N12-36, N12-37.

**N12-34** **(31# 1235)**

**Kátai, I.**

**Eine Bemerkung zur "Comparative prime-number theory I–VIII" von S. Knapowski und P. Turán.**

*Ann. Univ. Sci. Budapest. Eötvös Sect. Math.* **7** (1964), 33–40.

Write $\psi(x, k, l) = \sum_{n \leqq x, n \equiv l(k)} \Lambda(n)$, $\pi(x, k, l) = \sum_{p \leqq x, p \equiv l(k)} 1$, where $\Lambda(n)$ stands for the Dirichlet-von Mangoldt function and $p$ runs through primes. The author uses an idea of Littlewood to prove

$$\limsup_{x \to \infty} \frac{\psi(x, k, l_1) - \psi(x, k, l_2)}{\sqrt{x}} > 0 \qquad (l_1 \not\equiv l_2 \pmod k)$$

in case there are no zeros of $L(s, \chi)$-functions mod $k$ in $0<s<1$. Further, he shows

$$\limsup_{x \to \infty} \frac{\pi(x, k, l_1) - \pi(x, k, l_2)}{\sqrt{x}/\log x} > 0$$

if, additionally, the congruences $y^2 \equiv l_1 \pmod k$ and $y^2 \equiv l_2 \pmod k$ have the same number of solutions. He also obtains more precise information by assuming the full Riemann hypothesis for $L(s, \chi)$-functions mod $k$. The author can localize the sign changes to intervals of type $(\omega, \mathscr{A}\omega)$ for $\omega > \omega_0$, with ineffective $\mathscr{A}$ and $\omega_0$. So, for example, for the location of the first sign-change, no result follows.

{The papers mentioned in the title appeared in Acta Math. Akad. Sci. Hungar. **13** (1962), 299–314, 315–342, 343–364; MR **26** #3682a–c; ibid. **14** (1963), 31–42, 43–63, 65–78; MR **26** #3683a–c; ibid. **14** (1963), 241–250, 251–268; MR **28** #70a–b.}

*S. Knapowski* (Gainesville, Fla.)

Citations: MR 26# 3682a = N12-23; MR 26# 3682b = N12-23; MR 26# 3682c = N12-23; MR 26# 3683a = N12-24; MR 26# 3683b = N12-24; MR 26# 3683c = N12-24; MR 28# 70a = N12-25; MR 28# 70b = N12-25.

Referred to in N44-39.

**N12-35** **(31# 2221)**

**Knapowski, S.; Turán, P.**

**On an assertion of Čebyšev.**

*J. Analyse Math.* **14** (1965), 267–274.

For given $l_1, l_2$ with $l_1 \not\equiv l_2 \pmod 8$, let $\varepsilon_p = +1$ for $p \equiv l_1 \pmod 8$, $-1$ for $p \equiv l_2 \pmod 8$, 0 otherwise ($p$ prime),

$$g(x) = \sum_p \varepsilon_p e^{-px}, \qquad g^*(x) = \sum_p \varepsilon_p \log p \cdot e^{-px} \qquad (x > 0).$$

Let

$$\Delta = \exp\left(\frac{\log(1/\delta) \log_3(1/\delta)}{\log_2(1/\delta)}\right) \qquad (0 < \delta < 1),$$

where $\log_n$ denotes an $n$-fold logarithm. In a previous paper [Acta Math. Acad. Sci. Hungar. **14** (1963), 251–268; MR **28** #70b] the authors proved that, if $l_1$, $l_2$ are any two of 3, 5, 7 (quadratic non-residues of 8) and if $\delta < c$ (a suitable numerical constant), then

$$\max_{\delta \leq x \leq \delta^{1/3}} g^*(x) > \delta^{-1/2}\Delta^{-22},$$

$$\min_{\delta \leq x \leq \delta^{1/3}} g^*(x) < -\delta^{-1/2}\Delta^{-22}.$$

Here they consider the more difficult problem of $g(x)$ and prove

(I) $$\max_{\delta \leq x \leq \delta^{1/3}} |g(x)| \geqq \delta^{-1/2}\Delta^{-23}.$$

The proof connects $g^*(x)$ with $g(x)$ by means of the formula

$$\log \nu = \int_0^\infty \frac{e^{-t}-e^{-\nu t}}{t}\,dt \qquad (\nu > 0),$$

using ideas of G. Szegö. The authors state that, by combining their methods with those of Hardy-Littlewood-Landau, they can also prove (I) for $l_1 = 1$, $l_2 = 3, 5, 7$; with a similar result for modulus 4 and $l_1 = 1$, $l_2 = 3$. They hope to return to the problem of one-sided inequalities.

*A. E. Ingham* (Cambridge, England)

Citations: MR 28# 70b = N12-25.

## N12-36 (31# 4773)

**Knapowski, S.; Turán, P.**

**Further developments in the comparative prime-number theory. III.**

*Acta Arith.* **11** (1965), 115–127.

This is a continuation of a series of papers dealing with the behavior, as $x \to +\infty$, of a sum

$$S(l_1, l_2, k) = \sum_{p \equiv l_1(k)} \log p \cdot e^{-p/x} - \sum_{p \equiv l_2(k)} \log p \cdot e^{-p/x},$$

summed over all primes as indicated. It is conjectured that this behavior depends on whether $l_1$ and $l_2$ have the same quadratic character mod $k$ or not. In particular, if $l_1$ and $l_2$ have the same quadratic character mod $k$, the generalized Riemann conjecture holds for all $L(s, \chi)$ functions mod $k$, and if the so-called Haselgrove condition holds for $k$ ($k$ is then called a "good" value), then there is no definite preponderance of primes $p \equiv l_1 \pmod k$ over those that are $\equiv l_2 \pmod k$ in a sense that is explained in terms of the fluctuations of the sum $S(l_1, l_2, k)$. In the present paper this fact is proved in the case $l_1 = 1$, $l_2 =$ quadratic residue mod $k$.

Part II appeared in same Acta **10** (1964), 293–313 [MR **30** #4739]. *H. W. Brinkmann* (Swarthmore, Pa.)

Citations: MR 30# 4739 = N12-33.

Referred to in N12-37.

## N12-37 (32# 99)

**Knapowski, S.; Turán, P.**

**Further developments in the comparative prime-number theory. IV, V.**

*Acta Arith.* **11** (1965), 147–161; *ibid.* **11** (1965), 193–202.

The first of these two papers (IV) is a direct continuation of the problem considered in Parts II and III [Acta Math. Acad. Sci. Hungar. **13** (1962), 315–342; 343–364; MR 26 #3682b, c].* This time the primes contained in two residue classes $\equiv l_1 \pmod k$ and $\equiv l_2 \pmod k$, where $l_1$, $l_2$ are both quadratic non-residues mod $k$, are compared. In order to prove the appropriate comparison theorem, it turns out that a somewhat more stringent condition than the Haselgrove condition has to be satisfied (i.e., the values of $k$ must be not merely "good" but "super-good").

In the second paper (V), the authors prove a slightly weaker form of the theorem proved, under less stringent conditions, in Part II, using a new method, different in principle from the method used before. The new method consists in using a two-sided result in the theory of diophantine approximations instead of a one-sided one. The idea involved can also be used in attacking other similar problems; a simplification of the proof usually results. *H. W. Brinkmann* (Swarthmore, Pa.)

*This reference is incorrect. It should be [Acta Arith. **10** (1964) 293–313; ibid. **11** (1965), 115–127; MR **30** #4739; **31** #4773]. Ed.

Citations: MR 30# 4739 = N12-33; MR 31# 4773 = N12-36.

Referred to in N12-39.

## N12-38 (32# 5613)

**van Lint, J. H.; Richert, H.-E.**

**On primes in arithmetic progressions.**

*Acta Arith.* **11** (1965), 209–216.

Improving considerably on earlier results of Brun-Titchmarsh and Klimov [Prachar, *Primzahlverteilung*, Satz 4.1, p. 44, Springer, Berlin, 1957; MR **19**, 393; Klimov, Uspehi Mat. Nauk **16** (1961), no. 3 (99), 181–188; MR **23** #A2398], the authors obtain, by a careful treatment of the remainder term in Selberg's sieve method, sharp upper estimates for $\pi(x; k, l)$ (the number of primes $p \leqq x$, $p \equiv l \bmod k$), and for the difference $\pi(x; k, l) - \pi(x-y; k, l)$, where $(k, l) = 1$, $1 \leqq k < y \leqq x$. The result for $\pi(x; k, l)$ is

$$\pi(x; k, l) < \frac{1}{\varphi(k)} \cdot \frac{x}{\log(x/k)} \cdot \min\left\{3, 2 + \frac{16}{\log(x/k)}\right\}.$$

In the process, the authors get an estimate, useful for large $k$, for the number of $n \leqq x$, $n$ prime to $k$:

$$\sum_{n \leqq x,\,(n,k)=1} 1 < \frac{15}{2} \cdot \frac{\varphi(k)}{k} \cdot x$$

for $x \geqq 10^3$, provided that the greatest prime factor of $k$ is $\leqq x$. *W. Schwarz* (Freiburg)

Citations: MR 19, 393b = N02-7; MR 23# A2398 = N28-43.

Referred to in M55-80, N02-12.

## N12-39 (34# 149)

**Knapowski, S.; Turán, P.**

**Further developments in the comparative prime-number theory. VI. Accumulation theorems for residue-classes representing quadratic residues** mod $k$.

*Acta Arith.* **12** (1966), 85–96.

As in Part IV [same Acta **11** (1965), 147–161; MR **32** #99], the primes contained in two residue classes $\equiv l_1 \pmod k$ and $\equiv l_2 \pmod k$ are compared, but it is now assumed that $l_1$ and $l_2$ are both quadratic residues mod $k$. The resulting comparison theorems are of the same type as in Part IV, and they are obtained under the same conditions, i.e., the values of $k$ must again be "super-good".

{Part V appeared ibid. **11** (1965), 193–202 [MR **32** #99].}

*H. W. Brinkmann* (Swarthmore, Pa.)

Citations: MR 32# 99 = N12-37.

Referred to in N02-14.

## N12-40 (34# 156)

**Davenport, H.; Halberstam, H.**

**Primes in arithmetic progressions.**

*Michigan Math. J.* **13** (1966), 485–489.

Put $\psi(x; q, a) = \sum_{n \leq x,\, n \equiv a \bmod q} \Lambda(n)$ with $\Lambda(n) = \log p$ for $n = p^k$, $\Lambda(n) = 0$ otherwise. For $q \leqq \log^A x$ the Siegel-Walfisz prime number theorem [cf. K. Pracher, *Primzahl-*

*verteilung*, Springer, Berlin, 1957; MR **19**, 393] yields $E(x; q, a) = |\psi(x; q, a) - x/\varphi(q)| = O(x \exp(-C \log^{1/2} x))$. The authors estimate this error term $E$ "in the mean", namely: for any fixed $A > 0$ and any $Q \leqq x(\log x)^{-A}$, one has

$$\sum_{q \leqq Q} \sum_{1 \leqq a \leqq q, (a,q)=1} (E(x; q, a))^2 = O(x^2 (\log x)^{5-A}).$$

The proof is based on a "large-sieve" theorem of the authors [Mathematika **13** (1966), 91–96; MR **33** #5592] and the Siegel-Walfisz theorem.

A weaker theorem of the same kind was proved by M. B. Barban [Vestnik Leningrad. Univ. Ser. Mat. Meh. Astronom. **18** (1963), no. 4, 5–13; MR **28** #57; Uspehi Mat. Nauk **21** (1966), no. 1 (127), 51–102, Theorem 3.2; MR **33** #7320]. *W. Schwarz* (Freiburg)

Citations: MR 19, 393b = N02-7; MR 28# 57 = P48-8; MR 33# 5592 = M55-45; MR 33# 7320 = Z02-53.

Referred to in M55-52, N12-41, N16-36, R46-32.

## N12-41 (38# 2099 )

**Davenport, H.; Halberstam, H.**

**Corrigendum: "Primes in arithmetic progression".**

*Michigan Math. J.* **15** (1968), 505.

Die Verfasser ersetzen einen in ihrer Arbeit in demselben J. **13** (1966), 485–489 [MR **34** #156] verwendeten Hilfssatz über das "große Sieb" durch einen etwas abgewandelten Satz, den sie in einer Notiz in Mathematika **14** (1967), 229–232 [MR **36** #2569] bewiesen hatten. Das Hauptergebnis der obengenannten Arbeit ändert sich nicht. *W. Schwarz* (Freiburg)

Citations: MR 34# 156 = N12-40; MR 36# 2569 = M55-46.

## N12-42 (34# 2545 )

**Grosswald, Emil**

**Oscillation theorems of arithmetical functions.**

*Trans. Amer. Math. Soc.* **126** (1967), 1–28.

The old method of Landau is employed, and results in a long list of arithmetic oscillation-theorems. As the author points out, most of the contents of this paper have essentially been discovered before. However, he does include some new results, proving, e.g., that the functions $\pi(x, k, a) - \pi(x, k, b)$ change sign infinitely often in all admissible cases, for $k = 43, 67, 163$. Naturally, owing to the imperfection of Landau's method, the really deep oscillatory problems—e.g., those concerning the sign-changes of $\pi(x) - \operatorname{li} x$, of the summatorial Liouville function, the comparison of the distribution of primes mod 4—had to be left out. *S. Knapowski* (Coral Gables, Fla.)

## N12-43 (34# 5793 )

**Rieger, G. J.**

**Über die natürlichen und primen Zahlen der Gestalt $[n^c]$ in arithmetischer Progression.**

*Arch. Math.* (*Basel*) **18** (1967), 35–44.

Let $k$, $l$ and $n$ be natural numbers, $F_c$ the sequence $\{[n^c]\}$, and $x$ and $c$ any real numbers with the properties $x \geqq 2$, $2 > c > 1$. First the author proves a theorem concerning the function $s_c(x, k, l)$ denoting the number of positive integers $a$ such that $a \in F_c$, $a \leqq x$ and $a \equiv l \pmod{k}$; namely, $s_c(x, k, l) = (1/k)x^{1/c} + O_c(g(x)^{1/7})$, with a constant in the remainder term depending only on $c$. Here $g(x) = x^{1+\lambda}(\log x)^3$, where $\lambda$ is the Legendre symbol $(5/c)$. Then he also proves an asymptotic formula with regard to the function $\pi_c(x; k, l)$, the number of primes $p \leqq x$ with $p \equiv l \pmod{k}$, $p \in F_c$ and $(k, l) = 1$. Finally, some applications of these results are given, among them a generalization of a theorem of L. G. Šnirel'man [Math. Ann. **107** (1933), 649–690]. {On p. 40, read $8c$ instead of $7c$ (4 times).} *W. Ljunggren* (Oslo)

## N12-44 (35# 4177 )

**Koshiba, Zen'ichirô; Uchiyama, Saburô**

**On the existence of prime numbers in arithmetic progressions.**

*J. Math. Anal. Appl.* **19** (1967), 431–443.

This paper gives a new nonelementary proof of Dirichlet's theorem on the infinitude of primes in arithmetic progressions. The basic idea is analogous to that in Dirichlet's original proof, except that power series are used instead of Dirichlet series.

For any integer $h$ relatively prime to $k$, $k \geqq 1$, the authors define the power series $g_h(s) = \sum_{n=0}^{\infty} b_n(h) e^{-ns}$ for $s > 0$, where $b_n(h) = \sum (\log p)/p$, the sum being extended over all primes $p$ satisfying the conditions $e^n \leqq p < e^{n+1}$, $p \equiv h \pmod{k}$. The proof consists in showing that $g_h(s)$ is unbounded as $s \to 0+$. The authors express the last sum in terms of characters modulo $k$ and obtain the formula $\phi(k) g_h(s) = s^{-1} + \sum_{\chi \neq \chi_0} \bar{\chi}(h) f(s, \chi) + O(1)$, where $f(s, \chi) = \sum_{n=0}^{\infty} a_n(\chi) e^{-ns}$, $a_n(\chi) = \sum_{e^n \leqq p < e^{n+1}} \chi(p)(\log p)/p$. Here $\chi_0$ denotes the principal character modulo $k$. The major portion of the proof is devoted to proving that for $\chi \neq \chi_0$, $f(s, \chi) = O(\log 1/s)$ as $s \to 0+$. This part of the proof uses a modification of Selberg's inequality [A. Selberg, Ann. of Math. (2) **50** (1949), 297–304; MR **10**, 595] and a stability argument for an asymptotic nonlinear differential equation satisfied by $f(s, \chi)$. This gives $g_h(s) = \{s\phi(k)\}^{-1} + O(\log 1/s)$, from which it follows that $g_h(s)$ is unbounded as $s \to 0+$. *T. M. Apostol* (Pasadena, Calif.)

Citations: MR 10, 595a = N20-2.

## N12-45 (35# 6634 )

**Kolesnik, G. A.**

**The distribution of primes in sequences of the form $[n^c]$. (Russian)**

*Mat. Zametki* **2** (1967), 117–128.

Let $\pi_c(x)$ denote the number of primes $\leqq x$ contained in the sequence $[n^c]$. I. I. Pjateckiĭ-Šapiro [Mat. Sb. (N.S.) **33 (75)** (1953), 559–566; MR **15**, 507] proved, for $1 < c < 12/11$, that $\pi_c(x) \sim A x^{1/c}/\log x$ for some constant $A$. The author extends this result to the range $1 < c < 10/9$. The proof is based on estimates of exponential sums. *H.-E. Richert* (Marburg)

Citations: MR 15, 507e = N12-8.

## N12-46 (37# 5169 )

**Turán, P.**

**On a comparative theory of primes.**

*Proc. Fourth All-Union Math. Congr.* (*Leningrad*, 1961) (*Russian*), *Vol. II, pp.* 137–142. *Izdat. "Nauka", Leningrad*, 1964.

This paper is devoted to the statement of some important results whose proofs have appeared [S. Knapowski and the author, Acta Math. Acad. Sci. Hungar. **14** (1963), 31–42; MR **26** #3683a; ibid. **14** (1963), 43–63; MR **26** #3683b; ibid. **14** (1963), 65–78; MR **26** #3683c]. Let $\pi(x, k, l)$ be the number of primes $p \leqq x$ with $p \equiv l \pmod{k}$ (where $1 \leqq l < k$, $(l, k) = 1$). Put $\psi(x, k, l) = \sum_{n \leqq x; n \equiv l \pmod{k}} \Lambda(n)$, and $F(\nu, k, l) = \sum_{p \equiv l \pmod{k}} e^{-p\nu} \log p$. Then for all $T$ greater than a certain constant $c_1$, the interval $\exp[(\log_3 T)^{1/50}] \leqq x \leqq T$ contains numbers $x_1$ and $x_2$ such that

$$(1) \quad [\pi(x_1, 4, 1) - \pi(x_1, 4, 3)] x_1^{-1/2} \log x_1 > \log_5 T,$$

and (2) $[\pi(x_2, 4, 1) - \pi(x_2, 4, 3)] x_2^{-1/2} \log x_2 < -\log_5 T$; here $\log_n T$ means the $n$th iterate of $\log T$. For $T > c_2$, the interval $T^{1/3} \leqq x \leqq T$ contains a sign change of the function

$\psi(x, 4, 1)-\psi(x, 4, 3)$. Analogous results hold for the modulus $k=6$. When $k=8$, the analogues of (1) and (2) hold for the functions $\pi(x, 8, 1)-\pi(x, 8, l)$ $(l=3, 4, 7)$. If $1\neq l_1\neq l_2\neq 1$ and $T>c_3$, one has the stronger inequality $\pi(x, 8, l_1)-\pi(x, 8, l_2)>T^{1/2}e^{-\log T/(\log\log T)^{1/2}}$ for some $x$ in the interval $T^{1/3}\leqq x\leqq T$. If $l=3$, 5, or 7, then

$$\lim_{\nu\to 0}[F(\nu, 8, 1)-F(\nu, 8, l)] = -\infty$$

if and only if the functions $L(x, \chi)$, where $\chi$ is a character mod 8 with $\chi(l)\neq 1$, do not vanish for $\sigma>\frac{1}{2}$. If $1\neq l_1\neq l_2\neq 1$, and $0<\delta<e^{-e}$, then there is a value $\nu_0$ in the interval $\delta\leqq\nu_0\leqq\delta^{1/3}$, such that (3) $F(\nu_0, 8, l_1)-F(\nu_0, 8, l_2)>\delta^{-1/2}\times \exp[\log\delta/(\log\log\delta^{-1})^{1/2}]$. When $k=5$, analogues of (1) and (2) hold for $\pi(x, 5, 1)-\pi(x, 5, l)$ $(l=2, 3)$, and $\pi(x, 5, 2)-\pi(x, 5, 3)$. The analogue of (3) holds for $F(\nu, 5, 3)-F(\nu, 5, 2)$ and $F(\nu, 5, 2)-F(\nu, 5, 3)$. On the other hand, if $l_1=1$ or 4 and $l_2=2$ or 3, then $\lim[F(\nu, 5, l_1)-F(\nu, 5, l_2)]=-\infty$ if and only if no $L(s, \chi)$, where $\chi$ is a character mod 5, vanishes for $\sigma>\frac{1}{2}$. The analogue of (3) holds for $F(\nu, 5, 1)-F(\nu, 5, 4)$ if no such $L(s, \chi)$ vanishes for $\sigma>1-\{\log\log(|t|+e^e)\}^{-1/3}$.

For general $k$, the authors formulate analogues of the above results, which involve grouping the residue classes $l$ (mod $k$) according to the number of solutions of the congruence $x^2\equiv l$ (mod $k$). Some of these analogues are as yet unproved, while others have been proved under the assumption that no $L(s, \chi)$ vanishes on the interval $0\leqq s\leqq 1$ (where $\chi$ is a character mod $k$). Others require the further hypothesis that $L(s, \chi)\neq 0$ for $\sigma>\frac{1}{2}$, $|t|\leqq k^{10}$.

*B. Gordon* (Los Angeles, Calif.)

Citations: MR 26# 3683a = N12-24; MR 26# 3683b = N12-24; MR 26# 3683c = N12-24.

## N12-47 (38# 126)

**Kátai, Imre**

**A distribution problem in prime number theory. (Hungarian)**

*Magyar Tud. Akad. Mat. Fiz. Oszt. Közl.* **15** (1965), 5–8.

Let $k$, $l_1$ and $l_2$ be natural numbers, with $(k, l_1)=(k, l_2)=1$, and let $\Lambda(n)$ be the von Mangoldt function. Let $\Delta_k(x)\overset{\text{def}}{=}\sum_{n\leqq x}\varepsilon(n)\Lambda(n)$, where $\varepsilon(n)=1$ if $n\equiv l_1$ (mod $k$), $\varepsilon(n)=-1$ if $n\equiv l_2$ (mod $k$) and $\varepsilon(n)=0$ in all other cases. The author shows that the function $\Delta_k(x)x^{-1/2}$ does not have a limiting boundary distribution if $x\to\infty$, under the conditions that, in the case of $\chi$ taken modulo $k$, $L(s, \chi)\neq 0$ for $\operatorname{Re} s>\frac{1}{2}$ and also $L(\frac{1}{2}, \chi)\neq 0$. Earlier Wintner showed that, if the Riemann hypothesis holds for $\zeta(s)$ and $\psi(x)\overset{\text{def}}{=}\sum_{n\leqq x}\Lambda(n)$, then the function $(\psi(e^t)-e^t)e^{-t/2}$ has a limiting distribution as $t\to\infty$. *K. Korradi* [*K. Corrádi*] (RŽMat **1966** #1 A102)

## N12-48 (38# 5724)

**Gallagher, P. X.**

**Bombieri's mean value theorem.**

*Mathematika* **15** (1968), 1–6.

The author presents a short and relatively simple proof of E. Bombieri's theorem [Mathematika **12** (1965), 201–225; MR **33** #5590] which asserts that for each positive constant $A>0$ there is a constant $B=B(A)$ such that if $Q=x^{1/2}(\log x)^{-B}$, then

$$\sum_{q\leqq Q}\max_{y\leqq x}\max_{(a,q)=1}\left|\psi(y, q, a)-\frac{y}{\phi(q)}\right| \ll x(\log x)^{-A};$$

here $\psi(y, q, a)=\sum_{n\leqq x; n\equiv a(q)}\Lambda(n)$ as usual. Bombieri's proof depended on a density theorem for the zeros of $L$-functions in the critical strip, which is in itself of great interest. By contrast, the author has been able largely to avoid the critical strip, although his ingenious method otherwise follows the classical pattern in several important respects. In particular, the Siegel-Walfisz theorem is used in the usual way to dispose of the small $q$, and the "large sieve" again plays a central role in the estimation of character sums, upon which the whole argument is made to depend. Estimates obtained in this way tend to be good for small $t=\mathscr{I}s$ only, and the author has sidestepped this difficulty by means of a certain "smoothing" device: namely, writing $\psi_k(y, \chi)=(1/k!)\sum_{n\leqq y}\chi(n)\Lambda(n)\log^k(y/n)$, he works with $\psi_3(y, \chi)$ in place of $\psi(y, \chi)=\psi_0(y, \chi)$. As in Bombieri's approach, the problem reduces to estimating the average of $\max_{y\leqq x}|\psi_k(y, \chi)|$ with respect to primitive $\chi$ mod $q$ over large $q\leqq Q$. The author sets out from the integral formula

$$\psi_k(y, \chi) = \frac{1}{2\pi i}\int_{\alpha-i\infty}^{\alpha+i\infty}\frac{y^s}{s^{k+1}}\left(-\frac{L'}{L}(s, \chi)\right)ds,$$

$\alpha=1+1/(\log x)$, and then replaces $L'/L$ in the classical manner by $(L'/L)(1-LS)^2+(2L'S-L'LS^2)=f+g$, say, where $S$ is a finite sum approximating to $L^{-1}$ (so that $1-LS$ is small); $S$ is bounded and analytic in $\mathscr{R}s\geqq\frac{1}{2}$. The average of the integral corresponding to $f$ is then dealt with by the large sieve, whilst the integral corresponding to $g$ is first moved back almost up to $\mathscr{R}s=\frac{1}{2}$ before its average is dealt with in a similar way. The final unsmoothing procedure involves no new difficulties and no appreciable loss of precision.

This clarification of the nature of Bombieri's theorem is a very useful addition to the literature. Workers in the field may like to know that the author has since found a further simplification; it turns out from a more careful analysis of his method that substantially the same argument succeeds with $\psi_1$ in place of $\psi_3$. {The author has allowed the reviewer to add this remark to the present review.} *H. Halberstam* (Nottingham)

Citations: MR 33# 5590 = M55-43.
Referred to in R46-32.

## N12-49 (41# 1660)

**Montgomery, H. L.**

**Primes in arithmetic progressions.**

*Michigan Math. J.* **17** (1970), 33–39.

Das "große Sieb" erlaubt es, das mittlere Fehlerquadrat $D(x, Q)=\sum_{q\leqq Q}\sum_{1\leqq a\leqq q,(a,q)=1}|\psi(x; q, a)-x/\varphi(q)|^2\ll Qx\log x$ (für $Q\leqq x$) nach oben abzuschätzen [man vgl. P. X. Gallagher, Mathematika **14** (1967), 14–20; MR **35** #5411]. Der Verfasser beweist für $D(x, Q)$ sogar eine asymptotische Beziehung, nämlich (*) $D(x, Q)=Qx\log x+O(Qx\log(2x/Q))+O(x^2(\log x)^{-A})$ für $Q\leqq x$, und eine ähnliche Formel gilt für $Q>x$. {Leider sagt (*) für kleine $Q$ weniger aus als die mit dem "großen Sieb" erzielten Abschätzungen.} Beim Beweis vermeidet der Verfasser die Anwendung des großen Siebes; er stützt sich auf eine obere Abschätzung der Summe

$$\sum_{k\leqq\frac{1}{2}x}\{\sum_{k<n\leqq x}\Lambda(n)\Lambda(n-2k)-(x-2k)\cdot A(k)\}^2$$

von A. F. Lavrik [Dokl. Akad. Nauk SSSR **132** (1960), 1013–1015; translated as Soviet Math. Dokl. **1** (1960), 700–702; MR **28** #1183]. *W. Schwarz* (Frankfurt a.M.)

Citations: MR 28# 1183 = P40-13; MR 35# 5411 = M55-52.

## N12-50 (42# 4504)

**Glatfeld, Martin**

**Primzahlverteilung und Taubersche Asymptotik.**

B.I-Hochschultaschenbücher 247/247a.

*Überblicke Math.* **3** (1969), 71–95.

N. Wiener has clarified by his general theory of Tauberian theorems the two avenues of approach to the prime number theorem to the effect that the number of primes less than $x$ is asymptotically equal to $x/\log x$. Following the two aspects separately, the author gives proofs for the prime number theorem for arithmetical progressions: (1) $\pi(x; k, l)=\sum_{p\leq x, p\equiv l(k)} 1=(1/\varphi(k))x/\log x+o(x/\log x)$, where $k, l$ are fixed integers, $k>0$, $(k, l)=1$.

In the first place the author applies the Lambert series type approach of Wiener [Ann. of Math. (2) **33** (1932), 1–100, pp. 39–44] to the proof of asymptotic formulae for the sums $\sum_{n\leq x}\chi(n)\mu(n)/n$ and $\sum_{n\leq x}\chi(n)\mu(n)$, where $\chi(n)$ is a character (mod $k$) and $\mu(n)$ is the Möbius function, and the truth of (1) is then inferred from equivalence theorems of H. N. Shapiro [Comm. Pure Appl. Math. **2** (1949), 293–308; MR **11**, 419]. This essentially covers the author's paper [J. London Math. Soc. **32** (1957), 67–73; MR **18**, 874]. And in the second place he uses the Ikehara-Wiener theorem [Wiener, loc. cit., pp. 44–47] to give two proofs of (1) in its equivalent form (2) $\psi(u; k, l)=\sum_{n\leq u, n\equiv l(k)}\Lambda(n)=u/\varphi k+o(u)$, where $\Lambda(p^k)=\log p$ and $\Lambda(n)=0$ if $n$ is not of the form $p^k$. The first proof starts with the theorem: if $\psi_\chi(u)=\sum_{n\leq u}\chi(n)\Lambda(n)$, then $\psi_\chi(u)=o(u)$ for $\chi\neq\chi_0$ and $\psi_\chi(u)=u+o(u)$ for $\chi=\chi_0$. From this he deduces (2). For a second new proof he again applies the Ikehara-Wiener theorem directly to $\psi(e^u; k, l)$ to prove (2) [see, G. J. Rieger, Arch. Math. **10** (1959), 257–260; MR **21** #5614].

*S. Ikehara* (Tokyo)

Citations: MR 11, 419d = N12-4; MR 18, 874a = N12-11; MR 21# 5614 = R44-12.

## N12-51 (43# 3222)

**Riesel, Hans; Göhl, Gunnar**

**Some calculations related to Riemann's prime number formula.**

*Math. Comp.* **24** (1970), 969–983.

The authors describe machine calculations relating the complex zeros of the Riemann zeta function $\zeta(s)$ to the distribution of prime numbers. The analysis depends on a new relation obtained from the Riemann-Mangoldt formula expressing $\pi(x)$, the number of primes $\leq x$, in terms of the logarithmic integral $\mathrm{li}(x)$. By considering only the first 29 pairs of complex zeros $\rho=\frac{1}{2}\pm i\alpha$, $\alpha<100$, the authors obtain $\pi(x)$ correctly up to about $x=1000$.

*T. M. Apostol* (Pasadena, Calif.)

## N12-52 (44# 6642)

**Stark, H. M.**

**A problem in comparative prime number theory.**

*Acta Arith.* **18** (1971), 311–320.

The author combines existing ideas to prove several theorems concerning differences $\varphi(k)\pi(y; k, a)-\varphi(K)\pi(y; K, A)$. (The constraints on $k, K, a, A$ should be strengthened to eliminate consideration of such pairs of arithmetic progressions as $3n+1$, $6n+1$; this may be accomplished by requiring that $k\not\equiv 2 \pmod 4$, $K\not\equiv 2 \pmod 4$.) The proofs are simpler than those of S. Knapowski and R. Turán [Acta Math. Acad. Sci. Hungar. **13** (1962), 299–314; MR **26** #3682a; ibid. **13** (1962), 315–342; MR **26** #3682b; ibid. **13** (1962), 343–364; MR **26** #3682c; ibid. **14** (1963), 31–42; MR **26** #3683a; ibid. **14** (1963), 43–63; MR **26** #3683b; ibid. **14** (1963), 65–78; MR **26** #3683c; ibid. **14** (1963), 241–250; MR **28** #70a; ibid. **14** (1963), 251–268; MR **28** #70b] because no attempt is made to localize the asymptotic behaviour. The author performs a numerical calculation which with his theorems leads to the new result that

$$\lim\sup(\pi(y; 5, 4)-\pi(y; 5, 2))y^{-\frac{1}{2}}\log y>0.$$

Unfortunately, the details of the calculation are difficult to reconstruct.

{In the course of his numerical argument the author remarks upon his "pleasant surprise" that a term arising from the trivial zeros makes a beneficial contribution. It seems to the reviewer that this contribution can be shown to occur in certain circumstances, so that the following result can be proved: Let $p$ be prime, $p>p_0$, and suppose that no $L$-function mod $p$ has a real zero in the open interval $(\frac{1}{2}, 1)$. Then $\lim\sup(\pi(y; p, -1)-\pi(y; p, b))y^{-\frac{1}{2}}\log y>0$ for each fixed $b$ satisfying $1\leq b\leq p-2$.}

*H. L. Montgomery* (Cambridge, England)

Citations: MR 26# 3682a = N12-23; MR 26# 3682b = N12-23; MR 26# 3682c = N12-23; MR 28# 70a = N12-25; MR 28# 70b = N12-25.

# N16 PRIMES IN PROGRESSIONS: LOCAL QUESTIONS

See also Section R44.

See also reviews A18-52, A32-27, A40-32, A42-1, M02-3, M20-35, M25-61, M25-64, M25-90, M50-27, M55-48, M55-79, N02-14, N08-27, N08-35, N08-44, N12-2, N12-26, N12-29, N12-33, N12-34, N12-36, N12-37, N12-38, N12-39, N12-46, N24-52, N24-65, N32-40, N32-44, N80-14, N80-17, N80-28, N80-48, P16-6, P32-77, R44-19, R44-21.

## N16-1 (1, 135e)

**Turán, Paul. Über die Primzahlen der arithmetischen Progression.** (II.) Acta Litt. Sci. Szeged **9**, 187–192 (1939).

Let $P(k, l)$ denote the smallest prime of the form $kx+l$. It was proved by Chowla [J. Indian Math. Soc. (2) **1**, 1–3 (1934)] that if no $L$-function vanishes for $\sigma>1/2$, then $P(k, l)<c_1\phi(k)^{2+\epsilon}$, where $\epsilon$ is arbitrarily small and $c_1=c_1(\epsilon)$. The author now shows that a similar result follows from a weaker hypothesis. Suppose that there are constants $\delta$, $0<\delta\leq 1/2$, and $\alpha$, such that no $L$-function vanishes for $1-\delta<\sigma\leq 2$, $|t|\leq\alpha$. Then $P(k, l)<c_3\phi(k)^{c_4}$, where $c_3$ is an absolute constant, and $c_4=c_4(\alpha, \delta)$, $c_4>1/\delta$.

*E. C. Titchmarsh* (Oxford).

## N16-2 (1, 293b)

**Vinogradow, I. Distribution of primes of an arithmetical progression to a given modulus.** Bull. Acad. Sci. URSS. Sér. Math. [Izvestia Akad. Nauk SSSR] **4**, 27–36 (1940). (Russian. English summary)

It is proved that, if $N>2$, $0<q\leq N$, $0\leq L<Q$, $(Q, L)=1$, $(Q, q)=1$, then

$$(1)\qquad \sum_{\substack{N-A<p\leq N\\ p\equiv L \pmod Q}} e^{2\pi i\alpha p}=O(R),\quad \alpha=\frac{a}{q};\ (a, q)=1;\ 1\leq A\leq N,$$

$$(2)\qquad T_1-\sigma T=O(R),\qquad 0<\sigma\leq 1;\ Q\leq A\leq N,$$

where $T$ is the number of primes $p$ in the range of summation in (1), $T_1$ is the number of these $p$ for which $0\leq p<\sigma q \pmod q$,

$$R=\frac{A}{Q}N^{\epsilon}\left(\frac{1}{q}+\frac{N^{\frac{1}{2}}Q}{A}+\frac{NQ^2q}{A^2}\right)^{\frac{1}{2}},$$

and the constants of the $O$'s depend only on $\epsilon(>0)$. The proof of (1), from which (2) is deduced, is by the methods used in the author's previous estimations of trigonometrical sums involving primes.

*A. E. Ingham.*

**N16-3** **(6, 259j)**

**Linnik, U. V. On the possibility to avoid Riemann's extended hypothesis in the investigation of primes in progressions.** C. R. (Doklady) Acad. Sci. URSS (N.S.) **44**, 135–138 (1944).

The author outlines a method of attack on the problem of the magnitude of the least prime in a progression $Dx+l$ in which he assumes, instead of the generalized Riemann hypothesis, a weaker "density property." This assumption is that each of the Dirichlet $L$-functions (mod $D$), with possibly a bounded number of exceptions, has the property that the ratio of the number of zeros in any one circle of radius $1/\log D$ with center in the rectangle $9/10 \leqq \sigma \leqq 1$, $|t| \leqq \log^3 D$ to the number of zeros in any other such circle does not exceed an absolute constant. This paper is superseded by that reviewed in the second review below, where the need for this assumption is surmounted.

*H. Davenport* (London).

**N16-4** **(6, 260a)**

**Linnik, U. V. On Dirichlet's $L$-series and prime-number sums.** Rec. Math. [Mat. Sbornik] N.S. **15**(57), 3–12 (1944). (English. Russian summary)

In a previous paper [C. R. (Doklady) Acad. Sci. URSS (N.S.) **41**, 145–146 (1943); these Rev. **6**, 58] the author stated an upper bound for the number of zeros of $L$-functions (mod $D$) which have a zero in the rectangle $1-\theta \leqq \sigma \leqq 1$, $|t| \leqq \log^3 D$. [In the previous paper the last inequality read $|t| \leqq D^{\eta/2}$, which was presumably a misprint.] In the present paper he proves a stronger result, which is a step toward a later paper [see the following review]. Let $\lambda > 0$ be arbitrarily small, and let $\theta$ satisfy $\frac{1}{3} \geqq \theta \geqq (\log D)^{\lambda-1}$. Let $Q$ denote the number of $L$-functions (mod $D$) which have a zero in the rectangle $1-\theta \leqq \sigma \leqq 1$, $|t| \leqq \log^3 D$. Then $Q < \exp(A(\lambda)\theta \log D)$, where $A(\lambda)$ is a positive constant depending only on $\lambda$. The proof seems to be very difficult reading.

*H. Davenport* (London).

Citations: MR 6, 58b = M25-8.

Referred to in M02-3, M25-27, N12-27, N12-28, N16-14, N16-15, P32-8, P32-12, R44-2.

**N16-5** **(6, 260b)**

**Linnik, U. V. On the least prime in an arithmetic progression. I. The basic theorem.** Rec. Math. [Mat. Sbornik] N.S. **15**(57), 139–178 (1944). (English. Russian summary)

The author's object is to prove, without any hypothesis, that the least prime in an arithmetic progression $Dx+l$ (where $l$, $D$ are coprime, and $1 \leqq l \leqq D-1$) does not exceed $D^{C_0}$, where $C_0$ is an absolute constant. This first section is devoted mainly to the proof of the "basic theorem." Let $\psi(D)$ be any number satisfying $\frac{1}{3}\log D \geqq \psi(D) \geqq 2$. Let $\theta = \psi(D)/\log D$ and let $Q$ denote the number of $L$-functions (mod $D$) which have a zero in the rectangle $1-\theta \leqq \sigma \leqq 1$, $|t| \leqq \min\{\log^3 D, \psi^{100}(D)\}$. Then $Q < \exp(A\psi(D))$, where $A$ is an absolute constant. The proof appears to be very formidable, and is particularly difficult to follow because a detailed knowledge of the author's previous papers is assumed. [Cf. the preceding and following reviews.]

*H. Davenport* (London).

Referred to in M02-3, M25-54, M25-58, M25-59, M25-90, M50-2, N02-12, N08-10, N12-29, N16-14, N16-15, N16-22, N16-29, N68-6, N68-8, P32-8, R44-16.

**N16-6** **(6, 260c)**

**Linnik, U. V. On the least prime in an arithmetic progression. II. The Deuring-Heilbronn phenomenon.** Rec. Math. [Mat. Sbornik] N.S. **15**(57), 347–368 (1944). (English. Russian summary)

[Cf. the preceding review.] The author proves a "second basic theorem" which is a new formulation of a phenomenon discovered by Deuring [Math. Z. **37**, 405–415 (1933)] and Heilbronn [Quart. J. Math., Oxford Ser. **5**, 150–160 (1934)]. It is well known that there exists a constant $c_0$ such that there are no zeros of any $L$-functions (mod $D$) in the rectangle $1 \geqq \sigma \geqq 1 - c_0/\log D$, $|t| \leqq D$, except possibly one real zero $\beta_0$ of a particular $L$-function formed with a real character. Let $\sigma_0 = 1-\beta_0$ and $\mu_0 = 1/(\sigma_0 \log D) \geqq 1$. Then the rectangle $1 \geqq \sigma \geqq 1 - c_3 \log(c_4\mu_0)/\log D$, $|t| \leqq \log^3 D$ contains no zero of any $L$-function formed with any modulus not exceeding $D^2$, except for the zero $\beta_0$ of the particular function. Using this and the results of section I, the author proves his main theorem on the least prime in the progression $Dx+l$.

*H. Davenport* (London).

Referred to in L20-8, M25-54, M25-90, N02-12, N08-10, N12-29, N16-15, N16-22, N16-29, N68-6, N68-8, R44-16.

**N16-7** **(6, 260d)**

**Linnik, U. V. On the distribution of characters.** C. R. (Doklady) Acad. Sci. URSS (N.S.) **42**, 323–325 (1944).

The author announces two results on the distribution of the values of characters (mod $D$). One is that, if $\chi(n)$ is a complex character (mod $D$) of bounded order, then

$$N^{-1} \sum_{p>2} \chi(p) \log p \cdot \exp(-p/N) = O\{(\log D)^{-1} + \exp(-\log N/\log D)\}.$$

The other result is for the character $(-D/n)$, where $-D$ is a fundamental discriminant and differs in having an additional term $\exp(-h \log N/\sqrt{D})$ on the right, where $h$ is the class number of the field $k(\sqrt{(-D)})$. The proof appears to be very deep, and the outline given is too short to be intelligible to the reviewer. In an addendum the author states that he has proved that the least prime equivalent to $l$ (mod $D$), where $(l, D)=1$, is less than $\exp(c \log D \log\log\log D)$, where $c$ is a constant.

*H. Davenport* (London).

**N16-8** **(9, 499a)**

**Rodosskiĭ, K. A. On the distribution of prime numbers in short arithmetic progressions.** Izvestiya Akad. Nauk SSSR. Ser. Mat. **12**, 123–128 (1948). (Russian)

This paper is concerned with the determination of the number of primes in comparatively short arithmetic progressions. More precisely, assuming $(D, l)=1$, and letting $\pi(x, D, l) = \sum 1$ summed over $p \leqq x$, $p \equiv l$ (mod $D$), the author proves the following theorem. Let $\epsilon$ be any small fixed positive number and $\log^{1+\epsilon} D \leqq \log x \leqq \log^{9/4} D$, $D \geqq D_0(\epsilon)$. Then

$$\pi(x, D, l) = \frac{1}{\varphi(D)} \sum_{2 \leqq n \leqq x} 1/\log n - E\frac{\chi_1(l)}{\varphi(D)} \sum_{2 \leqq n \leqq x} n^{\beta_1 - 1}/\log n + \frac{x}{\varphi(D)\log x} O\left(\exp\left\{-A(\epsilon)\frac{\log x}{\log D}\right\}\right),$$

where $A>0$ depends on $\epsilon$; the $O$ is uniform in $D$; $\chi_1$ is a certain exceptional character; $E=0$ or 1 and $\beta_1$ is a zero of $L(s, \chi_1)$. An analogous result is given for $\psi(x, D, l) = \sum \Lambda(n)$ summed over $n \leqq x$, $n \equiv l$ (mod $D$), where $(D, l)=1$, $\Lambda(n) = \log n$ for $n = p^\alpha$ and 0 otherwise. In order to obtain the theorem stated above the author utilizes his previous results [same Izvestiya Ser. Mat. **12**, 47–56 (1948); these Rev. **9**, 413] concerning upper estimates for the number of $L$-series (with characters modulo $D$) which have zeros in certain rectangles.

*H. N. Shapiro* (New York, N. Y.).

Citations: MR 9, 413d = M25-27.

Referred to in M25-29.

**N16-9** **(9, 499b)**

**Čudakov, N. G. On the limits of variation of the function** $\psi(x, k, l)$. Izvestiya Akad. Nauk SSSR. Ser. Mat. **12**, 31–46 (1948). (Russian)

It has been proved by Ingham [Quart. J. Math., Oxford Ser. **8**, 255–266 (1937)] that

$$\pi(x+u)-\pi(x)\sim u(\log x)^{-1},\quad u=x^{\theta},\ \theta>(1+4c)/(2+4c),$$

if $\zeta(\frac{1}{2}+ti)=O(|t|^c)$. Titchmarsh [Quart. J. Math., Oxford Ser. **13**, 11–17 (1942); these Rev. **4**, 131] proved this result for all $c>19/116$, thus confirming Ingham's theorem for all $\theta>48/77$. Using Ingham's method the author extends these results to primes in an arithmetic progression. He obtains in the usual notation

$$\pi(x+u;k,l)-\pi(x;k,l)\sim u(\varphi(k)\log x)^{-1}$$

provided that $u=x^{\theta}$, $\log k=O(\log x)^{1-\tau}$, where $\tau>\frac{3}{4}$ is an arbitrary constant. This holds uniformly in $k$ (for fixed $k$ the generalization of Ingham's theorem would be almost trivial). Starting from the inequality $L(\frac{1}{2}+ti)=O(k|t|^c)$ the author proves that the Dirichlet $L$-series $L(s,\chi)$ has at most $O(k^{2(1-\sigma_1)}T^{b(1-\sigma_1)}\log^5(kT))$ zeros in the rectangle $\sigma_1\leqq\sigma<1$, $|t|\leqq T$, where $\chi$ is a character mod $k$ and $b>2(1+2c)$ is a constant. From this inequality the result follows in the classical way, but a further complication arises from the fact that for given $k$ one $L(s,\chi)$ may have a real zero near $s=1$, which requires separate treatment. The paper suffers from various misprints and minor inaccuracies.

*H. Heilbronn* (Bristol).

Citations: MR 4, 131b = M15-3.

Referred to in M02-3, N16-11, N16-31.

**N16-10** **(10, 684c)**

**Erdös, P. On some applications of Brun's method.** Acta Univ. Szeged. Sect. Sci. Math. **13**, 57–63 (1949).

Let $P(k,l)$ denote the least prime in the arithmetic progression $kx+l$, $0<l<k$, $(l,k)=1$; let $\phi(k)$ denote the Euler function; let $c_1$, $c_3$ and $c_5$ be arbitrary positive constants. The author employs the V. Brun method to prove the following three theorems. (I) There exist a constant $c_2=c_2(c_1)$ and infinitely many integers $k$ so that $P(k,l)>(1+c_1)\phi(k)\log k$ for more than $c_2\phi(k)$ values of $l$. (II) There exists a constant $c_4=c_4(c_3)$ such that for $c_4\phi(k)$ values of $l$, $P(k,l)<c_3\phi(k)\log k$. (III) Let $n$ be sufficiently large. Then there exists a constant $c_6=c_6(c_5)$ and a sequence of primes $p_k<p_{k+1}<\cdots<p_{k+r}<n$, $r=[c_6\log n]$, so that $p_{k+i+1}-p_{k+i}>c_5$, $i=0,1,\cdots,r-1$. The proof uses results of Schnirelmann [Landau, Nachr. Ges. Wiss. Göttingen. Math.-Phys. Kl. **1930**, 255–276], Page [Proc. London Math. Soc. (2) **39**, 116–141 (1935)] and the author [Proc. Cambridge Philos. Soc. **33**, 6–12 (1937)] on the distribution of primes. Theorem III is an improvement on a result obtained by Sierpiński [Colloquium Math. **1**, 193–194 (1948); these Rev. **10**, 431]. *A. L. Whiteman.*

Citations: MR 10, 431b = N08-8.

**N16-11** **(14, 249b)**

**Tatuzawa, Tikao. On the zeros of Dirichlet's** $L$**-functions.** Proc. Japan Acad. **26**, no. 9, 1–13 (1950).

The author sharpens the recent results of Čudakov [Izvestiya Akad. Nauk SSSR. Ser. Mat. **12**, 31–46 (1948); these Rev. **9**, 499] on the finite differences of $\psi(x;k,l)$ so that the "short" arithmetic progressions of Rodosskiĭ are also treated. Let $(k,l)=1$ and $L(s,\chi)\neq 0$ for $\sigma>1-d/(\log t)^{\mu}$ and $t>t_0(k)$. Let $\zeta(\frac{1}{2}+it,w)-w^{-1/2-it}=O(t^c)$; actually, only the following consequence of this assumption is used: $L(\frac{1}{2}+it,\chi)=O(k^{1/2}t^c)$. Also let $x^{(1+4c)/(2+4c)+\epsilon}\leqq y\leqq x$. A reformulation of the author's result is that there exist suitable positive numbers $A$, $B$, $C$ depending on $\epsilon$ such that

$$\psi(x+y;k,l)-\psi(x;k,l)=\frac{y}{\varphi(k)}-\frac{E(k)}{\varphi(k)}\frac{(x+y)^{\beta_1}-x^{\beta_1}}{\beta_1}+\frac{y}{\varphi(k)}O(R),$$

where $E(k)=1$ if the exceptional real zero $\beta_1$ exists and $E(k)=0$ otherwise; also

$$\log R=\begin{cases}-A\log x/\log k & \text{if}\quad C\log k\log\log k\leqq\log x\leqq B(\log k)^{1/\mu}\\ -A(\log x)^{1-\mu} & \text{if}\quad B(\log k)^{1/\mu}\leqq\log x.\end{cases}$$

And, by Siegel's result on the real zeros, the term involving $E(k)$ may be discarded if $k^{\delta}<\log x$.

The principal tool is the result that the number of zeros in $\sigma\leqq\Re(s)\leqq 1$, $|\Im(s)|\leqq T$ of all $L$-functions with modulus $k$ is

$$O(k^{4(1-\sigma)}T^{4c(1-\sigma)}(T+k)^{2(1-\sigma)}\log^8 kT)$$

if $\frac{1}{2}\leqq\sigma\leqq 1$. This is proved by a method of Ingham. Results related to this are due to Rodosskiĭ [ibid. **12**, 47–56 (1948); **13**, 315–328 (1949); these Rev. **9**, 413; **11**, 84] and to Haselgrove [J. London Math. Soc. **26**, 273–277 (1951); these Rev. **13**, 438].

The author also states without proof the result that each large odd integer $N$ is the sum of three primes $p$ such that $|p-N/3|<N/\log^m N$ for each given $m$; but this result is weaker than Haselgrove's estimate of $N^{\vartheta}$ for some $\vartheta<1$.

*L. Schoenfeld* (Urbana, Ill.).

Citations: MR 9, 413d = M25-27; MR 9, 499b = N16-9; MR 11, 84e = M25-29; MR 13, 438e = P32-17.

Referred to in M25-34, M25-47.

**N16-12** **(14, 727d)**

**Prachar, K. Über Primzahldifferenzen. II.** Monatsh. Math. **56**, 307–312 (1952).

Let $q_1<q_2<\cdots$ be the sequence of consecutive primes $\equiv l \pmod D$, $(l,D)=1$. The author proves that the density of integers of the form $q_{k+1}-q_k$ is positive; also that $\liminf\,(q_{k+1}-q_k)/\log q_k<\phi(D)$; for $D=1$ this is a result of the reviewer [Duke Math. J. **6**, 438–441 (1940); these Rev. **1**, 292].

Denote by $\Delta^k a_n$ the $k$th difference of the sequence $a_n$. The author proves that $\sum_{q_n<x}\Delta^k(q_{n+1}-q_n)/q_n>c\log x$; for $k=1$, $D=1$ this was proved by the reviewer and Rényi [Simon Stevin **27**, 115–125 (1950); these Rev. **11**, 644].

*P. Erdös* (Los Angeles, Calif.).

Citations: MR 1, 292h = N08-1; MR 11, 644d = N08-11.

Referred to in N08-12.

**N16-13** **(14, 728d)**

**Kanold, Hans-Joachim. Abschätzungen bei Kreisteilungspolynomen und daraus hergeleitete Bedingungen für die kleinsten Primzahlen gewisser arithmetischer Folgen.** Math. Z. **55**, 284–287 (1952).

The author proves that the least prime $q$ of the arithmetic progression $mx+1$ with $m\geqq 4$ is less than or equal to $5\cdot 2^{\varphi(m)-2}$ where $\varphi(m)$ denotes Euler's function. This result is improved further in the cases $m$ odd, $m\equiv 2 \pmod 4$, and $m\equiv 0 \pmod 4$, respectively. *A. Brauer.*

Referred to in C15-27.

**N16-14** **(15, 202b)**

**Rodosskiĭ, K. A. On the number of** $L$**-functions having zeros in some rectangle.** Ukrain. Mat. Žurnal **3**, 399–403 (1951). (Russian)

The author proves that for $\Delta<1$ the number of $L$-functions (formed by characters mod $D$) which have zeros in the rectangle $\Delta \leqq \sigma \leqq 1$, $|t-T| \leqq \frac{1}{2}$ is $O(\log^8 (DT)(D^2T)^{3(1-\Delta)/\Delta})$. Similar results were proved by Linnik [Mat. Sbornik N.S. **15**(57), 3–12, 139–178 (1944); these Rev. **6**, 260]. The author's proof is surprisingly short. *H. Heilbronn.*

Citations: MR 6, 260a = N16-4; MR 6, 260b = N16-5.
Referred to in R42-19.

## N16-15 (15, 202c)

**Rodosskiĭ, K. A. On the least prime number in an arithmetic progression and the zeros of $L$-functions.** Doklady Akad. Nauk SSSR (N.S.) **88**, 753–756 (1953). (Russian)

Using the results of the paper reviewed above, the author simplifies the proof of Linnik's theorem [see references cited above and Mat. Sbornik N.S. **15**(57), 347–368 (1944); these Rev. **6**, 260] that the smallest prime $p \equiv l \pmod D$ satisfies for $(D, l)=1$ the inequality $p=O(D^c)$, where $c$ is an absolute constant. *H. Heilbronn* (Bristol).

Citations: MR 6, 260a = N16-4; MR 6, 260b = N16-5; MR 6, 260c = N16-6.
Referred to in N16-16.

## N16-16 (15, 935e)

**Rodosskiĭ, K. A. On the least prime number in an arithmetic progression.** Mat. Sbornik N.S. **34**(76), 331–356 (1954). (Russian)

This is a more detailed account of the author's previous paper [Doklady Akad. Nauk SSSR (N.S.) **88**, 753–756 (1953); see also Ukrain. Mat. Žurnal **3**, 399–403 (1951); these Rev. **15**, 202]. The following are the two main results. (1) Let $D$ be an integer $\geqq 3$, $\psi$ a real number between 2 and 0.1 ln $D$ and $Q(D, \psi)$ the number of $L$-functions (formed with characters for modulus $D$) having at least one zero in the rectangle $1-\psi \ln^{-1} D \leqq \sigma \leqq 1$, $|t| \leqq e^{\psi} \ln^{-1} D$. Then $Q(D, \psi) < e^{A_1\psi}$, $A_1$ being a positive absolute constant. (2) Linnik's theorem: Let $P_{\min}(D, l)$ denote the least prime number in the progression $nD+l$, $(D, l)=1$. Then $P_{\min}(D, l) < D^{A_2}$, $A_2$ being a positive absolute constant. *W. H. Simons.*

Citations: MR 15, 202c = N16-15.
Referred to in M25-54, N12-29, N16-18, N16-22, R44-16.

## N16-17 (17, 14g)

**Rodosskiĭ, K. A. The exceptional zero and the distribution of prime numbers in short arithmetic progressions.** Mat. Sb. N.S. **36**(78), 341–348 (1955). (Russian)

The following two theorems are proved. (1) Let $(D, l)=1$, $14 \ln D \leqslant \ln x \leqslant \ln^3 D$. Then positive absolute constants $D_1$, $A_1$, $A_2$ exist such that

$$\left|\psi(x, D, l)-\frac{x}{\varphi(D)}\{1-E(D)\tilde{\chi}(l)\tilde{\beta}^{-1}x^{\tilde{\beta}-1}\}\right| < \frac{x}{\varphi(D)}\left\{A_2 \ln^{12} D\left(\frac{eA_1}{\delta_0 \ln D}\right)^{-(A_1 \ln x)/2 \ln D}+\frac{1}{D}\right\}$$

for $D>D_1$. $\varphi(D)$ is Euler's $\varphi$-function, and

$$E(D)=1,\ \delta_0=1-\tilde{\beta} \quad \text{if } 1-\tilde{\beta} \geq A_1 \ln^{-1} D,$$
$$E(D)=0,\ \delta_0=A_1 \ln^{-1} D \text{ if } 1-\tilde{\beta} > A_1 \ln^{-1} D.$$

(2) Positive absolute constants $D_2$, $A_3$, $A_4$, $A_5$ exist such that if $x^{1-A_3} \leq u \leq x$, $\ln x/\ln\ln x \geq A_4 \ln D$ and $D \geq D_2$, then

$$\left|\psi(x+u, D, l)-\Psi(x, D, l)-\frac{u}{\varphi(D)}\{1-E(D)\tilde{\chi}(l)x^{\tilde{\beta}-1}\}\right| < A_5 \delta_0 \frac{u}{\varphi(D)},$$

$E(D)$ and $\delta_0$ being defined as above. The proofs of the above make use of an improved estimate for $N(\Delta, T, D)$ for $0.9 \leq \Delta \leq 1$, $T \geq 3$, $\ln D \geq 12$. *W. H. Simons.*

## N16-18 (17, 240d)

**Fogels, È. K. On prime numbers at the beginning of an arithmetic progression.** Dokl. Akad. Nauk SSSR (N.S.) **102** (1955), 455–456. (Russian)

The author announces that by methods of Rodosskiĭ [Mat. Sb. N.S. **34(76)** (1954), 331–356; MR **15**, 935] he has obtained the following results. 1) For any $\varepsilon>0$ there exists an absolute constant $A=A(\varepsilon)>24/\varepsilon$ such that in the interval $(D^A, D^{A(1+\varepsilon)})$ is situated at least one prime of the progression $Du+l$, $(u=0, 1, 2, \cdots; (D, l)=1)$. 2) For any $\varepsilon>0$, and for every $A>A_0(\varepsilon)>30/\varepsilon$, $\pi(D^A; D, l) > D^{A(1-\varepsilon)}$. *W. H. Simons* (Vancouver, B.C.).

Citations: MR 15, 935e = N16-16.
Referred to in R44-25.

## N16-19 (21# 4140)

**Pan, Cheng-tung. On the least prime in an arithmetical progression.** Sci. Record (N.S.) **1** (1957), 311–313.

Let $P_{\min}(D, l)$ denote the least prime in an arithmetic progression $nD+l$, where $1 \leqq l \leqq D-1$ and $(l, D)=1$. K. A. Rodosskiĭ showed in 1954 that there exists a positive absolute constant $A$ such that $P_{\min}(D, l) < D^A$ but gave no indication of the size of $A$. In the paper here reviewed the author announces the result that $A \leqq 10^4$. A detailed proof is not given but the necessary fundamental lemmas needed to obtain the result are mentioned without proof. *W. H. Simons* (Vancouver, B.C.)

Referred to in N12-29, N16-20, N16-29.

## N16-20 (23# A1614)

**Fluch, W.**
**Verwendung der Zeta-Funktion beim Sieb von Selberg.**
*Acta Arith.* **5**, 381–405 (1959).

The author applies the Riemann zeta function to certain sums arising in connection with the lower estimates in Selberg's sieve method [cf. A. I. Vinogradov, Mat. Sb. (N.S.) **41** (**83**) (1957), 49–80, 415–416; MR **20** #3836; see also Vinogradov, Vestnik Leningrad. Univ. **11** (1956), no. 13, 142–146; MR **20** #3835]. He obtains the result that for $\varepsilon>0$, $k>k_0(\varepsilon)$, every arithmetical progression $l$, $l+k$, $l+2k$, $\cdots$ contains a number $<k^{15+\varepsilon}$ which is a prime or a product of two primes. A stronger result was recently announced by Cheng-tung Pan [Science Abstracts of China No. 1 (1958), 7–8; see also Sci. Record (N.S.) **1** (1957), 311–313; MR **21** #4140], stating that the exponent $c$ in Linnik's theorem can be taken $\leqq 5448$. [Linnik's theorem says that the progression contains a prime $<k^c$; see K. Prachar, *Primzahlverteilung*, Springer-Verlag, Berlin, 1957; MR **19**, 393.] *N. G. de Bruijn* (Eindhoven)

Citations: MR 19, 393b = N02-7; MR 20# 3835 = P32-35; MR 20# 3836 = P32-36; MR 21# 4140 = N16-19.

## N16-21 (23# A2399)

**Prachar, K.**
**Über die kleinste Primzahl einer arithmetischen Reihe.**
*J. Reine Angew. Math.* **206** (1961), 3–4.

Let $k$ be a positive integer, $l$ a positive integer less than and prime to $k$, and $p(k, l)$ the least prime number which is congruent to $l \pmod k$. Upper bounds for $p(k, l)$ have been obtained by a number of writers, and in particular by Ju. V. Linnik [see, e.g., K. Prachar, *Primzahlverteilung*, Springer, Berlin, 1957, Chapter X; MR **19**, 393]. In the present paper the author proves a result in the opposite direction: given any $l$, there exist infinitely many $k$ such that, for a suitable positive constant $c$ (independent of $k$),

$$p(k, l) > ck \log k \cdot \log_2 k \cdot \log_4 k/(\log_3 k)^2.$$

The proof is elementary and depends on Brun's sieve method and on R. A. Rankin's estimate of the number of integers below a given bound whose prime factors are subject to a certain restriction [J. London Math. Soc. **13** (1938), 242–247]. *L. Mirsky* (Sheffield)

Citations: MR 19, 393b = N02-7.
Referred to in N16-27.

**N16-22** **(23# A2402 )**

**Fogels, È. K.**

**Prime numbers in short arithmetic progressions.**

*Dokl. Akad. Nauk SSSR* **133** (1960), 1038–1040 (*Russian*); *translated as Soviet Math. Dokl.* **1** (1961), 949–951.

A method of proof is given for the following theorem. There exist positive constants $c$ and $c'$, not depending on $k$ or $l$, such that for any positive number $\varepsilon \leqq c$ and for all $k \geqq k_0(\varepsilon)$ and all $x \geqq k^{c' \log(c/\varepsilon)}$, there is a prime $p \equiv l \pmod k$ $((k, l)=1)$ in the interval $(x, xk^\varepsilon)$. The general features of the proof are similar to those of Rodosskiĭ's proof [Mat. Sb. (N.S.) **34 (76)** (1954), 331–336; MR **15**, 935], which is a simplified version of Ju. V. Linnik [ibid. **15 (57)** (1944), 139–178, 347–368; MR **6**, 260]. *S. Ikehara* (Tokyo)

Citations: MR 6, 260b = N16-5; MR 6, 260c = N16-6; MR 15, 935e = N16-16.

**N16-23** **(23# A2403 )**

**Fogels, E.**

**On the existence of primes in short arithmetical progressions.**

*Acta Arith.* **6** (1960/61), 295–311.

The author proves by methods of Linnik, simplified (and slightly weakened) by Rodosskiĭ, the following result: There are absolute constants $c>0$, $c'>0$ such that for any positive $\varepsilon \leqq c$, for all $k \geqq k_0(\varepsilon)$ and all $x \geqq k^{c' \log(c/\varepsilon)}$, there is at least one prime $p \equiv l \pmod k$, $(k, l)=1$, in the interval $(x, xk^\varepsilon)$. There are even more than $x/\varphi(k)k^{2\varepsilon}$ primes $\equiv l \pmod k$ for $x<\exp k^\varepsilon$, $k>k_1(\varepsilon)$. A corollary of this result is:

(1) $$\pi(x; k, l) > x/\varphi(k)k^{3\varepsilon}$$

for all $x \in (k^{c' \log(c/\varepsilon)+\varepsilon}, \exp k^\varepsilon)$, $k>k_2(\varepsilon)$. (The constant $k_0(\varepsilon)$ depends on Siegel's theorem and cannot be calculated at present.) To prove this the method of Linnik-Rodosskiĭ is supplied with two more parameters and another dissection of the critical strip is used. The above theorems fill a gap between Linnik's theorem, that $\pi(x; k, l)>0$ for $x>k^{c_1}$ with $c_1$ independent of $k$, and Tschudakow's generalisation of Hoheisel's theorem, that there is a prime $p$, $p \equiv l \pmod k$, between $x$ and $x+x^{3/4}$ if $x \geqq \exp k^{\varepsilon_1}$, $k>k_0(\varepsilon_1)$ (actually 3/4 can be replaced by a value $<5/8$ as was proved by Ingham and others). For $x \geqq \exp k^{\varepsilon_1}$ it is also well known that $\pi(x; k, l)> c(\varepsilon)x/\varphi(k)\log x$ ($\pi(x; k, l)$ the number of primes $\leqq x$ and $\equiv l \pmod k$). $x=1$, $\varepsilon=c$ gives Linnik's result.—(1) gives for the first time a lower estimate of $\pi(x; k, l)$ for every $l$ (which tends to infinity with $x \to \infty$) for a region of $x$-values with $x \leqq \exp k^\varepsilon$. It seems interesting to compare this with the following conditional result, which is easily proved if the Riemann hypothesis for $L$-functions is supposed true: There is always a prime $\equiv l \pmod k$ between $x$ and $x+k^{2+\varepsilon}$ if $x<k^{2+\varepsilon}$ and between $x$ and $x+x^{1/2+\varepsilon}\varphi(k)$ if $x>k^{2+\varepsilon}$; $\pi(x; k, l) \sim x/\varphi(k)\log x$ for $x>k^{2+\varepsilon}$. *K. Prachar* (Vienna)

Referred to in R44-19.

**N16-24** **(25# 5042 )**

**Tatuzawa, Tikao**

**On Bertrand's problem in an arithmetic progression.**

*Proc. Japan Acad.* **38** (1962), 293–294.

In this note, the author proves the following theorem. There exists a positive constant $c$ such that if $x \geqq \exp(c \log k \log\log k)$ and $k$ is sufficiently large, then $\pi(2x; k, l)-\pi(x; k, l)>0$ is true for all $l$ satisfying $(k, l)=1$. *B. K. Ghosh* (Calcutta)

**N16-25** **(26# 2415 )**

**Fomenko, O. M.**

**Two hypotheses in the theory of prime numbers. (Russian)**

*Rev. Math. Pures Appl.* **6** (1961), 745–746.

Hypothesis 1: There is at least one prime of the form $kx+l$, where $(k, l)=1$, between $(kn)^2$ and $(k(n+1))^2$, where $k, l, n$ denote arbitrary natural numbers. Hypothesis 2: Let $p_m$ denote the $m$th prime, $P_t=p_1 \cdot p_2 \cdots p_t$. Let $2p_t>k$. Consider the natural numbers of the form $kx+l$ which are less than $kP_t$ and prime to $P_t$. Then the difference between consecutive members of the numbers under consideration is smaller than $k(2p_t-k)$.

The author proves that Hypothesis 1 follows from Hypothesis 2 (these hypotheses were mentioned by Landau [Proc. 5th Internat. Congr. Math. (Cambridge, England, 1912), Vol. I, pp. 93–108, Cambridge Univ. Press, Cambridge, England, 1913]). *S. Chowla* (Boulder, Colo.)

**N16-26** **(27# 92 )**

**Sierpiński, W.**

**L'hypothèse de M. A. Schinzel sur les nombres premiers et les progressions arithmétiques.**

*Univ. Beograd. Publ. Elektrotehn. Fak. Ser. Mat. Fiz. No.* 101–106 (1963), 7–8.

Let $a$ and $b$ be positive integers and consider the arithmetic progression $\{ak+b\}$, $k=1, 2, \cdots$. Clearly, a necessary condition for this progression to contain infinitely many pairs of consecutive terms which are prime numbers is that $a$ be even and $b$ be relatively prime to $a$. Whether this condition is also sufficient is an open question. In fact, an affirmative answer in the special case, $a=2$, $b=1$, would mean the existence of an infinitude of prime pairs. In this paper it is shown by elementary methods (1) that the sufficiency of the condition is another of the implications of A. Schinzel's conjecture known as Hypothesis H [Acta Arith. **4** (1958), 185–208; erratum, ibid. **5** (1959), 259; MR **21** #4936]; (2) that the consequence $C_{13}$ of Hypothesis H [ibid. **7** (1961/62), 1–8; MR **24** #A70] implies that, if the condition is met, the progression contains infinitely many pairs of consecutive terms which are consecutive primes; and (3) that for any even $a$, if, for every $b$ prime to $a$, the progression $\{ak+b\}$ contains at least one pair of consecutive terms that are primes, then it contains an infinite number of such pairs. *R. J. Levit* (San Francisco, Calif.)

Citations: MR 21# 4936 = N32-20; MR 24# A70 = A26-53.

**N16-27** **(27# 118 )**

**Schinzel, Andrzej**

**Remark on the paper of K. Prachar "Über die kleinste Primzahl einer arithmetischen Reihe".**

*J. Reine Angew. Math.* **210** (1962), 121–122.

K. Prachar [same J. **206** (1961), 3–4; MR **23** #A2399] had shown that for every positive integer $l$ there exists a positive constant $c=c(l)$ such that the least prime number $p(k, l)$ which is congruent to $l \pmod k$ satisfies the inequality

$$p(k, l) > ck (\log k) \log_2 k (\log_4 k)/(\log_3 k)^2$$

for infinitely many values of $k$. The author of the present paper points out that a very small modification in Prachar's argument suffices to establish the above result with an absolute value of $c$. *L. Mirsky* (Sheffield)

Citations: MR 23# A2399 = N16-21.

**N16-28** **(29# 1193)**

**Barban, M. B.; Linnik, Ju. V.; Čudakov, N. G.**

**On the distribution of primes in short progressions mod $p^n$. (Russian)**

*Dokl. Akad. Nauk SSSR* **154** (1964), 751–753.

Consider the remainder in

$$\pi(x, D, k) = \varphi(D)^{-1}[\mathrm{li}(x)+R(x, D, k)],$$

where $x$, $D$, $k$ denote positive integers, $(k, D)=1$. The authors are interested in the dependence of $R$ on $D$. It is stated that, for each constant $A>0$, we have

$$R(x, D, k) = O(x(\log D)^{-A})$$

provided: (I) $D$ is restricted to the powers $p^n$ of a fixed prime $p$; (II) $x \gg D^{8/3+\varepsilon}$.

The proof is outlined in some detail. Use is made of: (i) An upper bound involving $D$, due to M. B. Barban [Mat. Sb. (N.S.) **61** (**103**) (1963), 418–425], on the total number of zeros inside $\sigma \leq \sigma' \leq 1$, $|t| \leq T$, of the functions $L(s, \chi)$ having $D$ as modulus; (ii) A zero-free region near $\sigma=1$, depending on $D$, of the $L(s, \chi)$ with $D=p^n$, analogous to one by S. M. Rozin [Izv. Akad. Nauk SSSR Ser. Mat. **23** (1959), 503–508; MR **22** #4680].

*J. H. B. Kemperman* (Rochester, N.Y.)

Citations: MR 22# 4680 = M25-46.

**N16-29** **(32# 5611)**

**Chen Jing-run [Ch'en Ching-jun]**

**On the least prime in an arithmetical progression.**

*Sci. Sinica* **14** (1965), 1868–1871.

Denote by $p_{\min}(k, l)$ the least prime $\equiv l \bmod k$, where $(k, l)=1$, $1 \leq l < k$. Linnik [Mat. Sb. (N.S.) **15** (**57**) (1944), 139–178; 347–368; MR **6**, 260] proved the existence of an absolute constant $C$, such that $p_{\min}(k, l) < k^C$. P'an Ch'eng-tung proved $C \leq 5448$ [Sci. Record **1** (1957), 311–313; MR **21** #4140; Acta Sci. Natur. Univ. Pekinensis **4** (1958), 1–34]. The author announces the result $C \leq 777$ for sufficiently large $k$, and states the main lemmas for the proof.

*W. Schwarz* (Freiburg)

Citations: MR 6, 260b = N16-5; MR 6, 260c = N16-6; MR 21# 4140 = N16-19.

Referred to in N16-35.

**N16-30** **(33# 2610)**

**Baženova, T. M.**

**A stronger form of a theorem on finite differences for the function $\pi(x)$. (Russian)**

*Proc. First Sci. Conf. Math. Dept. Ped. Inst. Volga Region* (*May*, 1960) (*Russian*), *p.* 3. *Kuĭbyšev. Gos. Ped. Inst., Kuybyshev*, 1961.

With the usual notation in the prime number theorem for arithmetic progressions, the author announces the following result:

$$\psi(x+u, k, l)-\psi(x, k, l) = uh^{-1}+O(uh^{-1}e^{-c(\log x)^{1/4-\varepsilon}}),$$

where $u=x^{\vartheta}$, $\vartheta<1$, $k=O((\log x)^c)$.

*S. Chowla* (University Park, Pa.)

**N16-31** **(33# 5584)**

**Klimov, N. I.**

**Cugiani chains of isolated prime numbers. (Russian)**

*Proc. First Sci. Conf. Math. Dept. Ped. Inst. Volga Region* (*May*, 1960) (*Russian*), *pp.* 8–11. *Kuĭbyšev. Gos. Ped. Inst., Kuybyshev*, 1961.

Several theorems are given on the variation of differences between successive primes in arithmetic progressions with increasing modulus, based on an application of the sieve method and results of N. G. Čudakov [Izv. Akad. Nauk SSSR Ser. Mat. **12** (1948), 31–46; MR **9**, 499].

*V. G. Sprindžuk* (RŽMat **1962** #9 A82)

Citations: MR 9, 499b = N16-9.

**N16-32** **(34# 4226)**

**Kátai, I.**

**$\Omega$-theorems for the distribution of prime numbers. (Russian)**

*Ann. Univ. Sci. Budapest. Eötvös Sect. Math.* **9** (1966), 87–93.

Using standard notation, the author shows that for arbitrarily small $\varepsilon_1>0$, $\varepsilon_2>0$ there exists an (ineffective) $T_0=T_0(k, \varepsilon_1, \varepsilon_2)$ such that

$$\int_{T^{1-\varepsilon_1}}^{T} |\psi(x, k, l_1)-\psi(x, k, l_2)|x^{-1}\,dx > T^{\theta_1-\varepsilon_2}$$

for $T>T_0$; here $l_1 \not\equiv l_2 \pmod k$, $(l_1, k)=(l_2, k)=1$, and $\theta_1$ is the lowest upper bound of real parts of singular points of the function $\sum_\chi (\bar\chi(l_1)-\bar\chi(l_2))(\mathscr{L}'/\mathscr{L})(s, \chi)$, where $\chi$ runs through all characters mod $k$.

*S. Knapowski* (Coral Gables, Fla.)

Referred to in N44-39.

**N16-33** **(38# 2103)**

**Kátai, I.**

**On oscillation of the number of primes in an arithmetical progression.**

*Acta Sci. Math.* (*Szeged*) **29** (1968), 271–282.

In connection with Littlewood's result that there exist values of $x$ for which $\pi(x)>\mathrm{li}\,x$, the author proves some results regarding oscillation of the number of primes in an arithmetical progression. The following notations are used in the statement of the theorems. $\pi(x, k, l)$ as usual denotes the number of primes $\equiv l \pmod k$ and $\leq x$. $\sigma(x, k, l)=\sum_{p\equiv l \pmod k} e^{-p/x}$, $s(x)=\sum_{n=2}^{\infty} e^{-n/x}\log n$. Throughout $k$ is restricted to take the values 3, 4, 5, 6, 7, 8, 9, 10, 11, 12, 19, 24, and $N_k(l)$ denotes the number of solutions of the congruence $x^2\equiv l \pmod k$. $\delta$ and $c$ are positive numerical constants which can be explicitly determined (not necessarily the same in the statement of each theorem). Also, $\chi=(2+\sqrt{3})^2$. Theorem 1: For $T>c$,

$$\max_{T\leq x\leq T^\chi}(\pi(x, 4, 3)-\tfrac{1}{2}\,\mathrm{li}\,x)/((\sqrt{x})/\log x) > \delta$$

and

$$\min_{T\leq x\leq T^\chi}(\pi(x, 4, 3)-\tfrac{1}{2}\,\mathrm{li}\,x)/((\sqrt{x})/\log x) < -\delta.$$

Theorem 2: For $T>c$ and for all pairs $l_1$, $l_2$ for which $N_k(l_1)=N_k(l_2)$, $l_1\not\equiv l_2 \pmod k$,

$$\max_{T\leq x\leq T^\chi}(\pi(x, k, l_1)-\pi(x, k, l_2))/((\sqrt{x})/\log x) > \delta,$$

$$\min_{T\leq x\leq T^\chi}(\pi(x, k, l_1)-\pi(x, k, l_2))/((\sqrt{x})/\log x) < -\delta.$$

Theorem 3: For $T>c$ and for all $l$ for which $N_k(l)=0$,

$$\max_{T\leq x\leq T^\chi}(\pi(x, k, l)-(\mathrm{li}\,x)/\varphi(k))/((\sqrt{x})/\log x) > \delta,$$

$$\min_{T\leq x\leq T^\chi}(\pi(x, k, l)-(\mathrm{li}\,x)/\varphi(k))/((\sqrt{x})/\log x) < -\delta.$$

Theorem 4: For $T>c$ and for all $l$ for which $N_k(l)=0$,

$$\max_{T\leq x\leq T^\chi}(\sigma(x, k, l)-s(x)/\varphi(k))/((\sqrt{x})/\log x) > \delta,$$

$$\min_{T\leq x\leq T^\chi}(\sigma(x, k, l)-s(x)/\varphi(k))/((\sqrt{x})/\log x) < -\delta.$$

Theorem 5: For $T>c$ and for all $l_1$, $l_2$ for which $N_k(l_1)=N_k(l_2)$, $l_1\not\equiv l_2 \pmod k$,

$$\max_{T\leq x\leq T^\chi}(\sigma(x, k, l_1)-\sigma(x, k, l_2))/((\sqrt{x})/\log x) > \delta.$$

*K. Thanigasalam* (University Park, Pa.)

**N16-34** **(42# 3030)**

**Motohashi, Yoichi**

**A note on the least prime in an arithmetic progression with a prime difference.**

*Acta Arith.* **17** (1970), 283–285.

Define $\pi(N, k)$ to be the number of primes not exceeding $N$ and $\equiv 1 \pmod{k}$. Then

$$\log \prod_{p \leq N} (p-1) = \sum_{q^\alpha < N} \pi(N, q^\alpha) \log q,$$

where $p$ runs over all primes not exceeding $N$, $q$ runs over all primes less than $N$ and $\alpha$ is an integer. The author then splits the sum over $q^\alpha < N$ into four parts one of which is $N^\zeta < q < N$, $\alpha = 1$. The remaining three parts are summed using the mean-value theorem of Bombieri, partial summation and the theorem of Brun-Titchmarsh. The author is thus able to show that $\sum_{N^\zeta < q < N} \pi(N, q) \log q > 0$ for $\zeta < 1 - \frac{1}{2}e^{-1/4}$. Let $P(k, l)$ be the least prime in the arithmetic progression $n \equiv l \pmod{k}$, where $(k, l) = 1$. The following theorem then follows: For any fixed $l$ there exist infinitely many primes $q$ such that $P(q, l) < c(\varepsilon) q^{\theta + \varepsilon}$, where $\theta = 2e^{1/4}(2e^{1/4} - 1)^{-1} = 1.63773 \ldots$.

*E. M. Horadam* (Armidale)

**N16-35** **(42# 5939)**

**Jutila, Matti**

**A new estimate for Linnik's constant.**

*Ann. Acad. Sci. Fenn. Ser. A I No.* 471 (1970), 8 *pp.*

A famous theorem of Linnik asserts that given a positive integer $D \geqq 2$, there exists an absolute constant $L$ such that the least prime in the arithmetical progression $\{Dn + k\}$ with $(D, k) = 1$ is $\ll D^L$. Amongst others, Ch'en Ching-jun [Sci. Sinica **14** (1965), 1868–1871; MR **32** #5611] obtained the estimate $L < 777$ for $L$. The author sharpens this to $L < 550$.

*K. Thanigasalam* (Bronx, N.Y.)

Citations: MR 32# 5611 = N16-29.

**N16-36** **(42# 7609)**

**Elliott, P. D. T. A.; Halberstam, H.**

**The least prime in an arithmetic progression.**

*Studies in Pure Mathematics (Presented to Richard Rado), pp.* 59–61. *Academic Press, London,* 1971.

Es bezeichne $P(q, h)$ die kleinste Primzahl $p \equiv h \bmod q$. Die Verfasser zeigen, daß "fast immer" $P(q, h) < \varphi(q) \cdot (\log q)^{1+\delta}$ gilt, genauer: zu jedem $\delta > 0$ gibt es eine Folge $Q$ natürlicher Zahlen der Dichte Null, so daß für $q \notin Q$ die Anzahl der primen Restklassen $h$ mod $q$, für die $P(q, h) < \varphi(q) \cdot (\log q)^{1+\delta}$ gilt, asymptotisch gleich $\varphi(q)$ ist. Der Beweis folgt aus der von H. Davenport und dem zweiten Verfasser [Michigan Math. J. **13** (1966), 485–489; MR **34** #156] und P. X. Gallagher [Mathematika **14** (1967), 14–20; MR **35** #5411] mit Hilfe des großen Siebes für $\sum_{q \leq X} \sum'_{h \bmod q} (\theta(x; q, h) - \varphi^{-1}(q) \cdot x)^2$ gegebenen Abschätzung. Die Verfasser führen aus, daß sich das Ergebnis noch geringfügig verschärfen läßt.

*W. Schwarz* (Frankfurt a.M.)

Citations: MR 34# 156 = N12-40; MR 35# 5411 = M55-52.

**N16-37** **(42# 7610)**

**Knapowski, S.; Turán, P.**

**Über einige Fragen der vergleichenden Primzahltheorie.**

*Number Theory and Analysis (Papers in Honor of Edmund Landau), pp.* 157–171. *Plenum, New York,* 1969.

This paper is concerned with two types of problem from the domain of "comparative number theory". Typical of the first type of problem is the following theorem, to be proved elsewhere: For $T > c_1$ there exist $U_1, U_2, U_3, U_4$ such that $\log_3 T \leqq U_2 \exp(-\log^{9/10} U_2) < U_1 < U_2 \leqq T$, $\log_3 T \leqq U_4 \exp(-\log^{9/10} U_4) < U_3 < U_4 \leqq T$, and

$$(1) \quad \sum_{U_1 < p < U_2, p \equiv 1 (\bmod 4)} \log p - \sum_{U_1 < p < U_2, p \equiv 3 (\bmod 4)} \log p > U_2^{1/2},$$

$$\sum_{U_3 < p < U_4, p \equiv 1 (\bmod 4)} \log p - \sum_{U_3 < p < U_4, p \equiv 3 (\bmod 4)} \log p < -U_4^{1/2};$$

here $\log_3 T$ denotes the iterated logarithm. It is an unremarked consequence of work of Hardy and Littlewood that there exist infinitely many pairs $p_\nu, p_{\nu+1}$ of consecutive primes that are both congruent to 1 modulo 4. The inequality (1) enables one to deduce more, namely, that for $T > c_1$ there exist consecutive primes in the interval $(\log_3 T, T)$ both congruent to 1 modulo 4. The corresponding result for 3 modulo 4 can be proved for a smaller interval, namely $(T \exp(-\log^{11/12} T), T)$.

The second type of problem concerns sequences of integers $y$ for which $\pi(y, 4, 1)$ exceeds its average value $\frac{1}{2} \operatorname{Li} y$ and generalizations of this problem. The results are too complicated to be stated concisely.

*R. A. Rankin* (Glasgow)

# N20 ELEMENTARY PROOFS OF THE PRIME NUMBER THEOREM AND SIMILAR THEOREMS

Elementary proofs of special cases of Dirichlet's theorem are reviewed in **A42**.

See also Section N80.

See also reviews A02-4, A34-9, M45-6, N02-5, N04-14, N04-31, N04-54, N12-16, N12-50, N36-16, N36-63, N80-3, R44-1, R44-6, R44-10, R44-17, R44-20, R44-31, R44-42, R46-8, Z15-92.

**N20-1** **(10, 594f)**

**Zassenhaus, Hans. Über die Existenz von Primzahlen in arithmetischen Progressionen.** Comment. Math. Helv. **22**, 232–259 (1949).

The purpose of this paper is to give an "elementary" proof of Dirichlet's theorem concerning primes in arithmetical progressions. The author calls a mathematical argument "elementary" when it can be carried out in a finite number of steps without the use of limiting processes. Thus the use of the differential and integral calculus and of functions such as the logarithm is forbidden although complex numbers and the simpler properties of ideals and cyclotomic fields are allowed. The sequence of ideas is very roughly the same as that used in the classical analytical proof, but since they have to be presented in "elementary" form the Dirichlet $L$-functions have to be replaced by finite sums, and statements concerning continuity and limits by inequalities. Also, an appreciable part of the paper is devoted to the construction and investigation of the properties of an "ersatz" logarithm $l_n(z)$ which is defined for every nonnegative integer $n$ and algebraic numbers $z$, which are not zero nor negative real numbers, to be $2^n\{z^{2^{-n}} - 1\}$. The establishment of the relevant properties of these finite analogues adds considerably to the complication of the algebra which is, fortunately, carried out in full.

It is not possible to give an adequate summary of this paper here, but it may be stated that the final result depends upon the inequalities

$$\left|\varphi(m)\sum_{p\equiv a(m);p\leqq N} p^{-s}-\sum_{p\leqq N;p\nmid m} p^{-s}\right|\leqq\sum_{\chi\neq\chi_1}\left|\sum_{p\leqq N}\frac{\chi(p)}{p^s}\right|<6\varphi(m),$$

where $p$ denotes a prime, $\varphi(m)$ is Euler's function, $(a, m)=1$, $\chi$ is any character modulo $m$ and $\chi_1$ the principal character. Since, in "nonelementary" language, the second sum diverges for $s=1$ as $N\rightarrow\infty$, the result will follow if $s$ can be chosen sufficiently near to unity $(s>1)$. The chief difficulty of the proof lies in obtaining a value of $s$ which satisfies the inequalities stated and which is sufficiently close to unity to entail the desired conclusion. *R. A. Rankin.*

## N20-2 (10, 595a)

**Selberg, Atle. An elementary proof of Dirichlet's theorem about primes in an arithmetic progression.** Ann. of Math. (2) **50**, 297–304 (1949).

The author proves that, for every positive integer $k$, there exist positive numbers $C$ and $x_0$ depending only on $k$ such that, when $(k, l)=1$,

$$Q_l(x)=(1/\log x)\sum_{p\leqq x;p\equiv l(k)} p^{-1}\log p>C$$

($p$ prime). It follows that every arithmetical progression $ky+l$, where $(k, l)=1$, contains an infinity of primes. The proof does not employ the complex characters modulo $k$ and only finite sums are considered. The formulae

$$\sum_{p\leqq x} p^{-1}\log p=\log x+O(1) \quad\text{and}\quad \pi(x)=O(x/\log x)$$

are used; these can be proved by elementary methods. It will therefore be seen that the author's interpretation of the word "elementary" is not so strict as that of Zassenhaus [see the preceding review]. Agreement on interpretation could no doubt be attained without difficulty at the cost of considerable expansion of the algebra. The proof is of interest not only because of its elementary character but because it has so little in common with the classical analytical proof.

By means of the relations $\sum_{d|n}\mu(d)\log^2(x/d)=$ (a) $\log^2 x$ $(n=1)$, (b) $\log p\log(x^2/p)$ $(n=p^\alpha, \alpha\geqq 1)$, (c) $2\log p\log q$ $(n=p^\alpha q^\beta, \alpha\geqq 1, \beta\geqq 1, p, q$ different primes), (d) 0 otherwise, which are summed over all $n\equiv l \pmod k$, $n\leqq x$, and by repeated partial summation, it is shown that

$$(1)\quad Q_l(x)\geqq\tfrac{2}{27}\sum_{m_1m_2m_3\equiv l(k)} Q_{m_1}(x^{\frac13})Q_{m_2}(x^{\frac13})Q_{m_3}(x^{\frac13})-O(1/\log x),$$

and

$$(2)\qquad Q_l(x)\leqq 2/\varphi(k)+O(\log\log x/\log x).$$

The next step is to show that, for every real nonprincipal character $\chi(n)$ modulo $k$,

$$(3)\qquad \sum_{p\leqq x;\chi(p)=1} p^{-1}\log p>\tfrac{1}{9}\log x,\qquad x>x_0.$$

The proof makes use of (i) the fact that $\chi(p)$ can be written as the quadratic residue symbol $(D/p)$, where $D$ is an integer which is not a square, and $|D|<k^2$, (ii) the product $P=\prod'|u^2-Dv^2|$ taken over all integers $u$ and $v$ such that $|u|\leqq\{\frac12 x\}^{\frac12}$, $|v|\leqq\{\frac12 x/|D|\}^{\frac12}$, $(u, v)\neq(0, 0)$. The inequalities

$$x|D|^{-\frac12}\log x<\log P<8x|D|^{-\frac12}\sum_{p\leqq x;(D/p)=1} p^{-1}\log p+O(x)$$

are derived, the second one being obtained by estimating the number of factors of $P$ which are divisible by each prime power $p^\alpha$; (3) follows at once.

It can be deduced from (2) and (3) that there is a set $S$ of at least $\frac12\varphi(k)$ incongruent residue classes $m$ for which

$$Q_m(x^{\frac13})>\tfrac{1}{20}\{\varphi(k)\}^2,\qquad x>x_0,$$

and $S$ contains unity and two members $m, m'$ such that $mm'\equiv l \pmod k$, provided that $Q_l(x)<1/\{30\varphi(k)\}$. It is shown that this implies that $S$ contains three members $m_1, m_2, m_3$ such that $m_1m_2m_3\equiv l \pmod k$, and (1) then gives

$$Q_l(x)\geqq\tfrac{2}{27}Q_{m_1}(x^{\frac13})Q_{m_2}(x^{\frac13})Q_{m_3}(x^{\frac13})-O(1/\log x)>(20)^{-4}\{\varphi(k)\}^{-6},$$

which proves the theorem. Although the general trend of the argument is clear the paper is not easy to read since the algebraic steps necessary for the estimation of the order of magnitude of sums are mostly omitted. *R. A. Rankin.*

Referred to in N12-44, N20-6, N20-20, N20-34, N20-57, R44-11.

## N20-3 (10, 595b; 10, 595c)

**Selberg, Atle. An elementary proof of the prime-number theorem.** Ann. of Math. (2) **50**, 305–313 (1949).

**Erdös, P. On a new method in elementary number theory which leads to an elementary proof of the prime number theorem.** Proc. Nat. Acad. Sci. U. S. A. **35**, 374–384 (1949).

The prime number theorem (PNT) asserts that

$$\pi(x)\sim x/\log x,\qquad x\rightarrow\infty,$$

where $\pi(x)$ is the number of primes $p\leqq x$. All previous proofs have been by "transcendental" arguments involving some appeal to the theory of functions of a complex variable. Successive proofs have moderated the demands on this theory, or invoked alternative analytical theories (e.g., Fourier transforms), but there remained a nucleus of complex variable theory, namely the proposition that the Riemann zeta-function $\zeta(s)=\zeta(\sigma+it)$ has no zeros on the line $\sigma=1$; and this could hardly be avoided, except by a radically new approach, since the PNT is in a clearly definable sense "equivalent" to this property of $\zeta(s)$. It has long been recognised that an "elementary" proof of the PNT, not depending on analytical ideas remote from the problem itself, would (if indeed possible) constitute a discovery of the first importance for the logical structure of the theory of the distribution of primes. An elementary (though not easy) proof is given, in various forms, in these two papers. Since the papers are in some ways complementary, it seems clearest to review them together.

The starting point is A. Selberg's formula

$$(1)\qquad \sum_{p\leqq x}\log^2 p+\sum_{pq\leqq x}\log p\log q\sim 2x\log x,$$

where $p, q$ run over primes. The formula might be deduced from the PNT or its equivalent $\vartheta(x)\equiv\sum_{p\leqq x}\log p\sim x$, but this, on the classical theory of the distribution of primes, would give it a transcendental basis. The significant events to record are: (a) the discovery by Selberg of an elementary proof (indeed with "$\sim 2x\log x$" replaced by "$=2x\log x+O(x)$," though this refinement is not required for the application); and (b) the recognition that the formula nevertheless embodied facts previously accessible only to the analytical theory of primes. The hope that (1) might therefore be made the basis of an elementary proof of the PNT itself was justified, but the deduction was by no means obvious. The first proof (by Selberg) used, besides (1) (and parts of the elementary theory of primes), the following provisional result (deduced from (1) by Erdös): (2) For any $\lambda>1$ the number of primes in $(x, \lambda x)$ is at least $Kx/\log x$ for $x>x_0$ $(K=K(\lambda)>0,\ x_0=x_0(\lambda))$. Later it was found possible to argue directly from (1) without the intervention of (2).

Selberg's paper contains his proof of (1), a statement of (2), his deduction of the PNT from (1) and (2), and his final direct deduction of the PNT from (1). Erdös's paper contains a statement of (1), an allusion to Selberg's final proof of the PNT (not published at the time), and an account of other proofs in chronological order; the account includes Erdös's own proof of (2), Selberg's deduction of the

PNT from (1) and (2), a sketch of Selberg's simplified proof of (2), and the joint simplified direct deduction of the PNT from (1). It is stated (in both papers) that the method can be adapted to the prime number theorem for arithmetical progressions.

Selberg's proof of (1) is, in accordance with the general spirit of the investigation, expressed in arithmetical form. But in a brief summary it is quicker to treat the formula as the result of equating coefficient-sums in the formal identity $(\zeta'/\zeta)'+(\zeta'/\zeta)^2=\zeta''/\zeta$, where $\zeta=\zeta(s)$, $\zeta'=\zeta'(s)$, $\cdots$. The left hand side gives substantially the left hand side of (1). As to the right hand side we can write

$$\zeta''=2\zeta^3+b\zeta^2+c\zeta+\delta,$$

where $b$, $c$ are certain constants and $\delta$ is a Dirichlet's series $\sum d_n n^{-s}$ with coefficient-sum $D(x)\equiv\sum_{n\leqq x}d_n=O(x^\alpha)$ $(0<\alpha<1)$, by elementary theorems on divisor functions. The coefficient-sum of $\zeta''/\zeta=2\zeta^2+b\zeta+c+\zeta^{-1}\delta$ can now be estimated with an error $O(x)$, and (1) follows. [This is the general idea; but Selberg, besides avoiding even the formal use of Dirichlet's series, arranges the details rather differently so that the coefficients $d_3(n)$ in $\zeta^3$ do not enter.]

Of the various deductions from (1) the joint simplified proof of the PNT is perhaps the easiest to summarise. In this, (1) is used in the equivalent form

$$(1)' \qquad \vartheta(x)\log x+\sum_{p\leqq x}\vartheta(x/p)\log p\sim 2x\log x,$$

which may be rewritten as

$$(1)'' \qquad s(x)+\frac{1}{\log x}\sum_{p\leqq x}\epsilon_p s(x/p)\to 2,$$

where $s(x)=\vartheta(x)/x$ and $\epsilon_p=(\log p)/p$; and we wish to deduce that $\vartheta(x)\sim x$, i.e., $s(x)\to 1$. We have, by elementary theory: (3) $\sum_{p\leqq x}\epsilon_p\sim\log x$; so the second term in (1)″ is essentially a weighted average of $s(x)$. [The situation now recalls Mercer's theorem; a certain linear combination of a function and its average tends to a (finite) limit, and it is required to deduce that the function itself tends to a limit. The proof (by "compensation") has some features in common with Knopp's proof of Mercer's theorem, but it uses special properties of $s(x)$ that have no counterpart in Mercer's theorem, for example the "Tauberian" condition "$xs(x)$ positive and increasing" and the connection of $s(x)$ with the weights $\epsilon_p$.] Suppose that

$$a=\liminf s(x)<\limsup s(x)=A.$$

We have $a>0$ by elementary theory; and it is an easy deduction from (1)″, (3) that: (4) $A+a=2$. Consider a (large) $x$ for which $s(x)$ is large (i.e., near $A$). From (1)″, (3) we deduce that (to compensate): ($\alpha$) $s(x/p)$ is small (i.e., near $a$) for a set $X$ of primes comprising almost all $p\leqq x$ (where "almost all" means "except for a subset over which $\sum\epsilon_p$ is small compared with the same sum taken over the whole set"). Take a particular (small) $p_1$ in $X$. Then similarly: ($\beta$) $s(x/p_1p)$ is large for a set $Y$ of primes comprising almost all $p\leqq x/p_1$. Next, it follows easily from (1)′, (4) and the fact that $\vartheta(\cdot)$ is an increasing function that: ($\gamma$) points $x'$, $x$ $(x'>x)$ where $s(\cdot)$ is large and small (or vice versa) must be so far apart that $x'/x>(A/a)-\epsilon$ $(=\lambda$, say) for large $x$. [This is the sense of lemma 5 of Erdös's paper, but the inequality signs in the conclusion and in most of the proof have become reversed. A list of further misprints (supplied by Erdös) includes: (Lemmas 1, 2) for $r$ read $p$; (p. 377, line 1) for $X$ read $C$; (p. 377, line 14 from below) for $\vartheta(x)$ read $\vartheta(x/p)$; (p. 378 (14)) move last square bracket two places to the right; (p. 376, line 9 from below; p. 383, line 3) symbols following $c'>C-$ and $I_i=$ badly printed (but meaning clear).] Now ($\alpha$), ($\beta$), ($\gamma$) involve a contradiction. The proof of this, the most difficult step, is presented in alternative forms. The simpler version is based on a study of the sum $S=\sum\epsilon_p\epsilon_q$ taken over all pairs of primes $(p, q)$ for which $p$ is in $X$, $\lambda^{-1}p<p_1q\leqq\lambda p$. Writing $S=\sum_p\epsilon_p\sum_q\epsilon_q$, we have $\sum_q\geqq(\lambda p/p_1)^{-1}\{\vartheta(\lambda p/p_1)-\vartheta(\lambda^{-1}p/p_1)\}>c>0$ by the definition of $a$, $A$, since $a\lambda>A\lambda^{-1}$; whence $S>(c-\epsilon)\log x$, since, by ($\alpha$), $\sum_p$ extends over almost all $p\leqq x$. On the other hand, writing $S=\sum_q\epsilon_q\sum_p\epsilon_p$, we have

$$\sum_p\leqq(\lambda^{-1}p_1q)^{-1}\vartheta(\lambda p_1q)<C;$$

whence $S<\epsilon\log x$, since, by ($\gamma$), $q$ can never belong to $Y$ (because $x/p_1q$ is too near to $x/p$ for some $p$ of $X$), so that, by ($\beta$), $\sum_q$ extends over "almost no" primes. This contradiction shows that $a=A$ $(=1$ since $A+a=2)$. Selberg, in his own final proof, proceeds on somewhat different lines, by "successive approximation." He first derives from (1) an inequality involving (on both sides) the function $R(x)=\vartheta(x)-x$, and then infers from it (and elementary properties of $R(x)$) that, if $|R(x)/x|<\alpha$ $(<8)$ $(x>x_0)$, then $|R(x)/x|<\alpha_1$ $(x>x_1)$, where $\alpha_1=\alpha(1-k\alpha^2)$ and $k$ is a positive absolute constant; whence by repeated application $|R(x)/x|<\alpha_n$ $(x>x_n)$ where $\alpha_n\to 0$ as $n\to\infty$. [The logical arrangement on p. 311 is confusing, since the proof that (3.2) still holds if $R(n)$ changes sign does not seem to be valid until the order of $x'/x$ has been suitably restricted. Also the argument of the text seems to use a sharpened version of (1), though the full form with error $O(x)$ is not required. The claim in the "final remark" that (1) itself suffices would seem to presuppose the use of the alternative form of inequality referred to in footnote 4 on p. 311.]

It may be useful to view the elementary proof against its analytical background, in order to see how the argument, while omitting all reference to analytical facts known to be inseparable from the truth of the PNT, nevertheless avoids the danger of coming into conflict with these facts (and thereby proving too much). Let $f$ be a function of the complex variable $s=\sigma+it$, to be taken as $-\zeta'/\zeta$ in the application but subject at present only to the following restrictions: (i) $f=\sum a_n n^{-s}$ $(\sigma>1$; $a_n$ real); (ii) $f$ is regular in $\sigma\geqq 1$ except possibly for simple poles on $\sigma=1$; (iii) $g\equiv -f'+f^2=\sum b_n n^{-s}$ $(\sigma>1)$, where $B(x)\equiv\sum_{n\leqq x}b_n\sim 2x\log x$. (When $f=-\zeta'/\zeta$, (iii) is equivalent to Selberg's formula (1).) Then, by (iii), $g$ cannot have a double pole at a point $s\neq 1$ of $\sigma=1$; whence any possible pole of $f$ at such a point must have residue $R$ satisfying $R+R^2=0$, i.e., $R=-1$; and the example

$$f(s)=\zeta(s)-\zeta(s-i\alpha)-\zeta(s+i\alpha)$$

$(\alpha>0)$ shows that this is actually possible. Thus our present assumptions are consistent with the existence of poles of $f$ at points $s\neq 1$ on $\sigma=1$; and this may be taken as a "reason" why it is possible to give an elementary proof of (1) without becoming involved in the question of the existence of zeros of $\zeta$ on $\sigma=1$. Now introduce the further assumption: (iv) $a_n\geqq 0$. Then it can be proved, as in Hadamard's classical argument, that a pole of $f$ at $s=1+it$ with $R=-1$ implies a pole at $s=1+2it$ with $R=+1$, and this is impossible; so $f$ can have no pole on $\sigma=1$ except at $s=1$. Thus the properties (i)–(iv) of $f=-\zeta'/\zeta$ do embody the essential analytical fact on which previous proofs of the PNT have been based. What Selberg and Erdös do is to deduce the PNT directly from the arithmetical counterparts of (i), (iii), (iv), without the explicit intervention of the analytical fact. In principle this opens up the possibility of a new approach, in which the old logical arrangement is reversed and analytical properties of $\zeta(s)$ are deduced from arithmetical properties of the sequence of primes. How far the practical effects of this revolution of ideas will penetrate into the structure of the subject, and how much of the theory will ultimately have to be rewritten, it is too early to say.

*A. E. Ingham* (Cambridge, England).

Referred to in A34-9, M45-34, N20-5, N20-6, N20-7, N20-8, N20-10, N20-13, N20-14, N20-24, N20-39, N20-42, N20-43, N20-52, N20-53, N20-57, N20-58, N20-62, N20-67, N36-16, R44-1, R44-31, Z15-92.

## N20-4 (10, 597a)

**van der Corput, J. G. Démonstration élémentaire du théorème sur la distribution des nombres premiers.** Math. Centrum Amsterdam, Scriptum no. 1, 32 pp. (1948).

This mimeographed pamphlet is a connected account of the elementary proof of the prime number described in the preceding review. Based on lectures by Erdös, it follows the general lines of the joint simplified proof of Selberg and Erdös, but it has been cast into its present form by van der Corput. The author has adopted a very elementary standpoint, so that the text includes proofs of results that would normally be quoted from elementary analysis. The most substantial change is in the concluding stages of the argument; here the result ($\gamma$) [see the preceding review] is not used explicitly, but the double sum $S$ is replaced by a triple sum $\sum \epsilon_p\epsilon_q\epsilon_r$. The exposition is clear and precise, and it is only in these final stages, which remain the most difficult part of the proof, that the reader is seriously taxed.

*A. E. Ingham* (Cambridge, England).

Referred to in N20-36, N20-57.

## N20-5 (11, 161d)

**Jarník, Vojtěch. Une démonstration nouvelle de la loi de la distribution des nombres premiers.** Časopis Pěst. Mat. Fys. **74**, D51–D54 (1949). (Czech. French summary)

A brief account of the work of Selberg [Ann. of Math. (2) **50**, 305–313 (1949)] and Erdös [Proc. Nat. Acad. Sci. U. S. A. **35**, 374–384 (1949)]; cf. these Rev. **10**, 595.

Citations: MR 10, 595b = N20-3; MR 10, 595c = N20-3.

## N20-6 (11, 419c)

**Selberg, Atle. An elementary proof of the prime-number theorem for arithmetic progressions.** Canadian J. Math. **2**, 66–78 (1950).

This is an elementary proof of the formula $\vartheta_{k,l}(x)\sim x/\varphi(k)$, where $(k,l)=1$, and $\vartheta_{k,l}(x)=\vartheta_l(x)=\sum\log p$ summed over the range $p\leqq x$, $p\equiv l \pmod k$ ($p$ prime). The proof follows the general lines of the author's treatment of the case $k=1$ [Ann. of Math. (2) **50**, 305–313 (1949); these Rev. **10**, 595; quoted as (ii)]. The starting point is the formula

$$(1)\quad \sum_{p\leqq x;\, p\equiv l\ (k)}\log^2 p+\sum_{pq\leqq x;\, pq\equiv l\ (k)}\log p\log q=\frac{2}{\varphi(k)}x\log x+O(x)$$

($p$, $q$ prime). From this it is first deduced that

$$(2)\quad |R_l(x)|\leqq\frac{1}{\varphi(k)\log x}\sum_\alpha\sum_{n\leqq x}|R_\alpha(x/n)|+O\left(\frac{x\log\log x}{\log x}\right),$$

$$(3)\quad \sum_{n\leqq x}n^{-1}\log nR_l(n)=-\sum_{n\leqq x}n^{-1}\sum_{\alpha\beta\equiv l\ (k)}R_\alpha(n)R_\beta(x/n)+O(x),$$

where $R_l(x)=\vartheta_l(x)-x/\varphi(k)$, and $\alpha$, $\beta$ run over reduced sets of residues (mod $k$). The general idea is then to show that $|R_l(x)/x|<\sigma_n/\varphi(k)$ $(x>x_n)$, where $\sigma_n$ satisfies a recurrence relation implying that $\sigma_n\to 0$ as $n\to\infty$. But the extension to $k>1$ brings new difficulties. One of these entails the introduction of (3) in place of a more elementary result that sufficed when $k=1$. But the main difficulty arises from the need for a sufficiently elementary proof that $\vartheta_l(x)/x>c(k)>0$ $(x>x_0)$. This the author resolves, with the help of a little of the theory of real (but not complex) characters, by borrowing and developing ideas from his elementary treatment of Dirichlet's theorem on the existence of primes in arithmetical progressions [Ann. of Math. (2) **50**, 297–304 (1949); these Rev. **10**, 595; quoted as (i)].

The proof of (1) itself is pieced together from the author's papers (i) and (ii). In (i) it was proved that $T_{k,l}(x)=S_k(x)+O(x)$, where $T_{k,l}(x)$ is the left hand side of (1) and $S_k(x)$ is independent of $l$; from which it was deduced, by summation over $l$, that $\varphi(k)T_{k,l}(x)=T_{1,0}(x)+O(x)$. The problem of the asymptotic behaviour of $T_{k,l}(x)$ was thus reduced to the case $k=1$; and this was dealt with in (ii) by an elementary estimation of $S_1(x)$. The actual form of $S_k(x)$ used was

$$S_k(x)=xk^{-1}\sum_{d\leqq x;\ (d,k)=1}d^{-1}\mu(d)\log^2(x/d).$$

(This is equivalent, to order $O(x)$, to the sum of those coefficients $b_n$ in $\zeta''(s)/\zeta(s)=\sum b_nn^{-s}$ for which $n\leqq x$, $n\equiv l$ (mod $k$), but was discussed by the author without reference to Dirichlet's series.) *A. E. Ingham.*

Citations: MR 10, 595a = N20-2; MR 10, 595b = N20-3.

Referred to in N20-57, N20-63, R44-31.

## N20-7 (11, 419e)

**Shapiro, Harold N. On a theorem of Selberg and generalizations.** Ann. of Math. (2) **51**, 485–497 (1950).

For integral $k\geqq 2$ write

$$V_k(x)=\sum_{n\leqq x}d^{-1}\mu(d)\log^k(x/d).$$

By successive applications of the Möbius inversion formula it is shown that $V_2(x)=2\log x+O(1)$, and from this result Selberg's lemma [Ann. of Math. (2) **50**, 305–313 (1949); these Rev. **10**, 595]

$$\sum_{p\leqq x}\log^2 p+\sum_{pq\leqq x}\log p\log q=2x\log x+O(x)$$

is deduced ($p$ and $q$ denote primes). Both results are then generalised (induction is used and the inversion formula is applied to $f(x)=x\log^{k-1}x$) to prove that

$$V_k(x)=k\log^{k-1}x+\sum_{i=1}^{k-2}c_i^{(k)}\log^i x+O(1),$$

where the $c_i^{(k)}$ are constants depending on $k$, and that

$$\frac{(k+1)!\theta_{k+2}(x)}{x\log^{k+1}x}+\frac{k!\theta_{k+1}(x)}{x\log^k x}=2+O(1/\log x),$$

where

$$\theta_r(x)=\sum\log p_1\log p_2\cdots\log p_r$$

summed over $p_1p_2\cdots p_r\leqq x$. By means of this result $\theta_k(x)$ can be expressed in terms of $\theta_1(x)=\theta(x)$ and a further generalisation to sums

$$\sum_{p_1p_2\cdots p_k\leqq x}\log^{m_1}p_1\log^{m_2}p_2\cdots\log^{m_k}p_k$$

is proved. If an asymptotic equality for any of these functions can be obtained it will imply $\theta(x)\sim x$, i.e., the prime number theorem. *R. A. Rankin* (Cambridge, England).

Citations: MR 10, 595b = N20-3.

Referred to in N20-13, N20-14, N20-16, N20-25, N20-37, N20-41.

## N20-8 (11, 420a)

**Erdös, P. On a Tauberian theorem connected with the new proof of the prime number theorem.** J. Indian Math. Soc. (N.S.) **13**, 131–144 (1949).

This is a further contribution to the logic of the prime number theorem [see A. Selberg, Ann. of Math. (2) **50**, 305–313 (1949); P. Erdös, Proc. Nat. Acad. Sci. U. S. A. **35**, 374–384 (1949); these Rev. **10**, 595]. It is proved [theorem 1] that, if $1<p_1<p_2<\cdots$ and

$$(1)\qquad \sum_{p_i\leqq x}(\log p_i)^2+\sum_{p_ip_j\leqq x}\log p_i\log p_j=2x\log x+O(x),$$

then $\vartheta(x)\equiv\sum_{p_i\leqq x}\log p_i\sim x$. The effect of this, when the $p_i$ are the primes, is that from Selberg's asymptotic formula in its sharper form we can deduce the prime number theorem without assuming independently any results from the elementary theory of primes. It is deduced, in fact, from (1) that (2) $\sum_{p_i\leqq x}p_i^{-1}\log p_i=\log x+O(1)$; and theorem 1 then follows from the earlier work of Selberg and Erdös. The deduction of (2) from (1) is based on the Tauberian theorem [theorem 2]: let $a_k\geqq 0$, $s_m=\sum_{k=1}^m a_k$, and suppose $S(n)=\sum_{k=1}^n a_k(s_{n-k}+k)=n^2+O(n)$; then $s_n=n+O(1)$. The proof of this theorem is elementary, but too intricate for a brief summary. The main difficulty arises from the sharpness of the final error term; to illustrate this the author begins by discussing in succession the simpler versions with final errors $o(n)$, $o(n^\epsilon)$, $O(\log n)$. A generalisation [theorem 2′] is stated, in which the errors in hypothesis and conclusion are replaced by $O[nf(n)]$ and $O[f(n)]$, where $f(n)>c>0$, $f(n)/n\to 0$. *A. E. Ingham* (Cambridge, England).

Citations: MR 10, 595b = N20-3; MR 10, 595c = N20-3.

Referred to in G20-46, N20-42.

## N20-9 (11, 420b)

**Erdös, P. Supplementary note.** J. Indian Math. Soc. (N.S.) **13**, 145–147 (1949).

This is a discussion of some further points arising out of theorem 2 of the paper reviewed above. Use the notation of that theorem, and write

$$S(n)=\sum_{k=1}^n a_ks_{n-k}+\sum_{k=1}^n ka_k=S_2(n)+S_1(n),$$

say. The author proves: (i) if $a_k\geqq 0$ and $S_1(n)=\frac{1}{2}n^2+O(n)$, then $s_n=n+O(\log n)$; (ii) if $a_k\geqq 0$ and $S_2(n)=\frac{1}{2}n^2+O(n)$, then $s_n=n+o(n)$. It is shown by examples that in (i) the final error cannot be improved, while in (ii) it certainly cannot be improved to $o(n^{\frac{1}{2}})$. (This emphasises the distinctive feature of theorem 2; if we separate the two constituents of $S(n)$, we no longer obtain anything sufficiently precise for the prime number theorem.) Another example shows that the conclusion of theorem 2 cannot be improved to $s_n=n+o(1)$ even if we replace $O(n)$ by $O(1)$ in the hypothesis. A generalisation of theorem 2 is given, but one that is quickly reduced to the special case. [Note: (i) is true, by partial summation, without the condition $a_k\geqq 0$.] *A. E. Ingham* (Cambridge, England).

Referred to in G20-46.

## N20-10 (11, 644f)

**Wiener, Norbert, and Geller, Leonard. Some prime-number consequences of the Ikehara theorem.** Acta Sci. Math. Szeged **12**, Leopoldo Fejér et Frederico Riesz LXX annos natis dedicatus, Pars B, 25–28 (1950).

[The second author's name is misprinted Gellert in the original.] This paper arises out of the Selberg-Erdös elementary proofs of the prime number theorem [Selberg, Ann. of Math. (2) **50**, 305–313 (1949); Erdös, Proc. Nat. Acad. Sci. U. S. A. **35**, 374–384 (1949); these Rev. **10**, 595]. The object is to adduce reasons, from the analytical side, for the possibility of such proofs. The starting point is the identity $\zeta''/\zeta=(\zeta'/\zeta)'+(\zeta'/\zeta)^2$ in the integrated form

$$\text{(a)}\qquad -\int\frac{\zeta''(z)}{\zeta(z)}dz=\int_0^\infty u^{-z}d\psi(u)+\int_0^\infty u^{-z}d\chi(u)\quad(x=\Re z>1)$$

with $\psi(u)$ and $\chi(u)$ nondecreasing and $\psi(u)=\sum_{p^m\leqq u}\log p$ so that $\psi(u)\sim u$ $(u\to\infty)$ is equivalent to the prime number theorem. Ikehara's theorem (in general form) gives (b) $\psi(u)+\chi(u)\sim 2u$. The possibility that $\zeta(z)$ may have zeros on $x=1$ is irrelevant so far, since such zeros (necessarily simple) only give rise to logarithmic singularities of the function on the left of (a) and these do not affect Lebesgue integrability. But this possibility must now be excluded. If $\zeta(1+i\lambda)=0$, then $g(z)\equiv f(z)+\frac{1}{2}f(z+i\lambda)+\frac{1}{2}f(z-i\lambda)$ (where $f(z)=-\zeta'(z)/\zeta(z)$) is a Dirichlet series with nonnegative coefficients having no singularity at $z=1$, from which it is "easy to show" that it has none on $x=1$. A weak form of Ikehara's theorem then gives:

$$\text{(c)}\qquad \int_0^u\{1+\cos(\lambda\log u)\}d\psi(u)=o(u).$$

Write $\psi(u)=\psi_1(u)+\psi_2(u)$, where $\psi_1(u)$ and $\psi_2(u)$ are nondecreasing, and increase only in those intervals where $1+\cos(\lambda\log u)\geqq\epsilon$ and $<\epsilon$ respectively. By (c), $\psi_1(u)=o(u)$ (for fixed $\epsilon>0$). By differencing (b) over intervals of variation of $\psi_2(u)$, using the fact that $\chi(u)$ is nondecreasing, and summing over the relevant intervals, it is proved that $\limsup\psi_2(u)/u\leqq\delta(\epsilon)$, where $\delta(\epsilon)$ is small with $\epsilon$. It follows that $\psi(u)=o(u)$, contrary to an elementary theorem of Chebyshev. The possibility $\zeta(1+i\lambda)=0$ is thus excluded, and the prime number theorem then follows from Ikehara's theorem, applied to $f(z)$ on classical lines. [Notes by reviewer. (i) There are several misprints and minor inaccuracies. (ii) The logical basis of the proof that $\zeta(1+i\lambda)\neq 0$ is unfortunately obscured by the words quoted. On the natural assumptions about $\zeta(z)$ we could complete the proof at once by saying that, since $g(z)$ is regular at $1+i\lambda$, therefore $\zeta(z)$ must have a pole at $1+2i\lambda$ (the classical contradiction); but this can hardly be intended, since it would render otiose all the applications of Ikehara's theorem except the classical one.] *A. E. Ingham* (Cambridge, England).

Citations: MR 10, 595b = N20-3; MR 10, 595c = N20-3.

## N20-11 (12, 81a)

**Shapiro, Harold N. On primes in arithmetic progressions. I.** Ann. of Math. (2) **52**, 217–230 (1950).

The author establishes by elementary methods the analogue of Selberg's formula for arithmetical progressions, namely,

$$\text{(A)}\qquad \sum_{\substack{p\leqq x\\ p\equiv B(A)}}\log^2 p+\sum_{\substack{pq\leqq x\\ pq\equiv B(A)}}\log p\log q=\frac{2}{\varphi(A)}x\log x+O(x),$$

where $(B,A)=1$ and $p$ and $q$ are primes. This formula together with

$$\text{(B)}\qquad \sum_{\substack{p\leqq x\\ p\equiv 1(A)}}\frac{\log p}{p}\to\infty,$$

which is obtained by using certain results of algebraic number theory applied to the field obtained from the rational field by adjoining the $A$th roots of unity, is used to deduce that

$$\sum_{\substack{p\leqq x\\ p\equiv B(A)}}\log^2 p\to\infty$$

[in (1.4) $\log p$ should be replaced by $\log^2 p$], from which Dirichlet's theorem follows. In addition, it can be shown from (A) without the use of (B) that at least half of the progressions modulo $A$ (which are relatively prime to $A$) contain an infinity of primes. In the special case when $A=p^\alpha$ ($p\geqq 2$) it is possible to deduce from this and (A) that, if $B$ is a quadratic nonresidue modulo $A$, then there are infinitely many primes congruent to $B$ (mod $A$).

*R. A. Rankin* (Cambridge, England).

Referred to in N20-41.

## N20-12 (12, 81b)

**Shapiro, Harold N. On primes in arithmetic progression. II.** Ann. of Math. (2) **52**, 231–243 (1950).

The author considers the series

$$L_0(\chi)=\sum_{n=1}^{\infty}\frac{\chi(n)}{n},\quad L_1(\chi)=\sum_{n=1}^{\infty}\frac{\chi(n)\log n}{n},$$

where $\chi$ is a nonprincipal character modulo $A$. It can be shown by elementary methods that, if $\chi$ is real, $L_0(\chi)\neq 0$. A sketch of the proof given by Landau [Handbuch der Lehre von der Verteilung der Primzahlen, Teubner, Leipzig-Berlin, 1909, § 106] is given. By means of repeated applications of a generalisation of the Möbius inversion formula and by considering $L_0(\chi)$ and $L_1(\chi)$ it is shown that

$$\text{(C)}\qquad \sum_{p\leqq x}\frac{\chi(p)\log p}{p}=\begin{cases} O(1) \text{ if } L_0(\chi)\neq 0,\\ -\log x+O(1) \text{ if } L_0(\chi)=0.\end{cases}$$

From this it is deduced that

$$\varphi(A)\sum_{\substack{p\leqq x\\ p\equiv 1\,(A)}}\frac{\log p}{p}=(1-N)\log x+O(x),$$

where $N$ is the number of nonprincipal characters $\chi$ for which $L_0(\chi)=0$. Since the left-hand side is positive, $N=0$ or 1. This means that $L_0(\chi)\neq 0$ for a complex character, as otherwise it would follow that $N\geqq 2$ since $L_0(\bar\chi)=\overline{L_0(\chi)}$ and $\chi$ and $\bar\chi$ are different characters. (C) then gives

$$\sum_{p\leqq x}p^{-1}\chi(p)\log p=O(1),$$

and it follows easily that

$$\text{(D)}\qquad \sum_{\substack{p\leqq x\\ p\equiv B\,(A)}}\frac{\log p}{p}=[\varphi(A)]^{-1}\log x+O(1).$$

The only processes in the deduction of (D) which are not strictly elementary are those involving the use of the infinite series $L_0(\chi)$ and $L_1(\chi)$. A sketch of a method of proof in which these are replaced by finite sums is given. Let

$$\vartheta_B(x)=\sum_{\substack{p\leqq x\\ p\equiv B\,(A)}}\log p.$$

By means of (D) and (A) [see the preceding review] the author shows that

$$\liminf \vartheta_B(x)/x+\limsup \vartheta_B(x)/x=2/\varphi(A)$$

for each $B$ with $(B,A)=1$, and that the lower limit, and therefore the upper limit, is the same for each $B$. From the prime ideal theorem (this can be proved by elementary methods; see the author [Comm. Pure Appl. Math. **2**, 309–323 (1949); these Rev. **11**, 501]) it can be deduced that, for $B=1$, each limit is $1/\varphi(A)$ and from this it follows that $\vartheta_B(x)\sim x/\varphi(A)$ for all $(B,A)=1$. *R. A. Rankin.*

Citations: MR 11, 501h = R44-1.
Referred to in N20-34, N20-41, R44-10.

## N20-13 (13, 536d)

**Tanaka, Minoru. An elementary proof of the prime number theorem.** Sûgaku (Mathematics) **3**, 136–143 (1951). (Japanese)

This is a clear presentation of Selberg's proof of the prime-number theorem [Ann. of Math. (2) **50**, 305–313 (1949); these Rev. **10**, 595], using, in part, H. N. Shapiro's paper [ibid. **51**, 485–497 (1950); these Rev. **11**, 419].

*S. Ikehara* (Tokyo).

Citations: MR 10, 595b = N20-3; MR 11, 419e = N20-7.

## N20-14 (13, 725f)

**Tatuzawa, Tikao, and Iseki, Kanesiroo. On Selberg's elementary proof of the prime-number theorem.** Proc. Japan Acad. **27**, 340–342 (1951).

Let $\Lambda(n)=\log p$ for $n=p^l$ ($p$ prime) and 0 otherwise. Put $\psi(x)=\sum_{n\leqq x}\Lambda(n)$. Applying the Möbius inversion formula, the author establishes the formula

$$\psi(x)\log x+\sum_{n\leqq x}\psi(x/n)\Lambda(n)=2x\log x+O(x).$$

The analysis resembles Shapiro's derivation [Ann. of Math. (2) **51**, 485–497 (1950); these Rev. **11**, 419] of Selberg's lemma [Ann. of Math. (2) **50**, 305–313 (1949); these Rev. **10**, 595]. The author's result may be used in place of Selberg's lemma to prove the prime number theorem.

*A. L. Whiteman* (Los Angeles, Calif.).

Citations: MR 10, 595b = N20-3; MR 11, 419e = N20-7.
Referred to in N20-22, N20-57, N20-60, N20-62, N20-67.

## N20-15 (13, 824a)

**Fogels, È. K. On an elementary proof of the prime number theorem.** Latvijas PSR Zinātņu Akad. Fiz. Mat. Inst. Raksti. **2**, 14–45 (1950). (Russian. Latvian summary)

The author proposes that an "elementary" proof of the prime number theorem should be carried out entirely within the domain of rational numbers. Thus he wishes also to remove from the work of A. Selberg and P. Erdös the presence of such "transcendental" elements as the functions $\log x$, $\log\log x$, $x^r$, etc. This program is effected by replacing the use of $e^x$ by

$$E(x)=1+\frac{x}{1!}+\frac{x^2}{2!}+\cdots+\frac{x^N}{N!}$$

where $N$ is a suitable function of the total range $X$ entering into the discussion. Then for $M=M(X)$ another such function of $X$ (which serves as a sort of common denominator for the rational numbers in the proof) for any rational number $\xi\geqq 1$ let $k$ be the integer such that $E(k/M)\leqq\xi<E((k+1)/M)$ and define $L(\xi)=k/M$. This function $L(x)$ is then used to replace $\log x$. Carrying out this replacement systematically, and following A. Selberg's method of proof very closely, the prime number theorem is derived in the form $\pi(x)\sim x/\sum_{n\leqq x}n^{-1}$. Proofs of a similar category are then derived for $\sum_{n\leqq x}\mu(n)=o(x)$, and $\sum_{n\leqq x}\mu(n)/n=o(1)$.

*H. N. Shapiro* (New York, N. Y.).

Referred to in N20-19, N20-30.

## N20-16 (14, 137d)

**Wright, E. M. The elementary proof of the prime number theorem.** Proc. Roy. Soc. Edinburgh. Sect. A. **63**, 257–267 (1952).

A complete elementary proof of the prime number theorem is given (following the method of A. Selberg) in which no previous knowledge of number theory is presumed.

Selberg's fundamental formula

(1) $$\psi(x)\log x+\sum_{mn\leq x}\Lambda(m)\Lambda(n)=2x\log x+O(x)$$

is proved by a procedure which is essentially the same as the proof given by Selberg in that it stems from a consideration of the sum

(2) $$\sum_{d|n}\mu(d)\log^2\frac{x}{d}.$$

However the proof is arranged in such a manner as to avoid explicit reference to any sums involving the divisor function, and is in this direction very similar to a proof given by the reviewer [Ann. of Math (2) **51**, 485–497 (1950); these Rev. **11**, 419]. In this connection it should be pointed out that the use of (2) is slightly misleading, and that the arithmetic identity which underlies Selberg's formula is

(3) $$\sum_{d|n}\mu(d)\log^2\frac{n}{d}=\Lambda(n)\log n+\sum_{d|n}\Lambda(d)\Lambda\left(\frac{n}{d}\right).$$

This identity can be proved arithmetically by observing that

$$\log^2 n=\log n\sum_{d|n}\Lambda(d)=\sum_{d|n}\Lambda(d)\log\frac{n}{d}+\sum_{d|n}\Lambda(d)\log d$$
$$=\sum_{d|n}\left\{\Lambda(d)\log d+\sum_{c|d}\Lambda(c)\Lambda\left(\frac{d}{c}\right)\right\}.$$

Applying the Möbius inversion formula to this yields (3).

In his derivation of the prime number theorem from (1) the author follows Selberg's method except that in the concluding argument sums are replaced by integrals. This tends to elucidate somewhat the idea behind Selberg's proof.

*H. N. Shapiro* (New York, N. Y.).

Citations: MR 11, 419e = N20-7.

Referred to in N04-54, N20-63, N20-65, N20-67, Z01-28.

## N20-17 (14, 355d)

**Wright, E. M. Functional inequalities in the elementary theory of primes.** Duke Math. J. **19**, 695–704 (1952).

In this paper the author analyzes the functional inequalities behind Selberg's proof of the prime number theorem. Assuming real functions $\chi(x)>0$, $f(x)$, given, which are bounded and integrable in every finite interval $a\leqq x\leqq X$, and such that

(1) $$|f(x_2)-f(x_1)|\leqq A_1|x_2-x_1|+A_2x_1^{-\delta},\qquad A_1>0,\ A_2\geqq 0,\ \delta>0,$$

(2) $$\left|\int_{x_1}^{x_2}f(y)dy\right|\leqq A_3,\quad A_3>0,$$

(3) $$x|f(x)|\leqq\int_a^x|f(y)|dy+\chi(x);$$

the problem considered concerns the manner in which the order of $f(x)$ depends on the order of $\chi(x)$. The main theorem is the following. Theorem I: Under the above assumptions, if $\chi(x)=O(x\phi^3)$, where $\phi=\phi(x)>0$ is nonincreasing and (a) $\lim_{x\to\infty}\phi(x)=0$, (b) $\phi(x)(\log x)^{1/2}$ nondecreasing, then $f(x)=O(\phi(x))$ as $x\to\infty$. The special case where all that is known is that $\chi(x)=o(x)$ yields $f(x)=o(1)$, which is the relevant result for the proof of the prime number theorem (no error term). It is proved that Theorem I is best possible in the sense of Theorem II: If $\phi(x)$ satisfies the conditions of Theorem I, and $\chi(x)=x\phi^3$, there exists an $f(x)$ satisfying (1), (2), and (3) such that $f(x)\neq o(\phi)$ as $x\to\infty$.

*H. N. Shapiro* (New York, N. Y.).

## N20-18 (15, 201e)

**Gupta, Hansraj. A generalization of the Möbius function.** Scripta Math. **19**, 121–126 (1953).

The function considered by the author is denoted by $v_r(n)$, and could be defined by the identity

$$\sum_{n=1}^{\infty}v_r(n)n^{-s}=\zeta(rs)/\zeta(s).$$

This function includes the function $\mu$ of Möbius for $r=0$ the function $\lambda$ of Liouville for $r=2$ and the "unit function" $[1/n]$ for $r=1$. The author generalizes some of the lemmas in the Selberg-Erdös-van der Corput proof of the Prime Number Theorem. For example,

$$\left|\sum_{n\leq x}n^{-1}v_r(n)\right|\leqq 1+x^{-1/r}$$

$$-\sum_{n\leq x}g(n)=\sum_{k=1}^{\infty}\theta(x/K^n)+o(x),$$

where $g(n)=\sum_{d|n}v_r(d)\log d$. *D. H. Lehmer.*

Referred to in N20-64.

## N20-19 (15, 507d)

**Fogel', È. K. An elementary proof of formulae of de la Vallée Poussin.** Latvijas PSR Zinātņu Akad. Vestis **1950**, no. 11 (40), 123–130 (1950). (Russian. Latvian summary)

The author discusses by elementary methods, involving only finite sums and the properties of $a^x$, $\log x$, $\sin x$, $\cos x$, the asymptotic relations

$$\sum_{\substack{p\leq x\\ p\equiv l(k)}}1\sim\frac{x}{h\log x},\quad \sum_{\substack{n\leq x\\ n\equiv l(k)}}\lambda(n)=o(x),\quad \sum_{\substack{n\leq x\\ n\equiv l(k)}}\mu(n)=o(x),$$

where $(l,k)=1$, $h=\varphi(k)$, $p$ runs through primes, and $\lambda(n)$ and $\mu(n)$ are the functions of Liouville and Möbius. The proof of the first formula follows the lines of A. Selberg's elementary proof of the prime number theorem (the special case $k=1$). A substantial part of the argument is taken up with a proof, according to the author's canons, of the formula

$$\sum_{\substack{p\leq x\\ p\equiv l(k)}}\frac{\log p}{p}=\frac{1}{h}\log x+O(1)$$

of Mertens; this involves the use of real and complex characters. (In a footnote the author acknowledges Selberg's treatment of the general case $k\geqq 1$ by the use of real characters, his own work having been done in ignorance of this.) It is stated that the second and third results can be deduced from the first by methods used in a previous paper by the author [Latvijas PSR Zinātņu Akad. Fiz. Mat. Inst. Raksti. **2**, 14–45 (1950); these Rev. **13**, 824]. The concluding section is devoted to analogues concerning primes representable by a positive definite binary quadratic form.

*A. E. Ingham* (Cambridge, England).

Citations: MR 13, 824a = N20-15.

## N20-20 (16, 117b)

**Briggs, W. E. An elementary proof of a theorem about the representation of primes by quadratic forms.** Canadian J. Math. **6**, 353–363 (1954).

H. Weber [Math. Ann. **20**, 301–329 (1882)] proved that every binary quadratic form $ax^2+2bxy+cy^2$ which is properly primitive (i.e., $(a, 2b, c)=1$, $a>0$) is capable of representing infinitely many prime numbers. The author gives an elementary proof of this theorem using the methods of A. Selberg [Ann. of Math. (2) **50**, 297–304 (1949); these Rev. **10**, 595]. *H. S. A. Potter* (Aberdeen).

Citations: MR 10, 595a = N20-2.

Referred to in N20-40.

## N20-21 (16, 449a)

**Eda, Yoshikazu. On Selberg's function.** Proc. Japan Acad. **29**, 418–422 (1953).

The author considers generalizations of Selberg's identity

$$\sum_{\substack{p\leq x\\ p\equiv\lambda(a)}} \log^2 p + \sum_{\substack{pq\leq x\\ pq\equiv\lambda(a)}} \log p \log q = \frac{2}{\varphi(a)} x \log x + O(x), \quad (\lambda, a)=1,$$

to identities for

$$\sum_{\substack{p_1^{\alpha_1}\cdots p_r^{\alpha_r}\leq x\\ p_1^{\alpha_1}\cdots p_r^{\alpha_r}\equiv\lambda(a)}} \log^{\alpha_1} p_1 \cdots \log^{\alpha_r} p_r.$$

Use is made of the umbral calculus of E. T. Bell.

*H. N. Shapiro* (New York, N. Y.).

## N20-22 (16, 450b)

**Ayoub, R. G. On Selberg's lemma for algebraic fields.** Canad. J. Math. **7**, 138–143 (1955).

A simple proof of Selberg's fundamental lemma in the theory of the distribution of primes has recently been given by Tatuzawa and Iseki [Proc. Japan Acad. **27**, 340–342 (1951); MR **13**, 725] who employed an ingenious application of the Möbius inversion formula. In this paper the author shows that this proof may be extended to yield a corresponding result for algebraic fields. Shapiro [Comm. Pure Appl. Math. **2**, 309–323 (1949); MR **11**, 501] earlier derived the same result using Selberg's methods and deduced as a consequence the prime-ideal theorem.

*A. L. Whiteman* (Los Angeles, Calif.).

Citations: MR 11, 501h = R44-1; MR 13, 725f = N20-14.

## N20-23 (16, 677a)

**Karamata, J. Evaluation élémentaire des sommes typiques de Riesz de certaines fonctions arithmétiques.** Acad. Serbe Sci. Publ. Inst. Math. **7**, 1–40 (1954).

The author obtains estimates of the Rieszian sums

$$\sum_{n\leq x} a_n \log^k\left(\frac{x}{n}\right).$$

In particular, if $na_n=\mu(n)$ and $k=2$, the value of the sum is $2\log x+O(1)$; for the case $na_n=\Lambda(n)$ and $k=3$, he obtains $c_4\log^4 x+\cdots+c_1\log x+O(1)$, where the $c$'s are constants. Both sums are of interest in analytic prime number theory. The proofs are elementary. *S. Chowla.*

## N20-24 (16, 904f)

**Breusch, Robert. Another proof of the prime number theorem.** Duke Math. J. **21**, 49–53 (1954).

Another elementary derivation of the prime-number theorem from Selberg's identity

$$\sum_{p\leq x} \log^2 p + \sum_{pq\leq x} \log p \log q = 2x\log x + O(x)$$

is given. The proof is close in spirit to that given by Erdös [Proc. Nat. Acad. Sci. U. S. A. **35**, 374–384 (1949); MR **10**, 595] but is considerably simpler. *H. N. Shapiro.*

Citations: MR 10, 595c = N20-3.

## N20-25 (16, 905d)

**Fischer, Günter. Verallgemeinerungen einer Selbergschen Formel.** Mitt. Math. Sem. Giessen no. **50**, i+31 pp. (1954).

Certain identities involving the sums over primes of the form

$$\sum_{p_1\cdots p_k\leq x} \log^{\alpha_1} p_1 \cdots \log^{\alpha_k} p_k$$

are derived. The results and proofs are similar to those given in a paper of the reviewer [Ann. of Math. (2) **51**, 485–497 (1950); MR **11**, 419]. Whereas in the aforementioned paper various identities involving the zeta function are used to obtain certain arithmetic identities, the derivation given in this paper avoids the use of the zeta function.

*H. N. Shapiro* (New York, N. Y.).

Citations: MR 11, 419e = N20-7.

## N20-26 (16, 905e)

**Popken, J. On convolutions in number theory.** Nederl. Akad. Wetensch. Proc. Ser. A. **58**=Indag. Math. **17**, 10–15 (1955).

The multiplication theorem for Dirichlet series provides that for suitably convergent series

$$\sum f(n)n^{-s}\sum g(n)n^{-s}=\sum h(n)n^{-s}$$

where $h(n)=\sum_{d|n} f(d)g(n/d)$, and suggests various identities between arithmetic functions. The author defines the "convolution" of $f(n)$ and $g(n)$ as $h=f*g$, develops various properties of it, and gives a proof of Selberg's identity, utilizing this notion. *H. N. Shapiro* (New York, N. Y.).

Referred to in N20-69, N20-71, N80-22.

## N20-27 (17, 587d)

**Kuhn, P. Eine Verbesserung des Restgliedes beim elementaren Beweis des Primzahlsatzes.** Math. Scand. 3 (1955), 75–89.

Using elementary methods, it is shown that the Selberg identity

$$(1)\quad \theta(x)\log x+\sum_{p\leq x}\theta\left(\frac{x}{p}\right)\log p=2x\log x+O(x)$$

yields

$$(2)\quad \theta(x)=x+O(x\log^{-c} x);\ c=1/10.$$

Though it is not difficult to see that the method (which is an adaptation of that of Selberg) will produce some constant $c>0$ for which (2) is a consequence of (1), the calculations necessary for obtaining $c=1/10$ are a bit involved. *H. N. Shapiro* (New York, N.Y.).

Referred to in N20-36, N20-43, N20-46, N20-51, N20-52, N20-53, R44-42.

## N20-28 (17, 587e)

**Postnikov, A. G.; and Romanov, N. P. A simplification of A. Selberg's elementary proof of the asymptotic law of distribution of prime numbers.** Uspehi Mat. Nauk (N.S.) **10** (1955), no. 4(66), 75–87. (Russian)

The underlying idea of this paper is to give an elementary proof of the prime-number theorem in the form

$$(1)\quad M(x)=\sum_{n\leq x}\mu(n)=o(x).$$

This deduction is made from the elementary identity

$$(2)\quad M(x)\log x+\sum_{p\leq x}M\left(\frac{x}{p}\right)\log p=O(x).$$

This is an old identity which appeared in Landau's thesis, and a direct simple path from (2) to (1) would be rather interesting. However, in addition to (2), the authors use the Selberg identity

$$(3)\quad \theta(x)\log x+\sum_{p\leq x}\theta\left(\frac{x}{p}\right)\log p=2x\log x+O(x).$$

This is applied to eliminate the explicit appearance of the primes in (2), converting it into the inequality

$$(4)\quad |M(x)|\leq\frac{1}{\log x}\sum_{n\leq x}\left|M\left(\frac{x}{n}\right)\right|+O\left(\frac{x\log\log x}{\log x}\right).$$

Then applying an iteration scheme analogous to that used by Selberg, (1) is deduced from (4). The only "advantage" gained by dealing with $M(x)$ rather than $\theta(x)$ stems from the fact that $M(x)$ has limited jumps at the integers (since $|\mu(n)|\leq 1$). *H. N. Shapiro.*

Referred to in N20-29.

**N20-29** **(41# 3429)**

**Postnikov, A. G.** **A remark on an article by A. G. Postnikov and N. P. Romanov. (Russian)** *Uspehi Mat. Nauk* **24** (1969), *no.* 5 (149), 263.

The original article [the author and N. P. Romanov, same Uspehi **10** (1955), no. 4 (66), 75–87; MR **17**, 587] developed the method of A. Selberg in the following version: $\sum_{n\leqq x}\mu(n)/n=O(1)$ implies $\sum_{n\leqq x}\mu(n)=o(x)$ implies $\pi(x)\sim x/\ln x$.

The present note corrects an error in the earlier paper.
*A. I. Vinogradov* (Leningrad)

Citations: MR 17, 587e = N20-28.

**N20-30** **(17, 587f)**

**Eda, Yoshikazu.** **On the prime number theorem.** Sci. Rep. Kanazawa Univ. **2** (1953), no. 1, 23–33.

The elementary proof of the prime number theorem as given by Selberg is "detranscendentalized" by replacing the function $\log x$ by $\sum_{n\leqq x}1/n$. Though this paper is substantially the same in spirit as that of Fogels [Latvijas PSR Zinātņu Akad. Fiz. Mat. Inst. Raksti **2** (1950), 14–45; MR **13**, 824], the details are carried out much more neatly here. *H. N. Shapiro* (New York, N.Y.).

Citations: MR 13, 824a = N20-15.

**N20-31** **(17, 587g)**

**Eda, Yoshikazu.** **On the Selberg's inequality.** Sci. Rep. Kanazawa Univ. **2** (1953), no. 1, 7–13.

Selberg's identity

$$(1)\qquad \theta(x)\log x+\sum_{p\leqq x}\theta\left(\frac{x}{p}\right)\log p=2x\log x+O(x)$$

may be viewed as a translation in terms of primes of

$$(2)\qquad \sum_{n\leqq x}\frac{\mu(n)}{n}\log^2\frac{x}{n}=2\log x+O(1).$$

This last has been generalized by the reviewer to

$$(3)\qquad V_K(x)=\sum_{n\leqq x}\frac{\mu(n)}{n}\log^k\frac{x}{n}$$
$$=k\log^{k-1}x+\sum_{j=1}^{k-2}k_j\log^j x+O(1).$$

In this paper the constants $k_j$ are determined in terms of certain "Euler constants". A generalization of (1) is then obtained by expressing $V_K(x)$ in terms of primes.
*H. N. Shapiro* (New York, N.Y.).

**N20-32** **(17, 827h)**

**Lambek, J.; and Moser, L.** **Rational analogues of the logarithm function.** Math. Gaz. **40** (1956), 5–7.

The authors explore the use of the rational function

$$l_r(n)=h(rn)-h(r),$$

where $h(m)=\sum_{k=1}^m k^{-1}$ is the harmonic series as far as $m$ terms, as a substitute for the transcendental function $\log x$ in making elementary proofs about the distribution of primes. Theorems like

$$|l_r(xy)-l_r(x)-l_r(y)|<2r^{-1}$$

are proved by elementary means for rational numbers $x, y$.
*D. H. Lehmer* (Berkeley, Calif.).

**N20-33** **(17, 1055i)**

**Egan, M. F.** **The harmonic logarithm.** Math. Gaz. **40** (1956), 8–10.

Let $x>0$, put $x=[x]+\alpha$, $0\leqq\alpha<1$. The author defines the harmonic logarithm $L(x)$ of $x$ as

$$L(x)=L([x])=\sum_{r=1}^{[x]}\frac{1}{r}\quad(L(0)=0).$$

He proves various inequalities for $L(x)$ using only simple inequalities on rational numbers [see also Broderick, J. London Math. Soc. **14** (1939), 303–310; Proc. Roy. Irish. Acad. Sect. A. **46** (1940), 17–24; MR **1**, 41, 292].
*P. Erdös* (Jerusalem).

Citations: MR 1, 41c = A38-1; MR 1, 292g = A38-3.

**N20-34** **(18, 18d)**

**Yamamoto, Koichi.** **Theory of arithmetic linear transformations and its application to an elementary proof of Dirichlet's theorem.** J. Math. Soc. Japan **7** (1955), 424–434.

The author gives a proof of Dirichlet's theorem on the infinitude of primes in arithmetic progression which is essentially the same as given previously by the reviewer [Ann. of Math. (2) **52** (1950), 231–243, pp. 232–236; MR **12**, 81]. Also included is a simplifying remark concerning the original method of A. Selberg [ibid. **50** (1949), 297–304; MR **10**, 595]. *H. N. Shapiro* (New York, N.Y.).

Citations: MR 10, 595a = N20-2; MR 12, 81b = N20-12.

Referred to in N20-35, N20-41.

**N20-35** **(18, 719g)**

**Yamamoto, Koichi.** **Theory of arithmetic linear transformations and its application to an elementary proof of Dirichlet's theorem about the primes in an arithmetic progression.** Proceedings of the international symposium on algebraic number theory, Tokyo & Nikko, 1955, pp. 266–267. Science Council of Japan, Tokyo, 1956.

This article has appeared previously in greater detail [J. Math. Soc. Japan **7** (1955), 424–434; MR **18**, 18]. No bibliography is given in this shortened version.

Citations: MR 18, 18d = N20-34.

**N20-36** **(18, 112a)**

**Van der Corput, J. G.** **Sur le reste dans la démonstration élémentaire du théorème des nombres premiers.** Colloque sur la Théorie des Nombres, Bruxelles, 1955, pp. 163–182. Georges Thone, Liège; Masson and Cie, Paris, 1956.

Starting from Selberg's celebrated inequality

$$(1)\qquad \frac{\vartheta(x)}{x}+\frac{1}{x\log x}\sum_{p\leqq x}\vartheta\left(\frac{x}{p}\right)\log p=2+O\left(\frac{1}{\log x}\right),$$

the author obtains

$$\vartheta(x)=x+O\left(\frac{x}{(\log x)^{1/200}}\right).$$

A little earlier P. Kuhn [Math. Scand. **3** (1955), 75–89; MR **17**, 587] proved that (1) implies $\vartheta(x)=x+O\left(\frac{x}{(\log x)^{1/10}}\right)$.

Starting from (1), (assuming for the error term on the right side only $o(1)$) he obtains a simplified version of his proof of the prime number theorem [Math. Centrum Amsterdam, Scriptum no. **1** (1948); MR **10**, 597]. *P. Erdös*.

Citations: MR 10, 597a = N20-4; MR 17, 587d = N20-27.

Referred to in N20-43, N20-52.

**N20-37** **(19, 1161c)**

**Rieger, G. J.** **Bemerkungen zu einem zahlentheoretischen Satz von Shapiro.** Arch. Math. **8** (1957), 251–254.

An elementary derivation is given for the relation

$$\sum_{\substack{n\leq x\\(n,k)=1}} \frac{\mu(n)}{n}\log^r\frac{x}{n}=\frac{rk}{\varphi(k)}\log^{r-1}x+\sum_{m=1}^{r-2} b_m^{(r)}\log^m x+O(1),$$

where $\mu$ denotes the Möbius function, $r\geqq 2$ is an integer, and the $b_m^{(r)}$ are constants depending on $m$, $r$, and $k$. This generalizes a result of the reviewer [Ann. of Math. (2) **51** (1950), 485–497; MR **11**, 419] which corresponds to the case $k=1$ of the above. *H. N. Shapiro.*

Citations: MR 11, 419e = N20-7.

## N20-38 (20# 6398)

**Corrádi, Keresztély. Über die Zusammenhang der Primzahlsätze arithmetischer Progressionen desselben Differenzes.** Mat. Lapok **9** (1958), 67–90. (Hungarian. Russian and German summaries)

The author proves by elementary methods the following result: Let $k$ be any integer. If we assume that the prime number theorem for arithmetic progressions holds for one progression $l$ (mod $k$), $(l, k)=1$, then it holds for every such progression.

The author does not use Selberg's formula.

*P. Erdös* (Birmingham)

## N20-39 (20# 7172)

**Pitt, H. R. A general Tauberian theorem related to the elementary proof of the prime number theorem.** Proc. London Math. Soc. (3) **8** (1958), 569–588.

The author proves a general Tauberian theorem, which can be used in the elementary proof of the prime number theorem as given by Selberg [Ann. of Math. (2) **50** (1949), 305–313; MR **10**, 595]. Transformations of the form

$$(*)\qquad g(x)=s(x)+\frac{1}{x}\int_0^x s(x-y)dk(y)\quad (x>0)$$

are abelian, in the sense that $s(x)\to A$ implies that $g(x)\to 2A$, provided that $k(0)=0$, $k(x)$ increases for $x\geqq 0$, and $k(x)\sim x$ as $x\sim\infty$. Furthermore, it is assumed that $\lim\sup[k(x)-k(x-\delta)]=\eta(\delta)<\infty$ for every positive constant $\delta$. The object of this paper is to find conditions under which the Tauberian theorem that $g(x)\to 2A$ implies that $s(x)\to A$ can be asserted. It is found that the appropriate Tauberian condition is that $s(x)$ should satisfy the Schmidt slowly decreasing condition that $\lim\inf[s(x')-s(x)]\geqq 0$ as $x\to\infty$, $x'\geqq x$, $x'-x\to 0$ [Math. Z. **22** (1924), 89–152; see pp. 127–142].

It is to be noted that the Tauberian theorem fails (with $s(x)=\cos(\pi x/\lambda)$) if $k(x)$ is a step function with positive increments $2\lambda$ at the points $(2j+1)\lambda$ ($j=0$, 1, 2, $\cdots$), so that some further condition is required on $k(x)$ to avoid this situation.

If we put $k(x)=\sum\log p/p$ ($p$ prime, $\log p\leqq x$) and $s(x)=e^{-x}\vartheta(e^x)-1$, $\vartheta(u)=\sum\log p$ ($p\leqq u$), (*) becomes the kernel of Selberg's proof, and this deduction of the prime number theorem is essentially the same as Selberg's. [For a general account, see § 6.3 of the author's *Tauberian theorems*, Oxford Univ. Press, London, 1958.]

*S. Ikehara* (Tokyo)

Citations: MR 10, 595b = N20-3.

## N20-40 (21# 4135)

**Ehlich, Hartmut. Ein elementarer Beweis des Primzahlsatzes für binäre quadratische Formen.** J. Reine Angew. Math. **201** (1959), 1–36.

The author gives an elementary proof of the prime number theorem for quadratic forms, namely:

$$\pi(x, D, f)\sim\frac{x}{\varepsilon h(\log x)},$$

where $h=h(D)$ is the number of classes of equivalent primitive forms of discriminant $D$, $f=au^2+buv+cv^2$, $D=b^2-4ac$, $\varepsilon$ is 1 or 2 according as $f$ is non-ambiguous or ambiguous, and $\pi(x, D, f)$ denotes the number of primes not greater than $x$ which are represented by the form. The proof uses in no sense obvious analogues of some results of Selberg.

An immediate consequence of this result is Dirichlet's theorem that an infinite number of primes are represented by any primitive binary form, for which an elementary proof was given by W. E. Briggs [Canad. J. Math. **6** (1954), 353–363; MR **16**, 117]. The author points to an "error" in Briggs' paper, which seems really to be a misinterpretation of the following sums of Briggs:

$$\sum\omega_n=\sum\lambda_d\sum 1,$$

where the first sum is over all $n\leqq x$, $n=f$, $(n, 2D)=1$, the third sum is over all divisors of $n$ with the above restrictions on $n$ and the second sum is over all $d\leqq x$ with $(d, 2D)=1$; $\lambda_d=\mu(d)\log^2(x/d)$ and $\omega_n$ is the sum of $\lambda_d$ over the divisors, $d$, of $n$. The author draws unwarranted and incorrect conclusions from Briggs' results. But the author's proof of the prime number theorem seems to be valid. *B. W. Jones* (Mayaguez, P.R.)

Citations: MR 16, 117b = N20-20.

## N20-41 (21# 4138)

**Amitsur, S. A. On arithmetic functions.** J. Analyse Math. **5** (1956/57), 273–314.

Verf. verallgemeinert den Selbergschen Beweis des Primzahlsatzes auf eine gewisse Klasse von arithmetischen Funktionen. Er benutzt die Beweisanordnungen von H. N. Shapiro [Ann. of Math. (2) **51** (1950), 485–497; **52** (1950), 217–230, 231–243; MR **11**, 419; **12**, 81] und K. Yamamoto [J. Math. Soc. Japan. **7** (1955), 424–434; MR **18**, 18]. Es wird dabei einer arithmetischen Funktion $g(n)$ eine durch

$$(S_g f)(x)=\sum_{n\leqq x} g(n)f\left(\frac{x}{n}\right)$$

definierte lineare Transformation im linearen Raum $\mathfrak{M}$ der für $x\geqq 1$ definierten und auf jedem endlichen Intervall beschränkten komplexwertigen Funktionen $f$ zugeordnet. Der Faltung ("convolution")

$$(g*h)(x)=\sum_{d|n} g(d)\,h\left(\frac{n}{d}\right)$$

zweier arithmetischer Funktionen $g$ und $h$ entspricht das Produkt der zu $g$ und $h$ gehörigen linearen Transformationen. Die Algebra der arithmetischen Funktionen (mit "Faltung" statt "gewöhnlicher Multiplikation") ist isomorph mit der Algebra $A$ der zugehörigen linearen Transformationen von $\mathfrak{M}$. Die Multiplikation einer arithmetischen Funktion mit $\log x$ (oder allgemeiner mit einer additiven Funktion) induziert in $A$ eine Ableitung ("derivation"). Verf. betrachtet jetzt den Teilraum $\mathfrak{L}$ von $\mathfrak{M}$, der aus allen Polynomen in $\log x$ besteht. Mit Hilfe eines symbolischen Kalküls erhält er (für die in Betracht kommenden arithmetischen Funktionen $g$) asymptotische Formeln für $I_g f$ (wo $I_g=S_{gx^{-1}}$), in denen die Hauptglieder Funktionen aus $\mathfrak{L}$ sind. Diese Formeln entsprechen der Selbergschen fundamentalen Ungleichung. Der Hauptsatz des Verf. verkörpert eine Verallgemeinerung des Verfahrens, mit dem Selberg den Primzahlsatz aus der fundamentalen Ungleichung herleitet. Er lautet folgendermaßen: Es sei $f$ eine beschränkte Funktion aus $\mathfrak{M}$ mit den folgenden Eigenschaften:

$$(1)\qquad |f(x)|\log x\leqq\sum_{n\leqq x}\Lambda(n)f\left(\frac{x}{n}\right)+o(\log x)$$

($\Lambda$ ist die aus der Primzahltheorie bekannte Faltung der Funktion $\mu$ von Moebius mit $\log x$); (2) Es gibt ein positives ganzes $k$ derart, daß

$$\sum_{n\leqq x}\left|f\left(\frac{x}{n}\right)-f\left(\frac{x}{n+1}\right)\right| = O(\log^k x);$$

(3) $\sum_{n\leqq x}f(n)/n=O(1)$; (4) $|f(tx)-f(x)|=o(1)$ falls $t\to 1$ und $x\to\infty$. Dann gilt $f(x)=o(1)$. Falls $f(x)=\sum_{n\leqq x}\mu(n)/n$ erhält man den Primzahlsatz. Verf. beweist auch den Dirichletschen Satz über Primzahlen in einer arithmetischen Progression. *H. D. Kloosterman* (Zbl **81**, 43)

Citations: MR 11, 419e = N20-7; MR 12, 81a = N20-11; MR 12, 81b = N20-12; MR 18, 18d = N20-34.

Referred to in A22-49, N20-47, N20-48, N80-9, R44-31.

**N20-42** **(22# 2581)**

**Shapiro, Harold N. Tauberian theorems and elementary prime number theory.** Comm. Pure Appl. Math. **12** (1959), 579–610.

A. Selberg proved the celebrated formula

$$(1)\qquad \sum_{p\leqq x}(\log p)^2+\sum_{pq\leqq x}\log p\log q = 2x\log x+O(x)$$

in an elementary way and Selberg [Ann. of Math. (2) **50** (1949), 305–313; MR **10**, 595] and the reviewer [Proc. Nat. Acad. Sci. U.S.A. **35** (1949), 374–385; MR **10**, 595] deduced the prime number theorem $\vartheta(x)=x+o(x)$ from (1) in an elementary way. To analyse the relation of (1) and the prime number theorem the reviewer proved [J. Indian Math. Soc. (N.S.) **13** (1949), 131–144; MR **11**, 420] that if $1<p_1<p_2<\cdots$ is any sequence of real numbers satisfying (1) then

$$(2)\qquad \frac{1}{x}\sum_{p_i\leqq x}\log p_i = 1+o(1)$$

(i.e., it was not assumed that $\sum_{p_i\leqq x}\log p_i>cx$ as in the proof of the prime number theorem). The proof of (2) was very complicated. The author first of all gives a simpler proof of (2).

The reviewer also asked the following question: Assume that $1<p_1<p_2<\cdots$ is any sequence of real numbers which satisfies (1) with an error term $o(x\log x)$. Does this weakened form of (1) also imply (2)? The reviewer was unable to answer this question. The author answers this question affirmatively; his proof is elementary but fairly complicated.

Some other related questions are also discussed.

*P. Erdős* (Budapest)

Citations: MR 10, 595b = N20-3; MR 10, 595c = N20-3; MR 11, 420a = N20-8.

**N20-43** **(22# 4685)**

**Breusch, Robert. An elementary proof of the prime number theorem with remainder term.** Pacific J. Math. **10** (1960), 487–497.

The author proves the prime number theorem with error term, in an elementary but fairly complicated way. He proves that

$$(1)\qquad \sum_{p^m\leqq x}\frac{\log p}{p^m} = \log x+a_x,$$

where $a_x=-A_0+o((\log x)^{-1/6+\epsilon})$ and $A_0$ is Euler's constant; as is well known, (1) implies

$$\vartheta(x) = \sum_{p\leqq x}\log p = x+o(x(\log x)^{-1/6+\epsilon}).$$

He uses an asymptotic formula similar to the celebrated formula of A. Selberg.

{For other elementary proofs of the prime number theorem see Selberg [Ann. of Math. (2) **50** (1949), 305–313; MR **10**, 595] and Erdös [Proc. Nat. Acad. Sci. U.S.A. **35** (1949), 374–384; MR **10**, 595]; for the prime number theorem with an error term see P. Kuhn [Math. Scand. **3** (1955), 75–89; MR **17**, 587] and Van der Corput [Colloque sur la Théorie des Nombres (Bruxelles, 1955), pp. 163–182, Georges Thone, Liège, 1956; MR **18**, 112].}

*P. Erdös* (Budapest)

Citations: MR 10, 595b = N20-3; MR 10, 595c = N20-3; MR 17, 587d = N20-27; MR 18, 112a = N20-36.

Referred to in N20-52, N20-53, N20-58, N20-65, N20-71.

**N20-44** **(23# A1618)**

**Ehlich, Hartmut**

**Über die elementaren Beweise der Primzahlsätze.**

*J. Reine Angew. Math.* **203** (1960), 143–153.

Since P. Erdös and A. Selberg have proved the prime-number theorem in an elementary way, successful attempts have been made to give alternative proofs, as well as to supply proofs for similar questions, e.g., those concerning the prime-ideal theorem and the prime-number theorem for primitive binary quadratic forms. All such proofs consist of two parts: (1) a proof of the so-called Selberg formula (or its analogue); (2) a process of iteration leading to the particular prime-number theorem. The present author gives two general theorems (proving them in a rather simple way) which enable one to settle the second part simultaneously for all cases considered.

*S. Knapowski* (Poznań)

**N20-45** **(24# A1892)**

**Kasara, I. Ja.**

**Linear operators and their applications in number theory. (Russian. Uzbek summary)**

*Izv. Akad. Nauk UzSSR Ser. Fiz.-Mat.* **1961**, *no.* 2, 33–40.

Define $a_n$ and $b_n$ by

$$F(s) = \sum_1^\infty a_n/n^s,\quad F'(s)/F(s) = -\zeta(s)+1,$$

$$\Phi(s) = \sum_1^\infty b_n/n^s,\quad \Phi'(s)/\Phi(s) = \zeta(s)-1,$$

where $\zeta(s)$ is Riemann's zeta function. We may then define $Lf(x)=\sum_{n\leqq x}a_nf(x/n)$, $L^{-1}f(x)=\sum_{n\leqq x}b_nf(x/n)$ and $\tau f(x)=f(x)\log_e x+\sum_{n\leqq x}f(x/n)$. The author proves

$$(1)\qquad \tau f(x) = L^{-1}[(\log x+1)Lf(x)].$$

The author's applications of (1) to the prime number theorem and Selberg's fundamental lemma are heuristic, not rigorous, proofs of these theorems.

*S. Chowla* (Boulder, Colo.)

**N20-46** **(25# 2048)**

**Levin, B. V.**

**On the distribution of primes of an arithmetic progression. (Russian. Uzbek summary)**

*Izv. Akad. Nauk UzSSR Ser. Fiz.-Mat. Nauk* **1961**, *no.* 5, 15–28.

The fundamental publications of Erdős and Selberg on the elementary theory of prime numbers were followed by a number of papers offering extensions, variants, and refinements of their ideas. In particular, P. Kuhn [Math. Scand. **3** (1955), 75–89; MR **17**, 587] gave an elementary proof of the prime number with an explicit error term by proving the relation

$$\pi(x) = \frac{x}{\log x} + O\left\{\frac{x}{(\log x)^{11/10}}\right\}.$$

In the present paper, a simplification of Kuhn's method enables the author to deal with the problem of the distribution of primes in arithmetic progressions and to prove that

$$\pi(x; k, l) = \frac{1}{\phi(k)}\frac{x}{\log x} + O\left\{\frac{x}{(\log x)^{1.14}}\right\},$$

where the $O$-constant depends on $k$. A noteworthy feature of the argument, which is entirely elementary, is its independence of the theory of Dirichlet characters and, indeed, of the notion of a complex number. In this respect the present treatment differs decisively from all earlier discussions of the problem. *L. Mirsky* (Sheffield)

Citations: MR 17, 587d = N20-27.

**N20-47** **(26# 67)**

**Amitsur, S. A.**

**Some results on arithmetic functions.**

*J. Math. Soc. Japan* **11** (1959), 275–290.

Let $g(n)$ denote a function defined for all positive integers $n$. To $g(n)$ corresponds the linear operator $I_g(f)$ defined by

$$(I_g f)(x) = \sum_{n\leq x} \frac{g(n)}{n} f\left(\frac{x}{n}\right).$$

Let $G(D)=\sum_{r=-p}^{\infty} g_r D^r$ be a power series in $D$ with only a finite number of negative exponents; here $D$ stands for $d/d\log x$. The notation $I_g = G(D)+O(\phi_u)$ means $I_g \log^n x - G(D)\log^n x = O(\phi_n(x))$. In a previous paper [J. Analyse Math. **5** (1956/57), 273–314; MR **21** #4138], the author showed that

$$(*)\qquad I_g I_h = G(D)H(D)+O(\rho_n).$$

However, the bound obtained for $\rho_n$ was not symmetric in $g$ and $h$; moreover, the product $G(D)H(D)$ had to be computed as $G(D)[H(D)f]$ and not by the ordinary product of the power series $[G(D)H(D)]f$. In the present paper a more satisfactory bound for $\rho_n$ is obtained; also, it is proved that in (*) the product $G(D)H(D)$ is in the ring of power series in $D$. Unfortunately, the main result is too complicated to permit brief quotation.

As an application, a number of asymptotic formulas are obtained, in particular, for $\sum_{n\leq x} d(n)/n$, $\sum_{n\leq x} d^2(n)/n$, $\sum_{n\leq x} |\mu(n)|/n$; the error terms are $O(x^\beta)$, where $\beta = -\frac{1}{2}$, $-\frac{1}{6}+\varepsilon$, $-\frac{1}{3}$, respectively.

The second part of the paper improves the main theorem of the earlier paper [loc. cit.]. In particular, an asymptotic formula is obtained for $\sum_{n\leq x} n^{-1}\Lambda_2(n)\log(x/n)$, where $\Lambda_2 = \mu * \log^2 x$ (the function used in Selberg's formula).

*L. Carlitz* (Durham, N.C.)

Citations: MR 21# 4138 = N20-41.

Referred to in N20-48.

**N20-48** **(26# 1290)**

**Amitsur, S. A.**

**On a lemma in elementary proofs of the prime number theorem.**

*Bull. Res. Council Israel Sect. F* **10F**, 101–108 (1962).

In three previous papers concerning the elementary proof of the prime number theorem and related questions [J. Analyse Math. **5** (1956/57), 273–314; MR **21** #4138; J. Math. Soc. Japan **11** (1959), 275–290; MR **26** #67; Canad. J. Math. **13** (1961), 83–109; MR **23** #A1616] the author used a basic lemma in various forms. In this paper he proves a more general proposition that covers all the preceding forms of the lemma. This result, which is also interesting in itself, can be formulated as follows. Let $1\leq\beta_1\leq\beta_2\leq\cdots$ be a non-decreasing sequence and $\beta_\nu\to\infty$ as $\nu\to\infty$. Let $\{\alpha_\nu\}$ be a second sequence ($\alpha_\nu>0$). Put $N(x)=\sum_{\beta_\nu\leq x}\alpha_\nu$ and assume the following conditions:

$$N(\tau x)/N(x)\to 1 \text{ as } x\to\infty, \text{ for } \tau>\tau_0;$$

$$\inf_{x,y}\frac{N(tx)-N(x)}{N(Ty)-N(y)} > 0,$$

for $1<t<t_0$, $T>T_0$, $y\geq Y_0$, $y\leq x<tx\leq Ty$. Let $h(x)$ be a real function defined for $x\geq 1$, satisfying the conditions: $h(x)$ bounded in every finite interval; $h(tx)-h(x)\to 0$ as $(t, x)\to(1, \infty)$. Finally assume that

$$(*)\qquad h(x)G(x) = \sum_{\beta_\nu\leq x}\alpha_\nu h\left(\frac{x}{\beta_\nu}\right)+o(G(x)),$$

where $G(x)\sim N(x)$. Under these conditions the following result holds. Let $\{z_\nu\}$ be a non-decreasing sequence of real numbers with $z_\nu\to\infty$ and $\limsup(z_{\nu+1}/z_\nu)<\infty$; then $\lim h(x)=\lim h(z_\nu)$ if $\lim h(z_\nu)$ exists. By assuming the condition (*) in different weaker forms, analogous propositions can be obtained, which concern the lim sup $h(x)$ and the lim inf $h(x)$. Several interesting consequences are deduced and some connected questions are also treated.

*M. Cugiani* (Milan)

Citations: MR 21# 4138 = N20-41; MR 23# A1616 = N80-9; MR 26# 67 = N20-47.

Referred to in N20-49.

**N20-49** **(38# 4390)**

**Amitsur, S. A.**

**Correction to "Arithmetic linear transformations".**

*Canad. J. Math.* **21** (1969), 1–5.

Verfasser korrigiert einige Aussagen, Beweise und Druckfehler früherer Arbeiten [dasselbe J. **13** (1961), 83–109; MR **23** #A1616; Bull. Res. Council Israel Sect. F **10F**, 101–108 (1962); MR **26** #1290].

Ein grundlegender Hilfssatz, aus dem er früher Folgerungen im Hinblick auf seinen elementaren Beweis des Primzahlsatzes und auf Primzahlen in arithmetischen Progressionen gezogen hat, läßt sich in der allgemeinen Form nicht aufrecht erhalten [vgl. P. R. Ahern, Trans. Amer. Math. Soc. **118** (1965), 221–242; MR **31** #4771], jedoch wird er in der vorliegenden Arbeit in modifizierter Gestalt bewiesen. Glücklicherweise bleiben die Hauptergebnisse der früheren Arbeiten mit diesem abgeänderten Hilfssatz beweisbar. *H. J. Kanold* (Braunschweig)

Citations: MR 23# A1616 = N80-9; MR 26# 1290 = N20-48; MR 31# 4771 = R44-31.

**N20-50** **(26# 2416)**

**Nevanlinna, Veikko**

**Über den elementaren Beweis des Primzahlsatzes.**

*Soc. Sci. Fenn. Comment. Phys.-Math.* **27** (1962), *no.* 3, 8 *pp.*

The author gives a surprisingly simple elementary proof of the prime number theorem. Put $\psi(x)=\sum_{p\leq x}\log p$, $r(x)=e^{-x}\psi(e^x)-1$. From Selberg's well-known asymptotic formula the author deduces

$$(1)\qquad |r(x)| \leq \frac{1}{x}\int_0^x |r(t)|\,dt+o(1).$$

He further uses the well-known result of Mertens in the form $\int_0^x \psi|t|/t^2=\log x+O(1)$ and deduces

$$(2)\qquad \left|\int_u^v r(t)\,dt\right| < c$$

for every $0<u<v$, where $c$ is an absolute constant. Using

Chebyshev's result $\psi(x) < c_1x$ the author deduces from (1) and (2) by elementary Tauberian arguments $r(x) = o(x)$, which is the prime number theorem.

The proof is similar to that given by E. M. Wright [see G. H. Hardy and E. M. Wright, *An introduction to the theory of numbers*, 3rd ed., Clarendon, Oxford, 1954; MR **16**, 673], but is in the opinion of the reviewer somewhat simpler.

*P. Erdős* (London)

Citations: MR 16, 673b = Z01-28.
Referred to in N20-57, N20-65.

**N20-51** **(27# 117)**

**Dusumbetov, A.**

**An elementary proof of the asymptotic law for the distribution of prime numbers.** **(Russian. Uzbek summary)**

*Izv. Akad. Nauk UzSSR Ser. Fiz.-Mat. Nauk* **1963**, *no.* 2, 24–31.

Using the "fundamental lemma" of A. Selberg, the author improves P. Kuhn's estimate of the difference $\sum_{p\leq x} \log p - x$ from $O(x(\log x)^{-1/10})$ to $O(x(\log x)^{-1+\varepsilon})$, where $\varepsilon$ is an arbitrary positive number [see Kuhn's paper, Math. Scand. **3** (1955), 75–89; MR **17**, 587].

*S. Chowla* (Boulder, Colo.)

Citations: MR 17, 587d = N20-27.

**N20-52** **(27# 119)**

**Wirsing, Eduard**

**Elementare Beweise des Primzahlsatzes mit Restglied. I.**

*J. Reine Angew. Math.* **211** (1962), 205–214.

An elementary proof of the prime number theorem was first given by P. Erdős and A. Selberg [P. Erdős, Proc. Nat. Acad. Sci. U.S.A. **35** (1949), 374–384; MR **10**, 595; A. Selberg, Ann. of Math. (2) **50** (1949), 305–313; MR **10**, 595], by showing the relation $\psi(x) \sim x$. Later this relation was replaced by

(*) $$\psi(x) = x + O(x/\log^m x)$$

with $m = 1/200$ [J. G. van der Corput, Colloq. Théorie Nombres (Bruxelles, 1955), pp. 163–182; G. Thone, Liège, 1956; MR **18**, 112] with $m = 1/10$ [P. Kuhn, Math. Scand. **3** (1955), 75–89; MR **17**, 587] with $m = 1/6$ [R. Breusch, Pacific J. Math. **10** (1960), 487–497; MR **22** #4685].

In this paper it is proved that (*) holds with $m = 3/4$ and it is announced that (*) is true for every large $m$. The proof is quite elementary. The main tool is the celebrated Selberg lemma and a very nice geometrical lemma.

In a footnote the author mentions that P. Erdős has pointed out to him a private communication by E. Bombieri who claims to have proved by a similar method the same result for every $m$ (see also E. Bombieri [#120 below]).

*M. Cugiani* (Milan)

Citations: MR 10, 595b = N20-3; MR 10, 595c = N20-3; MR 17, 587d = N20-27; MR 18, 112a = N20-36; MR 22# 4685 = N20-43.
Referred to in N20-56, N20-58.

**N20-53** **(27# 120)**

**Bombieri, Enrico**

**Maggiorazione del resto nel "Primzahlsatz" col metodo di Erdős-Selberg.**

*Ist. Lombardo Accad. Sci. Lett. Rend. A* **96** (1962), 343–350.

In the 1949 papers by Selberg [Ann. of Math. (2) **50** (1949), 297–304; MR **10**, 595; ibid. **50** (1949), 305–313; MR **10**, 595] and Erdős [Proc. Nat. Acad. Sci. U.S.A. **35** (1949), 374–384; MR **10**, 595] the prime number theorem was proven by elementary methods in the form of an asymptotic equality, without estimation of an error term. Breusch [Pacific J. Math. **10** (1960), 487–497; MR **22** #4685; see also Kuhn, Math. Scand. **3** (1955), 75–89; MR **17**, 587] showed by elementary methods that $\theta(x) = x + O(x(\log x)^{\varepsilon - 1/6})$. The present paper contains a sketch of an elementary proof of (*) $\theta(x) = x + O(x \log^{-m} x)$ for any constant $m$. It should be mentioned that the same result has been obtained by Wirsing [#119 above], and that Jurkat has even announced the elementary proof of (*) with an error term $O(x \exp(-c_1 \log^{c_2} x))$ [Internat. Congr. Math. (Stockholm, 1962)]. The present author uses Amitsur's [Canad. J. Math. **13** (1961), 83–109; MR **23** #A1616] approach and notations. If $f(n)$ is an arithmetic function and $\varphi(x)$ is defined for $x \geqq 1$, set $S_f\varphi = \sum_{n\leq x} f(n)\varphi(x/n)$. Concepts of order and weight of $S_f$ are introduced and the class of transformations $S_f$ of order $\leqq h$ and weight $\leqq m$ is denoted by $\mathfrak{G}_{h,m}$. Besides usual notations like $f * g(n) = \sum_{hk=n} f(h)g(k)$, $\mu$ (Möbius function), $\Lambda$ (von Mangoldt function), the author also defines $L^k = \log^k x$, $\Lambda_k = \mu * L^k$ (observe that $\Lambda_1 = \mu * L = \Lambda$) and $V_k(\eta, f) = e^{-\eta}/k! S_f L^k(e^\eta))$. It is shown that (*) is equivalent to $V_0(\eta, \Lambda - 1) = O(\eta^{-N})$, valid for all $N$. The latter inequality is proven, using among others a generalized version of the Selberg formula, which, in the present terminology, reads: from $h \geqq 1$ and $S_g \in \mathfrak{G}_{h,m}$ follows $S_{gL^{n+1}} + h\binom{h+n}{n} S_{\Lambda L^n} S_g \in \mathfrak{G}_{h+n,m+n+1}$.

*E. Grosswald* (Philadelphia, Pa.)

Citations: MR 10, 595b = N20-3; MR 10, 595c = N20-3; MR 17, 587d = N20-27; MR 22# 4685 = N20-43; MR 23# A1616 = N80-9.
Referred to in R44-42.

**N20-54** **(27# 2491)**

**Dusumbetov, A.**

**An elementary proof of the asymptotic law of the distribution of primes in an arithmetic progression.** **(Russian. Uzbek summary)**

*Izv. Akad. Nauk UzSSR Ser. Fiz.-Mat. Nauk* **1963**, *no.* 3, 5–12.

The author gives another proof of the theorem mentioned in the title. With the usual notation his result is that

$$\sum_{\substack{n\leq x \\ n\equiv l (\mathrm{mod}\ k)}} \Lambda(n) = \frac{x}{\varphi(k)} + O(x \log^{-1+\varepsilon} x),$$

where $(l, k) = 1$, and $\varepsilon > 0$ is arbitrary.

*S. Chowla* (University Park, Pa.)

**N20-55** **(27# 4804)**

**Bombieri, Enrico**

**Sulle formule di A. Selberg generalizzate per classi di funzioni aritmetiche e le applicazioni al problema del resto nel "Primzahlsatz".** **(English summary)**

*Riv. Mat. Univ. Parma* (2) **3** (1962), 393–440.

Author's summary: "Using the elementary method of Erdős and Selberg, one proves the result $\vartheta(x) = x + O(x/\log^m x)$ for every $m$."

*S. W. Golomb* (La Canada, Calif.)

Referred to in N20-56, N20-71.

**N20-56** **(29# 3457)**

**Wirsing, Eduard**

**Elementare Beweise des Primzahlsatzes mit Restglied. II.**

*J. Reine Angew. Math.* **214/215** (1964), 1–18.

The author continues his researches concerning the elementary proof of the prime number theorem; the formula

(1) $$\psi(x) = x+O(x/\log^{\alpha}x)$$

is now proved for every $\alpha$ as announced in a previous paper [same J. **211** (1962), 205–214; MR **27** #119]. The author also sketches the proof of the corresponding result concerning primes in an arithmetical progression.

The main tool in the proof is an analogue of the celebrated Selberg formula. If we set

(2) $$\rho(x) = \sum_{n \leqq \exp x} \left(\frac{1}{n} - \frac{\Lambda(n)}{n}\right) - 2C,$$

the fundamental result in the paper is the proof that

(3) $$\rho(x) = O(x^{-\alpha}) \quad \text{for every } \alpha,$$

from which (1) can be easily deduced.

The author follows in the proof a cyclic method. From (3) he deduces the relations:

(4) $$\rho(x) = \frac{1}{x}\int_{0-}^{x} \rho(x-y)\,d\rho(y)+O(x^{-\beta}),$$
$$|\rho(x)-\rho(y)| \leqq |x-y|+O(x^{-\beta})$$

for $\beta<\alpha+1$, and from (4) he can also deduce (3) with $\beta$ instead of $\alpha$. The deduction of (3) from (4) is given only for a certain $\alpha'>\beta-1$. The proof for $\alpha=\beta$ is only briefly sketched.

The proof of (1) for every $\alpha$, as is pointed out by the author, was obtained at the same time by E. Bombieri following a different method founded on an important extension of the Selberg formula [Riv. Mat. Univ. Parma (2) **3** (1962), 393–440; MR **27** #4804]. *M. Cugiani* (Milan)

Citations: MR 27# 119 = N20-52; MR 27# 4804 = N20-55.

Referred to in N20-71, N36-63, N80-35, R44-42.

## N20-57 (29# 5800)

**Nevanlinna, Veikko**

**Über die elementaren Beweise der Primzahlsätze und deren äquivalente Fassungen.**

*Ann. Acad. Sci. Fenn. Ser. A I No.* 343 (1964), 52 *pp.*

The prime number theorem (PNT) asserts that

(I) $$\pi(x) \sim x/\log x, \qquad x\to\infty,$$

where $\pi(x)$ is the number of primes $p\leqq x$. (I) is known to be equivalent to the following assertions:

(II) $$\vartheta(x) \sim x, \qquad x\to\infty,$$

where $\vartheta(x)$ denotes the sum $\vartheta(x)=\sum_{p\leqq x}\log p$, and

(III) $$\psi(x) = \sum_{p^{\nu}\leqq x}\log p = \sum_{n\leqq x}\Lambda(n) \sim x, \qquad x\to\infty,$$

where the function $\Lambda(n)$ is defined as being $\log p$ when $n$ is a prime $p$ or one of its powers and 0 otherwise [e.g., A. E. Ingham, *The distribution of prime numbers*, p. 13, Cambridge Univ. Press, London, 1932].

All previous proofs up to 1948 have been by "transcendental" arguments involving some appeal to the theory of functions of a complex variable, but then A. Selberg and P. Erdős [see, e.g., J. G. van der Corput, Math. Centrum Amsterdam Scriptum No. 1 (1948); MR **10**, 597] succeeded in producing an elementary proof of the PNT, not depending on analytical ideas remote from the problem itself. In various versions elementary proofs were given by A. Selberg [Ann. of Math. (2) **50** (1949), 305–313; MR **10**, 595], P. Erdős [Proc. Nat. Acad. Sci. U.S.A. **35** (1949), 374–384; MR **10**, 595], and others.

The purpose of this paper is essentially to give a simple elementary proof of the PNT and to deduce its equivalent formulas while exhibiting the parallelism running through the proofs. The starting point in the first chapter of this paper is Selberg's asymptotic formula:

(a) $$\rho(x)\log x+\int_{1-}^{x+}\rho(x/t)\,d\psi(t) = O(x) \quad (\rho(x)=\psi(x)-x),$$

which is effected to this form from Selberg's original formula through application of the method of T. Tatuzawa and K. Iseki [Proc. Japan Acad. **27** (1951), 340–342; MR **13**, 725]. The PNT is then deduced first by eliminating the differential $d\psi$ to get Selberg's inequality:

(b) $$|\rho(x)|\log^2 x \leqq 2\int_1^x |\rho(x/t)|\log t\,dt+O(x\log x).$$

After the substitution of $r(x)=e^{-x}\rho(e^x)=e^{-x}\psi(e^x)-1$ the author deduces from this inequality by elementary arguments $r(x)=o(1)$, which is equivalent to the PNT [Soc. Sci. Fenn. Comment. Phys.-Math. **27** (1962), no. 3; MR **26** #2416].

The second chapter starts with the following notations:

$$\varepsilon(x) = \int_{1-}^{x+} d\psi(t)/t-\log x+C,$$
$$M(x) = \sum_{n\leqq x}\mu(n),$$
$$B(x) = \sum_{n\leqq x}\mu(n)/n = \int_{1-}^{x+} dM(t)/t,$$

where $C$ is the Euler constant, and $\mu$ denotes the Möbius function. Then it is shown that as $x\to\infty$

(IV) $$\varepsilon(x) = o(1),$$

(V) $$M(x) = o(x),$$

(VI) $$B(x) = o(1)$$

are each equivalent to the formula (III). Selberg's asymptotic formula is derived for the function $\varepsilon(x)$, and through the use of the ideas of Pitt [*Tauberian theorems*, Oxford Univ. Press, London, 1958; MR **21** #5109] and Selberg, a new variant of Selberg's proof is given. The equivalence of (III), (IV), (V), and (VI) is proved by showing the logical relations among them. It is shown that if $\rho(x)$ in (a) and (b) is replaced by $M(x)$ or $B(x)$, then an almost complete analogy for the asymptotic expression and inequality of Selberg holds.

In the third chapter the author deduces the PNT for arithmetical progressions corresponding to (I), (II), and (III), which was first proved in an elementary way by Selberg [Canad. J. Math. **2** (1950), 66–78; MR **11**, 419]. Here again, the lemma of Tatuzawa and Iseki is used to derive Selberg's asymptotic formula and inequality. Then the method in the chapter is carried out, resulting in the almost complete analogy with the first chapter. Finally, an elementary proof is given of Dirichlet's theorem about primes in arithmetic progressions [cf., e.g., A. Selberg, Ann. of Math. (2) **50** (1949), 297–304; MR **10**, 595].

*S. Ikehara* (Tokyo)

Citations: MR 10, 595a = N20-2; MR 10, 595b = N20-3; MR 10, 595c = N20-3; MR 10, 597a = N20-4; MR 11, 419c = N20-6; MR 13, 725f = N20-14; MR 21# 5109 = M45-34; MR 26# 2416 = N20-50.

## N20-58 (31# 2223)

**Levinson, N.**

**A variant of the Selberg inequality.**

*Proc. London Math. Soc.* (3) **14a** (1965), 191–198.

A. Selberg's elementary proof of the prime number theorem [Ann. of Math. (2) **50** (1949), 305–313; MR **10**, 595] was based on the inequality

$$\psi(x)\log x+\sum_{n\leq x}\Lambda(n)\psi(x/n) = 2x\log x+O(x),$$

where $\Lambda(n)=\log p$ for $n=p^k$ ($p$ prime, $k=1, 2, \cdots$), $\Lambda(n)=0$ for other $n$ and $\psi(x)=\sum_{n\leq x}\Lambda(n)$. Other inequalities for similar purposes were proved by R. Breusch [Pacific J. Math. **10** (1960), 487–497; MR **22** #4685] and E. Wirsing [J. Reine Angew. Math. **211** (1962), 205–214; MR **27** #119]. In the present paper, an elementary proof of the inequality

$$\psi(x)+\sigma\sum_{n\leq x}n^{-\sigma}\Lambda(n)\psi(x/n) = 2x+O(\sigma x+x^{1-\sigma}),\quad 0\leq\sigma\leq\tfrac{1}{2}$$

is given. *E. Fogels* (Riga)

Citations: MR 10, 595b = N20-3; MR 22# 4685 = N20-43; MR 27# 119 = N20-52.

## N20-59 (32# 98 )

**Bang, Thøger S. V.**

**An inequality for real functions of a real variable and its application to the prime number theorem.**

*On Approximation Theory* (*Proceedings of Conference in Oberwolfach*, 1963), *pp.* 155–160. *Birkhäuser, Basel*, 1964.

The author uses the isoperimetric inequality to estimate a Stieltjes integral. He then applies his result to give a variant of an elementary proof of the prime number theorem. *S. Knapowski* (Gainesville, Fla.)

## N20-60 (32# 5615 )

**Rieger, G. J.**

**Zur Selbergschen Gleichung für die arithmetische Progression.**

*Elem. Math.* **20** (1965), 36–39.

The proof of Selberg's formula by Tatuzawa and Iseki [Proc. Japan Acad. **27** (1951), 340–342; MR **13**, 725] is adapted to give a simple proof of

$$\psi(x;k,l)\log x+\sum_{n\leq x,\,(n,k)=1}\psi\left\{\frac{x}{n};k,ln'\right\}\Lambda(n) = \frac{2}{\varphi(k)}\cdot x\log x+O(x),$$

where $(l,k)=1$, $nn'\equiv 1 \bmod k$.

{In the formulation of the result (Formula (3)), read $(n,k)=1$ instead of $n\equiv l \bmod k$.}

*W. Schwarz* (Freiburg)

Citations: MR 13, 725f = N20-14.

## N20-61 (35# 1561 )

**Koshiba, Zen'ichirô; Uchiyama, Saburô**

**On the existence of prime numbers in arithmetic progressions.**

*Proc. Japan Acad.* **42** (1966), 696–701.

Let $k$, $l$ be integers with $k>0$, $(l,k)=1$, and let $p$, $q$ run over primes. An elementary proof of the familiar result

(1) $\sum_{p\leq x;\,p\equiv l\,(\mathrm{mod}\,k)}p^{-1}\log p\sim\log x/\varphi(k)\quad(x\to\infty)$

is obtained by way of Selberg's formula

(2) $$\sum_{p\leq x;\,p\equiv l\,(\mathrm{mod}\,k)}p^{-1}\log^2 p+\sum_{pq\leq x;\,pq\equiv l\,(\mathrm{mod}\,k)}(pq)^{-1}\log p\log q = (\log^2 x)/\varphi(k)+O(\log x)$$

and the fact that (3) for $l=1$, the left-hand side of (1) is greater than $c\log x$ for $x>x_0$, where $c=c(k)>0$. By grouping terms into blocks $e^\nu\leq p<e^{\nu+1}$ ($\nu=0, 1, \cdots$) and introducing certain power series in $e^{-s}$ with coefficients involving characters $\chi$ (mod $k$), the authors link (2) with the differential equation $y'-y^2=-2\varepsilon s^{-2}+O(s^{-1})$ ($s\downarrow 0$), where $y'\equiv dy/ds$ and $\varepsilon=\varepsilon(\chi)$ is 1 if $\chi$ is the principal character and 0 otherwise. Supplementing a result of Korevaar [Bull. Amer. Math. Soc. **62** (1956), 42] with one of their own (Lemma 2), they conclude that $y=as^{-1}+O(\log s^{-1})$, $a=\varepsilon$ or $-1-\varepsilon$. The second alternative is excluded by (3), and an analogue of (1) for Abel means is deduced; whence (1) itself follows by the Abel-Tauber theorem of Hardy and Littlewood on power series with positive coefficients. The authors note that (3) still serves its purpose if $c\log x$ is replaced by $(\log\log x)^\alpha$ with a fixed $\alpha>1$. *A. E. Ingham* (Cambridge, England)

## N20-62 (35# 2837 )

**Nevanlinna, Veikko**

**A refinement of Selberg's asymptotic equation.**

*Pacific J. Math.* **21** (1967), 537–540.

The author gives a refinement of Selberg's asymptotic equation in the elementary proofs of the prime number theorem [A. Selberg, Ann. of Math. (2) **50** (1949), 305–313; MR **10**, 595; P. Erdős, Proc. Nat. Acad. Sci. U.S.A. **35** (1949), 374–384; MR **10**, 595]. The method is based on the lemma of T. Tatuzawa and K. Iseki [Proc. Japan Acad. **27** (1951), 340–342; MR **13**, 725], and, assuming the prime number theorem, on an estimation of remainder integral more áccurate than earlier ones. *S. Ikehara* (Tokyo)

Citations: MR 10, 595b = N20-3; MR 10, 595c = N20-3; MR 13, 725f = N20-14.

## N20-63 (35# 2839 )

**Corrádi, K. A.**

**A remark on the theory of multiplicative functions.**

*Acta Sci. Math.* (*Szeged*) **28** (1967), 83–92.

The main theorem of this paper is a generalization of a result used by E. M. Wright [Proc. Roy. Soc. Edinburgh Sect. A **63** (1952), 257–267; MR **14**, 137] in his modification of the elementary proof of the prime number theorem. The theorem is as follows. Let $f(n)$ be a number-theoretic function which takes the three values 0, 1, $-1$ only, and suppose that $f(n)$ is multiplicative, so that $f(mn)=f(m)f(n)$ when $(m,n)=1$. Let $k$ be a positive integer. Suppose that there exists a natural number $l$ for which $l\leq k$ and $(l,k)=1$ and the relation $\sum_{n\leq x,n\equiv l(\mathrm{mod}\,k)}f(n)/n=O(1)$ is satisfied. Then for all $u$ with $1\leq u\leq k$, $(u,k)=1$, the relation $\sum_{n\leq x,n\equiv u(\mathrm{mod}\,k)}f(n)=o(x)$ holds. The case $k=1$, $l=1$, $f(n)=\mu(n)$, where $\mu(n)$ is the Möbius function, leads to the following equivalent formulation of the prime number theorem: $\sum_{n\leq x}\mu(n)=o(x)$. The author's method of proof shows a great formal similarity to that of Wright. However, the two methods differ in the way some of the original formulas of A. Selberg [Canad. J. Math. **2** (1950), 66–78; MR **11**, 419] are extended. The author observes "that the result of the paper does not seem to be obtainable by analytical methods, thus in this case elementary methods seem to go further than those of the theory of functions". *A. L. Whiteman* (Princeton, N.J.)

Citations: MR 11, 419c = N20-6; MR 14, 137d = N20-16.

## N20-64 (35# 6614 )

**Evelyn, C. J. A.**

**Relations between arithmetical functions.**

*Proc. Cambridge Philos. Soc.* **63** (1967), 1027–1029.

Let $S_h(x)=\sum_{d\leq x}\lambda(d)[\log(x/d)]^h$, where $\sum_{d|m}\lambda(d)=1$ or 0, according as $m$ is or is not an $N$th power, $N$ being a fixed positive integer.

For $h=0$ and 1, the author proves that if $T$ runs through all natural numbers $\leq x$, which are not divisible by an $N$th power $>1$, then (*) $\sum_T S_h(x/T) = (\log x)^h$. The reviewer [Scripta Math. **19** (1953), 121–126; MR **15**, 201] had considered sums of the form

$$f_h(x, n) = \sum_{d|n} \lambda(d)[\log (x/d)]^h.$$

For $N=0$, $\lambda(d)$ becomes the Möbius function and (*) still holds, $T$ of course running through all natural numbers $\leq x$, in this case. *H. Gupta* (Allahabad)

Citations: MR 15, 201e = N20-18.

## N20-65 (36# 1398 )

**Levinson, N.**

**On the elementary proof of the prime number theorem.**

*Proc. Edinburgh Math. Soc.* (2) **15** (1966/67), 141–146.

The author gives a simple and elementary proof of the prime number theorem. The proof is similar to the proof of Wright and Nevanlinna [E. M. Wright, Proc. Roy. Soc. Edinburgh Sect. A **63** (1952), 257–267; MR **14**, 137; V. Nevanlinna, Soc. Sci. Fenn. Comment. Phys.-Math. **27** (1962), no. 3; MR **26** #2416]. Put $R(x) = \psi(x) - x$, $S(y) = \int_2^y (R(x)/x)\,dx$. The author deduces from Selberg's inequality that

$$(*) \quad \log^2 y|S(y)| \leq 2\int_2^y (\log u)|S(y/u)|\,du + cy\log y$$

and deduces from (*) the prime number theorem in a way similar to that of Nevanlinna (see also R. Breusch [Pacific J. Math. **10** (1960), 487–497; MR **22** #4685]). *P. Erdős* (Budapest)

Citations: MR 14, 137d = N20-16; MR 22# 4685 = N20-43; MR 26# 2416 = N20-50.

Referred to in N20-67.

## N20-66 (36# 2574 )

**Kalecki, M.**

**A simple elementary proof of $M(x) = \sum_{n\leq x} \mu(n) = o(x)$.**

*Acta Arith.* **13** (1967/68), 1–7.

The author proves the stated result through a sequence of lemmas. In the first he shows

$$M(x)\log^2 x = -\sum_{p\leq x} M(x/p)\log^2 p + \sum_{pp'\leq x} M(x/pp')\log p \log p' + O(x\log x)$$

by considering $\sum_{n\leq x} \mu(n)\log^2 n$. Using this, together with Selberg's theorem in the form

$$\sum_{p\leq y} \log^2 p + \sum_{pp'\leq y} \log p \log p' = 2y\log y + O(y),$$

he shows $\frac{1}{2}|M(x)|\log^2 x \leq \int_1^x |M(x/t)|\log t\,dt + o(x\log^2 x)$, and then $\int_1^x M(x/t)\log t\,dt \leq \frac{1}{2}g(1-\lambda)x\log^2 x$, where $g = \limsup|M(x)/x|$ and $\lambda$ is a constant $>0$ if $g>0$. The last two imply $|M(x)/x| \leq g(1-\lambda) + o(1)$, a contradiction. Thus $g=0$. *R. A. MacLeod* (Victoria, B.C.)

## N20-67 (39# 2712 )

**Levinson, Norman**

**A motivated account of an elementary proof of the prime number theorem.**

*Amer. Math. Monthly* **76** (1969), 225–245.

The prime number theorem asserts that the number of primes not exceeding $x$ is asymptotically equal to $x/\log x$. This striking result was proved independently, by Hadamard and de la Vallée Poussin in 1896. But an elementary proof was not discovered until 1949 when P. Erdős [Proc. Nat. Acad. Sci. U.S.A. **35** (1949), 374–384; MR **10**, 595] and A. Selberg, using a formula previously proved by Selberg in an elementary way, jointly succeeded in giving several elementary proofs. These proofs and another one of A. Selberg [Ann. of Math. (2) **50** (1949), 305–313; MR **10**, 595] are not simple, though elementary.

Now the author gives a self-contained and motivated account of an elementary proof of the prime number theorem by the use of the Tatuzawa-Iseki identity [T. Tatuzawa and K. Iseki, Proc. Japan Acad. **27** (1951), 340–342; MR **13**, 725] to obtain the Selberg formula, and by simplifications introduced by Wright [G. H. Hardy and E. M. Wright, *An introduction to the theory of numbers*, Clarendon, Oxford, 1938; third edition, 1954; MR **16**, 673; fourth edition, 1960; German translation of the third edition, Oldenbourg, Munich, 1958; MR **20** #828; E. M. Wright, Proc. Roy. Soc. Edinburgh Sect. A **63** (1952), 257–267; MR **14**, 137] and by the author [Proc. Edinburgh Math. Soc. (2) **15** (1966/67), 141–146; MR **36** #1398]. *S. Ikehara* (Tokyo)

Citations: MR 10, 595b = N20-3; MR 10, 595c = N20-3; MR 13, 725f = N20-14; MR 14, 137d = N20-16; MR 16, 673b = Z01-28; MR 20# 828 = Z01-29; MR 36# 1398 = N20-65.

## N20-68 (41# 6772 )

**Kalecki, M.**

**A short elementary proof of the prime number theorem.**

*Prace Mat.* **13** (1969), 51–55.

The prime number theorem is proved in the form $\psi(x) = x + o(x)$, where $\psi(x) = \sum_{p^k\leq x} \log p = \sum_{n\leq x} \Lambda(n)$. Define $\psi_1(x) = \psi(x) + \log x$ and then the equivalent of Selberg's approximation is proved in the form $\sum_{n\leq x} \Lambda(n)\psi_1(x/n) + \psi_1(x)\log x = 2x\log x + O(x)$. The author introduces an auxiliary function $r(x)$ defined by $r(x) = (\psi_1(x)/x) - 1$. It is proved that if $\varepsilon > 0$ is fixed and $x$ chosen in such a way that $r(x) = r + o(1)$, then there exists an integer $a \leq x^\varepsilon$ such that $r(x/a) = -r + o(1)$. The prime number theorem will then follow if it can be proved that $r=0$. This is done by considering intervals in which $r(x/n') \leq -\varepsilon$ and those in which $r(x/am') \geq \varepsilon$. *E. M. Horadam* (Armidale)

## N20-69 (41# 6800 )

**Buschman, R. G.**

**Identities involving products of number-theoretic functions.**

*Proc. Amer. Math. Soc.* **25** (1970), 307–309.

For three different multiplications which are defined on the set of number-theoretic (arithmetical) functions, the author uses the following notation: $f\cdot g$ if $(f\cdot g)(n) = f(n)g(n)$, $f*g$ if $(f*g)(n) = \sum (f(k)g(m): km=n)$, $f\#g$ if $(f\#g)(x) = \sum (f(k)g(x/k): 1\leq k\leq x)$.

The following identities are then proved: $f\#(g\#h) = (f*g)\#h$, $a\#(l\cdot(b\#c)) = (a*b)\#(c\cdot l) + (a*(b\cdot l))\#c$, where $a$, $b$, $c$ are any arithmetical functions and $l$ is the logarithm function. The second identity enables the author to prove the Tatuzawa-Iseki identity in the form $\mu\#(l\cdot(\nu_0\#c)) = c\cdot l + \Lambda\#c$, where $\mu$ is the Möbius function, $\nu_0$ the constant function for which $\nu_0(n)=1$ and $\Lambda$ is the von Mangoldt function for which $\Lambda(n) = \log p$ if $n=p^m$ and $\Lambda(n)=0$ otherwise. It is interesting to compare the methods of this paper with those of J. Popken [Nederl. Akad. Wetensch. Proc. Ser. A **58** (1955), 10–15; MR **16**, 905]. *E. M. Horadam* (Armidale)

Citations: MR 16, 905e = N20-26.

## N20-70 (42# 4503 )

**Breusch, Robert**

**The prime number theorem and its proofs.**

*Math. Chronicle* **1** (1970), *part* 2, 61–70.

Elementary expository survey.

**N20-71** **(43# 6169)**

**Diamond, Harold G.; Steinig, John**
**An elementary proof of the prime number theorem with a remainder term.**
*Invent. Math.* **11** (1970), 199–258.

The prime number theorem, which asserts that the number of primes not exceeding $x$ is asymptotic to $x/\log x$ as $x \to \infty$, was first proved by Hadamard and de la Vallée Poussin, independently, in 1896. A few years later de la Vallée Poussin obtained an estimate for the remainder term, which may be written as (1) $\psi(x) - x = O\{x \exp(-c \log^\alpha x)\}$, where $\psi(x) = \sum_{p^a \leq x} \log p$, $\alpha = 1/2$, $c > 0$, and "$O$" is Landau's symbol. The analytic methods in prime number theory gave a better error term while the elementary methods yielded an error term $\psi(x) - x = O(x \log^{-m} x)$ with estimates of $m$ smaller than $1/6$ [R. Breusch, Pacific J. Math. **10** (1960), 487–497; MR **22** #4685], and later with arbitrarily large positive values of $m$ [E. Bombieri, Riv. Mat. Univ. Parma (2) **3** (1962), 393–440; MR **27** #4804; E. Wirsing, J. Reine Angew. Math. **214/215** (1964), 1–18; MR **29** #3457].

The object of this paper is to prove the following theorem by elementary methods: If $\log\log x \geq 100$, then $|\psi(x) - x| = x \exp\{-(\log x)^{1/7}(\log\log x)^{-2}\}$. The proof is elementary in the sense that it uses neither Laplace transforms nor any properties of the Riemann zeta function. This result is weaker than that of de la Vallée Poussin or the more recent estimates of Vinogradov, Hua and others [cf. A. Z. Val'fiš, *Weylsche Exponentialsummen in der neueren Zahlentheorie*, p. 187, VEB Deutsch. Verlag der Wiss., Berlin, 1963; MR **36** #3737], which give (1) with $\alpha$ near $3/5$.

Most of the formulas in the present paper are expressed in terms of multiplicative convolution, and measures are used in place of arithmetical functions [cf. the first author, Illinois J. Math. **14** (1970), 12–28; MR **40** #5555]. The authors generalize Selberg's formula [cf. J. Popken, Nederl. Akad. Wetensch. Proc. Ser. A **58** (1955), 10–15; MR **16**, 905] and in the course of the proof they command very many explicit estimates to obtain an analogue of the Dirichlet divisor problem [E. C. Titchmarsh, *The theory of the Riemann zeta-function*, Clarendon Press, Oxford, 1951; MR **13**, 741] and an extension of Wirsing's inequality [loc. cit., p. 2], and conclude by the Tauberian argument patterned on that of Wirsing. *S. Ikehara* (Tokyo)

Citations: MR 13, 741c = M02-2; MR 16, 905e = N20-26; MR 22# 4685 = N20-43; MR 27# 4804 = N20-55; MR 29# 3457 = N20-56; MR 36# 3737 = L02-8; MR 40# 5555 = N80-54.

# N24 DISTRIBUTION OF INTEGERS WITH CONSTRAINTS ON THE NUMBER OR MULTIPLICITY OF PRIME FACTORS

See also Sections N60, P16.

See also reviews A22-67, A26-96, A38-46, A38-52, A40-18, B28-19, B48-17, L20-4, L99-4, M45-28, M45-39, M55-13, M55-15, M55-66, N16-20, N16-25, N20-47, N28-9, N28-38, N28-41, N28-42, N36-8, N36-13, N40-75, N44-32, N48-26, N48-30, N56-6, N60-6, N60-58, N60-67, N60-71, N60-83, N60-85, N64-2, N64-6, N64-35, N72-29, N80-18, N80-19, N80-20, N80-39, N80-43, P16-7, P28-70, R14-35, R46-2, R48-22, Z10-6.

**N24-1** **(1, 293a)**

**Pillai, S. S. Generalisation of a theorem of Mangoldt.** Proc. Indian Acad. Sci., Sect. A. **11**, 13–20 (1940).

Let $N_{r,t}(x)$ denote the number of numbers not exceeding $x$, whose number of prime factors (each counted according to its multiplicity) belongs to the residue class $t$ mod $r$, and $N'_{r,t}(x)$ the number of such squarefree numbers. Then

$$(1) \qquad N_{r,t}(x) \sim \frac{x}{r},$$

$$(2) \qquad N'_{r,t}(x) \sim \frac{6}{\pi^2}\frac{x}{r}.$$

The author's proof holds for primes $r$ only; but in an appendix the result is proved for all cases by an argument due to Chowla. (1) is a generalization of von Mangoldt's theorem

$$L(x) = \sum_{n \leq x} (-1)^{\rho(n)} = o(x)$$

($\rho(n)$: the number of prime factors of $n$), which is equivalent to $N_{2,0}(x) \sim N_{2,1}(x) \sim x/2$; von Mangoldt also proved that $N'_{2,0}(x) \sim N'_{2,1}(x)$. A different proof of (2) is due to S. Selberg [Math. Z. **44**, 306–316 (1938)]. *F. A. Behrend.*

Referred to in L20-2, N24-29.

**N24-2** **(2, 42e)**

**Sambasiva Rao, K. Generalisation of a theorem of Pillai-Selberg.** Proc. Indian Acad. Sci., Sect. A. **11**, 502–504 (1940).

The following theorem is established: Let $N^k_{r,t}(x)$ denote the number of $k$th power-free integers not exceeding $x$, the number of whose prime factors (taking into consideration the degree of multiplicity) is congruent to $t$ modulo $r$. Then $N^k_{r,t}(x) \sim x/\zeta(k)$, where $\zeta(k) = \sum_{n=1}^{\infty}(1/n^k)$. Special cases of this result are due to von Mangoldt, Pillai [Proc. Indian Acad. Sci., Sect. A. **11**, 13–20 (1940); these Rev. **1**, 293] and Selberg [Math. Z. **44**, 306–318 (1939)]. The main point of the proof is to show that $L_r^{(k)}(x) = O(x)$, where $L_r^{(k)}(x) = \sum \lambda_r(n)$, summed over all $k$th power-free integers not exceeding $x$; $\lambda_r(n) = \exp(2\pi i t(n)s/r)$, $s = 1, \cdots, r-1$; and $t(n)$ is the number of prime factors of $n$, each prime factor being counted according to its degree of multiplicity. This follows at once from the corresponding result in the paper of Pillai referred to above. *R. D. James.*

**N24-3** **(2, 249c)**

**Selberg, Sigmund. Über die zahlentheoretische Funktion $\pi_n(x)$.** Norske Vid. Selsk. Forh. **13**, 30–33 (1940).

The formula

$$\pi_n(x) \sim \frac{x}{\log x}\frac{(\log\log x)^{n-1}}{(n-1)!},$$

where $\pi_n(x)$ is the number of positive square-free integers not greater than $x$ which are products of $n$ primes, is proved by means of a consideration of the functions $\pi_{\nu,n}(\xi, x)$ which designate the number of positive square-free integers not greater than $x$ which are products of $\nu$ primes not greater than $\xi$ and $n-\nu$ primes greater than $\xi$. These methods can be used to obtain more refined asymptotic formulas involving $\pi_n(x)$. *H. S. Zuckerman* (Seattle, Wash.).

**N24-4** **(8, 316f)**

**Ramaswami, V., and Sambasiva Rao, K. On the probability that two $k$th power-free integers belonging to an assigned arithmetic progression should be prime to one another.** J. Indian Math. Soc. (N.S.) **9**, 88–92 (1945).

**N24-5** **(8, 446g)**

**Selberg, Sigmund. An asymptotic formula for the distribution of the two-factorial integers.** C. R. Dixième Congrès Math. Scandinaves 1946, pp. 59–64. Jul. Gjellerups Forlag, Copenhagen, 1947.

Let $\pi_2(x)$ be the number of integers not exceeding $x$ which can be represented as a product of two different primes. The author proves the formula

$$\pi_2(x)=x\sum_{n=1}^{r-1}(n!\log\log x+a_n)(\log x)^{-n-1}+O(x(\log x)^{-r-1}),$$

where $r$ is a positive integer and $a_1, a_2, \cdots$ are real constants. The formula was given by Shah [Indian Phys. Math. J. **4**, 47–53 (1933)] but the author states that Shah's proof was not correct. The author proves the formula in the classical way by an investigation of the integral $\int x^s s^{-1}\log^2\zeta(s)ds$. He also states that the formula can be proved by elementary methods. *H. Heilbronn.*

**N24-6** **(8, 502i)**

**Selberg, Sigmund. On the distribution of the positive integers of the form $pp_1^{\alpha_1}p_2^{\alpha_2}\cdots p_n^{\alpha_n}$.** Norske Vid. Selsk. Forh., Trondhjem **16**, no. 24, 87–90 (1943).

This paper contains a proof of a formula for the number of integers $m\leqq x$ for which $m=pp_1^{\alpha_1}p_2^{\alpha_2}\cdots p_n^{\alpha_n}$, where $p, p_1, p_2, \cdots, p_n$ are distinct primes. The proof is made by induction on $n$ from the case $n=0$ (the prime number theorem). Applications are made to the number of integers represented as a product of $n$ primes, not necessarily distinct, and to the number of integers which have exactly $n$ divisors. *R. D. James* (Vancouver, B. C.).

**N24-7** **(8, 503a)**

**Selberg, Sigmund. On the sum $\sum_{m\leq x}\frac{1}{m}$, where $m$ is of a given standard form.** Norske Vid. Selsk. Forh., Trondhjem **16** (1943), no. 27, 99–102 (1944).

Let $n$ be a positive integer and $2^\nu$ the highest power of 2 dividing $n$. Let $S_n(x)=\sum 1/m$, summed over $1\leqq m\leqq x$ and $d(m)=n$, and $w_n(x)=\sum 1$ over the same range. The author proves, for any $q>0$, $S_n(x)=x^{-1}w_{2n}(x)\log x+O(\log\log^{-q}x)$ and

$$S_n(x)=\sum_{k=1}^{\nu+1}\frac{c_k}{(\nu-k+1)!}(\log\log x)^{\nu-k+1}+O(\log\log^{-q}x),$$

where $c_1, \cdots, c_{\nu+1}$ depend on $2^{-\nu}n$ only. These results are deduced from two previous papers by the author [Skr. Norske Vid. Akad. Oslo. I. **1942**, no. 5; these Rev. **6**, 57, and the paper reviewed above]. *H. Heilbronn* (Bristol).

Citations: MR 6, 57h = N28-9.

**N24-8** **(8, 503c)**

**Kuhn, Pavel. Zur Viggo Brun'schen Siebmethode. I.** Norske Vid. Selsk. Forh., Trondhjem **14** (1941), no. 39, 145–148 (1942).

Using a result of Tartakowski [C. R. (Doklady) Acad. Sci. URSS (N.S.) **23**, 121–125, 126–129 (1939); the author's reference is incorrect] based on the Brun sieve method, the author proves the following theorem. For sufficiently large $x$ there are 2.3 $e^{-C}x^{\frac{1}{2}}/\log x$ numbers between $x$ and $x+x^{\frac{1}{2}}$ which are divisible by at most four primes. Here $C$ is the Euler constant. *R. D. James* (Vancouver, B. C.).

Referred to in P32-35.

**N24-9** **(9, 333b)**

**Erdös, P. On the integers having exactly $K$ prime factors.** Ann. of Math. (2) **49**, 53–66 (1948).

Let $\pi_k(n)$ denote the number of integers not exceeding $n$ which have exactly $k$ prime factors, multiple factors being counted only once. The author proves that, for $k$ in the interval $(x-cx^{\frac{1}{2}}, x+cx^{\frac{1}{2}})$, where $x=[\log\log n]$ and $c$ is a constant, $\pi_k(n)=(1+o(1))(n/\log n)x^{k-1}/(k-1)!$. The proof requires estimates for sums such as $\sum 1/a_i^{(k)}$, where the $a_i^{(k)}$ are the integers not exceeding $n$ having exactly $k$ prime factors. At one point only, the prime number theorem is used. The author states two analogous results, one for the case when the multiple factors are counted according to their multiplicity, and the other for the case of square-free integers not exceeding $n$. He then raises several questions which he is unable to answer at present. *R. D. James.*

Referred to in B28-37, K30-15, N24-15.

**N24-10** **(11, 83h)**

**Mirsky, L. On the distribution of integers having a prescribed number of divisors.** Simon Stevin **26**, 168–175 (1949).

Denote by $\Delta(x, k)$ the number of positive integers not exceeding $x$ and having exactly $k$ divisors. An asymptotic expression is obtained for $\Delta(x, k)$ for fixed $k$ and as $x\rightarrow\infty$. In the proof of the result use is made of the prime number theorem and known estimates for the sums $\sum_{p\leqq x}p^{-1}$ and $\sum_{p\leqq x}p^{-1}\log p$. An asymptotic formula is also given for the number of positive integers not exceeding $x$ and having at most $k$ divisors. *W. H. Simons* (Vancouver, B. C.).

**N24-11** **(11, 644c)**

**Linnik, Yu. V. A remark on products of three primes.** Doklady Akad. Nauk SSSR (N.S.) **72**, 9–10 (1950). (Russian)

The author sketches a proof of the following result. If $x$ is large, then in the interval $[x, x+x^{\frac{1}{2}}\exp\{(\log x)^{0.99}\}]$ there exist integers which are products of exactly three prime factors. *P. T. Bateman* (Urbana, Ill.).

**N24-12** **(13, 208d)**

**Roth, K. F. On the gaps between squarefree numbers.** J. London Math. Soc. **26**, 263–268 (1951).

Let $q_n$ denote the $n$th square-free number. By means of a simple elementary argument it is shown that

$$q_{n+1}-q_n=O(x^{\frac{1}{4}});$$

a more elaborate argument leads to $q_{n+1}-q_n=O(x^{\frac{1}{5}+\epsilon})$. Finally, using a theorem of van der Corput [Math. Z. **28**, 301–310 (1928), Th. 3], it is shown that

$$q_{n+1}-q_n=O(n^{3/13}(\log n)^{4/13}).$$

*L. Carlitz* (Durham, N. C.).

**N24-13** **(13, 208e)**

**Halberstam, H., and Roth, K. F. On the gaps between consecutive $k$-free integers.** J. London Math. Soc. **26**, 268–273 (1951).

For $k\geqq 2$, let $q_k(n)$ denote the $n$th $k$-free integer (number not divisible by any $k$th power other than 1). It is proved that

$$q_k(n+1)-q_k(n)=O(n^{\frac{1}{2k}+\epsilon}).$$

(For $k=2$, see the preceding review.) It is stated that it is possible to improve this result and obtain an exponent less than $1/2k$. *L. Carlitz* (Durham, N. C.).

Referred to in N32-12.

**N24-14** **(13, 627a)**

**Erdös, P. Some problems and results in elementary number theory.** Publ. Math. Debrecen **2**, 103–109 (1951).

Let $p_1 < p_2 < \cdots$ denote a sequence of primes such that

$$\sum_{p_i < x} \frac{1}{p_i} = f(x) \to \infty \quad \text{as} \quad x \to \infty;$$

also let $v_1 < v_2 < \cdots$ denote the integers which are either not divisible by $p_i$ or are divisible by $p_i^2$. Then it is proved that

$$v_{i+1} - v_i > ce^{f(\log v_i)} \frac{\log v_i}{\log \log v_i}$$

for infinitely many $i$. A corollary of this result is

$$u_{i+1} - u_i > c \frac{\log u_i}{(\log \log u_i)^{1/2}}$$

where $u_1 < u_2 < \cdots$ denotes the sequence of integers $x^2 + y^2$. It is remarked that the latter result can be proved (without Brun's method) by making use of Landau's theorem that the number of integers $x^2 + y^2 \leqq t$ is $O(t/(\log t)^{1/2})$. (The formula $u_{i+1} - u_i < cu_i^{1/4}$ which is due to Chowla and Bambah is easily obtained.)

In the next place let $s_1 < s_2 < \cdots$ denote the sequence of squarefree integers. The author states that he can prove

$$\sum_{s_{k+1} < x} (s_{k+1} - s_k)^\alpha = C_\alpha x + o(x),$$

for $\alpha < A$, where $A$ is a certain constant between 2 and 3. The proof is given for $\alpha = 2$. *L. Carlitz.*

## N24-15 (15, 103a)

**Sathe, L. G. On a problem of Hardy on the distribution of integers having a given number of prime factors. I.** J. Indian Math. Soc. (N.S.) 17, 63–82 (1953).

This is the first part of a paper in which the author proves (among others) the following results: Denote by $\pi_\nu(x)$ the number of squarefree integers having $\nu$ prime factors. Put $\nu = k \log \log x$. Let $k < e$. Then

$$\pi_\nu(x) = (1 + o(1)) f(k) \frac{x}{\log x} \frac{(\log \log x)^{\nu-1}}{(\nu - 1)!}$$

where ($p$ runs through all primes)

$$f(k) = \frac{1}{\Gamma(k+1)} \left[ \prod_p \left(1 - \frac{1}{p}\right) e^{1/p} \right]^k \prod_p \left(1 + \frac{k}{p} e^{-k/p}\right).$$

Similar asymptotic formulas are obtained for $\sigma_\nu(x)$ and $\rho_\nu(x)$, where $\sigma_\nu(x)$ denotes the number of integers $\leqq x$ having $\nu$ prime factors, multiple factors counted multiply, and in $\rho_\nu(x)$ multiple factors are counted only once.

The proofs are very complicated. These results strengthen and supersede all previous ones and were found about simultaneously with those of the reviewer [Ann. of Math. (2) **49**, 53–66 (1948); these Rev. **9**, 333] which are special cases ($\nu = \log \log x + c(\log \log x)^{1/2}$) of those of the author.

*P. Erdös* (South Bend, Ind.).

Citations: MR 9, 333b = N24-9.
Referred to in N24-16, N24-17.

## N24-16 (15, 401i)

**Sathe, L. G. On a problem of Hardy on the distribution of integers having a given number of prime factors. II.** J. Indian Math. Soc. (N.S.) 17, 83–141 (1953).

The author completes the proof of the results announced in the first part of this paper [same vol., 63–82 (1953); these Rev. **15**, 103]. *P. Erdös* (South Bend, Ind.).

Citations: MR 15, 103a = N24-15.
Referred to in N24-17, N24-22.

## N24-17 (16, 221b; 16, 221c)

**Sathe, L. G. On a problem of Hardy on the distribution of integers having a given number of prime factors. III.** J. Indian Math. Soc. (N.S.) 18, 27–42 (1954).

**Sathe, L. G. On a problem of Hardy on the distribution of integers having a given number of prime factors. IV.** J. Indian Math. Soc. (N.S.) 18, 43–81 (1954).

In these two parts the author completes the proofs of the theorems stated in part I [same J. (N.S.) **17**, 63–82 (1953); these Rev. **15**, 103] and partly carried out in part II [ibid. (N.S.) **17**, 83–141 (1953); these Rev. **15**, 401]. In addition, he shows in part IV that the asymptotic formulas obtained in part I for $\sigma_\nu(x)$, $\nu < (2-\epsilon) \log \log x$, fail to hold for $\nu = 2[\log \log x] + 1$. *P. Erdös* (Jerusalem).

Citations: MR 15, 103a = N24-15; MR 15, 401i = N24-16.
Referred to in N24-22.

## N24-18 (15, 289c)

**Richert, H.-E. On the difference between consecutive squarefree numbers.** J. London Math. Soc. 29, 16–20 (1954).

The following theorem is proved. Let $s_n(q, l)$ denote the $n$th squarefree number in the arithmetic progression $mq + l$, $1 \leqq l \leqq q$, $(q, l) = 1$, $m = 0, 1, \cdots$, $q = O(n^{2/7})$. Then as $n \to \infty$, $s_{n+1}(q, l) - s_n(q, l) = O(q^{11/9} n^{2/9} \log n)$, uniformly in $n$, $q$, and $l$. In particular, if $s_n$ is the $n$th squarefree number, then $s_{n+1} - s_n = O(n^{2/9} \log n)$. *L. Carlitz.*

Referred to in N24-30.

## N24-19 (15, 603b)

**Richert, Hans-Egon. Über quadratfreie Zahlen mit genau $r$ Primfaktoren in einer arithmetischen Progression.** J. Reine Angew. Math. 192, 180–203 (1953).

Consider the square-free numbers with exactly $r$ factors and let $\pi_r(x; k, l)$ denote the number of such numbers $\leqq x$ that are congruent to $l$ (mod $k$). The first main result of the paper is an asymptotic formula for $\pi_r(x; k, l)$ in which the error term is uniform in $k$. The result is too elaborate to reproduce here. For $r = 1$ it reduces to the well known theorem of Page-Siegel-Walfisz. As an application of this result the writer obtains an asymptotic formula for the number of solutions of $n = p_1 + p_2 + p_3 p_4$, $p_3 < p_4$, where the $p_i$ are primes. This includes a theorem of Estermann [Quart. J. Math., Oxford Ser. **8**, 32–38 (1937)].

*L. Carlitz* (Durham, N. C.).

Referred to in N24-33, N24-54, P16-28, R46-7.

## N24-20 (16, 114a)

**Bellman, Richard, and Shapiro, Harold N. The distribution of squarefree integers in small intervals.** Duke Math. J. 21, 629–637 (1954).

Let $Q(u, v)$ denote the number of square-free integers $q$ such that $u < q \leqq v$. It is proved first that if $\phi(x)$ is any function such that $\phi(x) \to \infty$ as $x \to \infty$, then for almost all $n$ the interval $(n, n + \phi(n))$ contains a square-free integer. While proved independently, this is a consequence of the following theorem. If $\phi(n)$ is any strictly monotone function such that $\phi(x) \to \infty$ as $x \to \infty$, then $Q(n, n + \phi(n))$ has the normal order $6\phi(n)/\pi^2$. Finally this result is sharpened as follows. If $k(n) \to \infty$ as $n \to \infty$, then for almost all $n$

$$\frac{6}{\pi^2}\phi(n) - k(n)\phi^{1/2}(n) \leqq Q(n, n + \phi(n)) \leqq \frac{6}{\pi^2}\phi(n) + k(n)\phi^{1/2}(n),$$

provided $\phi(n)$ satisfies certain additional requirements.

*L. Carlitz* (Durham, N. C.).

Referred to in N24-69.

**N24-21** **(16, 448e)**

**Wright, E. M. A simple proof of a theorem of Landau.** Proc. Edinburgh Math. Soc. (2) **9**, 87–90 (1954).

Let $\sigma_k(x)$ be the number of integers $n=p_1\cdots p_k\leqq x$ which are the products of exactly $k$ primes, and let $\pi_k(x)$ be the number of such $n$ for which all the $p_i$ are distinct. The theorem in question asserts that

$$\pi_k(x)\sim\sigma_k(x)\sim\frac{x(\log\log x)^{k-1}}{(k-1)!\log x}.$$

In the present paper this theorem is proved in an elementary way assuming

$$\sum_{p\leqq x}\log p\sim x,\quad \sum_{p<x}\frac{1}{p}\sim\log\log x.$$

*L. Carlitz* (Durham, N. C.).

Referred to in N28-62.

**N24-22** **(16, 676a)**

**Selberg, Atle. Note on a paper by L. G. Sathe.** J. Indian Math. Soc. (N.S.) **18**, 83–87 (1954).

The author obtains short and simple proofs of the results of Sathe [same J. (N.S.) **17**, 83–141 (1953); **18**, 27–42, 43–81 (1954); MR **15**, 401; **16**, 221] on $\pi_k(x)$, the number of positive integers $\leqq x$ containing exactly $k$ prime factors.

*S. Chowla* (Boulder, Colo.).

Citations: MR 15, 401i = N24-16; MR 16, 221b = N24-17; MR 16, 221c = N24-17.

Referred to in K30-15, N24-81, N36-46, N60-36.

**N24-23** **(17, 944f)**

**Rényi, Alfred. On the density of certain sequences of integers.** Acad. Serbe Sci. Publ. Inst. Math. **8** (1955), 157–162.

If $A$ is a set of positive integers and if $\lim_{x\to\infty}A(x)/x=d$, then $d$ is called the density of $A$. Let $n=p_1^{a_1}\cdots p_r^{a_r}$ be the prime decomposition of $n$ and consider the set $A_k$ of integers for which $a_1-1+\cdots+a_r-1=k$. The author shows that $A_k$ has density $d_k$ where

$$\sum_{k=0}^{\infty}d_kz^k=\prod_p(1-p^{-1})(1-(p-z)^{-1}),$$

where the product is extended over all primes. [There is a misprint in the formula at the bottom of page 157.]

*H. B. Mann* (Columbus, Ohio).

Referred to in N24-37, N24-56, N24-73, N52-25, N52-46, N60-37, N60-58, N60-67, N60-87, N60-91, Q15-13, Q15-17.

**N24-24** **(17, 944g)**

**Kac, M. A remark on the preceding paper by A. Rényi.** Acad. Serbe Sci. Publ. Inst. Math. **8** (1955), 163–165.

The author gives a probabilistic proof of the theorem of Rényi stated in the paper reviewed above.

*H. B. Mann* (Columbus, Ohio).

**N24-25** **(17, 945c)**

**Mycielski, Jan. On powers.** Bull. Acad. Polon. Sci. Cl. III. 3 (1955), 129–132.

Denote by $P$ the sequence of integers which are not powers. Clearly every integer can be uniquely represented in the form

$$P_1^{P_2^{\cdot^{\cdot^{\cdot^{P_k}}}}}$$

The author obtains various asymptotic formulas for sums $\sum_{P<x}(\log P)^{\alpha}$, and $\sum_{P<x}P^{\alpha}$ and various other asymptotic formulas.

*P. Erdös* (Haifa).

**N24-26** **(18, 18c)**

**Hornfeck, Bernhard. Dichtentheoretische Sätze der Primzahltheorie.** Monatsh. Math. **60** (1956), 96–109.

Let $\mathfrak{M}$ be a set of positive integers. Then $\mathfrak{M}^k$ is defined as the set of all integers which can be represented in the form $m_1\cdots m_k$, $m_i\in\mathfrak{M}$ $(i=1,\cdots,k)$. Denote by $M(x)$ the number of $m\in\mathfrak{M}$, $m\leqq x$. If $\phi(x)\to\infty$ as $x\to\infty$ and the limit $\lim_{x=\infty}M(x)/\phi(x)=\tau$ exists and is positive, then $\tau$ is said to be the $\phi(x)$-density of $\mathfrak{M}$.

The present paper is concerned with relations between the densities of a set and its powers. As a typical result we may quote the following. Let $\mathfrak{T}$ be a set of primes and suppose that it has $(x/\log x)$-density $\tau$; then $\mathfrak{T}^k$ has $\{x(\log\log x)^{k-1}/(k-1)!\log x\}$-density $\tau^k$. When $\mathfrak{T}$ is the set of all primes, this result reduces to a well-known asymptotic formula of Landau [Bull. Soc. Math. France **28** (1900), 25–38].

In addition to theorems about subsets of primes, the author also obtains more general relations involving sets of pairwise coprime integers. *L. Mirsky* (Sheffield).

Referred to in K30-17, N28-42, N28-76.

**N24-27** **(18, 18f)**

**Obláth, Richard. Sur la répartition des nombres sans diviseur quadratique.** Publ. Math. Debrecen **4** (1956), 131–134.

The author proves that if $x$ is sufficiently large and if $n=O(x)$ then the number of square-free integers within each of the intervals $[1,x]$, $[x,2x]$, $\cdots$, $[(n-1)x,nx]$, is asymptotically uniform and equal to $6x/\pi^2$. Assuming the Riemann hypothesis, the conclusion still holds if the condition $n=O(x)$ is replaced by $n=O(x^{3/2-\varepsilon})$. In line 6 of p. 132, read $o(\sqrt{mx})$ instead of $o(\sqrt{m}x)$.

*T. M. Apostol* (Pasadena, Calif.).

**N24-28** **(18, 720a)**

**Delange, Hubert. Sur la distribution des entiers ayant certaines propriétés.** Ann. Sci. Ecole Norm. Sup. (3) **73** (1956), 15–74.

This paper is concerned with a number of problems whose type is best stated as finding an equivalent expression for the number of numbers not exceeding $x$ for $x\to\infty$, and possessing one or more given properties. The best known example is the prime number theorem, which asserts that the number of primes not exceeding $x$ is asymptotic to $x/\log x$. The author has generalized a Tauberian theorem appropriate for the proof of the prime number theorem [cf. D. V. Widder, The Laplace transform, Princeton, 1942; MR **3**, 232] in a series of papers [C. R. Acad. Sci. Paris **232** (1951), 465–467, 589–591; Ann. Sci. Ecole Norm. Sup. (3) **71** (1954), 213–242; MR **12**, 405, 497; **16**, 921].

Some of his generalized theorems were applied to prove certain asymptotic formulae in the theory of numbers related to $\omega(n)$ and $\Omega(n)$, which denote, respectively, the number of distinct prime factors, and the total number of primes in the positive integer $n$ [C. R. Acad. Sci. Paris **232** (1951), 1392–1393; Mém. Soc. Roy. Sci. Liége (4) **16** (1955), no. 1–2; Univ. e Politec. Torino. Rend. Sem. Mat. **14** (1954–55), 87–103; MR **12**, 677; **17**, 965]. The present paper gives a complete proof for a comprehensive group of problems, including many interesting new results. A first group of theorems imposes various conditions on integers such as $\omega(n)=q$, and $\Omega(n)\equiv r \pmod{q'}$ when $q$ and $q'>1$ and $r$ are integers, and $n$ may be also "quadratfrei". A second group deals with integers belonging to an arithmetical progression while $\omega(n)$ and $\Omega(n)$ are restricted as above. For example, the number of numbers not exceeding $x$ such that $(k,l)=1$, $n\equiv l \pmod{k}$ and $\Omega(n)\equiv r$

(mod $q$) tends to $x/kq$ as $x\to\infty$. A particular case of $q=2$ is found in Landau, Handbuch der Primzahlen [Bd. 2, 2nd ed., Chelsea, New York, 1953, p. 630; MR **16**, 904]. A third group is studied on certain set $E$ of prime numbers while primes for integers $n$ in $\omega(n)$ and $\Omega(n)$ are restricted to this set. And finally, further generalizations are given by limiting integers to a form $n=p_1^{k_1}p_2^{k_2}\cdots p_n^{k_n}m$, where primes $p$'s belong to the set $E$ and no $p$'s divide $m$.

*S. Ikehara* (Tokyo).

Citations: MR 12, 405a = M45-13; MR 12, 497d = M45-14; MR 12, 677d = N28-23; MR 16, 904d = N02-3; MR 16, 921e = M45-24; MR 17, 965c = M45-28; MR 17, 965d = M45-29.

Referred to in K30-15, N24-42, N60-22, N60-29, N80-46, R12-40.

## N24-29 (19, 17c)

**Addison, A. W. A note on the compositeness of numbers.** Proc. Amer. Math. Soc. **8** (1957), 151–154.

The "compositeness" of the number $n=p_1^{\alpha_1}p_2^{\alpha_2}\cdots p_m^{\alpha_m}$ is defined by $\Omega(n)=\alpha_1+\alpha_2+\cdots+\alpha_m$. If for any $q\geqq 3$ we partition the integers into $q$ classes $\{C_{q,i}\}$ $(i=0, 1, \cdots, q-1)$ according to whether $\Omega(n)\equiv 0, 1, \cdots, q-1 \pmod q$, and let $C_{q,i}(x)$ be the corresponding counting functions, the author proves that

$$C_{q,i}(x)-x/q=\Omega_\pm(x/\log^r x)\ (i=0, 1, \cdots, q-1),$$

where $r=1-\cos(2\pi/q)$. The leading term $x/q$, with error of $o(x)$, has already been established by S. Selberg [Math. Z. **44** (1938), 306–318] and S. S. Pillai [Proc. Indian Acad. Sci. Sect. A. **11** (1940), 13–20; MR **1**, 293].

*S. Ikehara* (Tokyo).

Citations: MR 1, 293a = N24-1.

## N24-30 (19, 392b)

**Yüh, Ming-I. On the differences between squarefree numbers.** Sci. Record (N.S.) **1** (1957), no. 3, 13–16.

Combining van der Corput's method with an estimate of Vinogradov's, the author improves a former estimate by the reviewer [J. London Math. Soc. **29** (1954), 16–20; MR **15**, 289] for the difference $s_{n+1}-s_n$ of two consecutive squarefree numbers. However, Rankin in his paper on van der Corput's method of exponent pairs [Quart. J. Math. Oxford Ser. (2) **6** (1955), 147–153; MR **17**, 240] has pointed out that this method leads to an estimate, namely $s_{n+1}-s_n=O(n^{\gamma+\varepsilon})$, $\gamma=0.22198215\cdots$, which is superior to that given by the author. The paper is somewhat condensed, and there are some misprints.

*H E. Richert* (Göttingen).

Citations: MR 15, 289c = N24-18; MR 17, 240a = L99-4.

## N24-31 (19, 1160g)

**Prachar, Karl. Über die kleinste quadratfreie Zahl einer arithmetischen Reihe.** Monatsh. Math. **62** (1958), 173–176.

Let $Q(x, k, l)$ denote the number of integers $m\leqq x$ which are $\equiv l \pmod k$, and such that $m$ is squarefree. It is proved that (with $(k, l)=1$)

$$Q(x, k, l)=Axk^{-1}+O(x^{\frac12}k^{-\frac14+\varepsilon}+k^{\frac12+\varepsilon})$$

for any given $\varepsilon>0$, where

$$A=\frac{6}{\pi^2}\prod_{p|k}\left(1-\frac{1}{p^2}\right)^{-1},$$

and the $O$ is uniform in $k$. From this it is concluded that, for $q_1(k, l)=$the smallest squarefree number in the arithmetic progression of integers $\equiv l \pmod k$, one has

$$q_1(k, l)<k^{3/2+\varepsilon}.$$

Analogous results are given for $r$th-power-free integers.

*H. N. Shapiro* (New York, N.Y.).

Referred to in N24-38, N24-65, N24-80.

## N24-32 (20# 2305)

**Bateman, Paul T.; and Grosswald, Emil. On a theorem of Erdös and Szekeres.** Illinois J. Math. **2** (1958), 88–98.

Let $h$ be a given integer $>1$, and let $N_h(x)$ denote the number of positive integers $n\leqq x$ which have the property that $p^h|n$ for every prime factor $p$ of $n$. It was proved by Erdös and Szekeres [Acta Sci. Math. Szeged **7** (1934), 95–102] that $N_h(x)=\gamma_0x^{1/h}+O(x^{1/(h+1)})$, where $\gamma_0$ is a constant. The present authors derive more precise information. If $h>2$, they show that $N_h(x)=\gamma_0x^{1/h}+\gamma_1x^{1/(h+1)}+O(x^{1/(h+2)})$. If $h=2$, when the generating Dirichlet series is $\zeta(2s)\zeta(3s)/\zeta(6s)$, they replace the $O$-term by $O(x^{1/6}\exp(-a\omega(x)))$, where $\omega(x)=(\log x)^{4/7}(\log\log x)^{-3/7}$. In the case $h>2$ they also give an estimate with $r+1$ major terms instead of two, where $r$ is the largest integer $<(2h)^{\frac12}$. These results are obtained by writing the generating Dirichlet series as a product of a series belonging to a lattice point problem (and which is a product of $\zeta$'s) and a series with a relatively small abscissa of absolute convergence.

*N. G. de Bruijn* (Amsterdam)

Referred to in N24-75.

## N24-33 (20# 3108)

**Rieger, G. J. Verschärfung des Satzes von Richert über die Verteilung der quadratfreien Zahlen mit genau $r$ Primfaktoren in einer arithmetischen Progression.** J. Reine Angew. Math. **199** (1958), 215–220.

The author sharpens previous results of Richert on the number of squarefree numbers having exactly $r$ prime factors in an arithmetic progression [Richert, J. Reine Angew. Math. **192** (1953), 180–203; MR **15**, 603].

*P. Erdös* (Haifa)

Citations: MR 15, 603b = N24-19.

Referred to in N24-54, R46-14.

## N24-34 (20# 3832)

**Christopher, John. The asymptotic density of some $k$-dimensional sets.** Amer. Math. Monthly **63** (1956), 399–401.

Let $A$ be a subset of the set of $k$-tuples $(a_1, \cdots, a_k)$ of positive integers, where $k\geqq 1$. Let $A_n$ be the number of elements in $A$ with every $a_i\leqq n$. Then the asymptotic density $\delta(A)$ of $A$ (namely, the probability that a random $k$-tuple of positive integers will be in $A$) is defined by $\delta(A)=\lim_{n\to\infty}\{A_n/n^k\}$.

The author proves that if $A$ is the set of $k$-tuples whose greatest common divisor is square-free, then $\delta(A)=1/\zeta(2k)$, where $\zeta$ is the Riemann zeta-function, and if, for $k>1$, $A$ is the set of $k$-tuples whose g.c.d. is $t$, with $t\geqq 1$, then $\delta(A)=t^{-k}/\zeta(k)$.

*S. H. Gould* (Providence, R.I.)

Referred to in A99-20.

## N24-35 (21# 5615)

**Wang, Yuan. On sieve methods and some of their applications.** Acta Math. Sinica **9** (1959), 87–100. (Chinese. English summary)

The author gives detailed proofs of the following results. For $k>5$ denote by $w$ the smallest integer satisfying

$$w+1\geqq\frac{5.64527}{4.8396}+\frac{3.65}{4.8396}\log\frac{5k-w}{w+5},$$

and put $n=k+1$ if $1\leqq k\leqq 5$, but $n=k+w$ if $k>5$. (1) If $F(x)$ is an irreducible integral-valued polynomial of degree $k$ without fixed prime divisor, there are infinitely many integers $x$ such that $F(x)$ is the product of at most $n$ primes. (2) For sufficiently large $x$ at least one integer between $x$ and $x+x^{1/k}$ has at most $n$ prime factors. (3) For sufficiently large $x$ at least one integer between $x$ and $x+x^{10/17}$ has at most two prime factors; at least one between $x$ and $x+x^{20/49}$ has at most three prime factors; and at least one between $x$ and $x+x^{9/902}$ has at most 100 prime factors. *K. Mahler* (Manchester)

Referred to in N24-36.

## N24-36 (26# 3685)

**Wang, Yuan**

**On sieve methods and some of their applications.**

*Sci. Sinica* **11** (1962), 1607–1624.

The Chinese version of this paper [Acta Math. Sinica **9** (1959), 87–100] was reviewed in MR **21** #5615.

Citations: MR 21# 5615 = N24-35.

Referred to in M55-34, N32-42.

## N24-37 (22# 34)

**Bodmer, W. F. The limiting frequencies of integers with a given partitional characteristic.** J. Roy. Statist. Soc. Ser. B **21** (1959), 134–143.

Let $n$ be a positive integer and let $q(n)$ be the quotient of $n$ by its largest square-free divisor. The decomposition of $q(n)$ into powers of primes may be arranged so that like powers are grouped together. This gives a characteristic partition $Q$ of the total number of prime factors of $q(n)$. Thus for $n$ a number like $2^4 5^2 7^4 29$ we have $q(n)=(2\cdot 7)^3\cdot 5$ and the partition $(3^2 1)$ of the seven prime factors of $q(n)$. The paper considers the problem of calculating the density $N(Q)$ of the set of integers $n$ that lead to a given partition $Q$. Thus $N(3^2 1)=.000027$. Again, for the null partition, $q(n)=1$, $N(0)=.607927=6\pi^{-2}$, which is the familiar density of square-free integers. By a general method involving symmetric functions the author has computed all densities $N(Q)$ which exceed $10^{-5}$. As a test the 330 numbers from 8446 to 8775 were classified and tallied and the results compared with the expected ones. The sum $d_k$ of $N(Q)$ over all partitions $Q$ of $k$ is also given for $k=0(1)5$. This function was first studied by Rényi [Acad. Serbe Sci. Publ. Inst. Math. **8** (1955), 163–165; MR **17**, 944]. *D. H. Lehmer* (Berkeley, Calif.)

Citations: MR 17, 944f = N24-23.

## N24-38 (22# 9476)

**Erdös, P. Über die kleinste quadratfreie Zahl einer arithmetischen Reihe.** Monatsh. Math. **64** (1960), 314–316.

Let $a$, $d$ be coprime integers such that $1\leqq a<d$, and denote by $q(a, d)$ the smallest positive square-free number which is $\equiv a \pmod{d}$. It was shown by K. Prachar [Monatsh. Math. **62** (1958), 173–176; MR **19**, 1160] that, for suitable absolute constants $c_1$, $c_2$,

$$q(a, d) \leqq c_1 d^{3/2} 2^{c_2 \log d/\log\log d}.$$

In the present paper this estimate is improved to

$$q(a, d) \leqq c_3 d^{3/2}/\log d,$$

where $c_3$ is again an absolute constant. The author conjectures that, in fact, $q(a, d)=o(d^{1+\varepsilon})$ and states that an easy argument leads to the conclusion

$$q(a, d) = \Omega(d \log d/\log\log d).$$

*L. Mirsky* (Sheffield)

Citations: MR 19, 1160g = N24-31.

## N24-39 (24# A1898)

**Cohen, Eckford**

**Some sets of integers related to the $k$-free integers.**

*Acta Sci. Math. Szeged* **22** (1961), 223–233.

$Q_k^*(x)$ is the number of $n\leqq x$ such that in the representation $n=p_1^{l_1}\cdots p_t^{l_t}$ ($p$'s distinct primes) we have $l_i \not\equiv 0 \pmod{k}$ for $1\leqq i\leqq t$. Theorem: $Q_k^*(x)=\alpha_k x+O(x^{1/k})$. Besides this theorem, the author obtains a number of generalizations. *S. Chowla* (Boulder, Colo.)

## N24-40 (25# 2049)

**Cohen, Eckford**

**Arithmetical notes. VIII. An asymptotic formula of Rényi.**

*Proc. Amer. Math. Soc.* **13** (1962), 536–539.

Pour VI voir Michigan Math. J. **9** (1962), 277–282.* Désignons par $K$ l'ensemble des entiers $n$ admettant ou bien des diviseurs premiers tous à la première puissance seulement, ou bien, à côté des précédents, un seul facteur premier à la deuxième puissance; soit $K(x)$ le nombre des entiers $n\in K$ tels que $n\leqq x$. Rényi a déterminé la densité asymtotique de $K$, soit

$$\delta \equiv \lim_{x\to\infty} \frac{K(x)}{x} = \frac{6\alpha}{\pi^2}, \quad \alpha \equiv \sum_p \frac{1}{p(p+1)},$$

la somme s'étendant à tous les nombres premiers $p$. L'auteur renforce le résultat de Rényi en démontrant la formule

$$K(x) = \frac{6\alpha x}{\pi^2} + O(x^{1/2}\log\log x), \quad x\geqq 3.$$

La démonstration de Rényi ne permettant pas d'obtenir une évaluation du reste, l'auteur se base essentiellement, pour démontrer son théorème, sur les propriétés de la fonction $\mu(n)$ de Moebius, sur les approximations bien connues $\sum_{n>x} 1/n^2 = O(1/x)$ et $\sum_{p\leqq x} 1/p = O(\log\log x)$ (ici $x\geqq 3$), et sur la remarque que tout entier $n$ admet une représentation unique $n=ec^2$, $c>0$, $e\in Q$, $Q$ étant l'ensemble des entiers n'admettant pas de facteur carré.

L'auteur annonce la parution d'une vaste extension du résultat signalé ici sans indiquer la revue dans laquelle il compte la faire paraître. *A. Gloden* (Luxembourg)

*See MR **25** #3897 = N56-13.

Citations: MR 25# 3897 = N56-13.

Referred to in N24-43, N60-58.

## N24-41 (25# 3887)

**Prachar, K.**

**Sätze über quadratfreie Zahlen.**

*Monatsh. Math.* **66** (1962), 306–312.

The author proves the following theorem, previously stated without proof by Erdős: For every positive number $\varepsilon$, there is a number $C$ such that for every natural number $k$ there are at least $(1-\varepsilon)\phi(k)$ different natural numbers $l$ such that $l\leqq k$ and $(l, k)=1$, and that there is a square-free natural number $q$ such that $q\equiv l \pmod{k}$ and $q<Ck$.

He also proves two other theorems of a similar type. *T. Estermann* (London)

## N24-42 (25# 3910)

**Delange, Hubert**

**Sur certains entiers.**

*Bull. Soc. Roy. Sci. Liège* **30** (1961), 404–415.

Let $k$, $l$, $q$ be fixed positive integers, $(l, k)=1$. $S_1$ is the set of integers having exactly $q$ different prime divisors, $S_2$ is the set of numbers which are products of $q$ primes (not necessarily distinct) and $S_3$ is the set of products of $q$ distinct primes. In a previous paper [Ann. Sci. École Norm. Sup. (3) **73** (1956), 15–74; MR **18**, 720] it was shown that, for each $i$, the number of integers $n$ with $1\leqq n\leqq x$, $n\equiv l \pmod{k}$, $n\in S_i$ is asymptotically

$$(\varphi(k))^{-1} x(\log\log x)^{q-1}\{(q-1)!\log x\}^{-1}$$

if $x\to\infty$. The present paper gives a more elementary

derivation of this result, based upon the prime number theorem for residue classes. The case $k = 1$ is a classical result by Landau [*Handbuch der Lehre von der Verteilung der Primzahlen*, Bd. I, Kap. 13, pp. 205–213, Teubner, Leipzig, 1909]. *N. G. de Bruijn* (Eindhoven)

Citations: MR 18, 720a = N24-28.
Referred to in N80-46.

## N24-43 (26# 2406)

**Cohen, E.**
**Arithmetical notes. IX. On the set of integers representable as a product of a prime and a square.**
*Acta Arith.* **7** (1961/62), 417–420.

Pour VIII voir Proc. Amer. Math. Soc. **13** (1962), 536–539 [MR **25** #2049]. Soit $A(x)$ le nombre des entiers $n \leqq x$ représentables comme produit d'un nombre premier par un carré. L'auteur démontre que, pour $x \geqq 2$, on a la relation

$$A(x) = \frac{\pi^2}{6}\cdot\frac{x}{\log x}+O\left(\frac{x}{\log^2 x}\right).$$

Il en résulte une détermination asymptotique de $A(x)$ si $x \to \infty$. Si $A^*(x)$ désigne le nombre des entiers $n \leqq x$ tels que $n = pe^2$, $p$ étant un nombre premier $\nmid e$, l'auteur démontre que, pour $x \geqq 2$, $A^*(x)$ vérifie la même relation que $A(x)$. *A. Gloden* (Luxembourg)

Citations: MR 25# 2049 = N24-40.
Referred to in A22-67, N24-62.

## N24-44 (26# 6105)

**Cohen, Eckford**
**On the distribution of certain sequences of integers.**
*Amer. Math. Monthly* **70** (1963), 516–521.

Let $S$ denote the set of positive integers $n$ such that each prime factor of $n$ occurs with multiplicity at least 2. Sharpening earlier work, Bateman proved that

$$S(x) = \sum_{\substack{n\leqq x\\ n\in S}} 1 = \alpha x^{1/2}+\beta x^{1/3}+O(x^{1/5}).$$

The author proves that

$$S_{a,b}(x) = \sum_{n\leqq x} P_{a,b}(n) = \gamma x^{1/a}+\delta x^{1/b}+O(x^{1/(a+b)}),$$

where $b > a > 1$, $(a, b) = 1$ and $P_{a,b}(n)$ is defined by

$$F(s) = \sum_{1}^{\infty}\frac{P_{a,b}(n)}{n^s} = \frac{\zeta(as)\zeta(bs)}{\zeta(abs)},$$

while $\gamma$, $\delta$ are expressed in terms of the residues of $F(s)$ at $s = 1/a, 1/b$, respectively. *S. Chowla* (Boulder, Colo.)

Referred to in N24-75.

## N24-45 (27# 2490)

**Mientka, Walter E.**
**An application of the Selberg sieve method.**
*J. Indian Math. Soc. (N.S.)* **25** (1961), 129–138 (1962).

It was proved by V. Brun [Skr. Vid. Kristiania I Mat.-Naturvid. Kl. **1920**, Bd. 1, no. 3] that for large $x$ there is at least one integer between $x$ and $x+x^{1/2}$ which has at most 11 prime factors. The author shows that 11 can be replaced by 9, by proving that the interval $(x, x+x^{1/2})$ contains at least one number whose smallest prime factor exceeds $x^{1/(10-\varepsilon)}$. This is derived by means of estimates for the lower bound in Selberg's sieve method, for which the author refers to a companion paper which has not yet appeared. *N. G. de Bruijn* (Eindhoven)

Referred to in N24-48.

## N24-46 (28# 1188)

**Cohen, E.; Robinson, Richard L.**
**On the distribution of the $k$-free integers in residue classes**; errata, ibid. **10** (1964/65), 443.
*Acta Arith.* **8** (1962/63), 283–293.

The literature of the theory of numbers contains a few fragmentary results on the distribution of power-free integers in arithmetic progressions: here the complex of questions concerned with this problem is treated systematically. The arguments used are elementary throughout and the two principal (but by no means sole) results derived in the present paper are as follows. (i) If $(a, h)$ is $k$-free, then the number $Q_k(x; a, h)$ of $k$-free integers $n \leqq x$ such that $n \equiv a \pmod h$ is given by $Q_k(x; a, h) = f(a, h, k)x + O(x^{1/k})$ uniformly in $h$ and $a$; here $f(a, h, k)$ is an explicitly given but complicated expression. (ii) The $k$-free integers are said to be equidistributed (mod $h$) if the density of these integers in each residue class (mod $h$) where they occur at all is the same. It is shown that the $k$-free integers are equidistributed (mod $h$) if and only if every prime factor of $h$ divides $h$ at least to the $k$th power. *L. Mirsky* (Sheffield)

Referred to in N24-47, N28-72.

## N24-47 (41# 8380)

**Cohen, E. [Cohen, Eckford]; Robinson, Richard L.**
**Correction to the paper: "On the distribution of the $k$-free integers in residue classes".**
*Acta Arith.* **16** (1969/70), 439.

The original paper appeared in same Acta **8** (1962/63), 283–293 [MR **28** #1188].

Citations: MR 28# 1188 = N24-46.

## N24-48 (28# 2101)

**Uchiyama, Saburô**
**On a theorem concerning the distribution of almost primes.**
*J. Fac. Sci. Hokkaido Univ. Ser. I* **17** (1963), 152–159.

Recently W. Mientka [J. Indian Math. Soc. (N.S.) **25** (1961), 129–138; MR **27** #2490] improved a theorem of V. Brun by showing that for all large $x$ there is at least one integer between $x$ and $x+x^{1/2}$ which has at most 9 prime factors. Mientka's method is refined in this paper, and there is a substantial improvement in the result: for every integer $k \geqq 2$ it is true that for all large $x$ the interval $(x, x+x^{1/k})$ contains at least one integer which has at most $2k$ prime factors. *N. G. de Bruijn* (Eindhoven)

Citations: MR 27# 2490 = N24-45.

## N24-49 (29# 74)

**Cohen, Eckford**
**Arithmetical notes. II. An estimate of Erdős and Szekeres.**
*Scripta Math.* **26**, 353–356 (1963).

Part I appeared in Proc. Amer. Math. Soc. **12** (1961), 214–217 [MR **24** #A1239]. The problem of counting the number of abelian groups of a given order has been raised by Erdős and Szekeres [Acta Litt. Sci. Szeged **7** (1934), 95–102] who actually solved a somewhat more general number-theoretic problem. This has been generalized and refined further by Richert [Math. Z. **56** (1952), 21–32; MR **14**, 349] and by Bateman and the reviewer [Illinois J. Math. **2** (1958), 88–98; MR **20** #3205]. The present author generalizes the corresponding number-theoretic problem as follows. Let $n = p_1^{e_1}p_2^{e_2}\cdots p_t^{e_t}$, where $e_i = ak$ or $e_i = ak+b$ ($k \geqq 0$, $a > 0$, $b > 0$ are all integers; $i = 1, 2, \cdots, t$). The number of such $n \leqq x$ is denoted by $R_{a,b}(x)$. If $\tau_{a,b}(n)$ is the number of decompositions of $n$ in the form $n=d^a\delta^b$, and $T_{a,b}(x)=\sum_{n\leq x}\tau_{a,b}(n)$, then

$$R_{a,b}(x) = \sum_{n\leq x^{1/2b}} \mu(n)T_{a,b}(x/n^{2b}).$$

Using different estimates for $T_{a,b}(x)$, the author obtains corresponding results for $R_{a,b}(x)$. The best error term is obtained by using Richert's [loc. cit.] estimate for $T_{a,b}(x)$ and is given by $R_{a,b}(x)=\alpha^*x^{1/a}+\beta^*x^{1/b}+E(x)$, where $\alpha^*=\zeta(b/a)/\zeta(2b/a)$, $\beta^*=\zeta(a/b)/\zeta(2)$ and

$$\begin{aligned} E(x) &= O(x^{1/2b}) \quad \text{if} \quad 2b < 5a, \\ &= O(x^{1/2b}\log x) \quad \text{if} \quad 2b = 5a, \\ &= O(x^{2/(2b+5a)}) \quad \text{if} \quad 2b > 5a. \end{aligned}$$

*E. Grosswald* (Philadelphia, Pa.)

Citations: MR 14, 349e = N52-13; MR 24# A1239 = N36-28.

Referred to in N24-53.

## N24-50 (29# 3413)

**Sierpiński, W.**

**Sur une conséquence d'une hypothèse sur les polynômes.**

*Rend. Circ. Mat. Palermo* (2) **11** (1962), 283–284.

L'auteur déduit d'une conjecture de Bouniakovsky [cf. L. E. Dickson, *History of the theory of numbers*, Vol. I, p. 333, Stechert, New York, 1934] la proposition suivante: Si $f(x)$ est un polynôme en $x$ aux coefficients entiers et s'il existe une infinité de nombres naturels $x$ tels que $f(x)$ est un nombre premier, alors, quelque soit le nombre naturel $s$, il existe une infinité de nombres naturels $x$ tels que $f(x)$ est un produit de $s$ nombres premiers distincts.

L'auteur démontre cette proposition pour le cas d'un polynôme linéaire. *A. Schinzel* (Columbus, Ohio)

## N24-51 (30# 66)

**Cohen, Eckford**

**Remark on a set of integers.**

*Acta Sci. Math. (Szeged)* **25** (1964), 179–180.

Let $k$ be a fixed integer $>1$ and let $Q_k^*(x)$ denote the number of positive integers $n\leq x$ with the property that the multiplicity of each prime divisor of $n$ is not a multiple of $k$. The author gives a very simple proof that

$$Q_k^*(x) = \alpha_k x + O(x^{1/k}),$$

where

$$\alpha_k = \zeta(k)\prod_p \left\{1-\frac{2}{p^k}+\frac{1}{p^{k+1}}\right\}$$

and $p$ runs over all primes.

*S. Chowla* (University Park, Pa.)

## N24-52 (30# 1108)

**Uchiyama, Saburô**

**On the distribution of almost primes in an arithmetic progression.**

*J. Fac. Sci. Hokkaido Univ. Ser. I* **18** (1964), 1–22.

Let $V(n)$ denote the sum of the multiplicities of the prime divisors of $n$. The author proves a theorem, of which the following result is a particular case: Let $k$ and $l$ be a relatively prime pair of integers, with $k$ assumed positive, and define $a(k, l)$ to be the least positive $n$ ($\neq 1$) such that $n\equiv l \pmod k$ and $V(n)\leq 2$; then $a(k, l)=O(k^{7/2})$, uniformly in $k$ and $l$. The proof is based on the sieve method of A. Selberg in connection with a refined form of the prime number theorem. *E. Cohen* (Knoxville, Tenn.)

Referred to in M55-48.

## N24-53 (31# 153)

**Cohen, Eckford**

**Arithmetical notes. III. Certain equally distributed sets of integers.**

*Pacific J. Math.* **12** (1962), 77–84.

For Parts I and II of the series, see Proc. Amer. Math. Soc. **12** (1961), 214–217 [MR **24** #A1239]; Scripta Math. **26**, 353–356 (1963) [MR **29** #74]. For an arbitrary set $A$ of positive integers $n$, the characteristic function $a(n)$ and the inversion function $b(n)$ are determined by

$$\sum_{d\mid n} b(d) = a(n) \equiv \begin{cases} 1 & (n\in A), \\ 0 & (n\notin A). \end{cases}$$

Let $Z$ denote the set of positive integers, $k\in Z$, $P_k$ the set of $k$th powers of elements of $Z$, $Q_k$ the set of $k$-free integers in $Z$, $R_k$ the set of $k$-full positive integers, i.e., 1, together with those integers $n=p_1^{e_1}\cdots p_m^{e_m}$ ($m>0$) which have the property $e_i\geq k$ for all $i$. Let $\lambda_k(n)$ be the inversion function for $P_k$, $\mu_k(n)$ the inversion function for $R_k$ or $Q_k$, respectively, when $k>1$ or $k=1$.

The author studies the functions $\lambda_k(n)$ and $\mu_k(n)$, and then obtains the following estimates: $\sum_{n\leq x}\mu_k(n)=o(x)$, $k\geq 1$, $\sum_{n\leq x}\lambda_k(n)=o(x)$, $k\geq 2$. He also obtains other results for questions in this area.

{Reviewer's remark: In the statement of Theorem 3.2, in place of $\sum_{n\leq x}\mu_k(n)$ one should read $\sum_{n\leq x}\lambda_k(n)$.}

*O. Fomenko* (RŽMat **1963** #11 A83)

Citations: MR 24# A1239 = N36-28; MR 29# 74 = N24-49.

Referred to in N28-48.

## N24-54 (32# 94)

**Lu Hong-wen [Lu Hung-wen]**

**On the number of square-free numbers in an arithmetical progression which are the products of exactly $r$ prime factors.**

*Acta Math. Sinica* **14** (1964), 882–891 *(Chinese); translated as Chinese Math.—Acta* **6** (1965), 284–293.

Let $\pi_r(x, k, l)$ denote the number of products of different primes $p_1\cdots p_r\leq x$ which are $\equiv l \bmod k$. The analogue of the Page-Siegel-Walfisz theorem, i.e., the asymptotic formula for $\pi_r(x, k, l)$ holding uniformly in $k$, was first proved by the reviewer [J. Reine Angew. Math. **192** (1953), 180–203; MR **15**, 603]. The estimate of the remainder term, $R$ say, has been improved by G. J. Rieger [ibid. **199** (1958), 215–220; MR **20** #3108] by using more recent results on the zeros of Dirichlet's $L$-functions. The present author proves a general estimate of $R$ in terms of upper bounds for the zeros of $L$-functions, thus generalizing a theorem of Tatuzawa [Japan. J. Math. **21** (1951), 93–111; MR **15**, 202; erratum, MR **15**, p. 1139]. He then indicates that the latest version of I. M. Vinogradov's method [Izv. Akad. Nauk SSSR Ser. Mat. **22** (1958), 161–164; MR **21** #2624] leads to a new improvement in the estimate of $R$. *H.-E. Richert* (Marburg)

Citations: MR 15, 202d = N12-7; MR 15, 603b = N24-19; MR 20# 3108 = N24-33; MR 21# 2624 = M15-19.

## N24-55 (32# 100)

**Kalecki, M.**

**A theorem on sums of the type $\sum \sigma(N/r)$ and its application. (Polish. English summary)**

*Prace Mat.* **9** (1965), 129–135.

Let $\{s_j\}$, $\{r_i\}$ denote two positive non-decreasing sequences such that $s_j\to\infty$, $r_i\to\infty$, and $\sigma(x)$ and $\rho(x)$ the number of terms in $\{s_j\}$ and $\{r_i\}$ which are $\leq x$, respectively. Theorem 1: Let $\sigma(N)$ and $\rho(N)$ be asymptotically equal to non-decreasing functions $\sigma'(N)=N/f(\log N)$, $\rho'(N)=N/\varphi(\log N)$, respectively, such that $f(ux)/f(x)\to u^q$,

$\varphi(ux)/\varphi(x) \to u^\gamma$ when $x \to \infty$ and $0 < u \leqq 1$, where $g$, $\gamma$ are non-negative constants. Moreover, let $\sum_{r_i \leqq N} 1/r_i$ and $\sum_{s_j \leqq N} 1/s_j$ be equal asymptotically to functions $S(\log N)$ and $R(\log N)$ such that $S(x) \to \infty$, $R(x) \to \infty$, $S(ux)/S(x) \to 1$, $R(ux)/R(x) \to 1$, as $x \to \infty$, for each $0 < u \leqq 1$. Then

$$(1) \quad \sum_{r_i \leqq N} \sigma\left(\frac{N}{r_i}\right) = \{\sigma'(N)R(\log N) + \rho'(N)S(\log N)\}(1+o(1)).$$

The author derives from (1) in a direct way the well-known [G. H. Hardy and E. M. Wright, *An introduction to the theory of numbers*, fourth edition, pp. 369–370, Clarendon, Oxford, 1960] Theorem 2: Let $\tau_k(N)$ denote the number of integers $\leqq N$ which have $k$ prime factors and $\pi_k(N)$ the number of integers $\leqq N$ which have $k$ distinct prime factors. Then $\tau_k(N)$ and $\pi_k(N)$ both equal asymptotically $N(\log\log N)^{k-1}/(k-1)!\log N$.

{Reviewer's remark: In the English summary, one should read "$\varphi(ux)/\varphi(x)$" instead of "$\varphi(ux)/f(x)$", and "$x \to \infty$" instead of "$N \to \infty$".}

*J. W. Andrushkiw* (S. Orange, N.J.)

**N24-56** **(32# 2386)**

**Robinson, R. L.**

**An estimate for the enumerative functions of certain sets of integers.**

*Proc. Amer. Math. Soc.* **17** (1966), 232–237.

Let $r = \prod_{i=1}^m p_i^{e_i}$, $\Delta(r) = \sum_{i=1}^m (e_i - 1)$. Denote by $d_n$ the density of the integers satisfying $\Delta(r) = n$. The author proves that

$$(1) \qquad d_n = \frac{6}{\pi^2} \sum_{\Delta(r)=n} \frac{l_2(r)}{\psi(r)},$$

where $l_2(r) = 1$ if all $e_i$ are not less than 2 and is 0 otherwise, and $\psi(r) = r\prod_{p|r}(1+1/p)$. (1) should be compared with a formula of Rényi [Acad. Serbe Sci. Publ. Inst. Math. **8** (1955), 157–166; MR **17**, 944] and M. Kac [*Statistical independence in probability, analysis and number theory*, Wiley, New York, 1959; MR **22** #996].

The author further proves several other results.

*P. Erdős* (Budapest)

Citations: MR 17, 944f = N24-23; MR 22# 996 = Q15-7.

Referred to in N24-57, N28-73.

**N24-57** **(33# 5594)**

**Robinson, R. L.**

**Errata: "An estimate for the enumerative functions of certain sets of integers".**

*Proc. Amer. Math. Soc.* **17** (1966), 1474.

Correction of misprints in an article in same Proc. **17** (1966), 232–237 [MR **32** #2386].

Citations: MR 32# 2386 = N24-56.

**N24-58** **(32# 4110)**

**Duncan, R. L.**

**The Schnirelmann density of the $k$-free integers.**

*Proc. Amer. Math. Soc.* **16** (1965), 1090–1091.

Let $T_k(n)$ denote the number of $k$-free integers not exceeding $n$, and let $d(T_k) = \inf_{n \geqq 1}(T_k(n)/n)$ and $\delta(T_k) = \lim_{n\to\infty}(T_k(n)/n)$. The author proves by an elementary argument that

$$\delta(T_k) < d(T_{k+1}) \leqq \delta(T_{k+1}).$$

For $k=2$, K. Rogers [same Proc. **15** (1964), 515–516; MR **29** #1192] showed that $d(T_2) = 53/88$.

*O. H. Körner* (Marburg)

Citations: MR 29# 1192 = A38-46.

**N24-59** **(33# 7310)**

**Stark, H. M.**

**On the asymptotic density of the $k$-free integers.**

*Proc. Amer. Math. Soc.* **17** (1966), 1211–1214.

A positive integer is said to be $k$-free ($k \geqq 2$) if it contains no perfect $k$th power factor greater than 1. Let $S(x)$ be the number of $k$-free integers $\leqq x$, and let $T(x) = S(x) - [x]/\zeta(k)$, where $\zeta(s)$ is the Riemann zeta function. Using a Tauberian theorem of A. E. Ingham [Amer. J. Math. **64** (1942), 313–319; MR **3**, 271], the author proves the following theorem. Let $r_j = \frac{1}{2} + g_j$ ($j = 1, 2$) denote the first two zeros of $\zeta(s)$ above the real axis ($g_1 \approx 14$, $g_2 \approx 21$). Let $a = \zeta(r_1/k)/[\zeta'(r_1)r_1]$ and $L = 2(1 - g_1/g_2)|a|$. Then $\liminf_{x\to\infty} x^{-1/2k}T(x) \leqq -L$ and $\limsup_{x\to\infty} x^{-1/2k}T(x) \geqq L$.

*O. H. Körner* (Marburg)

Citations: MR 3, 271c = N44-4.

Referred to in N24-76.

**N24-60** **(34# 7447)**

**Ryan, J. T.**

**One more "many-more" assertion.**

*Amer. Math. Monthly* **74** (1967), *no.* 1, *part I*, 19–24.

Let $m > 1$ be an integer. Let $\phi(m)$ denote the number of numbers $< m$ and prime to $m$ and let $R(m)$ be the number of these which are quadratic residues of $m$. Let $C_a$ be the class of all products of $a$ primes distinct or not. From an examination of the first 2,000,000 numbers, the author is led to the following conjecture which he supports with numerical evidence for the cases $m = 8$, 10, 12: Among all members of $C_a$ in the vicinity of $x$, the density of those congruent to $c$ modulo $m$ depends only on the quadratic character of $c$ modulo $m$. When $c$ is a quadratic non-residue of $m$, the density is $[1 + (-1)^{a+1}R(m)x^{-1/2}]/\phi(m)$. This is a generalization of a conjecture of D. Shanks [Math. Tables Aids Comput. **13** (1959), 272–284; MR **21** #7186].

*D. H. Lehmer* (Berkeley, Calif.)

Citations: MR 21# 7186 = N12-14.

**N24-61** **(37# 172)**

**Bojarincev, A. E.**

**Asymptotic expressions for the $n$th composite number. (Russian)**

*Ural. Gos. Univ. Mat. Zap.* **6**, *tetrad'* 1, 21–43 (1967).

Let $C_n$ denote the $n$th composite number, such a number having, by definition, more than two distinct positive factors. It is shown that $C_n = n\{1 + \nu + 2\nu^2 + 4\nu^3 + 19\nu^4/2 + 181\nu^5/6 + o(\nu^5)\}$, where $\nu = 1/\log n$. Put $C_n^{(1)} = C_n$, $C_n^{(2)} = C_{C_n}$, etc. The properties of $C_n^{(\kappa)}$ are also investigated.

*R. A. Rankin* (Glasgow)

**N24-62** **(37# 174)**

**Schwarz, Wolfgang**

**Eine Bemerkung über die Anzahl der Zahlen $pr^2$ unterhalb $x$.**

*Colloq. Math.* **19** (1968), 117–120.

Let $A(x)$ be the number of integers of the form $pr^2$ ($p$ a prime, $r$ a natural integer) not exceeding $x$. It is shown by entirely elementary considerations that $A(x) = \sum_{n=0}^k C_n x(\log x)^{-n-1} + O_k(x(\log x)^{-k-2})$, where $C_0 = \zeta(2)$ $(=\pi^2/6)$ and, for $n \geqq 1$, $C_n = (-2)^n\zeta^{(n)}(2) + nC_{n-1}$. In fact,

$$A(x) = \sum_{r^2 \leqq x} \pi(xr^{-2}) = \sum_{r \leqq B} \pi(xr^{-2}) = \sum_{r \leqq B} (\operatorname{li} z + O(z(\log z)^{-k-2})),$$

where $z = xr^{-2}$, $B = (\frac{1}{2}x)^{1/2}$, $\operatorname{li} z = \int_2^z (\log v)^{-1}\,dv = 2x\int_b^B u^{-3}(\log xu^{-2})^{-1}\,du$ and $b = (x/z)^{1/2}$; now invert the order of summation and integration and estimate the resulting integral, obtaining the stated result. This generalizes one by E. Cohen [Acta Arith. **7** (1961/62), 417–420; MR **26** #2406], which corresponds to $k=0$; further possible generalizations are indicated and the question is raised to find a formula of the type $A(x)=$ (principal term) $+O(R(x))$, with $R(x)$ the error term in the prime number theorem. *E. Grosswald* (Philadelphia, Pa.)

Citations: MR 26# 2406 = N24-43.
Referred to in N24-79.

## N24-63 (38# 2115)

**Orr, Richard C.**
**On the Schnirelmann density of the sequence of $k$-free integers.**
*J. London Math. Soc.* **44** (1969), 313–319.

Eine natürliche Zahl $m$ heißt $k$-frei, wenn sie nicht teilbar ist durch die $k$-te Potenz irgendeiner Primzahl. Es sei $Q_k(n)$ die Anzahl der $k$-freien $m\leqq n$. Die Schnirelmann-Dichte $d(k)$ der Menge der $k$-freien $m$ ist $d(k)=\inf_{1\leqq n<\infty} Q_k(n)n^{-1}$. Das Hauptergebnis ist der Satz: Für $k\geqq 5$ ist $d(k)$ gleich $Q_k(n)n^{-1}$ für wenigstens ein $n$, welches $5^k\leqq n<6^k$ erfüllt, und für kein $n$ außerhalb dieses Intervalls. Es ist $d(3)=314/378$ bzw. $d(4)=2320/2512$, und diese Werte werden nur angenommen bei $n=378$ bzw. $n=2512$. *H. J. Kanold* (Braunschweig)

## N24-64 (39# 1390)

**Duncan, R. L.**
**On the density of the $k$-free integers.**
*Fibonacci Quart.* **7** (1969), 140–142.

If $T_k$ is the set of $k$-free integers and $T_k(n)$ the number of such numbers not exceeding $n$, then $d(T_k)=\inf T_k(n)/n$ and $\delta(T_k)=\lim_{n\to\infty} T_k(n)/n$. The author's theorem is that $(\delta(T_{k+1})-d(T_{k+1}))/(\delta(T_{k+1})-\delta(T_k))<2^{-k}$.

## N24-65 (39# 6840)

**Fluch, Wolfgang**
**Bemerkung über quadratfreie Zahlen in arithmetischen Progressionen.**
*Monatsh. Math.* **72** (1968), 427–430.

Let $q_r(k,l)$ denote the least squarefree number in the arithmetic progression $l$ mod $k$ $(0<l<k,\ (l,k)=1)$ having at most $r$ prime factors. The author shows that $q_3(k,l)<ck^{(5/3)+\varepsilon}$ and $q_4(k,l)<ck^{(3/2)+\varepsilon}$. The latter result may be regarded as sharpening the result of K. Prachar [same Monatsh. **62** (1958), 173–176; MR **19**, 1160] that the progression $l$ mod $k$ contains a squarefree number less than $ck^{(3/2)+\varepsilon}$. It would be very interesting to reduce the obstinate exponent $\frac{3}{2}$; in this connection note that H.-E. Richert [Mathematika **16** (1969), 1–22; MR **40** #119] has proved that $l$ mod $k$ contains a number less than $ck^{11/8}$ having at most 4 prime factors. The basis of the author's method is the lower bound sieve of Jurkat-Richert [W. B. Jurkat and H.-E. Richert, Acta Arith. **11** (1965), 217–240; MR **34** #2540]. *H. Halberstam* (Nottingham)

Citations: MR 19, 1160g = N24-31; MR 34# 2540 = M55-48; MR 40# 119 = M55-66.

## N24-66 (40# 2623)

**Vaidya, A. M.**
**On the order of the error function of the square-free numbers.**
*Proc. Nat. Inst. Sci. India Part A* **32** (1966), 196–201.

The number of square-free integers $\leqq x$ is $\sum_{n\leqq x}\mu^2(n)=6x/\pi^2+O(x^{1/2})$, where $\mu$ is the Möbius function. The author shows that under the Riemann hypothesis, the error term can be improved to $O(x^{2/5+\varepsilon})$. He also treats the related function $\sum_{n\leqq x}\mu^2(n)n^k$ for integer $k\geqq 0$.
*T. M. Apostol* (Pasadena, Calif.)

## N24-67 (41# 1633)

**Urazbaev, B. M.**
**The growth of the number of real quadratic fields with positive discriminant. (Russian)**
*Proc. Second Kazakhstan Interuniv. Sci. Conf. Math. Mech.* (1965) (*Russian*), *pp.* 15–20. *Izdat. "Nauka" Kazah. SSR, Alma-Ata*, 1968.

Let $N(x)$ denote the number of odd square-free numbers less than $x$. The author proves, using contour integration, etc., the asymptotic formula $N(x)=\pi^{-2}4x+O(x^{a+\varepsilon})$, where $\frac{3}{4}<a<1$. {By more elementary methods one can obtain a stronger result with the last term $O(\sqrt{x})$; see G. H. Hardy and E. M. Wright [*An introduction to the theory of numbers*, third edition, Clarendon, Oxford, 1954; MR **16**, 673; German translation, Oldenbourg, Munich, 1958; MR **20** #828; fourth edition, Clarendon, Oxford, 1960].} *J. Browkin* (Warsaw)

Citations: MR 16, 673b = Z01-28; MR 20# 828 = Z01-29.

## N24-68 (41# 3430)

**Warlimont, Richard**
**On squarefree numbers in arithmetic progressions.**
*Monatsh. Math.* **73** (1969), 433–448.

Let $q(k,l)$ denote the least squarefree number in the arithmetic progression $l+mk$, $m=0,1,\cdots$, where $0\leqq l\leqq k$ and $(l,k)=1$. One theorem proved in the first part of the paper is: Given $C\geqq 1$ there exists some $\varepsilon=\varepsilon(C)>0$ such that for infinitely many $k$'s the inequality $q(k,l)\geqq Ck$ holds for at least $\varepsilon\phi(k)$ numbers $l$. The second part of the paper is concerned with finding a type of average error term for square-free numbers in arithmetic progressions analogous to those found by Davenport and Halberstam, and P. X. Gallagher for primes in arithmetic progressions [Gallagher, Mathematika **14** (1967), 14–20; MR **35** #5411].

Large sieve methods are used to estimate $S(x,y)=\sum_{k\leq y}\sum_{l\leq k,(l,k)=1}|\sum_{n\leq x,n\equiv l(k)}\mu^2(n)-xF(k)|^2$; $1\leqq y\leqq x$, with $F(k)=(\sum_{d=1,(d,k)=1}^{\infty}\mu(d)/d^2)/k$ and, in particular, the author shows that $S(x,y)\ll xy$ for $x^{1/3}\log^{10/3}x\leqq y\leqq x$.
*E. M. Horadam* (Armidale)

Citations: MR 35# 5411 = M55-52.
Referred to in N24-80, N40-75.

## N24-69 (41# 5313)

**Emerson, W. R.**
**Covering theorems with applications to some questions on normal orders.**
*Trans. Amer. Math. Soc.* **145** (1969), 287–307.

In einer früheren Arbeit [R. Bellman und H. N. Shapiro, Duke Math. J. **21** (1954), 629–637; MR **16**, 114] wurde der folgende Satz bewiesen: $\Phi$ sei eine monotone Funktion, welche die Menge der natürlichen Zahlen in die Menge der positiven reellen Zahlen abbildet und $\lim_{n\to\infty}\Phi(n)=+\infty$ erfüllt. Dann gilt: $Q_\Phi(n)=Q(n,n+\Phi(n))$ hat die Größenordnung $6\cdot\pi^{-2}\cdot\Phi(n)$, wobei $Q(u,v)$ die Anzahl der quadratfreien natürlichen Zahlen $q$ mit $u<q\leqq v$ bedeutet. In der vorliegenden Arbeit wird die Monotonie von $\Phi$ durch schwächere Bedingungen ersetzt.
*H. J. Kanold* (Braunschweig)

Citations: MR 16, 114a = N24-20.

## N24-70 (42# 1780)

**Golomb, S. W.**
**Powerful numbers.**
*Amer. Math. Monthly* **77** (1970), 848–855.

Define a positive integer $r$ to be a powerful number if $p^2$ divides $r$ whenever the prime $p$ divides $r$. Then every powerful number can be represented uniquely in the form

$r=n^2m^3$ if $m$ is square-free. Let $k(x)$ denote the number of powerful numbers $\leqq x$ and put

$$F(s) = \prod_p (1+p^{-2s}+p^{-3s}+p^{-4s}+\cdots) = \sum_{r\in K} r^{-s},$$

where $K$ is the set of powerful numbers. By writing $k(x)=\sum_{m=1}^{\infty} \mu^2(m)[(x/m^3)^{1/2}]$, it is proved that $k(x)\sim c\sqrt{x}$, where $c=\zeta(3/2)/\zeta(3)$. Also,

$$F(s) = \sum_{n=1}^{\infty} n^{-2s} \sum_{m=1}^{\infty} \mu^2(m)m^{-3s} = \zeta(2s)\zeta(3s)/\zeta(6s)$$

and so $F(1)$ = the sum of the reciprocals of the powerful numbers $=315\zeta(3)/(2\pi^4)$.

It is also shown that any solution $x_1, y_1$ of the Pell equation $x^2-dy^2=\pm 1$ with the extra condition that $d|y_1^2$, leads to an infinite family of consecutive powerful numbers. For gaps between powerful numbers it has been conjectured that 6 cannot be represented in any way as a difference between two powerful numbers. It is further conjectured that there are infinitely many numbers which cannot be so represented. *E. M. Horadam* (Armidale)

## N24-71 (42# 1781)

**Kátai, I.; Mogyoródi, J.**

**On the density of certain sequences of integers.**

*Publ. Math. Debrecen* **16** (1969), 17–23.

An integer $n$ will be called square-full if all its prime factors occur at least to the second power. Every integer can be written uniquely as the product of two relatively prime integers, one square-free the other square-full. The authors consider functions of $n$ which depend only on the square-full part of $n$. Several interesting, though complicated, results on the local-distribution of such functions are stated and proved. *A. R. Freedman* (Burnaby, B.C.)

## N24-72 (42# 5927)

**Suryanarayana, D.; Sitaramachandra Rao, R.**

**On the order of the error function of the $k$-free integers.**

*Proc. Amer. Math. Soc.* **28** (1971), 53–58.

Let $Q_k(x)$ and $Q_k'(x)$ denote the number and sum, respectively, of the $k$-free integers $\leqq x$. Then $\Delta_k(x)=Q_k(x)-x/\zeta(k)$ and $\Delta_k'(x)=Q_k'(x)-\frac{1}{2}x^2/\zeta(k)$ represent the error functions in the asymptotic formulas for $Q_k(x)$ and $Q_k'(x)$. Assuming the Riemann hypothesis in the form $\sum_{n\leq x}\mu(n) =O(x^{1/2+\varepsilon})$, the authors prove that $\Delta_k'(x)-x\Delta_k(x)= O(x^{1+3/(4k+1)+\varepsilon})$ and $(1/x)\int_1^x \Delta_k(t)\,dt=O(x^{3/(4k+1)+\varepsilon})$ for every $\varepsilon>0$. They use this as evidence in favor of the conjecture $\Delta_k(x)=O(x^{3/(4k+1)+\varepsilon})$. The best known result on $\Delta_k(x)$, proved by A. Z. Val'fiš [*Weylsche Exponentialsummen in der neueren Zahlentheorie*, VEB Deutsch. Verlag Wissensch., Berlin, 1963; MR **36** #3737] without any hypothesis, is $\Delta_k(x)=O(x^{1/k}\exp(-c_k \log^{3/5} x(\log\log x)^{-1/5}))$, where $c_k>0$. *T. M. Apostol* (Pasadena, Calif.)

Citations: MR 36# 3737 = L02-8.

## N24-73 (42# 7611)

**Schwarz, Wolfgang**

**Eine Bemerkung zu einer asymptotischen Formel von Herrn Rényi.**

*Arch. Math.* (*Basel*) **21** (1970), 157–166.

Let $K$ denote the set of all natural numbers $n$ having prime decomposition $n=p_1^{\alpha_1}\cdots p_r^{\alpha_r}$ with exactly one exponent $\alpha$ equal to 2 and all the others equal to 1; and let $K(x)$ denote the number of elements of $K$ not exceeding $x$. The principal result of this paper is an asymptotic expansion for $K(x)$: for each $r=1, 2, \cdots$, $K(x)= (6/\pi^2)\alpha x+(x^{1/2}/\log x)\sum_{k=0}^{r-1} b_k(\log x)^{-k}+O(x^{1/2}(\log x)^{-r-1})$, where $\alpha=\sum_p 1/(p(p+1))$, $b_0=0$, $b_1=-4\zeta(\frac{1}{2})$ $(\neq 0)$ and the remaining coefficients $b_k$ $(k=2, 3, \cdots)$ are given by a certain (complicated) formula. The asymptotic relation $K(x)\sim(6/\pi^2)\alpha x$ is the special case $l=1$ of a general result of A. Rényi [Acad. Serbe Sci. Publ. Inst. Math. **8** (1955), 157–162; MR **17**, 944] concerning the asymptotic density $d_l$ of the sequence $D_l$ of numbers $n$ for which $\Omega(n)-\omega(n)=l$. The author now improves on results of E. Cohen [Trans. Amer. Math. Soc. **112** (1964), 214–227; MR **29** #3458]; he reports in an addendum that his asymptotic expansion of $K(x)$ has also been established by a pupil of Delange, and that Delange himself has found an asymptotic expansion for $D_l(x)$. *H. Halberstam* (Nottingham)

Citations: MR 17, 944f = N24-23; MR 29# 3458 = N52-25.

Referred to in N24-79.

## N24-74 (42# 7623)

**Deshouillers, Jean-Marc**

**Sur les nombres admettant un nombre de facteurs premiers déterminé.**

*C. R. Acad. Sci. Paris Sér. A-B* **271** (1970), A1197–A1199.

Let $\omega(n)$ be the number of distinct prime factors of the integer $n$, and let $\Omega(n)$ be the number of prime factors of $n$ counted with their multiplicities. Let $A$ be a strictly increasing sequence of integers, let $A(x)$ be the number of integers of $A$ less than or equal to $x$, let $d(A)=\lim A(x)/x$ (if this limit exists), let $\underline{d}(A)=\liminf A(x)/x$, and let $\overline{d}(A)=\limsup A(x)/x$, all limits being taken as $x$ goes to infinity. Finally, let $E_A=\{n\colon \omega(n)\in A\}$ and let $F_A=\{n\colon \Omega(n)\in A\}$. Outlines of the proofs of the following four theorems are given. (1) If the elements $a_i$ of $A$ satisfy $a_i=i/d(A)+o(i^{1/2})$ as $i$ goes to infinity, then $d(E_A)=d(F_A)=d(A)$. (2) The theorem (1) is best possible, in the sense that there exists a sequence $A$ with elements $a_i$ satisfying $a_i=2i+o(i^{1/2})$ as $i$ goes to infinity and such that neither $d(E_A)$ nor $d(F_A)$ exists. (3) If $\underline{d}(A)=0$ then $d(E_A)$ (or $d(F_A)$) exists if and only if for any positive real number $c$, $A(x+cx^{1/2})-A(x-cx^{1/2})=o(x^{1/2})$, and then $d(E_A)=d(F_A)=0$. (4) $\overline{d}(A)=0$ then $d(E_A)$ (or $d(F_A)$) exists if and only if the elements $a_i$ of $A$ satisfy $a_i= i+o(i^{1/2})$, and then $d(E_A)=d(F_A)=1$.

*B. Garrison* (San Diego, Calif.)

## N24-75 (43# 146)

**Cohen, Eckford; Davis, K. Joseph**

**Elementary estimates for certain types of integers.**

*Acta Sci. Math.* (*Szeged*) **31** (1970), 363–371.

The main purpose of the paper seems to be the proof of the following theorem: For any integer $k\geqq 2$, let $L_k(x)$ be the number of positive integers $n$, with the property that each of their prime factors divides them at least to the $k$th power; then $L_k(x)=c_kx^{1/k}+c_k'x^{1/(k+1)}+O(x^{1/(k+2)})$, with explicitly known coefficients $c_k$, $c_k'$, independent of $x$. This result (actually even in a stronger form and with an essentially elementary proof) was known [see P. T. Bateman and the reviewer, Illinois J. Math. **2** (1958), 88–98; MR **20** #2305], but the proof used the uniqueness theorem for Dirichlet series. The present authors avoid that, and their proof, which is by no means easy, is entirely elementary. The paper ends with a really very simple proof of a slightly weaker version of the same theorem (error term $O(x^{1/(k+2)}\log x)$). The method of proof is a refinement of that by which P. Erdős and G. Szekeres [Acta Litt. Sci. Szeged **7** (1934), 95–102] proved $L_k(x)=c_kx^{1/k}+O(x^{1/(k+1)})$. {Reviewer's remark: The paper is rather difficult to read. For about three references (that could easily have been added to the bibliography) the reader is directed to the bibliography of an earlier paper by the first author [Amer.

Math. Monthly **70** (1963), 516–521; MR **26** #6105]. The numbering of the lemmas must have been changed at the last moment and was done rather carelessly. Lemma 5 is followed by Lemma 8 and reference is made in the proofs to Lemma 4c, Lemma 6 and Lemma 7, nowhere to be found.} *E. Grosswald* (Philadelphia, Pa.)

Citations: MR 20# 2305 = N24-32; MR 26# 6105 = N24-44.

## N24-76 (43# 167)

**Saffari, Bahman**

**Ω-théorèmes sur le terme résiduel dans la loi de répartition des entiers non divisibles par une puissance $r^{\text{ième}}$, $r>1$ ("$r$-free").**

*C. R. Acad. Sci. Paris Sér. A-B* **272** (1971), A95–A97.

Author's summary: "Amélioration d'un Ω-théorème 'quantitatif' de H. M. Stark [Proc. Amer. Math. Soc. **17** (1966), 1211–1214; MR **33** #7310] grâce à une généralisation de l''inégalité taubérienne' de A. E. Ingham [Amer. J. Math. **64** (1942), 313–319; MR **3**, 271] et à des résultats de 'limitation' sur les zéros communs à $\zeta(s)$ et à $\zeta(rs)$ dans la bande critique."

Citations: MR 3, 271c = N44-4; MR 33# 7310 = N24-59.

## N24-77 (44# 147)

**Suryanarayana, D.**

**Semi-$k$-free integers.**

*Elem. Math.* **26** (1971), 39–40.

A positive integer $n$ is said to be semi-$k$-free if the multiplicity of each prime factor of $n$ is not equal to $k$. The integer 1 is semi-$k$-free. For $x \geqq 1$, let $Q_k(x)$ denote the number of semi-$k$-free integers $\leqq x$. The author proves that $Q_k(x)=\alpha_k x+O(x^{1/k})$, where $\alpha_k=\prod_p (1-1/p^k+1/p^{k+1})$, the product being extended over all primes $p$.
*R. Alter* (Lexington, Ky.)

## N24-78 (44# 2716)

**Subbarao, M. V.; Feng, Y. K.**

**On the distribution of generalized $K$-free integers in residue classes.**

*Duke Math. J.* **38** (1971), 741–748.

An integer $n$ is $K$-free whenever it is not divisible by the $K$th power of any prime. In this paper, the notion of $K$-free integers is generalized as follows: Let $q$ and $r$ be fixed integers such that $0<q<r$. Any integer $n>1$ has the unique representation $n=a^r b$, where $b$ is $r$-free. If, in addition, $b$ is $q$-free, then $n$ is a generalized $q$-free integer or an $(r, q)$-integer. Let $Q_{r,q}(x; a, h)$ denote the number of $(r, q)$-integers which are $\leqq x$ and which lie in the residue class consisting of numbers of the form $n\equiv a \pmod h$. Then results from a paper by the first author and V. C. Harris [J. London Math. Soc. **41** (1966), 595–604; MR **34** #133] and the properties of a multiplicative function are used to obtain an asymptotic estimate for $Q_{Kr,Kq}(x; a, h)$ where $K$ is an integer $>1$. A second theorem gives an estimate for the number of representations of the integer $n$ as the sum of a $(K_1r_1, K_1q_1)$-integer and a $(K_2r_2, K_2q_2)$-integer, where $K_1>1$, $0<q_1<r_1$, $K_2>1$, $0<q_2<r_2$, and $K_2q_2 \leqq K_1$. *E. M. Horadam* (Armidale)

Citations: MR 34# 133 = A36-55.

## N24-79 (44# 3971)

**Duttlinger, J.**

**Eine Bemerkung zu zwei asymptotischen Entwicklungen aus der Zahlentheorie.**

*Arch. Math. (Basel)* **22** (1971), 70–71.

Es bezeichne $A(x)$ bzw. $K(x)$ die Anzahl der natürlichen Zahlen $n \leqq x$, die sich in der Gestalt $n=p\cdot r^2$ bzw. $n=p^2e$ darstellen lassen, wobei $p$ eine Primzahl bedeutet, $r$ eine natürliche Zahl und $e$ eine quadratfreie, zu $p$ teilerfremde natürliche Zahl. Frühere Ergebnisse von W. Schwarz [Colloq. Math. **19** (1968), 117–120; MR **37** #174; Arch. Math. (Basel) **21** (1970), 157–166; MR **42** #7611] werden verschärft zu

$$A(x) = \sum_{0\leqq n<(4e)^{-1}\log x} C_n x(\log x)^{-n-1}+O(x\exp(-c_2\log^{1/2}x)),$$

$$K(x) = 6\pi^{-2}\alpha x+(x^{1/2}/\log x)\sum_{m=0}^{r(x)-1} b_m \log^{-m} x +O(x^{1/2}\exp(-c_3\log^{1/4}x)).$$

*H. J. Kanold* (Braunschweig)

Citations: MR 37# 174 = N24-62; MR 42# 7611 = N24-73.

## N24-80 (44# 3973)

**Orr, Richard C.**

**Remainder estimates for squarefree integers in arithmetic progression.**

*J. Number Theory* **3** (1971), 474–497.

Let $Q(x; k, l)$ be the number of squarefrees $q$ such that $q\leqq x$ and $q\equiv l \bmod k$, where $(k, l)$ is squarefree. Let $R(x; k, l)$ be the corresponding remainder term $R(x; k, l)=Q(x; k, l)-A(k, l)x/k$, where

$$A(k, l) = \prod_{p\nmid k}(1-p^{-2})\prod_{p\mid k, p\nmid k/(k,l)}(1-1/p).$$

K. Prachar [Monatsh. Math. **62** (1958), 173–176; MR **19**, 1160] proved the result (significant when $k<x^{2/3-\delta}$) $R(x; k, l)=O(x^{1/2}k^{-1/4+\varepsilon}+k^{1/2+\varepsilon})$, when $(k, l)=1$. The author gives some applications of his own theorems

$$\sum_{k\leqq x^{2/3}/(\log x)^{A+1}} \max_{k,l}|R(x; k, l)| = O(x/(\log x)^A),$$

$$\sum_{k\leqq y}\sum_{1\leqq l\leqq k} R^2(x; k, l) = O(xy+x^{8/5}(\log x)^5) \quad (y\leqq x),$$

for the proofs of which reference is made to a paper of R. Warlimont [ibid. **73** (1969), 433–448; MR **41** #3430]. Let $q$, $q_1$ and $q_2$ be squarefree. The results include asymptotic estimates for $\sum_{l<q\leqq x} d_3(q-l)$ and $\sum_{q_1\leqq\sqrt{x}, l<q_1q_2\leqq x} d(q_1q_2-l)$, where $d$ and $d_3$ are the usual divisor functions. The author observes that the corresponding problems in which $q$, $q_1$ and $q_2$ are prime were considered, respectively, by P. D. T. A. Elliott and H. Halberstam [Mathematika **13** (1966), 196–203; MR **34** #5788] (see also J. W. Porter [Proc. London Math. Soc. (3) **24** (1972), 15–26]) and by M. B. Barban [Vestnik Leningrad. Univ. Ser. Mat. Meh. Astronom. **18** (1963), no. 4, 5–13; MR **28** #57].
*G. Greaves* (Cardiff)

Citations: MR 19, 1160g = N24-31; MR 28# 57 = P48-8; MR 34# 5788 = P36-50; MR 41# 3430 = N24-68.

## N24-81 (44# 6623)

**Delange, Hubert**

**Sur des formules de Atle Selberg.**

*Acta Arith.* **19** (1971), 105–146. (*errata insert*)

The author considers sums of the type $\sum \chi(n)z^{f(n)}$, where $f$ is an additive arithmetic function taking non-negative integer values and $\chi$ is a multiplicative function taking the values 0 and 1 only and such that $\chi(p)=1$ for all primes $p$. For example, let $\Omega(n)$ be the number of prime factors of $n$ counted according to multiplicity. A. Selberg [J. Indian Math. Soc. (N.S.) **18** (1954), 83–87; MR **16**, 676] showed that $\sum_{n\leqq x} z^{\Omega(n)}=xH(z)(\log x)^{z-1}+O\{x(\log x)^{\operatorname{Re} z-2}\}$, where $H(z)=\{\Gamma(z)\}^{-1}\prod_p(1-z/p)^{-1}(1-1/p)^z$ and for each $\rho<2$ the estimate holds uniformly in $|z|<\rho$. In his more general case the author obtains more precise estimates of the form $x(\log x)^{z-1}\{\sum_{0\leqq j\leqq q} A_j(z)/(\log z)^j+O((\log x)^{-q-1})\}$, valid, for each integer $q>0$, uniformly in $|z|\leqq\rho$ for each $\rho$ for which the sum $\sum_{p,k\geqq 2}\chi(p^k)\rho^{f(p^k)}/p^{k_\sigma}$ converges for some $\sigma<1$. He uses his results to infer similarly precise estimates for the quantities $\sum_{n\leqq x, f(n)=\nu}\chi(n)$ and $\sum_{n\leqq x}\chi(n)f(n)^{\nu}$. *G. Greaves* (Cardiff)

Citations: MR 16, 676a = N24-22.

# N28 DISTRIBUTION OF INTEGERS WITH OTHER MULTIPLICATIVE CONSTRAINTS

See also Section N60.

See also reviews A32-11, B28-45, D40-61, E24-29, E28-2, E76-2, E76-4, M55-25, M55-37, M55-53, N12-38, N24-14, N24-26, N24-28, N32-21, N56-3, N56-8, N56-19, N80-19, P28-8, R20-92, R46-9, R46-19, R46-23.

## N28-1 (2, 40c)

**Segal, B. On integers of standard form of a definite type.** Bull. Acad. Sci. URSS. Sér. Math. [Izvestia Akad. Nauk SSSR] **1939**, 519–538 (1939). (Russian. English summary)

Let $p_1, \cdots, p_l$ be distinct given primes, $l\geqq 2$, $n_1, n_2, \cdots$ the sequence of integers of the form $p_1^{\alpha_1}\cdots p_l^{\alpha_l}$, in order of magnitude. Then $n_{j+1}/n_j\to 1$. This remains true if $l\geqq 3$ and the $\alpha_i$ are restricted to primes. For $l=2$ Segal had proved [C. R. (Doklady) Acad. Sci. URSS (A) **1933**, 39–44] Theorem 1: let $I_N$ be the number of solutions of $N=dp_1^{\alpha_1}p_2^{\alpha_2}$ with positive integers $\alpha_i$, and $1\leqq d\leqq e^{\Delta_1}$, $\Delta_1\log\log N=\log\log\log N$; then

$$I_N=\Delta_1(\log N)/\beta_2+O(\log N/\log\log N).$$

Here $\beta_l=\log p_1\cdots\log p_l$. Using a result of A. Gelfond [same vol., 509–518; cf. these Rev. **1**, 295], $\Delta_1$ can be replaced by $\Delta=e^{-\rho}$, $\rho=(\log\log N)^{\frac{1}{2}-\epsilon}$, $\epsilon>0$; and Segal proves Theorem 2: Let $l\geqq 3$, $I_{N,l}$ the number of solutions of $N=dp_1^{\alpha_1}\cdots p_l^{\alpha_l}$ with positive integral $\alpha_i$ and $e^{-\Delta}\leqq d\leqq e^{\Delta}$; then

$$I_{N,l}=E+O((\log N)^{l-1}e^{-\rho_0}),$$

where $E=(2/(l-1)!)(\log N)^{l-1}\Delta/\beta_l$, $\rho_0=(\log\log N)^{\frac{1}{2}-\epsilon_0}$, $0<\epsilon_0<\epsilon$. Using also results by Vinogradow [see the preceding review],* Segal restricts the $\alpha_i$ to be primes, when the asymptotic formula becomes $E(\log\log N)^{-l}(1+O(\Delta_1))$. A similar result is given for $N=dp_1^{\pi}p_2^{\alpha}$, where $\pi$ runs over primes, $\alpha$ over positive integers. *G. Pall.*

*MR 2, 40B = L20-2.

Citations: MR 1, 295c = J80-1; MR 2, 40b = L20-2.

Referred to in N28-2.

## N28-2 (2, 150d)

**Segal, B. On certain sets of integers.** Bull. Acad. Sci. URSS. Sér. Math. [Izvestia Akad. Nauk SSSR] **4**, 319–334 (1940). (Russian. English summary)

Let $n\geqq 2$ be an integer, $l\geqq r+1$, $r$ the greatest even number less than $4\cdot 81n(n+1)(n+2)\log n$. Let $p_1, \cdots, p_l$ be given primes, and let $\sigma_1, \cdots, \sigma_l$ range over integer $n$th powers. Write $\nu=1/n$, $\rho=(\log\log N)^{\frac{1}{2}-\epsilon}$, $\rho_0=(\log\log N)^{\frac{1}{2}-\epsilon_0}$, $\beta_l=\log p_1\cdots\log p_l$, $\gamma=(\Gamma(1+\nu))^l/\Gamma(l\nu)$. Then the number $I_N$ of representations of $N$ in the form $N=dp_1^{\sigma_1}\cdots p_l^{\sigma_l}$, with $e^{-\Delta}\leqq d\leqq e^{\Delta}$ and $\Delta=e^{-\rho}$, is given by

$$I_N=2(\gamma/\beta_l^{\nu})(\log N)^{l\nu-1}\Delta+O((\log N)^{l\nu-1}e^{-\rho_0}),$$

where $0<\epsilon_0<\epsilon$. The case where the $\sigma_i$ range over all integers or all primes was considered in earlier articles [same Bull. **3**, 519–538 (1939); cf. these Rev. **2**, 40]. Estimates of sums due to I. M. Vinogradow and A. D. Gelfond are used. Lemmas 7 and 8 are alternative to, and are said to have wider applicability than, some estimates by van der Corput [Nederl. Akad. Wetensch., Proc. **42**, 461–467 (1939)]. *G. Pall* (Princeton, N. J.).

Citations: MR 2, 40c = N28-1.

## N28-3 (3, 69d)

**Kac, M. Two number-theoretic remarks.** Revista Ci., Lima **43**, 177–182 (1941).

The author proves the following results: (1) Denote by $d(a, h, k)$ the density of integers $n$ which have exactly $k$ prime divisors between $a$ and $a^{e^h}$. Then $\lim_{a\to\infty}d(a, h, k)=e^{-h}h^k/k!$.

$$(2)\qquad \sum_{k=0}^{\infty}(-1)^k\frac{d(2k+1)}{2k+1}=\frac{\pi^2}{16}.$$

This was a problem proposed by Ramanujan. *P. Erdös.*

## N28-4 (3, 269b)

**Pillai, S. S. On numbers of the form $2^a\cdot 3^b$. I.** Proc. Indian Acad. Sci., Sect. A. **15**, 128–132 (1942).

Ramanujan asserted that, if $N(x)$ is the number of integers of the form $2^a3^b$ which are less than $x$, then approximately

$$(1)\qquad N(x)=\frac{\log 2x\log 3x}{2\log 2\log 3}.$$

Let $\Delta(x)=N(x)-F(x)$, where $F(x)$ is the right member of (1). The order of $\Delta(x)$ may be obtained from the Hardy-Littlewood results on the problem of lattice points in a right angled triangle. In this paper formulas for $N(2^r\cdot 3^s)$ and $\Delta(2^r\cdot 3^s)$ are derived by the ingenious use of recursion formulas connecting $N(x)$ and $\Delta(x)$ with $N(\frac{1}{2}x)$, $N(\frac{1}{3}x)$ and $\Delta(\frac{1}{2}x)$, $\Delta(\frac{1}{3}x)$, respectively. A table is given of integers of the form $2^a\cdot 3^b$ up to $2^{10}\cdot 3^6$. *R. D. James.*

## N28-5 (3, 269c)

**Pillai, S. S. and George, Alleyamma. On numbers of the form $2^a\cdot 3^b$. II.** Proc. Indian Acad. Sci., Sect. A. **15**, 133–134 (1942).

From the results and table of part I [see the preceding review] with additional tables it is shown that $-1.9<\Delta(x)<2.4$ for $x\leqq 2^{1000}$. *R. D. James* (Saskatoon, Sask.).

## N28-6 (4, 210c)

**Pillai, S. S. On a congruence property of the divisor function.** J. Indian Math. Soc. (N.S.) **6**, 118–119 (1942).

Let $d(n)$ denote the number of divisors of $n$ and $N(k, x)$ the number of $n\leqq x$ for which $d(n)$ is a multiple of $k$. The author gives a short proof of the results

$$N(k, x)=Ax+O(x^{1/(k-1)}\log x),\quad k\geqq 3,\ \text{prime},$$
$$N(2, x)=[x]-[\sqrt{x}].$$

Here

$$A=\sum_{q,r}((-1)^{f(q)-1}\varphi(q)/q^{rk}),$$

where $f(q)$ is the number of different prime factors of $q$ and $\varphi(q)$ is the Euler $\varphi$-function. *R. D. James.*

Referred to in N28-7, N28-11.

## N28-7 (6, 36h)

**Sathe, L. G. On a congruence property of the divisor function. I.** J. Indian Math. Soc. (N.S.) **7**, 143–145 (1943).

Let $N(k, x)$ denote the number of $n\leqq x$ for which $d(n)$, the number of divisors of $n$, is a multiple of $k$. It is proved that, for any odd prime $k$,

$$N(k, x)=A_kx+O(x^{1/(k-1)}\log x),$$

where

$$A_k = 1 - \prod_p \{1-(p-1)/(p^k-1)\},$$

$p$ running through all primes. The author states that this corrects an erroneous result by S. S. Pillai [J. Indian Math. Soc. (N.S.) **6**, 118–119 (1942); these Rev. **4**, 210]. There is a misprint in the equation for $A_k$ in the statement of the theorem on page 143. *I. Niven* (Lafayette, Ind.).

Citations: MR 4, 210c = N28-6.
Referred to in N28-11.

## N28-8 (6, 37a)

**Sathe, L. G. On a congruence property of the divisor function. II.** J. Indian Math. Soc. (N.S.) **7**, 146–151 (1943).

Extending the result stated in the preceding review, the author proves: (1) $N(k, x) \neq o(x)$ for any positive integer $k$; (2) $N(2k, x) \sim N(k, x)$ for $k$ odd; (3) for $k = m_1 m_2$, $m_1 < m_2$, $m_1$ and $m_2$ being odd primes,

$$N(k, x) = C_k x + O(x^{1/(m_1-1)+\epsilon})$$

for every $\epsilon > 0$, $C_k$ being a positive constant.
*I. Niven* (Lafayette, Ind.).

## N28-9 (6, 57h)

**Selberg, Sigmund. Über die Verteilung einiger Klassen quadratfreier Zahlen, die aus einer gegebenen Anzahl von Primfaktoren zusammengesetzt sind.** Skr. Norske Vid. Akad. Oslo. I. no. **5**, 49 pp. (1942).

Let $\pi_n(x)$ be the number of integers not greater than $x$ which are a product of exactly $n$ different primes; it is known [E. Landau, Bull. Soc. Math. France **28**, 25–38 (1900)] that

$$\pi_n(x) = \frac{x}{\log x} \frac{(\log\log x)^{n-1}}{(n-1)!} + O\left(\frac{x}{\log x}(\log\log x)^{n-2}\right).$$

The author obtains the better result:

$$\frac{\log x}{x}\pi_n(x) = \sum_{\nu=1}^{n} \frac{a_\nu}{(n-\nu)!}(\log\log x)^{n-\nu} + O((\log\log x)^{-q});$$

the numbers $a_1, a_2, \cdots$ are absolute constants, and $q$ is arbitrarily large; this is deduced as an elementary consequence of the prime number theorem. If $m$ is any product of $n$ different primes, let $P_m$ denote the largest prime factor of $m$. The author proves that the number of $m < x$ satisfying the condition

$$P_m < x^{1-(\log x)^{-\phi(x)}}$$

is $o(x)$, where $n$ is given and $\phi(x)$ is any positive function such that $\phi(x) \to 0$, $\phi(x) \log\log x \to \infty$, as $x \to \infty$.
*C. L. Siegel* (Princeton, N. J.).

Referred to in M45-39, N24-7, N28-10, N28-13.

## N28-10 (7, 48a)

**Selberg, Sigmund. Ein elementarer Satz über den grössten Primfaktor einer quadratfreien Zahl, die aus einer gegebenen Anzahl von Primfaktoren zuzammengesetzt ist.** Arch. Math. Naturvid. **45**, no. 4, 53–60 (1942).

Denote by $a_1 < \cdots < a_x \leqq n$ the integers having exactly $k$ prime factors. It is well known that

$$x = (1+o(1))(n/\log n)(\log\log n)^{k-1}/(k-1)!.$$

Denote by $p(a_i)$ the greatest prime factor of $a_i$. Let $c$ be arbitrary, $0 < c < 1$. The author proves that $p(a_i) > n^c$ for all but

$$o\left(\frac{n}{\log n} \cdot \frac{(\log\log n)^{k-1}}{(k-1)!}\right)$$

values of $n$. [A sharper result obtained by the author has already been reviewed [Skr. Norske Vid. Akad. Oslo. I. **1942**, no. 5 (1942); these Rev. **6**, 57].] *P. Erdös.*

Citations: MR 6, 57h = N28-9.

## N28-11 (7, 49g)

**Sathe, L. G. On a congruence property of the divisor function.** Amer. J. Math. **67**, 397–406 (1945).

Let $N(k, r, x)$ denote the number of $n \leqq x$ for which $d(n) \equiv r \pmod k$, $d(n)$ being the number of divisors of $n$. The author proves that, if $2^m$ is the highest power of 2 which divides $k$, then there is a constant $B = B(k, r) > 0$ such that $N(k, r, x) \sim Bx$ if $2^m | r$, and $N(k, r, x) = o(x)$ otherwise. For $k$ prime and $r = 0$ this result was given by Pillai [J. Indian Math. Soc. (N.S.) **6**, 118–119 (1942); these Rev. **4**, 210], whose work contained an error corrected by Sathe [J. Indian Math. Soc. (N.S.) **7**, 143–145 (1943); these Rev. **6**, 36]. Two miscellaneous results are obtained: it is shown that $B(k, r) = B(k', r')$ under certain conditions on $k, r, k', r'$; and $B(k, r)$ is evaluated in terms of the zeta function in case $r = 0$ and $k = 2^m p$, $p$ a prime. *I. Niven.*

Citations: MR 4, 210c = N28-6; MR 6, 36h = N28-7.
Referred to in N28-46.

## N28-12 (8, 317a)

**Selberg, Sigmund. The number of cancelled elements in the sieve of Eratosthenes.** Norsk Mat. Tidsskr. **26**, 79–84 (1944). (Norwegian)

Let $k$ be the product of all primes not exceeding $\xi = x^\alpha \geqq 2$, and denote by $A(\xi, x)$ the number of positive integers prime to $k$ and not exceeding $x$. The author proves the following relation, valid for $0 < \alpha < \frac{1}{2}$:

$$\lim_{x\to\infty} \frac{A(\xi, x)}{x/\log x} = a,$$

where the positive number $a$ depends only on $\alpha$. His proof is based on the prime number theorem. *T. Nagell.*

## N28-13 (9, 272c)

**Chowla, S. A theorem in analytic number theory.** Proc. Nat. Inst. Sci. India **13**, 97–99 (1947).

The author announces the following theorem. Let $k$ and $r$ be given positive integers. Then almost all positive integers $n$ are of the form $n'\prod_{i=1}^{r} p_i^{2\alpha_i+1}$, where each prime $p$ is of the form $kx-1$. The proof is given for $r=2$ and depends on the prime number theorem. For $r>2$ the proof is said to depend on a recent result of S. Selberg [Skr. Norske Vid. Akad. Oslo. I. **1942**, no. 5; these Rev. **6**, 57]. It follows from the general theorem that, for almost all $n$, Ramanujan's function $\tau(n)$ is divisible by an arbitrarily high power of $p$, for $p = 2, 3, 5, 7, 23$ and 691. *D. H. Lehmer.*

Citations: MR 6, 57h = N28-9.

## N28-14 (9, 332d)

**Chowla, S. D., and Vijayaraghavan, T. On the largest prime divisors of numbers.** J. Indian Math. Soc. (N.S.) **11**, 31–37 (1947).

Let $g(m)$ denote the largest prime divisor of $m$ and let $\phi(x, \theta)$, $0 < \theta < 1$, denote the number of numbers $m \leqq x$ for which $g(m) > x^\theta$. It is shown that $\lim_{x\to\infty} \phi(x, \theta)/x = A(\theta)$ exists, and that $A(\theta)$ is a strictly decreasing continuous function in the interval $0<\theta<1$, with $A(1-0)=0$, and $A(+0)=1$. *R. Bellman* (Stanford University, Calif.).

Referred to in N28-18, N28-19, N28-26, N28-63, N28-68, R46-33.

**N28-15** **(9, 332l)**

**Selberg, Sigmund. An upper bound for the number of cancelled numbers in the sieve of Eratosthenes.** Norske Vid. Selsk. Forh., Trondhjem **19**, no. 2, 3–6 (1946). (Norwegian)

Denote by $P(N)$ the product of all primes not exceeding $N$ and by $A(N_1, N)$ the number of positive integers not exceeding $N$ which are relatively prime to $P(N_1)$. The author proves the existence of an absolute constant $c$ such that $A(N_1, N)<cN/\log N_1$ for all integers $N$ and $N_1$ with $2\leqq N_1<N$. *T. Nagell* (Uppsala).

**N28-16** **(10, 17b; 10, 17c; 10, 17d)**

**Ramaswami, V. On the number of integers $\leqslant X$ and free of prime divisors $>X^c$.** Science and Culture **13**, 503 (1948).

**Ramaswami, V. On the number of integers $\leqslant X$ and free of prime divisors $>X^c$, and a problem of S. S. Pillai.** Science and Culture **13**, 503 (1948).

**Ramaswami, V. On the number of positive integers $<X$ and free of prime divisors $>X^c$.** Science and Culture **13**, 465 (1948).

In letters to the editor, the author gives asymptotic formulas for $f(x, c)$, the number of positive integers less than $x$ and free of prime divisors greater than $x^c$. Proofs will appear elsewhere. *R. D. James* (Vancouver, B. C.).

**N28-17** **(10, 597b)**

**Ramaswami, V. The number of positive integers $\leqq x$ and free of prime divisors $>x^c$, and a problem of S. S. Pillai.** Duke Math. J. **16**, 99–109 (1949).

Let $f(x, c)$ denote the number of integers specified in the title. The main results of the paper are the formulas

$$f(x, c)=x\varphi(c)+q(c)(x/\log x)+O(x^c/\log x)+O(x/\log^2 x),\qquad \tfrac{1}{2}\leqq c<1;$$

$$f(x, c)=x\varphi(c)+q(x)(x/\log x)+O(x/(\log x)^{\frac{3}{2}}),\qquad c<\tfrac{1}{2} \text{ or } c\geqq 1.$$

Here $\varphi(c)$ is bounded and positive for $c>0$ and $q(c)$ is bounded, positive for $0<c<1$, and zero elsewhere. Explicit formulas are given for the functions $\varphi(c)$ and $q(c)$ and it is shown that they have derivatives of all orders except at $c=1/n$, where $n$ is a positive integer. The functions also satisfy certain inequalities of which $\Gamma(1/c)\varphi(c)<Ac$ for $c>0$ is an example. The problem of Pillai referred to in the title is that of answering the question: is $f(x, c)<Ax^c$ for $c\geqq(\log 2)/(\log x)$? It follows from the formulas of this paper and the inequalities satisfied by $\varphi(c)$ that the answer is "yes."

The proof of the main results uses the prime number theorem in the form $\pi(x)=\int_2^x(\log x)^{-1}dx+O(x/\log^3 x)$. The first result quoted above follows from this by noting that

$$f(x, 1)-f(x, c)=\sum_{n=1}^{r}\pi(x/n)-r\pi(x^c),$$

where $r=[x^{1-c}]$ and $\frac{1}{2}\leqq c<1$. In a note at the end of the paper, the author states a generalization of his results. *R. D. James* (Vancouver, B. C.).

Referred to in N28-18, N28-19, N28-24, N28-63.

**N28-18** **(11, 84b)**

**Buhštab, A. A. On those numbers in an arithmetic progression all prime factors of which are small in order of magnitude.** Doklady Akad. Nauk SSSR (N.S.) **67**, 5–8 (1949). (Russian)

The author proves the following theorem. Suppose $l<k$, $(l, k)=1$; denote by $B_l(k, x, y)$ the number of positive integers in the progression $kn+l$ not exceeding $x$ and free of prime factors greater than $y$; then for $\alpha\geqq 1$ we have $B_l(k, x, x^{1/\alpha})=x\omega(\alpha)/k+O(x\{\log x\}^{-\frac{1}{2}})$, where $\omega(\alpha)$ is a positive continuous monotonically decreasing function of $\alpha$ given for $N\leqq\alpha\leqq N+1$ by

$$\omega(\alpha)=1+\sum_{n=1}^{N}(-1)^n\int_n^\alpha\int_{n-1}^{z_1-1}\cdots\times\int_1^{z_{n-1}-1}(z_1\cdots z_n)^{-1}dz_1\cdots dz_n.$$

The proof is by induction on the positive integer $N$. The author seems to be unaware that the case $k=1$ was treated earlier by Chowla and Vijayaraghavan [J. Indian Math. Soc. (N.S.) **11**, 31–37 (1947); these Rev. **9**, 332]; the generalization to any $k$ is straightforward.

It is not difficult [cf. Ramaswami, Duke Math. J. **16**, 99–109 (1949), lemma 2(a); these Rev. **10**, 597] to prove that $\alpha^{-2\alpha}<\omega(\alpha)<1/\Gamma(\alpha+1)$ for $\alpha>1$. Using the integro-difference equation

$$\omega(\alpha)-\omega(\beta)=\int_\alpha^\beta z^{-1}\omega(z-1)dz$$

satisfied by $\omega(\alpha)$, the author improves the first of these inequalities by proving that for $\alpha\geqq 6$ we have

(*) $\omega(\alpha)>\exp(-\alpha\{\log\alpha+\log\log\alpha+6(\log\log\alpha)/(\log\alpha)\})$.

[N. G. de Bruijn has recently obtained still sharper results which are as yet unpublished.]

Finally the author points out that, if $m$ is an integer not less than 2, $p$ is a prime, $m\,|\,(p-1)$, and $\omega(\alpha)>1/m$, then the least $m$th-power nonresidue modulo $p$ is less than $p^{1/(2\alpha)}$ for sufficiently large $p$. Using this remark and (*) the author proves that for $m>e^{33}$ the least $m$th-power nonresidue modulo $p$ is less than $p^{(\log\log m+2)/(2\log m)}$ for sufficiently large $p$; this improves a result of Vinogradov [Trans. Amer. Math. Soc. **29**, 218–226 (1927), theorem 4] by roughly a factor 2 in the exponent. *P. T. Bateman* (Princeton, N. J.).

Citations: MR 9, 332d = N28-14; MR 10, 597b = N28-17.

Referred to in N28-19, N28-63, R14-73, R46-33.

**N28-19** **(11, 233f)**

**Ramaswami, V. On the number of positive integers less than $x$ and free of prime divisors greater than $x^c$.** Bull. Amer. Math. Soc. **55**, 1122–1127 (1949).

The author proves that the number of positive integers less than $x$ and free of prime divisors greater than $x^c$ is equal to $x\phi(c)+O(x/\log x)$, where $\phi(c)>0$ for $c>0$ and the $O$-term is uniform for $c\geqq\delta>0$; moreover $\phi(c)$ is a continuous function of $c$ for all real $c$ and an increasing function of $c$ for $0<c<1$. Weaker versions of this theorem have been proved by Chowla and Vijayaraghavan [J. Indian Math. Soc. (N.S.) **11**, 31–37 (1947); these Rev. **9**, 332] and by Buhštab [Doklady Akad. Nauk SSSR (N.S.) **67**, 5–8 (1949); these Rev. **11**, 84], although Ramaswami seems actually to have obtained his result earlier than these other authors. (Buchstab considered more generally the positive integers of an arithmetic progression, which presents little additional difficulty.) It is a corollary to Ramaswami's proof that

$$\phi(b)-\phi(a)=\int_a^b \phi(u/(1-u))u^{-1}du$$

for $0<a<b\leqq 1$. In a paper which has already appeared [Duke Math. J. **16**, 99–109 (1949); these Rev. **10**, 597], but which is logically a sequel to the present one, the author has studied the function $\phi(c)$ in great detail. [Cf. also the following review.] *P. T. Bateman* (Princeton, N. J.).

Citations: MR 9, 332d = N28-14; MR 10, 597b = N28-17; MR 11, 84b = N28-18.

## N28-20 (11, 233g)

**Ramaswami, V. Sequences satisfying $a_1=1$ and $(r+1)^{-1}a_r\leqq a_r-a_{r+1}\leqq r^{-1}a_{r-1}$ for $r>1$.** Math. Student **16** (1948), 31–33 (1949).

[In the original the subscript is omitted from $a_1$ in the title.] The function $\phi$ of the paper reviewed above is such that the sequence $a_r=\phi(1/r)$, $r=1, 2, \cdots$, satisfies the properties mentioned in the title of the present paper. The author raises the question here whether these properties alone imply the known fact that $0\leqq\phi(1/r)\leqq 1/\Gamma(r)$. The sequence $a_r=\lambda/r+(1-\lambda)/\Gamma(r)$, $0<\lambda\leqq 1$, shows that this is not the case. However, the author proves the following weaker statement: If a sequence $\{a_r\}$ satisfies the conditions in the title, then $a_r\geqq 0$ for $r\geqq 2$, $ra_r\leqq(r+1)a_{r+1}$ for $r\geqq 2$, and either $ra_r$ has a positive limit as $r$ tends to infinity or else $a_r\leqq 1/\Gamma(r)$ for all $r$. *P. T. Bateman* (Princeton, N. J.).

## N28-21 (11, 500f)

**Specht, Wilhelm. Zahlenfolgen mit endlich vielen Primteilern.** S.-B. Math.-Nat. Kl. Bayer. Akad. Wiss. **1948**, 149–169 (1949).

Let $\mathfrak{B}$ denote the sequence $1=b_1<b_2<\cdots$ of integers which contain no prime factors other than the $m$ given primes $p_1, \cdots, p_m$ $(m\geqq 2)$, and let $B(x)$ be the number of members of $\mathfrak{B}$ which do not exceed $x$. Put $P=(p_1p_2\cdots p_m)^{\frac{1}{2}}$, $Q=(m!\log p_1\log p_2\cdots\log p_m)^{1/m}$. The author improves on certain results given by G. Pólya and himself concerning the sequence $\mathfrak{B}$. Thus he proves that, for large $n$ and $x$,

$$(1)\qquad \log b_n=Qn^{1/m}-\log P+o(1),$$

$$(2)\qquad B(x)=\{(\log x)/Q\}^m+o\{(\log x)^{m-1}\},$$

$$(3)\qquad b_{n+1}\sim\frac{1}{P}\exp(Qn^{1/m}),$$

$$(4)\qquad \log(b_{n+1}-b_n)\sim\log b_n\sim Qn^{1/m}.$$

In order to prove (1), (2) and (3) he considers the set $\Delta_m(\xi,\alpha)$ of points $(x_1, x_2, \cdots, x_m)$ with nonnegative integral coordinates which satisfy the inequality $\sum_{\nu=1}^n\alpha_\nu x_\nu\leqq\xi$, where $\xi>0$ and $\alpha_\nu>0$ $(\nu=1, \cdots, m)$. The number of points in $\Delta_m(\xi,\alpha)$ he calls $A_m(\xi,\alpha)$ and proves that, if the ratios $\alpha_\nu/\alpha_1$ are not all rational then

$$(5)\qquad A_m(\xi,\alpha)=\frac{\{\xi+\frac{1}{2}(\alpha_1+\alpha_2+\cdots+\alpha_m)\}^m}{m!\alpha_1\alpha_2\cdots\alpha_m}+o(\xi^{m-1})$$

as $\xi\to\infty$. Relation (5) is deduced from some general results on uniform distribution of functions $f(x,\alpha)$ with respect to $\Delta_m(\xi,\alpha)$ and is applied to evaluate $B(x)$ and $b_n$ by taking $\xi=\log x$, $\alpha_i=\log p_i$ $(1\leqq i\leqq m)$. The proof of (4) requires the Thue-Siegel theorem which is used to show that the Diophantine inequalities $0<Ax^p-By^p\leqq Cy^{p-2\sqrt{p}}$ ($A$, $B$ positive integers, $p\geqq 5$ a prime and $C>0$ an arbitrary constant) has only a finite number of solutions. By putting $b_{n+1}=Ax^p$, $b_n=By^p$ where $A$ and $B$ are divisible by no $p$th powers, it is deduced that the inequality $b_{n+1}-b_n\leqq b_n^{1-\epsilon}$ $(\epsilon>0)$ can hold for a finite number of values of $n$ only and (4) follows.

*R. A. Rankin* (Cambridge, England).

Referred to in N28-36.

## N28-22 (12, 11d)

**De Bruijn, N. G. On the number of uncancelled elements in the sieve of Eratosthenes.** Nederl. Akad. Wetensch., Proc. **53**, 803–812 = Indagationes Math. **12**, 247–256 (1950).

For $x>0$, $y\geqq 2$, let $\Phi(x,y)$ denote the number of positive integers less than or equal to $x$ which have no prime factors less than $y$. The author derives estimates for $\Phi(x,y)$ in the regions $y^n\leqq x\leqq y^{n+1}$, $n=1, 2, \cdots$, which hold uniformly in $n$. His results and methods are improvements on those of Buchstab [Rec. Math. [Mat. Sbornik] N.S. **2(44)**, 1239–1246 (1937)]. Use is made of the Buchstab function $\omega(u)$ defined by $\omega(u)=1/u$, $1\leqq u\leqq 2$, and $(u\omega(u))'=\omega(u-1)$, $u\geqq 2$, where for $u=2$ the right-hand derivative has to be taken. Let $\pi(y)$ denote the number of primes less than or equal to $y$, li $y$ the logarithmic integral, $\gamma$ the Euler constant, $C$ an absolute constant not necessarily the same each time it occurs. Put $\Phi(x,y)=x\prod_{p<y}(1-p^{-1})\cdot\psi(x,y)$. Then the main estimates are: (1) $|\psi(y^u,y)-e^\gamma\log y\int_1^u y^{t-u}\omega(t)dt|<CR(y)$, $u\geqq 1$, $y\geqq 2$, where $R(y)$ is a positive function satisfying $R(y)\downarrow 0$ for $y\to\infty$, $R(y)>1/y$ and $|\pi(y)-\mathrm{li}\,y|<yR(y)/\log y$, $\int_y^\infty|\pi(t)-\mathrm{li}\,t|t^{-2}dt<R(y)$, $y\geqq 2$;

(2) $|\psi(y^u,y)-1|<C\log^3 y\exp(-u\log u-u\log\log u+Cu)$, $1\leqq u\leqq 4y^{\frac{1}{2}}/\log y$, $y\geqq 2$;

(3) $|\psi(y^u,y)-1|<C\exp(-\frac{1}{3}u\log y)$, $u>4y^{\frac{1}{2}}/\log y$, $y\geqq 2$. *A. L. Whiteman.*

Referred to in N28-27, N28-28, N28-32, N28-37, N28-75, N80-38, P32-62.

## N28-23 (12, 677d)

**Delange, Hubert. Quelques formules asymptotiques de la théorie des nombres.** C. R. Acad. Sci. Paris **232**, 1392–1393 (1951).

Several results are stated which may be proved by the author's Tauberian theorems [same vol. 465–467, 589–591 (1951); these Rev. **12**, 405, 497], based solely on the facts that the Riemann $\zeta$-function and Dirichlet's $L$-function do not vanish for $\Re(s)\geqq 1$. Let $k$ be an integer greater than 1 and $(l)$ be a system of integers $l_1, l_2, \cdots, l_r$, all prime to $k$ and not congruent (mod $k$) to each other. Denote by $E[k,(l)]$ the set of integers $n$ with the property that each prime factor $p$ of $n$ satisfies one of the congruences: $p\equiv l_1$, $p\equiv l_2$, $\cdots$, $p\equiv l_r$ (mod $k$). Define $\omega(n)$ as the number of different prime factors of $n$, and $\Omega(n)$ as the total number of prime factors in the decomposition of $n$. Let $\phi(k)$ denote the number of integers not greater than and prime to $k$. Landau showed [Handbuch der Lehre von der Verteilung der Primzahlen, Teubner, Leipzig-Berlin, 1909, p. 668] that the ratio of $E[k,(l)]$ to $x[(\log x)^{1-r/\phi(k)}]^{-1}$ tends to a finite positive limit as $x\to\infty$. Related formulas are stated when additional conditions are imposed on $\Omega(n)$ and on the system of integers $(l)$. Other results are also stated such as $\sum_{3\leqq n\leqq x}[\omega(n)-\log\log n]^2/\log\log n\sim Ax$ when $x\to\infty$, where $A$ is a positive constant. *S. Ikehara.*

Citations: MR 12, 405a = M45-13; MR 12, 497d = M45-14.

Referred to in M45-24, N24-28.

## N28-24 (13, 14f)

**Ramaswami, V. Number of integers in an assigned A. P., $\leq x$ and prime to primes greater than $x^c$.** Proc. Amer. Math. Soc. **2**, 318–319 (1951).

Let $f(m, v, k, x, c)$ denote the number of integers of the form $m(v+nk)$, $(v, k)=1$, $n=1, 2, 3, \cdots$, that do not exceed $x$ and are prime to primes greater than $x^c$. The case $m=v=k=1$ was treated previously by the author [Duke Math. J. **16**, 99–109 (1949); these Rev. **10**, 597]. By suitably generalizing the proofs used in the special case, similar formulas are found for the general case. *R. D. James.*

Citations: MR 10, 597b = N28-17.
Referred to in N72-55.

## N28-25 (13, 15a)

**Selberg, Sigmund. A theorem in analytic number theory.** Norske Vid. Selsk. Forh., Trondheim **23**, 1–2 (1951).

Let $P$ denote a set of primes $p$ such that

$$\sum_{p\leq x,\, p\varepsilon P} \frac{1}{p} > \frac{1}{h} \log\log x - c,$$

where $c>0$, $h\geqq 1$, and let $A(x; P)$ denote the number of integers $\leqq x$ which are divisible by none of the numbers of $P$. Then the author proves that there exists a constant $D$ such that $A(x; P) < Dx(\log x)^{-1/h}$. The special case of the theorem in which $P$ consists of the primes in an arithmetic progression has been applied by E. Jacobsthal [Norske Vid. Selsk. Forh., Trondheim **22**, no. 41, 193–197 (1950); these Rev. **11**, 715]. *L. Carlitz* (Durham, N. C.).

Citations: MR 11, 715f = A08-16.

## N28-26 (13, 326f)

**de Bruijn, N. G. The asymptotic behaviour of a function occurring in the theory of primes.** J. Indian Math. Soc. (N.S.) **15**, 25–32 (1951).

The function $\Psi(x, y)$, defined as the number of positive integers $\leqq x$ which are free of prime divisors $>y$, has been investigated by several writers in recent years. In particular, it was shown by S. D. Chowla and T. Vijayaraghavan [J. Indian Math. Soc. (N.S.) **11**, 31–37 (1947); these Rev. **9**, 332] that, for any fixed positive $u$,

$$\operatorname{Lim}_{y\to\infty} y^{-u}\Psi(y^u, y) = \rho(u),$$

where $\rho(u)$ is continuous for $u>0$ and uniquely defined by the relations

$$(1)\quad \rho(u)=1 \quad (0\leqq u\leqq 1); \qquad u\rho'(u) = -\rho(u-1) \quad (u>1).$$

In the present paper the author uses these relations to prove that, for $u\to\infty$,

$$(2)\qquad \rho(u) \sim \frac{e^\gamma}{\sqrt{(2\pi u)}} \exp\left\{-\int_0^\xi \frac{se^s-e^s+1}{s}ds\right\},$$

where $\gamma$ is Euler's constant and, for $u>1$, $\xi$ is the positive root of the equation $e^\xi - 1 = u\xi$. To obtain (2) we first note that, in virtue of (1),

$$u\rho(u) = \int_0^1 \rho(u-t)dt \qquad (-\infty < u < \infty),$$

where we put $\rho(u)=0$ for $u<0$. Now an earlier paper due to the author [Nederl. Akad. Wetensch., Proc. **53**, 813–821 (1950); these Rev. **12**, 30] states that if $F(u)$, $F_0(u)$ are continuous and both satisfy

$$(3)\qquad uF(u) = \int_0^1 F(u-t)dt$$

for $u>0$ and if $F_0(u)$ is positive and non-increasing for $u\geqq 1$, then $F(u) = \{C+O(u^{-\frac{1}{2}})\}F_0(u)$ $(u\to\infty)$, where $C$ is a constant. It therefore follows that

$$F_1(u) = \{C+O(u^{-\frac{1}{2}})\}\rho(u),$$

where $F_1(u)$ is any continuous solution of (3). Taking

$$F_1(u) = \frac{1}{2\pi i}\int_W \exp\left\{-uz + \int_0^z \frac{e^s-1}{s}ds\right\}dz,$$

where $W$ is a suitable contour, and using the saddle point method we prove that

$$F_1(u) \sim \frac{1}{\sqrt{(2\pi u)}} \exp\left\{-\int_0^\xi \frac{se^s-e^s+1}{s}ds\right\}.$$

A second, and more difficult, application of the saddle point method leads to the relation $C=e^{-\gamma}$, and so to (2).

In addition to the asymptotic formula (2), the author also establishes an exact formula for $\rho(u)$, namely

$$\rho(u) = \frac{e^\gamma}{2\pi i}\int_{-i\infty}^{i\infty} \exp\left\{-uz + \int_0^z \frac{e^s-1}{s}ds\right\}dz \quad (u>0).$$

Here the outer integral is taken along the imaginary axis. *L. Mirsky* (Bristol).

Citations: MR 9, 332d = N28-14.
Referred to in M55-36, N28-28, N28-57.

## N28-27 (13, 626h)

**Buhštab, A. A. On an asymptotic estimate of the number of numbers of an arithmetic progression which are not divisible by "relatively" small prime numbers.** Mat. Sbornik N.S. **28(70)**, 165–184 (1951). (Russian)

If $l$ and $k$ are relatively prime positive integers, let $\pi_l(k, x, y)$ denote the number of positive integers in the progression $kn+l$ not exceeding $x$ and free of prime factors less than $y$. The author has proved previously [Mat. Sbornik N.S. **2(44)**, 1239–1246 (1937)] that if $\alpha$ is a fixed positive number greater than unity, then

$$(*)\quad \pi_l(k, x, x^{1/\alpha}) = \psi(\alpha)x/\{\phi(k)\ln x\} + O(x\{\ln x\}^{-3/2}),$$

where $\psi(\alpha)=1$ for $1<\alpha\leqq 2$ and $\psi(\alpha) = 1+\int_1^{\alpha-1}\psi(z)z^{-1}dz$ for $\alpha>2$. In the present paper the author proves that there is a constant $C$ such that

$$|\psi(\alpha) - e^{-\gamma}\alpha| < \exp\{-\alpha(\ln\alpha + \ln\ln\alpha - 1 + C\ln\ln\alpha/\ln\alpha)\},$$

where $\gamma$ is Euler's constant. He does this by using an improved form of Brun's method to get upper and lower estimates for $\pi_l(k, x, x^{1/\alpha})$ and then comparing these with (*). The weaker result $\psi(\alpha) = e^{-\gamma}\alpha + O(1/\Gamma(\alpha))$ has been given by de Bruijn [Nederl. Akad. Wetensch., Proc. **53**, 803–812, p. 805 = Indagationes Math. **12**, 247–256 (1950), p. 249; these Rev. **12**, 11], who also gives results on $\pi_l(k, x, y)$. *P. T. Bateman* (Urbana, Ill.).

Citations: MR 12, 11d = N28-22.
Referred to in P32-30, P32-62.

## N28-28 (13, 724e)

**de Bruijn, N. G. On the number of positive integers $\leq x$ and free of prime factors $>y$.** Nederl. Acad. Wetensch. Proc. Ser. A. **54**, 50–60 (1951).

Let $\Psi(x, y)$ denote the quantity specified in the title. It was proved by Dickman [Ark. Mat. Astr. Fys. **22**, no. A10 (1930)] that if $u$ is a fixed positive number, then $\lim_{y\to\infty} y^{-u}\Psi(y^u, y) = \rho(u)$, where $\rho(u)$ is a continuous function of $u$ defined by the properties $\rho(u)=1$ for $0<u\leqq 1$ and $u\rho'(u) = -\rho(u-1)$ for $u>1$. (Dickman's result has been rediscovered recently by several other authors listed in the bibliography of the present paper). In another paper [J. Indian Math. Soc. (N.S.) **15**, 25–32 (1951); these Rev. **13**, 326] the author has made a detailed study of the function $\rho(u)$. In the present paper he constructs and studies a function $\Lambda(x, y)$ which is a closer approximation to $\Psi(x, y)$ than $x\rho(\log x/\log y)$. This function $\Lambda(x, y)$ is defined as

$x\int_0^x \rho((\log x-\log t)/\log y)d([t]/t)$ if $x$ is not an integer and as $\Lambda(x+0, y)$ if $x$ is an integer. He proves that if $x>0$ and $y\geqq 2$ then $|\Psi(x, y)-\Lambda(x, y)|<Cx(\log x/\log y)^2R(y)$, where $R(y)$ is any function such that

$$R(y)\downarrow 0\ (y\to\infty),\quad R(y)>y^{-1}\log y\ (y\geqq 2),$$

and $|\pi(y)-\mathrm{li}\, y|<yR(y)/\log y\ (y\geqq 2)$. The method of proof is similar to that used by the author in an earlier paper [Nederl. Akad. Wetensch, Proc. **53**, 803–812 = Indagationes Math. **12**, 247–256 (1950); these Rev. **12**, 11] to prove an analogous estimate for $\Phi(x, y)$, the number of positive integers $\leqq x$ and free of prime factors $<y$. The author also applies his main result in proving that if $g(n)$ denotes the largest prime divisor of the positive integer $n$, then $\sum_{n=2}^{x}\log g(n)=ax\log x+O(x)$, where $a=\int_0^\infty(1+u)^{-2}\rho(u)du$.
*P. T. Bateman* (Urbana, Ill.).

Citations: MR 12, 11d = N28-22; MR 13, 326f = N28-26.
Referred to in A18-14, L20-15, M55-36, N08-36, N28-63, N80-38, Q10-9, R46-19, R46-33.

## N28-29 (15, 289b)

**Prachar, Karl. Über Zahlen der Form $a^2+b^2$ in einer arithmetischen Progression.** Math. Nachr. **10**, 51–54 (1953).

The author considers the problem of determining the number of elements $A(x)$ of the arithmetic progression $1+Dn$, $n=1, 2, \cdots$, which are less than $x$ and representable as a sum of two squares. Following the classical procedure of Landau [Handbuch der Lehre der Verteilung der Primzahlen, Bd. 2, Teubner, Leipzig-Berlin, 1909, Kap. 55–58], he considers the associated Dirichlet series. The asymptotic relation is, as in Landau's case, $A(x)\sim bx/\sqrt{\log x}$. There is now a certain amount of difficulty in determining the constant $b$. *R. Bellman* (Santa Monica, Calif.).

Referred to in N28-66.

## N28-30 (16, 569h)

**Kanold, Hans-Joachim. Über die Dichte von gewissen Zahlenmengen.** J. Reine Angew. Math. **193**, 250–252 (1954).

Let $a, d, \cdots$ denote positive integers. For every $a$ let $(Q(a))^2$ be the largest perfect square dividing $a$. Then for a given $d$

$$\lim_{N\to\infty}\frac{1}{N}\sum_{\substack{a\leqq N\\ Q(a)=d}}1=\frac{6}{\pi^2d^2}$$

and

$$\lim_{N\to\infty}\frac{1}{N}\sum_{\substack{a\leqq N\\ Q(a)>d}}1=1-\frac{6}{\pi^2}\sum_{j=1}^{d-1}\frac{1}{j^2}.$$

Let $f$ be squarefree and prime to $d$. Then

$$\lim_{N\to\infty}\frac{1}{N}\sum_{\substack{a\leqq N\\ Q(a)=d\\ (a,f)=1}}1=\frac{6}{\pi^2d^2}\prod_{p\mid f}\frac{p}{p+1}.$$

The proofs of these formulas are based on the following formula: $\lim_{N\to\infty}N^{-1}\sum_{a\leqq N}\mu^2(a)=6\pi^{-2}$ [cf. E. Landau, Handbuch der Lehre von der Verteilung der Primzahlen, Bd II, Teubner, Leipzig-Berlin, 1909, pp. 580 ff.].
*P. Scherk* (Saskatoon, Sask.).

Referred to in A22-27, N28-34, N52-25, N80-7, N80-19, N80-20.

## N28-31 (16, 675h)

**LeVeque, W. J. The distribution of values of multiplicative functions.** Michigan Math. J. **2** (1953–54), 179–192 (1955).

The author investigates the asymptotic behaviour, as $x\to\infty$ for fixed $k$, of $T_k(x)$ and $R_k(x)$; here $T_k(x)$ denotes the number of positive integers $\leqq x$ with exactly $k$ divisors, and $R_k(x)$ denotes the number of positive integers $\leqq x$ with exactly $k$ representations as a sum of two squares. If $k=p_1^{\nu_1}\cdots p_s^{\nu_s}$, where $p_1<p_2<\cdots<p_s$, it is shown that

$$T_k(x)\sim\frac{Ax^\alpha(\log\log x)^{\nu_1-1}}{(\nu_1-1)!\log x},$$

where $\alpha=(p_1-1)^{-1}$ and $A$ is a positive constant depending on $k$ which is expressed as a multiple sum. The proof is analytical, and is based on the idea of expressing the relevant generating functions as (essentially) polynomials in $\log\zeta(s)$, $\log\zeta(2s)$, $\cdots$. The asymptotic expressions that are obtained for $R_k(x)$ take different forms according as $k$ is (a) even, (b) odd and not divisible by 3, (c) odd and divisible by 3. They disprove a conjecture of P. Lévy [Atti Accad. Sci. Torino **75**, 177–183 (1939); MR **1**, 201].
*H. Davenport* (London).

Citations: MR 1, 201f = E76-3.

## N28-32 (17, 127l)

**Chowla, S., and Briggs, W. E. On the number of positive integers $\leqq x$ all of whose prime factors are $\leqq y$.** Proc. Amer. Math. Soc. **6** (1955), 558–562.

Recently de Bruijn [Nederl. Akad. Wetensch. Proc. **53**, 803–812 = Indag. Math. **12** (1950), 247–256; MR **12**, 11] estimated the functions $f(x, y)$ and $g(x, y)$, where $f(x, y)$ denotes the number of positive integers $\leqq x$, all of whose prime factors are $\leqq y$, and where $g(x, y)$ denotes the number of positive integers $\leqq x$, all of whose prime factors are $>y$. An interesting special case is the estimate $f[x, (\log x)^h]=O(x^{1-1/h+\epsilon})$, where $h>2$. The present authors give a new proof of this formula and a corresponding formula for $g[x, (\log x)^h]$. Although they follow de Bruijn very closely their analysis is considerably simpler.
*A. L. Whiteman* (Los Angeles, Calif.).

Citations: MR 12, 11d = N28-22.

## N28-33 (18, 18b)

**Roux, Delfina. Sulla distribuzione degli interi rappresentabili come somma di due quadrati.** Ist. Lombardo Sci. Lett. Rend. Cl. Sci. Mat. Nat. (3) **21(90)** (1956), 137–140.

Let $A(\xi)$ denote the number of integers representable as the sum of two squares and not exceeding $\xi$. Making a simple application of the sieve method of Viggo Brun the author derives the upper bound: $A(\xi)<k\xi/(\log\xi)^{\frac{1}{2}}$ for $\xi>\xi_1$. *A. L. Whiteman* (Los Angeles, Calif.).

## N28-34 (18, 284b)

**Scherk, Peter. Bemerkungen zu einer Arbeit von Herrn Kanold.** J. Reine Angew. Math. **196** (1956), 133–136.

Let $a$, $d$, $f$ be positive integers such that $(d, f)=1$. For every $a$ let $(Q(a))^2$ be the largest perfect square dividing $a$. It is proved that

$$\lim_{n\to\infty}\frac{1}{n}\sum_{\substack{a=1\\(a,f)=1\\Q(a)\geqq d}}^{n}1=\prod_{p\mid f}\frac{p-1}{p}-\frac{6}{\pi^2}\prod_{p\mid f}\frac{p}{p+1}\cdot\sum_{\substack{b=1\\(b,f)=1}}^{d-1}\frac{1}{b^2}.$$

This generalizes a theorem of H.-J. Kanold [same J. **193** (1954), 250–252; MR **16**, 569]. The writer also gives alternative proofs of some of Kanold's results.
*I. Niven* (Eugene, Ore.).

Citations: MR 16, 569h = N28-30.
Referred to in N28-38, N80-7, N80-19, N80-20.

## N28-35 (18, 642f)

**Wirsing, Eduard. Über die Zahlen, deren Primteiler einer gegebenen Menge angehören.** Arch. Math. **7** (1956), 263–272.

Let $\mathfrak{T}$ be a subset of the primes whose relative density in the set of all primes is $\tau$, let $\mathfrak{M}$ be the set of all integers whose prime factors are in $\mathfrak{T}$, and let $M(x)$ denote the number of integers of $\mathfrak{M}$ not exceeding $x$. From a consideration of special cases [in particular, Landau, Handbuch der Lehre von der Verteilung der Primzahlen, Bd. 2, Teubner, Leipzig-Berlin, 1909, pp. 641–669], it might be expected that $M(x) \sim cx/(\log x)^{1-\tau}$, where $c$ is a constant. The author proves that this is so if and only if $\sum 1/p = \tau \log\log x + c' + o(1)$, where the summation is over all $p \in \mathfrak{T}$, $p \leqq x$, and $c'$ is a constant. He also proves, without assuming the result for $\sum 1/p$, that there is an explicit asymptotic formula for $M(x)$. The proof uses Tauberian theorems for infinite series and a theorem on Laplace transforms. *R. D. James* (Vancouver, B.C.).

Referred to in N28-41, N28-70, N80-46, P64-22.

**N28-36** **(18, 643b)**

**Lochs, Gustav. Über die Unregelmässigkeit der Abstände aufeinander folgender Zahlen mit gegebenen Primfaktoren und einen damit zusammenhängenden allgemeineren Satz.** Arch. Math. **7** (1956), 259–262.

The author proves the following result: Let $\alpha_i$ $(i=1, \cdots, k)$ be $k$ given positive numbers with $\alpha_i < \alpha_{i+1}$ and such that no relation $\sum_{i=1}^k a_i\alpha_i = 0$ holds with rational $a_i$. Consider all numbers of the form $\sum_{i=1}^k x_i\alpha_i$, where the $x_i$ are non-negative integers, and arrange them in an increasing sequence. Denote the $n$th term of the sequence by $\lambda_n$ and let $\lambda_{n+1} - \lambda_n = \mu_n$, $\mu_n\mu_{n+1} = c_n$. Then

(1) $\limsup c_n \geqq 1$ and $c_n > 1$ infinitely often,

(2) $\liminf c_n \leqq 1$,

(3) $\limsup c_n - \liminf c_n \geqq (3-\sqrt{5})/2$.

In particular, if $\alpha_i = \log p_i$ $(i=1, \cdots, k)$, where the $p_i$ are distinct primes, then $\lambda_n = \log z_n$, where $z_n$ is the $n$th term of the sequence of integers whose only prime factors are the $p_i$. In this case, $(z_{n+1} - z_n)/(z_{n+2} - z_{n+1}) \sim c_n$ and (3) shows that, although the difference $z_{n+1} - z_n \to \infty$ [W. Specht, S-B. Math. -Nat.Kl. Bayer. Akad. Wiss. **1948**, 149–169; MR **11**, 500], it behaves in an irregular manner. For $k=2$ better results than (1)–(3) are proved and the author suggests that they may also be true for $k \geqq 3$.
*R. D. James* (Vancouver, B.C.).

Citations: MR 11, 500f = N28-21.

**N28-37** **(19, 16f)**

**Vinogradov, A. I. On numbers with small prime divisors.** Dokl. Akad. Nauk SSSR (N.S.) **109** (1956), 683–686. (Russian)

Let $F(x, z)$ denote the number of positive integers, not exceeding $x$, whose maximum prime factor does not exceed $z$. Many authors have estimated $F(x, z)$ in recent years, notably de Bruijn [Nederl. Akad. Wetensch. Proc. **53** (1950), 803–812; MR **12**, 11]. Writing $z = x^\alpha$ where ($\lambda$ is a certain positive absolute constant)

$$\frac{\lambda(\log\log x)^{7/4}}{(\log x)^{1/4}} \leqq \alpha \leqq \frac{1}{e},$$

the author obtains an asymptotic formula for $F(x, z)$, which is sharper than previous estimates. The formula is too long to be quoted here. *S. Chowla.*

Citations: MR 12, 11d = N28-22.

Referred to in N28-53, N32-36, R14-37.

**N28-38** **(19, 636b)**

**Volkmann, Bodo. Einige Sätze über $k$-freie Zahlen.** J. Reine Angew. Math. **198** (1957), 7–9.

For $k \geqq 2$ and $a \geqq 1$ put $a = t_k(a)(P_k(a))^k$, where $(P_k(a))^k$ is the greatest $k$th power dividing $a$. If $P_k(a) = 1$, $a$ is $k$-free; let $\mathfrak{C}^k$ denote the set of $k$-free integers. Also let $\mathfrak{C}_f{}^k$ denote the set of $k$-free integers $a$ with $(a, f) = 1$; $\mathfrak{T}_{f,d}{}^k$ the set of $a$ with $(a, f) = 1$ and $P_k(a) = d$, where $(f, d) = 1$; $\mathfrak{A}_{f,d}{}^k$ the set of $a$ with $(a, f) = 1$ and $P_k(a) \geqq d$. For each of these sets let $M(N)$ denote the number of the elements of the set that are $\leqq N$; if $\lim M(N)/N$ exists for $N \to \infty$, it defines the natural density $D^*$. Generalizing results of Scherk in the case $k=2$ [same J. **196** (1956), 133–136; MR **18**, 284], the following results are obtained:

$$D^*(\mathfrak{C}^k) = \frac{1}{\zeta(k)};$$

$$D^*(\mathfrak{C}_f{}^k) = \frac{1}{\zeta(k)} \prod_{p|f} \frac{p^{k-1}}{1+p+\cdots+p^{k-1}};$$

$$D^*(\mathfrak{T}_{f,d}{}^k) = \frac{1}{d^k} D^*(\mathfrak{C}_f{}^k);$$

and an explicit formula for $D^*(\mathfrak{A}_{f,d}{}^k)$. *L. Carlitz.*

Citations: MR 18, 284b = N28-34.

Referred to in N80-20.

**N28-39** **(20# 6399)**

**Kanold, Hans-Joachim. Über quadratfreie Zahlen mit vorgeschriebener Primteileranzahl.** Arch. Math. **9** (1958), 46–53.

Let $A_k(x)$ denote the number of integers $m \leqq x$ which may be represented as the product of $k$ distinct primes $p_1 < \cdots < p_k$. It is well known that $A_k(x) \sim [x/\log x] \cdot [(\log\log x)^{k-1}/(k-1)!]$. The author proves that the same result holds if certain conditions are imposed: either (1) $p_1 > \exp(\log x)^{\varepsilon(x)}$, $p_k > x^{1-\log\log x}$, where $\varepsilon(x)$ is any function tending to 0 as $x \to \infty$; or (2) $(\sigma_r(m), m) = (\varphi_r(m), m) = 1$, where $\varphi_r(m) = m^r \prod_{p|m} (1-p^{-r})$, $\sigma_r(m) = \sum_{d|m} d^r$. The proofs are straightforward, using known results on the distribution of primes, and the results are not entirely unexpected. *R. D. James* (Vancouver, B.C.)

**N28-40** **(21# 3387)**

**Erdös, P. Some remarks on prime factors of integers.** Canad. J. Math. **11** (1959), 161–167.

The following theorems are proved. I. Let $\varepsilon_p > 0$, $\delta_p = \min(\varepsilon_p, 1)$. Then the divergence of $\sum_p \delta_p/p$ is a necessary and sufficient condition that all integers except for a set of density zero should have two prime factors $p$ and $q$ satisfying the inequality $p < q < p^{1+\varepsilon_p}$. II. The density of integers $n$ which have two prime factors $p$ and $q$ such that $p < q < p^{1+c/\log\log n}$ equals $1 - e^{-c}$.

In the proof of I, Turán's method of the second moment is used; in the proof of II, a sieve argument occurs.
*W. J. LeVeque* (Ann Arbor, Mich.)

**N28-41** **(22# 698)**

**Hornfeck, Bernhard. Über natürliche Zahlen, deren Primteiler in mindestens $k$-ter Potenz auftreten.** Math. Ann. **138** (1959), 442–449.

Let $\mathfrak{T}$ be a subset of the primes such that $T(x)$, the number of $p \leqq x$, $p \in \mathfrak{T}$, satisfies $T(x) \sim (\tau x)/\log x$, $\tau > 0$, $x \to \infty$. Let $\mathfrak{M}_k(x)$ be the set of natural numbers whose prime factors (a) occur to the $k$th power at least and (b) belong to $\mathfrak{T}$. The author proves that $M_k(x)$, the number of $n \leqq x$, $n \in \mathfrak{M}_k$, has the asymptotic formula $M_k(x) \sim (Cx^{1/k})/\log x$, $x \to \infty$, where $C$ depends on $k$ and $\mathfrak{T}$ (in particular, on $\sum_{p \leqq x^{1/k}, p \in \mathfrak{T}} (1/p)$). For $k=1$, this specializes to the result of Wirsing [Arch. Math. **7** (1956), 263–272; MR **18**, 642] and when $\mathfrak{T}$ is the set of all primes $(\tau = 1)$, to $M_k(x) \sim C^* x^{1/k}$.
*R. D. James* (Vancouver, B.C.)

Citations: MR 18, 642f = N28-35.

**N28-42** **(22# 5615)**

**Hornfeck, Bernhard. Zur Verteilung gewisser Primzahlpotenzprodukte.** Math. Ann. **139**, 14–30 (1959).

This paper is mainly concerned with the distribution of

integers of the form

(1) $$p_1^{b_1} \cdots p_k^{b_k},$$

where $k$ is fixed, while $p_1, \cdots, p_k$ are primes and $b_1, \cdots, b_k$ are integers about which additional assumptions are made. Thus, for example, when $p_1, \cdots, p_k$ are given distinct primes and, for $1 \leqq i \leqq k$, $b_i$ belongs to the given set of integers $\mathfrak{B}_i$ with positive density $\beta_i$, then the number of integers of the form (1) which do not exceed $x$ is asymptotic to

$$\frac{1}{k!} \prod_{i=1}^{k} \frac{\beta_i}{\log p_i} \cdot (\log x)^k.$$

This result generalizes an earlier theorem of G. Pólya [Math. Z. **1** (1918), 143–148]. Another problem considered is the distribution of the numbers (1) when $p_1, \cdots, p_k$ are distinct primes belonging to a given set and $(b_1, \cdots, b_k)$ is a given $k$-tuple. The asymptotic formula obtained in this case includes, in particular, Landau's formula for the distribution of square-free numbers with exactly $k$ prime factors [*Handbuch der Lehre von der Verteilung der Primzahlen*, B. G. Teubner, Leipzig, 1909; vol. I, § 56]. Several variants and generalizations of these problems are also discussed.

A theorem of a somewhat different type proved in the last section of the paper states that if $\mathfrak{T}$ is a set of primes with a positive $(x/\log x)$-density, and if the primes of $\mathfrak{T}$ are distributed uniformly among the residue classes (mod $n$) and prime to $n$, then this latter property is inherited by the numbers of the form $p_1 \cdots p_k$, where $k$ is fixed and $p_1, \cdots, p_k \in \mathfrak{T}$.

The methods used are in part classical and in part constitute a further development of ideas introduced by the author in an earlier publication [Monatsh. Math. **60** (1956), 96–109; MR **18**, 18]. *L. Mirsky* (Sheffield)

Citations: MR 18, 18c = N24-26.

## N28-43 (23# A2398)

**Klimov, N. I.**

**Almost prime numbers. (Russian)**

*Uspehi Mat. Nauk* **16** (1961), *no.* 3 (99), 181–188.

Almost prime numbers are integers with a bounded number of prime divisors. The author gives in the first part of the paper, using Selberg's sieve method, some upper estimate of number-theoretic functions connected with the almost prime numbers. E.g., an upper estimate is supplied of $\pi_{l,h}(k; x, x^{1/\alpha})$, the number of numbers $P \equiv l (\mathrm{mod}\ k)$, $h < P \leqq h + x$, such that $p | P$ implies $p > x^{1/\alpha}$ ($p$ prime). In the second part of the paper the author presents some applications of his estimates. One of his results here is the following. Denoting by $J^{(1)}(x, y)$ the number of primes $p \leqq x$ such that (1) $p+2$ is almost prime, (2) there is no prime $q \neq p$, $p - y \leqq q \leqq p + y$, such that $q+2$ is almost prime, one gets for $0 < \varepsilon < c_1$, $x \geqq c_2$: $J^{(1)}(x, \varepsilon \log x) > c_3(x/\log^3 x)$. *S. Knapowski* (Poznań)

Referred to in N12-38, Z10-22.

## N28-44 (23# A3720)

**Èrdeš, P. [Erdös, P.]**

**An asymptotic inequality in the theory of numbers. (Russian. English summary)**

*Vestnik Leningrad. Univ.* **15** (1960), *no.* 13, 41–49.

Es sei $A(n)$ die Anzahl der verschiedenen Zahlen $m \leqq n$ mit $m = xy$, $1 \leqq x \leqq \sqrt{n}$, $1 \leqq y \leqq \sqrt{n}$. Der Verfasser beweist: zu jedem $\varepsilon > 0$ gibt es ein $n_0(\varepsilon)$, so dass für $n > n_0(\varepsilon)$ die Ungleichung

$$\frac{n}{(\ln n)^{1+\varepsilon}} (e \ln 2)^{\ln \ln n / \ln 2} < A(n) < \frac{n}{(\ln n)^{1+\varepsilon}} (e \ln 2)^{\ln \ln 2 / \ln 2}$$

besteht. *H.-E. Richert* (Syracuse, N.Y.)

Referred to in P36-32.

## N28-45 (24# A77)

**Cohen, E.**

**Unitary products of arithmetical functions.**

*Acta Arith.* **7** (1961/62), 29–38.

The author continues his study of "unitary divisors", that is, divisors which are relatively prime to their complementary divisor [see E. Cohen, Math. Z. **74** (1960), 66–80; MR **22** #3707]. Using natural analogues of the Möbius function, the Euler totient etc., he obtains several asymptotic estimates, of which the following are typical.

Let $a, b$ be positive integers, and let $S_{ab}(x)$ count the number of positive integers below $x$ which are the product of an $a$th power and a $b$th power relatively prime to each other. Let $S_{ab}^*(ax)$ count only those integers for which the above representation is unique. For $b > a > 1$, $(a, b) = 1$, $x \geqq 2$, it is shown that

$$S_{ab}(x) = Ax^{1/a} + Bx^{1/b} + O(x^{1/(a+b)} \log x),$$

where

$$A = \zeta(b/a)\zeta(b) \prod_p (1 - 2p^{-b} + p^{-b-1} + p^{-b-b/a} - p^{-1-b/a}),$$

$$B = \zeta(a/b)\zeta(a) \prod_p (1 - 2p^{-a} + p^{-a-1} + p^{-a-a/b} - p^{-1-a/b}),$$

and also

$$S_{ab}^*(x) = A^*x^{1/a} + B^*x^{1/b} + O(x^{1/(a+b)} \log x),$$

where

$$A^* = A\zeta(b) \prod_p (1 - 2p^{-b}),$$

$$B^* = B\zeta(a) \prod_p (1 - 2p^{-a}).$$

*E. G. Straus* (Los Angeles, Calif.)

Citations: MR 22# 3707 = N52-19.

Referred to in T55-45.

## N28-46 (24# A1863)

**Cohen, Eckford**

**Arithmetical notes. V. A divisibility property of the divisor function.**

*Amer. J. Math.* **83** (1961), 693–697.

Part IV will appear in J. Tenn. Acad. Sci. Let $k$ and $n$ denote positive integers, $k$ fixed, and let $\tau(n)$ denote the number of divisors of $n$. The set of all $n$ such that $k | \tau(n)$ is denoted by $S_k$, and the enumerative function of $S_k$ is denoted by $S_k(x)$. Sathe [same J. **67** (1945), 397–406; MR **7**, 49] has proved that, for odd $k > 1$,

$$S_k(x) \sim \alpha_k x \qquad (x \to \infty),$$

where $\alpha_k$ is a positive constant; the proof depends on a result that is equivalent to the prime number theorem. In the present paper, using elementary methods, the author proves that if $k$ is odd and greater than 1, then

$$S_k(x) = \alpha_k x + O(x^{1/2} \log^2 x).$$

*L. Carlitz* (Durham, N.C.)

Citations: MR 7, 49g = N28-11.

Referred to in N56-13.

## N28-47 (26# 4977)

**de Bruijn, N. G.**

**On the number of integers $\leqq x$ whose prime factors divide $n$.**

*Illinois J. Math.* **6** (1962), 137–141.

Using a Tauberian theorem of Hardy and Ramanujan, the author obtains the asymptotic estimate

$$\log E(x) \sim \log (F(x)/x) \sim \log (G(x)/x) \sim (8 \log x)^{1/2} (\log \log x)^{-1/2}.$$

$E$, $F$, and $G$ are the partial sums for $n \leqq x$, respectively, of the reciprocal of the product of the different primes dividing $n$, of the number of integers $\leqq x$ which divide $n^x$, and of the number of integers $\leqq n$ which divide $n^n$ (i.e., all of whose prime factors divide $n$).

*J. L. Selfridge* (Seattle, Wash.)

Referred to in N28-52, N36-41, N36-44.

**N28-48** **(26# 6103 )**

**Cohen, Eckford**

**Arithmetical notes. IV. A set of integers related to the divisor function.**

*J. Tennessee Acad. Sci.* **37** (1962), 119–120.

Pour III, voir Pacific J. Math. **12** (1962),77–84.*Soit $q$ un nombre premier impair donné. Désignons par $\tau(n)$ le nombre des diviseurs de l'entier positif $n$, et par $S_q(x)$ le nombre des $n \leqq x$ tels que $q|\tau(n)$. L'auteur précise une évaluation donnée par Pillai en démontrant la formule

$$S_q(x) = (1-c_q)x + O(x^{1/(q-1)}), \quad x \geqq 1,$$

$c_q = \zeta(q)/\zeta(q-1)$, $\zeta(s)$ étant la fonction $\zeta$ de Riemann.

La méthode appliquée dans cette note est indépendante de l'emploi de fonctions génératrices et est à considérer comme élémentaire sous tous les rapports. Soit $Q_k$ l'ensemble des entiers n'admettant aucun facteur à la $k^e$ puissance $\neq 1$. Si $n = p_1^{e_1} \cdots p_s^{e_s}$, $p_1, \cdots, p_s$ étant des diviseurs premiers distincts, et si, pour $k \geqq 1$, $R_k$ est l'ensemble des entiers tels que $e_i \not\equiv -1 \pmod k$, $i = 1, \cdots, s$, $S_q$ et $R_q$ sont complémentaires par rapport à l'ensemble des entiers positifs $n$. Soient encore $q_k(n)$ et $r_k(n)$ les fonctions caractéristiques de $Q_k$ et de $R_k$. La démonstration se base essentiellement sur l'identité arithmétique (I) $r_k(n) = \sum q_{k-1}(d)$, valable pour des entiers $k > 1$, avec $n = de^k$, obtenue à partir d'une formule d'inversion se réduisant dans le cas particulier $k = 1$ à celle de Möbius, et sur la formule asymptotique connue pour $Q_k(x)$, fonction énumérative de $Q_k$.

Dans une remarque jointe à la note, l'auteur indique qu'il a obtenu d'importantes généralisations de ces résultats. Elles constituent l'objet d'une nouvelle note [#6104]. Cette note donne aussi une démonstration plus simple de l'identité (I).

*A. Gloden* (Luxembourg)

Citations: MR 31# 153 = N24-53.

**N28-49** **(26# 6104 )**

**Cohen, Eckford**

**Arithmetical notes. XIII. A sequel to Note IV.**

*Elem. Math.* **18** (1963), 8–11.

Soit $n$ un entier positif arbitraire. Si $n = p_1^{e_1} \cdots p_r^{e_r}$, $p_1, \cdots, p_r$ étant les diviseurs premiers de $n$, désignons par $t(n)$ l'ordre de multiplicité le plus élevé de $n$. Pour un entier positif arbitraire $k$, soit $n_k$ le nombre $n/m$, $m$ étant la plus grande puissance d'ordre $k$ de $n$. Soit encore $t_k(n)$ l'ordre de multiplicité le plus élevé de $n_k$.

L'auteur définit deux suites d'entiers $U_{k,s}$ et $V_{k,s}$ de la manière suivante. Si $s$ désigne un entier positif donné, $U_{k,s}$ est l'ensemble des $n$ pour lesquels $t_k(n) < s$, et $V_{k,s}$ l'ensemble des $n$ pour lesquels $t_k(n) = s$.

Il démontre pour $U_{k,s}(x)$, fonction énumérative de l'ensemble $U_{k,s}$, le Théorème 1: Si $1 < s < k$, on a, pour $x \geqq 1$,

$$U_{k,s}(x) = (\zeta(k)/\zeta(s))x + O(x^{1/s}),$$

$\zeta(s)$ étant la fonction $\zeta$ de Riemann, et pour $V_{k,s}(x)$, fonction énumérative de l'ensemble $V_{k,s}$, le Théorème 2: Si $1 < s < k$, on a

$$V_{k,s}(x) = c_{k,s}x + O(x^{1/s})$$

avec

$$c_{k,s} = \zeta(k)(\zeta^{-1}(s+1) - \zeta^{-1}(s)) \quad \text{si} \quad s < k-1,$$
$$= 1 - \zeta(k)\zeta^{-1}(k-1) \quad \text{si} \quad s = k-1,$$

si $k > 2$,

$$V_{k,1}(x) = (\zeta(k)/\zeta(2))x + O(x^{1/2}).$$

En désignant par $U_k$ l'ensemble des entiers $n = p_1^{e_1} \cdots p_r^{e_r}$ pour lesquels $e_i \not\equiv -1 \pmod k$, $i = 1, \cdots, r$, on a $U_k = U_{k,k-1}$ si $k > 1$. $U_k$ coïncide avec l'ensemble $R_k$ de la note précédente [#6103] et l'évaluation asymptotique de $R_k(x)$ est retrouvée ici par $U_k(x)$. Si $V_k$ représente l'ensemble des $n$ pour lesquels $k|\tau(n)$, $\tau(n)$ étant le nombre des diviseurs de $n$, on a, $k$ étant un nombre premier impair, $V_k = V_{k,k-1}$. $V_k$ coïncide avec l'ensemble $S_k$ de la note susmentionnée, et l'évaluation asymptotique de $S_k(x)$ est retrouvée ici par $V_k(x)$.

Ajoutons que l'auteur utilise dans la démonstration du théorème 1 un lemme généralisant l'identité arithmétique établie dans la note susmentionnée dont il donne ici une démonstration plus simple.

*A. Gloden* (Luxembourg)

**N28-50** **(27# 5741 )**

**Hooley, C.**

**On the difference of consecutive numbers prime to $n$.**

*Acta Arith.* **8** (1962/63), 343–347.

Let $1 = a_1 < \cdots < a_{\varphi(n)} = n-1$ be the integers relatively prime to $n$. The reviewer conjectured that

$$\sum_{i=1}^{\varphi(n)-1} (a_{i+1}-a_i)^2 = O(n^2/\varphi(n)).$$

The author proves that for every $1 \leqq \alpha < 2$

$$\sum_{i=1}^{\varphi(n)-1} (a_{i+1}-a_i)^\alpha = O(n(n/\varphi(n))^{\alpha-1}),$$

$$\sum_{i=1}^{\varphi(n)-1} (a_{i+1}-a_i)^2 = O(n \log\log n).$$

*P. Erdős* (Vancouver, B.C.)

Referred to in N28-60, N28-61, N60-86, N72-44.

**N28-51** **(28# 2391 )**

**Shanks, Daniel**

**The second-order term in the asymptotic expansion of $B(x)$.**

*Math. Comp.* **18** (1964), 75–86.

If $B(X)$ is the number of integers $\leqq X$ that are expressible in the form $w^2+v^2$, then $B(X) \sim bX/\sqrt{\log X}$, where $b$ is a known constant. The main objective of this article is to investigate the next term in the asymptotic expansion of $B(X)$. The result obtained is

$$B(X) = \frac{bX}{\sqrt{\log X}}\left[1 + \frac{c}{\log X} + O\left(\frac{1}{\log^2 X}\right)\right],$$

where $c$ is also a known constant. This result contradicts a statement of Hardy and exhibits the error made by Ramanujan's integral approximation to $B(X)$. With the aid of IBM 7090 computations, a table of $B(X)$ and two approximate functions is exhibited for $X = 2, 4, \cdots, 2^k, \cdots, 2^{26}$.

*W. Sangren* (San Diego, Calif.)

Referred to in N56-21.

**N28-52** **(28# 2995 )**

**de Bruijn, N. G.; van Lint, J. H.**

**On the number of integers $\leqq x$ whose prime factors divide $n$.**

*Acta Arith.* **8** (1962/63), 349–356.

Let $f(n, x)$ be the number of integers not exceeding $x$ which are products of powers of prime factors of $n$. In an earlier paper [Illinois J. Math. **6** (1962), 137–141; MR **26** #4977], de Bruijn showed that if

$$F(x) = \sum_{n \leqq x} f(n, x), \qquad G(x) = \sum_{n \leqq x} f(n, n),$$

then

$$\log(x^{-1}F(x)) \sim \log(x^{-1}G(x)) \sim (8 \log x)^{1/2} (\log\log x)^{-1/2}.$$

In the present paper it is shown that $F(x) \sim G(x)$. The proof quickly reduces to showing that

$$\sum_{k \leqq x} \frac{k}{\alpha(k)} = o\left(x \sum_{k \leqq x} \frac{1}{\alpha(k)}\right)$$

as $x \to \infty$, where $\alpha(k) = \prod_{p|k} p$ is the maximal square-free factor of $k$; the verification of this is somewhat intricate.

*W. J. LeVeque* (Boulder, Colo.)

Citations: MR 26# 4977 = N28-47.

## N28-53 (29# 1194)

**Barban, M. B.; Vinogradov, A. I.**

**On the number-theoretic basis of probabilistic number theory. (Russian)**

*Dokl. Akad. Nauk SSSR* **154** (1964), 495–496.

With $m$ as a positive integer, let $(m)_r$ denote the largest divisor of $m$ having all its prime factors $\leqq r$. Then

(1) $$N_n\{(m)_r \geqq u\} \leqq n \exp(-c_1\beta),$$

as was shown by M. B. Barban [Izv. Akad. Nauk UzSSR Ser. Fiz.-Mat. Nauk **1961**, no. 5, 3–9; MR **25** #2051]. Here $n$, $r$ and $u$ are variable integers $\geqq 2$, $c_1$ is an absolute constant, $\beta = \log u/\log r$, while $N_n\{\cdot\}$ denotes the number of integers $1 \leqq m \leqq n$ having the stated property. The result (1) appears as one of the two so-called fundamental lemmas (namely, Lemma 1.2) in the book of J. Kubilius [*Probabilistic methods in the theory of numbers* (Russian), Second, enlarged edition, Gosudarstv. Izdat. Politič. i Naučn. Lit. Litovsk. SSR, Vilna, 1962; MR **26** #3691; English transl., Amer. Math. Soc., Providence, R.I., 1964; MR **28** #3956]. In the present note, the authors improve (1) to

(2) $$N_n\{(m)_r \geqq u\} \leqq n \exp(-c_2\beta \log \beta).$$

In fact, (2) turns out to be an easy consequence of a bound on $N_n\{(m)_r = m\}$ due to A. I. Vinogradov [Dokl. Akad. Nauk SSSR **109** (1956), 683–686; MR **19**, 16]. Using (2), and further a method due to R. V. Uždavinis [Dissertation, Vilna, 1961], the authors also obtain a more precise form for the remainder term in a central limit theorem for strongly additive functions; the new remainder is smaller by a factor $[\log\log(1/\mu_n)]^{-1}$, where $\mu_n$ has the usual meaning; see Kubilius, op. cit., p. 108.

*J. H. B. Kemperman* (Rochester, N.Y.)

Citations: MR 19, 16f = N28-37; MR 25# 2051 = M55-25; MR 26# 3691 = N60-38; MR 28# 3956 = N60-39.

Referred to in N32-36.

## N28-54 (30# 1111)

**Rieger, G. J.**

**Über die Anzahl der als Summe von zwei Quadraten darstellbaren und in einer primen Restklasse gelegenen Zahlen unterhalb einer positiven Schranke. I.**

*Arch. Math.* **15** (1964), 430–434.

The author uses a previous result [J. Reine Angew. Math. **214/215** (1964), 373–385; MR **29** #86], based on the sieve method, to find an upper bound for $H(x+y; k, l) - H(y; k, l)$. Here $H(x; k, l)$ is the number of integers $n < x$ such that $n \equiv l \pmod{k}$ and such that the greatest odd divisor of $n$ has all its prime divisors $\equiv 1 \pmod 4$. This in turn is used to estimate $B(x+y; k, l) - B(y; k, l)$, where $B(x; k, l)$ is the number of integers $m < x$ with the properties listed in the title of this note. (Any such $m$ is of the form $m = 2^\alpha ab^2$, where $a \in \mathfrak{D}_1$, $b \in \mathfrak{D}_3$; here $\mathfrak{D}_1$ and $\mathfrak{D}_3$ are, respectively, the set of those integers whose prime divisors are all $\equiv 1 \pmod 4$ and $\equiv 3 \pmod 4$, respectively. The referee adds a remark at the end of the note pointing out that the result could be generalized to those integers $m$ represented by a positive-definite primitive binary quadratic form, since there is an analogous characterization of the prime divisors of $m$.)

A third theorem also uses a previous result and is concerned with the number of integers $m$ representable as $m = v^+ - v$, where $v \in \mathfrak{D}_1$ and $v^+$ is the least integer in $\mathfrak{D}_1$ greater than $v$. It is similar to the results for the differences $d_i = p_i - p_{i-1}$ of consecutive primes.

*R. D. James* (Vancouver, B.C.)

Citations: MR 29# 86 = P36-37.

Referred to in N28-58.

## N28-55 (30# 1997)

**Erdős, P.**

**On some applications of probability to analysis and number theory.**

*J. London Math. Soc.* **39** (1964), 692–696.

The author gives a review of applications of probability to the theory of power and Fourier series with gaps. He lists some new number theoretic results obtained by probabilistic considerations.

To every positive $\varepsilon_1$ and $\varepsilon_2$ there corresponds an $n_0$ so that if $n > n_0$ and $m < 2^{(1-\varepsilon_1)\log\log n}$, then more than $(1-\varepsilon_2)n$ positive integers $u \leqq m$ have divisors in every residue class mod $m$. From this result the author deduces that the number of positive integers $m \leqq n$ which do not have a divisor of the form $p(kp+1)$ is

$$(1+o(1)) \frac{e^{-\gamma}n}{\log 2 \cdot \log\log n}.$$

For every $\eta > 0$ the density of integers $n$ which have two divisors $d_1$ and $d_2$ satisfying

$$1 < d_2/d_1 < 1 + (e/3)^{(1-\eta)\log\log n}$$

is 1, but the density of integers $n$ which have two divisors $d_1$ and $d_2$ for which

$$1 < d_2/d_1 < 1 + (e/3)^{(1+\eta)\log\log n}$$

is 0.

*J. Kubilius* (Vilnius)

## N28-56 (30# 4731)

**de Bruijn, N. G.; van Lint, J. H.**

**Incomplete sums of multiplicative functions. I, II.**

*Nederl. Akad. Wetensch. Proc. Ser. A* **67** = *Indag. Math.* **26** (1964), 339–347, 348–359.

Let $\lambda$ be a non-negative multiplicative function defined on the positive integers, and let $P(n)$ denote the largest prime divisor of $n$. Put $\Lambda_a(x, y) = \sum \lambda(n) n^a$, where the summation is over those $n \leqq x$ satisfying $P(n) \leqq y$, and where $a \geqq 0$. The authors obtain asymptotic formulas for $\Lambda_a(y^u, y)$ whenever $\lambda$ satisfies certain restrictions. These formulas and restrictions are too lengthy to state here. Certain standard asymptotic formulas, such as

$$\prod_{p \leqq y} (1 - 1/p) \sim (e^\gamma \log y)^{-1},$$

are special cases of these formulas.

*D. G. Cantor* (Los Angeles, Calif.)

Referred to in N28-57, N80-38.

**N28-57** **(34# 4736)**

**Uchiyama, Saburô**

**On a differential-difference equation.**

*J. Fac. Sci. Hokkaido Univ. Ser. I* **19** (1966), 59–65.

If $s \geqq 0$ then $f_s(x)$ is defined by (i) $f_s(x)=0$ for $x<0$, (ii) $f_s(x)$ continuous for $x>0$, (iii) $f_s(x)=x^{s-1}$ for $0<x\leqq 1$, and (iv) $xf_s'(x)=(s-1)f_s(x)-sf_s(x-1)$ for $x>1$. The author shows that for $x\neq 0$,

$$2\pi i f_s(x)e^{-Cs}(\Gamma(s))^{-1} = \lim_{T\to\infty}\int_{-iT}^{iT}\exp[-xt+s\int_0^t(e^z-1)z^{-1}\,dz]\,dt,$$

where $C$ is Euler's constant. The special case $s=1$ is due to the reviewer [J. Indian Math. Soc. (N.S.) **15** (1951), 25–32; MR **13**, 326]. The general case is the Laplace transform of a result obtained by the reviewer and J. H. van Lint [Nederl. Akad. Wetensch. Proc. Ser. A **67** (1964), 339–347, 348–359; MR **30** #4731], but the author's method is different. *N. G. de Bruijn* (Eindhoven)

Citations: MR 13, 326f = N28-26; MR 30# 4731 = N28-56.

**N28-58** **(30# 4734)**

**Rieger, G. J.**

**Über die Anzahl der als Summe von zwei Quadraten darstellbaren und in einer primen Restklasse gelegenen Zahlen unterhalb einer positiven Schranke. II.**

*J. Reine Angew. Math.* **217** (1965), 200–216.

For $x>2$, $\tau$ any positive number, let $k$ and $l$ be integers with $(k,2l)=1$ and $k<\log^\tau x$. Let $B(x;k,l)$ denote the number of integers $n<x$, $n\equiv l \pmod k$, such that $n$ is a sum of two squares. Improving on a theorem of Landau, the author proves (Theorem 1) that

$$B(x;k,l) = C_1 q_1(k)(x/\sqrt{\log x})\left\{1+O_\tau\left(\frac{\log\log 4k}{\log x}\right)\right\},$$

where $C_1=\{2\prod_1(1-p^{-2})\}^{-1/2}$, $q_1(k)=k^{-1}\prod_2(1+p^{-1})$, the product $\prod_1$ being over all primes $p\equiv 3 \pmod 4$, and the product $\prod_2$ over all primes $p|k$, $p\equiv 3 \pmod 4$. The constant in the error term depends only on $\tau$. (In Part I [Arch. Math. **15** (1964), 430–434; MR **30** #1111], the author used the Brun sieve method to obtain an approximation to $B(x;k,l)$ from above.)

In this paper, the author uses a more-or-less classical approach to prove his main results. Some of the lemmas go back to Landau [*Handbuch der Lehre von der Verteilung der Primzahlen*, Teubner, Leipzig, 1909; 2 Bände, zweite Auflage, Chelsea Publishing Co., New York, 1953; MR **16**, 904], and others are similar to those in Chapter IV of Prachar [*Primzahlverteilung*, Springer, Berlin, 1957; MR **19**, 393]. There are (predictable) results analogous to Theorem 1 for $D(x;k,l)=\sum\delta(n)$, where $\delta(n)=1$ if every $p|n$ is congruent to 1 (mod 4), and $\delta(n)=0$ otherwise (Theorem 2); and for $A(x;k,l)=\sum\alpha(n)$, where $\alpha(n)=1$ if $n$ is squarefree and a sum of two squares, and $\alpha(n)=0$ otherwise (Theorem 3). (Note that $\alpha(n)=|\mu(n)|\theta(n)=|\mu(n)|\delta(n)$, where $\theta(n)=1$ if $n$ is a sum of two squares, and $\theta(n)=0$ otherwise.)

In the concluding section, the author states certain relationships between the constants in Theorems 1, 2, and 3, and indicates various generalizations of the theorems. The generalizations are of the following sort. Instead of $B(x;k,l)$, one considers $\sum 1$, where the summation is over all $n<x$, $n\in N$, $n\equiv l \pmod k$, and $N$ is a certain set of integers of the form $n=\prod_{p|n}p^{a_p}$, characterized by primes belonging to pairwise different residue classes. *R. D. James* (Vancouver, B.C.)

Citations: MR 16, 904d = N02-3; MR 19, 393b = N02-7; MR 30# 1111 = N28-54.

Referred to in N28-66.

**N28-59** **(31# 147)**

**Rieger, G. J.**

**Aufeinanderfolgende Zahlen als Summen von zwei Quadraten.**

*Nederl. Akad. Wetensch. Proc. Ser. A* **68** = *Indag. Math.* **27** (1965), 208–220.

The author proves (among others) the following theorems. The number of integers $n\leqq x$ for which both $n$ and $n+1$ are the sums of two squares is less than $c_1x/\log x$. The number of solutions of $n=u+v$, where both $u$ and $v$ are the sums of two squares, is less than

$$\frac{c_2 n}{\log n}\prod_{p|n,\,p\equiv 3 \pmod 4}\left(1+\frac{1}{p}\right).$$

Denote by $v_1<v_2<\cdots$ the integers which can be written as the sum of two squares; then

$$c_3\log^{3/2}x < \sum_{v_k<x}\left|\frac{v_{k+1}}{k+1}-\frac{v_k}{k}\right| < c_4\log^{3/2}x.$$

*P. Erdős* (Budapest)

**N28-60** **(32# 4099)**

**Hooley, Christopher**

**On the difference between consecutive numbers prime to $n$. II.**

*Publ. Math. Debrecen* **12** (1965), 39–49.

Let $1=a_1<a_2<\cdots<a_{\varphi(n)}=n-1$ be the integers relatively prime to $n$. Denote by $f_n(c)$ the number of integers $i$ for which $a_{i+1}-a_i<c^n/\varphi(n)$. Then if $n/\varphi(n)\to\infty$,

$$(1) \qquad f_n(c) = (1+o(1))\varphi(n)(1-e^{-c})$$

uniformly in $c$ if $c$ is bounded away from 0 and $\infty$. (1) confirms and considerably strengthens a conjecture of the reviewer [Magyar Tud. Akad. Mat. Kutató Int. Közl. **6** (1961), 221–254; MR **31** #2106].

The author further proves that if $n/\varphi(n)\to\infty$ and $0\leqq\alpha<2$, then

$$\sum_{i=1}^{\varphi(n)-1}(a_{i+1}-a_i)^\alpha = (1+o(1))\Gamma(\alpha+1)n\left(\frac{n}{\varphi(n)}\right)^{\alpha-1}.$$

The conjecture of the reviewer, $\sum_{i=1}^{\varphi(n)-1}(a_{i+1}-a_i)^2<cn^2/\varphi(n)$ is left open.

{Part I appeared in Acta Arith. **8** (1962/63), 343–347; MR **27** #5741; Part III appeared in Math. Z. **90** (1965), 355–364; MR **32** #1182.} *P. Erdős* (Budapest)

Citations: MR 27# 5741 = N28-50; MR 31# 2106 = Z05-10; MR 32# 1182 = N28-61.

Referred to in N60-86.

**N28-61** **(32# 1182)**

**Hooley, Christopher**

**On the difference between consecutive numbers prime to $n$. III.**

*Math. Z.* **90** (1965), 355–364.

Let $n$ be an integer, and $1=a_1<a_2<\cdots<a_{\varphi(n)}$ the integers relatively prime to $n$. Assume $n/\varphi(n)\to\infty$. The author proves that

$$(1) \qquad \sum_{\substack{1\leqq i<\varphi(n)\\ i\equiv 0 \pmod 2}}(a_{i+1}-a_i) = (\tfrac{1}{2}+o(1))n.$$

(1) has special interest in view of the conjecture of Pillai,

$$(2) \qquad \sum_{\substack{p_i<x\\ i\equiv 0 \pmod 2}}(p_{i+1}-p_i) = (\tfrac{1}{2}+o(1))x,$$

where the $p$'s are the primes. (2) is probably unattainable with present methods.

Denote by $g_n(c_1,\cdots,c_t)$ the number of integers $i$ for which $a_{i+j}-a_{i+j-1}\leqq c_jn/\varphi(n)$. Let $c_1,\cdots,c_t$ lie in some range $R$ that is bounded at each end by positive constants. The author proves that if $n/\varphi(n)\to\infty$ then uniformly in $R$,

$$(3) \qquad g_n(c_1,\cdots,c_t)=(1+o(1))\varphi(n)\prod_{j=1}^{t}(1-e^{-c_j}).$$

A conjecture which is analogous to (3) can be formulated about the primes but is probably unattackable by present methods.

(The author has two papers about similar subjects, Acta Arith. **8** (1962/63), 393–397 [MR **27** #5741] and Publ. Math. Debrecen **12** (1965), 39–49.) *P. Erdős* (Budapest)

Citations: MR 27# 5741 = N28-50.
Referred to in A26-85, N28-60, N60-86.

## N28-62 (34# 2541)

**Miech, R. J.**
**An asymptotic property of the Euler function.**
*Pacific J. Math.* **19** (1966), 95–107.

Denote by $\Phi'(k,x)$ the number of positive square-free integers $m\leqq x$ which have exactly $k$ prime factors, and which have a factor in common with $\phi(m)+1$, where $\phi(m)$ is the Euler totient function. The author proves that $\Phi'(k,x)\sim\lambda_k x(\log\log x)^{k-2}(\log x)^{-1}$ as $x\to\infty$, where $\lambda_k$ is a positive constant depending on $k$.

This result is derived from the stronger result (A) $\Phi(k,x)=\alpha_k x(\log\log x)^{k-2}(\log x)^{-1}[1+O((\log_{k+1}x)^{-1/2k})]$, where $\log_{k+1}x$ denotes the $(k+1)$st iterated logarithm, $\alpha_k$ is a positive constant depending on $k$, and $\Phi(k,x)$ is the number of odd integers $m\leqq x$ with all the above properties.

The main tools used in the proof of (A) are a deep version of the prime number theorem for arithmetic progressions with a variable modulus, the Brun-Titchmarsh theorem, and a generalization of an idea of E. M. Wright [Proc. Edinburgh Math. Soc. (2) **9** (1954), 87–90; MR **16**, 448] to arithmetic progressions.

The proof involves many careful estimations.
*S. L. Segal* (Rochester, N.Y.)

Citations: MR 16, 448e = N24-21.

## N28-63 (34# 5770)

**de Bruijn, N. G.**
**On the number of positive integers $\leqq x$ and free of prime factors $>y$. II.**
*Nederl. Akad. Wetensch. Proc. Ser. A* **69** = *Indag. Math.* **28** (1966), 239–247.

For $x>0$, $y\geqq 2$ denote by $\Psi(x,y)$ the number of positive integers not exceeding $x$ which contain no prime factors greater than $y$. An upper bound for $\Psi(x,y)$ was given by R. A. Rankin [J. London Math. Soc. **13** (1938), 242–247]:

$$(1)\quad \Psi(x,y)<x\exp\{-(\log_3 y/\log y)\log x+\log_2 y+O(\log_2 y/\log_3 y)\}.$$

The author [Nederl. Akad. Wetensch. Proc. Ser. A **54** (1951), 50–60; MR **13**, 724] sharpened (1) by a different method, and, in particular, proved that for iog $y>(\log x)^{2/3}$, (2) $\Psi(x,y)\sim x\rho(u)$, where $u=\log x/\log y$ and $\rho(u)$ is the solution of the differential-difference equation $u\rho'(u)=-\rho(u-1)$ for $u>1$ and with initial conditions $\rho(u)=1$ for $0\leqq u\leqq 1$, $\rho(u)$ continuous at $u=1$. (2) was established in the smaller region $\log y>c\log x$ (for any positive $c<1$) by K. Dickman [K. Ark. Mat. Astronom. Fys. **22** (1930), no. A10, 1–14], the reviewer and T. Vijayaraghavan [J. Indian Math. Soc. (N.S.) **11** (1947), 31–37; MR **9**, 332], V. Ramaswami [Duke Math. J. **16** (1949), 99–109; MR **10**, 597] and A. A. Buštab [Dokl. Akad. Nauk SSSR **67** (1949), 5–8; MR **11**, 84]. Also, the special (and very sharp) result $\log\Psi(x,\log x)\sim(\log 4)\times(\log x)(\log_2 x)^{-1}$ was obtained by Erdős [Wisk. Opgaven **21** (1963), 133–135; problem and solution No. 136]. The author now obtains two theorems, the first an asymptotic formula for $\log\Psi(x,y)$, effective if $y\to\infty$, $u\to\infty$. The second theorem (which also uses the method of Rankin) improves his previous result. His results are as follows. Theorem 1: Writing $Z=\{\log(1+y/\log x)\}(\log x)/(\log y)+\{\log(1+y^{-1}\log x)\}y/\log y$, we have, uniformly for $2<y\leqq x$, $\log\Psi(x,y)=Z\{1+O(\log y)^{-1}+O(\log_2 x)^{-1}+O(u+1)^{-1}\}$. Theorem 2: If $c$ is a constant, $c>1$, we have for $(\log x)^c\leqq y\leqq x$, $x\geqq 2$, uniformly $\log\Psi(x,y)\leqq\log x\rho(u)+\frac{1}{2}\log(1+u)+O(\log_2 y)+O((\log x)^2/y)+O(R)$, where $R=\int_1^{\log y}\exp\{s\eta/\log y\}V(e^s)\,ds$, $\eta=\log u+\log_2(u+1)$ and $V$ is a continuous positive function whose integral can be used as error-term in the prime-number theorem, $\pi(y)-\mathrm{li}(y)=O(\int_e^y V(t)\,dt)$, $\mathrm{li}(y)=\int_e^y dt/\log t$.
*S. Chowla* (University Park, Pa.)

Citations: MR 9, 332d = N28-14; MR 10, 597b = N28-17; MR 11, 84b = N28-18; MR 13, 724e = N28-28.
Referred to in N28-65.

## N28-64 (34# 7474)

**Erdős, P.**
**On the distribution of divisors of integers in the residue classes** (mod $d$).
*Bull. Soc. Math. Grèce (N.S.)* **6 I** (1965), *fasc.* 1, 27–36.

Let $k,l$ be integers such that $0<l<k$, $(l,k)=1$. Let $f(x;k,l)$ be the number of integers less than $x$ having a divisor congruent to $l$ (mod $k$), $F(x;k)$ the number of integers less than $x$ with a divisor congruent to $l$ (mod $k$) for every possible $l$, $Q(x)$ the number of integers less than $x$ with no divisor of the form $p(kp+1)$, and $d(n;k,l)$ the number of divisors of $n$ congruent to $l$ (mod $k$).

It is proved that if $k<2^{(1-\varepsilon)\log\log x}$, then $F(x;k)=x+o(x)$ uniformly in $k$. Since it was already known from work of G. H. Hardy and S. Ramanujan [Quart. J. Pure Appl. Math. **48** (1917), 76–92] that $F(x;k)=o(x)$ if $k>2^{(1+\varepsilon)\log\log x}$, we have that $2^{\log\log x}$ is, in a sense, a critical value of $k$, on the two sides of which the behavior of $F(x;k)$ is quite different.

Proofs in outline are given of the following results. For $k>2^{(1+\varepsilon)\log\log x}$, $f(x;k,l)=x/l+o(x)$ uniformly in $k$ and $l$. (Thus almost all the contribution to $f(x;k,l)$ is from the factors which are less than $k$.) $Q(x)=(1+o(1))e^{-\gamma}x\times(\log 2\log\log x)^{-1}$, where $\gamma$ is Euler's constant. If $k<2^{((1-\varepsilon)\log\log x)/2}$ then for every $\eta>0$ and every $l_1$ and $l_2$, $1-\eta<d(n;k,l_1)/d(n;k,l_2)<1+\eta$ holds for all but $o(x)$ integers less than $x$.

A number of conjectures are made about possible strengthening of these results and about similar results.
*H. J. Godwin* (Swansea)

Referred to in N64-42.

## N28-65 (35# 2836)

**Erdős, P.; van Lint, J. H.**
**On the number of positive integers $\leqq x$ and free of prime factors $>y$.**
*Simon Stevin* **40** (1966/67), 73–76.

Let $\Psi(x,y)$ be the number of integers specified in the title. Various estimates and formulas for $\Psi(x,y)$ have been given (see N. G. de Bruijn [Nederl. Akad. Wetensch. Proc. Ser. A **54** (1951), 50–60; MR **13**, 724] and references therein). The present authors give the following theorem which is related to a recent result of de Bruijn [ibid. **69** (1966), 239–247; MR **34** #5770]: For $2<y\leqq x$ one has, for $x\to\infty$ and uniformly in $y$, $\log\Psi(x,y)\sim\log\binom{\pi(y)+u}{u}$, where $u=[(\log x)/\log y]$. {Authors' correction: The condition $2<y\leqq x$ should be replaced by $2<y\leqq x^{\varepsilon(x)}$, where

$\varepsilon(x)$ is any function of $x$ which tends to 0 as $x \to \infty$.}
*J. B. Roberts* (Portland, Ore.)

Citations: MR 34# 5770 = N28-63.

**N28-66** **(37# 1327 )**

**Bekić, Hans**

**Über die Anzahl der Zahlen $a^2+b^2$ in einer arithmetischen Reihe großer Differenz.**

*J. Reine Angew. Math.* **226** (1967), 120–131.

Denote by $A(x, k, l)$ the number of natural numbers $n \leqq x$, $n=a^2+b^2$, $n \equiv l \bmod k$. Using the method of complex integration and the theory of $L$-functions, an asymptotic formula for $A(x, k, l)$ is proved which is uniform for $k \leqq \exp(c (\log x)^{1/2})$. For related results, see K. Pracher [Math. Nachr. **10** (1953), 51–54; MR **15**, 289] and the reviewer [J. Reine Angew. Math. **217** (1965), 200–216; MR **30** #4734]. Under the extended Riemann hypothesis, this asymptotic formula holds for $k \leqq x^{\alpha-\varepsilon}$ with $\alpha = 3-\sqrt{8}$ and arbitrary $\varepsilon > 0$.

{See also #1328 below.} *G. J. Rieger* (Buffalo, N.Y.)

Citations: MR 15, 289b = N28-29; MR 30# 4734 = N28-58.

**N28-67** **(37# 1328 )**

**Prachar, K.**

**Bemerkung zu der Arbeit von Herrn H. Bekić.**

*J. Reine Angew. Math.* **229** (1968), 28.

Using stronger theorems from prime number theory [see the author's book *Primzahlverteilung*, pp. 315–318, Springer, Berlin, 1957; MR **19**, 393], the asymptotic formula for $A(x, k, l)$ of the preceding review [#1327] is proved uniformly for $k \leqq \exp((\log x)^{2/3-\varepsilon})$.

*G. J. Rieger* (Buffalo, N.Y.)

Citations: MR 19, 393b = N02-7.

**N28-68** **(38# 2206 )**

**Dornhoff, Larry**

**Simple groups are scarce.**

*Proc. Amer. Math. Soc.* **19** (1968), 692–696.

The author proves the following interesting theorem. Theorem 1: Let $r(x)$ denote the number of integers $n \leqq x$ such that every group of order $n$ has a normal Sylow subgroup. Then $\lim_{x\to\infty} r(x)/x = 1$. This theorem justifies the title of the author's paper.

The author also proves Theorem 4: If $p(x)$ is the number of integers $n \leqq x$ with a prime divisor greater than $\sqrt{n}$, then $\lim_{x\to\infty} p(x)/x = \log_e 2$. Results of this type have been proved before by several authors, e.g., Buchstab, De Bruijn, Ramaswami, the reviewer and T. Vijayaraghavan [the last two in J. Indian Math. Soc. (N.S.) **11** (1947), 31–37; MR **9**, 332]. See also the reviewer and J. Todd [Canad. J. Math. **1** (1949), 297–299; MR **11**, 14].

*S. Chowla* (University Park, Pa.)

Citations: MR 9, 332d = N28-14; MR 11, 14d = N32-4.

**N28-69** **(39# 5492 )**

**Ennola, Veikko**

**On numbers with small prime divisors.**

*Ann. Acad. Sci. Fenn. Ser. A I No.* 440 (1969), 16 *pp.*

The author investigates the function $\psi(x, y)$, namely, the number of integers in the interval $(1, x)$ whose prime factors are all $\leqq y$. Chief consideration is given to the very small factors from the interval $y \leqq (\ln x)^\theta$, $\theta \leqq 1$. In this case he obtains asymptotic estimates for $\psi(x, y)$.

*A. I. Vinogradov* (Leningrad)

**N28-70** **(40# 4217 )**

**Rieger, G. J.**

**Zahlentheoretische Anwendung eines Taubersatzes mit Restglied.**

*Math. Ann.* **182** (1969), 243–248.

Let $T$ be an infinite set of primes $p$ and suppose (*) $\sum_{p\leq x, p\in T} (\log p)/p = \tau(1+\nu(x)) \log x$ (as $x\to\infty$), where $\tau$ is a positive constant, and $\nu(x) = O((\log x)^{-\delta})$ for some $\delta > 0$. Making earlier results ($\nu(x)=o(1)$) more precise, the author proves that (*) implies that $\sum_{m\leq x, m\in\mathscr{M}} 1/m = e^{-c\tau}/\Gamma(\tau+1) \prod_{p\leq x, p\in T} (1-1/p)^{-1}(1+O(1/\log\log x))$, where $\mathscr{M}$ is the set of all positive integers $m$ such that if $p|m$, then $p\in T$, and $c$ is Euler's constant. ($\nu(x)=o(1)$ gives $o(1)$ in place of $O(1/\log\log x)$ in the above formula.)

The proof depends upon a corresponding improvement in the Tauberian theorem used by E. Wirsing to prove the earlier results [Arch. Math. **7** (1956), 263–272; MR **18**, 642]. *S. L. Segal* (Rochester, N.Y.)

Citations: MR 18, 642f = N28-35.

**N28-71** **(41# 3426 )**

**van de Lune, J.; Wattel, E.**

**On the frequency of natural numbers $m$ whose prime divisors are all smaller than $m^\alpha$.**

*Math. Centrum Amsterdam Afd. Zuivere Wisk.* **1968**, ZW-007, 35 *pp.*

If $\alpha$ is a real number and $n$ is a positive integer, let $G(n, \alpha)$ denote the number of positive integers $m \leqq n$ such that all prime divisors of $m$ are smaller than $m^\alpha$. Let $G(\alpha) = \lim_{n\to\infty} G(n, \alpha)/n$. It is shown that this limit exists for all $\alpha$, and that, for $0<\alpha<1$, the function $G(\alpha)$ is differentiable and satisfies the differential equation $\alpha G'(\alpha) = G(\alpha/(1-\alpha))$. A simple integral formula for the Laplace transform of the function $H(x) = G(1/x)$ is obtained. Methods for computing $H(x)$ are discussed, and a short numerical table is included.

*D. Rearick* (Boulder, Colo.)

**N28-72** **(41# 6796 )**

**Suryanarayana, D.**

**The number and sum of $k$-free integers $\leqq x$ which are prime to $n$.**

*Indian J. Math.* **11** (1969), 131–139.

Let $Q_k(x, n)$ denote the number of $k$-free integers $\leqq x$ which are relatively prime to $n$. Then $Q_k(x, n) = (n^{k-1}\Phi(n)/J_k(n))x/\zeta(k) + O((\Phi(n)\gamma(n)/n)x^{1/k})$, where $\Phi(n)$ is Euler's $\Phi$-function, $J_k(n)$ is Jordan's totient (so $\Phi(n) = J_1(n)$), $\zeta(k)$ is the Riemann zeta function, and $\gamma(n)$ the number of square-free divisors of $n$.

Similar results are given for the sum of the integers counted above, and for the average order of the sum of unitary $k$-free divisors of $n$. The cited result improves on one of E. Cohen and R. L. Robinson [Acta Arith. **8** (1962/63), 283–293; errata, ibid. **10** (1964/65), 443; MR **28** #1188]. *S. L. Segal* (Rochester, N.Y.)

Citations: MR 28# 1188 = N24-46.

**N28-73** **(41# 6797 )**

**Suryanarayana, D.**

**Uniform $O$-estimates of certain error functions connected with $k$-free integers.**

*J. Austral. Math. Soc.* **11** (1970), 242–250.

Let $Q_k(x, n)$ denote the number of $k$-free integers $\leqq x$ and prime to $n$ and let $Q_k'(x, n)$ denote the sum of the reciprocals of these integers. The author proves the following results.

For $0 \leqq s < 1/k$,

$$(*) \qquad Q_k(x, n) = nx/(\zeta(k)\psi_k(n)) + O(\sigma_{-s}^*(n)x^{1/k})$$

and $Q_k'(x, n) = (n/(\zeta(k)\psi_k(n)))\{\log x + \gamma - k\zeta'(k)/\zeta(k) + \alpha(n) - k\alpha_k(n)\}$, where $\psi_k(n) = n\prod_{p|n}(1+1/p+\cdots+1/p^{k-1})$, $\alpha(n) = \sum_{p|n}(p-1)^{-1}\log p$, $\alpha_k(n) = \sum_{p|n}(p^k-1)^{-1}\log p$, $\sigma_t^*(n)$ is the sum of the $t$th powers of the squarefree divisors of $n$ and $\gamma$ is Euler's constant. The author notes that (*)

was stated by R. L. Robinson [Proc. Amer. Math. Soc. **17** (1966), 232–237; MR **32** #2386; correction, ibid. **17** (1966), 1473; MR **33** #5594] with the error term $O(\sigma_0^*(n)x'^{(k)})$; the case $k=2$ had been proved by E. Cohen [Math. Z. **74** (1960), 66–80; MR **22** #3707]. *L. Carlitz* (Durham, N.C.)

Citations: MR 22# 3707 = N52-19; MR 32# 2386 = N24-56; MR 32# 5594 = J24-40.

## N28-74 (42# 211)

**Levin, B. V.; Faĭnleĭb, A. S.**

**The generalized problem of numbers with small and large prime divisors and its applications. (Russian. Uzbek summary)**

*Dokl. Akad. Nauk UzSSR* **1966**, *no.* 5, 3–7.

The authors investigate the distribution of integers with given boundaries for prime divisors. They obtain a general asymptotic law of the behavior of multiplicative functions on such sets. *A. I. Vinogradov* (Leningrad)

## N28-75 (42# 225)

**Warlimont, Richard**

**Eine Bemerkung zu einem Ergebnis von N. G. de Bruijn.**

*Monatsh. Math.* **74** (1970), 273–276.

For $x>0$, $y\geqq 2$, let $\varphi(x,y)$ be the number of positive integers $\leqq x$ with no prime divisors $<y$. Put $\varphi(x,y)=\psi(x,y)x\prod_{p<y}(1-p^{-1})$. It was shown by W. B. Jurkat and H.-E. Richert [Acta Arith. **11** (1965), 217–240; MR **34** #2540] by means of the Selberg sieve method that $\varphi(x,y)=1+O((\log x)^{-1})$ for $\log y\leqq(\log x)/(2\log\log 3x)$. The author shows that this estimate holds for all $x>0$ and all $y\geqq 2$, bridging the gap by means of a result of the reviewer [Nederl. Akad. Wetensch. Proc. Ser. A **53** (1950), 803–812; MR **12**, 11]. *N. G. de Bruijn* (Eindhoven)

Citations: MR 12, 11d = N28-22; MR 34# 2540 = M55-48.

## N28-76 (42# 1774)

**Lucht, Lutz**

**Dichtentheoretische Sätze der Zahlentheorie.**

*J. Reine Angew. Math.* **243** (1970), 192–218.

From the prime number theorem $\pi(x)\sim x/\log x$, Landau deduced the generalization

$$\pi_k(x) \sim x(\log\log x)^{k-1}/(k-1)!\log x$$

using only elementary combinatorial arguments. The author considers the corresponding problem in which the set $\mathfrak{P}$ of primes is replaced by an arbitrary set $\mathfrak{A}$ of relatively prime positive integers with counting-function $A(x)=\sum_{a\leqq x,a\in\mathfrak{A}}1$, and $\mathfrak{A}^k$ denotes the $k$-fold complex product of $\mathfrak{A}$ with itself. Among several results concerning the counting-function $A_k(x)$ of $\mathfrak{A}^k$, the following direct generalization of Landau's formula is representative: If $A(x)\sim\alpha x^\tau/\log x$, then

$$A_k(x) \sim \alpha^k\tau^{k-1}x^\tau(\log\log x)^{k-1}/(k-1)!\log x.$$

Another result justifies the "obvious" integral approximation for certain sums extended over the elements of a set $\mathfrak{A}$ of positive integers whose counting-function is asymptotic to a differentiable function $\psi(x)$, viz. $\sum_{b\leqq a\leqq x,a\in\mathfrak{A}}F(a,x)\sim\int_b^x F(t,x)\psi'(t)\,dt$. If $\mathfrak{A}$ is specialized to $\mathfrak{P}$, another theorem of Landau results.

The present work is related to that of B. Hornfeck [Monatsh. Math. **60** (1956), 96–108; MR **18**, 18] who supervised this doctoral dissertation. *D. Rearick* (Boulder, Colo.)

Citations: MR 18, 18c = N24-26.
Referred to in N28-77.

## N28-77 (43# 3220)

**Lucht, Lutz**

**Ergänzung zu meinem Beitrag "Dichtentheoretische Sätze der Zahlentheorie" in Band 243.**

*J. Reine Angew. Math.* **244** (1970), 220.

Author's text: "In den Sätzen 5 und 7 auf den Seiten 208 bzw. 215 befinden sich Setzfehler. Die jeweils 7. Zeile muß richtig heißen: (b) $h(x^q)\leqq dh(x)$ für alle $q$, $q_0\leqq q\leqq 1$, und alle $x\geqq 1$. Beim Beweis von Satz 6 ist die Gleichheit in Formel (46) auf Seite 213 durch eine asymptotische Gleichheit zu ersetzen, Das versehentlich nicht aufgeführte Restglied $S(\sqrt{x})T(\sqrt{x})$ ist ein $o(S(x)+T(x))$ wegen $h(x)=o(1)$. Letzteres ist aus der vorausgesetzten Konvergenz der Reihe $\sum_{t\in\mathfrak{T}}t^{-\sigma}$ unter Verwendung von (34 b) ableitbar. Entsprechend ist auf Seite 214, 17. Zeile, für das zweite Gleichheitszeichen ein asymptotisches Gleichheitszeichen zu setzen."

{The original article appeared in same J. **243** (1970), 192–218 [MR **42** #1774].} *D. Rearick* (Boulder, Colo.)

Citations: MR 42# 1774 = N28-76.

## N28-78 (42# 4489)

**Rieger, G. J.**

**Zur Satz von Landau über die Summe aus zwei Quadraten.**

*J. Reine Angew. Math.* **244** (1970), 198–200.

Let $B(x)$ be the number of integers $\leqq x$ which are the sum of two squares of rational integers. With a method of Landau, using complex integration, one can prove $B(x)=cx\log^{-1/2}x(1+O((\log x)^{-1}))$ for $x\to\infty$ with an absolute constant $c>0$ [see E. Landau, *Handbuch der Lehre von der Verteilung der Primzahlen*, Band II, § 183, Teubner, Leipzig, 1909; second edition, Chelsea, New York, 1953; MR **16**, 904]. The author gives an elementary proof of the weaker result $B(x)=cx\log^{-1/2}x(1+O((\log\log x)^{-1}))$ for $x\to\infty$. His proof is based on the prime number theorem for arithmetic progressions and a Tauberian theorem, both with a remainder term. *R. Tijdeman* (Princeton, N.J.)

Citations: MR 16, 904d = N02-3.

## N28-79 (42# 4509)

**Halberstam, H.**

**On integers all of whose prime factors are small.**

*Proc. London Math. Soc.* (3) **21** (1970), 102–107.

Let $\Psi(x,y)$ denote the number of positive integers not exceeding $x$ free of prime factors greater than $y$, and put $x=y^u$. The author obtains a new lower bound for the function $\Psi(y^u,y)$ in the case $u\geqq 3$, namely, $\Psi(y^u,y)\geqq 2y^u\exp\{-u\log u-u\log\log u-u\log\log u/\log u-u/\log u+u\log\log u/\log^2 u-4u/\log^2 u-14\}$ if $y\geqq y_1(u)$. An elementary proof is given. The gap between this and known upper bounds is comparatively narrow. *D. Rearick* (Boulder, Colo.)

## N28-80 (43# 165)

**Nicolas, Jean-Louis**

**Répartition des nombres hautement composés de Ramanujan.**

*Canad. J. Math.* **23** (1971), 116–130.

Let $d(n)$ denote the number of divisors of $n$. S. Ramanujan [Proc. London Math. Soc. (2) **14** (1915), 347–409] has defined a positive integer $A$ to be highly composite if $d(M)<d(A)$ for any positive integer $M$ less than $A$, and has defined $A$ to be superior highly composite if there exists $\varepsilon>0$ such that $d(M)/M^\varepsilon\leqq d(A)/A^\varepsilon$ for any positive integer $M$. Let $Q(X)$ be the number of highly composite integers less than $X$. Ramanujan proved $\lim_{X\to\infty}Q(X)/\log X=+\infty$, and P. Erdős [J. London Math. Soc. **19** (1944),

130–133; MR 7, 145] showed $Q(X) \geqq (\log X)^{1+c}$ where $c \leqq 3/32$. In the paper being reviewed, this inequality is obtained for a slightly larger $c$. Also, it is shown that there exists a constant $c$ such that if $N$ and $N'$ are consecutive superior highly composite numbers, then $Q(N') - Q(N) = O(\log N)^c$. For this same $c$, and for any $X$, $Q(X) = O(\log X)^{1+c}$. *B. Garrison* (San Diego, Calif.)

Citations: MR 7, 145d = A32-11.

**N28-81** **(43# 1942)**

**Erdős, Paul**

**Some extremal problems in combinatorial number theory.** *Mathematical Essays Dedicated to A. J. Macintyre, pp.* 123–133. *Ohio Univ. Press, Athens, Ohio,* 1970.

This paper contains a number of results concerning the density of some sequences of positive integers that have certain divisibility properties. The most striking of these results are the following. (1) The density of those integers that have three pairwise relatively prime divisors $b_1, b_2, b_3$ with $b_1 < b_2 < b_3 < 2b_1$ exists and is less than unity. (2) Let $F(k, x)$ denote the maximum number of positive integers $a_1, a_2, \cdots, a_s$, with $a_1 < a_2 < \cdots < a_s \leqq x$ and with the property that no $k$ of them have pairwise the same least common multiple; then, as a consequence of (1), it follows that the relation $F(k, x) = o(x)$ does not hold for $k \geqq 4$; for $k = 3$ the question is still open. (3) Let $A_t$, for integral $t$, denote the set of those integers $n$ such that $t$ can be written as a sum of distinct divisors of $n$; then the density of $A_t$ exists for all $t$ and tends to zero, as $t \to \infty$. (4) An integer $n$ is said to have the property $P$ if all the $2^{d(n)}$ possible sums of distinct divisors of $n$ are distinct from one another; the density of the set of integers having the property $P$ exists and is positive. The author remarks that some of the results of the paper (not those mentioned above) are the joint work of the author with A. Sárközi and E. Szemerédi.

*F. Herzog* (E. Lansing, Mich.)

## N32 MULTIPLICATIVE STRUCTURE OF POLYNOMIAL VALUES

Many of the papers in this section are either heuristic or conjectural, and might therefore have been included in **A42**, for example. But obviously the questions themselves are not elementary.

See also reviews A18-31, A26-53, A38-62, A44-1, A44-16, A46-18, A46-25, A46-40, A46-42, A46-46, A50-1, C10-16, D12-32, D12-41, D12-51, D12-72, D60-82, E16-11, E16-43, E16-59, E16-68, E16-79, E24-37, E24-41, E24-64, E76-10, E76-20, E76-24, J80-29, M55-13, M55-15, M55-33, M55-37, M55-53, M55-66, N12-6, N20-19, N20-20, N20-40, N24-35, N36-5, N36-8, N40-1, N40-16, N40-19, N40-25, N40-26, N40-32, N40-43, N40-47, N40-66, N40-69, N40-81, N48-12, N48-14, N48-16, N48-29, N52-14, N52-32, N52-34, N52-40, N56-39, N60-15, N60-21, N60-32, N60-37, N60-41, N60-44, N60-45, N60-50, N60-56, N60-69, N60-73, N60-75, N60-84, N80-41, P02-5, P32-62, P36-29, P36-33, P36-40, P40-7, P40-22, P52-12, R08-22, R42-49, R44-19, R44-21, R44-43, R46-14, R46-18, R46-24, R46-34, U05-52, Z10-47, Z15-70.

**N32-1** **(4, 34c)**

**Mahler, Kurt. Remarks on ternary Diophantine equations.** Amer. Math. Monthly **49**, 372–378 (1942).

In a previous paper [Math. Ann. **107**, 691–730 (1933)], the author obtained the following generalization of Thue's theorem: If the greatest prime factor of a binary form $F(x, y)$ is bounded for an infinite number of relatively prime pairs $x, y$, then $F(x, y)$ is a power of a linear or quadratic form. He proves now by simple examples that the assertions of Thue's theorem and of his generalization are no longer true if the binary form $F(x, y)$ is replaced by a ternary form $F(x, y, z)$. *C. L. Siegel* (Princeton, N. J.).

**N32-2** **(8, 5a)**

**Brauer, Alfred. A theorem of M. Bauer.** Duke Math. J. **13**, 235–238 (1946).

A generalization of a theorem of M. Bauer [J. Reine Angew. Math. **131**, 265–267 (1906)] is the author's theorem I. Let $f(x)$ be a polynomial with rational integral coefficients which has at least one real root. Let $G(k)$ be the group of the residue classes relatively prime to $k$ and $H$ a subgroup which does not contain the class of numbers congruent to $-1 \pmod{k}$. Then, for integral values of $x$, $f(x)$ takes values divisible by infinitely many primes which do not belong to the classes of $H$. The author obtains other results from this theorem. His proof is simple and such that the Dirichlet theorem is only essentially employed when the degree of $f(x)$ is even. *R. Hull* (Lincoln, Neb.).

**N32-3** **(8, 503b)**

**Selmer, Ernst S. Über Primzahlen von der Form $x^2+1$.** Norske Vid. Selsk. Forh., Trondhjem **15** (1942), no. 39, 149–152 (1943).

Hardy and Littlewood [Acta Math. **44**, 1–70 (1922)] conjectured an asymptotic formula for $P(n)$, the number of primes of the form $x^2+1$ less than $n$. In this paper a similar formula for primes of the form $x^2+k$ is stated and verified for $n = 2981^2$ and $k = 1, 2, \cdots, 10$. With one or two exceptions the agreement between the calculated value and the actual count is surprisingly good considering the many number-theoretic tables involved in the computation.

*R. D. James* (Vancouver, B. C.).

**N32-4** **(11, 14d)**

**Chowla, S. D., and Todd, John. The density of reducible integers.** Canadian J. Math. **1**, 297–299 (1949).

Let $P(m)$ denote the greatest prime factor of $m$. The authors call an integer $n$ reducible if $P(n^2+1) < 2n$, and they adduce numerical evidence in support of the conjecture that the set of reducible integers possesses a density which is approximately equal to 0.3. They also prove that the set of integers $n$ such that $P(n) < 2n^{\frac{1}{2}}$ has density $1 - \log 2$. This result is obtained by estimating in turn the number of positive integers $n \leqq x$ for which $P(n) > 2x^{\frac{1}{2}}$ and $2n^{\frac{1}{2}} \leqq P(n) \leqq 2x^{\frac{1}{2}}$ respectively, and using in both cases the classical asymptotic formula for $\sum_{p \leqq x} p^{-1}$. The authors observe, moreover, that a similar argument will show that the density of the set of numbers $n$ such that $P(n) > An^{\alpha}$, where $A \geqq 1$, $\frac{1}{2} \leqq \alpha < 1$, is $\log(1/\alpha)$. [This is erroneously stated as $\log \alpha$ in the paper. The authors have informed the reviewer that the table on page 297 contains numerous minor errors, and they have supplied an amended table. They also point out that the words "right" and "left" on page 297, § 1, lines 4 and 5, should be interchanged.]

*L. Mirsky* (Sheffield).

Referred to in N28-68, N32-7.

**N32-5** **(11, 14e)**

**Mirsky, L. A property of square-free integers.** J. Indian Math. Soc. (N.S.) **13**, 1–3 (1949).

Let $q_1, q_2, \cdots, q_s$ be any nonzero integers. Then the set of those positive integers $n$ for which all the numbers $n^2+q_1, n^2+q_2, \cdots, n^2+q_s$ are square-free is either empty or has positive lower density. *T. Estermann* (London).

**N32-6** **(11, 159d)**

**Todd, John. A problem on arc tangent relations.** Amer. Math. Monthly **56**, 517–528 (1949).

The problem considered is that of expressing the arctangent of an integer $m$ as a linear combination of arctangents of integers less than $m$, the linear combination having integral coefficients. Those integers $m$ for which such an expression is possible are termed reducible. The author proves that each of the following conditions is necessary and sufficient for the reducibility of $m$. (A) All prime factors of $1+m^2$ divide $\prod_{n=1}^{m-1}(1+n^2)$. (B) The prime factors of $1+m^2$ are all less than $2m$. In proving the sufficiency of (A) an algorithm for actually carrying out the reduction of $m$ is given. There are infinitely many reducible and infinitely many irreducible integers. It is conjectured that the density of irreducible integers is approximately .7. The irreducible integers 1, 2, 4, 5, 6, 9, 10, 11, 12, 14, $\cdots$ form a basis for arctan $m$ and for arctan $(a/b)$. The expansion of arctan $m$ in terms of arctangents of irreducible integers is given for each reducible integer not exceeding 342, as well as that of arctan $(a/b)$ for integers $a, b$, such that $a^2+b^2$ is a prime not exceeding 409. *D. H. Lehmer.*

Referred to in D99-10, Z30-35.

**N32-7** **(12, 481k)**

**Knödel, W. Reduzible Zahlen.** Monatsh. Math. **54**, 308–312 (1950).

S. D. Chowla and J. Todd [Canadian J. Math. **1**, 297–299 (1949); these Rev. **11**, 14] conjectured that the set of integers $x$, such that $x^2+1$ has no prime factor exceeding $2x$, possesses a density, and that this density is approximately equal to 0.3. The author proves the following result connected with the problem of Chowla and Todd. Let $f(x)=o(x \log x)$ and denote by $N(A)$ the number of integers $x \leqq A$ such that $x^2+1$ possesses no prime factor exceeding $f(x)$. Then $\limsup_{A\to\infty} N(A)/A \leqq 0.5$. The argument depends essentially on the use of well-known estimates in prime number theory. The reviewer observes that in the last equation on p. 311 and in the first equation on p. 312 the term $o(A \log A)$ has been omitted; moreover in the second equation on p. 312 the term $o(A)$ has been omitted. *L. Mirsky* (Bristol).

Citations: MR 11, 14d = N32-4.

**N32-8** **(13, 914a)**

**Erdös, P. On the greatest prime factor of $\prod_{k=1}^{x} f(k)$.** J. London Math. Soc. **27**, 379–384 (1952).

Let $f(x)$ be a polynomial with integral coefficients which is not the product of linear factors with integral coefficients. $P_x$ denotes the greatest prime factor of $\prod_{k=1}^{x} f(k)$. The author shows that, for some $c>0$,

$$P_x > x\,(\log x)^{c \log\log\log x};$$

thus improving Nagell's inequality $P_x > cx \log x$ [Abh. Math. Sem. Univ. Hamburg **1**, 179–194 (1922)]. The main lemmas are: (1) The number of positive integers $t \leqq x$ for which $f(t)$ is divisible by a number in the interval $(x/\log\log x, x)$ is greater than

$$cx\,(\log\log x)(\log\log\log x)/\log x;$$

(2) (due to Nagell) if $f(k)=A_kB_k$, where the prime factors of $A_k$ are $\leqq x$, and those of $B_k$ are $>x$, then we have

$$\sum_{k=1}^{x} \log A_k < x \log x + O(x).$$

The author states that he is able to prove, in a much more complicated way, that $P_x > x \exp((\log x)^c)$. *N. G. de Bruijn* (Delft).

Referred to in N32-18, N32-54.

**N32-9** **(13, 914d)**

**Cugiani, Marco. Sull'aritmetica dei polinomi di esponenziali a valori interi.** Boll. Un. Mat. Ital. (3) **7**, 38–43 (1952).

Let $F(y)=c_0y^n+c_1y^{n-1}+\cdots+c_n$ ($c_0\neq 0$, $c_n\neq 0$, $n\geqq 1$) be an irreducible polynomial with integral coefficients. Let $P_x$ denote the largest prime divisor of the product $F(a)F(a^{2^m})\cdots F(a^{x^m})$ ($a$, $x$, $m$ integers, $m\geqq 1$, $|a|\geqq 2$, $(a, c_n)=1$). The author proves that there exists a positive number $\gamma$ independent of $x$ such that $P_x > \gamma(x \log x)^{1/2}$ for sufficiently large $x$. The proof is based upon the following three lemmas in which the letter $p$ stands for a prime. I. For $(k, p)=1$ the congruence $y^m \equiv k \pmod{p^s}$ possesses at most $2m$ solutions $\pmod{p^s}$. II. The number $N(\xi)$ of solutions of the congruence $x^m \equiv kp^r \pmod{gp^s}$ (where $(k, p)=(g, p)=1$, $0<r<s$) which do not exceed a given real number $\xi$, satisfies the inequality $N(\xi)\leqq 2m(\xi p^{-s/m}+1)$. III. If $x$ is a real number then $\sum_{p\leqq x} p = O(x^2/\log x)$. The author's theorem is an extension of a result previously obtained by G. Ricci [same Boll. **12**, 222–228 (1933)]. *A. L. Whiteman* (Princeton, N. J.).

Referred to in N32-28.

**N32-10** **(14, 137f)**

**dos Reis, Manuel. On conjectured asymptotic formulas concerning the distribution of prime numbers.** Gaz. Mat., Lisboa **12**, no. 50, 83–90 (1951). (Portuguese)

Using the sieve method in conjunction with some probabilistic arguments, several conjectural formulas are established. Some of them correspond to well-known theorems (the prime number theorem for all integers and for arithmetic progressions; the Hardy-Littlewood-Vinogradov asymptotic formula for the number of representations of an odd number as a sum of three odd primes [Vinogradov, Mat. Sbornik **2**(44), 179–195 (1937)]), others were conjectured by Hardy and Littlewood [Acta Math. **44**, 1–70 (1923)] and others still, of the same general type, seem new, as, e.g.,

$$P(n) \sim n^{1/4}(\log n)^{-1}\prod_{p\geqq 3}\{1-(-1/p)(p-1)^{-1}\} \times \prod_{p\equiv 1 \,(\mathrm{mod}\ 4)} \{1-(-1/p)_4\cdot 2/(p-2)\}$$

for the number of primes not exceeding $n$ and of the form $x^4+1$. Here $(-1/p)_4=1$ (respectively, $=-1$) if $-1$ is biquadratic residue (resp., non-residue) mod $p$. The fact that some of the formulas obtained by his method are known to be true indicates, in the author's opinion, that also the others have a high degree of probability of being true. Some of the arguments used in the paper do not seem very convincing to the reviewer, even when considered as purely heuristical ones. *E. Grosswald* (Philadelphia, Pa.).

**N32-11** **(15, 15b)**

**Rényi, Kató. The distribution of numbers not divisible by a $k$th power of an integer greater than one in the set of values of a polynomial having rational roots.** Comptes Rendus du Premier Congrès des Mathématiciens Hongrois, 27 Août–2 Septembre 1950, pp. 493–506. Akadémiai Kiadó, Budapest, 1952. (Hungarian. Russian summary)

Let $P(x)$ be a polynomial of degree $r$ whose roots are all rational. Then the density of integers $n$ for which $P(n)$ is $k$th power free exists and is positive except if $P(x)$ has a $k$-fold root or if $P(x)$ is such that there exists a $p$ so that, for every $n$, $P(n)\equiv 0 \pmod{p^k}$. Clearly the density in question is 0 in the exceptional cases. The second exceptional case is discussed in detail. The proofs are elementary.

*P. Erdös* (South Bend, Ind.).

## N32-12 (15, 102g)

**Cugiani, Marco. Sugli intervalli fra i valori dell'argomento pei quali un polinomio risulta libero da potenze.** Rivista Mat. Univ. Parma **4**, 95–103 (1953).

If an integer does not have a $k$th power other than 1 for a divisor, it is said to be $k$-free ($k\geqq 2$). Let $F(x)$ be an integral-valued polynomial of degree $g$ with rational coefficients and discriminant different from zero. For $g \geqslant 1$ and a fixed integer $l\geqq 1$ put $k=g+l$. The author considers sequences of integers $1\leqq q_1<q_2<\cdots<q_n<\cdots$ which are such that the corresponding polynomial values $F(q_1), \cdots, F(q_n), \cdots$ are all $k$-free integers. Halberstam and Roth [J. London Math. Soc. **26**, 268–273 (1951); these Rev. **13**, 208] proved in the particular case $F(x)=x$ ($q_n$ is now the $n$th $k$-free integer) that $\delta_n=O(n^{(1/2k)+\epsilon})$, where $\delta_n=q_{n+1}-q_n$. Employing only elementary arguments in conjunction with the method of Viggo Brun the author obtains preliminary results about the asymptotic behaviour of $\delta_n$ in the general case. Let $\nu(m)$ denote the number of solutions of the congruence $F(x)\equiv 0 \pmod{m}$. For a fixed integer $s\geqq 2$ put $\Lambda_s=\prod(1-\nu(p^s)/p^s)$, where the product extends over all the primes. Then the author establishes the following three results: (a) $\liminf \delta_n\leqq 1/\Lambda_k$; (b) $\limsup \delta_n \log\log n/\log n\geqq h/gk$; (c) $\delta_n=O(n^{(g/k)-\alpha}/(\log n)^\beta)$, where $\alpha=g/(k^2+k)$, $\beta=k/(k+1)$ for $g\leqq l$, and $\alpha=l/(k^2-k)$, $\beta=1$ for $g>l$.

*A. L. Whiteman* (Princeton, N. J.).

Citations: MR 13, 208e = N24-13.

## N32-13 (15, 104f)

**Erdös, P. Arithmetical properties of polynomials.** J. London Math. Soc. **28**, 416–425 (1953).

Let $f(x)$ denote a polynomial of degree $l$ whose coefficients are integers with highest common factor 1 and with positive highest coefficient. The writer first notes the known result that there are infinitely many positive integers $n$ such that $f(n)$ is $l$th power free. He then proves that if $l\geqq 3$ then there are infinitely many positive integers $n$ such that $f(n)$ is $(l-1)$th power free. It is necessary to exclude an exceptional case; this is done by assuming that when $l$ is a power of 2 there exists an $n$ such that $f(n)\not\equiv 0 \pmod{2^{l-1}}$. In the exceptional case it follows from the proof of the main result that there are infinitely many $n$ for which $f(n)=2^{l-1}u_n$, where $u_n$ is odd and $(l-1)$th power free. It is remarked in conclusion that the method of proof of the present paper should allow one to prove that every sufficiently large positive integer is the sum of an $l$th power and an $(l-1)$th power-free integer.

*L. Carlitz* (Durham, N. C.).

Referred to in N32-56, N40-66, N52-40.

## N32-14 (15, 289d)

**Mahler, K. On the greatest prime factor of $ax^m+by^n$.** Nieuw Arch. Wiskunde (3) **1**, 113–122 (1953).

In this note the following result is established: Let $m\geqq 2$, $n\geqq 3$, $a\neq 0$, $b\neq 0$ be four integers, and let $x$ and $y$ be two integral variables which are relatively prime. Then, as $\max(|x|, |y|)$ increases indefinitely, the greatest prime factor of $ax^m+by^n$ tends to infinity. The proof follows the idea which Landau has applied for the proof of Theorem 695 in his Vorlesungen über Zahlentheorie [Bd. 3, Hirzel, Leipzig, 1927, pp. 60–64]; however, instead of the Thue-Siegel theorem, Mahler uses its $\mathfrak{p}$-adic generalization. In the proof the condition "$(x, y)=1$" is replaced by "$(x, y)$ is bounded", and it is shown that still less is required.

*J. F. Koksma* (Amsterdam).

## N32-15 (16, 998m)

**Katz, Stanley. On the representation of powerfree integers by systems of polynomials.** Abridgment of a dissertation, New York University, 1951. 3 pp.

The following result is stated. Let $f_i(x)$ be polynomials with integral coefficients such that

$$f_i(x)=c_i\prod_{j=1}^{b_i}(g_{ij}(x))^{d_{ij}} \quad (1\leqq i\leqq a,\ b_i\geqq 0),$$

where the $c_i$ are integers $\neq 0$ and each $g_{ij}(x)$ is an irreducible polynomial with integral coefficients and of content 1. Let $r_i>d_{ij}\geqq 1$; $1\leqq i\leqq a$, $1\leqq j\leqq b_i$, and let $\phi(n)$ be any complex-valued periodic function with an integral period. Put

$$V(z)=\sum_{1\leqq n\leqq z}\phi(n)\prod_{i=1}^{a}\mu_{r_i}(f_i(n)),$$

where $\mu_r(n)=1$ if $N$ is $r$-free, $=0$ otherwise. Then there exists a constant $\lambda$ independent of $z$ such that

$$(*)\qquad V(z)-z\lambda=o(z) \quad (z\to\infty),$$

provided that a certain constant $\leqq 1$. Moreover, if $\phi(n)\geqq 0$ and if, for some integer $n$, $\phi(n)\prod_1^a \mu_{r_i}(f_i(n))>0$, then $\lambda>0$. A more precise result than (*) is stated but this requires additional notation.

*L. Carlitz* (Durham, N. C.).

## N32-16 (17, 462d)

**Knapowski, S. On the greatest prime factors of certain products.** Ann. Polon. Math. 2 (1955), 56–63.

Generalizing theorems of Chebyshev, Ivanov and Størmer [E. Landau, Handbuch der Lehre von der Verteilung der Primzahlen, Bd. 1, Teubner, Leipzig-Berlin, 1909, pp. 559–564] the writer proves the following results. I. Let $\{a_n\}$ be a sequence of integers $0<a_1<a_2<\cdots$ and $A$ a positive integer. Let $P_x$ denote the greatest prime factor of $\prod_1^x(A+a_n^2)$. If

$$\liminf_{n=\infty}\frac{\log(a_1\cdots a_n)}{a_n\log a_n}>\tfrac{1}{2},$$

then $\lim_{x=\infty}P_x/a_x=\infty$; and if

$$\liminf_{n=\infty}\frac{\log(a_1\cdots a_n)}{a_n\log n}>\tfrac{1}{2},$$

then $\lim_{x=\infty}P_x/x=\infty$. II. Let $\{a_n\}$ be a sequence of integers $0<a_1<a_2<\cdots$ and let either

$$\liminf_{n=\infty}\frac{\log(a_1\cdots a_n)}{a_n\log a_n}>\tfrac{1}{2}$$

or

$$\liminf_{n=\infty}\frac{\log(a_1\cdots a_n)}{a_n\log n}>\tfrac{1}{2} \text{ and } a_n=O(n).$$

Then among the numbers $i(i-a_1)\cdots(i-a_2)$ at most a finite number are real or pure imaginary. In addition two further theorems are proved.

*L. Carlitz.*

## N32-17 (18, 718j)

**Cugiani, M. Sulla estensione ai polinomi di un teorema di Sylvester-Schur-Erdös.** Riv. Mat. Univ. Parma 6 (1955), 261–268.

The author proves among others the following theorems. 1) Let $f(x)$ be an irreducible polynomial of degree $n$ and $\delta$ and $\varepsilon$ two arbitrary constants satisfying $0<\delta<1$, $\delta<\varepsilon n$. Denote by $P_{x,y}$ the greatest prime factor of $\prod_{0\leq k\leq y}f(x-k)$. Then for $x\geqq x_0$ and $y_0\leqq y<x^\delta$, $P_{x,y}>(1-\varepsilon)y\log y$. 2) Let $\eta$, $\varepsilon$, $\delta$ be given satisfying $\eta<1$, $\delta<\frac{1}{2}(1-\eta)n$, then for $x\geqq x_0$, $y_0\leqq y<\exp((\sigma\log x\log\log x)^{\frac{1}{2}})$

we have

$$P_{x,y} > y(\log y + \eta \operatorname{loglog} y).$$

Several corollaries are deduced. *P. Erdős.*

**N32-18** **(19, 635h)**

**Knapowski, S. Zur arithmetik der Polynome.** J. London Math. Soc. **32** (1957), 319–321.

Let $f(x)$ be a primitive irreducible polynomial with integer coefficients, and let $S$ be the set of primes $q$ for which $f(y) \equiv 0 \pmod q$ has an integral solution. The author shows that, for $x$ sufficiently large, the smallest $q \in S$ which does not divide $P_x = \prod_{k=1}^{x} f(k)$ is less than $(n(n-1)+\varepsilon)x \log x$. — The converse problem about the greatest $q$ dividing $P_x$ was dealt with by T. Nagell and by P. Erdös [same J. **27** (1952), 379–384; MR **13**, 914].
*N. G. de Bruijn* (Amsterdam).

Citations: MR 13, 914a = N32-8.

**N32-19** **(20# 4531 )**

**Wang, Yuan. On some properties of integral valued polynomials.** Advancement in Math. 3 (1957), 416–423. (Chinese. English summary)

Let $F(x)$ be an irreducible integral-valued polynomial of degree $k$ without fixed prime divisors, and let $\pi(N; F(x))$ denote the numbers of primes represented by $F(x)$ for $x = 1, 2, \cdots, N$. Let $h_m(k!m)$ denote the number of solutions of $F(x) \equiv 0 \pmod m$ with $0 \leqq x < k!m$, and let $\omega(m) = h_m(k!m)/k!$. Then, by means of Selberg's method, the author proves that

$$\pi(N; F(x)) \leqq 2 \prod_p \left(\frac{1-\omega(p)/p}{1-1/p}\right) \cdot \frac{N}{\log N} + o\left(\frac{N}{\log N}\right).$$

He also considers similar problems for reducible polynomials and gives, e.g., an upper bound for the number of $x$'s for which both $x^2+1$ and $x^2+3$ are primes.
*K. Mahler* (Manchester)

Referred to in N32-55.

**N32-20** **(21# 4936 )**

**Schinzel A.; et Sierpiński W. Sur certaines hypothèses concernant les nombres premiers.** Acta Arith. **4** (1958), 185–208; erratum **5** (1959), 259.

The authors derive many consequences of "Hypothesis H": if $f_1(x), f_2(x), \cdots, f_r(x)$ are integral-valued polynomials, $\prod_j f_j(a) \not\equiv 0 \pmod p$ for any prime $p$ and some $a$, then there exist infinitely many integers $n$ for which $f_1(n), f_2(n), \cdots, f_r(n)$ are all primes. Examples of such consequences: (1) There are infinitely many pseudo-primes [see preceding review].* (2) If $a$ is a square-free integer and $|a| > 1$, then there exist infinitely many primes for which $a$ is a primitive root.

Many of these consequences are much weaker than the "H Hypothesis". The "H Hypothesis" would have many interesting consequences in the structure of finite groups which are not mentioned here.
*N. C. Ankeny* (Cambridge, Mass.)

*MR 21 #4935 = A18-18.

Citations: MR 21# 4935 = A18-18.

Referred to in A18-38, A18-55, A26-53, A26-65, A46-40, A46-46, A50-81, A52-60, A64-17, B40-43, D08-33, D08-37, N16-26, N32-27, N32-31, N32-42, N32-46, N32-51.

**N32-21** **(21# 4937 )**

**Schinzel, A. Sur un problème concernant le nombre de diviseurs d'un nombre naturel.** Bull. Acad. Polon. Sci. Sér. Sci. Math. Astr. Phys. **6** (1958), 165–167.

It has been proved by A. Wintner [*The theory of measure in arithmetical semi-groups*, Baltimore, Md., 1944; MR **7**, 367, p. 14] and more recently in a different way by S. Golomb [Nordisk Mat. Tidskr. **4** (1956), 24–29; MR **17**, 944] that for every integer $k > 1$ there is an integer $c$ such that $\mu(c+1) = \mu(c+2) = \cdots = \mu(c+k)$, where $\mu(n)$ is the Möbius function. It is not known whether an analogous theorem is true for some of the other familiar numerical functions, in particular for $\theta(n)$, the number of divisors of $n$. It is shown in this paper that from a conjecture made by the author and W. Sierpiński ["Hypothesis H", preceding review] it would follow that there are infinitely many integers $c$ for each $k$ such that $\theta(c+1) = \theta(c+2) = \cdots = \theta(c+k)$. *R. J. Levit* (San Francisco, Calif.)

Citations: MR 7, 367a = Z02-5; MR 17, 944b = N64-6.

**N32-22** **(22# 2586 )**

**Shanks, Daniel. A note on Gaussian twin primes.** Math. Comput. **14** (1960), 201–203.

The Gaussian integers $n-1+i$ and $n+1+i$ are a pair of Gaussian twin primes whenever $(n-1)^2+1$ and $(n+1)^2+1$ are rational primes. Let $g(N)$ be the number of such pairs for $4 \leqq n+1 \leqq N$. The author determines $g(N)$ for $N = 500(500)18500$ from a table due to him giving the largest prime factor of $n^2+1$ for $n = 1(1)18500$. The author notes that the numerical data so obtained bear out the truth of the conjectured relationship

$$g(N) \sim c \int_2^N \frac{dx}{(\log x)^2},$$

$$c = \frac{\pi^2}{8} \prod_{p \equiv 1 \pmod 4} \left(1 - \frac{4}{p}\right)\left(\frac{p+1}{p-1}\right)^2 = 0.48762\cdots.$$

*M. Newman* (Washington, D.C.)

**N32-23** **(22# 7985 )**

**Levin, B. V. Estimates from below for the number of nearly-prime integers belonging to some general sequences.** Vestnik Leningrad. Univ. **15** (1960), no. 7, 48–65. (Russian. English summary)

It is not known whether the polynomial sequence $\{n^2+1\}$ contains infinitely many primes; the result is probably true, but a proof seems out of the reach of existing methods. The author proves the corresponding simpler problem for almost-primes. He proves that: The sequence $\{n^2+1\}$ $(n = 1, 2, \cdots, N)$ contains at least $aN/(\log N) + O(N \log\log N/(\log N)^{3/2})$ members each having at most five prime factors. The prime factors exceed $N^{1/2.91}$ and $a$ is a certain positive constant. The author bases his proof on A. I. Vinogradov's account of A. Selberg's 'lower bound' sieve method [Mat. Sb. (N.S.) **41** (**83**) (1957), 49–80, 415–416; MR **20** #3836]. The paper ends with a generalisation. *H. Halberstam* (London)

Citations: MR 20# 3836 = P32-36.

Referred to in N32-29.

**N32-24** **(22# 10941 )**

**Shanks, Daniel. On numbers of the form $n^4+1$.** Math. Comput. **15** (1961), 186–189.

Let $Q(x)$ denote the number of primes of the form $n^4+1$ not exceeding $x^4+1$. This function is tabulated, from data given by A. Gloden, for $x = 100(100)1000$ and compared with the conjectured approximate formula

$$Q(x) \doteq .66974 \int_2^x dt/\log t$$

where the constant is given by

$$\frac{1}{4} \prod \left\{1 - \frac{\chi(-1)+\chi(2)+\chi(-2)}{p-1}\right\}$$

Here $\chi(h)$ is the Legendre symbol $(h/p)$ and the product is over odd primes. This slowly convergent product is evaluated by means of Dirichlet $L$-series and zeta-functions. The problem is compared with the corresponding one for the function $n^2+1$.

*D. H. Lehmer* (Berkeley, Calif.)

## N32-25 (22# 10960)

**Shanks, Daniel. On the conjecture of Hardy & Littlewood concerning the number of primes of the form $n^2+a$.** Math. Comp. **14** (1960), 320–332.

A famous and as yet unproved conjecture of G. H. Hardy and J. E. Littlewood [Acta Math. **44** (1923), 1–70] states that, if the integer $a$ is not equal to a negative square, then the number $P_a(N)$ of primes of the form $n^2+a$ with $1\leq n\leq N$ satisfies, for $N\to\infty$, the asymptotic relation

$$(*)\qquad P_a(N) \sim \frac{1}{2}\prod_{p\nmid a}\left\{1-\left(\frac{-a}{p}\right)\frac{1}{p-1}\right\}\int_2^N \frac{du}{\log u}.$$

It was verified by A. E. Western [Proc. Cambridge Philos. Soc. **21** (1922/23), 108–109] that, for $a=1$ and $N\leq 15{,}000$, the agreement between $P_a(N)$ and the right-hand side of $(*)$ is good. In the present paper the discussion of the numerical evidence is taken a stage further. First of all the infinite product in $(*)$ is transformed into a more rapidly converging product; this step facilitates its computation. Next, by considering the range $N\leq 180{,}000$, the author shows that $(*)$ is almost certainly valid for $a=1$, $\pm 2$, $\pm 3$, 4. Finally, he presents a heuristic sieve method which suggests the validity of $(*)$ for all values of $a$.

*L. Mirsky* (Sheffield)

Referred to in M05-35, N32-34.

## N32-26 (23# A1617)

**Simakova, Eleonora [Simacova, Elenora]**

**On the prime divisors of a polynomial with integer coefficients (Russian. English, French and German summaries)**

*Bul. Inst. Politehn. Bucureşti* **20** (1958), *no.* 4, 13–26.

The following generalization of a theorem of Čebyšev [E. Landau, *Handbuch der Lehre vor der Verteilung der Primzahlen, Vol. I*, Teubner, Leipzig, 1909; p. 559] is proved. Let $f(x)=a_0x^n+\cdots+a_n$ $(a_0\neq 0, n>1)$ be a primitive polynomial with rational integral coefficients, and let $p_N$ be the largest prime divisor of the product $f(1)f(2)\cdots f(N)$. Then $p_N/N\to\infty$ when $N\to\infty$. The proof makes use of some lemmas concerning the congruence $f(x)\equiv 0 \pmod{p^m}$ and also some properties of the Dedekind zeta-function.

*L. Carlitz* (Durham, N.C.)

## N32-27 (25# 1128)

**Sierpiński, W.**

**Sur quelques conséquences d'une hypothèse de M. A. Schinzel.**

*Bull. Soc. Roy. Sci. Liège* **31** (1962), 317–320.

The author shows that the following propositions follow from a certain hypothesis H of A. Schinzel [Acta Arith. **4** (1958), 185–208; p. 188; MR **21** #4936]: (P1) For arbitrary $n$, there exist infinitely many positive integers $x$ such that $x^{2^n}+1$, $x^{2^n}+3$, $x^{2^n}+7$, $x^{2^n}+9$, $x^{2^n}+13$ are prime. (P2) There exist infinitely many positive integers $x$ such that $x+1, x+5, x+7, x+11, x+13, x+17$ are prime. (P3) For arbitrary $n$, there exist infinitely many positive integers $x$ such that $x^{2^n}+37$, $x^{2^n}+41$, $x^{2^n}+43$, $x^{2^n}+47$, $x^{2^n}+53$ are prime.

*L. Carlitz* (Durham, N.C.)

Citations: MR 21# 4936 = N32-20.

## N32-28 (25# 2046)

**Bacchiani, Romana; Spera, Angela M.**

**Sui grandi divisori primi dei polinomi di esponenziali a coefficienti interi. (English summary)**

*Boll. Un. Mat. Ital.* (3) **16** (1961), 412–424.

Let $F(y)$ be a polynomial and, for integral $a$ with $|a|\geq 2$ and $m\geq 1$, set $G(x)=F(a^{x^m})$. If $F(a^{x^m})=0$ has integral roots, let $x_M$ be the largest and select an integral $x_0>x_M$. Define $\Pi(x)=\prod_{n=x_0}^{x} G(n)$. Denote by $P_x$ the largest prime divisor of $\Pi(x)$ and, for any $K>0$, let $N_K(x)$ and $S_K(x)$, respectively, stand for the number and the sum of those distinct prime divisors of $\Pi(x)$ that exceed $K\sqrt{(x\log x)}$; finally, let $Q_K(x)$ denote the largest divisor of $\Pi(x)$ containing only prime factors in excess of $K\sqrt{(x\log x)}$. The authors prove the following. As $x\to\infty$, for every $K>0$, $\log Q_K(x)\sim\log\Pi(x)$ and $S_K(x)/x\to\infty$. From the last result it follows that, for every $K>0$, $\max\{P_x/x, N_K(x)\}\to\infty$, which in turn implies $P_x(x\log x)^{-1/2}\to\infty$, both for $x\to\infty$. These results generalize and add precision to (partly well-known) theorems due to Pólya [J. für Math. **151** (1920), 19–21], Ricci [Boll. Un. Mat. Ital. **12** (1933), 222–228] and Cugiani [ibid. (3) **7** (1952), 38–43; MR **13**, 914]. Besides elementary considerations, the proofs are based mainly on estimates for the number of solutions of certain Diophantine equations; the reviewer was unable to follow some of the details of the proofs.

*E. Grosswald* (Philadelphia, Pa.)

Citations: MR 13, 914d = N32-9.

## N32-29 (26# 3677)

**Levin, B. V.**

**The weak Landau problem and its generalization. (Russian)**

*Uspehi Mat. Nauk* **16** (1961), *no.* 2 (98), 123–125.

The author reports the following result, which goes some way towards Landau's conjecture that the sequence $\{n^2+1\}$ contains infinitely many primes: Let $J(N)$ denote the number of integers in the sequence $\{n^2+1\}$, $n\leq N$, which have at most three prime factors. Then

$$J(N) > A\frac{N}{\log N}+O\left(\frac{N(\log\log N)^2}{(\log N)^{3/2}}\right),$$

where

$$A = \frac{2}{\pi}\prod_{p\equiv 1 \pmod 4}\left(1-\frac{1}{(p-1)^2}\right)\prod_{p\equiv 3 \pmod 4}\left(1-\frac{1}{p^2}\right)^{-1}.$$

The proof, of which a sketch is provided, uses Selberg's sieve and analytic methods developed by A. I. Vinogradov [Mat. Sb. (N.S.) **41 (83)** (1957), 49–80; correction, 415–416; MR **20** #3836]; see also B. V. Levin [Vestnik Leningrad. Univ. **15** (1960), no. 7, 48–65; MR **22** #7985].

*H. Halberstam* (Dublin)

Citations: MR 20# 3836 = P32-36; MR 22# 7985 = N32-23.

## N32-30 (26# 4971)

**Környei, I.**

**Eine Bemerkung zur Theorie der durch quadratischen Formen darstellbaren Primzahlen.**

*Ann. Univ. Sci. Budapest. Eötvös Sect. Math.* **5** (1962), 95–108.

Let $Q(x, y)$ denote a primitive binary quadratic form with integral coefficients. Hecke has shown that in any sector ("Winkelraum") such a form represents infinitely many primes. P. Turán has asked the question if a similar result holds also for certain regions which contain no sector. Using a theorem of Erdős and Turán, three theorems are proved in this paper, the last of which is: If $c$ is a sufficiently small positive constant and $\varphi$, $r$ denote the polar coordinates of a point, then each positive form $Q(x, y)$ represents infinitely many primes in the following region:

$$|\varphi-\varphi_0| \leqq \exp(-c\sqrt{(\log r)}).$$

*Burton W. Jones* (Boulder, Colo.)

**N32-31** **(26# 6139)**

**Bateman, Paul T.; Horn, Roger A.**

**A heuristic asymptotic formula concerning the distribution of prime numbers.**

*Math. Comp.* **16** (1962), 363–367.

Let $f_1(x), f_2(x), \cdots, f_k(x)$ be distinct irreducible polynomials with all coefficients integral and leading coefficients positive, their degrees being $h_1, h_2, \cdots, h_k$, respectively. Suppose that $f_1(x)\cdot f_2(x)\cdot \cdots \cdot f_k(x)$ has no constant factor $>1$. Let $Q(f_1, f_2, \cdots, f_k; N)$ denote the number of positive integers $n$ between 1 and $N$ such that $f_1(n)$, $f_2(n), \cdots, f_k(n)$ are all primes. The authors give a heuristic asymptotic formula

$$Q(f_1, \cdots, f_k; N) \sim h_1^{-1}h_2^{-1}\cdots h_k^{-1}C(f_1, \cdots, f_k)\int_2^N (\log u)^{-k}\,du,$$

where

$$C(f_1, \cdots, f_k) = \prod_p \{(1-1/p)^{-k}(1-\omega(p)/p)\},$$

the product being taken over all primes and $\omega(p)$ being the number of solutions of the congruence $f_1(x)f_2(x)\cdots f_k(x)\equiv 0 \pmod p$. This formula is a generalization of six conjectures of Hardy and Littlewood [Acta Math. **44** (1923), 1–70] and may be regarded as a quantitative form of a conjecture of the reviewer [Acta Arith. **4** (1958), 185–208, p. 188; erratum, **5** (1959), 259; MR **21** #4936].

*A. Schinzel* (Warsaw)

Citations: MR 21# 4936 = N32-20.

Referred to in N32-32, N32-42, N32-45.

**N32-32** **(27# 3609)**

**Schinzel, A.**

**A remark on a paper of Bateman and Horn.**

*Math. Comp.* **17** (1963), 445–447.

Let $f_1, f_2, \cdots, f_k$ be distinct irreducible polynomials with integral coefficients and with the highest coefficient positive, such that $f(x)=f_1(x)f_2(x)\cdots f_k(x)$ has no fixed divisor $>1$. Denote by $P(N)$ the number of positive integers $x\leqq N$ such that all numbers $f_1(x), f_2(x), \cdots, f_k(x)$ are primes.

P. T. Bateman and R. A. Horn [Math. Comp. **16** (1962), 363–367; MR **26** #6139] gave the heuristic estimate

$$P(N) \sim \frac{N}{\log^k N}(h_1\cdots h_k)^{-1}\prod_p\left(1-\frac{\omega(p)}{p}\right)\left(1-\frac{1}{p}\right)^{-k},$$

where $h_i$ is the degree of $f_i$ and $\omega(p)$ is the number of solutions of $f(x)\equiv 0 \pmod p$.

This formula contains as special cases six well-known conjectures of Hardy and Littlewood [Acta Math. **44** (1923), 1–70]. The author suggests the following conjecture, which also includes as special cases some of the conjectures in Hardy and Littlewood's celebrated paper cited above [namely, conjectures $C$, $G$, $L$ and $A$, $H$, $I$].

Let polynomials $f_1, f_2, \cdots, f_k$ $(k\geqq 0)$, $f=f_1f_2\cdots f_k$ satisfy the same conditions as above. Let $g$ be a polynomial with integral coefficients and the highest coefficient positive. Let $n$ be a positive integer such that $n-g(x)$ is irreducible and $f(x)(n-g(x))$ has no fixed divisor $>1$. Denote by $N(n)=N$ the number of positive integers $x$ such that $n-g(x)>0$ and by $P(n)$ the number of $x$'s such that all numbers $f_1(x), \cdots, f_k(x)$ and $n-g(x)$ are primes. Then for large $n$,

$$P(n) \sim \frac{N}{\log^{k+1} N}(h_0\cdots h_k)^{-1}\prod_p\left(1-\frac{\omega(p)}{p}\right)\left(1-\frac{1}{p}\right)^{-k-1},$$

where $h_0$ is the degree of $g$ and $\omega(p)$ is the number of solutions of $f(x)(n-g(x))\equiv 0 \pmod p$.

[Other references: the reviewer, Acta Arith. **1** (1935), 115–122; Ju. V. Linnik, Izv. Akad. Nauk SSSR Ser. Mat. **24** (1960), 629–706; MR **23** #A130.]

*S. Chowla* (University Park, Pa.)

Citations: MR 23# A130 = P36-26; MR 26# 6139 = N32-31.

Referred to in N32-42.

**N32-33** **(28# 1163)**

**Lenskoĭ, D. N.**

**On the representation of prime numbers by polynomials of two variables. (Russian. English summary)**

*Vestnik Leningrad. Univ. Ser. Mat. Meh. Astronom.* **18** (1963), *no.* 4, 150–154.

Let $f_1(x, y), f_2(x, y), \cdots, f_n(x, y)$ be integral-valued polynomials. For a prime number $p$ let $\omega(p)$ be the number of solutions of the congruence $f_1(x, y)\cdots f_n(x, y)\equiv 0$ $(p)$ and suppose that $\omega(p)<p^2$ (all $p$). Then the number $\pi(N)$ of pairs $(x, y)$ of integers in $1\leqq x\leqq N$, $1\leqq y\leqq N$ for which all the $f_j(x, y)$ are prime satisfies

$$\pi(N) \leqq 2^k\cdot k!\prod_p \frac{1-\omega(p)/p^2}{(1-1/p)^k}\frac{N^2}{\log^k N}(1+o(1)).$$

The proof uses a variant of Selberg's sieve. The author remarks that if $\omega(p)=p^2$ for any $p$, much stronger estimates hold.

*J. W. S. Cassels* (Cambridge, England)

**N32-34** **(28# 3013)**

**Shanks, Daniel**

**Supplementary data and remarks concerning a Hardy-Littlewood conjecture.**

*Math. Comp.* **17** (1963), 188–193.

Let $P_a(N)$ be the number of primes of the form $n^2+a$ for $1\leqq n\leqq N$. Let $\Pi_a(N)$ be the number of primes $\leqq N$ having $-a$ as a non-residue. Let $h_a$ be the infinite product

$$h_a = \prod_{p>2}\left(1-\left(\frac{-a}{p}\right)\frac{1}{p-1}\right).$$

According to a conjecture of Hardy and Littlewood, $P_a(N)/\Pi_a(N)\sim h_a$. Previous numerical data on $P_a$ and $\Pi_a$ were given for $a=1$, $\pm 2$, $\pm 3$, and 4 [the author, Math. Comp. **14** (1960), 320–332; MR **22** #10960]. This note supplies further data for $a=\pm 5$, $\pm 6$, and $\pm 7$. More precisely, the two functions $P_a(N)$ and $\Pi_a(N)$ and their ratio are tabulated for $N=10^4(10^4)18\cdot 10^4$. Agreement when $a=\pm 6$ is good. For $a=\pm 5$ and $\pm 7$ no accurate values of $h_a$ are known but the ratios $P_a/\Pi$ are well-behaved. The most popular form is $n^2+7$. There is a discussion of the computation of the constant $h_a$, and an irregular graph for $-20\leqq a\leqq 9$ is given.

*D. H. Lehmer* (Berkeley, Calif.)

Citations: MR 22# 10960 = N32-25.

Referred to in M05-35.

**N32-35** **(28# 3975)**

**Hmyrova, N. A.**

**On polynomials with small prime divisors. (Russian)**

*Dokl. Akad. Nauk SSSR* **155** (1964), 1268–1271.

Let $f(y)$ denote a polynomial of the form

$$y^n+a_1y^{n-1}+\cdots+a_n$$

with integral coefficients. Denote by $F_f(x, z)$ the number of $m \leqq x$ such that $p|f(m)$ implies $p \leqq z \leqq x$. Here $\alpha = \log z/\log x$. If

$$\frac{\log \log x}{\log x} \leqq \alpha \leqq 1,$$

the author obtains the estimate

$$F_f(x, z) \leqq c(K)x \exp\left(-\frac{1}{4\alpha} \log \frac{1}{\alpha}\right),$$

where $c(K)$ is a constant depending only on the normal field $K$ generated by the roots of $f$.

The literature cited includes references to papers by I. M. Vinogradov, Ju. V. Linnik, A. A. Buchstab, N. G. de Bruijn, the reviewer and W. E. Briggs, A. I. Vinogradov. One might add also the reviewer and T. Vijayaraghavan, V. Ramaswami. *S. Chowla* (University Park, Pa.)

Referred to in N32-36.

**N32-36** **(34# 7475)**

**Hmyrova, N. A.**

**On polynomials with small prime divisors. II.** (Russian)

*Izv. Akad. Nauk SSSR Ser. Mat.* **30** (1966), 1367–1372.

With the notation of the review of Part I [Dokl. Akad. Nauk SSSR **155** (1964), 1268–1271; MR **28** #3975] the author now proves: $F_f(x, z) < c(f)x \exp(\alpha^{-1} \ln \alpha e)$ for $\ln \ln x/\ln x \leqq \alpha = \ln z/\ln x \leqq 1/e$; and for arbitrary $\varepsilon > 0$ in $(0, \frac{1}{2})$, $F_f^{(\pi)}(x, z) < (c(f)/\varepsilon)\pi(x) \exp\{(1-\varepsilon)\alpha^{-1} \ln \alpha e\}$ with $\ln \ln x/\ln x \leqq \alpha \leqq 1/e$. Here $c(f)$ is a positive constant depending only on the degree $n$ of the polynomial $f$ and on its coefficients. (References are to M. B. Barban and A. I. Vinogradov [cf. ibid. **154** (1964), 495–496; MR **29** #1194; A. I. Vinogradov, ibid. **109** (1956), 683–686; MR **19**, 16], amongst others.) *S. Chowla* (University Park, Pa.)

Citations: MR 19, 16f = N28-37; MR 28# 3975 = N32-35; MR 29# 1194 = N28-53.

**N32-37** **(29# 1174)**

**Miech, R. J.**

**Almost primes generated by a polynomial.**

*Acta Arith.* **10** (1964/65), 9–30.

An "almost prime" in a given sequence of integers is an integer with a bounded number of prime factors. The author considers the sequence $G(1), G(2), \cdots$, where $G(n)$ is an integer-valued polynomial and proves that infinitely many almost primes exist in this sequence. The actual theorems proved are somewhat too complicated to state in a short review, but roughly speaking, he shows that there are infinitely many integers $m$ such that $G(m)$ has at most $9h/5 + k \log k$ prime factors, where $G(n)$ is of degree $h$ and is the product of $k$ polynomials irreducible over the rationals. A corollary of his work, for example, is that there are infinitely many integers of the form $n^2+1$ with at most 4 prime factors. The methods of proof are sieve methods and involve generalizations of Selberg's methods for the twin prime case.

*Morris Newman* (Washington, D.C.)

Referred to in N32-42, N32-48, Z10-47.

**N32-38** **(29# 3423)**

**Shanks, Daniel**

**An analytic criterion for the existence of infinitely many primes of the form $\frac{1}{2}(n^2+1)$.**

*Illinois J. Math.* **8** (1964), 377–379.

Let $f(z) = \sum_{n=0}^{\infty} z^{n(n+1)/2}$, and write $g(z) = f^2(z) - 3f(z) = -2 + \{f(z)-1\}^2 - \{f(z)-1\} = \sum_{m=0}^{\infty} a_m z^m$, say. The author points out that, for $m > 0$, $4m+1$ is a prime of the form $\frac{1}{2}(n^2+1)$ if and only if $a_m = (1/m!)g^{(m)}(0) < 0$. Consequently there exist infinitely many primes of the form $\frac{1}{2}(n^2+1)$ if and only if $g$ possesses infinitely many negative coefficients in its Taylor expansion near $z=0$.

*H. Halberstam* (Nottingham)

**N32-39** **(29# 4746)**

**Sierpinski, W. [Sierpiński, Waclaw]**

**Les binômes $x^2+n$ et les nombres premiers.**

*Bull. Soc. Roy. Sci. Liège* **33** (1964), 259–260.

This note contains a brief, elementary proof of the theorem that for each positive integer $m$ there exists a positive integer $n$ such that $x^2+n$ is a prime for more than $m$ distinct values of $x$. The proof is based on the inequality $\pi(n) > n/(12 \log n)$, $n \geqq 2$. *R. D. James* (Vancouver, B.C.)

**N32-40** **(31# 138)**

**Kalnin', I. M.**

**On primes which can be represented by a quadratic form.** (Russian. Latvian and English summaries)

*Latvijas PSR Zinātņu Akad. Vēstis Fiz. Tehn. Zinātņu Sēr.* **1964**, *no.* 5, 37–42.

The author gives a sketch of a proof of an analogue of Ingham's theorem concerning primes in intervals $[x, x+x^\theta]$, in the case of binary quadratic forms with negative discriminant. *S. Knapowski* (Marburg)

**N32-41** **(31# 140)**

**Wójcik, J.**

**On the representation of primes by quadratic forms.** (Polish. English summary)

*Prace Mat.* **9** (1965), 19–21.

Author's summary: "For arbitrary integers $a, b, c, \xi, \eta, m, n$ satisfying the condition $amn(n\xi^2 - m\eta^2) \neq 0$, there exist only finitely many primes $p$ representable in the form

$$p = (ax^2 + b\xi x + c\xi^2)/m = (ay^2 + b\eta y + c\eta^2)/n,$$

where $x$ and $y$ are integers." *J. Kubilius* (Vilnius)

**N32-42** **(31# 1234)**

**Bateman, Paul T.; Horn, Roger A.**

**Primes represented by irreducible polynomials in one variable.**

*Proc. Sympos. Pure Math., Vol. VIII, pp.* 119–132. *Amer. Math. Soc., Providence, R.I.,* 1965.

The authors comment on their conjecture [Math. Comp. **16** (1962), 363–367; MR **26** #6139] concerning the asymptotic distribution of positive integers which when substituted into $k$ given polynomials $f_1(x), f_2(x), \cdots, f_k(x)$ produce primes, and on a related conjecture of the reviewer [ibid. **17** (1963), 445–447; MR **27** #3609]. Numerical data supporting the former conjecture are collected for the case when $k=1$ and the Galois group of the equation $f_1(x)=0$ is nonabelian. When that group is abelian, the constant occurring in the asymptotic formula is more easily computed and the numerical evidence for this case of the conjecture was given in the paper quoted above. Other references are G. H. Hardy and J. E. Littlewood [Acta Math. **44** (1923), 1–70], G. Ricci [Ann. Scuola Norm. Sup. Pisa (2) **6** (1937), 71–116], the reviewer and W. Sierpiński [Acta Arith. **4** (1958), 185–208; erratum, ibid. **5** (1959), 259; MR **21** #4936], Y. Wang [Sci. Sinica **11** (1962), 1607–1624; MR **26** #3685], and R. J. Miech [Acta Arith. **10** (1964/65), 9–30; MR **29** #1174; ibid. **11** (1965), 35–56; MR **31** #3390].

*A. Schinzel* (Warsaw)

Citations: MR 21# 4936 = N32-20; MR 26# 3685 = N24-36; MR 26# 6139 = N32-31; MR 27# 3609 = N32-32; MR 29# 1174 = N32-37; MR 31# 3390 = N32-43.

Referred to in N32-45.

**N32-43** **(31# 3390)**

**Miech, R. J.**

**Primes, polynomials and almost primes.**

*Acta Arith.* **11** (1965), 35–56.

The author makes use of Brun's sieve method and results of Rényi's on the distribution of the zeros of $L$-series to prove the following result. Let $F$ be an integral valued polynomial. Let $K, c$ be arbitrary integers such that $(K, c)=1$. Then there is a positive constant $A$, which depends on $F$, such that there are infinitely many primes $p \equiv c \pmod K$ for which $F(p)$ has at most $A$ prime factors.

*Morris Newman* (Washington, D.C.)

Referred to in N32-42.

**N32-44** **(32# 5612)**

**Levin, B. V.**

**On the least almost prime number in an arithmetic progression and the sequence $k^2x^2+1$. (Russian)**

*Uspehi Mat. Nauk* **20** (1965), *no.* 4 (124), 158–162.

The author gives several applications of a theorem on sieve methods he proved in an earlier paper [Mat. Sb. (N.S.) **61** (**103**) (1963), 389–407; MR **30** #1991]. The smallest number in an arithmetic progression $kx+l$, $(l, k)=1$, $0<l<k$, having at most two prime factors, is $\leqq k^{2.3696}$ (here the exponent can be replaced by $25/11+\varepsilon$; cf. W. B. Jurkat and the reviewer [Acta Arith. **11** (1965), 217–240]). The smallest number in the sequence $k^2x^2+1$ having at most three prime factors is $\leqq k^{10.9578}$.

*H.-E. Richert* (Marburg)

Citations: MR 30# 1991 = P32-62.

**N32-45** **(32# 5632)**

**Davenport, H.; Schinzel, A.**

**A note on certain arithmetical constants.**

*Illinois J. Math.* **10** (1966), 181–185.

Denote by $f_1, \cdots, f_k$ distinct irreducible polynomials with integral coefficients. Bateman and Horn [Math. Comp. **16** (1962), 363–367; MR **26** #6139; compare also Hardy and Littlewood, Acta Math. **44** (1923), 1–70] made a conjecture on the number of $n \leqq N$ such that $f_1(n), \cdots, f_k(n)$ are all primes; the conjecture involves the constant

$$C = C(f_1, \cdots, f_k) = \prod_p \{(1-p^{-1})^{-k}(1-p^{-1}\omega(p))\},$$

where $\omega(p)$ denotes the number of solutions of $f_1(x)\cdots f_k(x) \equiv 0 \pmod p$.

Improving on a result of Bateman and Horn [Proc. Sympos. Pure Math., Vol. 8, pp. 119–132, Amer. Math. Soc., Providence, R.I., 1965; MR **31** #1234], the authors express $C$ by absolutely convergent products over primes and by constants such as the discriminant, regulator and class-number of the fields $K_i$, generated by a root of $f_i$. As an application, the constants $C(x^3 \pm 2)=1.29\ldots$ and $C(x^3 \pm 3)=1.38\ldots$ are computed. *W. Schwarz* (Freiburg)

Citations: MR 26# 6139 = N32-31; MR 31# 1234 = N32-42.

**N32-46** **(33# 5585)**

**Sierpiński, W.**

**Remarque sur la distribution de nombres premiers.**

*Mat. Vesnik* **2** (**17**) (1965), 77–78.

The author remarks that although the sequence $(2n+1)^2-2$ $(n=1, 2, \cdots)$ is particularly rich in primes, every set of four consecutive values contains a multiple of 7. Hence 7, 23, 47, 79 is the only set of four consecutive values that are all primes. The existence of infinitely many examples of three consecutive values that are all primes would follow from Hypothesis H of Schinzel [Acta Arith. **4** (1958), 185–208; erratum, ibid. **5** (1959), 259; MR **21** #4936].

Similar remarks are made about the sequence $4n^2+1$, where 3 and 5 replace 4 and 7.

*D. H. Lehmer* (Berkeley, Calif.)

Citations: MR 21# 4936 = N32-20.

Referred to in N32-51.

**N32-47** **(33# 7316)**

**Levin, B. V.; Maksudov, I. G.**

**Distribution of almost prime numbers in polynomials in $n$ variables. (Russian. Uzbek summary)**

*Izv. Akad. Nauk UzSSR Ser. Fiz.-Mat. Nauk* **10** (1966), *no.* 3, 15–23.

Verfasser geben obere und untere Abschätzungen für die Anzahl von Primzahlen und Fastprimzahlen in Polynomen. Anstatt jedoch die in den Behauptungen auftretende Gesamtanzahl der Primfaktoren abzuschätzen, werden Abschätzungen lediglich für die Anzahl der verschiedenen Primfaktoren bewiesen. Dieselbe Bemerkung gilt für mehrere Arbeiten des erstgenannten Verfassers [vgl. z.B. Mat. Sb. (N.S.) **61** (**103**) (1963), 389–407; MR **30** #1991; Acta Arith. **10** (1964/65), 387–397; MR **31** #4774].

*H.-E. Richert* (Marburg)

Citations: MR 30# 1991 = P32-62; MR 31# 4774 = M55-37.

**N32-48** **(34# 1287)**

**Miech, R. J.**

**A uniform result on almost primes.**

*Acta Arith.* **11** (1966), 371–391.

The author continues his earlier work [same Acta **10** (1964/65), 9–30; MR **29** #1174] and proves the following result. Let $f_i(x)$ be an irreducible polynomial with integral coefficients of degree $n_i$, $1 \leqq i \leqq k$, and suppose that these polynomials are pairwise relatively prime. Put $F(x)=f_1(x)\cdots f_k(x)$ and assume that $F(x)$ has no fixed prime divisors. Let $A(f_i)$ denote the maximum of the absolute values of the coefficients of $f_i$, and set $B(F)=A(f_1)\cdots A(f_k)$. Let $n$ be the maximum of the $n_j$ and define $L(k)=k\sum_{j=1}^k (1/j)$. Then for any $\delta>0$ there is a constant $c$ depending on $k$, $\delta$ and $n$, and a positive integer $m \leqq \exp(cB(F)^\delta)$ for which $F(m)$ has at most $n_1+\cdots+n_k+L(k)+k\log(2n+1)+1$ prime factors, multiple prime factors being counted multiply.

*Morris Newman* (Washington, D.C.)

Citations: MR 29# 1174 = N32-37.

**N32-49** **(34# 1288)**

**Pleasants, P. A. B.**

**The representation of primes by cubic polynomials.**

*Acta Arith.* **12** (1966), 23–45.

Let $\phi(\mathbf{x})=C(\mathbf{x})+Q(\mathbf{x})+L(\mathbf{x})+N$ be a cubic polynomial with rational integral coefficients, where $C(\mathbf{x})$ denotes the cubic part of $\phi(\mathbf{x})$, $Q(\mathbf{x})$ the quadratic part, etc. An obvious necessary condition that $\phi(\mathbf{x})$ represent an infinity of primes is that for any given integer $m>1$ there is an integral point $\mathbf{a}$ such that $m \nmid \phi(\mathbf{a})$. The author proves that this condition is also sufficient provided $C(\mathbf{x})$ satisfies a further condition which arises from the method of proof. The supplementary condition is that $h^*(C) \geqq 8$, where $h$ is the least positive integer such that $C(\mathbf{x})$ is rationally equivalent to one in the shape $\sum_1^h y_i Q_i(\mathbf{y})$ (whence $n-h$ is the dimension of the maximal linear rational space on the surface $C=0$) and $h^*$ is the greatest integer such that $C(\mathbf{x})$ is rationally equivalent to one of the shape $\sum_1^s C_i(\mathbf{y})$, with $h^*=h(C_1)+\cdots+h(C_s)$ and the $C_i$ forms in disjoint sets of variables. Thus $1 \leqq h \leqq h^* \leqq n$, and $h^*=n$ exactly when $C(\mathbf{x})$ is equivalent to an additive form. There is no discussion whether or not this or some other supplementary condition is actually needed. The author obtains an asymptotic formula for the number of primes represented by integral points in an expanded parallelepiped $\mathscr{P}$ (where the parallelepiped $\mathscr{P}$ is suitably chosen), the main term being $\mathfrak{S}VP^n/\log P^3$, where $V$ is the volume of $\mathscr{P}$ and $\mathfrak{S}$ is the singular series for this problem. The derivation of this result follows methods and ideas (with added embellishments by the author) to be found in H. Davenport [Philos. Trans. Roy. Soc. London Ser. A **251** (1959), 193–232; MR **21** #4136; *Analytic methods for Diophantine equations and Diophantine inequalities*, Ann Arbor Publishers, Ann Arbor, Mich., 1962; MR **28** #3002] and in H. Davenport and the reviewer, [J. London Math. Soc. **39** (1964), 657–671; MR **29** #4731].

*D. J. Lewis* (Ann Arbor, Mich.)

Citations: MR 21# 4136 = D72-19; MR 28# 3002 = D02-19; MR 29# 4731 = D72-37.
Referred to in N32-50.

## N32-50 (35# 143)

**Pleasants, P. A. B.**

**The representation of primes by quadratic and cubic polynomials.**

*Acta Arith.* **12** (1966/67), 131–163.

In this paper the author completes his study of the integral representation of primes by cubic polynomials, which was begun in same Acta **12** (1966), 23–45 [MR **34** #1288]. The author proves that if $\varphi$ is a nondegenerate, irreducible cubic polynomial with integer coefficients in $n>10$ variables, such that for each integer $m>1$ there is an integral point $\mathbf{x}_m$ for which $\varphi(\mathbf{x}_m)\not\equiv 0 \pmod m$, then, with integer values for the variables, $\varphi$ represents infinitely many positive primes. His method of proof fails to give rise to an asymptotic formula for the number of primes represented. In the earlier paper an asymptotic formula was given provided the invariant $h(\varphi)$ was large (approximately 8), where $n-h(\varphi)$ is the dimension of the maximal rational linear space on $C=0$, and $C$ is the cubic part of $\varphi$. In this paper he first studies the representation of primes by quadratic polynomials. He then shows that when $h(\varphi)$ is small one can fix some of the variables so as to get a quadratic polynomial. {This approach is reminiscent of recent work of G. L. Watson [see, e.g., Proc. London Math. Soc. (3) **17** (1967), 271–295; MR **35** #2846].}

*D. J. Lewis* (Ann Arbor, Mich.)

Citations: MR 34# 1288 = N32-49; MR 35# 2846 = D72-51.

## N32-51 (34# 1289)

**Sierpiński, Wacław**

**Les résultats de W. A. Golubew et l'hypothèse de A. Schinzel. (Serbo-Croatian summary)**

*Glasnik Mat.-Fiz. Astronom. Ser. II Društvo Mat. Fiz. Hrvatske* **20** (1965), 43–49.

V. A. Golubev [Anz. Öster. Akad. Wiss. Wien Math.-Natur. Kl. **100** (1963), 237–244] has examined the numbers $x^2+5$ for $x=0(1)10^4$ and found 82 values of $x$ for which $x^2+5$ and $x^2+7$ are both primes. He has conjectured the existence of infinitely many such values of $x$; similarly for the pair $x^2+20$ and $x^2+22$. The author discusses more general conjectures concerning pairs and quadruplets of primes that are consequences of Hypothesis (H) of Schinzel [A. Schinzel and the author, Acta Arith. **4** (1958), 185–208; erratum, ibid. **5** (1959), 259; MR **21** #4936; see also the author, Mat. Vesnik **2** (**17**) (1965), 77–78; MR **33** #5585].

*D. H. Lehmer* (Berkeley, Calif.)

Citations: MR 21# 4936 = N32-20; MR 33# 5585 = N32-46.

## N32-52 (34# 2526)

**Wójcik, J.**

**Diophantine equations involving primes.**

*Ann. Polon. Math.* **18** (1966), 315–321.

Let $f$, $g$ be irreducible polynomials in one variable, with degree $r>2$ and integer coefficients. Suppose that $f$, $g$ have the same leading coefficient and the same minimal splitting field. Let $m$, $n$ be non-zero integers with $m/n$ not an $r$th power. The author shows how to find all primes representable in the form (*) $p=f(x)/m=g(y)/n$ with $x$, $y$ integral.

It is routine to show that (*) has only finitely many solutions; the interest of the result lies in the method by which all the solutions $p$ may be obtained effectively.

*B. J. Birch* (Oxford)

The hypotheses given in the review should be changed as follows: in lines 3–4 replace "the same minimal splitting field" by "arbitrarily chosen roots of $f$ and $g$ generate the same normal field".
Referred to in N32-53.

## N32-53 (38# 4402)

**Wójcik, J.**

**Diophantine equations involving primes. II.**

*Ann. Polon. Math.* **20** (1968), 259–266.

The author generalizes earlier work [same Ann. **18** (1966), 315–321; MR **34** #2526] concerning integral polynomials $f$ and $g$ for which $p=f/m=g/n$ takes on only a finite number of prime values. Here $f$ and $g$ are such that arbitrary roots generate the same normal field. {The author points out that the review cited, MR **34** #2526, should be amended to clarify this condition.} In the present work the author cites cases such as $(x^4+15x^2+9)/25=225y^4+51y^2+1$ and $(4x^4-2x^2+1)/3=(2y^2+1)/3$ which have infinitely many solutions of which only a finite number produce common prime values. The extension theorems, typically, involve $f, f_1, \cdots, f_k$, irreducible polynomials over $Q$ with roots (one of each) $\eta$, $\xi_1, \cdots, \xi_k$ such that each $Q(\xi_j)$ is normal and contains $\eta$. Let there exist infinitely many integers $x$, $y$ such that $f_1(x)f_2(x)\cdots f_k(x)=f(y)$ and all $f_j(x)$ are primes. Then there exists an integral polynomial $h(x)$ and integers $a$, $b$ such that $f_1(ax+b)\cdots f_k(ax+b)=f(h(x))$, the polynomials $f_j(ax+b)$ all have integer coefficients and $f(h(x))$ has no constant factor $>1$. The result is extended to polynomials over imaginary quadratic fields.

*Harvey Cohn* (Tucson, Ariz.)

Citations: MR 34# 2526 = N32-52.

## N32-54 (34# 4225)

**Hooley, Christopher**

**On the greatest prime factor of a quadratic polynomial.**

*Acta Math.* **117** (1967), 281–299.

Let $D$ be a positive integer which is not a perfect square. Denote by $P_x$ the greatest prime factor of $\prod_{\sqrt{|D|}<n\leq x}(n-D)$. Combining the method of Čebyšev [see E. Landau, *Handbuch der Lehre von der Verteilung der Primzahlen*, § 147–149, Teubner, Leipzig, 1909; second edition, Chelsea, New York, 1953; MR **16**, 904] with both the sieve method and a method involving trigonometrical sums (see the author's paper in Acta Math. **110** (1963), 97–114 [MR **27** #3610]), the author obtains the result: $P_x>x^{11/10}$ for all sufficiently large $x$. He indicates that for negative $D$ the same statement holds, the proof being similar in principle. Thus the estimate $P_x>xe^{\log^c x}$ $(0<c<1)$ by P. Erdős [J. London Math. Soc. **27** (1952), 379–384; MR **13**, 914] is improved.

*O. H. Körner* (Marburg)

Citations: MR 13, 914a = N32-8; MR 16, 904d = N02-3; MR 27# 3610 = N40-47.

**N32-55** **(35# 4178)**

**Lenskoĭ, D. N.**

**On certain generalizations of twins.** **(Russian)**

*Volž. Mat. Sb. Vyp.* 1 (1963), 114–118.

Let $f$ be an integer valued polynomial with positive leading coefficient, irreducible over the field of rationals. Let $\omega(p)$ be the number of solutions of the congruence $xf(x) \equiv 0 \pmod p$, and $\pi_f(N)$ the number of primes $p \leqq N$ such that $f(p)$ is also prime. The author's objective is to obtain a good upper estimate for $\pi_f(N)$, and he takes as his point of departure the upper bound sieve of Selberg. For a good result, this approach involves finding an asymptotic formula or accurate lower bound for a certain sum (see, for example, H. Halberstam and K. F. Roth [*Sequences*, Vol. I, Chapter IV, Theorem 3, Clarendon, Oxford, 1966; MR **35** #1565], where the sum in question is denoted by $Q$); and this the author does only in outline. The result he states is (after correcting an obvious misprint) $\pi_f(N) \leqq 8(1+o(1)) \prod_p (1-\omega(p)/p)(1-1/p)^{-2} N(\log N)^{-2}$ $(N \to \infty)$, provided $\omega(p) < p$. In a footnote, the author draws attention to an earlier short paper by Wang Yuan [Advancement in Math. **3** (1957), 416–423; MR **20** #4531] in which his result has been anticipated. For an accessible and detailed account of the case $f(x) = x + 2k$, see E. Bombieri and H. Davenport [Proc. Roy. Soc. Ser. A **293** (1966), 1–18, Theorem 2 and section 4; MR **33** #7314].

*H. Halberstam* (Nottingham)

Citations: MR 20# 4531 = N32-19; MR 33# 7314 = N08-43; MR 35# 1565 = B02-3.

**N32-56** **(35# 5405)**

**Hooley, C.**

**On the power free values of polynomials.**

*Mathematika* **14** (1967), 21–26.

Let $f(x)$ be an irreducible polynomial of degree $r$ having integral coefficients. Denote by $N(x)$ the number of integers $1 \leqq n \leqq x$ for which $f(n)$ is not divisible by an $(r-1)$th power of an integer greater than 1. Assume that $f(n)$ has no fixed $(r-1)$th power divisors greater than 1 (i.e., there is no $l > 1$ such that $f(n) \equiv 0 \pmod{l^{r-1}}$ for all $n > 0$). The reviewer proved that $N(x) \to \infty$ as $x \to \infty$ [J. London Math. Soc. **28** (1953), 416–425; MR **15**, 104].

Denote by $\rho(l)$ the number of roots of the congruence $f(v) \equiv 0 \pmod l$. The author proves that

$$N(x) = x \prod_p (1-\rho(p^{r-1})/p^{r-1}) + O(x/(\log x)^{c/\log\log\log x}),$$

which is a very considerable sharpening of the reviewer's result. For $f(x)$ a cubic polynomial, the author obtained $N(x) = Ax + O(x/(\log x)^{2/3})$ in a previous paper ["On the square-free values of cubic polynomials", to appear in J. Reine Angew. Math.].*

*P. Erdős* (Budapest)

*See MR **36** #3738 = N32-57.

Citations: MR 15, 104f = N32-13; MR 36# 3738 = N32-57.

Referred to in N52-40.

**N32-57** **(36# 3738)**

**Hooley, Christopher**

**On the square-free values of cubic polynomials.**

*J. Reine Angew. Math.* **229** (1968), 147–154.

Let $N(x)$ be the number of positive integers $n$ not exceeding $x$ for which $4n^3 + k$ is square-free, where $k$ is not a multiple of 4. Let $\rho(l)$ be the number of roots (mod $l$) of the congruence $4\nu^3 + k \equiv 0 \pmod l$. Then, as $x \to \infty$, $N(x) = x \prod_p (1-\rho(p^2)/p^2) + O(x \log^{-2/3} x)$, the product being taken over all positive primes $p$. The positive integers $n$ for which $4n^3 + k$ is square-free have positive density.

*B. Garrison* (San Diego, Calif.)

Referred to in N32-56.

**N32-58** **(36# 6363)**

**Shanks, Daniel**

**Lal's constant and generalizations.**

*Math. Comp.* **21** (1967), 705–707.

The author evaluates the constant $\lambda$ in the heuristic asymptotic formula $h(N) \sim \lambda \int_2^N (\log n)^{-2}\, dn$, where $h(N)$ denotes the number of pairs of primes $(m-1)^4 + 1$ and $(m+1)^4 + 1$, $m + 1 \leqq N$. It is shown that $\lambda$ can be evaluated from the product $C = \prod_{p=8k+1} p(p-8)/(p-4)^2$, which is evaluated by using Dirichlet series. Up to five decimal places, $C$ and $\lambda$ are given by 0.88307 and 0.79220, respectively. The same technique is shown to be useful for evaluation of a large class of such constants. *M. S. Cheema* (Tucson, Ariz.)

**N32-59** **(38# 2104)**

**Rieger, G. J.**

**On polynomials and almost-primes.**

*Bull. Amer. Math. Soc.* **75** (1969), 100–103.

Applying the method of Selberg's sieve in the improved form given by W. B. Jurkat and H.-E. Richert [Acta Arith. **11** (1965), 217–240; MR **34** #2450], the author obtains the result: There are infinitely many primes $p$ such that $p^2 - 2$ has at most five prime factors (multiplicities included). Using Kuhn's device the author can give more precise statements about the order of magnitude of the primes dividing $p^2 - 2$.

To estimate the remainder term which occurs in Selberg's sieve, the author applies Bombieri's prime number theorem for arithmetic progressions [E. Bombieri, Mathematika **12** (1965), 201–225; MR **33** #5590]. Proofs are only indicated and not given in detail. {Misprints: Page 101, line 5: replace "[6]" by "[7]"; page 102, line 4: read $A(M_a, \rho)/(y^* R(\rho))$ instead of $A(M_a, \rho)$ (author's correction).}

It should be mentioned that the above result is also contained in H.-E. Richert's forthcoming paper ("Selberg's sieve with weights", Theorem 7, to appear ibid. June, 1969): Let $F(x)$ $(\neq \pm x)$ be an irreducible polynomial of degree $g \geqq 1$ with integral coefficients and without any fixed prime divisor. Let $\rho(p)$ denote the number of solutions of $F(m) \equiv 0 \pmod p$ and suppose that $\rho(p) < p - 1$ for $p \nmid F(0)$ and $p \leqq g + 1$. Then there are infinitely many primes $p$ such that $F(p)$ has at most $2g + 1$ prime factors (multiplicities included).

*W. G. H. Schaal* (E. Lansing, Mich.)

Citations: MR 33# 5590 = M55-43.

**N32-60** **(40# 4242)**

**Grölz, Wolfgang**

**Primteiler von Polynomen.**

*Math. Ann.* **181** (1969), 134–136.

Let $f_i(x)$, $i = 1, 2, 3, \cdots, m$, denote polynomials with coefficients from $Z$ and with degrees $n_i > 0$. Further, let $P(f_i)$ denote the set of all primes dividing $f_i(n)$, $n = 1, 2, 3, \cdots$. Then the author proves that $P(f_1) \cap \cdots \cap P(f_m)$ is an infinite set. This theorem is included in a more general one due to T. Nagell, later generalized by L. Fjellstedt [Ark. Mat. **3** (1955), 193–198; MR **16**, 906].

The author's proof is of interest because he makes use of the concept of ultraproduct of algebraic structures.

*W. Ljunggren* (Oslo)

Citations: MR 16, 906e = R08-26.

**N32-61** **(41# 1689)**

**Keates, M.**

**On the greatest prime factor of a polynomial.**

*Proc. Edinburgh Math. Soc.* (2) **16** (1968/69), 301–303.

If $f(x)$ is a polynomial with rational integral coefficients and if, for integral $x$, $P(x)$ is the greatest positive prime factor of $f(x)$, then $P(x) > C \log\log |x|$ for $|x|$ sufficiently large, provided either (a) $f(x)$ is quadratic or cubic with distinct roots and $C=10^{-7}$ or (b) $f(x)=Ax^k+B$, $A$ and $B$ non-zero, $k \geqq 3$ and $C=(10k)^{-6}$.

*L. K. Durst* (Providence, R.I.)

## N32-62 (41# 8344)

**Gendler, Stephen I.; Gendler, Joyce**

**Primes in an angle of an ellipse.**

*Indian J. Pure Appl. Math.* **1** (1970), *no.* 2, 178–179.

E. Hecke [Math. Z. **6** (1920), 11–51] has shown that if $F(x, y)$ is a binary quadratic form, then the number of integral points $(x, y)$ which lie in a sector of the plane and for which $F(x, y)$ is prime is asymptotically proportional to the non-Euclidean measure of the angle of the sector. The authors give here some numerical results for $F(x, y)=x^2+2y^2$ and the sectors of the ellipse $x^2+2y^2 \leqq N$ $(N \leqq 5000)$ in the first quadrant with $x \geqq y$ and with $x<y$.

*E. S. Barnes* (Adelaide)

## N32-63 (41# 8356)

**Maksudov, I. G.**

**Distribution of almost primes in certain sequences. (Russian. Uzbek summary)**

*Dokl. Akad. Nauk UzSSR* **1966**, *no.* 7, 3–6.

Let $f$ be a polynomial of $n$ variables with integral coefficients that is irreducible in the field of rational numbers. Let $F_r=\prod_{i=1}^r f_i$. The author considers the sequence $F_r(x_1, \cdots, x_k, p_{k+1}, \cdots, p_n)$ when one part of the variables of $F_r$ admits all integral rational values and the other part admits primes.

For these general sequences he obtains estimates from above and from below for a number of almost prime numbers of form $F_r$. In the proof he complements A. Selberg's lattice method by A. Weil's theorem.

*A. V. Vinogradov* (RŽMat **1967** #3 A83)

## N32-64 (41# 8361)

**Greaves, G.**

**On the divisor-sum problem for binary cubic forms.**

*Acta Arith.* **17** (1970), 1–28.

Let $f(x, y)$ denote a fixed binary cubic form $f(x, y)=a_0x^3+a_1x^2y+a_2xy^2+a_3y^3$, irreducible over the integers, having non-zero discriminant $D=a_1{}^2a_2{}^2-4a_0a_2{}^3-4a_1{}^3a_3-27a_0{}^2a_3{}^2+18a_0a_1a_2a_3$. Let $d(n)$ denote the number of positive divisors of $n$. The principal result of this paper states that there exist constants $C_1, C_2$, depending on $f$, such that, as $Z \rightarrow \infty$, $\sum_{|f(r,s)| \leq Z} d(|f(r, s)|)=C_1Z^{2/3}\log Z+C_2Z^{2/3}+O(Z^{9/14+\varepsilon})$, for any fixed $\varepsilon>0$. The method of proof is an extension of previous methods developed by P. Erdős [J. London Math. Soc. **27** (1952), 7–15; MR **13**, 438] and C. Hooley [Acta Math. **110** (1963), 97–114; MR **27** #3610] and depends on a consideration of the exponential sum

$$S(g, h; l) = \sum_{1 \leq r, s \leq l, f(r,s) \equiv 0 \,(\mathrm{mod}\, l)} \exp(2\pi i(gr+hs)/l).$$

The analysis is intricate and ingenious and is developed in a sequence of eleven lemmas. The author does not claim that the estimate $O(Z^{9/14+\varepsilon})$ for the error term is anything like the best possible; in fact, he believes that an appreciably better estimate should be obtainable by suitable improvements in the arguments that he uses.

*A. L. Whiteman* (Los Angeles, Calif.)

Citations: MR 13, 438f = N40-19; MR 27# 3610 = N40-47.

## N32-65 (41# 8384)

**Hornfeck, Bernhard**

**Primteiler von Polynomen.**

*J. Reine Angew. Math.* **243** (1970), 120.

The polynomial $f(x) \in Z[x]$ is said to have the prime divisor $p$ if there exists an integer $a$ such that $p | f(a)$. The author gives an elementary proof of the following theorem: Let $f_i(x)$ $(i=1, 2, \cdots, k)$ be non-constant polynomials of $Z[x]$ and let $M_i$ be the set of prime divisors of $f_i(x)$. Then $M_1 \cap M_2 \cap \cdots \cap M_k$ is infinite.

*W. Ledermann* (Brighton)

## N32-66 (42# 5909)

**Greaves, George**

**Large prime factors of binary forms.**

*J. Number Theory* **3** (1971), 35–59.

The author obtains results about the order of magnitude of the largest prime factor of integers represented by cubic forms with integer coefficients. He proves Theorem 1: Let $f$ be an irreducible binary form of degree three. Let $\alpha=0{,}754\cdots$ be the unique positive root of $3\alpha+\log(3\alpha-1)=5/2$. Then for any $\varepsilon>0$ the greatest prime factor of the integers $f(r, s)$, $1 \leqq |f(r, s)| \leqq Z$ exceeds $Z^{\alpha-\varepsilon}$. The proof depends on an application of Selberg's upper sieve method; for this purpose a careful investigation of the function

$$N(x, 1) = \sum_{1 \leq r, s \leq x, f(r,s) \equiv 0 \,(\mathrm{mod}\, 1)} 1$$

is required. To estimate $\sum_{|f(r,s)| \leq t} 1$ a weak form of the Thue-Siegel-Roth theorem is used.

Another result of the paper deals with almost primes represented by forms with integer coefficients. Theorem 2: Let $f$ be an irreducible binary form of degree $n \geqq 3$, and suppose the numbers $f(r, s)$ have no nontrivial fixed divisor. Let $P_k$ denote a number having at most $k$ prime factors ($k$ contains the multiplicities of the prime factors). Then the numbers $f(r, s)$ for which $1 \leqq r, s \leqq x$ include at least $Ax^2(\log x^2)^{-1}$ of the type $P_k$, where $k=\frac{1}{2}(n+2)$ if $2|n$; $k=\frac{1}{2}(n+1)$ if $2 \nmid n$, $A$ is a constant. All the prime factors of the $P_k$ counted above exceed $x^{1/2-\varepsilon}$.

The proof depends on a slightly adjusted form of a theorem by H.-E. Richert [Mathematika **16** (1969), 1–22; MR **40** #119]. The applications of this theorem also requires results about the numbers $N(x, 1)$.

*W. G. H. Schaal* (Marburg)

Citations: MR 40# 119 = M55-66.

## N32-67 (44# 3961)

**Sprindžuk, V. G.**

**The greatest prime divisor of a binary form. (Russian)**

*Dokl. Akad. Nauk BSSR* **15** (1971), 389–391.

Let $f=f(x, y)$ be an irreducible binary form with integral coefficients, of degree $n$. For any two co-prime integers $x$ and $y$ put $X=\max(|x|, |y|)$ and denote by $P$ the greatest prime divisor of $f(x, y)$. The author improves on earlier estimates by himself [same Dokl. **12** (1968), 293–297; MR **37** #6247; ibid. **14** (1970), 681–684; MR **43** #3267] and by J. Coates [Acta Arith. **16** (1969/70), 399–412; MR **41** #8341; ibid. **16** (1969/70), 425–435; MR **41** #8342] and proves that if $n \geqq 5$ and $X$ is sufficiently large, then $P>c(\log\log X)(\log\log\log X)^{-1}$, where $c$ depends only on the form $f$. This estimate may not be far from the best possible result; it has since been improved by the author to $P>c \log\log X$, except for certain special forms (unpublished).

*K. Mahler* (Canberra)

Citations: MR 37# 6247 = D24-71; MR 41# 8341 = D40-57; MR 41# 8342 = D40-58; MR 43# 3267 = J68-67.

## N32-68 (44# 5284)

**Motohashi, Yoichi**

**On the distribution of prime numbers which are of the form $x^2+y^2+1$.**

*Acta Arith.* **16** (1969/70), 351–363.

Der Verfasser beweist zwei bedeutende Sätze und schließt

daran einige Bemerkungen und eine Vermutung an.

Bezeichnet man mit $r(n)$ die Anzahl der Darstellungen von $n$ als Summe zweier Quadrate, so lautet Satz 1: Es existiert eine Konstante $c_1$ so, daß $\sum_{p\leq N} r^2(p-1)\leq c_1 N$ gilt. Satz 2: Es gibt unendlich viele Primzahlen $p$ der Gestalt $p=x^2+y^2+1$.

Ihre Anzahl in der Menge $\{1,\cdots,N\}$ ist größer als $c_2 N(\log N)^{-2}$; $c_2$ ist konstant. Die Vermutung besagt, daß diese Anzahl asymptotisch gleich

$$(3/2)\prod_{p\equiv -1(4)}(1-1/p^2)^{-1/2}(1-1/(p(p-1)))N(\log N)^{-3/2}$$

ist. In einer späteren Arbeit [#5285 unten] wird eine obere Schranke dieser Größenordnung als richtig nachgewiesen.
*H. J. Kanold* (Braunschweig)

**N32-69** **(44# 5285 )**

**Motohashi, Y.**
**On the distribution of prime numbers which are of the form "$x^2+y^2+1$". II.**
*Acta Math. Acad. Sci. Hungar.* **22**(1971/72),207–210.

In dieser Arbeit wird eine frühere Abschätzung verschärft [#5284 oben].

Bezeichnet man mit $I(N)$ die Anzahl der Primzahlen $p\leq N$ der Gestalt $p=x^2+y^2+1$, so wird der folgende Satz bewiesen: $I(N)\leq c_1 N(\log N)^{-3/2}$ mit einer positiven Konstanten $c_1$. Der Beweis ist ziemlich kompliziert und benutzt Methoden von A. Selberg, Bombieri und Brun-Titchmarsh. Am Schluß wird eine Verallgemeinerung auf quadratische Zahlkörper angegeben.
*H. J. Kanold* (Braunschweig)

# N36 ESTIMATES OF SUMS OF ARITHMETIC FUNCTIONS: GENERAL THEOREMS

See also reviews A22-88, A36-30, A36-42, A36-46, B28-33, M40-6, M55-72, M99-6, N04-1, N08-3, N20-47, N40-2, N56-1, P28-55, P28-64, P28-75, P28-89, Q20-9, Q20-16, Q20-18, Q20-41, Z02-4, Z05-14, Z10-20, Z10-35.

**N36-1** **(6, 118e)**

**Wintner, Aurel. The Lebesgue constants of Möbius' inversion.** Duke Math. J. **11**, 853–867 (1944).

Let $f$ and $f'$ be connected by the relation

$$f(n)=\sum_{d|n} f'(d)$$

and the corresponding Möbius inverse. The author considers the problem of the equality of

$$\lim_{n\to\infty}(f(1)+f(2)+\cdots+f(n))/n$$

and $\sum_{n=1}^{\infty} f'(n)/n$. He determines the exact order of the "Lebesgue constants" of the linear transformations connecting these two expressions, thus showing that the existence of one does not necessarily imply the existence of the other. He also obtains a Tauberian restriction under which the existence of one does imply that of the other. The special case $f'(n)=\mu(n)$ shows the relation of the problem to the prime number theorem. The limits of summation on page 859 are incorrect but the final result is correct. Formula (37) should read $f'(p^k)=f(p)$. This necessitates a number of minor changes in the following work but does not affect the validity of the corollary. *H. S. Zuckerman.*

**N36-2** **(6, 150f)**

**Wintner, Aurel. A summation method associated with Dirichlet's divisor problem.** Amer. J. Math. **66**, 579–590 (1944).

The transformation

$$D_n(s)=\sum_{m=1}^{n}(n/m-[n/m])s_m/n$$

of the sequence $s_1, s_2, \cdots$ into the sequence $D_1(s), D_2(s), \cdots$ defines the summation method considered. It is compared with $(C, 1)$ summation, defined by $M_n(s)=\sum_{m=1}^{n} s_m/n$. These two methods are shown to be incomparable but not inconsistent and other properties of the $D$-process are discussed. The presentation is marred by a number of misprints and errors. *H. S. Zuckerman* (Seattle, Wash.).

**N36-3** **(7, 147a)**

**Wintner, Aurel. Mean-values of arithmetical representations.** Amer. J. Math. **67**, 481–485 (1945).

The author proves that every multiplicative function which is bounded and nonnegative has a mean value. That is, $\lim_{n\to\infty}\{f(1)+f(2)+\cdots+f(n)\}/n$ exists.
*P. Erdös* (Stanford University, Calif.).

Referred to in Q15-13.

**N36-4** **(8, 9b)**

**Wintner, Aurel. Square root estimates of arithmetical sum functions.** Duke Math. J. **13**, 185–193 (1946).

In Gauss's circle problem it can be proved by elementary methods that $\sum_{m=1}^{N} f(m)=\pi n+O(n^{\frac{1}{2}})$, where $f(m)$ is the number of representations of $m$ as a sum of two squares. More generally, the author shows that, for an arbitrary function $f(m)$,

$$\text{(A)}\qquad \sum_{m=1}^{n} f(m)=n\sum_{m=1}^{\infty} m^{-1}f'(m)+O(n^{\frac{1}{2}})$$

provided that (B) $\sum_{m=1}^{n} f'(m)=O(1)$, where $f(n)=\sum_{d|m} f'(d)$. The exponent $\theta=\frac{1}{2}$ in the error term in (A) can, of course, be improved in special cases (for example, in the circle problem). The author proves, however, that in the general case nothing more than (A) can be concluded from (B); that is, functions $f(m)$ exist for which the error term cannot be replaced by one of order lower than $n^{\frac{1}{2}}$. Thus "the possibility of improving the Gauss-Dirichlet exponent $\theta=\frac{1}{2}$ is due to the explicit nature of their problem" and not to "a general arithmetical fact depending only on that peculiarity of the sequence 1, 2, $\cdots$ which makes possible the application of the underlying sieve process." Use is made of the Lebesgue-Toeplitz "norm" principle [Toeplitz, Prace Mat.-Fiz. **22**, 113–119 (1913)]. A similar result is shown to hold for problems of the type of Dirichlet's divisor problem.

The reviewer observes that the inequality following (13) and the last paragraph on page 188 are incorrect but can be modified so as to leave the final conclusions unaltered. Furthermore, on page 187, line 7 and elsewhere the symbol $O(n^{\frac{1}{2}})$ is used in a more restricted sense than is customary. There are also several minor misprints. *R. A. Rankin.*

**N36-5** **(9, 499e)**

**Bellman, Richard. On the average value of arithmetic functions.** Proc. Nat. Acad. Sci. U. S. A. **34**, 149–152 (1948).

The author announces a new method of estimating sums of the form $S=\sum_{n=1}^{N} f(g(n))$, where $f(n)$ is an arithmetic function such as the Euler $\varphi$-function, and $g(n)$ is either a polynomial in $n$, a term of the form $ap_n+b$, where $p_n$ is the $n$th prime, or a term of the form $ak^n+b$. The point of the

method is to express $f(n)$ in terms of Ramanujan's function $c_q(n)$ and then, for the polynomial case, to use Hua's result on exponential sums [J. Chinese Math. Soc. **2**, 301–312 (1940); these Rev. **2**, 347]. An asymptotic formula for $\sum_{n=1}^{N}\sigma(g(n))$ is proved, where $\sigma(n)$ is the sum of the divisors of $n$ and $g(n)$ is a polynomial in $n$ of degree $k$ with integral coefficients having no factor in common. [In the theorem, $n$ is misprinted $x$, and in lemma 1, $\sum a_k x^k$ should be $\sum a_l n^l$.]
*R. D. James* (Vancouver, B. C.).

Citations: MR 2, 347h = L05-2.
Referred to in N40-16.

## N36-6 (10, 235a)

**Mirsky, L. Note on a theorem of Carlitz.** Duke Math. J. **15**, 803–815 (1948).

Asymptotic formulae, for $n\to\infty$, are obtained for certain sums of the form

$$\sum_{n_1+\cdots+n_s=n} n_1^{\alpha_1}\cdots n_s^{\alpha_s}F_1(n_1)\cdots F_s(n_s),$$

where $\alpha_1, \cdots, \alpha_s$ are nonnegative numbers, and $F_1, \cdots, F_s$ are arithmetic functions satisfying given conditions. Included is a theorem of Carlitz [Quart. J. Math., Oxford Ser. **2**, 97–106 (1931); **3**, 273–290 (1932)], but with an improved estimate of the remainder term for $s>2$. The general results are used to obtain asymptotic formulae for the following: (a) the problem of Evelyn and Linfoot [see J. Reine Angew. Math. **164**, 131–140 (1931)] and Page [see J. London Math. Soc. **7**, 24–27 (1932)];

(b) $$\sum_{n_1+\cdots+n_s=n}\varphi_{\alpha_1}(n_1)\cdots\varphi_{\alpha_s}(n_s),$$

where $\varphi_k(n)=n^k\prod_{p|n}(1-p^{-k})$, $k>0$;

(c) $$\sum_{n_1+\cdots+n_s=n}\sigma_{\alpha_1}(n_1)\cdots\sigma_{\alpha_s}(n_s),$$

where $\sigma_k(n)=\sum_{d|n}d^k$. *W. H. Simons* (Vancouver, B. C.).

## N36-7 (11, 15a)

**Mirsky, L. Summation formulae involving arithmetic functions.** Duke Math. J. **16**, 261–272 (1949).

Let $F_1, \cdots, F_s$ be arithmetic functions, and $k_1, \cdots, k_s$ given fixed integers. The author obtains general asymptotic formulae, for $x\to\infty$, for sums of the form

$$\sum_{0<n\leqq x} F_1(n+k_1)\cdots F_s(n+k_s)$$

under various sets of assumptions about $F_1, \cdots, F_s$. The general results are used to obtain asymptotic expressions for sums of the above type when the $F$'s are (a) functions $\mu_k(n)$ defined to be 1 or 0 according as $n$ is or is not $k$-free, (b) Euler's $\varphi$-function $\varphi(n)$. *W. H. Simons.*

Referred to in A22-88.

## N36-8 (11, 15b)

**Atkinson, F. V., and Cherwell. The mean-values of arithmetical functions.** Quart. J. Math., Oxford Ser. **20**, 65–79 (1949).

Let $\{A_n\}$, $\{a_n\}$ be two sequences connected by the relation $A_n=\sum_{m|n}a_m$. The authors first prove that if $\lambda(n)$ is a positive nondecreasing function of $n$, such that $\lambda(n)/\log n$ is nonincreasing, and if $\sum_1^N a_n=o(N/\lambda(n))$, $\log(N^{-1}\sum_1^N|a_n|)=O(\lambda(N))$, then $N^{-1}\sum_1^N A_n\to\sum_1^N a_n/n$ as $N\to\infty$. Next, this result is extended to cover the case when $n$ runs through an arithmetic progression. Finally, a generalized theorem about the average of products of the $A_n$ when $n$ runs through a polynomial sequence is established. The results are derived by elementary methods and include many of the standard mean-value and distribution formulae of the theory of numbers. Among the numerous applications the following theorem may be cited. The number of $k$th-power-free numbers not exceeding $N$, of the form $n^l+h$, where $h\neq 0$, is asymptotic to $N^{1/l}\prod((1-(\chi(p)/p^k))$, provided that $k\geqq l$, $k\geqq 2$. Here $\chi(m)$ denotes the number of solutions of the congruence $x^l+h\equiv 0 \pmod{m^k}$. A corresponding estimate for numbers of the form $p^l+h$, where $p$ is a prime, is based upon results related to the prime number theorem. *A. L. Whiteman* (Los Angeles, Calif.).

Referred to in N36-28, N36-30, P16-9.

## N36-9 (15, 11g)

**Pérez-Cacho, L. On the function $E(x)$ (integral part of $x$).** Revista Mat. Hisp.-Amer. (4) **13**, 188–195 (1953). (Spanish)

The author shows how a number of known results concerning sums of the form $\sum_{x=1}^{n}f(x)E(n/x)$ may be derived in a systematic fashion, and deduces corresponding results for the function $q(n)$ which is the number of odd terms in the sequence $\{E(n/x)\}$, $x=1, 2, \cdots, n$. *R. Bellman.*

## N36-10 (16, 1089c)

**Ricci, Giovanni. Funzioni aritmetiche e quasi-asintoticità.** Rend. Sem. Mat. Fis. Milano **24** (1952–53), 88–106 (1954).

In this paper, which is partly expository in nature, the author reviews various problems concerned with the order of magnitude of arithmetical functions. The notions of asymptoticity in the mean, quasi-asymptoticity and quasi-asymptoticity in the mean are defined and discussed. All of these concepts are copiously illustrated with examples taken from the classical literature. *A. L. Whiteman.*

## N36-11 (16, 1089d)

**Ricci, Giovanni. Sul pennello di quasi-asintoticità della differenza di interi primi consecutivi. I, II.** Atti Accad. Naz. Lincei. Rend. Cl. Sci. Fis. Mat. Nat. (8) **17**, 192–196 (1954); **17** (1954), 347–351 (1955).

Let $b_n>0$ for all subscripts $n$ with the possible exception of the values $n_k$ of a sequence $\{n_k\}$ of asymptotic density zero. Then $a_n$ is said to be quasi-asymptotic to $b_n$ as $n\to\infty$ (written $q\lim a_n/b_n=1$) if for every $\epsilon>0$ the sequence $n(\epsilon, h)$ $(h=1, 2, \cdots)$ of the indices $n$ for which

$$(1-\epsilon)b_n<a_n<(1+\epsilon)b_n$$

has asymptotic density 1. The sequence $\{a_n, b_n\}$ determines a quasi-asymptotic pencil of the sequence $\{x_n\}$ if $q\liminf x_n/a_n=1$ and $q\limsup x_n/b_n=1$. Theorem I. If $p_n$ denotes the $n$th prime, then $p_{n+1}-p_n$ is not quasi-asymptotic to any monotonic function $\psi(n)$. Theorem II. Let $\{\alpha\log p_n, \beta\log p_n\}$ be a quasi-asymptotic pencil of the sequence $p_{n+1}-p_n$. Then the uniquely determined constants $\alpha$ and $\beta$ satisfy the inequalities $\alpha\leqq 1-H/C$, $\beta\geqq\alpha+2H/C$, where $H=\prod(1-(p-1)^{-2})$ (the product extending over odd primes) and $0\leqq C\leqq 16H$. Theorem III. Let $\psi_1(n)$ and $\psi_2(n)$ be two monotonic functions forming a quasi-asymptotic pencil of the sequence $p_{n+1}-p_n$. Then $\psi_2(n)\to\infty$ and

$$\liminf \psi_1(n)/\log p_n\leqq 1-H/C,$$
$$\limsup (\psi_2(n)-\psi_1(n))/\log p_n\geqq 2H/C.$$

*A. L. Whiteman* (Los Angeles, Calif.).

## N36-12 (18, 31d)

**Richert, Hans-Egon. Summierbarkeit Dirichletscher Reihen und asymptotische Zahlentheorie.** Colloque sur la Théorie des Nombres, Bruxelles, 1955, pp. 85–92. Georges Thone, Liège; Masson and Cie, Paris, 1956.

Consider the Riesz mean, $C_k(x)=\sum_{1\leqq n\leqq x}c_n\log^k x/n$, associated with the infinite series, $\sum_{n=1}^{\infty}c_n$. The author defines a nonlinear summability method by the condition

$$\int_1^x |C_x(u)-c\log^k u|^2 \frac{du}{u} = o(\log^{2k+1} x).$$

If this condition holds, the series $\sum_{n=1}^{\infty} c_n$ is said to be $|R, k|^2$-summable to $c$.

Using the Parseval theorem for Fourier integrals, a precise relation is obtained between the $|R, k|^2$-abscissa of convergence of a Dirichlet series, $f(s)=\sum_{n=1}^{\infty} a_n n^{-s}$, and the Carlson function obtained from the consideration of the mean value $T^{-1}\int_{-T}^{T} |f(s+it)|^2 dt$. *R. Bellman.*

## N36-13 (19, 1162b)

**Richert, Hans-Egon. Über Dirichletreihen mit Funktionalgleichung.** Acad. Serbe Sci. Publ. Inst. Math. **11** (1957), 73–124.

The author estimates partial sums $S_0(x)=\sum_{1\le n\le x} f(n)$, and more generally, $S_\kappa(x)=\sum_{1\le n\le x} f(n)(x-n)^\kappa$, where the $f(n)$ are coefficients of a Dirichlet series $Z(s)=\sum_1^\infty f(n)n^{-s}$. It is assumed that there is a second Dirichlet series $Z_1(s)$ which is related to $Z(s)$ by an equation of the type

$$Z(s)=C^{as+b}Z_1(\gamma-s)\prod_{j=1}^{M}\frac{\Gamma(\beta_j-b_js)}{\Gamma(\delta_j+d_js)}.$$

In the case $\kappa=0$, the problem was treated by Landau [Nachr. Ges. Wiss. Göttingen, Math.-Phys. Kl. **1912**, 687–771]. The present author removes some of Landau's supplementary conditions, and also considers $\kappa>0$, but his main achievement is that one of the major error terms is replaced by an exponential sum of the form

$$Cx^\eta \sum_{1\le n\le N} f_1(n)n^c \cos(\lambda(xn)^\rho+\Phi),$$

where $C, \eta, c, \lambda, \rho, \Phi$ are certain constants, and the $f_1(n)$ are the coefficients of $Z_1(s)$.

In many special cases non-trivial estimates for this exponential sum are available. The author uses estimates obtained in a previous paper [Math. Z. **58** (1953), 204–218; MR **15**, 11] in connection with the Dirichlet divisor problem. In this way he obtains the error term $O(x^{15/46+\varepsilon})$ in the following problems: (i) The number of products $n_1n_2\le x$, where $n_1$ and $n_2$ are restricted to $n_1\equiv l_1 \pmod{k_1}$, $n_2\equiv l_2 \pmod{k_2}$; (ii) the number of ideals with norm $\le x$ in a quadratic number field; (iii) the coefficient problem for the product of two Dirichlet $L$-series; (iv) the coefficient problem for the Eisenstein series $G_1(\tau; a_1, a_2, N)$.

Furthermore, the author applies his results to questions about the abscissa of Riesz summability $(R, \log n, \kappa)$ of $Z(s)$. In particular he considers the Dirichlet series arising from modular cusp forms. *N. G. de Bruijn.*

Citations: MR 15, 11h = N40-22.
Referred to in N36-52.

## N36-14 (21# 659)

**Tull, J. P. Dirichlet multiplication in lattice point problems.** Duke Math. J. **26** (1959), 73–80.

The author establishes a theorem which he states is a generalization of a theorem on the convergence of the Dirichlet product given by Landau [E. Landau, *Handbuch der Lehre von der Verteilung der Primzahlen*, Teubner, vol. II, Leipzig, 1909; pp. 755–758]. Theorem: $A(x)$ and $B(x)$ are of bounded variation on each interval $(1, x)$ with $A(1)=B(1)=0$: for $x\ge 1$,

$$A(x) = \sum_{\mu=1}^{h} x^{\alpha_\mu}P_\mu(\log x)+O(x^\alpha \log^l (x+1)),$$

$$B(x) = \sum_{\nu=1}^{k} x^{\beta_\nu}Q_\nu(\log x)+O(x^\beta \log^{l'} (x+1)),$$

and the total variations of the main terms of the above are of order of magnitude

$$V_A(x) = O(x^\rho \log^m (x+1)),\quad V_B(x) = O(x^\tau \log^{m'} (x+1)),$$

respectively, where $\alpha, \beta, \rho, \tau, l, l', m, m'$ are non-negative real numbers; $\alpha_\mu, \beta_\nu$ are complex numbers; $P_\mu$ and $Q_\nu$ are polynomial functions. $C(x)$ is the Stieltjes resultant of $A$ and $B$; i.e., $C(x)=\int_1^x A(x/u)dB(u)$. Then there is a function $T(x)$ of the same form as the main terms in $A(x)$ and $B(x)$ such that

$$C(x) = T(x)+O\{x^\omega \log^q (x+1)\},$$
$$\omega = (\rho\tau-\alpha\beta)/(\rho+\tau-\alpha-\beta),$$
$$q = \max\{r+r'+1,\ [(l+m')(\rho-\beta)+(l'+m)(\tau-\alpha)]/(\rho+\tau-\alpha-\beta)\}$$

if $\max(\alpha, \beta)<\min(\rho, \tau)$. If the last condition is not satisfied, other values for $\omega$ and $q$ are obtained which are given in detail in the paper. Furthermore the total variation of $C(x)$ is given by $V_C(x)=O\{x^{\max(\rho,\tau)}\log^{m''}(x+1)\}$, where $m''=m, m'$, or $m+m'+1$ according as $\rho>\tau$, $\rho<\tau$, or $\rho=\tau$, respectively. *D. Moskovitz* (Pittsburgh, Pa.)

Referred to in N36-15.

## N36-15 (21# 6362)

**Tull, J. P. Dirichlet multiplication in lattice point problems. II.** Pacific J. Math. **9** (1959), 609–615.

[For part I, see Duke Math. J. **26** (1959), 73–80; MR **21** #659.] The author generalizes his earlier result on the Stieltjes resultant $C(x)$ given in I. In the place of the functions $P\mu(\log x)$ in asymptotic formulae for $A(x)$ and $B(x)$ [see the cited review], the author uses more general slowly oscillating functions in the sense of Karamata [Bull. Soc. Math. France **61** (1933), 55–62] with the canonical representation

$$L(x) = a\exp\left(\int_1^x t^{-1}\delta(t)dt\right),\quad a>0,\quad \delta(x)\to 0,\quad x\to\infty,$$

$\delta$ is bounded and $L$-integrable on each bounded interval. Then the main terms in the Stieltjes resultant of $A(x)$ and $B(x)$, i.e., in $C(x)=\int_1^x A(x/u)dB(u)$, have the same form as the main terms in $A(x)$ and $B(x)$. Very precise $O$-remainder terms in asymptotic formulas for $C(x)$ are expressed by means of $x^\alpha L(x)$ and their integrals. *M. Tomić* (Belgrade)

Citations: MR 21# 659 = N36-14.
Referred to in N40-42.

## N36-16 (21# 1960)

**Karamata, J. Sur les inversions asymptotiques des produits de convolutions.** Glas Srpske Akad. Nauka **228** Od. Prirod.-Mat. Nauka (N.S.) **13** (1957), 23–59. (Serbo-Croatian. French summary)

Define

$$F(x) = \sum_{n\le x} f(n),\quad G(x) = \sum_{n\le x} F(x/n) = \sum_{n\le x} f(n)[x/n],$$

where $[w]$ denotes the greatest integer contained in $w$. What are the conditions on $p(x)$ so that from (1) $G(x)=Ax\log x+p(x)$ we can deduce that (2) $F(x)=Ax+o(x)$? The author discusses known results in this direction, and obtains the following: Theorem 5: If

$$p(x) = Bx+Cx/\log x+o(x/\log x)$$

and if $f(n)\ge -M$ $(n=1, 2, 3, \cdots)$, then (1)→(2). The idea of the proof is that of A. Selberg in his elementary proof of the Prime Number Theorem [Ann. of Math. (2) **50** (1949), 305–313; MR **10**, 595]. See also the succeeding review. *S. Chowla* (Boulder, Colo.)

Citations: MR 10, 595b = N20-3.

**N36-17** **(21# 1961 )**

**Karamata, J. Sur les inversions asymptotiques de certains produits de convolution.** Bull. Acad. Serbe Sci. (N.S.) **20** Cl. Sci. Math.-Nat. Sci. Math. **3** (1957), 11–32.

The author proves (we use the notation of the preceding review) the sharper result: If $p(x)=Bx+o(x)$, then $\int_1^x t^{-1}F(t)dt=Ax+o(x)$; and if, in addition, $f(n)\geqq -M$, then equation (2) (of the preceding review) holds.

*S. Chowla* (Boulder, Colo.)

**N36-18** **(21# 3390 )**

**Buschman, R. G. Asymptotic expressions for $\sum n^a f(n) \log^r n$.** Pacific J. Math. **9** (1959), 9–12.

There exists a class of Tauberian theorems which assert that if $F(t)$ is a non-negative, non-decreasing function in $0\leqq t<\infty$ and various regularity conditions are satisfied, an asymptotic expression for the Laplace transform $\mathscr{L}\{F\}$ of $F$ implies a related asymptotic expression for $F(t)$ [see H. Delange, Ann. Sci. École Norm. Sup. (3) **71** (1954), 213–242; MR **16**, 921]. Such theorems have a number of well-known applications in number theory. The author applies this method to functions $F(t)=\sum_{1\leqq n\leqq e^t} n^a f(n)\log^r n$ where $f$ is a non-negative number-theoretic function, and lists a large number of results, several of them proved in some detail. *H. Halberstam* (London)

Citations: MR 16, 921e = M45-24.

**N36-19** **(22# 4667 )**

**Ciesielski, Z. On multiplicative sequences.** Colloq. Math. **7** (1959/60), 265–268.

Let $f(n)=\pm 1$ be a multiplicative number-theoretic function. It has been conjectured that

$$(1)\qquad \lim_{n=\infty}\frac{1}{n}\sum_{k=1}^{n} f(k)$$

always exists. Define the real number $t$ $(0\leqq t\leqq 1)$ as follows: $t=\sum_{n=1}^{\infty}(1+f(p_n))/2^{n+1}$, where $p_n$ is the $n$th prime. The author proceeds to prove that (1) holds for almost all multiplicative functions. He also proves this for all complex-valued multiplicative functions satisfying $|f(n)|=1$ (see also A. Wintner)*. *P. Erdös* (Haifa)

*See MR 7. 367A = Z02-5.

Citations: MR 7, 367a = Z02-5.

**N36-20** **(22# 9466 )**

**Cohen, Eckford. The average order of certain types of arithmetical functions: generalized $k$-free numbers and totient points.** Monatsh. Math. **64** (1960), 251–262.

Let $M$ denote any set of positive integers and $Z$ the set of all positive integers, $\rho_M(n)$ the characteristic function of the set $M$ and $\mu_M(n)$ the inversion function of $M$ given implicitly by the relation $\rho_M(n)=\sum_{d/n}\mu_M(d)$. Introducing $F_M(n)=\sum_{de=n,\ e\in M} f(d)$ and $F(n)=F_Z(n)$ for any given arithmetical function $f(n)$, the author proves the identity $F_M(n)=\sum_{d/n}\mu_M(d)F(n/d)$, which is a generalization of Mertens identity. Using this identity and a related identity he gives new proofs for known estimations of the arithmetical functions considered in the Dirichlet divisor problems, Mertens totient problem and Gauss' circle problem. He also gives estimations of generalizations of these functions. *H. Bergström* (Göteborg)

**N36-21** **(22# 9477 )**

**Chandrasekharan, Komaravolu; Narasimhan, Raghavan. Sur l'ordre moyen de quelques fonctions arithmétiques.** C. R. Acad. Sci. Paris **251** (1960), 1333–1335.

Defining $\Delta(x)$ by $\sum_{n=1}^{x} d(n)=x\log x+(2\gamma-1)x+\Delta(x)$, where $d(n)$ is the number of divisors of $n$ and $\gamma$ is Euler's constant, the authors refer to the $\Omega$-theorem that $\Delta(x)/x^{1/4}$ has upper and lower limits $+\infty$ and $-\infty$ as $x\to\infty$. They note that the generating function $\varphi(s)=\zeta^2(s)=\sum d(n)n^{-s}$ of the coefficients $d(n)$ satisfies a functional equation (1) $\Gamma^2(\frac{1}{2}s)\varphi(s)=\Gamma^2(\frac{1}{2}-\frac{1}{2}s)\psi(1-s)$, where $\varphi(s)$ and $\psi(s)$ have Dirichlet expansions $\varphi(s)=\sum a_n\lambda_n^{-s}$ and $\psi(s)=\sum b_n\mu_n^{-s}$ in certain half-planes. They then observe that there are other solutions of (1) (e.g., $\zeta$-functions of real quadratic fields), and enunciate $\Omega$-theorems for the error terms in asymptotic formulae for the Riesz sums $\sum_{\lambda_n\leqq x} a_n(x-\lambda_n)^\rho$ in a wide class of such cases. {The second sentence in the statement of Theorem I is somewhat obscure. The intended meaning seems to be: Suppose that the sequence $\{\lambda_n\}$ contains a part $\{\lambda_{nk}\}$ such that no $\lambda_n^{1/2}$ can be represented as a linear combination of the numbers $\{\lambda_{nk}^{1/2}\}$ with coefficients $\pm 1$, unless $\lambda_n^{1/2}=\pm\lambda_{nr}^{1/2}$ for some $r$, in which case $\lambda_n^{1/2}$ has no other representation. It seems to the reviewer, however, that this condition should relate to the sequence $\{\mu_n\}$ rather than $\{\lambda_n\}$.}

*A. E. Ingham* (Cambridge, England)

Referred to in N36-25, N36-32, N36-77.

**N36-22** **(22# 10947 )**

**Rubel, L. A. An Abelian theorem for number-theoretic sums.** Acta Arith. **6** (1960), 175–177.

The author considers pairs of functions $f(n)$, $f^*(n)$ connected by the equivalent relations

$$f(n)=\sum_{d|n} f^*(d),\quad f^*(n)=\sum_{d|n} f(d)\mu\left(\frac{n}{d}\right).$$

There are known Abelian and Tauberian theorems connecting convergence or limitability of the sequence $\{f(n)\}$ with convergence or summability of the series $\sum_1^\infty f^*(n)/n$ (with equality of limit and sum) [A. Wintner, *Eratosthenian averages*, Baltimore, Md., 1943; MR **7**, 366; §§ 8–12, §§ 18–24; G. H. Hardy, *Divergent series*, Clarendon, Oxford, 1949; MR **11**, 25; Appendix IV]. To these the author adds the Abelian theorem: If $f(n)\to L$ (finite) as $n\to\infty$, then $\sum_1^\infty f^*(n)/n$ converges to $L$. The author's argument is based on the claim that the conditions for regularity of the appropriate matrix transformation are equivalent to the known results (a) $N(k)\to 0$ as $k\to\infty$, (b) $\sum_{k=1}^{\infty}|N(k)|/k<\infty$, of prime number theory, where $N(x)=\sum_{k\leqq x}\mu(k)/k$. In a later correction, however, he notes that (as pointed out by P. T. Bateman) the argument is inadequate at the point where (b) is used. To repair the omission he applies the known theorem that $|N(k)|\log^2 k<H$, where $H$ is a constant. This is stronger than (a) and (b), and is more than sufficient for regularity of the transformation.

*A. E. Ingham* (Cambridge, England)

Referred to in N36-23.

**N36-23** **(23# A3705 )**

**Rubel, L. A.**

**Correction to "An Abelian theorem for number-theoretic sums".**

*Acta Arith.* **6** (1960/61), 523.

The author refers to a previous paper of his own [Acta Arith. **6** (1960), 175–177; MR **22** #10947], and corrects an error pointed out by P. T. Bateman. In order to estimate a certain sum, the author had used the well-known result that $\sum k^{-1}|N(k)|<\infty$, where $N(x)\equiv\sum_{k\leqq x}k^{-1}\mu(k)$. The argument proves to be inadequate, and in order to repair the deficiency the author now uses the stronger (known) result that $|N(k)|\leqq H(\log k)^{-2}$ $(k\geqq 2)$.

*A. E. Ingham* (Bombay)

Citations: MR 22# 10947 = N36-22.

**N36-24** **(23# A868)**

**Chandrasekharan, K.; Narasimhan, Raghavan**
**On Hecke's functional equation.**
*Bull. Amer. Math. Soc.* **67** (1961), 182–185.

This is a relatively short announcement in which, with a general functional equation

$$(2\pi)^{-s}\Gamma(s)\varphi(s) = (2\pi)^{s-\delta}\Gamma(\delta-s)\psi(\delta-s),$$

$\varphi(s)=\sum a_n\lambda_n^{-s}$, $\psi(s)=\sum b_n\mu_n^{-s}$, there are associated two families of "modular" relations with "residual" terms (as originally envisaged by this reviewer), and then, by rather precise employment of syllogisms (due mainly to A. Zygmund and A. E. Ingham), statements are obtained which, in particular, subsume extant estimates for various arithmetical functions, some estimates being in their best known scope or even better.

*S. Bochner* (Princeton, N.J.)

**N36-25** **(23# A3719)**

**Chandrasekharan, K.; Narasimhan, Raghavan**
**Hecke's functional equation and the average order of arithmetical functions.**
*Acta Arith.* **6** (1960/61), 487–503.

Write, as usual, $s=\sigma+it$, and let $\varphi(s)=\sum_{n=1}^{\infty} a_n\lambda_n^{-s}$ (convergent for $\sigma>\alpha$) and $\psi(s)=\sum_{n=1}^{\infty} b_n\mu_n^{-s}$ (convergent for $\sigma>\delta-\beta$) satisfy

$$(*)\qquad (2\pi)^{-s}\Gamma(s)\varphi(s) = (2\pi)^{s-\delta}\Gamma(\delta-s)\psi(\delta-s).$$

Denoting the common value of either side of (*) by $\chi(s)$, and setting $P(x)=(2\pi i)^{-1}\int_{\mathscr{C}}\chi(s)(2\pi/x)^s ds$ (with $\mathscr{C}$ an appropriately chosen closed curve), Bochner [Ann. of Math. (2) **53** (1951), 332–363; MR **13**, 920] has shown that (*) is equivalent to a certain modular relation (which, for $\varphi(s)=\zeta(s)$ reduces to a well-known identity in the theory of theta functions). In continuation of some earlier work [Ann. of Math. (2) **74** (1961), 1–23; see also C. R. Acad. Sci. Paris **251** (1960), 1333–1335; MR **22** #9477], the authors multiply this modular relation by certain factors and obtain by integration some new and interesting relations, somewhat too complex to be reproduced here. In the statements of the main result occur a certain condition (L) [quoted in detail, in the paper reviewed as MR **22** #9477] to be satisfied by a subset $\Lambda$ of the increasing sequence $\lambda_n$, the Riesz means

$$B_\mu{}^\rho(x)=(\Gamma(\rho+1))^{-1}\sum_{\mu_n\le x}{}' b_n(x-\mu_n)^\rho \ (\rho\ge 0),$$

and $Q_\rho(x)=(2\pi i)^{-1}\int_{\mathscr{C}'}\chi(s)(2\pi)^s x^{s+\rho}/\Gamma(\rho+1+s)\,ds$. Theorem I: If $(L)$ holds and $\sum_{\lambda_n\in\Lambda}|\mathrm{Re}\,a_n|\lambda_n^{-\frac12(\delta+\rho+\frac12)}$ diverges for some $\rho\ge 0$, then

$$\lim_{x\to\infty}{}^{\sup}_{\inf}\ \mathrm{Re}(B_\mu{}^\rho(x)-Q_\rho(x))x^{-\frac12(\delta+\rho-\frac12)} = {}^{+\infty}_{-\infty}$$

and the corresponding statement for the imaginary parts. Theorem II: If Re $a_n\ne 0$ for at least one $n$, then, for $\rho\ge 0$, $\mathrm{Re}(B_\mu{}^\rho(x)-Q_\rho(x))=\Omega_\pm(x^{\frac12(\rho+\delta-\frac12)})$, and similarly for the imaginary parts. The theorems may be applied to $\varphi(s)=\sum_{n=1}^{\infty}\tau(n)n^{-s}$ (where $\tau(n)$ is the Ramanujan function) and leads to Pennington's [Proc. Cambridge Philos. Soc. **47** (1951), 668–678; MR **13**, 209] result that

$$\lim_{x\to\infty}{}^{\sup}_{\inf}\ x^{-23/4}\sum_{n\le x}\tau(n) = {}^{+\infty}_{-\infty}$$

and certain generalizations. Taking

$$\varphi(s) = \zeta_k(s) = \sum_{n=1}^{\infty} r_k(n)n^{-s}$$

($r_k(n)$ is the number of lattice points on a $k$-dimensional sphere of radius $n^{1/2}$), one obtains a generalization of Ingham's results that

$$\lim_{x\to\infty}{}^{\sup}_{\inf}\ x^{-1/4}\Big(\sum_{n\le x} r_2(n)-\pi x\Big) = {}^{+\infty}_{-\infty}.$$

{More applications are indicated. There are some annoying misprints.}

*E. Grosswald* (Philadelphia, Pa.)

Citations: MR 13, 209d = F35-32; MR 13, 920b = M40-7; MR 22# 9477 = N36-21.
Referred to in N36-32, N36-33, N36-36, N36-65, N36-77, N36-78, R46-31.

**N36-26** **(23# A3723)**

**Richert, Hans-Egon**
**Zur multiplikativen Zahlentheorie.**
*J. Reine Angew. Math.* **206** (1961), 31–38.

In the context of a general investigation on the theory of strong Riesz summability [Nachr. Akad. Wiss. Göttingen Math.-Phys. Kl. II **1960**, 17–75; MR **24** #A358], the author had obtained a number of results concerning lower estimates of error terms in general asymptotic formulae. The present paper, which is independent of this work, attacks the problem directly. The principal result established here is as follows. Let $k\ge 2$ be an integer, let $\{c_n\}$ be a sequence of complex numbers, and suppose that, for any $\varepsilon>0$, $\sum_{n\le x}c_n=O(x^{(k-1)/2k+\varepsilon})$. Suppose, further, that the relation $\sum_{n\le x}|c_n|^2=O(x^\beta)$ is false for every $\beta<1$ and that $\sum_{n_1\cdots n_k\le x}c_{n_1}\cdots c_{n_k}=O(x^\alpha)$. Then $\alpha\ge(k-1)/2k$. The argument depends on a very penetrating discussion of Dirichlet series associated with the sequences $\{c_n\}$ and $\{b_n\}$, where $b_n=\sum_{n_1\cdots n_k=n}c_{n_1}\cdots c_{n_k}$; and use is made of some earlier results due to the author [Nachr. Akad. Wiss. Göttingen Math.-Phys. Kl. IIa **1956**, 77–125; MR **18**, 123] and to Carlson [Ark. Mat. Astronom. Fys. **16** (1922), no. 18]. From the general theorem stated above, the following deduction is made. Let $k\ge 2$, and let $\{a_n\}$ be a sequence of complex numbers. Suppose that, for every $\varepsilon>0$, $\sum_{n\le x}a_n=x+O(x^{(k-1)/2k+\varepsilon})$ and suppose, further, that

$$\sum_{n_1\cdots n_k\le x} a_{n_1}\cdots a_{n_k} = xP_{k-1}(\log x)+O(x^\alpha),$$

where $P_{k-1}$ is a polynomial of degree $k-1$. Then $\alpha\ge(k-1)/2k$. This result contains, in particular, Hardy's theorems on the error terms in the divisor problems of Piltz and Dirichlet [Hardy, Proc. London Math. Soc. (2) **15** (1916), 1–25].

*L. Mirsky* (Sheffield)

Citations: MR 18, 123h = M40-16; MR 24# A358 = N36-27.
Referred to in N36-45, N36-58.

**N36-27** **(24# A358)**

**Richert, Hans-Egon**
**Einführung in die Theorie der starken Rieszschen Summierbarkeit von Dirichletreihen.**
*Nachr. Akad. Wiss. Göttingen Math.-Phys. Kl. II* **1960**, 17–75.

As the title implies, the author studies the theory of strong summability of Dirichlet series. Let $a$, $b$ be two real numbers, $a>0$, $0<b\le 1$; then the series $\sum_{n=1}^{\infty}c_n$ is said to be summable $|R, \log n, a|^{1/b}$ to the sum $c$ if there exists a constant $c$ such that

$$\int_1^x |C_{a-b}(u)-c\log^{a-b}u|^{1/b}\,\frac{\partial u}{u} = O(\log^a x),$$

where $C_m(x)=\sum_{n\le x}c_n\log^m(x/n)$ are the Riesz sums.

It is not possible to give a detailed account of the results of this long paper which continues work on strong Riesz summability by the author himself [Nachr. Akad. Wiss. Göttingen Math.-Phys. Kl. IIa. **1956**, 77–125; MR **18**,

123] and Glatfeld [Proc. Glasgow Math. Assoc. **3** (1957), 123–131; MR **22** #9761].

Applications are given to some functions of analytic number theory. For the Piltz problem, the author proves: If

$$\theta_k = \inf\{\xi \mid \sum_{n\leq x} d_k(n) - \operatorname{res} \frac{x^s}{s}\zeta^k(s) = O(x^\xi)\},$$

then $\theta_k \leq 1 - c/k^{2/3}$ for some constant $c$. $d_k(n)$ is the number of solutions of $n_1 n_2 \cdots n_k = n$.

He studies in addition the corresponding problem for a cyclotomic field. *R. G. Ayoub* (University Park, Pa.)

Citations: MR 18, 123h = M40-16.
Referred to in N36-26.

## N36-28 (24# A1239)

**Cohen, Eckford**

**Arithmetical notes. I. On a theorem of van der Corput.**
*Proc. Amer. Math. Soc.* **12** (1961), 214–217.

Let $g(n)$ be a complex-valued arithmetical function and define $f(n) = \sum_{d|n} g(d)$. It is known that if (1) $\alpha = \sum g(n)/n$ is absolutely convergent, then $\lim_{x\to\infty}(x^{-1}\sum_{n\leq x} f(n))$ exists and is equal to $\alpha$ [J. G. van der Corput, Nederl. Akad. Wetensch. Proc. **42** (1939), 859–866; MR **1**, 66; F. V. Atkinson and Lord Cherwell, Quart. J. Math. Oxford Ser. **20** (1949), 65–79; MR **11**, 15]. The author obtains the following generalisation: If

$$f_k(n) = \sum_{dd_1d_2\cdots d_k = n} g(d) = \sum_{d|n} g(d)\tau_k(n/d)$$

and (1) is true, then $\lim_{x\to\infty}(x^{-1}(\log x)^{-k+1}\sum_{n\leq x} f_k(n))$ exists and is equal to $\alpha/(k-1)!$ ($\tau_k(n)$ is the number of representations of $n$ as a product of $k$ factors; in usual notation, $\tau_2(n) = \tau(n)$.) The proof is by induction on $k$, and quite simple. *H. Halberstam* (London)

Citations: MR 1, 66a = N40-2; MR 11, 15b = N36-8.
Referred to in N24-49, N24-53, N36-34.

## N36-29 (24# A1561)

**Cohen, Eckford**

**Fourier expansions of arithmetical functions.**
*Bull. Amer. Math. Soc.* **67** (1961), 145–147.

In the notation of the author's paper [#A1239 above], Wintner [A. Wintner, *Eratosthenian averages*, Baltimore, Md., 1943; MR **7**, 366] proved that if condition (1) above holds, $f(n)$ is almost periodic ($B$) with absolutely convergent Fourier expansion $f(n) \sim \sum_{r=1}^{\infty} a_r c(n, r)$, $a_r = \sum_{n=1, r|n}^{\infty} g(n)/n$, where $c(n, r)$ is Ramanujan's trigonometric sum; he showed further that if (2) $\sum_{n=1}^{\infty} \tau(n)|g(n)|n^{-1}$ converges, $f(n)$ is equal to its Fourier series for all $n$. The author announces that for certain important classes of multiplicative functions, the latter result holds even without condition (2), provided (1) is true. A proof is not given; the author refers the reader to another paper on almost even functions of finite abelian groups to appear later. *H. Halberstam* (London)

Citations: MR 7, 366a = Z02-4.

## N36-30 (24# A1241)

**Wirsing, Eduard**

**Das asymptotische Verhalten von Summen über multiplikative Funktionen.**
*Math. Ann.* **143** (1961), 75–102.

The principal result of this paper is the following (Theorem 1): If $f(n)$ is a non-negative multiplicative arithmetic function satisfying (1) $f(p^\nu) \leq \gamma_1\gamma_2^\nu$ with $\gamma_2 < 2$, $p$ prime and $\nu = 2, 3, \cdots$, and (2) $\sum_{p\leq x} f(p) \sim \tau x/(\log x)$ as $x\to\infty$, then, as $x\to\infty$,

$$\sum_{n\leq x} f(n) \sim \frac{e^{-c\tau}}{\Gamma(\tau)}\frac{x}{\log x}\prod_{p\leq x}\left(1+\frac{f(p)}{p}+\frac{f(p^2)}{p^2}+\cdots\right);$$

where $c$ is Euler's constant. From Theorem 1 the author deduces a result about the mean values of complex-valued multiplicative functions, which he uses to derive equidistribution properties for members of a large class of arithmetic functions; in the process, he proves again or extends results of Delange, Erdős and other authors [a full bibliography is given; see especially H. Delange, C. R. Acad. Sci. Paris **246** (1958), 514–517; MR **20** #2311; ibid. **246** (1958), 2205–2207; MR **20** #2312]. The author poses, among other problems, the question of finding the weakest hypotheses under which the result of Theorem 1 holds; in particular, he asks whether (2) can be replaced by

$$(2') \qquad \sum_{p\leq x} \frac{f(p)}{p}\log p \sim \tau\log x.$$

The author's proof of Theorem 1 is carried out by elementary methods in two steps; in the first and easier step, he shows that $\log x\sum_{n\leq x} f(n) \sim \tau x\sum_{n\leq x} f(n)/n$, and here he needs the full force of (2); the second step, leading ingeniously to the main result, can be accomplished with the aid of (2′) only. {In this connection, see P. Erdős, Ann. of Math. (2) **47** (1946), 1–20 [MR **7**, 416] and perhaps also F. V. Atkinson and Lord Cherwell, Quart. J. Math. Oxford Ser. **20** (1949), 65–79 [MR **11**, 15].} *H. Halberstam* (London)

Citations: MR 7, 416c = N60-7; MR 11, 15b = N36-8; MR 20# 2311 = K30-16; MR 20# 2312 = K30-17.
Referred to in N36-41, N36-43, N36-62, N36-63, N36-68, N36-70, N48-17, N60-64, N80-38, N80-46.

## N36-31 (25# 54)

**Swetharanyam, S.**

**Asymptotic expressions for certain type of sums involving the arithmetic functions in the theory of numbers.**
*Math. Student* **28** (1960), 9–28.

This paper illustrates various elementary techniques for deducing asymptotic estimates for summations, $\sum_{n\leq x} f(n)n^{-a}$, $a$ real, on the basis of known results in the case $a = 0$; $f$ is used here to denote an arithmetical function of divisor or totient type. The principal tool is the technique of partial summation and its variants, in connection with formulas based on the greatest integer function. The results are conveniently summarized in tabular form at the end. {Reviewer's remark: The author's discussion of the Euler $\phi$-function is based on the Val'fiš estimate of 1953 [Dokl. Akad. Nauk SSSR **90** (1953), 491–493; MR **15**, 11; Akad. Nauk Gruzin. SSR Trudy Tbiliss. Mat. Inst. Razmadze **19** (1953), 1–31; MR **16**, 338], which has been recently superseded by a refinement due to Saltykov [Vestnik Moskov. Univ. Ser. I Mat. Meh. **1960**, no. 6, 34–50; MR **23** #A2395].} *E. Cohen* (Knoxville, Tenn.)

Citations: MR 15, 11f = N48-2; MR 16, 338d = N48-3; MR 23# A2395 = N48-10.

## N36-32 (25# 3911)

**Chandrasekharan, K.; Narasimhan, Raghavan**

**Functional equations with multiple gamma factors and the average order of arithmetical functions.**
*Ann. of Math.* (2) **76** (1962), 93–136.

This is a further development of earlier work by the same authors [Ann. of Math. (2) **74** (1961), 1–23; Acta Arith. **6** (1960/61), 487–503; MR **23** #A3719; C. R. Acad. Sci. Paris

**251** (1960), 1333–1335; MR **22** #9477; erratum, p. 2547]. It is assumed that a functional equation $\Delta(s)\varphi(s) = \Delta(\delta - s)\psi(\delta - s)$ is satisfied, where $\Delta(s) = \prod_1^N \Gamma(\alpha_\nu s + \beta_\nu)$ ($\alpha_\nu > 0$, $A \equiv \sum_1^N \alpha_\nu \geqq 1$), $\delta$ is real, $\varphi(s)$ and $\psi(s)$ have absolutely convergent Dirichlet expansions $\sum_1^\infty a_n \lambda_n^{-s}$ and $\sum_1^\infty b_n \mu_n^{-s}$ in some half-plane, and the equation is to be understood in the sense that the two sides have a common analytic continuation $\chi(s)$ in a domain $\mathscr{D}$ which is the exterior of a bounded closed set $S$, such that $\chi(s) \to 0$ uniformly in every fixed finite interval $\sigma_1 \leqq \sigma \leqq \sigma_2$ as $t \to \pm\infty$ ($s = \sigma + it$). The main object is to obtain $\Omega_-$ and $O$-theorems relating to $R_\lambda^\rho(x) = A_\lambda^\rho(x) - Q_\rho(x)$, where $\Gamma(\rho+1)A_\lambda^\rho(x)$ is the Riesz sum of order $\rho \geqq 0$ and type $\{\lambda_n\}$ of the coefficients $a_n$ and $Q_\rho(x)$ is a certain function arising from the singularities of $\varphi(s)$ and $\Gamma(s)$. It is proved (Theorem 3.2) that the real (or imaginary) part of $R_\lambda^\rho(x)$ is $\Omega_\pm(x^\theta)$, where $2A\theta = A\delta + \rho(2A - 1) - \frac{1}{2}$, if $b_n' \neq 0$ for some $n$, where $b_n'$ is the real (or imaginary) part of $b_n$; and (Theorem 3.1) that the conclusion may be strengthened to $\Omega_\pm(x^\theta\omega(x))$, where $\omega(x) \to \infty$ with $x$, if the set $\{n\}$ of positive integers has a subset $M = \{n_k\}$ such that (i) no number $\mu_n^{1/(2A)}$ is representable as a linear combination of numbers $\mu_m^{1/(2A)}$ ($m \in M$) with coefficients $\pm 1$, apart from a trivial representation $\mu_n^{1/(2A)} = \mu_m^{1/(2A)}$ if $n \in M$, and (ii) $\sum_{m \in M} |b_m'| \mu_m^{-\tau} = \infty$, where $2A\tau = A\delta + \rho + \frac{1}{2}$. It is also proved that Theorem 3.2 is best possible for large $\rho$, in that $R_\lambda^\rho(x) = O(x^\theta)$ if $\sum_1^\infty |b_n| \mu_n^{-\tau} < \infty$. The proofs make use of explicit formulae involving functions $I(x)$ that have convenient approximations by Bessel and trigonometric functions, combined with a known adaptation to $\Omega$-problems of a device used in an analytical proof of Kronecker's theorem on Diophantine approximation. For smaller $\rho$ the $O$-results are less precise. The authors concentrate on $R_\lambda^0(x)$, for which they use Landau's method of taking a $\rho$th difference of $A_\lambda^\rho(x)$ with a sufficiently large integer $\rho$. The full result (Theorem 4.1) is rather elaborate, but it includes classical estimates in special cases, such as the errors $O(x^{1/3} \log x)$ and $O(x^{1/3})$ in Dirichlet's divisor problem and the problem of the lattice points of a circle, the corresponding $\Omega$-results of Theorem 3.1 being $\Omega_\pm(x^{1/4}\omega(x))$. (Mention may be made of the work of K. S. Gangadharan [Proc. Cambridge Philos. Soc. **57** (1961), 699–721; MR **24** #A92] which, in the parts of these two problems not already covered by stronger results of G. M. Hardy, replaces the unspecified $\omega(x)$ by explicit functions tending to infinity with $x$.)

The authors note that, although the condition $A \geqq 1$ is not essential for results of the above general character, one cannot have a functional equation with $A < 0$ and the same main features as before, since the explicit formula would imply unlimited differentiability of $A_\lambda^\rho(x)$ for suitable $\rho$. As an incidental consequence, the existence of an infinity of complex zeros of $\zeta(s)$ (for example) is inferred from a consideration of $1/\zeta(s)$.

*A. E. Ingham* (Cambridge, England)

Citations: MR 22# 9477 = N36-21; MR 23# A3719 = N36-25; MR 24# A92 = N40-4.
Referred to in N36-33, N36-36, N36-77, N36-78, N36-80, P20-39, R46-35.

## N36-33 (27# 114)

**Chandrasekharan, K.; Narasimhan, Raghavan**

**The average order of arithmetical functions, and the approximate functional equation for a class of zeta-functions.**

*Rend. Mat. e Appl.* (5) **21** (1962), 354–363.

This is a survey of results already published on the average order of arithmetical functions [Acta Arith. **6** (1960/61), 487–503; MR **23** #A3719; Ann. of Math. (2) **76** (1962), 93–136; MR **25** #3911], and an announcement of forthcoming results (to appear in Math. Ann.) on the derivation of an approximate functional equation from a functional equation under general conditions.

*A. E. Ingham* (Cambridge, England)

Citations: MR 23# A3719 = N36-25; MR 25# 3911 = N36-32.

## N36-34 (28# 2074)

**Narkiewicz, W.**

**On a summation formula of E. Cohen.**

*Colloq. Math.* **11** (1963), 85–86.

E. Cohen [Proc. Amer. Math. Soc. **12** (1961), 214–217; MR **24** #A1239] has proved the following theorem: If the series $\sum_1^\infty g(n)/n$ is absolutely convergent and $g_s(n) = \sum_{d|n} g(d)\tau_s(n/d)$, where $\tau_1(n) = 1$, $\tau_{s+1}(n) = \sum_{d|n} \tau_s(d)$, then

$$\lim_{x=\infty} \frac{1}{x(\log x)^{s-1}} \sum_{n \leqq x} g_s(n) = \frac{1}{(s-1)!} \sum_{n=1}^{\infty} \frac{g(n)}{n} \quad (s = 1, 2, \cdots).$$

The present paper contains another proof of this result. The author also remarks that the same method yields the following result. If $\sum_1^\infty g(n)/n$ is absolutely convergent and $f(n) = \sum_{cd=n,(c,d)=1} g(d)$, then

$$\lim_{x=\infty} \frac{1}{x} \sum_{n \leqq x} f(n) = \sum_{n=1}^{\infty} \frac{g(n)\phi(n)}{n}.$$

*L. Carlitz* (Durham, N.C.)

Citations: MR 24# A1239 = N36-28.

## N36-35 (28# 3965)

**Cohen, Eckford**

**A generalization of Axer's theorem and some of its applications.**

*Math. Nachr.* **27** (1963/64), 163–177.

Let $Z$ denote the multiplicative semi-group of the positive integers, and for a fixed $r \in Z$, let $Z_r$ denote the subsemigroup of $Z$ consisting of the integers relatively prime to $r (Z = Z_1)$. Let $T_r$ denote the set of all functions from $Z_r$ into the complex field and place $T = T_1$. A function $f$ of $T$ induces a function $f^{(r)}$ of $T_r$ by placing $f^{(r)}(n) = f(n)$ for each $n \in T_r$. Let $\varphi(x, r)$ denote the number of $n$ in $Z_r$ not exceeding $x$. The relative mean value $M_r$ of a function $f$ of $T_r$ is defined to be the limit (if it exists)

$$(1) \qquad M_r(f) = \lim_{x \to \infty} \frac{1}{\varphi(x, r)} \sum_{\substack{n \leqq x \\ n \in Z_r}} f(n).$$

The relative norm $N_r$ of $f$ in $T_r$ is defined by the equation (1) when we change $M$ to $N$, replace lim by lim sup, and replace $f(n)$ by $|f(n)|$.

The author proves the theorem: Let $f$ and $g$ be functions of $T_r$ related by $f(n) = \sum_{d|n} g(d)$, $n \in Z_r$, and suppose that $g$ has relative mean value $\alpha_r$ and is of finite relative norm. Then

$$\lim_{x \to \infty} \left\{ \frac{r}{x\phi(r)} \sum_{\substack{n \leqq x \\ n \in Z_r}} f(n) - \sum_{\substack{n \leqq x \\ n \in Z_r}} \frac{g(n)}{n} \right\} = -\frac{\alpha_r}{r} \{\Phi(r) + \beta\phi(r)\},$$

where $\beta = 1 - \gamma = \Gamma'(2)$ and $\Phi(r)$ is defined for each $r$ in $Z$ by

$$\Phi(r) = \sum_{d\delta = r} \mu(d)\delta \log d.$$

The author cites the following example. Let $C(n)$ denote the number of solutions of the congruence

$$x_1^2 + x_2^2 + x_3^2 - x_4^2 - x_5^2 - x_6^2 \equiv 1 \pmod{n};$$

then the mean value of $C(n)/n^5$ over the odd integers exists and is equal to $96/\pi^4$.

*S. Chowla* (University Park, Pa.)

**N36-36** **(28# 3976)**

**Chandrasekharan, K.; Narasimhan, Raghavan**

**On the mean value of the error term for a class of arithmetical functions.**

*Acta Math.* **112** (1964), 41–67.

The authors continue their study of functional equations which formally resemble the functional equation of the Riemann $\zeta$-function. Earlier papers dealt with $\Omega$- and $O$-results [Acta Arith. **6** (1960/61), 487–503; MR **23** #A3719; Ann. of Math. (2) **76** (1962), 93–136; MR **25** #3911] and approximate functional equations [Math. Ann. **152** (1963), 30–64; MR **27** #3605]. In this paper corresponding problems about the mean value of error terms are considered.

Let $s=\sigma+it$. Suppose $\sum_{n=1}^{\infty} a_n\lambda_n^{-s}$ $(0<\lambda_1<\cdots<\lambda_n\to\infty$, not all $a_n$ are 0) is a Dirichlet series absolutely convergent in some half-plane where it represents a meromorphic function $\phi(s)$. Let

$$E(y) = \sum_{\lambda_n \leqq x}' a_n - \frac{1}{2\pi i}\int_C \frac{x^s}{s}\phi(s)\,ds,$$

where $C$ is a simple closed path containing all the singularities of the integrand in its interior and $\sum'$ means that the last term is to be halved if $\lambda_n=x$. The authors obtain estimates for $\int_1^x (E(y))^2\,dy$ when $\phi(s)$ satisfies the same general conditions as in the last two papers cited above when these satisfy further numerical restrictions. The general conditions are: Suppose $\sum_{n=1}^{\infty} b_n\mu_n^{-s}$ $(0<\mu_1<\cdots<\mu_n\to\infty$, not all $b_n$ are 0) is also absolutely convergent in some half-plane where it represents a function $\psi(s)$. Let $\delta$ be real. Let $\Delta(s)=\prod_{\nu=1}^{N}\Gamma(\alpha_\nu s+\beta_\nu)$ where $N\geqq 1$, $\beta_\nu$ is complex and $\alpha_\nu>0$. The functional equation $\Delta(s)\phi(s)=\Delta(\delta-s)\psi(\delta-s)$ is said to hold if there exists a domain $D$ which is the exterior of some closed bounded set $S$ in which there exists a holomorphic function $\chi$ such that $\lim_{|t|\to\infty}\chi(\sigma+it)=0$ uniformly in every interval $-\infty<\sigma_1\leqq\sigma\leqq\sigma_2<\infty$ and $\chi(s)=\Delta(s)\phi(s)$ for $\sigma>c_1$, $\chi(s)=\Delta(\delta-s)\psi(\delta-s)$ for $\sigma<c_2$, where $c_1$ and $c_2$ are constants.

The estimates for $\int_1^x (E(y))^2\,dy$ are obtained subject to the additional conditions: $\delta>0$, $\sum_{\nu=1}^{N}\alpha_\nu=A\geqq 1$, $\lambda_n=c''n$, $\mu_n=c'n$, where $c''$ and $c'$ are constants, and also certain order conditions are imposed on $\sum_{\mu_n\leqq x} b_n^2$ and sometimes also on $\sum_{\lambda_n\leqq x} a_n^2$.

When specialized to particular $\phi(s)$ the estimates lead sometimes to new results, sometimes to the best known old ones, and sometimes to slightly poorer than the best known results. In particular, the results for $\zeta_K(s,\mathscr{L})$, the Dedekind $\zeta$-functions for the ideal class $\mathscr{L}$ in the algebraic number field $K$ of degree $n$ over the rationals, are new.

There are several minor misprints.

*S. L. Segal* (Rochester, N.Y.)

Citations: MR 23# A3719 = N36-25; MR 25# 3911 = N36-32; MR 27# 3605 = M40-33.

**N36-37** **(30# 71)**

**Delange, Hubert**

**Un théorème sur les fonctions arithmétiques multiplicatives et ses applications.**

*Ann. Sci. École Norm. Sup.* (3) **78** (1961), 1–29.

In the application of probability theory to number theory, much, if not quite all, of the attention has been given to questions connected with the distribution of values of multiplicative and additive functions. (Here, as usual, an "arithmetic" function $f$ (a complex-valued function whose domain is the set of natural numbers) is "multiplicative" ["additive"] if $f(mn)=f(m)f(n)$ $[f(mn)=f(m)+f(n)]$ whenever $m$ and $n$ are relatively prime.) This is natural, not only because so many of the functions of interest in number theory are themselves multiplicative or additive, but also because the structure of such functions permits inferences about their overall behavior from their behavior on relatively small sets: sets of primes or prime powers. Such inferences are among the basic tools of the expert in probabilistic number theory and it is to the elaboration and application of these tools that the present paper and the one reviewed below [#72] are devoted.

In reviewing these papers, it is convenient to introduce and extend some of the author's conventions. Thus, use of $p$ as an index indicates that the process involved, e.g., the summation in (*) is carried out over primes only. If the limit as $x\to\infty$ of $M_x(f;P)$ exists, where

$$(*)\qquad M_x(f;P) = \frac{\log x}{x}\sum_{p\leqq x} f(p),$$

then this limit is denoted by $M(f;P)$. Similarly, the limit of $M_x(f)$, where

$$M_x(f) = \frac{1}{x}\sum_{n\leqq x} f(n),$$

is denoted by $M(f)$ whenever it exists. Note in particular that $M(f)=0$ if and only if $M_x(f)=o(x)$. We distinguish the set $\mathfrak{M}_0$ of those multiplicative functions $f$ satisfying the condition $|f(n)|\leqq f(1)=1$ for all $n$.

The theorem of the title can be stated as follows. Let $f$ be in $\mathfrak{M}_0$ and, in addition, satisfy the conditions: (i) $M(f;P)$ exists, (ii) The series $\sum_p (1-\operatorname{Re} f(p))/p$ diverges. Then $M(f)$ exists and $M(f)=0$; also $M(f,\chi_Q)=0$, where $\chi_Q$ is the characteristic function of the set of square-free numbers. (Condition (ii) actually is stated only in case $M(f;P)=1$; in all other cases, as the author shows, (i) implies (ii).)

This theorem had previously been announced by the author without proof [C. R. Acad. Sci. Paris **246** (1958), 514–517; MR **20** #2311; ibid. **246** (1958), 2205–2207; MR **20** #2312]. Some of these results had previously been obtained by the author in a different way [Illinois J. Math. **2** (1958), 81–87; MR **20** #2310]. The present paper supplies the complete proof of the title theorem and goes on to a detailed exposition of the applications. One very special result will serve to illustrate these applications. Let $\lambda$, $\mu$ be irrational numbers, linearly independent in the sense that the equation $\lambda x+\mu y=z$ has no integer solutions $x, y, z$ other than $x=y=z=0$. Let $\omega(n)$ denote the number of prime divisors of $n$ (note that $\omega$ is additive and that the function $f_z$ defined by $f_z(n)=z^{\omega(n)}$ is in $\mathfrak{M}_0$ for $|z|\leqq 1$), and let $\Omega(n)$ similarly denote the total number, counting multiplicities, of prime divisors of $n$. Let $\{x\}$ denote the fractional part of $x$, i.e., the difference between $x$ and the largest integer not exceeding $x$. Then the points $(\{\lambda\omega(n)\}, \{\mu\Omega(n)\})$ are uniformly distributed over the unit square. This means that if $(x,y)$ is a point in the unit square, and $f_{(x,y)}$ is the arithmetic function defined by $f_{(x,y)}(n)=1$ if $\{\lambda\omega(n)\}\leqq x$, $\{\mu\Omega(n)\}\leqq y$, $f_{(x,y)}(n)=0$ otherwise, then $M(f_{(x,y)})$ exists and equals $xy$.

*A. Sklar* (Chicago, Ill.)

Citations: MR 20# 2310 = K30-15; MR 20# 2311 = K30-16; MR 20# 2312 = K30-17.

Referred to in B48-21, N36-42, N36-54, N36-60, N36-61, N36-63, N60-78, Q15-21.

**N36-38** **(30# 72)**

**Delange, Hubert**

**Sur les fonctions arithmétiques multiplicatives.**

*Ann. Sci. École Norm. Sup.* (3) **78** (1961), 273–304.

Conventions are the same as in the preceding review [#71]. The principal results of the paper are contained in the following pair of theorems, which should be compared with the theorem of the title of the preceding review. Theorem 1: Let $f$ be in $\mathfrak{M}_0$ and let $M(f)$ exist and be distinct from 0; then the series $\sum_p (1-f(p))/p$ converges, and there is at least one $r \geqq 1$ for which $f(2^r) \neq -1$. Theorem 2: Let $f$ be in $\mathfrak{M}_0$ and let the series $\sum_p (1-f(p))/p$ converge; then $M(f)$ exists and is given by

$$M(f) = \prod_p \left(1-\frac{1}{p}\right)\left(1+\sum_{r=1}^{\infty}\frac{f(p^r)}{p^r}\right).$$

Moreover, $M(f)=0$ if and only if $f(2^r)=-1$ for all $r \geqq 1$.

The significance of these results lies in the fact that if $g$ is a real-valued additive function, then for every real $t$, the function $f_t$ defined by $f_t(n)=\exp(itg(n))$ belongs to $\mathfrak{M}_0$. Now the existence of $M(f_t)$ for all real $t$ and the continuity at 0 of $M(f_t)$ as a function of $t$ are necessary and sufficient conditions for $g$ to have a distribution function [cf. M. Kac, *Statistical independence in probability, analysis and number theory*, p. 43, Wiley, New York, 1959; MR **22** #996; J. Kubilius, *Probabilistic methods in the theory of numbers*, pp. 20–21, Amer. Math. Soc., Providence, R.I., 1964; MR **28** #3956]. This last statement means that if $x$ is any real number and $h_x$ is the arithmetic function defined by $h_x(n)=1$ if $g(n)<x$, $h_x(n)=0$ otherwise, then $M(h_x)$ exists; the actual distribution function $\sigma$ is defined by $\sigma(x)=M(h_x)$.

Thus the author's results have direct application to existence criteria for distribution functions of real additive functions. In fact, these results enable him to recover, in a remarkably simple fashion, the celebrated Erdős-Wintner theorem, which can be stated as follows. Let $g$ be a real additive function and let $g^*(n)=g(n)$ if $|g(n)|<1$, $g^*(n)=1$ if $|g(n)| \geqq 1$. Then a necessary and sufficient condition for $g$ to have a distribution function $\sigma$ is that the two series

$$\sum_p \frac{g^*(p)}{p}, \qquad \sum_p \frac{(g^*(p))^2}{p}$$

converge. Necessity was shown by P. Erdős [J. London Math. Soc. **13** (1938), 119–127] and sufficiency by P. Erdős and A. Wintner [Amer. J. Math. **61** (1939), 713–721; MR **1**, 40]. The author's methods have since been adapted by Kubilius to his own treatment of the Erdős-Wintner theorem [op. cit., pp. 74–85]. *A. Sklar* (Chicago, Ill.)

Citations: MR 1, 40c = N60-1; MR 22# 996 = Q15-7; MR 28# 3956 = N60-39.

Referred to in N36-47, N36-55, N36-63, N36-79.

## N36-39 (30# 73)

**Delange, Hubert**

**On a class of multiplicative arithmetical functions.**

*Scripta Math.* **26**, 121–141 (1963).

Denote by $M_0$ the class of all multiplicative functions $f(n)$ for which $f(1)=1$ and $|f(n)| \leqq 1$ for all integers $n$. Sharpening some of his previous results [see #72 above] the author proves the following results. Theorem 1: There is a function $C(f)$ continuous for $f \in M_0$ for which $C(f)=0$ if and only if $f(2^r)=-1$ for all $r \geqq 1$; further, if $f \in M_0$, then as $x \to \infty$

$$\prod_{p \leqq x}\left(1-\frac{1}{p}\right)\left[1+\sum_{j=1}^{\infty}\frac{f(p^j)}{p^j}\right] = C(f)\exp\left(-\sum_{p \leqq x}\frac{1-f(p)}{p}\right)+o(1).$$

Theorem 2: Suppose that for every $\varepsilon>0$ we have $\sum 1/p < +\infty$, $\Re f(p) < 1-\varepsilon$. Then as $x \to \infty$ we have

$$\frac{1}{x}\sum_{n \leqq x} f(n) = \prod_{p \leqq x}\left(1-\frac{1}{p}\right)\left[1+\sum_{j=1}^{\infty}\frac{f(p^j)}{p^j}\right]+o(1).$$

Using these theorems the author obtains a new proof of a result of the reviewer [Ann. of Math. (2) **47** (1946), 1–20; Theorem II, p. 2; MR **7**, 416], and he also proves several new results on additive number-theoretical functions. *P. Erdős* (London)

Citations: MR 7, 416c = N60-7.

Referred to in N36-63.

## N36-40 (30# 4099)

**Segal, S. L.**

**Dirichlet convolutions and the Silverman-Toeplitz conditions.**

*Acta Arith.* **10** (1964), 287–291.

The author proves the following abelian theorem for a wide class of arithmetical functions $f$. Suppose that $\lim_{n\to\infty} h(n)=L$, where $L$ is finite, and let $h_f$ denote the Dirichlet product of $f$ and $h$; then $\sum_{n=1}^{\infty} h_f(n)/n = L$. The proof uses some deep estimates of Landau for the Möbius $\mu$-function, together with the Toeplitz-Silverman theorem. *E. Cohen* (Knoxville, Tenn.)

## N36-41 (31# 132)

**Schwarz, Wolfgang**

**Einige Anwendungen Tauberscher Sätze in der Zahlentheorie.**

Habilitationsschrift vorgelegt zur Erlangung der venia legendi für Mathematik der Hohen Naturwissenschaftlich-Mathematischen Fakultät der Albert-Ludwigs-Universität zu Freiburg i. Br.

*Dissertation, Freiburg,* 1964. xviii + 103 *pp.*

Die Arbeit behandelt das Problem der asymptotischen Entwicklung von $\sum_{n\leqq x} f(n)$ für multiplikative Funktionen $f(n)$ mit der Voraussetzung $\sum_{p\leqq x} f(p)\log p = Kx\log^{\alpha} x + R(x)$, $R(x)$ Restglied. Allgemein wurde die Fragestellung mit Erfolg von E. Wirsing [Math. Ann. **143** (1961), 75–102; MR **24** #A1241] für $\alpha \leqq 0$ beantwortet; hier wird auch der Fall $\alpha>0$ ausführlich behandelt. Die Voraussetzung der Multiplikativität ergibt eine Produktzerlegung für die zugeordnete Dirichletreihe $\sum_{n=1}^{\infty} f(n)/n^s$. Ein Taubersatz von Hardy und Ramanujan liefert zunächst eine Entwicklung für $\log \sum_{n\leqq x} f(n)$. Der Inghamsche Taubersatz wird angewandt, um $\sum_{n\leqq x} f(n)/n$ zu entwickeln, woraus dann nach einer Idee von Wirsing auf $\sum_{n\leqq x} f(n)$ geschlossen wird. Die Voraussetzungen sind: $R(x)=O(x)$, $f(p)=o(p(\log p)^{-(\alpha+1)})$, und es gebe ein $\delta>0$, so daß für $v=2, 3, \cdots$, $f(p^v) \leqq \gamma p^{v-1-\delta}/v^2$. Der letzte Abschnitt der Arbeit führt Untersuchungen von de Bruijn [Illinois J. Math. **6** (1962), 137–141; MR **26** #4977] und de Bruijn-van Lint [Acta Arith. **8** (1962/63), 349–356; MR **28** #2995] weiter. Für $\alpha(n)=\prod_{p|n} p$ wird bewiesen

$$\sum_{n \leqq x}\frac{1}{\alpha(n)} = \frac{1+o(1)}{\sqrt{(4\pi\sqrt{2})}}\sqrt[4]{\left(\frac{\log\log x}{\log x}\right)}\exp(-R(\log x)),$$

wo $-R(u) \sim 2\sqrt{2}\sqrt{(u/\log u)}$. *H.-E. Richert* (Marburg)

Citations: MR 24# A1241 = N36-30; MR 26# 4977 = N28-47.

## N36-42 (31# 4770)

**Tull, Jack P.**

**A theorem in asymptotic number theory.**

*J. Austral. Math. Soc.* **5** (1965), 196–206.

Let $\alpha(n)$ be a multiplicative arithmetic function. Delange [Ann. Sci. École Norm. Sup. (3) **78** (1961), 1–29; MR **30** #71] proved that if $|\alpha(n)| \leqq 1$ and if, for a certain constant $\rho$, $\sum_{p\leqq x}\alpha(p) \sim \rho x/\log x$ $(x\to\infty)$, where $\rho=1$ implies $\sum_p (1-\operatorname{Re}\alpha(p))/p = +\infty$, then $\sum_{n\leqq x}\alpha(n)=O(x)$ $(x\to\infty)$. The present author improves this result. He shows, for example, that if $\alpha(n)$ is multiplicative, $|\alpha(n)| \leqq 1$, and $\sum_{p\leqq x}\alpha(p) = \rho \operatorname{li} x + O[xL(x)/\log x]$, where $\rho \neq 1$ and $L(x)$ is a monotonic slowly varying function such that $L(x)\to 0$

as $x \to \infty$, then for $x \geqq e^2$,

$$\sum_{n \leqq x} \alpha(n) = O[xL^*(x)/\log x] + O[\rho x/\log\log x],$$

where $L^*(x) = \int_1^x u^{-1}L(u)\,du$.

*L. Carlitz* (Durham, N.C.)

Citations: MR 30# 71 = N36-37.

## N36-43 (32# 2387)

**Schwarz, Wolfgang**

**Einige Anwendungen Tauberscher Sätze in der Zahlentheorie. A.**

*J. Reine Angew. Math.* **219** (1965), 67–96.

E. Wirsing [Math. Ann. **143** (1961), 75–102; MR **24** #A1241] proved that if a non-negative multiplicative arithmetic function $f$ satisfies $f(p^\nu) \leqq \gamma_1\gamma_2^\nu$, with $\gamma_2 < 2$, $p$ prime, $\nu = 2, 3, \cdots$, and $\sum_{p \leqq x} f(p) \sim Kx/\log x$ $(x \to \infty)$ with a positive constant $K$, then

$$\sum_{n \leqq x} f(n) \sim (\Gamma(K))^{-1} e^{-cK} x(\log x)^{-1} \prod_{p \leqq x} \left( \sum_{\nu=0}^{\infty} p^{-\nu} f(p^\nu) \right),$$

where $c$ is Euler's constant. In Part I of the paper, this result is extended to a theorem where, in $\sum f(p)$ and in $\sum f(n)$, summation is restricted to residue classes mod $m$.

In Part II, the author starts from the assumption that $\sum_{p \leqq x} f(p) \log p \sim Kx(\log x)^\alpha$ with $\alpha > 0$ (the case $\alpha = 0$, which is much simpler, was treated by Wirsing). He shows that the problem of $\sum_{n \leqq x} f(n)$ can be reduced to that of $\sum_{n \leqq x} n^{-1} f(n)$, and for this he obtains asymptotic formulas whose form is slightly different for the cases $\alpha < 1$, $\alpha = 1$, $\alpha > 1$. In the simplest case, $0 < \alpha < 1$, it is

$$\sum_{n \leqq x} n^{-1} f(n) \sim C_1(\log x)^{-\rho/2} \exp(C_2(\log x)^\rho),$$

where $\rho = \alpha/(\alpha + 1)$, and $C_1$, $C_2$ are positive constants.

In the proofs an essential rôle is played by a Tauberian theorem of Ingham [Ann. of Math. (2) **42** (1941), 1075–1090; MR **3**, 166], which gives the asymptotic behaviour of $A(u)$ for $u \to 0$ if $\int_0^\infty e^{-us}\,dA(u)$ is of the type $\exp(Cs^{-\alpha})$, or of a similar nature. *N. G. de Bruijn* (Eindhoven)

Citations: MR 3, 166a = P72-3; MR 24# A1241 = N36-30.

Referred to in N36-70.

## N36-44 (32# 2388)

**Schwarz, Wolfgang**

**Einige Anwendungen Tauberscher Sätze in der Zahlentheorie. B.**

*J. Reine Angew. Math.* **219** (1965), 157–179.

Let $\alpha(n)$ be the product of all primes dividing $n$, and put $P(x) = \sum_{n \leqq x} (\alpha(n))^{-1}$. It was shown by the reviewer [Illinois J. Math. **6** (1962), 137–141; MR **26** #4977] that $\log P(x) \sim 8^{1/2}(\log x/\log\log x)^{1/2}$. Using Ingham's Tauberian theorem quoted in the preceding review [#2387], the author succeeds in getting an asymptotic formula for $P(x)$ itself. It can be presented in the following form (which is easier to describe than the one given by the author):

$$\sum_{n \leqq x} (\alpha(n))^{-1} \sim (4\pi)^{-1/2} 2^{-1/4} \left( \frac{\log\log x}{\log x} \right)^{1/4} Q(x),$$

where $Q(x) = \min_{0 < \sigma < \infty} x^\sigma \sum_{n=1}^{\infty} (\alpha(n))^{-1} n^{-\sigma}$.

*N. G. de Bruijn* (Eindhoven)

Citations: MR 26# 4977 = N28-47.

## N36-45 (32# 2389)

**Warlimont, Richard**

**Über einen Satz von H.-E. Richert zur multiplikativen Zahlentheorie.**

*J. Reine Angew. Math.* **221** (1966), 197–202.

The following theorem about the error term in asymptotic formulas is proved. Let $l_n$ be a strictly increasing sequence of real numbers, $l_n \to \infty$, and for a suitable $l > 0$, assume $(\log l_n - \log l_{n-1})^{-1} = O(l_n^{\,l+\varepsilon})$. Let $a_n$ be an arbitrary sequence satisfying (1) $\sum_{l_n \leqq x} a_n = x + O(x^{1-l/2-\delta})$ for some $\delta > 0$. Then, from $\sum_{l_m l_n \leqq x} a_m a_n = x \log x + cx + R(x)$ and $(x^{-1} \int_1^x |R(u)|^2\,du)^{1/2} = O(x^\alpha)$, it follows that $\alpha \geqq 1 - \frac{3}{4}l$. In another theorem, condition (1) is replaced by some conditions about $Z(s)$ which are too complicated to be stated here. For $l_n = n$, and only estimating $R(x)$ itself, this result was proved by the reviewer [same J. **206** (1961), 31–38; MR **23** #A3723]. *H.-E. Richert* (Marburg)

Citations: MR 23# A3723 = N36-26.

## N36-46 (32# 4102)

**Dixon, R. D.**

**On a generalized divisor problem.**

*J. Indian Math. Soc.* (*N.S.*) **28** (1964), 187–196 (1965).

Let $f(s, z) = \sum_{n=1}^{\infty} a(n, z) n^{-s}$. Under certain general conditions for $f(s, z)$ (too complicated to be stated here), an asymptotic expansion for the summatory function $\sum_{n \leqq x} a(n, z)$ is derived. This theorem is similar to that given by Kienast [Math. Z. **45** (1939), 554–558; MR **1**, 41]. For example, it is applicable to the summatory function $D(x, z)$ belonging to $f(s, z) = \zeta^z(s)$ for all complex $z$, whereas Kienast's theorem was only concerned with real $z$. The proof follows essentially ideas of A. Selberg [J. Indian Math. Soc. (N.S.) **18** (1954), 83–87; MR **16**, 676], who already proved an asymptotic relation for $D(x, z)$ for all complex $z$. *O. H. Körner* (Marburg)

Citations: MR 1, 41d = N04-1; MR 16, 676a = N24-22.

## N36-47 (32# 7538)

**Rényi, Alfréd**

**A new proof of a theorem of Delange.**

*Publ. Math. Debrecen* **12** (1965), 323–329.

The author gives a new quite simple proof of the following theorem of H. Delange. Let $g(n)$ be a strongly multiplicative complex-valued number-theoretical function. Suppose that $|g(n)| \leqq 1$ for $n = 1, 2, \cdots$ and that the series $\sum_p (g(p) - 1)/p$ is convergent. Here $p$ runs over all primes. Then $\sum_{n=1}^{N} g(n)/N$ tends to the product $\prod_p (1 + (g(p) - 1)/p)$ as $N \to \infty$.

Delange has given two different proofs for this theorem. The first [Ann. Sci. École Norm. Sup. (3) **78** (1961), 273–304; MR **30** #72] is analytic and makes use of deep Tauberian theorems; the second [*Seminaire Delange-Pisot*, 1ère année: 1959/60, Secrétariat mathématique, Paris, 1962; MR **26** #3568; ibid., 2ième année: 1960/61; MR **26** #3569] is based on Selberg's sieve method. The author's proof is based on the inequality proved by the reviewer [*Probabilistic methods in the theory of numbers* (Russian), Lemma 3.1, Gosudarstv. Izdat. Političesk. i Naučn. Lit. Litovsk. SSR, Vilnius, 1962; MR **26** #3691; English translation, Amer. Math. Soc., Providence, R.I., 1964; MR **28** #3956] by generalizing an inequality of P. Turán [J. London Math. Soc. **11** (1936), 125–133].

*J. Kubilius* (Vilnius)

Citations: MR 26# 3568 = Z10-9; MR 26# 3569 = Z10-10; MR 26# 3691 = N60-38; MR 28# 3956 = N60-39; MR 30# 72 = N36-38.

Referred to in N36-55.

## N36-48 (33# 4038)

**Segal, S. L.**

**On prime-independent additive functions.**

*Arch. Math.* (*Basel*) **17** (1966), 329–332.

The author investigates arithmetic functions $h(n)$ with the following properties: $h(nm) = h(n) + h(m)$ for $(n, m) = 1$, and $h(p^k)$ depends only on $k$ for all primes $p$. Among other things, he proves in an elementary way the following theorem: If $h(p^m)=O(2^{m/2})$, then $\sum_{n\leq x} h(n)=h(p)x\log\log x+Ax+O(x/\log x)$, where $A$ is a constant.

*O. H. Körner* (Marburg)

## N36-49 (33# 6304)

**Grosswald, Emil**

**On some generalizations of theorems by Landau and Pólya.**

*Israel J. Math.* **3** (1965), 211–220.

From the author's summary: "If $F(s)$, the Mellin transform of $f(x)$ (real valued), satisfies certain regularity conditions and if its behaviour on the abscissa of convergence is known, then theorems of Landau and Pólya give information concerning sign changes of $f(x)$. In the present paper, corresponding conclusions are obtained when $F(s)$ does not satisfy the regularity conditions of the theorems of Landau and Pólya." *R. K. Saxena* (Jodhpur)

## N36-50 (33# 7740)

**Warlimont, Richard**

**Fatou-Rieszsche Sätze in der Theorie der starken Rieszschen Summierbarkeit von Dirichletreihen.**

*J. Reine Angew. Math.* **218** (1965), 129–142.

The series $\sum a_n$ is said to be strongly summable in the sense of Riesz, with type $\lambda$ and order $k$, and index $p$—symbolically, summable $[R, \lambda, k]^p$—to the sum $a$, if $\int_0^x |A_\lambda{}^k(\omega)-a\omega^k|^p\,d\omega=o(x^{kp+1})$ as $x\to\infty$, where $A_\lambda{}^k(\omega)$ is the classical Riesz sum of type $\lambda$ and order $k$, $p\geqq 1$, $kp+1>0$. $\sum a_n$ is said to be bounded $[R, \lambda, k]^p$ if $\int_0^x |A_\lambda{}^k(\omega)|^p\,d\omega=O(x^{kp+1})$ as $x\to\infty$. These are briefly written as $\sum a_n=a\ [R, \lambda, k]^p$; $\sum a_n=O(1)\ [R, \lambda, k]^p$. Corresponding to a Dirichlet series $\sum a_n e^{-\lambda_n s}$ there always exists an abscissa $c=c(k, p)$ $(-\infty\leqq c\leqq\infty)$ such that $\sum a_n e^{-\lambda_n s}=f(s)\ [R, \lambda, k]^p$ (Re $s>c$), whereas, for Re $s<c$, there is nowhere summability $[R, \lambda, k]^p$.

In the first part of this paper summability $[R, \lambda, k]^p$ of the Dirichlet series on the line Re $s=c$ is studied, and the following interesting analogue of the well-known theorem of Riesz on typical means is established. Theorem 1: Let $kp+1>0$, $c\geqq 0$, and $\int_0^x |A_\lambda{}^k(\omega)e^{-c\omega}|^p\,d\omega=o(x^{kp+1})$ or $O(x^{kp+1})$. Then

$$\sum a_n e^{-\lambda_n s} = f(s) = (s^{k+1}/\Gamma(k+1))\int_0^\infty A_\lambda{}^k(u)e^{-su}\,du$$

$[R, \lambda, k]^p$ for Re $s>c$. If the function $f(s)$, holomorphic for Re $s>c$, is also holomorphic at $s_0=c+it_0$, then $\sum a_n e^{-\lambda_n s_0}=f(s_0)$ $[R, \lambda, k]^p$ (case $o$), $\sum a_n e^{-\lambda_n s_0}=O(1)$ $[R, \lambda, k]^p$ (case $O$), (1) for $k=[k]$ and $c\geqq 0$, and (2) for any $k$ with $kp+1>1$, but $c>0$, and indeed uniformly in each bounded closed interval $t_1\leqq t_0\leqq t_2$, not containing the origin, in which the function is holomorphic. The supposition about holomorphy is essentially weakened in Theorem 2.

In the second part of the paper, the analogue of Theorem 1 for the summability $[R, l, k]^p$ of the Dirichlet series $\sum a_n l_n{}^{-s}$ is proved. *T. Pati* (Jabalpur)

Referred to in N36-51.

## N36-51 (36# 1402)

**Warlimont, Richard**

**Fatou-Rieszsche Sätze bei starker Rieszscher Summierbarkeit von Laplace-Integralen.**

*J. Reine Angew. Math.* **228** (1967), 139–143.

Continuation of the author's work on Fatou-Riesz theorems in the theory of strong Riesz summability of Dirichlet series [same J. **218** (1965), 129–142; MR **33** #7740]. Let $F(x)$ be measurable and $\int_0^x |F(u)|^2\,du=O(x)$. Then $f(s)=\int_0^\infty F(u)e^{-su}\,du$ exists and is holomorphic for $\Re(s)>0$. (i) If $f(s)$ is holomorphic at $s=it_0$ then (1) $y^{-1}\int_0^y |\int_0^x F(u)e^{-it_0u}\,du-f(it_0)|^2\,dx=O(1)$. (ii) If $f(s)$ is an entire function, then the preceding estimate holds for all $s=it$ and with $O(1)$ replaced by $o(1)$. Let $f(s)$ be meromorphic with only a finite number of poles where those on the imaginary axis are simple and have residues $r_k$ $(k=1, 2, \cdots, n)$. Then (1) holds for $s=it_0$, $t_0\neq t_k$ and with a right member $\sum_{k=1}^n |r_k|^2(t_0-t_k)^{-2}+o(1)$. Similar theorems hold for integrals of the form $F(s)=\int_1^\infty F(u)u^{-s-1}\,du$. In (1) we take integrals with lower limit 1 instead of 0 and replace $e^{-it_0u}$ by $u^{-it_0-1}$. An application is given to the Dirichlet divisor problem where $D(s)=\zeta^2(s)+\zeta'(s)-2C\zeta(s)=\sum_{n=1}^\infty a_n n^{-s}=s\int_1^\infty A(u)u^{-s-1}\,du$ and $a_n=d(n)-\log n-2C$. Here $A(u)=\Delta(u)+O(\log u)$, where $\Delta(u)$ is the remainder in the divisor problem. From H. Cramér's estimate $\int_1^x |\Delta(u)|^2\,du\sim Kx^{3/2}$ it follows that $B(u)=u^{-1/4}A(u)$ satisfies $x^{-1}\int_1^x |B(u)|^2\,du\sim 3K/2$ and

$$y^{-1}\int_1^y |\textstyle\sum_{n<x} a_n n^{-s}-D(s)|^2\,dx = 3K/2+o(1)$$

for all $s=\frac{1}{4}+it$. Here the remainder is $O(y^{-1/4+\varepsilon})$. See also the next review [#1403]. *E. Hille* (Eugene, Ore.)

Citations: MR 33# 7740 = N36-50.

## N36-52 (36# 1403)

**Warlimont, R.**

**Eine Bemerkung über Dirichletreihen mit Funktionalgleichung.**

*J. Reine Angew. Math.* **228** (1967), 144–158.

Let $Z(s)=\sum_{n=1}^\infty f(n)n^{-s}$, $Z_1(s)=\sum_{n=1}^\infty f_1(n)n^{-s}$ be two Dirichlet series related by the functional equation $Z(s)=C^{\vartheta s+\theta}\prod_{j=1}^M(\Gamma(\beta_j-b_js)/\Gamma(\delta_j+d_js))Z_1(\gamma-s)$. Estimates for $S_\kappa(x)=\sum_{1\leq n\leq x} f(n)(x-n)^\kappa$ were obtained by E. Landau [Nachr. Akad. Wiss. Göttingen Math.-Phys. Kl. II **1912**, 687–771] for $\kappa=0$ under restrictive assumptions on the constants entering in the $\Gamma$-quotient. Some of these restrictions were removed by H.-E. Richert [Acad. Serbe Sci. Publ. Inst. Math. **11** (1957), 73–124; MR **19**, 1162], who also considered $\kappa>0$ and managed to replace one of the error terms by an exponential sum. The present author now allows complex constants and improves the estimates of the error terms (details too complicated for a review). In particular, he brings in quadratic mean values of the type considered in the paper reviewed above [#1402]. Thus for $Z(s)=\zeta^2(s+\frac{1}{4}+it_0)$ he obtains

$$\int_1^y |\textstyle\sum_{n\leq x} a_n n^{-s_0}-f(s_0)|^2\,dx = y(4\pi^2)^{-1}\sum_{m=1}^\infty [d(m)]^2 m^{-3/2}+O(y^{3/4+\varepsilon}).$$

Here $a_n=d(n)-\log n-2C$, $f(s)=\zeta^2(s)+\zeta'(s)-2C\zeta(s)$, $s_0=\frac{1}{4}+it_0$. Similar results are obtained for the quadratic mean of the error terms in the Dirichlet divisor problem, in the lattice point problem for the circular disk and for the norm problem in algebraic fields of degree $n$.

*E. Hille* (Eugene, Ore.)

Citations: MR 19, 1162b = N36-13.

## N36-53 (34# 1283)

**Èl'natanov, B. A.**

**Asymptotic estimate of special arithmetic sums taken over numbers with "large" and "small" prime divisors. (Russian. Tajiki summary)**

*Dokl. Akad. Nauk Tadžik. SSR* **9** (1966), *no.* 8, 8–13.

Es seien $\beta_\nu$ reelle Zahlen, $0=\beta_0<\beta_1<\cdots<\beta_k=t$, und $M_\nu$ die Menge aller natürlichen Zahlen, für deren Primteiler $x^{\beta_{\nu-1}}<p\leqq x^{\beta_\nu}$ gilt; dann ist für $n\leqq x^t$ eindeutig $n=n_1\cdots n_k$ mit $n_\nu\in M_\nu$. Weiter werde für willkürliche multiplikative Funktionen $f_1(n), \cdots, f_k(n)$ gesetzt $f(n)=f_1(n_1)\cdots f_k(n_k)$. Verschiedene Autoren [B. V. Levin und A. S. Feĭnleĭb, Dokl. Akad. Nauk UzSSR **1965**, no. 11,

5–8; ibid. **1966**, no. 5, 3–7; B. M. Urazbaev, Izv. Akad. Nauk Kazah. SSR **1959**, no. 8 (12), 70–87; ibid. **1959**, no. 8 (12), 88–91; der Verfasser, Dokl. Akad. Nauk Tadžik. SSR **9** (1966), no. 5, 3–6] haben das asymptotische Verhalten von $\sum_{n\leq x^t} f(n)$ studiert. Verfasser betrachtet für eine additive Funktion $g(n)$ die Asymptotik von $\sum_{n\leq x^t} f(n)g(n)$. Der Wortlaut der Sätze ist zu umfangreich um hier wiedergegeben zu werden.

*H.-E. Richert* (Marburg)

[The first and third of the above references are 37 #5172 = N36-66 and 37 #5173 = N36-67.]

Citations: MR 37# 5172 = N36-66; MR 37# 5173 = N36-67.

Referred to in N36-71.

## N36-54 (34# 2536)

**Corrádi, K. A.; Kátai, I.**

**On the theory of multiplicative functions.**

*Ann. Univ. Sci. Budapest. Eötvös Sect. Math.* **9** (1966), 147–155.

The investigations in this paper are confined to the class $T$ of complex-valued multiplicative functions $\alpha(n)$ satisfying $|\alpha(n)|\leq 1$ for positive integers $n$. Let $P$ denote a given infinite set (not necessarily proper) of rational primes. Put $A_x=\sum_{p\leq x, p\in P} p^{-1}$, $M(x)=\sum_{n\leq x}\alpha(n)$, and suppose that $A_x\to\infty$ when $x\to\infty$. First, the authors derive a number of interesting results from the formula $M(x)A_x=\sum_{p\leq x, p\in P}\alpha(p)M(x/p)+O(xA_x^{1/2})$. The following theorem is typical. Let $g(n)$ be an arbitrary real-valued additive function, i.e., $g(mn)=g(m)+g(n)$ for $(m,n)=1$. Let $k$, $l$ and $m$ be given natural numbers with the property $(k,l)=(k,m)=1$. Suppose that the sequence $g(kn+l)$ $(n=1,2,\cdots)$ is uniformly distributed mod 1. Then the same is true for the sequence $g(kn+m)$ $(n=1,2,\cdots)$. Next, the authors suppose that $\alpha(n)$ is an arbitrary multiplicative function which takes the values $\pm 1$ only, and for which the series $\sum p^{-1}$ diverges when $p$ runs over the primes satisfying $\alpha(p)=-1$. P. Erdős [Magyar Tud. Akad. Mat. Kutató Int. Közl. **6** (1961), 221–254; MR **31** #2106] conjectured that for such a function $M(x)=o(x)$ holds. The authors make what appears to be a step toward settling this conjecture. Finally, they establish the following extension of a theorem of H. Delange [Ann. Sci. École Norm. Sup. (3) **78** (1961), 1–29; MR **30** #71]. Let $\alpha(n)$ be any multiplicative function belonging to $T$. Suppose that $\sum_{p\leq x}|\alpha(p)-\rho|p^{-1}=o(\log_2 x)$, where $|\rho|\leq 1$, $\rho\neq 1$. Then $M(x)=o(x)$.

*A. L. Whiteman* (Los Angeles, Calif.)

Citations: MR 30# 71 = N36-37; MR 31# 2106 = Z05-10.

## N36-55 (34# 2537)

**Erdős, Paul; Rényi, A.**

**On the mean value of nonnegative multiplicative number-theoretical functions.**

*Michigan Math. J.* **12** (1965), 321–338.

If $g$ is an arithmetic function (a complex-valued function on the natural numbers) then $g$ is said to have a mean value if the limit $M(g)=\lim_{N\to\infty} N^{-1}\sum_{n=1}^{N} g(n)$ exists. Many questions in number theory hinge on the existence and magnitude of mean values; they have therefore been the object of many investigations. The known results generally relate the existence of $M(g)$ to the convergence of certain infinite series, notably the series (0.2) $\sum_p (g(p)-1)/p$, where the use of $p$ as an index, here and elsewhere, indicates that the process involved is carried out over primes only. The authors prove several results of this type, most of them involving strongly multiplicative functions. (As usual, an arithmetic function $g$ is multiplicative if $g(mn)=g(m)g(n)$ for all pairs $m$, $n$ of relatively prime integers; a multiplicative function $g$ is strongly multiplicative if $g(p^k)=g(p)$ for all primes $p$ and all positive integers $k$.) Probably the most significant of these results is contained in Theorem 7, which can be stated as follows. Let $g$ be a nonnegative strongly multiplicative function for which (0.2) converges, and such that, for every $\varepsilon>0$, there exist $\delta>0$ and $N>0$ such that (0.6) $\sum_{n\leq p\leq n(1+\varepsilon)} p^{-1}g(p)\log p\geqq\delta$ for all $n\geqq N$. Then $M(g)$ exists, and is positive or 0 according as the series (0.5) $\sum_p g^2(p)/p^2$ converges or diverges; in either case, $M(g)$ is given by (4.3) $M(g)=\lim_{x\to\infty}\prod_{p\leq x}(1+(g(p)-1)/p)$. The proof of this result involves the use of an analytic method of H. Delange [Ann. Sci. École Norm. Sup. (3) **78** (1961), 273–304; MR **30** #72]. The second author [Publ. Math. Debrecen **12** (1965), 323–329; MR **32** #7538] has given a much simpler proof of Delange's theorem, but Delange's original method is still required for the theorems of this paper. The authors give examples, due to E. Wirsing, to show that conditions like (0.6) are necessary in Theorem 7 and elsewhere.

The authors show that an earlier theorem of the first author [Bull. Amer. Math. Soc. **53** (1947), 536–544; MR **9**, 12] follows from their present results, and on the basis of these they make the following conjecture: For any non-negative multiplicative function $g$, define $E(p)=1+\sum_{k=1}^{\infty}(g(p^k)-g(p^{k-1}))/p^k$. Then (admitting $+\infty$ as a possible value) $M(g)$ exists if and only if $\lim_{x\to\infty}\prod_{p<x}E(p)$ exists; and whenever they exist, the mean value and the above limit are equal.

*A. Sklar* (Chicago, Ill.)

Citations: MR 30# 72 = N36-38; MR 32# 7538 = N36-47.

## N36-56 (34# 2544)

**Segal, S. L.**

**A note on Dirichlet convolutions.**

*Canad. Math. Bull.* **9** (1966), 457–462.

The following results are proved. Theorem 1: If $\sum_{n=1}^{\infty} n^{-1}\sum_{d|n} f(d)$ converges absolutely to $A$ and $\lim_{n\to\infty} h(n)=L$, $L$ finite, then $\sum_{n=1}^{\infty} n^{-1}\sum_{d|n} f(d)h(n/d)=AL$. Theorem 2: Define $g(n)$ by means of $\sum_{n=1}^{\infty} g(n)n^{-s}=-\zeta'(s)/\zeta^3(s)$. Assume there exists a fixed $\varepsilon>0$ such that $\zeta(s)\neq 0$ for $1-\varepsilon\leqq\sigma\leqq 1$. If $\lim_{n\to\infty} h(n)=L$, $L$ finite, then $\sum_{n=1}^{\infty} n^{-1}\sum_{d|n} g(d)h(n/d)=L$, $\sum_{n=1}^{\infty} n^{-1}\sum_{d|n} g(d)=1$, but convergence is not absolute. The author notes that these results can be reformulated in the following way. If $\sum_{n=1}^{\infty} n^{-1}|\sum_{d|n} f(d)|$ converges then

$$\sup_r \sum_{n\leq r} n^{-1}|\sum_{m\leq r/n} f(m)/m|<\infty,$$

but not conversely.

*L. Carlitz* (Durham, N.C.)

Referred to in N36-74.

## N36-57 (34# 4219)

**Duncan, R. L.**

**A general class of arithmetical functions.**

*Duke Math. J.* **33** (1966), 507–510.

In this paper the author generalizes some previous results of his, concerning certain classes of arithmetic functions [Amer. Math. Monthly **69** (1962), 34–36; MR **24** #A1864; ibid. **72** (1965), 882–884; MR **32** #1150]. Let $g(n)$ be an arithmetic function, $0=g(0)\leqq g(1)\leqq g(2)\leqq\cdots$, and define $a(1)=0$, $a(n)=\sum_i g(\alpha_i)$, where the $\alpha_i$ are the exponents in the canonical representation of $n$, and $b(n)=\sum_{d|n}\{g(d)-g(d-1)\}\,d\mu(n/d)$. The two main results of the paper are based on the hypothesis that $g(n)=o(n^{-\lambda}2^n)$, where $\lambda>1$, and can be described as follows. (1) An asymptotic expression is given for $\sum_{n\leq x} a(n)$ whose two principal terms are

$g(1)x \log\log x + Bx$, where $B$ is a constant that depends only on the function $g$. (2) For $s>1$, $\sum_n a(n)n^{-s} = \zeta(s)\sum_n b(n)n^{-1}\log\zeta(ns)$, with both series converging absolutely. Several examples are given; for instance, by specializing $g(n)=1$ or $n$, one obtains $a(n)=\omega(n)$ or $\Omega(n)$, respectively, and $b(n)=\mu(n)$ or $\phi(n)$, respectively. {It should be noted that throughout pages 507 and 508, all the $o$'s should be replaced by $O$'s.}

*F. Herzog* (E. Lansing, Mich.)

Citations: MR 24# A1864 = N52-23; MR 32# 1150 = A34-30.

**N36-58** **(34# 5774)**

**Dixon, R. D.**

**An analytic continuation for certain functions defined by Dirichlet series.**

*Illinois J. Math.* **11** (1967), 13–20.

Author's introduction: "The problem which motivated this research is that of obtaining $\Omega$ results of the type obtained by G. H. Hardy [Proc. London Math. Soc. (2) **15** (1916), 1–25] and E. Landau [Nachr. Akad. Wiss. Göttingen Math.-Phys. Kl. II **1924**, 137–150 (1925)]. P. Erdős and W. Fuchs [J. London Math. Soc. **31** (1956), 67–73; MR **17**, 586] and later P. Bateman, E. Kohlbecker and J. Tull [Proc. Amer. Math. Soc. **14** (1963), 278–284; MR **26** #2417] have generalized the classical $\Omega$ result for the circle problem. H.-E. Richert [J. Reine Angew. Math. **206** (1961), 31–38; MR **23** #A3723] showed that the classical $\Omega$ results for the divisor problems are also indicative of results in a class of problems involving the multiplication of Dirichlet series. In particular, his results concerned series whose generating functions have only finitely many poles in a strip to the left of the region of convergence. In this paper we present some preliminary work necessary to extend his results to a class of Dirichlet series and Laplace Transforms whose generating functions are analytic in a strip to the left of the region of convergence with the possible exception of a bounded region. This class of functions is interesting because of the unity of exposition it allows and because there are available in this class examples which show why certain restrictions imposed by Richert are necessary if a proof is to be given along his lines."

*A. L. Whiteman* (Los Angeles, Calif.)

Citations: MR 17, 586d = B16-9; MR 23# A3723 = N36-26; MR 26# 2417 = B16-18.

**N36-59** **(35# 139)**

**Halász, G.**

**A note on the distribution of multiplicative number-theoretical functions.**

*Studia Sci. Math. Hungar.* **1** (1966), 113–117.

Let $f$ be a complex-valued multiplicative function. It is assumed that $\sum_p (p^{-2}|f(p^2)| + p^{-3}|f(p^3)| + \cdots) < \infty$, and that there exists a complex constant $c$ such that $\operatorname{Re} c < 0$, $|f(p)-c| \leqq 1$ for all $c$, $\sum_p p^{-1}(1-|f(p)-c|) = +\infty$. Comparing $\sum f(n)n^{-s}$ with $(\zeta(s))^c$, the author proves the existence of $\lim_{N\to\infty} N^{-1}\sum_{n\leqq N} f(n)$.

{Reviewer's remark: For the special case that $|f(n)| \leqq 1$ for all $n$, stronger results have recently been obtained by E. Wirsing.} *N. G. de Bruijn* (Eindhoven)

Referred to in N36-81.

**N36-60** **(35# 2838)**

**Corrádi, K. A.; Kátai, I.**

**On multiplicative characters.**

*Acta Sci. Math. (Szeged)* **28** (1967), 71–76.

Let $f(n)$ be a multiplicative number-theoretic function, so that $f(mn)=f(m)f(n)$ whenever $(m,n)=1$. A theorem of H. Delange [Ann. Sci. École Norm. Sup. (3) **78** (1961), 1–29; MR **30** #71] states that a sufficient condition for the relation $\sum_{n\leqq x} f(n) = o(x)$ to hold is given by (*) $|f(n)| \leqq 1$ $(n=1,2,\cdots)$ together with $\sum_p (1-\operatorname{Re} f(p))/p = +\infty$. It is natural to ask for a condition which turns out to be besides (*) sufficient for the relation $M(x;k,l) = \sum_{n\leqq x;\, n\equiv l(\mathrm{mod}\, k)} f(n) = o(x)$ to hold. The present authors obtain the following theorem. Let $f(n)$ be an arbitrary but fixed multiplicative function satisfying (*). Let $k$ and $l$ be given natural numbers with $(k,l)=1$. Suppose that $f(p)=\alpha$ if $p\equiv l \pmod k$ and $p$ is a prime. Suppose also that the value of $\alpha$ is different from all the values $\chi(l)$ taken by any character $\chi \bmod k$. Then $M(x;k,m)=o(x)$ holds for every $m$ satisfying $(m,k)=1$. The prime number theorem for arithmetic progressions and P. Turán's generalization [J. London Math. Soc. **11** (1936), 125–133] of a theorem of Hardy and Ramanujan are used in the course of the proof.

*A. L. Whiteman* (Princeton, N.J.)

Citations: MR 30# 71 = N36-37.

**N36-61** **(35# 2840)**

**Delange, Hubert**

**A theorem on multiplicative arithmetic functions.**

*Proc. Amer. Math. Soc.* **18** (1967), 743–749.

The author proves by quite elementary means the following theorem. Let $f$ be a bounded multiplicative arithmetic function. Suppose that, as $x$ tends to infinity, $\sum_{p\leqq x} f(p)\log p = rx + O(xL(x))$, where $r$ is a constant $\neq 1$ and $L$ is a positive function, defined for $x\geqq 1$, nonincreasing, and such that $L(x)=o(1)$. Then, as $x$ tends to infinity, $x^{-1}\sum_{n\leqq x} f(n) = O(L^*(x)/\log x)$ if $r=0$ or $s<0$, and $= O((\log x)^{s-1}\int_2^x L^*(t)/(t\log^{s+1} t)\,dt)$ otherwise, where $s$ denotes the real part of $r$ and $L^*(x) = \int_1^x L(t)/t\,dt$. He obtained a less precise version of this theorem in a previous paper [Ann. Sci. École Norm. Sup. (3) **78** (1961), 1–29; MR **30** #71] with the aid of a classical Tauberian theorem. *O. H. Körner* (Marburg)

Citations: MR 30# 71 = N36-37.

Referred to in Z10-35.

**N36-62** **(36# 123)**

**Levin, B. V.; Faĭnleĭb, A. S.**

**On a method of summation of multiplicative functions. (Russian)**

*Izv. Akad. Nauk SSSR Ser. Mat.* **31** (1967), 697–710.

The principal result of this paper is a proof of the following theorem. Let $f(n)$ be a complex multiplicative function for which $\sum_{p\leqq x} f(p) \sim \tau x/\log x$, $\sum_{p\leqq x}|f(p)| = O(x/\log x)$, and $f(p^r) = O((2p)^{\gamma r})$ $(0<\gamma<\frac{1}{2},\ r\geqq 2)$, where $p$ denotes a prime. Then, as $x\to\infty$, $\sum_{n\leqq x} f(n) = (e^{-C\tau}/\Gamma(\tau))(x/\log x)\prod_f(x) + o((x/\log x)\prod_{|f|}(x))$, where $C$ is Euler's constant and $\prod_f(x) = \prod_{p\leqq x}\{1+\sum_{r=1}^{\infty} f(p^r)/p^r\}$. A similar result has been obtained under somewhat weaker conditions by E. Wirsing [Math. Ann. **143** (1961), 75–102; MR **24** #A1241]. The proof expresses the integers $n$ summed over in the form $n=n_1n_2$, where the prime divisors of $n_1$ and $n_2$ are, respectively, less than and greater than a suitably chosen number $y$. Estimates for sums of the type $\sum_{n_1\leqq x} f(n_1)/n_1$ and $\sum_{n_2\leqq x} f(n_2)$ are obtained and combined to prove the theorem. An extension to sums of the type $\sum_{n\leqq x} f(n_1)g(n_2)$ is stated. *R. A. Rankin* (Glasgow)

Citations: MR 24# A1241 = N36-30.

Referred to in N36-72.

**N36-63** **(36# 6366)**

**Wirsing, E.**

**Das asymptotische Verhalten von Summen über multiplikative Funktionen. II.**

*Acta Math. Acad. Sci. Hungar.* **18** (1967), 411–467.

In this substantial memoir the author obtains asymptotic formulae for averages of multiplicative arithmetic functions of a very general kind. In doing so he extends both his own earlier work on the same theme [Math. Ann. **143** (1961), 75–102; MR **24** #A1241; J. Reine Angew. Math. **214/215** (1964), 1–18; MR **29** #3457] and several theorems of H. Delange [Ann. Sci. École Norm. Sup. (3) **78** (1961), 1–29; MR **30** #71; ibid. (3) **78** (1961), 273–304; MR **30** #72; Scripta Math. **26** (1963), 121–141; MR **30** #73]. For example, the author settles, as a special case of his Satz 1.2.2, the following difficult old problem of Wintner (see A. Wintner, *The theory of measure in arithmetical semigroups* [Baltimore, Md., 1944; MR **7**, 367], which contains a fallacious proof of the problem): If $\lambda$ is a multiplicative arithmetic function which assumes only the values $\pm 1$, then

$$\lim_{x\to\infty} x^{-1}\sum_{n\leq x}\lambda(n) = \lim_{x\to\infty}\prod_{p\leq x}(1-1/p)(1+\lambda(p)/p+\lambda(p^2)/p^2+\cdots).$$

It is not possible in a brief review to describe all the results contained in the paper. However, the following theorems indicate the power and scope of the author's method. Satz 1.1: Let $\lambda$ be a non-negative multiplicative arithmetic function satisfying (1) $\sum_{p\leq x}(\log p/p)\lambda(p)\sim\tau\log x$ $(\tau>0)$, (2) $\lambda(p)\ll 1$, (3) $\sum_{p,\nu\geq 2}\lambda(p^\nu)p^{-\nu}<\infty$, and, if $\tau\leq 1$, (4) $\sum_{p,\nu\geq 2,p^\nu\leq x}\lambda(p^\nu)\ll x/\log x$. Then $\sum_{n\leq x}\lambda(n)\sim (e^{-c\tau}/\Gamma(\tau))(x/\log x)\prod_{p\leq x}\{1+\lambda(p)/p+\lambda(p^2)/p^2+\cdots\}$, where $c$ is Euler's constant. Satz 1.1.1: The same conclusion holds for a complex-valued multiplicative $\lambda$ provided (1) holds, (2), (3) and (4) (in case $\tau\leq 1$) hold with $|\lambda|$ in place of $\lambda$, and if, in addition, also (5) $\sum_p p^{-1}\{|\lambda(p)|-\operatorname{Re}\lambda(p)\}<\infty$. Satz 1.2.2: If $\lambda$ is as in Satz 1.1 and $\lambda^*$ is real, multiplicative and satisfies $|\lambda^*|\leq\lambda$, then

$$\lim_{x\to\infty}\left(\sum_{n\leq x}\lambda^*(n)\right)\left(\sum_{n\leq x}\lambda(n)\right)^{-1} = \prod_p\left(\sum_{\nu=0}^\infty\lambda^*(p^\nu)/p^\nu\right)\left(\sum_{\nu=0}^\infty\lambda(p^\nu)/p^\nu\right)^{-1}.$$

There are several other theorems of this order of generality about complex-valued multiplicative functions; an account of applications and further extensions; a section on outstanding problems; and a discussion showing that the principal results are, or come close to being, best possible.

In devising his method the author has built on his own earlier work and on his elementary proof of the prime number theorem with an error term. The general problem is translated into questions concerning the distribution of values of certain convolution integrals, and the solution, using Tauberian methods, of some approximate integral equations. Let $\xi=\log x$, and $f(\xi)=e^{-\xi}\sum_{n\leq x}\lambda(n)$. One can show that $\xi f(\xi)=\int_0^\xi f(\xi-\eta)\,dk(\eta)+$error term, where $k(\xi)=\sum_{p\leq x}(\log p/p)\lambda(p)\sim\tau\xi$. Approximating to the step function $k$ by a piecewise linear function $h$, and writing $h'=\tau g$, give $\xi f(\xi)=\tau\int_0^\xi f(\xi-\eta)g(\eta)\,d\eta+$error term, subject to $\int_0^\xi g(\eta)\,d\eta\sim\xi$, $g(\xi)\ll 1$, and subject also to the further condition $\int_0^\xi f(\eta)\,d\eta\sim\xi^\tau L(\xi)$, where $L$ is a certain slowly oscillating function, which derives from known information about $\sum_{n\leq x}\lambda(n)/n$. To deduce from these facts that $f(\xi)\sim\tau\xi^{\tau-1}L(\xi)$ represents the major difficulty the author had to overcome, and the method of solution (in Sections 2 and 3) is a formidable achievement, of quite independent interest also in analysis (see, for example, Satz 1.3). *H. Halberstam* (Nottingham)

Citations: MR 7, 367a = Z02-5; MR 24# A1241 = N36-30; MR 29# 3457 = N20-56; MR 30# 71 = N36-37; MR 30# 72 = N36-38; MR 30# 73 = N36-39.

Referred to in B48-21, N36-68, N36-69, N36-82, N36-83.

**N36-64** **(37# 4038)**

**Faĭnleĭb, A. S.**

**Some asymptotic formulas for sums of multiplicative functions and their applications.** (Russian. Lithuanian and English summaries)

*Litovsk. Mat. Sb.* **7** (1967), 535–546 (1968).

The author finds asymptotical formulas for the sums of the form $\sum_{n\leq x}f(n)$ by using other functions with known behaviour. *T. T. Tonkov* (Leningrad)

Referred to in N36-85.

**N36-65** **(37# 5167)**

**Steinig, John**

**Sur les changements de signe du reste dans l'évaluation asymptotique de certaines fonctions arithmétiques.**

*C. R. Acad. Sci. Paris Sér. A-B* **263** (1966), A905–A906.

The author announces the following result, which he obtained by a method of G. Pólya [Nachr. Gesell. Wiss. Göttingen Math.-Phys. Kl. (1930), 19–27] from an identity of K. Chandrasekharan and R. Narasimhan [Acta Arith. **6** (1960/61), 487–503; MR **23** #A3719]: Let $f(s)=\sum a_n e^{-l_n s}$ and $p(s)=\sum b_n e^{-m_n s}$ be functions expressed by Dirichlet series satisfying a functional equation of the type $(2\pi)^{-s}\times\Gamma(s)f(s)=(2\pi)^{s-d}\Gamma(d-s)p(d-s)$ for complex $s$ and some real $d$. For $r\geq 0$, $x>0$, put $B_m{}^r(x)\Gamma(r+1)=\sum_{m_n\leq x}b_n(x-m_n)^r$, where the last term of the sum is to be multiplied by $\frac{1}{2}$ if $r=0$ and $x=m_n$ for some $n$. Furthermore, put $Q_r(x)=(1/2\pi i)\int\Gamma(s)p(s)/\Gamma(s+r+1)x^{s+r}\,ds$, where the contour of integration encloses the singularities of the integrand. If $r+d+\frac{1}{2}$ is an integer and if $W(x)$ denotes the number of changes of sign of $B_m{}^r(u)-Q_r(u)$ in the interval $0<u\leq x$, then $\limsup_{x\to\infty}W(x)/\sqrt{x}>0$. Interesting applications of this result are pointed out. *O. H. Körner* (Marburg)

Citations: MR 23# A3719 = N36-25.

**N36-66** **(37# 5172)**

**Levin, B. V.; Faĭnleĭb, A. S.**

**The asymptotic behavior of sums of multiplicative functions.** (Russian)

*Dokl. Akad. Nauk UzSSR* **1965**, *no.* 11, 5–8.

The authors introduce an analogue of von Mangoldt's function, namely, the function $\Lambda_f(n)$ defined by $f(n)\times\log n=\sum_{d\mid n}f(d)\Lambda_f(n/d)$, where $f(n)$ is a multiplicative function. They use this function to obtain information about the asymptotic behavior of the function $\sum_{n\leq x}f(n)$, given information about the behavior of $f(n)$ at powers of the primes. Their methods and results are described in greater detail in their survey article [#5174 below]. (From the review of O. Fomenko in RŽMat **1966** #5 A81.)

Referred to in N36-53, N36-71.

**N36-67** **(37# 5173)**

**Èl'natanov, B. A.**

**Asymptotic estimate of special arithmetic sums.** (Russian. Tajiki summary)

*Dokl. Akad. Nauk Tadžik. SSR* **9** (1966), *no.* 5, 3–6.

Zu einer multiplikativen zahlentheoretischen Funktion $f(n)$ bilde man (in Verallgemeinerung der von Mangoldtschen Funktion $\Lambda(n)$) die Funktion $\Lambda_f(n)$, definiert durch $f(n)\log n=\sum_{d\mid n}f(d)\Lambda_f(n/d)$. Dann läßt sich, wie B. V. Levin und A. S. Faĭnleĭb [siehe #5172 oben] systematisch untersucht haben, beispielsweise unter der Voraussetzung einer asymptotischen Entwicklung für $\sum_{n\leq x}\Lambda_f(n)/n$ eine solche für $\sum_{n\leq x}f(n)$ herleiten. Verfasser verallgemeinert dieses Problem, indem er zu einer additiven Funktion $g(n)$ eine Funktion $\Lambda_f{}^{(g)}(n)$ durch

$f(n)g(n) = \sum_{d|n} f(d)\Lambda_f^{(g)}(n/d)$ erklärt und dann unter weiteren entsprechenden Voraussetzungen über $\Lambda_f^{(g)}(n)$ eine asymptotische Entwicklung für $\sum_{n\le x} f(n)g(n)$ herleitet. Eine umfassende Behandlung ähnlicher Fragen mit ausführlichen Literaturangaben findet sich in der neueren Arbeit von B. V. Levin und A. S. Faĭnleĭb [#5174 unten].

*H.-E. Richert* (Marburg)

Referred to in N36-53.

## N36-68 (37# 5174)

**Levin, B. V.; Faĭnleĭb, A. S.**

**Application of certain integral equations to questions of the theory of numbers.** **(Russian)**

*Uspehi Mat. Nauk* **22** (1967), *no.* 3 (135), 119–197.

The paper deals with the asymptotic evaluation of sums $\sum_{n\le x} f(n)$, where $f(n)$ is a multiplicative function, under conditions involving the values $f(p)$, where $p$ runs over primes. Results of this type were obtained previously by E. Wirsing [Math. Ann. **143** (1961), 75–102; MR **24** #A1241].

{Reviewer's remark: Independently of the authors and at about the same time Wirsing developed his results much further in another paper in Acta Math. Acad. Sci. Hungar. **18** (1967), 411–467 [MR **36** #6366] in a direction similar to the authors'.} Instead of the usual analytic method, the authors use a method consisting of reducing the problem in question to the study of the asymptotic behaviour of the solution $z(t)$ of the integral equation $t\cdot z(t) = \int_0^t K(t-u)z(u)\,du$, where $K(t)$ is a given step function. A large number of theorems is proved, the formulation of which is too complicated to be stated here in detail. We mention only one of the results (Theorem 2.3.2). For a certain class of additive number theoretical functions, it is shown that their distribution on the set $\{1, 2, \cdots, n\}$, suitably normalized, differs from the standard normal distribution by an error term having order of magnitude $(\log\log n)^{-1/2}$. This result generalizes a theorem of the reviewer and P. Turán [Acta Arith. **4** (1958), 71–84; MR **20** #3112]. Under stronger restrictions the authors give (Theorem 2.3.3) an asymptotic expansion in powers of $(\log\log n)^{-1/2}$ for the remainder term in the above mentioned theorem, thereby generalizing a result of J. Kubilius [*Probabilistic methods in the theory of numbers* (Russian), Gosudarstv. Izdat. Politič. Naučn. Lit. Litovsk. SSR, Vilnius, 1959; MR **23** #A134; second enlarged edition, 1962; MR **26** #3691; English translation, Amer. Math. Soc., Providence, R.I., 1964; MR **28** #3956].

{This article has appeared in English translation [Russian Math. Survey **22** (1967), no. 3, 119–204].}

*A. Rényi* (Budapest)

Citations: MR 20# 3112 = N60-31; MR 23# A134 = N60-37; MR 24# A1241 = N36-30; MR 26# 3691 = N60-38; MR 28# 3956 = N60-39; MR 36# 6366 = N36-63.

Referred to in M55-57.

## N36-69 (37# 6254)

**Halász, G.**

**Über die Mittelwerte multiplikativer zahlentheoretischer Funktionen.**

*Acta Math. Acad. Sci. Hungar.* **19** (1968), 365–403.

Eine zahlentheoretische Funktion $f(n)$ heisst multiplikativ, wenn aus $(a, b) = 1$ stets $f(ab) = f(a)f(b)$ folgt. Verfasser betrachtet die Summen $M(x) = \sum_{n\le x}^{\infty} f(n)$ und fragt nach asymptotischen Formeln für $M(x)$. Im Gegensatz zu einer Arbeit von E. Wirsing [dieselben Acta **18** (1967), 411–467; MR **36** #6366] werden hier funktionentheoretische Hilfsmittel verwendet, die die Beziehungen

$$F(s) = \sum_{n=1}^{\infty} f(n)/n^s = \prod_p (1 + f(p)/p^s + f(p^2)/p^{2s} + \cdots)$$

($p$ = Primzahl), $s = \sigma + it$ ausnützen. Von den Ergebnissen seien u.a. erwähnt Satz 2 (Vermutung von E. Wirsing): Ist $f(n)$ eine beliebige multiplikative Funktion mit $|f(n)| \le 1$, so existieren eine komplexe Konstante $C_0$, eine reelle Konstante $a_0$ und eine Funktion $L(n)$ mit den Eigenschaften $|L(n)| = 1$, $L(n_1)/L(n) \to 1$ gleichmäßig für $n \to \infty$, $n \le n_1 \le 2n$, so daß $M(x) = C_0 L(\log x) x^{1+ia_0} + o(x)$. Satz 3: Unter den Voraussetzungen (a) $f(n)$ multiplikativ, (b) $f(p) = O(1)$ oder nur $\sum_p (|f(p)|^{1+\delta}/p^\sigma) \log p = O(1/(\sigma-1))$ mit einem $\delta > 0$, (c) $\sum_{p,k;k\ge 2} f(p^k)/p^k < +\infty$, (d) keiner der Faktoren von $F(s)1 + f(p)/p^s + \cdots$ verschwindet auf der Geraden $\sigma = 1$, (e) $F(s) = C/(s-1) + o(|s|/(\sigma-1))$ gleichmäßig für $\mathrm{Re}\, s = \sigma$, folgt $M(x) = Cx + o(x)$.

*H. J. Kanold* (Braunschweig)

Citations: MR 36# 6366 = N36-63.

Referred to in M40-48, N36-82, N36-87.

## N36-70 (38# 124)

**Schwarz, Wolfgang**

**Schwache asymptotische Eigenschaften schnell wachsender multiplikativer zahlentheoretischer Funktionen.**

*Monatsh. Math.* **72** (1968), 355–367.

Let $\lambda$ be a non-negative multiplicative arithmetic function, with $\sum \lambda^2(p)p^{-2}$ convergent and the values $\lambda(p^2)$, $\lambda(p^3)$, $\cdots$ zero or "small". The problem considered is that of deducing, from asymptotic information about the sum $t(x) = \sum_{p<x} \lambda(p) \log p \cdot p^{-1}$, asymptotic information about the sum $\Lambda(x) = \sum_{n<x} \lambda(n)n^{-1}$. This problem was introduced and discussed by E. Wirsing [Math. Ann. **143** (1961), 75–102; MR **24** #A1241], and some results of this kind have been obtained previously by the author [J. Reine Angew. Math. **219** (1965), 67–96; MR **32** #2387]. The present paper is devoted to establishing three further theorems of this type. The proofs given are non-elementary and are based on a generalized form of a classical Tauberian theorem of Hardy and Ramanujan. Two of the theorems are reversible, with the specified conditions on $t(x)$ shown to be necessary as well as sufficient for the stated asymptotic behavior of $\Lambda(x)$.

*D. Rearick* (Boulder, Colo.)

Citations: MR 24# A1241 = N36-30; MR 32# 2387 = N36-43.

## N36-71 (38# 5729)

**Èl'natanov, B. A.**

**Once again on estimates of special arithmetic sums.** **(Russian. Tajiki summary)**

*Dokl. Akad. Nauk Tadžik. SSR* **11** (1968), *no.* 5, 13–15.

In an earlier paper [same Dokl. **9** (1966), no. 8, 8–13; MR **34** #1283] the author investigated under assumptions introduced by B. V. Levin and A. S. Faĭnleĭb [Dokl. Akad. Nauk UzSSR **1965**, no. 11, 5–8; MR **37** #5172] the behavior of $\sum_{n\le x} f(n)g(n)$, where $f(n)$ and $g(n)$ are multiplicative and additive functions, respectively. In the present note these investigations are extended to the forms $\sum_{n\le x} f(n)\binom{g(n)}{k}$ and $\sum_{n\le x} f(n)g^k(n)$, where $k$ is a natural number. The idea of the proof consists of studying the multiplicative function $f(n)z^{g(n)}$.

*H.-E. Richert* (Marburg)

Citations: MR 34# 1283 = N36-53; MR 37# 5172 = N36-66.

## N36-72 (39# 164)

**Baĭbulatov, R. S.**

**Distribution of values of certain classes of additive arithmetic functions in algebraic number fields.** **(Russian)**

*Mat. Zametki* **4** (1968), 63–73.

The author generalizes to the set of Hecke's ideal numbers

a theorem of B. V. Levin and A. S. Faĭnleĭb [Izv. Akad. Nauk SSSR Ser. Mat. **31** (1967), 697–710; MR **36** #123] concerning the asymptotic behavior of sums of the form $\sum_a f(a_1)g(a_2)$, where $a = a_1 a_2$ is the decomposition of $a$ into factors, one of which has all its prime divisors less than $y$, and the other larger than $y$, $f(x)$ and $g(x)$ are multiplicative functions satisfying some conditions, which are too long to be quoted here, and $y$ depends on a parameter. As a corollary he obtains an analogue of the theorem of P. Erdős and A. Wintner [Amer. J. Math. **61** (1939), 713–721; MR **1**, 40]. *W. Narkiewicz* (Wrocław)

Citations: MR 1, 40c = N60-1; MR 36# 123 = N36-62.

## N36-73 (39# 6843)

**Corrádi, C. A. [Corrádi, K. A.]; Kátai, I.**

**Some problems concerning the convolutions of number-theoretical functions.**

*Arch. Math.* (*Basel*) **20** (1969), 24–29.

For a function $f$ defined on the set of natural members, put $h(n) = \sum_{\nu=1}^{n-1} f(\nu)f(n-\nu)$. Let $A$ be the class of functions $f$ taking the values $+1$ and $-1$ only. The general aim of the paper is to find conditions, for $f \in A$, under which $h(n)$ will be $o(n)$ as $n \to \infty$.

Put $C(f) = \sum_{f(p)=-1} 1/p$, $p$ running through the primes. It is proved that if $f \in A$ and is multiplicative, then $h(n) = o(n)$ will imply that $C(f) = \infty$. The converse of this is false. Theorem 1 says that if $f \in A$ and is absolutely multiplicative, and $C(f) < \infty$, then $\liminf_n n^{-1} \cdot h(n) \geqq -1/3$. Theorem 3 asserts that if $f \in A$, $\limsup_n n^{-1/2}|h(n)| \geqq 1$. The author conjectures that if $f \in A$, then

$$\limsup_n n^{-1/2}|h(n)| = \infty.$$

*E. M. Paul* (Calcutta)

## N36-74 (40# 4220)

**Ayoub, R.; Chowla, S.**

**On a problem in elementary number theory.**

*Norske Vid. Selsk. Forh.* (*Trondheim*) **42** (1969), 74–75.

The authors prove that the function $g(n)$ defined by $\sum_1^\infty n^{-s}g(n) = \zeta'(s)/\zeta^3(s)$, $s > 1$, satisfies the condition $\sum_1^x n^{-1}g(n) = O(\log^{-q} x)$ for arbitrary $q > 1$. This is a stronger result than the one needed to answer a question raised by S. L. Segal [Canad. Math. Bull. **9** (1966), 457–462; MR **34** #2544].

Citations: MR 34# 2544 = N36-56.

## N36-75 (40# 4224)

**Smith, R. A.**

**An error term of Ramanujan.**

*J. Number Theory* **2** (1970), 91–96.

An old result of Ramanujan states that $\sum_{n \leq x} \sigma^2(n) = 5\zeta(3)x^3/6 + E(x)$, where $\sigma(n)$ is the sum of the divisors of $n$, $\zeta(s)$ is the Riemann zeta function, and $E(x) = O(x^2 \log^2 x)$. The author improves the error term to $O(x^2 \log^{5/3} x)$. He first proves the following lemma referring to an arbitrary arithmetical function $h(n)$. Let $H(x) = \sum_{n \leq x} h(n)$, $nb(n) = \sum_{d|n} h(d)$, $B(x) = \sum_{n \leq x} b(n)[x/n]$. If $\sum_{n \leq x} |h(n)| = O(x)$ and $H(x) = hx + O(x^\delta)$, $0 < \delta < 1$, then $B(x) = \zeta(2)Hx - (h \log^2 x)/4 - P(x) + O(\log x)$, where $H = \sum_1^\infty h(n)n^{-2}$, $P(x) = \sum_{n \leq x} n^{-1}h(n)\rho(x/n)$, and $\rho(x) = \sum_{n \leq x} n^{-1}(x/n - [x/n] - \frac{1}{2})$. By specializing $h(n)$ and using the estimate $\rho(x) = O(\log^{2/3} x)$ of A. Val'fiš [*Weylsche Exponentialsummen in der neueren Zahlentheorie*, VEB Deutsch. Verlag der Wissensch., Berlin, 1963; MR **36** #3737], the author shows that $\sum_{n \leq x} \sigma^2(n)/n^2 = 5\zeta(3)x/2 - (\log^2 x)/4 + O(\log^{5/3} x)$. Partial summation in this formula gives the improved estimate in Ramanujan's theorem. He also proves that the average value of $E(x)$ is $\zeta(0)x^2(\log x)/6$, thus showing that $E(x) \neq o(x^2 \log x)$, a result stated by Ramanujan without proof.

*T. M. Apostol* (Pasadena, Calif.)

Citations: MR 36# 3737 = L02-8.

## N36-76 (40# 5568)

**Levin, B. V.; Faĭnleĭb, A. S.**

**Mean values of multiplicative functions. (Russian)**

*Dokl. Akad. Nauk SSSR* **188** (1969), 517–519.

In this paper some new results concerning the sums of multiplicative functions are announced. Also, the author gives some applications in the probabilistic theory of numbers.

{This article has appeared in English translation [Soviet Math. Dokl. **10** (1969), 1142–1145].}

*N. Popescu* (Bucharest)

## N36-77 (41# 1658)

**Steinig, J.**

**The changes of sign of certain arithmetical error-terms.**

*Comment. Math. Helv.* **44** (1969), 385–400.

G. Pólya [Math. Z. **29** (1928), 549–640] refined E. Landau's theorem [Math. Ann. **61** (1906), 527–550] and considered, as a particular case, the problem of estimating the number of changes of sign of the error-term $\psi(x) - x$ in the interval $1 < x \leq t$, where $\psi(x)$ is the Chebyshev function in the prime number theorem. If $N(t)$ denotes that number, then Pólya's result implies that $\limsup N(t)/\log t > 0$. The author has now filled a gap in the original proof of Pólya's theorem, which he applies to the error-term associated with the arithmetical function $r_k(n)$, the number of representations of an integer $n$ as a sum of $k$ squares ($k \geqq 2$). This application is made possible by the fact that the Dirichlet series $\sum_1^\infty r_k(n)n^{-s}$ represents the Epstein zeta-function $\zeta_k(s)$, which satisfies Hecke's functional equation $\pi^{-s}\Gamma(s)\zeta_k(s) = \pi^{s-k/2}\Gamma(k/2-s)\zeta_k(k/2-s)$, and this implies a fundamental identity given by K. Chandrasekharan and R. Narasimhan [Acta Arith. **6** (1960/1961), 487–503; MR **23** # A3719; C. R. Acad. Sci. Paris **251** (1960), 1333–1335; MR **22** #9477; erratum, MR **22**, p. 2547].

Given an equation such as (*) $\Delta(s)\varphi(s) = \Delta(\delta - s)\varphi(\delta - s)$, where $\delta$ is a real number, $\Delta(s)$ is a product of a finite number of gamma functions, say, $\Delta(s) = \prod_1^N \Gamma(\alpha_\nu s + \beta_\nu)$ and $\varphi(s) = \sum_1^\infty a_n \lambda_n^{-s}$, we define for $\rho \geqq 0$, $A_\lambda^\rho(x) = (\Gamma(\rho+1))^{-1} \sum_{\lambda_n \leq x}^{1} a_n(x - \lambda_n)^\rho$, which is the fractional integral of order $\rho$ of the summatory function $A_\lambda^0(x) \equiv A(x) = \sum_{\lambda_n \leq x}^{1} a_n$. Chandrasekharan and Narasimhan have shown [Ann. of Math. (2) **76** (1962), 93–136; MR **25** #3911] that corresponding to the equation (*) there exists a "residual function" $S_\rho(x)$ such that $\mathrm{Re}\{A_\lambda^\rho(x) - S_\rho(x)\} = \Omega_\pm(x^\Theta)$, where $\Theta = \{A\delta + 2(A-1)\rho - \frac{1}{2}\}/2A$ with $A = \sum_1^N \alpha_\nu$. (A similar result for the imaginary part of $A_\lambda^\rho(x) - S_\rho(x)$.) The general $\Omega$-theorem clearly implies that the real part of the "error-term" $A_\lambda^\rho(x) - S_\rho(x)$ has an infinity of changes of sign in the interval $0 < x < \infty$. The author obtains a lower bound for the number of changes of sign of $\mathrm{Re}\{A_\lambda^\rho(x) - S_\rho(x)\}$, and of $\mathrm{Im}\{A_\lambda^\rho(x) - S_\rho(x)\}$ in a given interval, while Pólya's theorem gives only a "lim sup result". In the case $\rho = 0$, this paper gives a lower bound for the number of changes of sign, in any interval, of the error-term associated with such arithmetical functions as $d(n)$, or $r_k(n)$, or Ramanujan's function $\tau(n)$.

*S. Ikehara* (Tokyo)

Citations: MR 22# 9477 = N36-21; MR 23# A3719 = N36-25; MR 25# 3911 = N36-32.

Referred to in N04-55.

**N36-78** **(41# 5310)**

**Berndt, Bruce C.**

**On the average order of some arithmetical functions.**

*Bull. Amer. Math. Soc.* **76** (1970), 856–859.

$\{a_n\}$, $\{b_n\}$ seien zwei Folgen komplexer Zahlen, keine von ihnen bestehe aus lauter Nullen. Ferner sei $s=\sigma+i\tau$ und seien $\{\lambda_n\}$ und $\{\mu_n\}$ monoton gegen unendlich wachsende Folgen reeller Zahlen.

$\Phi(s)=\sum_{n=1}^{\infty} a(n)\lambda_n^{-s}$, $\Psi(s)=\sum_{n=1}^{\infty} b(n)\mu_n^{-s}$ seien zwei Dirichlet-Reihen, welche in gewissen Halbebenen konvergieren, es sei $\sigma_a{}^*$ die Abszisse der absoluten Konvergenz von $\Psi$. Setzen wir noch $\Delta(s)=\prod_{\upsilon=1}^{N}\Gamma(\alpha_\upsilon s+\beta_\upsilon)$, wobei $\alpha_\upsilon>0$ und i.a. $\beta_\upsilon$ komplex sind und fordern wir für reelle $r$, daß $\Delta(s)\Phi(s)=\Delta(r-s)\Psi(r-s)$ gilt, so werden in drei Sätzen Größenordnungsaussagen über $\mathrm{Re}(P_q(x))$ gemacht, wobei $A_q(x)=(\Gamma(q+1))^{-1}\sum_{\lambda_n\leq x} a(n)(x-\lambda_n)^q$ $(q\geqq 0)$, $\alpha=\sum_{\upsilon=1}^{N}\alpha_\upsilon$, $Q_q(x)=(2\pi i)^{-1}\int\Gamma(s)\Phi(s)x^{s+q}(\Gamma(s+q+1))^{-1}\,ds$ (das Integral über einen passend gewählten Kreis erstreckt) und $P_q(x)=A_q(x)-Q_q(x)$ bedeuten. Der Verfasser gibt ohne ausführliche Beweise Resultate an, welche frühere Untersuchungen [K. Chandrasekharan and Raghavan Narasimhan, Acta Math. **6** (1960/61), 487–503; MR **23** #A3719; Ann. of Math. (2) **76** (1962), 93–136; MR **25** #3911] verfeinern. Die Beweise sollen in zwei weiteren Arbeiten des Verfassers, welche im J. Number Theory erscheinen werden, durchgeführt werden.

*H. J. Kanold* (Braunschweig)

Citations: MR 23# A3719 = N36-25; MR 25# 3911 = N36-32.

**N36-79** **(41# 6801)**

**Delange, Hubert**

**A remark on multiplicative functions.**

*Bull. London Math. Soc.* **2** (1970), 183–185.

Define the mean value $M(f)$ of an arithmetical function $f$ to be the limit as $N\to\infty$ of $N^{-1}\sum_{n=1}^{N} f(n)$, if it exists. The author proves that if $f$ and $g$ are multiplicative functions satisfying $|f(n)|\leqq 1$, $|g(n)|\leqq 1$ and if both $M(f)$ and $M(g)$ exist and are nonzero, then $M(fg)$ also exists. He shows that the series $\sum[1-f(p)g(p)]/p$ converges when extended over all primes and then invokes one of his earlier theorems [Ann. Sci. École Norm. Sup. (3) **78** (1961), 273–304; MR **30** #72] to deduce that $M(fg)$ exists.

*T. M. Apostol* (Pasadena, Calif.)

Citations: MR 30# 72 = N36-38.

**N36-80** **(41# 8359)**

**Berndt, Bruce C.**

**On the average order of ideal functions and other arithmetical functions.**

*Bull. Amer. Math. Soc.* **76** (1970), 1270–1274.

A famous theorem of E. Landau [Nachr. Ges. Wiss. Göttingen Math.-Phys. Kl. **1915**, 209–243], whose formulation takes more than three pages, concerns $O$-results for error-terms of average orders of a general class of arithmetical functions. The author states a result whose "proof is a slight modification of Landau's" in which the error-term is allowed in addition to vary with respect to a certain parameter and in the context of the investigations of K. Chandrasekharan and R. Narasimhan concerning functional equations with multiple gamma factors [e.g., Ann. of Math. (2) **76** (1962), 93–136; MR **25** #3911].

*S. L. Segal* (Rochester, N.Y.)

Citations: MR 25# 3911 = N36-32.

**N36-81** **(42# 3038)**

**Gilquin, Emmanuel**

**Comportement des fonctions arithmétiques complexes, multiplicatives, à valeurs dans le disque $|z|\leqq 1$.**

*Séminaire Delange-Pisot-Poitou: 1968/69, Théorie des Nombres, Fasc. 1, Exp. 13, 8 pp. Secrétariat mathématique, Paris,* 1969.

Let $f(n)$ be a multiplicative function satisfying $|f(n)|\leqq 1$ and $M(x)=\sum_{n\leq x} f(n)$. It was proved by G. Halász [Studia Sci. Math. Hungar. **1** (1966), 113–117; MR **35** #139] that $M(x)=C_0L_0(lgx)x^{1+ia_0}+o(x)$, where $|L_0(u)|=1$, and moreover, $L_0(u)$ is slowly oscillating. The author gives a new proof which seems simpler, using some theorems of H. Delange.

{The reviewer feels it is still somewhat recondite but perhaps no easier proof is possible.}

*P. Barrucand* (Paris)

Citations: MR 35# 139 = N36-59.

**N36-82** **(42# 4510)**

**Levin, B. V.; Timofeev, N. M.**

**Sums of multiplicative functions.** **(Russian)**

*Dokl. Akad. Nauk SSSR* **193** (1970), 992–995.

E. Wirsing [Acta Math. Acad. Sci. Hungar. **18** (1967), 411–467; MR **36** #6366] conjectured, and the reviewer [ibid. **19** (1968), 365–403; MR **37** #6254] proved, that for any multiplicative function $f(n)$ with $|f(p^k)|\leqq 1$, $\sum_{n\leq x} f(n)=(CL(\log x)+o(1))x^{1+ia}$ with an explicitly given complex constant $C$, a real constant $a$ and a slowly oscillating function $L(u)$ with $|L(u)|=1$. The authors generalize this essentially for the case $|f(p)|\leqq\tau$ (in a certain average sense), giving rise to a $\log^{\tau-1}x$ in the formula, under the condition $\tau>\frac{1}{2}$. The proof, which follows that of the reviewer, is rather sketchy. The last remark, "asymptotic differentiation", needs more explanation when $|f(p)|\leqq\tau$ is assumed only in the average.

{Reviewer's remark: It will be shown in a forthcoming paper of the reviewer ("On the distribution of additive and the mean values of multiplicative arithmetic functions", to appear in Studia Sci. Math. Hungar.) how to drop the unnecessary condition $\tau>\frac{1}{2}$.}

{This article has appeared in English translation [Soviet Math. Dokl. **11** (1970), 1062–1066].}

*G. Halász* (Budapest)

Citations: MR 36# 6366 = N36-63; MR 37# 6254 = N36-69.

**N36-83** **(42# 5920)**

**Halász, G.**

**On the mean value of multiplicative number theoretic functions.**

*Number Theory (Colloq., János Bolyai Math. Soc., Debrecen, 1968), pp. 117–121. North-Holland, Amsterdam,* 1970.

Let $f(n)$ be a multiplicative function with mean (where it exists) defined by $\lim_{x\to\infty} x^{-1}\sum_{n\leq x} f(n)$. Among other things E. Wirsing [Acta Math. Acad. Sci. Hungar. **18** (1967), 411–467; MR **36** #6366] has shown, by elementary methods, that the mean always exists if $f(n)=\pm 1$ or 0. The author discusses an analytic method for proving theorems of this type starting from the Dirichlet series: $F(s)=\sum_{n=1}^{\infty} f(n)/n^s=\prod_p(1+f(p)/p^s+f(p^2)/p^{2s}+\cdots)$; $s=\sigma+it$. From the properties of $F(s)$ a Tauberian theorem is needed to infer the asymptotic behaviour of $f(s)$. In fact, Theorem 1 states that if $|f(n)|\leqq 1$ and $F(s)=C/(s-1)+o(|s|/(\sigma-1))$ uniformly as $1<\mathrm{Re}\,s=\sigma\to 1$, then $M(x)=\sum_{n\leq x} f(n)=C(x)+o(x)$.

*E. M. Horadam* (Armidale)

Citations: MR 36# 6366 = N36-63.

**N36-84** **(43# 4784)**

**Wolke, Dieter**

**Einige Anwendungen des großen Siebes auf zahlentheoretische Funktionen.**

Habilitationsschrift.
*Philipps-Universität Marburg/Lahn, Marburg/Lahn,* 1970. i+37 *pp.*
Der Verfasser untersucht das asymptotische Verhalten von Summen der Gestalt $S(f;x)=\sum_{n\leq x} d(n)\cdot f(n+a)$, wobei $d(n)$ die Anzahl der Teiler von $n$ und $f$ eine multiplikative Funktion bezeichnet, die geeignet eingeschränkt ist. In Spezialfällen wurden solche Summen u.a. von A. E. Ingham [J. London Math. Soc. **2** (1927), 202–208], C. Hooley [Proc. London Math. Soc. (3) **7** (1957), 396–413; MR **19**, 839] und Ju. V. Linnik [*The dispersion method in binary additive problems* (Russian), Izdat. Leningrad. Univ., Leningrad, 1961; MR **25** #3920; English translation, Amer. Math. Soc., Providence, R.I., 1963; MR **29** #5804] studiert. Der Verfasser verlangt, daß $0\leq f(p^a)\leq C'\cdot a^C$ und $\sum_{p\leq x}|f(p)-\tau|\ll x^{1-\eta}$ mit $\eta>0$, $\tau>5/2$ ist. Um $S(f;x)$ zu bestimmen, benötigt der Autor einen Satz vom Bombierischen Typ für die Funktion $f$; er weist für jedes positive $\varepsilon$ die Existenz von Konstanten $D(f)$ und $\gamma=\gamma(f,\varepsilon)>0$ nach, so daß die Abschätzung

$$(*)\quad \sum_{k\leq x^{1/2-\varepsilon}} \max_{(b,k)=1} \Big|\sum_{n\leq x, n\equiv b \bmod k} f(n)-(D(f)/\varphi(k)) \times\prod_{p|k}(1+f(p)/p+\cdots)\cdot x(\log x)^{\tau-1}\Big| \ll x(\log x)^{\tau-\gamma}$$

besteht; für den Beweis wird ein ganzes Arsenal analytischer Methoden benutzt (großes Sieb, Abschätzungen der Mittelwerte multiplikativer Funktionen, komplexe Integration). Aus der Abschätzung (*) folgt die asymptotische Formel $S(f;x)\sim C(f,a)\cdot x\log^\tau x$. Auf ähnlichem Wege wird für additive Funktionen $g$, die $0\leq g(p^a)\leq C'\cdot a^C$ und $\sum_{p\leq x}p^{-1}g(p)\sim C(g)\cdot\log\log x$ erfüllen, die asymptotische Formel

$$\sum_{n\leq x} f(n)g(n+a)\sim C(f,g,a)(x/\log x)\log\log x\cdot\prod_{p\leq x}(1+f(p)/p+\cdots)$$

bewiesen.
{Der Verfasser hat dem Referenten brieflich weitere Verbesserungen der oben genannten Ergebnisse mitgeteilt; insbesondere kann $\gamma$ auf der rechten Seite von (*) beliebig groß vorgeschrieben werden, und $k$ darf bis $x^{1/2}(\log x)^{-B}$ mit $B=B(\gamma)$ laufen.} *W. Schwarz* (Frankfurt a.M.)

Citations: MR 19, 839c = N40-30; MR 25# 3920 = P02-18; MR 29# 5804 = P02-19.

## N36-85 (44# 168)

**Tuljaganova, M. I.**
**Asymptotic formulae for sums of multiplicative functions that are determined on a normed semigroup.** (**Russian. Uzbek summary**)
*Izv. Akad. Nauk UzSSR Ser. Fiz.-Mat. Nauk* **13** (1969), *no.* 4, 30–35.
The author substitutes a more general semigroup for the natural series in the Levin-Faĭnleĭb theorems [see A. S. Faĭnleĭb, Litovsk. Mat. Sb. **7** (1967), 535–546 (1968); MR **37** #4038]. *A. I. Vinogradov* (Leningrad)

Citations: MR 37# 4038 = N36-64.

## N36-86 (44# 1636)

**Berndt, Bruce C.**
**On the average order of a class of arithmetical functions. I.**
*J. Number Theory* **3** (1971), 184–203.
G. H. Hardy [Proc. London Math. Soc. (2) **15** (1916), 1–25] and G. Szegő [Math. Z. **25** (1926), 388–404] studied the average order of the error term $P_k(x)$ defined by $\sum_{n\leq x} r_k(n) = (\pi x)^{\frac{1}{2}k}/\Gamma(\frac{1}{2}k+1)+P_k(x)$. The present author applies Szegő's methods to a class of arithmetical functions generated by Dirichlet series satisfying functional equations with Γ-factors. The results of Hardy and Szegő are obtained as special cases.
*L. K. Durst* (Providence, R.I.)

## N36-87 (44# 5286)

**Tuljaganova, M. I.**
**A certain extension of a theorem of Halasz.** (**Russian. Uzbek summary**)
*Izv. Akad. Nauk UzSSR Ser. Fiz.-Mat. Nauk* **14** (1970), *no.* 5, 35–40.
The author proves the following theorem, which is an extension of a theorem of G. Halász [Acta Math. Acad. Sci. Hungar. **19** (1968), 365–403; MR **37** #6254]. (1) Let $f(n)$ be a multiplicative function satisfying $|f(p^k)|\leq r^k$, $r>\frac{1}{2}$; then there exist a complex constant $C_0$, real number $a_0$ and a function $L(u)$ with the property that $|L(u)|=1$, $L(u_1)/L(u)\to 1$ uniformly for $u\to\infty$, $u\leq u_1\leq 2u$, such that $\sum_{n\leq x} f(n)=C_0L(\log x)x^{1+ia_0}$, $\log^{r-1}x+o(x\log^{r-1}x)$. The proof depends on the following result which is also proved. Let $|f(p^k)|\leq r^k$, $r>\frac{1}{2}$, $f(n)$ a multiplicative function, and $F(s)=\sum_{n=1}^\infty f(n)/n^s=CL(1/(\sigma-1))/[s-(1-ia)]^r+o(1/(\sigma-1)^r)$ $(s=\sigma+it,\ \sigma\to 1+0)$ uniformly for $|t|\leq k$, $k$ arbitrary, $a$ real and $L(u)$ as above; then $\sum_{n\leq x} f(n)=(CL(\log x)/(\Gamma(r)(1+ia)^2))x^{1+ia}\log^{r-1}x+o(x\log^{r-1}x)$.
*W. H. Simons* (Corvallis, Ore.)

Citations: MR 37# 6254 = N36-69.

## N36-88 (44# 6629)

**Wolke, Dieter**
**Multiplikative Funktionen auf schnell wachsenden Folgen.**
*J. Reine Angew. Math.* **251** (1971), 54–67.
Let $\mathfrak{A}=\{a_1,a_2,\cdots\}$ be a sequence of positive integers and put $A(x,d)=\sum_{n\leq x, d|a_n} 1=\rho(d)/dx+R(x,d)$. Let $f$ be a non-negative multiplicative arithmetic function and put $F(\mathfrak{A},x)=\sum_{n\leq x} f(a_n)$, $S(\mathfrak{A},x)=\sum_{p\leq x}\rho(p)/p(f(p)-1)$. Under certain technical assumptions on the sequence $\mathfrak{A}$ and the function $f$, the asymptotic behavior of $F(\mathfrak{A},x)$ is investigated. In particular, it is shown that $F(\mathfrak{A},x)\ll x\exp S(\mathfrak{A},x)$ if $f(p^l)$ grows relatively slowly with $l$, with the $\ll$ sign being reversed if $f(p^l)$ grows relatively rapidly with $l$, while if $f(p^l)\to 1$ as $p\to\infty$ for all $l\geq 1$, then $F(\mathfrak{A},x)\sim cx\exp S(\mathfrak{A},x)$. The assumed conditions on $\mathfrak{A}$ are weak enough to apply to all cases in which $a_n$ is the value of a polynomial $G(n)$ with integer coefficients, and moreover to the case $a_n=[n^t]$, where $1<t<2$. The results strengthen those of M. B. Barban [Izv. Akad. Nauk UzSSR Ser. Fiz.-Mat. Nauk **1964**, no. 6, 13–19; MR **31** #1239]. *D. Rearick* (Boulder, Colo.)

Citations: MR 31# 1239 = N48-16.

# N40 ESTIMATES OF SUMS OF ARITHMETIC FUNCTIONS: DIVISOR FUNCTIONS $d_r(n)$, $\sigma_r(n)$

For sums over the "shifted primes" $p+a$, see **P48**.

See also reviews A22-5, A28-17, A28-18, A36-45, A36-46, B28-31, B28-33, K10-7, L15-20, L15-21, L15-29, L20-15, L99-4, M02-3, M05-41, M15-2, M15-11, M15-28, M15-31, M40-16, M40-35, N12-28, N20-47, N24-80, N28-3, N36-2, N36-4, N36-20, N36-26, N36-27, N36-28, N36-32, N36-44, N36-46, N36-51, N36-75, N36-84, N44-3, N48-4, N48-6, N48-18, N48-20, N48-22, N48-24, N48-26, N48-28, N48-34, N52-3, N52-15, N52-29, N52-40, N80-1, N80-6, N80-18, N80-32, P02-5, P02-10, P02-18, P02-21, P24-10, P28-57, P28-58, P28-72, P28-89, P28-92, P36-43, P48-4, P48-15, P48-24, Q20-7, R46-4, R46-5, R46-13, R46-16, R46-22, R46-27, Z10-30.

**N40-1** **(1, 41b)**

**van der Corput, J. G. Une inégalité relative au nombre des diviseurs.** Nederl. Akad. Wetensch., Proc. **42**, 547–553 (1939).

The paper discusses principally sums of the type

$$S=\sum_{y=1}^{X}\tau^l(y)T(y),$$

where $\tau(y)$ is the number of divisors of $y$, $l$ a natural number, and $T(y)\geqq 0$. The problem is to impose on $T(y)$ suitable and applicable conditions such that

$$S\leqq C\cdot(\log X)^\omega$$

for certain $C$ and $\omega$. Such a condition (that one assumed in Theorem 1) is that there exist three numbers $A$, $\gamma$, $\eta$ such that for all positive integers $v\leqq X^\gamma$ we have

$$\sum_{\substack{y=1\\ y\equiv 0 \pmod v}}^{X} T(y)\leqq A\cdot v^{-1}\tau^\eta(v).$$

A second theorem introduces a weaker but more complicated condition, which cannot conveniently be reproduced here. The proof of Theorem 2 (of which Theorem 1 is shown to be a special case) is based on a peculiar factorization of $y$.

By means of his Theorem 1 and a lemma due to Hua [J. London Math. Soc. **13**, 54–61 (1938)] the author finally proves a third theorem: If $\psi(h)$ is a polynomial of integral coefficients and $l$ a positive integer, then there exists a number $\Omega$ such that, for all $Z\geqq 3$,

$$\sum_{\substack{h=1\\ \psi(h)\neq 0}}^{Z} \tau^l(|\psi(h)|)\leqq Z(\log Z)^\Omega.$$

*H. Rademacher* (Swarthmore, Pa.).

Referred to in N40-66.

**N40-2** **(1, 66a)**

**van der Corput, J. G. Sur quelques fonctions arithmétiques élémentaires.** Nederl. Akad. Wetensch., Proc. **42**, 859–866 (1939).

Let $f(n)$ be a multiplicative arithmetical function and $k>0$ be an integer such that the product

$$\prod_p\left(1+\frac{|g(p)|}{p}+\frac{|g(p^2)|}{p^2}+\cdots\right)$$

extended over the primes converges, where

$$g(p^\rho)=f(p^\rho)-\binom{k}{1}f(p^{\rho-1})+\binom{k}{2}f(p^{\rho-2})-\cdots+(-1)^\rho\binom{k}{\rho}f(1).$$

The author proves

$$(1)\qquad x^{-1}(\log x)^{1-k}\sum_{n\leqq x}f(n)\to\frac{P}{(k-1)!},$$

where $P$ denotes the product

$$P=\prod_p\left\{\left(1-\frac{1}{p}\right)^k\left(1+\frac{f(p)}{p}+\frac{f(p^2)}{p^2}+\cdots\right)\right\}.$$

Let $\tau_r(n)$ be the number of the representations of $n$ as a product of $r$ positive integers. Then it follows from (1) that for every positive integer $l$

$$(2)\qquad x^{-1}(\log x)^{1-r^l}\sum_{n\leqq x}\tau_r{}^l(n)\to\frac{P}{(r^l-1)!},$$

with

$$P=\prod_p\left\{\left(1-\frac{1}{p}\right)^r\left(1+\frac{\binom{r}{1}^l}{p}+\frac{\binom{r+1}{2}^l}{p^2}+\cdots\right)\right\}.$$

From (2) it follows, for $r=3$ and $l=2$, that $\sum_{n\leqq x}\tau_3{}^2(n)$ has the order of magnitude $x(\log x)^8$, whereas Vinogradow [Bull. Acad. Sci. URSS, Cl. Sci. Math. Nat. **1938**, 399–416] obtained $x(\log x)^5$ erroneously.

*A. Brauer* (Princeton, N. J.).

Referred to in N36-28.

**N40-3** **(2, 149f)**

**Ingham, A. E. On two classical lattice point problems.** Proc. Cambridge Philos. Soc. **36**, 131–138 (1940).

The object of this note is to prove

$$\limsup\frac{P(x)}{x^{\frac14}}=+\infty,\quad \liminf\frac{\Delta(x)}{x^{\frac14}}=-\infty,$$

where $P(x)$ is the error term in the problem of the lattice points of a circle, and $\Delta(x)$ the error term in Dirichlet's divisor problem. *J. G. van der Corput* (Groningen).

Referred to in F35-32, N40-4.

**N40-4** **(24# A92 )**

**Gangadharan, K. S.**

**Two classical lattice point problems.**

*Proc. Cambridge Philos. Soc.* **57** (1961), 699–721.

The author obtains refinements of the results of Ingham [same Proc. **36** (1940), 131–138; MR **2**, 149].

*T. Estermann* (London)

Citations: MR 2, 149f = N40-3.

Referred to in N36-32, N40-67, R46-31.

**N40-5** **(3, 269d)**

**Atkinson, F. V. A divisor problem.** Quart. J. Math., Oxford Ser. **12**, 193–200 (1941).

If $d_k(n)$ is the number of ways of expressing $n$ as the product of $k$ factors then Piltz's formula is $\sum_{n<x}d_k(n)=xf_k(\log x)+\Delta_k(x)$, where $f_k(x)$ is the residue of $\zeta^k(s)x^{s-1}/s$ at $s=1$ and $\Delta_k(x)=O(x^\alpha)$. It is shown that, if $\alpha_k$ denotes the lower bound of the $\alpha$ for which the estimate holds, then $\alpha_3\leqq 37/75$. This is somewhat better than the results $\alpha_3\leqq 43/87$ [Walfisz] and $\alpha_k\leqq\max(\frac12,(k-1)/(k+2))$ [Hardy and Littlewood]. *H. S. Zuckerman* (Seattle, Wash.).

Referred to in N40-36.

**N40-6** **(4, 131c)**

**Titchmarsh, E. C. Some problems in the analytic theory of numbers.** Quart. J. Math., Oxford Ser. **13**, 129–152 (1942).

The problems considered are those of determining the

asymptotic behavior of sums of the type

$$\sum_{n=1}^{\infty} d(n)d_3(n+r)e^{-2n\delta}$$

as $\delta\to 0$, where $d(n)$ is the number of divisors of $n$ and $d_3(n)$ is the number of ways in which $n$ can be expressed as a product of three factors. Asymptotic formulas for $\sum d(n)^2e^{-2n\delta}$ and $\sum d(n)d(n+r)e^{-2n\delta}$ are already known. The author points out that these can be obtained by forming the appropriate generating function, replacing it by its dominant part on each Farey arc and integrating around a circle. Without estimating the error terms, the author applies the same procedure to (1) $\sum d_3^2(n)e^{-2n\delta}$, (2) $\sum d(n)d_3(n)e^{-2n\delta}$, (3) $\sum d_3(n)d_3(n+r)e^{-2n\delta}$, (4) $\sum d_3(n)d(n+r)e^{-2n\delta}$. He also obtains true asymptotic formulas for (1) and (2) by other methods. The results agree for (2) but do not for (1). It is interesting to note that the two results for (1) differ only by a factor 255/256. The author does not have alternative methods for (3) and (4) but is led by analogy to conjecture that his result for (4) is probably true but that (3) is more doubtful. *H. S. Zuckerman* (Seattle, Wash.).

Referred to in N40-17, N40-30.

## N40-7 (5, 35d)

**Peng, H. Y. A result in divisor problem.** Acad. Sinica Science Record **1**, 69–72 (1942).

It was proved by Walfisz [Ann. Scuola Norm. Super. Pisa (2) **5**, 289–298 (1936)] that, if

$$\tau(x)=\sum_{n\leqq x}(x-n)\sum_{d\mid n}1/d,$$

then

$$\tau(x)=(\pi^2/12)x^2-\tfrac{1}{2}x\log x-\tfrac{1}{2}(\gamma-1+\log 2\pi)x+R(x),$$

where $R(x)=O(x^{3/10})$. Here van der Corput's method is used to prove that $R(x)=O(x^{2/7}\log x)$. *E. C. Titchmarsh.*

## N40-8 (7, 275d)

**Brun, Viggo. Méthode élémentaire pour évaluer des fonctions énumératives. I.** Skr. Norske Vid. Akad. Oslo. I. **1941**, no. 12, 14 pp. (1942).

This article studies the function

$$D(x)=[x/1]+[x/2]+[x/3]+\cdots,$$

that is, the number of lattice points within the hyperbola $uv=x$. Use is made of the symbols

$$L(x^s\psi(s))=\lim_{s\to\infty}\left(\frac{2\psi(s)x^s}{1!}-\frac{3\psi(2s)x^{2s}}{2!}+\frac{4\psi(3s)x^{3s}}{3!}-\cdots\right),$$

$$UA(x)=\int_1^\infty A(x/u)du-\sum_{u=1}^{\infty}A(x/u)+\tfrac{1}{2}A(x),$$

and the expression $[x]=\phi(x)+\phi(x/2)+\phi(x/3)+\cdots$, where $\phi(x)=1$ if $x\geqq 1$, $\phi(x)=0$ if $0\leqq x<1$. The final result is

$$x^{-1}\int_0^x D(x)dx=\tfrac{1}{2}x\log x+(E-\tfrac{3}{4})x+\tfrac{1}{4}+\theta(\tfrac{1}{8}\log x+\tfrac{1}{12}+3/x),$$

or the equivalent formula for $\Delta(x)=D(x)-x\log x-(2E-1)x$,

$$x^{-1}\int_0^x \Delta(x)dx=\theta(\tfrac{1}{8}\log x+\tfrac{1}{3}+3/x),$$

valid for $x>1$. Here $E$ is Euler's constant and $-1<\theta<1$. Cramér's formula $\frac{1}{4}+O(x^{-\frac{1}{4}})$ for the mean value of $\Delta(x)$ was only asymptotic. *G. Pall* (Montreal, Que.).

Referred to in N40-11.

## N40-9 (8, 137b)

**Kuhn, Pavel. An elementary formula for medium values of Dirichlets divisor problem.** Norske Vid. Selsk. Forh., Trondhjem **18**, no. 50, 204–207 (1946).

The author obtains, by elementary methods, an approximate formula with explicit error terms for $\int_0^x f(y)dy$, where $f(y)\equiv\sum_{\nu=1}^{\infty}[y/\nu]$. The integral represents a mean value of $f(y)$ and $f(y)=\sum_{m=1}^{[y]}d(m)$, where $d(m)$ is the number of divisors of $m$. *R. D. James* (Vancouver, B. C.).

## N40-10 (8, 503d)

**Kuhn, Pavel. Zu den Mittelwerten zahlentheoretischer Funktionen.** Norske Vid. Selsk. Forh., Trondhjem **14** (1941), no. 42, 157–160 (1942).

In this paper the integral

$$\int_0^x dx_1\int_0^{x_1}dx_2\cdots\int_0^{x_{m-1}}[x_m/n]dx_m$$

is expressed in terms of Bernoulli polynomials of order $m+1$. The proof is made by induction on $m$ and the result is applied to the function $A(x,u)=[x/1]+[x/2]+\cdots+[x/u]$, where $u=x^{\frac{1}{2}}$. *R. D. James* (Vancouver, B. C.).

## N40-11 (8, 503e)

**Kuhn, Pavel. Zur elementaren Abschätzung des Mittelwertes der Dirichletschen Teilerfunktion.** Norske Vid. Selsk. Forh., Trondhjem **15**, no. 8, 29–32 (1942).

Let $D(x)$ denote Dirichlet's divisor function and write $D(x)=x\log x+(2C-1)+E(x)$, where $C$ is the Euler constant. Brun [Skr. Norske Vid. Akad. Oslo. I. **1941**, no. 12 (1942); these Rev. **7**, 275] found an explicit upper bound for $|x^{-1}\int_0^x E(t)dt|$. In this note a refinement of Brun's method leads to a smaller bound. *R. D. James.*

Citations: MR 7, 275d = N40-8.

## N40-12 (9, 11h)

**Bellman, Richard. The Dirichlet divisor problem.** Duke Math. J. **14**, 411–417 (1947).

It is proved that, if $d(n)$ denotes the number of divisors of $n$, and $D(x)=\sum_{n<x}d(n)=x\log x+(2C-1)x+\Delta(x)$, then

$$\int_1^T\{\Delta(x)\}^2x^{-\frac{3}{2}}dx\sim c_1\log T,\qquad T\to\infty,$$

where $c_1$ is a positive constant. A corresponding result is obtained in the theory of Euler's $\phi$-function. As the author points out, more general problems of this kind had been considered by A. Walfisz [J. Reine Angew. Math. **169**, 111–130 (1933)] and S. Chowla [Math. Z. **35**, 279–299 (1932)]. The method used here, depending on the Riemann zeta-function, is, however, different from that of Walfisz and Chowla. *E. C. Titchmarsh* (Oxford).

## N40-13 (9, 500c)

**Titchmarsh, E. C. On series involving divisors.** J. London Math. Soc. **22** (1947), 179–184 (1948).

In this note the author investigates the asymptotic behavior of the function $f(z)=\sum d(n)z^n=\sum z^n/(1-z^n)$, as $z$ approaches the unit circle, by a method which avoids the use of the Riemann zeta-function. The substitution $z=\exp(2\pi ih/k-\delta)$, where $\Re(\delta)>0$, changes $f(z)$ into $F(\delta,h,k)=\sum_{r=1}^{k}\sum_{m=0}^{\infty}g_r(m)$, where $g_r(m)=z^{r+mk}/(1-z^{r+mk})$.

Using the summation formula

$$\lim_{N\to\infty}\left[\sum_{m=0}^{N} g_r(m)-\int_0^N g_r(x)dx\right]$$

$$=\tfrac{1}{2}g_r(0)+\int_0^\infty (x-[x]-\tfrac{1}{2})g_r'(x)dx,$$

the sum for $F(\delta, h, k)$ splits into four parts, three of which are estimated directly with appropriate error terms. The fourth is in integral form and is evaluated by suitably altering the path of integration. Different paths of integration are required for different ranges of arg $\delta$. A sample result is $F(\delta, h, k)=1/(k\delta)(\log(1/\delta)-2\log h+\gamma)+O(k\log k)$ for $k^2|\delta|\leqq\pi$, $0\leqq\arg\delta\leqq\frac{1}{4}\pi$. *R. D. James.*

## N40-14 (10, 431g)

**Halberstam, H. Four asymptotic formulae in the theory of numbers.** J. London Math. Soc. **24**, 13–21 (1949).

The author obtains asymptotic formulae, with error terms, for $\sum_{\nu=1}^{x}\phi(\nu)\phi(\nu+k)$ as $x\to\infty$, for $\sum_{\nu=1}^{n-1}\phi(\nu)\phi(n-\nu)$ as $n\to\infty$, for $\sum_{\nu=1}^{x}\sigma_r(\nu)\sigma_s(\nu+k)$ as $x\to\infty$, and for $\sum_{\nu=1}^{n-1}\sigma_r(\nu)\sigma_s(n-\nu)$ as $n\to\infty$. Here $\phi(n)$ is Euler's function, $\sigma_r(n)$ is the sum of the $r$th powers of the divisors of $n$, $k$ is a fixed positive integer, and $r$ and $s$ are fixed positive numbers. The proofs, which are elementary, are similar to those used by Ingham [same J. **2**, 202–208 (1927)] to obtain asymptotic formulae for $\sum_{\nu=1}^{x}d(\nu)d(\nu+k)$ and $\sum_{\nu=1}^{n-1}d(\nu)d(n-\nu)$, where $d(n)$ is the number of divisors of $n$. *P. T. Bateman.*

## N40-15 (11, 15c)

**Davenport, H. A divisor problem.** Quart. J. Math., Oxford Ser. **20**, 37–44 (1949).

Let $\sigma(n)$ denote the sum of the divisors of $n$, and consider the problem of determining a bound for the error term $R(x)$ in the formula $\sum_{n\leq x}\sigma(n)=\pi^2x^2/12+xR(x)$. If $\rho(x)=\sum_{m\leq x}\psi(x/m)/m$, $\psi(u)=u-[u]-\frac{1}{2}$, it is easy to prove that $R(x)=-\rho(x)+O(1)$. The inequality $\rho(x)=O(\log x)$ is obvious. Using Weyl's inequality for exponential sums, Walfisz improved this to $\rho(x)=O(\log x/\log\log x)$, and then to $O(\log x)^{\frac{3}{4}+\epsilon}$ by applying the more refined inequalities of Vinogradov [references are given in the paper]. Davenport gives another proof of this result, also using Vinogradov's inequalities. *R. Bellman* (Stanford University, Calif.).

## N40-16 (11, 715h)

**Bellman, Richard. Ramanujan sums and the average value of arithmetic functions.** Duke Math. J. **17**, 159–168 (1950).

By a method which was outlined in a preceding paper [Proc. Nat. Acad. Sci. U. S. A. **34**, 149–152 (1948); these Rev. **9**, 499] the author proves that, for $\Re(s)>0$, $N\to\infty$, we have

(1) $$\sum_{n\leq N}\sigma_{-s}(f(n))\sim c_5(s)N,$$

(2) $$\sum_{p\leq N}\sigma_{-s}(f(p))\sim c_6(s)N/\log N.$$

Without proof, he states that

(3) $$\sum_{n\leq N}\sigma_{-s}(f(n))^r\sim C_r(s)N,\qquad r=1, 2, 3, \cdots.$$

Here $\sigma_{-s}=\sum_{k|n}k^{-s}$, and $f(x)$ is a polynomial with integer coefficients (the theorems are stated for integer-valued polynomials, but the proofs do not consider this generalization). The functions $c_5(s)$ and $c_6(s)$ are, respectively,

$$c_5(s)=\zeta(1+s)\sum_{n=1}^{\infty}\rho(n)n^{-1-s};\quad c_6(s)=\zeta(1+s)\sum_{n=1}^{\infty}\rho'(n)n^{-s}/\phi(n).$$

Both series converge absolutely for $\Re(s)>0$. Here $\rho(n)$ denotes the number of solutions of $f(x)\equiv 0 \pmod n$ if $x$ runs through a complete set of residues mod $n$; $\rho'(n)$ is the corresponding number for a reduced set. In formula (2.3), $\mu(n/d)$ should be $\mu(q/d)$; this leads to the error term $O(d(n))$ instead of $O(d(n)\log Y)$. *N. G. de Bruijn* (Delft).

Citations: MR 9, 499e = N36-5.

Referred to in N40-25, N40-26, N40-47.

## N40-17 (12, 80e)

**Bellman, Richard. On some divisor sums associated with Diophantine equations.** Quart. J. Math., Oxford Ser. (2) **1**, 136–146 (1950).

Let $d(n)$ and $d_j(n)$ be respectively the number of divisors of $n$ and the number of representations of $n$ as a product of $j$ integers. The following asymptotic formulas are obtained:

$$S_3=\sum_{n\leq N}d(n)d_3(n+r)\sim c_3(r)N\log^3 N$$

and

$$S_4=\sum_{n\leq N}d(n)d_4(n+r)=c_4(r)N\log^4 N.$$

The first step is the reduction of the problem to that of estimating the sums $T_j=\sum_{n\leq N}d_j(kn+r)$ for $j=3, 4$. Then an application of the Perron formula gives rise to a Dirichlet series, and the calculation of the mean value of the fourth power of this series constitutes the main part of the proof. Details are given for the case $r=1$, with an indication at the end of the paper of the necessary modifications for the general case. A heuristic treatment of $S_3$ was given by Titchmarsh [same J., Oxford Ser. (1) **13**, 129–152 (1942); these Rev. **4**, 131] following the circle method of Hardy and Littlewood *I. Niven* (Eugene, Ore.).

Citations: MR 4, 131c = N40-6.

## N40-18 (12, 804e)

**Venkataraman, C. S. An order result relating to the number of divisors of $n$ in an arithmetic progression.** Math. Student **18** (1950), 19–21 (1951).

Let $d(a, b|n)$ denote the number of divisors of $n$ of the form $ar+b$ ($r=0, 1, 2, \cdots$). Then the author proves that there exists a constant $\alpha=\alpha(a, b)$ such that as $x\to\infty$

$$a\sum_{n\leq x}d(a, b|n)=x\log x+\alpha x+O(x^{\frac{1}{2}}).$$

The proof follows along the lines of Dirichlet's argument in the well-known case of $a=b=1$. It may be worth noting that $\alpha(a, b)=\log a-\psi(b/a)-\psi(2)$ where $\psi(x)$ is the logarithmic derivative of $\Gamma(x)$. *D. H. Lehmer* (Berkeley, Calif.).

## N40-19 (13, 438f)

**Erdös, P. On the sum $\sum_{k=1}^{x}d(f(k))$.** J. London Math. Soc. **27**, 7–15 (1952).

Let $d(n)$ denote the number of divisors of a positive integer $n$, and let $f(k)$ be an irreducible polynomial with integer coefficients. The author proves that there exist two positive constants $c_1$ and $c_2$ such that $c_1x\log x<\sum_{k\leq x}d(f(k))<c_2x\log x$ for $x\geqq 2$. For $f(k)$ a quadratic the result, and even an asymptotic equality, had previously been established by the reviewer and Shapiro [Ann. of Math. (2) **49**, 333–340 (1948); these Rev. **9**, 414]. The lower inequality is readily established, but the upper inequality requires some extremely ingenious and involved estimations. In the course of the proof, an earlier result of van der Corput, $\sum_{k\leq x}d(f(k))=O(x\log x^c)$, where $c$ depends upon $f(k)$, is used. It is further stated that Brun's method combined with the technique of the paper would enable one to establish $\sum_{p\leq x}d(f(p))=O(x)$, where $p$ runs through the primes $p$ less than or equal to $x$.

*R. Bellman* (Stanford University, Calif.).

Citations: MR 9, 414a = N52-7.

Referred to in C05-39, N32-64, N40-66, N40-69, N40-82, N52-40, N60-75.

**N40-20** **(14, 536h)**

**Iseki, Kanesiroo. A divisor problem involving prime numbers.** Jap. J. Math. **21** (1951), 67–92 (1952).

The paper deals with the function $D(x)=\sum_{p<x}d(x-p)$, where $x$ denotes a positive integer, $p$ a prime, and $d(n)$ the number of positive divisors of $n$. It is shown that

$$A_1\frac{\phi(x)}{\log\log x}\leqq D(x)\leqq A_2\phi(x)\quad(x\geqq 3)$$

and, on the extended Riemann hypothesis,

$$D(x)=\phi(x)\prod_{p\nmid x}\left(1+\frac{1}{p(p-1)}\right)+O\left(\frac{\log\log x}{\log x}\phi(x)\right),$$

where $A_1$ and $A_2$ are positive constants, and $\phi(x)$ is Euler's function. A refinement of a theorem of Titchmarsh [Rend. Circ. Mat. Palermo **54**, 414–429 (1930)] concerning the function $D_p(x)=\sum_{l<p\leqq x}d(p-l)$ is also obtained.

*T. Estermann* (London).

**N40-21** **(14, 956b)**

**Richert, Hans-Egon. Ein Gitterpunktproblem.** Math. Ann. **125**, 467–471 (1953).

Let $D(x;q_1,h_1,q_2,h_2)$ denote the number of lattice points $u$, $v$ in the region $u>0$, $v>0$, $uv\leqq x$, which satisfy $u\equiv h_1$ (mod $q_1$), $u\equiv h_2$ (mod $q_2$). Further put $x-[x]-\frac{1}{2}=\psi(x)$. From a previous paper [Math. Z. **58**, 71–84 (1953); these Rev. **14**, 945] the author borrows the formula

$$\sum_{0<n\leqq y}\psi(n^{-1}x+\omega)=O(1)+O(x^{-1/2}y^{3/2})+O(x^{11/41}y^{6/41}),$$

uniformly in $x$, $y$, $\omega$, $\theta$, where $x>0$, $y>0$, $\omega$ real, and $\theta^{-1}$ is a positive integer. By a well-known classical argument the author derives that

$$D(x;q_1,h_1,q_2,h_2)=X\log X$$
$$-\left(\frac{\Gamma'}{\Gamma}\left(\frac{h_1}{q_1}\right)+\frac{\Gamma'}{\Gamma}\left(\frac{h_2}{q_2}\right)+1\right)X+O(X^{27/82}),$$

where $X=x/(q_1q_2)$, uniformly in $x$, $q_1$, $q_2$, $h_1$, $h_2$ $(q_1q_2\leqq x)$. The result can be applied to the circle problem, and more generally to the problem of the number of ideals with norm $\leqq x$ in a quadratic field. The special case $\omega=0$, $\theta=1$ gives Nieland's result for Dirichlet's divisor problem [Thesis, Groningen, 1933]. The author announces that he will show in a forthcoming paper that the error term in the divisor problem can be reduced to $O(x^{15/46}\log^{12/23}x)$.

*N. G. de Bruijn* (Amsterdam).

**N40-22** **(15, 11h)**

**Richert, Hans-Egon. Verschärfung der Abschätzung beim Dirichletschen Teilerproblem.** Math. Z. **58**, 204–218 (1953).

The author applies a two-dimensional version of the Van der Corput method to the estimation of the remainder term, $\Delta(x)$, in the Dirichlet divisor problem. The method was previously applied to the circle problem by Titchmarsh [Proc. London Math. Soc. (2) **38**, 96–115 (1934)] and Hua [Quart. J. Math., Oxford Ser. **13**, 18–29 (1942); these Rev. **4**, 190]. The problem is essentially more difficult in the present case because of the possible vanishing of a crucial determinant, a Hessian, and the appearance of hyperbolic rather than circular sectors. Using a method followed by Min [Trans. Amer. Math. Soc. **65**, 448–472 (1949); these Rev. **11**, 84] to overcome the first difficulty and some non-trivial estimates to meet the second, the author obtains the estimate $\Delta(x)=O(x^{15/46}\log^{30/23}x)$ which is superior to the best previous, $\Delta(x)=O(x^{27/82})$, derived recently by Nieland.

*R. Bellman* (Santa Monica, Calif.).

Citations: MR 4, 190e = P20-2; MR 11, 84c = M15-8.
Referred to in N36-13, N40-38, N40-41.

**N40-23** **(15, 935g)**

**Val'fiš, A. Z. On the theory of prime numbers.** Soobščeniya Akad. Nauk Gruzin. SSR **14**, 77–83 (1953). (Russian)

Under the assumption of the Extended Riemann Hypothesis (that is, the conjecture that the real parts of the zeros of the Dirichlet $L$-functions do not exceed $\frac{1}{2}$) the author proves that

$$\sum_{1<p<N}d(N-p)=\frac{315\zeta(3)}{2\pi^4}N\prod_{p\mid N}\frac{(p-1)^2}{p^2-p+1}+O\left(\frac{N(\log\log N)^2}{\log N}\right),$$

where $N$ is a positive integer $>2$, $p$ runs over the prime numbers, and $d(n)$ is the number of divisors of the positive integer $n$. The proof, which is straightforward and uses only well-known results, is similar to the proof given by Titchmarsh (also under the assumption of the E. R. H.) for a somewhat analogous asymptotic formula for $\sum_{l<p\leqq x}d(p-l)$, where $l$ is a fixed non-zero integer [Rend. Circ. Mat. Palermo **54**, 414–429 (1930); **57**, 478–479 (1933)]. Remark: The reviewer does not know how to justify the assertion on the next to the last line of p. 78, namely, that if $N$ is any positive integer, $M=N^{\frac{1}{4}}$, and $n$ is any positive integer $\leqq M$, then $|\pi(N;n,N)-\pi(N-nM;n,N)-\pi(nM;n,N)|$ is less than an absolute constant, $\pi(y;k,l)$ being the number of prime numbers not exceeding $y$ and congruent to $l$ modulo $k$. However, the proof can easily be modified so that the statement in question is not used. One need only replace $\pi(nM;n,N)$ in the statement of Lemma 2 and in its three occurrences on the third from the last line of p. 82 by $\pi(N;n,N)-\pi(N-nM;n,N)$ and also replace $\int_2^{nM}dz/\log z$ on the next to the last line of p. 82 by $\int_{N-nM}^{N}dz/\log z$.

*P. T. Bateman* (Urbana, Ill.).

Referred to in P36-33.

**N40-24** **(16, 116c)**

**Iseki, Kanesiroo. On the divisor-problem generated by $\zeta^\alpha(s)$.** Nat. Sci. Rep. Ochanomizu Univ. **4**, 175 (1954).

For real $\alpha>0$, put

$$\zeta^\alpha(s)=\sum_{n=1}^{\infty}d_\alpha(n)n^{-s}\quad(\text{Re } s>1),\qquad D_\alpha(x)=\sum_{n\leqq x}d_\alpha(n).$$

Then

$$(*)\qquad D_\alpha(x)\sim\frac{1}{\Gamma(\alpha)}x(\log x)^{\alpha-1}\quad(x\to\infty).$$

It is stated that (*) is deduced from a lemma which may be proved by the Ikehara-Wiener-Landau method for Tauberian theorems. Details of the proof are not given.

*L. Carlitz* (Durham, N. C.).

Referred to in F25-8.

**N40-25** **(16, 1089f)**

**Arzt, Sholom. On a mean value theorem for certain divisor functions taken over exponential sequences.** Abridgment of a dissertation, New York University, 1951. 5 pp.

The author summarizes some results obtained in his doctoral dissertation concerning the asymptotic evaluation of sums of the type $\sum_{n\leqq x}\sigma_{-s}(f(n))$, where $f(n)=g(b_1^n,b_2^n)$, with $g(x,y)$ a homogeneous polynomial and $b_1$, $b_2$ positive or negative integers. Previous results of this nature were obtained by the reviewer [Duke Math. J. **17**, 159–168

(1950); MR **11**, 715] for the case where $f(n)$ is a polynomial in $n$. *R. Bellman* (Santa Monica, Calif.).

Citations: MR 11, 715h = N40-16.

## N40-26 (17, 238e)

**Erdös, P. On some problems of Bellman and a theorem of Romanoff.** J. Chinese Math. Soc. (N.S.) **1** (1951), 409–421. (Chinese summary)

Let $\sigma_s(n)$ denote $\sum d^s$ where the sum ranges over all divisors $d$ of $n$. It is proved that if $f(x)$ is a polynomial with integral coefficients and $a$ is any integer then there exists a constant $A$ such that

$$\sum_{k=1}^{x} \sigma_{-1}f(a^k)=Ax+o(x).$$

This is a partial extension of results by R. Bellman [Duke Math. J. **17** (1950), 159–168; MR **11**, 715] who treated sums $\sum \sigma_{-s}f(k)$. Also there is a positive constant $c$ such that for $0<s<c$

$$\lim_{x\to\infty}\frac{1}{x}\sum_{k=1}^{x}\sigma_{-s}(a^k-1)=\infty.$$

For fixed $a$ and $f(x)$ it is established that the asymptotic density of integers of the form $p+f(a^n)$ is positive. This generalizes a theorem of N. P. Romanoff [Math. Ann. **109** (1934), 668–678] who treated the case $f(x)=x$.
*I. Niven* (Berkeley, Calif.).

Citations: MR 11, 715h = N40-16.

## N40-27 (17, 349b)

**Tong, Kwang-Chong. On divisor problems.** J. Chinese Math. Soc. **2** (1953), 258–266. (Chinese. English summary)

From the convexity of Lindelöf's function $\mu(\sigma)$ in the Riemann zeta-function [cf. Titchmarsh, The theory of the Riemann zeta-function, Oxford, 1951, Chap. V; MR **13**, 741] the author proves that

| $k=$ | 4 | 5 | 6 | 7 | 8 | 9 | 10 | 11 |
|---|---|---|---|---|---|---|---|---|
| $\alpha_k\leqq$ | 1/2 | 4/7 | 5/8 | 71/107 | 41/59 | 31/43 | 26/35 | 19/25 |
| $\beta_k\leqq$ | 23/54 | 1/2 | 35/62 | 11/18 | 149/230 | | | |

where $\alpha_k$ and $\beta_k$ (cf. Titchmarch, loc. cit. Chap. XII) have their usual meanings in the divisor problem.
*L. K. Hua* (Zbl **51**, 280).

Citations: MR 13, 741c = M02-2.

## N40-28 (17, 462c)

**Tong, Kwang-Chang. On division problems. I.** Acta Math. Sinica **5** (1955), 313–324. (Chinese. English summary)

Let $d_k(n)$ be the number of positive integral solutions of $n=n_1\cdots n_k$; let $D_k(x)=\sum_{n\leqq x}d_k(n)$; let

$$R_k(x)=x(a_{k0}+a_{k1}\log x+\cdots+a_{k,k-1}\log^{k-1}x)$$

be the residue of $\zeta(s)^k x^s/s$ at $s=1$; and let $\Delta_k(x)=D_k(x)-R_k(x)$. The author proves the following results. (1) Let $N\geqq 0$; let the integer $h$ be large compared with $k/2$; and let $\min(x, x+hy)>0$. Then

$$\int_0^y\cdots\int_0^y \Delta_k(x+y_1+\cdots+y_h)dy_1\cdots dy_h=\frac{y^h}{(-2)^k}$$
$$+\sum_{n\leqq N}d_k(n)\int_0^y\cdots\int_0^y I_{k,0}(n, x+y_1+\cdots+y_h)dy_1\cdots dy_h$$
$$+\sum_{l=0}^{h}(-1)^{h-l}\binom{h}{l}\sum_{n>N}d_k(n)I_{k,h}(n, x+ly).$$

Here

$$I_{k,j}(n,x)=\frac{2^k}{2\pi i}\int_{C_j}\frac{x^{j+1-s}}{(2\pi)^{ks}n^s}\frac{(\Gamma(s)\cos\frac{1}{2}\pi s)^k}{(1-s)(2-s)\cdots(j+1-s)}ds$$
$$(x>0;\ n=1, 2, 3, \cdots),$$

where $C_j$, $j=0, 1, 2, \cdots$, is the polygon with vertices at

$$-i\infty,\ -i,\ j+\frac{3}{2}-i,\ j+\frac{3}{2}+i,\ i,\ i\infty.$$

(2) If $nx$ is large, then

$$I_{k,j}(n,x)\sim\sum_{m=0}^{\infty}c_{kjm}x^{j+1}(nx)^{-\frac{(k+1)}{2k}-\frac{(j+m)}{k}}\cos\{2k\pi(nx)^{1/k}+\theta_{kjm}\}$$

where $c_{kj0}=(2^j\pi^{1+j}\sqrt{k})^{-1}$, $\theta_{kj0}=\frac{1}{2}\pi(\frac{1}{2}(k-3)-j)$, and $c_{kjm}$ and $\theta_{kjm}$ are real numbers. From these two lemmas, and with the help of a further asymptotic result, the following two main theorems are deduced: (3) There exist two positive constants $c_k$ and $C_k$ such that, if $x\geqq 1$ and $-C_kx^{(k-1)/2k}\leqq t\leqq C_kx^{(k-1)/2k}$, there is at least one $y$ satisfying $x\leqq y\leqq x+c_kx^{1-1/k}$ and $\Delta_k(y)=t$. (4) There exists a positive constant $\tilde{C}_k$ such that

$$\left\{\frac{1}{x}\int_0^x|\Delta_k(y)|^\lambda dy\right\}^{1/\lambda}\geqq\tilde{C}_kx^{\frac{k-1}{2k}}$$

for every $\lambda\geqq 1$ and every $x\geqq 1$. [See G. Voronoi, Ann. Sci. Ecole norm. Sup. (3) **21** (1904), 207–267, 459–533; G. H. Hardy, Proc. London Math. Soc. (2) **15** (1916), 1–25; E. C. Titchmarsh, The theory of the Riemann zeta-function, Oxford, 1951, ch. 12, in particular p. 272; MR **13**, 741.] *K. Mahler* (Manchester).

Citations: MR 13, 741c = M02-2.
Referred to in N40-33.

## N40-29 (18, 874b)

**Halberstam, H. An asymptotic formula in the theory of numbers.** Trans. Amer. Math. Soc. **84** (1957), 338–351.

The formula in question is

$$\sum_{\nu=1}^{n-1}\sigma_\alpha(\nu)\sigma_\beta(n-\nu)=A_1\sigma_{\alpha+\beta+1}(n)+A_2n^\alpha\sigma_{-\alpha+\beta+1}(n)+$$
$$A_3n^\beta\sigma_{\alpha-\beta+1}(n)+A_4n^{\alpha+\beta}\sigma_{-\alpha-\beta+1}(n)+O(n^\omega\log^\lambda n),$$

where $\sigma_r(m)$ is the sum of the $r$th powers of the (positive) divisors of the positive integer $m$, and $A_1$, $A_2$, $A_3$, $A_4$, $\omega$, $\lambda$ are constants depending on the positive constants $\alpha$, $\beta$. This is an improvement of previous results, stated by the reviewer and proved by the author, involving the first explicit term and weaker error terms. The improvement affects the case $\alpha+\beta<1$ and amounts in the main to a reduction of $\omega$ from $\max(\alpha,\beta)+1$ to $\frac{3}{4}+\frac{1}{2}(\alpha+\beta)$ or $\frac{1}{2}+(\alpha+\beta)$ according as $\alpha+\beta<\frac{1}{2}$ or $\geqq\frac{1}{2}$. This is achieved by the use, in place of the original elementary method, of an analytical method (the Hardy-Ramanujan-Littlewood 'circle method') on the lines of Estermann's treatment of the corresponding problem with $\alpha=\beta=0$ [Proc. London Math. Soc. (2) **31** (1930), 123–133]. The present method uses A. Weil's estimate [Proc. Nat. Acad. Sci. U.S.A. **34** (1948), 204–207; MR **10**, 234]) of Kloosterman sums. Estermann used earlier estimates of these sums.
*A. E. Ingham* (Cambridge, England).

Citations: MR 10, 234e = T25-5.

## N40-30 (19, 839c)

**Hooley, C. An asymptotic formula in the theory of numbers.** Proc. London Math. Soc. (3) **7** (1957), 396–413.

Let $d(n)$ be the number of divisors of $n$ and $d_3(n)$ be the number of representations of $n$ as the product of three factors. In this paper the author investigates the difficult problem of obtaining asymptotic formulae for the sums

$$A_0(x)=\sum_{n\leqq x}d_3(n)d(n+a),\quad B_0(x)=\sum_{n\leqq x}d_3(n+a)d(n).$$

His results confirm formulae involving these sums which were conjectured earlier by Titchmarsh [Quart. J. Math. Oxford Ser. **13** (1942), 129–152; MR **4**, 131]. The main theorem is as follows. As $x \to \infty$,

$$A_0(x) = \tfrac{1}{2}A(a)x\log^3 x + O\{x(\log x \log\log x)^2\},$$

where $A(m) = \sum_{n=1}^{\infty} c_n(m)\psi(n)/n^2$, $\psi(n) = \sum_{d|n} \phi(d)/d$, and $c_n(m)$ is the Ramanujan sum. This theorem is also valid when $A_0(x)$ is replaced by $B_0(x)$. The analysis depends upon a detailed study of the auxiliary sums

$$C_\alpha(x, k) = \sum_{\substack{n \leq x \\ n \equiv a \pmod{k}}} n^\alpha d(n), \quad D_\alpha(x, k) = \sum_{\substack{n \leq x \\ n \equiv a \pmod{k}}} n^\alpha d^2(n),$$

where $\alpha$ is a suitable positive constant. The estimate of the Kloosterman sum due to Weil [Proc. Nat. Acad. Sci. U.S.A. **34** (1948), 204–207; MR **10**, 234] is also required. By employing similar methods the author has derived formulae for the 'conjugate' sum $\sum_{v=1}^{m-1} d_3(m-v)d(v)$ and for the sums $\sum_{n \leq x} d_3(n)r(n+a)$, $\sum_{v=1}^{m-1} d_3(m-v)r(v)$, where $r(n)$ is the number of representations of $n$ as the sum of two integral squares. *A. L. Whiteman.*

Citations: MR 4, 131c = N40-6; MR 10, 234e = T25-5.
Referred to in N36-84, N40-48, N48-28, P02-18.

## N40-31 (20# 831)

**Vinogradov, A. I.; and Linnik, Yu. V. Estimate of the sum of the number of divisors in a short segment of an arithmetic progression.** Uspehi Mat. Nauk (N.S.) **12** (1957), no. 4(76), 277–280. (Russian)

Suppose that $(l, D) = 1$ and $0 < l < D$. Let $S = \sum_{nD+l \leq x} \tau(nD+l)$, where $\tau(m)$ denotes the number of divisors of $m$. An upper bound for $S$ is obtained when $D \leq x^{1-\alpha}$, where $\alpha$ is fixed and $0 < \alpha < \frac{1}{2}$, namely

$$(*) \qquad S < C(\alpha)\frac{x}{D}\log\frac{x}{D}\prod_{p|D}(1-p^{-1}),$$

where $C(\alpha)$ depends on $\alpha$. The same expression, with a different $C(\alpha)$, also gives a lower bound for $S$, as is easily seen. The proof of (*) is technically elementary, using division into several cases. The question is raised: how should $C(\alpha)$ behave as $\alpha \to 0$? *H. Davenport* (London)

Referred to in N60-75.

## N40-32 (20# 3107)

**Hooley, Christopher. On the representation of a number as the sum of a square and a product.** Math. Z. **69** (1958), 211–227.

This paper is concerned with the asymptotic behaviour of the sum

$$\kappa(n) = \sum_{|\nu| < \sqrt{n}} d(n-\nu^2),$$

i.e. the number of solutions of $n = \lambda\mu + \nu^2$ in integers $\lambda, \mu, \nu$ $(\lambda, \mu > 0)$, when the integer $n$ is large and not a square. By elementary transformations familiar in this type of problem it is first proved that

$$\kappa(n) = 4\sqrt{n}\sum_{\lambda < \sqrt{n}} \frac{\rho(\lambda)}{\lambda} + O\Big(\sum_{\lambda < \sqrt{n}} \rho(\lambda)\Big) = \kappa_1 + O(\kappa_2),$$

where $\rho(\lambda)$ is the number of roots of the quadratic congruence $\nu^2 \equiv n \pmod{\lambda}$. By the theory of such congruences, $\kappa_1$ and $\kappa_2$ are then reduced to sums involving characters $\chi_{d_1}(l) = (d_1|l)$ ($l$ odd), or 0 ($l$ even), where $(d_1|l)$ is Jacobi's symbol, and $d_1$ ranges over certain divisors of $n$. This, however, does not determine the asymptotic behaviour of $\kappa_1$ and $\kappa_2$ in simple explicit terms. Nevertheless, by a series of analytical devices, including, among others, the Selberg sieve method and the estimation of character sums, the author is able to prove that $\kappa_2 = o(\kappa_1)$, and so obtain an asymptotic formula for $\kappa(n)$. The final result is of the form

$$\kappa(n) = 4\sqrt{n}\Big\{1 + O\Big(\frac{\log\log n}{\log n}\Big)\Big\}F(n) \sim 4\sqrt{n}F(n).$$

Here, $F(n) = (\log\sqrt{n} + \gamma)f_n(1) + f_n'(1)$; $\gamma$ is Euler's constant; and

$$f_n(s) = \frac{K(s)}{\zeta(2s)}\sum_{d^2|n;\,(d,2)=1} \frac{d}{d^{2s}} L_{n/d^2}(s),$$

where $K(s)$ is defined for $s > \frac{1}{2}$ by an absolutely convergent power series in $2^{-s}$, and $L_{d_1}(s) = L(s, \chi_{d_1})$.

By way of contrast, the author mentions the 'conjugate' problem of

$$N(x, n) = \sum_{0 < \nu \leq x} d(\nu^2 - n),$$

i.e. the number of solutions of $n = \nu^2 - \lambda\mu$, $\nu \leq x$ in integers $\lambda, \mu, \nu$ $(\lambda, \nu > 0)$, when $x \to \infty$ but $n$ is now fixed. Here, $d_1$ is confined to a fixed finite set of values and the major difficulties of the problem of $\kappa(n)$ do not arise. *A. E. Ingham* (Cambridge, England)

Referred to in E20-88, N40-47.

## N40-33 (20# 5173)

**Tong, Kwang-Chang. On divisor problems. II, III.** Acta Math. Sinica **6** (1956), 139–152, 515–541. (Chinese. English summary)

Let $d_k(n)$ be the number of integral solutions of $n = n_1 \cdots n_k$; let $D_k(x) = \sum_{n \leq x} d_k(n)$; let $R_k(x)$ be the residue of $\zeta^k(s)x^s/s$ at $s = 1$; and let $\Delta_k(x) = D_k(x) - R_k(x)$. The author continues the work of his earlier paper with the same title [same Acta **5** (1955), 313–324; MR **17**, 462]. He proves in part II that, if $l$ is any positive integer, then

$$\limsup_{x \to \infty} \frac{(-1)^{[(k-1)/4]}\Delta_k(x)}{(x\log x)^{(k-1)/2k}(\log\log x)^{k-1}} > 0 \quad \text{if } k \neq 4l+1,$$

$$\liminf_{x \to \infty} \frac{(-1)^{[(k-1)/4]}\Delta_k(x)(\log\log\log x)^{(k+1)(k-2)/2k}}{x^{(k-1)/2k}(\log x)^{(k-2)/2k}(\log\log x)^{k-2}} < 0 \quad \text{if } k = 2l,$$

$$\liminf_{x \to \infty} \frac{(-1)^{[(k-1)/4]}\Delta_k(x)(\log\log\log x)^{(k-1)(k-3)/2k}}{x^{(k-1)/2k}(\log x)^{(k-3)/2k}(\log\log x)^{k-2}} < 0 \quad \text{if } k = 4l-1,$$

$$\lim_{x \to \infty} \begin{Bmatrix}\sup \\ \inf\end{Bmatrix} \frac{\Delta_k(x)(\log\log\log x)^{(k^2-1)/2k}}{(x\log x)^{(k-1)/2k}(\log\log x)^{k-2}} \begin{Bmatrix} > \\ < \end{Bmatrix} 0 \quad \text{if } k = 4l+1.$$

Let, further, $\sigma_k$ be the lower bound of $\sigma$ for which

$$\int_{-\tau}^{+\tau} |\zeta(\sigma+it)|^{2k} dt \ll \tau^{1+\varepsilon},$$

where $\varepsilon > 0$ is arbitrarily small. The main result of part III is then that

$$\int_0^x \Delta_k(y)^2 dy = \frac{1}{(4k-2)\pi^2}\sum_{n=1}^{\infty} \frac{d_k(n)^2}{n^{1+1/k}} x^{2-1/k} + \begin{cases} O(x^{2+\varepsilon-(3-4\sigma_k)/(2k(1-\sigma_k)-1)}) & \text{if } k > 2, \\ O(x(\log x)^5) & \text{if } k = 2. \end{cases}$$

*K. Mahler* (Manchester)

Citations: MR 17, 462c = N40-28.

## N40-34 (21# 30)

**Erdös, P. Asymptotic formulas for some arithmetic functions.** Canad. Math. Bull. **1** (1958), 149–153.

Let $\alpha$ be an irrational number, and let $d(n, m)$ denote the number of divisors of the greatest common divisor of $n$ and $m$. The author proves that $\sum_{n=1}^{x} d(n, [\alpha n]) \sim \frac{1}{6}\pi^2 x$ if and only if, for every positive number $c$, there are only a finite number of pairs of positive integers $a$, $b$ for which $\alpha < a/b < \alpha + (1+c)^{-b}$. He states, without proof, the corresponding result with the number of divisors replaced by the sum of the divisors. *T. Estermann* (London)

## N40-35 (21# 34)

**Linnik, Yu. V. Dispersion of divisors and quadratic forms in progressions and certain binary additive problems.** Dokl. Akad. Nauk SSSR **120** (1958), 960–962. (Russian)

Let $d(m)$ denote the number of divisors of $m$, and let

$r(m)$ denote the number of representations of $m$ by $Q(x, y)$, a positive primitive binary quadratic form of discriminant $d<0$. Let

$$f(n) = \sum_{\substack{m=1 \\ m\equiv l \pmod{D}}}^{n} d(m), \qquad g(n) = \sum_{\substack{m=1 \\ m\equiv n \pmod{D}}}^{n} r(m),$$

where $1\leq l\leq D$ and $(l, D)=1$. The author first states that asymptotic formulae for $f(n)$, $g(n)$ as $n\to\infty$, valid for $D<n^{\frac{2}{3}-\varepsilon}$, can be proved by using André Weil's estimate for Kloosterman sums. These are of the form

$$f(n) = F(n, D)+O(n^{1-\alpha}), \qquad g(n) = G(n, D)+O(n^{1-\alpha}),$$

where explicit values for $F(n, D)$, $G(n, D)$ are given, the latter being somewhat complicated. The author goes on to announce results on the mean square deviation of $f(n)$ and $g(n)$ when $D$ varies in an interval less restricted than that mentioned above. Theorem 1. Suppose $n^{\frac{1}{2}}\leq D_1<n^{1-\eta}$, $D_2=D_1^{1-\zeta}$, $l\leq n$, where $\eta$, $\zeta$ are fixed small positive numbers. Then

$$\sum_{\substack{D=D_1 \\ (D,l)=1}}^{D_2} (f(n)-F(n, D))^2 = O(n^{2-\tau}D_2D_1^{-2}),$$

for some $\tau>0$, with a similar result for $g(n)$ but without the condition $(D, l)=1$. Several applications are also announced. One is to an asymptotic formula for

$$\sum_{m=1}^{n} d(m)d_k(m+l),$$

where $d_k(\nu)$ denotes the number of expressions for $\nu$ as a product of $k$ factors, and $k\geq 3$. Another is that if $D$ is given and $n>n_0(D)$ then $n$ is representable as $\Pi_1+\Pi_2$, where $\Pi_1$ is a product of primes $\equiv 1 \pmod 4$ and $\Pi_2$ is a product of primes $\equiv 1 \pmod D$. {Obviously $n$ must be understood to be even if $D$ is even.}

*H. Davenport* (Cambridge, England)

Referred to in P36-27.

## N40-36 (21# 35)

**Yüh, Ming-i. A divisor problem.** Sci. Record (N.S.) **2** (1958), 326–328.

It is a question of the lower bound $\alpha_3$ of $\alpha$ for which $\sum_{n\leq x} d_3(n)=xP_3(\log x)+O(x^\alpha)$, where $P_3$ is a quadratic polynomial. The author announces the result $\alpha_3\leq 14/29$, improving on the reviewer's 37/75 [Quart. J. Math. Oxford Ser. **12** (1941), 193–200; MR **3**, 269] and also on the (not cited) value $0.493\cdots$ of R. A. Rankin [ibid. (2) **6** (1955), 147–153; MR **17**, 240]. The paper reproduces the breaking up of the main sum into subsums, but not the actual estimation, said to depend on methods of both van der Corput and Vinogradov.

*F. V. Atkinson* (Canberra)

Citations: MR 3, 269d = N40-5; MR 17, 240a = L99-4.
Referred to in N40-37, N40-39, N40-41.

## N40-37 (21# 1959)

**Yüh, Ming-i. A divisor problem.** Acta Math. Sinica **8** (1958), 496–506. (Chinese. English summary)

The paper gives details of the proof that the remainder term in the asymptotic formula for $\sum_{n\leq x} d_3(n)$ is $O(x^{14/29+\varepsilon})$; the result was announced previously in Sci. Record (N.S.) **2** (1958), 326–328 [MR **21** #35].

*F. V. Atkinson* (Canberra)

Citations: MR 21# 35 = N40-36.

## N40-38 (21# 1287)

**Yin, Wen-lin. On Dirichlet's divisor problem.** Sci. Record (N.S.) **3** (1959), 6–8.

Let

$$\Delta(x) = \sum_{n\leq x} d(n)-x\log x-(2\gamma-1)x,$$

and let $\theta$ be the inf. of the positive numbers $\alpha$ such that $\Delta(x)=O(x^\alpha)$. It was proved by T. T. Chin [Sci. Rep. Tsing Hua Univ. **5** (1950), 402–427] and H.-E. Richert [Math. Z. **58** (1953), 204–218; MR **15**, 11] that $\theta\leq 15/46$. In analogy with a result of L. K. Hua [Quart. J. Math. **13** (1942), 18–29; MR **4**, 190] on the circle problem, it is announced in the present paper that $\theta\geq 13/40$. There are brief remarks on the method of proof, indicating that it is similar to Hua's.

*W. J. LeVeque* (Ann Arbor, Mich.)

Citations: MR 4, 190e = P20-2; MR 15, 11h = N40-22.
Referred to in N40-41.

## N40-39 (21# 3388)

**Yin, Wen-lin. Piltz's divisor problem for $k=3$.** Sci. Record (N.S.) **3** (1959), 169–173.

Let $\theta$ be the lower bound of $\alpha$ such that $\sum_{n\leq x} d_3(n)=xP(\log x)+O(x^\alpha)$, where $P$ is a certain quadratic. Improving on a recent result of Yüh Ming-I [same Record **2** (1958), 326–328; MR **21** #35], the author gives the result $\theta\leq 25/52$, and indicates the main lemmas and steps in the proof. Other methods are stated to yield the even better results $\theta\leq 10/21$, $\theta\leq 8/17$.

*F. V. Atkinson* (Canberra)

Citations: MR 21# 35 = N40-36.

## N40-40 (22# 2582)

**Chih, Tsung-tao. A divisor problem.** Acad. Sinica Science Record **3** (1950), 177–182.

Let $d(n)$ be the number of divisors of $n$ and put $D(x)=\sum_{n\leq x} d(n)$. In this paper the following two theorems are proved. Theorem 1: Let $\phi(x)$ be positive and increasing and $\phi(x)/x$ decreasing for $x>0$. Further suppose that $\phi(x)/x\to 0$ and $\phi(x)/\log^2 x\to\infty$ as $x\to\infty$. Then we have for almost all $x>0$: $D(x+\phi(x))-D(x)\sim\phi(x)\log x$. Theorem 2: Let $\phi(x)$ be positive and increasing and $\phi(x)/x$ decreasing for $x>0$. Further suppose that $\phi(x)/x\to 0$ and $\phi(x)/\log^6 x\to\infty$ as $x\to\infty$. Then we have for almost all $x>0$:

$$D(x+\phi(x))-D(x) = \phi(x)\log x+2\gamma\phi(x)+o(\phi(x)),$$

where $\gamma$ is Euler's constant. The method employed is essentially that used by A. Selberg [Arch. Math. Naturvid. **47** (1943), no. 6, 87–105; MR **7**, 48] to study the normal density of primes in small intervals, and the difference between consecutive primes.

*A. L. Whiteman* (Princeton, N.J.)

Citations: MR 7, 48e = N08-4.

## N40-41 (22# 2583)

**Chih, Tsungtao. The Dirichlet's divisor problem.** Sci. Rep. Nat. Tsing Hua Univ. Ser. A **5** (1950), 402–427.

Let $d(n)$ denote the number of divisors of $n$. Dirichlet's divisor problem is concerned with the estimation of

$$\Delta(x) = \sum_{n\leq x} d(n)-x\log x-(2\gamma-1)x,$$

where $\gamma$ is Euler's constant. Employing Titchmarsh's [Proc. London Math. Soc. (2) **38** (1934), 96–115] two-dimensional version of Van der Corput's method, the author proves that $\Delta(x)=O(x^{15/46}\log^{10/9} x)$. Because of the appearance of hyperbolic rather than circular sectors the analysis is essentially more intricate than in the circle problem. A difficult point, which involves the possible vanishing of a certain Hessian, is overcome by following a method due to Min [Trans. Amer. Math. Soc. **65** (1949), 448–472; MR **11**, 84].

{Note: To the best of the reviewer's knowledge the result in this 1950 paper has not subsequently been superseded. In 1953 H. E. Richert [Math. Z. **58** (1953), 204–218; MR **15**, 11] proved independently that

$$\Delta(x) = O(x^{15/46}\log^{30/23} x).$$

Other important related papers published after 1950 are: R. A. Rankin [Quart. J. Math. Oxford Ser. (2) **6** (1955), 147–153; MR **17**, 240]; Yüh, Ming-i [Sci. Record (N.S.) **2** (1958), 326–328; MR **21** #35]; Yin, Wen-lin [ibid. **3** (1959), 6–8; MR **21** #1287].}

*A. L. Whiteman* (Princeton, N.J.)

Citations: MR 11, 84c = M15-8; MR 15, 11h = N40-22; MR 17, 240a = L99-4; MR 21# 35 = N40-36; MR 21# 1287 = N40-38.

## N40-42 (22# 10943)

**Tull, J. P. Average order of arithmetic functions.** Illinois J. Math. **5** (1961), 175–181.

Making use of a theorem of a previous paper [Pacific J. Math. **9** (1959), 609–615; MR **21** #6362] the author obtains estimates for the sums $\sum_{n<x}\mu_k(n)$, $\sum_{n<x}\mu_k(n)/n$, $\sum_{n<x}2^{\nu(n)}$, $\sum_{n<x}2^{\nu(n)}/n$, $\sum_{n<x}d(n^2)$, $\sum_{n<x}d(n^2)/n$, $\sum_{n<x}d(n)^2$, $\sum_{n<x}d(n)^2/n$, $\sum_{n<x}d_k(n)/n$, where $\mu_k$ is the characteristic function of the $k$th-power-free integers, $\nu(n)$ is the number of distinct prime factors of $n$, $d_k(n)$ is the number of solutions of $x_1x_2\cdots x_k=n$ and $d(n)=d_2(n)$.

*L. Carlitz* (Durham, N.C.)

Citations: MR 21# 6362 = N36-15.

## N40-43 (22# 12076)

**Vinogradov, A. I. On an estimate for quadratic forms used in arithmetics.** Vestnik Leningrad. Univ. **14** (1959), no. 19, 60–63. (Russian. English summary)

An estimate is given for the sum $\sum_{x=1}^{P}\tau^4(C+Bx-Ax^2)$, where $\tau(y)$ denotes the number of divisors of $y$ and $P$, $A$, $B$, $C$ and $D=B^2+4AC$ are integers for which constants $N$ and $\alpha>0$ exist such that $|D|<N$ and $P>N^{\alpha}$.

*W. H. Simons* (Vancouver, B.C.)

## N40-44 (22# 12081)

**Buhštab, A. A. An asymptotic estimate of certain numerical functions connected with the number of divisors.** Moskov. Gos. Ped. Inst. Uč. Zap. **108** (1957), 45–53. (Russian)

[An estimate for $\Sigma_{n\leqslant x, n\in\Omega(y)}d_k(n)$, where $\Omega(y)$ is the set of integers all of whose prime factors are $\leqslant y$. Ed.]

## N40-45 (23# A124)

**Cohen, Eckford**

**The number of unitary divisors of an integer.**

*Amer. Math. Monthly* **67** (1960), 879–880.

A short proof of Mertens' theorem:

$$T^*(x) \equiv \sum_{n\leq x} t(n) = \frac{x}{\zeta(2)}\left(\log x+2\gamma-1-\frac{2\zeta'(2)}{\zeta(2)}\right)+O(\sqrt{x}\log x),$$

where $t(n)$ is the number of "unitary" divisors of $n$; that is, the number of (ordered) factorizations of $n$ into two relatively prime factors.

*E. G. Straus* (Los Angeles, Calif.)

Referred to in N48-18.

## N40-46 (25# 3012)

**Linnik, Yu. V. [Linnik, Ju. V.]**

**Divisor problems and related binary additive problems. (Russian)**

*Proc. Internat. Congress Math.* 1958, *pp.* 313–321. *Cambridge Univ. Press, New York*, 1960.

The author displays asymptotic formulas for the sums $\sum_{n\leq x}\tau_2(n)\tau_k(n+1)$, $x\to\infty$, $k\geq 2$, where $\tau_k(m)$ stands for the number of integer solutions of the equation $\xi_1\xi_2\cdots\xi_k=m$. At the same time he presents some related results concerning the representation of integers by binary quadratic forms.

*S. Knapowski* (New Orleans, La.)

## N40-47 (27# 3610)

**Hooley, Christopher**

**On the number of divisors of a quadratic polynomial.**

*Acta Math.* **110** (1963), 97–114.

The author proves that if $-a$ is not a perfect square, then ($d(n)$ denotes the number of divisors of $n$)

$$\sum_{n\leq x} d(n^2+a) = A_2(a)x\log x+A_3(a)x+O(x^{8/9}(\log x)^3).$$

The proof uses the theory of binary quadratic forms and exponential sums, and is ingenious and complicated.

The author states that by his method he can obtain corresponding asymptotic formulas for $\sum_{n\leq x}d(an^2+bn+c)$ and $\sum_{n\leq x}r(an^2+bn+c)$, where $r(n)$ denotes the number of solutions of $n=x^2+y^2$.

Finally, the author shows that in the congruence $V^2\equiv D \pmod k$, $D$ fixed, $k$ variable, the ratio $V/k$ is uniformly distributed [see R. Bellman, Duke Math. J. **17** (1950), 159–168; MR **11**, 715; the author, Math. Z. **69** (1958), 211–227; MR **20** #3107; errata, MR **20**, p. 1372; Acta Math. **97** (1957), 189–210; MR **19**, 532; A. E. Ingham, J. London Math. Soc. **2** (1927), 202–208].

*P. Erdős* (Edmonton, Alta.)

Citations: MR 11, 715h = N40-16; MR 19, 532a = P36-17; MR 20# 3107 = N40-32.

Referred to in E20-92, N32-54, N32-64.

## N40-48 (27# 3611)

**Bredihin, B. M.**

**Binary additive problems of indefinite type. III. The additive problem of divisors. (Russian)**

*Izv. Akad. Nauk SSSR Ser. Mat.* **27** (1963), 777–794.

Part II appeared in same Izv. **27** (1963), 577–612 [MR **27** #121]. The author denotes by $Q(n)$ the number of solutions of the equation $xy-x_1x_2\cdots x_k=a$, where $x, y, x_1, x_2, \cdots, x_k$ are natural numbers, and $xy\leq n$; $a$ is a fixed integer (positive or negative). For large $n$ he obtains, for $k\geq 2$,

$$Q(n) = \frac{1}{(k-1)!}A_kB_k(a)n(\log n)^k + O(n(\log n)^{k-1}(\log\log n)^4),$$

where

$$A_k = \sum_{g=1}^{\infty}\frac{\mu(g)}{g^2}\prod_{p|a}p\left\{1-\left(1-\frac{1}{p}\right)^{k-1}\right\},$$

$$B_k(a) = \prod_{p|a}f(p)g(p,a).$$

Here

$$f(p) = \left\{1+\frac{1}{p}\left(1-\frac{1}{p}\right)^{k-2}\right\}^{-1},$$

$$g(p,a) = 1+\left(1-\frac{1}{p}\right)^k\sum_{t=1}^{\alpha(p)}\sum_{m=t}^{\infty}\frac{S_k(m)}{p^m} + \frac{1}{p}\left(1-\frac{1}{p}\right)^{k-2}\frac{S_k(\alpha(p))}{p^{\alpha(p)}},\qquad S_k(m) = \sum_{\substack{\beta_1+\cdots+\beta_k=m\\ \beta_i\geq 0}}1,$$

$\alpha(p)$ is the exact power of $p$ contained in $a$.

The case $k=2$ (much easier) was settled by Ingham [J. London Math. Soc. **2** (1927), 202–208], the (hard) case $k=3$ by Hooley [Proc. London Math. Soc. (3) **7** (1957), 396–413; MR **19**, 839]. The author settles the really difficult case $k \geq 4$ by the "dispersion method" of Linnik.
*S. Chowla* (University Park, Pa.)

Citations: MR 19, 839c = N40-30; MR 27# 121 = P36-29.
Referred to in N40-65, P36-40.

## N40-49 (27# 5740)

**Yüh, Ming-i; Wu, Fang**
**On the divisor problem for $d_3(n)$.**
*Sci. Sinica* **11** (1962), 1055–1060.

If $d_3(n)$ is the number of ways in which a positive integer $n$ can be expressed as a product of three factors, then

$$\sum_{n \leq x} d_3(n) = xP_3(\log x) + \Delta_3(x),$$

where $P_3(\log x)$ is a polynomial of degree 2 in $\log x$ and the best estimate of the error term $\Delta_3(x)$ so far obtained is

$$\Delta_3(x) = O(x^{14/29}).$$

This estimate is due to Yin [Acta Sci. Nat. Univ. Pekin. **5** (1959), 193–196].

By applications of a lemma of van der Corput, together with Schwarz's inequality, the authors succeed in replacing 14/29 by the smaller exponent 8/17.
*R. A. Rankin* (Bloomington, Ind.)

Referred to in N40-50, N40-55, N40-56, N40-57.

## N40-50 (28# 56)

**Yüh, Ming-i; Wu, Fang**
**On the divisor problem for $d_3(n)$.**
*Acta Math. Sinica* **12** (1962), 170–174 (*Chinese*); *translated as Chinese Math.* **3** (1963), 184–189.

This is the same paper as in Sci. Sinica **11** (1962), 1055–1060 [MR **27** #5740]. *R. A. Rankin* (Bloomington, Ind.)

Citations: MR 27# 5740 = N40-49.
Referred to in N40-56.

## N40-51 (28# 1186)

**Gordon, B.; Rogers, K.**
**Sums of the divisor function.**
*Canad. J. Math.* **16** (1964), 151–158.

Let $\tau(n)$ denote the number of divisors of a positive integer $n$, and let $u$ denote a positive square-free integer. The authors derive the following refinement of a result of Shapiro and Warga [Comm. Pure Appl. Math. **3** (1950), 153–176; MR **12**, 244]:

$$\sum_{\substack{n \leq x \\ (n,u)=1}}' \frac{\tau(n)}{n} =$$

$$\frac{1}{2} A \log^2 x + (A+B) \log x + C + O\left(x^{-1/2+\varepsilon} \exp \frac{c\sqrt{\log 3u}}{\log\log 3u}\right)$$

for some constant $c>0$. Here the dash $'$ beside the summation symbol indicates that $n$ runs over square-free integers satisfying the summation conditions. The letters $A$, $B$, $C$ are defined as follows:

$$A = \prod_{p \mid u} \frac{p}{p+2} \cdot \prod_{p} \frac{(p-1)^2(p+2)}{p^3},$$

$$B = A\left\{(2\gamma-1) + 2\sum_{p \mid u} \frac{\log p}{p-1} + 6 \sum_{p \nmid u} \frac{(p-1)\log p}{p^2(p+2)}\right\},$$

$$C = C(u) = O\left(\exp \frac{c\sqrt{\log 3u}}{\log\log 3u}\right),$$

where $\gamma$ denotes Euler's constant. The method employs a sieve process which is used to sum $\tau(n)$ itself over the same range. *A. L. Whiteman* (Los Angeles, Calif.)

Citations: MR 12, 244c = P32-15.
Referred to in N40-74, N80-44.

## N40-52 (28# 3972)

**Chowla, S.; Walum, H.**
**On the divisor problem.**
*Norske Vid. Selsk. Forh.* (*Trondheim*) **36** (1963), 127–134.

Let $[x]$ be the greatest integer in $x$, and let $\psi(x) = x-[x]-\frac{1}{2}$. The well-known conjecture that the error term in Dirichlet's divisor problem is $O(x^{1/4+\varepsilon})$ for every $\varepsilon>0$ is, as is well known, equivalent to $\sum_{n \leq \sqrt{x}} \psi(x/n) = O(x^{1/4+\varepsilon})$ for every $\varepsilon>0$. The authors prove that

$$\sum_{n \leq \sqrt{x}} n\left(\psi^2\left(\frac{x}{n}\right) - \frac{1}{12}\right) = O(x^{3/4}).$$

This leads them to the following conjecture. For $0<x\leq 1$, let $g_1(x) = x-\frac{1}{2}$, $g_2(x) = x^2-x+\frac{1}{6}$, $\cdots$, where $g_r(x)$ is determined recursively by the conditions $g_r'(x) = rg_{r-1}(x)$ and $\int_0^1 g_r(x)\,dx = 0$, and define $g_r(x+1) = g_r(x)$. Let $G_{a,r}(x) = \sum_{n \leq \sqrt{x}} n^a g_r(f(x/n))$ where $a$ is a non-negative integer and $f(x)$ is the fractional part of $x$. (This is clearly the intended definition of $G_{a,r}(x)$; in the text $\psi$ is written for $f$.) The authors then conjecture that $G_{a,r}(x) = O(x^{a/2+1/4+\varepsilon})$ for every $\varepsilon>0$.

It will be observed that the result of this paper is somewhat stronger in the case $a=1$, $r=2$, while the divisor problem conjecture is the case $a=0$, $r=1$. The work of Hardy and Ingham on the divisor problem shows that the $\varepsilon$ cannot be omitted in this latter case of the conjecture.

There are several minor misprints in addition to the one noted above. *S. L. Segal* (Rochester, N.Y.)

## N40-53 (30# 4733)

**Chowla, S.; Walum, H.**
**On the divisor problem.**
*Proc. Sympos. Pure Math., Vol. VIII, pp.* 138–143. *Amer. Math. Soc., Providence, R.I.*, 1965.

Let $d(n)$ denote the number of divisors of $n$. It has been conjectured that $\sum_{n=1}^{x} d(n) = x\log x + (2\gamma-1)x + O(x^{1/4+\varepsilon})$, for every positive $\varepsilon$. If one writes $\psi(x) = x-[x]-\frac{1}{2}$, this conjecture about the order of the remainder can be put in the form $\sum_{n=1}^{\sqrt{x}} \psi(x/n) = O(x^{1/4+\varepsilon})$. In this paper the authors prove a related result; namely,

$$\sum_{n=1}^{\sqrt{x}} n\{\psi^2(x/n) - 1/12\} = O(x^{3/4}).$$

The proof is elementary, though intricate.
*H. W. Brinkmann* (Swarthmore, Pa.)

Referred to in N40-58.

## N40-54 (30# 1625)

**Gotusso, Laura**
**Studio dell'andamento del resto nel problema dei divisori.**
*Atti Sem. Mat. Fis. Univ. Modena* **13** (1964), 209–220.

The author reports on a numerical exploration of the error term $\Delta = \Delta(x)$ in the divisor problem

$$\sum_{n \leq x} d(n) = x(\log x + 2\gamma - 1) + \Delta(x)$$

for $x$ in the ranges 15000–16000, 60000–62000, 240000–243000, 960000–964000, 3601800–3604800. The extreme values of $\Delta$ in these ranges are compared with the functions

$$\Delta_1 = x^{15/46} \quad \text{and} \quad \Delta_2 = (x \log x)^{1/4} \log\log x.$$

The data would support either of the hypotheses

$$|\Delta(x)| < 2\Delta_1, \qquad |\Delta(x)| < \Delta_2.$$

The largest value of $\Delta$ was found to be $\Delta(3603600) = 222$. There are sample tables of 210 consecutive values of $\Delta(x)$ for each of the five regions.

*D. H. Lehmer* (Berkeley, Calif.)

**N40-55** **(30# 3869)**

**Chen, Jing-run**

**An improvement of asymptotic formulae for $\sum_{n\leq x} d_3(n)$ where $d_3(n)$ denotes the number of solutions of $n=pqr$.**

*Sci. Sinica* **13** (1964), 1185–1188.

The problem considered is that of the lower bound $\theta$ of constants $\alpha<1$ for which $\sum_{n\leq x} d_3(n) = xP_3(\log x) + O(x^\alpha)$ as $x \to \infty$, where $d_3(n)$ is the number of solutions of $n=pqr$ in positive integers $p, q, r$, and $P_3$ is a polynomial of degree 2. The paper is modelled on one by Ming-i Yüh and Fang Wu [Sci. Sinica **11** (1962), 1055–1060; MR **27** #5740], and the author claims to improve the result $\theta \leqq 8/17$ of that paper to $\theta \leqq 5/11$. The present paper, however, introduces gratuitous (if unimportant) mistakes, such as the omission of coefficients $\delta(y)$ when a sum $\sum_{p,q,r} f(pqr)$ is (or should be) rewritten as $\sum_{y,r} \delta(y) f(yr)$, and suppresses much essential detail in the development and application of the basic inequalities. The main novelty seems to lie in the use, not only of non-trivial estimates of trigonometric sums as in the earlier paper, but also of van der Corput's "approximate functional equation" for such sums. Details have, however, not been filled in by this reviewer.

*A. E. Ingham* (Cambridge, England)

Citations: MR 27# 5740 = N40-49.

**N40-56** **(30# 4732)**

**Chen, Jing-run**

**On the divisor problem for $d_3(n)$.**

*Acta Math. Sinica* **14** (1964), 549–558 *(Chinese); translated as Chinese Math.—Acta* **5** (1964), 591–601.

If $d_3(n)$ is the number of ways in which a positive integer $n$ can be expressed as a product of three factors, then $\sum_{n\leq x} d_3(n) = xP_3(\log x) + \Delta_3(x)$, where $P_3(\log x)$ is a polynomial of degree 2 in $\log x$, and the best estimate of the error term $\Delta_3(x)$ so far obtained is $\Delta_3(x) = O(x^{8/17})$. This estimate is due to Ming-i Yüh and Fang Wu [Sci. Sinica **11** (1962), 1055–1060; MR **27** #5740; Acta Math. Sinica **12** (1962), 170–174; MR **28** #56]. By applications of two lemmas of Vinogradov on trigonometric sums [Izv. Akad. Nauk SSSR Ser. Mat. **24** (1960), 777–786; MR **23** #A860], the author succeeds in replacing 8/17 by the smaller exponent 5/11.

*R. A. Rankin* (Glasgow)

Citations: MR 23# A860 = P20-19; MR 27# 5740 = N40-49; MR 28# 56 = N40-50.

**N40-57** **(32# 2384)**

**Chen Jing-run [Ch'en Ching-jun]**

**On the divisor problem for $d_3(n)$.**

*Sci. Sinica* **14** (1965), 19–29.

A further improvement in the error term in the formula

$$\sum_{n\leq x} d_3(n) = xP_3(\log x) + O(x^\alpha)$$

is obtained. Here $d_3(n)$ is the number of ways in which $n$ can be expressed as a product of three factors and $P_3$ is a polynomial of degree 2. Yüeh Min-i and Wu Fang [Sci. Sinica **11** (1962), 1055–1060; MR **27** #5740] proved that $\alpha_3 = \inf \alpha \leqq 8/17$. By complicated methods of van der Corput type, it is shown here that $\alpha_3 \leqq 5/11$.

*R. A. Rankin* (Glasgow)

Citations: MR 27# 5740 = N40-49.

**N40-58** **(31# 3391)**

**Segal, Sanford L.**

**A note on the average order of number-theoretic error terms.**

*Duke Math. J.* **32** (1965), 279–284.

Let $\tau(n)$ denote the number of divisors of $n$,

$$\Delta(x) = \sum_{n\leq x} \tau(n) - \{x \log x + (2\gamma - 1)x\}.$$

The reviewer and Walum [Proc. Sympos. Pure Math., Vol. VIII, pp. 138–143, Amer. Math. Soc., Providence, R.I., 1965; MR **30** #4733] used the result

$$\sum_{n\leq x} \Delta(n) = \tfrac{1}{2}x \log x + (\gamma - \tfrac{1}{4})x + O(x^{3/4})$$

which they attributed to Voronoĭ [Ann. Sci. École Norm. Sup. **(3) 21** (1904), 213–216; 245–249; 258–267; 472–480; 480–514] "in whose work of 1904 (unavailable to the authors) it is implicit". The author says "we reprove Voronoĭ's relatively inaccessible result". This he does by establishing a lemma of wide applicability.

If $\phi(n)$ is Euler's totient function, Mertens proved that if $E(x) = \sum_1^x \phi(n) - 3x^2/\pi^2$, then $E(x) = O(x \log x)$. Pillai and the reviewer [J. London Math. Soc. **5** (1930), 95–101] proved that $\sum_1^x E(n) \sim 3x^2/2\pi^2$. The author's result shows that this can be re-written as $\int_2^x E(u)\,du = o(x^2)$.

*S. Chowla* (University Park, Pa.)

Citations: MR 30# 4733 = N40-53.

Referred to in N40-59, N40-60.

**N40-59** **(32# 95)**

**Segal, Sanford L.**

**Erratum: A note on the average order of number-theoretic error terms.**

*Duke Math. J.* **32** (1965), 765.

Two errata are given to the article which appeared in same J. **32** (1965), 279–284 [MR **31** #3391]. To Condition (1) of the lemma on page 279 should be added the further hypothesis that $g''(x)$ is of constant sign for $x \geqq 1$. The second erratum refers to a misprint and is itself incorrect. An additional misprint occurs on page 282, Equation (8), where $(1+O)/y$ should be replaced by $1 + O(1/y)$.

Citations: MR 31# 3391 = N40-58.

**N40-60** **(33# 5575)**

**Segal, Sanford L.**

**Errata: "A note on the average order of number-theoretic error terms".**

*Duke Math. J.* **33** (1966), 821.

The author corrects some errors in his article in same J. **32** (1965), 279–284 [MR **31** #3391].

Citations: MR 31# 3391 = N40-58.

**N40-61** **(32# 7519)**

**Rieger, G. J.**

**Zum Teilerproblem von Atle Selberg.**

*Math. Nachr.* **30** (1965), 181–192.

Der Verfasser behandelt das A. Selbergsche Teilerproblem in arithmetischen Progressionen, d.h. die asymptotische Entwicklung von $\sum_{n<x,\, n\equiv l \bmod k} d_z(n)$, wo für beliebiges komplexes $z$, $d_z(n)$ durch $(\zeta(s))^z = \sum_{n=1}^\infty d_z(n) n^{-s}$ $(\sigma > 1)$ erklärt ist. Die Abschätzung geschieht gleichmäßig für $z$ in einer festen Kreisscheibe um $z=0$ und $k$ unterhalb einer festen Potenz von $\log x$. Anschließend wird ein allgemeinerer Satz hergeleitet, aus dem sich entsprechende Anwendungen für

$$\sum_{\substack{n<x\\ n\equiv l \bmod k}} z^{\omega(n)} \quad \text{und} \quad \sum_{\substack{n<x\\ n\equiv l \bmod k}} (d_z(n))^r$$

mit beliebigem ganzzahligem $r$ ergeben.

*H.-E. Richert* (Marburg)

**N40-62** **(34# 1284 )**

**Soni, Kusum**

**Some relations associated with an extension of Koshliakov's formula.**

*Proc. Amer. Math. Soc.* **17** (1966), 543–551.

The author considers seven formulae involving as parameters sequences $\{a_n\}$, $\{b_n\}$, $\{\lambda_n\}$, $\{l_n\}$ and numbers $\alpha$, $\alpha'$, $\beta$, $\beta'$. He shows that under certain conditions imposed on the parameters, the first formula implies each of the others, and under additional conditions, conversely, each of the others implies the first, so that they are all shown to be equivalent. For special values of the parameters, these are known formulae such as the functional equation of $\zeta^2(s)$, a summation formula of Voronoĭ, and a formula of Košljakov [see N. S. Košljakov, Messenger of Math. **58** (1928), 1–23].

*S. Knapowski* (Coral Gables, Fla.)

**N40-63** **(34# 5771 )**

**Erdős, P.**

**Asymptotische Untersuchungen über die Anzahl der Teiler von $n$.**

*Math. Ann.* **169** (1967), 230–238.

Let $d(n)$ denote the number of divisors of $n$. The following theorems are proved. (1) Let $h(x)$ be an arbitrary increasing function such that $h(x)\to\infty$ as $x\to\infty$. Let $f(x)>(\log x)^{2\log 2-1}e^{h(x)(\log\log x)^{1/2}}$. Then, for almost all $x$, $\sum_{u=1}^{f(x)} d(x+u)=(1+o(1))f(x)\log x$, and this cannot be improved. (2) Let $h(x)$ be an arbitrary function such that $h(x)\to\infty$ as $x\to\infty$. Then, for every $\varepsilon>0$, the density of numbers $x$ such that for every $t>(\log x)^{2\log 2-1}e^{h(x)(\log\log x)^{1/2}}$ one has $1-\varepsilon<(t\log x)^{-1}\sum_{i=1}^{t} d(x+i)<1+\varepsilon$ is equal to 1. (3) A similar result holds for $r(n)$, the number of solutions of $n=u^2+v^2$. (4) Let $h(x)$ be an arbitrary function such that $h(x)\to\infty$ as $x\to\infty$. Let $g(n)$ be a multiplicative real-valued function for which the series $\sum_{p,\alpha}(g(p^\alpha)-1)p^{-\alpha}$ and $\sum_{p,\alpha}(g(p^\alpha)-1)^2p^{-\alpha}$ converge. It is known that the mean value $\lim_{n=\infty} n^{-1}\sum_{k=1}^{n} g(k)=\alpha$, $\alpha\neq 0$, $\alpha\neq\infty$, exists. Let $\varepsilon>0$. Then the density of numbers $x$ such that $(1-\varepsilon)\alpha< t^{-1}\sum_{i=1}^{t} g(x+i)<(1+\varepsilon)\alpha$ for all $t>h(x)$ is equal to 1.

*L. Carlitz* (Durham, N.C.)

Referred to in N40-80.

**N40-64** **(34# 5778 )**

**Lavrik, A. F.**

**On the problem of divisors in segments of arithmetical progressions. (Russian)**

*Dokl. Akad. Nauk SSSR* **164** (1965), 1232–1234.

Let $\tau_k(n)$ denote the number of ways of expressing the integer $n$ as the product of $k$ positive integers. The author states a number of results, including an asymptotic formula for $\sum_{n\leq x, n\equiv l (\bmod D)}\tau_k(n)$ for integers $k$, $l$, $D$ satisfying $k\geqq 4$, $0\leqq l<D$, $(l,D)=1$, and which holds uniformly for $D$ up to a positive power (less than one) of $x$. Amongst the related results he gives a form of approximate functional equation for Dirichlet functions $L(s,\chi)$ formed with primitive characters $\chi$. This can then be used to estimate $L(\frac{1}{2}+it,\chi)$.

The method used is said to be a generalisation of that of Ju. V. Linnik [Mat. Sb. (N.S.) **53 (95)** (1961), 3–38; MR **22** #10964], who considered the case $k=4$. No further details are given.

{This article has appeared in English translation [Soviet Math. Dokl. **6** (1965), 1362–1364].}

*P. D. T. A. Elliott* (Nottingham)

Citations: MR 22# 10964 = P36-25.

Referred to in M05-48.

**N40-65** **(35# 1562 )**

**Pergel, J.**

**Generalization of Linnik's asymptotic formula for the additive problem of divisors to Gaussian numbers.**

*Studia Sci. Math. Hungar.* **2** (1967), 133–151.

Let $\tau_k(z)$ be the number of factorizations of the Gaussian integer $z$ as a product $\xi_1\xi_2\cdots\xi_k$ of Gaussian integers, with $\tau_2=\tau$, and let $\Omega$ be a star region, containing the origin as an inner point, in the complex plane. The author uses Ju. V. Linnik's "dispersion method" to obtain an asymptotic estimate

$$\sum_{z\in x\Omega}\tau(z+l)\tau_k(z) = (A_kB_k(l)/(k-1)!)|\Omega|x^2\log^k x + O(x^2\log^{k-1}x(\log\log x)^c),$$

where $|\Omega|$ is the area of $\Omega$, $c$ is a constant, and $A_k$ and $B_k(l)$ are explicitly given but complicated functions of the indicated parameters $k$, $l$. The analogous formula for the case in which $z$ and its factors are required to be rational integers and $\Omega$ is an interval has been proved by Linnik [*Dispersion method in binary additive problems* (Russian), Izdat. Leningrad. Univ., Leningrad, 1961; MR **25** #3920; English translation, Amer. Math. Soc., Providence, R.I., 1963; MR **29** #5804] and B. M. Bredihin [Izv. Akad. Nauk SSSR Ser. Mat. **27** (1963), 439–462; MR **26** #6149; ibid. **27** (1963), 777–794; MR **27** #3611].

*W. J. LeVeque* (Ann Arbor, Mich.)

Citations: MR 25# 3920 = P02-18; MR 26# 6149 = P48-7; MR 27# 3611 = N40-48; MR 29# 5804 = P02-19.

**N40-66** **(35# 4179 )**

**McDonagh, Sean**

**On the sum $\sum_{t<N^{1/k}} d(N-t^k)$.**

*Proc. Edinburgh Math. Soc.* (2) **15** (1967), 215–219.

The author proves the following theorem: If $N$, $k$, $l$ are positive integers, then $\sum (d(N-t^k))^l<N^{1/k}(\log N)^{c_{kl}}$. The author uses a method due to J. G. van der Corput [Nederl. Akad. Wetensch. Proc. **42** (1939), 547–553; MR **1**, 41]. See also the reviewer [J. London Math. Soc. **27** (1952), 7–15; MR **13**, 438; ibid. **28** (1953), 416–425; MR **15**, 104].

*P. Erdős* (Budapest)

Citations: MR 1, 41b = N40-1; MR 13, 438f = N40-19; MR 15, 104f = N32-13.

**N40-67** **(35# 6635 )**

**Corrádi, Keresztély; Kátai, Imre**

**A comment on K. S. Gangadharan's paper entitled "Two classical lattice point problems". (Hungarian. English summary)**

*Magyar Tud. Akad. Mat. Fiz. Oszt. Közl.* **17** (1967), 89–97.

The paper deals with lower estimation of the error term in the circle-problem and divisor-problem. The following theorem is proved. Let $r(n)$ be the number of representations of $n=x^2+y^2$, $d(n)$ the number of divisors of $n$. Put $R(x)=\sum_{n\leq x}r(n)=\pi x+P(x)$, and $D(x)=\sum_{n\leq x}d(n)=x\log x+(2\gamma-1)x+\Delta(x)$. Then

$$P(x) = \Omega_+(x^{1/4}\exp(c(\log\log x)^{1/4}(\log\log\log x)^{-3/4})),$$

$$\Delta(x) = \Omega_-(x^{1/4}\exp(c(\log\log x)^{1/4}(\log\log\log x)^{-3/4})),$$

as $x \to \infty$. The result is an improvement of a result of K. S. Gangadharan [Proc. Cambridge Philos. Soc. **57** (1961), 699–721; MR **24** #A92]. *P. Szüsz* (Stony Brook, N.Y.)

Citations: MR 24# A92 = N40-4.

## N40-68 (36# 1406)

**Žogin, I. I.**

**Certain asymptotic equations connected with the problem of Dirichlet on divisors. A generalization of the Dirichlet theorem. (Russian)**

*Sverdlovsk. Gos. Ped. Inst. Učen. Zap.* **31** (1965), 87–96.

Let $\tau(n; q, p)$ denote the number of divisors of $n$ which are congruent to $p$ (mod $q$). The author extends Dirichlet's classical estimate for the case $q=p=1$, by evaluating

$$(1/n)\sum_{t=1}^{n}\tau(t; q, p) = (1/p)\{\log n + 2\gamma - 1 - \log p + p/q - \int_0^1 [(1-t^{q/p})/(1-t)]\,dt\} + O(1/\sqrt{n}),$$

where $\gamma$ is Euler's constant.

*S. Chowla* (University Park, Pa.)

## N40-69 (38# 5730)

**Ennola, Veikko**

**A note on a divisor problem.**

*Ann. Univ. Turku. Ser. A I No.* 118 (1968), 11 *pp.*

Let $f(x) = \prod_{i=1}^{q}(f_i(x))^{\gamma_i}$ be an arbitrary polynomial with rational integral coefficients. The polynomials $f_i(x)$ are distinct, irreducible over the rational field and $f_i(x) > 0$ when $x > 0$. Put $\gamma = \sum_{i=1}^{q}\gamma_i$. Let $d(a)$ denote the number of positive divisors of the natural number $a$. In the case $q=\gamma=1$, i.e., when $f(x)$ is irreducible, P. Erdős [J. London Math. Soc. **27** (1952), 7–15; MR **13**, 438] proved that for $N \geqq 2$, $C_1 N \log N < \sum_{n=1}^{N-1} d(f(n)) < C_2 N \log N$, where $C_1$ and $C_2$ are positive constants. Applying Erdős' method, the author shows that for an arbitrary polynomial $f(x)$, as above, one has $C_1 N \log^\gamma N < \sum_{a=1}^{N} d(f(n)) < C_2 N \log^\gamma N$, for suitable positive $C_1$ and $C_2$.

*J. B. Kelly* (Tempe, Ariz.)

Citations: MR 13, 438f = N40-19.

## N40-70 (39# 145)

**Diamond, Harold George**

**Interpolation of the Dirichlet divisor problem.**

*Acta Arith.* **13** (1967/68), 151–168.

The divisor problem of Dirichlet is that of finding an asymptotic formula as $x \to \infty$ of the number of ordered pairs of positive integers $(m, n)$ whose product does not exceed $x$. This may be reformulated as the problem of estimating $\int_1^x dn * dn$, where $dn$ is the counting measure on the positive integers; such estimates are well known, as well as estimates for $\int_1^x dn^k$, the $k$-fold convolution.

The author's purpose is to give meaning to the expression $dA^z$ for $z$ an arbitrary complex number and $dA$ any real Borel measure on $[1, \infty)$, with positive point mass at 1. The method is essentially to reduce to a binomial series, in which one has an infinite expansion in terms of integral powers, whose meaning is already known.

A principal result is the following expression for the integral $\int_1^x dn^z$: (1) $\sum_{j=1}^{J} c_j \times (\log x)^{z-j} + O(x\exp(-\log x)^{a'})$, where the $c_j$'s depend on $z$, $J = (\log x)^a$, $a'$ a positive constant.

As a converse, the author proves the following: Suppose for some integers $\nu \geqq 2$ the equation (2) $\int_1^x dn^z = \sum_{j=1}^{\nu-1} c_j(\log x)^{z-j} + O(x(\log x)^{z-\nu})$ holds uniformly for all $z$ in some real interval $(0, \varepsilon)$, where the $c_j$'s are those appearing in (1). Then the prime number theorem follows.

In the course of his proofs the author obtains the expansion

$$(1/\Gamma(z))\sum_{n=0}^{\infty}(\Gamma(n+z)/\Gamma(n+1)^2)(\log x)^n = \sum_{n=1}^{N} a_n x \log x)^{z-n} + 2a_N\theta x(\log x)^{z-N} + O(\log^k x),$$

where $x \geqq x_0 = x_0(K)$, $N \leqq \frac{1}{2}\log x$, $\theta$ is a complex number of modulus less than one, and $K$ is a fixed compact set containing $z$.

The proof of this depends on elegant contour integration methods.

*B. Berlowitz* (Berkeley, Calif.)

## N40-71 (39# 4103)

**Krätzel, Ekkehard**

**Ein Teilerproblem.**

*J. Reine Angew. Math.* **235** (1969), 150–174.

Let $\sigma_{v,u}(a, b; k) = \sum_{n^a m^b = k} n^{av} m^{bu}$ and $D_{v,u}(a, b; x) = \sum_{k \leq x}\sigma_{v,u}(a, b; k)$, abbreviating $D_{0,0}(a, b; x)$ by $D(a, b; x)$. The latter function arises in a generalization of the Dirichlet divisor problem formulated by H.-E. Richert [Math. Z. **56** (1952), 21–32; MR **14**, 349]. The principal question involved is the determination of the least constant $\theta(a, b)$ in the error term $O(x^{\theta(a,b)})$ of the asymptotic formula for $D(a, b; x)$. The author's main result is $\theta(a, b) \geqq 1/(2a+2b)$. It is deduced from a generalization of the Voronoi identity which holds for the restricted case $a = b = 1$. The methods used, although suggested by Mellin transform theory, are basically methods of classical real analysis, following to some extent the ideas of Landau who in 1915 proved $\theta(1, 1) \geqq \frac{1}{4}$. The author also obtains integral and series representations of certain functions associated with $D_{v,u}(a, b; x)$.

*D. Rearick* (Boulder, Colo.)

Citations: MR 14, 349e = N52-13.

## N40-72 (41# 162)

**Erdős, P.; Kátai, I.**

**On the sum $\sum d_4(n)$.**

*Acta Sci. Math. (Szeged)* **30** (1969), 313–324.

Let $d_1(n)$ denote the number of divisors of $n$, and $d_k(n) = d_1(d_{k-1}(n))$ for $k \geqq 2$. It was conjectured by R. Bellman and H. N. Shapiro [Ann. of Math. (2) **49** (1948), 333–340; MR **9**, 414] that $\sum_{n \leq x} d_k(n) = (1+o(1))c_k x \log_k x$, where $\log_k$ denotes the $k$-fold logarithm. This conjecture was proved for $k=2$ and $k=3$ by the second author [Acta Sci. Math. (Szeged) **29** (1968), 199–206; MR **39** #5496; Publ. Math. Debrecen **16** (1969), 3–15]. In the present paper, by a complicated dissection, the conjecture is proved for $k=4$.

*H.-E. Richert* (Marburg)

Citations: MR 9, 414a = N52-7; MR 39# 5496 = N52-40.

## N40-73 (41# 1659)

**Kolesnik, G. A.**

**An improvement of the remainder term in the divisor problem. (Russian)**

*Mat. Zametki* **6** (1969), 545–554.

For the remainder in Dirichlet's divisor problem, the author obtains the exponent 12/37. 15/46 was known.

{This article has appeared in English translation [Math. Notes **6** (1969), 784–791].} *A. I. Vinogradov* (Leningrad)

## N40-74 (41# 1665)

**Kátai, I.**

**A note on a paper of Gordon and Rogers.**

*Ann. Univ. Sci. Budapest. Eötvös Sect. Math.* **12** (1969), 29–33.

Let $\tau(n)$ denote the number of divisors of $n$ and $\mu(n)$ the Möbius function. R. Gordon and K. Rogers [Canad. J. Math. **61** (1964), 151–158; MR **28** #1186] estimated the sums $D(x, u)=\sum_n |\mu(n)|\tau(n)$, $E(x, u)=\sum_n |\mu(n)|\tau(n)/n$, where the summation is over all positive integers $n$ not exceeding $x$ and relatively prime to $u$. They proved that $D(x, u) = Ax \log x + Bx + R_1(x)$, $E(x, u) = \frac{1}{2}A \log^2 x + (A+B) \log x + G + R_2(x)$, where

$$A = \prod_{p|u} (p/(p+2)) \prod_p p^{-3}(p-1)^2(p+2),$$

and

$$B = A\{(2\gamma-1)+2 \sum_{p|u} \log p/(p-1) + 6 \sum_{p\nmid u} (p-1) \log p/(p^2(p+2))\},$$

and where $\gamma$ is Euler's constant. Putting $K(u)=\exp(c(\log 3u)^{1/2} \log\log 3u)$, the present author proves that $R_1(x)=O(x^{1/2}(\log x)^3K(u))$, $R_2(x)=O(x^{-1/2}(\log x)^3K(u))$, $G=O(K(u))$, thereby improving corresponding estimates of Gordon and Rogers. The method of proof is simple and has previously been applied by the author [Magyar Tud. Akad. Mat. Fiz. Oszt. Közl. **16** (1966), 269–273; MR **38** #5726] to treat other problems.

*A. L. Whiteman* (Los Angeles, Calif.)

Citations: MR 28# 1186 = N40-51; MR 38# 5726 = N60-71.

## N40-75 (41# 3431 )

**Warlimont, Richard**

**On divisor problems in connection with squarefree numbers.**

*Monatsh. Math.* **74** (1970), 154–165.

Let $d(n)$ denote the divisor function and let $D(x)=\sum d(q_1q_2)$, $E(n)=\sum d(n-q_1q_2)$, the sums being taken, respectively, over squarefree numbers $q_1 \leqq \sqrt{x}$, $q_2 \leqq \sqrt{x}$ and $q_1 < \sqrt{x}$, $q_2 < \sqrt{x}$. Using estimates from an earlier paper [MR **41** #3430], the author derives the asymptotic formulas $D(x) \sim c_1 x \log^2 x$, $E(n) \sim c_2 M(n) n \log n$, where $c_1$, $c_2$ are constants and $M(n)$ is an explicitly determined multiplicative function.

*T. M. Apostol* (Pasadena, Calif.)

Citations: MR 41# 3430 = N24-68.

## N40-76 (41# 6793 )

**Kátai, I.**

**On the iteration of the divisor-function.**

*Publ. Math. Debrecen* **16** (1969), 3–15.

Let $d_1(n)$ denote the number of divisors of $n$, let $d_r(n)=d_{r-1}(d(n))$, $r=2, 3, \cdots$, let $D_r(x)=\sum_{n\leqq x} d_r(n)$, let $\bar{D}_r(x)=\sum_{p\leqq x} d_r(p-1)$, and let $\log_r x=\log(\log_{r-1} x)$, where $\log_1 x = \log x$. It is well-known that $D_1(x)=(1+o(1))x \log x$ as $x\to\infty$. R. Bellman and H. N. Shapiro [Ann. of Math. (2) **49** (1948), 333–340; MR **9**, 414] have conjectured that $D_r(x)=c_r(1+o(1))x \log_r x$ as $x\to\infty$ for every $r\geqq 1$. It is proved that this is the case when $r$ is 2 or 3. It is also shown that $\bar{D}_2(x)=(1+o(1))k_2(x/\log x) \log_2 x$ as $x\to\infty$.

*B. Garrison* (San Diego, Calif.)

Citations: MR 9, 414b = T15-15.

## N40-77 (41# 6802 )

**Erdős, P.**

**On the sum $\sum_{n=1}^{x} d[d(n)]$.**

*Math. Student* **36** (1968), 227–229 (1969).

Let $d(n)$ denote the number of divisors of $n$. The author proves the following theorem:

$$\lim_{x\to\infty}(\log\log x)^{-1} \sum_{n=1}^{x} d\{d(n)\} = d_2.$$

where $0<d_2<\infty$ is a constant.

Put $d(n)=d_1(n)$, $d_k(n)=d\{d_{k-1}(n)\}$ and denote by $\log_k(n)$ the $k$ fold integrated logarithm. The author verifies the result $\lim_{x\to\infty}(1/\log_k x) \sum_{n=1}^{x} d_k(n)=d_k$ for $k=3$ and states that a similar proof can be given for the general case but he has not carried out the details.

*J. M. Gandhi* (Macomb, Ill.)

## N40-78 (42# 1786 )

**Motohashi, Yoichi**

**An asymptotic formula in the theory of numbers.**

*Acta Arith.* **16** (1969/70), 255–264.

This paper establishes

$$\sum_{n\leqslant N}\tau^2(n)\tau(n+1) = P\cdot(N(\log N)^4)+O(N(\log N)^3 \log\log N),$$

where $\pi^2P = \Pi(1-P^{-1}+P^{-1}(1-P^{-1})^2(1+P^{-1})^{-1})$. This proof uses the large sieve, Dirichlet $L$-series and Ramanujan like identities.

*J. H. Jordan* (Pullman, Wash.)

## N40-79 (42# 4508 )

**Erdős, P.**

**On the sum $\sum_{d|2^n-1} d^{-1}$.**

*Israel J. Math.* **9** (1971), 43–48.

Let $\sigma(n)$ denote the sum of the divisors of $n$. It is shown that $\sigma(2^n-1)/(2^n-1)=\sum_{d|2^n-1} 1/d<c_1 \log\log n$, where $c_1$ is a positive absolute constant. Apart from the value of $c_1$ this result is best possible.

*B. Garrison* (San Diego, Calif.)

## N40-80 (42# 4511 )

**Motohashi, Yoichi**

**On the sum of the number of divisors in a short segment.**

*Acta Arith.* **17** (1970), 249–253.

Der Autor verschärft ein Ergebnis von P. Erdős [Math. Ann. **169** (1967), 230–238; MR **34** #5771] und beweist, auf Ergebnissen von T. Estermann [J. Reine Angew. Math. **164** (1931), 173–182] aufbauend, folgenden Satz: Ist $g(x)\leqq\log^2 x$, $g(x)\nearrow\infty$ für $x\to\infty$, so gilt (mit der Abkürzung $t=g(x)\cdot\log^3 x$) für "fast alle" $n\leqq x$ die asymptotische Formel $\sum_{j\leqq t} \tau(n+j)=t\cdot(\log n+2\gamma)+o(t)$. {Die Bedingung $g(x)\leqq\log^2 x$ sollte noch entfernt werden.}

*W. Schwarz* (Frankfurt a.M.)

Citations: MR 34# 5771 = N40-63.

## N40-81 (44# 166 )

**Babaev, G.**

**The number of divisors of irreducible polynomials. (Russian. Tajiki summary)**

*Dokl. Akad. Nauk Tadžik. SSR* **12** (1969), *no.* 5, 7–8.

For any real number $x$, we write $S_f(x)=\sum_{n\leqq x} d(f(n))$, where $d(m)$ is the number of positive divisors of the integer $m$ and $f(y)$ is an irreducible polynomial with integer coefficients, such that $\deg f\geqq 2$ and the coefficient of the greatest power of $y$ is a positive number. Then $S_f(x)=Ax \ln x+O(x)$, where $A$ is a fixed positive real number.

*N. Popescu* (Bucharest)

## N40-82 (44# 6624 )

**Delmer, Francine**

**Sur la somme de diviseurs $\sum_{k\leqq x} \{d[f(k)]\}^s$.**

*C. R. Acad. Sci. Paris Sér. A-B* **272** (1971), A849–A852.

In J. London Math. Soc. **27** (1952), 7–15 [MR **13**, 438], P. Erdős proved that if $f(k)$ is an irreducible polynomial of degree $m$ with integral coefficients, then there exist positive constants $c_1$ and $c_2$ such that (*) $c_1x \log x< \sum_{k\leqq x} d(f(k))<c_2x \log x$, where $d(n)$ denotes the number of

divisors of $n$. However, the proof contains an error. (In Lemma 5 the condition $p^\alpha \leqq x$ is missing: in particular, Erdős' Lemma 5 as it stands would imply that there are infinitely many integers $n$ for which $f(n)$ is square-free, a probably true, but as yet unproved, result.)

The author indicates a correct Lemma 5 (take $\alpha > m$ instead of $>1$ in the statement); only a small addition to Erdős' proof is required, and then the result (*) can actually be proved. Aside from the modified Lemma 5, the proof is by citation of Erdős, since all goes through as in his paper. The author also shows that Erdős' method in fact will give the following somewhat more general result: There exist positive constants $c_1$ and $c_2$ such that $c_1 x(\log x)^l < \sum_{k \leqq x} (d(f(k)))^s < c_2 x(\log x)^l$, where $l = 2^s - 1$.

*S. L. Segal* (Rochester, N.Y.)

Citations: MR 13, 438f = N40-19.

## N44 ESTIMATES OF SUMS OF ARITHMETIC FUNCTIONS: $\mu(n)$, $\lambda(n)$

See also reviews L20-4, L20-12, M20-17, M25-81, M30-4, M30-9, M30-10, M30-12, M30-14, M30-18, M30-19, M30-22, M30-27, M30-43, M30-46, M30-49, M30-51, M45-33, M45-46, N04-28, N04-52, N04-54, N12-4, N12-11, N20-19, N20-28, N20-57, N20-63, N20-66, N24-1, N24-53, N48-4, N48-31, N72-1, Q20-17, Q20-40, R44-34, R46-10, Z02-4, Z30-28, Z30-51, Z30-60.

### N44-1 (2, 248h)

**Kuhn, Pavel. Eine Formel für die Summe der Möbiusfaktoren.** Norske Vid. Selsk. Forh. **13**, 112–114 (1940).

A formula for the sum $\sigma(x) = \sum_{n=1}^{x} \mu(n)$ is transformed to obtain a formula for $\sigma(x) - \sigma(x/2)$ which could be used to compute values of $\sigma(x)$.

*H. S. Zuckerman.*

### N44-2 (2, 248i)

**Gupta, Hansraj. On a table of values of $L(n)$.** Proc. Indian Acad. Sci., Sect. A. **12**, 407–409 (1940).

This note gives data on the behavior of the function $L(x) = \sum_{m \leqq x} \lambda(m)$, where $\lambda(m)$ is Liouville's purely multiplicative function for which $\lambda(p^\alpha) = (-1)^\alpha$, $p$ a prime. Thus $L(x)$ is the excess of the number of those integers not exceeding $x$ which have an even number of prime factors over the number of those having an odd number of prime factors (e.g., $2^3 \cdot 3^2 \cdot 7$ has 6 prime factors). For $x \geqq 2$, $L(x) \leqq 0$ according to a conjecture of Pólya, who verified this fact for $x \leqq 1500$ [Jber. Deutsch. Math. Verein. **28**, 38–40 (1919)]. The author has extended this verification to $x \leqq 20000$, and publishes three small tables giving data as follows. For each integer $t$ from 0 to 10, the first table gives the greatest value of $n \leqq 20000$ for which $L(n) = -t$. Only the first two or three entries in this table are of much interest, since $L(48512) = -2$. The greatest $n$ for which $L(n)$ is known to be zero is 586. The second table gives for each $k \leqq 150$ the least value of $n$ for which $L(n) = -k$. For $n \leqq 20000$, $L(n)$ has a minimum of $-150$ at $n = 15810$. The third table gives 19 extreme values of $L(n)$ for $n \leqq 20000$. For this range the function $L^2(n)/n$ is greatest for 9840, where it has the value 1.66504, from which it appears that $L(x) = O(x^{1/2})$.

*D. H. Lehmer* (Berkeley, Calif.).

Referred to in N44-5.

### N44-3 (3, 69c)

**Fogels, E. On average values of arithmetic functions.** Proc. Cambridge Philos. Soc. **37**, 358–372 (1941).

This paper deals with the problem of finding functions $h = h(x)$ for which the mean relation $\sum_{n=1}^{x} a(n) \sim A\psi(x)$, $x \to \infty$, can be extended to (1) $\sum_{n=x}^{x+h} a(n) \sim A\psi(x+h) - A\psi(x)$, $x \to \infty$. By using a method of Heilbronn [Math. Z. **36**, 394–423 (1933)] and a convexity theorem of Ingham [Quart. J. Math. **8**, 255–266 (1937), Th. 2], the author proves that (1) holds when $a(n)$ is either of the arithmetical functions $\Lambda(n)$, $\lambda(n)$ or $\mu(n)$ and $h(x) = x^\theta$, $\theta > (1+4c)/(2+4c)$, where $c$ is a constant for which $\zeta(\frac{1}{2} + it) = O(t^c)$, $t \to \infty$. [The result for $\Lambda(n)$ had been proved earlier in another manner by Ingham, loc. cit.] Similar results are obtained for the arithmetical functions $q(n)$, $2^{\nu(n)}$, $d(n^2)$ and $d^2(n)$.

*P. Hartman.*

### N44-4 (3, 271c)

**Ingham, A. E. On two conjectures in the theory of numbers.** Amer. J. Math. **64**, 313–319 (1942).

The conjectures referred to are that $M(x) = \sum_{n \leqq x} \mu(n) = O(x^{\frac{1}{2}})$ and $L(x) = \sum_{n \leqq x} \lambda(n) \geqq 0$, $x \geqq 2$. A consequence of either of these conjectures is the Riemann hypothesis and the fact that all the zeros of the zeta-function are simple. In this paper it is further shown that the imaginary parts of all the zeros above the real axis must be linearly dependent. It is proved that if the imaginary parts of the zeros are connected by no, or only a finite number of, linear relations with integral coefficients, then $\underline{\lim}\, x^{-\frac{1}{2}} M(x) = -\infty$, $\overline{\lim}\, x^{-\frac{1}{2}} M(x) = +\infty$, $\underline{\lim}\, x^{-\frac{1}{2}} L(x) = -\infty$, $\overline{\lim}\, x^{-\frac{1}{2}} L(x) = +\infty$, as $x \to \infty$.

*H. S. Zuckerman* (Seattle, Wash.).

Referred to in M30-9, N24-59, N24-76, N44-5, N44-10, N44-20.

### N44-5 (5, 199e)

**Gupta, Hansraj. A formula for $L(n)$.** J. Indian Math. Soc. (N.S.) **7**, 68–71 (1943).

The function $L$ referred to is the sum function

$$L(x) = \sum_{n \leqq x} \lambda(n) \tag{1}$$

of the well-known purely multiplicative function $\lambda(n)$ of Liouville for which $\lambda(p) = -1$ for $p$ any prime. The interesting function $L(x)$ is, according to a conjecture of Pólya, nonnegative. This conjecture, which implies rather more than the Riemann hypothesis [see A. E. Ingham, Amer. J. Math. **64**, 313–319 (1942); these Rev. **3**, 271], was verified recently for $x \leqq 20000$ by a table of $L(x)$ computed by the author [Proc. Indian Acad. Sci., Sect. A. **12**, 407–409 (1940); these Rev. **2**, 248]. The present paper considers the problem of obtaining isolated values of $L(x)$ for $x > 20000$. A complicated formula for $L(n)$ involving $L(n/m)$ summed over odd $m$'s whose prime factors are distinct and bounded, as well as the function $\pi(a, b)$ giving the number of primes between $a$ and $b$, is derived from Meissel's well-known formula and the identity

$$L(x) + \sum_{\nu=1}^{\infty} L_{\nu-1}(x/p_\nu) = 1,$$

where $L_k(x)$ is obtained from (1) by deleting those terms for which $n$ is divisible by one of the first $k$ primes. This formula serves to calculate $L(N)$ given a table of $L(x)$ for $x \leqq N/3$ and a list of primes. It is applied by the author to verify a remark by the reviewer that $L(48512) = -2$. To facilitate the use of his formula the author lists on page 71 all products $m < 51051$ of odd distinct primes not greater than 31 arranged according to the parity of the number of prime factors of $m$.

*D. H. Lehmer* (Berkeley, Calif.).

Citations: MR 2, 248i = N44-2; MR 3, 271c = N44-4.

## N44-6 (8, 446c)

**Brun, Viggo. La somme des facteurs de Möbius.** C. R. Dixième Congrès Math. Scandinaves 1946, pp. 40–53. Jul. Gjellerups Forlag, Copenhagen, 1947.

This lecture contains a number of interesting remarks about the sum $M(x)=\sum_{n\leq x}\mu(n)$ and about associated questions. *H. Davenport* (London).

Referred to in N44-8, N44-13.

## N44-7 (10, 597c)

**Wintner, Aurel. A note on Mertens' hypothesis.** Revista Ci., Lima **50**, 181–184 (1948).

The author notes that the statements

$$(1)\quad \sum_{n=1}^{x}\mu(n)=O(x^{\frac{1}{2}}),\qquad (2)\quad \sum_{n=1}^{x}\mu(n)/n^{\frac{1}{2}}=O(1),$$

of which (1) is a famous (but doubtful) hypothesis of Stieltjes and Mertens, stand in the following logical relation. By partial summation, (2)$\rightarrow$(1), but not conversely. However, by a theorem of M. Riesz [Acta Math. **40**, 349–361 (1916), p. 350, footnote 4] (1)(3)$\rightarrow$(2), where (3) is the statement: $1/\zeta(s)$ is regular at $s=\frac{1}{2}$. Since (3) is true, (1) and (2) are thus both true or both false. *A. E. Ingham.*

Referred to in R46-10.

## N44-8 (11, 234f)

**Gupta, Hansraj. On a conjecture of Miller.** J. Indian Math. Soc. (N.S.) **13**, 85–90 (1949).

Let $\mu(n)$ be Möbius' inversion function and let $M_1(x)=\sum_{n\leq x}\mu(n)$. The conjecture of Miller is that the function $M_2(x)=\sum_{n\leq x}M_1(n)$ is negative for $x\geqq 3$. The paper presents a table of $M_2(25m)$ for $m=1(1)800$, showing that the conjecture holds for $x\leqq 20000$. The average $A(n)=M_2(n)/n$ is also tabulated for $n=100(100)20000$. According to an informal argument of Brun [C. R. Dixième Congrès Math. Scandinaves 1946, pp. 40–53 (1947); these Rev. **8**, 446], $A(n)=-2+12n^{-1}+\cdots$. The table fails to bear this out. The author conjectures that $A(n)=O(\log n)$. *D. H. Lehmer* (Berkeley, Calif.).

Citations: MR 8, 446c = N44-6.
Referred to in N44-13, N44-26.

## N44-9 (12, 674a)

**Gupta, Hansraj. A table of values of Liouville's function $L(t)$.** Res. Bull. East Panjab Univ. **1950**, 45–63 (1950).

The function $L(x)$ is defined by $L(x)=\sum_{n\leq x}\lambda(n)$ where $\lambda(n)$ is the Liouville function whose value is $+1$ or $-1$ according as the number of prime factors of $n$, each counted with its multiplicity, is even or odd. The author has condensed an original table of $L(n)$ for $n=1(1)20000$ by giving $L(n)$ for $n=5(5)20000$ and a device for reading out the missing values. The purpose of the table is to study the as yet unproved conjecture of Pólya to the effect that, for $n>1$, $L(n)$ is nonpositive. The conjecture is verified as far as 20000, though there are such examples as $L(19680)=-10$. The table would support the conjecture $L(x)=O(x^{\frac{1}{2}})$ which, like Pólya's conjecture, would imply the Riemann hypothesis. *D. H. Lehmer* (Berkeley, Calif.).

## N44-10 (13, 327c)

**Fawaz, A. Y. The explicit formula for $L_0(x)$.** Proc. London Math. Soc. (3) **1**, 86–103 (1951).

Let

$$L(x)=\sum_{n\leq x}\lambda(n),\quad L_0(x)=\tfrac{1}{2}[L(x+0)+L(x-0)]=\sum_{n\leq x}{}'\lambda(n),$$

where $\lambda(n)$ is Liouville's arithmetical function defined by

$$\frac{\zeta(2s)}{\zeta(s)}=\sum_{n=1}^{\infty}\frac{\lambda(n)}{n^s}\quad (s=\sigma+it,\ \sigma>1)$$

and $\sum'$ indicates that, when $x$ is an integer, the term corresponding to $n=x$ is to have the factor $\frac{1}{2}$. The functions $L(x)$ and $L_0(x)$ differ only when $x$ is an integer, their difference then being $\pm\frac{1}{2}$. It has been conjectured by Pólya [Jber. Deutsch. Math. Verein. **28**, 31–40 (1919)] that $L(x)\leqq 0$ for $x\geqq 2$, and by Ingham [Amer. J. Math. **64**, 313–319 (1942); these Rev. **3**, 271] that lim sup (inf) $L(x)/x^{\frac{1}{2}}=+\infty(-\infty)$. In the present paper the author gives an explicit formula for $L_0(x)$ on the assumption that the Riemann hypothesis is true and that the zeros of $\zeta(s)$ are all simple. *W. Simons* (Vancouver, B. C.).

Citations: MR 3, 271c = N44-4.
Referred to in N44-11.

## N44-11 (14, 537a)

**Fawaz, A. Y. On an unsolved problem in the analytic theory of numbers.** Quart. J. Math., Oxford Ser. (2) **3**, 282–295 (1952).

The title refers to the two conflicting conjectures by Pólya and Ingham regarding the number-theoretic function $L(x)$ [Fawaz, Proc. London Math. Soc. (3) **1**, 86–103 (1951); these Rev. **13**, 327]. In the cited paper the author obtained an explicit formula for $L_0(x)$ ($L_0(x)$ differs from $L(x)$ only when $x$ is an integer, the difference then being $\pm\frac{1}{2}$) in which appears the integral

$$I(x)=\frac{1}{2\pi i}\int_{(a)}\frac{\zeta(2s)}{s\zeta(s)}x^s ds\quad (0<a<\tfrac{1}{2}).$$

In the present paper he proves that

$$\liminf_{x\to\infty} x^{-\frac{1}{2}}L(x)=-\limsup_{x\to 0+} x^{-\frac{1}{2}}I(x),$$

$$\limsup_{x\to\infty} x^{-\frac{1}{2}}L(x)=-\liminf_{x\to 0+} x^{-\frac{1}{2}}I(x),$$

so that information about $I(x)$ can be applied to $L(x)$. *W. H. Simons* (Vancouver, B. C.).

Citations: MR 13, 327c = N44-10.

## N44-12 (14, 847c)

**Larsen, Otto. Epreuve numérique d'une supposition de P. Turán.** Mat. Tidsskr. B. **1952**, 28 (1952).

Let $L_s(n)=\sum_{m=1}^{n}\lambda(m)m^{-s}$, where $\lambda(m)$ is Liouville's function ($\lambda(m)=(-1)^\mu$ when $m$ is a product of $\mu$ equal or distinct primes). Turán conjectured that $L_1(n)>0$ $(n\geqq 1)$ [Danske Vid. Selsk. Mat.-Fys. Medd. **24**, no. 17 (1948); these Rev. **10**, 286]. Numerical evidence in support of this is here given for the range $1000<n\leqq 4528$. The author also reports that he has repeated previous calculations up to $n=1000$ and found minor discrepancies (in the fifth place of decimals). The least value found is $L_1(2837)=0.0002393$. Turán's conjecture is on much the same footing as Pólya's conjecture $L_0(n)\leqq 0$ $(n\geqq 2)$, and is open to similar doubts. *A. E. Ingham* (Cambridge, England).

Citations: MR 10, 286b = M30-9.

## N44-13 (15, 779b)

**Gupta, H., Cheema, M. S., and Gupta, O. P. On Möbius means.** Res. Bull. Panjab Univ. no. 42, 16 pp. (1 plate) (1954).

The authors give tables which serve to test the conjectures of Brun and Siegel about the function $\mu_2(n)=\sum_{k=1}^{n}\mu_1(n)$, where $\mu_1(n)=\sum_{k=1}^{n}\mu(n)$, for the Möbius function $\mu$. The conjecture is that on the average

$$n^{-1}\mu_2(n-1)=-2+12n^{-1}-\beta n^{-2},$$

where $\beta=18$ according to Brun and $\beta=2\pi^2/\zeta(3)=16.421$ according to Siegel. [See Brun, C. R. Dixième Congrès Math. Skandinaves, 1946, Gjellerup, Copenhagen, 1947, pp. 40–53; these Rev. **8**, 446; Gupta, J. Indian Math. Soc. (N.S.) **13**, 85–90 (1949); these Rev. **11**, 234.] The authors tabulate

$$F(n)=T_0(n)=n\mu_2(n-1)+2n^2-12n$$

and its successive means

$$T_k=n^{-1}\sum_{\nu=1}^{n}T_{k-1}(\nu)\quad(k=1,2,3,4,5)$$

for $n=1(1)750$. Over the last half of the table $T_5(n)$ descends gradually from $-14$ to $-15$. *D. H. Lehmer.*

Citations: MR 8, 446c = N44-6; MR 11, 234f = N44-8.

## N44-14 (17, 348f)

**Selberg, Sigmund. Über die Summe $\sum_{n\leq x}\frac{\mu(n)}{n}$.** Norske Vid. Selsk. Forh., Trondheim **28** (1955), 37–41.

The author shows that the partial sums of the title cannot be of one sign for large $x$. *R. Bellman.*

Referred to in N44-15.

## N44-15 (18, 194e)

**Selberg, Sigmund. Über eine zahlentheoretische Summe.** Math. Scand. **4** (1956), 129–142.

In earlier papers [Norske Vid. Selsk. Forh., Trondheim **26** (1953), 89–93; **28** (1955), 37–41; MR **15**, 607; **17**, 348], the author proved that the sum

$$\sigma_k(x)=\sum_{r=1}^{k}\left\{x\left[\frac{r}{x}\right]-(x+1)\left[\frac{r}{x+1}\right]\right\}$$

satisfied the condition $\sigma_k(x)\geq 0$ and that $\lim_{k\to\infty}\sigma_k(x)/k=\frac{1}{2}$. In this paper, he demonstrates that $\sigma_k(x)\leq k$.

*R. Bellman* (Santa Monica, Calif.).

Citations: MR 15, 607a = A34-13; MR 17, 348f = N44-14.

## N44-16 (18, 18g)

**Selberg, Sigmund. Über eine Vermutung von P. Turan.** Norske Vid. Selsk. Forh., Trondheim **29** (1956), 33–35.

Let

$$L(x)=\sum_{n=1}^{x}\frac{\lambda(n)}{n},\quad H(x)=\sum_{n=1}^{x}L(n),$$

where $\lambda(n)$ is Liouville's function, i.e. $\lambda(n)=(-1)^{\Omega(n)}$, where $\Omega(n)$ is the number of (equal or distinct) prime factors of $n$. Let $H$ and $h$ be the upper and lower limits, respectively, of $H(x)/\sqrt{x}$ as $x\to\infty$; and let $a=-2/\zeta(\frac{1}{2})$ ($=1.37$ approximately). The author notes first that, by a classical theorem of Landau, $H\geq a\geq h$. Turán's conjecture (T) is that $L(x)>0$ $(x\geq 1)$ [Danske Vid. Selsk. Mat.-Fys. Medd. **24** (1948), no. 17; MR **10**, 286]. The aim of this paper is to show that $T$ implies that $h\geq\frac{2}{3}$ and $H<10$. The method is elementary and is based on properties of the function

$$\sigma_x(n)=\sum_{t=1}^{x}\left\{n\left[\frac{t}{n}\right]-(n+1)\left[\frac{t}{n+1}\right]\right\}$$

introduced by E. Jacobsthal.

{Notes by the reviewer: (1) By a classical method of E. Schmidt and Landau the inequalities $H\geq a\geq h$ may be strengthened to $H\geq a+c>a-c\geq h$, where $c$ is a (finite or infinite) positive constant depending on the complex zeros of $\zeta(s)$. (2) As the author observes, the hypothesis (S) that $H(x)/\sqrt{x}$ is bounded above or below implies (like T) the Riemann hypothesis, i.e. that the complex zeros of $\zeta(s)$ are of the form $\frac{1}{2}\pm i\gamma_n$ $(\gamma_n>0)$ (and, it may be added, are all simple, so that the $\gamma_n$ are distinct). Now $T$ implies $S$ (obviously, with 0 as a lower bound), and indeed more (by the main result of this paper), so $S$ is to this extent weaker than $T$. It is also more plausible in that it does not (like $T$) compel us to accept the (improbable) conclusion that the $\gamma_n$ are linearly dependent [see the review quoted above].} *A. E. Ingham* (Cambridge, England).

Citations: MR 10, 286b = M30-9.

## N44-17 (20# 3113)

**Knapowski, S. On the Möbius function.** Acta Arith. **4** (1958), 209–216.

Denote by $\mu(n)$ the Möbius function. Put $M(x)=\sum_{n=1}^{x}\mu(n)$. It is known that the Riemann hypothesis is equivalent with

$$M(x)=O(x^{\frac{1}{2}+\epsilon}).$$

It has been conjectured that $M(n)<\sqrt{n}$ for $n>1$. Put $\psi(x)=\sum_{p<x}\log p$. Turán proved [Eine neue Methode in der Analysis und deren Anwendungen, Akadémiai Kiado, Budapest, 1953; MR **15**, 688] that

$$(1)\qquad \max_{1\leq x\leq T}|\psi(x)-x|>T^{\beta_0}\exp\left(-21\frac{\log T}{\sqrt{(\log\log T)}}\right),$$

where $\beta_0+i\gamma_0$, $\beta_0\geq\frac{1}{2}$, is any complex root of $\zeta(s)$. The author proves, using Turán's method, that assuming the unproved and well known conjecture

$$(2)\qquad \int_1^T\left(\frac{M(x)}{x}\right)^2dx=O(\log T),$$

we have

$$\max_{1\leq x\leq T}|M(x)|>T^{\frac{1}{2}}\exp\left(-\frac{\log T}{\sqrt{(\log\log T)}}\right).$$

(It is well known that (2) implies the Riemann hypothesis.) *P. Erdös* (Haifa)

Citations: MR 15, 688b = M50-2.
Referred to in N44-18.

## N44-18 (20# 7005)

**Knapowski, S. On the distribution of values of the Möbius function.** Colloque sur la théorie des suites, tenu à Bruxelles du 18 au 20 décembre 1957, pp. 161–164. Centre Belge de Recherches Mathématiques. Librairie Gauthier-Villars, Paris; Établissements Ceuterick, Louvain; 1958. 167 pp. 220 fr. belges.

A full proof of the results announced here has appeared in Acta Arith. **4** (1958), 209–216 [MR **20** #3113].

*N. G. de Bruijn* (Amsterdam)

Citations: MR 20# 3113 = N44-17.

## N44-19 (20# 5178)

**Wintner, Aurel. On the $\lambda$-variant of Mertens' $\mu$-hypothesis.** Amer. J. Math. **80** (1958), 639–642.

The author considers the conjecture $\sum_{n=1}^{x}\lambda(n)=O(\sqrt{x})$ $(\lambda(n)=(-1)^{\alpha+\beta+\cdots},\ n=p_1^{\alpha}p_2^{\beta}\cdots)$ and proves that the above conjecture is equivalent to $\sum_{n=1}^{x}(\lambda(n)/\sqrt{n})=c\log x+O(1)$. *P. Erdös* (Haifa)

## N44-20 (21# 3391)

**Haselgrove, C. B. A disproof of a conjecture of Pólya.** Mathematika **5** (1958), 141–145.

The conjecture of Pólya asserts that for every $x\geq 2$ there are at least as many numbers $\leq x$ having an odd number of prime factors as there are numbers with an even number of prime factors. More precisely, if we adopt Liouville's function

$$\lambda(n) = (-1)^{a_1+\cdots+a_\nu} \quad (n = p_1^{a_1}p_2^{a_2}\cdots p_\nu^{a_\nu}),$$

then $L(x)=\sum_{n\leqq x}\lambda(n)$ is never positive for $x\geqq 2$. This conjecture had been verified as far as 800000 by R. S. Lehman and W. G. Spohn. The author shows that the conjecture is false. Furthermore there is a good reason to believe $L(x)>0$ for $x$ near $e^{831.847}=1.845\cdot 10^{361}$. In a note added in proof, the author announces that he has disproved also the conjecture of Turán, namely that $L_1(x)=\sum_{n\leqq x}\lambda(n)/n$ is never negative.

The method is based on results of A. Ingham [Amer. J. Math. **64** (1942), 313–319; MR **3**, 271] involving the two functions

$$A(u) = e^{-u/2}L(e^u),$$
$$A_T^*(u) = \alpha_0+2\operatorname{Re}\{\sum(1-\gamma_n/T)\alpha_n\exp(iu\gamma_n)\},$$

where the sum extends over those values of $n$ for which $0<\gamma_n<T$ and $\gamma_n$ is the imaginary part of the $n$th complex zero $\rho_n$ of the Riemann zeta-function. Also

$$\alpha_0 = 1/\zeta(1/2), \quad \alpha_n = \zeta(2\rho_n)/(\rho_n\zeta'(\rho_n)).$$

The conjecture of Pólya implies the Riemann Hypothesis and so to disprove the former we may assume the latter. Ingham showed that on the assumption of the Riemann Hypothesis

$$A_T^*(u) \leqq \limsup A_T^*(u) \leqq \limsup A(u),$$

and so to disprove the Pólya conjecture it suffices to discover $T$ and $u$ for which $A_T^*(u)>0$. Such a pair is $T=1000$, $u=831.847$ for which $A_T^*(u)=.00495$. This discovery was based on a calculation of the first 1500 zeros $\rho_n$ and the corresponding values $\alpha_n$. The latter complex constants and $\gamma_n$ are tabulated on p. 141 for $n=1\,(1)\,50$ to 80. There is also a short table of $A^*_{1000}(u)$ for $u=831.800\,(.001)\,831.859$. {There is obviously something wrong at $u=831.857$. Presumably the value should be $-0.06321$, not $-1.56321$.} To show that $A_T^*(u)$ and $A(u)$ are not very far apart there is a graph of both functions (for $T=200$) for $x=e^u=44400\,(200)\,51600$, showing the near miss at $x=48512$ where $L(x)=-2$.

The calculations were made independently on EDSAC I and Manchester University's Mark I. They have since been confirmed by R. S. Lehman using an IBM 701. The author believes that Merten's conjecture $\sum_{n\leqq x}\mu(n)<x^{1/2}$ may be disproved by the use of very much faster machines.

*D. H. Lehmer* (Berkeley, Calif.)

Citations: MR 3, 271c = N44-4.
Referred to in M15-23, N44-22.

## N44-21 (22# 6762)

**Lehmer, D. H.; Selberg, S. A sum involving the function of Möbius.** Acta Arith. **6** (1960), 111–114.

From the introduction: "Let $\mu(n)$ be the Möbius function. The sum $g(x)=\sum_{n\leqq x}\mu(n)/n$ may itself be summed to give $G(x)=\sum_{n\leqq x}g(n)$. In this note we show that $G(x)-2$ changes sign infinitely often. Some numerical calculations of the first 56 sign changes are described. These show that these 'zeros' of $G(x)-2$ are remarkably close to being in geometric progression with two exceptions. An heuristic explanation of this phenomenon is given."

*A. L. Whiteman* (Princeton, N.J.)

## N44-22 (22# 10955)

**Lehman, R. Sherman. On Liouville's function.** Math. Comp. **14** (1960), 311–320.

Liouville's function $\lambda(n)$ is defined by $\lambda(n)=(-1)^r$ where $r$ is the number of prime factors of $n$, multiple factors being counted according to their multiplicity. Pólya conjectured that the function $L(x)=\sum_{n\leqq x}\lambda(n)$ was negative or zero for all $x>2$, but this conjecture was proved false by the reviewer [Mathematika **5** (1958), 141–145; MR **21** #3391]. In this paper the author confirms the reviewer's calculations of the sum

$$A_T^*(u) = \sum_{|\gamma_n|<T}\alpha_n\left(1-\frac{|\gamma_n|}{T}\right)e^{i\gamma_n u},$$

where $\gamma_n$ runs through the imaginary parts of the zeros $\rho_n$ of the Riemann zeta function and where $\alpha_0=1/\zeta(\tfrac{1}{2})$, $\alpha_n=\zeta(2\rho_n)/\rho_n\zeta'(\rho_n)$. For $T=1000$, $A_T^*(u)$ is found to be positive for $u=831.847$, taking the value 0.0050. This confirms the reviewer's result. However $A_T^*(u)$ is also found to be positive for $u=814.492$ where it takes the much larger value 0.0782. These results suggest, but do not prove, that $L(x)$ is positive for these values of $u=\log x$.

It was found that $A_T(u)=\sum_{|\gamma_n|<T}\alpha_n e^{i\gamma_n u}$ nearly became positive for $T=1000$ and $u=20.62$. This suggested that $L(x)$ might become positive for $x$ near $9.05\times 10^8$. By direct calculation of $L(x)$ it was found that $L(9061\,80359)=+1$ and that $L(x)$ is positive over a considerable number of ranges of $x$ in the intervals 9061 70000 to 9062 00000 and 9064 70000 to 9065 00000. Some of the 167 values of $x$ found in the range for which $L(x)=0$ are listed.

*C. B. Haselgrove* (Manchester)

Citations: MR 21# 3391 = N44-20.

## N44-23 (24# A3121)

**Knapowski, S.**
**Mean-value estimations for the Möbius function. I.**
*Acta Arith.* **7** (1961/62), 121–130.

Writing $M(x)=\sum_{n\leqq x}\mu(n)$, where $\mu(n)$ denotes the Möbius function, the author, in a previous paper [Acta Math. Acad. Sci. Hungar. **10** (1959), 375–390; MR **22** #2584] proved the following. Suppose

$$(1) \qquad \int_1^T \frac{|M(x)|}{x}\,dx < aT^{1/2}$$

($T\geqq 1$, $a$ independent of $T$).

Then

$$(2) \qquad \int_1^T \frac{|M(x)|}{x}\,dx > T^{1/2}\exp(-\log T/(\log\log T)^{1/2})$$

for $T>\operatorname{Max}(c_2, e^a)$, $c_2$ being a numerical constant. In this paper, the author assumes (1), then he proves the Theorem I:

$$\int_{T/H}^T \frac{|M(x)|}{x}\,dx > \frac{1}{H}T^{1/2}$$

for $T\geqq(a+2)^{c_3}=H$, where $c_3$ can be numerically calculated. The author also states another theorem (Theorem II) without giving any proof. (He wishes to prove it in the second part of this paper.)

*B. K. Ghosh* (Calcutta)

Citations: MR 22# 2584 = N04-28.

## N44-24 (26# 69)

**Knapowski, S.**
**Mean-value estimations for the Möbius function. II.**
*Acta Arith.* **7** (1961/62), 337–343.

Writing $M(x)=\sum_{n\leqq x}\mu(n)$, where $\mu(n)$ denotes the Möbius function, the author proves the following theorem which he announced in a previous paper on the subject [same Acta **7** (1961/62), 121–130; MR **24** #A3121]. If all the zeros of $\zeta(s)$ in the rectangle $0<\sigma<1$, $|t|\leqq\omega$ are simple and have $\sigma = \frac{1}{2}$, then

$$\int_x^T |M(x)|x^{-1}\,dx > T^{1/2}\exp\left(-12\frac{\log T}{\log\log T}\log\log\log T\right),$$

with

$$X = T\exp\left(-100\frac{\log T}{\log\log T}\log\log\log T\right),$$

for $c_1 \leqq T \leqq \exp(\omega^{10})$, where $c_1$ is a positive numerical constant. *B. K. Ghosh* (Calcutta)

Citations: MR 24# A3132 = J04-44.

## N44-25 (27# 3607)

**Staś, W.**

**Zur Theorie der Möbiusschen $\mu$-Funktion.**

*Acta Arith.* **7** (1961/62), 409–416.

Hardy and Littlewood [Acta Math. **41** (1918), 119–196] proved that the estimate

$$(1) \qquad \sum_{k=1}^{\infty} \frac{(-x)^k}{k!\zeta(2k+1)} = O(x^{-1/4})$$

is equivalent to the Riemann hypothesis. Here $\zeta(s)$ is Riemann's zeta function. We can write (1) as follows:

$$(2) \qquad \sum_{n=1}^{\infty} \frac{\mu(n)}{n} e^{-\beta^2/n^2} = O\left(\frac{1}{\sqrt{\beta}}\right),$$

where $\mu(n)$ is the Möbius function, and $\beta \to +\infty$. Write

$$(3) \qquad M(x) = \sum_{n \leqq x} \mu(n).$$

The author proves the following theorem: If

$$(4) \qquad \int_1^T \left(\frac{M(x)}{x}\right)^2 dx < \alpha \log T,$$

then for

$$(5) \qquad T > \max(c_0, e^{\sqrt{\alpha}})$$

we have the following estimate

$$(6) \qquad \max_{Te^{-\varphi(T)} \leqq \beta \leqq T} \left|\sum_{n=1}^{\infty} \frac{\mu(n)}{n} e^{-\beta^2/n^2}\right| \geqq \frac{1}{\sqrt{T}} e^{-3\log T \log\log\log\log T/\log\log T}$$

where

$$\varphi(T) = \frac{\log T \log\log\log T}{\log\log T}$$

and $c_0$ is an explicit constant.

The method used is due to Turán [*Eine neue Methode in der Analysis und deren Anwendungen*, Akad. Kiadó, Budapest, 1953; MR **15**, 688].

*S. Chowla* (University Park, Pa.)

Citations: MR 15, 688b = M50-2.
Referred to in M30-43, N44-28.

## N44-26 (27# 5721)

**Neubauer, Gerhard**

**Eine empirische Untersuchung zur Mertensschen Funktion.**

*Numer. Math.* **5** (1963), 1–13.

Let $\mu(n)$ be the function of Möbius. The author reports on an extensive numerical investigation of the functions

$$M_1(x) = \sum_{n \leqq x} \mu(n), \quad M_2(x) = \sum_{n \leqq x} M_1(n).$$

Two conjectures are disproved. One by von Sterneck asserts that

$$(1) \qquad |M_1(x)| < \tfrac{1}{2}x^{1/2} \qquad (x > 200).$$

The author finds that $M_1(7760000000) = 47465$ whereas $\frac{1}{2}(7760000000)^{1/2} < 44046$. The other conjecture, by J. C. P. Miller [H. Gupta, J. Indian Math. Soc. (N.S.) **13** (1949), 85–90; MR **11**, 234] and verified by H. Gupta for $x < 20000$, asserts that $M_2(x)$ is negative for $x \geqq 3$. The first failure of this conjecture occurs at $M_2(21067) = 2$. For $10^6 < x < 10^8$ about half of the values of $M_2(x)$ are positive. A sketch of $M_2(x)/(x \log x)$ oscillates wildly over this range of $x$.

An extensive rough graph of the function $M_1(x)$ is given for $x < 10^{10}$. It shows that the inequality (1) comes close to failure more than a score of times but fails definitely only in the neighborhood of $8 \cdot 10^9$.

The calculation had for its basic information a table of $M_1(x)$ and $M_2(x)$ for $x = 1(1)10^8$. Beyond this limit only isolated values of $M_1(x)$ were computed by methods known to von Sterneck. Various errata in the latter's tables are cited. *D. H. Lehmer* (Berkeley, Calif.)

Citations: MR 11, 234f = N44-8.

## N44-27 (27# 5736)

**Knapowski, S.**

**On oscillations of certain means formed from the Möbius series. I.**

*Acta Arith.* **8** (1962/63), 311–320.

Let $M(x) = \sum_{n \leqq x} \mu(n)$, where $\mu(n)$ denotes the Möbius function. This is the first of a series of papers (to appear) in which the author wishes to deal with the oscillatory properties of $M(x)$ and of some related functions.

Let $\log_k$ and $e_k$ denote the $k$-fold iterates of the logarithm and exponential functions, and let $c_3, c_4, \cdots$ denote positive numerical constants. The author proves the following main result. Let all the zeros of $\zeta(s)$ $(s = \sigma + it)$ in the rectangle $0 < \sigma < 1$, $|t| \leqq \omega$, lie on the line $\sigma = \frac{1}{2}$, then for $c_3 \leqq T \leqq e^{\omega^{10}}$,

$$\max_{1 \leqq x \leqq T} M(x) \geqq T^{1/2} e_1\left(-15\frac{\log T}{\log_2 T}\log_3 T\right),$$

$$\min_{1 \leqq x \leqq T} M(x) \leqq -T^{1/2} e_1\left(-15\frac{\log T}{\log_2 T}\log_3 T\right).$$

(On the basis of Riemann's conjecture the above holds for all $T$ sufficiently large.)

In the proof of the above result the author uses two lemmas, the first of them a modification of P. Turán's one-sided theorem [Acta Math. Acad. Sci. Hungar. **12** (1961), 455–468; MR **24** #A2565].

*B. K. Ghosh* (Calcutta)

Citations: MR 24# A2565 = M50-26.
Referred to in N44-29.

## N44-28 (27# 5737)

**Staś, W.**

**Über eine Reihe von Ramanujan.**

*Acta Arith.* **8** (1962/63), 261–271.

The author improves an earlier result [same Acta **7** (1961/62), 409–416; MR **27** #3607] relating to

$$(1) \qquad S(\beta) = \sum_{n=1}^{\infty} \frac{\mu(n)}{n} e^{-\beta^2/n^2} = O(\beta^{-1/2}) \qquad (\beta \to \infty)$$

(where $\mu(n)$ is the Möbius function), which is equivalent to the Riemann Hypothesis [Hardy-Littlewood]. Write

$$(2) \qquad \varphi(\beta, \pi/\beta) = \pi^{1/2}S(\pi/\beta) - \beta S(\beta),$$

$$(3) \qquad K =_{\text{def}} \max_{\langle e^{1/2}, e\rangle} |\varphi(\beta, \pi/\beta)|,$$

$$(4) \qquad K = |\varphi(\beta_0, \pi/\beta_0)|, \qquad e^{1/2} \leqq \beta_0 \leqq e.$$

The author proves the following theorem: If all zeros of

$\zeta(s)$ are simple and lie on $\sigma=\frac{1}{2}$, then for

$$T > \max(c_1, \exp\exp(1/K)),$$

we have

$$\max_{T^{1-o(1)}\leqq\beta\leqq T} |S(\beta)| > T^{-1/2-o(1)},$$

where $c_1$ is an explicitly determinable numerical constant, and $K$ is the constant from (2)–(4).

{Minor correction: For the '$l$' that occurs in the last summation of (1.5) read '$k$'.}

*S. Chowla* (University Park, Pa.)

Citations: MR 27# 3607 = N44-25.
Referred to in M30-43.

## N44-29 (30# 3073)

**Knapowski, S.**

**On oscillations of certain means formed from the Möbius series. II.**

*Acta Arith.* **10** (1964/65), 377–386.

Part I appeared in same Acta **8** (1962/63), 311–320 [MR **27** #5736]. This paper contains new results on the distribution of values of $\mu(n)$ in certain intervals $a\leqq n\leqq b$. Thus it is proved that there exist infinitely many intervals $(U_1, U_2)$, with $U_2^{1-o(1)}\leqq U_1\leqq U_2$ (as $U_2\to\infty$), such that $\sum_{U_1\leqq n\leqq U_2}\mu(n)>U_2^{1/2-o(1)}$; a similar result is obtained for an estimate in the opposite direction. The proofs given depend on the assumption of the Riemann hypothesis concerning the roots of the $\zeta$-function; detailed estimates of the $\zeta$-function are needed in the proof.

*H. W. Brinkmann* (Swarthmore, Pa.)

Citations: MR 27# 5736 = N44-27.

## N44-30 (33# 3984)

**Evelyn, C. J. A.**

**A relationship for the Möbius function.**

*Quart. J. Math. Oxford Ser.* (2) **17** (1966), 281.

The relationship in question is that if $M(x)=\sum_{n\leqq x}\mu(n)$, where $\mu(n)$ is the Möbius function, then $M(x^{1/N})=\sum_{T\leqq x}M(x/T)$, where $N$ is fixed and $T$ is divisible by no $N$th power.

*A. A. Armendáriz* (Ann Arbor, Mich.)

## N44-31 (34# 7444)

**Fröberg, Carl-Erik**

**Numerical studies of the Möbius power series.**

*Nordisk Tidskr. Informations-Behandling* **6** (1966), 191–211.

This paper is concerned with the two functions $f(z)=\sum_{n=1}^{\infty}\mu(n)z^n$, $g(z)=\sum_{n=1}^{\infty}\mu(n)z^n/n$, where $\mu(n)$ is the well-known inversion function of Möbius. The author studies the behavior of these power series for $z$ on and just inside the unit circle. By using Mellin transforms of $f(e^{-t})$, interesting expansions for very small values of $t$ are obtained in a sometimes heuristic way.

By using a computer, numerical values of $f(z)$ and $g(z)$ can be found for $|z|$ very close to 1. There are four tables of these values.

Table I: $4D$ values of $f(z)$ and $g(z)$ for $|z|=.1(.2).9$, .98, .995, .999, .9998, .99995, .99999, $\arg(z)=0(\pi/12)\pi$.

Table II: $6D$ values of $f(z)$ for $|z|=.999$, .9998, .99995, .99999, $\arg(z)=0(\pi/12)\pi$.

Table III: $12D$ values of $f(z)$ for $|z|=.999$, .9995, .9998, .9999, .99995, .99998, .99999, $\arg(z)=0$, $\pi/3$, $\pi/2$, $2\pi/3$, $\pi$.

Table IV: $4D$ values of $g(z)$ for $|z|=1$ and $\arg(z)=0(\pi/36)\pi$.

Table IV was obtained by taking 500000 terms of the power series. The values in all these tables are the real and imaginary parts of the function and are too isolated to permit interpolation.

There are five graphs $g(z)$, including a map of the semicircle $z=e^{i\theta}$, $0\leqq\theta\leqq\pi$, that can only be described as fantastic.

Various conjectures are made, as, for example, that $2g(\exp 5\pi i/6)$ and $g(\exp 3\pi i/4)$ have the same imaginary part.

*D. H. Lehmer* (Berkeley, Calif.)

## N44-32 (34# 7480)

**Kátai, I.**

**Comparative theory of prime numbers. (Russian)**

*Acta Math. Acad. Sci. Hungar.* **18** (1967), 133–149.

The author works out several $\Omega$-type theorems for various arithmetical functions. He obtains explicit estimates in a number of cases (like those involving the distribution of primes modulo 8, the Möbius function $\mu(n)$, $k$th-power-free integers, etc.). A sample: For $T>c_1$ we have $\sum_{n\leqq x}\mu(n)>c_2\sqrt{x_1}$ and $\sum_{n\leqq x_2}\mu(n)<-c_2\sqrt{x_2}$ for some $x_1, x_2\in[T, T^{(2+\sqrt{3})^2}]$. Also, he gives some non-effective $\Omega$-theorems relating to the distribution of primes mod $\Delta$, $\Delta$ unspecified. The work is based on an idea of K. A. Rodosskiĭ [Uspehi Mat. Nauk **17** (1962), no. 3 (105), 189–191; MR **25** #2047].

*S. Knapowski* (Coral Gables, Fla.)

Citations: MR 25# 2047 = N04-38.
Referred to in N44-39.

## N44-33 (35# 138)

**Dusumbetov, A.**

**A proposition on the sum of the Möbius function. (Russian)**

*Taškent. Gos. Ped. Inst. Učen. Zap.* **61** (1966), 5–9.

Denote by $\mu(n)$ the Möbius function; put $M(x)=\sum_{n\leqq x}\mu(n)$, and $N(x)=\sum_{mn\leqq x}\mu(n)\mu(m)$. Assuming the estimation $N(x)=O(x^\gamma)$, $0<\gamma<1$, the author proves by elementary arguments that $M(x)=O(x^{(3-\gamma)(5-3\gamma)^{-1}}\log x)$. Voronoĭ's estimate $\sum_{n\leqq x}\sum_{d|n}1-x(\log x+2C-1)=O(x^{1/3})$ is used in the proof.

*W. Schwarz* (Freiburg)

## N44-34 (36# 1405)

**Kátai, I.**

**On investigations in the comparative prime number theory.**

*Acta Math. Acad. Sci. Hungar.* **18** (1967), 379–391.

The author obtains inequalities for several functions occurring in analytic number theory. He begins by proving a general theorem on Dirichlet integrals of the form $f(s)=\int_1^\infty x^{-s}\,dA(x)$, $s=\sigma+it$, absolutely convergent in a half-plane $\sigma>\sigma_1$. It is assumed that $A(x)$ is real, that $|A(x)|\leqq c_1x^{\theta_1}$ if $x\geqq 1$, where $c_1>0$ and $\theta_1>0$, that $f(s)$ can be continued into the half-plane $\sigma>\theta_2-\delta_1$ for some $\delta_1>0$ and $0<\theta_2<\theta_1$, and that $\rho=\theta_2+i\gamma$ ($\gamma\neq 0$) is a pole of $f(s)$ of multiplicity $k$. Let $Q(x)=x^{-\theta_2}(\log x)^{1-k}A(x)$. Then there exist positive constants $\delta$ and $c_2$ (numerically calculable once $f$ is known) such that for $T>c_2$ one has

$$\max_{T\leqq x\leqq T^\kappa} Q(x) > \delta, \qquad \min_{T\leqq x\leqq T^\kappa} Q(x) < -\delta,$$

where $\kappa=(\theta_1/\theta_2+\{(\theta_1/\theta_2)^2-1\}^{1/2})^2$.

Many interesting corollaries follow from this theorem. For example, if $M(x)=\sum_{n\leqq x}\mu(n)$, where $\mu$ is the Möbius function, then for $T>c_2$ and $\kappa=(2+\sqrt{3})^2$ one has

$$\max_{T\leqq x\leqq T^\kappa} x^{-1/2}M(x)\geqq\delta, \quad \min_{T\leqq x\leqq T^\kappa} x^{-1/2}M(x)\leqq -\delta,$$

where $c_2>0$ and $\delta>0$ are numerically calculable constants. Analogous results are obtained for $M_0(x)=\sum_{n\leqq x}n^{-1}\mu(n)$, $S(x)=\sum_{n=1}^{\infty}n^{-1}\mu(x)\exp(-x^2/n^2)$, $m(x)=\sum_{n=1}^{\infty}\mu(n)\exp(-n/x)$, and for sums involving $k$-free numbers and prime numbers in different arithmetic progressions. All the estimates are obtained without assuming the Riemann hypothesis or other unproved conjectures.

*T. M. Apostol* (Pasadena, Calif.)

Referred to in N44-37.

**N44-35** **(36# 2575)**

**MacLeod, R. A.**

**A new estimate for the sum $M(x)=\sum_{n\leq x}\mu(n)$.**

*Acta Arith.* **13** (1967/68), 49–59.

The estimate $|M(x)|<x/80$ for $x\geqq 1119$ is proved in an elementary way and as an application the inequality $g(x)=\sum_{n\leq x}\mu(n)/n\geqq g(13)$ is obtained. Although $M(x)=o(x)$, it would probably not be easy to obtain the former inequality even using the non-elementary explicit estimates of J. B. Rosser and L. Schoenfeld [Illinois J. Math. **6** (1962), 64–94; MR **25** #1139]. *A. Schinzel* (Warsaw)

Citations: MR 25# 1139 = N04-37.

Referred to in N44-36, N44-40.

**N44-36** **(39# 6847)**

**MacLeod, R. A.**

**Errata to the paper "A new estimate for the sum $M(x)=\sum_{n\leq x}\mu(n)$".**

*Acta Arith.* **16** (1969/70), 99–100.

The original paper appeared in same Acta **13** (1967/68), 49–59 [MR **36** #2575].

Citations: MR 36# 2575 = N44-35.

**N44-37** **(36# 2577)**

**Kátai, I.**

**On oscillations of number-theoretic functions.**

*Acta Arith.* **13** (1967/68), 107–122.

Recently the author obtained effective localized omega-estimations for several functions occurring in analytic number theory [Acta Math. Acad. Sci. Hungar. **18** (1967), 379–391; MR **36** #1405]. The following result is typical. If $M(x)=\sum_{n\leq x}\mu(n)$, where $\mu$ is the Möbius function, then for $T>c_1$ and $\kappa=(2+\sqrt{3})^2$ we have $\max_{T\leq x\leq T^\kappa} x^{-1/2}M(x)>\delta$, $\min_{T\leq x\leq T^\kappa} x^{-1/2}M(x)<-\delta$, where $c_1>0$ and $\delta>0$ are numerically calculable constants. In this paper the author refines the localization in these and similar inequalities by showing that inequalities of the same type hold in the interval $T^\kappa\leqq x\leqq T$ for $T>c_2$, where $\kappa$ and $c_2$ depend on regions of nonvanishing of the Riemann zeta function $\zeta(\sigma+it)$ for $\sigma>\frac{1}{2}$. Recent computations of B. J. Rosser and L. Schoenfeld ("The first two million zeros of the Riemann zeta-function are on the critical line", lecture presented at Internat. Congr. Math., Moscow, 1966) showing that the first two million zeros of $\zeta(\sigma+it)$ are on the critical line enable the author to choose $\kappa=0.36$. For the same $\kappa$ but a different $c_2$ the author also proves that $\int_1^T x^{-1}|M(x)|\,dx>\delta T^{\kappa/2}$. Similar inequalities are obtained for $M_0(x)=\sum_{n\leq x} n^{-1}\mu(n)$, $S(x)=\sum_{n=1}^{\infty} n^{-1}\mu(n)\exp(-x^2/n^2)$, $m(x)=\sum_{n=1}^{\infty}\mu(n)\exp(-n/x)$, and other functions. The remarkable feature of all these estimates is that they make no use of the Riemann hypothesis or other unproved hypotheses. The results are deduced from a refinement of a general theorem on Dirichlet integrals of the form $f(s)=\int_1^\infty x^{-s}\,dA(x)$ proved in the earlier paper.

*T. M. Apostol* (Pasadena, Calif.)

Citations: MR 36# 1405 = N44-34.

**N44-38** **(38# 129)**

**Kátai, Imre**

**The Ω-estimation of the arithmetic mean of the Möbius function. (Hungarian)**

*Magyar Tud. Akad. Mat. Fiz. Oszt. Közl.* **15** (1965), 15–18.

Let $M(x)\stackrel{\text{def}}{=}\sum_{n\leq x}\mu(n)$, where $\mu(n)$ is the Möbius function. If the Riemann hypothesis holds, then one can find a constant $c$ such that $\max_{1\leq x\leq T} M(x)\geqq T^{1/2}\exp(-c\log_2{}^2 T)$ and $\min_{1\leq x\leq T} M(x)\leqq -T^{1/2}\exp(-c\log_2{}^2 T)$ hold for any $T\geqq 2$. The proof can be modified so that the "finite" form of the Riemann hypothesis again yields an $\Omega_\pm$-estimate for $M(x)$. The accuracy of this estimate depends on the ordinate $t>0$ for which, when $\operatorname{Re} s>\frac{1}{2}$, it is known that if $|\operatorname{Im} s|\leqq t$ then $\zeta(s)\neq 0$. Previously Knapowski has proved an $\Omega_\pm$-estimate for $M(x)$ on the basis of the Riemann hypothesis in the "finite" form.

*K. Korradi* [*K. Corrádi*] (RŽMat **1966** #1 A110)

Referred to in N44-39.

**N44-39** **(39# 2714)**

**Kátai, Imre**

**Omega-type investigations in prime number theory. (Hungarian. English summary)**

*Magyar Tud. Akad. Mat. Fiz. Oszt. Közl.* **16** (1966), 369–396.

The author outlines the proof of various results on the changes of signs of number theoretic functions. Here we state only one of his numerous results: Put $M(x)=\sum_{n=1}^{x}\mu(n)$, where $\mu(n)$ is the Möbius function. Then there is a $\delta>0$ such that for $T>0$, $\max_{T\leq x\leq T^\alpha} x^{-1/2}M(x)\geq\delta$, $\min_{T\leq x\leq T^\alpha} x^{-1/2}M(x)\leq-\delta$. Detailed proofs of this and the other results have appeared in his various publications (see, e.g., Ann. Univ. Sci. Budapest. Eötvös Sect. Math. **7** (1964), 33–40 [MR **31** #1235] and several of his papers which are in print [Magyar Tud. Akad. Mat. Fiz. Oszt. Közl. **15** (1965), 9–13; MR **38** #128; ibid. **15** (1965), 15–18; MR **38** #129; Acta Math. Acad. Sci. Hungar. **18** (1967), 133–149; MR **34** #7480; Ann. Univ. Sci. Budapest. Eötvös Sect. Math. **9** (1966), 87–93; MR **34** #4226; ibid. **9** (1966), 95–102; MR **34** #4214]). *P. Erdős* (Kensington)

Citations: MR 31# 1235 = N12-34; MR 34# 4214 = M30-46; MR 34# 4226 = N16-32; MR 34# 7480 = N44-32; MR 38# 128 = M30-49; MR 38# 129 = N44-38.

**N44-40** **(39# 2716)**

**Schoenfeld, Lowell**

**An improved estimate for the summatory function of the Möbius function.**

*Acta Arith.* **15** (1968/69), 221–233.

Let $\mu(n)$ be the Möbius function and let $M(x)=\sum_{1\leq n\leq x}\mu(n)$ be its summatory function. The reviewer showed [same Acta **13** (1967/68), 49–59; MR **36** #2575] that $|M(x)|<x/80$ for $x\geqq 1119$ and $|M(x)|\leqq(x+1)/80+11/2$ for $x\geqq 0$. The author proves stronger results of the type $|M(x)|<ax/(\log x)^\alpha$, for $x>1$, where $a$ and $\alpha$ are, respectively, 1.2 and 2/3, 12 and 1, and 26 and 10/9. The proofs are based primarily on inequalities of J. B. Rosser and the author [Illinois J. Math. **6** (1962), 64–94; MR **25** #1139]. Using the recently announced result of J. B. Rosser, L. Schoenfeld and J. M. Yohe ("Rigorous computation and the zeros of the Riemann zeta function", Proc. Fourth Internat. Federation Information Processing Congr. (Edinburgh, 1968), North-Holland, Amsterdam, to appear) that the first 3,500,000 zeros of $\zeta(s)$ are on the critical line, the author obtains for $a$ and $\alpha$, 0.47 and 2/3 ($x\geqq 6$), 2.9 and 1, and 5.3 and 10/9.

*R. A. MacLeod* (Victoria, B.C.)

Citations: MR 25# 1139 = N04-37; MR 36# 2575 = N44-35.

**N44-41** **(42# 7607)**

**Saffari, Bahman**

**Sur les oscillations des fonctions sommatoires des fonctions de Möbius et de Liouville.**

*C. R. Acad. Sci. Paris Sér. A-B* **271** (1970), A578–A580.

An announcement of results. Proofs will be published at a later date.

**N44-42** **(43# 6167)**

**Saffari, Bahman**

**Sur la fausseté de la conjecture de Mertens. (With discussion)**

*C. R. Acad. Sci. Paris Sér. A-B* **271** (1970), A1097–A1101.

Let $\mu(n)$ be the Möbius function and $M(x)=\sum_{1\leq n<x}\mu(n)$ for positive $x$. F. Mertens [S.-B. Akad. Wien Math.-Naturwiss. Kl. Abt. 2 **106** (1897), 761–830] and T. J. Stieltjes [see C. Hermite and Stieltjes, *Correspondance d'Hermite et de Stieltjes*, two volumes, letter 79, Gauthier-Villars, Paris, 1905] conjectured that $|M(x)|<\sqrt{x}$ for $x>1$. The author shows that this conjecture can be disproved, if a certain finite computational question has a positive answer. More precisely, he proves that $\limsup_{x\to\infty}|M(x)|/\sqrt{x}>1.179$ under the hypothesis that $P(h)$ is true for $h=28000$. Here $P(h)$ is the statement that all sums of the form $\sum_{k=1}^{N} a_k c_k$ do not vanish for arbitrary integers $a_k$ not all zero and $\max(N, \sum_{k=1}^{N}|a_k|)\leq h$, $c_k$ denoting the imaginary part of the $k$th zero of the Riemann zeta function on the critical line above the real axis. So far only a fact somewhat close to $P(20)$ has been established. *O. H. Körner* (Ulm)

# N48 ESTIMATES OF SUMS OF ARITHMETIC FUNCTIONS: OTHER MULTIPLICATIVE FUNCTIONS

**See also reviews L15-29, M15-18, M20-23, M20-31, M30-18, M40-3, M40-31, M40-48, N04-54, N20-23, N20-63, N28-56, N36-6, N36-41, N36-42, N36-63, N36-82, N40-14, N40-42, N40-51, N40-58, N40-59, N40-60, N40-74, N44-3, N44-34, N52-13, N60-61, N60-83, N80-45, P36-59, P48-1, P48-14.**

**N48-1** **(13, 535i)**

**Erdös, Paul, and Shapiro, Harold N. On the changes of sign of a certain error function.** Canadian J. Math. **3**, 375–385 (1951).

Let $\varphi(n)$ be Euler's function, $R(x)=\sum_{n=1}^{x}\varphi(n)-3\pi^{-2}x^2$. The authors prove that neither the upper nor the lower limit of the function $R(x)x^{-1}(\log\log\log\log x)^{-1}$ equals zero, and that $R(x)$ changes sign infinitely often. The proof is based on an "elementary" calculation of the average of the function

$$H(x)=\sum_{n=1}^{x}\varphi(n)n^{-1}-6\pi^{-2}x,$$

taken over individual residue classes mod $\prod_{p<y}p$. It has been proved by Pillai and Chowla [J. London Math. Soc. **5**, 95–101 (1930)] that $R(x)\neq o(x\log\log\log x)$. *H. Heilbronn* (Bristol).

Referred to in N48-21.

**N48-2** **(15, 11f)**

**Val'fiš, A. Z. On Euler's function.** Doklady Akad. Nauk SSSR (N.S.) **90**, 491–493 (1953). (Russian)

Let $R(x)=\sum_{n\leq x}\phi(n)-3x^2/\pi^2$ where $\phi(n)$ is the Euler $\phi$-function. It is well-known that $R(x)=O(x\log x)$, a result due to Mertens. The author, using estimation techniques of the Vinogradoff variety, establishes the better estimate $R(x)=O(x(\log x)^{3/4}(\log\log x)^2)$. *R. Bellman.*

Referred to in N36-31, N48-3.

**N48-3** **(16, 338d)**

**Val'fiš, A. Z. On Euler's function.** Akad. Nauk Gruzin. SSR. Trudy Tbiliss. Mat. Inst. Razmadze **19**, 1–31 (1953). (Russian)

This paper is a complete account of the derivation of the following result, reported in the author's note of the same title [Doklady Akad. Nauk SSSR (N.S.) **90**, 491–493 (1953); these Rev. **15**, 11]:

$$\sum_{n\leq x}\varphi(n)=\frac{3}{\pi^2}x^2+O(x(\log x)^{3/4}(\log\log x)^2),$$

where $\varphi(n)$ is Euler's $\varphi$-function. Briefly, the method is as follows. It is first shown that

$$(*)\qquad \sum_{n\leq x}\varphi(n)=\frac{3}{\pi^2}x^2-x\sum_{n\leq x}\frac{\mu(n)}{n}\psi\left(\frac{x}{n}\right)+Bx,$$

where $\mu(n)$ is the Möbius function and $\psi(v)=v-[v]-\frac{1}{2}$. $\psi(x/n)$ is expanded in a Fourier series and improved estimates for the trigonometric sums arising from the right side of (*) are obtained using Vinogradoff techniques. The bulk of the paper is devoted to obtaining these estimates. *W. H. Simons* (Vancouver, B. C.).

Citations: MR 15, 11f = N48-2.

Referred to in N02-3, N36-31.

**N48-4** **(16, 338c)**

**Selberg, Sigmund. Über die Summe $\sum_{n\leq x}\frac{\mu(n)}{nd(n)}$.** Tolfte Skandinaviska Matematikerkongressen, Lund, 1953, pp. 264–272 (1954). 25 Swedish crowns (may be ordered from Lunds Universitets Matematiska Institution).

The author discusses the sum above, giving first some elementary estimates and then a precise asymptotic estimate obtained by means of classical analytic techniques. *R. Bellman* (Santa Monica, Calif.).

**N48-5** **(17, 588f)**

**Grosswald, Emil. The average order of an arithmetic function.** Duke Math. J. 23 (1956), 41–44.

Let $F(n)$ stand for the number of prime divisors of $n$, distinct or not, and set $a(n)=2^{F(n)}$. The author's main result is:

$$(1)\qquad \sum_{n\leq x}a(n)=(r+1)C_1x\log(2^{-r/2}x)-(r+1)C_2x+O(x^c)$$

where

$$C_1=\tfrac{1}{4}\prod_{p\geq3}(1+(p^2-2p)^{-1}),$$

$$C_2=C_1(2\sum_{p\geq3}\log p/(p-1)(p-2)-2\log2-2\gamma+1),$$

$\gamma$ is Euler's constant, $r=[\log x/\log 2]$, and the constant $c$ satisfies $c<0.84$. The classical method of evaluating sums of coefficients of Dirichlet series is applied to the function

$$f(s)=\prod_{p\geq3}(1-2p^{-s})^{-1}=\sum_{n=1}^{\infty}a_nn^{-s},$$

where $a_n=a(n)$ if $n$ is odd, and $a_n=0$ otherwise. Some difficulties have had to be overcome in the accompanying process of contour integration. The paper concludes with some remarks on the likely true order of magnitude of the error term in (1). *H. Halberstam* (Berkeley, Calif).

Referred to in M15-16, N48-7, N48-8.

**N48-6** **(18, 642b)**

**Pan, Cheng-Tung. On $\sigma(n)$ and $\varphi(n)$.** Bull. Acad. Polon. Sci. Cl. III. **4** (1956), 637–638.

Let $\sigma(n)$ denote the sum of the divisors of $n$, and $\phi(n)$ Euler's totient function. Writing

$$\sum_{n\le x}\sigma(n)=\frac{\pi^2}{12}x^2+\Delta(x),\quad \sum_{n\le x}\varphi(n)=\frac{3}{\pi^2}x^2+R(X),$$

the author announces the following theorems. Theorem 1.

$$\Delta(x)=O\{x(\log x\log\log x)^{3/4}\}.$$

Theorem 4.

$$\sum_{n\le x}\frac{R(n)}{n},=\frac{3}{\pi^2}x+O\{x\exp(-A\log^{4/7-\varepsilon}x)\},$$

where $A$ is a positive number and $\varepsilon$ an arbitrarily small positive number.

Theorem 1 improves a result of Walfisz and Davenport [see, e.g., Walfisz, Math. Z. **26** (1927), 66–88]. Theorem 4 improves a result of Pillai and the reviewer [J. London Math. Soc. **5** (1930), 95–101]. *S. Chowla.*

**N48-7** **(19, 392a)**

**Yüh, Ming-I. A note on an arithmetical function.** Sci. Record (N.S.) **1** (1957), no. 2, 9–12.

Let $F(n)$ be the number of prime divisors of $n$, distinct or not, and let $C_2, \cdots, C_7$ denote certain well-defined constants. The reviewer proved [Duke Math. J. **23** (1956), 41–44; MR **17**, 588] that

(1) $$\sum_{n\le x}2^{F(n)}=C_6x\log^2x+C_7x\log x+O(x)$$

(the argument used in the proof of reviewer's Theorem 3 does not give any sharper result) and

(2) $$\sum_{\substack{2\nmid n\\ n\le x}}2^{F(n)}=C_2x\log x-C_5x+O(x^c)$$

for $c>c_0(=.84\cdots)$, and conjectured that (2) holds for any $c>d=(\log 2)/(\log 3)$. The author proves this conjecture. In his inference from (2) with $c=d+\varepsilon$ to a sharpened version of (1) with error term $O(x^{d+\varepsilon})$, the author repeats an oversight of the reviewer. In fact, the left-hand member of (1) has a discontinuity of saltus $x$ whenever $x=2^k$, and the error term cannot be of lower order. The author asserts (without proof) also the validity of

(3) $$\sum_{n\le x}2^{F(n)}=C_1x\log^2x+C_2x\log x+C_3x+C_4x^d+O(x^{1/2+\varepsilon}).$$

Consideration of $x=2^k$ or $x=3^k$ shows that (3) cannot hold. Several misprints make the reading difficult. *E. Grosswald* (Philadelphia, Pa.).

Citations: MR 17, 588f = N48-5.

**N48-8** **(19, 1040a)**

**Bateman, Paul T. Proof of a conjecture of Grosswald.** Duke Math. J. **25** (1957), 67–72.

For $n=p_1^{\alpha_1}p_2^{\alpha_2}\cdots p_r^{\alpha_r}$ let $F(n)=\alpha_1+\cdots+\alpha_r$ and $a(n)=2^{F(n)}$. Grosswald [same J. **23** (1956), 41–44; MR **17**, 588] proved with certain absolute constants $A$, $B$ as $x\to\infty$

(1) $$\sum_{n\le x}{}' a(n)=Ax\log x+Bx+O(x^c)$$

with a certain $c<0.84$ and where $\Sigma'$ denotes summation over the odd positive integers $n$. Furthermore he conjectured that (1) holds with the exponent log 2/log 3. The author proves this conjecture, which gives a best possible result. For the analogous problem with summation over all positive integers an error in the paper of Grosswald is corrected. By the same method further results on expansions of $\sum_{n\le x}^{(k)}a(n)$ (summation over the positive integers $n$ not divisible by any of the first $k$ primes) are obtained. *H.-E. Richert* (Göttingen).

Citations: MR 17, 588f = N48-5.

**N48-9** **(20# 6382 )**

**McCarthy, Paul J. On a certain family of arithmetic functions.** Amer. Math. Monthly **65** (1958), 586–590.

Let $r$ be a positive integer. An integer is said to be $r$-free if it is not divisible by the $r$th power of any prime, and the function $T_r(n)$ is defined to be the number of integers $k$ such that $1\le k\le n$ and the greatest common divisor $(k, n)$ is $r$-free. It is shown that $T_r(n)$ is multiplicative in the usual number-theoretic sense, and hence it is given explicitly by $T_r(n)=n\prod(1-p^{-r})$, where $p$ ranges over all primes such that $p^r|n$. For $r>1$ it is shown that

$$\sum_{m=1}^{n}T_r(m)=\frac{n^2}{2\zeta(2r)}+O(n),$$

where $\zeta(s)$ is the Riemann zeta function. From this it follows that the probability that the greatest common divisor of two positive integers be $r$-free is $1/\zeta(2r)$. *W. H. Mills* (New Haven, Conn.)

Referred to in A26-89.

**N48-10** **(23# A2395 )**

**Saltykov, A. I.**

**On Euler's function. (Russian. English summary)**

*Vestnik Moskov. Univ. Ser. I Mat. Meh.* **1960**, *no.* 6, 34–50.

Suppose that under appropriate conditions on the coefficients $\alpha_1, \cdots, \alpha_{n+1}$ it is known that

(1) $$\left|\sum_{y=1}^{P}\exp\{2\pi i(\alpha_1y+\cdots+\alpha_{n+1}y^{n+1})\}\right|<e^{c_1n^{\gamma_1}}P^{1-c_2/n^{\gamma_2}}.$$

It is shown here that then

(2) $$\sum_{k\le x}\varphi(k)=3\pi^{-2}x^2+O(x\log^\gamma x(\log\log x)^{1+\varepsilon}),$$

where $\varepsilon>0$ is arbitrary and $\gamma=(\gamma_1+\gamma_2)/(\gamma_1+\gamma_2+1)$. An estimate of the form (1) has been given by N. M. Korobov [Uspehi Mat. Nauk **13** (1958), no. 4 (82), 185–192; MR **21** #4939] with $\gamma_1=0$, $\gamma_2=2$, and it follows that (2) holds with $\gamma=2/3$. This improves the heretofore best known result, due to A. Val'fiš [Acta Arith. **4** (1958), 108–180; MR **21** #2623], in which $\gamma$ was 3/4. *W. J. LeVeque* (Ann Arbor, Mich.)

Citations: MR 21# 2623 = M15-18; MR 21# 4939 = L15-21.

Referred to in N36-31.

**N48-11** **(24# A2554 )**

**Cohen, Eckford**

**A property of Dedekind's $\psi$-function.**

*Proc. Amer. Math. Soc.* **12** (1961), 996.

Let

$$\psi(n)=n\prod_{p|n}\left(1+\frac{1}{p}\right),$$

the product extending over all prime divisors of $n$. The author proves the formula $\sum_{n\in L}1/\psi(n)=\pi^2/6$, where $L$ is the set of positive integers whose prime factors are all multiple. *L. Carlitz* (Durham, N.C.)

**N48-12** **(25# 2052 )**

**Schwarz, Wolfgang**

**Über die Summe $\sum_{n\le x}\varphi(f(n))$ und verwandte Probleme.**

*Monatsh. Math.* **66** (1962), 43–54.

The author obtains asymptotic formulae for $\sum_{n\leq x}\varphi(f(n))$, where $\varphi$ is Euler's totient function and $f(n)$ is a polynomial (primitive) with integer coefficients. He uses an estimate for $\sum_{n\leq x} d(f(n))$, where $d$ is the 'number of divisors' function [Hua, *Additive Primzahltheorie*, Satz 3, p. 12, Teubner, Leipzig, 1959; MR **23** #A1620], as well as the well-known Siegel-Walfisz estimate for $\pi(x; k, 1)$.

*S. Chowla* (Boulder, Colo.)

Citations: MR 23# A1620 = P02-7.

## N48-13 (25# 3916)

**Cohen, Eckford**

**An elementary method in the asymptotic theory of numbers.**

*Duke Math. J.* **28** (1961), 183–192.

The author obtains asymptotic formulae for sums of the form $\sum_{n\leq x} f(n)$, where $f(n)$ is an arithmetic function of the form $f(n)=\sum_{d\delta=n,\gamma(\delta)\mid d} g(d)h(\delta)$. Here $\gamma(n)$ denotes the maximal square-free divisor of $n$, so that the summation is confined to those divisors of $n$ which are multiples of $\gamma(n)$. Two special classes of such functions are considered. (1) Let $S_{k,n}$ denote the set of integral vectors $(x_1,\cdots,x_k)$ where each $x_i$ $(i=1,2,\cdots,k)$ runs through a complete residue system (mod $n$). Let $T_{k,n}$ be the subset of these vectors for which the g.c.d. $(x_1,\cdots,x_k)$ is prime to $n$. Let $T^*_{k,n}$ be the subset of $S_{k,n}$ for which the g.c.d. of $x_1,\cdots,x_k$ is not divisible by a unitary factor $d$ of $n$. ($d$ is a unitary factor if $d\delta=n$ and $(d,\delta)=1$.) Let Let $J_k(n)$ and $J_k{}^*(n)$ be the number of vectors in sets $T_{k,n}$ and $T^*_{k,n}$, respectively. The author shows that $J_k(n)=\sum_{d\delta=n}\mu(d)\delta^k$ and $J_k{}^*(n)=\sum_{d\delta=n,\gamma(\delta)\mid d} J_k(d)$. He then proves that

$$\sum_{n\leq x} J_k{}^*(n) = \alpha_k\frac{x^{k+1}}{k+1}+O(x^k),$$

where $\alpha_k=\prod_p(1-(p-1)/p(p^{k+1}-1))$. Similar results are obtained for other arithmetic functions of this type. (2) A general asymptotic formula is given for sums of the form $\sum_{n\leq x} r_{s,t}(n)$, where $r_{s,t}(n)=\sum_{d\delta=n,\gamma(\delta)\mid d} d^s\mu^2(d)/\gamma^t(\delta)$. In particular $\sum_{n\leq x}\gamma(n)=\frac{1}{2}\alpha x^2+O(x^{3/2})$ with $\alpha=\prod_p(1-1/(p^2+p))$.

*W. H. Simons* (Vancouver, B.C.)

Referred to in A36-51, N52-25.

## N48-14 (26# 2396)

**Scourfield, E. J.**

**The divisors of a quadratic polynomial.**

*Proc. Glasgow Math. Assoc.* **5**, 8–20 (1961).

For a fixed modulus $k>1$ let $d(m;h)$ denote the number of divisors $d$ of $m$ which satisfy $d\equiv h$ (mod $k$), where $(h,k)=1$. Let $f(n)=an^2+bn+c$ be an irreducible quadratic polynomial with integer coefficients and discriminant $D=b^2-4ac$ relatively prime to $k$. Assume also that for all integers $n>0$ the integer $f(n)$ is positive and relatively prime to $k$. The author's main theorem is the asymptotic formula

$$(1)\qquad \sum_{n=1}^{x} d(f(n);h) = A_1x\log x+O(x\log\log x)$$

for large $x$, where $A_1$ is a constant depending on $k$ and on the coefficients of $f$. The proof depends on the estimation of certain character sums. Interesting applications of this theorem are made by specializing the polynomial $f$. For example, if $f(n)$ is odd for all $n>0$, if $f(n)\equiv 1$ (mod 4) for some integers $n$, if $-D$ is the square of an integer, and if $r(m)$ is the number of representations of $m$ as a sum of two squares, then (1) implies

$$(2)\qquad \sum_{n=1}^{x} r(f(n)) = Ax\log x+O(x\log\log x),$$

where $A$ is a constant depending on $f$. Formula (2), in turn, can be used to prove that $\sum_{n\leq x} r(n^2+1)=(8/\pi)x\log x+O(x\log\log x)$. The author also indicates how the error terms in these asymptotic formulas could be improved.

*T. M. Apostol* (Pasadena, Calif.)

## N48-15 (29# 4723)

**Cohen, Eckford**

**Some analogues of certain arithmetical functions.**

*Riv. Mat. Univ. Parma* (2) **4** (1963), 115–125.

For positive integers $n$ and $r$ define the unique factoring of $n$ into relatively prime integers $\alpha_r(n)$ and $\beta_r(n)$ by the following rule: If $p^k$ is the highest power of a prime dividing $n$, let $p^k$ be a factor of $\alpha_r(n)$ or $\beta_r(n)$ according as $k\leqq r$ or $k>r$. Define $\phi_r(n)=\beta_r(n)\phi(\alpha_r(n))$, where $\phi$ is the Euler totient function. The author studies $\phi_r(n)$ and related functions. This involves the use of the analogue of the Möbius function defined as the multiplicative function such that $\mu_r(p^e)=p^r$, $-1$, or 0 according as $e=r+1$, $e=1$, or otherwise. The following typical results are cited. First, $\phi_r(n)=n\sum\mu_r(d)/d$, where the sum is taken over all divisors $d$ of $n$. Also $\sum_{n\leq x}\phi_r(n)/n=a_rx+O(\log^2 x)$, where $a_r=\prod(1-p^{-2}+p^{-r-2})$, the product being taken over all primes. The sum $\sum_{n\leq x}\phi_r(n)=\frac{1}{2}a_rx^2+O(x\log^2 x)$. These estimates are obtained by using classical properties of Dirichlet series.

*I. Niven* (Eugene, Ore.)

## N48-16 (31# 1239)

**Barban, M. B.**

**Multiplicative functions of ${}^\Sigma R$-equidistributed sequences. (Russian. Uzbek summary)**

*Izv. Akad. Nauk UzSSR Ser. Fiz.-Mat. Nauk* **1964**, *no.* 6, 13–19.

A sequence $\{a_n\}$ of integers is said to be ${}^\Sigma R'(y,z)$-equidistributed if

$$\sum_{D\leqq y}\max_{(l,D)=1}\left|A(x,D,l)-\frac{A(x)}{\varphi(D)}\right| < \frac{A(x)}{z},$$

where $A(x)=\sum_{a_n\leqq x}1$, $A(x,D,l)=\sum_{a_n\equiv l(D),a_n\leqq x}1$. A sequence $\{a_n\}$ is called dense if $A(x)>x\log^{-c}x$ for $x>x_0$ ($c>0$, a constant). The author proves the following theorem. Let $t(n)$ be a multiplicative function satisfying $t(p^k)=O(k^{c_1})$, $t(p^{k+1})\geqq t(p^k)$ $(k\geqq 0$, $p$ a prime). Then for an arbitrary irreducible polynomial $g(m)$ and an arbitrary dense sequence $\{a_n\}$ which is ${}^\Sigma R'(x^\alpha, c(B)\log^B x)$-equidistributed, one has

$$\sum_{a_n\leqq x} t(g(a_n)) \asymp A(x)\exp\left(\sum_{p\leqq x}\frac{L(p)}{p}(t(p)-1)\right),$$

where $L(p)$ is the number of solutions of the congruence $g(m)\equiv 0$ $(p)$ ($f_1\asymp f_2$ means $c_2<f_1/f_2<c_3$).

*S. Knapowski* (Gainesville, Fla.)

Referred to in N36-88, N60-75, Z02-53.

## N48-17 (33# 5576)

**Stronina, M. I.**

**An elementary proof of Urazbaev's asymptotic formula. (Russian)**

*Izv. Vysš. Učebn. Zaved. Matematika* **1966**, *no.* 3 (52), 156–158.

For a fixed prime $l$, let $I(n)$ be the multiplicative function defined for prime powers $p^m$ as follows: $I(p^m)=l-1$ if $m=1$ and $p\equiv 1$ (mod $l$), and $I(p^m)=0$ otherwise. Then $\sum_{n\leq x} I(n)\sim\lambda x$ as $x\to\infty$, where $\lambda=\lambda(l)$ is a positive constant for which various (complicated) explicit expressions can be given. In a stronger form, with error term, this was proved by B. M. Urazbaev [Dokl. Akad. Nauk SSSR (N.S.) **95** (1954), 935–938; MR **15**, 937] by classical methods of contour integration based on a study of the generating function $f(s)=\sum I(n)n^{-s}$ for complex $s$. In the present paper, the author deduces the result (in the form stated) from the prime-number theorem for the arithmetical progression $n\equiv 1 \pmod{l}$ by means of a general theorem of E. Wirsing [Math. Ann. **143** (1961), 75–102; MR **24** #A1241]. Wirsing's proof of his theorem, and the author's application of the theorem, make no use of the generating function. But in order to identify the form of $\lambda$ given by this method with that obtained by Urazbaev, the author uses an Abelian argument based on a consideration of $f(s)$ for real $s>1$. *A. E. Ingham* (Cambridge, England)

Citations: MR 15, 937d = R20-19; MR 24# A1241 = N36-30.

## N48-18 (34# 2538)

**Gioia, A. A.; Vaidya, A. M.**

**The number of squarefree divisors of an integer.**

*Duke Math. J.* **33** (1966), 797–799.

Denote by $\theta(n)$ the number of squarefree divisors of $n$. The authors improve the remainder term in $\sum_{n\leq x}\theta(n)=c_1x\log x+c_2x+O(x^{1/2}\log x)$ (cf. F. Mertens [J. Reine Angew. Math. **77** (1874), 289–338] and E. Cohen [Amer. Math. Monthly **67** (1960), 879–880; MR **23** #A124]) to $O(x^{1/2})$. *W. Schwarz* (Freiburg)

Citations: MR 23# A124 = N40-45.

Referred to in N48-22.

## N48-19 (36# 2567)

**Žogin, I. I.**

**Notes on the theory of functions and theory of numbers. (Russian)**

*Mat. Prosvešč.* **1958**, *vyp.* 3, 147–155.

Setting $c_n=\sum_{d|n}a_db_{n/d}$, the author shows that if $A(z)=\sum_{n=1}^{\infty}a_nz^n$ and $B(z)=\sum_{n=1}^{\infty}b_nz^n$ have positive radii of convergence, then so also does their "Dirichlet product" $C(z)=\sum_{n=1}^{\infty}c_nz^n$. In the common circle of convergence, intersected with the unit circle, he shows $\sum_{n=1}^{\infty}a_nB(z^n)=\sum_{n=1}^{\infty}b_nA(z^n)=\sum_{n=1}^{\infty}c_nz^n$. Setting $b_n=1$, he obtains the ordinary Lambert series formula [K. Knopp, *Theorie und Anwendung der unendlichen Reihen*, Springer, Berlin, 1922; second edition, 1924; English translation, Blackie, London, 1928; third revised edition, Springer, Berlin, 1931; fourth edition, Springer, Berlin, 1947; MR **10**, 446; English translation, Hafner, New York, 1950; fifth corrected edition, Springer, Berlin, 1964; MR **32** #1473]. For a sequence of integers $n_i$ satisfying $1\leq n_1\leq n_2\leq\cdots$, he defines $\sigma_\alpha(n, n_N)$ as the sum of the $\alpha$th powers of the divisors of $n$ appearing in the first $N$ terms of the sequence $n_i$. He obtains the formula $\sum_{n=1}^{\infty}\{\sigma_\alpha(n, n_N)-\sum_{j=1}^{N}(n_j)^{\alpha-1}\}/n=-\sum_{j=1}^{N}(n_j)^{\alpha-1}\ln n_j$. Specializing to $n_j=j^q$, he obtains by a difficult double limit inversion, that for $q$ integral and $\geq 2$, $\sum_{n=1}^{\infty}(\tau^{(q)}(n)-\zeta(q))/n=q\zeta'(q)$, where $\zeta(s)$ is the Riemann zeta function and $\tau^{(q)}(n)$ is the number of divisors of $n$ which are $q$th powers. Next, he obtains formulas relating to the $\psi(x)$ of prime number theory, and an asymptotic formula for $\sum_{n\leq x}\tau^{(q)}(n)/n$. Other specializations give formulas for $\ln N$, and Euler's constant. {On line 2 of page 148, the $=$'s should be $\leq$'s.}

See also #2568 below. *R. Spira* (E. Lansing, Mich.)

Referred to in A28-18.

## N48-20 (36# 2568)

**Žogin, I. I.**

**Lambert series. I. (Russian)**

*Sverdlovsk. Gos. Ped. Inst. Učen. Zap.* **31** (1965), 97–105.

The author considers generalized Lambert series, $f(z)=\sum_{n=1}^{\infty}a_nz^n/(1-z^n)^\alpha$, where $\alpha$ is complex. Using the results of his paper reviewed above [#2567], he shows that if $\sum_{n=1}^{\infty}a_nz^n$ converges for $|z|<1$, so does the series for $f(z)$. He then restricts $\alpha$ to be $>0$, and studies the behavior of $f(z)$ on radial approach to primitive roots of unity. Specializing to particular cases, he shows that $\sum_{n=1}^{\infty}\sigma_\alpha(n)z^n$ and $\sum_{n=1}^{\infty}\varphi_\alpha(n)z^n$ have the unit circle as natural boundary where $\sigma_\alpha(n)=\sum_{d|n}d^\alpha$ and $\varphi_\alpha(n)=n^\alpha\prod_{p|n}(1-1/p^\alpha)$, the Jordan totient function.

{In the remark after (10), he means to apply Abel's test to the series whose partial sum is opposite "(10)". The last $=$ sign in (11) should be a $+$. At the start of § 4, he is using the $M$-test. In the remark in parentheses after (13) he means $0\leq\alpha\leq 1$ and is using Abel's uniform convergence test. There are other misprints.}

*R. Spira* (E. Lansing, Mich.)

## N48-21 (36# 2576)

**MacLeod, R. A.**

**The minimum of $\Phi(x)/x^2$.**

*J. London Math. Soc.* **42** (1967), 652–660.

Let $\varphi(n)$ denote Euler's totient function. Define $\Phi(x)=\sum_{n\leq x}\varphi(n)$ and let $R(x)$ denote the difference between this sum and $3x^2/\pi^2$, $R(x)=\sum_{n\leq x}\varphi(n)-3x^2/\pi^2$. It is well-known that $R(x)=O(x\log x)$. S. S. Pillai and the reviewer [same J. **5** (1930), 95–101] proved that $R(x)\neq o(x\log\log\log x)$ and that $\sum_{n\leq x}R(n)\sim 3x^2/2\pi^2$. M. L. N. Sarma [Proc. Indian Acad. Sci. Sect. A **3** (1936), 338] showed that $R(820)<0$, while P. Erdős and H. Shapiro [Canad. J. Math. **3** (1951), 375–385; MR **13**, 535] showed that $R(x)$ changes sign for infinitely many positive integers $x$.

The author studies the minimum of $R(x)/x^2$ over all integers $x>0$ and shows that this minimum occurs at $x=1276$ (1276 is the second integer $x$ for which $R(x)<0$). Here it has the value $-0.2466\times 10^{-4}$ approximately. He proves this result by showing that for $x>150{,}000$, $|R(x)/x^2|<|R(1276)/1276^2|$ and using the computer to check for $x\leq 150{,}000$. *S. Chowla* (University Park, Pa.)

Citations: MR 13, 535i = N48-1.

## N48-22 (36# 3739)

**Saffari, Bahman**

**Sur le nombre de diviseurs "$r$-free" d'un entier. Cas $r=2$ et $r=3$.**

*C. R. Acad. Sci. Paris Sér. A-B* **265** (1967), A705–A707.

Let $d_r(n)$ denote the number of $r$-free divisors of $n$ and let $d(n)$ denote the total number of divisors. Put $\sum_{n\leq x}d(n)=x\log x+(2\gamma-1)x+\Delta(x)$, $\sum_{n\leq x}d_r(n)=(1/\zeta(r))x\log x+((2\gamma-1)/\zeta(r)-r\zeta(r)/\zeta^2(r))x+\Delta_r(x)$. It is well known that $\Delta(x)=O(x^c)$ for some $c<\frac{1}{3}$, and A. A. Gioia and A. M. Vaidya [Duke Math. J. **33** (1966), 797–799; MR **34** #2538] have proved that $\Delta_2(x)=O(x^{1/2})$. The present author obtains results of the type $\Delta_2(x)=O(x^{1/2})$, $\Delta_3(x)=O(x^{1/3})$. The author promises to treat the case $\gamma\geq 4$ in another paper. *L. Carlitz* (Durham, N.C.)

Citations: MR 34# 2538 = N48-18.

Referred to in N48-24.

## N48-23 (37# 176)

**Il'jasov, I.**

**The summation of composite functions of Euler's function. (Russian)**

*Dokl. Akad. Nauk SSSR* **178** (1968), 529–532.

Let $\phi$ be Euler's function and $F$ be continuous on [0, 1]. It can be shown [cf. M. Kac, *Statistical independence in probability, analysis and number theory*, Chapter 4, Section 2, Wiley, New York, 1959; MR **22** #996] that $A(F)=\lim_{N\to\infty}N^{-1}\sum_{n\leq N}F(\phi(n)/n)$ exists. The author proves that $N^{-1}\sum_{n\leq N}F(\phi(n)/n)-A(F)=O((\log N)^{-2})$ if $F$ is differentiable and satisfies the Lipschitz condition of first order on [0, 1]. This improves, by a factor $(\log\log N)^2$, the estimate found by M. M. Tjan [Litovsk. Mat. Sb. **6** (1966), 105–119; MR **34** #5780]. As Tjan showed, imposing further smoothness conditions on $F$ leads to better estimates; the author asserts that here too he is able to sharpen Tjan's results, but that the proofs become rather complicated.

{This article has appeared in English translation [Soviet Math. Dokl. **9** (1968), 130–134].}

*H. Halberstam* (Nottingham)

Citations: MR 22# 996 = Q15-7; MR 34# 5780 = N60-61.

**N48-24** **(37# 6252)**

**Saffari, Bahman**

**Sur le nombre des diviseurs "$r$-libres" d'un entier, et sur les points à coordonnées entières dans certaines régions du plan.**

*C. R. Acad. Sci. Paris Sér. A-B* **266** (1968), A601–A603.

Let $d_r(n)$ be the number of "$r$-free" divisors of $n$, $d_{r,s}(n)$ the number of solutions of $n=q_rq_s$, where $q_r$ is "$r$-free", $T_r(x)=\sum_{1\leq n\leq x} d_r(n)$, $T_{r,s}(x)=\sum_{1\leq n\leq x} d_{r,s}(n)$. Theorem 2 states that if

$$T_{r,s}(x) = \frac{x\log x}{\zeta(r)\zeta(s)} + \left(\frac{2\gamma-1}{\zeta(r)\zeta(s)} - \frac{r\zeta'(r)\zeta(s)+s\zeta'(s)\zeta(r)}{(\zeta(r)\zeta(s))^2}\right)x + \Delta_{r,s}(x),$$

where $r=2$ or 3, $s\geqq 2$, then assuming the Riemann hypothesis,

$$\Delta_{r,s}(x) = O\left[x^a \exp\left(\frac{b\log x}{\log\log x} + O\left(\frac{\log x}{(\log\log x)^2}\right)\right)\right],$$

where $a$ and $b$ are certain positive constants depending on $r$, $s$, with $a<\{\min(r,s)\}^{-1}$. A similar estimate is stated for the error term $\Delta_r(x)$ in $T_r(x)$ for $r=2$ or 3, again assuming the Riemann hypothesis. Inequalities for $\liminf_{x\to\infty} \Delta_{r,s}(x)$ and $\limsup_{x\to\infty} \Delta_{r,s}(x)$ are also given. There are no proofs but some methods used are named [cf. the author, same C. R. **265** (1967), A705–A707; MR **36** #3739; ibid. **266** (1968), A109–A112; MR **38** #131].

*I. Danicic* (Aberystwyth)

Citations: MR 36# 3739 = N48-22; MR 38# 131 = N48-25.

Referred to in N48-25.

**N48-25** **(38# 131)**

**Saffari, Bahman**

**Sur le nombre de diviseurs "$r$-free" d'un entier. Cas $r\geqq 4$.**

*C. R. Acad. Sci. Paris Sér. A-B* **266** (1968), A109–A112.

Let $\Delta(x)$ be the error term arising in the ordinary divisor problem. The author gives estimates for $\Delta_r(x)$ $(r\geqq 4)$ in terms of $\Delta(x)$, the following being typical (for the definition of $\Delta_r(x)$, see the review of the author's paper in same C. R. **266** (1968), A601–A603 [MR **37** #6252]). If $\rho(x)$ is an increasing unbounded function such that

$$R \equiv \limsup_{x\to\infty} x^{-1/4}\Delta(x)/\rho(x) > 0,$$

then for $r\geqq 5$, $\limsup_{x\to\infty} x^{-1/4}\Delta_r(x)/\rho(x) \geqq R/\zeta(r/4)$, which leads to $\limsup_{x\to\infty} \Delta_r(x)/(x^{1/4}(\log x)^{1/4}\log\log x) \geqq H/\zeta(r/4)$ $(r\geqq 5)$, where $H$ is a positive constant arising from Hardy's estimate for $\limsup \Delta(x)$. {A misprint in the paper at this point states "$\leqq$" instead of "$\geqq$".}

*I. Danicic* (Aberystwyth)

Citations: MR 37# 6252 = N48-24.

Referred to in N48-24.

**N48-26** **(38# 4428)**

**Suryanarayana, D.**

**The number of $k$-ary divisors of an integer.**

*Monatsh. Math.* **72** (1968), 445–450.

Ein Teiler $d$ von $n$ heißt "$k$-är", wenn aus $t^k|(d, n/d)$ schon $t=1$ folgt. Bezeichnet $\tau_{(k)}(n)$ $[\tau_k{}^*(n)]$ die Anzahl der $k$-freien ["$k$-ären"] Teiler von $n$, so zeigt der Verfasser die Beziehung $\tau_k{}^*(n)=\tau_{(2k)}(n)$ und leitet mit bekannten elementaren Methoden asymptotische Formeln für $\sum_{n\leq x}\tau_k{}^*(n)$ $[\sum_{n\leq x}\tau_{(k)}(n)]$ (gültig für $k\geqq 2$ [für $k\geqq 3$]) her.

*W. Schwarz* (Freiburg)

**N48-27** **(39# 1414)**

**Vaidya, A. M.**

**On the changes of sign of a certain error function connected with $k$-free integers.**

*J. Indian Math. Soc. (N.S.)* **32** (1968), 105–111.

Let $Q_k(x)$ be the number of $k$-free integers that are $\leq x$. It is well known that $Q_k(x)\sim x/\zeta(k)$. Let $E_k(x)=Q_k(x)-x/\zeta(k)$. The author shows, utilizing either the validity of the Riemann hypothesis or the existence of a simple zero of $\zeta(ks)$ on the line $\sigma=1/2k$ which is not a zero of $\zeta(s)$, that (i) there is a sequence $\{x_j\}$ with $\lim_{j\to\infty} x_j=\infty$ such that $|E_k(x_j)|>Cx_j$, where $C$ is a positive constant independent of $x$, (ii) for any $\varepsilon>0$ there are infinitely many integers $n$ for which $E(n)>n^{1/2k-\varepsilon}$ and there are infinitely many integers $m$ for which $E(m)<-m^{1/2k-\varepsilon}$, (iii) there are infinitely many $n$ for which $0\leqq E(n)<1$, (iv) there are infinitely many $n$ for which $Q_k(n)=n/\zeta(k)$ or $Q_k(n)=[n/\zeta(k)+1]$ and (v) the Schnirelmann density of the $k$-free integers is $<1/\zeta(k)$.

Standard type arguments are used with the inequalities implicit in the assumption of the validity of the Riemann hypothesis.

*J. H. Jordan* (Pullman, Wash.)

**N48-28** **(40# 2622)**

**Smith, R. A.**

**On $\sum r(n)r(n+a)$.**

*Proc. Nat. Inst. Sci. India Part A* **34** (1968), 132–137.

Author's summary: "In 1932, T. Estermann [Proc. London Math. Soc. (2) **34** (1932), 280–292] obtained an asymptotic formula for the sum $\sum_{n\leq x} r(n)r(n+a)$, where $r(n)$ denotes the number of representations of $n$ as a sum of two squares and $a$ is a fixed positive integer. His method is entirely elementary. In this paper, we use an analytic method of C. Hooley [ibid. (3) **7** (1957), 396–413; MR **19**, 839] to find the asymptotic formula for this sum. The method depends on the asymptotic formula for the sum $\sum_{n\leq x, n\equiv b \pmod k} r(n)$, with a 'reasonably sharp' error term. The result is in course of publication elsewhere (C. Hooley, "The circle problem in an arithmetic progression", Canad. Math. Bull., to appear) and so is only quoted in this paper as a lemma."

Citations: MR 19, 839c = N40-30.

**N48-29** **(40# 4221)**

**Barban, M. B.; Vehov, P. P.**

**Summation of multiplicative functions of polynomials. (Russian)**

*Mat. Zametki* **5** (1969), 669–680.

The authors estimate the precise order of magnitude of sums of multiplicative functions for which the Möbius inversion is sign-reversing (i.e., for functions of the type of norms of integral ideals of algebraic number fields). The estimates for this class of functions essentially differ from estimates for functions whose Möbius inversion is sign-preserving (for example, for functions of the type of $d(n)$, the number of divisors of $n$). The new results are applied to the problem of the distribution of integral points on a sphere.

{This article has appeared in English translation [Math. Notes **5** (1969), 400–407].}

*A. I. Vinogradov* (Leningrad)

**N48-30** **(40# 5564 )**

**Suryanarayana, D.**

**Asymptotic formula for $\sum_{n\leq x}\mu^2(n)/n$.**

*Indian J. Math.* **9** (1967), 543–545 (1968).

Proof of $\sum_{n<x}\mu^2(n)/n=(1/\xi(2))(\log x+\gamma-2\zeta'(2)/\zeta(2))+o(\sqrt{x})$. A slightly better estimation of the error term, not using the Riemann conjecture, is also given.

*P. Barrucand* (Paris)

**N48-31** **(40# 7212 )**

**Apostol, Tom M.**

**Möbius functions of order $k$.**

*Pacific J. Math.* **32** (1970), 21–27.

Given a positive integer $k$, define the function $\mu_k$ by $\mu_k(1)=1$; $\mu_k(n)=0$ if $p^{k+1}|n$ for some prime $p$; $\mu_k(n)=(-1)^r$ if $n=p_1{}^k\cdots p_r{}^k\prod_{i>r}p_i{}^{A_i}$ with $0\leq A_i<k$ for each $i>r$, and $\mu_k(n)=1$ otherwise. Then $\mu_1(n)=\mu(n)$. It is proved that for $k\geq 2$, $\sum_{n\leq x}\mu_k(n)=A_kx+O(x^{1/k}\log x)$, where $A_k=(1/\zeta(k))\sum_{n=1}^{\infty}(\mu(n)/n^k)\prod_{p|n}(1-p^{-1})/(1-p^{-k})$.

*K. Thanigasalam* (University Park, Pa.)

**N48-32** **(41# 163 )**

**Il'jasov, I. I.**

**An estimate of the remainder term of the sum $\sum_{n\leq x}(\varphi(n)/n)^\alpha$. (Russian)**

*Izv. Akad. Nauk Kazah. SSR Ser. Fiz.-Mat.* **1969**, *no.* 3, 77–79.

Der Verfasser benützt nach bekanntem Vorbild [A. Z. Val'fiš, *Weylsche Exponentialsummen in der neueren Zahlentheorie*, Kapitel IV, VEB Deutsch. Verlag Wissensch., Berlin, 1963; MR **36** #3737] Exponentialsummen, um für $0\leq\alpha\leq 1$ das Restglied in $\sum_{n\leq x}(\varphi(n)/n)^\alpha=Cx+O(\log x)$ auf $O\{(\log x)^{2/3}(\log\log x)^{4/3}\}$ zu verschärfen.

*W. Schwarz* (Frankfurt a.M.)

Citations: MR 36# 3737 = L02-8.

**N48-33** **(41# 6798 )**

**Suryanarayana, D.**

**Extensions of Dedekind's $\psi$-function.**

*Math. Scand.* **26** (1970), 107–118.

The Dedekind $\psi$-function is defined by

$$\psi(n) = \sum_{d|n} d\phi((d, n/d))(d, n/d)^{-1},$$

where $\phi$ is the Euler totient. The author introduces three generalizations $\psi_k$, $\Psi_k$ and $\psi_{(k)}$, each of which reduces to $\psi$ when $k=1$. The definitions of the former two utilize Cohen's and Klee's totients, respectively, rather than Euler's. Several multiplicative identities are proved, and the average orders of the functions are found.

*D. Rearick* (Boulder, Colo.)

**N48-34** **(43# 172 )**

**Ufimceva, L. I.**

**A generalization of the additive problem of divisors. (Russian)**

*Mat. Zametki* **7** (1970), 477–482.

Die Dispersionsmethode und die Methode des "großen Siebes" brachten viele neue Ergebnisse über Summen, die Teilerfunktionen enthalten. So leitete etwa B. M. Bredihin [Uspehi Mat. Nauk **22** (1965), no. 2 (122), 89–130; MR **32** #5618] für die Summe $\sum_{m<n}\tau_{k_1}(m)\tau_{k_2}(n-m)$ eine asymptotische Formel her. Verfasser verallgemeinert dieses Ergebnis (für $k_2=2$) und beweist: Ist $f\geq 0$ eine multiplikative Funktion, die $f(p)=f_0>1$, $f_0$ ganz, für alle Primzahlen $p$ erfüllt, und die mit einer passenden Konstanten $c$ der Abschätzung $f(m)=O(\tau^c(m))$ genügt, so gilt für $n\rightarrow\infty$,

$$\sum_{m<n}f(m)\tau(n-m) = n\sigma(n)(\log n)^{f_0}+O(n(\log n)^{f_0-1}(\log\log n)^{c_1});$$

hierbei kann die Singuläre Reihe durch $\sigma(n)\gg(\log\log n)^{-c_2}$ abgeschätzt werden.

{In seiner Habilitationsschrift ["Einige Anwendungen des großen Siebes auf zahlentheoretische Funktionen", Univ. Marburg, Marburg, 1970] hat D. Wolke Summen der Gestalt $\sum_{n\leq x}\tau(n)f(n+a)$ behandelt, wobei die multiplikative Funktion $f\geq 0$ erheblich weniger eingeschränkt ist als oben.}

{This article has appeared in English translation [Math. Notes **7** (1970), 289–292].} *W. Schwarz* (Frankfurt a.M.)

Citations: MR 32# 5618 = P36-43.

**N48-35** **(43# 176 )**

**Galambos, J.**

**A probabilistic approach to mean values of multiplicative functions.**

*J. London Math. Soc.* (2) **2** (1970), 405–419.

In an earlier paper the author introduced a class $(K)$ of dependent random variables and obtained a generalization of the Kolmogorov three series theorem. In the present paper, the author translates a number theoretical method of A. Rényi into a probabilistic method and obtains a considerably more general theorem. One of several applications which the author presents is the following result which generalizes Delange's theorem to polynomials. Theorem 3: Let $f(x)>0$ be an irreducible polynomial of degree $s$ having integral coefficients. Then, if $g(u)$ is a strongly multiplicative complex valued function satisfying the conditions $|g(u)|\leq 1$ and $\lim_{k\to\infty}g(q_k)=0$, where $q_1$, $q_2$, $\cdots$ is the sequence of rational primes and furthermore, if the series $\sum_{k=1}^{\infty}(g(q_k)-1)\rho(q_k)/q_k$ converges where $\rho(q)$ is the number of residue classes mod $q$ for which $g(x)\equiv 0$ mod $q$, then

$$\lim_{N=+\infty}N^{-1}\sum_{j=1}^{N}g(f(j)) = \prod_{k=1}^{\infty}(1+(g(q_k)-1)\rho(q_k)/q_k).$$

{The reader may wish to refer to a survey written by the author in Ann. Inst. H. Poincaré Sect. B (N.S.) **6** (1970), 281–305. It contains a comprehensive bibliography on the subject.} *M. C. Wunderlich* (De Kalb, Ill.)

**N48-36** **(44# 6625 )**

**Erdős, P.; Kátai, I.**

**Non complete sums of multiplicative functions.**

*Period. Math. Hungar.* **1** (1971), *no.* 3, 209–212.

If $f$ is an arithmetic function, let

$$C(n) = \max_{1\leq z\leq n}|\sum_{d|n,d\leq z}f(d)|$$

and let $P$ denote the set of primes $p$ for which $f(p)=-1$. The authors prove that if $f$ is multiplicative, $|f(n)|\leq 1$ and $\sum_{p\in P}1/p=\infty$, then $C(n)<2^{\alpha\omega(n)}$ for almost all $n$, where $\omega(n)$ denotes the number of distinct prime divisors of $n$ and $\alpha$ is any constant greater than $\frac{1}{2}$.

If $f$ is taken to be the Möbius function, and $C(n)$ is renamed $M(n)$ to conform with earlier usage, this theorem represents an improvement on previous upper estimates of $M(n)$. The authors also conjecture a lower estimate for $M(n)$; as stated it contradicts the upper estimate, and the reviewer believes that what was meant is $M(n) > (\log n)^{\frac{1}{2}-\varepsilon}$ for every positive $\varepsilon$ and almost all $n$.

*D. Rearick* (Boulder, Colo.)

# N52 ESTIMATES OF SUMS OF ARITHMETIC FUNCTIONS: OTHER SPECIAL FUNCTIONS

See also reviews A22-6, A30-13, A36-9, A44-21, A62-83, B56-13, F35-32, K10-7, N04-47, N28-28, N28-72, N36-8, N40-42, N68-31, N72-33, P08-10, P28-70, P48-1, R46-8.

## N52-1 (3, 165b)

**Erdös, P. On some asymptotic formulas in the theory of the "factorisatio numerorum."** Ann. of Math. (2) **42**, 989–993 (1941).

Let $1 < a_1 \leqq a_2 \leqq \cdots$ be a sequence of integers. Denote by $f(n)$ the number of representations of $n$ as a product of the $a$'s, where two representations are considered equal only if they contain the same factors in the same order. The author assumes $\sum a_n^{-1-\epsilon}$ convergent for $\epsilon > 0$ and that not all $a$'s are powers of $a_1$. He shows by elementary considerations that

$$F(n) = \sum_{r=1}^{n} f(r) = Cn^{\rho}[1+o(1)],$$

where $\sum a_n^{-\rho} = 1$. For the case $a_n = n+1$, he states the existence of constants $c_1$ and $c_2$, $0 < c_2 < c_1 < 1$, such that $f(n) > n^{\rho} \exp[-(\log n)^{c_1}]$ for infinitely many $n$ and $f(n) < n^{\rho} \exp[-(\log n)^{c_2}]$ for all large $n$. These results extend previous results of L. Kalmár [Acta Litt. Sci. Szeged **5**, 95–107 (1930)] and the reviewer [Acta Arith. **2**, 134–146 (1937), where the result $f(n) < n^{\rho-\epsilon}$ for infinitely many $n$ is proved].

*E. Hille* (Palo Alto, Calif.).

Referred to in N52-2, N56-5.

## N52-2 (5, 172c)

**Erdös, P. Corrections to two of my papers.** Ann. of Math. (2) **44**, 647–651 (1943).

[For the review of the first correction, cf. these Rev. **5**, 180.] The second correction refers to the paper "On some asymptotic formulas in the theory of factorisatio numerorum" [Ann. of Math. (2) **42**, 989–993 (1941); these Rev. **3**, 165], in which the main theorem was stated incorrectly. It should read as follows. Let $1 < a_1 < a_2 < \cdots$ be a sequence of integers such that, for some $\rho$, $\sum_1^\infty a_k^{-\rho} = 1$ and $\sum_1^\infty a_k^{-\rho} \log a_k < \infty$, while not all the $a_k$'s are powers of $a_1$. Let $f(n)$ be the number of factorizations of $n$ into the $a_k$'s, order being taken into account, $f(1) = 1$, $F(n) = \sum_1^n f(k)$. Then

$$(1) \qquad F(n) = Cn^{\rho}[1+o(1)].$$

The proof is unchanged. The author discusses the three alternatives which arise when the assumptions on the $a_k$'s are not satisfied. (1) If $\sum_1^\infty a_k^{-\sigma}$ diverges for all $\sigma$, then $F(n)n^{-\sigma} \to \infty$ for all $\sigma$. [This case requires $a_k = a_{k+1}$ infinitely often which would seem to be excluded by the nature of the problem.] (2) $\sum_1^\infty a_k^{-\sigma} < 1$ whenever the series converges. If $\sigma_0$ is the abscissa of convergence, then $F(n) = o(n^{\sigma_0})$ and not $O(n^{\sigma})$ for any $\sigma < \sigma_0$. (3) There is a $\rho$ such that $\sum_1^\infty a_k^{-\rho} = 1$ but $\sum_1^\infty a_k^{-\rho} \log a_k = \infty$; here the author can prove merely $\liminf n^{-\rho} F(n) = 0$. The case in which the $a_k$'s have all their prime factors in a given finite or infinite set of primes has been studied by E. Hille [Acta Arithmetica **2**, 134–144 (1936)] who found formula (1) with $C = \{\rho \sum_1^\infty a_k^{-\rho} \log a_k\}^{-1}$ in generalization of a formula by L. Kalmar for the case $a_k = k$. The author calls attention to the fact that this formula seems to presuppose $\sum_1^\infty a_k^{-\rho} \log a_k < \infty$. In an addendum, p. 651, E. Hille acknowledges the error but points out that his Ikehara-Wiener argument tacitly presupposed $\rho > \sigma_0$, in which case the condition is satisfied, and states that the argument does not apply if either $\rho = \sigma_0$ or $\sum a_k^{-\rho} < 1$ for $\sigma > \sigma_0$. [As reviewer I have to differ from myself as author: the Ikehara-Wiener theorem actually applies in the second case and gives $F(n) = o(n^{\sigma_0})$ in agreement with Erdös's result in case (2) above.] Finally the author acknowledges the priority rights of K. Mahler and K. Knopp to some results in his paper in Ann. of Math. (2) **43**, 437–450 (1942) [these Rev. **4**, 36].

*E. Hille.*

Citations: MR 3, 165b = N52-1; MR 4, 36a = P72-5.

## N52-3 (7, 365h)

**Ikehara, Shikao. On Kalmár's problem in "Factorisatio Numerorum." II.** Proc. Phys.-Math. Soc. Japan (3) **23**, 767–774 (1941).

[Part I appeared in the same Proc. **21**, 208–219 (1939).] The following result is proved. Let $k(n)$ denote the number of representations of an integer $n$ as a product of factors; let $K(x) = \sum_{m=1}^{[x]} k(m)$; let $\rho$ be the positive root of the equation $\zeta(s) = 2$. Then $n^{-\rho}K(n) = \rho^{-1}R^{-1} + F(n)$, where $R = -\zeta'(\rho)$, $F(n) = O\{\exp(-\alpha(\log\log n)^{\gamma})\}$, $\gamma^{-1} = \frac{3}{4} + \epsilon$ for any $\epsilon > 0$, and $0 < \alpha < \frac{1}{2}$. The bound for $F(n)$ is an improvement on previous results. The proof uses the results of Vinogradov on Weyl's sums.

*R. D. James* (Vancouver, B. C.).

## N52-4 (9, 226c)

**Kendall, D. G., and Rankin, R. A. On the number of Abelian groups of a given order.** Quart. J. Math., Oxford Ser. **18**, 197–208 (1947).

It is known that the number $a(n)$ of Abelian groups of order $n = p_1^{\alpha} p_2^{\beta} \cdots p_l^{\lambda}$ equals $P(\alpha)P(\beta) \cdots P(\lambda)$, where $P(\alpha)$ is the number of partitions of $\alpha$ into positive parts. Using $\sum a(n)n^{-s} = \zeta(s)\zeta(2s)\zeta(3s) \cdots$ and a theorem of Landau [Nachr. Ges. Wiss. Göttingen. Math.-Phys. Kl. **1915**, 209–243], the authors prove that $\sum_{n \leq x} a(n) = \alpha x - \beta x^{\frac{1}{2}} + O(x^{\frac{1}{3}} \log x)$, where $\alpha = \zeta(2)\zeta(3) \cdots$ and $\beta = -\zeta(\frac{1}{2})\zeta(\frac{3}{2})\zeta(\frac{4}{2})\zeta(\frac{5}{2}) \cdots$.

It also is shown in an elementary manner that the sequence $a(1), a(2), \cdots$ possesses an asymptotic distribution function, a mean value, and that the first moment of the distribution function exists and equals the mean value. The distribution of $a(1), a(2), \cdots, a(1000)$ is computed and compared with the asymptotic distribution of the entire sequence.

*P. Hartman* (Baltimore, Md.).

Referred to in N52-13, N52-47.

## N52-5 (9, 332i)

**Koksma, J. F. On Euler's indicator.** Nieuw Tijdschr. Wiskunde **35**, 189–195 (1947). (Dutch)

It is proved that for natural numbers $a$, $b$ and $N$ we have

$$\sum_{n=1}^{N} (am+b)^{-1}\varphi(am+b) = AN + \theta(1+2c+\log(aN+b)),$$

where

$$c = (a, b), \quad A = 6\pi^{-2}c^{-1}\varphi(c)\prod_{p|a}(1-p^{-2})^{-1}, \quad |\theta| \leqq 1.$$

*N. G. de Bruijn* (Delft).

## N52-6 (9, 413f)

**Tietze, Heinrich. Eine Bemerkung zum Lehmerschen Problem.** S.-B. Math.-Nat. Abt. Bayer. Akad. Wiss. **1944**, 163–170 (1944).

The Lehmer problem consists of the determination of the asymptotic order as $x \to \infty$ of the sum $S_1(x) = \sum A_1(n)$, $n \leqq x$,

$n\varepsilon G$, where $A_1(n)$ is the number of squarefree divisors of $n$, and $G$ is some subset of the positive integers. The problem was solved in some particular cases by Lehmer [Amer. J. Math. **22**, 293–335 (1900)] and in the general case by Landau [Amer. J. Math. **31**, 86–102 (1909)]. The author considers the general sum $S_g(x)=\sum A_{g-1}(n)$, $n\leqq x$, $n\varepsilon G$, where $A_g(n)$ is the number of $g$th-power free divisors of $n$. Analytic methods are used. *R. Bellman.*

**N52-7** **(9, 414a)**

**Bellman, Richard, and Shapiro, Harold N. On a problem in additive number theory.** Ann. of Math. (2) **49**, 333–340 (1948).

The authors consider the arithmetical function $\alpha(n)$, defined as the number of terms in the binary representation of $n$, which is in some respects analogous to $d(n)$, the number of divisors of $n$. They write $\alpha_r(n)=\alpha(\alpha_{r-1}(n))$, $\alpha_0(n)=n$, $A_r(x)=\sum_{n\leqq x}\alpha_r(n)$, and obtain the following results for $x\to\infty$: (1) $A_1(x)=x\log x/2\log 2+O(x\log\log x)$; (2) $\sum_{n\leqq x}2^{-n}A_2(2^n)\sim x\log x/2\log 2$; (3) $A_r(x)$ is not asymptotic to any elementary function for $r\geqq 2$. Result (1) is established by making use of the fact that $\alpha(2^L+r)=1+\alpha(r)$ if $1\leqq r<2^L$. It is stated in a footnote that the error term can, in fact, be reduced to $O(x)$. Result (2) is proved by means of a Tauberian theorem due to Hardy and Littlewood [Proc. London Math. Soc. (2) **13**, 174–191 (1914), theorem 8]. Result (3) (which, as the authors observe, is surprising since iteration might be expected to have a smoothing effect) is proved in several stages. It is first shown that, if $A_r(x)$ is asymptotic to an elementary function, that function must be $x\log_r x/2\log 2$, where $\log_r x=\log(\log_{r-1}x)$, $\log_1 x=\log x$; next it is shown that $A_2(x)$ is not asymptotic to any elementary function; finally (3) is deduced from the fact that the relation $A_r(x)\sim x\log_r x/2\log 2$ would imply $A_{r-1}(x)\sim x\log_{r-1}x/2\log 2$.

There is a misprint in the identity (3.1) which should read

$$\left(\sum_{k=0}^{\infty}\frac{x^{2^k}}{1+ax^{2^k}}\right)\prod_{k=0}^{\infty}(1+ax^{2^k})=\sum_{n=1}^{\infty}\alpha(n)a^{\alpha(n)-1}x^n.$$

Furthermore, the factor $2^{-n-1}$ has been omitted from the right-hand side of (6.1). This omission does not, however, affect the argument. *L. Mirsky* (Sheffield).

Referred to in N40-19, N40-72, N52-16.

**N52-8** **(11, 83g)**

**Mirsky, L. A theorem on representations of integers in the scale of $r$.** Scripta Math. **15**, 11–12 (1949).

Let $\alpha^{(r)}(n)$ denote the sum of the digits of the representation of $n$ in the scale of $r$. The author proves easily

$$\sum_{n=1}^{x}\alpha^{(r)}(n)=\tfrac{1}{2}(r-1)x\log x/\log r+O(x)$$

and shows that this result is best possible.

*H. Heilbronn* (Bristol).

**N52-9** **(11, 714c)**

**Kühnel, Ullrich. Über die Anzahl der Produktdarstellungen der positiven ganzen Zahlen.** Arch. Math. **2**, 216–219 (1950).

Let $f(n)$ be the number of different representations of $n$ as a product of factors greater than 1. Two representations which differ only by the order of the factors are considered as different. The function $f(n)$ was studied by Kálmár [Acta Litt. Sci. Szeged **5**, 95–107 (1931)] and Hille [Acta Arith. **2**, 134–144 (1936)]. The author states some new formulas for $f(n)$ without proof, the proofs having been given in the author's unpublished dissertation. From his formulas the author obtained some relations for binomial coefficients.

*A. Brauer* (Chapel Hill, N. C.).

**N52-10** **(12, 316i)**

**Šapiro-Pyateckiĭ, I. I. On an asymptotic formula for the number of Abelian groups whose order does not exceed $n$.** Mat. Sbornik N.S. **26**(68), 479–486 (1950). (Russian)

Let $A(n)$ be the number of Abelian groups of order $n$ and write

$$S(x)=\sum_{n\leqq x}A(n),\quad S(x;k,l)=\sum_{n\leqq x,\,n\equiv l\,(\mathrm{mod}\,k)}A(n).$$

It is shown that, for large $x$,

$$(1)\qquad S(x)=\gamma x+O(x^{\frac{1}{2}+\epsilon}),$$

$$(2)\qquad S(x;k,l)=\gamma x\frac{A(d)}{k}\prod_{p|k/d}\prod_{n=2}^{\infty}(1-p^{-n})+O(k^{\frac{1}{2}}x^{\frac{1}{2}+\epsilon}),$$

where $\gamma=\prod_{k=2}^{\infty}\zeta(k)$, $k\geqq 2$, $d=(l,k)<k$. A similar result is given for $l=0$. To obtain these results the properties of the Dirichlet series $\sum\chi(n)A(n)n^{-s}=\prod_{r=1}^{\infty}L(rs,\chi^r)$ are considered for characters modulo $k$. The proof of (2) appears to be valid only for $d=1$, since otherwise it is not necessarily true that $S(x;k,l)=A(d)S(x/d;k/d,l/d)$. Similarly, the treatment of the case $l=0$ breaks down when $k$ is not prime as it is not then possible to separate out the factors $A(k^n)$ from the sum considered. As mentioned by the author in a note added after submission the result (1) has already been obtained in a sharper form by Kendall and the reviewer [Quart. J. Math., Oxford Ser. (1) **18**, 197–208 (1947); these Rev. **9**, 226]. (There is an error in the main theorem. Landau's parameter $g$ is 1 and not 0, which means that the error term must be multiplied by $\log x$ giving $S(x)=\alpha x-\beta x^{\frac{1}{2}}+O(x^{\frac{1}{3}}\log^2 x)$.) It should also be mentioned that the result (1) is originally due to Erdös and Szekeres [Acta Litt. Sci. Szeged **7**, 95–102 (1934)], a fact unknown also to the reviewer and Kendall until recently.

*R. A. Rankin* (Cambridge, England).

Citations: MR 9, 226d = H30-8.

Referred to in N52-13.

**N52-11** **(12, 392i)**

**LeVeque, W. J. On representations as a sum of consecutive integers.** Canadian J. Math. **2**, 399–405 (1950).

If $m$ and $s$ are positive integers, then $\gamma_1(m,s)$ denotes the number of representations

$$m=r+(r+s)+(r+2s)+\cdots+(r+(k-1)s);$$

and $\gamma(m,s)$ denotes the number of solutions under the restriction $r>0$. It is shown that $\gamma_1(m,s)$ equals the number of divisors of $m$ if $s$ is even, and twice the number of odd divisors of $m$ if $s$ is odd. The author determines the average order of $\gamma_1(m,s)$ and of $\gamma(m,s)$. [In the last line of theorem 5 the factor $\frac{1}{2}$ should be omitted. The proof of theorem 6 can be simplified considerably by the remark that $\sum_{m=1}^{n}\gamma(m,s)$ equals the number of lattice points $(x,y)$ satisfying $x>0$, $y>0$, $xy\leqq 2n$, $y>(x-1)s$, $y\equiv(x-1)s\ (\mathrm{mod}\ 2)$.]

*N. G. de Bruijn* (Delft).

**N52-12** **(14, 20h)**

**Mycielski, Jan. Sur les représentations des nombres naturels par des puissances à base et exposant naturels.** Colloquium Math. **2** (1951), 254–260 (1952).

Let $n$ be an integer. Consider all representations $n=a_i^{b_i}$, $a_i$, $b_i$ integers, $n=a_1>a_2>\cdots>a_{\gamma(n)}$, $b_1=1<b_2<\cdots<b_{\gamma(n)}$ (i.e., $\gamma(n)$ denotes the number of representations of $n$ in the form $k^l$). Put $\tau(n)=\sum_{i=1}^{\gamma(n)}b_i$. The author proves, among other things, that $\sum_{n=2}^{\infty}(\tau(n)-1)/n=\pi^2/6+1$. *P. Erdös.*

**N52-13** **(14, 349e)**

**Richert, Hans-Egon. Über die Anzahl Abelscher Gruppen gegebener Ordnung. I.** Math. Z. **56**, 21–32 (1952).

Let $a_0(n)$ denote the number of essentially different

abelian groups of order $n$ and put $A_0(x)=\sum_{n\leq x}a_0(n)$. Then D. G. Kendall and the reviewer [Quart. J. Math., Oxford Ser. **18**, 197–208 (1947); these Rev. **9**, 226; for errata see review of a paper by Šapiro-Pyateckiĭ, Mat. Sbornik N.S. **26**(68), 479–486 (1950); these Rev. **12**, 316] showed that

$$A_0(x)=C_1x+C_2x^{1/2}+O(x^{1/3}\log^2 x)$$

where $C_1$ and $C_2$ are certain constants. This result was obtained by applying a famous theorem of Landau to the function $\zeta(s)\zeta(2s)$ which consists of the first two factors of the generating function

$$\sum_{n=1}^{\infty} a_0(n)n^{-s}=\prod_{\nu=1}^{\infty}\zeta(\nu s).$$

By dispensing with this theorem and applying instead van der Corput's method to estimate the sum-function of the coefficients of the first three factors $\zeta(s)\zeta(2s)\zeta(3s)$, the author obtains the sharper result

$$A_0(x)=C_1x+C_2x^{1/2}+C_3x^{1/3}+O(x^{3/10}\log^{9/10}x).$$

For this purpose estimates of the sums

$$D(x;\mu,\nu)=\sum_{m^{\mu}n^{\nu}\leq x}1 \quad (x\geqq 1,\ \mu>\nu>0)$$

are needed and these involve estimates of sums of the type

$$\sum_{n\leq x^{\alpha}}\left\{\frac{x^{\beta}}{n^{\beta}}-\left[\frac{x^{\beta}}{n^{\beta}}\right]-\frac{1}{2}\right\}.$$

These latter sums are essentially trigonometric sums and it is to them that van der Corput's theory of exponent-pairs, as simplified by Phillips [Quart. J. Math., Oxford Ser. (1) **4**, 209–225 (1933)], is applied. The index 3/10 appears as a result of taking the exponent-pair (2/7, 4/7); as the author remarks, a minute diminution of the index could be achieved by making a different choice of exponent-pair. The reviewer confirms this as his calculations show that 3/10 exceeds the smallest index which the method can yield by less than 0.00007. *R. A. Rankin* (Birmingham).

Citations: MR 9, 226c = N52-4; MR 12, 316i = N52-10.
Referred to in N24-49, N40-71, N52-44, P28-70.

## N52-14 (14, 726e)

**Prachar, K. On the sum $\sum_{p\leq x}\omega(f(p))$.** J. London Math. Soc. **28**, 236–239 (1953).

Let $v(n)$ denote the number of distinct prime divisors of $n$. The author proves that $\sum_{p\leq x}v(f(p))>cx\log\log x/\log x$ if $f(x)$ is an irreducible polynomial with integral coefficients $\neq ax$. The proof depends upon a theorem of Titchmarsh concerning an estimate for $\pi(x,a,k)$, the number of primes in the arithmetic progression $k+an$, $1\leqq n\leqq x$, where $a$ may depend upon $x$. *R. Bellman* (Santa Monica, Calif.).

Referred to in N60-16.

## N52-15 (16, 904h)

**Prachar, K. Über die Anzahl der Teiler einer natürlichen Zahl, welche die Form $p-1$ haben.** Monatsh. Math. **59**, 91–97 (1955).

Let $d(m)$ denote the number of divisors of $n$ and $\delta(n)$ the number of divisors of the form $p-1$, where $p$ is prime; the function $\delta(n)$ has occurred in a recent paper by W. Nöbauer [Monatsh. Math. **58**, 181–192 (1954), p. 190; MR **16**, 338]. The following results are proved in the present paper.

(1) $$\sum_{n\leq x}\delta(n)=x\log\log x+Bx+O(x/\log x),$$

where $B$ is a constant. (2) $\delta(n)>\exp\{c\log n/(\log\log n)^2\}$ for infinitely many $n$ and some $c>0$. (3) Assuming the Riemann hypotheses for the Dirichlet $L$-series,

$$\delta(n)>\exp\{(\tfrac{1}{2}-\epsilon)\log n\log 2/\log\log n\}$$

for infinitely many $n$. (4) $\sum_{n\leq x}\delta^2(n)=O(x\log^2 x)$. Thus the results for $\delta(n)$ are analogous to known results for $d(n)$, although, as the author points out, according to (1) $(\delta n)$ is on the average smaller than $d(n)$, while according to (3) $\delta(n)$ can presumably become as large as $d(n)$.

*L. Carlitz* (Durham, N. C.).

Citations: MR 16, 338e = R08-15.
Referred to in A26-44, P48-3.

## N52-16 (17, 828b)

**Cheo, Peh-Hsuin; and Yien, Sze-Chien. A problem on the $k$-adic representation of positive integers.** Acta Math. Sinica **5** (1955), 433–438. (Chinese. English summary)

Let $x=\sum_{\tau=1}^{t}a_\tau k^{n_\tau}$, where $n_1>n_2>\cdots>n_k>0$, $1\leqq a_\tau\leqq k-1$, be the representation of the integer $x\geqq 1$ to the fixed integral basis $k\geqq 2$. Put $\alpha(x)=\sum_{\tau=1}^{t}a_\tau$, $A(x)=\sum_{y\leq x}\alpha(y)$, and denote for fixed integral $m\geqq 1$ by $B_m(x)$ the number of integers $y\leqq x$ satisfying $\alpha(y)=m$. In the identity

$$A(x)=\frac{n_1(k-1)}{2}\sum_{\tau=1}^{t}a_\tau k^{n_\tau}-\frac{k-1}{2}\sum_{\tau=1}^{t}(n_1-n_\tau)a_\tau k^{n_\tau}$$
$$+\tfrac{1}{2}\sum_{\tau=1}^{t}a_\tau(a_\tau-1)k^{n_\tau}+\sum_{\tau=1}^{t}a_\tau+\sum_{\tau=1}^{t}\left(\sum_{\sigma=1}^{\tau-1}a_\sigma\right)a_\tau k^{n_\tau}$$

the first sum equals $\tfrac{1}{2}(k-1)[\log x/\log k]x$, while the four other sums are $O(x)$; hence

(1) $$A(x)=\frac{k-1}{2}\frac{x\log x}{\log k}+O(x).$$

Here the error term is best possible, as is seen on taking $x=(k-1)k^n$. The author further shows that

$$B_m(x)\sim\frac{1}{m!}\left(\frac{\log x}{\log k}\right)^m \quad\text{as } x\to\infty.$$

[For the case $k=2$ of (1) see Bellman and Shapiro, Ann. of Math. (2) **49** (1948), 333–340; MR **9**, 414.]

*K. Mahler* (Manchester).

Citations: MR 9, 414a = N52-7.
Referred to in N52-17.

## N52-17 (27# 85)

**Tang, S. C.**
**An improvement and generalization of Bellman-Shapiro's theorem on a problem in additive number theory.**
*Proc. Amer. Math. Soc.* **14** (1963), 199–204.

The substance of this paper appears to be virtually identical in both form and content to an earlier paper by Cheo and Yien [Acta Math. Sinica **5** (1955), 433–438; MR **17**, 828]. The proofs of Lemmas 1 and 2 of Tang's paper involve a change of $k$ to $K$ in the material to be found on page 434 of the Chinese paper. The material on pp. 201–202 of Tang's paper is identical, except for the same change, with that to be found on pp. 435–437 of the Chinese paper. Every displayed formula in the remainder of Tang's paper may be found in the proper sequence in the Chinese paper. The two theorems stated in the English summary of the Chinese paper seem identical in substance with the two theorems stated in Tang's paper.

*A. J. Lohwater* (Providence, R.I.);
*Alex Rosenberg*, Managing Editor,
Proc. Amer. Math. Soc.

Citations: MR 17, 828b = N52-16.

## N52-18 (20# 3106)

**Urazbaev, B. M. Asymptotic estimation of an arithmetic sum.** Akad. Nauk Kazah. SSR. Trudy Sektor. Mat. Meh. **1** (1958), 160–174. (Russian)

Let $l>0$ be prime. The author shows that

$$(0)\quad \sum_{\substack{p_1p_2\cdots p_k\leq x\\ p_j\equiv 1 \pmod l}} k(l-1)^k = 2\lambda_0 x(\log\log x+C)+O(x\exp\{-\mu(\log x)^{\frac{1}{2}}\}) +O\left(x\exp\left\{-\frac{\mu\log x}{3\log l}+\mu(\log x)^{\frac{1}{2}}-\log\log x\right\}\right),$$

where the sum on the left is over all products of primes $p_j\equiv 1 \pmod l$, $C$ is Euler's constant, $\mu>0$ is an absolute constant and $\lambda_0>0$ is a number depending only on $l$. The author says that his method gives estimates for the corresponding sums in which $k(l-1)^k$ is replaced by $m_1{}^k k^m(l-1)^k$, where $m_1$, $m$ are natural numbers, and for similar sums. An estimate, when $k(l-1)^k$ is replaced by $(l-1)^k$, has already been given by him [Dokl. Akad. Nauk SSSR (N.S.) **95** (1954), 935–938, MR **15**, 937], but the present problem is more complicated. The earlier problem had an interpretation in the estimation of the number of abelian fields with group of a certain type and discriminant below a certain bound, but no such interpretation is given for the present results.

For $0<\tau\leq 1$ the author considers the function defined for $\Re s>1$ by

$$L(s,\tau,X)=\prod_p\left(1-\frac{\tau X(p)}{p^s}\right)^{-1}=\sum\frac{\tau^k X(p_1\cdots p_k)}{(p_1\cdots p_k)^s},$$

where $X$ is a character to modulus $l$ and the product and sum are over all primes $p$ and all sets of not necessarily distinct primes $p_1,\cdots,p_k$, respectively, so $L(s,1{:}X)=L(s{:}X)$ is the usual $L$-function. Since $\log L(s,\tau{:}X)-\tau\log L(s{:}X)$ has a unique analytic continuation in $\Re s>\frac{1}{2}$, the zeros of the many-valued function $L(s,\tau{:}X)$ in $\Re s>\frac{1}{2}$ are precisely those of $L(s{:}X)$. In particular, if $\mu>0$ is an absolute constant such that no $L$-function has a zero in

$$(1)\quad \sigma\geqq 1-\frac{\mu}{\log\{l(|t|+3)\}},$$

where $s=\sigma+it$ (such $\mu$ exist), then the product

$$(2)\quad \prod_X L(s,\tau{:}X)$$

over all characters $X$ to modulus $l$, has in (1) only a singularity at $s=1$ arising from the singularity of $L(s,\tau{:}X_0)$, where $X_0$ is the principal character: in general this singularity is a branch-point. If one were to go through the usual motions with the function (2), one would obtain an estimate for

$$(3)\quad \sum_{\substack{p_1\cdots p_k\leq x\\ p_j\equiv 1 \pmod l}} t^k(l-1)^k.$$

The left hand side of (0) is just the differential of (3) with respect to $t$, when $t=1$. The asymptotic relation (0) is got from the expression for (3), in which the remainder is expressed as a contour integral, by differentiating under the integral sign and then estimating. More precisely, it is not (3) that is estimated, but the average of (3) over $x\leqq y$ (say); and the routine transition from the average to the function averaged is made with the left hand side of (0). *J. W. S. Cassels* (Cambridge, England)

Citations: MR 15, 937d = R20-19.

## N52-19 (22# 3707)

**Cohen, Eckford. Arithmetical functions associated with the unitary divisors of an integer.** Math. Z. **74** (1960), 66–80.

The author considers the unitary convolution $f(n)=\sum_{d\delta=n,(d,\delta)=1} g(d)h(\delta)$ of two arithmetical functions $g(n)$ and $h(n)$. By elementary methods asymptotic estimates are found for $\sum_{n\leq x} f(n)$ in a number of special cases. From one of these an asymptotic estimate is found for the average order of the core of $n$, where the core $\gamma(n)$ of $n$ is the maximal square-free divisor of $n$. From another special case information is obtained about the distribution of exponentially odd integers, that is, integers in whose canonical prime-power factorization all occurring exponents are odd. The precise results are $\sum_{n\leq x}\gamma(n)=\frac{1}{2}\alpha x^2+O(x^{3/2})$ and $Q^*(x)=\alpha x+O(x^{1/2}\log x)$, where $Q^*(x)$ denotes the number of exponentially odd integers less than or equal to $x$, and $\alpha$ is a constant.

*W. H. Mills* (Berkeley, Calif.)

Referred to in A22-86, A22-90, A22-93, A26-77, A36-51, A36-77, N28-45, N28-73, N52-37, N80-11, T55-45.

## N52-20 (22# 9535)

**Cohen, E. On the average number of direct factors of a finite abelian group.** Acta Arith. **6** (1960), 159–173.

Let $G$ be an abelian group. $\tau(G)$ denotes the number of direct factors of $G$ and $t(G)$ denotes the number of direct decompositions of $G$ into two relatively prime direct factors (two factors $H_1$ and $H_2$ of $G$ are called relatively prime if the identity is the only common direct factor of $H_1$ and $H_2$).

The author proves by elementary methods that

$$(1)\quad T(x)=\sum{}'\tau(G) = \alpha' x(\log x+2\gamma-1)+\beta' x+O(x^{1/2}(\log x)^2)$$

and

$$(2)\quad T^*(x)=\sum{}' t(G) = c_1x(\log x+2\gamma-1)+c_2x+O(x^{1/2}\log x).$$

The dash in the summation indicates that the summation is extended over all the abelian groups of order not exceeding $x$. The constants in (1) and (2) are defined as follows: $\gamma$ is Euler's constant. Put $Z_K(s)=\prod_{i=K}^{\infty}\zeta(is)$ ($\zeta(s)$ is Riemann's zeta function), $H(s)=Z_2{}^2(s)/Z_1(s)$, $c_1=H(1)$, $c_2=H'(1)$, $Z_2{}^2(s)=L(s)$, $\alpha'=L(1)$, $\beta'=L'(1)$.

*P. Erdös* (Budapest)

## N52-21 (23# A1581)

**Duncan, R. L.**

**Note on the divisors of a number.**

*Amer. Math. Monthly* **68** (1961), 356–359.

Let $\tau(n)$ be the number of divisors of $n$ and $\nu(n)$ the number of its distinct prime divisors, and define $\alpha(n)=[\sum_{d|n}\nu(d)]/\tau(n)$. The author shows that, if the representation of $n$ as a product of powers of distinct primes is $n=p_1{}^{\alpha_1}\cdots p_r{}^{\alpha_r}$, then $\alpha(n)=\sum_{i=1}^r \alpha_i/(\alpha_i+1)$. He also obtains an asymptotic formula for $\alpha(n)$ from which he proves that the average order and the normal order of $\alpha(n)$ are both $\nu(n)/2$. *R. J. Levit* (San Francisco, Calif.)

## N52-22 (24# A1260)

**Golubev, V. A.; Fomenko, O. M.**

**On the functions $\varphi_2(n)$, $\mu_2(n)$, $\zeta_2(s)$. (Russian)**

*Ann. Polon. Math.* **11** (1961), 13–17.

The authors define (1) $\varphi_2(n)$ to be the number of natural pairs $a_1$, $a_2$ such that $a_2-a_1=2$, $(a_1,n)=1$, $(a_2,n)=1$, $a_1\leq n$; (2) $\mu_2(n)=(-1)^{k+1}2^k$ if $n=2p_1p_2\cdots p_k$, $p>2$, $\mu_2(n)=(-2)^k$ if $n=p_1p_2\cdots p_k$, $p>2$, $\mu_2(n)=\mu(n)$ for the remaining $n$; (3) $\zeta_2(s)=(1-2^{-s})^{-1}\prod(1-2p^{-s})^{-1}$, where the product is taken over all primes $p>2$, $s=\sigma+it$; (4) $\Delta(1)=0$, $\Delta(n)=\alpha+\beta+\cdots+\lambda$ if $n=2^\theta p_1{}^\alpha p_2{}^\beta\cdots p_k{}^\lambda$, $p_i>2$. By the help of the functions $\zeta(s)$ and $\zeta_2(s)$ it is shown that (1) $\sum_{d|q,dd'=q}2^{\Delta(d')}\mu_2(d)=1$ if $q=1$, $=0$ if $q>1$; (2) $\sum_{d|n}\mu_2(d)=0$ for $n$ even, $=(-1)^k$ for $n=p_1{}^\alpha p_2{}^\beta\cdots p_k{}^\lambda$, $p>2$; (3) $\varphi_2(n)=\sum_{d|n}\mu_2(d)(n/d)$. The authors also prove an asymptotic formula for $\sum_{k=1}^n\varphi_2(k)$ and a density theorem (analogous to that of $\varphi(n)$) for the set of numbers $\varphi_2(n)/n$ in the interval (0, 1) for $k$ odd, and in the interval (0, 1/2) for $n$ even. Finally, it is shown that given a natural $k$ there exists a natural $m$ such that the equation $\varphi_2(x)=m$ has more than $k$ natural solutions.

*J. W. Andrushkiw* (Newark, N.J.)

**N52-23** **(24# A1864 )**

**Duncan, R. L.**

**A class of additive arithmetical functions.**

*Amer. Math. Monthly* **69** (1962), 34–36.

Additive arithmetical functions of the type $f(n)$, for which $f(mn)=f(m)+f(n)$ whenever $(m,n)=1$, are considered. Taking $n=p_1^{\alpha_1}\cdots p_r^{\alpha_r}$ as the representation of $n$ as a product of powers of distinct primes, an additive function $\Omega_k(n)=\alpha_1^k+\cdots+\alpha_r^k$ is defined, where $k$ is an arbitrary non-negative integer. An asymptotic formula for $\sum_{n\leqq x}\Omega_k(n)$ is derived, whence it is inferred that the average order of $\Omega_k(n)$ is $\log\log n$ for every $k$. It is also indicated that $\Omega_k(n)$ has the normal order $\log\log n$.

*P. K. Ghosh* (Calcutta)

Referred to in N36-57.

**N52-24** **(28# 2149 )**

**Connell, Ian G.**

**A number theory problem concerning finite groups and rings.**

*Canad. Math. Bull.* **7** (1964), 23–34.

The number of abelian groups of order $n=\prod p_i^{e_i}$ is given by $f_1(n)=p_1(e_1)p_1(e_2)\cdots$, where $p_1$ is the partition function. The number of semi-simple rings of order $n$ is $f_2(n)=p_2(e_1)p_2(e_2)\cdots$. Here, $p_2(n)$ is the coefficient of $x^n$ in $P_2(x)$; $p_1(n)$ is the coefficient of $x^n$ in $P_1(x)$; and these generating functions are related by $P_2(x)=P_1(x)P_1(x^4)\times P_1(x^9)\cdots$. The average orders of $f_1(n)$, $f_2(n)$ are 2.3 and 2.5, respectively; Erdős and Szekeres found $\sum_1^n f_1(j)=2.29\cdots n+O(\sqrt{n})$. The author conjectures a certain refinement of this formula, and establishes $\log p_2(n)=\frac{1}{3}\pi^2\sqrt{n}+o(n)$.

*J. L. Brenner* (Palo Alto, Calif.)

**N52-25** **(29# 3458 )**

**Cohen, Eckford**

**Some asymptotic formulas in the theory of numbers.**

*Trans. Amer. Math. Soc.* **112** (1964), 214–227.

Denote by $Q^2(n)$ the largest square divisor of $n$. Let $\alpha$ be an arbitrary non-negative real number and $S$ any non-empty set of positive integers. Then for $x\to\infty$,

$$\sum_{\substack{n\leqq x\\ Q(n)\in S}}\left(\frac{n}{Q^2(n)}\right)^{\alpha} = \frac{6x^{\alpha+1}}{\pi^2(\alpha+1)}\sum_{\substack{n=1\\ n\in S}}^{\infty} n^{-2\alpha-2}+O(x^{\alpha+1/2}R_\alpha(x,S))$$

uniformly in $S$, where

$$R_\alpha(x,S) = \sum_{\substack{n\leqq\sqrt{x}\\ n\in S}} n^{-2\alpha-1},$$

if this sum is non-empty; otherwise, $R_\alpha(x,S)=1$.

The author proves two more asymptotic formulas: (1) for an analogous sum with the additional condition $(n,Q^2(n))=1$, and (2) for an analogous sum with summands $(n/Q^*(n))^\alpha$, where $Q^*(n)$ is the largest divisor of $n$ with no simple prime factors.

He deduces from these results 42 corollaries, which yield estimates due to Cesàro [Ann. Mat. Pura Appl. (2) **13** (1885), 251–268], Feller and Tornier [Math. Ann. **107** (1932), 188–232], Kanold [J. Reine Angew. Math. **193** (1954), 250–252; MR **16**, 569], Rényi [Acad. Serbe Sci. Publ. Inst. Math. **8** (1955), 157–162; MR **17**, 944] and the author [Duke Math. J. **28** (1961), 183–192; MR **25** #3916].

*J. Kubilius* (Vilnius)

Citations: MR 16, 569h = N28-30; MR 17, 944f = N24-23; MR 25# 3916 = N48-13.

Referred to in N24-73.

**N52-26** **(33# 2604 )**

**de Bruijn, N. G.; van Lint, J. H.**

**On partial sums of $\sum_{d\mid M}\varphi(d)$.**

*Simon Stevin* **39** (1965/66), 18–22.

Let $\varphi$ denote Euler's function and suppose $f$ is a positive, real-valued function defined on the positive integers. For $M$ a positive integer, put $h(M)=\sum_d\varphi(d)$, where the sum is over those positive integers $d$ which divide $M$ and satisfy $d\leqq M/f(M)$. The authors are interested in relating the growth rates, as $M\to\infty$, of $f(M)$ and $h(M)$. They prove: (1) If $\log f(x)/\log\log x\to\infty$ as $x\to\infty$, then $h(M)=o(M)$; (2) if $h(M)=o(M)$, then $\limsup\log f(x)/\log\log x=\infty$; (3) if $f(x)\to\infty$ as $x\to\infty$, then $x^{-1}\sum_{M\leqq x}h(M)\to 0$ as $x\to\infty$.

*D. G. Cantor* (Los Angeles, Calif.)

**N52-27** **(33# 5724 )**

**Schwarz, Wolfgang**

**Über die Anzahl Abelscher Gruppen gegebener Ordnung. I.**

*Math. Z.* **92** (1966), 314–320.

Let $A(x)$ denote the number of abelian groups of order $n\leqq x$. Several authors have proved an asymptotic formula of the form $A(x)=A_1x+A_2x^{1/2}+A_3x^{1/3}+F(x)$ with $A_j=\prod_{\nu\neq j}\zeta(\nu/j)$ and $F(x)$ a remainder term. By refining previous arguments and applying van der Corput's method once more, the author gives an improved estimate of the error term, namely, $F(x)=O(x^\vartheta(\log x)^{\vartheta'})$, where $\vartheta=20/69$.

{In a footnote it is mentioned that P. G. Schmidt has reported, in a letter to the author, that he has obtained the result $\vartheta=5/18$.}

*H.-E. Richert* (Marburg)

Referred to in N52-28, N52-33.

**N52-28** **(35# 6631 )**

**Schwarz, Wolfgang**

**Über die Anzahl Abelscher Gruppen gegebener Ordnung. II.**

*J. Reine Angew. Math.* **228** (1967), 133–138.

Let $a(n)$ denote the number of Abelian groups of order $n$ and set $A(x)=\sum_{n\leqq x}a(n)$. Assuming the truth of the Riemann hypothesis, it is proved that a result $A(x)=\sum_{j=1}^6 A_jx^{1/j}+O(x^{1/6-\varepsilon})$, where $A_j=\prod_{\nu=1;\nu\neq j}^{\infty}\zeta(\nu/j)$, is impossible for any $\varepsilon>0$.

{Part I appeared in Math. Z. **92** (1966), 314–320 [MR **33** #5724].}

*H.-E. Richert* (Marburg)

Citations: MR 33# 5724 = N52-27.

**N52-29** **(34# 7477 )**

**Rieger, G. J.**

**Asymptotische Formeln für einige arithmetische Funktionen.**

*Math. Nachr.* **33** (1967), 31–37.

Let $\alpha,\beta$ be real numbers satisfying $0\leqq\alpha<\beta$ and define $\varphi_{\alpha,\beta}(n)=\sum_{a\mid n}\mu(a)a^\alpha(n/a)^\beta$ $(n=1,2,3,\cdots)$. The author proves theorems of the following type. Let $x\geqq 2$; for integers $k_1>0$, $k_2>0$, $b_1>-k_1$, $b_2>-k_2$ satisfying $b_1k_2\neq b_2k_1$ and $(k_1k_2,b_1k_2-b_2k_1)=1$, the following formula holds:

$$\sum_{0<m\leqq x} d(k_1m+b_1)\varphi_{\alpha,\beta}(k_2m+b_2) = C(\alpha,\beta,k_1,k_2,b_1,b_2)x^{\beta+1}\log x+O(x^{\beta+1}),$$

where $d(n)$ denotes the number of positive divisors of $n$; the $O$-constant depends on $\alpha,\beta,k_1,k_2,b_1,b_2$. The proofs use only elementary methods. (Compare also A. E. Ingham [J. London Math. Soc. **2** (1927), 202–208].)

*Werner G. H. Schaal* (Marburg)

**N52-30** **(34# 7478 )**

**Subbarao, M. V.**

**An arithmetic function and an associated probability theorem.**

*Nederl. Akad. Wetensch. Proc. Ser. A* **70** = *Indag. Math.* **29** (1967), 93–95.

Let $k$ and $q$ be integers, $1\leqq q<k$. By a well-known ele-

mentary method, the author derives an asymptotic formula for $S = \sum_{r \leq N} \varphi_{k,q}(r)$, where $\varphi_{k,q}(r)$ is defined by $\zeta(s-1)\zeta(ks)\zeta^{-1}(qs) = \sum \varphi_{k,q}(r)r^{-s}$; $S$ is the number of pairs $n, m \leq N$ such that the $k$th-power-free part of the greatest common divisor $(n, m)$ is $q$th-power-free.

*W. Schwarz* (Freiburg)

## N52-31 (35# 2849)

**Galambos, János**

**A distribution problem in number theory. (Hungarian)**

*Mat. Lapok* **14** (1963), 88–97.

Denote by $F(n, d)$ the number of solutions of $a_{i+1} - a_i = d$, where $1 = a_1 < a_2 < \cdots < a_{\varphi(n)} = n-1$ are the integers relatively prime to $n$. The author determines for every $d \geq 1$ the value of $\varphi(d) = \lim_{N=\infty}(1/N^2)\sum_{n=1}^{N} F(n, d)$. $\varphi(d)$ is given by a complicated formula:

$$\varphi(1) = (\pi^2/6)\prod_p (1-2/p^2),$$

$$\varphi(2) = \tfrac{3}{8}\prod_{p>2}(1-2/p^2) - \tfrac{1}{4}\prod_{p>2}(1-3/p^2).$$

*P. Erdős* (Budapest)

## N52-32 (35# 2850)

**Elliott, P. D. T. A.**

**On certain additive functions.**

*Acta Arith.* **12** (1966/67), 365–384.

Generalizing a previous result of J. Kubilius [*Probabilistic methods in the theory of numbers* (Russian), Gos. Izdat. Politič. i Naučn. Lit. Litovsk. SSR, Vilnius, 1959; MR **23** #A134; second enlarged Russian edition, 1962; MR **26** #3691; English translation, Amer. Math. Soc., Providence, R.I., 1964; MR **28** #3956], the author proves the following theorem. Let $g(t)$ be an irreducible polynomial with integer coefficients. Let $\varepsilon_x \to 0$ as $x \to \infty$ and let $\nu(n)$ denote the number of prime factors of $n$. Let $a_1 < a_2 < \cdots$ be a sequence of integers satisfying (1) $A(x) = \sum_{a_i \leq x} 1 > x\exp(-\varepsilon_x \log\log x)$. Then for every integer $k$, (2) $\sum \nu^k(g(a_i)) = (1+o(1))A(x)(\log\log x)^k$.

The author in fact proves a much more general theorem (where $v(n)$ is replaced by a non-negative additive function). He also shows that (1) is a best possible condition.

Further interesting problems and results of probabilistic number theory are discussed. *P. Erdős* (Budapest)

Citations: MR 23# A134 = N60-37; MR 26# 3691 = N60-38; MR 28# 3956 = N60-39.

Referred to in N52-34.

## N52-33 (36# 6305)

**Schmidt, Peter Georg**

**Zur Anzahl Abelscher Gruppen gegebener Ordnung.**

*J. Reine Angew. Math.* **229** (1968), 34–42.

$a(n)$ bezeichne die Anzahl der nicht-isomorphen Abelschen Gruppen der Ordnung $n$, und es werde mit gewissen Konstanten $c_i$, $\sum_{n \leq x} a(n) = c_1x + c_2x^{1/2} + c_3x^{1/3} + R(x)$ gesetzt. W. Schwarz [Math. Z. **92** (1966), 314–320; MR **33** #5724] hat (1) $R(x) \ll x^{20/69}\log^{21/23}x$ gezeigt. Bei diesem Problem handelt es sich hauptsächlich um Abschätzungen von Summen der Gestalt $S = \sum\sum B\{f(m, n)\}$, wobei $B(u) = u - [u] - \frac{1}{2}$, und der Verfasser führt bei diesem unsymmetrischen Gitterpunktproblem die Dirichletsche Summationsweise ein. Ein elementarer Satz von I. M. Vinogradov zur Behandlung von $S$ führt zu $R(x) \ll x^{2/7}\log^{6/7}x$, und mittels einer Abschätzung des Referenten für $S$ verschärft er (1) zu $R(x) \ll x^{34/123}$. Eine weitere Verbesserung ist inzwischen erschienen [der Verfasser, Acta Arith. **13** (1967/68), 405–417; MR **37** #190].

*H.-E. Richert* (Marburg)

Citations: MR 33# 5724 = N52-27.

## N52-34 (37# 175)

**Elliott, P. D. T. A.**

**On certain additive functions. II.**

*Acta Arith.* **14** (1967/68), 51–64.

Let $g(y)$ be an irreducible polynomial with integer coefficients, $f(n) \geq 0$ an additive function. $\rho(u)$ is the number of solutions of $g(r) \equiv 0 \pmod u$, $1 \leq r \leq u$. Put $l(x) = \max_{p^\alpha \leq x} f(p^\alpha)$ and $S(x) = \sum_{p^\alpha \leq x} \rho(p^\alpha)f(p^\alpha)p^{-\alpha}$. Let $a_1 < \cdots$ be a sequence of integers, $A(x) = \sum_{a_i < x} 1$. Assume that $l(x) = o(S(x))$ and $A(x) > x\exp(-\varepsilon(x)l^{-1}(x)S(x))$, where $\varepsilon(x) \to 0$ as $x \to \infty$. The author proves

(*) $\qquad \sum_{a_i < x}(f(g(a_i)))^k = (1+o(1))A(x)(S(x))^k.$

He observes that (*) implies that $f(g(a_i))$ is almost always asymptotic to $S(a_i)$.

(*) extends a previous result of the author [same Acta **12** (1966/67), 365–384; MR **35** #2850]. The proof of (*) is fairly complicated and uses nine lemmas.

*P. Erdős* (Budapest)

Citations: MR 35# 2850 = N52-32.

## N52-35 (37# 6253)

**Götze, Friedhelm**

**Über Fareysche Brüche.**

*Wiss. Z. Friedrich-Schiller-Univ. Jena/Thüringen* **14** (1965), 363–368.

Put $f_s(x) = \int (2\pi x)^{-t}\Gamma(t)\zeta(t)\zeta(s-t)\,dt$, where $\zeta(t)$ is the Riemann zeta function, $\Gamma(t)$ is Euler's gamma function, and the integral is taken over $\operatorname{Re}(t) = \operatorname{Re}(s)/2$ and $-\infty \leq \operatorname{Im}(t) \leq \infty$. This integral converges when $\operatorname{Re}(s) > 2$ and $|\arg(x)| < \pi/2$. The author proves that $f_s(x)$ is a meromorphic function of $x$ and $s$, and determines its poles and residues when it is considered as a function of one of the two variables $x$ or $s$.

With the aid of these results and with certain observations about lattice points he generalizes a classical result of Mertens. Put $\varphi_m(k) = \sum_h (h/k)^m$ where the sum is over those $h$ relatively prime to $k$ and satisfying $1 \leq h < k$. The author proves that $F_r(m) = \sum_{k=1}^{r} \varphi_m(k) = 3(r/\pi)^2/(m+1) + O(r\log r)$ (Mertens' result is the case $m = 1$). Finally he obtains certain complicated linear relations among the $F_r(m)$. *D. G. Cantor* (Los Angeles, Calif.)

## N52-36 (38# 1054)

**Gupta, Hansraj**

**An arithmetical sum.**

*Indian J. Math.* **10** (1968), 83–86.

The author proves, for a fixed square free integer $m \geq 1$, that $\sum_{1 \leq n;(n,m)=1} \lambda_r(n)[x/n] \sim x^{1/r}\sum_{d|m^{r-1}} d^{-1/r}$, as $x \to \infty$, where $\lambda_r(n)$ $(r \geq 2)$ is the multiplicative function defined by $\lambda_r(p^i) = 1$ if $i \equiv 0 \pmod r$, $\lambda_r(p^i) = -1$ if $i \equiv 1 \pmod r$, and $\lambda_r(p^i) = 0$ otherwise. The method used is elementary.

*K. S. Williams* (Ottawa, Ont.)

## N52-37 (38# 2105)

**Chidambaraswamy, J.**

**Sum functions of unitary and semi-unitary divisors.**

*J. Indian Math. Soc.* (*N.S.*) **31** (1967), 117–126 (1968).

If $f$ and $g$ are arithmetic functions, let $F^*$ denote their unitary product, and put $F^{s*}(n) = \sum f(d)g(n/d)$, summed over all semi-unitary divisors $d$ of $n$. The average orders of magnitude of $F^*$ and $F^{s*}$ are found, in the cases in which $g$ is bounded and either $f(n) = n^r$ or $f(n) = n^r\mu^2(n)$, $r \geq 1$. Certain results of E. Cohen [Math. Z. **74** (1960), 66–80; MR **22** #3707] appear as special cases.

*D. Rearick* (Boulder, Colo.)

Citations: MR 22# 3707 = N52-19.

**N52-38** **(39# 2713)**

**Niven, Ivan**

**Averages of exponents in factoring integers.**

*Proc. Amer. Math. Soc.* **22** (1969), 356–360.

For any positive integer $m>1$, let $m=p_1^{\alpha_1}p_2^{\alpha_2}\cdots p_r^{\alpha_r}$, and define $h(m)=\min(\alpha_1,\alpha_2,\cdots,\alpha_r)$ and $H(m)=\max(\alpha_1,\alpha_2,\cdots,\alpha_r)$, where for convenience $h(1)=H(1)=1$. The author proves that $\lim_{n\to\infty} n^{-1}\sum_{j=1}^n h(j)=1$ and

$$\lim_{n\to\infty} n^{-1}\sum_{j=1}^n H(j) = 1+\sum_{k=2}^{\infty}\{1-\zeta(k)^{-1}\}$$

and in fact that $\sum_{j=1}^n h(j)=n+c\sqrt{n}+o(\sqrt{n})$, where $c=\zeta(3/2)/\zeta(3)$. The argument depends on obtaining elementary estimates for $T_k(n)=\{m\leqq n\ni h(m)\geqq k\}$, for $k=2$ and 3. *R. A. MacLeod* (Victoria, B.C.)

**N52-39** **(39# 2715)**

**Kátai, I.**

**On the sum of digits of prime numbers.**

*Ann. Univ. Sci. Budapest. Eötvös Sect. Math.* **10** (1967), 89–93.

For a fixed integer $k>1$, any positive integer $n$ has a unique representation $n=a_0k^0+a_1k^1+\cdots+a_tk^t$, with digits $a_\tau$, $0\leqq a_\tau<k$; denote by $\alpha(n)=\sum a_\tau$ the sum of the digits $a_\tau$ of $n$. The author is concerned with the asymptotic behavior of $B(x)=\sum_{p\leqq x}\alpha(p)$. Assuming the density hypothesis $N(\sigma,T)=O\{T^{2(1-\sigma)}\log^2 T\}$ (for $\frac{1}{2}\leqq\sigma\leqq 1$) for Riemann's zeta-function, the author proves $B(x)=\frac{1}{2}(k-1)\cdot x/\log k+O\{x(\log\log x)^{-1/3}\}$. Also the author corrects an error in his paper in same Ann. **8** (1965), 61–64 [MR **33** #1295]. *W. Schwarz* (Freiburg)

Citations: MR 33# 1295 = N08-41.

**N52-40** **(39# 5496)**

**Kátai, I.**

**On the sum $\sum dd(f(n))$.**

*Acta Sci. Math. (Szeged)* **29** (1968), 199–206.

Let $f(x)$ denote an irreducible polynomial with integer coefficients, not of the form $cx$, such that $f(n)>0$ for $n\geqq 1$. Let $d(n)$ denote the number of divisors of $n$, and let $dd(n)$ stand for $d(d(n))$. The author investigates the average order of $dd(f(n))$ and $dd(f(p))$, where $p$ denotes a prime. Specifically, he proves that if degree $f(x)\leqq 3$, then $\sum_{n\leqq x} dd(f(n))=cx\log\log x+O(x\sqrt{\log\log x})$, and if degree $f(x)\leqq 2$, then $\sum_{p\leqq x} dd(f(p))=c'\operatorname{li} x\log\log x+O(\operatorname{li} x\sqrt{(\log\log x\log\log\log x)})$, where $c$ and $c'$ are positive constants depending on the polynomial.

The methods of proof are elementary, drawing upon earlier results of P. Turán [J. London Math. Soc. **11** (1936), 125–133], C. Hooley [Mathematika **14** (1967), 21–26; MR **35** #5405] and P. Erdős [J. London Math. Soc. **27** (1952), 7–15; MR **13**, 438; ibid. **28** (1953), 416–425; MR **15**, 104] on arithmetic properties of the numbers $f(n)$, and upon the prime number theorem for arithmetic progressions as well as upon the sieve method of E. Bombieri [Mathematika **12** (1965), 201–225; MR **33** #5590]. The restrictions on the degree of $f(x)$ are imposed by adapting earlier work, and the author suspects that they may be unnecessary in the present paper. *D. Rearick* (Boulder, Colo.)

Citations: MR 13, 438f = N40-19; MR 15, 104f = N32-13; MR 33# 5590 = M55-43; MR 35# 5405 = N32-56.

Referred to in N40-72.

**N52-41** **(40# 1352)**

**Cohen, Eckford**

**On the mean parity of arithmetical functions.**

*Duke Math. J.* **36** (1969), 659–668.

$f(n)$ bezeichne eine komplexwertige Funktion der natürlichen Zahl $n$; $b$, $m$ seien ganz rational, $b>0$. $P_{m,b}$ sei die Menge der $n\equiv m\pmod b$. Für reelles $x\geqq 1$ sei $P_{m,b}(x)$ die Anzahl der $n\leqq x$, $n\in P_{m,b}$. Es sei ferner (1) $M_{m,b}(f)=b\lim_{x\to\infty}(1/x)\sum_{n\leqq x,n\in P_{m,b}}f(n)$, falls dieser Grenzwert existiert. Ferner sei $M_{0,b}(f)=M_b(f)$,

$$M_1(f) = \lim_{x\to\infty}(1/x)\sum_{n\leqq x}f(n),$$

$M_b{}^*(f)=M_{1,b}(f)$.

Eine Funktion $f$ heiße "im Mittel gerade" (even in the mean), wenn $M_{m,b}(f)$ existiert und gerade (mod $b$) ist für jedes $b$. Mit diesen Begriffsbildungen werden einige interessante Sätze formuliert und bewiesen, für die als Beispiel der folgende dienen soll: Sei $f(n)=\sum_{d|n}g(d)$; entweder sei $g(n)=O(n^{-\varepsilon})$ für geeignete $\varepsilon>0$ oder es gelte für geeignete natürliche $k>1$ die Beziehung $g(n)=0$, wenn $n$ keine $k$-te Potenz ist, $g(n)=O(1)$, wenn $n$ eine $k$-te Potenz ist. Dann ist in jedem Fall $f$ im Mittel gerade und $M_{m,b}(f)=\sum_{n=1,(n,b)|m}^{\infty}g(n)(n,b)/n$ für jedes ganze $b>0$ und jedes ganze $m$. *H. J. Kanold* (Braunschweig)

**N52-42** **(40# 1354)**

**Stronina, M. I.**

**Integral points on circular cones.** (Russian)

*Izv. Vysš. Učebn. Zaved. Matematika* **1969**, *no.* 8 (87), 112–116.

The author derives the asymptotic behavior of the sum $\sum_{n=1}^N r(n^2)$ from the properties of the generating Dirichlet series in the critical strip, $r(n^2)$ being the number of solutions of the equation $n^2=x^2+y^2$ in the integers $x$, $y$. *A. I. Vinogradov* (Leningrad)

**N52-43** **(40# 5532)**

**Duncan, R. L.**

**On the factorization of integers.**

*Proc. Amer. Math. Soc.* **25** (1970), 191–192.

If $n=\prod_{i=1}^r p_i^{a_i}$, let $a(n)=(a_1+\cdots+a_r)/r$ be the average of the exponents. The author proves in an elementary way that $\sum_{n\leqq x}a(n)=x+O(x/\log\log x)$, from which it follows that $a(n)$ has average order 1. *T. M. Apostol* (Pasadena, Calif.)

**N52-44** **(41# 6794)**

**Krätzel, Ekkehard**

**Teilerprobleme in drei Dimensionen.**

*Math. Nachr.* **42** (1969), 275–288.

Let $a$, $b$, $c$ be three positive integers with $1\leqq a\leqq b\leqq c$. For arbitrary $k$, denote by $d(a,b,c;k)$ the number of decompositions $k=n_1{}^a n_2{}^b n_3{}^c$. Put

$$D(a,b,c;x) = \sum_{1\leqq k\leqq x} d(a,b,c;k).$$

The author shows that $D(a,b,c;x)$ has the form

$$\Delta(a,b,c;x) = \zeta(b/a)\zeta(c/a)x^{1/a}+\zeta(a/b)\zeta(c/b)x^{1/b} + \zeta(a/c)\zeta(b/c)x^{1/c}+\Delta(a,b,c;x),$$

with a certain error term $\Delta(a,b,c;x)$. He derives various estimates for this term. A typical result is as follows. For $b=2a$, $2c<9$ one has

$$\Delta(a,b,c;x) = O((x^{20}\log^{9(a+2c)}x)^{1/(27a+14c)}).$$

This generalizes and ameliorates a result of H. E. Richert [Math. Z. **56** (1952), 21–32; MR **14**, 349] according to which $\Delta(1,2,3;x)=O(x^{3/10}\log^{9/10}x)$. The author's method is a refinement of Richert's. *C. G. Lekkerkerker* (Amsterdam)

Citations: MR 14, 349e = N52-13.

**N52-45** **(41# 8351)**

**Ayoub, R.; Chowla, S.**

**On a theorem of Müller and Carlitz.**

*J. Number Theory* **2** (1970), 342–344.

Let $r(n)$ denote the number of representations of $n$ as a

sum of two squares. C. Müller [Abh. Math. Sem. Univ. Hamburg **19** (1954), no. 1–2, 62–65; MR **15**, 940] proved that (*) $\sum_{r\leq x} r(n)\log(x/n)=Ax+B\log x+C+O(x^{-1/4})$, where $A$, $B$, $C$ are explicit constants. The reviewer [ibid. **21** (1957), 87–89; MR **19**, 731] gave a simpler proof of (*) but did not evaluate $C$. In the present paper the following more general problem is treated. Let $K$ denote an imaginary quadratic field with discriminant $d$ and put $\zeta_K(s)=\sum_{n=1}^{\infty} F(n)n^{-s}=\zeta(s)L_d(s)$, where $L_d(s)=\sum_{n=1}^{\infty}\chi_d(n)n^{-s}$ and $\chi_d(n)=(d/n)$, the Kronecker symbol. It is proved that $\sum_{n\leq x} F(n)\log(x/n)=L_d(1)x+\zeta_K(0)\log x+\zeta_K'(0)+O(x^{-1/4})$. It is known that $\zeta_K(0)=-h/w$, where $h$ is the class number of $K$ and $w$ is the number of roots of unity in $K$. Moreover, $\zeta_K'(0)=(h/w)\log(\frac{1}{2}|d|/\pi)-\frac{1}{2}\sum_{r=1}^{|d|-1}\chi_d(r)\log\Gamma(r/|d|)$. In particular, if $K$ is the Gaussian field, $4\zeta_K'(0)=-\log(\frac{1}{4}\Gamma^4(\frac{1}{4})/\pi)$ in agreement with Müller's result.

*L. Carlitz* (Durham, N.C.)

Citations: MR 15, 940a = P28-18; MR 19, 731g = P20-15.

## N52-46 (42# 3037)

**Saffari, Bahman**

**Sur quelques applications de la "méthode de l'hyperbole" de Dirichlet à la théorie des nombres premiers.**

*Enseignement Math.* (2) **14** (1968), 205–224 (1970).

The author makes an ingeneous use of the method of hyperbola [e.g., H. Rademacher, *Lectures on elementary number theory*, p. 100, Blaisdell, New York, 1964; MR **30** #1079] to obtain asymptotic values of certain arithmetic functions. He first deals with $\omega(n)$, which denotes the number of different prime factors of $n$ $(n=1,2,\cdots)$. G. H. Hardy and S. Ramanujan proved [Quart. J. Pure Appl. Math. **48** (1917), 76–92; reprinted in *Collected papers of Sriniva Ramanujan*, pp. 262–275, especially p. 263, Chelsea, New York, 1962] that when $x\to\infty$, $\sum_1^n\omega(n)=x\log\log x+Bx+O(x/\log x)$, where $B$ is a constant. They stated that the result could be improved by transcendental methods [loc. cit., p. 347], which has, however, apparently never been published. The author now proves the following theorem: Let $\pi_{k,l}(x)$ be the number of primes, $p\leqslant x$, $p\equiv l$ (mod $k$), and let there exist three constants $C$, $\alpha$ and $\beta$ $(C>0, \alpha>0)$ such that when $x\to\infty$,

$$\pi_{k,l}(x) = (1/\varphi(k))\int_2^x(\log t)^{-1}\,dt + O[x\exp(-C(\log x)^\alpha(\log\log x)^\beta)].$$

Then there exist a constant $C'>0$ such that, when $x\to\infty$,

$$\sum_{1\leq n\leq x}\omega_{k,l}(n) = (x\log\log x)/\varphi(k) + B_{k,l}x-(x/\varphi(k))\int_1^{\sqrt{x}}(t^{-2}\{t\}/(\log x-\log t))\,dt + O[x\exp(-C'(\log x)^\alpha(\log\log x)^\beta)],$$

where $\omega_{k,l}(n)$ is the number of different prime factors $p$ of $n$ such that $p\equiv l$ (mod $k$). The error term above is shown to be sharpened if the Riemann hypothesis is assumed concerning the Dirichlet $L$-series relative to the character modulo $k$.

The method of hyperbola applied to the sum $\sum_{1\leq n\leq x}\omega_{k,l}(n)$ is extended to get analogous results for the sum $\sum_{1\leq n\leq x}(\omega_{k,l}(n))^h$, where $h$ is an integer $\geqq 2$, but the case beyond $h\geqq 3$ becomes too complicated. Let $\Omega(n)$ denote the number of all prime factors of $n$, and for each nonnegative integer $m$, let $\nu_m(x)$ denote the number of natural numbers $n\leqq x$ for which $\Omega(n)-\omega(n)=m$. A. Rényi has shown that a density $d_m$ exists to the effect: $\nu_m(x)=d_mx+O(x)$ [Acad. Serbe Sci. Publ. Inst. Math. **8** (1955), 157–162; MR **17**, 944]. This result has been improved by H. Delange [Acta Arith. **11** (1965), 241–252; MR **34** #1282; ibid. **13** (1967/68), 339–362; MR **37** #4037] and I. Kátai [Magyar Tud. Akad. Mat. Fiz. Oszt. Közl. **16** (1966), 269–273; MR **38** #5726]. Better results are found, and those of Rényi and Delange are derived in an elementary way.

The author mentions that the method of hyperbola has its own limitations because of its elementary nature, and that the results of this paper have been superseded by analytical methods of Delange [Acta Arith. **16** (1969/70), 195–206; MR **40** #7218], and two forthcoming papers in the same journal.

*S. Ikehara* (Tokyo)

Citations: MR 17, 944f = N24-23; MR 30# 1079 = Z01-57; MR 34# 1282 = N60-58; MR 37# 4037 = N60-67; MR 38# 5726 = N60-71; MR 40# 7218 = N60-83.

## N52-47 (42# 3171)

**Krätzel, Ekkehard**

**Die maximale Ordnung der Anzahl der wesentlich verschiedenen abelschen Gruppen $n$-ter Ordnung.**

*Quart. J. Math. Oxford Ser.* (2) **21** (1970), 273–275.

Let $a(n)$ denote the number of Abelian groups of order $n$. The main result of this note is the following theorem: For any fixed $\varepsilon>0$, each of the inequalities $a(n)<5^{(1+\varepsilon)\log n/4\log\log n}$ and $a(n)>5^{(1-\varepsilon)\log n/4\log\log n}$ is valid for infinitely many $n$. The proof employs several estimates of $p(m)$, the number of unrestricted partitions of $m$, one of which is $p(m)\leqq 5^{m/4}$. These results improve a previous estimate of D. G. Kendall and R. A. Rankin [same Quart. **18** (1947), 197–208; MR **9**, 226] of the form $a(n)=O(\exp(b\log n/\log\log n))$.

*R. L. Graham* (Murray Hill, N.J.)

Citations: MR 9, 226c = N52-4.

## N52-48 (42# 5931)

**Suryanarayana, D.**

**The number of unitary, square-free divisors of an integer. I, II.**

*Norske Vid. Selsk. Forh.* (*Trondheim*) **42** (1969), 6–13; *ibid.* **42** (1969), 14–21.

Let $\tau'(n)$ denote the number of unitary squarefree divisors of $n$. The author derives an asymptotic formula of the form $\sum_{n\leq x}\tau'(n)=Ax\log x+Bx+O(x^{3/4})$, where $A$ and $B$ are constants. He also shows that the error term can be replaced by $O(x^{7/10+\varepsilon})$ for every $\varepsilon>0$ if the Riemann hypothesis is true.

*T. M. Apostol* (Pasadena, Calif.)

## N52-49 (44# 1639)

**Fedulova, T. M.**

**A solution of certain additive problems.** (Russian)

*Volž. Mat. Sb. Vyp.* 7 (1969), 184–189.

The author's object is to prove that, for large $n$,

$$\sum_{x_1x_2\cdots x_k\leq n} 2^{\nu(n-x_1x_2\cdots x_k)} = \sigma(n,k)n(\log n)^k+E(n),$$

where $E(n)=O\{n(\log n)^{k-1}(\log\log n)^{a(k)}\}$. Here $\nu(m)$ denotes the number of different prime divisors of $n$. The sum is carried out over all positive integers $x_1, x_2, \cdots, x_k$ whose product does not exceed $n$. In the error term, $a(k)$ is presumably some exponent depending on $k$. In the main term $\sigma(n,k)$ is a "singular series" whose form is not made precise, nor is any positive lower bound obtained for it, as far as the reviewer can ascertain.

*R. A. Rankin* (Glasgow)

## N52-50 (44# 5282)

**Saparnijazov, O.**

**Certain arithmetical estimations.** (Russian. Uzbek summary)

*Izv. Akad. Nauk UzSSR Ser. Fiz.-Mat. Nauk* **14** (1970), *no.* 4, 26–31.

Let $a_n=\sum_{d|n}\ln(d,n/d)\chi(d)$. Then it is shown that $\sum_{n=1}^{\infty}a_n/n^s=-\frac{1}{2}(L'/L)(2s,\chi)L(s,\chi)\zeta(s)$, where $L'(s,\chi)$ denotes the derivative of the Dirichlet $L$-function $L(s,\chi)$.

Assuming the validity of the extended Riemann hypothesis an estimate is obtained for $\sum_{n\le x} a_n$. Similar results are obtained for $a_n=\sum_{d|n}\ln(d, n/d)\chi(n)$. Finally, it is proved that if the usual Riemann hypothesis is true and if $S(x)=\sum_{n\le x}\sum_{d|n}\ln(d, n/d)\chi(d)=-\frac{1}{2}\lambda x+O\{(Dx)^{1/4+\varepsilon}\}$, where $\lambda=(L'/L)(2, \chi)L(1, \chi)$ and $D$ is the modulus of the character $\chi(n)$, then the extended Riemann hypothesis is true.
*W. H. Simons* (Corvallis, Ore.)

# N56 RATE OF GROWTH OF MISCELLANEOUS ARITHMETIC FUNCTIONS

See also reviews A22-29, A26-68, A34-34, A54-48, A99-20, D16-11, D16-17, D16-18, E16-77, E24-10, E24-118, M40-34, N24-20, N28-81, N32-68, N52-1, N52-9, N52-21, N52-23, N60-91, N60-93, N64-13, N72-55, N80-24, N80-33, N80-51, N80-58, P48-11, P80-2.

## N56-1 (2, 42a)

**Hartman, Philip and Kershner, Richard. On upper limit relations for number theoretical functions.** Amer. J. Math. **62**, 780–786 (1940).

The proof of a result of the form

$$\limsup_{x\to\infty} f(x)g(x)=1,$$

where $f(x)$ is a number theoretical function and $g(x)$ is elementary, is often made by first proving $\lim_{n\to\infty} f(r_n)g(r_n)=1$, where $r_n$ is the product of the first $n$ primes. It is then necessary to show that the second result implies the first. The aim of this paper is to find general conditions under which this implication is valid. The main result is a theorem which gives conditions that are sufficient to imply

$$\limsup_{x\to\infty} f(x)g(x)=1,$$

where $f(x)$ is additive and $g(x)=\log\log x/\log x$. Similar results are given for the case where $f(x)$ is strongly additive or strongly multiplicative and $g(x)$ is a non-increasing function. These theorems are based on a lemma which gives conditions sufficient to imply

$$\limsup_{x\to\infty} f(x)g(x)=1$$

from $\lim_{n\to\infty} f(r_n)g(r_n)=1$, where the $r_n$ form an increasing sequence of integers. *H. S. Zuckerman* (Seattle, Wash.).

## N56-2 (4, 240c)

**Pillai, S. S. On $\sigma_{-1}(n)$ and $\phi(n)$.** Proc. Indian Acad. Sci., Sect. A. **17**, 67–70 (1943).

Results on the orders of $\sigma_{-1}(n)$ and $\phi(n)$ due to Wigert [Acta Math. **37**, 113–140 (1914)] and Landau [Handbuch der Verteilung der Primzahlen, Leipzig, 1909, p. 216] are obtained with certain estimates of error terms.
*H. S. Zuckerman* (Seattle, Wash.).

## N56-3 (4, 240g)

**Pall, Gordon. The distribution of integers represented by binary quadratic forms.** Bull. Amer. Math. Soc. **49**, 447–449 (1943).

In this paper the author proves that the number $c(x)$ of positive integers $n\leqq x$ which can be represented by positive primitive binary quadratic forms of a given negative discriminant $d$ is given by

$$cx/(\log x)^{\frac{1}{2}}+O(x/\log x),$$

where $c$ is positive and depends on $d$ alone. This result is deduced from the theorem of R. D. James [Amer. J. Math. **60**, 737–744 (1938)] which states that the above formula with a different constant in place of $c$ gives the number $B(x)$ of all those $n\leqq x$ in the above, for which $(n, d)=1$.
*A. E. Ross* (St. Louis, Mo.).

Referred to in N56-23.

## N56-4 (10, 594d)

**Erdös, P. Some asymptotic formulas in number theory.** J. Indian Math. Soc. (N.S.) **12**, 75–78 (1948).

Let $A(n)$ denote the number of integers $m\leqq n$ for which $(m, \varphi(m))=1$. The author shows that

$$A(n)=(1+o(1))\frac{ne^{-\gamma}}{\log\log\log n},$$

where $\gamma$ is Euler's constant. *W. H. Simons.*

Referred to in N56-32.

## N56-5 (14, 356b)

**Sklar, Abe. On the factorization of squarefree integers.** Proc. Amer. Math. Soc. **3**, 701–705 (1952).

The problem of "Factorisatio numerorum" is concerned with the number $f(n)$ of representations of an integer $n$ as an ordered product of factors greater than 1; it has been studied by Kalmár [Acta Litt. Sci. Szeged **5**, 95–107 (1931)], Hille [Acta Arith. **2**, 134–144 (1936)], Erdös [Ann. of Math. (2) **42**, 989–993 (1941); these Rev. **3**, 165], Sen [Bull. Calcutta Math. Soc. **33**, 1–8 (1941); these Rev. **3**, 269], and others. The author defines, for integral $r$, $h(r)=f(S_r)$, where $S_r$ represents any square-free integer with $r$ prime factors, and proves, among other results, a (convergent) asymptotic expansion:

$$h(r)=2^{-1}r!(\log 2)^{-r-1}\{1+R_r\},$$

where the remainder $R_r$ is expressed in an infinite series, involving two products of properly defined cosine terms. Using this result he determines a "normal" order of $f(n)$ for all $n$. *S. Ikehara* (Tokyo).

Citations: MR 3, 165b = N52-1; MR 3, 269e = A34-2.

## N56-6 (14, 356d)

**Bellman, Richard, and Shapiro, Harold N. On the normal order of arithmetic functions.** Proc. Nat. Acad. Sci. U. S. A. **38**, 884–886 (1952).

Given an arithmetic function $f(n)$ the normal order of $F(x, y)=\sum f(n)$ taken over the range $x\leqq n\leqq x+y$ is defined to be $g(x)$ if for any $\epsilon>0$, we have

$$(1-\epsilon)g(x)\leqq F(x, y)\leqq(1+\epsilon)g(x)$$

for all $x\leqq z$ except for a set of total number $o(z)$ as $z\to\infty$. In this note a technique for deriving the normal order of $F(x, y)$ for a large class of arithmetical functions is indicated. The method employed is intimately connected to the methods introduced by Schnirelman [see E. Landau, Über einige neuere Fortschritte der additiven Zahlentheorie, Cambridge Univ. Press, 1937, pp. 40–59] and Turán [J. London Math. Soc. **9**, 274–276 (1934)]. The authors apply their results to the problem of the distribution of squarefree numbers and prove: (I) If $y(x)$ is any function such that $\lim_{x\to\infty} y(x)=\infty$, then the number of $n\leqq z$ such that the interval $(n, n+y(n))$ contains no squarefree integer is $o(z)$ as $z\to\infty$. (II) If $\lim_{x\to\infty} y(x)=\infty$, and for some $\lambda$, $0<\lambda<1$, $y(x)/y(\lambda x)$ is bounded, then the normal order of $\sum\mu^2(n)$ taken over the range $x\leqq n\leqq x+y$ is $(6/\pi^2)y$. Here $\mu(n)$ is the Möbius function. *A. L. Whiteman.*

**N56-7** **(16, 336g)**

**Gel'fond, A. O. On the partition of the natural series into classes by the group of linear substitutions.** Izvestiya Akad. Nauk SSSR. Ser. Mat. **18**, 297–306 (1954). (Russian)

Let $m \geqq 2$, $p_0 \geqq 1$, $p_1 \geqq 0, \cdots, p_{m-1} \geqq 0$ be integers, and consider the set of linear substitutions

$$L_k(x) = mx + p_k m + k \quad (0 \leqq k \leqq m-1).$$

Denote by $L_k^{-1}(x)$ the integer $y$, if it exists, such that $x = L_k(y)$. Two positive integers $N$ and $n$ are said to belong to the same class if there exists a relation of the type

$$L_{k_1}^{\epsilon_1} \cdots L_{k_s}^{\epsilon_s}(N) = L_{q_1}^{\delta_1} \cdots L_{q_r}^{\delta_r}(n),$$

where the $\epsilon$'s and $\delta$'s have the values $\pm 1$, and the $k$'s and $q$'s belong to the range $[0, m-1]$. In this way the set of positive integers is partitioned into disjoint classes, and it is not difficult to verify that the number of these classes is finite.

Let $\nu$ be the least integer of some class, and denote by $N_\nu(x)$ the number of integers, not exceeding $x$, which belong to the same class as $\nu$. The main object of the paper under review is to study the behaviour of $N_\nu(x)$ for $x \to \infty$. The author shows, in the first place, that

$$N_\nu(x) = x\phi_\nu\left(\frac{\log x}{\log m}\right) + O(1),$$

where $\phi_\nu(t)$ is a periodic function with period 1. Now, let $\nu = n_0 < n_1 < n_2 < \cdots$ be the integers of the class of $\nu$. By investigating the properties of the power series $f_\nu(x) = \sum_{k=0}^\infty x^{n_k}$ and making use of the methods of complex function theory the author obtains an explicit, though complicated, formula for $\phi_\nu(t)$. The paper concludes with a discussion of the zeta-function associated with the class of $\nu$, i.e. the function $\zeta_\nu(s) = \sum_{k=0}^\infty n_k^{-s}$. *L. Mirsky* (Sheffield).

**N56-8** **(20# 1654)**

**Erdös, Paul. On an elementary problem in number theory.** Canad. Math. Bull. **1** (1958), 5–8.

Quoting from the paper: "Let $0 < x \leqq y$. Estimate the smallest $f(x)$ so that there should exist integers $u$ and $v$ satisfying (1) $0 \leqq u, v < f(x)$ and $(x+u, y+v) = 1$. — I am going to prove that for every $\varepsilon > 0$ there exist arbitrarily large values of $x$ satisfying (2) $f(x) > (1-\varepsilon)(\log x/\log\log x)^{\frac{1}{2}}$ but that for a certain $c > 0$ and all $x$, and (3) $f(x) < c\log x/\log\log x$. — A sharp estimation of $f(x)$ seems to be a difficult problem. It is clear that $f(p) = 2$ for all primes $p$. ... By similar methods as used in the proof of (3) we can prove the following theorem. Let $g(x)(\log x/\log\log x)^{-1} \to \infty$, $0 < x < y$. Then the number of pairs $0 \leqq u, v < g(x)$ satisfying $(x+u, y+v) = 1$ equals $(1+o(1))(6/\pi^2)g^2(x)$. ··· We can show by methods used in the proof of (2) in our theorem that we cannot have $g(x)$ less than $c(\log x/\log\log x)^{\frac{1}{2}}$, i.e., $g(x)(\log x/\log\log x)^{-\frac{1}{2}} \to \infty$ is necessary for the truth of our theorem. An exact estimation of $g(x)$ seems difficult."

A footnote states: "L. Moser informs me that he independently obtained this result (2) and its generalization to an $m$-dimensional lattice."

*A. J. Kempner* (Boulder, Colo.)

**N56-9** **(20# 2297)**

**Kanold, Hans-Joachim. Ein Satz über zahlentheoretische Funktionen.** Math. Nachr. **18** (1958), 36–38.

For any positive integers $r$ and $n$, let $\sigma_r(n) = \sum_d d^r$; $\varphi_r(n) = \prod_p (p^r - 1)/p^r$, where $d$ ranges over all divisors and $p$ over all prime divisors of $n$. Denote by $M(x)$ the number of positive integers $m \leqq x$ which are prime to either $\sigma_r(m)$ or $\varphi_r(m)$ or both. In this paper it is shown that $\lim_{x\to\infty} M(x)/x = 0$. *R. J. Levit* (San Francisco, Calif.)

**N56-10** **(22# 4658)**

**Veržbinskiĭ, M. L. The primeness deficiency of an integer.** Zap. Leningrad. Gorn. Inst. **36** (1958), no. 3, 5–12. (Russian)

The primeness deficiency of the natural number $n$ is defined to be $\kappa(n) = \sum_1^{n-1}(m, n) - (n-1)$, where $(m, n)$ is the greatest common divisor. Then it is shown that

(1) $$\kappa(n) < n^{1+[\log\log(4\log n) - \log\log 2]/\log\log n} - 2n + 1$$

"asymptotically" for all large $n$. Clearly $\kappa(n)$ is zero only when $n$ is prime, and the author shows that

$$\kappa(n) > (n^{1/2} - 1)^2$$

when $n$ is composite. He also obtains bounds below for $\kappa(n)$ depending on the number of prime factors of $n$. The proofs are all elementary. {It appears to the reviewer that "asymptotically" in connection with (1) means that the inequality with $(1+\varepsilon)$ multiplying the $\log\log(4\log n)$ term is true for all sufficiently large $n$.}

*J. W. S. Cassels* (Cambridge, England)

**N56-11** **(23# A864)**

**Erdös, P.**

**On a problem of G. Golomb.**

*J. Austral. Math. Soc.* **2** (1961/62), 1–8.

Let the sequence $\{q_i\}$ be defined as follows: $q_1 = 3$, $q_2 = 5$, $\cdots$, $q_i$ is the smallest prime greater than $q_{i-1}$ for which $q_i \not\equiv 1 \pmod{q_j}$, $1 \leqq j < i$. Denoting by $A(x)$ the number of $q_i \leqq x$, the following result is obtained:

$$A(x) = (1+o(1))\frac{x}{\log x \log\log x}, \quad x \to \infty.$$

The proof depends on a skilful application of Brun's method. *S. Knapowski* (Poznań)

**N56-12** **(23# A2404)**

**Vinogradov, A. I.**

**Generalization of a lemma of Erdös.** (Russian. English summary)

*Vestnik Leningrad. Univ.* **15** (1960), *no.* 19, 124–126.

Let $n$, $d$ and $r$ be relatively prime in pairs, with $n \geqq 10dr$. It is shown that the number of positive integers $Q_1, Q_2$ having the property that every prime divisor of $Q_1Q_2$ is larger than $n^\alpha$, and such that $n = dQ_1 + rQ_2$, is smaller than

$$\frac{cn}{rd}\left(\log^{-2}\frac{n}{rd} + (\alpha\log n)^{-4}\right)\log\log^2 n \cdot \log\log^2\frac{n}{rd}.$$

That which was generalized is not disclosed.

*W. J. LeVeque* (Ann Arbor, Mich.)

**N56-13** **(25# 3897)**

**Cohen, Eckford**

**Arithmetical notes. VI. Simultaneous binary compositions involving coprime pairs of integers.**

*Michigan Math. J.* **9** (1962), 277–282.

Part V appeared in Amer. J. Math. **83** (1961), 693–697 [MR **24** #A1863]. The author finds an asymptotic formula for the number $Q(m, n)$ of solutions of

(1) $$m = x_1 + y_1, \quad n = x_2 + y_2$$

in non-negative integers $x_1, y_1, x_2, y_2$ subject to

(2) $$(x_1, x_2) = (y_1, y_2) = 1.$$

It has the form

(3) $$Q(m, n) \sim mn\alpha(m, n) \quad (n \geqq m, m \to \infty),$$

where

$$(4) \qquad \alpha(m, n) = \prod_{p|(m,n)} \left(1-\frac{1}{p^2}\right) \prod_{p\nmid(m,n)} \left(1-\frac{2}{p^2}\right).$$

From (4) the author deduces

$$(5) \qquad A_1 < \frac{Q(m, n)}{mn} < A_2,$$

where $A_1$, $A_2$ are positive constants independent of $m$, $n$.
*S. Chowla* (Boulder, Colo.)

Citations: MR 24# A1863 = N28-46.
Referred to in N24-40, N56-16.

## N56-14 (26# 2411 )

**Erdős, Pál [Erdős, Paul]**
**Some remarks on number theory. II. (Hungarian. Russian and English summaries)**
*Mat. Lapok* **12** (1961), 161–169.

Author's summary: "Let $\phi(n)=\phi_1(n)$ be Euler's $\phi$ function and put $\phi_k(n)=\phi(\phi_{k-1}(n))$. The author proves that if we neglect a sequence of density 0, then for $k\geqq 2$

$$\lim_{n\to\infty} \frac{\phi_k(n)\log\log\log n}{\phi_{k-1}(n)} = e^{-C},$$

where $C$ is Euler's constant. Several other problems and results are stated about the $\phi$ function."

Referred to in A30-28.

## N56-15 (26# 6141 )

**Jager, H.**
**On the number of pairs of integers with least common multiple not exceeding $x$.**
*Nederl. Akad. Wetensch. Proc. Ser. A* **65** = *Indag. Math.* **24** (1962), 346–350.

Der Verfasser behandelt die Frage nach der Anzahl der (geordneten) Paare natürlicher Zahlen $(a, b)$, deren kleinstes gemeinsames Vielfaches $[a, b]\leqq x$ ist. Für die Anzahl $\theta(x)$ dieser Paare beweist er bei $x\to\infty$

$$\theta(x) = c_0x\log^2 x+c_1x\log x+c_2x+O(x^{1/2+\varepsilon}),$$

wo $c_0=1/2\zeta(2)$, $c_1$ und $c_2$ absolute Konstanten bezeichnen. Die erzeugende Funktion von $[a, b]=n$ ist $\zeta^3(s)/\zeta(2s)$, und der Beweis wird unter Anwendung eines allgemeinen Satzes über Dirichletsche Reihen zur Behandlung derartiger Fragen vom Referenten [Nachr. Akad. Wiss. Göttingen Math.-Phys. Kl. IIa **1956**, 77–125; MR **18**, 123] geführt. Ein elementarer Beweis mit einem etwas schwächeren Restglied wird angekündigt.
*H.-E. Richert* (Syracuse, N.Y.)

Citations: MR 18, 123h = M40-16.
Referred to in N56-36.

## N56-16 (28# 3964 )

**Cohen, Eckford**
**Arithmetical notes. XII. A sequel to Note VI.**
*Norske Vid. Selsk. Forh.* (*Trondheim*) **36** (1963), 10–15.

Part VI appeared in Michigan Math. J. **9** (1962), 277–282 [MR **25** #3897]. For positive integers $m$, $n$ let $Q(m, n)$ denote the number of sets of ordered pairs $[x_1, x_2]$, $[y_1, y_2]$ of positive integers $x_1, x_2, y_1, y_2$ such that

$$(1) \quad m = x_1+y_1,\ n = x_2+y_2,\quad (x_1, x_2) = (y_1, y_2) = 1.$$

The author proves the theorem: If $n\geqq m$, then

$$Q(m, n) = \alpha((m, n))mn+O(n\log^2 m) \text{ if } n \geqq m^2,$$
$$= \alpha((m, n))mn+O(mn^{1/2}\log^2 m) \text{ if } n < m^2.$$

Here

$$\alpha(t) = \prod_{p|t}\left(1-\frac{1}{p^2}\right)\prod_{p\nmid t}\left(1-\frac{2}{p^2}\right)$$

and $(x, y)$ denotes, as usual, the greatest common divisor of $x$ and $y$. *S. Chowla* (University Park, Pa.)

Citations: MR 25# 3897 = N56-13.

## N56-17 (30# 3870 )

**Mąkowski, A.; Schinzel, A.**
**On the functions $\varphi(n)$ and $\sigma(n)$.**
*Colloq. Math.* **13** (1964), 95–99.

It is an easy observation that $\liminf \sigma(n)/n=1$, where $\sigma(n)$ denotes the sum of the divisors of $n$. In this paper, the authors prove by elementary methods that $\liminf \sigma(\sigma(n))/n<\infty$, and, in fact, that this limit is 1. An analogous result for the Euler $\phi$-function is also proved, but the proof is not elementary.
*E. Cohen* (Knoxville, Tenn.)

Referred to in N56-22.

## N56-18 (34# 124 )

**Brun, Viggo**
**Un procédé qui ressemble au crible d'Eratosthène. (Romanian and Russian summaries)**
*An. Şti. Univ. "Al. I. Cuza" Iaşi Secţ. I a Mat. (N.S.)* **11B** (1965), 47–53.

Denote by $[\beta]$ the largest integer $\leqq\beta$. Define a sequence $x_n$ by $x_1=x>0$, $x_n=x_{n-1}-[x_{n-1}/n]$, $n=2, 3, \cdots$; put $\alpha(x)=\lim_{n\to\infty} x_n$. The asymptotic behaviour of $\alpha(x)$ (for $x\to\infty$) is known [Nordisk Mat. Tidskr. **5** (1957), 114–117, solution of problem 167]. The author proves that $\alpha(x)=2\pi^{-1/2}x^{1/2}(1+\omega x^{-1/8})$ for $x>5^8$, where $|\omega|<1$.
*W. Schwarz* (Freiburg)

## N56-19 (34# 4220 )

**Erdős, P.**
**On some properties of prime factors of integers.**
*Nagoya Math. J.* **27** (1966), 617–623.

Let the canonical decomposition of the positive integer $n$ be denoted by $n=\prod_{i=1}^{\nu(n)} p_i^{\alpha_i}$. Define $\gamma_j(n)=(\sum_{i=1}^{j-1}\alpha_i\log p_i)\times(\log p_j)^{-1}$ for $2\leqq j\leqq\nu(n)$, and $P(n)=\max\{\gamma_j(n): 2\leqq j\leqq\nu(n)\}$. The author proves that, except for a sequence of $n$'s with density 0, one has $P(n)=(1+o(1))(\log_3 n)(\log_4 n)^{-1}$ ($\log_k$ is the $k$-fold iterated logarithm).

The most difficult part of the proof is the following lemma, which is interesting in itself. Let $r$ run through the integers between $\frac{1}{2}\log_2 x$ and $\log_2 x$, put

$$a_r = \exp\{[1+(\log_4 x)^{-1}]^r\},$$

and let $I_r$ be the interval $(a_r, a_{r+1})$. The lemma states that if $\varepsilon>0$ then all but $o(x)$ integers $n\leqq x$ have the property that there exists an $r$ such that $n$ has at least $(1-\frac{1}{2}\varepsilon)(\log_3 x)(\log_4 x)^{-1}$ distinct prime factors in $I_r$.

The author sketches the proofs of two further results. Theorem 2: There exists a continuous strictly increasing function $\varphi$ on $0\leqq x\leqq\infty$, with $\varphi(0)=0$, $\varphi(\infty)=1$, such that for every $c$ $(0\leqq c\leqq\infty)$ the number of $j$'s with $\gamma_j(n)\leqq c$ is $(\varphi(c)+o(1))\log_2 n$ except for a sequence of integers $n$ of density zero. Theorem 3: The density of integers $n$ for which $\min\{\gamma_j(n): 2\leqq j\leqq\nu(n)\}<c/\log_2 n$ is $\psi(c)$ $(0\leqq c\leqq\infty)$; again $\psi$ is continuous strictly increasing, $\psi(0)=0$ and $\psi(\infty)=1$. *N. G. de Bruijn* (Eindhoven)

## N56-20 (34# 5789 )

**van Lint, J. H.**
**Representation of 0 as $\sum_{K=-N}^{N}\varepsilon_k k$.**
*Proc. Amer. Math. Soc.* **18** (1967), 182–184.

Let $A(N)$ denote the number of representations of 0 in the form $\sum_{k=-N}^{N}\varepsilon_k k$, where $\varepsilon_k=0$ or 1 for $-N\leqq k\leqq N$. Being the constant term in the expansion of $\prod_{k=-N}^{N}(1+x^k)$, the number $A(N)$ can be treated by means of Cauchy's integral theorem. In this way, the author obtains easily that $A(N)\sim(3/\pi)^{1/2}2^{2N+1}N^{-3/2}$, thus answering a recent question of P. Erdős. *O. H. Körner* (Marburg)

Referred to in N56-24.

**N56-21** **(35# 1564)**

**Shanks, Daniel; Schmid, Larry P.**

**Variations on a theorem of Landau. I.**

*Math. Comp.* **20** (1966), 551–569.

Let $B(x)$ denote the number of integers $\leqq x$ that are the sum of two squares. The theorem of the title is that $B(x)\sim bx(\log x)^{-1/2}$ for a constant $b=.764223654$. As in an earlier paper by the first author [Math. Comp. **18** (1964), 75–86; MR **28** #2391], the authors are concerned with the next term in the expansion not only of $B(x)$ but also of its generalizations $B_n(x)$, $B_{a,b}(x)$ and $B_{a,b,c}(x)$ which are, respectively, the number of integers $\leqq x$ of the form $u^2+nv^2$, $au^2+bv^2$ and $au^2+buv+cv^2$. According to H.-H. Ostmann [*Additive Zahlentheorie, I, Allgemeine Untersuchungen, II, Spezielle Zahlenmengen*, Ergeb. Math. Grenzgeb. (N.F.), Hefte 7, 11, Springer, Berlin, 1956; MR **20** #5176],

$$B_n(x) = b_nx(\log x)^{-1/2}+O(x/\log x),$$

but the authors show that this is false for $n=14$ since

$$B_{14}(x) = b_{14}x(\log x)^{-1/2}[1-\beta_{14}(\log x)^{-1/4}+O(1/\log x)],$$

while for several values of $n$ it can be shown that

$$B_n(x) = b_nx(\log x)^{-1/2}[1+\beta_n/\log x+O((\log x)^{-2})].$$

The variations mentioned in the title result from elaborate special cases that go with the quadratic form representing $m\leqq x$. The $B_n(x)$, as well as $B_{a,b}(x)$ and $B_{a,b,c}(x)$, are especially sensitive to the number of classes per genus among the forms equivalent to the corresponding forms defining these functions. These cases are too numerous and varied to set forth in a review.

Table 1 gives $9D$ values of $b_n$ for 28 values of $n$ between $-34$ and 256 including $n=1(1)10$. For $n=11$, 13 and 14 only $3D$ values are given. These are derived from values of $L$-series and certain infinite products over primes. Tables of the exact values of $B_n(x)$ are given for $n=-2$, 1, 2, 3, 4, 6, 10, 12, 16, of $B_{a,b}(x)$ for $(a,b)=(2,3)$, $(2,5)$ and $(3,4)$, and of $B_{4,4,5}(x)$ all for $x=2^t$ $(t=0(1)26)$.

For the many remarkable details we can only refer the reader to the paper itself.

*D. H. Lehmer* (Berkeley, Calif.)

Citations: MR 20# 5176 = Z02-30; MR 28# 2391 = N28-51.

**N56-22** **(36# 2573)**

**Erdős, P.**

**Some remarks on the iterates of the $\varphi$ and $\sigma$ functions.**

*Colloq. Math.* **17** (1967), 195–202.

Let $\sigma(n)$ denote the sum of the divisors of $n$. Put $\sigma_1(n)=\sigma(n)$ and, for $k>1$, $\sigma_k(n)=\sigma_1(\sigma_{k-1}(n))$. A. Makowski and A. Schinzel [same Colloq. **13** (1964/65), 95–99; MR **30** #3870] proved that for $k=2$, (*) $\lim\inf(\sigma_k(n)/n)<\infty$. In fact, they showed that this limit is 1. The author is presently unable to prove (*) for $k=3$, but he is able to establish a theorem which shows certain differences between the cases $k=2$ and $k=3$. Denote by $N_\sigma(k,\alpha,x)$ the number of integers $n\leqq x$ for which $\sigma_k(n)<\alpha n$. Theorem: We have, for every $t$, if $x>x_0(t)$,

$$N_\sigma(2, 2, x) > (x/\log x)(\log\log x)^t,$$

and for every $\alpha>0$ and $\varepsilon>0$, if $x>x_0(\varepsilon,\alpha)$,

$$N_\sigma(2, \alpha, x) < (x/\log x)(\log x)^\varepsilon,$$

$$N_\sigma(3, \alpha, x) < (x/(\log x)^2)(\log x)^\varepsilon.$$

Furthermore, the inequality for $N_\sigma(2,2,x)$ is best possible in the sense that $\alpha=2$ cannot be replaced by any smaller number. The author also obtains an analogous result for the Euler $\phi$-function. The non-elementary proofs employ the prime number theorem for arithmetic progressions, the Viggo Brun sieve and a theorem of Titchmarsh-Prachar [see K. Prachar, *Primzahlverteilung*, p. 44, Theorem 4.1, Springer, Berlin, 1957; MR **19**, 393].

*A. L. Whiteman* (Princeton, N.J.)

Citations: MR 19, 393b = N02-7; MR 30# 3870 = N56-17.

**N56-23** **(37# 2686)**

**Heupel, Wolfgang**

**Die Verteilung der ganzen Zahlen, die durch quadratische Formen dargestellt werden.**

*Arch. Math.* (*Basel*) **19** (1968), 162–166.

Verfasser beweist den Satz: Sei $C(x)$ die Anzahl der natürlichen Zahlen $m\leqq x$, die sich durch eine positive, primitive, ganzzahlige, binäre quadratische Form mit der Diskriminante $d\leqq -3$ darstellen lassen. Dann gilt $C(x)=ux(\log x)^{-1/2}(1+v(\log x)^{-1/2}+O(\log^{-2}x))$. Hierbei sind $u>0$ und $v$ durch längere Ausdrücke gegebene Konstanten. Die Arbeit schließt sich methodisch an G. Pall [Bull. Amer. Math. Soc. **49** (1943), 447–449; MR **4**, 240] an, sie verbessert das dort angegebene Fehlerglied.

*H. J. Kanold* (Braunschweig)

Citations: MR 4, 240g = N56-3.

**N56-24** **(37# 5138)**

**Entringer, R. C.**

**Representation of $m$ as $\sum_{k=-n}^{n}\varepsilon_kk$.**

*Canad. Math. Bull.* **11** (1968), 289–293.

Let $A(n,m)$ denote the number of representations any integer $m$ has in the form stated in the title with $\varepsilon_k=0$ or 1 for $-n\leqq k\leqq n$. Then $A(n,m)=A(n,-m)$ is, for $m\geqq 0$, the coefficient of $x^{n(n+1)/2+m}$ in $2\prod_{k=1}^{n}(1+x^k)^2$. The author proves that $A(n,m)$ is a non-increasing function of $|m|$. He then shows that for $m=O(n)$, $A(n,m)\sim(3/\pi)^{1/2}2^{2n+1}n^{-3/2}$. J. H. van Lint has proved this result for $m=0$ [Proc. Amer. Math. Soc. **18** (1967), 182–184; MR **34** #5789].

*H. Gupta* (Allahabad)

Citations: MR 34# 5789 = N56-20.

**N56-25** **(39# 1392)**

**James, R. D.**

**The factors of a square-free integer.**

*Canad. Math. Bull.* **11** (1968), 733–735.

Let $n=p_1\cdots p_m$, where the $p$'s are distinct primes, so that $n$ is a square free integer. Then if $F(m)$ denotes the number of ordered nontrivial factorizations of $n$, it is shown that $\lim\sup_{m\to\infty}|2F(m)/m!-1/(m+1)|^{1/m} = 1/(\log^2 2+4\pi^2)^{1/2}$ and that $2F(m)/m!=1/(\log 2)^{m+1}+O(1/(2\pi)^m)$.

*K. Thanigasalam* (University Park, Pa.)

**N56-26** **(39# 5495)**

**Erdős, P.**

**On the distribution of prime divisors.**

*Aequationes Math.* **2** (1969), 177–183.

Denote by $V(n;u,v)$ the number of prime factors $p$ of $n$ satisfying $u<p<v$. Let $u=u(x)$, $v=v(x)$, and assume that $\log_2 v-\log_2 u\to\infty$. P. Turán [J. London Math. Soc. **9** (1934), 274–276] proved that for all but $o(x)$ integers $n<x$, (*) $V(n;u,v)=(1+o(1))(\log_2 v-\log_2 u)$ ($\log_k$ denotes the $k$-fold iterated logarithm).

The author investigates the case when $u$ and $v$ depend on $n$. If the dependence is regular, Turán's method carries through without too much difficulty. In the general case, $\log_2 v-\log_2 u\to\infty$ is not sufficient for (*), but the present paper shows that the result holds uniformly in $u$ and $v$ under rather mild conditions. A best possible theorem reads: Assume $(\log_2 v-\log_2 u)/\log_3 n\to\infty$. Then we have for almost all $n$, uniformly in $u$ and $v$, $V(n;u,v)=(1+o(1))(\log_2 v-\log_2 u)$.

This theorem can be generalised for a large class of

additive functions, and the probabilistic theorem corresponding to the above theorem is formulated. A few results are stated without proof about prime factors of integers, which can be obtained by standard methods of probabilistic number theory [the author and M. Kac, Amer. J. Math. **62** (1940), 738–742; MR **2**, 42; J. P. Kubilius, Uspehi Mat. Nauk **11** (1952), no. 2 (68), 31–66; MR **18**, 17; translated in Amer. Math. Soc. Transl. (2) **19** (1962), 47–85; MR **24** #A1266]. *S. Ikehara* (Tokyo)

Citations: MR 2, 42c = N60-4; MR 18, 17d = Q15-4; MR 24# A1266 = Q15-5.

## N56-27 (40# 5559)

**Erdős, P.; Kátai, I.**

**On the growth of $d_k(n)$.**

*Fibonacci Quart.* **7** (1969), 267–274.

Let $d(n)$ be the number of divisors of $n$, and define $d_k(n)$ by $d_k(n)=d(d_{k-1}(n))$ $(k\geqq 2)$, $d_1(n)=d(n)$. Let $\log_s$ denote the $s$-fold iterated logarithm. The authors prove (in Theorem 1) that $\lim\sup_{n\to\infty}(\log_2 d_k(n))/\log_2 n=1/l_k$, where $l_k$ is the $(k+1)$st term of the Fibonacci sequence 1, 1, 2, 3, 5, $\cdots$—a surprising result that goes far beyond some old results of Ramanujan. They prove also (Theorem 2) that if $K(n)$ is the least positive integer $k$ such that $d_k(n)=2$, then $0<\lim\sup K(n)/\log_3 n<\infty$; and they conjecture that $n^{-1}\sum_{m=1}^n K(m)$ grows roughly like $L(n)$, where $L(n)$ is the least positive integer such that $\log_{L(n)} n<1$. There are several misprints, of which the most confusing is the misstatement of Wigert's result at the very beginning of the paper (where one should read log 2 for $\log_2$). *H. Halberstam* (Nottingham)

## N56-28 (40# 7213)

**Drozdova, A. A.; Freĭman, G. A.**

**The estimation of certain arithmetic functions. (Russian)**

*Elabuž. Gos. Ped. Inst. Učen. Zap.* **3** (1958), 160–165.

Let the canonical decomposition of a positive integer $N$ into prime factors have the form: $N=p_1^{\alpha_1}\cdots p_r^{\alpha_r}$. Let $f(\alpha)$ be a function that assumes positive values for integers $\alpha$ and satisfies the condition: $f(\alpha)=f(\alpha-1)(1+O(1/\alpha))$. The authors evaluate an arithmetic function of the form: $F(N)=f(\alpha_1)\cdots f(\alpha_r)$. They prove in an elementary way that

$$\ln F(N) \leqq \sup(1/m)\ln f(m)\ln N/(\ln\ln N) + O((\ln N/(\ln\ln N)^2)\ln\ln\ln N).$$

This result is used to obtain an upper bound for the number of representations of the positive integer $N$ in the form of a product of $k$ positive factors, for the number of divisors of the positive integer $N$, that are divisible by any prime number entering into $N$, and for the number of choices of $k$ numbers whose least common multiple equals $N$. *V. I. Nečaev* (RŽMat **1960** #95)

## N56-29 (40# 7215)

**Freĭman, G. A.**

**Dense sequences in the theory of partitions. (Russian)**

*Elabuž. Gos. Ped. Inst. Učen. Zap.* **3** (1958), 120–137.

We denote by $q_n$ the number of solutions of the inequality $2^{\alpha_2}3^{\alpha_3}\cdots n^{\alpha_n}\leqq n$ in positive* integers $\alpha_2, \alpha_3, \cdots, \alpha_n$. The author deduces the asymptotic formula

$$q_n = (2\sqrt{(\pi)}(\ln n)^{3/4})^{-1}ne^{2\sqrt{\ln n}}(1+O(1/(\ln n)^{1/8-\varepsilon}))$$

by an analytical method and proves in an elementary way that the inequalities $ne^{c_1\sqrt{\ln n}}\leqq q_n\leqq ne^{c_2\sqrt{\ln n}}$ are valid for certain positive constants $c_1$ and $c_2$ for all sufficiently large natural $n$. *V. I. Nečaev* (RŽMat **1960** #85)

[* Presumably, nonnegative. Original not accessible. Ed.]

## N56-30 (40# 7222)

**Anderson, Ian**

**A variance method in combinatorial number theory.**

*Glasgow Math. J.* **10** (1969), 126–129.

The set $D_n$ of divisors of a natural number $n$ ordered by division forms a lattice. A collection of incomparable elements in $D_n$ is called a Sperner collection, and $s(n)$, the maximal cardinality over all Sperner collections in $D_n$, is called the Sperner number of $D_n$. Let $p_1, \cdots, p_r$ denote distinct primes, let $a_1, \cdots, a_r$ denote natural numbers, and suppose $n=p_1^{a_1}\cdots p_r^{a_r}$. E. Sperner [Math. Z. **27** (1928), 544–548] proved that if $a_1=\cdots=a_r=1$, then $s(n)=r!/([r/2]!(r-[r/2])!)$, and N. G. de Bruijn, Ca. Tengbergen and D. Kruyswijk [Nieuw Arch. Wisk. (2) **23** (1951), 191–193; MR **13**, 207] showed that $s(n)$ is a function of $(a_1, \cdots, a_r)$ defined as follows: let $A=a_1+\cdots+a_r$, and let $a$ denote the greatest integer in $A/2$, then $s(n)=S(a_1, \cdots, a_r)$ is the coefficient of $x^a$ in the polynomial $\prod_{i=1}^{i=r}(1+x+\cdots+x^{a_i})=(1-x)^{-r}\prod_{i=1}^{i=r}(1-x^{a_i+1})$. In the paper now under review, and in an earlier paper [J. London Math. Soc. **42** (1967), 137–148; MR **35** #147], the author is interested in the behavior of $S(a_1, \cdots, a_r)$ as $A$ tends to infinity. Using ingenious elementary methods, he is able to show that there exist constants $C_1$ and $C_2$ such that $(S(a_1, \cdots, a_r))^2$ is bounded above and below by

$$C_j\prod_{i=1}^{i=r}(1+a_i)^2/(-r+\sum_{i=1}^r(1+a_i)^2)$$

for $j=1, 2$, respectively. The lower bound is proved by using the decomposition of $D_n$ into chains described by de Bruijn, Tengbergen, and Kruyswijk. The upper bound depends on ideas given by the author in ibid. **43** (1968), 410–418 [MR **37** #6235]. *D. A. Klarner* (Eindhoven)

Citations: MR 13, 207f = A24-2; MR 35# 147 = B28-31; MR 37# 6235 = A28-14.

## N56-31 (42# 3032)

**Scourfield, E. J.**

**On the divisibility of a modified divisor function.**

*Proc. London Math. Soc.* (3) **21** (1970), 145–159.

Let $\chi$ be a non-principal real character mod $Q$ and $k$ a positive integer. The author studies the function $\sigma_k(n, \chi)=\sum_{d\mid n}\chi(d)d^k$ and finds asymptotics for the number of positive integers $n\leqq x$ for which a given prime-power $p^m$ divides exactly $\sigma_k(n, \chi)$. These asymptotics are of the form $Ax(\log\log x)^a/(\log x)^b$ with rational positive $b$, integral nonnegative $a$ and positive $A$. In the case $p=2$ the constant $A$ is explicitly evaluated. This result is a modification of a previous theorem of the author, concerning the $\sigma_k(n)$ function [Acta Arith. **10** (1964), 245–285; MR **30** #3074]. *W. Narkiewicz* (Wrocław)

Citations: MR 30# 3074 = N64-20.

## N56-32 (42# 3047)

**Hall, R. R.**

**On the probability that $n$ and $f(n)$ are relatively prime.**

*Acta Arith.* **17** (1970), 169–183.

Let $g(n)$ be an integer-valued number-theoretic function and let $T_g(x)$ be the number of integers $n\leqq x$ for which $(n, g(n))=1$. It is shown that when $g(n)$ is the sum of the distinct prime factors of $n$,

$$T(x) = 6\pi^{-2}x+O(x/(\log_3 x)^{1/4}(\log_4 x)^{3/4}),$$

where $\log_n x$ is the $n$-fold iterate of $\log x$.

Asymptotic estimates had been obtained earlier for $T_g(x)$ when $g(n)=[f(n)]$ ($f$ a suitably smooth function [G. L. Watson, Canad. J. Math. **5** (1953), 451–455; MR **15**, 292; P. Erdős and G. G. Lorentz, Acta Arith. **5** (1958), 35–44

(1959); MR **21** #37]) and when $g(n)=\phi(n)$ or $\sigma(n)$ [Erdős, J. Indian Math. Soc. (N.S.) **12** (1948), 75–78; MR **10**, 594].

*W. J. LeVeque* (Claremont, Calif.)

**Citations: MR 10, 594d = N56-4; MR 15, 292a = B52-4; MR 21# 37 = B52-9.**

**Referred to in N56-39.**

## N56-33 (42# 3048)

**Kátai, I.**

**Statistical theorems for the number of prime factors of integers.**

*Ann. Univ. Sci. Budapest. Eötvös Sect. Math.* **11** (1968), 71–78.

The author studies the asymptotic behavior of sums that are a generalization of sums for a number of divisors for shifted prime numbers and $\sum_{p\leq x} r(p+1)$, where $r(n)$ is the number of representations of a number $n$ in the form of a sum of two squares. The proof for the theorem is only briefly sketched. One of the four theorems. Theorem 1: Let $c_1>1$, $c_2>1$, $\varepsilon>0$ be constants. Then

(1) $$R(x, c_1, c_2) \asymp x(\ln x)^{c_1+c_2-2},$$

(2) $$R(x, c_1, c_2) = (1+o(1)) \sum_{n\leq x, n\in A(c_1,\varepsilon), n+1\in A(c_2,\varepsilon)} c_1^{U(n)} c_2^{U(n+1)},$$

(3) $$(\ln x)^{-\varepsilon \ln c_1 c_2} \ll r(x, c_1, c_2, \varepsilon)/(x(\ln x)^{c_1+c_2-(c_1\ln c_1+c_2\ln c_2)}) \ll (\ln x)^{\varepsilon \ln c_1 c_2},$$

where $R(x, c_1, c_2)=\sum_{n\leq x} c_1^{U(n)}c_2^{U(n+1)}$, $U(n)$ is the number of different prime divisors of a number $n$, $A(c,\varepsilon)$ is the set of such $n$ for which $|U(n)-c\ln\ln x|<\varepsilon \ln\ln x$, and $r(x, c_1, c_2, \varepsilon)=\sum_{n\leq x, n\in A(c_1,\varepsilon), n+1\in A(c_2,\varepsilon)} 1$. There are misprints.

*A. Judin* (RŽMat **1969** #8 A150)

## N56-34 (42# 6109)

**Greenberg, Leon; Newman, Morris**

**Some results on solvable groups.**

*Arch. Math.* (*Basel*) **21** (1970), 349–352.

Let $a_1, a_2, \cdots, a_r$ be fixed odd integers greater than 1 and $s$ the arithmetic function defined by: $s(n)=1$ if a solvable group of order $n$ exists generated by elements $x_1, x_2, \cdots, x_r$ such that $x_1^{a_1}=x_2^{a_2}=\cdots=x_r^{a_r}=1$ and $s(n)=0$ otherwise. If $S(x)=\sum_{n\leq x} s(n)$, then $x^{-1}S(x)=O((\log x)^{-1/(2h)})$ where $h=\varphi(a_1a_2\cdots a_r)$. In particular, $\lim_{x\to\infty} x^{-1}S(x)=0$. The group theoretical section of the proof consists of showing that, for any solvable group $G$ of order $n$ generated by elements $x_1, \cdots, x_r$ such that $x_1^{a_1}=\cdots=x_r^{a_r}=1$, and any prime $p$ dividing $n$ to the first power while $p\nmid a_1\cdots a_r$, we have $(p-1, a)>1$. Using this result and a well-known result on arithmetic progressions by E. Landau [Amer. J. Math. **26** (1904), 209–222; ibid. **31** (1909), 86–102], the following lemma yields the above theorem: Let $\omega$ be the arithmetic function defined by $\omega(1)=1$, $\omega(n)=1$ if all primes dividing $n$ do so to a power bigger than the first, $\omega(n)=0$ otherwise, and $\Omega(x)=\sum_{n\leq x}\omega(n)$. Then $\omega(n)=\sum_{d^3|n}|\mu(d)|q(n/d^3)$, $\Omega(x)\leq(\zeta(3/2)/\zeta(3))x^{1/2}$, where $q(n)$ is the characteristic function for squares.

*H. Lausch* (Vienna)

## N56-35 (43# 163)

**Pons, Francisco Tomás**

**Some problems relative to the distribution of the digits in the representations of $a$ with base $p\leq a$.** (Spanish)

*An. Inst. Mat. Univ. Nac. Autónoma México* **9** (1969), 53–78.

Notations: $\pi(x)=\sum_{p\leq x} 1$; $a_{n,i}$ = coefficient of $n^i$ in the $n$-adic expansion of $a=\sum_{i\geq 0} a_{n,i}n^i$ $(0\leq a_{n,i}<n)$; $[x]$ = greatest integer not exceeding $x$; $\{x\}=x-[x]$ = fractional part of $x$. For $t\in[0,1]$, $N_{\alpha,\beta}(x,t)$ = number of primes not exceeding $x^\alpha$ such that $\{xp^{-1/\beta}\}\leq t$; $\Phi_{\alpha,\beta}(t)=\lim_{x\to\infty}(N_{\alpha,\beta}(x,t)/\pi(x^\alpha))$ (if the limit exists). $\varphi_r(a)=\prod_{i=1}^a i_r$, where $i_r$ is the highest $r$th power that divides the integer $i$; in particular, for $r=1$, $i_1=i$ and $\varphi_1(a)=a!$. Given $b$, for every $p\leq b$ and $2\leq q\in \mathbf{Z}$ let $b_p'$ be the (unique) solution of $b_p'\equiv b^q \pmod p$, with $0\leq b_p'<p$. For odd prime $q$, let $P_q(b)$ be the set of primes $p\leq b$ such that $q\nmid(p-1)$, and let $\pi_q(b)$ stand for the number of primes in $P_q(b)$; denote by $r_p(b)$ the (unique) solution of $r_p(b)^q\equiv b \pmod p$, $0\leq r_p(b)<p$; finally, let $B_q$ stand for the set of $q$th powers and define $f_q(b)=(1/\pi_q(b))\sum_{p\in P_q(b)} r_p(b)/p$. With these notations a certain number of problems are raised and assertions are made (with proofs). Proposition 1: For $\alpha\geq\beta>0$, the limit $\Phi_{\alpha,\beta}(t)$ exists. Proposition 2: For $\alpha\geq\beta>0$, $\lim_{x\to\infty}(\pi(x^\alpha))^{-1}\sum_{p\leq x^\alpha}\{xp^{-1/\beta}\}$ exists. Lemma: For $\alpha>0$, and integer $r$,

$$(\pi(a^\alpha))^{-1}\sum_{p\leq a^\alpha}\{a/p^r\} = (\pi(a^\alpha))^{-1}\sum_{p\leq a^\alpha}(a_{p,r-1}/p)+o(1).$$

In case $\alpha\geq 1/r$, this answers affirmatively Problem 1: Does $\lim_{a\to\infty}(\pi(a^\alpha))^{-1}\sum_{p\leq a^\alpha}(a_{p,r-1}/p)$ exist? Problem 2: If $\beta>\alpha>0$, does the limit $\Phi_{\alpha,\beta}(t)$ exist? This problem is left unanswered. An affirmative answer would solve Problem 1 for $\alpha<1/r$. It is shown that $\Phi_{\alpha,\alpha}(t)=\sum_{n=1}^\infty(n^{-\alpha}-(n+t)^{-\alpha})$, that $\lim_{x\to\infty}(\pi(x^\alpha))^{-1}\sum_{p\leq x^\alpha}\{xp^{-1/\alpha}\}=1-\int_0^1\Phi_{\alpha,\alpha}(t)\,dt$ and that, for $\alpha>\beta$, the corresponding limit exists and equals zero, while $\lim_{x\to\infty}(\pi(x^\alpha))^{-1}N_{\alpha,\beta}(x,t)=1$ if $t>0$ and $=0$ if $t=0$. The particular case $\alpha=\frac{1}{2}$, $\beta=1$ of Problem 2 is discussed, but not solved. For $r>1$, $\ln\varphi_r(a)=-a\zeta'(r)/\zeta(r)+(r/(1-r)+\int_0^1\Phi_{1/r,1/r}(t)\,dt)a^{1/r}+o(a^{1/r})$. For $r=1$,

$$\lim_{a\to\infty}\sum_{p\leq a}(a_{p,0}/p) = 1-C \quad (C=\text{Euler constant}).$$

Problem 1′: Does $\lim_{b\to\infty}(\pi(b))^{-1}\sum_{p\leq b}(b_p'/p)$ exist? Does $\lim_{b\to\infty, b\notin B_q}(\pi(b))^{-1}\sum_{p\in P_q(b)}(r_p(b)/p)$ exist? (No, if $q=2$.) The author quotes numerical work by Ignacio Canales, who computed $f_q(b)$ for $q=3$ and $a\leq 345$. {It is not always easy to understand exactly what the author wants to assert, nor the connection between the different problems raised. Some questions seem to be pursued only up to the point where it becomes clear that they can be solved. So, e.g., combining several statements of the paper and doing some computing, it would seem that the limit discussed in Problem 1 is zero for $r>1/\alpha$, equals

$$1-\sum_{n=1}^\infty((n+1)^\alpha(1-\alpha/(n+1))-n^\alpha)/((1-\alpha)n^\alpha(n+1)^{\alpha-1})$$

for $r=1/\alpha$ (if $1/\alpha$ is an integer) and is not known to exist for $r<1/\alpha$. These statements, however, are nowhere to be found in the paper. The reviewer was unable to follow most of the arguments offered as proofs.}

*E. Grosswald* (Philadelphia, Pa.)

## N56-36 (43# 171)

**Sitaramachandra Rao, R.; Suryanarayana, D.**

**The number of pairs of integers with L.C.M. $\leq x$.**

*Arch. Math.* (*Basel*) **21** (1970), 490–497.

Let $\theta(x)$ denote the number of ordered pairs of integers $a$ and $b$ with least common multiple less than or equal to $x$. The authors improve the error term $E(x)$ for $\theta(x)$ shown by H. Jager [Nederl. Akad. Wetensch. Proc. Ser. A **65** (1962), 346–350; MR **26** #6141] to be $O(x^{1/2+\varepsilon})$, where $\varepsilon>0$. In this paper $E(x)$ is proved to be $O(x^{1/2}\delta(x))$, where $\delta(x)=\exp\{-A\log^{3/5}x(\log\log x)^{-1/5}\}$ and $A$ is a positive constant. Beginning from $\sum_{n\leq x}\mu(n)=O(x\delta(x))$, the authors use partial summation to evaluate $\sum_{n\leq x}\mu(n)/n^s$, $\sum_{n\leq x}(\mu(n)\log n)/n^s$ and $\sum_{n\leq x}(\mu(n)\log^2 n)/n^s$. Since $(\theta x)=\sum_{d^2\delta\leq x}\mu(d)\tau_3(\delta)$, where $\tau_3(n)$ denotes the number of ordered triads of positive integers $a, b, c$ such that $abc=n$; and using the known sum for $\sum_{n\leq x}\tau_3(n)$, the value of $\theta(x)$

may be calculated. On the assumption of the Riemann hypothesis, there is a further improvement in $E(x)$.

*E. M. Horadam* (Armidale)

Citations: MR 26# 6141 = N56-15.

## N56-37 (43# 3225)

**Olivier, Michel**

**Sur le développement en base $g$ des nombres premiers.**

*C. R. Acad. Sci. Paris Sér. A-B* **272** (1971), A937–A939.

Let $n=\sum_{i=0}^{t} a_i g^i$, $0\leqq a_i<g$, and $s_g(n)=\sum_{i=1}^{t} a_i$. The author outlines the proof of the following theorem: Suppose that $m>2$, $g>2$, $p$ is a prime and $(m, g-1)=1$, and denote by $T_j(x, g, m)$ the number of primes $p<x$ for which $s_g(p)\equiv j \pmod m$; then $T_j(x, g, m)=\pi(x)/m+o(x^{\lambda+\varepsilon})$, where $\lambda=(1/(2\log g))(\log g \sin(\pi/(2m))-\log\sin(\pi/(2mg)))$.

Several related results are stated.

*P. Erdős* (Waterloo, Ont.)

## N56-38 (43# 7406)

**Erdős, P.; Guy, R. K.**

**Distinct distances between lattice points.**

*Elem. Math.* **25** (1970), 121–123.

The authors investigate how many points $(x_i, y_i)$, $1\leqq i\leqq k$, with integer coordinates $0<x_i, y_i\leqq n$, may be chosen with all mutual distances distinct. By means of a construction they show that $k>n^{2/3-\varepsilon}$ for any $\varepsilon>0$ and sufficiently large $n$. Lower and upper bounds for $k$ are also given in the case of $d$ dimensions. Some open problems are presented, as well as the conjectures $k<c_4 n^{2/3}(\log n)^{1/6}$ $(d=2)$ and $k<c_8 d^{2/3} n^{2/3}(\log n)^{1/3}$ $(d\geqq 3)$, $c_4$ and $c_8$ being positive constants.

*L. Beran* (Prague)

## N56-39 (44# 6627a; 44# 6627b)

**Hall, R. R.**

**On the probability that $n$ and $f(n)$ are relatively prime. II.**

*Acta Arith.* **19** (1971), 175–184.

**Hall, R. R.**

**Corrigendum to the paper "On the probability that $n$ and $f(n)$ are relatively prime".**

*Acta Arith.* **19** (1971), 203–204.

The author calls an integer-valued function $g$ a pseudo-polynomial if $g(n+k)\equiv g(n) \pmod k$ for all $n$ and $k$. For such $g$ and for each prime $p$ define $B(p)$ as the maximum number of solutions of the congruence $g(x)\equiv b \pmod p$, for $0\leqq b\leqq p-1$, and suppose that $g$ satisfies the following conditions: (i) for each square-free $q$ there exists an $a$, prime to $q$, for which $g(a)\not\equiv 0 \pmod q$; (ii) the series $\sum_p p^{-1}(B(p)/p)^{1/2}$ is convergent; and (iii) $\log(1+|g(n)|)=O(\exp(A\log n/\log_3 n))$. Put $f(n)=\sum_{p|n} g(p)$. The author shows that there exists an absolute constant $C$ such that

$$\sum_{n<x,(n,f(n))=1} 1 = 6x/\pi^2+O(x\sum_{p\geqq C\log_3 x} p^{-1}(B(p)/p)^{1/2}+x/\sqrt{\log_3 x}).$$

He constructs a pseudo-polynomial that is not a polynomial satisfying (i) and (ii); however, no such function is known that also satisfies (iii).

The proof of Lemma 2 is incorrect, and an alternative proof of the theorem, independent of the lemma, is given in the Corrigendum.

This generalizes a theorem proved in Part I [same Acta **17** (1970), 169–183; MR **42** #3047].

*W. J. LeVeque* (Claremont, Calif.)

Citations: MR 42# 3047 = N56-32.

# N60 DISTRIBUTION FUNCTIONS ASSOCIATED WITH ADDITIVE AND POSITIVE MULTIPLICATIVE FUNCTIONS

See also Section A32.

See also reviews A26-90, A52-68, B48-17, L99-7, L99-8, M15-1, M20-15, M55-72, N04-3, N08-34, N12-47, N24-15, N24-23, N24-24, N24-81, N28-14, N28-17, N28-53, N28-62, N28-76, N36-37, N36-68, N36-72, N48-23, N52-4, N52-34, N52-46, N56-26, N64-16, N64-37, N80-30, N80-43, N80-56, P48-5, P48-6, P48-20, P80-4, P80-5, Q15-4, Q15-7, Q15-8, Q15-15, Q15-17, Q15-21, Q20-10, R46-2, Z02-4, Z10-10.

## N60-1 (1, 40c)

**Erdös, Paul and Wintner, Aurel. Additive arithmetical functions and statistical independence.** Amer. J. Math. 61, 713–721 (1939).

A real arithmetical function $f(n)$ (that is, a function defined for $n=1, 2, \cdots$) is called additive if $f(n_1n_2)=f(n_1)+f(n_2)$ whenever $(n_1, n_2)=1$. If there exists a monotone function $\sigma=\sigma(x)$, $-\infty<x<+\infty$, satisfying the boundary conditions $\sigma(-\infty)=0$, $\sigma(+\infty)=1$, such that for any continuity point of $\sigma(x)$ the set of $n$-values at which $f(n)<x$ has a relative density represented by $\sigma(x)$, then $f$ is said to have an asymptotic distribution function $\sigma$. The problem of finding conditions for the existence of $\sigma(x)$ has been treated by Schoenberg and Davenport by statistical methods (moments and Fourier transforms) and by Erdös by elementary methods. The present paper contains a complete solution of this problem: (i) Placing $y^+=y$ or $y^+=1$ according as $|y|<1$ or $|y|\geqq 1$, a necessary and sufficient condition for the existence of $\sigma(x)$ is the convergence of the two series $\sum f^+(p)/p$ and $\sum f^+(p)^2/p$, where the summation is over all primes $p$. The sufficiency of this condition had already been proved by Erdös; its necessity also follows by elementary considerations. An additive arithmetical function always satisfies the condition $f(1)=0$; it is uniquely determined by its values on prime powers, and these values may be arbitrarily chosen. Denoting by $f^{(k)}(n)$ the additive function which coincides with $f(n)$ on the powers of the $k$th prime $p_k$ and is zero on all other prime powers, one has $f(n)=\sum_{k=1}^{\infty} f^{(k)}(n)$. Evidently every function $f^{(k)}(n)$ possesses an asymptotic distribution function $\sigma^{(k)}=\sigma^{(k)}(x)$, namely the step function which has at $x=f(p_k{}^l)$ the jump $p_k{}^{-l}-p_k{}^{-(l+1)}$. It is also easily seen that, for every $k$, the additive function $f_k(n)=\sum_{j=1}^{k} f^{(j)}(n)$ possesses an asymptotic distribution function $\sigma_k=\sigma_k(x)$, which is the convolution $\sigma_k=\sigma^{(1)}*\cdots*\sigma^{(k)}$. Combining these facts with known results, one is led to the following theorems: (ii) A necessary and sufficient condition for the existence of $\sigma(x)$ is that $f_k(n)$ converges to $f(n)$ in relative measure, in which case $\sigma_k\to\sigma$. (iii) A necessary and sufficient condition for the existence of $\sigma(x)$ is that the infinite convolution $\sigma^{(1)}*\sigma^{(2)}*\cdots$ is convergent, in which case $\sigma^{(1)}*\sigma^{(2)}*\cdots=\sigma$. (iv) The function $\sigma(x)$ is, when it exists, either a step function, or singular, or absolutely continuous. (v) It is a step function if and only if the series $\sum_{f(p)\neq 0}(1/p)$ is convergent. For results regarding the two other cases see the following paper. (vi) If $\sigma(x)$ exists, its spectrum is the closure of the set of values of $f(n)$.

*B. Jessen* (Copenhagen).

Referred to in N36-38, N36-72, N60-8, N60-51, N60-59, N60-69, N60-83, N60-95.

**N60-2** **(1, 41a)**

**Erdös, Paul. On the smoothness of the asymptotic distribution of additive arithmetical functions.** Amer. J. Math. **61**, 722–725 (1939).

Let $f(n)$ be an additive arithmetical function which possesses an asymptotic distribution function $\sigma=\sigma(x)$; as shown in the preceding paper, $\sigma(x)$ is either a step function, or singular, or absolutely continuous, and it is a step function if and only if the series $\sum_{f(p)\neq 0}(1/p)$ is convergent. The author now discusses certain extreme cases of functions $f(n)$ with continuous $\sigma(x)$ in which it is possible to distinguish between singular and absolutely continuous behavior of $\sigma(x)$. Let $f(p^l)=f(p)$ for all $p$ and $l$. Sections 1 and 2 depend on estimates of the Fourier transform of $\sigma(x)$, which is given by

$$L(u)=\int_{-\infty}^{+\infty} e^{iux}d\sigma(x)=\Pi\left(1-\frac{1-\exp(if(p)u)}{p}\right).$$

If $f(p)=(-1)^{(p-1)/2}(\log\log p)^{-\alpha}$ $(\alpha>\frac{1}{2})$, a simple application of Merten's result

$$\prod_{p<t}(1-1/p)\backsim e^{-\gamma}/\log t$$

leads to an estimate $L(u)=O(\exp-C|u|^{1/\alpha})$ for a positive constant $C$; hence $\sigma(x)$ may be continued to an entire function $\sigma(z)=\sigma(x+iy)$ if $\frac{1}{2}<\alpha<1$, to a function regular at least in the strip $|y|<C$ if $\alpha=1$, and has at least derivatives of arbitrarily high order if $\alpha>1$. If $f(p)=1/\log p$, one finds $L(u)=O(|u|^{-\frac{1}{2}-\epsilon})$ for some $\epsilon>0$; by Plancherel's theorem this implies the absolute continuity of $\sigma(x)$. If $f(p)=2^{-p}$, one finds $L(u)\neq o(|u|)$; hence $\sigma(x)$ is singular. In section 3 it is shown by elementary considerations that, if $f(p)=O(p^{-c})$ for some $c>0$, then $\sigma(x)$ is singular. This result is particularly interesting, since it contains the case $f(n)=\log n/\varphi(n)$, where $\varphi(n)$ is Euler's function. It may be mentioned that the assumption $f(p^l)=f(p)$ for all $p$ and $l$ is not necessary, since the character of $\sigma(x)$ depends only on the values of $f(n)$ on the primes. *B. Jessen.*

**N60-3** **(2, 42b)**

**Hartman, Philip and Wintner, Aurel. On the standard deviations of additive arithmetical functions.** Amer. J. Math. **62**, 743–752 (1940).

The existence of an asymptotic distribution function is in general not sufficient to insure almost periodicity. However, in the case of arithmetical functions this is enough. The authors prove that an additive function $f(n)$ is almost periodic $(B^2)$ if and only if its asymptotic distribution function possesses a second moment

$$\int_{-\infty}^{\infty} x^2 d\sigma(x)<\infty.$$

*S. Bochner* (Princeton, N. J.).

**N60-4** **(2, 42c)**

**Erdös, P. and Kac, M. The Gaussian law of errors in the theory of additive number theoretic functions.** Amer. J. Math. **62**, 738–742 (1940).

If an arithmetical function satisfies $f(m)+f(n)=f(mn)$ for $(m, n)=1$ and $f(p^\alpha)=f(p)$, $|f(p)|\leqq 1$ for all prime numbers $p$, put

$$A_n=\sum_{p<n} p^{-1}f(p),\quad B_n^2=\sum_{p<n} p^{-1}f^2(p).$$

Suppose that $B_n\to\infty$ as $n\to\infty$. If $K_n$ denotes, for a real $\omega$, the number of integers $m$ between $l$ and $n$ for which $f(m)<A_n+\omega\sqrt{2}B_n$, then

$$\lim_{n\to\infty}\frac{K_n}{n}=\pi^{-\frac{1}{2}}\int_{-\infty}^{+\infty}\exp(-u^2)du.$$

The analogy of this theorem to a classical statistical limit theorem is obvious. The proof consists in the justification of the interchange of two limiting processes. The one is $n\to\infty$ of the theorem; the other consists in letting $l\to\infty$ in the case when only the first $l$ primes are considered. The interchange is based on some of the deeper "elementary" arithmetical methods, in particular on a method of Vigo Brun's classical memoir concerning the sieve of Eratosthenes.

*E. R. van Kampen* (Baltimore, Md.).

Referred to in N56-26, N60-5, N60-7, N60-9, N60-13, N60-14, N60-15, N60-18, N60-20, N60-24, N60-26, N60-27, N60-28, N60-31, N60-35, N60-42, N60-63, N60-74, N60-77, P48-6.

**N60-5** **(3, 69e)**

**Kac, M. Note on the distribution of values of the arithmetic function** $d(m)$. Bull. Amer. Math. Soc. **47**, 815–817 (1941).

The author proves the following theorem: Denote by $r_n(\omega)$ the number of integers $m\leqq n$ for which

$$d(m)\leqq 2^{\log\log n+\omega(2\log\log n)^{\frac{1}{2}}}$$

($d(m)$ denotes the number of divisors of $m$). Then

$$\lim_{n\to\infty} r_n(\omega)/n=\pi^{-\frac{1}{2}}\int_{-\infty}^{\omega} e^{-u^2}du.$$

The proof follows from a joint result of the author and reviewer [Amer. J. Math. **62**, 738–742 (1940); cf. these Rev. **2**, 42]. *P. Erdös* (Philadelphia, Pa.).

Citations: MR 2, 42c = N60-4.

Referred to in N60-41.

**N60-6** **(3, 271b)**

**Wintner, Aurel. The distribution of primes.** Duke Math. J. **9**, 425–430 (1942).

Let $f(n)$ be an additive arithmetical function such that, for every prime $p$, (a) $f(p)=1$, (b) $f(p^k)>0$ $(k=2, 3, \cdots)$. Furthermore, let $f_m(x)$ denote the number of integers $j<x$ for which $f(j)=m$. The author proves the asymptotic relationship

$$f_m(x)\sim\frac{x(\log x)^{-1}(\log\log x)^{m-1}}{(m-1)!},\quad m=1, 2, \cdots.$$

The result is first approached heuristically by means of the Poisson probability distribution and then proved rigorously using the prime number theorem and some of its consequences. *M. Kac* (Ithaca, N. Y.).

Referred to in Z02-4.

**N60-7** **(7, 416c)**

**Erdös, P. On the distribution function of additive functions.** Ann. of Math. (2) **47**, 1–20 (1946).

Let $f(n)$ be an additive function of the positive integer $n$, that is, $f(m_1m_2)=f(m_1)+f(m_2)$ if $(m_1, m_2)=1$. Let $p$ be an arbitrary prime and let $f'(p)=f(p)$ if $|f(p)|\leqq 1$ and $f'(p)=1$ otherwise. The author shows that, if $\sum(f'(p))^2/p=\infty$ and if $f(p)\to 0$ as $p\to\infty$, then the sequence $f(n)-[f(n)]$ $n=1, 2, \cdots$, is equidistributed on the interval $[0, 1]$. The methods are similar to those used by Erdös and Kac [Amer. J. Math. **62**, 738–742 (1940); these Rev. **2**, 42] and depend on a strengthening of the central limit theorem due to Berry [Trans. Amer. Math. Soc. **49**, 122–136 (1941); these Rev. **2**, 228].

Most of the other theorems in the paper depend on the following result. There exists a constant $c$ such that, if $f^+(n)$ is defined by $f^+(n)=f(n)-c\log n$, then $\sum(f^{+\prime}(p))^2/p<\infty$ if and only if there exist two positive constants $c_1$, $c_2$ such that, for infinitely many $n$, there are integers $a_1<a_2<\cdots<a_n(<n)$ for which $|f(a_i)-f(a_j)|<c_1$ and $x>c_2n$. The proof of "only if" depends on the device of estimating $\sum_{m=1}^{\infty}(f(m))^2$ by splitting the corresponding double sum at

$\sqrt{n}$. The proof of "if" is more difficult and depends on methods used by Turán [J. London Math. Soc. **11**, 125–133 (1936)] and by Erdös [J. London Math. Soc. **12**, 9–10 (1937)]. This theorem leads to the following characterizations of the additive function $f(n)=c\log n$: $f(n)=c\log n$ if and only if $f(n+1)\geqq f(n)$ holds for all $n$; also, if and only if $f(n+1)-f(n)\to 0$ as $n\to\infty$. The author makes several conjectures along these lines. He also deduces, from the main theorem, a generalization of his theorem concerning the continuity of the asymptotic distribution of additive functions [J. London Math. Soc. **13**, 119–127 (1938), in particular, p. 121]. If $\sum_{f(p)\neq 0}1/p=\infty$ and if $a_1<a_2<\cdots<a_x\leqq n$ are integers such that $|f(a_i)-f(a_j)|<\epsilon$, then $x<\delta n$, where $\delta=\delta(\epsilon)\to 0$ as $\epsilon\to 0$.

The paper contains other related theorems. A number of annoying misprints occur: the statement of theorem II should involve $\phi(m)$, not $f(m)$; the statement "$\delta\to 0$ as $\epsilon\to 0$" should be included in theorem IV; $\sum_p(f^{+\prime}(p))^2/p$ should replace $\sum_p(f^{+\prime}(p)/p)^2$ in theorem V; lemma 7 is not accurately stated, etc. *P. Hartman* (Flushing, N. Y.).

Citations: MR 2, 42c = N60-4.

Referred to in K30-20, N36-30, N36-39, N60-15, N60-37, N64-3, N64-21, N64-23, N64-24, N64-29, N64-33, N64-34, N64-36, N64-40, N64-44, N64-45, N64-46, N64-47.

## N60-8 (7, 507g)

**Erdös, P. Some remarks about additive and multiplicative functions.** Bull. Amer. Math. Soc. **52**, 527–537 (1946).

It is known that the distribution function $f_1(x)$ of the multiplicative number-theoretic function $n/\phi(n)$ is purely singular and has as its spectrum the half-axis $1\leqq x\leqq\infty$. The author obtains sharp asymptotic inequalities for the distribution function $f_1(x)$ at the ends of the spectrum $x=1$ and $x=\infty$. It is also shown that, if $g(n)$ is any function such that $\log\log\log n=o(g(n))$, $n\to\infty$, then

$$\sum_{m=n}^{n+g(n)}\phi(m)/m=(1+o(1))6g(n)/\pi^2$$

and that the number of integers $m$ between $n$ and $n+g(n)$ for which $m/\phi(m)\leqq x$ is equal to $(1+o(1))g(n)f_1(x)$. These results do not hold if $\log\log\log n\neq o(g(n))$. Similar theorems are stated concerning the distribution of the function $\sigma(n)/n$. The methods of proof are direct counting processes depending on elementary estimates.

The author states the following theorem. Let $f(n)$ be an additive function possessing an asymptotic distribution function $F(x)$. Let $|f(p^k)|\leqq C$. Then, for any $c>0$, $1-F(x)<\exp(-cx)$ for sufficiently large $x$. However, it seems to the reviewer that in the proof [cf. the fifth formula line on p. 536] the assumption $f(p^k)\geqq 0$ is implicitly used. The proof of this theorem is made to depend on the following result. Let $g(n)\geqq 0$ be a multiplicative function. Then $g(n)$ possesses an asymptotic distribution function if and only if the two series $\sum_p(g(p)-1)'/p$, $\sum_p((g(p)-1)')^2/p$ converge, where $(g(p)-1)'$ denotes 1 or $g(p)-1$ according as $|g(p)-1|$ does or does not exceed 1. The proof of this theorem is reduced to the case of additive functions [Erdös and Wintner, Amer. J. Math. **61**, 713–721 (1939); these Rev. **1**, 40] by considering $\log g(n)$. This, however, supposes that $g(n)$ is positive, rather than nonnegative.

The paper also contains a discussion of the distribution of the numbers $b=b_i(n)$ defined by the equation $(p_i^{\alpha_i})^b=p_{i+1}^{\alpha_{i+1}}$, where $n=p_1^{\alpha_1}p_2^{\alpha_2}\cdots p_k^{\alpha_k}$, $p_1^{\alpha_1}<p_2^{\alpha_2}<\cdots<p_k^{\alpha_k}$. *P. Hartman* (Baltimore, Md.).

Citations: MR 1, 40c = N60-1.

## N60-9 (11, 83i)

**LeVeque, Wm. J. On the size of certain number-theoretic functions.** Trans. Amer. Math. Soc. 66, 440–463 (1949).

The major results of this paper are the following. (I) Let $d(m)$ and $\nu(m)$ denote the number of divisors of $m$ and the number of distinct prime divisors of $m$, respectively; let $\omega$ be a real number. The number of positive integers $m\leqq n$ for which $d(m)<2^{e(n)}$, $e(n)=\log_2 n+\omega(\log_2 n)^{\frac{1}{2}}$, or for which $\nu(m)<e(n)$, is $nD(\omega)+O(n\log_3 n/(\log_2 n)^{\frac{1}{2}})$, where

$$D(\omega)=(2\pi)^{-\frac{1}{2}}\int_{-\infty}^{\omega}e^{-x^2/2}dx.$$

(II) Let $f(m)$ be a strongly additive function, that is, $f(mn)=f(m)+f(n)$ if $(m,n)=1$ and $f(p^\alpha)=f(p)$. Suppose that $|f(p)|\leqq 1$ for all primes $p$. Let $\sum_p f^2(p)/p=\infty$, and let $\omega_1$, $\omega_2$ be any real numbers. Then the number of positive integers $m\leqq n$ for which simultaneously $f(m)<A_n+\omega_1B_n$ and $f(m+1)<A_n+\omega_2B_n$, where

$$A_n=\sum_{p\leqq n}f(p)/p,\quad B_n^2=\sum_{p\leqq n}f^2(p)/p,$$

is $nD(\omega_1)D(\omega_2)+o(n)$. This implies a result stated without proof by Erdös [Ann. of Math. (2) **47**, 1–20 (1946); these Rev. **7**, 416]. (III) The number of $m\leqq n$ for which $d(m)<2^{f(n)}d(m+1)$, $f(n)=\omega(2\log_2 n)^{\frac{1}{2}}$, or for which $\nu(m)<\nu(m+1)+f(n)$ is $nD(\omega)+o(n)$. These theorems are extensions in various directions of results obtained by Erdös and Kac [Amer. J. Math. **62**, 738–742 (1940); these Rev. **2**, 42] and are derived by similar methods. The principal tools are the central limit theorem from the theory of probability and the Viggo Brun sieve method. Improvements in error terms are obtained by using a hitherto unpublished theorem of J. B. Rosser and W. J. Harrington which states a complicated result obtained by the use of Brun's method. *A. L. Whiteman* (Los Angeles, Calif.).

Citations: MR 2, 42c = N60-4.

Referred to in N60-15, N60-21, N60-31, N60-35, N60-36, N60-41, N60-42.

## N60-10 (11, 161b)

**Kac, M. Probability methods in some problems of analysis and number theory.** Bull. Amer. Math. Soc. **55**, 641–665 (1949).

Report on recent literature. Part I reviews problems on gap series, e.g., $\sum_1^\infty c_k\sin(2\pi n_k t)$, $n_{k+1}/n_k>q>1$, which show, in many respects, the same behaviour as the Rademacher series $\sum_1^\infty c_n r_n(t)$, $r_n(t)=\operatorname{sgn}\sin(2^n\pi t)$. In the latter case the functions $r_n(t)$ are statistically independent, so that probabilistic methods can be applied immediately. Some of the results and methods can be transferred to the general gap series. Part II reviews papers of Erdös, Kac and others on additive functions $f(n)$ $(n=1,2,\cdots)$ (which satisfy $f(mn)=f(m)+f(n)$ whenever $(m,n)=1$). The Hardy-Ramanujan theorem (almost every integer $m$ has about $\log\log m$ prime factors) appears to be a legitimate application of the law of large numbers. After that the problem is considered whether the central limit theorem of probability may be applied. Instead of $\nu(n)$ (the number of prime divisors of $n$) general additive functions are considered also. Finally the problem of which additive functions possess a distribution function is discussed. *N. G. de Bruijn.*

Referred to in N60-11, N60-13, N60-18, N60-23, Q15-4.

## N60-11 (15, 201f)

**Delange, Hubert. Sur le nombre des diviseurs premiers de $n$.** C. R. Acad. Sci. Paris **237**, 542–544 (1953).

The author proves that the values of

$$(\omega(n)-\log\log n)/(\log\log n)^{\frac{1}{2}},$$

where $\omega(n)$ is the number of different prime divisors of $n$, are normally distributed. His proof depends on estimates for the moments $S_r(x)=\sum_{n\le x}(\omega(n)-\log\log n)^r$. To this end the author considers $\prod_r(x)=\sum_{k\le x, k\varepsilon S}k^{-1}$, where $S$ is the set of all products of $r$ different primes. The latter sum can be estimated by using a tauberian theorem proved in a previous paper [same C. R. **232**, 589–591 (1951); these Rev. **12**, 497].

The author seems not to be acquainted with a paper of Erdös and Kac [Amer. J. Math. **62**, 738–742 (1940); these Rev. **2**, 42], where the same result was obtained from a general theorem on the distribution of the values of additive number-theoretic functions. He also overlooked Kac's report on probability methods in analysis and number theory [Bull. Amer. Math. Soc. **55**, 641–665 (1949); these Rev. **11**, 161], where several aspects of the present problem were discussed, and the idea to use the moments was suggested.

*N. G. de Bruijn* (Amsterdam).

Citations: MR 11, 161b = N60-10; MR 12, 497d = M45-14.

Referred to in N60-19, N60-36.

## N60-12 (16, 448f)

**Erdös, Paul, and Shapiro, H. N. The existence of a distribution function for an error term related to the Euler function.** Canad. J. Math. 7, 63–75 (1955).

If

$$H(x)=\sum_{n\le x}\frac{\phi(n)}{n}-\frac{6}{\pi^2}x,$$

where $\phi(n)$ is the number of positive integers not exceeding $n$ and relatively prime to $n$, the authors prove that $H(x)$ possesses a continuous distribution function. An essential tool in the proof is the estimate

$$\int_1^x H^2(u)du\sim\frac{x}{2\pi^2}$$

due to the reviewer [Math. Z. **35**, 279–299 (1932)].

*S. Chowla* (Boulder, Colo.).

## N60-13 (16, 569g)

**Halberstam, H. On the distribution of additive number-theoretic functions.** J. London Math. Soc. **30**, 43–53 (1955).

Let $f(n)$ be an additive function. Put

$$A_n=\sum_{p<n}\frac{f(p)}{p},\quad B_n=\sum_{p<n}\frac{(f(p))^2}{p}.$$

Assume that $|f(p)|<c$ and that $B_n\to\infty$ as $n\to\infty$. The author proves that for every positive integer $k$

$$(1)\quad \lim_{n=\infty}\sum_{m=1}^{n}(f(m)-A_n)^k/nB_n^{k/2}=(2\pi)^{-1/2}\int_{-\infty}^{\infty}x^ke^{-x^2/2}dx.$$

The proof is elementary but fairly complicated. The author then deduces from (1) the theorem of Erdös and Kac [Amer. J. Math. **62**, 738–742 (1940); MR **2**, 42] without using the central-limit theorem and Brun's method, this fulfills a desideratum of Kac [Bull. Amer. Math. Soc. **55**, 641–665 (1949); MR **11**, 161]. *P. Erdös.*

Citations: MR 2, 42c = N60-4; MR 11, 161b = N60-10.

Referred to in N60-14, N60-15, N60-18, N60-19, N60-21, N60-24, N60-26, N60-28, N60-77.

## N60-14 (17, 239d)

**Kubilyus, I. P. An analogue of A. N. Kolmogorov's theorem on Markov processes in the theory of prime numbers.** Dokl. Akad. Nauk SSSR (N.S.) **103** (1955), 361–363. (Russian)

Let $f(p)$, defined on the sequence of primes $p$, be any function satisfying: (i) $B_u^2=\sum_{p\le u}f^2(p)/p\to\infty$, (ii) $\Lambda_u=\max_{p\le u}|f(p)|=o(B_u)$, as $u\to\infty$. Put $A_u=\sum_{p\le u}f(p)/p$ and $f_u(m)=\sum_{p|m, p\le u}f(p)$. The distribution of values of $f_m(m)$ has been discussed by Erdös and Kac [Amer. J. Math. **62** (1940), 738–742; MR **2**, 42] and more recently by the reviewer [J. London Math. Soc. **30** (1955), 43–53; MR **16**, 569] under conditions less general than (i) and (ii), but the methods of both papers succeed also with (i) and (ii). Erdös and Kac grounded their method on the Central-Limit (or Liapounoff's) Theorem, and the author now derives from a generalization of this theorem by Kolmogorov [Izv. Akad. Nauk SSSR. Otd. Mat. Estest. Nauk (7) **1933**, 363–372] the following result about the distribution of values of the partial sums $f_u(m)$: Let $a(t)$, $b(t)$ be two real functions defined on (0, 1), possessing continuous first derivatives and satisfying $a(t)<0<b(t)$. Then the number of integers $m\le n$ satisfying the set of inequalities

$$a(B_p/B_n)<\{f_p(m)-A_p\}/B_n<b(B_p/B_n)\qquad(p=2, 3, 5, \cdots; p\le n),$$

and the number of integers $m\le n$ satisfying the set of inequalities

$$a(B_p/B_n)<\{f_p(m)-f_p(m+1)\}/(B_n\sqrt{2})<b(B_p/B_n)\qquad(p=2, 3, 5, \cdots; p\le n),$$

are, as $n\to\infty$, each equal to $nv(0, 0)+o(n)$, where $v(x, t)$ is that solution of the partial differential equation $\partial v/\partial t+\frac{1}{2}\partial^2v/\partial x^2=0$ for which $v(x, 1)=1$, $a(t)<x<b(t)$, $v\{a(t),x\}=0$, $0\le t<1$, $v\{b(t), x\}=0$, $0\le t<1$. An alternative expression for $v(0, 0)$ is stated. The proof is given in outline only.

*H. Halberstam* (Providence, R.I.).

Citations: MR 2, 42c = N60-4; MR 16, 569g = N60-13.

Referred to in N60-18.

## N60-15 (17, 461d)

**Halberstam, H. On the distribution of additive number-theoretic functions. II.** J. London Math. Soc. **31** (1956), 1–14.

Let $f$ be a function defined initially on the primes, and for $m$ and $n$ positive integers put

$$f(m)=\sum_{p|m}f(p),$$

$$A_n=\sum_{p<n}\frac{f(p)}{p},\quad B_n=\sum_{p<n}\frac{f^2(p)}{p}.$$

Erdös [Ann. of Math. (2) **47** (1946), 1–20; MR **7**, 416] pointed out that a method developed by him and Kac [Amer. J. Math. **62** (1940), 738–742; MR **2**, 42] could be used to prove the following theorem: Let $k_n(\omega_1, \omega_2)$ be the number of positive integers $m\le n$ for which simultaneously

$$f(m)<A_n+\omega_1B_n^{\frac{1}{2}},\quad f(m+1)<A_n+\omega_2B_n^{\frac{1}{2}},$$

and let $s_n(\omega)$ be the number of such integers for which

$$f(m)<f(m+1)+\omega(2B_n)^{\frac{1}{2}}.$$

Then if $|f(p)|\le 1$ for all $p$ and $B_n\to\infty$ with $n$,

$$\lim_{n\to\infty}n^{-1}k_n(\omega_1, \omega_2)=\phi(\omega_1)\phi(\omega_2),$$

$$\lim_{n\to\infty}n^{-1}s_n(\omega)=\phi(\omega),$$

where

$$\phi(\xi)=(2\pi)^{-\frac{1}{2}}\int_{-\infty}^{\xi}e^{-u^2/2}du.$$

The proof, using Brun's method and the central-limit theorem, was given by the reviewer [Trans. Amer. Math. Soc. **66** (1949), 440–463; MR **11,** 83]. In the present paper the author uses his method of moments [J. London Math. Soc. **30** (1955), 43–53; MR **16,** 569] to strengthen this theorem; the requirement $|f(p)|\leqq 1$ is replaced by $f(p)=o(B_p^{\frac{1}{2}})$.

The same method is used to show that the frequency of solutions $m\leqq n$ of the inequality $f(g(m))<A(n)+\omega(B(n))^{\frac{1}{2}}$ is also asymptotically normal; here $g$ is an irreducible polynomial with integral coefficients,

$$A(n)=\sum_{p<n}\frac{f(p)r(p)}{p},\quad B(n)=\sum_{p<n}\frac{f^2(p)r(p)}{p},$$

and $r(a)$ is the number of solutions of $g(m)\equiv 0 \pmod a$, $0\leqq m<a$. *W. J. LeVeque* (Ann Arbor, Mich.).

Citations: MR 2, 42c = N60-4; MR 7, 416c = N60-7; MR 11, 83i = N60-9; MR 16, 569g = N60-13.

Referred to in N60-17, N60-18, N60-21, N60-23, N60-63.

## N60-16 (17, 461e)

**Halberstam, H. On the distribution of additive number-theoretic functions. III.** J. London Math. Soc. **31** (1956), 14–27.

Let $f$ be an irreducible polynomial with integral coefficients, and let $\omega(m)$ be the number of distinct primes dividing $m$. Improving a result of Prachar [same J. **28** (1953), 236–239; MR **14,** 726], it is shown that

$$\sum_{p\leqq m}\omega(f(p))\sim\frac{n\log\log n}{\log n}$$

and the same method shows that for all but $o(n/\log n)$ primes $p\leqq n$, $\omega(f(p))\equiv\log\log n$. By a result on moments similar to those mentioned in the preceding review, a general theorem is proved which has the following as a special case: If $\varkappa_n(\vartheta)$ is the number of primes $p\leqq n$ for which

$$\omega(f(p))<\log\log n+\vartheta(\log\log n)^{\frac{1}{2}},$$

then

$$\lim_{n\to\infty}\frac{\varkappa_n(\vartheta)}{\pi(n)}=\phi(\vartheta).$$

The proof of this last theorem uses a deep result on primes in an arithmetic progression. *W. J. LeVeque.*

Citations: MR 14, 726e = N52-14.

Referred to in N60-17, N60-18, N60-21, N60-23, N60-63.

## N60-17 (17, 946d)

**Halberstam, H. Über additive zahlentheoretische Funktionen.** J. Reine Angew. Math. **195** (1955), 210–214 (1956).

An announcement of results whose proofs have already appeared [J. London Math. Soc. **31** (1956), 1–14, 14–27; MR **17,** 461].

*W. J. LeVeque* (Ann Arbor, Mich.).

Citations: MR 17, 461d = N60-15; MR 17, 461e = N60-16.

Referred to in N60-28.

## N60-18 (17, 588c)

**Kubilyus, I. P. Probability methods in number theory.** Vestnik Leningrad. Univ. **10** (1955), no. 11, 59–60. (Russian)

A real function $f(m)$, defined on the sequences of all natural numbers, is called strongly additive if (i) $f(mn)=f(m)+f(n)$, $(m,n)=1$, and (ii) $f(p^\alpha)=f(p)$, $p$ prime and $\alpha=2,3,\cdots$. Set $A_n=\sum_{p\leqq n}f(p)/p$, $B_n^2=\sum_{p\leqq n}f^2(p)/p$ and assume that (iii) $B_n\to\infty$ as $n\to\infty$ [see Erdös and Kac, Amer. J. Math. **62** (1940), 738–742; MR **2,** 42; Kac, Bull. Amer. Math. Soc. **55** (1949), 641–665; MR **11,** 161; Halberstam, J. London Math. Soc. **30** (1955), 43–53; **31** (1956), 1–14, 14–27; MR **16,** 569; **17,** 461]. The author states, without proof, the following theorem, of interest in that, to the reviewer's knowledge, it is the first published result of an "if and only if" nature about the distribution of strongly additive functions subject to condition (iii):

Assume that there exists a function $r(n)$ such that (iv) $B_{r(n)}=B_n(1+o(1))$, $\ln r(n)=o(\ln n)$. Then the number of positive integers $m\leqq n$ satisfying $f(m)<A_n+B_nx$ is equal to $nF(x)+o(n)$ at points of continuity of $F(x)$, where $F(x)$ is some distribution function, if and only if there exists a non-decreasing function $K(u)$ with variation one such that for all $u\neq 0$

$$B_n^{-2}\sum_{p\leqq n,\,f(p)\leqq B_nu}f^2(p)/p\to K(u),\quad n\to\infty.$$

If these conditions are satisfied, the characteristic function $\phi(t)$ corresponding to $F(x)$ is given by

$$\ln\phi(t)=\int_{-\infty}^{\infty}(e^{itu}-1-itu)u^{-2}dK(u).$$

Also stated is a corollary and a second theorem which, however, was already announced by the author in a preceding note [Dokl. Akad. Nauk SSSR (N.S.) **103** (1955), 361–363; MR **17,** 239].

If $f(p)=O(1)$ it is seen that (iv) is satisfied, that $K(u)=1$ if $u>0$ and 0 if $u<0$, $\ln\phi(t)=-\frac{1}{2}t^2$, and that the corresponding distribution is therefore normal. However, if $f(p)=o(B_p)$ (iv) may no longer be true, and thus the widest class of functions subject to (iii) hitherto discussed (see above ref.) is not covered by the present theorem.

*H. Halberstam* (Berkeley, Calif.).

Citations: MR 2, 42c = N60-4; MR 11, 161b = N60-10; MR 16, 569g = N60-13; MR 17, 239d = N60-14; MR 17, 461d = N60-15; MR 17, 461e = N60-16.

Referred to in N60-26.

## N60-19 (17, 946e)

**Delange, Hubert. Sur un théorème d'Erdös et Kac.** Acad. Roy. Belg. Bull. Cl. Sci. (5) **42** (1956), 130–144.

The author gives a new proof of the following theorem due to the reviewer [J. London Math. Soc. **30** (1955), 43–53; MR **16,** 569]: Let $f(m)$ be a real strongly additive function defined on the set of positive integers by the properties (i) $f(mn)=f(m)+f(n)$, $(m,n)=1$, (ii) $f(p^\alpha)=f(p)$, $p$ prime and $\alpha=2,3,\cdots$. Define $A_k(x)=\sum_{p<x}[f(p)]^k/p$ and assume that (iii) $A_2(x)\to\infty$ as $x\to\infty$, (iv) $f(p)=O(1)$. Then $\sum_{n\leqq x}[f(n)-A_1(x)]^q=(\mu_q+o(1))x[A_2(x)]^{q/2}$, where $\mu_q=(2\pi)^{-\frac{1}{2}}\int_{-\infty}^{\infty}t^qe^{-t^2/2}dt$. The author was the first to prove this theorem in the special case $f(p)=1$ [C. R. Acad. Sci. Paris **237** (1953), 542–544; MR **15,** 201], and in his present proof of the general result he gains, by introducing certain types of generating function, some simplicity and elegance in method, although he sacrifies the entirely elementary nature of the reviewer's proof.

The author also proves briefly that the theorem remains true even if (iv) is sharpened to (v) $f(p)=o([A_2(p)]^{\frac{1}{2}})$.

*H. Halberstam* (Exeter).

Citations: MR 15, 201f = N60-11; MR 16, 569g = N60-13.

Referred to in N60-24, N60-26.

## N60-20 (18, 113c)

**Shapiro, Harold N. Distribution functions of additive arithmetic functions.** Proc. Nat. Acad. Sci. U.S.A. **42** (1956), 426–430.

Let $f(m)$ be an additive arithmetic function, set $A_x=\sum_{p<x}f(p)/p$, $B_x^2=\sum_{p<x}f^2(p)/p$ ($p$ prime), and suppose that $B_x\to\infty$ as $x\to\infty$. The author proves that if, for any $\eta>0$,

$$(1)\qquad \sum_{p<n,\,|f(p)|>\eta B_n}f^2(p)/p=o(B_n^2)$$

as $n\to\infty$, the distribution of $(f(m)-A_n)/B_n$ $(m\leqq n)$ is asymptotically Gaussian; this sharpens a well-known theorem of Erdös and Kac [Amer. J. Math. **62** (1940), 738–742; MR **2**, 42]. He conjectures that (1) is also a necessary condition for the truth of the Erdös-Kac theorem. *H. Halberstam* (Exeter).

Citations: MR 2, 42c = N60-4.

Referred to in N60-26, N60-28.

## N60-21 (18, 563a)

**Tanaka, Minoru. On the number of prime factors of integers.** Jap. J. Math. **25** (1955), 1–20 (1956).

The author proves (among others) the following theorem: Let $f_i(x)$ $(1\leqq i\leqq k)$ be a set of non-constant polynomials which are pairwise relatively prime. Assume that $f_i(x)$ is the product of $r_i$ irreducible polynomials (multiple factors are counted only once). Let $E$ be any Jordan measurable set in $k$ dimensional space and $V(n)=\sum_{p|n}1$. $A(x;E)$ denotes the number of integers $n<x$ for which the point $(\mu_1(n), \mu_2(n), \cdots, \mu_k(n))$ belongs to $E$, where

$$\mu_i(n)=\frac{V(f_i(n))-r_i\log\log n}{\sqrt{(r_i\log\log n)}}.$$

Then

$$\lim_{x\to\infty}\frac{A(x;E)}{x}=\frac{1}{(2\pi)^{k/2}}\int_E\exp\left(-\tfrac{1}{2}\sum_{i=1}^{k}\mu_i^2\right)d\mu_1\cdots d\mu_k.$$

This generalizes previous results of Hardy-Ramanujan, Turán, Erdös-Kac, Delange and others [cf. also some recent results of Leveque, Trans. Amer. Math. Soc. **66** (1949), 440–463; MR **11**, 83; and Halberstam, J. London Math. Soc. **30** (1955), 43–53; **31** (1956), 1–14, 14–27; MR **16**, 569; **17**, 461].

The author discusses several interesting special cases of his theorem. *P. Erdös.*

Citations: MR 11, 83i = N60-9; MR 16, 569g = N60-13; MR 17, 461d = N60-15; MR 17, 461e = N60-16.

Referred to in N60-27, N60-32, N60-41, N60-84.

## N60-22 (19, 17b)

**Delange, Hubert. Sur la distribution des valeurs de certaines fonctions arithmétiques.** Colloque sur la Théorie des Nombres, Bruxelles, 1955, pp. 147–161. Georges Thone, Liège; Masson and Cie, Paris, 1956.

This lecture deals with distribution properties of the functions $\omega_E(n)$ and $\Omega_E(n)$, defined by a set $E$ of prime numbers in the following way: $\omega_E(n)=\sum_{p\in E, p|n}1$, $\Omega_E(n)=\sum_{p\in E, p|n}\lambda(n)$ ($\lambda(n)$ is the maximal $\lambda$ such that $p^\lambda|n$). It is assumed that the set $E$ has the property (H): There is a constant $\alpha$ $(0<\alpha\leqq 1)$ such that $\sum_{p\in E}p^{-s}+\alpha\log(s-1)$ is regular throughout the closed halfplane $\operatorname{Re}s\geqq 1$. For example, the set of all $p$ has the property (H), and so has the set of all $p$ in any given arithmetic progression. Using some of his work on Tauberian theorems [Ann. Sci. Ecole Norm. Sup. (3) **71** (1954), 213–242; MR **16**, 921], the author shows that the values of $\omega_E(n)$ are equally distributed over the residue classes mod $q$, for integer $q$. The same thing holds for $\Omega_E(n)$. Moreover, if $f$ and $g$ are functions $\omega$ (or $\Omega$) belonging to disjoint sets $E_1$ and $E_2$, both having property (H), then the residue classes of $f(n)$ mod $q$ and $g(n)$ mod $q$ are statistically independent. And, if only those $n$ are considered for which $f(n)$ equals a given integer $h$, then $g(n)$ is still equally distributed over the residue classes mod $q$. In some cases these results remain true if $n$ is assumed to run over all squarefree integers $>0$ instead of over all integers $>0$. In the proofs, a central role is played by sums $\sum_1^\infty z^{f(n)}n^{-s}$, where $z$ is a root of unity. [For details, the author refers to Ann. Sci. Ecole Norm. Sup. (3) **73** (1956), 15–74; MR **18**, 720.] It is conjectured that the condition (H) can be replaced by the more natural condition $\sum_{p\in E}p^{-1}=\infty$. *N. G. de Bruijn.*

Citations: MR 16, 921e = M45-24; MR 18, 720a = N24-28.

Referred to in K30-15, N60-29.

## N60-23 (19, 393d)

**Erdös, P. On additive arithmetical functions and applications of probability to number theory.** Proceedings of the International Congress of Mathematicians, 1954, Amsterdam, vol. III, pp. 13–19. Erven P. Noordhoff N.V., Groningen; North-Holland Publishing Co., Amsterdam, 1956. $7.00.

An additive function $f(n)$ is one defined for positive integers $n$ which takes real values and has the property that $f(mn)=f(m)+f(n)$ if $m$ and $n$ are relatively prime. The main problem discussed is that of the existence of a distribution function $\psi(c)$ such that the asymptotic density of the integers $n$ for which $f(n)<c$ exists and equals $\psi(c)$. Many other problems arise from this. The present survey is partly complementary to that of M. Kac [Bull. Amer. Math. Soc. **55** (1949), 641–665; MR **11**, 161]. Besides giving an account of the considerable body of knowledge now attained on the distribution problem and related problems, the author mentions many questions (both general and special) still awaiting an answer. Since 1954 further progress in the subject has been made by Kubilyus, whose article [Uspehi Mat. Nauk (N.S.) **11** (1956), no. 2(68), 31–66; MR **18**, 17] should be read in conjunction with that of Erdös. Some other recent contributions are by H. Delange [see the paper reviewed below], and H. Halberstam [J. London Math. Soc. **31** (1956), 1–14, 14–27; MR **17**, 461]. *H. Davenport.*

Citations: MR 11, 161b = N60-10; MR 17, 461d = N60-15; MR 17, 461e = N60-16; MR 18, 17d = Q15-4.

## N60-24 (19, 394a)

**Delange, Hubert. Sur les fonctions arithmétiques fortement additives.** C. R. Acad. Sci. Paris **244** (1957), 1307–1309.

Let $E$ be a set of positive integers of positive density $D(E)$, $f(n)$ a real strongly additive function defined on the positive integers, and define $A(f,x)=\sum_{p\leqq x}f(p)/p$, $B(f,x)=\{\sum_{p\leqq x}f^2(p)/p\}^{\frac{1}{2}}$ with $p$ prime. The author states that the 'moment' method, as developed by the reviewer [J. London Math. Soc. **30** (1955), 43–53; MR **16**, 569] and by the author himself [Acad. Roy. Belg. Bull. Cl. Sci. (5) **42** (1956), 130–144; MR **17**, 946, 1437], may be extended to prove the following asymptotic formulae. If $B(f,x)\to\infty$ as $x\to\infty$ and $f(p)=o(B(f,p))$ as $p\to\infty$, then, for each fixed integer $q\geqq 0$,

$$(*)\qquad \lim_{x\to\infty}x^{-1}\sum_{\substack{n_0\leqq n\leqq x\\ n\in E}}\left[\frac{f(n)-A(f,n)}{B(f,n)}\right]^q=D(E)\mu_q,$$

where $\mu_q$ is the $q$th moment of the Gaussian distribution, mean 0 and standard deviation 1, and $E$ can be any one of a number of different sets. For instance, $E$ may be an arithmetic progression, or it may be an arithmetic progression whose members obey the added condition that the number of prime factors of each member also lies in a certain arithmetic progression. For the latter case properties of Riemann's $\zeta$-function and Dirichlet's $L$-functions in the critical strip are required. Let $N_E(f,x,t)$ be the number of positive integers $n\leqq x$, $n\in E$, such that $f(n)\leqq A(f,x)+tB(f,x)$. The author points out that the mean value formulae (*) entail

$$\lim_{x\to\infty}\frac{1}{x}N_E(f,x,t)=D(E)(2\pi)^{-\frac{1}{2}}\int_{-\infty}^{t}e^{-\frac{1}{2}u^2}du$$

[cf. Erdös and Kac, Amer. J. Math. **62** (1940), 738–742; MR **2**, 42]. *H. Halberstam* (London).

**Citations: MR 2, 42c = N60-4; MR 16, 569g = N60-13; MR 17, 946e = N60-19.**

## N60-25 (19, 394b)

**Delange, Hubert. Sur les fonctions arithmétiques fortement additives.** C. R. Acad. Sci. Paris **244** (1957), 1604–1606.

The author states results which extend the theorems described in the preceding review to the simultaneous distribution of $m$ linearly independent strongly additive functions $f_i(n)$ $(i=1, 2, \cdots, m)$ with $n \in E$, where $E$ is either the set of all positive integers, or one of the sets described in the note reviewed above. *H. Halberstam.*

**Referred to in N60-65.**

## N60-26 (19, 394c)

**Delange, Hubert. Sur les fonctions arithmétiques fortement additives.** C. R. Acad. Sci. Paris **244** (1957), 2122–2124.

With the notation of the two preceding reviews, a recent theorem of Kubilyus [Vestnik Leningrad. Univ. **10** (1955), no. 11, 59–60; MR **17**, 588, but ignore last sentence of this review] states that if (i) $\lim_{x\to\infty} B(f, x) = +\infty$, (ii) for $\lambda>1$, $B(f, x^\lambda) \sim B(f, x)$ as $x\to\infty$, then setting

$$K_x(t) = B^{-2}(f, x) \sum_{\substack{p\leq x \\ f(p)\leq tB(f,x)}} f^2(p)/p,$$

there exists a distribution function $F$ such that

$$\lim_{x\to\infty} x^{-1}N(f, x, t) = F(t)$$

at all continuity points of $F$, if, and only if, there exists a function $K(t)$, non-decreasing in $(-\infty, \infty)$, with the property that $\lim_{x\to\infty} K_x(t) = K(t)$ at all continuity points of $K$. When this is the case, then for all real $t$,

$$\int_{-\infty}^{\infty} e^{itu} dF(u) = \exp\left\{\int_{-\infty}^{\infty} \frac{e^{itu}-1-itu}{u^2} dK(u)\right\}.$$

The theorem of Kubilyus generalises a well-known theorem of Erdös and Kac [Amer. J. Math. **62** (1940), 738–742; MR **2**, 42], and, indeed, contains as special cases all previous generalisations of the Erdös-Kac theorem. [See H. N. Shapiro, Proc. Nat. Acad. Sci. U.S.A. **42** (1956), 426–430; MR **18**, 113; Halberstam, J. London Math. Soc. **30** (1955), 43–53; MR **16**, 569; Delange, Acad. Roy. Belg. Bull. Cl. Sci. (5) **42** (1956), 130–144; MR **17**, 946, 1437.]

The author explains, without giving details, that one may replace the Vigo Brun method in the proof of Kubilyus' theorem by the moment method applied to a related strongly additive function. He further illustrates the effectiveness of the moment method in this subject by stating, without proof, that the mean value formulae of equation (*) [see the review second above] hold, subject to the conditions of Kubilyus' theorem and the one extra condition $f(p) = O(B(f, p))$ (and do not hold without some such extra condition), with $\mu_q$ equal to $\int_{-\infty}^{\infty} t^q dF(t)$. Thus the author's result stands in the same relation to Kubilyus' theorem as the reviewer's does to the Erdös-Kac theorem. *H. Halberstam* (London).

**Citations: MR 2, 42c = N60-4; MR 16, 569g = N60-13; MR 17, 588c = N60-18; MR 17, 946e = N60-19; MR 18, 113c = N60-20.**

## N60-27 (19, 636c)

**Tanaka, Minoru. On the number of prime factors of integers. II.** J. Math. Soc. Japan **9** (1957), 171–191.

[For Part I see Jap. J. Math. **25** (1955), 1–20; MR **18**, 563.] Let $\pi_1, \pi_2, \cdots, \pi_k$ be a family of disjoint subsets of primes, satisfying $\sum_{p\in\pi_i} 1/p = \infty$ for all $i$, $1\leq i\leq k$. Put

$$y_i(n) = \sum_{p\leq n,\, p\in\pi_i} 1/p, \quad \omega_i(n) = \sum_{p|n,\, p\in\pi_i} 1.$$

Define further $u_i(n) = (\omega_i(n) - y_i(n))/\sqrt{(y_i(n))}$. Then to each integer $n$ there corresponds a point

$$U(n) = (u_1(n), u_2(n), \cdots, u_k(n))$$

of $k$-dimensional space. Let $E$ be a Jordan-measurable set in $k$-dimensional space, and denote by $A(x, E)$ the number of integers $n\leq x$ for which $U(n)$ belongs to $E$. The author proves that

$$\lim_{x\to\infty} \frac{A(x, E)}{x} = (2\pi)^{-k/2} \int_E \exp(-\tfrac{1}{2} \sum_{i=1}^{k} u_i^2) du_1 \cdots du_k.$$

This generalizes a result of the reviewer and Kac [Amer. J. Math. **62** (1940), 738–742; MR **2**, 42; see also Part I, loc. cit.] *P. Erdös* (Toronto, Ont.).

**Citations: MR 2, 42c = N60-4; MR 18, 563a = N60-21.**
**Referred to in N60-32, N60-41.**

## N60-28 (19, 1163c)

**Delange, H.; and Halberstam, H. A note on additive functions.** Pacific J. Math. **7** (1957), 1551–1556.

Let $f(n)$ be an additive arithmetic function, and set

$$A_n = \sum_{p<n} f(p)/p, \quad B_n = \sum_{p<n} f^2(p)/p.$$

One of the problems concerning the distribution of values of additive arithmetic functions is the determination of conditions under which the distribution of

$$\frac{f(m) - A_n}{B_n^{\frac{1}{2}}}$$

is asymptotically Gaussian. This was proved first by Erdös and Kac [Amer. J. Math. **62** (1939), 738–742; MR **2**, 42] under the hypothesis

(1) $$f(p) = O(1).$$

The reviewer later derived this [Proc. Nat. Acad. Sci. U.S.A. **42** (1956), 426–430; MR **18**, 113] under the weaker assumption

(2) $$\lim_{n\to\infty} B_n^{-1} \sum_{\substack{p<n \\ |f(p)|>\varepsilon B_n^{1/2}}} \frac{f^2(p)}{p} = 0, \text{ for every } \varepsilon>0.$$

Delange [Acad. Roy. Belg. Bull. Cl. Sci. (5) **42** (1956), 130–144; MR **17**, 946] and Halberstam [J. London Math. Soc. **30** (1955), 43–53; MR **16**, 569] (independently), by means of moment calculations, had also derived the result under the assumption that

(3) $$f(p) = o(B_p^{\frac{1}{2}}).$$

More precisely, they derived that for each fixed integer $k\geq 1$,

(4) $$\lim_{n\to\infty} \frac{\sum_{m=1}^{n} (f(m) - A_n)^k}{nB_n^{k/2}} = (2\pi)^{-\frac{1}{2}} \int_{-\infty}^{\infty} \omega^k e^{-\frac{1}{2}\omega^2} d\omega.$$

In this paper, they show that (4) may be derived from (2) together with

(5) $$f(p) = O(B_p^{\frac{1}{2}}).$$

It is also shown that either (2) or (5) alone does not imply (4). *H. N. Shapiro* (New York, N.Y.).

**Citations: MR 2, 42c = N60-4; MR 16, 569g = N60-13; MR 17, 946d = N60-17; MR 18, 113c = N60-20.**

## N60-29 (19, 1164a)

**Delange, Hubert. Sur certaines fonctions arithmétiques.** C. R. Acad. Sci. Paris **245** (1957), 611–614.

Using some of his Tauberian theorems [Ann. Sci. Ecole Norm. Sup. (3) **73** (1956), 15–74; Colloque sur la Théorie des Nombres, Bruxelles, 1955, Thone, Liège, 1956, pp. 147–161; MR **18**, 720; **19**, 17] the author studies the distribution properties of the functions $\omega_E$ and $\Omega_E$, which are respectively defined by a set $E$ of prime numbers as the number of distinct prime factors and the total number of primes from $E$ in the positive integer $n$. It is assumed that $E$ is regular and of density $\alpha$, i.e., there exists a non-negative number $\alpha\leqq 1$ such that, for $\Re(s)\geqq 1$, $\sum_{p\in E} P^{-s}=\alpha\log(s-1)^{-1}+r(s)$, where $r(s)$ is a holomorphic function for $\Re(s)\geqq 1$. The set $E$ here is of the form: $E=E_1\cup E_2-E_3$, where (1) $E_1$ is the set, supposed infinite, of all primes belonging to a given arithmetical progression, or to the union of two or more given arithmetical progressions, (2) $E_2\cap E_1=\emptyset$ and $E_3\subset E_1$, and (3) the set $E_j$ ($j=2, 3$) is empty or finite or the series $\sum_{p\in E_j} P^{-\sigma}$ is convergent for $\sigma<1$. Denote by ($\Phi$) the family formed by all the sets of this form. Corresponding to the sets of the family ($\Phi$) we designate by ($\mathscr{F}$) the family formed by all functions $\omega_E$ and $\Omega_E$. In order to study the distribution of values of a function of the family ($\mathscr{F}$) the method is to evaluate the series $P_x(z)=\sum_{n\leq x, n\in A} z^{f(n)}$ ,where $z$ is a complex variable. Several asymptotic formulae are obtained by imposing various conditions on $f$ and the set $A$.

*S. Ikehara* (Tokyo).

Citations: MR 18, 720a = N24-28; MR 19, 17b = N60-22.

## N60-30 (19, 1164b)

**Delange, Hubert. Sur certaines fonctions arithmétiques.** C.R. Acad. Sci. Paris **245** (1957), 1197–1200.

This paper treats two functions simultaneously of the family ($\mathscr{F}$) (terminology same as in the preceding review). Let $f$ be one of the functions $\omega_{E_1}$ and $\Omega_{E_1}$, and $g$ one of the functions $\omega_{E_2}$ and $\Omega_{E_2}$, $E_1$ and $E_2$ being two disjoint sets of the family ($\Phi$). Let us denote by $\alpha$ and $\beta$ the respective densities of $E_1$ and $E_2$ with respect to the set of all prime numbers. If $A$ is the set of all positive integers, or set of squarefree integers, the author derives, when $x\to\infty$, a formula of the form:

$$\sum_{n\leq x,\, n\in A} u^{f(n)}v^{g(n)}= G(u, v)x(\log x)^{\alpha u+\beta v-\alpha-\beta}+O(x(\log x)^{\alpha Ru+\beta Rv-\alpha-\beta-1})$$

valid uniformly for $|u|\leqq u_0$, $|v|\leqq v_0$ if $u_0$ and $v_0$ are positive numbers satisfying $u_0<U$, $v_0<V$, where $U$ and $V$ are appropriately defined, and $G(u, v)$ is holomorphic in $u$ and $v$. From the above formula are deduced several asymptotic expressions for the number of positive integers $n\leqq x$ by giving conditions, among others, on both $f(n)$ and $g(n)$. *S. Ikehara* (Tokyo).

## N60-31 (20# 3112)

**Rényi, A.; and Turán, P. On a theorem of Erdös-Kac.** Acta Arith. **4** (1958), 71–84.

Denote by $v(n)$ the number of prime factors of $n$ (multiple factors counted multiply). Denote by $N_n(v, x)$ the number of integers $k\leqq n$ for which

$$\frac{v(k)-\log\log n}{\sqrt{(\log\log n)}}<x$$

The reviewer and M. Kac proved [Amer. J. Math. **62** (1940), 738–742; MR **2**, 42] that

$$(1)\qquad \lim_{n=\infty} N_n(v, x)/n=\phi(x),$$

where $\phi(x)=(2\pi)^{-\frac{1}{2}}\int_{-\infty}^{x} e^{-u^2/2}du$. LeVeque proved [Trans. Amer. Math. Soc. **66** (1949), 440–463; MR **11**, 83] that

$$(2)\qquad \frac{N_n(v, x)}{n}=\phi(x)+O\left(\frac{\log\log\log n}{(\log\log n)^{\frac{1}{4}}}\right),$$

and conjectured that the error term in (2) is of the order $(\log\log n)^{-\frac{1}{2}}$. Kubelius improved the error term to $O\left(\frac{\log\log\log n}{(\log\log n)^{\frac{1}{2}}}\right)$ [Uspehi Mat. Nauk (N.S.) **11** (1956), no. 2(68), 31–66; MR **18**, 17].

By combining the methods of analytic number theory with a theorem of Esseen [Acta Math. **77** (1945), 1–125; MR **7**, 312] the authors prove LeVeque's conjecture; in fact, they show that uniformly in $x$

$$(3)\qquad N(v, x)/n=\phi(x)+O((\log\log n)^{-\frac{1}{2}}).$$

A simple argument shows that the error term in (3) is best possible. The authors further apply their method to more general additive functions. *P. Erdös* (Haifa)

Citations: MR 2, 42c = N60-4; MR 7, 312a = P20-5; MR 11, 83i = N60-9; MR 18, 17d = Q15-4.

Referred to in N36-68, N60-36, N60-37, N60-38, N60-40, N60-42, N60-51, N60-53, N60-63, N60-68, P48-6, Q15-8.

## N60-32 (20# 3842)

**Tanaka, Minoru. On the number of prime factors of integers. III.** Jap. J. Math. **27** (1957), 103–127

The author proves the following theorem: Let $f_i(x)$, $1\leqq i\leqq k$, be a set of polynomials with integral coefficients. Denote by $v_i(p)$ the number of solutions of $f_i(x)\equiv 0$ (mod $p$). Let further $\pi_i$, $1\leqq i\leqq k$, be a set of prime numbers. Assume that for every $i$, $1\leqq i\leqq k$, $\sum_{p\in\pi_i} v_i(p)/p$ diverges. Define

$$\omega_i(n)=\sum_{\substack{p|n\\ p\in\pi_i}} 1,\quad y_i(n)=\sum_{\substack{p\leq n\\ p\in\pi_i}}\frac{v_i(p)}{p},\quad u_i(n)=\frac{\omega_i(f_i(n))-y_i(n)}{(y_i(n))^{\frac{1}{2}}}.$$

Let $E$ be a Jordan-measurable set in $k$-dimensional space. Denote by $A(x, E)$ the number of integers $1\leqq n\leqq x$ for which the point $\{u_i(n)\}$, $1\leqq i\leqq k$, belongs to $E$. Then

$$\lim\frac{A(x,E)}{x}=(2\pi)^{-k/2}\int_E\exp\left(-\tfrac{1}{2}\sum_{i=1}^{k}u_i^2\right)du_1\cdots du_k.$$

Special cases of this theorem have been proved by the author in two previous papers [same J. **25** (1955), 1–20; J. Math. Soc. Japan **9** (1957), 171–191; MR **18**, 563; **19**, 636], and the proof is similar to the one used in these papers. *P. Erdös* (Haifa)

Citations: MR 18, 563a = N60-21; MR 19, 636c = N60-27.

Referred to in N60-41.

## N60-33 (20# 7004)

**Erdös, P. On the distribution function of additive arithmetical functions and on some related problems.** Rend. Sem. Mat. Fis. Milano **27** (1957), 45–49.

An additive arithmetical function $f(n)$ is one with the property that $f(mn)=f(m)+f(n)$ whenever $m$, $n$ are relatively prime. The corresponding distribution function $\psi(c)$ is the asymptotic density (if it exists) of those $n$ for which $f(n)<c$. The paper gives a brief survey of known results, many of which are due to the author, and mentions several unsolved problems.

*H. Davenport* (Cambridge, England)

Referred to in N64-29, N64-38.

## N60-34 (21# 4945)

**Kubilyus, I. P. Convolutions of arithmetic functions and limit theorems for sums of independent random variables.** Vestnik Leningrad. Univ. **14** (1959), no. 1, 30–33. (Russian. English summary)

Let $a_k(m)$ ($k=1, 2, \cdots$) be a sequence of arithmetic functions with the properties (1) $a_k(m)\geqq 0$ for all $m$ and $k$, (2) the series $\sum_{m=1}^{\infty} a_k(m)=s_k$ are convergent and $s_k\neq 0$. Define $A_n(m)=\sum_{m_1m_2\cdots m_n=m} a_1(m_1)a_2(m_2)\cdots a_n(m_n)$ and $\Phi_n(x)=(s_1s_2\cdots s_n)^{-1}\sum_{\ln m<x} A_n(m)$; $A_n(m)$ is called the convolution of the arithmetic functions $a_1(m), \cdots, a_n(m)$. The author puts $F_k(x)=s_k^{-1}\sum_{\ln m<x} a_k(m)$, and notes that since $F_k(x)$ and $\Phi_n(x)$ are monotonic, non-decreasing, continuous from the left, both tend to 0 as $x\to-\infty$ and to 1 as $x\to\infty$, and since $\Phi_n(x)$ is the convolution of

$F_1(x), \cdots, F_n(x)$ in the function-theoretic sense, the behaviour of $\Phi_n(x)$ for large $n$ may be described with the help of probability limit theorems for sums of independent variables. He then states three general theorems of this kind, analogues respectively of theorems due to Gnedenko and Groshev, Lindeberg and Feller, and Esseen [see Gnedenko and Kolmogorov, *Predel'nye raspredeleniya dlya summ nezavisimyh slučaĭnyh veličin*, Gosudarstv. Izdat. Tehn.-Teor. Lit., Moscow-Leningrad, 1949; translated by K. L. Chung as *Limit distributions for sums of independent random variables*, Addisón-Wesley, Cambridge, Mass., 1954; MR **12**, 839; **16**, 52]. By way of illustration, it will suffice for the purpose of this review to state a special case of the author's third theorem: Let $a_1(m) = a_2(m) = \cdots = a_n(m) = m^{-2}$, when $m^2A_n(m)$ becomes $\tau_n(m)$, the number of representations of $m$ as a product of $n$ integers. Then

$$(6/\pi^2)^n \sum_{\ln m < x\sigma\sqrt{n}+cn} \tau_n(m)m^{-2} = (2\pi)^{-1/2}\int_{-\infty}^{x} e^{-u^2/2}du + \beta(1-x^2)(6\sigma^3\sqrt{(2\pi n)})^{-1}e^{-x^2/2}+O(n^{-1})$$

where $c$, $\sigma$ and $\beta$ are certain numerical constants associated with $\sum_{m=1}^{\infty} m^{-2}$. *H. Halberstam* (London)

## N60-35 (22# 2588)

**Kubilyus, I. P. [Kubilius, J. P.] On asymptotic distribution laws of certain number-theoretic functions.** Vilniaus Valst. Univ. Mokslo Darbai. Mat. Fiz. Chem. Mokslų Ser. **4** (1955), 45–59. (Russian. Lithuanian summary)

Let $\nu(m)$ be the number of distinct prime factors of the positive integer $m$, $N\{\cdots\}$ the number of $m \leqq x$ satisfying the conditions in $\{\cdots\}$, and

$$G(\omega) = \frac{1}{\sqrt{(2\pi)}}\int_{-\infty}^{\omega} e^{-u^2/2}du, \quad \Delta(m) = \frac{\nu(m)-\ln_2 x}{\sqrt{(\ln_2 x)}},$$

where $\ln_k$ denotes a $k$-times repeated logarithm. It is proved that, for fixed distinct integers $a_1, \cdots, a_s \geqq 0$, and for a fixed integer $a > 0$, we have

$$(1)\quad x^{-1}N\{\Delta(m+a_1) < \omega_1, \cdots, \Delta(m+a_s) < \omega_s\} = G(\omega_1)\cdots G(\omega_s)+R_1,$$

$$(2)\quad x^{-1}N\{\nu(m) < \nu(m+a)+\omega\sqrt{(2\ln_2 x)}\} = G(\omega)+R_2,$$

where

$$R_1 = O[(\ln_2 x)^{-1/2}(\ln_3 x)^2],$$

and

$$R_2 = O[(\ln_2 x)^{-1/3}(\ln_3 x)^{5/3}],$$

uniformly for all real $\omega_1, \cdots, \omega_s$, and $\omega$, as $x \to \infty$. With $s=1$, $a_1=0$, $R_1=o(1)$, (1) was proved by P. Erdös and M. Kac [Amer. J. Math. **62** (1940), 738–742; MR **2**, 42]; it represents a statistical development of the Hardy-Ramanujan theorem that the normal order of $\nu(m)$ is $\ln_2 m$ [G. H. Hardy and E. M. Wright, *An introduction to the theory of numbers*, Clarendon, Oxford, 1938; Theorem 436]. A different proof was given by H. Delange [C. R. Acad. Sci. Paris **237** (1953), 542–544; MR **15**, 201]. In the same special case W. J. LeVeque improved the error to $R_1=O[(\ln_2 x)^{-1/4}(\ln_3 x)]$, and conjectured that $R_1=O[(\ln_2 x)^{-1/2}]$; he also proved (1) with $s=2$, $a_1=0$, $a_2=1$, $R_1=o(1)$, and (2) with $a=1$, $R_2=o(1)$ [Trans. Amer. Math. Soc. **66** (1949), 440–463; MR **11**, 83]. The extensions and refinements of the present paper are obtained by a combination of the sieve method with probability arguments, as in the work of Erdös-Kac and LeVeque, but the details are more complicated owing to the number of variables involved. The probability element enters in connection with the formula

$$e^{-y}\sum_{k<y+\omega\sqrt{y}} \frac{y^k}{k!} = G(\omega)+O\left(\frac{1}{\sqrt{y}}\right) \text{ (uniformly in } \omega),$$

which can, of course, be proved directly. An elaborate generalization of (2) is stated; and analogues of (1) and (2) are proved or stated for some other arithmetical functions. *A. E. Ingham* (Cambridge, England)

Citations: MR 2, 42c = N60-4; MR 11, 83i = N60-9; MR 15, 201c = P72-19.

## N60-36 (22# 4668)

**Delange, Hubert. Sur des formules dues à Atle Selberg.** Bull. Sci. Math. (2) **83** (1959), 101–111.

Let $\omega(n)$ represent the number of distinct prime factors of the positive integer $n$. Then a particularization of a theorem of Selberg [J. Indian Math. Soc. (N.S.) **18** (1954), 83–87; MR **16**, 676] yields the following formula:

$$(1)\quad \sum_{n\leqq x} z^{\omega(n)} = x(\log x)^{z-1}F(z)+O(x(\log x)^{z-2}).$$

In (1), $x$ is positive and large, $z$ is an arbitrary complex number, and $F$ denotes the entire function defined by:

$$F(z) = (\Gamma(z))^{-1}\prod_p (1-1/p)^z(1+z/(p-1)),$$

where the infinite product extends over all primes. The $O$-term in (1) is uniform in $z$ for $z$ bounded in modulus.

With (1) as a starting point, the author derives, or indicates the derivation of, numerous results concerning $\omega(n)$, both old and new. In particular, a short proof leads from (1) to the fact that, for any non-negative integer $m$,

$$\sum_{n\leqq x}(\omega(n)-\log\log x)^m = m!xA_m(x) + O(x(\log\log x)^{m/2}/\log x),$$

where $A_m(x)$ is the coefficient of $\zeta^m$ in the Maclaurin expansion of $F(e^\zeta)\exp((e^\zeta-1-\zeta)\log\log x)$. Thus $A_m(x)$ is a polynomial in $\log\log x$ of degree $[m/2]$, where $[x]$ denotes, as usual, the greatest integer function. This estimate is an improvement over a previous one due to the author [C. R. Acad. Sci. Paris **237** (1953), 542–544; MR **15**, 201].

Another result, stated by the author without proof (which is to appear elsewhere) is the following. Let $N(x, t)$ denote the number of positive integers $n \leqq x$ for which $\omega(n) \leqq \log\log x + t(\log\log x)^{1/2}$. Then

$$N(x,t)/x = (2\pi)^{-1/2}\int_{-\infty}^{t}\exp(-u^2/2)du + (2\pi\log\log x)^{-1/2}\exp(-t^2/2) \times (a-t^2/6-\{\log\log x+t(\log\log x)^{1/2}\}) + O(\log\log x)^{-1},$$

where $\{x\}$ denotes the fractional part of $x$, and $a=2/3-F'(1)=0.40516\cdots$. This improves upon the results of Rényi and Turán [Acta Arith. **4** (1958), 71–84; MR **20** #3112], who, in demonstrating the validity of a conjecture of LeVeque [Trans. Amer. Math. Soc. **66** (1949), 440–463; MR **11**, 83], showed that

$$N(x,t)/x = (2\pi)^{-1/2}\int_{-\infty}^{t}\exp(-u^2/2)du+O(\log\log x)^{-1/2}.$$

Formulas similar in form to (1) apply when the left-hand side of (1) is replaced by a summation extending only over squarefree $n$, or when the function $\omega(n)$ is replaced by $\Omega(n)$, the total number of prime factors, distinct or not, of $n$. Accordingly, results corresponding to those flowing from (1) are to be expected in these latter cases as well; various examples of such corresponding results are provided by the author.

*A. Sklar* (Chicago, Ill.)

Citations: MR 11, 83i = N60-9; MR 15, 201f = N60-11; MR 16, 676a = N24-22; MR 20# 3112 = N60-31.

**N60-37** **(23# A134)**

**Kubilius, J. [Кубилюс, И.]**

**Probability methods in number theory [Вероятностные методы в теории чисел].**

*Akad. Nauk Litovsk. SSR, Inst. Fiz. Mat., Vyp.* 2. *Gosudarstv. Izdat. Polit. Naučn. Lit. Litovsk. SSR, Vilna,* 1959. 164 *pp.*

This monograph is almost entirely devoted to the statistics of the distribution of the values taken by an additive function, i.e., a function $f(n)$ of the positive integer $n$ such that $f(mn)=f(m)+f(n)$ when $m, n$ are coprime. It can best be described briefly as an expansion of § 1 of the author's report, Uspehi Mat. Nauk **11** (1956), no. 2 (68), 31–63 [MR **18**, 17]. There is a detailed exposition of several important results, several of them due to the author. Much of the detail of the proofs and several of the results do not seem to have appeared in print before or have appeared only in comparatively inaccessible journals. There is comparatively little discussion of the history of the subject or of how the results obtained fit into the general framework of what is known about additive functions. There is, however, a pretty full bibliography which covers a much wider field than the book itself. The monograph is to be welcomed as a useful addition to the literature of a topic of considerably current interest.

Synopsis of contents:

§ 1. Application of the Sieve of Eratosthenes. This section gives the purely number-theoretic lemmas required. The principal lemma is rather elaborate and gives a fairly precise estimate of the number of integers $m$ in $1 \leqq m \leqq n$ which satisfy certain congruences and do not satisfy others. It is more precise than that enunciated by the author in his report and proved in his paper [Naučn. Trudy Fiz.-Tehn. Inst. Akad. Nauk Litovsk. SSR **1** (1955), 5–24].

§ 2. Additive arithmetical functions and stochastic variables. A formal account in general terms of how the general theory of stochastic processes can be applied to the arithmetical situation.

§ 3. The law of large numbers. If $P(m, n)$ is a statement about the integers $m, n$, the author denotes by $\nu_n\{P(m, n)\}$ the proportion of the integers in $1 \leqq m \leqq n$ for which $P(m, n)$ holds. The most important result here is Theorem 1: Let $f(m)$ be an additive function and put

$$A(n) = \sum_{p \leqq n} \frac{f(p)}{p}, \quad \{D(n)\}^2 = \sum_{p^\alpha \leqq n} \frac{|f(p^\alpha)|^2}{p^\alpha},$$

where $p$ (as always) denotes a prime. Then for any $t>0$ we have

$$\nu_n\{|f(m)-A(n)| < tD(n)\} = 1+O(t^{-2}),$$

where the constant implied by the $O$ depends only on the function. The proof uses a rather complicated estimation of the variance.

§ 4. One-dimensional asymptotic integrals and local laws of distribution. In this section "strongly additive" functions $f$ are considered, i.e., $f(p^\alpha)=f(p)$ $(\alpha=2, 3, \cdots)$. Write $(B(n))^2 = \sum_{p \leqq n} |f(p)|^2/p$. A strongly additive function is said to belong to class $H$ if $B(n) \to \infty$ and there exists a function $r(n)$ of $n$ for which

$$\frac{\log r}{\log n} \to 0, \quad \frac{B(r(n))}{B(n)} \to 1.$$

(The significance of this in the proofs is that the $p \geqq r$ make comparatively little contribution usually to the $f(m)$ $(m \leqq n)$; the $p<r$ are small enough in comparison to $n$ for them to be amenable to the statistical laws.) Theorem 3: Let $f(m)$ be real, strongly additive and in class $H$. A necessary and sufficient condition that

$$\nu_n\left\{\frac{f(m)-A(n)}{B(n)} < x\right\}$$

should tend to a limiting distribution with variance 1 as $n \to \infty$ is that there should exist a nondecreasing function $K(u)$ $(-\infty<u<\infty)$ with $K(\infty)-K(-\infty)=1$ such that

$$\frac{1}{B^2(n)} \sum_{\substack{p \leqq n \\ f(p)<uB(n)}} \frac{f^2(p)}{p} \to K(u).$$

The logarithm of the characteristic function $\phi(t)$ of the limit law is then given by Kolmogorov's formula

$$\log \phi(t) = \int_{-\infty}^{\infty} \frac{e^{itu}-1-itu}{u^2}\, dK(u).$$

The section also includes a new proof of the theorem of Erdös [Ann. of Math. (2) **47** (1946), 1–20; MR **7**, 416] that if $f(m)$ is real and strongly additive and if $B(n) \to \infty$, $f(b) \to 0$ $(n \to \infty, p \to \infty)$ then $f(m)$ is uniformly distributed modulo 1 (Theorem 5).

Finally there is the following generalization of a result of Rényi [Acad. Serbe Sci. Publ. Inst. Math. **8** (1955), 157–162; MR **17**, 944]. Theorem 6: Let $f(m)$ be an integer-valued additive, but not strongly additive, function such that $f(p)=0$ for all primes $p$. Then

$$\lim_{n \to \infty} \nu_n\{f(m) = k\} = \lambda_k,$$

where the $\lambda_k$ are given by the following identity in $t$:

$$\sum_{k=-\infty}^{\infty} \lambda_k e^{itk} = \prod_p \left\{\left(1-\frac{1}{p}\right)\left(1+\frac{1}{p}+\sum_{\alpha \geqq 2} \frac{e^{itf(p^\alpha)}}{p^\alpha}\right)\right\}.$$

§ 5. Asymptotic laws for the sums of additive functions. Let $f_j(m)$ $(1 \leqq j \leqq s)$ be additive functions and let $a_j$ $(1 \leqq j \leqq s)$ be distinct integers. The three quoted theorems of § 4 are generalized respectively by the substitution of

$$\sum_j \frac{f_j(m+a_j)-A_j(n)}{B_j(n)}, \quad \sum_j f_j(m+a_j), \quad f_1(m)-f_2(m+a_2)$$

for $(f(m)-A(n))/B(n)$, $f(m)$, $f(m)$ (in Theorems 3, 5, 6, respectively) with an appropriate modification.

§ 6. The estimation of the remainder term in the integral asymptotic laws. The main theorem here is Theorem 11: Let $f_j(m)$ $(1 \leqq j \leqq s)$ be real strongly additive functions such that

$$B_j(n) \to \infty \ (n \to \infty), \frac{1}{B_j(n)} \max_{p \leqq n} |f_j(p)| \leqq \mu_n \quad (1 \leqq j \leqq s),$$

where the suffix $j$ refers to $f_j$ and where $\mu_n$ tends monotonely to zero. Suppose that $a_j$ $(1 \leqq j \leqq s)$ are fixed distinct integers. Then for all $n \geqq n_1$ and for all $x$ we have

$$\nu_n\left\{\frac{1}{s^{1/2}} \sum_{j=1}^{s} \frac{f_j(m+a_j)-A_j(n)}{B_j(n)} < x\right\} = G(x)+O\{\mu_n(1+e^{-x^2/2}\log^2 \mu_n)\},$$

where $G(x)$ is the normalized Gaussian distribution (note that $n_1$ is independent of $x$).

In the particular case $s=1$, $f_1(m) = \omega(m) = \sum_{p/m} 1$, this gives an error term $O((\log\log\log n)^2/(\log\log n)^{1/2})$. By a conjecture of LeVeque recently proved by Rényi and Turán [Acta Arith. **4** (1958), 71–84; MR **20** #3112] the correct error term in this case is $O(1/(\log\log n)^{1/2})$. The reviewer notes (although the author does not) that the case $s=1$ of this theorem is appreciably weaker than the Theorem 6 of his report.

§ 7. The distribution of the sequence of cut-off functions. If $f(m)$ is a strongly additive function and $u$ is a positive integer the author denotes by $f(m)_u$ the "cut-off function" $\sum_{p|m,p\leq u} f(p)$. The following three theorems are proved, in all of which $f_j(m)$ $(1\leqq j\leqq s)$ are real strongly additive functions of class $H$ and $a_1, \cdots, a_s$ are distinct integers. Theorem 12: There exists a constant $C$ such that

$$\nu_n\left\{\max_{k\leqq n}\left|\sum_{j=1}^{s}\frac{f_j(m+a_j)_k-A_j(k)}{B_j(n)}\right|>\varepsilon\right\}<\frac{C}{\varepsilon^2}$$

for each $\varepsilon>0$ and all $n\geqq n_1(\varepsilon, C)$. Theorem 13: Suppose that there exists a function $B_n$ such that $B_j(n)\sim B_n$ $(1\leqq j\leqq s)$ and suppose that

$$\max_{p\leqq n}|f_j(p)| = o\left\{\frac{B_n}{\sqrt{(\log\log B_n)}}\right\}\quad(1\leqq j\leqq s).$$

Let $\varepsilon$, $\delta$ be arbitrarily small and $K$ be arbitrarily large. Then there exist $u\geqq K$ and $n_1$ such that

$$\nu_n\left\{\max_{k>u}\frac{\left|\sum_{j=1}^{s}(f_j(m+a_j)_k-A_j(k))\right|}{B_n\sqrt{(2s\log\log B_n)}}>1+\delta\right\}<\varepsilon,$$

$$\nu_n\left\{\max_{k>u}\frac{\left|\sum_{j=1}^{s}(f_j(m+a_j)_k-A_j(k))\right|}{B_n\sqrt{(2s\log\log B_n)}}<1-\delta\right\}>1-\varepsilon$$

for all $n\geqq n_1$ ("Law of the iterated logarithm"). Theorem 14: Suppose that

$$B_j(n)\to\infty,\quad\frac{1}{B_j(n)}\max_{p\leqq n}|f_j(p)|\leqq\mu_n\quad(1\leqq j\leqq s),$$

where $\mu_n$ tends monotonely to zero. Let $\psi_1(t)$ and $\psi_2(t)$ be defined for $0\leqq t\leqq 1$ and let them have continuous derivatives. Suppose that $\psi_1(t)<0<\psi_2(t)$. Let $Q_n$ be the number of $m\leqq n$ for which

$$\psi_1\left(\frac{1}{s}\sum_{j=1}^{s}\frac{B_j^2(k)}{B_j^2(n)}\right)<\frac{1}{\sqrt{s}}\sum_{j=1}^{s}\frac{f_j(m+a_j)_k-A_j(k)}{B_j(n)}$$
$$<\psi_2\left(\frac{1}{s}\sum_{j=1}^{s}\frac{B_j^2(k)}{B_j^2(n)}\right)$$

for $1\leqq k\leqq n$. Then $n^{-1}Q_n\to v(0,0)$ where $v(x,t)$ is the solution of

$$\frac{\partial v}{\partial t}+\frac{1}{2}\frac{\partial^2 v}{\partial x^2}=0$$

with the boundary conditions

$$v(x,1)=1\quad(\psi_1(1)<x<\psi_2(1)),$$
$$v(\psi_1(t),t)=v(\psi_2(t),t)=0\quad(0\leqq t<1).$$

§ 8. Many-dimensional asymptotic laws. In this section general theorems of probability theory are used to get rather elaborate necessary and sufficient conditions for the existence of $s$-dimensional distributions which are the limits of

$$\nu_n\left\{\frac{f_1(m)-A_1(n)}{B_1(n)}<x_1,\cdots,\frac{f_s(m)-A_s(n)}{B_s(n)}<x_s\right\},$$

$$\nu_n\left\{\frac{f_1(m+a_1)-A_1(n)}{B_1(n)}<x_1,\cdots,\frac{f_s(m+a_s)-A_s(n)}{B_s(n)}<x_s\right\}.$$

§ 9. Additive arithmetical functions in the Gaussian field. Several of the results of the preceding chapters are extended to the case when the variables are Gaussian integers.

{Misprints. In addition to the fairly long list of mainly minor errors supplied with the book, the reviewer noted the following two which may cause trouble. In (6.6) and in three places on p. 120, for $(\ln\ln n)^2$ read $(\ln\ln\ln n)^2$. On p. 131, l. 17, for $v(x,1)$ read $v(x,1)=1$.}

*J. W. S. Cassels* (Cambridge, England)

Citations: MR 7, 416c = N60-7; MR 17, 944f = N24-23; MR 18, 17d = Q15-4; MR 20# 3112 = N60-31.

Referred to in M55-25, N36-68, N52-32, N60-38, N60-44, N60-49, N60-54, N60-55, N60-57, N60-59, N60-70, N60-74, N60-83, N60-87, N80-43, P02-18, Q15-13.

## N60-38 (26# 3691)

**Kubilius, J. [Кубилюс, Й.]**

**Probabilistic methods in the theory of numbers [Вероятностные методы в теории чисел].**

Second, enlarged edition.

*Gosudarstv. Izdat. Politič. i Naučn. Lit. Litovsk. SSR, Vilna,* 1962. 221 *pp.* 0.82 *r.*

This new edition is considerably different from the original [MR **23** #A134], which was published in 1959. Use will be made here of notation introduced in the review of the first edition.

In Chapter 1 there is given a more general and more precise version of the kind of result arising from Selberg's sieve; the proof, while inherently complicated, is highly polished.

Chapter 2 is essentially unchanged. Chapter 3, dealing with the weak law of large numbers for additive functions, has been supplemented by the statement of weak laws for $f(R(m))$ and $f(R(p))$, where $f$ is an additive function and $R$ is a positive-valued polynomial with integral coefficients, the roles of mean and variance being played by the quantities

$$A_R(n)=\sum_{p\leqq n}\frac{\vartheta_R(p)f(p)}{p},\qquad B_R{}^2(n)=\sum_{p\leqq n}\frac{\vartheta_R(p)f^2(p)}{p},$$

respectively, where $\vartheta_R(p)$ is the number of solutions of $R(m)\equiv 0 \pmod p$.

The treatment of integral laws in Chapter 4 has been expanded to include the statement of a characterization due to L. Kubik [Studia Math. **18** (1959), 295–309; addendum, **19** (1960), 249; MR **22** #10004] of the Kolmogorov limit function $K(u)$ of the variance of a sum of independent random variables, and also the implication of this theorem for strongly additive functions.

Several of the theorems of Chapters 5 and 6 have been made more precise by the inclusion of specific error terms; these chapters are otherwise unchanged, and Chapters 7 and 8 are the same as in the first edition.

Chapter 9 of the present work, which is entirely new, is devoted to the investigation of the error term in the Erdős-Kac theorem for $\omega(m)$, the number of distinct prime divisors of $m$. The reviewer conjectured that the number $N_n(x)$ of positive integers $m\leqq n$ for which $\omega(m)<\log\log n+x(\log\log n)^{1/2}$ is $nG(x)+O(n(\log\log n)^{-1/2})$; this was proved by Rényi and Turán [Acta Arith. **4** (1958), 71–84; MR **20** #3112] using Dirichlet generating functions. Delange [ibid. **7** (1961/62), 191–215; MR **25** #58] recently extended the latter work, obtaining a complete asymptotic expansion for $N_n(x)$. The author discovered this same expansion independently, and presents his proof here.

Chapter 10 is essentially Chapter 9 of the first edition.

*W. J. LeVeque* (Ann Arbor, Mich.)

Citations: MR 20# 3112 = N60-31; MR 23# A134 = N60-37; MR 25# 58 = N60-42.

Referred to in N28-53, N36-47, N36-68, N52-32, N60-39, N60-54, N60-55, N60-57, N60-59, N60-70, N60-74, N60-83, N60-87, N60-91, N60-95, Q15-13, Z02-53.

**N60-39** **(28# 3956)**

**Kubilius, J.**

**Probabilistic methods in the theory of numbers.**
Translations of Mathematical Monographs, Vol. 11.
*American Mathematical Society, Providence, R.I.*, 1964.
xviii + 182 *pp.* $8.60.

The original Russian was reviewed earlier [second, enlarged edition, Gosudarstv. Izdat. Politič. i Naučn. Lit. Litovsk. SSR, Vilna, 1962; MR **26** #3691].

Citations: MR 26# 3691 = N60-38.
Referred to in N28-53, N36-38, N36-47, N36-68, N52-32, N60-54, N60-55, N60-57, N60-59, N60-70, N60-74, N60-83, N60-87, N60-91, N60-95, N80-43, Z02-53.

**N60-40** **(23# A3730)**

**Rieger, G. J.**

**Zur Statistik der Primfaktoren der natürlichen Zahlen in arithmetischen Progressionen.**
*J. Reine Angew. Math.* **206** (1961), 26–30.

Let $V(m)$ denote the total number of prime factors of $m$. Let $N(n, x, k, l)$ denote the number of positive integers $m \leqq n$ for which $V(m) < \log\log n + x\sqrt{(\log\log n)}$ and for which $m \equiv l \bmod k$. It is proved in the paper that

$$n^{-1}N(n, x, k, l) = k^{-1}\Phi(x) + O((\log\log n)^{-1/2}),$$

where $\Phi(x) = (2\pi)^{-1/2}\int_{-\infty}^{x} e^{-u^2/2}\,du$.

The method of the proof is that of the paper by A. Rényi and P. Turán [Acta Arith. **4** (1958), 71–84; MR **20** #3112] where the above theorem is proved for $k = 1$.

It is pointed out that the same method leads to a generalization for algebraic number fields.

*A. Rényi* (Budapest)

Citations: MR 20# 3112 = N60-31.

**N60-41** **(24# A3148)**

**Tanaka, Minoru**

**On the number of prime factors of integers. IV.**
*Japan J. Math.* **30** (1960), 55–83.

The author proves a general theorem about the distribution of the prime factors of polynomials. A very special case of one of his theorems is as follows: Let $f_i(x)$ $(1 \leqq i \leqq k)$ be a set of irreducible polynomials with integral coefficients of positive degree and denote by $\Omega(n)$ the number of prime factors of $n$, multiple factors counted multiply. Put

$$u_i(n) = \frac{\Omega(f_i(n)) - \log\log n}{(\log\log n)^{1/2}}, \qquad 1 \leqq i \leqq k.$$

Let $E$ be a Jordan measurable set in $k$-dimensional space. Denote by $A(x, E)$ the number of integers $1 \leqq n \leqq x$ for which the point $\{u_1(n), \cdots, u_k(n)\}$ is in $E$. Then

$$\lim_{x\to\infty} \frac{A(x, E)}{x} = (2\pi)^{-k/2}\int_E \exp\left(-\tfrac{1}{2}\sum_{i=1}^{k} u_i^2\right) du_1 \cdots du_k.$$

The author also proves a theorem on the number of factorisations of integers and states several special cases which contain previous results of Kac, LeVeque and the reviewer [Kac, Bull. Amer. Math. Soc. **47** (1941), 815–817; MR **3**, 69; W. J. LeVeque, Trans. Amer. Math. Soc. **66** (1949), 440–463; MR **11**, 83; the reviewer, Proc. Cambridge Philos. Soc. **32** (1936), 530–540].

The methods of the author are the same as in his previous papers I, II and III [Japan. J. Math. **25** (1955), 1–20; MR **18**, 563; J. Math. Soc. Japan. **9** (1957), 171–191; MR **19**, 636; Japan. J. Math. **27** (1957), 103–127; MR **20** #3842].

*P. Erdős* (Budapest)

Citations: MR 3, 69e = N60-5; MR 11, 83i = N60-9; MR 18, 563a = N60-21; MR 19, 636c = N60-27; MR 20# 3842 = N60-32.

**N60-42** **(25# 58)**

**Delange, H.**

**Sur le nombre des diviseurs premiers de $n$.**
*Acta Arith.* **7** (1961/62), 191–215.

Let $\omega(n)$ be the number of distinct prime divisors of $n$, and let $N(x, t)$ be the number of positive integers $m \leqq x$ for which $\omega(n) \leqq \log\log x + t(\log\log x)^{1/2}$. It was proved by Erdős and Kac [Amer. J. Math. **62** (1940), 738–742; MR **2**, 42] that

$$\lim_{x\to\infty} \frac{1}{x} N(x, t) = (2\pi)^{-1/2}\int_{-\infty}^{t} e^{-u^2/2}\,du = \Phi(t).$$

It was conjectured by the reviewer [Trans. Amer. Math. Soc. **66** (1949), 440–463; MR **11**, 83] and proved by Rényi and Turán [Acta Arith. **4** (1958), 71–84; MR **20** #3112] that as $x \to \infty$,

$$\frac{1}{x} N(x, t) = \Phi(t) + O((\log\log x)^{-1/2}).$$

The author gives a new proof of this last relation and of the following much stronger theorem: There is a sequence of functions $\varphi_1(t, x), \varphi_2(t, x), \cdots$, each bounded for $t$ arbitrary and $x > e$, such that for each positive integer $\nu$ the asymptotic expansion

$$\frac{1}{x} N(x, t) = \Phi(t) + \sum_{r=1}^{\nu} \frac{\varphi_r(t, x)}{(\log\log x)^{r/2}} + O(\log\log x)^{-(\nu+1)/2}$$

holds uniformly in $t$ as $x \to \infty$.

The proof is based on the following result, due to A. Selberg: for arbitrary complex $z$ and arbitrary $R > 0$,

$$\sum_{n \leqq x} z^{\omega(n)} = xF(z)(\log x)^{z-1} + O(x(\log x)^{z-2})$$

uniformly for $|z| \leqq R$, where

$$F(z) = (\Gamma(z))^{-1}\prod_p (1-p^{-1})^z(1+z/(p-1)).$$

{A significant fraction of the paper is devoted to various estimations of the sum

$$\sum_{j \leq l + t\sqrt{l}} \frac{l^j e^{-l}}{j!}.$$

The reviewer remarks that such results can be derived from the lattice-distribution case of C.-G. Esseen's theorems [Acta Math. **77** (1945), 1–125; MR **7**, 312], using the fact that the above sum represents the distribution function for a sum of Poisson variables.}

*W. J. LeVeque* (Ann Arbor, Mich.)

Citations: MR 2, 42c = N60-4; MR 7, 312a = P20-5; MR 11, 83i = N60-9; MR 20# 3112 = N60-31.
Referred to in N60-38, N60-47, N60-55, N80-43.

**N60-43** **(25# 1126)**

**Schoenberg, I. J.**

**On two theorems of P. Erdös and A. Rényi.**
*Illinois J. Math.* **6** (1962), 53–58.

An additive function of a positive integral variable is a function $f$ with the property that $f(mn) = f(m) + f(n)$ whenever $(m, n) = 1$. The theorem of Erdös states that, if $f$ is an additive function, and either $f$ is monotone or $f(n+1) - f(n) \to 0$ as $n \to \infty$, then $f(n) = C \log n$, where $C$ is constant. In the theorem of Rényi, $f(n)$ is the number of prime factors of $n$ minus the number of distinct prime factors of $n$, and $d_k$ is the density of the set of those natural numbers $n$ for which $f(n) = k$. The theorem states that $d_0, d_1, d_2, \cdots$ exist, and that, if $|z| < 2$, then $\sum_{k=0}^{\infty} d_k z^k = \prod_p\{(1-1/p)(1+1/(p-z))\}$. New proofs of these two theorems are given.

*T. Estermann* (London)

Referred to in N64-18.

## N60-44 (26# 100)

**Uždavinis, R. V.**

**On the joint distribution of values of additive arithmetic functions of integral polynomials. (Russian. Lithuanian summary)**

*Trudy Akad. Nauk Litov. SSR Ser. B* **1960**, *no.* 1 (21), 5–29.

The author considers the distribution of values of real strongly additive arithmetic functions $F_k(m)$ $(k=1,\cdots,s)$, i.e., functions of the positive integer $m$ such that $F_k(mn)=F_k(m)+F_k(n)$ when $m, n$ are coprime and $F_k(p^\alpha)=F(p)$ for all primes $p$ and all positive integers $\alpha$. Let $g_k(x)$ $(k=1,\cdots,s)$ be polynomials with integral coefficients of positive degree such that $g_k(m)>0$ for $m=1,2,\cdots$. Denote by $r_k(p)$ the number of residue classes satisfying the congruence $g_k(m)\equiv 0 \pmod p$,

$$A_k(n) = \sum_{p\le n} F_k(p)r_k(p)/p, \quad B_k^2(n) = \sum_{p\le n} F_k^2(p)r_k(p)/p,$$

where $p$ runs over prime numbers. Suppose that $\max_{p\le n}|F_k(p)|=\sigma(B_k(n))$ and put

$$G(x) = (2\pi)^{-1/2}\int_{-\infty}^{x} \exp(-u^2/2)\,du.$$

The author states the following theorems.

If the polynomials $g_k(m)$ are coprime, then the frequency of positive integers $m\le n$ for which

$$(*)\qquad F_k(g_k(m)) < A_k(n)+x_kB_k(n) \qquad (k = 1,\cdots,s)$$

tends to $G(x_1)\cdots G(x_s)$ as $n\to\infty$, and the frequency of positive integers $m\le n$ for which

$$\sum_{k=1}^{s} \frac{F_k(g_k(m))-A_k(n)}{B_k(n)} < x$$

tends to $G(xs^{-1/2})$.

If $g_1(x)=\cdots=g_s(x)$, then the characteristic function $\varphi(t_1,\cdots,t_s)$ of the limiting Gaussian distribution of the limiting distribution of the frequency of $m\le n$ satisfying (*) equals

$$\exp\{-\tfrac12 \lim_{\varepsilon\to0}\limsup_{n\to\infty} \textstyle\sum' (\sum_{k=1}^{s} t_kF_k(p)r_k(p)/p)^2\},$$

where the dash $'$ denotes the summation over the primes $p\le n$ satisfying the condition $\sum_{k=1}^{s} f_k^2(p)B_k^{-2}(n)<\varepsilon^2$.

The method of the author is a generalisation of that of the reviewer [*Probability methods in number theory* (Russian), Gosudarstv. Izdat. Politič. i Naučn. Lit. Litovsk. SSR, Vilna, 1959; MR **23** #A134].

*J. Kubilius* (Vilnius)

Citations: MR 23# A134 = N60-37.
Referred to in N60-50.

## N60-45 (26# 2390)

**Uždavinis, R.**

**Some limit theorems for additive arithmetic functions. (Russian. Lithuanian and German summaries)**

*Litovsk. Mat. Sb.* **1** (1961), *no.* 1–2, 355–364.

We shall denote by $N_n(\cdot)$ the number of positive integers $m\le n$ which satisfy the condition indicated inside the bracket. An arithmetical function $F(m)$ is called additive if $F(mn)=F(m)+F(n)$ whenever $m$ and $n$ are relatively prime. For any polynomial $g(m)$ with integral coefficients, we shall denote by $\vartheta(p)$ the number of integers $m$ such that $g(m)\equiv 0 \pmod p$ and $0\le m<p$. Further, we shall write

$$A(n) = \sum_{p\le n}\frac{F(p)\vartheta(p)}{p}, \quad D(n) = \Big\{\sum_{\substack{p^\alpha\le n\\ \alpha\ge1}}\frac{F^2(p^\alpha)\vartheta(p)}{p^\alpha}\Big\}^{1/2}.$$

In the present paper it is shown that, under suitable conditions,

$$(*)\quad \frac1n N_n\{F(|g(m)|)<A(n)+xD(n)\}\to(2\pi)^{-1/2}\int_{-\infty}^{x} e^{-u^2/2}\,du$$

as $n\to\infty$. The main purpose of the investigation is to obtain results about the rapidity of convergence in (*). The principal conclusion established by the author is as follows. Let $F(m)$ be a real-valued, arithmetical, additive function. Suppose that $g(m)$ is an irreducible, primitive polynomial with integral coefficients and without integral zeros. Suppose, further, that

$$D(n)\to\infty \quad (n\to\infty), \qquad \max_{\substack{p^\alpha\le n\\ \alpha\ge1}} |F(p^\alpha)| \le \mu_nD(n),$$

where $\mu_n$ is non-increasing and tends to zero. Then there exists a number $n_1$, independent of $x$, such that

$$\frac1n N_n\{F(|g(m)|) < A(n)+xD(n)\} = (2\pi)^{-1}\int_{-\infty}^{x} e^{-u^2/2}\,du+O\{\mu_n(e^{-x^2/2}\log^2\frac{1}{\mu_n}+1)\}$$

for all $n>n_1$ and all $x$, where the constant implied by the $O$-notation is independent of $n$ and $x$.

A number of special cases are also considered. In particular, it is deduced from the result just quoted that, if $\omega(m)$ is the number of distinct prime divisors of $m$, then

$$\frac1n N_n\{\omega(|g(m)|) < \log\log n+x(\log\log n)^{1/2}\} = (2\pi)^{-1/2}\int_{-\infty}^{x} e^{-u^2/2}\,du + O\{(\log\log n)^{-1/2}(e^{-x^2/2}(\log\log\log n)^2+1)\},$$

where the polynomial $g(m)$ is subject to the same restrictions as above.

*L. Mirsky* (Sheffield)

Referred to in N60-50.

## N60-46 (26# 2414)

**Rieger, G. J.**

**Über die Anzahl der Primfaktoren algebraischer Zahlen und das Gausssche Fehlergesetz.**

*Math. Nachr.* **24** (1962), 77–89.

Let $x$ be an arbitrary positive number, $K$ an algebraic number field of degree $n$, $\mathfrak f$ an integral ideal in $K$ of norm $N\mathfrak f$, $A\{\mathfrak p:\ldots\}$ the number of prime ideals $\mathfrak p$ of $K$ with $\ldots$, $\xi$ an integer in $K$ of norm $N\xi$, $\xi^j$ $(j=1,2,\cdots,n)$ the conjugates of $\xi$, $A\{\xi:\ldots\}$ the number of the integers $\xi$ of $K$ with $\ldots$, $|\xi|<x^{1/n}$ mean the system $|\xi^j|\le x^{1/n}$ $(j=1,2,\cdots,n)$, $c_1, c_2,\cdots$ positive constants dependent on $K$. Further, let $\sum_\xi{}'$ mean $\sum_{\xi\ne0}$; $v(\xi)=A\{\mathfrak p:\mathfrak p|\xi\}$. The author proves a number of theorems, some of which are mentioned below. Theorem 1: $x$, $\alpha$, $\beta$ are arbitrary real numbers with $x>c_3$ and $\alpha<\beta$. Let $\mathfrak f$ be an integral ideal of $K$ with $N\mathfrak f<e^{(\log\log x)^2}$, $\gamma$ an integer of $K$, and $\mu=\max(1,|\alpha|,|\beta|)$. Then for $z=x$ and $z=|N\xi|$ $(z>e)$, one has the formula

$$A\{\xi:\xi\equiv\gamma \bmod \mathfrak f,\ |\xi|<x^{1/n},\ \log\log z+\alpha(\log\log z)^{1/2}<v(\xi)<\log\log z+\beta(\log\log z)^{1/2}\} = \frac{c_1x}{(2\pi)^{1/2}\cdot N\mathfrak f}\int_\alpha^\beta e^{-u^2/2}\,du+O\Big(\frac{\mu^4x(\log\log\log x)^{1/2}}{N\mathfrak f\cdot(\log\log x)^{1/4}}\Big).$$

Theorem 3 and Theorem 5: For each real number $x \geqq 3$, each integral ideal $\mathfrak{f}$ of $K$ with $N\mathfrak{f} \leqq x$ and each integer $\gamma$ of $K$,

$$\sum'_{\substack{|\xi|<x^{1/n} \\ \equiv \gamma \bmod \mathfrak{f}}} v(\xi) = \frac{c_1 x}{N\mathfrak{f}} \log\log x + O\left(\frac{x}{N\mathfrak{f}} \log N\mathfrak{f}\right) + O\left(\frac{x}{\log x} N\mathfrak{f}^{1/n-1}\right),$$

$$\sum'_{\substack{|\xi|<x^{1/n} \\ \equiv \gamma \bmod \mathfrak{f}}} v^2(\xi) = \frac{c_1 x}{N\mathfrak{f}} (\log\log x)^2 + O\left(\frac{x}{N\mathfrak{f}} \log N\mathfrak{f} \cdot \log\log x\right) + O\left(\frac{x}{N\mathfrak{f}} \log^2 N\mathfrak{f}\right) + O\left(x N\mathfrak{f}^{1/n-1} \frac{\log\log x}{\log x}\right).$$

Theorem 6:

$$A\{\xi : |\xi| < x^{1/n}, |v(\xi) - \log\log x| > (\log\log x)^{1/n} f(x)\} = O\left(\frac{x}{f^2(x)}\right).$$

Finally, the function $f(x) > 0$ tends monotonically to infinity. *B. K. Ghosh* (Calcutta)

## N60-47 (27# 3616)

**Kubiljus, I. P. [Kubilius, J.]**

**Asymptotic expansion of the distribution laws of certain arithmetical functions. (Russian. Lithuanian and German summaries)**

*Litovsk. Mat. Sb.* **2** (1962), *no.* 1, 61–73.

The author proves, independently, the same result as H. Delange [Acta Arith. **7** (1961/62), 191–215; MR **25** #58], and in much the same way, except that he uses the simplifying device to which the reviewer of Delange's paper drew attention at the conclusion of his review. *H. Halberstam* (Dublin)

Citations: MR 25# 58 = N60-42.

## N60-48 (27# 4789)

**Tjan, M. M.**

**Remainder terms in the problem of the distribution of values of two arithmetic functions. (Russian)**

*Dokl. Akad. Nauk SSSR* **150** (1963), 998–1000.

Let $\phi$ denote Euler's function, and let $P_n(\phi(n)/n < \lambda)$ be the number of integers $n$ among $1, 2, 3, \cdots, N$ for which $\phi(n)/n < \lambda$. Schoenberg [Math. Z. **28** (1928), 171–199] proved that, for every real $\lambda$,

$$\lim_{N\to\infty} \frac{1}{N} P_N(\phi(n)/n < \lambda) = v(\lambda),$$

where $v$ is a certain function whose properties have since been investigated by B. A. Venkov [Leningrad. Gos. Univ. Učen. Zap. Ser. Mat. **16** (1949), 3–19]. The author states that

$$\frac{1}{N} P_N(\phi(n)/n < \lambda) = v(\lambda) + O\left(\frac{1}{\ln\ln\ln N}\right),$$

and gives estimates of the difference

$$\frac{1}{N}\sum_{n\leqq N} F\left(\frac{\phi(n)}{n}\right) - \int_0^1 F(x)\, dv(x)$$

for various general classes of functions $F$. He also states similar results for the arithmetic function $t(n) = \sum_{d|n} 2^{-d}$. No proofs are given. *H. Halberstam* (Dublin)

## N60-49 (27# 5745)

**Grigelionis, B.**

**On the distribution of values of multiplicative functions. (Russian. Lithuanian and English summaries)**

*Litovsk. Mat. Sb.* **2** (1962), *no.* 2, 107–125.

The author first remarks that if $f(m)$ is a positive multiplicative function, then $\log f$ is additive, so that the theorems of Kubiljus [*Probabilistic methods in number theory* (Russian), Gosudarstv. Izdat. Polit. Naučn. Lit. Litovsk. SSR, Vilna, 1959; MR **23** #A134] on value distribution of additive functions can be applied to give information about the values assumed by $f$. He then treats the more general case when $f(m)$ may be 0, assuming first that $f$ is strongly multiplicative, i.e., $f(p^\alpha) = f(p)$ for all primes $p$. Here the problem reduces to studying strongly additive functions on the semigroup $Q$ generated by the set $P$ of primes where $f(p) > 0$, and estimating the number of integers $\leqq x$ in $Q$. In the case where $P$ consists of the primes in a given set of residue classes (mod $k$), this is carried out in detail, and results similar to those of Kubiljus are obtained. If $f$ is not strongly multiplicative, but $\sum_{p\in P} f^2(p)/p = \infty$, then the values of $f$ have asymptotically the same distribution as those of the strongly multiplicative function $f^*$ defined by $f^*(p^\alpha) = f(p)$. An application is made to $f(m) = r_2(m)/4$, where $r_2(m)$ is the number of representations of $m$ as a sum of two squares. *B. Gordon* (Los Angeles, Calif.)

Citations: MR 23# A134 = N60-37.

## N60-50 (28# 1164)

**Uždavinis, R.**

**Arithmetic functions on the sets of values of integer-valued polynomials. (Russian. Lithuanian and German summaries)**

*Litovsk. Mat. Sb.* **2** (1962), *no.* 2, 253–280.

In the present paper a number of results established by the author in earlier publications [Trudy Akad. Nauk Litov. SSR Ser. B **1959**, no. 2 (18), 9–29; ibid. **1960**, no. 1 (21), 5–29; MR **26** #100; Litovsk. Mat. Sb. **1** (1961), no. 1–2, 355–364; MR **26** #2390] are refined and generalized. We state two of his three principal conclusions. Theorem 1: Let $g_1, \cdots, g_s$ be integral-valued, primitive, pairwise coprime polynomials with non-vanishing discriminants, and let $F_1, \cdots, F_s$ be real-valued additive arithmetic functions. Put

$$A_i(n) = \sum_{p\leqq n} p^{-1} F_i(p)\vartheta_i(p), \qquad B_i(n) = \sum_{p\leqq n} p^{-1} F_i^2(p)\vartheta_i(p),$$

where $\vartheta_i(p)$ denotes the number of incongruent solutions of the congruence $g_i(m) \equiv 0 \pmod p$. Suppose that, for $1 \leqq i \leqq s$,

$$\max_{p\leqq n} |F_i(p^\alpha)| = O(\alpha^k B_i(n)), \qquad B_i(|g_i(n)|) = O(B_i(n)).$$

Then, for any positive function $\psi(n)$ which tends to infinity with $n$,

$$\nu_n\left\{\left|\sum_{i=1}^s \frac{F_i(|g_i(m)|) - A_i(n)}{B_i(n)}\right| > \psi(n)\right\} \to 0$$

as $n\to\infty$, where $\nu_n\{\cdots\}$ denotes the frequency of integers $m \leqq n$ satisfying the condition stated inside the brackets. Theorem 2: Let $g_1, \cdots, g_s$ be as above. Let $a_1, \cdots, a_s$ be positive constants and write $a = \sum_{i=1}^s a_i^{-2}$. Suppose that the real-valued additive arithmetic functions $F_1, \cdots, F_s$ satisfy the conditions

$$F_i(p^\alpha) = O(\alpha^k |F_i(p)|), \quad B_i(n) \to \infty \quad (n \to \infty),$$

$$\max_{p\leqq n} |F_i(p)| \leqq \mu_n B_i(n),$$

where $\mu_n$ tends monotonically to zero as $n\to\infty$. Then

$$\nu_n\left\{a^{-1/2} \sum_{i=1}^s \frac{F_i(|g_i(m)|) - A_i(n)}{a_i B_i(n)} < x\right\} = (2\pi)^{-1/2} \int_{-\infty}^x e^{-u^2/2}\, du + O\left\{\mu_n\left(e^{-x^2/2} \log^k \frac{1}{\mu_n} + 1\right)\right\}$$

uniformly for $x$ and all sufficiently large values of $n$. The proofs, which are long and formidable, depend on the use of the sieve method of A. A. Buchstab and on certain limit theorems relating to the summation of independent random variables. *L. Mirsky* (Sheffield)

Citations: MR 26# 100 = N60-44; MR 26# 2390 = N60-45.

## N60-51 (29# 3414 )

**Rényi, A.**

**On the distribution of values of additive number-theoretical functions.**

*Publ. Math. Debrecen* **10** (1963), 264–273.

Let $f(n)$ be an additive number-theoretic function. Put

$$f^*(p) = f(p) \quad \text{if} \quad |(fp)| \leq 1,$$
$$f^*(p) = 1 \quad \text{if} \quad |f(p)| > 1.$$

The reviewer proved that if

$$(1) \qquad \sum_p f^*(p)/p \quad \text{and} \quad \sum_p (f^*(p))^2/p$$

both converge, then $f(n)$ has a distribution function [J. London Math. Soc. **13** (1938), 119–127].

The author gives a new analytic proof of this theorem. He uses a method developed by the author and Turán [Acta Arith. **4** (1958), 71–84; MR **20** #3112]. (The reviewer and Wintner proved [Amer. J. Math. **61** (1939), 713–721; MR **1**, 40] that the existence of the distribution function implies the convergence of the two series (1).) *P. Erdős* (Budapest)

Citations: MR 1, 40c = N60-1; MR 20# 3112 = N60-31.

Referred to in N60-78.

## N60-52 (30# 4741 )

**Juškis, Z.**

**Limit theorems for additive functions defined on ordered semigroups with a regular norm. (Russian. Lithuanian and German summaries)**

*Litovsk. Mat. Sb.* **4** (1964), 565–603.

Author's summary: "Let $G$ be a multiplicative semigroup with countably many generators of infinite order. Let $N$ be a homomorphism of the semigroup $G$ in the multiplicative semigroup of positive integers. The homomorphic image $N(m)$ is called the norm of the element $m$. We suppose that the number of elements of $G$ with $N(m) \leq x$ is $Cx^{\vartheta} + O(x^{\vartheta_1})$; $C$, $\vartheta$, $\vartheta_1$ constants, $C > 0$, $0 \leq \vartheta_1 < \vartheta$. A function $f(m)$ is called additive if it is defined on $G$ and satisfies $f(mn) = f(m) + f(n)$ for all relatively prime $m$ and $n$.

"In this paper some limit theorems about the distribution of the values of additive functions which are defined on ordered semigroups with regular norming, are proved. Among others the following theorem is proved. Let $f(m)$ be an additive real function, satisfying

$$\frac{1}{D(x)} \max_{N(p)^{\alpha} \leq x} |f(p^{\alpha})| \leq \mu(x), \qquad D(x) \to \infty \ (x \to \infty),$$

where $\mu(x)$ tends monotonically to 0. Further, let $\lambda_x\{(f(m) - A(x))/D(x) < y\}$ be the frequency of the elements $m \in G$ satisfying $N(m) \leq x$ and $f(m) < A(x) + y(D(x))$. Then

$$\lambda_x\left\{\frac{f(m) - A(x)}{D(x)} < y\right\} = (2\pi)^{-1/2} \int_{-\infty}^{y} e^{-u^2/2}\, du$$
$$+ O\left(\mu(x)\left(e^{-y^2/2} \ln \frac{1}{\mu(x)} + 1\right)\right)$$

uniformly for $x > x_0$ and all $y$ ($x_0$ is independent of $y$)." *J. E. Cigler* (Groningen)

Referred to in N60-70.

## N60-53 (31# 152 )

**Gyapjas, F.; Kátai, I.**

**Zur Statistik der Primfaktoren der natürlichen Zahlen.**

*Ann. Univ. Sci. Budapest. Eötvös Sect. Math.* **7** (1964), 59–66.

Denote by $V_{k,l}(m)$ the number of prime divisors of $m$ which are congruent to $l$ modulo $k$, counting multiplicity. Let $\varphi(k)$ be Euler's $\varphi$-function and let $(k, l) = 1$. The authors prove that the number of those positive integers $m \leq n$ for which $V_{k,l}(m) < \log\log n/\varphi(k) + x(\log\log n/\varphi(k))^{1/2}$ is $G(x) + O(\log\log n)^{-1/2}$ with $G(x) = (2\pi)^{-1/2} \int_{-\infty}^{x} e^{-u^2/2}\, du$.

The authors also give analogous formulae (a) for the function $V_{k,l_1}(m) - V_{k,l_2}(m)$, (b) for the number of representations of integers as the sum of two squares, and (c) for any additive number-theoretical function $f(m)$ such that $f(p) = 1$ for any prime $p \equiv l \bmod k$, $f(p) = 0$ for $p \not\equiv l \bmod k$, and $|f(p^s)| \leq s^a$ $(s = 1, 2, \cdots)$, where $a$ is a constant. The method is a straightforward modification of that of Rényi and Turán [Acta Arith. **4** (1958), 71–84; MR **20** #3112]. *J. Kubilius* (Vilnius)

Citations: MR 20# 3112 = N60-31.

## N60-54 (32# 7536 )

**Grigelionis, B.**

**The distribution of values of arithmetic multiplicative functions. (Lithuanian. Russian summary)**

*Vilniaus Valst. Univ. Mokslo Darbai Mat. Fiz.* **9** (1960), 71–73.

Let $f(m)$ be a non-negative strong multiplicative arithmetical function. Denote by $\mathfrak{A}$ the set of primes $p$ for which $f(p) = 0$, and by $P_n$ the number of $p \leq n$, $p \in \mathfrak{A}$. Let

$$A_n = \sum_{p \leq n, p \notin \mathfrak{A}} \frac{\log f(p)}{p}, \qquad B_n^2 = \sum_{p \leq n, p \notin \mathfrak{A}} \frac{\log^2 f(p)}{p},$$

$p_0 = 1 - \prod_{p \in \mathfrak{A}} (1 - 1/p)$. Suppose that $\log P_n = o(\log n)$ and that there exists a function $\alpha(n)$ such that $\log \alpha(n) = o(\log n)$, $B_n \sim B_{\alpha(n)}$ as $n \to \infty$.

By using the reviewer's method [*Probabilistic methods in the theory of numbers* (Russian), Gosudarstv. Izdat. Političesk. i Naučn. Lit. Litovsk. SSR, Vilnius, 1959; MR **23** #A134; second edition, 1962; MR **26** #3691; English translation, Amer. Math. Soc., Providence, R.I., 1964; MR **28** #3956], the author proves the following theorem. Let $f(m)$ satisfy the above conditions. A necessary and sufficient condition that the relative frequency of positive integers $m \leq n$ for which $f(m) < e^{A_n + B_n x}$ should tend to a limiting distribution with variance $1 - p_0$ as $n \to \infty$ is that there should exist a non-decreasing function $K(u)$ $(-\infty < u < \infty)$ with $K(\infty) - K(-\infty) = 1$ such that

$$\frac{1}{B_n^2} \sum_{\substack{p \leq n, p \notin \mathfrak{A} \\ \log f(p) < uB_n}} \frac{\log^2 f(p)}{p} \to K(u)$$

for $u \neq 0$. The characteristic function of the limit law is $p_0 + (1 - p_0)\varphi(t)$, where

$$\log \varphi(t) = \int_{-\infty}^{\infty} \frac{(e^{itu} - 1 - itu)}{u^2}\, dK(u).$$

*J. Kubilius* (Vilnius)

Citations: MR 23# A134 = N60-37; MR 26# 3691 = N60-38; MR 28# 3956 = N60-39.

## N60-55 (32# 7537 )

**Kubiljus, I. P. [Kubilius, J. P.]**

**On some problems in probabilistic number theory. (Russian)**

*Proc. Sixth All-Union Conf. Theory Prob. and Math. Statist. (Vilnius, 1960) (Russian), pp. 57–68. Gosudarstv. Izdat. Političesk. i Naučn. Lit. Litovsk. SSR, Vilnius,* 1962.

This is an early account of a result that has since been superseded in works already reviewed. The main result here is Theorem 1: For $n\to\infty$, $x=o\{\sqrt{(\ln\ln n)}\}$, we have

$$\nu_n\left\{\frac{\omega(m)-\ln\ln n}{\sqrt{(\ln\ln n)}}<x\right\} = G(x)e^{Q_n(x)}\left\{1+O\left(\frac{|x|+1}{\sqrt{(\ln\ln n)}}\right)\right\}$$

if $x\leqq 0$, and a complementary formula for $x\geqq 0$ with $<$ replaced by $>$ and $G(x)$ by $1-G(x)$. On the left-hand side, $\omega(m)$ is the number of distinct prime factors of $m$, and $\nu_n\{\cdots\}$ is the proportion of integers $m$ in $1\leqq m\leqq n$ for which the statement in $\{\cdots\}$ holds. On the right-hand side,

$$G(x) = \frac{1}{\sqrt{(2\pi)}}\int_{-\infty}^{x} e^{-u^2/2}\,du,$$

$$Q_n(x) = \sum_{k=3}^{\infty}\frac{(-1)^{k-1}}{k(k-1)}\left(\frac{x}{\sqrt{(\ln\ln n)}}\right)^k \ln\ln n.$$

In § 9 of the second edition of his book *Probabilistic methods in the theory of numbers* (Russian) [Gosudarstv. Izdat. Političesk. i Naučn. Lit. Litovsk. SSR, Vilnius, 1962; MR **26** #3691; English translation, Amer. Math. Soc., Providence, R.I., 1964; MR **28** #3956; first edition, 1959; MR **23** #A134] the author replaces the right-hand side by an asymptotic expansion (a result also obtained independently by Delange [Acta Arith. **7** (1961/62), 191–215; MR **25** #58]). *A. E. Ingham* (Cambridge, England)

Citations: MR 23# A134 = N60-37; MR 25# 58 = N60-42; MR 26# 3691 = N60-38; MR 28# 3956 = N60-39.

## N60-56 (32# 7539)

**Uždavinis, R. V.**

**On the problem of distribution of additive arithmetical functions of polynomials over the integers.** (Russian)

*Proc. Sixth All-Union Conf. Theory Prob. and Math. Statist.* (*Vilnius*, 1960) (*Russian*), *pp.* 125–127. *Gosudarstv. Izdat. Političesk. i Naučn. Lit. Litovsk. SSR, Vilnius*, 1962.

Let $g_1(m),\cdots,g_s(m)$ be irreducible relatively prime polynomials of positive degree with integer coefficients. Suppose that the coefficients of the polynomial $g_j(m)$ are relatively prime. Let $f_1(m),\cdots,f_s(m)$ be real additive arithmetical functions

$$A_{ij}(n) = \sum_{p\leqq n} f_i(p)\vartheta_j(p)/p,$$

$$B_j(n) = \Big(\sum_{p\leqq n} f_j^2(p)\vartheta_j(p)/p\Big)^{1/2} \qquad (i,j=1,\cdots,s),$$

where $p$ runs over all primes $p\leqq n$ and $\vartheta_j(p)$ is the number of residue classes which satisfy the congruence $g_j(m)\equiv 0$ mod $p$. Suppose that $B_j(n)\to\infty$, $\max_{p\leqq n}|f_j(p^\alpha)|=o(\alpha^k B_j(n))$ ($j=1,\cdots,s$; $\alpha=1,2,\cdots$) as $n\to\infty$, where $k$ is a constant. Let $G(x)=(2\pi)^{-1/2}\int_{-\infty}^{x}\exp(-u^2/2)\,du$. The author states the following theorems. The relative frequency of positive integers $m\leqq n$ for which

$$\frac{1}{\sqrt{s}}\sum_{j=1}^{s}\frac{f_j(|g_j(m)|)-A_{jj}(n)}{B_j(n)} < x$$

tends to $G(x)$ for $n\to\infty$, and the relative frequency of $m\leqq n$ for which

$$\frac{f_j(|g_j(m)|)-A_{jj}(n)}{B_j(n)} < x_j \qquad (j=1,\cdots,s)$$

tends to $G(x_1)\cdots G(x_s)$ as $n\to\infty$. If $\sum_{p\leqq n}(TL_n(p))^2\vartheta_j(p)/p$ tends to a non-negative quadratic form $\sigma(T)$ as $n\to\infty$, where $L_n(p)=(f_1(p)/B_1(n),\cdots,f_s(p)/B_s(n))$, $T=(t_1,\cdots,t_s)$, then the relative frequency of $m\leqq n$ for which

$$\frac{f_j(|g_1(m)|)-A_{j1}(n)}{B_j(n)} < x_j \qquad (j=1,\cdots,s)$$

tends to a limit law with the characteristic function $\exp(-\frac{1}{2}\sigma(T))$. *J. Kubilius* (Vilnius)

## N60-57 (33# 5595)

**Danilov, A. N.**

**On sequences of values of additive arithmetical functions defined on the set of ideals of a field $K$ of degree $n$ over the field of rational numbers.** **(Russian)**

*Leningrad. Gos. Ped. Inst. Učen. Zap.* **274** (1965), 59–70.

From the author's introduction: "In the present paper, using the methods which I. Kubilius used to investigate the sequence of values of an additive arithmetic function on the set 1, 2, 3, $\cdots$ [I. Kubilius, *Probability methods in number theory* (Russian), pp. 46–61, Gosudarstv. Izdat. Politič. Naučn. Lit. Litovsk. SSR, Vilnius, 1959; MR **23** #A134], we obtain analogous results for additive functions defined on the set of ideals of the field of the title." The relevant portion of Kubilius' book is the third chapter, pp. 30–42 of the American translation [Amer. Math. Soc., Providence, R.I., 1964; MR **28** #3956] of the second, enlarged edition published in 1962 [MR **26** #3691]. *J. W. S. Cassels* (Cambridge, England)

Citations: MR 23# A134 = N60-37; MR 26# 3691 = N60-38; MR 28# 3956 = N60-39.

## N60-58 (34# 1282)

**Delange, H.**

**Sur un théorème de Rényi.**

*Acta Arith.* **11** (1965), 241–252.

Let $\omega(n)$ denote the number of different prime factors and $\Omega(n)$ the total number of prime factors of $n$. Let $V_k(x)$ denote the number of positive integers $n\leqq x$ for which $\Omega(n)-\omega(n)=k$. It has been shown by the reviewer [Publ. Inst. Math. (Beograd) **8** (1955), 157–162; MR **17**, 944] that $\lim_{x\to+\infty}V_k(x)/x=d_k$ exists for $k=0,1,\cdots$ and one has $\sum_{k=0}^{\infty}d_kz^k=\prod_p(1-1/p)(1+1/(p-z))$, where $p$ runs over all primes and $|z|<2$. The author proves that for $x\to+\infty$ one has $V_k(x)=d_kx+o((\sqrt{x})(\log\log x)^k)$ ($k=0,1,2,\cdots$). For the special case $k=0$ (i.e., for the number $V_0(x)$ of square free numbers $\leqq x$) this was shown already by E. Landau [*Handbuch der Lehre von der Verteilung der Primzahlen*, Vol. II, Teubner, Leipzig, 1909; second edition, Chelsea, New York, 1953; MR **16**, 904], and for $k=1$ by E. Cohen [Proc. Amer. Math. Soc. **13** (1962), 536–539; MR **25** #2049]. The proof is based on the fact that the Riemann zeta-function $\zeta(s)$ ($s=\sigma+it$) has no zeros with $\sigma=1$, and on theorems of Tauberian type. *A. Rényi* (Budapest)

Citations: MR 16, 904d = N02-3; MR 17, 944f = N24-23; MR 25# 2049 = N24-40.

Referred to in N52-46, N60-67, N60-71.

## N60-59 (34# 4230)

**Kubiljus, I. [Kubilius, J.]**

**On asymptotic laws of distribution of additive arithmetical functions.** **(Russian. Lithuanian and French summaries)**

*Litovsk. Mat. Sb.* **5** (1965), 261–273.

Sei $f(m)$ eine reellwertige, streng additive, zahlentheoretische Funktion und $A_1, A_2,\cdots$ eine reelle Zahlenfolge, ferner $x$ reell und $\nu_n(x)$ die relative Häufigkeit der Zahlen $m$ im Abschnitt $1,\cdots,n$, für die $f(m)-A_n<x$ gilt. Der Verfasser beweist folgende Verallgemeinerung eines bekannten Satzes von P. Erdős und A. Wintner [Amer. J. Math. **61** (1939), 713–721; MR **1**, 40]: Dann und nur dann existiert eine Verteilungsfunktion $\varphi(x)$ mit $\lim_{n\to\infty}\nu_n(x)=\varphi(x)$ für jeden Stetigkeitspunkt von $\varphi(x)$, wenn es eine Zahl $c>0$ so gibt, dass die beiden Reihen

$\sum_{|f(p)|\geqq c} 1/p$, $\sum_{|f(p)|<c} f^2(p)/p$ und die Folge $A_n - \sum_{p\leqq n, |f(p)|<c} f(p)/p$ konvergieren. Die charakteristische Funktion von $\varphi(x)$ wird explizit angegeben und ferner bewiesen, dass $\varphi(x)$ diskret oder stetig ist, je nachdem ob die Reihe $\sum_{f(p)\neq 0} 1/p$ konvergiert oder divergiert.

Im Unterschied zu den bisherigen Beweisen von Erdős-Wintner selbst und von mehreren anderen Autoren ist der vorliegende Beweis stärker wahrscheinlichkeitstheoretisch orientiert. Er verwendet Hilfsmittel aus dem Buch des Verfassers über wahrscheinlichkeitstheoretische Methoden in der Zahlentheorie [*Probability methods in number theory* (Russian), Gosudarstv. Izdat. Politič. Naučn. Lit. Litovsk. SSR, Vilnius, 1959; MR **23** #A134; second, enlarged edition, 1962; MR **26** #3691; English translation, Amer. Math. Soc., Providence, R.I., 1964; MR **28** #3956].

{See also #4231 below.} *B. Volkmann* (Stuttgart)

Citations: MR 1, 40c = N60-1; MR 23# A134 = N60-37; MR 26# 3691 = N60-38; MR 28# 3956 = N60-39.

## N60-60 (34# 4231)

**Kubiljus, I. [Kubilius, J.]**

**Letter to the editor. (Russian)**

*Litovsk. Mat. Sb.* **6** (1966), 132.

Korrektur eines Fehlers auf Seite 268 des oben referierten Artikel [#4230], der jedoch den Gang des Beweises nicht wesentlich beeinflußt. *B. Volkmann* (Stuttgart)

## N60-61 (34# 5780)

**Tjan, M. M.**

**On the question of the distribution of values of the Euler function $\varphi(n)$. (Russian. Lithuanian and French summaries)**

*Litovsk. Mat. Sb.* **6** (1966), 105–119.

Let $P_N(\lambda)$ be the number of positive integers $n\leqq N$ satisfying the inequality $\varphi(n)/n<\lambda$, where $\varphi(n)$ is the Euler $\varphi$-function. I. J. Schoenberg [Trans. Amer. Math. Soc. **39** (1936), 315–330] has proved that $P_N(\lambda)/N$ tends to a continuous distribution function $v(\lambda)$, as $N\to\infty$. The author improves this result by showing that for $\lambda\in(0,1)$, $P_N(\lambda)/N=v(\lambda)+O((\lambda\ln\ln N)^{-1}+(\ln\ln\ln N)^{-1})$. He also gives an estimation of the expression $\sum_{n=1}^N F(\varphi(n)/n)/N-\int_0^1 F(x)\,dv(x)$ for some classes of functions $F$ which admit a good approximation by polynomials.

*J. Kubilius* (Vilnius)

Referred to in N48-23.

## N60-62 (34# 5794)

**Barban, M. B.; Vinogradov, A. I.; Levin, B. V.**

**Limit laws for functions of the class $H$ of I. P. Kubilius which are defined on a set of "shifted" primes. (Russian. Lithuanian and English summaries)**

*Litovsk. Mat. Sb.* **5** (1965), 5–8.

Let $f(m)$ be a real strongly additive arithmetic function. Put $A_n=\sum f(p)/p$, $B_n^2=\sum f^2(p)/p$, where the summations extend over all primes $p\leqq n$: Denote by $\nu_n(x)$ the frequency of primes $p\leqq n$ for which the inequality $f(p-l)<A_n+xB_n$ with a fixed integer $l\neq 0$ holds. In his earlier paper [Akad. Nauk Uzbek. SSR Trudy Inst. Mat. No. 22 (1961), 1–20; MR **30** #1990] the first author found a necessary and sufficient condition for the convergence of $\nu_n(x)$ to a limit distribution function as $n\to\infty$ in case the function $f(m)$ satisfies the following conditions: (1) there exists a function $r(n)$ of $n$ such that $\ln r(n)/\ln n\to 0$, $B(r(n))/B(n)\to 1$ as $n\to\infty$; (2) $f(p)=O(B_n)$ for all primes $p\leqq n$. The aim of this paper is to show that condition (2) is superfluous. *J. Kubilius* (Vilnius)

Citations: MR 30# 1990 = N12-28.

## N60-63 (34# 5796)

**de Kroon, J. P. M.**

**The asymptotic behaviour of additive functions in algebraic number theory.**

*Compositio Math.* **17**, 207–261 (1965).

This paper generalizes results of P. Erdős and M. Kac [Amer. J. Math. **62** (1940), 738–742; MR **2**, 42], I. P. Kubilius [Uspehi Mat. Nauk **11** (1956), no. 2 (68), 31–66; MR **18**, 17; translated in Amer. Math. Soc. Transl. (2) **19** (1962), 47–85; MR **24** #A1266], A. Rényi and P. Turán [Acta Arith. **4** (1958), 71–84; MR **20** #3112] and H. Halberstam [J. London Math. Soc. **31** (1956), 1–14; MR **17**, 461; ibid. **31** (1956), 14–27; MR **17**, 461] concerning the behavior of additive number-theoretic functions to algebraic number fields and algebraic function fields with finite fields of constants. E.g., for algebraic number fields, theorems of the following type are proved. Let $R$ be the ring of integers of a fixed algebraic number field of absolute degree $n$. For $r$ in $R$ put $\|r\|=\max|r_i|$, where $r_1,\cdots,r_n$ are the conjugates of $r$. Denote by $A$, $B$, $\cdots$ ideals, by $P$ prime ideals of $R$ and by $NP$ their norms. Consider a map $S$ of $R$ into $R$ with the property $S(r)\equiv S(r')\bmod P$ whenever $r\equiv r'\bmod P$ for any $P$. Let $l(P)$ be the number of incongruent solutions of the congruence $S(r)\equiv 0\bmod P$. For $x>0$ and for a map $f$ of the set of ideals of $R$ into the reals with the properties $f(AB)=f(A)+f(B)$ for $(A,B)=R$, $f(P^k)=f(P)$ for $k\geqq 1$, and $|f(P)|\leqq 1$, put $A(x)=\sum_P l(P)f(P)/NP$ and $B^2(x)=\sum_P l(P)f^2(P)/NP$, where the summation over the $P$ is subject to the condition $NP\leqq x$. For real $u$ define $G(x,u)$ as the number of all $r$ in $R$ with $\|r\|\leqq x^{1/n}$ and with $f((S(r)))\leqq A(x)+uB(x)$, and $H(x)$ as the number of all $r$ in $R$ with $\|r\|\leqq x^{1/n}$. Then, if $B(x)\to\infty$ as $x\to\infty$, for suitable functions $S$ (e.g., when $S(r)$ is a fixed polynomial of the variable $r$ with coefficients in $R$) we have $G(x,u)/H(x)=(2\pi)^{-1/2}\int_{-\infty}^u \exp(-t^2/2)\,dt+O((B(x))^{-1/2})$ uniformly in $u$ as $x\to\infty$. The method of proof is analogous to that of Erdős and Kac. *O. H. Körner* (Marburg)

Citations: MR 2, 42c = N60-4; MR 17, 461d = N60-15; MR 17, 461e = N60-16; MR 18, 17d = Q15-4; MR 20# 3112 = N60-31; MR 24# A1266 = Q15-5.

## N60-64 (34# 5797)

**Levin, B. V.; Faĭnleĭb, A. S.**

**Distribution of values of additive arithmetic functions. (Russian)**

*Dokl. Akad. Nauk SSSR* **171** (1966), 281–284.

Let $g(m)$ be a real additive arithmetic function. It is called measurable if there exists a distribution function $\Phi(x)$ such that (*) $(\pi(n))^{-1}\sum 1\to\Phi(x)$ as $n\to\infty$ at each point of continuity of $\Phi(x)$, where the summation is extended over all primes $p\leqq n$ with $g(p)\leqq x$, and $\pi(n)$ is the number of primes $p\leqq n$. For every distribution function $\Phi(x)$ there exists an additive function $g(m)$ satisfying (*).

Let $g_1(p)=g(p)$ if $|g(p)|\leqq 1$ and $g_1(p)=1$ if $|g(p)|>1$. Suppose that for a measurable additive function $g(m)$, the series $\sum_p g_1^2(p)/p$ diverges. The authors find a necessary and sufficient condition for the existence of sequences $\{A_n\}$ and $\{B_n\}$ such that the frequency of positive integers $m\leqq n$ satisfying the inequality $g(m)\leqq A_n+xB_n$ tends to a limiting distribution as $n\to\infty$.

The main tool of the proof is the following theorem. Let $f(m)$ be a multiplicative function depending on a parameter $\tau$ and satisfying the conditions $|f(m)|=1$ for all positive integers $m$, and $\sum_{p\leqq x} f(p)\sim\tau x/\log x$ uniformly in $\tau$ for $\operatorname{Re}\tau\geqq\delta$, where $\delta>0$ is any fixed number. Then $\sum_{m\leqq x} f(m)=(e^{-C\tau}/\Gamma(\tau))(x/\log x)\prod_{p\leqq x}\sum_{k=0}^\infty f(p^k)/p^k+o(x)$ uniformly in $\tau$, $\operatorname{Re}\tau\geqq\delta$. Here $C$ is Euler's constant and $\Gamma(\tau)$ is the gamma function. The proof of this theorem is based on some ideas of E. Wirsing [Math. Ann. **143** (1961), 75–102; MR **24** #A1241].

{This article has appeared in English translation [Soviet Math. Dokl. **7** (1966), 1474–1477].} *J. Kubilius* (Vilnius)

Citations: MR 24# A1241 = N36-30.
Referred to in N60-74.

## N60-65 (34# 5798)

**Misjavičjus, G. [Misevičius, G.]**

**The use of the method of moments in probabilistic number theory. (Russian. Lithuanian and English summaries)**

*Litovsk. Mat. Sb.* **5** (1965), 275–289.

Let $f(m)$ be a real strongly additive number-theoretic function. Put $A(n)=\sum_{p\leqq n}f(p)/p$, $B^2(n)=\sum_{p\leqq n}f^2(p)/p$, where $p$ runs over all primes not exceeding $n$. Suppose that there exists a function $r(n)$ of $n$ for which $\ln r(n)/\ln n\to 0$, $B(r(n))/B(n)\to 1$ as $n\to\infty$. Denote by $\mu_n(x)$ $[\nu_n(x)]$ the proportion of positive integers $m\leqq n$, for which $f(m)<A(n)+xB(n)$ $[f(m)-f(m+a)<xB(n)]$, respectively, where $a$ is a fixed positive integer. The reviewer proved [Uspehi Mat. Nauk **11** (1956), no. 2 (68), 31–66; MR **18**, 17; translated in Amer. Math. Soc. Transl. (2) **19** (1962), 47–85; MR **24** #A1266] a necessary and sufficient condition that $\mu_n(x)$ and $\nu_n(x)$ should tend to a limiting distribution. An essential part of the proof was achieved by the application of the sieve of Eratosthenes. H. Delange [C. R. Acad. Sci. Paris **244** (1957), 1604–1606; MR **19**, 394] gave an outline of another proof for $\mu_n(x)$ based on the moment method, which permits one to avoid a rather complicated application of the sieve of Eratosthenes.

The author obtains a full proof founded on the moment method for both $\mu_n(x)$ and $\nu_n(x)$. *J. Kubilius* (Vilnius)

Citations: MR 18, 17d = Q15-4; MR 19, 394b = N60-25; MR 24# A1266 = Q15-5.

## N60-66 (35# 6636)

**Faĭnleĭb, A. S.**

**Distribution of values of Euler's function. (Russian)**

*Mat. Zametki* **1** (1967), 645–652.

Let $\varphi(n)$ be Euler's function and $N\cdot\phi_N(x)$ be the number of integers $n$, $1\leqq n\leqq N$, satisfying $\varphi(n)/n<x$. J. Schoenberg [Math. Z. **28** (1928), 171–199] proved that $\lim_{N\to\infty}\phi_N(x)=\phi(x)$ exists and is continuous. The author proves three theorems. We quote the first: $\phi_N(x)=\phi(x)+O(1/\ln\ln N)$ uniformly in $x\in[0,1]$. *J. E. Cigler* (Groningen)

Referred to in N60-76, N80-56.

## N60-67 (37# 4037)

**Delange, H.**

**Sur un théorème de Rényi. II.**

*Acta Arith.* **13** (1967/68), 339–362.

Let $\Omega(n)$ denote the number of all prime factors and $\omega(n)$ the number of different prime factors of $n$ $(n=1,2,\cdots)$. For each nonnegative integer $q$, denote by $V_q(x)$ the number of natural numbers $n\leqq x$ for which $\Omega(n)-\omega(n)=q$. It has been shown by the reviewer [Acad. Serbe Sci. Publ. Inst. Math. **8** (1955), 157–162; MR **17**, 944] that $\lim_{x\to+\infty}V_q(x)/x=d_q$, where

$$\sum_{q=0}^{+\infty}d_qz^q=(6/\pi^2)\prod_p(1-z/(p+1))/(1-z/p);$$

here $p$ runs over all primes. In the first part of this paper [Acta Arith. **11** (1965), 241–252; MR **34** #1282] the author proved that (1) $V_q(x)=d_q\cdot x+o(x^{1/2}(\log\log x)^q)$ $(q=0,1,\cdots)$. His proof was analytic and used the fact that the Riemann zeta function $\zeta(s)$ $(s=\sigma+it)$ has no zeros on the line $\sigma=1$. This result was slightly improved by I. Kátai [Magyar Tud. Akad. Mat. Fiz. Oszt. Közl. **16** (1966), 269–273] to (2) $V_q(x)=d_q\cdot x+O(x^{1/2}(\log\log x)^{q-1})$ $(q\geqq 1)$. In the present paper (1) is deduced in an elementary way from the relation $\sum_{n\leqq x}\mu(n)=o(x)$; at the same time the theorem is generalized for $V_q(x,E)$ instead of $V_q(x)$, where $E$ is an arbitrary set of primes and $V_q(x,E)$ denotes the number of natural numbers $n\leqq x$ for which $\Omega(n,E)-\omega(n,E)=q$; here $\Omega(n,E)$ is the total number of prime factors and $\omega(n,E)$ the number of different prime factors of $n$ which belong to the set $E$. By the same method, using instead of $\sum_{n\leqq x}\mu(n)=o(x)$ the stronger estimate $\sum_{n\leqq x}\mu(n)=O(xe^{-c\sqrt{\log x}})$, where $c>0$, it is shown that (1) can be improved to the remarkably sharp estimate (3) $V_q(x)=d_q\cdot x+O(x^{1/2}(\log\log x)^{q-1}/\log x)$ $(q\geqq 1)$.
*A. Rényi* (Budapest)

Citations: MR 17, 944f = N24-23; MR 34# 1282 = N60-58; MR 38# 5726 = N60-71.
Referred to in N52-46, N60-83.

## N60-68 (37# 4039)

**Galambos, J.**

**On the distribution of prime-independent additive number-theoretical functions.**

*Arch. Math.* (*Basel*) **19** (1968), 296–299.

A number-theoretic function $f(n)$ is called prime-independent if $f(p^k)$ depends only on $k$ for all primes $p$.

In this paper the author proves a simple lemma (Theorem 3) which he then shows allows one to use the method of A. Rényi and P. Turán [Acta Arith. **4** (1958), 74–84; MR **20** #3112] to show that if $f(n)$ is a real-valued prime-independent additive ($f(mn)=f(m)+f(n)$ whenever $(m,n)=1$) number-theoretic function such that $f(p)\neq 0$ and $f(p^k)=O(k^{-1}2^{k/2})$, then $N_n(f,x)/n=(2\pi)^{-1/2}\times\int_{-\infty}^x e^{-t^2/2}\,dt+O((\log\log n)^{-1/2})$ uniformly in $x$, where $N_n(f,x)$ is the number of positive integers $k\leqq n$ such that $(f(k)-f(p)\log\log n)(f(p)(\log\log n)^{1/2})^{-1}<x$. (Rényi and Turán proved this theorem for $f(n)=\Omega(n)$, the number of prime factors of $n$ (multiple factors counted multiply) and observed that their method sufficed for any additive number-theoretic function for which $f(p)=1$ and $|f(p^k)|\leqq k^\alpha$, $\alpha$ a constant independent of $p$; thus the author's contribution consists in pointing out that the growth requirement can be weakened.) *S. L. Segal* (Rochester, N.Y.)

Citations: MR 20# 3112 = N60-31.

## N60-69 (37# 4041)

**Uždavinis, R. [Uždavinys, R.]**

**An analogue of the Erdős-Wintner theorem for the sequence of values of an integral polynomial. (Russian. Lithuanian and German summaries)**

*Litovsk. Mat. Sb.* **7** (1967), 329–338.

Sei $f$ eine reellwertige additive zahlentheoretische Funktion, $R$ ein Polynom mit ganzen Koeffizienten. Der Autor verallgemeinert den bekannten Satz von P. Erdős und A. Wintner über additive Funktionen [Amer. J. Math. **61** (1939), 713–721; MR **1**, 40]—unter gewissen milden Voraussetzungen über $f$ und über das Polynom $R$—zu folgendem Ergebnis: Für $n\to\infty$ konvergiert $n^{-1}\cdot N\{m\leqq n, f(R(m))<x\}$ genau dann gegen eine asymptotische Verteilungsfunktion $F(x)$, wenn die beiden Reihen

$$\sum_p p^{-1}f(p)L_R(p)$$

und $\sum_p p^{-1}f^2(p)L_R(p)$ konvergieren; hierbei bezeichnet $L_R(p)$ die Lösungsanzahl der Kongruenz $R(m)\equiv 0 \bmod p$ und $N\{\cdots\}$ die Anzahl der natürlichen Zahlen $m$ mit den in $\{\cdots\}$ angegebenen Eigenschaften. Die charakteristische Funktion der Verteilungsfunktion $F$ wird explizit gegeben.
*W. Schwarz* (Freiburg)

Citations: MR 1, 40c = N60-1.

**N60-70** **(38# 1065 )**

**Danilov, A. N.**

**Integral and local distribution laws for additive functions defined on the set of ideals of an algebraic number field** $K$**. (Russian)**

*Leningrad. Gos. Ped. Inst. Učen. Zap.* **302** (1967), 9–31.

This paper generalizes the reviewer's results [*Probabilistic methods in the theory of numbers* (Russian), Gosudarstv. Izdat. Politič. Naučn. Lit. Litovsk. SSR, Vilnius, 1959; MR **23** #A134; second edition, 1962; MR **26** #3691; English translation, Amer. Math. Soc., Providence, R.I., 1964; MR **28** #3956] concerning the behavior of additive number-theoretic functions in algebraic number fields.

More general results have been obtained by Z. Juškys [Litovsk. Mat. Sb. **4** (1964), 565–603; MR **30** #4741].

*J. Kubilius* (Vilnius)

Citations: MR 23# A134 = N60-37; MR 26# 3691 = N60-38; MR 28# 3956 = N60-39; MR 30# 4741 = N60-52.

**N60-71** **(38# 5726 )**

**Kátai, Imre**

**A remark on H. Delange's paper "Sur un théorème de Rényi". (Hungarian. English summary)**

*Magyar Tud. Akad. Mat. Fiz. Oszt. Közl.* **16** (1966), 269–273.

From the author's summary: "Let $\Omega(n)$, $\omega(n)$ be defined by $\Omega(p_1^{\alpha_1}\cdots p_r^{\alpha_r})=\alpha_1+\cdots+\alpha_r$, $\omega(p_1^{\alpha_1}\cdots p_r^{\alpha_r})=r$; let $q\geqq 0$ be any integer, and $\lambda_q(n)=1$ if $\Omega(n)-\omega(n)=q$, $\lambda_q(n)=0$ otherwise, and $\nu_q(x)=\sum_{n\leqq x}\lambda_q(n)$. H. Delange proved [Acta Arith. **11** (1965), 241–252; MR **34** #1282] that the estimation $\nu_q(x)=d_qx+o(x^{1/2}(\log\log x)^q)$ follows from the prime-number theorem. The proof is based on the use of Ikehara's tauberian theorem.

"In the present paper we prove that this estimation follows very simply from the relation $\nu_0(x)=d_0x+o(x^{1/2})$. Further, from the somewhat stronger estimation $\nu(x)=d_0x+O(x^{1/2}/\log x)$ follows the estimation $\nu_q(x)=d_qx+O(x^{1/2}(\log\log x)^{q-1})$. With a refinement of the proof we could prove that

$$\nu_q(x) = d_qx+x^{1/2}(\log\log x)^{q-1}P_{n,q}(1/\log\log x) + O(x^{1/2}(\log\log x)^{q-n-2}),$$

where $P_{n,q}(x)$ is a suitable polynomial of degree $n$."

Citations: MR 34# 1282 = N60-58.

Referred to in N40-74, N52-46, N60-67.

**N60-72** **(38# 5727 )**

**Kátai, Imre**

**On the distribution of the function** $dd(n)$**. (Hungarian. English summary)**

*Magyar Tud. Akad. Mat. Fiz. Oszt. Közl.* **17** (1967), 447–454.

Author's summary: "Let $d(n)$ denote the number of divisors of $n$, and let $dd(n)$ be the number of divisors of $d(n)$. Let $N(x,\alpha)$ denote the number of solutions of the inequality $dd(n)<\alpha z$, $n\leqq x$, where $z=\log\log x$. We prove the following assertion:

$$N(x,\alpha) = \{\textstyle\sum_{l\leqq[\alpha]-1} e_l+e_{[\alpha]}\Phi(\{\alpha\}z^{1/2}/[\alpha]) + e_{[\alpha]+1}\Phi((\{\alpha\}-1)z^{1/2}/([\alpha]+1))\}+O(x/z^{3/4})+R(x,\alpha),$$

where $R(x,\alpha)=O(x/z^{1/2})$, when $0\leqq\alpha\leqq 1$, and $R(x,\alpha)=O(x\alpha^{-M}/z^{1/2})$ when $\alpha\leqq 1$, $M$ an arbitrary constant, $\Phi(u)=(2\pi)^{-1/2}\int_{-\infty}^u e^{-t^2/2}\,dt$; further, $e_l\geqq 0$ for $l=1,2,\cdots$, and $\sum_{l=1}^\infty e_l=1$."

**N60-73** **(38# 5728 )**

**Kátai, I.**

**On the distribution of arithmetical functions.**

*Acta Math. Acad. Sci. Hungar.* **20** (1969), 69–87.

The author obtains various generalizations of results concerning the distribution of additive number theoretic functions. The existence and continuity of distribution functions in $S$ dimensions ($S$ being a natural number) associated with certain additive functions of integral valued polynomials subject to various restrictions are considered.

The explicit statement of the theorems requires various notations, and it would be too lengthy to quote them here.

*K. Thanigasalam* (University Park, Pa.)

Referred to in P48-21.

**N60-74** **(38# 5735 )**

**Levin, B. V.; Faĭnleĭb, A. S.**

**Integral limit theorems for certain classes of additive arithmetic functions. (Russian)**

*Trudy Moskov. Mat. Obšč.* **18** (1968), 19–54.

Let $\phi(n)$ be a measurable additive function on the natural numbers $n$ in the sense of the authors [Dokl. Akad. Nauk SSSR **171** (1966), 281–284; MR **34** #5797]. The authors investigate the existence of a distribution function of another additive function $\psi(m)$ by considering the "truncated" function $\psi_y(m)=\psi(m_1)+\phi(m_2)$, $m=m_1m_2$, where $y=y(n)$ is some function of $n$ such that $y(n)\to\infty$, $\ln(y)/\ln(n)\to 0$ $(n\to\infty)$ and $m_1$ is the product (with the appropriate multiplicities) of the prime divisors $p$ of $n$ with $p<y$. They introduce a class $H(\varphi)$ of $\psi$ for which this approach yields useful theorems (which are, however, rather too complicated to reproduce here). When $\phi(n)=0$ identically, the corresponding class $H(0)$ contains all the strongly additive functions of the class $H$ introduced by J. Kubilius [*Probabilistic methods in the theory of numbers* (Russian), Gosudarstv. Izdat. Politič. Naučn. Lit. Litovsk. SSR, Vilnius, 1959; MR **23** #A134; second enlarged edition, 1962; MR **26** #3691; translated in Amer. Math. Soc. Transl. No. 11 (1964); MR **28** #3956], and then the truncated function is the familiar one. The technique of proof is to use the theory of characteristic functions to cope with $\psi_y$ and then to use an analogue of Čebyšev's inequality to make the transition to $\psi$. The authors remark that, in particular, they extend the classical theorems of P. Erdős and M. Kac [Amer. J. Math. **62** (1940), 738–742; MR **2**, 42] and J. Kubilius [loc. cit., Theorem 4.1] from strongly additive to additive functions.

At the end of the paper the authors consider the analogous problems in which the function takes real values modulo one. *J. W. S. Cassels* (Cambridge, England)

Citations: MR 2, 42c = N60-4; MR 23# A134 = N60-37; MR 26# 3691 = N60-38; MR 28# 3956 = N60-39; MR 34# 5797 = N60-64.

Referred to in N60-94.

**N60-75** **(39# 131 )**

**Kátai, Imre**

**Estimating the number of prime divisors on Diophantinely smooth series. (Hungarian. English summary)**

*Magyar Tud. Akad. Mat. Fiz. Oszt. Közl.* **18** (1968), 147–154.

Author's summary: "Let $a_n$ denote a monotonically increasing sequence of integers, $A(x)=\sum_{a_n\leqq x}1$; $A(x,D,l)=\sum_{a_n\equiv l(D);\,a_n\leqq x}1$, for which the inequalities $A(x)\gg x/(\log x)^c$

and

$\sum_{D \leqq x^{\alpha}} \max_{l(D):(lD)=1} |A(x, D, l) - A(x)/\varphi(D)| \ll$

$$A(x)(\log x)^{-B}$$

hold with suitable constants $\alpha > 0$, $c > 0$ and with arbitrary constant $B$. Let $g(x)$ be an irreducible polynomial with integer coefficients differing from $cx$. Let $h(x)$ be an increasing function, $\lim_{x\to\infty} h(x) = \infty$; $U(n)$ denotes the number of different prime factors of $n$. For a constant $z > 1$ ($w = z-1$), let $N(x, z, h)$ denote the number of the $a_n$'s not exceeding $x$ for which $|U(g(a_n)) - z \log\log x| \leqq h(x)\sqrt{\log\log x}$. Combining the method of A. I. Vinogradov and Ju. V. Linnik [Uspehi Mat. Nauk (N.S.) **12** (1957), no. 4 (76), 277–280; MR **20** #831], P. Erdős [J. London Math. Soc. **27** (1952), 7–15; MR **13**, 438] and M. B. Barban [Izv. Akad. Nauk UzSSR Ser. Fiz.-Mat. Nauk **1964**, no. 6, 13–19; MR **31** #1239], we prove the following theorem:

$|\log(N(x, z, h)/(A(x)(\log x)^{w - z\log z}))| \ll h(x)(\log\log x)^{1/2}$."

Citations: MR 13, 438f = N40-19; MR 20# 831 = N40-31; MR 31# 1239 = N48-16.

## N60-76 (39# 146)

**Faĭnleĭb, A. S.**

**A generalization of Esseen's inequality and its application in probabilistic number theory. (Russian)**

*Izv. Akad. Nauk SSSR Ser. Mat.* **32** (1968), 859–879.

The main result is the following inequality. Let $F(x)$ and $G(x)$ be two distribution functions, $f(t)$ and $g(t)$ their characteristic functions. Then for every $T > 0$,

$$\sup_x |F(x) - G(x)| \leqq C(S_G(1/H) + \textstyle\int_0^T |f(t) - g(t)| t^{-1}\, dt),$$

where $C$ is an absolute constant and

$$S_G(h) = \sup_x \textstyle\int_0^h (G(x+u) - G(x-u))\, du.$$

This is a generalization of C. G. Esseen's inequality [Acta Math. **77** (1945), 1–125; MR **7**, 312].

Using this inequality some theorems on the distribution of number-theoretic functions are proved. We quote the following. Let $\varphi(m)$ be Euler's function and $N_n(\varphi(m)/m \leqq x)$ be the number of integers $m$, $1 \leqq m \leqq n$, satisfying $\varphi(m)/m \leqq x$. Then

$N_n(\varphi(m)/m \leqq x)/n =$

$$\Phi(x) + O(\log^{-1} n(\log\log n)^2(\log\log\log n)^{-2}),$$

where $\Phi(x)$ is a distribution function. This result is an improvement of the author's previous result [Mat. Zametki **1** (1967), 645–652; MR **35** #6636]. Analogous results are given for the number of representations of a given integer as a sum of eight squares and a more general class of number-theoretic functions.

*J. Kubilius* (Vilnius)

Citations: MR 7, 312a = P20-5; MR 35# 6636 = N60-66.

Referred to in E16-77.

## N60-77 (39# 3555)

**Billingsley, Patrick**

**On the central limit theorem for the prime divisor function.**

*Amer. Math. Monthly* **76** (1969), 132–139.

For any subset $A$ of the positive integers, the density of $A$ is defined to be $D(A) = \lim_n (N_n(A)/n)$, where $N_n(A)$ is the number of integers $m$, with $1 \leqq m \leqq n$, in $A$. For any positive integer $m$, $\nu(m)$ is the number of prime devisors of $m$, not counting multiplicity. The Hardy-Ramanujan theorem states that $D\{m : |(\nu(m) - \log\log m)/\sqrt{\log\log m}| \leqq g_m\} = 1$ for every sequence $\{g_m\}$ going to infinity. P. Erdős and M. Kac [Amer. J. Math. **62** (1940), 738–742; MR **2**, 42], using number theory techniques, proved a stronger result, namely, that, for $x \leqq y$,

(*) $D\{m : x \leqq (\nu(m) - \log\log m)/\sqrt{\log\log m} \leqq y\} =$

$$\textstyle\int_x^y \exp(-t^2/2)\, dt/\sqrt{2t}.$$

H. Halberstam [J. London Math. Soc. **30** (1955), 43–53; MR **16**, 569] proved (*) by a probabilistic method using the method of moments. The author further simplifies Halberstam's approach avoiding all tedious moment calculations by introducing some auxiliary independent random variables and makes the proof more transparent to the student of probability theory.

*J. Sethuraman* (Tallahassee, Fla.)

Citations: MR 2, 42c = N60-4; MR 16, 569g = N60-13.

## N60-78 (39# 5498)

**Kátai, I.**

**On distribution of arithmetical functions on the set prime plus one.**

*Compositio Math.* **19**, 278–289 (1968).

Let $f(n)$ be a real valued additive number theoretical function, and put $f^*(n) = f(n)$ for $|f(n)| \leqq 1$, $f^*(n) = 0$ for $|f(n)| > 1$, and $F_N(y) = (\mathrm{li}\, N)^{-1} \sum_{f(p+1)<y,\, p \leqq N} 1$, where $\mathrm{li}\, x = \int_2^x du/\log u$. Also assume (1) $\sum_p f^*(p)/p$ is convergent, (2) $\sum_p (f^*(p))^2/p < +\infty$, (3) $\sum_{|f(p)|>1} 1/p < +\infty$, where $p$ denotes a prime. Then the author proves Theorem 1: The distribution functions $F_N(y)$ for $N \to \infty$ tend to a limiting distribution function $F(y)$ at all points of continuity of $F(y)$. Further, $F(y)$ is a continuous function if and only if $\sum_{f(p)\neq 0} 1/p = \infty$.

As immediate corollaries it follows that the functions $\phi(p+1)/(p+1)$, $\sigma(p+1)/(p+1)$ ($\phi(n)$ being Euler's function and $\sigma(n)$ the sum of the divisors of $n$) have limiting functions.

A more general theorem, from which Theorem 1 can be obtained, has been proved. For other results of similar nature, reference may be made to P. Erdős [J. London Math. Soc. **13** (1938), 119–127], H. Delange [Ann. Sci. École Norm. Sup. (3) **68** (1961), 1–29; MR **30** #71] and A. Rényi [Publ. Math. Debrecen **10** (1963), 264–273; MR **29** #3414]. {Reviewer's remark: On page 279, line 27, "distribvtron-function" should read "distribution function".}

*J. M. Gandhi* (Macomb, Ill.)

Citations: MR 29# 3414 = N60-51; MR 30# 71 = N36-37.

Referred to in P48-21.

## N60-79 (40# 2630)

**Bakštis, A. [Bakštys, A.]**

**The distribution of values of multiplicative arithmetic functions. (Russian)**

*Dokl. Akad. Nauk SSSR* **187** (1969), 1215–1218.

The author investigates the question of the existence of a limiting distribution of multiplicative functions in the sense of the characteristic transformation of V. M. Zolotarev [same Dokl. **142** (1962), 788–791; MR **24** #A2402]. He reduces the problem to certain finiteness conditions for sums of multiplicative functions involving prime numbers. He announces several theorems in this direction.

{This article has appeared in English translation [Soviet Math. Dokl. **10** (1969), 1001–1005].}

*A. I. Vinogradov* (Leningrad)

**N60-80** **(40# 4231 )**

**Bakštis, A. [Bakštys, A.]**

**Limit laws of a distribution of multiplicative arithmetic functions. I, II. (Russian. Lithuanian and German summaries)**

*Litovsk. Mat. Sb.* 8 (1968), 5–20; *ibid.* 8 (1968), 201–219.

Let $g(m)$ denote a real-valued multiplicative function, let $x^* = x$ or 1, according as $|x| \leqq 1$ or $|x| > 1$. We say that $\nu_n\{g(m) < x\} = n^{-1} \sum_{g(m)<x, m \leqq n} 1$ has a limit-distribution function $F(x)$ if $\lim_{n\to\infty} \nu_n\{g(m) < x\} = F(x)$ at every point of continuity of $F(x)$ and $\nu_n\{g(m) < 0\} \to F(0)$, $\nu_n\{g(m) \leqq 0\} \to F(+0)$ unless $F(+0) - F(0) = 1$. $p$ denotes a prime number.

The following assertions are proven. (1) $g(n)$ has a nonsymmetrical limit-distribution if and only if the series $\sum_p (|g(p)|-1)^*/p$, $\sum_p ((|g(p)|-1)^*)^2/p$, $\sum_{g(p)<0} 1/p$ converge and $g(2^\alpha) \neq -1$ for at least one $\alpha$. (2) Suppose that $g(m)$ has a limit distribution $F(x)$ and $F(+0) - F(0) < 1$. Then $F(x)$ is symmetrical if and only if at least one of the following conditions holds: (a) the series $\sum_{g(p)<0} 1/p$ diverges, (b) $g(2^\alpha) = -1$ for every $\alpha = 1, 2, \cdots$. (3) Let $\rho(n)$ be an arbitrary convergent sequence of real numbers, $a_n = \exp(\rho(n) - \sum_{p\leqq n} (g(p)-1)^*/p)$. Suppose that for every $\lambda > 0$, $\sum_{x<p\leqq x^\lambda} (|g(p)|-1)^*/p \to 0$ as $x \to \infty$. Then $\nu_n\{a_n g(m) < x\} = n^{-1} \sum_{m \leqq n, a_n g(m) < x} 1 (n \to \infty)$ has a nonsymmetrical limit-distribution function if and only if both the series $\sum_p ((|g(p)|-1)^*)^2/p$, $\sum_{g(p)<0} 1/p$ converge and $g(2^\alpha) \neq -1$ for at least one $\alpha$.

For the proofs, the method of Delange is used.

*I. Kátai* (Budapest)

**N60-81** **(40# 4232 )**

**Bakštis, A. [Bakštys, A.]**

**Limit laws of a distribution of multiplicative arithmetic functions. III. (Russian. Lithuanian and German summaries)**

*Litovsk. Mat. Sb.* 8 (1968), 643–680.

Let $\nu_n\{\cdots\}$ be the density of the integers $m \leqq n$, for which the condition stated in the brackets holds, $\nu_n\{A|B\} = \nu_n\{A \cap B\}/\nu_n\{B\}$. Let $g(m)$ be a multiplicative number-theoretic function, $A(n) = \sum_{p \leqq n, g(p) \neq 0} p^{-1} \log|g(p)|$, $B^2(n) = \sum_{p\leqq n, g(p)\neq 0} p^{-1} \log^2|g(p)|$. There are stated necessary and sufficient conditions for the existence of the limit of $\nu_n\{e^{-A(n)/B(n)} \cdot |g(m)|^{1/B(n)} \operatorname{sgn} g(m) < x | g(m) \neq 0\}$ as $n \to \infty$, assuming that $g(m)$ belongs to the class $\mathfrak{M}_H$, i.e., when $\sum_{g(p)=0} 1/p < \infty$, $B(n) \to 0$ $(n \to \infty)$, there exists a function $r = r(n) \to \infty$ such that $(\log n)^{-1} \log r \to 0$, $B(r)/B(n) \to 1$, $\nu_n\{\prod_{p|m, p>r} g(p) < 0\} \to 0$.

{For Parts I and II, see the preceding review [#4231].}

*I. Kátai* (Budapest)

**N60-82** **(40# 5558 )**

**Kátai, Imre**

**A local limit theorem in number theory. (Hungarian. English summary)**

*Mat. Lapok* 20 (1969), 137–140.

Author's summary: "Let $\mathscr{K}$ be the set of integers all of whose prime factors occur with an exponent greater than 1. Clearly, every integer can be uniquely written in the form (1) $n = Km$, $K \in \mathscr{K}$, $(m, K) = 1$, $m$ square-free.

"Let $g(n)$ be an arbitrary complex-valued number-theoretical function such that $g(n) = g(K)$. Let $s_1, s_2, \cdots$ be the set of values of $g(n)$. Let $\nu_i(x) = x^{-1} \sum_{g(n)=s_i, n \leqq x} 1$. We prove the theorem: We have

$$\nu_i(x) = \lambda_i + O(\theta_i(x) x^{-1/2} \log x)$$

$(i = 1, 2, \cdots)$, where $\lambda_i > 0$ $(i = 1, 2, \cdots)$, $\Sigma\lambda_i = 1; 0 < \theta_i(x) \leqq 1$, $\sum \theta_i(x) \leqq 1$. The constant implied by the $O$ is an absolute one."

**N60-83** **(40# 7218 )**

**Delange, Hubert**

**Sur certaines fonctions additives à valeurs entières.**

*Acta Arith.* 16 (1969/70), 195–206.

Let $f$ be an additive arithmetic function with integral values, satisfying $f(p) = 0$ for every prime $p$. It has been shown by J. Kubilius [*Probabilistic methods in the theory of numbers* (Russian), Gos. Izdat. Politič. i Naučn. Lit. Litovsk. SSR, Vilna, 1959; MR **23** #A134; second edition, 1962; MR **26** #3691; English translation, p. 88, Amer. Math. Soc., Providence, R.I., 1964; MR **28** #3956] that for every integer $q$ the set of positive integers $n$ such that $f(n) = q$ has a density $d_q$, in fact that $\nu_q(x) = xd_q + O(x \log\log x/\log x)$, where $\nu_q(x)$ is the number of positive $n \leqq x$ such that $f(n) = q$. The author improves the remainder term to $O(x^{1/2})$, and even shows that there is an absolute constant $C$ such that for every $f$ under consideration and every $q$, $|\nu_q(x) - xd_q| \leqq Cx^{1/2}$ for all $x \geqq 1$. The analytic argument used is based on estimates of average orders of arithmetic functions. The author shows the relation of his and Kubilius' work to the P. Erdős and A. Wintner work [Amer. J. Math. **61** (1939), 713–721; MR **1**, 40] on asymptotic distribution functions. Also, the author points out that his result is a partial improvement of his Théorème A in an earlier paper [Acta Arith. **13** (1967/68), 339–362; MR **37** #4037], and then establishes the following result. If $g$ is a multiplicative arithmetic function with $g(n) = 0$ or 1 for all $n \geqq 1$ and $g(p) = 1$ for every prime $p$, then $\sum_{n \leqq x} g(n) = \delta x + o(x^{1/2})$ for some constant $\delta$.

*I. Niven* (Eugene, Ore.)

Citations: MR 1, 40c = N60-1; MR 23# A134 = N60-37; MR 26# 3691 = N60-38; MR 28# 3956 = N60-39; MR 37# 4037 = N60-67.

Referred to in N52-46.

**N60-84** **(41# 1671 )**

**Eda, Yosikazu; Yamano, Gôsuke**

**On the number of prime factors of integers.**

*Sci. Rep. Kanazawa Univ.* 14 (1969), 13–20.

Let $\omega(n)$ be the number of distinct prime factors of $n$. Let $f_i(\xi)$, $i = 1, \cdots, k$, be polynomials with integral coefficients that are pairwise relatively prime with the additional property that $f_i(\xi) > 0$ for $\xi \geqq 1$. Let $r_i$ be the number of primitive irreducible factors of $f_i(\xi)$. Let $u_i(n) = (\omega(f_i(n)) - r_i \ln\ln n)/\sqrt{(r_i \ln\ln n)}$. Let $E$ be a Jordan-measurable set in $R^k$ and $A(x; E)$ represent the cardinality of $\{3 \leqq n \leqq x : (f_1(n), f_2(n), \cdots, f_k(n)) \in E\}$.

M. Tanaka established [Japan. J. Math. **25** (1955), 1–20 (1956); MR **18**, 563]

$$\lim_{x\to\infty} A(x; E)/x = (2\pi)^{-k/2} \int_E \exp(-\tfrac{1}{2} \sum_{i=1}^k u_i^2)\, du_1 du_2 \cdots du_k.$$

This paper gives a more explicit result for special regions: Given real $\alpha_i$ and $\beta_i$, $i = 1, \cdots, k$, with $\alpha_i < \beta_i$, let $A(x) =$ cardinality of $C\{3 \leqq n \leqq x; r_i \ln\ln n + \alpha_i \sqrt{(r_i \ln\ln n)} < \omega(f_i(n)) < r_i \ln\ln n + \beta_i \sqrt{(r_i \ln\ln n)}\}$, $i = 1, \cdots, k$. Then

$$A(x)/x = (2\pi)^{-k/2} \prod_{i=1}^k \int_{\alpha_i}^{\beta_i} e^{-u_i^2/2}\, du_i + O(\mu^{2(k+1)} (\ln\ln x)^{1-1/(2k)}/(\ln\ln x)^{1/(4k)}),$$

where $\mu = \max_{1\leqq i \leqq k}(1, |\alpha_i|, |\beta_i|)$. The $O$ term is uniform with respect to sufficiently large $x$. The result is obtained by using Selberg's sieve and the method of Tanaka.

*J. H. Jordan* (Pullman, Wash.)

Citations: MR 18, 563a = N60-21.

**N60-85** **(41# 3422 )**

**Elliott, P. D. T. A.**

**Some applications of a theorem of Raikov to number theory.**

*J. Number Theory* 2 (1970), 22–55.

Let $X_1, \cdots, X_n$ be independent random variables with $E(X_i)=0$, $|X_i| \leqq 1$ $(i=1, \cdots, n)$. Put $S_n = X_1 + \cdots + X_n$ and $\sigma^2 = \mathrm{Var}(S_n)$, $\sigma \geqq 0$. The author starts out by establishing certain upperbounds on the quantity $E[\{|S_n| > z\sigma\}|S_n|^k]$, $k \geqq 0$. Many applications are with $k=0$ and then his result is that (1) $\Pr(|S_n| > z\sigma) \leqq 72\exp(-z^2/(12))$ when $0 \leqq z \leqq 2\sigma$. Actually, much more is known. Namely, it follows easily from an elementary exponential bound in M. Loève's *Probability theory. Foundations. Random sequences* [p. 254, Van Nostrand, New York, 1955; MR **16**, 598] that (2) $\Pr(|S_n| > z\sigma) \leqq 2\exp(-z^2/(4b))$ whenever $0 \leqq z \leqq b\sigma$ and $b \geqq 1$.

Besides presenting new results, the paper also contains an extensive survey of some known results which are on the border line of number theory and probability theory.

A well-known method for generating independent random variables in number theory is to use the Chinese remainder theorem. Thus, let $q_1 < q_2 < q_3 < \cdots$ be relatively prime positive integers and consider the residues $Z_j(n) = n - [n/q_j]q_j$ taking values in $B_j = \{0, 1, \cdots, q-1\}$. Consider further the probability space $\Omega(x) = \{1, 2, \cdots, x\}$ with the uniform distribution. Thus the probability of an event $A$ is precisely equal to the frequency $(1/x)$[no. of $n=1, \cdots, x: n \in A$]. Relative to $\Omega(x)$ the functions $Z_j(n)$ may be regarded as random variables. For $m$ fixed, the random variables $Z_1, \cdots, Z_m$ are exactly independent when $x$ is a multiple of $M = q_1 q_2 \cdots q_m$. And even when $m = m(x)$ tends to infinity, we have that $Z_1, \cdots, Z_m$ are at least "nearly" independent provided $q_1 q_2 \cdots q_{m(x)} = o(x)$. Thus the asymptotic frequency of an event based on $Z_1, \cdots, Z_{m(x)}$ can in this case be computed from the corresponding asymptotic probability based on the assumption of independent random variables $Z_j$, with $Z_j$ uniformly distributed in $B_j$. The author exploits this idea in deriving (Theorem 3) certain asymptotic results for the function $g(n) = \min\{j : y^2 \neq n \pmod{q_j}$, all $y\}$. Here, $q_j$ denotes the $j$th prime $(j = 1, 2, \cdots)$.

Section 6 contains an exposition of some work by Kubilius, Uzdavinis, Barban and the author on additive arithmetic functions. Use is made of the random variables $Z_p = Z_p(n) = \max\{r \geqq 0 : p^r | n\}$, where $p$ runs through the primes. The distribution of $Z_p$ is about of the type $\Pr(Z_p = r) = (1-p^{-1})p^{-r}$ $(r = 0, 1, \cdots)$.

In Section 7, using these same $Z_p(n)$ but a somewhat different distribution, the author shows that the number of "small" divisors has asymptotically a normal distribution. *J. H. B. Kemperman* (Rochester, N.Y.)

Referred to in M55-79.

## N60-86 (41# 5323)

**Rényi, A.**

**On the distribution of numbers prime to *n*.**

*Number Theory and Analysis (Papers in Honor of Edmund Landau)*, pp. 269–278. *Plenum, New York*, 1969.

Denote by $Q_n(h, r)$ the relative frequency of those intervals $(k, k+h)$ $(1 \leqq k < n-h)$ which contain exactly $r$ integers relatively prime to $n$. The author proves the following theorem: Let $n$ tend to infinity through values such that $n/\varphi(n) \to \infty$. Then for every $\lambda > 0$,

$$\lim_{n/\varphi(n) \to \infty} Q_n(\lambda n/\varphi(n), r) = \lambda^r e^{-\lambda}/r! \quad (r = 0, 1, \cdots).$$

The author uses several results of C. Hooley [Acta Arith. **8** (1962/63), 343–347; MR **27** #5741; Math. Z. **90** (1965), 355–364; MR **32** #1182; Publ. Math. Debrecen **12** (1965), 39–49; MR **32** #4099]. *P. Erdős* (Waterloo, Ont.)

Citations: MR 27# 5741 = N28-50; MR 32# 1182 = N28-61; MR 32# 4099 = N28-60.

## N60-87 (41# 6804)

**Kubilius, J.**

**On local theorems for additive number-theoretic functions.**

*Number Theory and Analysis (Papers in Honor of Edmund Landau)*, pp. 173–191. *Plenum, New York*, 1969.

An arithmetical function $f$ is called additive if $f(mn) = f(m) + f(n)$ whenever $(m, n) = 1$. An asymptotic formula for the number $N_n(a)$ of positive integers $m \leqq n$ for which $f(m)$ assumes a given value $a$ is called a local theorem. In his monograph [*Probabilistic methods in the theory of numbers*, Amer. Math. Soc., Providence, R.I., 1964; MR **28** #3956; Russian original, Gosudarstv. Izdat. Politič. i Naučn. Lit. Litovsk. SSR, Vilna, 1959; MR **23** #A134; second Russian edition, 1962; MR **26** #3691] the author proved a local theorem for every integer-valued additive $f$ satisfying the condition $f(p) = 0$ for all primes $p$, generalizing a theorem of A. Rényi [Acad. Serbe Sci. Publ. Inst. Math. **8** (1955), 157–162; MR **17**, 944] for the special case $f(m) = \Omega(m) - \omega(m)$, where $\omega(m)$ is the number of distinct prime factors of $m$ and $\Omega(m)$ the number of all prime factors of $m$. This paper proves three theorems under the assumption that $f(p) = 1$ for all primes $p$ with the exception of primes from a rare set. For example, assume $f$ is additive and integral-valued and satisfies the conditions

$$\sum_{f(p) \neq 1} (\log p)/p < \infty, \qquad \sum_{f(p) \neq 1} |f(p)|/p < \infty,$$
$$\sum_p \sum_{\alpha=2}^{\infty} |f(p^\alpha)|/p^\alpha < \infty.$$

Then $N_n(a) = n\varphi(y)/\lambda + Bn/\lambda^2$ uniformly for all integers $a$ and $n > 30$, where $\lambda = (\log\log n)^{1/2}$, $y = (a - \lambda^2)/\lambda$, and $\varphi(u) = (2\pi)^{-1/2}\exp(-u^2/2)$. Further restrictions on $f$ lead to more precise results on $N_n(a)$.

*T. M. Apostol* (Pasadena, Calif.)

Citations: MR 17, 944f = N24-23; MR 23# A134 = N60-37; MR 26# 3691 = N60-38; MR 28# 3956 = N60-39.

## N60-88 (42# 220)

**Judin, A. A.**

**A new proof of the Erdős-Turán theorem.** (Russian. Lithuanian and English summaries)

*Litovsk. Mat. Sb.* **9** (1969), 839–848.

The theorem in question concerns the maximum mean deviation in probabilistic number theory.

*A. I. Vinogradov* (Leningrad)

## N60-89 (42# 1785)

**Kátai, I.**

**Some remarks on additive arithmetical functions. (Lithuanian and Russian summaries)**

*Litovsk. Mat. Sb.* **9** (1969), 515–518.

The author proves: (1) If $f(n)$ is an additive function which is bounded on the primes, and there exists a distribution function $F(\alpha)$ for which $\lim_{x\to\infty}(\mathrm{li}\, x)^{-1}N\{p \leqq x | f(p+1) < \alpha\} = F(\alpha)$ holds at all its points of continuity, then $\sum_{|f(p)|<1} f(p)/p$, $\sum_{|f(p)|<1} f^2(p)/p$ and $\sum_{|f(p)|\geqq 1} 1/p$ all converge. (2) Assuming the validity of the extended Riemann hypothesis, if $f(n)$ is a completely additive function satisfying $|f(p+1)| \leqq C\log(p+1)$ for all primes, then $|f(n)| \leqq K(\log n)(\log\log 10n)$. Extensive use is made in the proofs of these theorems of the sieve methods of Brun, Barban, Vinogradov and others.

*A. R. Freedman* (Burnaby, B.C.)

## N60-90 (42# 5940)

**Dressler, Robert E.**

**A density which counts multiplicity.**

*Pacific J. Math.* **34** (1970), 371–378.

The author gives an elementary proof of the result that if

$f(x)$ denotes the number of integers $m$ such that $\Phi(m) \leqq x$ ($\Phi$ is Euler's $\Phi$-function), then

$$\lim_{x\to\infty} f(x)/x = \zeta(2)\zeta(3)/\zeta(6).$$

Motivated by the considerations necessary for this proof, a generalization of natural density to a density counting multiplicities is formulated, and the general theory of such a density initiated.

{Remarks: A proof of the result on the $\Phi$-function using the fact that the distribution function of $\Phi(n)/n$ exists (a result of Schoenberg's) was (as the author remarks) noted earlier by Erdős and Turán [see P. Erdős, Bull. Amer. Math. Soc. **51** (1945), 540–544, especially pp. 543–544; MR **7**, 49] without explicit evaluation of the constant limit; this, however, can also be obtained by analytic means. The Erdős-Turan proof, as noted by Erdős, will show the existence of analogous limits for any multiplicative function for which a distribution function exists. The "non-elementary" part of their proof is the existence of the distribution function; it is this that the author avoids.}

*S. L. Segal* (Rochester, N.Y.)

Citations: MR 7, 49f = N64-1.

## N60-91 (42# 7612)

**Faĭnleĭb, A. S.**

**Local theorems with a remainder term for a certain class of arithmetic functions.** (Russian)

*Acta Math. Acad. Sci. Hungar.* **21** (1970), 271–281.

Mit $q_n$ werde der Teil der kanonischen Zerlegung einer natürlichen Zahl $n$ bezeichnet, dessen Primzahlexponenten $\geqq 2$ sind (d. h. für quadratfreie $n$ ist $q_n=1$). Eine (komplexwertige) Funktion $f$ heißt zur Klasse $R$ gehörig, falls $f(n)=f(q_n)$ für alle $n$ gilt. Im Falle $f(n)=\Omega(n)-\omega(n)$, wo $\omega(n)$ die verschiedenen, $\Omega(n)$ alle Primteiler von $n$ bezeichnet, zeigte A. Rényi [Acad. Serbe Sci. Publ. Inst. Math. **8** (1955), 157–162; MR **17**, 944] $N^{-1}\sum_{n\leqq N, f(n)=k} 1 \sim \lambda_k$, und ein entsprechendes Ergebnis wurde durch J. Kubilius [*Probabilistic methods in the theory of numbers* (Russian), second edition, Gosudarstv. Izdat. Politič. i Naučn. Lit. Litovsk. SSR, Vilna, 1962; MR **26** #3691; English translation, Amer. Math. Soc., Providence, R.I., 1964; MR **28** #3956] für eine gewisse Klasse von additiven Funktionen bewiesen. Später haben verschiedene Autoren diese Entwicklungen auch mit Restgliedern erhalten. Die vorliegende Arbeit enthält bzw. verschärft alle früheren Ergebnisse dieser Art. Theorem 1 lautet: Sei $f$ eine Funktion der Klasse $R$ und sei $E$ eine beliebige Menge komplexer Zahlen. Dann gilt mit einer absoluten $O$-Konstanten $\sum_{n\leqq N, f(n)\in E} 1 = \lambda_E(f)N + O(\sqrt{N})$.

*H.-E. Richert* (Marburg)

Citations: MR 17, 944f = N24-23; MR 26# 3691 = N60-38; MR 28# 3956 = N60-39.

## N60-92 (43# 3224)

**Elliott, P. D. T. A.; Ryavec, C.**

**The distribution of the values of additive arithmetical functions.**

*Acta Math.* **126** (1971), 143–164.

A real-valued number-theoretic function $f(m)$ is said to be additive if $f(ab)=f(a)+f(b)$ whenever $(a,b)=1$. If in addition, for each prime $p$, $f(p)=f(p^2)=\cdots$, then the function is said to be strongly additive. The authors develop the properties of those strongly additive functions which, after suitable translation, possess a limiting distribution. They also find the characteristic functions (Fourier transforms) of the limiting distributions.

Let $f'(p)=f(p)$ if $|f(p)|\leqq 1$ and $f'(p)=1$ otherwise. For each positive integer $n$, define the frequency $v_n(m:\cdots)=n^{-1}\sum 1$ (the sum counts those integers $m$ for which the property $\cdots$ holds and $1\leqq m\leqq n$). The distribution functions are defined by $F_n(z)=v_n(m:f(m)<z)$, $n=1,2,3,\cdots,$ and $f(m)$ possesses a limiting distribution if there exists a left continuous function $F(z)$ with the properties that $F(-\infty)=0$ and $F(+\infty)=1$, such that $\lim F_n(z)=F(z)$ $(n\to\infty)$ for all real points $z$ at which $F(z)$ is continuous.

The following auxiliary results are useful in the proof of the main theorems: Let $\omega_1, \omega_2, \cdots$ be a sequence of real numbers for which the limit $\lim_{n\to\infty}\exp(it\omega_n)$ exists uniformly in some neighbourhood of the origin; then the sequence $\omega_1, \omega_2, \cdots$ itself tends to a limit. Let $h(m)$ be an additive function; for each real number $t$, we define the sum $S(n,t)$ by $S(n,t)=n^{-1}\sum_{m\leqq n}\exp(ith(m))$; then if there exists a set of positive measure on which $S(n,t)$ does not converge to zero as $n\to\infty$, the function $h(m)$ is of the form $h(m)=b\log m+u(m)$ where $\sum_p (u'(p))^2/p<\infty$ and $b$ is some constant.

Integration methods and theorems from probability are used to prove the following theorems (and some others). Let $f(m)$ be a strongly additive function; then there exist constants $\alpha_1, \alpha_2, \cdots$ such that the frequencies $v_n(m: f(m)-\alpha_n<z)$ possess a limiting distribution if and only if $f(m)$ is of the form $f(m)=c\log m+g(m)$, where $\sum_p (g'(p))^2p^{-1}<\infty$. In this case we can set $\alpha_n=c\log n+\sum_{p\leqq n} g'(p)p^{-1}+\text{constant}+o(1)$ and, apart from the last two terms in this expression, the choice of the numbers $\alpha_n$ is unique. The characteristic function of the limiting distribution, when it exists, will be of the form $\phi(t)=(1+itc)^{-1}\prod_p (1-1/p)(1+\sum_{k=1}^{\infty} e^{itg(p^k)}/p^k)e^{-itg'(p)/p}$, to within a factor $\exp(-it(\text{constant}))$. The distribution function will be continuous if and only if $\sum_{f(p)\neq 0}(1/p)=\infty$.

The following two propositions are equivalent. Proposition 1: $\lim\sup_{z\to\infty}\lim\sup_{n\to\infty} v_n(m: |f(m)|<z)=1$. Proposition 2: (i) $\lim\inf_{n\to\infty}|\sum_{p\leqq n} f'(p)/p|<\infty$ and (ii) $\sum_p (f'(p))^2/p<\infty$.

*E. M. Horadam* (Armidale)

## N60-93 (43# 4782)

**Duncan, R. L.**

**Some applications of the Turán-Kubilius inequality.**

*Proc. Amer. Math. Soc.* **30** (1971), 69–72.

Let $g(n)$ be a real valued arithmetical function for which $g(0)=0$ and $g(1)\neq 0$. Define $f(1)=0$ and $f(n)=g(a_1)+g(a_2)+\cdots+g(a_r)$ for $n>1$, where $n=p_1^{a_1}p_2^{a_2}\cdots p_r^{a_r}$. It has been shown that if $g(n)=O(2^{n/2})$, then $\sum_{n\leqq x} f(n)=g(1)x\log\log x+Ax+O(x/\log x)$. If $h(n)$ is an arbitrary additive arithmetical function, then the Turán-Kubilius inequality states that $\sum_{m\leqq n}|h(m)-A_n|^2\leqq BnB_n$, where $A_n=\sum_{p^a\leqq n} h(p^a)/p^a$ and $B_n=\sum_{p^a\leqq n}|h(p^a)|^2/p^a$. In this article a more explicit form of this inequality is derived and the result is applied to the study of sums of reciprocals and quotients of such functions. The following results are proved: (i) if $g(n)=O(b^{n/2})$, $0<b<2$, then

$$\sum_{n\leqq x}[f(n)-g(1)\log\log x]^2 \leqq Cx\log\log x;$$

(ii) if $g(n)=O(b^{n/2})$, $0<b<2$ and $g(n)\geqq t>0$, then there exist positive constants $c_1$ and $c_2$ such that $c_1x/\log\log x\leqq\sum_{n\leqq x}(1/f(n))\leqq c_2x/\log\log x$; (iii) if $g(n)=O(n^k)$, then $\sum_{n\leqq x} f(n)/w(n)=g(1)x+O(x/\log\log x)$, where $w(n)=r$ for $n=p_1^{a_1}p_2^{a_2}\cdots p_r^{a_r}$.

*M. S. Cheema* (Tucson, Ariz.)

## N60-94 (43# 6176)

**Levin, B. V.; Faĭnleĭb, A. S.**

**Multiplicative functions and probabilistic number theory.** (Russian)

*Izv. Akad. Nauk SSSR Ser. Mat.* **34** (1970), 1064–1109.

A real additive function $\varphi(m)$ is said to be weakly measurable if there exists a distribution function $\Phi(x)$ such that $\sum_{p\leqq n,\varphi(p)<x}((\log p)/p)/\sum_{p\leqq n}((\log p)/p)\to\Phi(x)$ as $n\to\infty$ at each point of continuity of $\Phi(x)$, where the sums are taken over all primes $p\leqq n$, $\varphi(p)<x$ and $p\leqq n$ correspondingly. In their previous paper [Trudy Moskov.

Mat. Obšč. **18** (1968), 19–54; MR **38** #5735] the authors used measurable additive functions for the approximation of additive functions in order to obtain limit distribution functions. Using weakly measurable functions instead of measurable ones and generalizing their own previous results on the mean values of multiplicative functions they enlarge the class of additive functions for which there exist limit distribution functions. *J. Kubilius* (Vilnius)

Citations: MR 38# 5735 = N60-74.

**N60-95** **(43# 6178 )**

**Toleuov, Ž.; Faĭnleĭb, A. S.**

**The distribution of values of arithmetic functions on certain subsets of a natural series. (Russian. Uzbek summary)**

*Izv. Akad. Nauk UzSSR Ser. Fiz.-Mat. Nauk* **13** (1969), *no.* 5, 23–27.

The authors study distributions of values of arithmetic functions on values that certain polynomials take on a sequence of natural numbers. The sequences considered are uniformly distributed in the sense $^{\Sigma}R(y, z, d)$ of M. B. Barban [see J. P. Kubilius, *Probabilistic methods in the theory of numbers* (Russian), Gos. Izdat. Politič. i Naučn. Lit. Litovsk. SSR, Vilnius, 1962; MR **26** #3691; English translation, Amer. Math. Soc., Providence, R.I., 1964; MR **28** #3956; P. Erdős and A. Winter, Amer. J. Math. **61** (1939), 713–721; MR **1**, 40]. Let $a_n$ be such a sequence of natural numbers. The following notations are introduced: $N(x)$ is the number of members of the sequence $a_n$ such that $a_n \leqq x$; $N\{\cdots\}$ is the number of members of the sequence $a_n$ which satisfy the condition in braces; $d(D)$ is a strongly multiplicative function with positive integral values satisfying the condition $d(D)|D$ for all $D$; $K(u)$ is a polynomial with integral coefficients and $K(a_n) \neq 0$; $w(D)$ is the number of the least positive residues $l$ mod $D$ such that $K(l) \equiv 0$ mod $D$, and $w^*(D)$ is the number of mentioned residues with the additional condition $(l, d(D)) = 1$; the prime numbers are designated by $p$.

It is stated (in Theorem 2) that $\sum_{a_n \leq x} f(|K(a_n)|) = CN(x) + o(N(x))$, where $f(n)$ is a strongly multiplicative function satisfying the conditions $|f(n)| \leqq 1$ for all $n$, $\lim_{p\to\infty, w(p)\neq 0} f(p) = 1$, $\sum_p ((f(p)-1)/p)w(p) < \infty$,

$$\sum_p ((f(p)-1)/p)w^*(p) < \infty;$$

$a_n$ is a uniformly distributed sequence in the sense $^{\Sigma}R(x^\alpha, z(x), d(D))$, satisfying conditions stated in the paper; $C$ is a constant which depends on the functions $d$, $f$ and $K$.

It is also stated (in Theorem 3) that, for $x \to \infty$, $N\{a_n \leqq x, \psi(|K(a_n)|) - \sum_{p\leq x} \psi(p)w^*(p)/p \leqq W\} \sim N(x)F(W)$, where $W$ is an arbitrary real number, $a_n$ is a sequence satisfying the conditions mentioned above, $\psi(m)$ is a strongly additive real function such that $\lim_{p\to\infty} \psi(p)w(p) = 0$ and $\sum_p \psi^2(p)w(p)/p < \infty$, and $F(W)$ is the distribution function determined by the corresponding characteristic function, given in the paper.

An interesting example is deduced: Let $\varphi(m)$ be Euler's function and $K(0) \neq 0$; then $N\{p \leqq x, \varphi(|K(p)|)/|K(p)| \leqq W\} \sim \Phi(W)(x/\ln x)$, where $\Phi(W)$ is the corresponding distribution function. *D. Ugrin-Šparac* (Zagreb)

Citations: MR 1, 40c = N60-1; MR 26# 3691 = N60-38; MR 28# 3956 = N60-39.

**N60-96** **(44# 3977 )**

**Kubilius, Jonas**

**On the distribution of number-theoretic functions.**

*Séminaire Delange-Pisot-Poitou: 1969/70, Théorie des Nombres, Fasc. 2, Exp. 23, 11 pp. Secrétariat mathématique, Paris,* 1970.

This is a survey of results and of methods in the study of the distribution of values taken by additive and multiplicative arithmetic functions belonging to various general classes. As such it forms a useful introduction to recent work in this field by the author and his associates; some of the work cited had not yet appeared at the time this article was published. *H. Halberstam* (Nottingham)

**N60-97** **(44# 3978 )**

**Popov, G. A.**

**Distribution of the values of an additive function on a progression. (Russian)**

*Dokl. Akad. Nauk SSSR* **200** (1971), 290–293.

In this paper the author proves the following theorem: Let $g(n)$ be a real additive function, $A_N = \sum_{p\leq N} g(p)/p$ and let $l$ and $k$ be relatively prime numbers; then the limiting distribution $F_{l,k}(x) = \lim_{N\to\infty} (k/N) \sum_R 1$, where the range of summation $R$ is defined by $n \leqq N$, $g(n) - A_N \leqq x$, $n \equiv l \pmod k$, exists if and only if there exists a distribution function $F(x)$ such that $F(x) = \lim_{N\to\infty} N^{-1} \sum_S 1$, where the range of summation $S$ is defined by $n \leqq N$, $g(n) - A_N \leqq x$.

{This article has appeared in English translation [Soviet Math. Dokl. **12** (1971), 1392–1395].} *D. Ugrin-Šparac* (Zagreb)

**N60-98** **(44# 3979 )**

**Timofeev, N. M.**

**An estimate of the remainder term in one dimensional asymptotic laws. (Russian)**

*Dokl. Akad. Nauk SSSR* **200** (1971), 298–301.

Let $g(n)$ be a real additive function such that $g(p^r) = O(p^{r\gamma})$, where $r \geqq 2$, $0 < \gamma < \frac{1}{4}$, $p$ a prime. Introduce the notation $B_N^2(b) = \sum_{p\leq N} (g(p) - b \ln p)^2/p$, $A_N = \sum_{p\leq N} g(p)/p$. If there exists a real number $b$ such that

$$(1/B_N(b)) \max_{p\leq N} |g(p) - b \ln p| = \mu_N \to 0$$

when $N \to \infty$, then $F_N(x) = \sum_R 1 = G(x) + O(\mu_N)$ uniformly with respect to $x$, where the summation extends over the set $R$ of all $n$ such that $n \leqq N$ and $(g(n) - A_N)/B_N(b) \leqq x$; the function $G(x)$ is $(1/\sqrt{(2\pi)}) \int_{-\infty}^{x} \exp(-u^2/2)\, du$.

{This article has appeared in English translation [Soviet Math. Dokl. **12** (1971), 1401–1405].} *D. Ugrin-Šparac* (Zagreb)

# N64 OTHER RESULTS ON THE DISTRIBUTION OF VALUES OR THE CHARACTERIZATION OF ARITHMETIC FUNCTIONS

See also Sections A22, A32.

See also reviews A22-27, A22-45, A26-25, A26-30, A26-33, A30-33, A48-13, B48-15, B48-17, B48-21, D60-26, K30-15, K30-20, L25-27, M55-72, N28-11, N28-46, N28-62, N32-21, N60-7, N60-43, N60-89, N60-96, Q20-2, Q20-3, Q20-4, Q20-5, Q20-6, Q20-7, Q20-8, Q20-9, Q20-10, Q20-16, Q20-18, Q20-19, Q20-24, R46-29.

**N64-1** **(7, 49f)**

**Erdös, Paul. Some remarks on Euler's $\phi$-function and some related problems.** Bull. Amer. Math. Soc. **51**, 540–544 (1945).

Let $f(n)$ be the number of integers $m \leqq n$ for which $\phi(x) = m$ has solutions, $\phi(x)$ being Euler's $\phi$-function. The author proves that $f(n)>cn(\log n)^{-1}\log\log n$, for some constant $c$. In an earlier paper he had proved that $f(n)=o(n(\log n)^{1-\epsilon})$ for every $\epsilon>0$ [Quart. J. Math., Oxford Ser. **6**, 205–213 (1935)]. The sharper result $f(n)>n(\log n)^{-1}(\log\log n)^k$, for every $k$, is stated but not proved. It is also proved that the number of integers $m\leqq n$ for which $\phi(m)\leqq cn$ is $cn+o(n)$; this result is due to the author and Turán. It is stated that exactly parallel results can be proved if $\phi(m)$ is replaced by $\sigma(m)$, the sum of the divisors of $m$. *H. W. Brinkmann.*

Referred to in N60-90.

## N64-2 (14, 249e)

**Schinzel, Andrzej. Sur une propriété du nombre de diviseurs.** Publ. Math. Debrecen **3** (1954), 261–262 (1955).

Let $\tau(n)$ denote the number of divisors of $n$. Then for any two natural numbers $h$ and $m$ there exists a natural number $n>1$ such that $\tau(n)/\tau(n\pm i)>m$ for $i=1, 2, \cdots, h$. The proof is elementary. *W. H. Simons.*

## N64-3 (15, 104a)

**Erdös, P., and Mirsky, L. The distribution of values of the divisor function $d(n)$.** Proc. London Math. Soc. (3) **2**, 257–271 (1952).

Let $d(n)$ denote the number of divisors of $n$, and let $D(x)$ denote the number of distinct values of $d(n)$ assumed in the range $1\leqq n\leqq x$. Let $A$ be the set of integers whose factorisation is of the form $\prod p^{a(p)}$, where $p$ runs through all primes, and $a(p)$ is a non-increasing function of $p$. An $A$-number is called a $B$-number if the sequence of numbers $a(p)+1$ is a sequence of primes (discarding those $a(p)$'s which are zero). $A(x)$ denotes the number of $A$-numbers not exceeding $x$; $B(x)$ is defined analogously. It was proved by Hardy and Ramanujan [same Proc. (2) **16**, 112–132 (1917)] that

$$\log A(x)\sim 2\pi\cdot 3^{-\frac{1}{2}}\cdot(\log x)^{\frac{1}{2}}/(\log\log x)^{\frac{1}{2}}\quad (x\rightarrow\infty).$$

The present authors determine the asymptotic behavior of $\log D(x)$ by showing that

$$\log D(x)\sim\log B(x)\sim 2^{\frac{1}{2}}\cdot(\log A(x))/(\log\log x)^{\frac{1}{2}}.$$

The relation between $D(x)$ and $B(x)$ is studied in detail. It is proved that

$$B(x)\leqq D(x)\leqq B(x)+B(x)O((\log\log x)^2/(\log x)^{\frac{1}{2}}).$$

Some minor problems concerning the distribution of values of $d(n)$ are also studied. *N. G. de Bruijn* (Amsterdam).

Citations: MR 7, 416c = N60-7.

Referred to in N64-21.

## N64-4 (17, 238d)

**Moser, L., and Lambek, J. On monotone multiplicative functions.** Proc. Amer. Math. Soc. **4**, 544–545 (1953).

Let $f(n)$ be a real-valued function defined for the positive integers. Assume that $f(m\cdot n)=f(m)\cdot f(n)$ for $(m, n)=1$, i.e., $f(n)$ is weakly multiplicative. The authors prove that if $f(m)\geqq f(n)$ for $m\geqq n$ and $f(n)\not\equiv 0$, then $f(n)=n^k$ where $k$ is a constant. The authors overlooked that this was proved by the reviewer [Ann. of Math. (2) **47**, 1–20 (1946), p. 17; these Rev. **7**, 416]. The proof of the authors is completely different and very much simpler than my own.

*P. Erdös* (South Bend, Ind.).

## N64-5 (17, 461c)

**Schinzel, A. On functions $\varphi(n)$ and $\sigma(n)$.** Bull. Acad. Polon. Sci. Cl. III. **3** (1955), 415–419.

Let $a_1, a_2, \cdots, a_h$ be any finite sequence of non-negative numbers or infinity. Then there exists an infinite sequence $n_1<n_2<n_3<\cdots$ of natural numbers such that

$$\lim_{k\rightarrow\infty}\frac{\phi(n_k+i)}{\phi(n_k+i-1)}=a_i \text{ for } i=1, 2, \cdots, h,$$

$\phi(n)$ being the Euler function. The same result holds for the sum of divisors function $\sigma(n)$. These results generalize previous work by the author [same Bull. **2** (1954), 467–469; MR **16**, 675] and by the author and W. Sierpiński [ibid. **2** (1954), 463–466; MR **16**, 675]. *I. Niven.*

Citations: MR 16, 675f = A26-30; MR 16, 675g = A26-31.

Referred to in N64-7, N64-10, N64-14.

## N64-6 (17, 944b)

**Golomb, Solomon W. Properties of consecutive integers.** Nordisk Mat. Tidskr. **4** (1956), 24–29.

Generalizing the familiar theorem: There are arbitrarily long runs of composite numbers, the author first proves: If $A_1=a_1n+b_1, \cdots, A_k=a_kn+b_k$, where $(a_i, a_j)=1$ for $i\neq j$, then there are $k$ consecutive integers $c+1, \cdots, c+k$ such that $c+j$ is in $A_j$ for $1\leqq j\leqq k$. He next gives a simple proof of the following theorem of Wintner [The theory of measure in arithmetical semi-groups, Baltimore, Md., 1944, p. 14; MR **7**, 367]: There are arbitrarily long runs of consecutive integers $c+1, \cdots, c+k$, such that $\mu(c+1)=\cdots=\mu(c+k)=0$, where $\mu(n)$ is the Möbius function. It is observed that there are arbitrarily long sequences of non-$k$th-power-free integers. It is next proved that, for given $M$, there are runs such that

$$\phi(c+1)\equiv\cdots\equiv\phi(c+k)\equiv 0 \pmod M,$$

where $\phi(n)$ is the Euler function. Like results are proved for the function $\sigma(n)$ and $d(n)$. The problem of whether for every $k$ there exists a number $c$ such that $d(c+1)=\cdots=d(c+k)$ is left open. *L. Carlitz* (Durham, N.C.).

Citations: MR 7, 367a = Z02-5.

Referred to in N32-21.

## N64-7 (18, 17c)

**Schinzel, A.; and Wang, Y. A note on some properties of the functions $\varphi(n)$, $\sigma(n)$ and $\theta(n)$.** Bull. Acad. Polon. Sci. Cl. III. **4** (1956), 207–209.

Results are announced without proof of extensions and refinements of previous results of A. Schinzel [same Bull. **2** (1954), 467–469; **3** (1955), 415–419; MR **16**, 675; **17**, 461]. *I. Niven* (Eugene, Ore.).

Citations: MR 16, 675g = A26-31; MR 17, 461c = N64-5.

Referred to in N64-8.

## N64-8 (18, 719d)

**Shao Pin-Tsung. On the distribution of the values of a class of arithmetical functions.** Bull. Acad. Polon. Sci. Cl. III. **4** (1956), 569–572.

This note announces some results on the distribution of values of certain classes of arithmetic functions. One class includes $\varphi(n)$ and $\sigma(n)$ and its definition is suggested by properties of these two functions. The results generalize those of Schinzel and Sierpiński [Bull. Acad. Polon. Sci. Cl. III. **2** (1954), 463–466, 467–469; MR **16**, 675] and include more recent results obtained independently by Schinzel and Wang [Bull. Acad. Polon. Sci. Cl. III. **4** (1956), 207–209; MR **18**, 17]. Proofs are to appear in Acta Scientiarum Naturalium Universitatis Pekinensis.

*R. D. James* (Vancouver, B.C.).

Citations: MR 16, 675f = A26-30; MR 18, 17c = N64-7.

Referred to in N64-16.

**N64-9** **(18, 791a)**

**Schinzel, A. Generalisation of a theorem of B.S.K.R. Somayajulu on the Euler's function $\varphi(n)$.** Ganita **5** (1954), 123–128 (1955).

The author proves that the set of numbers $\varphi(n+1)/\varphi(n)$ is dense in $(0, \infty)$. *P. Erdös* (Haifa).

**N64-10** **(20# 1655 )**

**Schinzel, A.; and Wang, Y. A note on some properties of the functions $\varphi(n)$, $\sigma(n)$ and $\theta(n)$.** Ann. Polon. Math. **4** (1958), 201–213.

Let $\varepsilon$ and $a_1, \cdots, a_h$ be fixed positive numbers. It is shown, using a modified Brun's method, that there are positive numbers $c$ and $X_0$, depending on $\varepsilon$ and the $a$'s, such that for $X>X_0$, the number of positive integers $n\leqq X$, for which

$$(*) \qquad \left|\frac{\varphi(n+i)}{\varphi(n+i-1)}-a_i\right|<\varepsilon \quad (i=1, 2, \cdots, h)$$

is greater than $cX/\log^{h+1}X$. This refines an earlier theorem of the first author [Bull. Acad. Polon. Sci. Cl. III **3** (1955), 415–419; MR **17**, 461] which asserted that the number of solutions of (*) is infinite. The theorem remains true if $\varphi(n)$ is replaced by $\sigma(n)$. A somewhat weaker result holds for $\theta(n)$ (the number of divisors of $n$), which implies that for arbitrary positive $a_1, \cdots, a_h$ there is a sequence $n_1, n_2, \cdots$ of positive integers such that

$$\lim_{k\to\infty}\frac{\theta(n_k+i)}{\theta(n_k+i-1)}=a_i \quad (i=1, 2, \cdots, h).$$

*W. J. LeVeque* (Göttingen)

Citations: MR 17, 461c = N64-5.

Referred to in N64-11, N64-16.

**N64-11** **(35# 142 )**

**Schinzel, A.; Wang, Y. [Wang Yuan]**
**Corrigendum to: "A note on some properties of the functions $\varphi(n)$, $\sigma(n)$ and $\theta(n)$".**
*Ann. Polon. Math.* **19** (1967), 115.

It is pointed out that the deduction of formula (19) from (18) on pages 206–207 of the original article [same Ann. **4** (1958), 201–213; MR **20** #1655] is incorrect. A new argument is provided.

*W. J. LeVeque* (Ann Arbor, Mich.)

Citations: MR 20# 1655 = N64-10.

**N64-12** **(20# 4533 )**

**Wang, Yuan. A note on some properties of the arithmetical functions $\varphi(n)$, $\sigma(n)$ and $d(n)$.** Acta Math. Sinica **8** (1958), 1–11. (Chinese. English summary)

Let $\varphi(n)$, $\sigma(n)$, and $d(n)$ be Euler's function, the sum, and the number, of the divisors of $n$. The following results are proved. (1) If $\varepsilon>0$, and if $a_1, \cdots, a_k$ are finitely many non-negative numbers, there exist positive constants $c_0(a, \varepsilon)$ and $X_0(a, \varepsilon)$ such that, for $x>X_0$, the interval $1<p\leqq x$ contains more than

$$\frac{c_0x}{(\log x)^{k+2}\log\log x}$$

primes $p$ satisfying

$$\left|\frac{\varphi(p+\nu+1)}{\varphi(p+\nu)}-a_\nu\right|<\varepsilon \quad (\nu=1,2, \cdots, k).$$

(2) A result of the same form holds if $\varphi$ is replaced by $\sigma$. (3) For every positive integer $k$ there exists a constant $\gamma>1$ as follows. If $a_0, a_1, \cdots, a_k$ are any $k+1$ positive integers, there are two positive constants $c_2(a)$ and $X_2(a)$ such that, if $x>X_2$, the interval $1<p\leqq x$ contains more than

$$\frac{c_2x}{(\log x)^{k+2}\log\log x}$$

primes $p$ satisfying

$$a_\nu\leqq d(p+\nu+1)\leqq\gamma a_\nu \quad (\nu=0, 1, 2, \cdots, k).$$

(4) If each of $a_1, \cdots, a_k$ is either 0 or $\infty$, there exists an infinite sequence of primes $\{p_j\}$ satisfying

$$\lim_{j\to\infty}\frac{\varphi(p_j+\nu+1)}{\varphi(p_j+\nu)}=a_\nu \quad (\nu=1, 2, \cdots, k).$$

*K. Mahler* (Manchester)

**N64-13** **(20# 4534 )**

**Erdős, Pál. Remarks on two problems of the Matematikai Lapok.** Mat. Lapok **7** (1956), 10–17. (Hungarian. Russian and English summaries)

"Let $L_n=[\log_3 n/\log_4 n]$ ($\log_r n$ denotes the $r$ times iterated logarithm). Then for every $\varepsilon$ and $n>n_0$ there exists an $a<n$ for which

$$\varphi(a)+\varphi(a+1)+\cdots+\varphi(a+L_n)<\varepsilon a.$$

On the other hand for every $\eta>0$

$$\lim_{a\to\infty}\frac{\varphi(a)+\varphi(a+1)+\cdots+\varphi(a+(1+\eta)L_n)}{a}=\infty.$$

Further, it is stated without giving the proof that

$$\lim_{a\to\infty}\frac{1}{a}\left\{\varphi(a)+\cdots+\varphi\left(a+\frac{\log_3 a}{\log_4 a-\log_5 a}+\frac{c\log_3 a}{(\log_4 a)^2}\right)\right\}=\frac{e^c}{\alpha},$$

$$\alpha=\prod_p(1-p^{-1})^{-1/p}.$$

Several other results are stated without proof; here we mention only one: Put $k_n=\log_3 n/\log_6 n$ and let $i_1, i_2, \cdots, i_{k_n}$ be any permutation of the integers $1, 2, \cdots, k_n$. Then for $n>n_0$ there exists an $a<n$ so that

$$\varphi(a+i_1)>\varphi(a+i_2)>\cdots>\varphi(a+i_{k_n}).$$

On the other hand, for $n>n_0(\varepsilon)$

$$\varphi(n)>\varphi(n+1)>\cdots>\varphi(n+(1+\varepsilon)k_n)$$

can not hold. The same results hold for $\sigma(n)$ instead of $\varphi(n)$." *Author's summary*

Referred to in N64-14.

**N64-14** **(22# 1539 )**

**Erdős, P. Some remarks on Euler's $\varphi$ function.** Acta Arith. **4** (1958), 10–19.

Let $A(n)$ denote the number of solutions of $\phi(m)=n$. According to a long unsettled conjecture of R. D. Carmichael, there is no integer $n$ for which $A(n)=1$. In this paper it is shown that, if there exists an integer $n$ with $A(n)=k$, there are infinitely many such integers. This is accomplished by proving that for infinitely many primes $p$, if $A(n)=k$, then also $A[n(p-1)]=k$. Another result is the following:

$$\liminf_{n\to\infty}[\max_{1\leqq i\leqq f(n)}\phi(n+i)/\min_{1\leqq j\leqq f(n)}\phi(n+j)]=1$$

for any sequence $f(n)$ tending to infinity with $n$ in such a way that $f(n)\leqq F(n)$, where $F(n)$ is a complicated function, which is shown to be the best possible dominant. The author corrects an earlier statement [Mat. Lapok **7** (1956), 10–17; MR **20** #4534; p. 15] of the following theorem. Let $\lim g(n)/\log\log\log n=0$. Then there exists an infinite sequence $\{n_k\}$ such that for all $i$, $1\leqq i\leqq g(n_k)$, we have $1-\varepsilon_k\leqq\phi(n_k+i)/\phi(n_k+i-1)<1+\varepsilon_k$, where $\varepsilon_k\to 0$ as $k\to\infty$. The above condition on $g(n)$ is stated to be the best possible also. Among other results presented without proof the following is noteworthy. Let $a_1, a_2, \cdots, a_k$ be any non-negative integers or infinity. Then there exists an infinite sequence of integers, $n_1<n_2<\cdots$ such that $\lim_{j\to\infty}h(n_j+i)/h(n_j+i-1)=a_i$ for $i=1, 2, \cdots, k$, where $h(n)=n^cf(n)$ is multiplicative and $f(n)$ satisfies the conditions: $f(p_m^e)\to 1$ as $p_m^e\to\infty$, and $\sum_m |f(p_m^{b_m})-1|=\infty$ for a certain sequence $b_m\geqq 1$ as $p_m$ runs through the sequence of primes. This theorem was previously proved by A. Schinzel [Bull. Acad. Polon. Sci. Cl. III **3** (1955), 415–419; MR **17**, 461] in the cases $h=\phi$ and $h=\sigma$, where $\sigma(n)$ is the sum of the divisors of $n$.

*R. J. Levit* (San Francisco, Calif.)

Citations: MR 17, 461c = N64-5; MR 20# 4534 = N64-13.

## N64-15 (23# A863)

**Erdös, Pál**

**Remarks on two problems.** (Hungarian. Russian and English summaries)

*Mat. Lapok* **11** (1960), 26–32.

Author's summary: "The author proves that for every sufficiently large $n$ there exists an $m<n$ so that

$$d(m) > \prod_{1\leqq i<c_1 \log n/(\log\log n)^2} d(m+i)d(m-i),$$

where $c_1$ is a suitable positive constant. He further shows that for $n>n_0$ and $c_4$ sufficiently large

$$d(n) < \prod d(n+i), \quad 1\leqq i < c_4 \log n/\log_2 n \log_3 n,$$

where $\log_k n$ is the $k$-fold iterated logarithm. Several similar problems are discussed."

## N64-16 (23# A3706)

**Erdös, P.; Schinzel, A.**

**Distributions of the values of some arithmetical functions.**

*Acta Arith.* **6** (1960/61), 473–485.

Let $f_s(n)$ be any positive multiplicative function satisfying the conditions: (I) For any positive integer $l$ and prime $p$, $\lim_{p\to\infty} f_s(p^l)/p^{ls}=1$. (II) There exists an interval $(a,b)$, $a=0$ or $b=\infty$, such that for any integer $M>0$, the set of numbers $f_s(N)/N^s$, $(N,M)=1$, is dense in $(a,b)$. Shao Pin-Tsung [Bull. Acad. Polon. Sci. Cl. III **4** (1956), 569–572; MR **18**, 719] proved the following result. For any sequence of $h$ non-negative numbers $a_1,\cdots,a_h$, and $\varepsilon>0$, there exist positive constants $c=c(a,\varepsilon)$, $x_0=x_0(a,\varepsilon)$, such that the number of positive integers $n\leqq x$ satisfying

$$(*)\qquad \left|\frac{f_s(n+i)}{f_s(n+i-1)}-a_i\right| < \varepsilon \qquad (1\leqq i\leqq h)$$

is greater than $cx/\log^{h+1}x$ whenever $x>x_0$. This was an extension of results by Schinzel and Wang [Ann. Polon. Math. **4** (1958), 201–213; MR **20** #1655] who proved (*) for $\phi(n)$ and $\sigma(n)$.

In the present paper, it is shown that, with condition (I) replaced by

$$(\mathrm{I}')\qquad \sum_p \{f_s(p)-p^s\}^2/p^{2s+1} < \infty,$$

there exist more than $C(a,\varepsilon)x$ positive integers $n\leqq x$ for which (*) holds. This follows from the stronger result:

Let $f(n)$ be an additive function satisfying the conditions: (1) $\sum_p \|f(p)\|^2/p$ is convergent, where $\|f\|=f(p)$ if $|f(p)|\leqq 1$ and $\|f\|=1$ if $|f(p)|>1$. (2) There exists a number $c_1$ such that, for any integer $M>0$, the set of numbers $f(N)$, $(N,M)=1$, is dense in $(c_1,\infty)$. Then, for any sequence of $h$ real numbers $a_1,\cdots,a_h$, and $\varepsilon>0$, there exist more than $C(a,\varepsilon)x$ positive integers $n\leqq x$ such that

$$|f(n+i)-f(n+i-1)-a_i| < \varepsilon \quad (1\leqq i\leqq h).$$

A second theorem, with the additional condition that the partial sums of $\sum \|f(p)\|/p$ are bounded, gives a similar result for $|f(n+i)-a_i|$, which is best possible.

The paper concludes with other theorems based on ideas and results from a previous paper by Erdös [J. London Math. Soc. **14** (1938), 119–127]. One of these is: Let $f(n)$ be an additive function satisfying condition (1) above and such that $\sum_{f(p)\neq 0} 1/p$ is divergent and $\sum \|f(p)\|/p$ is convergent. Then the distribution function of $h$-tuples $\{f(m+1),\cdots,f(m+h)\}$ exists and is a continuous function.

The proofs all use standard number-theoretic results, but with the Erdös touch.

*R. D. James* (Vancouver, B.C.)

Citations: MR 18, 719d = N64-8; MR 20# 1655 = N64-10.

## N64-17 (24# A99)

**Rieger, G. J.**

**Über die Anzahl der Produktzerlegungen ganzer Zahlen.**

*Math. Z.* **76** (1961), 226–234.

Denote by $R(n)$ the number of representations of the natural integer $n$, as a product of integral factors, a change in the order of factors not counting as a distinct representation. The main purpose of the paper is to show that if $k\geqq 1$ is a fixed natural integer, then the values of $R(n)$, with $(n,k)=1$, are distributed evenly in some sense over the $\varphi(k)$ prime residue classes mod $k$. For that purpose, the author establishes asymptotic formulae for the sums $\sum_{n\leqq x}\chi(n)R(n)\log(x/n)$, $\sum_{n\leqq x,\, n\equiv l (\mathrm{mod}\, k)} R(n)\log(x/n)$ and $\sum_{n\leqq x,\, n\equiv l(\mathrm{mod}\, k)} R(n)$ ($\chi$ an arbitrary character mod $k$, $(l,k)=1$). The simplest of the three results is the following. For $x\to\infty$,

$$\sum_{n\leqq x, n\equiv l\,(\mathrm{mod}\, k)} R(n) = B_k x(\log x)^{-3/4}\exp\{2(\varphi(k)k^{-1}\log x)^{1/2}\} \times (1+O(\log^{-1/2}x))$$

with $B_k=\{16\pi^2k\varphi^3(k)\}^{-1/4}e^g$, where

$$g = \lim_{s\to 1}\left\{\sum_{m=1}^{\infty}\frac{(L(ms)-1)}{m}-\frac{\varphi(k)}{k(s-1)}\right\}$$

and the $L$-function corresponds to the principal character mod $k$. A similar result is obtained also for $T(n)$, defined like $R(n)$, but where products of the same factors in different orders are counted as distinct representations. The method is analytic (contour integration) and use is made of several known estimates (such as that for $L(1+it,\chi)$) and of the Wiener-Ikehara Tauberian theorem. Several known theorems (due to Szekeres and Turán, Hille, Kalmár and Ikehara) are contained as particular cases of the present results. Some generalizations are indicated.

*E. Grosswald* (Philadelphia, Pa.)

## N64-18 (26# 1294)

**Besicovitch, A. S.**

**On additive functions of a positive integer.**

*Studies in mathematical analysis and related topics, pp.* 38–41. *Stanford Univ. Press, Stanford, Calif.*, 1962.

Let $f(n)$ be a function on the positive integers which satisfies $f(nm)=f(n)+f(m)$ for $(m,n)=1$. New proofs are given for the following theorems: (i) $f(n)$ monotonic implies $f(n)=c\log n$; (ii) $f(n+1)-f(n)=o(1)$ implies $f(n)=c\log n$. These theorems are due to P. Erdős, whose proofs were rather complicated. Simpler proofs of (i) were given by Lambek and the reviewer, of (i) and (ii) by Schoenberg and of (ii) by Rényi, who also showed that (ii) plays a role in information theory. The present proof of (i) is entirely different from the previous proofs, while that of (ii) is similar to that of Rényi. The proofs of Schoenberg referred to as unpublished have now appeared [Illinois J. Math. **6** (1962), 53–58; MR **25** #1126].

*L. Moser* (Edmonton, Alta.)

Citations: MR 25# 1126 = N60-43.

## N64-19 (26# 2407)

**Rankin, R. A.**

**The divisibility of divisor functions.**

*Proc. Glasgow Math. Assoc.* **5**, 35–40 (1961).

Let $\nu, k$ denote fixed positive integers. For a positive integer $n$, put $\sigma_\nu(n)=\sum_{d|n} d^\nu$; and for any real $x>1$ define $N(\nu, k; x)$ as the number of positive integers $n \leqq x$ for which $\sigma_\nu(n)$ is not divisible by $k$. It was proved by G. N. Watson [Math. Z. **39** (1935), 712–731] that, when $\nu$ is odd and $x \to \infty$,

(*) $$N(\nu, k; x) = O\{x(\log x)^{-1/\phi(k)}\}.$$

In the present paper it is shown that, when $k$ is an odd prime, this estimate can be replaced by an asymptotic formula. Let $\nu$ be arbitrary, let $q$ be an odd prime, and write $h=(q-1)/(\nu, q-1)$. Then, as $x\to\infty$, $N(\nu, q; x)$ is asymptotic to $Ax(\log x)^{-1/h}$ or $Bx$ according as $h$ is even or odd. The constants $A$ and $B$ depend only on $\nu$ and $q$ and are evaluated explicitly. The proof depends on the use of complex function theory and, in particular, on the Wiener-Ikehara theorem and results of Landau's for Dirichlet series. Some information is also obtained for the case of a composite modulus $k$; and Watson's estimate (*) is improved for all cases except when $k$ is a power of a prime or twice such a power. *L. Mirsky* (Sheffield)

Referred to in N64-20.

## N64-20 (30# 3074)

**Scourfield, E. J.**

**On the divisibility of $\sigma_\nu(n)$.**

*Acta Arith.* **10** (1964), 245–285.

Let $\sigma_\nu(n)$ denote, as usual, the sum of $\nu$th powers of positive divisors of $n$. Let $q$ be a prime number and $m$ a positive integer, and denote by $D_m(\nu, q; x)$ the number of positive integers $n\leqq x$ for which $q^m\|\sigma_\nu(n)$ (i.e., $q^m$ is the highest power of $q$ dividing $\sigma_\nu(n)$). Let $\gamma$ be defined by the relation $q^\gamma\|\nu$, and write $m'=[m/(\gamma+1)]$, $h=(q-1)/(\nu, q-1)$. The object of the paper is to determine the asymptotic behaviour of $D_m(\nu, q; x)$ for large values of $x$ and fixed $m, \nu, q$. The principal conclusions are as follows. (i) If $q$ and $h$ are both odd, then $D_m(\nu, q; x)\sim A_1x$. (ii) If $q$ is odd and $h$ is even, then $D_m(\nu, q; x)\sim A_2x(\log\log x)^{m'}(\log x)^{-1/h}$. (iii) $D_m(\nu, 2; x)\sim A_3x(\log\log x)^{m-1}(\log x)^{-1}$. Here $A_1$, $A_2$, $A_3$ are positive constants depending only on $m$, $\nu$, and $q$. The corresponding relations for $m=0$ have been established previously by R. A. Rankin [Proc. Glasgow Math. Assoc. **5** (1961), 35–40; MR **26** #2407]. Furthermore, the author's estimates lead to improvements in still earlier results of G. N. Watson [Math. Z. **39** (1935), 712–731]. Not surprisingly, the proofs of the asymptotic formulae stated above hinge on the study of the Dirichlet series $\sum_{n=1}^\infty a_m(n)n^{-s}$ (where $a_m(n)$ is 1 or 0 according as the relation $q^m\|\sigma_\nu(n)$ is or is not valid) and the representation of this series in terms of the zeta-function and the $L$-functions. However, the details of the argument are long and arduous. *L. Mirsky* (Sheffield)

Citations: MR 26# 2407 = N64-19.

Referred to in N56-31, N64-28.

## N64-21 (30# 3321)

**Pisot, Ch.; Schoenberg, I. J.**

**Arithmetic problems concerning Cauchy's functional equation.**

*Illinois J. Math.* 8 (1964), 40–56.

Erdős [Ann. of Math. (2) **47** (1946), 1–20, Theorem XI; MR **7**, 416] proved that if $F(n)$ is an additive arithmetic function (i.e., $F(mn)=F(m)+F(n)$ whenever $(m, n)=1$) and $F(n)\leqq F(n+1)$ for all integers $n$, then $F(n)=C\log n$. This result was rediscovered by Moser and Lambek [Proc. Amer. Math. Soc. **4** (1953), 544–545; MR **15**, 104] with an elegant proof, and several other proofs have been given since.

The authors study the following generalized situation. Let $P=\{p_1, \cdots, p_k\}$ be a finite set of primes and let $A$ be the set of integers all of whose prime divisors belong to $P$. Suppose the function $F(n)$, defined for $n\in A$, has the property

$$F(n) = F(p_1^{v_1}\cdots p_k^{v_k}) = F(p_1^{v_1})+F(p_2^{v_2})+\cdots+F(p_k^{v_k}),$$

and suppose $F$ is non-decreasing over $A$. Is it still true that $F(n)=C\log n$?

It proves convenient to make the transformation $f(x)=F(e^x)$, $\log P_i=\alpha_i$, and the question then becomes one of the linearity of the solutions of

(*) $$f(v_1\alpha_1+\cdots+v_k\alpha_k) = f(v_1\alpha_1)+\cdots+f(v_k\alpha_k),$$

where $f$ is non-decreasing and the $v_i$ are integers $\geqq 0$. The authors study in particular the cases $k=2$ and $k=3$ for general $\alpha_i$, and the case where the $\alpha_i$ are integers for general $k$, and prove among others the following interesting results.

If $f$ is a non-decreasing function satisfying (*) for $k=3$ and the ratios $\alpha_1/\alpha_2$, $\alpha_1/\alpha_3$, $\alpha_2/\alpha_3$ are all irrational, then $f(x)=\lambda x$. The proof proceeds by first showing that $\lim'_{x\to\infty} f(x)/x$ exists, where the $'$ means that the limit is taken over all $x$ of the form $\alpha_1v_1+\alpha_2v_2+\alpha_3v_3$.

If $k=2$ and $\alpha_1/\alpha_2$ is irrational, there always exist non-linear non-decreasing solutions of (*), and the authors construct all of them. It is still true in this case that $\lim'_{x\to\infty} f(x)/x$ exists, where the limit is restricted to $x$ of the form $\alpha_1v_1+\alpha_2v_2$.

The authors also construct all non-decreasing functions $g$ satisfying $g(m\alpha_1+n\alpha_2)=g(m\alpha_2)=g(m\alpha_1)+g(n\alpha_2)$, $\alpha_1/\alpha_2$ irrational, where $m$ and $n$ are now arbitrary (instead of non-negative) integers, which are extensions of a given non-decreasing solution $f(x)$ of (*) with $k=2$ and $\alpha_1/\alpha_2$ irrational. In the case where the $\alpha_i$ are integers and $k$ is any integer $\geqq 2$, the result is essentially that non-decreasing solutions of (*) are of the form $f(x)=\lambda x+\phi_1(x)+\cdots+\phi_k(x)$, where the $\phi_i(x)$ are certain periodic functions of known period.

*S. L. Segal* (Rochester, N.Y.)

Citations: MR 7, 416c = N60-7; MR 15, 104a = N64-3.

## N64-22 (30# 3322)

**Schoenberg, I. J.**

**Arithmetic problems concerning Cauchy's functional equation.**

*Compositio Math.* **16**, 169–175 (1964).

An exposition of some of the results of the paper by the author and Pisot reviewed above [#3321].

*S. L. Segal* (Rochester, N.Y.)

## N64-23 (30# 3323)

**Pisot, Ch.; Schoenberg, I. J.**

**Arithmetic problems concerning Cauchy's functional equation. II.**

*Illinois J. Math.* **9** (1965), 129–136.

Erdős proved that if $F(n)$ is an additive arithmetic function (i.e., $F(mn)=F(m)+F(n)$ whenever $(m, n)=1$) such that either (1) $F(n+1)\geqq F(n)$ for all integers $n$ or (2) $F(n+1)-F(n)=o(1)$ as $n\to\infty$ holds, then $F(n)=C\log n$ [Ann. of Math. (2) **47** (1946), 1–20, Theorems XI and XIII; MR **7**, 416], and several proofs of both results have been given since.

Motivated by (1), the authors studied (see #3321 above) the real-valued non-decreasing solutions of the functional equation

(*) $$f\left(\sum_{i=1}^m v_i\alpha_i\right) = \sum_{i=1}^m f(v_i\alpha_i),$$

where $f$ is presumed a function of a real variable, and the $v_i$ are non-negative integers, particularly for the cases $m=2$ and $m=3$.

In this paper, motivated in part by (2), they study the solutions of (*), where the $\alpha_i$ may now be elements of the real $n$-dimensional space $R^n$ and the range of $f$ is an arbitrary Banach space $B$, and $f$ is uniformly continuous (i.e., for each $\varepsilon > 0$ there exists $\delta > 0$ such that if $|x-y| < \delta$, $\|f(x)-f(y)\| < \varepsilon$).

Their main theorem may be stated as follows. Suppose $m > n$ and $\alpha_1, \alpha_2, \cdots, \alpha_m$ are elements of $R^n$ such that (a) every set of $n$ of the $\alpha_i$ are linearly independent over the reals, and (b) $\alpha_1, \cdots, \alpha_m$ are linearly independent over the rationals. Then if $f(x)$ is a function defined on and uniformly continuous over the set $S = \{x = \sum_{i=1}^n v_i\alpha_i : v_i$ integers $\geqq 0\}$, and if $f$ is a solution of (*), then

$$f(x) = \lambda(x) + \sum_{i=1}^{m} \phi_i(x),$$

where $\lambda(x)$ is a linear function from $R^n$ to $B$ and the $\phi_i(x)$ are certain specified periodic functions. From this result they deduce that, in the above notation, if $m \geqq n+2$, then $f(x)$ is the restriction to $S$ of a linear function from $R^n$ to $B$. Since, if $m \leqq n$, the linear independence of $\alpha_1, \cdots, \alpha_m$ over the rationals implies that there is a positive lower bound to the distance between points of $S$, and so uniform continuity has no meaning, there remains only the case $m = n+1$. Here again, all solutions may be characterized as restrictions of certain functions from $R^n$ to $B$.

The authors discuss as examples the special cases corresponding to their earlier paper in which $n = 1$, $B = R^1$ and $m = 2$ or 3, and mention an unsolved problem which is analogous to Erdős's result quoted above.

*S. L. Segal* (Rochester, N.Y.)

Citations: MR 7, 416c = N60-7.

## N64-24 (34# 2535 )

**Birch, B. J.**

**Multiplicative functions with non-decreasing normal order.**

*J. London Math. Soc.* **42** (1967), 149–151.

The author's introduction (with appropriate references added) is as follows: "Following G. H. Hardy and E. M. Wright [*An introduction to the theory of numbers*, Third edition, p. 356, Clarendon, Oxford, 1954; MR **16**, 673] we say that an arithmetic function $f$ has non-decreasing normal order $g$ if $g$ is a non-decreasing function such that for every $\varepsilon > 0$, $|f(n)-g(n)| < \varepsilon g(n)$ for all except $o(X)$ integers $n$ less than a given bound $X$. An arithmetic function $f$ is multiplicative if $f(mn) = f(m)f(n)$ whenever $(m, n) = 1$. We will show that the only unbounded multiplicative functions with a non-decreasing normal order are the powers of $n$; our proof will be utterly elementary. Our theorem generalizes recent results of S. L. Segal [J. London Math. Soc. **39** (1964), 400–404; MR **32** #5607; ibid. **40** (1965), 459–466]; possibly it is implicit in the far deeper work of P. Erdős [Ann. of Math. (2) **47** (1946), 1–20; MR **7**, 416], but I have been unable to locate it. In contrast to our result, the method of P. Turán [J. London Math. Soc. **9** (1934), 274–276; ibid. **11** (1936), 125–133] shows that there is a very wide class of multiplicative functions $f$ for which $\log f(n)$ has a non-decreasing normal order." *A. L. Whiteman* (Los Angeles, Calif.)

Citations: MR 7, 416c = N60-7; MR 16, 673b = Z01-28; MR 32# 5607 = A26-68.

Referred to in N64-26.

## N64-25 (34# 4234 )

**Máté, Attila**

**A new proof of a theorem of P. Erdős.**

*Proc. Amer. Math. Soc.* **18** (1967), 159–162.

The author gives a simple elementary proof for the following theorem of P. Erdős (Erdős' proof is as yet unpublished): Let $f(n)$ be a real valued function, defined for all positive integers, with $f(ab) = f(a) + f(b)$ for $(a, b) = 1$. If $\lim\inf\{f(n+1) - f(n)\} \geqq 0$, then $f(n) = c \log n$ for a suitable constant $c$. *O. H. Körner* (Marburg)

Referred to in N64-34, N64-39.

## N64-26 (35# 4180 )

**Segal, S. L.**

**On non-decreasing normal orders.**

*J. London Math. Soc.* **40** (1965), 459–466.

The author proves two general theorems on the existence of non-decreasing normal orders for arithmetic functions. {In the proof of Theorem I, $g(x)$ should be replaced by $g_1(x) = \min(g([x]), m([x]))$. The given proof that $\sigma(n)$ has no non-decreasing normal order fails on line 5 of page 464, where it is incorrectly concluded that $n = o(g(n))$. For a related paper, see B. J. Birch [same J. **42** (1967), 149–151; MR **34** #2535].} *R. Spira* (E. Lansing, Mich.)

Citations: MR 34# 2535 = N64-24.

## N64-27 (36# 3742 )

**Kátai, I.**

**On sets characterizing number-theoretical functions.**

*Acta Arith.* **13** (1967/68), 315–320.

A complex-valued function $f(n)$ is called totally additive if $f(nm) = f(n) + f(m)$ holds for all pairs $m, n$ of natural numbers. If $f(n)$ vanishes for all natural numbers $n$, then $f(n)$ is called singular. A set of natural numbers is called a set of uniqueness if the unique totally additive function which vanishes on $\mathscr{A}$ is a singular function. The set $\mathscr{A}$ is called a set of quasi-uniqueness if there exists a set $\mathscr{B}$ of finitely many elements such that $\mathscr{A} \vee \mathscr{B}$ is a set of uniqueness. Using the result that the Dirichlet $L$-function mod $q$ is non-vanishing on the half plane $\mathrm{Re}(s) > \frac{1}{2}$ for every sufficiently large prime $q$, the author proves that the set $\{p+1\}$ is a set of quasi-uniqueness. Using results of Vinogradov it is shown that the set $\{P_3+1\}$ is a set of uniqueness, where $P_3$ consists of numbers having at most three prime divisors. A number of hypotheses are stated whose proofs seem to be difficult.

*M. S. Cheema* (Tucson, Ariz.)

Referred to in N64-32.

## N64-28 (36# 6365 )

**Narkiewicz, W.**

**Divisibility properties of a class of multiplicative functions.**

*Colloq. Math.* **18** (1967), 219–232.

Let $f(n)$ be an integer-valued multiplicative function having the following property: there exists a polynomial $W(x)$ with integral coefficients such that, for all primes $p$, $f(p) = W(p)$. For any prime $q$, let $\beta(q)$ be the number of integers $n$ $(1 \leqq n \leqq q-1)$ such that $W(n) \not\equiv 0 \pmod q$ and let $R_f$ be the set of all primes $q$ with $\beta(q) = q-1$. If $q^m$ divides $N$ but $q^{m+1}$ does not, then we write $q^m \| N$. Finally, by $N(n \leqq x : P)$ we denote the number of positive integers $n \leqq x$ with the property $P$. The author proves the following two theorems.

Theorem I: Let $q$ be a prime and $m$ a non-negative integer such that the set $\{n : q^m \| f(n)\}$ is not void. Then the following asymptotic evaluations hold: (i) if $q \notin R_f$, $\beta(q) \neq 0$, then

$$N(n \leqq x : q^m \| f(n)) \sim C_1(q, m)x(\log\log x)^M(\log x)^a,$$

where $a = \beta(q)/(q-1) - 1$; (ii) if $q \notin R_f$, $\beta(q) = 0$, $M(q, m) \neq 0$, then $N(n \leqq x : q^m \| f(n)) \sim C_2(q, m)x(\log\log x)^{M-1}(\log x)^{-1}$; (iii) if $q \notin R_f$, $\beta(q) = M(q, m) = 0$, then $N(n \leqq x : q^m \| f(n)) = O(x^{1/2})$; (iv) if $q \notin R_f$, then $N(n \leqq x : q^m \| f(n)) \sim C_3(q, m)x$. Here $M = M(q, m) \leqq m$ is the degree of a certain polynomial and $C_i(q, m)$ are positive constants $(i = 1, 2, 3)$.

Theorem II: (i) If $D$ is a square-free integer which has no prime divisor in $R_f$, then either (a) $N_D(x) \sim$

$C(D)x(\log x)^{-A}$ with positive $A$ and $C(D)$, or (b) $N_D(x) = O(x^{1-\varepsilon})$ with a suitable $\varepsilon > 0$. (ii) If $D$ is a square-free integer having prime divisors in $R_f$, then (c) $N_D(x) \sim C(D)x$ with $C(D)$ positive.

In the particular cases $f(n) = \sigma_\nu(n)$, $\phi(n)$ or $d(n)$, Theorem I and some special cases of Theorem II were proved by E. J. Scourfield [Acta Arith. **10** (1964), 245–285; MR **30** #3074], whose work generalizes earlier work of G. N. Watson and the reviewer. *R. A. Rankin* (Glasgow)

Citations: MR 30# 3074 = N64-20.
Referred to in N64-48.

**N64-29** **(38# 130)**

**Kátai, I.**

**A remark on number-theoretical functions.**
*Acta Arith.* **14** (1967/68), 409–415.

A well-known theorem of Erdős states that if the additive arithmetical function $f$ satisfies the condition $f(n) \leqq f(n+1)$ for $n = 1, 2, 3, \cdots$, then $f(n) = c \log n$ for a suitable constant $c$ [Ann. of Math. (2) **47** (1946), 1–20; MR **7**, 416]. The author had for some time the following conjecture: Let $f$, $g$ be additive arithmetical functions and let $h = \max(f, g)$. If $h(n) \leqq h(n+1)$ for $n = 1, 2, \cdots$, then $h = c \log n$ for some constant $c$.

In the present paper, the author first gives a counterexample to show that the conjecture is false. Then he proves the following results which show that the conjecture is not far from the truth: (A) If neither of the sets $E\{n : f(n) \geqq g(n)\}$ and $E\{n : g(n) \geqq f(n)\}$ has density 1, $h(n) = c \log n$ for all $n$. (B) If $S = E\{n: f(n) \geqq g(n)\}$ has density 1, $f(n) = c \log n$ for all $n$ and so $h(n) = c \log n$ for all $n$ in $S$. Also, $\{h(n) - c \log n\} \to 0$ as $n \to \infty$. Some further details are also proved in the paper.

Incidentally, in Lemma 2, the author answers in the affirmative the following question raised by P. Erdős [Rend. Sem. Mat. Fis. Milano **27** (1957), 45–49; MR **20** #7004]: Let $f$ be an additive arithmetical function such that $f(n) \leqq f(n+1)$ for all $n$ in a set of density 1. Does it follow that $f(n) = c \log n$, $c$ being a constant?

*E. M. Paul* (Calcutta)

Citations: MR 7, 416c = N60-7; MR 20# 7004 = N60-33.
Referred to in N64-44.

**N64-30** **(38# 5731)**

**Narkiewicz, W.**

**Divisibility properties of some multiplicative functions. (Loose Russian summary)**
*Bull. Acad. Polon. Sci. Sér. Sci. Math. Astronom. Phys.* **16** (1968), 621–623.

Let $f(n)$ be a multiplicative integer-valued function for which there exists a polynomial $P(x)$ with integer coefficients such that, for all primes $p$, $f(p) = P(p)$ (most multiplicative functions in number theory have this property). Given the natural number $d$, let $M(d, x)$ be the number of positive integers $n \leqq x$ for which $d|f(n)$ and $(d, f(n)/d) = 1$. Then asymptotic results of the following type are obtained: $M(d, x) \sim cx(\log\log x)^\alpha(\log x)^{-\beta}$, where $\alpha, \beta \geqq 0$, $c > 0$, or, in some cases, $M(d, x) = O(x^{1-\varepsilon})$ ($\varepsilon > 0$). This generalizes previous work of Rankin, Scourfield, and the author. Proofs are to appear in the Proc. Colloq. Theory of Numbers (Debrecen, 1968).

*R. A. MacLeod* (Victoria, B.C.)

**N64-31** **(39# 6846)**

**Kátai, I.**

**On the determination of an additive arithmetical function by its local behaviour.**
*Colloq. Math.* **20** (1969), 265–267.

It is shown that for each pair of positive integers $k$, $N$, there is a positive integer $K$ with the following property: if $f$ is completely additive and $f(n) = 0$ for all $n$ in the interval $N \leqq n \leqq N + K$, then $f(p_i) = 0$ for $i = 1, 2, \cdots, k$, where $p_i$ is the $i$th prime. Denoting the smallest such $K$ by $\lambda_k(N)$, the author proves that $\lambda_k(N) \leqq c_1\sqrt{N}$ and $\limsup_{N\to\infty} \log \lambda_k(N)/\sqrt{(\log N \log\log\log N)} \geqq c_2$, where $c_1$ and $c_2$ depend only on $k$. *D. Rearick* (Boulder, Colo.)

**N64-32** **(40# 106)**

**Kátai, I.**

**On sets characterizing number-theoretical functions. II. The set of "prime plus one" s is a set of quasi-uniqueness.**
*Acta Arith.* **16** (1969/70), 1–4.

In an earlier paper [same Acta **13** (1967/68), 315–320; MR **36** #3742] the author proved that the set $p_1 = \{p + 1\}$, where $p$ runs over all primes, is a set of quasi-uniqueness under the assumption of the Riemann-Piltz conjecture. Here he proves this result using Bombieri's result in the theory of the large sieve. The main result is the following. There exists a numerical constant $K$ such that if $f(n)$ is a completely additive number theoretic function such that $f(p) = 0$ for $p \leqq K$ and $f(p+1) = 0$ for all primes $p$, then $f(n) = 0$ identically. *M. S. Cheema* (Tucson, Ariz.)

Citations: MR 36# 3742 = N64-27.

**N64-33** **(40# 4222)**

**Kátai, I.**

**On a problem of P. Erdős.**
*J. Number Theory* **2** (1970), 1–6.

The author proves that if $f(n)$ is an additive number-theoretic function (i.e., $f(mn) = f(m) + f(n)$ if $(m, n) = 1$) such that $\sum_{n\leqq x} |f(n+1) - f(n)| = o(x)$, then $f(n) = c \log n$ for some constant $c$. This result implies, in particular, two other characterizations of $\log n$ as an additive number-theoretic function, proved originally by P. Erdős [Ann. of Math. (2) **47** (1946), 1–20; MR **7**, 416], and which have led to an extensive literature.

An independent proof and a still further generalization of the author's results have been obtained by Wirsing, but have not yet appeared.

{Remark: It would seem that in Section 2 the assumption $(p, N+1) = 1$ is also necessary, but the proof goes through just the same.} *S. L. Segal* (Rochester, N.Y.)

Citations: MR 7, 416c = N60-7.

**N64-34** **(40# 5560)**

**Kátai, I.**

**Some results and problems in the theory of additive functions.**
*Acta Sci. Math. (Szeged)* **30** (1969), 305–311.

A function $f(n)$ of a positive integer is said to be restrictedly additive if $(n_1, n_2) = 1$ implies $f(n_1 n_2) = f(n_1) + f(n_2)$. If this equation is satisfied for any pair of integers $n_1$, $n_2$, then $f(n)$ is said to be completely additive. P. Erdős [Ann. of Math. (2) **47** (1946), 1–20; MR **7**, 416] proved that (A) if $f(n)$ is restrictedly additive and monotonic, then it is a constant multiple of $\log n$, (B) if $f(n)$ is restrictedly additive and $f(n+1) - f(n) \to 0$ ($n \to \infty$), then it is a constant multiple of $\log n$. Various generalizations of these theorems have been discussed recently by A. Máté [Proc. Amer. Math. Soc. **18** (1967), 159–162; MR **34** #4234] and the author [Ann. Univ. Sci. Budapest. Eötvös Sect. Math. **10** (1967), 81–83]. In the present paper, two more theorems of similar nature are proved.

Let a class of additive functions be defined by (i) $f(2n+1) - f(n) \to C$ ($C$ is constant). Then the author proves the theorem: If $f(n)$ is a completely additive function satisfying (i), then $f(n)=C(\log 2)^{-1}\log n$. The other theorem is too long to be quoted here.

*J. M. Gandhi* (Macomb, Ill.)

Citations: MR 7, 416c = N60-7; MR 34# 4234 = N64-25.

## N64-35 (40# 5561)

**Kátai, I.**

**On the values of multiplicative functions in short intervals.**

*Math. Ann.* **183** (1969), 181–184.

By using an estimate obtained by P. G. Schmidt in his dissertation [*Abschätzungen bei unsymmetrischen Gitterpunktproblemen*, Georg-August-Univ., Göttingen, Göttingen, 1964; MR **31** #5837] for the number of square free numbers in an interval, the author proves the following theorem: Let $f$ be an arbitrary complex-valued multiplicative number-theoretical function and let $I_N$ denote the interval $[N, N+N^\theta]$, where $\theta=0.6108$. Suppose that, for some infinite sequence of integers $N_1<N_2<N_3<\cdots$, $f(n)=A_j\neq 0$ for all $n\in I_{N_j}$ $(j=1,2,\cdots)$. Then $f(n)=1$ for all squarefree $n$. It follows immediately from this that the Möbius function $\mu(n)$ assumes both the values 1 and $-1$ in $[N, N+N^\theta]$ for all sufficiently large $N$.

*R. A. Rankin* (Glasgow)

Citations: MR 31# 5837 = P28-70.

## N64-36 (41# 164)

**Máté, Eörs**

**On a problem of P. Erdős.**

*Acta Sci. Math. (Szeged)* **30** (1969), 301–304.

A function $f$ defined on the positive integers is additive when $f(ab)=f(a)+f(b)$ for coprime $a, b$, completely additive when the above holds for all $a, b$. The author proves the following theorem: Suppose $f$ is additive, $f(n+1)-f(n)$ is bounded, $|f(n+1)-f(n)|\leqq M$. Then $f$ may be written as a sum $f=g+h$, where $g$ is completely additive, $h$ is bounded. In fact (see p. 304), $|h(n)|\leqq 4M$. It follows that $g, h$ are unique, with $g(n)=\lim_{t\to\infty}t^{-1}f(n^t)$. This partially verifies a conjecture of P. Erdős, who has predicted $g(n)=k\log n$ for some constant $k$ [Ann. of Math. (2) **47** (1946), 1–20; MR **7**, 416].

The author first shows (Lemmas 1, 2, 3) that

$$|f(n^s)-sf(n)|\leqq 2sM,$$

$4sM$ for the cases $(s, n-1)=1$, $s=2^k$, also $|f(n^t)-f(n^s)|\leqq 4|t-s|nM$. He then proves $\lim_{t\to\infty}t^{-1}f(n^t)=g(n)$ exists, first for $t=2^k$, then for arbitrary $t\to\infty$. The complete additivity of $f$ and the bound ($4M$) for $|f-g|$ follow easily.

{Reviewer's note: The author's proof of Lemma 1 can be rearranged to show that for any additive $f$ and any $s$ we have $f(n^s)-sf(n)=\Delta(n^s)-\Delta(n)+\sum_{j=1}^{s-1}\Delta(S_j)+\varepsilon$, where $\Delta(m)=f(m)-f(m-1)$, $S_k=S_{kn}=\sum_{i=0}^{k}n^i$, $\varepsilon=f(n^s-1)-f(n-1)-f(S_{s-1})$. For $f(n)=f(S_j-1)-f(S_{j-1})$, thus (sum over $j$) $(s-1)f(n)=f(S_{s-1})-\sum\Delta S_j$, etc. If also $(s, n-1)=1$, then $\varepsilon=0$.}

*G. K. White* (Vancouver, B.C.)

Citations: MR 7, 416c = N60-7.

## N64-37 (41# 168)

**Kátai, Imre**

**On the distribution of the solutions of special Diophantine equations. (Hungarian)**

*Mat. Lapok* **20** (1969), 117–122.

Let $n$ be an integer with the prime decomposition $n=p_1^{\alpha_1}\cdots p_r^{\alpha_r}$. Write $\tau(n,\alpha,\beta)=\sum_{d|n, n^\alpha\leqq d\leqq n^\beta}1$. The distribution of the values of $\tau(n,\alpha,\beta)$ is investigated, when $n$ runs over some increasing sequence of integers. We quote two theorems. Theorem 1: The relation

$$\tau(n_k, \tfrac{1}{2}-\varepsilon, \tfrac{1}{2}+\varepsilon)/\tau(n_k)\to 1 \qquad (k\to\infty)$$

holds if and only if $(\log P(n_k))/\log n_k\to 0$, where $P(y)$ is the greatest prime-power divisor of $y$. Theorem 2: Denote by $\bar{N}_n(x)$ the number of divisors $d$ of $n$ ($n$ is a natural number) for which $\log d<\frac{1}{2}\log n+x(\sum_{i=1}^{r}c_i\log^2 p_i)^{1/2}$, where $c_i=\alpha_i(\alpha_i+2)/12$. Then we have

$$|\bar{N}_n(x)-(\tau(n)/\sqrt{(2\pi)})\int_{-\infty}^{x}e^{-t^2/2}\,dt| < c((\log P(n))/\log n)^{1/2}\tau(n),$$

where $c$ is an absolute constant.

The proofs are based on classical limit theorems on independent random variables.

*P. Szüsz* (Stony Brook, N.Y.)

## N64-38 (41# 1666)

**Kátai, I.**

**A remark on additive arithmetical functions.**

*Ann. Univ. Sci. Budapest. Eötvös Sect. Math.* **10** (1967), 81–83.

This paper contains a short proof of the following theorem: Let $\varepsilon(n)$ be a sequence tending to zero; if $f$ is an additive function on the natural numbers (i.e., $(n,m)=1$ implies $f(nm)=f(n)+f(m)$) and if $f(n+1)-f(n)\geqq-\varepsilon(n)$, then $f$ is a constant multiple of log. This theorem was stated without proof by P. Erdős [Rend. Sem. Mat. Fis. Milano **27** (1957), 45–49; MR **20** #7004]. *G. J. Rieger* (Munich)

Citations: MR 20# 7004 = N60-33.

## N64-39 (41# 1667)

**Kátai, I.**

**Characterization of additive functions by its local behavior.**

*Ann. Univ. Sci. Budapest. Eötvös Sect. Math.* **12** (1969), 35–37.

Let $f(n)$ be a real-valued function defined for all positive integers with $f(ab)=f(a)+f(b)$ for $(a,b)=1$. Let $\Delta^1 f(n)=\Delta f(n)=f(n+1)-f(n)$ and $\Delta^k f(n)=\Delta^{k-1}f(n+1)-\Delta^{k-1}f(n)$ for $k=2,3,\cdots$. The following theorem is proved by induction: If $\liminf\Delta^k f(n)\geqq 0$, or $\limsup\Delta^k f(n)\leqq 0$ for some natural number $k$, then $f(n)$ is a constant multiple of $\log n$. The case $k=1$ was proved by the author and by A. Máté [Proc. Amer. Math. Soc. **18** (1967), 159–162; MR **34** #4234] and constitutes the first part of the induction hypothesis. *E. M. Horadam* (Armidale)

Citations: MR 34# 4234 = N64-25.

## N64-40 (41# 8599)

**Ricci, G.**

**Funzioni aritmetiche additive e condizioni unilaterali.**

*Period. Mat.* (4) **46** (1968), 500–509.

P. Erdős [Ann. of Math. (2) **47** (1946), 1–20; MR **7**, 416] proved the following, by now classical, theorem: If $f(n)$ is an additive, non-decreasing function, defined on the natural integers, then there exists a constant $c$ such that $f(n)=c\log n$. Several similar theorems have been proven since. The condition of monotonicity may be replaced by (*) $f(n+1)-f(n)\to 0$ and several versions of the theorem are now known. The present paper contains further variations on the same theme. In particular, (*) is required only on a subset of the integers. Specifically, for $2\leqq a\in\mathbf{Z}$, $1\leqq t\in\mathbf{Z}$, set $u_t=u(a,t)=a^t-(a^t-1)/(a-1)$ and $\nu_t=\nu(a,t)=a^t+(a^t-1)/(a-1)$. If $f(n)$ is an additive function such that $f(u_h+1)-f(u_h)\to 0$ on the sequence $\{u_h\}$, then $f(u_h)/\log u_h\to f(a)/\log a$. Similarly, from $f(\nu_h)-f(\nu_h-1)\to 0$ follows $f(\nu_h)/\log\nu_h=f(a)/\log a$. Similar conclusions follow also if one replaces $f(u_h+1)-f(u_h)\to 0$ by "one-sided" conditions (somewhat too technical for quotation), provided that $f(n)$ has "property $\mathscr{M}$" defined as follows: Let $\varphi(n_h)=f(n_h)$ and interpolate $\varphi(u)$ linearly between the integers $n_h$; then $f(n)$ is said to have property $\mathscr{M}$, provided that $\varphi(u) \leqq \varphi(x) + o(\log x)$ for $\alpha x < u \leqq x$, where $0 < \alpha < 1$. {Observe that on p. 502 the author switches from $\alpha$ ($<1$) to $1/\alpha$ without changing the symbol, as, e.g., in the inequalities $x/\alpha \leqq u < x$.}

*E. Grosswald* (Philadelphia, Pa.)

Citations: MR 7, 416c = N60-7.

## N64-41 (42# 215)

**Skof, Fulvia**

**Sulle funzioni $f(n)$ aritmetiche additive asintotiche a $c \log n$.**

*Ist. Lombardo Accad. Sci. Lett. Rend. A* **103** (1969), 931–938.

An arithmetical function $f$, i.e., a mapping of the set of natural numbers into the set of complex numbers, is called additive, if $f(mn) = f(m) + f(n)$ for every pair $m$, $n$ of relatively prime natural numbers. The author investigates such functions that have the additional property (A): $f(n) \sim c \log n$ as $n \to \infty$ for some constant $c$. For example, he proves: An additive arithmetical function $f$ satisfies (A) if $f(2^k) = kf(2)$ $(k = 0, 1, 2, 3, \cdots)$ and $f(2n+1) - f(2n) \to 0$ as $n \to \infty$. Furthermore, he derives some refinements of this theorem and conditions necessary for (A).

*O. H. Körner* (Marburg)

## N64-42 (42# 1792)

**Hall, R. R.**

**On the distribution of divisors of integers in residue classes** (mod $k$).

*J. Number Theory* **2** (1970), 168–188.

The author establishes mean value theorems for the variance of the distribution of the divisors of $n$ among the reduced residue classes (mod $k$) and shows that for almost all $n < x$, the distribution is very even provided that $k$ is not too large compared with $x$. In particular, if we let $\tau(n; k)$ denote the number of divisors of $n$ which are prime to $k$ and $\tau(n; k, h)$ the number of these congruent to $h$ (mod $k$), $1 \leqq h \leqq k$, $(h, k) = 1$, the author evaluates the sum $\sum_{n \leq x} y^{\omega(n)} \sum_{h=1,(h,k)=1} [\tau(n; k, h) - \tau(n; k)/\varphi(k)]^2$, where $y$ are certain complex numbers, and for $k$ "not too large" with respect to $x$. The author then uses his results to obtain the following result which is a more precise version of a theorem of P. Erdős [Bull. Soc. Math. Grèce (N.S.) **6 I** (1965), fasc. 1, 27–36; MR **34** #7474]. Theorem: There exists an absolute constant $\varepsilon_0 > 0$ such that for $k \leqq 2^{(1/2)(1-\varepsilon_0/\log\log\log x)\log\log x}$, for any $\eta > 0$, for almost all $n \leqq x$, and for all $h$ prime to $k$, $(1-\eta)(\tau(n; k)/\varphi(k)) < \tau(n; k, h) < (1+\eta)(\tau(n; k)/\varphi(k))$ and, furthermore, the number of exceptional $n$ does not exceed

$$C[1/(\log x)^{\varepsilon^2/4} + 1/n\sqrt{(\varepsilon)}(\log x)^{\varepsilon/8}],$$

where $\varepsilon$ is defined by $k^2 = 2^{(1-\varepsilon)\log\log x}$.

*M. C. Wunderlich* (De Kalb, Ill.)

Citations: MR 34# 7474 = N28-64.

Referred to in N64-43.

## N64-43 (43# 149)

**Hall, R. R.**

**Erratum: "On the distribution of divisors of integers in residue classes** (mod $k$)".

*J. Number Theory* **2** (1970), 509.

The author corrects an error in the proof of Theorem 5 of his earlier paper [same J. **2** (1970), 168–188; MR **42** #1792].

*M. C. Wunderlich* (De Kalb, Ill.)

Citations: MR 42# 1792 = N64-42.

## N64-44 (42# 4512)

**Ryavec, C.**

**On additive functions.**

*Michigan Math. J.* **16** (1969), 321–329.

A number-theoretic function $f$ is said to be additive if $f(mn) = f(m) + f(n)$ whenever $(m, n) = 1$. Denote the class of such functions by $\mathscr{A}$ and the subclass of functions of the form $f(n) = c \log n$ by $\mathscr{B}$. The paper discusses the conditions on functions $f$ in $\mathscr{A}$ under which $f$ is also in $\mathscr{B}$. (See also P. Erdős [Ann. of Math. (2) **47** (1946), 1–20; MR **7**, 416] and I. Kátai [Acta Arith. **14** (1967/68), 409–415; MR **38** #130].) Let $f \in \mathscr{A}$, and $\lim_{x\to\infty} x^{-1} \sum_{n \leqslant x} |f(n+1) - f(n)| = 0$; the author then proves by an iterative method that $f$ is completely additive. If in addition $f(n) = O(\log n)$, the author shows that $f \in \mathscr{B}$. This is done by writing $\sum_{n \leq x} f(n) = \sum_{k=1}^{n_i} \sum_{n \leq x, n \equiv k (\mathrm{mod}\ n_i)} f(n)$ where $n_i = n_1$ or $n_2$ and $n_1$ and $n_2$ are chosen so that $n_2/n_1 = 1 + \zeta$, where $\zeta$ is a small positive number. The author also proves that if $f \in \mathscr{A}$, $f(n) \geqq 0$ and

$$\lim_{x\to\infty} (\log x)^{-1} \sum_{n \leq x} |f(n+1)/(n+1) - f(n)/n| = 0,$$

then $f \in \mathscr{B}$.

*E. M. Horadam* (Armidale)

Citations: MR 7, 416c = N60-7; MR 38# 130 = N64-29.

## N64-45 (42# 5932)

**Wirsing, E.**

**A characterization of** $\log n$ **as an additive arithmetic function.**

*Symposia Mathematica, Vol. IV (INDAM, Rome, 1968/69), pp.* 45–57. *Academic Press, London,* 1970.

Let $f$ be an additive (in the restricted sense) arithmetic function which is either monotonic or satisfies the condition $f(n+1) = f(n) + o(1)$ as $n \to \infty$. Then P. Erdős has proved [Ann. of Math. (2) **47** (1946), 1–20; MR **7**, 416] that $f(n) = c \log n$ for some constant $c$. Erdős also conjectured that an additive function $f$ satisfying $f(n+1) = f(n) + O(1)$ must have the form $f(n) = c \log n + O(1)$. That conjecture is proved to be correct in this paper.

*B. Garrison* (San Diego, Calif.)

Citations: MR 7, 416c = N60-7.

## N64-46 (42# 7613)

**Kátai, I.**

**On number-theoretical functions.**

*Number Theory (Colloq., János Bolyai Math. Soc., Debrecen,* 1968), *pp.* 133–137. *North-Holland, Amsterdam,* 1970.

A list is given of some theorems and conjectures concerning restrictedly additive and completely additive arithmetic functions. For example, P. Erdős has proved [Ann. of Math. (2) **47** (1946), 1–20; MR **7**, 416] that if $f$ is restrictedly additive, i.e., if $(n_1, n_2) = 1$ implies $f(n_1 n_2) = f(n_1) + f(n_2)$, and if $f(n+1) - f(n) \to 0$, then $f(n)$ is a constant multiple of $\log n$.

*B. Garrison* (San Diego, Calif.)

Citations: MR 7, 416c = N60-7.

## N64-47 (42# 7614)

**Skof, Fulvia**

**Un criterio di completa additività per le funzioni aritmetiche riguardante successioni di densità irregolare.** (English summary)

*Atti Accad. Naz. Lincei Rend. Cl. Sci. Fis. Mat. Natur.* (8) **48** (1970), 10–13.

An arithmetic function $f(n)$ is additive if $f(mn) = f(m) + f(n)$ when $(m, n) = 1$. P. Erdős [Ann. of Math. (2) **47** (1946), 1–20; MR **7**, 416] has proved that if $f(n)$ is additive and $f(n+1) - f(n) \to 0$ as $n \to \infty$, then there exists a constant $c$ such that $f(n) = c \log n$. He has conjectured that it is enough to assume that $f(n+1) - f(n) \to 0$ on an increasing set of integers of density 1. In the present paper it is proved that if $f(n)$ is additive and there exists a sequence of integers $u_1 < u_2 < u_3 < \cdots$, such that (*) $\limsup k/u_k = 1$,

$f(u_k+1)-f(u_k)\to 0$, then $f(rs)=f(r)+f(s)$ for all positive integers $r, s$. Thus additivity together with (*) imply complete additivity. *L. Carlitz* (Durham, N.C.)

Citations: MR 7, 416c = N60-7.

**N64-48** **(43# 170)**

**Narkiewicz, W.**

**Divisibility properties of some multiplicative functions.** *Number Theory (Colloq., János Bolyai Math. Soc., Debrecen,* 1968), *pp.* 147–159. *North-Holland, Amsterdam,* 1970.

Consider a multiplicative arithmetic function $f(n)$ whose values on primes $p$ are expressible as a polynomial in $p$ with integer coefficients. For a fixed positive integer $d$ let $M(d, x)$ denote the number of positive integers $n\leqq x$ such that $d$ is a unitary divisor of $f(n)$. The author investigates the asymptotic behavior of $M(d, x)$ for large $x$. His result (which generalizes earlier work of himself [the author, Colloq. Math. **18** (1967), 219–232; MR **36** #6365] and others in which $d$ is a prime power) states that either $M(d, x)\sim cx(\log\log x)^a(\log x)^{-b}$ for some positive $c$ and non-negative $a$ and $b$, or else $M(d, x)=O(x^{1-\varepsilon})$ for some positive $\varepsilon$. The constants $a$ and $b$ are evaluated explicitly when $f(n)$ is the Euler totient $\varphi(n)$ or the divisor function $d(n)$. The result is deduced from the Tauberian theorems of Delange and Ikehara [H. Delange, Ann. Sci. École Norm. Sup. (3) **71** (1954), 213–242; MR **16**, 921], by essentially elementary methods. *D. Rearick* (Boulder, Colo.)

Citations: MR 16, 921e = M45-24; MR 36# 6365 = N64-28.

**N64-49** **(43# 1935)**

**Ryavec, C.**

**A characterization of finitely distributed additive functions.** *J. Number Theory* **2** (1970), 393–403.

The author uses a new method to establish Erdős's characterization theorem for finitely distributed additive functions which, loosely worded, asserts that an additive function is finitely distributed if and only if it approximates a constant multiple of the logarithm. The author's method is measure-theoretic in nature and is used to prove the necessity of the condition. {The second displayed line on page 393 contains a confusing misprint—it should read $|f(a_i)-f(a_j)|<c_2$, $1\leqq i, j\leqq n$.}
*M. C. Wunderlich* (De Kalb, Ill.)

# N68 DISTRIBUTION OF INTEGERS IN SPECIAL RESIDUE CLASSES: QUADRATIC RESIDUES AND NONRESIDUES

See also Sections L10, N72.

See also reviews A10-8, A14-25, A14-40, B48-5, D80-26, E16-19, E16-88, L05-11, L10-1, L10-23, L20-17, L20-25, L25-16, L25-20, N60-85, N72-6, N72-43, N76-25, Q15-11, R12-5, T45-5, Z02-48.

**N68-1** **(3, 66f)**

**Chung, Kai-Lai. Note on a theorem on quadratic residues.** Bull. Amer. Math. Soc. **47**, 514–516 (1941).

Short proof of the known theorem: For every prime $p\equiv 3$ mod 4 there are more quadratic residues between 0 and $p/2$ then between $p/2$ and $p$. This is equivalent to

$$\sum u(s, p)=\sum_{s=1}^{(p-1)/2}\{[2s^2/p]-2[s^2/p]\}\leqq(p-1)/4.$$

Using the sine Fourier series for $x-[x]-\frac{1}{2}$, we have

$$u(s, p)=\sum_n(\sin(4n\pi s^2/p)-2\sin(2\pi s^2/p))/n\pi,$$

with the first summation running from $n=1$ to $\infty$. Making use of Gaussian sums, it is shown easily that

$$\sum_n(1/n\pi)\sum_s\sin(4n\pi s^2/p)\leqq\sum_n(2/n\pi)\sum_s\sin(2n\pi s^2/p).$$

*A. J. Kempner* (Boulder, Colo.).

Referred to in N68-3.

**N68-2** **(4, 189a)**

**Linnik, U. V. A remark on the least quadratic non-residue.** C. R. (Doklady) Acad. Sci. URSS (N.S.) **36**, 119–120 (1942).

This note contains a proof of the following theorem. Let $\epsilon>0$ be any fixed number; let the primes $p$ for which there are no quadratic nonresidues on the segment $[1, p^\epsilon]$ be called exceptional. Then for $N$ sufficiently large, the number of exceptional primes on the segment $[N^\epsilon, N]$ does not exceed $320\pi(g+2)^g g!$, $g=[2\epsilon^{-2}+1]$. The proof uses a lemma due to Vinogradow and a theorem of the author [C. R. (Doklady) Acad. Sci. URSS (N.S.) **30**, 292–294 (1941); these Rev. **2**, 349]. *R. D. James* (Saskatoon, Sask.).

Citations: MR 2, 349a = M55-1.

Referred to in N68-6.

**N68-3** **(9, 272b)**

**Chowla, S. On a problem of analytic number theory.** Proc. Nat. Inst. Sci. India **13**, 231–232 (1947).

It is a well-known consequence of Dirichlet's class-number formula that, if $p$ is a prime of the form $4n+3$, there are more quadratic residues than nonresidues between 0 and $\frac{1}{2}p$. No elementary proof of this has yet been given. The note contains a proof which is certainly very simple, but it cannot be considered as elementary, in the sense appropriate to the problem, since it uses infinite series. [A similar proof was given by K.-L. Chung, Bull. Amer. Math. Soc. **47**, 514–516 (1941); these Rev. **3**, 66.] *H. Davenport.*

Citations: MR 3, 66f = N68-1.

Referred to in N68-12.

**N68-4** **(9, 336g)**

**Rédei, Ladislaus. Eine Anwendung der hypergeometrischen Reihen auf eine Faktorenzerlegung des Fermatschen Polynoms $1-x^{p-1}$ im Zusammenhang mit der Theorie der quadratischen Reste.** Math. Naturwiss. Anz. Ungar. Akad. Wiss. **62**, 335–348 (1943). (Hungarian. German summary)

This paper is concerned with the problem of the distribution of quadratic residues. For $p$ an odd prime the author defines four classes of integers $H_{\rho\sigma}$ ($\rho^2=\sigma^2=1$) as consisting of those integers $a$ for which

$$\left(\frac{a-1}{p}\right)=\rho,\quad\left(\frac{a}{p}\right)=\sigma,\qquad 2\leqq a\leqq p-1,$$

where these are Legendre symbols. Denote by $f_{\rho\sigma}(x)$ the polynomial whose roots are the members of $H_{\rho\sigma}$, without repetition. By a theorem of Lagrange the degree of $f_{\rho\sigma}$ is $d_{\rho\sigma}=[\frac{1}{4}(p-\rho\sigma-\rho-1)]$. The author considers the problem of finding the coefficients of $f_{\rho\sigma}(x)$ modulo $p$. If $F(\alpha, \beta, \gamma; x)$ denotes the hypergeometric function the author proves that $f_{\rho\sigma}(x)$ is congruent modulo $p$ to the polynomial of degree $d_{\rho\sigma}$ obtained by truncating the function

$$F(\tfrac{1}{4}(\sigma+2),\ \tfrac{1}{4}(2\rho\sigma+2\rho+\sigma),\ 1+\tfrac{1}{2}\rho;\ x).$$

Hence the elementary symmetric functions of the members of the class $H_{\rho\sigma}$ are readily obtained modulo $p$.
*D. H. Lehmer* (Berkeley, Calif.).

**N68-5** **(10, 356f)**

**Cugiani, M. Osservazioni relative alla questione dell' esistenza di un algoritmo euclideo nei campi quadratici.** Boll. Un. Mat. Ital. (3) **3**, 136–141 (1948).

The author proves the following lemma (all symbols denote positive integers). Suppose that $p$ is a prime, $p\equiv h \pmod k$, that $k'|k$, $h'<k'$, $d=(k', h-h')$, $h'\equiv(h-h')/d \pmod{k'/d}$, $d\geqq t$, $p>dtk'$, and that $-d$ is a quadratic non-residue of $p$. Then there exists a number congruent to $h' \pmod{k'}$ and less than $p/t$ which is a quadratic non-residue of $p$. He applies this lemma to fill an alleged gap in Hofreiter's proof [Monatsh. Math. Phys. **42**, 397–400 (1935)] that the Euclidean algorithm does not hold in $k(\sqrt{D})$ if $D\equiv 21 \pmod{24}$ and $D>21$. He also uses it to prove the same if $D\equiv 13$ or $27 \pmod{120}$ and $D$ is a prime greater than $15^3$. *H. Davenport* (London).

**N68-6** **(10, 684b)**

**Fridlender, V. R. On the least $n$th-power non-residue.** Doklady Akad. Nauk SSSR (N.S.) **66**, 351–352 (1949). (Russian)

Let $n$ be a positive integer greater than 1 and for every prime number $p\equiv 1 \pmod n$ let $T_n(p)$ denote the smallest positive integer which is not congruent to an $n$th power modulo $p$. Using Linnik's theorem that the smallest prime in the arithmetic progression $kx+l$, $(k, l)=1$, does not exceed $k^c$ for some positive constant $c$ [Rec. Math. [Mat. Sbornik] N.S. **15(57)**, 139–178, 347–368 (1944); these Rev. **6**, 260], the author proves that $T_2(p)=\Omega(\log p)$, i.e., $\limsup_{p\to\infty}\{T_2(p)/\log p\}>0$. He remarks that this result cannot be extended to $T_n(p)$ for $n>2$, since Linnik's theorem has not been carried over to cyclotomic fields. However, he points out that a theorem of Linnik on $T_2(p)$ [C. R. (Doklady) Acad. Sci. URSS (N.S.) **36**, 119–120 (1942); these Rev. **4**, 189] can be generalized to $T_n(p)$ for any $n>1$. *P. T. Bateman* (Princeton, N. J.).

Citations: MR 4, 189a = N68-2; MR 6, 260b = N16-5; MR 6, 260c = N16-6.

Referred to in N68-8, N72-37.

**N68-7** **(11, 230c)**

**Whiteman, Albert Leon. Theorems on quadratic residues.** Math. Mag. **23**, 71–74 (1949).

Dirichlet proved that if $p$ is a prime of the form $4j+3$ then among the integers $1, 2, 3, \cdots, (p-1)/2$ there are more quadratic residues than nonresidues. Hence

$$(1)\qquad \sum_{n=1}^{(p-1)/2}\left(\frac{n}{p}\right)\gtrless 0$$

according as $p\equiv 3$ or $1 \pmod 4$, $\left(\frac{n}{p}\right)$ being the Legendre symbol. In the present paper the author establishes the following identities:

$$(2)\quad \tfrac{1}{4}p^{-\frac{1}{2}}\sum_{m=1}^{p-1}\cot \pi m^2/p=\sum_{n=1}^{(p-1)/2}[n^2/p]-(p-1)(p-5)/24,$$

$$(3)\qquad \sum_{m=1}^{p-1}\cot \pi m^2/p=-2p^{-\frac{1}{2}}\sum_{n=1}^{p-1}n\left(\frac{n}{p}\right),$$

where $[x]$ denotes the greatest integer not exceeding $x$. The proofs of (2) and (3) depend upon the well-known Fourier expansion for $((x))=x-[x]-\frac{1}{2}$ and classical results about Gauss sums. Also it is shown that if $p$ is an odd prime then

$$(4)\qquad \sum_{n=1}^{(p-1)/2}\left(\frac{n}{p}\right)=-p^{-1}\left\{2-\left(\frac{2}{p}\right)\right\}\sum_{n=1}^{p-1}n\left(\frac{n}{p}\right).$$

By means of the results (1), (2), (3), (4) the author shows that

$$\text{(a)}\quad \sum_{m=1}^{p-1}\cot \pi m^2/p\gtrless 0 \text{ according as } p\equiv 3 \text{ or } 1 \pmod 4,$$

and

$$\text{(b)}\qquad \sum_{n=1}^{(p-1)/2}\left[\frac{n^2}{p}\right]\gtrless(p-1)(p-5)/24,$$

according as $p\equiv 3$ or $1 \pmod 4$. *W. H. Simons.*

**N68-8** **(11, 500e)**

**Salié, Hans. Über den kleinsten positiven quadratischen Nichtrest nach einer Primzahl.** Math. Nachr. **3**, 7–8 (1949).

Linnik has proved that if $l$ and $k$ are coprime positive integers, then the smallest prime number congruent to $l$ modulo $k$ does not exceed $k^c$, where $c$ is a positive absolute constant [Rec. Math. [Mat. Sbornik] N.S. **15(57)**, 139–178, 347–368 (1944); these Rev. **6**, 260]. From this result the author deduces that the smallest quadratic nonresidue modulo an odd prime $p$ is not $o(\log p)$ as $p$ tends to infinity. Independently Fridlender [Doklady Akad. Nauk SSSR (N.S.) **66**, 351–352 (1949); these Rev. **10**, 684] has already remarked that Linnik's theorem has this corollary. *P. T. Bateman* (Urbana, Ill.).

Citations: MR 6, 260b = N16-5; MR 6, 260c = N16-6; MR 10, 684b = N68-6.

Referred to in N68-33, N72-37.

**N68-9** **(11, 640i)**

**Nagell, Trygve. Sur les restes et les non-restes quadratiques suivant un module premier.** Ark. Mat. **1**, 185–193 (1950).

Let $\pi_p$ denote the smallest odd prime which is a quadratic residue of $p$, and similarly $\psi_p$ the smallest odd prime quadratic nonresidue. The paper continues an earlier discussion by the author [Skrifter utgit av Videnskapsselskapet i Kristiania. I. Math.-Nat. Kl. **1923**, no. 13 (1924)] in which it was established that if $p=4n+1$ then $\pi_p<p^{\frac{1}{2}}$ for $p>17$. It is now proved that if $p=8n+1$, then $\psi_p<p^{\frac{1}{2}}$; if $p=8n+5$, $\psi_p<(2p)^{\frac{1}{2}}$; if $7<p=8n-1$, $\pi_p\leqq 2p^{\frac{1}{2}}-1$ and $\psi_p<(2p)^{\frac{1}{2}}-1$. Moreover, there is a prime quadratic nonresidue $q\equiv 3 \pmod 4$ belonging to $p$ such that $q<2p^{\frac{1}{2}}-1$ if $p=8n-1$ and $q<2p^{\frac{1}{2}}+1$ if $p=8n+3$. Finally for $p=8n+3$ we have $\pi_p\leqq\{(p+16)/3\}^{\frac{1}{2}}-2$ except for $p=3$, 11, 19, 43, 67, 163 and perhaps one other value of $p$. *I. Niven.*

Referred to in N68-15.

**N68-10** **(12, 591b)**

**Rédei, L. Über die Wertverteilung des Jacobischen Symbols.** Acta Univ. Szeged. Sect. Sci. Math. **13**, 242–246 (1950).

Let $m$ be an odd, square free integer, $(x/m)$ the Jacobi symbol, and call $\sum_{\alpha\leqq x\leqq\beta}(x/m)$ the quadratic excess in the interval $(\alpha, \beta)$. Denote by $A_1\cdots A_8$, $B_1\cdots B_{10}$, $C_1\cdots C_{12}$ the quadratic excesses in the subintervals got by dividing $(0, m)$ into 8, 10, and 12 equal parts, respectively. Let $h_k$ denote the class number of $R(\sqrt{-km})$. Dirichlet [J. Reine Angew. Math. **21**, 134–155 (1840)] and Gauss [Werke, v. 2, Göttingen, 1876, remarks by Dedekind pp. 301–303] found expressions for the $A_i$ in terms of $h_1$ and $h_2$, and, when $3\nmid m$, for the $C_i$ in terms of $h_1$, $h_3$. The author here derives an expression for the $B_i$ in terms of $h_1$, $h_5$, in case $5\nmid m$ and $m\equiv 3 \bmod 4$. *G. Whaples* (Bloomington, Ind.).

**N68-11** **(12, 676c)**

**Inkeri, K. On the least prime quadratic residue.** Ann. Acad. Sci. Fennicae. Ser. A. I. Math.-Phys. no. **73**, 10 pp. (1950).

Since 2 is a quadratic residue of primes of the form $8n+1$, the problem of an upper bound for the least prime quadratic residue $r=r(p)$ of a prime $p$ is reduced to the two cases $p=8n+3$ and $p=8n+5$. A theorem is given in each of these cases: (I) With the exception of the primes 3, 7, 11, 19, 43, 67, 163, and at most one other prime $>5\cdot 10^9$, $r<(p/3)^{\frac{1}{2}}(1-p^{-e})$ for $p=8n+3$ and for every $e>0$. (II) With the exception of a finite number of primes $p=8n+5$, $r<(p/5)^{\frac{1}{2}}$. The proofs depend on estimates for the class number of the field $K((-p)^{\frac{1}{2}})$. Results of Heilbronn and Linfoot and of Siegel are used. *D. H. Lehmer* (Berkeley, Calif.).

## N68-12 (12, 804g)

**Moser, Leo. A theorem on quadratic residues.** Proc. Amer. Math. Soc. **2**, 503–504 (1951).

Dirichlet's class-number formula implies that, if $p$ is a prime of the form $4n+3$, there are more quadratic residues of $p$ than nonresidues between 0 and $\frac{1}{2}p$. No proof of this theorem has yet been given which does not employ infinite series. The author simplifies the standard proof by using the Fourier series $\sum_{m=1}^{\infty} \sin (2m-1)\theta/(2m-1)$ instead of the customary $\sum_{m=1}^{\infty} \sin m\theta/m$. [To the author's list of related proofs should be added the following: Chowla, Proc. Nat. Inst. Sci. India **13**, 231–232 (1947); these Rev. **9**, 272.]
*A. L. Whiteman* (Los Angeles, Calif.).

Citations: MR 9, 272b = N68-3.

## N68-13 (13, 538c)

**Ankeny, N. C. The least quadratic non residue.** Ann. of Math. (2) **55**, 65–72 (1952).

Let $p$ be a prime. Denote by $n(p)$ the least quadratic non residue mod $p$. Vinogradov proved that

$$n(p)=O(p^{1/2\sqrt{e}}(\log p)^2)$$

and Linnik proved, using the extended Riemann hypothesis, that $n(p)=o(p^\epsilon)$. The author proves, using the same hypothesis, that $n(p)=O((\log p)^2)$. In view of a remark of Chowla and Turán $n(p)>c\log p$ for infinitely many $p$; thus the author's estimate is not far from the best possible one.

The author further proves (under the same hypothesis) that the least primitive root $r(p)$ of $p$ satisfies

$$r(p)=O[2^{\nu(p-1)}(\log p)^2(\log [2^{\nu(p-1)}\log p])^2],$$

where $\nu(p-1)$ denotes the number of prime factors of $p-1$. Here Vinogradov proved without any hypothesis that $r(p)=O(p^{\frac{1}{2}+\epsilon})$. The author further states that he can prove (again assuming the extended Riemann hypothesis) that the least $d$th power non residue (mod $p$) and the least prime $g$ which is a quadratic residue (mod $p$), are both $O((\log p)^2)$.
*P. Erdös* (Los Angeles, Calif.).

Referred to in N76-12.

## N68-14 (14, 247f)

**Nagell, Trygve. Sur un théorème d'Axel Thue.** Ark. Mat. **1**, 489–496 (1952).

The theorem of Thue is that for any integer $a$ which is relatively prime to $p$, there exist positive integers $x<\sqrt{p}$ and $y<\sqrt{p}$ such that $a\equiv\pm x/y \pmod p$ for one or the other of the signs. The author proves that at most two such representations exist for any $a$, and that, except for $p=3, 7, 23, 47$, for every prime there exists at least one number $a$ having two representations, one of each sign. As a corollary the following known result is obtained: the smallest positive odd quadratic non-residue of $p\equiv 7 \pmod 8$ is less than $\sqrt{p}$, except for $p=7, 23$. *I. Niven* (Eugene, Ore.).

## N68-15 (14, 247g)

**Nagell, Trygve. Sur le plus petit non-reste quadratique impair.** Ark. Mat. **1**, 573–578 (1952).

A simple method is used to prove that $\psi_p$, the least positive odd quadratic non-residue of $p\equiv\pm 1 \pmod 8$ is less than $\sqrt{p}$ except for $p=7, 23$; that $\psi_p\leqq 2+\sqrt{(p-4)}$ for $p\equiv 5 \pmod 8$. It is stated that similar methods will prove that $\psi_p<\sqrt{p}+4$ for $p\equiv 3 \pmod 8$ except $p=131$. Stronger results were obtained for $p\equiv\pm 1 \pmod 8$ by Vinogradov [Trans. Amer. Math. Soc. **29**, 218–226 (1927)] by analytic methods, and for $p\equiv\pm 3 \pmod 8$ by A. Brauer [Math. Z. **33**, 161–176 (1931); **35**, 39–50 (1932)] by elementary methods. Other work has been done by the author [Ark. Mat. **1**, 185–193 (1950); these Rev. **11**, 640] and by H.-J. Kanold [J. Reine Angew. Math. **187**, 169–182 (1950); these Rev. **12**, 592]. See also the preceding review. *I. Niven.*

Citations: MR 11, 640i = N68-9; MR 12, 592b = C15-12.

Referred to in N68-22, N72-7.

## N68-16 (14, 248a)

**Nagell, Trygve. Sur les restes et les non-restes cubiques.** Ark. Mat. **1**, 579–586 (1952).

Let $\pi(p, n)$ and $\psi(p, n)$ denote the smallest positive prime $n$-ic residue and non-residue respectively modulo $p$. If $p\equiv 1 \pmod 6$, then $\pi(p, 3)\leqq\sqrt{(4p-27)}$ except $p=7$, and better, if $p$ is not of the form $(A^2+27)/4$, then

$$\pi(p, 3)\leqq\sqrt{((4p-1)/27)}.$$

The proof is obtained from a discussion of the representation $p=(A^2+27B^2)/4$, it being established that every divisor of $AB$ is a cubic residue modulo $p$. Also

$$\psi(p, n)\leqq -1+\sqrt{((p+5)/2)}$$

for $p\geqq 13$, odd $n\geqq 3$, $(n, p-1)>1$, the proof being given in detail in the case $n=3$. Finally it is proved that as $p\to\infty$, $\limsup \psi(p, n)=\infty$, $\limsup \pi(p, n)=\infty$ for $n=2, 3$. Related work on similar questions has been done by L. Rédei [Nieuw Arch. Wiskunde (2) **23**, 150–162 (1950); these Rev. **11**, 417] and H.-J. Kanold [J. Reine Angew. Math. **188**, 74–77 (1950); these Rev. **12**, 483]. See also the two preceding reviews. *I. Niven* (Eugene, Ore.).

Citations: MR 11, 417i = N72-2; MR 12, 483a = N72-3.

Referred to in N72-7.

## N68-17 (14, 248b)

**Delcourte, M. Sur les sommes des résidus quadratiques des nombres premiers.** Mathesis **61**, 73–79 (1952).

If $p\equiv 1 \pmod 4$, then among the integers $1, 2, \cdots, (p-1)/2$ there are as many quadratic residues as non-residues. However, Dirichlet discovered, in his researches on the class number of quadratic forms, that if $p\equiv -1 \pmod 4$, there are more quadratic residues than non-residues in the same range. In the present paper the sum $\sum_{s=1}^{(p-1)/2}(\frac{s}{p})$ is denoted by $E_p$ and is called the quadratic excess of $p$ (although it is not proved that this sum is positive). Formulas are obtained for the sums $\sum_s(\frac{s}{p})s$ in terms of $E_p$ for $s$ running from 1 to $p-1$ and, in the case $p\equiv -1 \pmod 4$, for $s$ from 1 to $(p-1)/2$. These are used to derive expressions for the sum of residues and the sum of non-residues among the integers $1, 2, \cdots, p-1$ and also among $1, 2, \cdots, (p-1)/2$.
*W. H. Simons* (Vancouver, B. C.).

## N68-18 (14, 450b)

**Perron, Oskar. Bemerkungen über die Verteilung der quadratischen Reste.** Math. Z. **56**, 122–130 (1952).

The distribution of quadratic residues and non-residues within a complete residue system is discussed. For example, in the case $p=4k-1$, if $r_1, r_2, \cdots, r_{2k}$ are the $2k$ quadratic residues (zero is considered as a residue) and $a$ any integer prime to $p$, then the set $r_1+a, r_2+a, \cdots, r_{2k}+a$ always contains $k$ residues and $k$ non-residues. A similar result holds for the set of non-residues. Taking $a=1$ and the residue system $0, 1, \cdots, p-1$ this result shows that there are exactly $k$ pairs of consecutive residues (including the pair 0, 1) and $k-1$ pairs of consecutive non-residues. In general, if the length of a pair $b$, $c$ is defined to be the least positive integer congruent to either $b-c$ or $c-b$, then for any $a\leqq\frac{1}{2}(p-1)$ there are exactly $k$ pairs of residues and $k-1$ pairs of non-residues of length $a$. Analogous results are obtained for the case $p=4k+1$. A schematic representation of the results for $p=4k-1$ is given. *W. H. Simons.*

Referred to in N68-38.

**N68-19** **(14, 621e)**

**Carlitz, L. Some sums connected with quadratic residues.** Proc. Amer. Math. Soc. **4**, 12–15 (1953).

A well-known theorem of Dirichlet asserts that if $p$ is a prime $\equiv 3 \pmod 4$, then $\sum_{h=1}^{(p-1)/2}(h|p)>0$, where $(h|p)$ denotes the Legendre symbol. In the present note the author indicates a generalization of this result. He shows in particular that for $p\equiv 3 \pmod 4$, $(-1)^{k+1}\sum(h|p)B_{2k+1}(h/p)$ and $(-1)^k\sum(h|p)E_{2k}(2h/p)$ are positive for $k\geqq 0$, while for $p\equiv 1 \pmod 4$,

$$(-1)^{k+1}\sum(h|p)B_{2k}(h/p) \text{ and } (-1)^k\sum(h|p)E_{2k-1}(2h/p)$$

are positive for $k\geqq 1$. In the last four sums the summations extend from $h=1$ to $h=(p-1)/2$, and $B_k(x)$, $E_k(x)$ denote the Bernoulli and Euler polynomials, respectively, of degree $k$. The method of proof employs Gauss sums and the infinite series expansions of $B_k(x)$ and $E_k(x)$. *A. L. Whiteman.*

Referred to in B80-20.

**N68-20** **(14, 949g)**

**Kustaanheimo, Paul. On the fundamental prime of a finite world.** Ann. Acad. Sci. Fennicae. Ser. A. I. Math.-Phys. no. **129**, 7 pp. (1952).

The author previously noted [Soc. Sci. Fenn. Comment. Phys.-Math. **15**, no. 19 (1950); these Rev. **12**, 630] that for small residues modulo a prime $p$ to have the order properties of rational numbers, it was necessary that $-1$ be a quadratic non-residue and that 2, 3, $\cdots$ up to some small $q$ be quadratic residues. If our world is a geometry over some finite field with $p$ elements, the author asks what can be said in terms of $q$ about this fundamental prime $p$. This is essentially the problem of the least quadratic non-residue for a prime $p$. *Marshall Hall* (Columbus, Ohio).

Citations: MR 12, 630c = A14-13.

**N68-21** **(14, 1064a)**

**Brauer, Alfred. On the distribution of the Jacobian symbols.** Math. Z. **58**, 226–231 (1953).

For $m$ odd define $M^{++}$ as the number of pairs $c$, $c+1$ in a complete residue system (mod $m$) such that the Jacobi symbols $(c/m)=(c+1/m)=+1$; the numbers $M^{+-}, \cdots, M^{00}$ are defined in a similar manner. Also let $\phi(m)$ denote the Euler $\phi$-function and

$$\phi_2(m)=m\prod_{p|m}\left(1-\frac{2}{p}\right)$$

the Schemmel function. It is shown that for $m$ squarefree the $M$'s can be evaluated in terms of $\phi$ and $\phi_2$. For example, $M^{++}=M^{+-}=M^{-+}=M^{--}=\frac{1}{4}(\phi_2(m)+1)$ if $m$ is divisible by an odd number of primes of the form $4k+1$. Also

$$M^{00}=m-2\phi(m)+\phi_2(m);$$

this result holds for arbitrary $m$. *L. Carlitz.*

Referred to in N68-27.

**N68-22** **(15, 102c)**

**Rédei, L. Die Existenz eines ungeraden quadratischen Nichtrestes mod $p$ im Intervall 1, $\sqrt{p}$.** Acta Sci. Math. Szeged **15**, 12–19 (1953).

Nagell has proved that if $p\equiv\pm 1 \pmod 8$, $p\neq 7$ or 23, then there exists an odd prime $q<p^{\frac{1}{2}}$ such that $(q/p)=-1$; if $p\equiv 3$ or 5 (mod 8), then there is a $q<2p^{\frac{1}{2}}+1$ or $(2p)^{\frac{1}{2}}$ such that $(q/p)=-1$. In the present paper the following sharper result is obtained. If $p\neq 3, 5, 7, 11, 13, 23, 59, 109, 131$, then there exists an odd prime $q<p^{\frac{1}{2}}$ such that $(q/p)=-1$. (It is noted in proof that part of this theorem had been proved earlier by T. Nagell [Ark. Mat. **1**, 573–578 (1951); these Rev. **14**, 247] and A. Brauer [Math. Z. **33**, 161–176 (1931)].) *L. Carlitz* (Durham, N. C.).

Citations: MR 14, 247g = N68-15.
Referred to in N68-23.

**N68-23** **(16, 675c)**

**Stolt, Bengt. Über den kleinsten positiven quadratischen Nichtrest.** Math. Scand. **2**, 187–192 (1954).

The author proves that if $p$ is any prime of the form $8m+5$, different from 5, 13, 37, 61, 109, then the least positive odd quadratic non-residue of $p$ is less than $(p/2)^{1/2}$. This improves by a factor of $2^{-1/2}$ the upper limit $p^{1/2}$ set by a recent result of Rédei [Acta Sci. Math. Szeged **15**, 12–19 (1953); MR **15**, 102] at least for the case $p\equiv 5 \pmod 8$. The author states that a similar result can be proved for primes $p$ of the form $8m+3, 7$. To avoid transient situations the cases $(p/2)^{1/2}<5$ (i.e. $p<50$) are taken up separately. For $e=[(p/2)^{1/2}]\geqq 5$ the author separates 24 cases, namely the residue classes (mod 24). In each case he exhibits two integers $a$, $b$, one of which is odd and neither of which exceeds $e$ in absolute value. Both are of the form $(p-3uv)/8$, where $u$ and $v$ are positive odd integers not exceeding $e$. It follows that one of 3, $a$, $b$, $u$, $v$ is an odd non-residue of $p$. However, in 12 of the 24 cases certain exceptional $e$'s are encountered. There are less than 100 and the corresponding primes are examined separately. All but 61 and 109 have small odd quadratic non-residues. [The author might have referred to a paper by H. J. Kanold, J. Reine Angew. Math. **188**, 74–77 (1950); MR **12**, 483.] *D. H. Lehmer.*

Citations: MR 12, 483a = N72-3; MR 15, 102c = N68-22.

**N68-24** **(16, 675d)**

**Skolem, Th. On the least odd positive quadratic non-residue modulo $p$.** Norske Vid. Selsk. Forh., Trondheim **27**, no. 20, 7 pp. (1954).

Let $p$ be any odd prime not of the form $8k+1$. It is established that there exists a constant $c$ such that every $p$ has a positive odd quadratic non-residue not exceeding $cp^{2/5}$. Admissible values of $c$ are computed in the three cases $p\equiv 3, 5, 7 \pmod 8$. For example, $c=6.74$ will suffice in case $p\equiv 7 \pmod 8$. A short bibliography of earlier work on this topic is to be found in the paper reviewed above. *I. Niven* (Eugene, Ore.).

**N68-25** **(17, 713b)**

**Ankeny, N. C. Quadratic residues.** Duke Math. J. **21** (1954), 107–112.

With the consent of the original reviewer [cf. MR **15**, 777], the following review should replace the first one.

The author attempts to prove that the least positive quadratic nonresidue $n(k)$ with respect to the prime modulus $k\equiv 3 \pmod 4$ satisfies the inequality

$$(1) \qquad n(k)<k^{\varepsilon}$$

for arbitrary $\varepsilon>0$ and $k>k_0(\varepsilon)$.

However, the author's reasoning is incorrect. In applying the relation

$$(2) \qquad \lim_{D\to\infty}\frac{\ln N_{mm^*}}{\ln D}\,\frac{\max_x|\sum_{n\leq x}\chi(n)|}{D^{\frac{1}{2}}\ln D}=0$$

[proved in the paper of Linnik and Rényi, Izv. Akad. Nauk SSSR. Ser. Mat. **11** (1947), 539–546, Th. IB; MR **9**, 333], the author does not notice that $N_{mm^*}$ designates the modulus of the power residue least in absolute value. In the case of interest, $D=k\equiv 3 \pmod 4$, the relation (2) is trivial since $\chi(-1)=-1$ and $N_{mm^*}=1$. If (2) were true only for positive nonresidues, then (1) really could be proved, and considerably simpler than in the paper.

*K. A. Rodosskiĭ* (RŽMat **1955,** no. 1079).

Citations: MR 9, 333d = N72-1.

## N68-26 (17, 1056g)

**Fjellstedt, Lars. A theorem concerning the least quadratic residue and non-residue.** Ark. Mat. 3 (1956), 287–291.

Let $\psi^*(p, 2)$ and $\pi^*(p, 2)$ denote the smallest odd prime quadratic non-residue and quadratic residue respectively modulo $p$. The author claims to prove that $\psi^*(p, 2) < 6 \log p$ and $\pi^*(p, 2) < 6 \log p$ for $p$ sufficiently large. The proof is incorrect (specifically, in the arguments after (4) on page 289). *P. T. Bateman* (Princeton, N.J.).

## N68-27 (17, 1188d)

**Vause, R. Z. On the distribution of the Jacobian symbols.** J. Elisha Mitchell Sci. Soc. 72 (1956), 15–24.

For $m$ prime to 6 define $M_{ijk}$ as the number of triplets $c, c+1, c+2$ in a complete residue system (mod $m$) such that the Jacobi symbols $(c/m)\equiv i \pmod 3$, $([c+1]/m)\equiv j \pmod 3$, $([c+2]/m)\equiv k \pmod 3$. Thus the range of $i, j, k$ may be taken as $0, \pm 1$. Let $\phi(m)$ denote the Euler function, and

$$\phi_3(m)=m\prod_{p|m}\left(1-\frac{3}{p}\right)$$

the Schemmel generalization. For square-free $m$ the values of $M_{ijk}$ are evaluated in terms of $\phi$ and $\phi_3$ and the similarly defined function $M_{ij}$. For example, in case $m$ has a prime factor of the form $8h+3$ then $M_{ijk}=\frac{1}{8}\phi_3(m)$ for $i, j, k=\pm 1$. The function $M_{ij}$ has been treated by A. Brauer [Math. Z. **58** (1953), 226–231; MR **14,** 1064]. The writer also evaluates $M_{ij}{}^d$, the number of elements $x$ in a complete residue system (mod $m$) such that $(x/m)\equiv i \pmod 3$ and $([x+d]/m)\equiv j \pmod 3$. *I. Niven* (Eugene, Ore.).

Citations: MR 14, 1064a = N68-21.

## N68-28 (20# 28)

**Burgess, D. A. The distribution of quadratic residues and non-residues.** Mathematika 4 (1957), 106–112.

This paper presents the first significant improvement on Vinogradov's estimate [Trans. Amer. Math. Soc. **29** (1927), 209–217] for the magnitude of the least positive quadratic non-residue $d$, modulo a prime $p>2$. The new result is $d=O(p^\alpha)$ as $p\to\infty$, for any fixed $\alpha>\frac{1}{4}e^{-\frac{1}{2}}$; the improvement being essentially a factor of $\frac{1}{2}$ in the exponent $\alpha$. The theorem on which this is based is as follows:

Theorem 1. Let $\delta$ and $\varepsilon$ be any fixed positive numbers and let $\left(\frac{n}{p}\right)$ denote the usual Legendre quadratic character. Then for all sufficiently large $p$ and $N$, we have

$$\left|\sum_{n=N+1}^{N+H}\left(\frac{n}{p}\right)\right|<\varepsilon H,$$

provided that $H>p^{\frac{1}{4}+\delta}$.

This is an important variation on the classical inequality

$$\left|\sum_{n=N+1}^{N+H}\left(\frac{n}{p}\right)\right|<p^{\frac{1}{2}}\log p,$$

and its derivation is altogether deeper; being a consequence of A. Weil's theorem [Sur les courbes algébriques et les variétés qui s'en déduisent, Hermann, Paris, 1948; MR **10,** 262; Chaps. II, IV] on a generalized Riemann hypothesis for algebraic function-fields.

*J. H. H. Chalk* (Hamilton, Ont.)

Citations: MR 10, 262c = G20-8.

Referred to in E12-143, M15-25, N72-26, N72-38, N72-42, N76-12, R14-49.

## N68-29 (21# 1963)

**Gordeev, N. V. On the mean length of intervals consisting of numbers of the same quadratic character with respect to a prime modulus.** Biĭsk. Gos. Ped. Inst. Uč. Zap. **1** (1957), 111–120. (Russian)

The author shows that for an odd prime $p$ the mean number of consecutive integers in the interval $(1, p-1)$ having the same quadratic character is equal to 3. To prove this he obtains an expression for $P$, the number of isolated quadratic residues and non-residues, and $Q$, the number of sets of consecutive integers having the same quadratic character. The average number of consecutive integers in each set of $Q$ is then given by $T=(p-1-P)/Q$. $T$ is of the form $(3p+a)/(p+b)$, where $a$ and $b$ are determined constants, dependent upon whether $p\equiv 1, 3, 5$ or $7 \pmod 8$. Thus $T\to 3$ as $p\to\infty$. The expressions for $P$ and $Q$ are obtained by evaluating certain sums of Legendre symbols.

*W. H. Simons* (Vancouver, B.C.)

## N68-30 (23# A129)

**Bhaskaran, M.**

**Two applications of a result of S. Chowla.**

*J. Indian Math. Soc.* (*N.S.*) **23** (1959), 133–137 (1961).

The theorem of Chowla referred to gives an estimate for the number of lattice points with relatively prime coordinates in the rectangle $[1\leqq x\leqq m, 1\leqq y\leqq n]$. The first application is to show that every sufficiently large prime $p$ has a quadratic non-residue in the interval $(p^{1/2}/12, p^{1/2})$. The method is the same as that given by LeVeque [*Topics in number theory, Vol.* 1, Addison-Wesley, Reading, Mass., 1956; p. 123; MR **18,** 283]. See also an abstract by the reviewer [Bull. Amer. Math. Soc. **57** (1951), 461]. The second application is to prove that a prime $p$ can be expressed in the form $U_1V_1+U_2V_2$, where $1\leqq U_r\leqq p^\varepsilon$, $1\leqq V_r\leqq p^{1-\varepsilon}$ $(r=1, 2;\ 0<\varepsilon<1)$ in $(12/\pi^2-1)p+O(p^{\max(\varepsilon,1-\varepsilon)}\log p)$ ways. *L. Moser* (Edmonton, Alta.)

Citations: MR 18, 283b = Z01-38.

## N68-31 (26# 2410)

**Erdős, Pál [Erdős, Paul]**

**Remarks on number theory. I. (Hungarian. Russian and English summaries)**

*Mat. Lapok* **12** (1961), 10–17.

Author's summary: "Denote by $n_k(p)$ the smallest positive $k$th power non-residue (mod $p$). Mirsky asked the author to find an asymptotic formula for $\sum_{p\leqq x} n_k(p)$. The author proves, using the large sieve of Linnik, that $p_1<p_2<\cdots$ are the sequence of consecutive primes

$$\sum_{p\leqq x} n_2(p) = (1+o(1))\sum_{k=1}^{\infty}\frac{p_k}{2^k}\frac{x}{\log x}.$$

It is very likely true that

$$\sum_{p<x} n_k(p) = (1+o(1))\frac{c_k x}{\log x}."$$

Referred to in L25-28, N72-33, Z02-53.

## N68-32 (31# 1225)

**Godwin, H. J.**

**On the least quadratic non-residue.**

*Proc. Cambridge Philos. Soc.* **61** (1965), 671–672.

Let $n$ be the least quadratic non-residue of a given prime $p$. Simple proofs are given of the following two results: (I) If $n \geqq 3$ and $p \equiv 1 \pmod 4$, then $p \geqq 2n^2 - n + 2$; (II) If $n \geqq 7$, then $p \geqq n^2 + 3n + 1$. *W. H. Mills* (Princeton, N.J.)

**N68-33** **(31# 2199)**

**Salié, Hans**

**Über die kleinste Primzahl, die eine gegebene Primzahl als kleinsten positiven quadratischen Nichtrest hat.**

*Math. Nachr.* **29** (1965), 113–114.

Let $n(p)$ denote the smallest positive quadratic nonresidue of the prime $p$. The author has proved [same Nachr. **3** (1949), 7–8; MR **11**, 500] that $n(p) \neq o(p)$.*Let $Q_h$ denote the set of primes $q$ such that $n(q) = p_h$, where $p_h$ is the $h$th prime; also let $q_h$ be the smallest number in $Q_h$. The following two properties of the sequence $Q = (q_1, q_2, q_3, \cdots)$ are stated: (a) $Q$ is not monotone increasing, and (b) the congruence $q_h \equiv -1 \pmod 8$ does not hold for all $h \geqq 2$. These statements are established by listing all elements of $Q$ that are less than $10^7$. It is found that $q_{14} < q_{13}$, thus establishing (a). As for (b) it is found that $q_h \equiv -1 \pmod 8$ for $2 \leqq h \leqq 14$, but $q_{15} \equiv q_{16} \equiv 1 \pmod 8$. *L. Carlitz* (Durham, N.C.)

[*$n(p) \neq o(\log p)$ was intended. Ed.]

Citations: MR 11, 500e = N68-8.

**N68-34** **(31# 4759)**

**Whyburn, Clifton T.**

**The second smallest quadratic non-residue.**

*Duke Math. J.* **32** (1965), 519–528.

A. Brauer [Math. Z. **33** (1931), 161–176; Amer. J. Math. **62** (1940), 697–716; MR **2**, 146] has proved, by elementary means, that for $p$ a prime of any form except $8n+1$, the least odd quadratic nonresidue $u$ is less than a certain quadratic polynomial in $p^{1/5}$. He showed also that for primes of the form $24n + 13 \geqq 421$, the second odd prime nonresidue $v$ satisfies $3uv < p$. The present author obtains the following results in an elementary way. (I) If $p = 24n + 23$ (so that $u \geqq 5$), then $v < (10p)^{2/5} + 27(10p)^{1/5}/2 - 1$. (II) If $p = 24n \pm 13$, then $v < 2(5\varepsilon p)^{2/5} + (240\varepsilon - 3)(5\varepsilon p)^{1/5} - 1$. Here and below $\varepsilon = 1$ if $p = 4n - 1$, $\varepsilon = \frac{1}{2}$ if $p = 4n + 1$. (III) If $p = 24n \pm 17$, then $v < (6\varepsilon p)^{2/5} + (27\varepsilon + 5/3)(6\varepsilon p)^{1/5} + 60\varepsilon - 1$. (IV) If $p = 24n \pm 5$, then $v < 2(3\varepsilon p)^{2/5} + (2585/6) \times (3\varepsilon p)^{1/5} - 1$. *L. Carlitz* (Durham, N.C.)

Citations: MR 2, 146d = R12-3.

**N68-35** **(34# 5765)**

**Burgess, D. A.**

**On the quadratic character of a polynomial.**

*J. London Math. Soc.* **42** (1967), 73–80.

Let $\Phi(x)$ be a fixed polynomial, with integer coefficients, that is not a constant multiple of a perfect square. The author investigates the quadratic character of $\Phi(x)$. In an earlier work [Proc. London Math. Soc. (3) **13** (1963), 537–548; MR **26** #6134] he showed that if the roots of $\Phi(x)$ are rational, then for each sufficiently large prime $p$ there is a positive integer $\alpha$ satisfying $\alpha = O(p^{1/4} \log p)$ for which $\Phi(\alpha)$ is a quadratic non-residue (mod $p$). Now he shows that if $\Phi(x) = x^2 + k$, $k$ is not the negative of a square, then for any $\varepsilon > 0$ there is, for each sufficiently large prime $p$, an $\alpha$ satisfying $\alpha = O(p^{(2/3\sqrt{e}) + \varepsilon})$ for which $\alpha^2 + k$ is a quadratic non-residue (mod $p$). In the general case, one has only $\alpha = O(p^{1/2} \log p)$. *J. B. Kelly* (Tempe, Ariz.)

Citations: MR 26# 6134 = N72-14.

Referred to in L25-26.

**N68-36** **(35# 125)**

**Vinogradov, A. I.; Linnik, Ju. V.**

**Hypoelliptic curves and the least prime quadratic residue. (Russian)**

*Dokl. Akad. Nauk SSSR* **168** (1966), 259–261.

Denote by $P_{\min}(\mathscr{D})$ the least prime quadratic non-residue for a prime modulus $\mathscr{D}$. I. M. Vinogradov conjectured that for any fixed $\varepsilon > 0$ the estimate $P_{\min}(\mathscr{D}) = O(\mathscr{D}^{\varepsilon})$ holds. By using D. A. Burgess' method [Proc. London Math. Soc. (3) **13** (1963), 524–536; MR **26** #6133; ibid. (3) **13** (1963), 537–548; MR **26** #6134] the authors prove the estimate $P_{\min}(\mathscr{D}) = O(\mathscr{D}^{1/4+\varepsilon})$.

They also show the following theorem. Let $k(\sqrt{\mathscr{D}})$ be a quadratic field with discriminant $\mathscr{D}$. Then for any fixed $\varepsilon > 0$ the number of integer ideals of $k(\sqrt{\mathscr{D}})$, whose norms do not exceed $x$, is $x(1 + O(|\mathscr{D}|^{-\gamma(\varepsilon)})) \sum_{n=1}^{\infty} (\mathscr{D}/n) n^{-1}$, where $x \geqq |\mathscr{D}|^{1/4+\varepsilon}$, $\gamma(\varepsilon) > 0$ and $(\mathscr{D}/n)$ is Kronecker's symbol.

{This article has appeared in English translation [Soviet Math. Dokl. **7** (1966), 612–614].} *J. Kubilius* (Vilnius)

Citations: MR 26# 6133 = L25-19; MR 26# 6134 = N72-14.

Referred to in N68-37, N72-38, N72-53, R14-107.

**N68-37** **(36# 2566)**

**Elliott, P. D. T. A.**

**A note on a recent paper of U. V. Linnik and A. I. Vinogradov.**

*Acta Arith.* **13** (1967/68), 103–105.

Let $p$ be an odd prime, and put $L(s, \chi) = \sum_{n=1}^{\infty} \chi(n) n^{-s}$, where $\chi(n) = (n/p)$. The author makes the hypothesis that there is a positive integer $k$ such that $L(1, \chi) > c(\log \log p)^k / \log p$ for all large $p$, where $c$ is an absolute constant whose value could in principle be effectively determined. Under this assumption he shows that $r_2(p)$, the least prime quadratic residue of $p$, satisfies $r_2(p) = O(p^{(1+\varepsilon)/4(k+2)})$, for any fixed $\varepsilon > 0$. (If the extended Riemann hypothesis is true, then the author's assumption is satisfied for any positive integer $k$, since then $L(1, \chi) > c'/\log \log p$.)

{The paper mentioned in the title appeared in Dokl. Akad. Nauk SSSR **168** (1966), 259–261 [MR **35** #125].} *B. Gordon* (Los Angeles, Calif.)

Citations: MR 35# 125 = N68-36.

Referred to in N68-39.

**N68-38** **(38# 2080)**

**Burde, Klaus**

**Zur Verteilung quadratischer Reste.**

*Math. Z.* **105** (1968), 150–152.

The author uses a reformulation of the results of O. Perron [same Z. **56** (1952), 122–130; MR **14**, 450] to prove in a simple way the following result: For each odd prime $p$ there exists a sequence of $\frac{1}{2}(p-1)$ consecutive relatively prime residue classes mod $p$ among which the number of quadratic residues exceeds the number of quadratic non-residues by at least $[\frac{1}{2}(\sqrt{p} + 1)]$. *H. Halberstam* (Nottingham)

Citations: MR 14, 450b = N68-18.

Referred to in N72-54.

**N68-39** **(39# 6842)**

**Wolke, D.**

**A note on the least prime quadratic residue** (mod $p$).

*Acta Arith.* **16** (1969/70), 85–87.

Let $p$ be an odd prime and let $r_2(p)$ denote the least prime quadratic residue mod $p$. The author proves (sharpening a result of P. D. T. A. Elliott [same Acta **13** (1967/68),

103–105; MR **36** #2566]) that if $\sum_{n=1}^{\infty} n^{-1}\left(\frac{p}{n}\right) > t(p)/\log p$, where $t(p)$ is a positive function, then for absolute constants $c_2, c_3 > 0$, $r_2(p) \leq c_2 p^{c_3(t(p))^{-1/2}}$.

*K. S. Williams* (Ottawa, Ont.)

Citations: MR 36# 2566 = N68-37.

## N68-40 (40# 111)

**Elliott, P. D. T. A.**

**A restricted mean value theorem.**

*J. London Math. Soc.* (2) **1** (1969), 447–460.

Let $a_1 < a_2 < \cdots < a_k$ be $k$ non-negative integers, let $\varepsilon_j$, $j = 1, \cdots, k$, be given each having one of the values $\pm 1$. For each prime $p$ define $f(p)$ to be the least positive integer $n$ for which (1) $\left(\frac{n+a_j}{p}\right) = \varepsilon_j$, $j = 1, \cdots, k$, where $\left(\frac{m}{p}\right)$ denotes Legendre's symbol; if (1) cannot be satisfied, put $f(p) = 0$. It was proved by H. Davenport [same J. **8** (1933), 46–52] that there is a constant $\delta > 0$ such that $f(p) = O(p^{1-\delta})$. The present author proves the following theorem: There are positive constants $\alpha$, $A$, depending on $k$, such that $0 < \alpha < 1$ and $(\pi(x))^{-1} \sum_{p \leq x} \min(f(p), x^{\alpha}) \to A$ for $x \to \infty$.

During the course of the proof of the theorem, it is also shown that $d_n = \lim_{x\to\infty} (\pi(x))^{-1} \cdot \sum_{p \leq x, f(p) = n} 1$ exists and that for any value of $\delta$ the series $A_\delta = \sum_{n=1}^{\infty} n^{\delta} d_n$ converges and that $A_1 = A$. The author deduces the following corollary from these remarks: For any $\eta \leq \alpha$,

$$(\pi(x))^{-1} \sum_{p \leq x} (f(p))^{\eta} \to A_{\eta}$$

for $x \to \infty$.

The proofs are too involved to be discussed here.

*W. G. H. Schaal* (Marburg)

## N68-41 (41# 3375)

**Singh, Sahib**

**Bounds of quadratic residues in arithmetic progression.**

*J. Number Theory* **2** (1970), 162–167.

It is easy to show that every prime $p > 5$ has a pair of consecutive positive residues, $r, r+1$, with $r \leq 9$. D. H. Lehmer and E. Lehmer have shown that there is no such upper bound for three consecutive positive residues [Proc. Amer. Math. Soc. **13** (1962), 102–106; MR **25** #2025]. In the present paper quadratic residues in an arbitrary arithmetic progression are discussed. It is shown that for any fixed positive integer $a$ there exists an upper bound $\Lambda$, depending only on $a$, such that every sufficiently large prime $p$ has a pair $r, r+a$ of positive quadratic residues with $r \leq \Lambda$. If $a \equiv \pm 1 \pmod 3$ or if $a \equiv \pm 2 \pmod 5$, there is no such upper bound for three positive quadratic residues of the form $r, r+a, r+2a$. It is conjectured that for all other values of $a$ there is such a bound, and this is demonstrated for $a = 6$ and $a = 9$. {The reviewer notes that for $a = 9$ the best possible upper bound is 36, and not 42 as claimed.}

*W. H. Mills* (Princeton, N.J.)

Citations: MR 25# 2025 = N72-10.

## N68-42 (42# 188)

**Apostol, Tom M.**

**Quadratic residues and Bernoulli numbers.**

*Delta (Waukesha)* **1** (1968/70), *no.* 4, 21–31.

Let $p$ denote a prime $> 3$ and let $a$ be any positive integer less than $p$. $R(a)$ and $N(a)$ denote the number of quadratic residues and non-residues (mod $p$), respectively, among the integers $1, 2, \cdots, a$, so that $R(a) + N(a) = a$. The author of this paper considers the difference $R(a) - N(a)$. He proves that (1) $R(a) - N(a) \equiv 2\{B_q(a+1) - B_q\} \pmod p$, where $q = (p+1)/2$, and $B_q$ is the $q$th Bernoulli number and $B_q(x)$ is the $q$th Bernoulli polynomial. (The Bernoulli numbers are given by $B_0 = 1$, $B_n = \sum_{r=0}^{n} \binom{n}{r} B_r$, $n \geq 2$, and the Bernoulli polynomials by $B_n(x) = \sum_{s=0}^{n} \binom{n}{s} B_s x^{n-s}$.) (1) generalizes the following classical result of A. L. Cauchy [Mém. Acad. Sci. **17** (1838), 249–768, Part IV (1840); reprinted in *Œuvres* (1), Vol. III, pp. 163–180, Gauthier-Villars, Paris, 1911]:

$$R((p-1)/2) - N((p-1)/2) \equiv 2\{(2/p) - 2\} B_q \pmod p$$

(example 2 of the paper), and the trivial result $R(p-1) - N(p-1) \equiv 0 \pmod p$ (example 1 of the paper). Many other special cases are given.

*K. S. Williams* (Ottawa, Ont.)

## N68-43 (42# 1783)

**Elliott, P. D. T. A.**

**On the mean value of $f(p)$.**

*Proc. London Math. Soc.* (3) **21** (1970), 28–96.

Let $f(x)$ denote a complex-valued function which is defined for all primes $p$. The author is concerned with asymptotic estimates for sums of the form $\sum_{p \leq x} f(p)$. Because of the considerable length of the paper only a few examples of theorems proved in the paper can be given here. Theorem 2: Let $a(p)$ be the least positive integer $a$ for which $(a/p) = ((a+1)/p) = -1$. (If there is no such $a$ put $a(p) = 0$.) Then $\pi(x)^{-1} \sum_{p \leq x} a(p) = A_1 + O((\log\log x)^{-1/2})$, $x \to \infty$. Here $A_1 = \sum_{n=1}^{\infty} n d_n$, $d_n$ being certain limiting frequencies.

Theorem 4: Let $k$ be a fixed positive integer For each prime $p$, let $b(p)$ denote the least positive integer of the form $x^2 + k$ which is a quadratic non-residue mod $p$. Then, $\pi(x)^{-1} \sum_{p \leq x} b(p) \to A_2$, $x \to \infty$.

The following theorem may serve as an example for a problem "reciprocal" to the above mentioned problems. Theorem 5: For each integer $a \geq 2$ let $c(a)$ be the least positive prime $p$ for which $(a/p) = -1$. Then $x^{-1} \sum_{a \leq x} c(a) \to A_3$, $x \to \infty$. ($A_2$, $A_3$ have meanings similar to that of $A_1$ for Theorem 2.)

Lemmas of the following type (Lemma 10) are essential for the various proofs; they replace a probabilistic argument (Lemma 1). Let $b_1, b_2, \cdots$ be a sequence of complex numbers, and let $x$, $H$ be real numbers such that $x \geq 3$, $H \geq 2$. Then

$$\sum_{p \leq x} \left|\sum_{n \leq H} b_n (n/p)\right|^2 \leq 4x \sum_{m,n \leq H, m \cdot n = t^2, 2t^2} |b_m b_n| + O(H \log H (\textstyle\sum_{n \leq H} |b_n|)^2).$$

Results concerning non-quadratic characters are proved in later sections of the paper.

*W. G. H. Schaal* (Marburg)

## N68-44 (42# 5889)

**Lehmer, D. H.; Lehmer, Emma; Shanks, Daniel**

**Integer sequences having prescribed quadratic character.**

*Math. Comp.* **24** (1970), 433–451.

Authors' summary: "For the odd primes $p_1 = 3$, $p_2 = 5, \cdots$, we determine integer sequences $N_p$ such that the Legendre symbol $(N/p_i) = \pm 1$ for all $p_i \leq p$ for a prescribed array of signs $\pm 1$ (i.e., for a prescribed quadratic character). We examine six quadratic characters having special interest and applications. We present tables of these $N_p$ and examine some applications, particularly to questions concerning extreme values for the smallest primitive root (of a prime $N$), the class number of the quadratic field $R(\sqrt{-N})$, the real Dirichlet $L$ functions, and quadratic character sums."

Referred to in N76-28.

**N68-45** (43# 150)

**Hudson, Richard H.**

**On sequences of consecutive quadratic nonresidues.**

*J. Number Theory* **3** (1971), 178–181.

Let $l_n$ be the maximum number of consecutive quadratic nonresidues for any prime $p$ satisfying $p \equiv 1 \bmod 24$. Using purely elementary methods the author proves that $l_n < \sqrt{p}$. This is done by subdividing the interval $(1, (p-1)/2)$ into intervals bounded by quadratic residues and finding the maximum length of these sub-intervals. Since for $p \equiv 1 \bmod 24$, $p - r$ is a quadratic residue if $r$ is a quadratic residue, only sequences of consecutive nonresidues less than $p/2$ need be considered. Using an elementary result of A. Brauer [Math. Z. **35** (1932), 39–50] for all primes $p \not\equiv 1 \bmod 24$, the author is able to conclude that $l_n < \sqrt{p} + (3/4)(\sqrt{2})\sqrt[4]{p} + 2$ for every prime $p$.

*E. M. Horadam* (Armidale)

**N68-46** (43# 153)

**Karacuba, A. A.**

**Distribution of power residues and non-residues in additive sequences.** (Russian)

*Dokl. Akad. Nauk SSSR* **196** (1971), 759–760.

Let $P$ be the set of prime numbers, $U$ an arbitrary set of positive integers, and let $\chi$ be a non-principal character modulo a prime $q$. The following theorem is stated: If $1 \leq MN < q$ then

$$\sum_{p \leq N, p \in P} \sum_{u \leq M, u \in U} \chi(p+u) \ll \pi(N) g(M) (q^{.5+.5\nu}/Ng(M))^{\gamma\nu},$$

where $\gamma$ is a positive absolute constant, $\nu = 1/k$, where $k$ is any integer $\geqq \ln q / \ln N$, and the implied constant is dependent only on $\nu$. ($\pi(N)$ is the number of primes not exceeding $N$, $g(M)$ is the number of elements of $U$ not exceeding $M$.) Two corollaries are given yielding information on the number of quadratic residues and nonresidues in certain special intervals. The proof of the theorem is said to parallel that of the main theorem given by the author in a previous paper [Izv. Akad. Nauk SSSR Ser. Mat. **34** (1970), 299–321; MR **42** #5923].

{This article has appeared in English translation [Soviet Math. Dokl. **11** (1970), 235–236].}

*J. B. Roberts* (Portland, Ore.)

Citations: MR 42# 5923 = L20-25.

# N72 DISTRIBUTION OF INTEGERS IN SPECIAL RESIDUE CLASSES: RESIDUES OF HIGHER DEGREE POLYNOMIALS; INTEGERS YIELDING SPECIFIED CHARACTER VALUES

See also Section T10.

See also reviews A14-73, A16-55, B44-12, B44-44, C15-12, D80-38, D80-51, D80-54, D80-66, D80-68, D80-70, D80-77, F65-22, L25-20, M25-5, M25-56, N28-18, N68-6, N68-16, N68-31, N76-17, Q15-20, R10-3, R14-73, T10-38, T10-40, T10-52, T25-1, T25-24, T40-38.

**N72-1** (9, 333d)

**Linnik, Yu. V., and Ren'i, A. A. On certain hypotheses in the theory of Dirichlet characters.** Izvestiya Akad. Nauk SSSR. Ser. Mat. **11**, 539–546 (1947). (Russian)

[The second author's name appears as Rényi in non-Russian publications.] The authors prove the following lemma. If $0 < \eta \leqq 1$, $0 \leqq \vartheta \leqq 1$, $k > 1$, $x > 1$, $a(m)$ is a multiplicative arithmetical function, $|a(m)| \leqq 1$, and if $f(y)$ is a function with period 1, then

$$|\sum n^{-1} a(n) f(n\vartheta)| \leqq c \max |\sum_{m=1}^{n} m^{-1} a(m) f(m\vartheta)|,$$

where $c$ is a constant depending only on $k$, where the sum on the left is taken over all $n \leqq \eta x$ whose prime divisors do not exceed $x^{1/k}$, and where the max is taken over the range $0 \leqq \vartheta \leqq 1$, $1 \leqq n \leqq x$. With the help of this lemma, the authors show that, if $\chi(n)$ is a nonprincipal Dirichlet character mod $D$, and if $\chi(n) = 1$ for $1 \leqq n \leqq x^{1/k}$, then

$$(*) \qquad \sum_{n=1}^{x} \chi(n) = o(D^{\frac{1}{2}} \log D)$$

as $D$ tends to infinity uniformly in $x$. If $\chi(n)$ is real and $\chi(n) = \mu(n)$ for $1 \leqq n \leqq x^{1/k}$, it is also proved that (*) holds with help of Davenport's theorem

$$\sum_{n=1}^{x} \mu(n) e^{2\pi i n\theta} = O(x \log^{-h} x)$$

uniformly in $\theta$ for fixed $k > 0$ [Quart. J. Math., Oxford Ser. **8**, 313–320 (1937)]. *H. Heilbronn* (Bristol).

Referred to in N68-25.

**N72-2** (11, 417i)

**Rédei, L. Über die Anzahl der Potenzreste mod $p$ im Intervall 1, $\sqrt{p}$.** Nieuw Arch. Wiskunde (2) **23**, 150–162 (1950).

Let $p$ be a prime greater than 3 and $l$ an integer greater than unity such that $l | (p-1)$. Let the integers prime to $p$ be divided into $l$ classes $C_0, \cdots, C_{l-1}$ in such a way that two integers are in the same class if and only if their quotient modulo $p$ is an $l$th-power residue modulo $p$. Under the additional restriction that $l$ divides $\frac{1}{2}(p-1)$ the author proves that the number of integers in the class $C_i$ $(i = 0, 1, \cdots, l-1)$ which lie in the interval 1, $\sqrt{p}$ is less than $\{1 - (2+\sqrt{2})^{-1}(1-1/l)\}[\sqrt{p}]$. For $l$ a divisor of $p-1$ but not of $\frac{1}{2}(p-1)$ the author considers only the case $l = 2$; he proves that for $p \equiv 3 \pmod 4$ the number of quadratic residues and the number of quadratic nonresidues which lie in the interval 1, $2\sqrt{(p/3)}$ are both less than $\{1 - (8+4\sqrt{3})^{-1}\}[2\sqrt{(p/3)}]$. The proofs are based on the following result of the author which is in the course of publication: If $K$ is a convex domain in the Cartesian $(x, y)$-plane which is symmetrical in the origin, has area $4p$, and is contained in the open square $|x|, |y| < p$, then modulo $p$ the ratio $y/x$ represents all nonzero residue classes modulo $p$ when $x$ and $y$ run over all pairs of nonzero integers such that $(x, y)$ is in $K$. *P. T. Bateman.*

Referred to in H05-22, N68-16, N72-3.

**N72-3** (12, 483a)

**Kanold, Hans-Joachim. Eine Bemerkung zur Verteilung der $r$-ten Potenznichtreste einer ungeraden Primzahl.** J. Reine Angew. Math. **188**, 74–77 (1950).

The main theorem of this paper is included in a theorem of Rédei [Nieuw. Arch. Wiskunde (2) **23**, 150–162 (1950); these Rev. **11**, 417, first result quoted]. However, the work of the author seems to be independent of and roughly simultaneous with that of Rédei. *P. T. Bateman.*

Citations: MR 11, 417i = N72-2.

Referred to in N68-16, N68-23.

**N72-4** (14, 21b)

**Skolem, Th. Existence of an $n$th non-power-residue mod $p$ less than $\sqrt{p}$.** Norsk Mat. Tidsskr. **33**, 123–126 (1951). (Norwegian)

By an analytic method and the use of a theorem of Aubrey-Thue the author shows that if $p$ is a sufficiently large prime, $n$ a natural integer for which there exists numbers which are not $n$th power residues (mod $p$), then there are non-residues which do not exceed $\sqrt{p}$. *O. Ore.*

**N72-5** **(14, 21c)**

**Nagell, T. The least positive $n$th non-power-residue modulo $p$.** Norsk Mat. Tidsskr. **34**, 13 (1952). (Norwegian)

Let $p \geqq 11$ be a prime and $n \geqq 3$ an odd integer; furthermore, let $x$ be the least positive integer which is not an $n$th power residue (mod $p$). It is shown through a simple elementary proof that $x < \sqrt{(\frac{1}{2}p)}$, thus improving a result by Skolem [see the preceding review]. *O. Ore.*

**N72-6** **(14, 1063h)**

**Davenport, H., and Erdös, P. The distribution of quadratic and higher residues.** Publ. Math. Debrecen **2**, 252–265 (1952).

Some problems concerning the distribution of $k$th power residues and nonresidues are discussed. Let $d$ denote the least quadratic nonresidue to the prime $p$. Then the authors show $d = O(p^{\frac{1}{4}\beta} \log^\beta p)$, where $\beta = e^{-1/2}$, which result is slightly better than a result of Vinogradov. The method is based on an elementary lemma on characters, which lemma, however, as the authors remark in a note added later, is already given by Vinogradov [Foundations of the theory of numbers, 5th ed., Gostehizdat, Moscow-Leningrad, 1949, p. 109; these Rev. **12**, 10]. Similar results are deduced for $k > 2$, which for $k \geqq 4$ are more precise than those known until now. Further, the authors give for $k \geqq 3$ an estimate for the order of magnitude of the least $k$th power nonresidue in any given one of the $k-1$ classes of nonresidues. They show that a positive number $\eta = \eta(k)$ (depending on $k$ only) exists, such that the estimate $O(p^{\frac{1}{4}-\eta})$ holds. In the case $k=3$ their result takes the form $O(p^{\gamma+\epsilon})$, where $\gamma = 1/2u = 0.383$ approximately, $u$ denoting the solution of the equation

$$\log u + \int_1^{2u-1} \frac{\log t}{t+1} dt = \frac{1}{3},$$

and $\epsilon$ being an arbitrary positive constant. Finally the distribution of the quadratic residues and nonresidues in sets of consecutive integers is considered. *J. F. Koksma.*

Citations: MR 12, 10e = A20-21.

Referred to in L25-18, N72-26.

**N72-7** **(17, 1056f)**

**Nagell, Trygve. Sur quelques problèmes dans la théorie des restes quadratiques et cubiques.** Ark. Mat. 3 (1956), 211–222.

Let $\pi(p, n)$ and $\psi(p, n)$ denote the smallest positive prime $n$-ic residue and non-residue respectively modulo $p$; let $\pi^*(p, n)$ and $\psi^*(p, n)$ denote the smallest odd primes with the same properties. Say that the density of a set $A$ of primes is lim inf $A(x)/\pi(x)$, where $A(x)$ denotes the number of primes in $A$ which are $\leqq x$ and $\pi(x)$ is the number of primes $\leqq x$. Write $p_n$ for the $n$th prime. For $n > 1$ the density of primes $p$ such that $\psi^*(p, 2) = p_n$ is $1/2^{n-1}$; similarly for $\pi^*(p, 2) = p_n$. For fixed $n$ the density of primes $p$ such that $\psi(p, 3) = p_n$ is positive; similarly for $\pi(p, 3) = p_n$. Necessary and sufficient conditions that 2 (or 3 or 5 or 7) be a cubic residue of a prime $p$ of the form $(x^2+27y^2)/4$ are given in terms of simple divisibility conditions on $x$ and $y$. The density of primes enjoying the property is shown to be 1/6 (or 1/6 or 1/4 or 1/4). From this it follows that the density of primes having 2 (or 3 or 5 or 7) as a cubic non-residue is 1/3 (or 1/3 or 1/4 or 1/4). Several of the proofs employ results in the field $R(\varrho)$, where $\varrho$ is a primitive cube root of unity. The author has done earlier work on similar problems [Ark. Mat. **1**, 185–193 (1950), 573–578, 579–586 (1952); MR **11**, 640; **14**, 247, 248]. *I. Niven* (Eugene, Ore.).

Citations: MR 11, 640d = Z01-12; MR 14, 247g = N68-15; MR 14, 248a = N68-16.

Referred to in R16-39.

**N72-8** **(18, 564b)**

**Rodosskiĭ, K. A. On non-residues and zeros of $L$-functions.** Izv. Akad. Nauk SSSR. Ser. Mat. **20** (1956), 303–306. (Russian)

Let $N_{\min}(D, k)$ be the least positive non-residue of exponent $k$ for prime modulus $D$. Let the function $L(s, x)$, with non-principal character of exponent $k$ for prime modulus $D > D_0$, not vanish in the rectangle

$$1 - \Psi \ln^{-1} D \leqq \sigma \leqq 1, \ |t| \leqq \min\{e^\Psi \ln^{-1} D, 1\},$$

where $\Psi \in [e, \frac{1}{2} \ln D]$. Then

$$N_{\min}(D, k) < D^{A\Psi^{-1} \ln \Psi},$$

where $D_0$ and $A$ are absolute positive constants.

*N. Levinson* (Cambridge, Mass.).

**N72-9** **(22# 10962)**

**Fomenko, O. M. On the distribution with respect to a prime modulus of the products of primes with a given value of a character.** Acta Arith. **6** (1960/61), 325–332.

Let $q \equiv 1 \pmod n$ be a prime; $w_l^{(s)}$ runs over all products of $l$ different prime factors with ind $w_l^{(s)} \equiv s \pmod n$, where the index is taken with respect to a fixed primitive root of $q$. Denote by $R_{l,\beta}^{(s)}(N)$ the number of the $w_l^{(s)}$ not exceeding $n$ whose smallest non-negative remainder mod $q$ is less than $\beta q$. Suppose that $N$ is large; put $\log N = r$, let $\varepsilon_0$ and $\varepsilon_1$ be arbitrarily small positive numbers, and assume exp $r^{\varepsilon_0} \leqq q \leqq N$ exp$(-r^{\varepsilon_0})$, $\Delta_1 = (1/q + q/N)^{0.5-\varepsilon_1} + N^{-0.2+\varepsilon_1}$. The author proves (1) $R_{l,\beta}^{(s)}(N) = \beta R_{l,1}^{(s)}(N) + O(N\Delta_1)$, which in some sense implies the equidistribution (mod $q$) of the indices of the numbers $w_l^{(s)}$. The author obtains (1) as a special case of a theorem dealing with the distribution of the fractional parts of $\alpha w_l^{(s)}$. The author uses the method of Vinogradoff.

*P. Erdös* (Budapest)

**N72-10** **(25# 2025)**

**Lehmer, D. H.; Lehmer, Emma**
**On runs of residues.**
*Proc. Amer. Math. Soc.* **13** (1962), 102–106.

It is known that for every sufficiently large prime $p$ there exists a run of $l$ consecutive integers that are $k$th power residues (mod $p$), where $l \geqq 2$ and $k \geqq 2$ are arbitrary integers. Let $r = r(k, l, p)$ be the least positive integer such that $r+i$ $(i = 0, 1, \cdots, l-1)$ are all $k$th power residues (mod $p$). The authors define $\Lambda$ by the relation $\Lambda = \Lambda(k, l) = \lim\sup_{p\to\infty} r(k, l, p)$ and study the behaviour of $\Lambda$.

Some relations previously known are mentioned in the paper: $\Lambda(2, 2) = 9$; $\Lambda(3, 2) = 77$; $\Lambda(4, 2) = 1224$. The main result in the paper is the proof of the following theorems: (a) $\Lambda(2, 3) = \infty$; (b) $\Lambda(k, 4) = \infty$, for $k \leqq 1048909$. The conjecture is also formulated that $\Lambda(k, 4) = \infty$ for every $k$.

*M. Cugiani* (Milano)

Referred to in B44-36, N68-41, N72-13, N72-15; N72-18, N72-20, N72-45.

**N72-11** **(25# 3928)**

**Moroz, B. Z.**
**The distribution of power residues and non-residues. (Russian. English summary)**
*Vestnik Leningrad. Univ.* **16** (1961), *no.* 19, 164–169.

Let $p$ be a prime $\equiv 1 \pmod l$. The author estimates the function (1) $E^{(l)}(\varepsilon_1, \cdots, \varepsilon_s, \Phi)$ which is defined as the number of solutions of (2) $\chi_l(\Phi(x+t))=\varepsilon_t$ $(1\leqq t\leqq s)$ with $x\in[0,p-1]$. Here $\varepsilon_1{}^l=\varepsilon_2{}^l=\cdots=\varepsilon_s{}^l=1$, $\Phi$ is any irreducible polynomial of degree $f$ over the finite field of $p$ elements $\chi_l$ is a character (mod $p$) of order $l$. He proves that the value of $E^{(l)}$ in (1) above is

$$\frac{p}{l^s}+\theta(f(l-1)s-1)p^{1/2}+\theta_1 fs,$$

where $|\theta|<1$, $-1\leqq\theta_1\leqq 0$. This sharpens a weaker result of Davenport [Acta Math. **71** (1939), 99–121; MR **1**, 41]. The author has used well-known estimations of A. Weil, derived from the Riemann hypothesis in algebraic function fields over a finite field.

He also finds an estimate for the number of solutions of (2) when $x$ is restricted to an interval $[p_1,p_2]$, where $0\leqq p_1\leqq p_2\leqq(p-1)$. In this case the dominant term is $(p_2-p_1)/l^s$ and the error term is $O(p^{1/2}\log p)$.

*S. Chowla* (Boulder, Colo.)

Citations: MR 1, 41e = T25-1.

**N72-12** **(26# 1277)**

**Cazacu, C.**

**Sur la distribution des restes d'un certain ordre $h$, modulo $p$. (Romanian. Russian and French summaries)**

*Acad. R. P. Romîne Fil. Iaşi Stud. Cerc. Şti. Mat.* **12** (1961), 205–211.

Author's summary: "On étudie le nombre des séries de longueur donnée, des restes et nonrestes de l'ordre $h$ modulo $p$, disposés dans un ordre préétabli. La méthode employée est fondée sur la notion de prédicat de la logique mathématique."

**N72-13** **(26# 3660)**

**Lehmer, D. H.; Lehmer, Emma; Mills, W. H.**

**Pairs of consecutive power residues.**

*Canad. J. Math.* **15** (1963), 172–177.

Nach einem Satz von A. Brauer [S.-B. Akad. Wiss. Berlin **1928**, 9–16] gibt es zu vorgegebenen natürlichen Zahlen $k$, $m$ für alle genügend grossen Primzahlen $p$ Sequenzen $r, r+1, \cdots, r+m-1$ natürlicher Zahlen, die sämtlich $k$te Potenzreste mod $p$ sind. Es sei $r(k,m,p)$ das kleinste solche $r$. Die vorliegende Arbeit beschäftigt sich mit der Funktion $\Lambda(k,m)=\mathrm{Max}_p\, r(k,m,p)$, wobei alle Primzahlen $p$ zugelassen sind, für die $r(k,m,p)$ sinnvoll ist. In einer früheren Arbeit der ersten beiden Autoren [Proc. Amer. Math. Soc. **13** (1962), 102–106; MR **25** #2025] wurde $\Lambda(k,m)=\infty$ für gerades $k$ und $m\geqq 3$ oder $2<k\leqq 1048909$ und $m\geqq 4$ gezeigt. Jetzt wird, wie bereits dort in Aussicht gestellt, $\Lambda(k,2)$ für $k\leqq 6$ berechnet. Neu sind die Resultate $\Lambda(5,2)=7888$, $\Lambda(6,2)=202124$. Ersteres bedeutet z.B., dass zu jeder Primzahl $p>101$ zwei aufeinanderfolgende natürliche Zahlen $\leqq 7889$ existieren, die 5te Potenzreste mod $p$ sind. Die angegebene Grenze ist optimal. Es ist nicht bekannt, ob $\Lambda(k,2)<\infty$ für alle $k$ richtig ist. Die Resultate wurden erreicht unter Verwendung elektronischer Rechenmaschinen, in der vorliegenden Arbeit wird der theoretische Hintergrund des verwendeten Programms geschildert.

*H. Klirgen* (Freiburg)

Citations: MR 25# 2025 = N72-10.

Referred to in N72-15, N72-20, N72-23, N72-45.

**N72-14** **(26# 6134)**

**Burgess, D. A.**

**On Dirichlet characters of polynomials.**

*Proc. London Math. Soc.* (3) **13** (1963), 537–548.

Let $\chi$ be a $q$th power character (mod $p$), $p$ prime, and let $f(x)$ be a polynomial that is not a $q$th power (mod $p$). It is known that $\sum_{x=N+1}^{N+H}\chi(f(x))\ll p^{1/2}\log p$, where $A\ll B$ means $|A|<kB$ for some constant $k$ (which depends on the degree of $f$). The main result of the present paper is the following estimate. (I) Let $q$ be a fixed integer and $f$ a non-linear polynomial that is a product of rational linear factors but is not a $q$th power. If $p\equiv 1 \pmod q$ and is sufficiently large and $\chi$ is a $q$th-order character (mod $p$) and $\varepsilon>0$, then for all integers $H$, $N$ such that $p^{1/4+\varepsilon}\leqq H\leqq p^{1/2}$ we have

$$H-\Big|\sum_{x=N+1}^{N+H}\chi(f(x))\Big|\gg H^2p^{-1/2},$$

the constant implied in the notation depending on $\varepsilon$, $q$ and $f$.

As a consequence of (I) the author obtains the following. (II) The maximum number $H$ of consecutive integers having the same value for $\chi(f(x))$ is $\ll p^{1/2}\log p$. (III) If $p$ is sufficiently large, and if

$$H\gg p^{11/24}(\log p)^{3/2},$$

then the sequence $N+1, N+2,\cdots,N+H$ includes a pair of consecutive quadratic residues and a pair of quadratic non-residues (mod $p$).

*L. Carlitz* (Durham, N.C.)

Referred to in N68-35, N68-36, N72-32.

**N72-15** **(27# 4787)**

**Bierstedt, R. G.; Mills, W. H.**

**On the bound for a pair of consecutive quartic residues of a prime.**

*Proc. Amer. Math. Soc.* **14** (1963), 628–632.

The following theorem on the distribution of quartic residues is proved: Every prime except 2, 3, 5, 13, 17, 41 possesses a pair $n, n+1$ of positive quartic residues with $n\leqq 1224$. Furthermore, infinitely many primes have 1224, 1225 as their first pair of consecutive quartic residues. This result extends to quartic residues a similar result, as yet unpublished, by M. Dunton for the cubic case.

The proof is by separation of many cases, a method that has since been "automated" to obtain similar results for 5th, 6th, and 7th power residues. In the present proof there are 5 main cases according as the quartic characters.

$$[\chi(2),\chi(5)]=[-1,-1],[-1,i],[i,-1],[i,i],[i,-i].$$

Subcases involve the consideration of $\chi(q)$ for primes $q\leqq 41$. Primes having the pair 1224, 1225 as their least pair of consecutive quartic residues are given as those for which $\chi(3)=1$ and $\chi(q)=i$ for all other primes $q<1224$. There is no upper bound for three consecutive quartic residues [the reviewer and E. Lehmer, same Proc. **13** (1962), 102–106; MR **25** #2025; the reviewer, E. Lehmer and W. H. Mills, Canad. J. Math. **15** (1963), 172–177; MR **26** #3660].

*D. H. Lehmer* (Berkeley, Calif.)

Citations: MR 25# 2025 = N72-10; MR 26# 3660 = N72-13.

Referred to in N72-23.

**N72-16** **(28# 71)**

**Mills, W. H.**

**Characters with preassigned values.**

*Canad. J. Math.* **15** (1963), 169–171.

The paper is concerned with the following question. Let $k$ and $t$ be positive integers; let $q_1,\cdots,q_t$ be distinct primes and let $\zeta_1,\cdots,\zeta_t$ be $k$th roots of unity, not necessarily primitive. Under what conditions do there exist primes $p$ that have a $k$th power character $\chi$ such that

$$(*)\qquad \chi(q_i)=\zeta_i\quad(1\leqq i\leqq t)?$$

If $k$ is a prime, it is known that for any $q_1,\cdots,q_t$, $\zeta_1,\cdots,\zeta_t$ there exist an infinite number of such primes $p$. For even values of $k$ there are certain restrictions. It is proved that when these restrictions are satisfied, then there exist primes that satisfy (*). In particular, this is always the case if $k$ is odd, if $k=2$, if $k=4$ or if $k=2Q$, where $Q$ is a prime of the form $4m+3$. Moreover, if one such prime exists, then there are infinitely many.

*L. Carlitz* (Durham, N.C.)

Referred to in N72-47.

## N72-17 (28# 1732)

**Lehmer, D. H.**

**Some high-speed logic.**

*Proc. Sympos. Appl. Math., Vol. XV, pp.* 141–145. *Amer. Math. Soc., Providence, R.I.*, 1963.

The author discusses theorem-proving programs for digital computers that have given mechanical proofs of theorems that are both interesting and humanly impractical. The following examples are given. Every set of 7 consecutive integers greater than 36 contains a multiple of a prime greater than 41. The theorem is false if 7 is replaced by 6, and the last sequence of 6 consecutive integers with 41 as a common factor is given. Further, similar results are to appear in a forthcoming paper. Another example, from a paper already available [the author, E. Lehmer, W. H. Mills and J. L. Selfridge, Math. Comp. **16** (1962), 407–415] is the theorem that all primes except 7, 13, 19, 31, 37, 43, 61, 67, 79, 127, 283 have three consecutive cubic residues. The first triple occurs not later than 23532, 23533, 23534. This result is best possible because there are infinitely many primes for which no three residues less than 23534 are consecutive.

*W. R. Utz* (Columbia, Mo.)

## N72-18 (28# 2078)

**Graham, R. L.**

**On quadruples of consecutive $k$th power residues.**

*Proc. Amer. Math. Soc.* **15** (1964), 196–197.

Let $k$ and $N$ be positive integers, $k \geqq 2$. A short and elegant proof is given that there exist an infinite number of primes $p$ that do not have four consecutive $k$th power residues, $r, r+1, r+2, r+3$, with $r \leqq N$. This proves a conjecture of Lehmer and Lehmer [same Proc. **13** (1962), 102–106; MR **25** #2025]. In the notation of Lehmer and Lehmer this result is written $\Lambda(k, 4) = \infty$.

The corresponding result is known to be false for 3 consecutive residues, at least when $k=3$ [Lehmer, Lehmer, Mills, and Selfridge, Math. Comp. **16** (1962), 407–415].

*W. H. Mills* (Princeton, N.J.)

Citations: MR 25# 2025 = N72-10.

Referred to in N72-48.

## N72-19 (28# 2085)

**Mordell, L. J.**

**On the least residue and non-residue of a polynomial.**

*J. London Math. Soc.* **38** (1963), 451–453.

Let $p$ be a prime and $f(x)$ a polynomial of degree $n$ with integer coefficients. The author considers the problems of finding: (a) the least non-negative residue $l$ of $f(x)$ (mod $p$); (b) the least non-negative non-residue $k$ of $f(x)$ (mod $p$). For (a) he obtains $l \leqq np^{1/2} \log p$, and for (b), if $n=3$, $k=O(p^{1/2} \log^2 p)$. These results depend on the deep estimate $|\sum_{x=0}^{p-1} e(f(x))| \leqq n\sqrt{p}$, where $e(f(x)) = \exp(2\pi i f(x)/p)$ [see Carlitz and Uchiyama, Duke Math. J. **24** (1957), 37–41; MR **18**, 563]. Problem (b) for $n \geqq 4$ seems to be very difficult.

*S. L. Segal* (Rochester, N.Y.)

Citations: MR 18, 563c = T25-12.

Referred to in N72-27, N72-28, N72-31, N72-32, T10-29, T10-31, T25-24, T40-38.

## N72-20 (28# 5028)

**Jordan, J. H.**

**Pairs of consecutive power residues or non-residues.**

*Canad. J. Math.* **16** (1964), 310–314.

Let $k$ be a positive integer, $p=k+1$ a prime and $g$ a primitive root of $p$. Let $g^{\mathrm{Ind}\, u} \equiv u \pmod p$.

Recently various authors [the reviewer and E. Lehmer, Proc. Amer. Math. Soc. **13** (1962), 102–106; MR **25** #2025; the reviewer, E. Lehmer and W. Mills, Canad. J. Math. **15** (1963), 172–177; MR **26** #3660] have been concerned with the function $\Lambda(k, m) = \max\{r(k, m, p)\}$, where $r(k, m, p)$ denotes the least $r$ for which

$$(1) \quad \mathrm{Ind}\,(r) \equiv \mathrm{Ind}\,(r+1) \equiv \cdots \equiv \mathrm{Ind}\,(r+m-1) \equiv 0 \pmod{p-1}$$

and the maximum is taken over all primes $p$ for which $r$ exists. $\Lambda(k, 2)$ increases rapidly with $k$: $\Lambda(2, 2) = 9$, $\Lambda(3, 2) = 77$, $\Lambda(4, 2) = 1224$, $\Lambda(5, 2) = 7888$, $\Lambda(6, 2) = 202124$, $\Lambda(7, 2) = 1649375$.

The author defines another function $\Lambda^*(k, m)$ obtained by deleting the condition of divisibility in (1) so that one asks only for the first appearance of $m$ consecutive integers whose $k$th power characters are identical. $\Lambda^*(k, 2)$ turns out to be very much smaller. The author has established that $\Lambda^*(2, 2) = 3$, $\Lambda^*(3, 2) = 8$, $\Lambda^*(4, 2) = 20$, $\Lambda^*(5, 2) = 44$, $\Lambda^*(6, 2) = 80$, $\Lambda^*(7, 2) = 343$. The proofs are short enough to be done "by hand", although the last two proofs are omitted to save space. The further results $\Lambda^*(2k, 3) = \Lambda^*(k, 4) = \infty$ are also obtained in the same manner as for $\Lambda$.

*D. H. Lehmer* (Berkeley, Calif.)

Citations: MR 25# 2025 = N72-10; MR 26# 3660 = N72-13.

## N72-21 (28# 5578)

**Lehmer, D. H.; Lehmer, E.; Mills, W. H.; Selfridge, J. L.**

**Machine proof of a theorem on cubic residues.**

*Math. Comp.* **16** (1962), 407–415.

Any set of three consecutive positive integers is called a triplet. It is known that for any prime $p \equiv 1 \pmod 6$, up to a finite number of exceptional primes, there exists a triplet whose members are $\leqq p-1$ and cubic residues mod $p$. The authors proved, by using a computer method, that (a) the only exceptional primes are 2, 3, 7, 13, 19, 31, 37, 43, 61, 67, 79, 127, 283; (b) every non-exceptional prime has a triplet of cubic residues not exceeding (23532, 23533, 23534); (c) there are infinitely many primes whose smallest triplet of cubic residues is the above one, so that (b) is the best possible result.

The authors' method of proof is as follows. Since the $p-1$ reduced residue classes mod $p$ form a multiplicative group of order 3 modulo the group of cubic residues, let $R(s)$ be an isomorphism of this group onto the additive group mod 3. Let $S = \{q_1, \cdots, q_t\}$ be a set of distinct primes $\equiv 1 \bmod 6$, and for any such prime $p \notin S$, $A = (R(q_1), \cdots, R(q_t))$ be called the $S$-vector belonging to $p$. Then, a number $n = q_1^{b_1} \cdots q_t^{b_t}$ is a cubic residue mod $p$ if and only if $R(n) = b_1 a_1 + \cdots + b_t a_t \equiv 0 \pmod 3$. If this is the case, the authors say that $n$ disposes of $A$. If a number $N$ and a set $S$ of primes are found such that for any of the $3^t$ possible $S$-vectors $A$ there exists a triplet whose members do not exceed $N+1$ and do dispose of $A$, then all primes $p \notin S$ are non-exceptional.

By testing all primes less than 11243 in a preliminary machine run, the primes in (a) are shown to be exceptional. Then, the following ingenious selections of $S$ and $N$ lead the authors to success. For the first machine run the set of all primes $\leqq 127$ and 283 (see (a)) are used as $S$ and 44224 as $N$, and (a) is already proved. $N$ was chosen by a probabilistic discussion in order to supply enough triplets whose prime divisors are restricted to those in $S$. Then $N$ is lowered successively to 2 to the power 17, 16, 15. In these three runs (a) is again proved either by the machine itself or by some simple additional computations by hand. Then in the fifth run the set of all primes less than the

51st was selected as $S$ and $3 \cdot 2^{13}$ as $N$. These runs, especially the last, gave information as to what kind of $S$-vectors were hard to be disposed of. So in the sixth run, (b) was proved with $N=24389$ instead of 23533. Then, with the intention of proving part (c), a case test program was written by using special $S$-vectors selected by the information of the previous machine runs. This run resulted in getting the number 23533. The final run was made with $S$ of all primes less than the 56th and $N=23533$. This run alone proves (a) and (b), and (c) was proved by the case test program.

Interesting techniques for reducing machine time by improving the computations so as to fit machine computation, and discussions for selecting suitable $S$ and $N$ are described. This paper represents a kind of machine proof of mathematical theorems which is absolutely impossible without using a computer, and the details of the proof lie in the programs the authors wrote and the output from the machine. *S. Kuroda* (College Park, Md.)

Referred to in N72-45.

## N72-22 (29# 1173 )

**Hooley, C.**

**On the distribution of the roots of polynomial congruences.**

*Mathematika* **11** (1964), 39–49.

Let $f(x)$ be an irreducible polynomial of degree $n>1$ having integer coefficients. Denote by $v_1, \cdots, v_{l_k}$ the roots of the congruence $f(v) \equiv 0 \pmod{k}$ and arrange the numbers $v_i/k$, $1 \leqq i \leqq l_k$, $1 \leqq k < \infty$, as a sequence $s_1, s_2, \cdots$ so that the corresponding denominators are in ascending order (the arrangement in a group corresponding to a fixed value of $k$ is immaterial).

The author proves that the sequence $s_1, s_2, \cdots$ is uniformly distributed in $(0, 1)$. He uses in his proof several lemmas of independent interest, and also applies his method to the estimation of Kloosterman sums.

*P. Erdős* (Budapest)

## N72-23 (29# 2214 )

**Brillhart, John; Lehmer, D. H.; Lehmer, Emma**

**Bounds for pairs of consecutive seventh and higher power residues.**

*Math. Comp.* **18** (1964), 397–407.

Using a computing machine, the authors show that every prime of the form $7n+1$, except 29, 71, 113, and 491, has a pair $n$, $n+1$ of positive seventh power residues with $n \leqq 1649375$. Moreover, this bound is best possible since there exist an infinite number of primes with 1649375, 1649376 as the first pair of consecutive seventh power residues. It is not known how to prove a theorem of this type without the use of high-speed computers. The corresponding question for sixth and smaller power residues has been previously settled by the Lehmers and others [D. H. Lehmer, E. Lehmer and W. H. Mills, Canad. J. Math. **15** (1963), 172–177; MR **26** #3660; R. G. Bierstedt and W. H. Mills, Proc. Amer. Math. Soc. **14** (1963), 628–632; MR **27** #4787]. For $k$th power residues with $k \geqq 8$, it is not known whether or not such a bound exists. For $k$ odd and greater than 3, or for $k$ twice a prime of the form $4N+3$, the authors show that if such a bound exists, it must be at least $5^k$. There is a brief discussion of the cases $k=8$, 9, and 10.

*W. H. Mills* (Princeton, N.J.)

Citations: MR 26# 3660 = N72-13; MR 27# 4787 = N72-15.

## N72-24 (30# 3055 )

**Dunton, M.**

**Bounds for pairs of cubic residues.**

*Proc. Amer. Math. Soc.* **16** (1965), 330–332.

The author proves four theorems concerning pairs of nontrivial cubic residues. We quote the first three theorems. (1) If $p \nmid 7 \cdot 13$, then there exists a consecutive pair of nontrivial cubic residues $\leqq (77, 78)$ modulo $p$. (2) There are infinitely many primes which have (77, 78) as their first pair of consecutive nontrivial cubic residues; this implies that (77, 78) is the best possible bound. 13,817,029 is the smallest such prime. (3) If $p \nmid 7 \cdot 13$, then there exist two pairs of nontrivial consecutive cubic residues $\leqq (125, 126)$. *L. Carlitz* (Durham, N.C.)

Referred to in N72-48.

## N72-25 (31# 1226 )

**Mills, W. H.**

**Bounded consecutive residues and related problems.**

*Proc. Sympos. Pure Math., Vol. VIII, pp. 170–174. Amer. Math. Soc., Providence, R.I.*, 1965.

The author discusses some general aspects of the problem of bounding the first appearance of two, or more, consecutive power residues. A table (p. 170) gives the most recent determination of the values of $\Lambda(k, s)$ defined as the maximum over all primes $p$ of the smallest positive $k$th power residue modulo $p$ which is the first of $s$ consecutive integers that are also $k$th power residues of $p$.

In a more general setting, consider a finite abelian group $G$ with unit element $e$ and a function $\chi(n)$ on positive integers $n$ whose values lie in $G$ and which is purely multiplicative, so that $\chi(m)\chi(n)=\chi(mn)$. Such a function is said to be of length $s$ in case an integer $r$ exists such that $\chi(r)=\chi(r+1)=\cdots=\chi(r+q-1)=e$ holds for $q \mp s$, while for no $r$ does it hold for $q=s+1$. The existence of such functions is closely connected with the possibility that $\Lambda(k, s)$ is infinite. Here the group $G$ is the cyclic group of order $k$. To illustrate the non-cyclic case the author chooses for $G$ the Klein fours-group and gives the following best possible result: Let $\chi$ be defined as above; then $\chi(r)=\chi(r+1)=e$ holds for some $r \leqq 120$.

The author makes the following conjecture. Let $\chi(n)=\pm 1$ be purely multiplicative and of length 2, so that $\chi(r)=\chi(r+1)=\chi(r+2)=1$ never holds. Then

$$(1) \qquad \chi(n) \equiv n \pmod{3} \quad (n \not\equiv 0 \pmod{3}).$$

The author has verified (1) for $n<3181$. {The reviewer has verified this for $n<2 \cdot 10^6$.}

*D. H. Lehmer* (Berkeley, Calif.)

Referred to in N72-48.

## N72-26 (32# 4078 )

**Jordan, James H.**

**The distribution of cubic and quintic non-residues.**

*Pacific J. Math.* **16** (1966), 77–85.

Denote by $\alpha_k$ the smallest number so that for every sufficiently large $p \equiv 1 \pmod{k}$, each class of $k$th power non-residues mod $p$ contains a positive integer smaller than $p^{\alpha_k+\varepsilon}$. Very likely $\alpha_k=0$, but this, if true, is very deep.

Davenport and the reviewer obtained some upper bounds for $\alpha_k$ [Publ. Math. Debrecen **2** (1952), 252–265; MR **14**, 1063]. Using the results of Burgess [Mathematika **4** (1957), 106–112; MR **20** #28], the author considerably improves those estimates if $k$ is a prime. In particular, he obtains $\alpha_3<0.235$, $\alpha_5<0.09$; the earlier results were $\alpha_3<55/112$, $\alpha_5<197/396$. *P. Erdős* (Budapest)

Citations: MR 14, 1063h = N72-6; MR 20# 28 = N68-28.

## N72-27 (33# 1280 )

**Williams, Kenneth S.**

**On the least non-residue of a quartic polynomial.**

*Proc. Cambridge Philos. Soc.* **62** (1966), 429–431.

Let $p$ be a prime and $f$ a polynomial with integral coefficients. Let $k$ be such that $f(x) \equiv r \pmod{p}$ has a solution for $0 \leqq r \leqq k-1$, but not for $r=k$. For $f$ a cubic it was proved by Mordell [J. London Math. Soc. **38** (1963), 451–453; MR **28** #2085] that $k=O(p^{1/2}(\log p)^2)$, and the author states that Mordell's method can be made to yield $k=O(p^{1/2}\log p)$. Taking $f$ to be a quartic, considering the discriminant of $f(x)-r$ (which is a cubic in $r$), and working on similar lines to Mordell, the author shows that $k=O(p^{1/2}\log p)$ in this case also.

*H. J. Godwin* (Swansea)

Citations: MR 28# 2085 = N72-19.

## N72-28 (34# 1265)

**Hudson, Margaret**

**On the least non-residue of a polynomial.**

*J. London Math. Soc.* **41** (1966), 745–749.

Continuing investigations of L. J. Mordell [same J. **38** (1963), 451–453; MR **28** #2085] on the magnitude of $k$, the least non-negative integer $r$ for which the polynomial congruence $f(x)\equiv r \pmod p$ to a prime modulus $p$ is insoluble, the author derives for quartic polynomials $f(x)$ the estimate $k=O(p^{1/2}\log p)$. This is obtained by using well-known estimates of A. Weil [Proc. Nat. Acad. Sci. U.S.A. **34** (1948), 204–207; MR **10**, 234] and L. Carlitz and S. Uchiyama [Duke Math. J. **24** (1957), 37–41; MR **18**, 563].

*O. H. Körner* (Marburg)

Citations: MR 10, 234e = T25-5; MR 18, 563c = T25-12; MR 28# 2085 = N72-19.

## N72-29 (34# 2539)

**Glazkov, V. V.**

**Distribution of the values of characters.** **(Russian)**

*Studies in Number Theory, No. I (Russian), pp.* 12–20. *Izdat. Saratov. Univ., Saratov*, 1966.

Suppose that $h$ is a (complex-valued) character (this means that $|h(n)|=0$ or $=1$ for all integers $n\geqq 1$, and $h$ is completely multiplicative) with $h(p)\neq 0$ for all primes $p$; assume that the number of values $h(n)\neq 0$ is finite and equal to a prime $q$. The author conjectures, for every $s$, the existence of an $n$ with $h(n)=h(n+1)=\cdots=h(n+s)$. He proves the existence of infinitely many $n$ with $h(n)=h(n+1)$, and a better, analogous result for real-valued $h$. Corollary: If $\Omega(n)$ denotes the total number of prime factors of $n$, then the congruence $\Omega(n)\equiv\Omega(n+1) \bmod m$, for any $m$, has infinitely many solutions $n$.

Finally, the author proves that if $h(p)=\chi(p)$ ($\chi$ a Dirichlet character) for all primes $p\neq p_\nu$, $\nu=1, 2, \cdots$, and if $\sum_{\nu\geqq 1} p_\nu^{-1}$ converges, then for any set $(\xi_1, \cdots, \xi_s)$ of $q$th roots of unity, there exists an integer $a\geqq 0$ with $h(a+k)=\xi_k$, $k=1, \cdots, s$.

*W. Schwarz* (Freiburg)

## N72-30 (34# 7448)

**Tietäväinen, Aimo**

**On non-residues of a polynomial.**

*Ann. Univ. Turku. Ser. A I No.* 94 (1966), 6 *pp.*

E. Bombieri and H. Davenport [Amer. J. Math. **88** (1966), 61–70; MR **34** #167] proved the following theorem: If $f(x)$ is a polynomial of degree $d\geqq 2$ over the finite field of $p$ elements, $p$ a prime, such that at least one of the irreducible factors (mod $p$) of $(f(x)-f(y))/(x-y)$ is absolutely irreducible, then there is a number $C(d)$ depending only on $d$ such that if $k$ is the least non-negative non-residue of $f(x)$ mod $p$, then $k<C(d)p^{1/2}\log p$ for all sufficiently large $p$.

The author improves this estimate by dropping the $\log p$. This result is obtained by repeating the argument of Bombieri and Davenport except at the point where it becomes necessary to estimate (*) $\sum_{a=1}^{p-1}|S(a)|^2$, $S(a)=\sum_{b=0}^{u}\exp(-2\pi iab/p)$, $u$ an integer $0\leqq u\leqq (p-1)/2$, at which point he substitutes an explicit evaluation of (*), due to himself [Ann. Univ. Turku. Ser. A I No. 87 (1966); MR **33** #5611], for the estimate used by Bombieri and Davenport.

*S. L. Segal* (Rochester, N.Y.)

Citations: MR 33# 5611 = T10-31; MR 34# 167 = T25-24.

Referred to in N72-39, N72-50.

## N72-31 (35# 2816)

**McCann, K.; Williams, K. S.**

**On the residues of a cubic polynomial** (mod $p$).

*Canad. Math. Bull.* **10** (1967), 29–38.

Let $f(x)$ be a cubic polynomial with integral coefficients. The number of residues of $f(x)$ mod $p$ among the integers $1, 2, \cdots, h$ is shown to be $2h/3+O(p^{1/2}\log p)$. The proof, using several estimates of sums, is given only for the special case $f(x)=x^3+ax$ to simplify notation. The result implies a theorem of L. J. Mordell [J. London Math. Soc. **38** (1963), 451–453; MR **28** #2085] that the least non-residue of $f(x)$ mod $p$ is $O(p^{1/2}\log p)$.

*I. Niven* (Eugene, Ore.)

Citations: MR 28# 2085 = N72-19.

Referred to in A12-54.

## N72-32 (35# 4194)

**Williams, Kenneth S.**

**Pairs of consecutive residues of polynomials.**

*Canad. J. Math.* **19** (1967), 655–666.

Let $f(x)=a_0+a_1x+\cdots+a_dx^d$ be a polynomial with integral coefficients of fixed degree $d\geqq 4$. Let $p$ be a prime and suppose $a_d\not\equiv 0 \pmod p$. The author considers the problem of estimating the least integer $e$ $(0\leqq e\leqq p-1)$ such that $e$ and $e+1$ are both residues of $f(x)$ mod $p$. (The problem of the least non-negative residue was considered earlier by L. J. Mordell [J. London Math. Soc. **38** (1963), 451–453; MR **28** #2085].)

Using a deep result of S. Lang and A. Weil [Amer. J. Math. **76** (1954), 819–827; MR **16**, 398] the author first proves that $e$ always exists for all sufficiently large primes $p$ (though it may not exist for small $p$).

He then proves that for all but $o(p^{d+1})$ polynomials of fixed degree $d\geqq 4$, $e\leqq K_dp^{1/2}\log p$, where $K_d$ is a constant depending only on $d$.

For $d=2$ a stronger result for all quadratic polynomials is due to D. A. Burgess [Proc. London Math. Soc. (3) **13** (1963), 537–548; MR **26** #6134], and the author announces that for $d=3$, he and K. McCann have proved $e\leqq Kp^{1/2}\log p$ for all cubic polynomials. He conjectures that the theorem of the previous paragraph is true for all polynomials of fixed degree $d$.

*S. L. Segal* (Rochester, N.Y.)

Citations: MR 16, 398d = G25-2; MR 26# 6134 = N72-14; MR 28# 2085 = N72-19.

Referred to in N72-39, N72-41.

## N72-33 (36# 3741)

**Elliott, P. D. T. A.**

**A problem of Erdős concerning power residue sums.**

*Acta Arith.* **13** (1967/68), 131–149.

Let $k$ be a positive integer, $p$ a rational prime. Let $n_k(p)$ be zero for $p\not\equiv 1 \bmod k$ and $n_k(p)$ be the least positive residue which is not a $k$th power mod $p$ for $p\equiv 1 \bmod k$. The following theorem is proved. For each $k$ and constant $\alpha$ which satisfies $\alpha<4e^{1-1/k}$, one has, as $x\to\infty$, the asymptotic relation $\sum_{p<x}(n_k(p))^\alpha\sim C_{k,\alpha}x/\log x$, where $C_{k,\alpha}$ is a constant. If $k$ is an odd prime, $C_{k,\alpha}=\sum_{\nu=1}^{\infty}k^{-r}q_\nu^{\alpha}$, where $q_r$ runs over all primes. The proof uses algebraic number theory, Burgess's estimate for character sums and Linnik's large sieve. The result with $\alpha=1$ was proved by P. Erdős for $k=2$ and conjectured by him for $k>2$

[Mat. Lapok **12** (1961), 10–17; MR **26** #2410]. M. B. Barban has stated without proof the cases $k=2$, $\alpha \leqq 6$ and $k>2$, $\alpha=1$ [Uspehi Mat. Nauk **21** (1966), no. 1 (127), 51–102; MR **33** #7320]. {Reviewer's remark: The formula $C_{k,\alpha}$ given above holds also for $k=2$.}

*A. Schinzel* (Warsaw)

Citations: MR 26# 2410 = N68-31; MR 33# 7320 = Z02-53.

Referred to in L25-28, N72-34, N72-52.

## N72-34 (37# 4031)

**Elliott, P. D. T. A.**

**Corrigendum: "A problem of Erdős concerning power residue sums".**

*Acta Arith.* **14** (1967/68), 437.

The author corrects a mistake in one of his lemmata. The mistake has not affected any succeeding argument [cf. the author, same Acta **13** (1967/68), 131–149; MR **36** #3741].

*A. Schinzel* (Warsaw)

Citations: MR 36# 3741 = N72-33.

Referred to in L25-28.

## N72-35 (37# 139)

**Whyburn, Clifton T.**

**The density of power residues and non-residues in subintervals of $[1, \sqrt{p}]$.**

*Acta Arith.* **14** (1967/68), 113–116.

The author extends results of L. Rédei [Nieuw Arch. Wisk. (2) **23** (1950), 150–162; MR **11**, 417] on the density of power residues and non-residues in certain intervals. The main theorem states: Let $d$ be a positive integer such that $d|p-1$ and $d \geqq 2$. Let $h$ be such that $q=h\sqrt{p}$ is a positive integer and $1>h^2>\pi^2/6d$. Denote by $C_0$ the set of $d$th power residues (mod $p$) and define the classes $C_1, C_2, \cdots, C_{d-1}$ by $x, y \in C_i$ if $x$ and $y$ are prime to $p$ and their quotient is congruent to an element of $C_0$ (mod $p$). If $\nu_i$ is the number of elements of $C_i$ in $[1, q]$, we have $\nu_i/q = \delta_i \leqq (1+(d-1)(1-6d/\pi^2(d-1)+1/(d-1)h^2)^{1/2})/d+o(1)$. The special case of the theorem with $d=2$ and $q=[\sqrt{p}]$ gives the corollary: For $p$ an (odd) prime "sufficiently large", the density of quadratic residues or non-residues in $[1, [\sqrt{p}]]$ is $\geqq 0.042$.

*O. P. Stackelberg* (Durham, N.C.)

Citations: MR 11, 417h = A60-8.

Referred to in L25-31.

## N72-36 (37# 1310)

**Jordan, James H.**

**The distribution of $k$th power residues and nonresidues.**

*Proc. Amer. Math. Soc.* **19** (1968), 678–680.

Let $p$ be a prime, $p-1=kt$. Let $E_j$, $j=1, \cdots, k-1$, be the classes of $k$th power non-residues mod $p$ and let $E_0$ be the class of $k$th power residues. Denote by $N_j(H)$ the number of positive integers not exceeding $H$ in $E_j$. Using a result of D. A. Burgess on character sums [Proc. London Math. Soc. (3) **12** (1962), 179–192; MR **24** #A2569], the author proves that for every positive integer $r$, (*) $|N_j(H)-H/K| < cH^{1-1/(r+1)}p^{1/4r}\log p$. (*) improves a special case of a result of I. M. Vinogradov [Trans. Amer. Math. Soc. **29** (1927), 209–217].

*P. Erdős* (Budapest)

Citations: MR 24# A2569 = L25-16.

## N72-37 (37# 4000)

**Elliott, P. D. T. A.**

**Some notes on $k$-th power residues.**

*Acta Arith.* **14** (1967/68), 153–162.

Let $k$ be a positive integer and $p$ a rational prime satisfying $p \equiv 1 \pmod k$. Define $n_k(p)$ to be the least positive integer which is not a $k$th power mod $p$ and $r_k(p)$ to be the least prime which is a $k$th power mod $p$ if $p \equiv 1 \bmod k$, $n_k(p)=r_k(p)=0$ otherwise. The author proves: (1) If $k$ is an odd prime there is a constant $d_k>0$ such that $n_k(p)>d_k \log p$ holds infinitely often. (2) If $\alpha<4$ then

$$\sum_{p<x}(r_2(p))^\alpha = g_\alpha \operatorname{Li}(x)+O(x\exp(-c\log_2 x/\log_3 x)),$$

where $g_\alpha$ and $c$ are positive constants, $c$ being arbitrary but fixed and $g_\alpha$ given explicitly. The proof uses E. Fogels' results on the distribution of prime ideals [same Acta **7** (1961/62), 255–269; MR **28** #5053] and the large sieve. It is conjectured that $\sum_{p<x} r_k(p) \sim e_k x(\log x)^{-1}$.

{Reviewer's remark: The result for $k=2$ similar to (1), attributed by the author to Chowla, was proved also by V. R. Fridlender [Dokl. Akad. Nauk SSSR **66** (1949), 351–352; MR **10**, 684], H. Salié [Math. Nachr. **3** (1949), 7–8; MR **11**, 500] and P. Turán [Math. Lapok **1** (1950), 243–266; MR **12**, 311].}

*A. Schinzel* (Warsaw)

Citations: MR 10, 684b = N68-6; MR 11, 500e = N68-8; MR 12, 311n = Z15-17; MR 28# 5053 = R44-25.

Referred to in N72-52.

## N72-38 (37# 6239)

**Linnik, Ju. V.**

**Sur une application du théorème d'André Weil à la théorie des caractères de Dirichlet.**

*Séminaire Delange-Pisot-Poitou: 1966/67, Théorie des Nombres, Fasc.* 1, *Exp.* 6, 7 *pp. Secrétariat mathématique, Paris*, 1968.

For $D \in \mathbf{Z}$ and $\chi$ a non-principal character modulo $D$, let $N_{\min}(D, \chi)$, $P_{\min}(D, \chi)$ and $d_{\max}(D, \chi)$ stand for the least non-residue, least prime residue (not a divisor of $D$) and maximal difference of consecutive non-residues (between 1 and $D-1$), respectively; then Vinogradov's conjectures state that all three are $O(D^\varepsilon)$ ($\varepsilon>0$, arbitrarily small). While the first two would follow from the generalized Riemann hypothesis, the last one would not. Using Weil's estimate $|N-(p+1)| \leqq gp^{1/2}$ of the number $N$ of solutions of $Q(x, y)=0$ (irreducible polynomial of genus $g$ over the field of residues mod $p$), D. A. Burgess [Mathematika **4** (1957), 106–112; MR **20** #28; J. London Math. Soc. **38** (1963), 253–256; MR **26** #6135] improved earlier estimates for $N_{\min}(D, \chi)$ and $d_{\max}(D, \chi)$. The author, using Burgess' method and a classical result of Siegel, obtains $P_{\min}(D, \chi) = O(D^{1/4+\varepsilon})$ ($\varepsilon>0$), the best result to date. The proof follows that in the joint paper of A. I. Vinogradov and the author [Dokl. Akad. Nauk SSSR **168** (1966), 259–261; MR **35** #125]. Several other remarks are contained in the paper; in particular, the author calls attention to the depth of Weil's estimate, which leads to results not implied even by the generalized Riemann hypothesis.

*E. Grosswald* (Philadelphia, Pa.)

Citations: MR 20# 28 = N68-28; MR 26# 6135 = L25-20; MR 35# 125 = N68-36.

## N72-39 (38# 2082)

**Williams, Kenneth S.**

**Note on pairs of consecutive residues of polynomials.**

*Canad. Math. Bull.* **11** (1968), 79–83.

Let $f(x)=a_0+a_1x+\cdots+a_dx^d$ be a polynomial with integral coefficients and of fixed degree $d$. Let $p$ be a prime and suppose $a_d \not\equiv 0 \pmod p$. The author considers the problem of estimating the least integer $e$ ($0 \leqq e \leqq p-1$) such that $e$ and $e+1$ are both residues of $f(x)$ mod $p$.

Improving some of his earlier results [in particular, Canad. J. Math. **19** (1967), 655–666; MR **35** #4194], he proves that there are constants $K_d$, $C_d$ depending only on $d$ such that for all primes $p \geqq C_d$, $e \leqq K_d p^{1/2}$.

The main result used is a lemma of E. Bombieri and H. Davenport [Amer. J. Math. **88** (1966), 61–70; MR **34** #167]. The author also uses a method used by A.

Tietäväinen [Ann. Univ. Turku. Ser. A I No. 94 (1966); MR **34** #7448] to improve the estimate for the least non-negative non-residue of $f(x)$ mod $p$ over that derived by Bombieri and Davenport from the same lemma.

*S. L. Segal* (Rochester, N.Y.)

Citations: MR 34# 167 = T25-24; MR 34# 7448 = N72-30; MR 35# 4194 = N72-32.

Referred to in N72-41.

## N72-40 (39# 1419)

**Norton, Karl K.**

**Upper bounds for $k$th power coset representatives modulo $n$.**

*Acta Arith.* **15** (1968/69), 161–179.

Let $n$ and $k$ be positive integers, let $C(n)$ denote the multiplicative group of the integers mod $n$ and prime to $n$. If $C_k(n)$ denotes the subgroup of $k$th powers and $\nu=\nu_k(n)$ is the index of $C_k(n)$ in $C(n)$, let $1=g_0(n,k)<g_1(n,k)<\cdots<g_{\nu-1}(n,k)$ be the least positive representative of the $\nu$ cosets of $C_k(n)$.

By using D. A. Burgess' recent estimates for character sums [Proc. London Math. Soc. (3) **12** (1962), 179–192; MR **24** #A2569; ibid. (3) **12** (1962), 193–206; MR **24** #A2570; ibid. (3) **13** (1963), 524–536; MR **26** #6133], some upper bounds for $g_m(n,k)$ $(0\leqq m\leqq\nu-1)$ are presented. It is observed that previous work on this problem was largely devoted to the cases when $n$ is prime, when $k$ is small (e.g., $k=2$, 3 or 5) and entirely to the cases $m=1$ or $\nu-1$.

*J. H. H. Chalk* (Toronto, Ont.)

Citations: MR 24# A2569 = L25-16; MR 24# A2570 = L25-17; MR 26# 6133 = L25-19.

Referred to in D80-78, N72-44, N72-55.

## N72-41 (39# 1433)

**Perel'muter, G. I.**

**A certain conjecture of K. Williams. (Russian)**

*Dokl. Akad. Nauk SSSR* **184** (1969), 282–284.

Let $p$ be a prime number and $f(x)$ be an arbitrary polynomial of degree $d$ with rational integer coefficients. Williams conjectured that, if $p$ is sufficiently large, there exists a least positive integer $m$ such that the congruences $f(x)\equiv m \pmod p$ and $f(x)\equiv m+1 \pmod p$ are both solvable with $m<(C\sqrt{p})\log p$, where $C$ is a constant depending only on $d$ [K. S. Williams, Canad. J. Math. **19** (1967), 655–666; MR **35** #4194]. He later proved this conjecture and obtained the better estimation $m<C\sqrt{p}$ [Canad. Math. Bull. **11** (1968), 79–83; MR **38** #2082]. The present author gives a generalization of this result as follows. Let $F(X)$ and $G(Y)$ be polynomials with integer coefficients, where $\deg F(X)=d$ and $\deg G(Y)=\delta$. If the polynomial $F(X)-G(Y)$ has only one factor which is absolutely irreducible over $Z/pZ$, then for all sufficiently large $p$ there exists a least positive integer $\nu$ such that $F(X)\equiv\nu \pmod p$ and $G(Y)\equiv\nu \pmod p$ are both solvable with $\nu<C\sqrt{p}$, where $C$ is a constant depending on $d$ and $\delta$ alone. By putting $G(Y)=F(Y)-1$ one obtains Williams' result. There is also given an analogous theorem on the least positive integer $\mu$ with the property that $F(X)\equiv\mu$ (mod $p$) is solvable but $G(Y)\equiv\mu$ (mod $p$) is not solvable.

{This article has appeared in English translation [Soviet Math. Dokl. **10** (1969), 67–69].}

*E. Inaba* (Tokyo)

Citations: MR 35# 4194 = N72-32; MR 38# 2082 = N72-39.

## N72-42 (39# 2696)

**Jordan, James H.**

**The distribution of $k$th power residues and non-residues in the Gaussian integers.**

*Tôhoku Math. J.* (2) **20** (1968), 498–510.

The estimates of I. M. Vinogradov [Ž. Fiz.-Mat. Obšč. (Perm) **1** (1918), 94–98; Trans. Amer. Math. Soc. **29** (1927), 209–217; ibid. **29** (1927), 218–226] and D. A. Burgess [Mathematika **4** (1957), 106–112; MR **20** #28; Proc. London Math. Soc. (3) **12** (1962), 179–192; MR **24** #A2569] for minimal non-residues are extended to the field of Gaussian integers.

*A. I. Vinogradov* (Leningrad)

Citations: MR 20# 28 = N68-28; MR 24# A2569 = L25-16.

## N72-43 (40# 1330)

**Brauer, Alfred**

**Combinatorial methods in the distribution of $k$th power residues. (With discussion)**

*Combinatorial Mathematics and its Applications (Proc. Conf., Univ. North Carolina, Chapel Hill, N.C., 1967), pp. 14–37. Univ. North Carolina Press, Chapel Hill, N.C.*, 1969.

This beautifully written expository paper is principally concerned with problems on the distribution of $k$th power residues that are amenable to combinatorial methods. The interaction between number theory and combinatorics is cogently developed. Especially noteworthy features of the paper are the illuminating historical comments and the excellent bibliography.

*A. L. Whiteman* (Los Angeles, Calif.)

## N72-44 (40# 4223)

**Norton, Karl K.**

**On the distribution of $k$th power residues and non-residues modulo $n$.**

*J. Number Theory* **1** (1969), 398–418.

Let $n$ and $k$ be positive integers with $n>1$, let $C(n)$ denote the multiplicative group consisting of the residue classes mod $n$ which are relatively prime to $n$, and let $C_k(n)$ denote the subgroup of $k$th powers. Write $\nu=\nu_k(n)=[C(n):C_k(n)]$, and let $1=g_0'<g_1<\cdots<g_{\nu-1}$ be the smallest positive representatives of the $\nu$ cosets of $C_k(n)$. In a previous paper [Acta Arith. **15** (1968/69), 161–179; MR **39** #1419] the author obtained various upper bounds for the $g_m$. In this paper he investigates the distribution of the members of $C(n)$ among the various cosets $g_sC_k(n)$. For example, he derives a number of asymptotic formulae for the number of $x$ satisfying $h+1\leqq x\leqq H$ and $x\in g_sC_k(n)$, where $h$, $H$ are integers with $0\leqq h<H$. As a consequence of one of these formulae he estimates the maximum number of consecutive members of $C(n)$ in the coset $g_sC_k(n)$.

For an arbitrary but fixed coset $g_sC_k(n)$, let $\alpha=\phi(n)/\nu$, and let $h_0<h_1<\cdots<h_\alpha$ be the $\alpha+1$ smallest positive members of this coset, so $h_\alpha=n+h_0$. Various estimates are given for the quantities $h_j$, $\max\{h_j-h_{j-1}: 1\leqq j\leqq\alpha\}$ and $\sum_{j=1}^{\alpha}(h_j-h_{j-1})^\beta$ $(\beta\geqq 1)$. Used in the estimation of the latter sum is the following character sum estimate due to Burgess: $\sum_{x=1}^{n}|\sum_{l=1}^{h}\chi(x+l)|^2\leqq nh\{d(n)\log n\}^2$, where $\chi$ is any non-principal residue character mod $n$, $h\geqq 1$, and $d(n)$ is the number of positive divisors of $n$.

The ideas used in this paper are based upon those of D. A. Burgess [Proc. London Math. Soc. (3) **13** (1963), 524–536; MR **26** #6133], developed for tackling problems of this type, and upon a method of C. Hooley [Acta Arith. **8** (1962/63), 343–347; MR **27** #5741].

{The editors have been informed that the abstract of this article was inadvertently omitted.}

*K. S. Williams* (Ottawa, Ont.)

Citations: MR 26# 6133 = L25-19; MR 27# 5741 = N28-50; MR 39# 1419 = N72-40.

**N72-45** **(40# 7194)**

**Jordan, James H.**

**Consecutive residues or non-residues in the Gaussian integers.**

*J. Number Theory* **1** (1969), 477–485.

Two Gaussian integers $\alpha$, $\beta$ are called consecutive if $|\alpha-\beta|=1$; $m$ Gaussian integers $\alpha_1, \cdots, \alpha_m$ are called consecutive if $|\alpha_1-\alpha_2|=1$ and $\alpha_1-\alpha_2=\alpha_j-\alpha_{j+1}$. The paper gives Gaussian analogues of results on $k$th power characters due to D. H. Lehmer and E. Lehmer [Proc. Amer. Math. Soc. **13** (1962), 102–106; MR **25** #2025], D. H. Lehmer, E. Lehmer and W. H. Mills [Canad. J. Math. **15** (1963), 172–177; MR **26** #3660] and D. H. Lehmer, E. Lehmer and J. L. Selfridge [Math. Comp. **16** (1962), 407–415; MR **28** #5578]. Let $\Lambda_G(k, m)$ be the least positive number such that in the circle $|z|\leqq\Lambda_G(k, m)$ there are $m$ consecutive Gaussian integers $\alpha_1, \cdots, \alpha_m$ with the property that $\chi(\alpha_j)=1$ for some $k$th power character $\chi$ modulo $p$ for all but a finite number of Gaussian primes $p$. $\Lambda_G^*(k, m)$ is defined analogously, the property $\chi(\alpha_j)=1$ being replaced by $\chi(\alpha_j)=\chi(\alpha_1)$. The values of $\Lambda_G(k, m)$ and $\Lambda_G^*(k, m)$ for all $m$ and $k$ except for $m=2$, $k>3$ and $m=3$, $k>2$ are given, e.g., $\Lambda_G(k, m)=\Lambda_G^*(k, m)=\infty$ for all $k$ and $m\geqq 4$; $\Lambda_G(2, 2)=\Lambda_G^*(2, 2)=2$, exceptional prime $1+i$.

*I. Danicic* (Aberystwyth)

Citations: MR 25# 2025 = N72-10; MR 26# 3660 = N72-13; MR 28# 5578 = N72-21.

**N72-46** **(41# 3443)**

**Mazur, L. E.**

**Consecutive residues and nonresidues of polynomials. (Russian)**

*Mat. Zametki* **7** (1970), 97–107.

For a polynomial $\phi(x, y)$ with coefficients from $Z_p$ ($Z_p$ denotes the field of residues mod $p$), let $\omega_p(\phi)$ denote the number of absolutely irreducible divisors of $\phi(x, y)$. For a function $f(x)-\varphi(y)=\phi(x, y)$ we use the notation $\omega_p(f, \varphi)$ instead of $\omega_p(\phi)$. We call the number $m$ an $f$-residue, if the congruence $f(x)\equiv m \pmod p$ is soluble. We call the number $\lambda>0$ a common-residue for the polynomials $f_1(x)$ and $f_2(x)$ when $\lambda$ is an $f_1$-residue and an $f_2$-residue too. The following assertions are proved. Theorem 1: Let $f_1(x)$ [$f_2(x)$] be polynomials of degree $d_1$ [$d_2$], $1\leqq d_1\leqq p-1$, $1\leqq d_2\leqq p-1$, $d=\max(d_1, d_2)$. If $\omega_p(f_1, f_2)\geqq 1$, then for every $N$ and $H\geqq c(d)p^{1/2}$ in the interval $[N+1, N+H]$, there exists a common-residue for $f_1(x)$ and $f_2(x)$. Theorem 2: Suppose that $\phi(x, y)$ has a linear-term and has no constant term. Then $\omega_p(\phi)\geqq 1$.

{This article has appeared in English translation [Math. Notes **7** (1970), 59–65].} *I. Kátai* (Budapest)

**N72-47** **(41# 6795)**

**Rabung, John R.**

**Preassigned character values in the Gaussian integers.**

*J. Number Theory* **2** (1970), 329–332.

Let $k$ be odd, let $\gamma_1, \gamma_2, \cdots, \gamma_t$ be distinct prime Gaussian integers, and let $\rho_1, \rho_2, \cdots, \rho_t$ be $k$th roots of unity. It is shown that there exists an infinite number of Gaussian prime numbers $\pi$ for which there is a $k$th power character $\chi$ satisfying $\chi(\gamma_i)=\rho_i$, $1\leqq i\leqq t$. Like the corresponding result for the rational case [the reviewer, Canad. J. Math. **15** (1963), 169–171; MR **28** #71], the proof is based on the Čebotarev density theorem.

*W. H. Mills* (Princeton, N.J.)

Citations: MR 28# 71 = N72-16.

**N72-48** **(41# 8332)**

**Singh, Sahib**

**Bounds of cubic residues in A.P.**

*Indian J. Pure Appl. Math.* **1** (1970), *no.* 2, 265–268.

Let $k$ and $d$ denote positive integers and let $p$ denote a prime $\equiv 1 \pmod 3$. The author defines $r(k, d, p)$ to be the least positive integer such that $r, r+d, r+2d, \cdots, r+(k-1)d$ are all cubic residues modulo $p$. He defines $\Lambda(k, d)=\limsup_{p\to\infty} r(k, d, p)$. M. Dunton [Proc. Amer. Math. Soc. **16** (1965), 330–332; MR **30** #3055] has proved $\Lambda(2, 1)=77$, $\Lambda(2, 2)\leqq 90$, $\Lambda(2, 5)\leqq 114$, $\Lambda(2, 6)\leqq 21$, $\Lambda(2, 7)=1$, $\Lambda(2, 8)\leqq 56$, $\Lambda(2, 9)\leqq 72$, and $\Lambda(2, d)=+\infty$ if $d\equiv\pm 3 \pmod 7$. The author claims to have proved in his Ph.D. Thesis ["Bounds of power residues in arithmetic progression", Ph.D. Thesis, Penn. State Univ., Univ. Park, Pa., 1968] that $\Lambda(2, 2)\leqq 25$. W. H. Mills [*Theory of numbers* (Proc. Sympos. Pure Math. Vol. VIII, Calif. Inst. Tech., Pasadena, Calif., 1963), pp. 170–174, Amer. Math. Soc., Providence, R.I., 1965; MR **31** #1226] has proved that $\Lambda(3, 1)=23532$. In this paper the author proves that $\Lambda(3, d)=\infty$ if $d\equiv\pm 2, \pm 3 \pmod 7$, $d\equiv\pm 2, \pm 3, \pm 4, \pm 6 \pmod{13}$ or $d\equiv\pm 2, \pm 3, \pm 4, \pm 5, \pm 6, \pm 9 \pmod{19}$. R. L. Graham [Proc. Amer. Math. Soc. **15** (1964), 196–197; MR **28** #2078] has proved that $\Lambda(4, 1)=\infty$. The author also discusses a function $\Lambda^*(k, d)$ defined in a way similar to $\Lambda(k, d)$.

*K. S. Williams* (Ottawa, Ont.)

Citations: MR 28# 2078 = N72-18; MR 30# 3055 = N72-24; MR 31# 1226 = N72-25.

**N72-49** **(41# 8381)**

**Jordan, James H.**

**The distribution of $k$-th power non-residues.**

*Duke Math. J.* **37** (1970), 333–340.

For a prime $p\equiv 1 \pmod k$, $k\geqq 2$, the reduced residue system $S$, modulo $p$, is a multiplicative group and has a proper multiplicative subgroup $R_k$ consisting of the $k$th power residues modulo $p$. The $k-1$ cosets formed with respect to $R_k$, say $N^1, N^2, \cdots, N^{k-1}$, are called classes of $k$th power non-residues modulo $p$. If $\alpha_1, \alpha_2, \cdots, \alpha_{k-1}$ are the smallest positive integers in $N^1, N^2, \cdots, N^{k-1}$, respectively, then a bound $f(k, p)$ is sought such that $\alpha_i\leqq f(k, p)$ for $i=1, 2, \cdots, k-1$. The smallest function is desirable. The author establishes that for any $\varepsilon>0$, $p^{(1-d)/4+\varepsilon}$ is an upper bound when $p>P_\varepsilon$, and where $d$, which depends on $k$, is a positive constant expressed as the solution of an equation involving sums of multiple integrals with variable limits of integration.

The purpose of this paper is to formulate the process for generating the $d$'s for each $k$. As an example of the magnitude of improvement, the $d(4)$ of H. Davenport and P. Erdős [Publ. Math. Debrecen **2** (1952), 252–265; MR **14**, 1063] is approximately .000000017 while the $d$ for 4 implicit in the theorem of this paper is larger than .025.

*S. Ikehara* (Tokyo)

**N72-50** **(42# 4478)**

**Perel'muter, G. I.**

**The smallest non-residue of a polynomial along an algebraic curve. (Russian)**

*Studies in Number Theory, No.* 3 (*Russian*), *pp.* 64–68. *Izdat. Saratov. Univ., Saratov,* 1969.

Let $f(X, Y)$ and $F(X, Y)$ be polynomials with rational integral coefficients and of degrees $d$, $\delta$, respectively. Then there is a constant $C$ depending only on $d$ and $\delta$ such that for all sufficiently large rational primes $p$ there exists an integer in the range $1\leqq m\leqq Cp^{1/2}$ for which there is no solution of the pair of congruences $f(X, Y)\equiv 0 \pmod p$, $F(X, Y)\equiv m \pmod p$, provided that the following conditions are satisfied: (i) the curve $\Gamma: f(X, Y)=0$ is absolutely irreducible, (ii) the curve $f(X, Y)=0, f(U, Z)=0$, $F(X, Y)=F(U, Z)$ is not contained in the diagonal of $\Gamma\times\Gamma$ and (iii) $F(X, Y)$ is not constant on $f(X, Y)=0$.

The proof uses E. Bombieri's results about the estimation of trigonometric sums along a curve [Amer. J. Math. **88** (1966), 71–105; MR **34** #166] and follows the method of Bombieri and H. Davenport [ibid. **88** (1966), 61–70; MR **34** #167] as modified by A. Tietäväinen [Ann. Univ. Turku. Ser. A I No. 94 (1966); MR **34** #7448].

*J. W. S. Cassels* (Cambridge, England)

Citations: MR 34# 166 = T25-23; MR 34# 167 = T25-24; MR 34# 7448 = N72-30.

## N72-51 (43# 3202)

**Rabung, J. R.; Jordan, J. H.**

**Consecutive power residues or nonresidues.**

*Math. Comp.* **24** (1970), 737–740.

For natural numbers $k$ and $l$ the number $\Lambda^*(k, l)$ is the smallest number $\alpha$ such that the following holds for all primes $p$ except for a finite number of exceptional primes: for every $k$th power character $\chi$ (mod $p$) there exists an $a<\alpha$ such that $\chi(a)=\chi(a+1)=\cdots=\chi(a+l-1)$.

For various pairs $(k, l)$ the value of $\Lambda^*(k, l)$ is known. Here it is stated that $\Lambda^*(8, 2)=399$, exceptional prime 2, and $\Lambda^*(3, 3)=2499$, exceptional primes 2, 3, 7, 13 and 19. This result was obtained with the aid of an IBM 360 model 67 computer; an outline of the method of programming is given. *I. Danicic* (Aberystwyth)

## N72-52 (43# 4773)

**Elliott, P. D. T. A.**

**The distribution of power residues and certain related results.**

*Acta Arith.* **17** (1970), 141–159.

The author continues his investigations in two earlier papers [same Acta **13** (1967/68), 131–149; MR **36** #3741; ibid. **14** (1967/68), 153–162; MR **37** #4000]. Let $k>1$ and $r$ be positive rational integers, and let $a_1, a_2, \cdots, a_r$ be $r$ further integers. These need not necessarily be distinct. Let $M$ denote the least common multiple of the $a_j$ ($j=1, 2, \cdots, r$). Further, let $\varepsilon_1, \varepsilon_2, \cdots, \varepsilon_r$ be $r$ $k$th roots of unity, and let $Q_k$ be the cyclotomic field generated by $\sqrt[k]{1}$ and $\bar{Q}_k$ its ring of algebraic integers.

Define $N(k, r)$ by

$$N(k, r) = \sum_{\substack{\nu_1=1 \\ \alpha_1^{\nu_1}\alpha_2^{\nu_2}\cdots\alpha_r^{\nu_r}=\beta^k}}^{k} \cdots \sum_{\nu_r=1}^{k} (\varepsilon_1^{\nu_1}\varepsilon_2^{\nu_2}\cdots\varepsilon_r^{\nu_r})^{-1},$$

where in the summation condition $\beta$ is an algebraic integer in $Q_k$. For each real number $x$ let

$$S(x, k, r) = S(x, k; a_1, a_2, \cdots, a_r; \varepsilon_1, \varepsilon_2, \cdots, \varepsilon_r)$$

be the number of prime ideals $\mathfrak{p}$ of $\bar{Q}_k$ satisfying $N\mathfrak{p}\leqq x$ for which the relations $(a_j/\mathfrak{p})_k=\varepsilon_j$ ($j=1, 2, \cdots, r$) are satisfied. The author gives estimates for the difference $S(x, k, r)-k^{-r}N(k, r)\pi(x)$, $\pi(x)$ denoting the number of rational primes not exceeding the real number $x$. As an example we quote one of his estimates: $O(x\exp(-c_1\sqrt{\log x}))$ if $k$ is odd and $M$ does not exceed $\exp(c_2\sqrt{\log x})$.

Now let $p\equiv 1 \pmod k$ and define $n_k(p)$ to be the least positive integer which is not a $k$th-power residue (mod $p$). For other primes we set $n_k(p)=0$. By means of the result just mentioned the author proves that for odd values of $k$ there are two positive constants $\alpha$ and $c_k$ so that $(\pi(x))^{-1}\sum_{p\leq x} n_k(p)=c_k+O(\exp(-\log x)^{\alpha})$.

Other applications of his estimates are also suggested. Finally the author makes some remarks concerning an old conjecture of Artin, stating that the rational primes for which the integer 2 is a primitive root have a positive limiting frequency amongst the sequence of all rational primes.

The proofs are quite complicated. Use is made of methods and results from various parts of number theory.

*W. Ljunggren* (Oslo)

Citations: MR 36# 3741 = N72-33; MR 37# 4000 = N72-37.

Referred to in A14-81.

## N72-53 (43# 7401)

**Elliott, P. D. T. A.**

**The least prime $k$-th-power residue.**

*J. London Math. Soc.* (2) **3** (1971), 205–210.

Let $k$ be a positive integer and $p$ a prime satisfying $p\equiv 1 \bmod k$. Denote by $r_k(p)$ the least prime that is a $k$-th power residue mod $p$; otherwise let $r_k(p)=0$. The author proves that $r_k(p)=O(p^{(k-1)/4+\varepsilon})$ for any fixed $\varepsilon>0$. This estimate and its proof generalize a theorem by A. I. Vinogradov and Ju. V. Linnik [Dokl. Akad. Nauk SSSR **168** (1966), 259–261; MR **35** #125] in the case $k=2$. From this result it follows that $\sum_{p\leq x} r_k(p)/\sum_{p\leq x} 1\to e_k$ ($k=2$, 3, 4) as $x\to\infty$, with suitable constants $e_k$. For odd $k$ slightly sharper results can be obtained.

*J. Kubilius* (Vilnius)

Citations: MR 35# 125 = N68-36.

## N72-54 (44# 3946)

**Burde, Klaus**

**Verteilungseigenschaften von Potenzresten.**

*J. Reine Angew. Math.* **249** (1971), 133–172.

In der vorliegenden Arbeit werden Fragen der Verteilung von Potenzresten diskutiert. Die erzielten Resultate ergeben sich im wesentlichen aus dem Satz: Sei $p$ eine ungerade Primzahl; $C_p$ sei die Charaktergruppe der Gruppe der teilerfremden Restklassen modulo $p$. Man bezeichne mit $\varepsilon$ den Hauptcharakter und setze, wie üblich, für $\chi\in C_p$ $\chi(a)=0$, falls $p|a$. Ferner sei $\gamma(\chi)$ eine feste zu $\chi$ gehörige Gaußsche Summe, wobei für alle $\chi\in C_p$ dieselbe primitive $p$-te Einheitswurzel gewählt wird. Dann stellt die Zuordnung $\tilde{A}(\chi)=(\chi(k-i)/\gamma(\chi)+1/p)$ falls $\chi\neq\varepsilon$, $\tilde{A}(\chi)=(\delta_{ik})=E$ falls $\chi=\varepsilon$ ($i, k=0, \cdots, p-1$) einen Homomorphismus von $C_p$ in die $p$-reihigen Matrizen dar: $\tilde{A}(\chi\cdot\psi)=\tilde{A}(\chi)\tilde{A}(\psi)$, außerdem $\tilde{A}(\chi)\tilde{A}^*(\chi)=E$, das heißt, es handelt sich hierbei um eine unitäre Darstellung der Gruppe $C_p$ vom Range $p$.

Der Charakter $\chi\in C_p$ habe die Ordnung $n$; es sei $\eta$ eine feste primitive $n$-te Einheitswurzel, $\lambda$ eine ganze Zahl mit $p\nmid\lambda$. Sei $\alpha_{ik}{}^{\lambda}$ die Anzahl der Paare $\nu, \nu+\lambda$ mit $\chi(\nu)=\eta^i$, $\chi(\nu+\lambda)=\eta^k$, wobei $\nu$ ein volles Restsystem modulo $p$ durchläuft. Mit Hilfe der obigen Matrizendarstellung gelingt es dem Autor, für die $\alpha_{ik}{}^{\lambda}$ ($i, k=0, \cdots, n-1$) ein lineares Gleichungssystem anzugeben, aus welchem diese bestimmt werden können. Allerdings muß man hierzu die Zerlegungen $p=\omega_n\bar{\omega}_n$ kennen, $\omega_n\in\mathbf{Q}(\eta)$. Im Falle $n=3$ werden die erforderlichen Rechnungen explizit durchgeführt.

In der zweiten Hälfte der Arbeit werden weitere Verteilungseigenschaften von Werten von Restklassencharakteren modulo $p$ aus der Tatsache gefolgert, daß die obige Matrizendarstellung unitär ist. Hierbei handelt es sich auch um Weiterführungen von Untersuchungen aus einer früheren Arbeit des Autors [Math. Z. **105** (1968), 150–152; MR **38** #2080]. *W. G. H. Schaal* (Marburg)

Citations: MR 38# 2080 = N68-38.

## N72-55 (44# 3948)

**Norton, Karl K.**

**Numbers with small prime factors, and the least $k$th power non-residue.**

Memoirs of the American Mathematical Society, No. 106.

*American Mathematical Society, Providence, R.I.*, 1971. ii+106 *pp.* \$2.10.

To describe the essential results of this instructive memoir, first some notation. Let $n$ and $k$ be positive integers. Denote by $\nu-1$ the number of incongruent $k$th power non-residues mod $n$ that are prime to $n$, and by $g(n, k)$ the least positive $k$th power non-residue mod $n$ that is prime to $n$. It is assumed that $g(n, k)$ exists, i.e., that $\nu\geqq 2$. Also, for real $x$ and $y$ with $x\geqq 1$ and $y\geqq 0$, consider the function

$\psi_n(x, y)$ defined to be the number of integers $m$ such that $1 \leqq m \leqq x$, $(m, n)=1$ and $m$ has no prime factor greater than $y$. If in addition the $m$ are restricted to the residue class mod $n$ of an integer $l$, their number is denoted by $B_1(n, x, y)$. In the sequel $O_{\delta,\varepsilon,\cdots}$ $[O]$ indicates an implied constant that depends at most on $\delta, \varepsilon, \cdots$ [is absolute].

In the first section of the treatise the author gives a rapid comprehensive survey of the literature on the functions $B_1$ and $\psi_n$ and points out errors in several papers. This seems worthwhile, since previous investigations are numerous and many different notations and techniques have been used in obtaining a variety of results (some of them incorrect).

In the second section the author derives asymptotic formulae for $B_1$. Both the main result and the method of proof are essentially due to V. Ramaswami [Proc. Amer. Math. Soc. **2** (1951), 318–319; MR **13**, 14], whose presentation was sketchy, however.

In the third section the asymptotic formulae for $B_1$ are used to obtain corresponding formulae for $\psi_n(x, y)$. The conditions for $x$ and $y$ and the remainder terms that are considered are such that they suffice for later application to $g(n, k)$. For example, it is proved that

$$\psi_n(x, x^{1/\alpha}) = n^{-1}\varphi(n)\rho(\alpha)x+\varphi(n)b(n)\rho(\alpha-1)(x/\log x) + O(\{\rho(\alpha-3)\xi(n)+\alpha n/\varphi(n)\}(x/\log^2 x)+2^{\omega(n)}x^{1-1/\alpha})$$

for $3<\alpha\leqq\sqrt{\log x}$ with no restriction on $n$. Here $\varphi(n)$ is Euler's function, $\omega(n)$ the number of distinct prime factors of $n$, $\rho(\alpha)$ Dickman's function,

$$b(n) = n^{-1}\{1-\gamma-\textstyle\sum_{p\mid n}(p-1)^{-1}\log p\} = O(\log\log(3n)/\varphi(n)),$$

$\gamma$ Euler's constant and

$$\xi(n) = (n/\varphi(n))\{(\textstyle\sum_{p\mid n}p^{-1}\log p)^2+\sum_{p\mid n}p^{-1}\log^2 p\} = O(\{\log\log(3n)\}^3).$$

In the fourth section the author gets as corollaries of his main results on $\psi_n$ and some of his previous work [Acta Arith. **15** (1968/69), 161–179; MR **39** #1419] two estimates for $g(n, k)$ that can be formulated as follows. Let $w$ be an integer with $\nu\geqq w\geqq 2$ and $\alpha_w$ the unique root of the equation $\rho(\alpha)=w^{-1}$; then for each $\delta>0$, (1) $g(n, k)=O_{w,\delta}(n^{3/(8\alpha_w)+\delta})$ in all cases, while if $n$ is cubefree or $k$ is odd and squarefree the stronger statement (2) $g(n, k)=O_{w,\delta}(n^{1/(4\alpha_w)+\delta})$ holds. (In fact, (2) is proved under more general conditions.) (1) and (2) generalize results of Wang Yuan [Shuxue Jinzhan **7** (1964), 78–83; MR **37** #5162], who essentially obtained (2) in the case when $n$ is a prime. One gets a feeling for the magnitude of the exponents of $n$ in (1) and (2), if one observes that $\alpha_2=e^{\frac{1}{2}}$, $\alpha_3=e^{\frac{2}{3}}$ and $\alpha_w\to\infty$ for $w\to\infty$. However the constants implied by the $O$-symbols are not explicit.

In the fifth section the author takes up the question of explicit upper bounds for $g(n, k)$ when $n$ is a prime $p>2$. First he gives a surprisingly short simple proof for the estimates $g(p, k)\leqq\sqrt{(p-\frac{3}{4})}+\frac{1}{2}$ or $\leqq\sqrt{(p-1)}$ for $(k, (p-1)/2)=1$ or $>1$, respectively, thus generalizing slightly results of A. Brauer and R. L. Reynolds [Canad. J. Math. **3** (1951), 367–374; MR **14**, 21]. Furthermore he shows that an estimate due to I. M. Vinogradov [Trans. Amer. Math. Soc. **29** (1927), 218–226] can be sharpened to $g(p, k)<(\sqrt{(p)}\log p)^{\beta}$, where

$$\beta = \exp\{-1+\nu^{-1}+6/\log p+20/\log^2 p\}.$$

Finally, he applies a method of D. A. Burgess [J. London Math. Soc. **38** (1963), 253–256; MR **26** #6135] and estimates of character sums by the latter to deduce $g(p, k)\leqq 4.7\,p^{\frac{1}{4}}\log p$, where the constant 4.7 can be replaced by 3.9 if $(k, (p-1)/2)>1$.

The memoir concludes with a specific estimate of $\omega(n)$, namely $\omega(n)<(\log n)/(\log\log n-1.4)$, for all integers $n\geqq 58$. This is shown to be a consequence of B. Rosser's theorem on the $n$th prime [Proc. London Math. Soc. (2) **45** (1938), 21–44]. *O. H. Körner* (Ulm)

Citations: MR 13, 14f = N28-24; MR 14, 21a = A10-8; MR 26# 6135 = L25-20; MR 37# 5162 = R14-73; MR 39# 1419 = N72-40.

## N76 DISTRIBUTION OF INTEGERS IN SPECIAL RESIDUE CLASSES: PRIMITIVE ROOTS

See also reviews B44-12, B44-44, M20-36, M55-32, M55-52, N32-20, N36-13, N68-44, N72-52, P48-1, R02-60, R46-25, T25-26, T30-4, Z30-37.

**N76-1** **(4, 130d)**

**Hua, Loo-keng. On the least primitive root of a prime.** Bull. Amer. Math. Soc. **48**, 726–730 (1942).

Let $g(p)$ denote the least positive primitive root of a prime $p$, and $h(p)$ the numerically least such root. It is proved that $|h(p)|<2^m p^{\frac{1}{2}}$, where $m$ denotes the number of different prime factors of $p-1$; hence if $p\equiv 1 \pmod 4$, $|g(p)|<2^m p^{\frac{1}{2}}$; if $p\equiv 3 \pmod 4$, $|g(p)|<2^{m+1}p^{\frac{1}{2}}$. This is better than a result by Vinogradow [C. R. (Doklady) Acad. Sci. URSS. Ser. A. **1930**, 7–11 (1930)]. The proof employs an average of character sums, for example, proving that

$$(A+1)^{-1}\Big|\sum_{a=0}^{A}\sum_{n=-a}^{a}\chi(n)\Big|\leqq p^{\frac{1}{2}}-(A+1)p^{-\frac{1}{2}},$$

and then manipulates the identity

$$0=\sum_{k\mid p-1}(\mu(k)/\phi(k))\sum_{\chi(k)}\sum_{a=0}^{|h(p)|-1}\sum_{n=-a}^{a}\chi^{(k)}(n),$$

valid when $n$ is not a primitive root mod $p$. *G. Pall.*

Referred to in D12-3, F05-4, L25-1, N76-3.

**N76-2** **(6, 36g)**

**Pillai, S. S. On the smallest primitive root of a prime.** J. Indian Math. Soc. (N.S.) **8**, 14–17 (1944).

The author proves that for infinitely many primes $p$ the least primitive root of $p$ is greater than $c\log\log p$. *P. Erdös* (Princeton, N. J.).

**N76-3** **(6, 170b)**

**Erdös, P. On the least primitive root of a prime $p$.** Bull. Amer. Math. Soc. **51**, 131–132 (1945).

The best result on the size of the least primitive root $g$ of a prime $p$ is that of Hua, who proved that $g<2^{m+1}p^{\frac{1}{2}}$, where $m$ denotes the number of different prime factors of $p-1$ [Bull. Amer. Math. Soc. **48**, 726–730 (1942); these Rev. **4**, 130]. Using the method of Brun, the author proves that $g<p^{\frac{1}{2}}(\log p)^{17}$ for large $p$. It is pointed out that this is better than Hua's result if $m$ is large, but worse if $m$ is small. *H. W. Brinkmann* (Swarthmore, Pa.).

Citations: MR 4, 130d = N76-1.

**N76-4** **(11, 328d)**

**Schwarz, Štefan. On the reducibility of binomial congruences and on the bound of the least integer belonging to a given exponent** mod $p$. Časopis Pěst. Mat. Fys. **74**, 1–16 (1949). (English. Czech summary)

The author considers the factorization of $x^n - a$ into irreducible polynomials (mod $p$), and gives an explicit formula for the number of irreducible polynomial factors of degree $k$. Some applications of the formula are made, and generalizations to the finite field $[p^f]$ are indicated. The author generalizes a result of Vinogradov by proving that if $l$ divides $p-1$, the least integer (mod $p$) which belongs to the exponent $l$ is $O(l^{\epsilon-1}p^{\frac{1}{2}})$. He generalizes similarly a result due to the reviewer [Quart. J. Math., Oxford Ser. **8**, 308–312 (1937)]. *H. Davenport* (London).

Referred to in T05-6.

**N76-5** **(13, 209a)**

**Vinogradov, I. M. An arithmetical method applied to questions of the distribution of numbers with a given property of the index.** Izvestiya Akad. Nauk SSSR. Ser. Mat. **15**, 297–308 (1951). (Russian)

Let $q$ be a prime, and $n$ a divisor of $q-1$. The author defines $\sigma_r(x)$ to be $1-n^{-1}$ if the index of $x$ (relative to a fixed primitive root mod $q$) is congruent to $r$ (mod $n$), and to be $-n^{-1}$ if it is not. This defines $\sigma_r(x)$ for all $x$ not divisible by $q$, and the definition is completed by putting $\sigma_r(x)=0$ for $x\equiv 0$ (mod $q$). The function $\sigma_r(x)$ is periodic in $x$ with period $q$, and periodic in $r$ with period $n$, and the sum of its values over either period is 0. Theorem 1 of the present paper relates to the sum $S=\sum_{x=M+1}^{M+Q}\sigma_r(x)$, where $q^{\frac{1}{2}}<Q<\frac{1}{2}q$. If $h=Qq^{-\frac{1}{2}}$, it is proved that $|S|<q^{\frac{1}{2}}(a\log h+2.5)$, where $a=2(\log 27)^{-1}$. The proof is entirely elementary, and is almost the same as that already indicated by the author in the second half of a recent note [Doklady Akad. Nauk SSSR **73**, 635–638 (1950); these Rev. **12**, 161]. The only difference is that the present proof is expressed in terms of $\sigma_r(x)$ instead of in terms of Dirichlet characters. Theorem 2 relates to a double sum over both $x$ and $r$ in the case when $n=q-1$. Let $W=\sum_{x=M+1}^{M+Q}\sum_{r=N+1}^{N+Z}\sigma_r(x)$, where $q^{\frac{1}{2}}<Q<\frac{1}{2}q$, $n^{\frac{1}{2}}<Z<\frac{1}{2}n$. Then

$$|W|<q^{\frac{1}{2}}(a\log h+2.5)(a\log t+2.5),$$

where $h=Qq^{-\frac{1}{2}}$, $t=Zn^{-\frac{1}{2}}$. The proof is of a similar character to that of Theorem 1. Finally, Theorem 3 concerns the sum $\sum_{p\leq N}\sigma_r(p+k)$, where $p$ runs through primes, and $k\not\equiv 0$ (mod $q$). If $N\geqq 55$, it is proved that the sum is $O(N^{1+\epsilon}\{q^{-1}+qN^{-1}+N^{-\frac{1}{3}}\}^{\frac{1}{2}})$. This result is similar to one proved earlier by the author [same Izvestiya Ser. Mat. **7**, 17–34 (1943); these Rev. **5**, 143], but the proof now given is entirely elementary. The proof depends on Lemma 6 of the paper last quoted, and also on lemmas relating to sums of the form $\sum\sum\xi(x)\eta(y)\sigma_r(xy+k)$, where $\xi(x)$ and $\eta(y)$ are bounded functions, and summation is over the region defined by $U<x\leqq U'$ $(\leqq 2U)$, $xy\leqq N$. *H. Davenport* (London).

Citations: MR 5, 143a = L20-6; MR 12, 161b = L25-3.

**N76-6** **(14, 538a)**

**Hasse, Helmut. Über die Artinsche Vermutung und verwandte Dichtefragen.** Ann. Acad. Sci. Fennicae. Ser. A. I. Math.-Phys. no. **116**, 17 pp. (1952).

Suppose that $M$ is the set of all primes for which a given integer $a$ $(\neq 0, \neq\pm 1)$ is a primitive root. Let $k_q$ denote $q(q-1)$ if $a$ is not a $q$th power, and $q-1$ if $a$ is a $q$th power, $q$ a prime. Then Artin conjectured that $M$ should have the Dirichlet density $\omega(M)=\prod_q(1-1/k_q)$ by virtue of an analogue to infinite product theorems in the theory of probabilities. Now let $K_q$ denote the normal field which is generated by $a^{1/q}$ and the $q$th roots of unity; furthermore, suppose that $\zeta_{a,q}(s)$ denotes the $\zeta$-function of $K_q$, in which the factors $(1-N(\mathfrak{p})^{-s})^{-1}$ for primes $\mathfrak{p}$ of $K_q$ dividing $a$ or $q$ are omitted. The author shows that Artin's conjecture will be proved if the sum $\sum_q(1/k_q)[\log\zeta_{a,q}(s)/\log\zeta(s)]$ can be shown to be uniformly convergent for $1<s\leqq s_0$, where $\zeta(s)$ is the $\zeta$-function of the rational number field. Furthermore, the author presents H. Bilharz' proof [Math. Ann. **114**, 476–492 (1937)] (using A. Weil's proof of the Riemann Hypothesis for function fields) of the corresponding conjecture for function fields. Finally he discusses an unpublished result of H. W. Knobloch which is related to Artin's conjecture, namely, that the set of all primes $p$ for which $p-1$ is squarefree has the density $\prod_q(1-1/q(q-1))$. *O. F. G. Schilling* (Chicago, Ill.).

**N76-7** **(16, 570d)**

**Brauer, Alfred. Elementary estimates for the least primitive root.** Studies in mathematics and mechanics presented to Richard von Mises, pp. 20–29. Academic Press Inc., New York, 1954. $9.00.

Using purely elementary methods the author obtains estimates for the least positive primitive root and the number of primitive roots (mod $p^h$) which are less than $p$. The following two results are typical. 1. Let $p$ be a prime of the form $4n+1$ and $k$ the number of different prime divisors of $p-1$. Put $r=2^k$. If $g_0$ is the smallest positive primitive root (mod $p$) then $g_0<p^{(r-1)/r}$. 2. For an odd prime $p$ there are at least $\frac{1}{2}\varphi(p-1)$ primitive roots (mod $p^h$) which are less than $p$. *W. Simons* (Vancouver, B. C.).

**N76-8** **(18, 642e)**

**Carlitz, L. Sets of primitive roots.** Compositio Math. **13** (1956), 65–70.

Let $f_1(x), \cdots, f_r(x)$ be polynomials (mod $p$), which are square-free and relatively prime in pairs. Let $N_r$ denote the number of integers $x$ (mod $p$) for which each of $f_1(x), \cdots, f_r(x)$ is a primitive root (mod $p$). Then, provided $r$ is fixed and the degrees of the polynomials are fixed, it is shown that

$$p^{r-1}N_r\{\varphi(p-1)\}^{-r}\to 1 \text{ as } p\to\infty$$

through primes. Some variations on this result are also proved. The proofs are straightforward: Satz 496 of Landau's Vorlesungen über Zahlentheorie [Bd. 2, Hirzel, Leipzig, 1927] together with the reviewer's estimates for character sums [Acta Math. **71** (1939), 99–121; MR **1**, 41], or the deeper results of André Weil [Proc. Nat. Acad. Sci. U.S.A. **27** (1941), 345–347; MR **2**, 345] which superseded them, could be used. *H. Davenport* (London).

Citations: MR 1, 41e = T25-1; MR 2, 345b = G20-3.

Referred to in K30-17.

**N76-9** **(20# 3830)**

**Erdös, Paul; and Shapiro, Harold N. On the least primitive root of a prime.** Pacific J. Math. **7** (1957), 861–865.

Let $g(p)$ be the positive least primitive root mod $p$. The authors prove that $g(p)=O(m^cp^{\frac{1}{2}})$, where $c$ is a constant and $m$ is the number of distinct prime factors of $p-1$. They use Brun's method and the following lemma concerning character sums. Let $\chi(n)$ be a non-principal character, mod $p$; then $|\sum\chi(u+v)|\leqq(pN(U)N(V))^{\frac{1}{2}}$, where $u$ and $v$ run over the sets $U$ and $V$ of distinct integers mod $p$, and $N(U)$, $N(V)$ are the number of integers in the sets. *L. K. Hua* (Peking)

Referred to in N76-12.

**N76-10** **(22# 4659)**

**Wang, Yuan. On the least primitive root of a prime.** Acta Math. Sinica **9** (1959), 432–441. (Chinese)

Let $p$ be a prime, $g(p)$ its smallest primitive root; let

further $w(n)$ be the number of distinct prime factors of $n$, and $m = w(p-1)$. The author proves that $g(p) = O(p^{\frac{1}{4}+\varepsilon})$ ($\varepsilon > 0$), and that, if the Riemann hypothesis holds, even $g(p) = O(m^6(\log p)^2)$. Both results are important improvements on what was known. The proofs of these theorems are based on the following two theorems: (A) Let $0 < \delta \leq \frac{1}{6}$. If $p > P(\delta)$ and $H > p^{\frac{1}{4}+\delta}$, then for every positive integer $N$ we have $|\sum_{n=N+1}^{N+H} \chi(n)| < H/p^{\eta}$, where $\eta = \delta^2/6$ and $\chi$ is a character (mod $p$) distinct from the principal one; (B) if the Riemann hypothesis holds and $\chi$ is not the principal character,

$$\sum_{n=1}^{\infty} \Lambda(n)\chi(n)e^{-n/x} = O(x^{1/2} \log p).$$

*K. Mahler* (Manchester)

Referred to in N76-11.

## N76-11 (24# A702)

**Wang, Yuan**

**On the least primitive root of a prime.**

*Sci. Sinica* **10** (1961), 1–14.

An English version of a paper previously published in Chinese [Acta Math. Sinica **9** (1959), 432–441; MR **22** #4659].

Citations: MR 22# 4659 = N76-10.

Referred to in N76-20.

## N76-12 (24# A1894)

**Wang, Yuan**

**A note on the least primitive root of a prime.**

*Sci. Record (N.S.)* **3** (1959), 174–179.

Verfasser beweist die folgende Verschärfung eines Resultates von D. A. Burgess [Mathematika **4** (1957), 106–112; MR **20** #28]. Zu gegebenen $\delta > 0$, $A > 0$ existiert ein $P = P(\delta, A)$, so daß $|\sum_{n=N+1}^{N+H} \chi(n)| < H/\log^A p$ für alle $p > P$, $H > p^{1/4+\delta}$ und ganzzahliges $N$ und jeden Nichthauptcharakter $\chi$ mod $p$. In Verbindung mit der Brunschen Methode ergibt sich hieraus für die kleinste positive primitive Wurzel $g(p)$ der Primzahl $p$ mit einer nur von $\varepsilon$ abhängigen $O$-Konstanten $g(p) = O(p^{1/4+\varepsilon})$. Dies verbessert das Resultat $g(p) = O(m^c p^{1/2})$, $m$ = Anzahl der Primteiler von $p-1$, von Erdös und Shapiro [Pacific J. Math. **7** (1957), 861–865; MR **20** #3830]. Unter Annahme der erweiterten Riemannschen Vermutung folgt über Ankeny [Ann. of Math. (2) **55** (1952), 65–72; MR **13**, 538] hinaus $g(p) = O(m^6 \log^2 p)$.

*H.-E. Richert* (Zbl **86**, 34)

Citations: MR 13, 538c = N68-13; MR 20# 28 = N68-28; MR 20# 3830 = N76-9.

## N76-13 (26# 2409)

**Lehmer, D. H.; Lehmer, Emma**

**Heuristics, anyone?**

*Studies in mathematical analysis and related topics, pp.* 202–210. *Stanford Univ. Press, Stanford, Calif.,* 1962.

From the authors' introduction: "Heuristic reasoning has been applied recently by Professor Pólya [Amer. Math. Monthly **66** (1959), 375–384; MR **21** #3392] to questions of densities of pairs of primes differing by a given constant. Such methods can also be used to study densities of primes having other interesting properties. It is the purpose of this paper to indicate how this kind of reasoning can be applied to questions having to do with primitive roots and, more generally, with numbers having a given residue index, thus serving to make plausible certain data that heretofore seemed to be chaotic or mysteriously irregular."

*T. Estermann* (London)

Citations: MR 21# 3392 = A46-23.

## N76-14 (26# 7128)

**Lehmer, D. H.**

**A note on primitive roots.**

*Scripta Math.* **26** (1963), 117–119.

It was conjectured by Artin that if the integer $g$ is not a power of some other integer, then approximately three-eighths of all primes will have $g$ for a primitive root. The conjecture requires modification for small $g$. The purpose of the present paper is to indicate that for some $g$'s there exist constants $c_g$ such that primes of the form $gn^2 + c_g$ have a much higher probability than 3/8 of having $g$ for a primitive root. The author limits himself to the cases $g = 10$ and 326. Numerical evidence suggests that about 87% of the primes $10n^2 + 7$ admit 10 as a primitive root. A heuristic explanation is given. Next, almost every prime of the form $326n^2 + 3$ seems to have 326 for a primitive root. In view of this it is of some interest to find the first prime $p = 326n^2 + 3$ for which 326 is not a primitive root. The author reports that there is no such prime less than $10^7$.

*L. Carlitz* (Durham, N.C.)

## N76-15 (26# 7129)

**Brenner, C.; Brenner, J. L.**

**The popularity of small integers as primitive roots.**

*Numer. Math.* **4** (1962), 336–342.

Cunningham in 1913 and Artin in 1930 conjectured that if $m$ is not a power, about 37 percent of all primes will have $m$ as a primitive root. Experiments made by the reviewer in 1958 showed that this conjecture requires modification since nearly 45 percent of all primes examined have $-3$ for a primitive root. For the general modulus $n$ one may consider what the authors call a $\lambda$-root, namely, an integer $m$ whose exponent modulo $n$ is the maximum possible for that $n$. The authors investigate for the first time the popularity of small integers $m$ as $\lambda$-roots modulo $n$ for the modest range $n = 3(1)3801$, for $m = -9(1)-2, 2(1)8$. The contest is won by 5 with a 45 percent score. Runners-up are $-7$, 7, $-5$, 5 and $-3$, the last having now a score of barely 38 percent. There is some discussion of ground rules for the event. For the benefit of those who may wish to extend these data, a complete program of the routine is given in ALGOL.

*D. H. Lehmer* (Berkeley, Calif.)

## N76-16 (32# 4111)

**Hasse, Helmut**

**Über die Dichte der Primzahlen $p$, für die eine vorgegebene ganzrationale Zahl $a \neq 0$ von durch eine vorgegebene Primzahl $l \neq 2$ teilbarer bzw. unteilbarer Ordnung mod. $p$ ist.**

*Math. Ann.* **162** (1965/66), 74–76.

For a fixed prime number $l \neq 2$ and a fixed rational integer $a \neq 0$, let $A$ denote the set of all prime numbers $p$, $p \nmid al$, such that the order of the residue class of $a$ mod $p$ is divisible by $l$. In the present paper, the author determines the Dirichlet density $\Delta(A)$ of the set $A$ as follows. If $a = \pm 1$, then $A$ is empty, so that $\Delta(A) = 0$. Let $a \neq \pm 1$ and let $a$ be an $l^e$th power but not an $l^{e+1}$th power in the rational field ($e \geq 0$). Then $\Delta(A) = l^{1-e}(l^2-1)^{-1}$. The proof is given by considering the decomposition of the prime number $p$ in the field $K_n$ ($n \geq 0$) which is generated over the rational field by all $l^n$th roots of $a$.

*K. Iwasawa* (Cambridge, Mass.)

## N76-17 (33# 115)

**Nečaev, V. I.; Stepanova, L. L.**

**The distribution of nonresidues and primitive roots in recurrence sequences over a field of algebraic numbers. (Russian)**

*Uspehi Mat. Nauk* **20** (1965), *no.* 3 (123), 197–203.

Let $\rho$ be a prime ideal of an algebraic number field and $N(\rho)$ its norm. Define a linear recursion of order $n$, modulo $\rho$, in the obvious way. First (Lemma 2) the authors show that there always exists a recursion of maximum period, $N^n(\rho)-1$.

The remainder of the paper is devoted to the proof of two theorems. The first of these is about the numbers $T_m$ and $T_m'$ of $m$-ic residues and non-residues among $\mu$ consecutive values of a recursion modulo $\rho$. Let $w=(N(\rho)-1)/mN(\rho)$. Bounds are obtained for $|T_m-w\mu|$ and $|T_m'-(1-w)\mu|$ in terms of an expression whose dominant term is $N^{(n+1)/2}(\rho)$. The second theorem gives an inequality for $M$, the number of primitive roots mod $\rho$ among $\mu$ successive terms of the recursion:

$$\left|M-\frac{\varphi(N(\rho)-1)}{N(\rho)}\mu\right| < cN^{((n+1)/2)+\varepsilon},$$

where $c=c(n,\varepsilon)$. *J. D. Swift* (Los Angeles, Calif.)

## N76-18 (34# 7445)

**Hooley, Christopher**

**On Artin's conjecture.**

*J. Reine Angew. Math.* **225** (1967), 209–220.

The purpose of this paper is to prove the following. Assume that the extended Riemann hypothesis holds for the Dedekind zeta function over Galois fields of the type $Q(^{k_1}\sqrt{b}, {}^k\sqrt{1})$, where $k$ is square-free and $k_1|k$. (a) For any given non-zero integer $a$ that is not equal to $\pm 1$ or to a perfect square, let $N_a(x)$ be the number of primes $p$ not exceeding $x$ for which $a$ is a primitive root mod $p$. Also, let $a_1$ be the square-free part of $a$, let $h$ be the largest integer with the property that $a$ is a perfect $h$th power, and let $C(h)=\prod_{q|h}(1-1/(q-1))\prod_{q\nmid h}(1-1/q(q-1))$. Then if $a_1\not\equiv 1 \pmod 4$ one has $N_a(x)=C(h)x/\log x+O(x\log\log x/\log^2 x)$ as $x\to\infty$, while if $a_1\equiv 1 \pmod 4$ one has $N_a(x)=C(h)\times[1-\mu(|a_1|)\prod_{q|(h,a_1)}(q-2)^{-1}\prod_{q\nmid h, q|a_1}(q^2-q-1)^{-1}]x/\log x+O(x\log\log x/\log^2 x)$ as $x\to\infty$. (b) If $a$ is neither $\pm 1$ nor a perfect square, then there are infinitely many primes $p$ for which $a$ is a primitive root.

There is, in particular, one sum $P_a(x,k)$ whose evaluation is of importance for the proof of the following result. Let $k$ be as above, let $q$ be a prime and denote the simultaneous conditions "$q|(p-1)$ and $\nu^q\equiv a \pmod p$ is soluble" by $R(q,p)$. Define $P_a(x,k)$ to be the number of all $p\leq x$, $p\nmid a$, such that $R(q,p)$ holds for all $q|k$. Let $\mathfrak{p}$ denote a prime ideal of the algebraic number field $Q(^{k_1}\sqrt{a}, {}^k\sqrt{1})$, where $Q$ is the field of rationals. It is shown that there is a relation between $P_a(x,k)$ and $\pi(x,k)=\sum_{\mathfrak{p}, N\mathfrak{p}\leq x}1$. Using this relation, an asymptotic formula is given for $P_a(x,k)$ by applying the extended Riemann hypothesis to the estimation of the sum $\sum_\rho x^\rho/\rho$ where $\rho=\beta+i\gamma$, $\gamma\neq 0$, are the complex zeros of the Dedekind zeta function of the field $Q(^{k_1}\sqrt{a}, {}^k\sqrt{1})$.

The author mentions that there are several ways in which it is possible to obtain a similar result with weaker hypotheses, particularly if one is content with an existence theorem instead of an asymptotic formula for $N_a(x)$.

*Werner G. H. Schaal* (Marburg)

Referred to in M55-52, N76-21, R24-42.

## N76-19 (37# 6240)

**Vegh, Emanuel**

**Pairs of consecutive primitive roots modulo a prime.**

*Proc. Amer. Math. Soc.* **19** (1968), 1169–1170.

The author of this interesting paper proves that if $p$ is a prime $>3$ such that $\phi(p-1)>\frac{1}{3}(p-1)$, then there exists at least one pair of consecutive primitive roots (mod $p$). To do this he requires the result that if $p$ is a prime $>3$, then exactly half the primitive roots (mod $p$) are followed by quadratic non-residues. A slightly different approach to the proof of this latter result suggests a possible line of attack on the similar question of existence of pairs $(\alpha,\beta)$ of primitive roots (mod $p$) with $\beta-\alpha=a\not\equiv 0 \pmod p$. Let $N_p(a)$ denote the number of primitive roots $\alpha$ (mod $p$) for which $\alpha+a$ is a quadratic non-residue (mod $p$). Then $N_p(a)=\frac{1}{2}\sum_\alpha'\{1-((\alpha+a)/p)\}+\delta_p(a)$, where the dash (′) denotes that the sum is taken over all primitive roots $\alpha$ (mod $p$) and $\delta_p(a)=-\frac{1}{2}$ if $-a$ is a primitive root (mod $p$), $\delta_p(a)=0$ otherwise. Hence $N_p(a)=\frac{1}{2}\phi(p-1)-\frac{1}{2}S_p(a)+\delta_p(a)$, where $S_p(a)=\sum_\alpha'((\alpha+a)/p)$. Now the transformation $\alpha\to\alpha^{p-2}$ permutes the primitive roots (mod $p$) so that $S_p(a)=\sum_\alpha'((\alpha^{p-2}+a)/p)=-\sum_\alpha'(\alpha/p)((\alpha^{p-2}+a)/p)$, as every primitive root is a quadratic non-residue. Thus $S_p(a)=-\sum_\alpha'((1+a\alpha)/p)=-\sum_\alpha'((a^{p-1}+a\alpha)/p)=-(a/p)\times\sum_\alpha'((\alpha+a^{p-2})/p)=-(a/p)S_p(a^{p-2})$. The special case $a=1$ gives $S_p(1)=0$, $N_p(1)=\frac{1}{2}\phi(p-1)$, which is the lemma of the author. To evaluate $S_p(a)$ for other values of $a$ seems difficult. There is one other special case which is easy, namely, when $p\equiv 1 \pmod 4$, $a=-1$, then $S_p(-1)=0$. If it could be shown that $|S_p(a)|\leq K_a\phi(p-1)$, where $K_a$ is a constant possibly depending on $a$ but not on $p$ such that $0\leq K_a<1$, a proof on the lines of the author would show that if $p$ is a prime $>3$ such that $\phi(p-1)>p/(3-K_a)$, then $p$ has a pair of primitive roots $(\alpha,\beta)$ with $\beta-\alpha=a$.

*K. S. Williams* (Ottawa, Ont.)

Referred to in N76-27.

## N76-20 (38# 5736)

**Burgess, D. A.; Elliott, P. D. T. A.**

**The average of the least primitive root.**

*Mathematika* **15** (1968), 39–50.

Denote by $g(p)$ the least primitive root to the prime modulus $p$. Using Weil's work on the zeros of congruence zeta functions, the first author [Proc. London Math. Soc. (3) **12** (1962), 179–192; MR **24** #A2569] showed earlier that $g(p)\ll p^{1/4+\varepsilon}$. Assuming the extended Riemann hypothesis, Wang Yuan [Sci. Sinica **10** (1961), 1–14; MR **24** #A702] obtained $g(p)\ll(\log p)^2(v(p-1))^6$, where $v(n)$ denotes the number of distinct prime divisors of $n$. On the other hand, P. Turán [Mat. Lapok **1** (1950), 243–266; MR **12**, 311] has shown $g(p)=\Omega(\log p)$. In the present paper, the authors prove $(\pi(X))^{-1}\sum_{p\leq X}g(p)\ll(\log X)^2(\log\log X)^4$ and point out that a similar estimate can be obtained for $\sum_{p\leq X}(g(p))^r$ with $r<4$. The proof uses a more recent version of the large sieve (Roth, Bombieri and others) and also the ordinary sieve (Brun-Titchmarsh). In the course of the proof, the least prime primitive root $g'(p)$ to the prime modulus $p$ plays a significant role. *G. J. Rieger* (Buffalo, N.Y.)

Citations: MR 12, 311n = Z15-17; MR 24# A702 = N76-11; MR 24# A2569 = L25-16.

## N76-21 (39# 2711)

**Goldfeld, Morris**

**Artin's conjecture on the average.**

*Mathematika* **15** (1968), 223–226.

A famous conjecture of Artin states that the number $N_a(x)$ of primes $p\leq x$ for which $a$ is a primitive root satisfies $N_a(x)\sim c(a)\,\mathrm{Li}(x)$ $(a\neq -1, m^2)$. Under assumption of the Riemann hypothesis for certain fields, C. Hooley [J. Reine Angew. Math. **225** (1967), 209–220; MR **34** #7445] proved this conjecture. The present author proves (without using the R.H.) that $N_a(x)=c\,\mathrm{Li}(x)+O(x/\log^D x)$ for each $D\geq 1$, for all integers $a\leq A\leq x$ with at most $C_1A^{9/10}(5\log x+1)^{\log x/\log A+D+2}$ exceptions. Here $c=\prod_p(1-1/p(p-1))$ and $C_1$ depends only on $D$.

*F. van der Blij* (Bilthoven)

Citations: MR 34# 7445 = N76-18.

**N76-22** **(39# 4086 )**

**Vegh, Emanuel**

**Primitive roots modulo a prime as consecutive terms of an arithmetic progression.**

*J. Reine Angew. Math.* **235** (1969), 185–188.

The author proves the following two theorems on primitive roots. Theorem 1: Given positive integers $s$ and $h$, there exists a positive integer $N(s)$ such that for each prime $p>N(s)$ there is an arithmetic progression having at least $s$ consecutive terms as primitive roots modulo $v$, where $v=p^h$. Moreover, the common difference is a primitive root modulo $v$. The first part of Theorem 1 also holds for $v=2p^h$. Theorem 2: Given a positive integer $s$ and arbitrary primes $q_1<q_2<\cdots<q_r$, there exists a positive integer $N=N(s, q_r)$ such that for each prime $p>N$ with $p-1=q_1^{\alpha_1}q_2^{\alpha_2}\cdots q_r^{\alpha_r}$, $\alpha_i\geqq 0$, there is an arithmetic progression, with common difference an arbitrary primitive root modulo $p$, that has at least $s$ consecutive terms as primitive roots modulo $p$. The proofs use A. Brauer's form of van der Waerden's theorem on arithmetic progressions [S.-B. Deutsch. Akad. Wiss. Berlin Kl. Math. Phys. Tech. **1928**, 9–16].

*T. M. Apostol* (Pasadena, Calif.)

Referred to in N76-24.

**N76-23** **(40# 104 )**

**Elliott, P. D. T. A.**

**The distribution of primitive roots.**

*Canad. J. Math.* **21** (1969), 822–841.

Let $N(H, p)$ be the number of primes $\leqq H$ that are primitive roots of $p$ and let $g^*(p)$ be the smallest positive prime that is a primitive root of $p$.

The author establishes the following four theorems: (i) If $\varepsilon$ and $B$ are arbitrary positive constants, then there is a positive constant $F(\varepsilon, B)$ and a set of exceptional positive primes $E$ such that for all $p$ not in $E$, the estimate (I) $N(H, p)=\varphi(p-1)\pi(H)\{1+O((\log H)^{-B})\}(p-1)^{-1}$ holds uniformly for all $H>\exp(F \log\log p \log\log\log p)$, then the number of elements of $E$ not exceeding $x$ is $O(x^{\varepsilon})$. (ii) If $\varepsilon$ is as above, then there is a second set of exceptional primes $E'$ and a positive constant $G$ such that (I) holds for $H>p^{\varepsilon}$ and the number of elements of $E'$ not exceeding $x$ is $O((\log x)^G)$. (iii) There are infinitely many primes $p$ for which $g^*(p)<475(\log p)^{1.6}$. (iv) If $(T_\alpha(x))$ is the number of primes $\leqq x$ which have the property that the odd divisors of $\varphi(p)$ are all $>x^\alpha$, then $\liminf g^*(p)\leqq(8[\alpha^{-1}]^2/e)^{2(1+\alpha)^{-1}}$. The proofs involve the large sieve of Bombieri, the small sieve of H. Halberstam, H. E. Richert and W. Jurkat [C. R. Acad. Sci. Paris Sér. A-B **264** (1967), A920–A923; MR **36** #6374], bounds for character sums, approximation for the number of primes in arithmetic progressions, and a bound for the number of ordered $m$-tuples.

*J. H. Jordan* (Pullman, Wash.)

Citations: MR 36# 6374 = M55-55.

**N76-24** **(42# 1755 )**

**Vegh, Emanuel**

**Arithmetic progressions of primitive roots of a prime. II.**

*J. Reine Angew. Math.* **244** (1970), 108–111.

The methods of an earlier paper [same J. **235** (1969), 185–188; MR **39** #4086] are used to prove the following generalization. Suppose the set $Z(p)$ of positive integers relatively prime to a prime $p$ is partitioned into $k$ classes $T_1, \cdots, T_k$ such that if $x\in Z(p)$ and $i\leqq k$, then $xT_i\in T_j$ for some $j\leqq k$. Then for every pair of positive integers $s$ and $h$ there is an integer $N=N(s, k)$ (independent of $h$) such that if $p>N$ some class $T_\sigma$ contains at least $s$ distinct primitive roots mod $p^h$ in arithmetic progression. Moreover, the common difference of the progression is itself a primitive root mod $p^h$ and belongs to $T_\sigma$. Applications are made to progressions of primitive roots of $p$ that can be found in the classes of $k$th power nonresidues of $p$. Also, for special primes new results are given concerning sequences of arbitrary length of consecutive primitive roots. For example, if $p$ is a prime of the form $1+p_1^{\alpha_1}\cdots p_t^{\alpha_t}$, $\alpha_i\geqq 0$, then for every positive integer $s$ there is an integer $N=N(s, t)$ such that if $p>N$ there is a sequence of at least $s$ consecutive primitive roots mod $p$.

*T. M. Apostol* (Pasadena, Calif.)

Citations: MR 39# 4086 = N76-22.

**N76-25** **(42# 7624 )**

**Elliott, P. D. T. A.**

**Mean value theorems by the method of high moments.**

*Number Theory (Colloq., János Bolyai Math. Soc., Debrecen,* 1968), *pp.* 31–34. *North-Holland, Amsterdam,* 1970.

Three theorems are mentioned in this lecture: (1) The first theorem deals with the number of prime primitive roots $q$ (mod $p$) which satisfy $q\leqq H$. (2) Let $g^*(p)$ denote the least primitive root (mod $p$). Then the second theorem asserts $g^*(p)<475 (\log p)^{8/5}$ infinitely often. (3) A result is given about the least integer $y$ such that the Legendre symbol satisfies $(y/p)=-1=((y+1)/p)$. The proofs are only indicated and rely on applications of the sieve, Selberg's sieve as well as the large sieve. For the third result Burgess' character estimate and the Siegel-Walfisz theorem are required.

*W. G. H. Schaal* (Marburg)

**N76-26** **(44# 1624 )**

**Vegh, Emanuel**

**A new condition for consecutive primitive roots of a prime.**

*Elem. Math.* **25** (1970), 113.

The author proves in an elementary way the existence of a pair of consecutive primitive roots modulo $p$ for primes $p\equiv 1$ (mod 4) having 2 as a primitive root.

*K. S. Williams* (Ottawa, Ont.)

**N76-27** **(44# 2694 )**

**Vegh, Emanuel**

**A note on the distribution of the primitive roots of a prime.**

*J. Number Theory* **3** (1971), 13–18.

The author [Proc. Amer. Math. Soc. **19** (1968), 1169–1170; MR **37** #6240] proved that if $p$ is a prime $>3$ such that $\phi(p-1)>\frac{1}{3}(p-1)$, then there exists at least one pair $(\alpha, \alpha+1)$ of consecutive primitive roots (mod $p$). Generalizing and improving this, the author proves in this article the following theorems. If $p=4k+1$ is a prime such that $\phi(p-1)>\frac{1}{4}(p-1)$, $b$ is a quadratic residue (mod $p$) and $b'$ is a solution of the congruence $bb'\equiv 1$ (mod $p$), then there exists at least one pair $(\alpha, \beta)$ of primitive roots (mod $p$) for which $\alpha-\beta\equiv b$ or $b'$ (mod $p$). The same conclusion holds for primes $p=4k+3$ such that $\phi(p-1)>\frac{1}{3}(p-1)$. The author shows by numerical examples that there are primes $p$ and integers $b$ for which there is no pair $(\alpha, \beta)$ of primitive roots (mod $p$) with $\alpha-\beta\equiv b$ (mod $p$). The only such primes $p<2000$ are $p=2, 3, 5, 7, 11, 13$, and 61.

*T. Hayashida* (Yokohama)

Citations: MR 37# 6240 = N76-19.

**N76-28** **(44# 5270 )**

**Brown, H.; Zassenhaus, H.**

**Some empirical observations on primitive roots.**

*J. Number Theory* **3** (1971), 306–309.

In this note the authors give two small tables having to do with primitive roots.

For each prime $p$ let $p_{k+1}$ be the least prime which is not a primitive root. Table I gives a list of those primes $p$ whose $k$ is larger than those of all smaller primes with the additional condition that $k \geqq [\log p]$. There are 18 such $p < 10^6$ with $k \leqq 13$. Six additional entries are examples [taken from the reviewer, E. Lehmer and D. Shanks, Math. Comp. **24** (1970), 433–451; MR **42** #5889] of larger $p$'s whose $k$'s considerably exceed $\log p$.

Table II gives the results of three calculations having to do with the density of primes $p$ for which the root $\alpha$ of a quadratic $f(x)$ is a primitive root in the field GF($p^2$), generated by $(1, \alpha)$. The three $f$'s considered are $x^2+5x+7$, $x^2+10x+10$ and $x^2+x+2$. They give remarkably uniform results with density about 1/7. The authors' Conjecture II needs further restrictions since it fails for $f(x)=x^2+2x+4$.

*D. H. Lehmer* (Berkeley, Calif.)

Citations: MR 42# 5889 = N68-44.

# N80 GENERALIZED PRIMES AND INTEGERS

For generalized characters, see **L25**.

See also reviews L25-4, L25-7, L25-8, L25-9, L25-10, L25-11, L25-14, L25-22, L25-25, L25-27, M45-32, N60-52, R46-11, Z02-5.

## N80-1 (9, 11f)

**Ramaswami, V. On the divisors of a multiplicative set.** J. Benares Hindu Univ. **7**, part 1, 177–178 (1943).

Let $a_1, a_2, \cdots$ be a sequence of real numbers with the properties that (i) $a_1=1$, (ii) $a_{n+1}>a_n$, (iii) to every pair of positive integers $m$ and $n$ there corresponds a third integer $p$ such that $a_p=a_m a_n$ and (iv) there exists a constant $c_1$ such that the number of $a_n$ not exceeding $x$ is $c_1x+O(1)$. By generalizing the standard proofs for the case where $a_n=n$, it is shown that properties (i), (ii) and (iv) imply the existence of an "Euler-Mascheroni constant" $c_2$, that is,

$$\sum_{a_n\leqq x} 1/a_n = c_1 \log x + c_2 + O(1/x)$$

and that properties (i)–(iv) imply the analogue of Dirichlet's formula,

$$\sum_{a_n\leqq x} d(a_n) = c_1^2 x \log x + (2c_1c_2 - c_1^2)x + O(x^{\frac{1}{2}}),$$

where $d(a_n)$ is the number of ordered pairs $(a_r, a_q)$ satisfying $a_n = a_r a_q$.

*P. Hartman* (Baltimore, Md.).

## N80-2 (11, 332b)

**Nyman, Bertil. A general prime number theorem.** Acta Math. **81**, 299–307 (1949).

This is a development of Beurling's generalised prime number theory [Acta Math. **68**, 255–291 (1937)]. The "primes" are the members $y_n$ of a given real sequence $(1<y_1<y_2<\cdots; y_n\to\infty)$, and the "numbers" are all possible products $x_n$ of them $(1<x_1\leqq x_2\leqq\cdots)$ with repetitions for multiple representations. Let $\pi(x)$ be the number of $y_n\leqq x$, $N(x)$ the number of $x_n\leqq x$, and $\zeta(s)=1+x_1^{-s}+x_2^{-s}+\cdots$ $(s=\sigma+it,\ \sigma>1)$. It is asserted that the following three statements are equivalent: $(A)$ $N(x)=ax+O(x(\log x)^{-n})$ as $x\to\infty$, for some fixed $a>0$ and every fixed $n>0$; $(B)$ $|\zeta^{(n)}(s)|<A|t|^{\epsilon}$, $|\zeta(s)|^{-1}<A|t|^{\epsilon}$ $(\sigma>1,\ |t|\geqq\epsilon)$, for every $\epsilon>0$, every integer $n\geqq 0$, and some $A=A(\epsilon, n)$; $(C)$ $\pi(x)=\mathrm{Li}\,(x)+O(x(\log x)^{-n})$ as $x\to\infty$, for every fixed $n>0$. The argument is based on the scheme of implications: (1) $A\to B$, (2) $B\to C$, (3) $C\to B$, (4) $B\to A$. Of these (1) and (3) are established by partial integration and, in case (1), Hadamard's classical deduction from the inequality $|\zeta^3(\sigma)\zeta^4(\sigma+it)\zeta(\sigma+2it)|\geqq 1$ $(\sigma>1)$; while (2) and (4) are based on Parseval's formula. By the use of derivatives of high order the operations are confined essentially to the open half-plane $\sigma>1$. [The argument does not seem to correspond logically to the enunciation, for under the headings $B\to C$ and $B\to A$ the author proves only $A\&B\to C$ and $C\&B\to A$, respectively. Indeed, $B$ can hardly be equivalent by itself to $A$ or $C$, since it does not specify the behaviour of $\zeta(s)$ near $s=1$. Thus, if $y_n=2^n$, $B$ is true but $A$ and $C$ are false. The main equivalence $A\leftrightarrow C$ is, however, valid.]

*A. E. Ingham* (Cambridge, England).

Referred to in N80-10, N80-12, N80-54.

## N80-3 (16, 114e)

**Forman, William, and Shapiro, Harold N. Abstract prime number theorems.** Comm. Pure Appl. Math. **7**, 587–619 (1954).

Let $G$ be a free Abelian group on a countable number of generators $g_i$ $(i=1, 2, \cdots)$, and $N$ a homomorphism of $G$ into the positive rationals such that the $g_i$ (and so all integral words $w$ of $G$) have integral images $Ng_i$ (and $Nw$). Let $G'$ be a subgroup of finite index $h=[G:G']$, and suppose that, for all cosets $H$ of $G/G'$,

$$B_H(x)\equiv \sum_{\substack{Nw\leqq x\\ w\,\varepsilon\, H}} 1 = c_Hx+O(x^\theta),\ 0\leqslant\theta<1,\ c_H\geqslant 0;\ \sum_H c_H>0.$$

Then, for each $H$,

$$\pi_H(x)\equiv \sum_{\substack{Ng\leqq x\\ g\,\varepsilon\, H}} 1 = \frac{d_Hx}{\log x}+o\left(\frac{x}{\log x}\right).$$

This abstract theorem includes the classical prime number theorems for arithmetical progressions and ideal classes. Thus, to cover the case of primes in arithmetical progressions of difference $A$, where $A$ is a given positive integer, we identify the $g_i$ with the (positive) primes not dividing $A$ [taking $Ng_i$ equal to $g_i$, presumably] and take $G'$ to be the set of positive rational numbers $r=m/n$ of $G$ for which $r\equiv 1 \pmod A$ [i.e. $(m, A)=(n, A)=1$, $m\equiv n \pmod A$]. In this case the $c_H$ are all equal, and when this is so we have $d_H=1/h$ for each $H$ (so that the $g_i$ "equi-distribute" over the cosets $H$). But this "classical" situation is very special. The authors give an exhaustive analysis of the general case (i.e. a complete specification of the values of the $d_H$). This hinges on a certain between-group $L$ $(G'\subset L\subset G)$, but the possibilities are too numerous for a short summary. When $\theta<\frac{1}{2}$, however, some of these possibilities are excluded by an argument modelled on one of the function-theoretical proofs of the non-vanishing of the Dirichlet $L$-functions $L(s, \chi)$ at $s=1$; and the situation then is that $d_H=1/[L:G']$ if $H\,\varepsilon\, L/G'$ (i.e. $H\subset L$) and $d_H=0$ otherwise (so that the $g_i$ are "almost all" in $L$ and "equi-distribute" among the cosets of $G'$ in $L$).

The proof of the general abstract theorem follows the lines of Selberg's elementary proof of the prime number theorem, as modified by Shapiro. The various possibilities are illustrated by examples based on ordinary integers and primes. In the examples designed to show that the simplification when $\theta<\frac{1}{2}$ is not universal, the Riemann hypothesis is assumed [though it would be sufficient to assume $\Theta<1$, where $\Theta$ is the upper bound of the real parts of the zeros of Riemann's $\zeta(s)$].

[Remarks by the reviewer: (1) The definition of "Dirichlet density" on p. 600 is subject to an "existence" qualification, but this is not referred to in later developments. Thus, in the proof of Lemma A on p. 601, some a priori reason should be given for the existence of all the densities used, or failing this the argument should be conducted initially in terms of "upper and lower densities" (suitably defined). (2) The proof of Theorem I on pp. 614–616 (i.e. the simplification when $\theta<\frac{1}{2}$) is obscure. The statement at the bottom of p. 615 that $g(s)$ is regular in the half-plane $\sigma>\theta$ may be vitiated by zeros of $\zeta_G(2s)$; but Landau's theorem only calls for regularity along the portion $s\geqq\frac{1}{2}$ of the real axis, and this can be asserted with safety (on the assumption that $L(1,\chi)=0$). The statement near the top of p. 616 that $h(s)$ is regular and $h(s)\neq 0$ for $\sigma\geqq\frac{1}{2}$ seems to be based on the fact that $h(s)=\prod_g\{1-\eta_g(s)\}$, where $\eta_g(s)$ is regular, $\eta_g(s)\neq 1$, and $|\eta_g(s)|<K(Ng)^{-2\sigma}$, in $\sigma\geqq\frac{1}{2}$; but this by itself only permits a conclusion in $\sigma>\frac{1}{2}$ (and incidentally it is not clear why the list of exceptional $g$ given in the bracket should not include those for which $Ng=3$). However, if the definition of $g(s)$ is modified so that only one factor $\zeta_G(2s)$ occurs in the denominator in (6.7), the classical situation seems to be paralleled, so that Landau's theorem can be applied directly to $g(s)$ (with no exceptional $g$'s).] *A. E. Ingham* (Cambridge, England).

Referred to in N80-9, R44-11.

## N80-4 (20# 5175)

**Bredihin, B. M. Free numerical semigroups with power densities.** Dokl. Akad. Nauk SSSR (N.S.) **118** (1958), 855–857. (Russian)

The author remarks that the elementary proof of the prime number theorem utilizes only the multiplicative and order properties of the integers and hence the method is available for asymptotic density theorems for multiplicative semi-groups of real numbers. Let $1=\alpha_1<\alpha_2<\alpha_3<\cdots$ be generated multiplicatively by a set of generators $1<\omega_1<\omega_2<\omega_3<\cdots$ so that each $\alpha$ is uniquely a product of powers of a finite number of $\omega$'s. Let $\nu(x)$ and $\pi(x)$ be the number of $\alpha$'s and $\omega$'s, respectively, not exceeding $x$. It is assumed that, for some $\theta>0$, $x^{-\theta}\nu(x)$ tends to a positive limit as $x\to\infty$. Then it is proved by elementary methods that

$$\pi(x)\sim y/\log y \quad (y=x^\theta).$$

Besides its application to Gaussian primes and prime ideals the author gives an application to the following "inverse" problem. Suppose that the number of solutions $(n_1, n_2, \cdots)$ in positive integers of the inequality $n_1\alpha_1+n_2\alpha_2+\cdots\leqq x$ is $Ce^{\theta x}+O(e^{\theta_1 x})$ for some $\theta>\theta_1>0$. Then $\nu(x)=y/\log y$ $(y=e^{\theta x})$. *D. H. Lehmer* (Berkeley, Calif.)

Referred to in N80-15, N80-35.

## N80-5 (21# 87)

**Bredihin, B. M. Free numerical semigroups with power densities.** Mat. Sb. N.S. **46** (**88**) (1958), 143–158. (Russian)

The Selberg approach is extended to yield an elementary proof of an asymptotic law for the distribution of generating elements in a free numerical semigroup. Let $G$ be a free commutative semigroup with a countable system $P$ of generators. Let $N$ be a homomorphism of $G$ onto a multiplicative semigroup of numbers such that, for a given number $x$, only finitely many elements $\alpha$ in $G$ have norm $N(\alpha)$ satisfying $N(\alpha)\leqq x$. Let $\nu(x)=\sum_{N(\alpha)\leqq x,\,\alpha\in G}1$ and $\pi(x)=\sum_{N(\omega)\leqq x,\,\omega\in P}1$. Given $\theta>0$, if $\lim_{x\to\infty}(\nu(x)/x^\theta)$ exists and is a positive number $C$, then $C$ is called the density, relative to the $\theta$ power, of the semigroup. The asymptotic law may be expressed as follows: if the free semigroup has the property that $\nu(x)=Cx^\theta+O(x^{\theta_1})$, where $C>0$, $\theta>0$, and $\theta_1<\theta$, then

$$\lim_{x\to\infty}\frac{\pi(x)}{x^\theta/\log x}=\theta^{-1}.$$

As special cases there are the classical prime number theorem, theory concerning the distribution of primes among the Gaussian complex numbers, and results on the distribution of zeros of the $\zeta$-function generalized to free semigroups. *R. A. Good* (College Park, Md.)

Referred to in N80-13, N80-23, N80-35, N80-37.

## N80-6 (21# 2626)

**Gutmann, Hans. Anwendung Tauberscher Sätze und Lambertscher Reihen in der zahlentheoretischen Asymptotik.** Verh. Naturf. Ges. Basel **69** (1959), 119–144.

As a generalization of the sequence of prime numbers the author considers a sequence $B$ of natural numbers, $b_1<b_2<\cdots<b_k<\cdots$, which are prime to one another, and studies problems of asymptotic behavior of the number of numbers (=$b$-numbers) in $B$, the sum, the sum of reciprocal values, the sum of logarithms of numbers not divisible by the numbers of $B$, as well as the divisors and the sum of divisors which are divisible by the numbers of $B$. The idea to replace the prime numbers by the $b$-numbers is due to A. Beurling [Acta Math. **68** (1937), 255–291].

Throughout the paper convergence is assumed for $\sum_1^\infty b_\nu^{-1}$ and $\sum_1^\infty b_\nu^{-1}\cdot\log b_\nu$. Let the functions $f_n(x)$ be defined by the following relations ($|x|\neq 1$):

$$f_0(x)=\frac{x}{1-x},\quad f_{n+1}(x)=f_n(x)-f_n(x^{b_{n+1}}),\ n=0,1,2,\cdots.$$

Then for $|x|<1$ and for any $n$ it is proved by mathematical induction that

$$f_n(x)=\sum_{\beta\in M^{(n)}}(-1)^{\omega^{(n)}(\beta)}\frac{x^\beta}{1-x^\beta},$$

where $M^{(n)}$ is the totality of the $b^2$-free numbers formed by the factors 1, $b_1$, $b_2$, $\cdots$, $b_n$, and $\omega^{(n)}(\nu)$ is the number of $b$-numbers by which $\nu$ is divisible. In connection with the functions $f_n(x)$ are defined two other similar functions with recurrent relations, and their limiting functions are studied when $n\to\infty$. The Lambert series $L(x)=\sum_1^\infty x^\nu/(1-x^\nu)$ plays an important role as may be seen from the form of the functions $f_n(x)$. It is deduced for $0\leqq x<1$ that

$$\sum_1^\infty\frac{\mu(\nu)x^\nu}{1-x^\nu}=x \quad\text{and}\quad \sum_1^\infty\frac{\mu(\nu)}{\nu}\log(1-x^\nu)^{-1}=x,$$

where $\mu(\nu)$ is the Möbius function. By applying Tauberian theorems of Hardy and Littlewood [G. H. Hardy, *Divergent series*, Clarendon Press, Oxford, 1949; MR **11**, 25; e.g. theorems 90, 91, 92, 96, 113] many interesting number-theoretic results are obtained. *S. Ikehara* (Tokyo)

Referred to in N80-8.

## N80-7 (22# 3708)

**Bredihin, B. M. Natürliche Dichten einiger Zahlhalbgruppen.** Ukrain. Mat. Ž. **11** (1959), 137–145. (Russian. German summary)

Some results of H.-J. Kanold [J. Reine Angew. Math. **193** (1954), 250–252; MR **16**, 569] and P. Scherk [same J. **196** (1956), 133–136; MR **18**, 284] for integers and primes in the classical sense are extended to more general systems. Let $G$ be a multiplicative semigroup of positive real numbers $\alpha\geqq 1$ $(1\in G)$ with an infinite basis $\{\omega_1,\omega_2,\cdots\}$ $(\omega_j>1)$ having no finite limit point. This means that any $\alpha$ can be expressed uniquely as $\alpha=\omega_1^{x_1}\omega_2^{x_2}\cdots$, where Greek letters denote members of $G$ and the $x_j$ are non-negative integers of which at most a finite number are non-zero. In the classical case the $\alpha$ are the positive integers and the $\omega$ the primes; and apart from terminology the extension is essentially that of A. Beurling [Acta Math. **68** (1937), 255–291]. Divisibility, H.C.F., the Möbius $\mu$-function, etc., are defined in the obvious way in terms of the $\omega$-products of the $\alpha$'s. The set $G$ is said to have natural density $C$ if

(1) $$\nu(x)\sim Cx \quad\text{as } x\to\infty,$$

where $\nu(x)$ is the number of $\alpha$'s in $G$ which are $\leqq x$; and similarly for subsets of $G$. The author considers in particular the subsets $g''$, $g'''$ defined by:

$$(g'') \qquad (\alpha, \mu) = 1, \quad Q(\alpha) = \delta,$$

$$(g''') \qquad (\alpha, \mu) = 1, \quad Q(\alpha) \geqq \delta,$$

where $\mu$, $\delta$ are fixed, and $(Q(\alpha))^2$ is the largest square divisor of $\alpha$ (so that $Q(\alpha)=\gamma$, where $\gamma$ is uniquely defined by $\alpha=\beta\gamma^2$, $\mu(\beta)\neq 0$). The main result (theorem 1) is that, if $G$ has natural density $C$, then $g''$ and $g'''$ have, respectively, the natural densities

$$\frac{C_G}{\delta^2}\prod_{\omega|\mu}\frac{\omega}{\omega+1} \quad (\text{if } (\delta, \mu) = 1),$$

$$C\prod_{\omega|\mu}\frac{\omega-1}{\omega}-C_G\prod_{\omega|\mu}\frac{\omega}{\omega+1}\sum_{\beta<\delta,(\beta,\mu)=1}\frac{1}{\beta^2},$$

where $C_G$ depends only on $G$. It is proved also (theorem 2) that, if the asymptotic formula (1) for $G$ is replaced by

$$\nu(x) = Cx+O(\sqrt{x}),$$

then the corresponding asymptotic formulae for $g''$ and $g'''$ implied by theorem 1 may be replaced by formulae involving an error $O(\sqrt{x}\cdot\log x)$. When $\delta=1$ the set $g''$ is denoted by $g'$. The theorems are first proved for this basic case, and the other results are then derived. All arguments are of an elementary nature.

*A. E. Ingham* (Cambridge, England)

Citations: MR 16, 569h = N28-30; MR 18, 284b = N28-34.

Referred to in N80-20.

**N80-8** **(22# 6761 )**

**Gutmann, Hans. Beitrag zur Zahlentheorie verallgemeinerter Primzahlen.** Verh. Naturf. Ges. Basel **70** (1959), 167–192.

As a generalization of the sequence of prime numbers, the author studies a sequence of natural numbers, $b_1<b_2<\cdots<b_n<\cdots$, which are prime to one another, and the sets of $b$-numbers which are free from $b$-squares, corresponding to the sets of square-free numbers in the usual theory. The author studies the behavior of analogues of classical number-theoretic functions and extends theorems in the analytic theory of numbers. This paper embodies simplifications and improvements of his dissertation [same Verh. **69** (1959), 119–144; MR **21** #2626].

*S. Ikehara* (Tokyo)

Citations: MR 21# 2626 = N80-6.

**N80-9** **(23# A1616 )**

**Amitsur, S. A.**

**Arithmetic linear transformations and abstract prime number theorems.**

*Canad. J. Math.* **13** (1961), 83–109.

This paper is an extension of two previous papers by the author [J. Analyse Math. **5** (1956/57), 273–314; MR **21** #4138; J. Math. Soc. Japan **11** (1959), 275–290]. The 'symbolic calculus' of these papers is now applied to the 'abstract prime number theory' as developed by W. Forman and H. N. Shapiro [Comm. Pure Appl. Math. **7** (1954), 587–619; MR **16**, 114, 1337]. The author prefers to work with semi-groups rather than groups, and the general situation contemplated is as follows. Let $W$ be a free Abelian multiplicative semi-group generated by a countable number of generators $p_i$. Let $N$ be a homomorphism of $W$ into the semi-group $\mathfrak{N}$ of all positive integers. Let $W'\subseteq W$ be such that $W/W'$ is a finite group of order $h$, and let $H$ be a generic class of $W/W'$. The problem then is to deduce from the assumptions

$$B_H(x) \equiv \sum_{\substack{Nw\leqq x\\ w\in H}} 1 = c_Hx+R_H(x), \quad c_H \geqq 0, \quad \sum_H c_H > 0,$$

with suitable estimates of $R_H(x)$, the 'prime number theorem for the classes $H$', namely,

$$\pi_H(x) \equiv \sum_{\substack{Np\leqq x\\ p\in H}} 1 = d_H\frac{x}{\log x}+o\left(\frac{x}{\log x}\right).$$

Forman and Shapiro assumed that $R_H(x)=O(x^\theta)$ $(0\leqq\theta<1)$. The author adopts the wider condition $R_H(x)=O(x/\log^\gamma x)$, where it is assumed that $\gamma>2$ in some arguments and $\gamma>3$ in others. The proofs make use of the characters $\chi(H)$ of the group $W/W'$, which are studied intensively for their own sake. The methods used are 'elementary' and follow the general lines of the three papers cited above, combining the formal developments of the 'symbolic calculus' with the generality of the 'abstract' approach. The paper contains numerous misprints and minor inaccuracies.

*A. E. Ingham* (Cambridge, England)

Citations: MR 16, 114e = N80-3; MR 21# 4138 = N20-41.

Referred to in N20-48, N20-49, N20-53.

**N80-10** **(24# A708 )**

**Horadam, E. M.**

**Arithmetical functions of generalized primes.**

*Amer. Math. Monthly* **68** (1961), 626–629.

Generalized primes were discussed by Beurling [Acta Math. **68** (1937), 255–291] and Nyman [ibid. **81** (1949), 299–307; MR **11**, 332]. The following definition is employed in the present paper. Given a finite or infinite sequence $\{p\}$ of real numbers (generalized primes) such that $1<p_1<p_2<\cdots$. Form the set $\{l\}$ of all possible products $p_1^{v_1}p_2^{v_2}\cdots$, where $v_1, v_2, \cdots$ are integers, of which all but a finite number are 0. Assume that no two $l$'s are equal and arrange them in an increasing sequence $1=l_1<l_2<l_3<\cdots$.

(1) The author proves a formula for the power of a generalized prime contained in $l_n!=l_nl_{n-1}\cdots l_1$. (2) If $\phi(m)$ is the number of $l$-numbers less than $m$ and prime to $m$, then $\phi(p^n)=[p^n]-[p^{n-1}]$; moreover, $\sum_{d/l}\phi(d)=[l]$, where $d/l$ means $d\in\{l\}$ and there exist $l_d\in\{l\}$ such that $dl_d=l$. (3) There are also several theorems on multiplicative functions: $\theta(l)$ is multiplicative provided $\theta(l_ml_n)=\theta(l_m)\theta(l_n)$ when $(l_m, l_n)=1$.

*L. Carlitz* (Durham, N.C.)

Citations: MR 11, 332b = N80-2.

Referred to in N80-16, N80-18, N80-21.

**N80-11** **(24# A3120 )**

**Horadam, E. M.**

**Arithmetical functions associated with the unitary divisors of a generalised integer.**

*Amer. Math. Monthly* **69** (1962), 196–199.

The author generalizes to arithmetical semigroups of real numbers the unitary inversion formula for arithmetical functions [cf. Cohen, Math. Z. **74** (1960), 66–80, Th. 2.3; MR **22** #3707]. This result is then employed to evaluate a generalization of the unitary totient function.

*E. Cohen* (Knoxville, Tenn.)

Citations: MR 22# 3707 = N52-19.

**N80-12** **(26# 87 )**

**Malliavin, Paul**

**Sur le reste de la loi asymptotique de répartition des nombres premiers généralisés de Beurling.**

*Acta Math.* **106** (1961), 281–298.

Im Anschluß an Beurling [dieselben Acta **68** (1937), 255–291] nennt man eine beliebige Folge reeller Zahlen $p_n>1$ (verallgemeinerte) "Primzahlen", die aus ihnen gebildeten Produkte "ganze Zahlen". Werden die Anzahlfunktionen mit $\pi(x)$ bzw. $n(x)$ bezeichnet, so bewies Beurling, daß aus $n(x)=ax+O(x\log^{-b}x)$ $(a>0,\ b>\frac{3}{2})$, $\pi(x)\sim x/\log x$ folgt; dies wurde von Nyman [ibid. **81** (1949), 299–307; MR **11**,

332] weiter präzisiert. Der Verfasser zeigt, wieder unter Betrachtung der zugehörigen Zetafunktion, jedoch mittels eines neuen Tauberschen Satzes, daß aus $n(x)=bx+O(x\ \exp(-\log^a x))$, $0<a\leqq 1$, $\pi(x)=\mathrm{li}\ x+O(x\ \exp(-\log^{a'} x))$ hergeleitet werden kann (und umgekehrt, jeweils mit gewisser Verkleinerung des Exponenten). Ferner wird bemerkt, daß dieser Satz von der Riemannschen Vermutung unabhängig ist. Ist $0<\beta<1$ gegeben, so existiert nämlich eine Zetafunktion $\zeta_1(s)=\prod 1/(1-p^{-s})$, die für $\sigma>0$ (mit Ausnahme eines einfachen Poles bei $s=1$ holomorph ist) und genau bei $s=\beta$ eine Nullstelle besitzt. *H.-E. Richert* (Syracuse, N.Y.)

Citations: MR 11, 332b = N80-2.
Referred to in N80-54.

## N80-13 (26# 92)

**Bredihin, B. M.**

**The remainder term in the asymptotic formula for $\nu_G(x)$. (Russian)**

*Izv. Vysš. Učebn. Zaved. Matematika* **1960**, *no.* 6 (19), 40–49.

$G$ sei eine freie kommutative Halbgruppe mit abzählbarer Basis $P$. Der Verfasser hat früher [Mat. Sb. (N.S.) **46 (88)** (1958), 143–158; MR **21** #87] aus dem asymptotischen Verhalten von $\nu_G(x)=\sum_{N(\alpha)\leq x,\alpha\in G} 1$ $(N(\alpha)=\mathrm{Norm})$ auf dasjenige von $\pi_G(x)=\sum_{N(\omega)\leq x,\omega\in P} 1$ geschlossen. Hier werden Sätze in der umgekehrten Richtung bewiesen, wobei die Zetafunktion von $G$ und ein Taubersatz von G. Freud [Acta Math. Acad. Sci. Hungar. **2** (1951), 299–308; MR **14**, 361] benutzt werden. Dies verschärft die Resultate des Verfassers [Mat. Sb. (N.S.) **50 (92)** (1960), 221–232; MR **26** #246]. Verschiedene Anwendungen werden betrachtet. *H.-E. Richert* (Syracuse, N.Y.)

Citations: MR 21# 87 = N80-5; MR 26# 246 = N80-15.

## N80-14 (26# 99)

**Fogels, È. K.**

**On the distribution of analogues of primes. (Russian)**

*Dokl. Akad. Nauk SSSR* **146** (1962), 318–321.

Let a semigroup (with multiplication) $G$ of reals $a\geqq 1$ be split into classes $H_1, H_2, \cdots, H_h$, $h\leqq D$, forming a group and subject to the condition

$$\sum_{a\leq x,\, a\in H_j} 1 = \alpha x+O(D^{c_1}x^{1-\vartheta}), \qquad \alpha = D^l,$$

with $l$, $c_1$, $0\leqq\vartheta<1$ independent of $j$. The author outlines a proof of existence of a basic number $b\in G$ in every class $H_j$ localized to a certain prescribed interval. The result covers Linnik's celebrated theorem on the least prime in arithmetical progression, as well as several of its extensions. *S. Knapowski* (New Orleans, La.)

Referred to in N80-17.

## N80-15 (26# 246)

**Bredihin, B. M.**

**Elementary solutions of inverse problems on bases of free semigroups. (Russian)**

*Mat. Sb. (N.S.)* **50 (92)** (1960), 221–232.

Sei $G$ eine freie, multiplikative, kommutative Halbgruppe mit abzählbar vielen Erzeugenden $\omega_1, \omega_2, \cdots$, in der eine reellwertige "Norm" $N(\alpha)\geqq 0$ mit $N(\alpha\beta)=N(\alpha)N(\beta)$ für alle $\alpha,\beta\in G$ erklärt und für jedes $x$ die Anzahl $\nu_G(x)$ der $\alpha\in G$ mit $N(\alpha)\leqq x$ endlich ist. Es werden mehrere Sätze bewiesen, die aus Dichteeigenschaften des Erzeugendensystems auf solche der Halbgruppe selbst schliessen, z.B. Satz 3: Wenn für die Anzahl $\pi_G(x)$ der $\omega_i$ mit $N(\omega_i)\leqq x$ eine Gleichung (1) $\pi_G(x)=ax/\log x+R(x)$ mit $R(x)=o(x/\log x)$ gilt und

$$(2) \qquad \lim_{s\to 1+0}\int_{N(\omega_1)}^{\infty} R(x)x^{-s-1}\,dx \neq \infty$$

existiert, folgt (3) $\nu_G(x)\sim C_G x\ \log^{a-1} x$. Umgekehrt wird bewiesen, daß auch aus (3) die Aussagen (1) und (2) folgen. Als Folgerungen ergeben sich analoge Sätze für den Fall, dass die Halbgruppe $G$ eine Potenzdichte besitzt, wie der Verfasser sie in einer früheren Arbeit [Dokl. Akad. Nauk SSSR **118** (1958), 855–857; MR **20** #5175] betrachtet hat. Der Schlussteil der Arbeit behandelt Anwendungen der bewiesenen Sätze; z.B. wird die Dichte der komplexen multiplikativen Halbgruppe bestimmt, die von der Menge der Gauss'schen ganzen Zahlen in einem gegebenen (endlichen) Kreissektor um 0 erzeugt wird. *B. W. Volkmann* (Mainz)

Citations: MR 20# 5175 = N80-4.
Referred to in N80-13.

## N80-16 (26# 3649)

**Horadam, E. M.**

**A generalised form of a theorem on integer quotients of products of factorials.**

*Math. Mag.* **36** (1963), 98–100.

In an earlier paper the author introduced sets of "generalized integers" $\{l_n\}$ [Amer. Math. Monthly **68** (1961), 626–629; MR **24** #A708]. She defines $l_n!=l_nl_{n-1}\cdots l_1$ and proves various theorems on quotients of products of these generalized factorials. For example, if $n=a+b+\cdots+k$, the quotient $l_n!/(l_a!l_b!\cdots l_k!)$ is a generalized integer. *T. M. Apostol* (Pasadena, Calif.)

Citations: MR 24# A708 = N80-10.

## N80-17 (26# 4969)

**Fogels, È.**

**On the abstract theory of prime numbers. (Russian. English summary)**

*Latvijas PSR Zinātņu Akad. Vēstis* **1963,** *no.* 1 (186), 75–80.

The author extends his abstract prime number theorem presented earlier [Dokl. Akad. Nauk SSSR **146** (1962), 318–321; MR **26** #99]. He obtains in particular an upper estimate of the smallest prime representable by a primitive binary quadratic form $\psi(u,v)$ with $(u,v)$ restricted to a given angle in the plane. *S. Knapowski* (New Orleans, La.)

Citations: MR 26# 99 = N80-14.

## N80-18 (26# 6148)

**Horadam, E. M.**

**The order of arithmetical functions of generalized integers.**

*Amer. Math. Monthly* **70** (1963), 506–512.

In a previous paper [same Monthly **68** (1961), 626–629; MR **24** #A708] the author has defined generalized integers as follows. Given a finite or infinite sequence $\{p\}$ of real numbers (generalized primes) such that $1<p_1<p_2<\cdots$, construct the set $\{b\}$ of all $p_1^{v_1}p_2^{v_2}\cdots$, where $v_1, v_2, \cdots$ are integers $\geqq 0$ of which all but a finite number are 0. The $\{b\}$ are called generalized integers; it is assumed that no two $b$'s are equal if their $v$'s are different. Number $\{b\}$ so that $1-b_1<b_2<\cdots$. Let $[x]$ denote the number of $b_j\leqq x$; assume $[x]=x+R(x)$, where $R(x)=O(x^\alpha)$, $\alpha<1$. The object of the paper is to extend classical results on the order of arithmetic functions to generalized integers. Among the results proved in the present paper the following may be cited. (1) The number of generalized primes is infinite. (2) A generalized $\mu$-function is defined and an inversion formula is obtained. (3) Let $\tau(b_n)$ denote the number of divisors of $b_n$. It is proved that the equation $\tau(b_n)=O((\log b_n)^\Delta)$ is false for every $\Delta$; on the other hand, $\tau(b_n)=O(b_n{}^\delta)$ for all $\delta>0$. Also $\sum_{b_n\leq x}\tau(b_n)=b_n\log b_n+O(b_n)$. (4) Let $\sigma(b_n)$ denote the sum of the divisors of $b_n$. Then

$$\sum_{r=1}^{n}\sigma(b_r) = \tfrac{1}{2}\zeta(2)b_n{}^2+O(b_n{}^{\alpha+1}),$$

where $\zeta(2)=\sum b_n^{-2}$. (5) If $Q(x)$ is the number of square-free $b_j \leqq x$, then

$$Q(x) = \frac{2}{\zeta(2)}+O(\sqrt{x})+O(x^{\alpha}).$$

*L. Carlitz* (Durham, N.C.)

Citations: MR 24# A708 = N80-10.

## N80-19 (26# 6150)

**Bredihin, B. M.**

**On power densities of certain subsets of free semigroups. (Russian)**

*Izv. Vysš. Učebn. Zaved. Matematika* **1958**, *no.* 3 (4), 24–30.

Let $G$ be a multiplicatively written free commutative semigroup with a denumerable set $\{\omega_1, \omega_2, \cdots\}$ of generators. Let $N$ be a homomorphism of $G$ onto the multiplicative semigroup of non-zero integers such that there is only a finite number of elements $\alpha \in G$ with $N(\alpha) \leqq x$. Denote $\nu_G(x)=\sum_{N(\alpha)\leqq x, \alpha\in G} 1$. If there exists $\lim_{x=\infty} (\nu_G(x)/x^{\theta})=C$ with $\theta>0$, $C>0$ the number $C$ is called the power $\theta$-density of $G$. Every $\alpha\in G$ can be written in an obvious way as $\alpha=\beta\gamma^2$, where $\gamma^2$ is the "largest" quadratic factor. Denote $Q(\alpha)=\gamma$. Consider the following three sets (with $\mu$, $\delta\in G$ fixed and in an obvious notation):

$$g' = \{\alpha\in G|(\alpha,\mu) = 1, Q(\alpha) = 1\},$$

$$g'' = \{\alpha\in G|(\alpha,\mu) = 1, Q(\alpha) = \delta\},$$

$$g''' = \{\alpha\in G|(\alpha,\mu) = 1, N(Q(\alpha)) \geqq N(\delta)\}.$$

Denote further

$$(*) \quad \nu'_{\mu} = \sum_{N(\alpha)\leqq x,\, \alpha\in g'} 1, \quad \nu''_{\mu,\delta}(x) = \sum_{N(\alpha)\leqq x,\, \alpha\in g''} 1,$$

$$\nu'''_{\mu,\delta}(x) = \sum_{N(\alpha)\leqq x,\, \alpha\in g'''} 1.$$

Theorem: If (for a given $N$) $G$ has a power $\theta$-density $C>0$, then the sets $g'$, $g''$, $g'''$ have power $\theta$-densities. For instance, for the set $g'$ it is equal to

$$C' = C_G \prod_{\omega|\mu} N(\omega)^{\theta}/(N(\omega)^{\theta}+1)$$

(where $C_G$ is a constant depending only on $G$ and $N$). Formulas for the densities of $g''$ and $g'''$ are also given.

Next, asymptotic formulas for the functions (*) are given. Theorem: Suppose that (for a fixed $N$) $\nu_G(x)=Cx^{\theta}+R(x)$ with $R(x)=O(x^{\theta_1})$, $\theta_1<\theta$. Then $\nu_{\mu}'(x)=C'x^{\theta}+r(x)$, where $r(x)=O(x^{\theta/2})$ if $\theta_1<\theta/2$, $r(x)=O(x^{\theta/2}\log x)$ if $\theta_1=\theta/2$, $r(x)=O(x^{\theta_1})$, if $\theta_1>\theta/2$. Analogous formulas are given for $\nu''_{\mu,\delta}$, $\nu'''_{\mu,\delta}$.

It is pointed out that these results contain a number of special cases of number-theoretical interest, in particular, the results of H. Kanold [J. Reine Angew. Math. **193** (1954), 250–252; MR **16**, 569] and P. Scherk [ibid. **196** (1956), 133–136; MR **18**, 284]. *Št. Schwarz* (Bratislava)

Citations: MR 16, 569h = N28-30; MR 18, 284b = N28-34.

## N80-20 (27# 125)

**Wegmann, Helmut**

**Über $k$-freie Elemente in Halbgruppen reeller Zahlen.**

*J. Reine Angew. Math.* **212** (1963), 180–182.

Generalizing results of Kanold [same J. **193** (1954), 250–252; MR **16**, 569] and Scherk [ibid. **196** (1956), 133–136; MR **18**, 284] in the case $k=2$, B. Volkmann proved several density theorems for the set of $k$-free integers [ibid. **198** (1957), 7–9; MR **19**, 636]. By Bredihin [Ukrain. Mat. Ž. **11** (1959), 137–145; MR **22** #3708] the results of Kanold and Scherk were extended to the more general case where integers are replaced by the elements of a multiplicative semigroup of positive real numbers with an infinite base $\{\omega_1, \omega_2, \cdots\}$ having no finite limit point ($\omega_i>1$). The author shows that in this case also the analogues of Volkmann's theorems hold.

*J. F. Koksma* (Amsterdam)

Citations: MR 16, 569h = N28-30; MR 18, 284b = N28-34; MR 19, 636b = N28-38; MR 22# 3708 = N80-7.

## N80-21 (27# 2467)

**Horadam, E. M.**

**The Euler $\phi$ function for generalized integers.**

*Proc. Amer. Math. Soc.* **14** (1963), 754–762.

In a previous paper [Amer. Math. Monthly **68** (1961), 626–629; MR **24** #708] the author defined generalized integers as follows. Given a finite or infinite sequence $\{p\}$ of real numbers (generalized primes) such that $1<p_1<p_2<\cdots$. Form the set $\{l\}$ of all possible $p$-products $p_1^{v_1}p_2^{v_2}\cdots$, where the $v_j$ are integers $\geqq 0$ of which all but a finite number are 0. Suppose that no two generalized integers are equal if their $v$'s are different. Then arrange $\{l\}$ in an increasing sequence $1=l_1<l_2<\cdots$.

Let $[x]$ be the number of generalized integers $\leqq x$. It is assumed that $[x]=x+O(x^{\alpha})$, $0<\alpha<1$. The author defines generalizations of the Euler function, Möbius function and the like. A number of identities and estimates are obtained. The main result of the paper is an asymptotic formula for the sum $\sum_{l_p,l_q\leqq x} f_k((l_p, l_q))$, where $f_k(l_n)=\sum_{d\delta=l_n} g(d)[\delta^k]$, and $g(l_n)$ is bounded. This generalizes some results due to E. Cohen on functions of a g.c.d. [Proc. Amer. Math. Soc. **11** (1960), 164–171; MR **22** #2575].

*L. Carlitz* (Durham, N.C.)

Citations: MR 22# 2575 = A36-30; MR 24# A708 = N80-10.

Referred to in N80-32.

## N80-22 (28# 5047)

**Horadam, E. M.**

**A calculus of convolutions for generalised integers.**

*Nederl. Akad. Wetensch. Proc. Ser. A* **66**=*Indag. Math.* **25** (1963), 695–698.

Let a finite or infinite sequence $\{p\}$ of real numbers $1<p_1<p_2<\cdots$ be given (generalized primes). We form the set $\{l\}$ of all possible $p$-products $p_1^{v_1}p_2^{v_2}\cdots$, where $v_1, v_2, \cdots$ are non-negative integers of which all but a finite number are 0. Suppose that no two of these "generalized integers" are equal if the $v$'s are different. Then arrange $\{l\}$ as an increasing sequence $1=l_1<l_2<l_3<\cdots$. {The reviewer remarks that in the case of an infinite sequence $\{p\}$ the possibility of such an ordering for the set $\{l\}$ is equivalent to the condition $p_n\to\infty$ as $n$ increases indefinitely; moreover, this implies $l_n\to\infty$.}

The author considers "arithmetical functions" $f(l)$ defined on the set $\{l\}$ and then introduces the "convolution" of two given arithmetical functions $f$ and $g$ by putting $f(l)*g(l)=\sum_{d\delta=1} f(d)g(\delta)$. Then she develops a calculus quite similar to the one given by the reviewer in the case of ordinary arithmetical functions [Nederl. Akad. Wetensch. Proc. Ser. A **58** (1955), 10–15; MR **16**, 905].

As applications the author proves a number of identities which are used in a following paper to deduce an analogue of Selberg's lemma for the prime number theorem; compare with the next review [#5048].

*J. Popken* (Amstelveen)

Citations: MR 16, 905e = N20-26.

**N80-23** **(28# 5048)**

**Horadam, E. M.**

**Selberg's inequality for generalised integers using the calculus of convolutions.**

*Nederl. Akad. Wetensch. Proc. Ser. A* **66** = *Indag. Math.* **25** (1963), 699–704.

Given a finite or infinite sequence $\{p\}$ of real numbers (generalized primes), $1<p_1<p_2<p_3<\cdots$, we form the set of all possible $p$-products $p_1^{a_1}p_2^{a_2}\cdots$, where $a_1, a_2, \cdots$ are non-negative integers of which ali but a finite number are 0. Suppose that no two of these numbers ("generalized integers") are equal (except in the trivial case). Then arrange $\{l\}$ as an increasing sequence $1=l_1<l_2<l_3<\cdots$. Let $\nu(x)=\sum_{l_n\leqq x}1$, $\pi(x)=\sum_{p_n\leqq x}1$.

Assume $\nu(x)=Cx^\theta+o(x^{\theta_1})$, where $C$, $\theta$, $\theta_1$ are positive constants, $\theta_1<\theta$. Then ("generalized prime number theorem")

$$(1)\qquad \lim_{x\to\infty}\frac{\pi(x)}{x^\theta/\log x}=\theta^{-1}.$$

The author applies what she calls "the calculus of convolutions" to obtain an analogue of Selberg's fundamental lemma. From the analogue one obtains the generalized prime number theorem (1) as Bredihin has shown [Mat. Sb. (N.S.) **46 (88)** (1958), 143–158; MR **21** #87].

*S. Chowla* (University Park, Pa.)

Citations: MR 21# 87 = N80-5.

Referred to in N80-59.

**N80-24** **(29# 3452)**

**Rémond, Paul**

**Évaluations asymptotiques dans certains semi-groupes.**

*C. R. Acad. Sci. Paris* **258** (1964), 4179–4181.

Let $\mathscr{E}(E^*)$ be a commutative semigroup having a subset of primes $E^*$ such that if $A\in\mathscr{E}$, then $A$ has a unique expression in the form

$$A=P_1^{\alpha_1}\cdots P_n^{\alpha_n}\qquad (P_i\in E^*,\ \alpha_i\in Z).$$

Assume that there is a norm $N$ from $\mathscr{E}$ to the natural numbers with $N(A)\geqq 2$ and $N(e)=1$. The purpose of this note is to extend certain results of H. Delange [Ann. Sci. École Norm. Sup. (3) **78** (1961), 1–29]. A normed semigroup $\mathscr{E}(E^*)$ is called a $D$ semigroup if

$$\sum_{A\in\mathscr{E}}N(A)^{-s}=u(s)(s-1)^{-\mu},$$

$s=\sigma+it$, $\sigma>1$, $\mu>0$, $u(s)$ holomorphic for $\sigma\geqq 1$, $u(s)\neq 0$ for $\sigma\geqq 1$. The set $E^*$ is said to be regular if, for $\sigma>1$,

$$\sum_{P\in E^*}N(P)^{-s}=-\mu\log(s-1)+r(s),$$

$\mu\geqq 0$ and $r(s)$ holomorphic for $\sigma\geqq 1$. $\mu$ is called the density of $E^*$. A normed semigroup $\mathscr{E}$ is a $D$ semigroup if and only if the set $E^*$ of primes is regular with density $\mu>0$. In addition, the author announces certain asymptotic relations for $D$ semigroups and deduces the following corollary. If $k=2, 4, p^\alpha, 2p^\alpha$, where $p$ is a rational prime $>2$,

$$\sum_{\substack{n\leqq x\\ n\equiv 1 \,(\mathrm{mod}\, k)}}1\sim\left(\frac{\phi(\phi(k))}{[\phi(k)]^{\phi(k)}[\phi(k)-1]!}\right)\left(\frac{x(\log\log x)^{\phi(k)-1}}{\log x}\right),$$

where the summation extends over those $n$ which are not the product of two integers congruent to 1 mod $k$.

*R. Ayoub* (University Park, Pa.)

Referred to in N80-25, N80-36.

**N80-25** **(31# 2224)**

**Rémond, Paul**

**Évaluations asymptotiques dans certains semi-groupes.**

*C. R. Acad. Sci. Paris* **260** (1965), 6250–6251.

Die kommutative Halbgruppe $\mathscr{E}(E^*)$ enthalte eine Untermenge $E^*$ von "Primzahlen", so daß jedes $A\in\mathscr{E}$ eindeutig als Produkt von "Primzahlen" darstellbar ist. Die Begriffe Norm, $D$-Halbgruppe, reguläre Menge und Dichte wurden in einer früheren Arbeit des Verfassers [dieselben C. R. **258** (1964), 4179–4181; MR **29** #3452] erklärt. Sei nun eine $D$-Halbgruppe $\mathscr{E}$ in Klassen $C_0, \cdots, C_k$ $(k\geqq 1)$ zerlegt, die eine abelsche Gruppe mit Einselement $C_0$ bilden, so daß die Menge der "Primzahlen" in jeder Klasse $C_\kappa$ regulär und von positiver Dichte ist. Für die Anzahl $n(B)$ der Darstellungen von $B\in C_0$ als Produkt unzerlegbarer Elemente aus $C_0$ kündigt der Autor (mit einem Polynom $P$) folgendes Ergebnis an:

$$\sum_{\substack{B\in C_0,\\ \mathrm{Norm}(B)\leqq x}}n(B)\sim x\cdot\exp\{P(\log\log x, \log\log\log x)\}\quad (x\to\infty).$$

Ferner kündigt der Autor die Anwendbarkeit seiner Ergebnisse auf Idealklassen algebraischer Zahlkörper an. So ist etwa die Anzahl der Hauptideale der Norm $\leqq x$, die nicht in ein Produkt zweier Hauptideale zerlegbar sind, $\sim K\cdot x\cdot(\log\log x)^{t-1}\cdot(\log x)^{-1}$ mit einer gewissen ganzen Zahl $t\geqq 1$.

*W. Schwarz* (Freiburg)

Citations: MR 29# 3452 = N80-24.

Referred to in N80-36.

**N80-26** **(29# 5795)**

**Horadam, E. M.**

**Ramanujan's sum for generalised integers.**

*Duke Math. J.* **31** (1964), 697–702.

Let $\{p\}$ be a sequence of real numbers (generalized primes) such that $0<1<p_1<p_2<\cdots$. Form the set $\{l\}$ of all $p$-products $p_1^{v_1}p_2^{v_2}\cdots$, where the $v_j$ are integers $\geqq 0$, of which all but a finite number are 0. These numbers are called generalized integers; it is assumed that no two are equal if their $v$'s are different. Also the $l$'s are numbered so that $0<1<l_2<l_3<\cdots$. Ramanujan's sum for $\{l\}$ is defined by means of

$$c(l_n, l_r)=\sum_{d\mid(l_n,l_r)}\mu(l_r/d)d.$$

More generally the author defines

$$c_k(l_n, l_r)=\sum_{\substack{d\mid l_r\\ d^k\mid l_n}}\mu(l_r/d)d^k,$$

thus generalizing the function

$$c_k(n, r)=\sum_{(x,r^k)_k=1}e(nx, r^k)$$

introduced by E. Cohen [same J. **22** (1955), 543–550; MR **17**, 238]. The present paper generalizes a number of results concerning $c_k(n, r)$, and also some properties of the class $E_k$ of $k$-even functions, that is, functions $f(l_n, l_r)$ such that

$$f(l_n, l_r)=f((l_n, l_r^k)_k, l_r).$$

The class $E_k$ for functions of integers has been studied by P. J. McCarthy [J. Reine Angew. Math. **203** (1960), 55–63; MR **22** #2574]. For example, it is proved that if $f(l_n, l_r)\in E_k$, then

$$f(l_n, l_r)=\sum_{d\mid l_r}\alpha(d)c_k(l_n, d),$$

where

$$\alpha(d)=\frac{1}{l_r^k}\sum_{\delta\mid l_r}f\left[\left(\frac{l_r}{\delta}\right)^k, l_r\right]c_k\left[\left(\frac{l_r}{d}\right)^k, \delta\right].$$

*L. Carlitz* (Durham, N.C.)

Citations: MR 17, 238g = A36-19; MR 22# 2574 = A36-29.

Referred to in N80-27, N80-53.

**N80-27** **(33# 7308)**

**Horadam, E. M.**

**Addendum to: "Ramanujan's sum for generalised integers".**

*Duke Math. J.* **33** (1966), 705–707.

The present paper is a continuation of the author's earlier paper [same J. **31** (1964), 697-702; MR **29** #5795] and assumes the notation, definitions and results of the latter. Put $C_k(l_n, l_r/l_m) = c_k(l_n, l_r/l_m)$ if $l_m | l_r$, $C_k(l_n, l_r/l_m) = 0$ otherwise. It is proved that a function $f(l_n, l_r)$ of the class $E_k$ can be represented in the form

$$f(l_n, l_r) = \sum_{l_m \leqq l_r} \alpha(l_r, l_m) C_k(l_n, l_r/l_m),$$

where $\alpha(l_r, l_m) = (1/l_r^k) \sum_{d | (l_r, l_m)} d^k w(l_r/d, d)$. Several applications of this result are given.

*L. Carlitz* (Durham, N.C.)

Citations: MR 29# 5795 = N80-26.

**N80-28** **(29# 5802)**

**Fogels, E.**

**On the abstract theory of primes. I.**

*Acta Arith.* **10** (1964/65), 137–182.

The theory in question arises from replacing the positive integers by a countable multiplicative semigroup $G$ of real numbers $a \geqq 1$ with some asymptotic distribution law. The role of the primes is taken over by the generators of $G$. To get the equivalent of arithmetic progressions, $G$ is split into classes $H_i$ $(i = 1, \cdots, h)$ forming a group $K$ under the multiplication given by: If $a \in H_i$, $a' \in H_j$, then $aa' \in H_k$ with $k = k(i, j)$. The class $H_i$ corresponds to an arithmetic progression.

The author's aim is to get, under suitable assumptions, an upper estimate for the smallest generator of $G$ in $H_i$, valid simultaneously for all $i$. A parameter $D$ is introduced corresponding to the common difference in an arithmetic progression, and it is supposed that $D > 3$, $1 \leqq h \leqq D^{c_0}$, $c_0 > 0$. The asymptotic distribution law which is assumed is $\sum 1 = \alpha x + O(D^{c_1} x^{1-\theta})$ for large $x$, where the summation is over all $a \in H_i$ such that $a \leqq x$, and $\alpha = D^l$; the constants $l$, $c_1$, $\theta$ do not depend on $i$.

For even $h$ let $K_j$ be any subgroup of $K$ with index 2. Then it is shown that

$$\lim_{x \to \infty} \Big( \sum_{a \in K, a \leqq x} a^{-1} - \sum_{a \notin K_j, a \leqq x} a^{-1} \Big) = C_j = C_j(D).$$

Now the main theorem is: (i) If $\theta > \frac{1}{2}$, there is a $c > 0$ such that for any $x \geqq 1$, $H_i$ has a generator in the interval $(x, xD^c)$. For odd $h$ this holds also if $\theta \leqq \frac{1}{2}$. (ii) For even $h$ and $\theta \leqq \frac{1}{2}$, the conclusion of (i) holds if there is a $c_2 > 0$ such that $C_j > D^{-c_2}$ for any $j$ (in this case $c$ also depends on $c_2$). (iii) Let $\pi(x, H_i)$ be the number of generators (generalized primes) in $H_i$ not exceeding $x$. Then constants $c_3$, $c_4$ exist such that $\pi(x, H_i) > D^{-c_4} x/\log x$ for $x > D^{c_3}$.

The proof, running to over twenty-five lemmas, is long, involved, and not easy to follow. The method is analytical in nature and employs the following zeta-functions and $L$-series: $\zeta(s, H) = \sum_{a \in H} a^{-s}$, $\zeta(s, \chi) = \sum_a \chi(a) a^{-s}$ ($\chi$ is a character of the group $K$ and $\chi(a)$ is $\chi(H)$ for all $a \in H$). One then has, as for the ordinary case, $\zeta(s, \chi) = \prod_b [1 - \chi(b) b^{-s}]^{-1}$, where $b$ runs over all generators of $G$.

*R. D. James* (Vancouver, B.C.)

Referred to in N80-29.

**N80-29** **(30# 4738)**

**Fogels, E.**

**On the abstract theory of primes. II.**

*Acta Arith.* **10** (1964/65), 333–358.

An abstract analogue of primes in arithmetic progressions is obtained here by considering an infinite semigroup $G$ on a countable number of generators. The elements of $G$ are divided into $h$ classes $H_i$, $1 \leqq h \leqq D$, forming a group $\Gamma$. (If $a \in H_i$, $a_1 \in H_j$, then $aa_1 \in H_p$, $p = p(i, j)$.) The classes $H_i$ correspond to arithmetic progressions with common difference $D$, and the generators correspond to primes (cf. the previous paper with the same title [same Acta **10** (1964/65), 137–182; MR **29** #5802]). A homomorphism $N$ of $G$ into the multiplicative semigroup of reals $\geqq 1$ leads to analogues $N(a)$ of absolute values. An asymptotic density law is assumed in the form $\sum 1 = D^l x + O(D^{c_1} x^{1-\theta})$, where the summation is over $a \in H_j$, $N(a) \leqq x$, with $0 < \theta \leqq 1$, and $l$, $c_1$, and $\theta$ independent of $j$. A homomorphism $\Phi$ of $G$ into the multiplicative semigroup of complex numbers is used, where

$$\Phi : a \to [N(a)]^{1/2} \exp(2\pi i \alpha), \qquad 0 \leqq \alpha < 1,$$

and $R(a) = \arg \Phi(a)$. In addition to the asymptotic density law above, it is assumed that $\sum 1 = \varphi D^l x + O(D^{c_1} x^{1-\theta_1})$ (where the summation is over $a \in H_j$, $N(a) \leqq x$, $0 \leqq R(a) < \varphi$), uniformly for the angle $\varphi$, $0 < \varphi \leqq 1$, and with $\theta_1$ independent of $j$ and satisfying $0 < \theta_1 \leqq \theta$. Let a fixed angular region $A$ be given by

$$A = \{z : \arg z \equiv \alpha_0 + \lambda\Delta \pmod 1\},$$

where $0 \leqq \lambda < 1$, $D^{-c_0} < \Delta \leqq 1$, and $c_0$ is arbitrarily large.

Under these conditions, the author obtains an estimate on the least norm $N(b)$ of a generator of $G$ whose image under $\Phi$ is in $A$. Theorem: (a) If $\theta > \frac{1}{2}$, there is a $c > 0$, $c = c(c_0, c_1, l, \theta, \theta_1)$, such that for any $x \geqq 1$ and any $H_j$, there is a generator $b \in H_j$ satisfying $x < N(b) < xD_1{}^c$, $R(b) \in A$, with $D_1 = D^{\log\log(8/\Delta)}$. For odd $h$, this holds also for $\theta \leqq \frac{1}{2}$. (b) Let $h$ be even and $\theta \leqq \frac{1}{2}$. Suppose that for any subgroup $\Gamma_1$ of $\Gamma$ of index 2, there is a $c_2$ such that the limit as $x \to \infty$ of $\sum_1 a^{-1} - \sum_2 a^{-1}$ is greater than $D^{-c_2}$, where the summation in $\sum_1$ is over $a \in \Gamma_1$, $N(a) \leqq x$, and in $\sum_2$, over $a \notin \Gamma_1$, $N(a) \leqq x$. Then the conclusion of (a) holds with $c = c(c_0, c_1, c_2, l, \theta, \theta_1)$. (c) (Corollary) Let $\pi(x, A, H_j)$ denote the number of generators $b \in H_j$ such that $\Phi(b) \in A$ and $N(b) \leqq x$. Then for appropriate constants $c_3$ and $c_4$, $\pi(x, A, H_j) > D_1{}^{-c_4}(x/\log x)$ for $x > D_1{}^{c_3}$.

*R. D. James* (Vancouver, B.C.)

Citations: MR 29# 5802 = N80-28.

Referred to in N80-41.

**N80-30** **(30# 1197)**

**Juškis, Z.**

**A theorem of P. Erdős and A. Wintner on ordered semigroups with regular norm. (Russian. Lithuanian and German summaries)**

*Litovsk. Mat. Sb.* **4** (1964), 429–450.

Let $E$ and $E_1$, respectively, be the set of all integers and the multiplicative semigroup of all positive real numbers. Suppose that $f$ is a real function defined on $E$ such that $f(m_1 m_2) = f(m_1) + f(m_2)$ for any $m_1, m_2 \in E$ with $(m_1, m_2) = 1$. For $y$, $n \in E$ let $M_n(y) = \{m : m \in E, m \leqq n, f(m) < y\}$, $\lambda_n(y) = (1/n) M_n(y)$. P. Erdős [J. London Math. Soc. **13** (1938), 119–127] and P. Erdős and A. Wintner [Amer. J. Math. **61** (1939), 713–721] proved a theorem concerning the limit of $\lambda_n(y)$ for $n \to \infty$. The author generalizes the theorem of Erdős and Wintner for the case in which $E$ is replaced by a commutative semigroup $G$ with a countable set of free generators; it is assumed that there exists a homomorphism $N : G \to E_1$ satisfying certain conditions, and by means of $N$ a relation $\leqq$ on $G$ is defined so that $G(\leqq)$ is a quasi-ordered set (not an ordered set, in general).

*J. Jakubík* (Košice)

**N80-31** **(32# 4094)**

**Horadam, E. M.**

**Exponential functions for arithmetical semi-groups.**

*J. Reine Angew. Math.* **222** (1966), 14–19.

Let $\{p\}$ be a finite or infinite sequence of real numbers such that $1<p_1<p_2<\cdots$. Let $\{b\}$ denote the set of all $p$-products, that is, products $p_1^{v_1}p_2^{v_2}\cdots$, where $v_1, v_2, \cdots$ are integers $\geqq 0$ of which all but a finite number are 0. The $p_j$ are called generalized primes, the $b_j$ generalized integers. It is assumed that the semi-group formed by the $b$'s is free; the $b$'s are numbered so that $1=b_1<b_2<b_3<\cdots$. The author defines divisibility and greatest common divisor in $\{b\}$ in the obvious way. She also defines a generalized Möbius function $\mu(b_n)$ by means of $\mu(b_n)=0$ if $b_n$ has a square factor, $\mu(b_n)=(-1)^k$ when $b$ is the prime of $k$ distinct primes. Other functions defined are

$$g(b_n, b_r) = \begin{cases} b_r & (b_r|b_n), \\ 0 & (b_r\nmid b_n), \end{cases}$$

$$c(b_n, b_r) = \sum_{d|b_r} \mu\left(\frac{b_r}{d}\right)g(b_n, d) = \sum_{d|(b_n, b_r)} \mu\left(\frac{b_r}{d}\right) d,$$

$$C\left(b_n, \frac{b_r}{b_m}\right) = \begin{cases} c(b_n, b_r/b_m) & (b_m|b_r), \\ 0 & (\text{otherwise}). \end{cases}$$

Thus, $c(b_n, b_r)$ is a generalization of the ordinary Ramanujan sum. The first theorem of the paper asserts that $\sum_{b_m\leqq b_r} C(b_m, b_r/b_m)=0$ ($b_r\neq$ square), $=b_r^{1/2}$ ($b_r=$ square). In Theorem 2, the sum $\sum_{b_m\leqq b_r b_s} C(b_a, b_r/b_m)C(b_c, b_s/b_m)$ is evaluated when $(b_a, b_r)=(b_c, b_s)=1$. In the latter part of the paper the author considers unitary divisors ($d$ is a unitary divisor of $b_n$ if $d\delta=b_n$ and $(d, \delta)=1$). Functions $\mu^*(b_n)$, $c^*(b_n, b_r)$, $C^*(b_n, b_r/b_m)$ are defined, and unitary analogues of Theorems 1 and 2 are proved.

*L. Carlitz* (Durham, N.C.)

## N80-32 (32# 4095)

**Horadam, E. M.**

**The number of unitary divisors of a generalised integer.**
*Amer. Math. Monthly* **71** (1964), 893–895.

Let $p_1, p_2, \cdots$ be real numbers, with $p_0=1<p_1<p_2<\cdots$, and let $\{l\}$ be the multiplicative semigroup generated by these "generalized primes". Suppose that $\{l\}$ has unique factorization, and let $\tau^*(l_n)$ be the number of "unitary divisors" of $l_n\in\{l\}$, i.e., the number of divisors $d$ such that $(d, l_n/d)=1$, in the obvious sense. Suppose also that $[x]=x+O(x^\alpha)$, $0<\alpha<1$, where $[x]$ is the number of $l_n\leqq x$. Put $\zeta(s)=\sum_{n=1}^\infty l_n^{-s}$. It is shown that

$$\sum_{l_n\leqq x} \tau^*(l_n) = \frac{x}{\zeta(2)}\left\{\log x - 2\frac{\zeta'(2)}{\zeta(2)} + 2\gamma_1 - 1\right\} + O(x^{(1+\alpha)/2}),$$

where $\gamma_1$ is the constant in the earlier result of the author [Proc. Amer. Math. Soc. **14** (1963), 754–762; MR **27** #2467]: $\sum_{l_n\leqq x} 1/l_n=\log x+\gamma_1+O(x^{\alpha-1})$.

*W. J. LeVeque* (Ann Arbor, Mich.)

Citations: MR 27# 2467 = N80-21.
Referred to in N80-47.

## N80-33 (32# 4096)

**Horadam, E. M.**

**The average order of the number of generalised integers representable as a product of a prime and a square.**
*J. Reine Angew. Math.* **217** (1965), 64–68.

The assumptions are the same as in the review above [#4095] except that it is now supposed that $[x]=Cx^\theta+O(x^{\theta_1})$, $C>0$, $\theta>\theta_1$. Let $A(x)$ be the number of "integers" (elements of $\{l\}$) which are the product of a prime and a square. It is shown that

$$A(x) = \frac{\gamma_\theta}{\theta}\frac{x^\theta}{\log x}+O\left(\frac{x^\theta}{\log^2 x}\right),$$

where $\gamma_\theta$ is a constant. An estimate is also given of the number of square-full "integers" not exceeding $x$.

*W. J. LeVeque* (Ann Arbor, Mich.)

## N80-34 (32# 4097)

**Wegmann, Helmut**

**Beiträge zur Zahlentheorie auf freien Halbgruppen. I.**
*J. Reine Angew. Math.* **221** (1966), 20–43.

The author considers a free abelian semigroup $G$ with a countable set $E$ of generators ("primes") $p_1, p_2, \cdots$, and with a norm-function, satisfying $|gg'|=|g|\cdot|g'|$, $|p_i|>1$, and $\lim_{i\to\infty}|p_i|=\infty$. For a subset $U\subset G$, putting $U(x)=\sum_{g\in U, |g|\leqq x} 1$, he defines the density $d(U)=\lim_{x\to\infty} U(x)/G(x)$ (if the limit exists). Under certain assumptions on $G(x)$, the author first gives analogues of theorems of elementary number theory, among other theorems the Möbius inversion formulae, properties of analogues of number-theoretic functions (number and sum of divisors, Euler's $\varphi$-function) and evaluation of the density of various subsets of $G$ (e.g., the density of the set of $k$-free elements of $G$).

Finally, the author constructs several Boolean algebras $\mathfrak{R}_j$, consisting of subsets $U\subset G$, such that every $U\in\mathfrak{R}_j$ possesses a density, and he gives the power (Mächtigkeit) of these algebras; for the semigroup of natural numbers similar problems were discussed by R. C. Buck [Amer. J. Math. **68** (1946), 560–580; MR **8**, 255]. If $G$ is the set of natural numbers, the author evaluates the Hausdorff dimension of $\Gamma(\mathfrak{R}_j)$, where the dyadic mapping $\Gamma$ is defined by $\Gamma(U)=\sum_{u\in U} 2^{-u}$ [compare Volkmann, J. Reine Angew. Math. **190** (1952), 199–230; MR **15**, 15].

*W. Schwarz* (Freiburg)

Citations: MR 8, 255f = B04-2; MR 15, 15e = B20-3.

## N80-35 (32# 4098)

**Wegmann, Helmut**

**Beiträge zur Zahlentheorie auf freien Halbgruppen. II.**
*J. Reine Angew. Math.* **221** (1966), 150–159.

Let $G$ be a free abelian semigroup with a countable set of generators ("primes") $p_1, p_2, \cdots$, and with a norm $|g|$, such that $|p_i|>1$ and $\lim_{i\to\infty}|p_i|=\infty$. Assuming asymptotic formulas for $G(x)=\sum_{g\in G, |g|\leqq x} 1$, several writers gave asymptotic formulas for the number $\pi(x)$ of "primes" $p$ with $|p|\leqq x$ [Beurling, Acta Math. **68** (1937), 255–291; Nyman, ibid. **81** (1949), 299–307; MR **11**, 332; Bredihin, Dokl. Akad. Nauk SSSR **118** (1958), 855–857; MR **20** #5175; Mat. Sb. (N.S.) **46 (88)** (1958), 143–158; MR **21** #87; Malliavin, Acta Math. **106** (1961), 281–298; MR **26** #87].

The author, adapting Wirsing's elementary proof [J. Reine Angew. Math. **214/215** (1964), 1–18; MR **29** #3457] of the prime number theorem with remainder term, shows: If $G(x)=Ax^\delta+O(x^\delta\log^{-\beta}x)$, $\beta>3$, $\delta>0$, then $\pi(x)=li(x^\delta)+O(x^\delta\log^{-\gamma}x)$ for all $\gamma<\frac{1}{2}(\beta-1)$.

{Reviewer's remark: In § 1 the results of Beurling and Malliavin are incorrectly cited.}

For Part I, see #4097 above. *W. Schwarz* (Freiburg)

Citations: MR 11, 332a = A40-10; MR 20# 5175 = N80-4; MR 21# 87 = N80-5; MR 29# 3457 = N20-56.
Referred to in N80-37.

## N80-36 (32# 5614)

**Rémond, Paul**

**Évaluations asymptotiques dans certains semi-groupes.**
*C. R. Acad. Sci. Paris Sér. A-B* **262** (1966), A271–A273.

Generalizing his former results [same C. R. **258** (1964), 4179–4181; MR **29** #3452; ibid. **260** (1965), 6250–6251;

MR **31** #2224], the author states three theorems on normed semigroups $\mathscr{E}$ with a set of "primes", possessing a "degree" $r \geqq 0$; that means that the number of "primes" with norm $\leqq x$ is $\sim \mu x\,(\log\log x)^r/\log x$. For instance, he announces that if the "primes" of each class of a partition of $\mathscr{E}$ into classes $C_i$ have a "degree", then $\sum_{B\in C_1, NB\leqq x} 1 \sim \sum_{B\in C_i, NB\leqq x} 1$.

*W. Schwarz* (Freiburg)

Citations: MR 29# 3452 = N80-24; MR 31# 2224 = N80-25.

## N80-37 (33# 1294)

**Bredihin, B. M.**

**Distribution of generating elements in ordered semigroups with a regular normalization. (Russian)**

*Proc. First Sci. Conf. Math. Dept. Ped. Inst. Volga Region (May,* 1960) *(Russian), pp.* 4–8. *Kuĭbyšev. Gos. Ped. Inst., Kuybyshev,* 1961.

Denote by $G$ a free abelian semigroup with a countable set $P$ of generators ("primes") and with a norm-function $N$. Assuming $\sum_{a\in G, N(a)\leqq x} 1 = C\cdot x^\theta + O(x^{\theta'})$, $\theta' < \theta$, the author proves (by the classical complex integration method) an asymptotic formula for the number of primes $p$ of $G$ with norm $\leqq x$,

$$\pi_G(x) = \sum_{p\in P, N(p)\leqq x} 1 = \mathrm{li}(x^\theta) + O(x^\theta\cdot\exp(-a\sqrt{\log x})),$$

with a constant $a > 0$, depending on $G$ and $N$. {This problem has also been treated by elementary methods; compare Bredihin [Mat. Sb. (N.S.) **46 (88)** (1958), 143–158; MR **21** #87] and Wegmann [J. Reine Angew. Math. **221** (1966), 150–159; MR **32** #4098].} Further, the author estimates the difference $\pi_G(x) - \mathrm{li}(x^\theta)$ from below.

*W. Schwarz* (Freiburg)

Citations: MR 21# 87 = N80-5; MR 32# 4098 = N80-35.

## N80-38 (33# 2605)

**Faĭnleĭb, A. S.**

**Summation of values of multiplicative functions defined on a normalized semigroup. (Russian. Uzbek summary)**

*Izv. Akad. Nauk UzSSR Ser. Fiz.-Mat. Nauk* **9** (1965), *no.* 6, 49–55.

The author considers multiplicative functions $f$, defined on a semigroup $\mathfrak{S}$ with norm $N$ and with unique factorization into primes $p$. He derives an asymptotic formula for $\sum_{N(a)\leqq x, a\in\mathfrak{S}} f(a)$ (more generally, $a$ lies in certain subclasses of $\mathfrak{S}$) from assumptions on the values $f(p^r)$. A very specialized form of his Theorem 1: If

$$\sum_{p\leqq x} f(p)\log p = \tau\cdot\log x + B + O(\exp(-\log^\alpha x)),$$

then $\sum_{n\leqq x} f(n)$ has an asymptotic expansion

$$\sim \log^\tau x\cdot\sum_{\nu\geqq 0} a_\nu\cdot(\log x)^{-\nu}$$

[cf. Wirsing, Math. Ann. **143** (1961), 75–102; MR **24** #A1241]. Another result is an asymptotic formula for the number of $a\in\mathfrak{S}$, $N(a)\leqq x^t$, such that $p|a$ implies $N(p) > x$ [cf. de Bruijn, Nederl. Akad. Wetensch. Proc. Ser. A **53** (1950), 803–812; MR **12**, 11; ibid. **54** (1951), 50–60; MR **13**, 724; de Bruijn and van Lint, ibid. **67** (1964), 339–347, 348–359; MR **30** #4731]. *W. Schwarz* (Freiburg)

Citations: MR 12, 11d = N28-22; MR 13, 724e = N28-28; MR 24# A1241 = N36-30; MR 30# 4731 = N28-56.

## N80-39 (33# 2611)

**Bredihin, B. M.**

**Converses of certain theorems on power densities of ordered semigroups. (Russian)**

*Kuĭbyšev. Gos. Ped. Inst. Učen. Zap. Vyp.* 29 (1959), 13–20.

Denote by $G$ a free abelian semigroup with a norm $N$. Put $\nu_G(x) = \sum_{\alpha\in G, N(\alpha)\leqq x} 1$, and $\nu'(x) = \sum^*_{\alpha\in G} 1$ (* means summation over the "squarefree" $\alpha$ with $N(\alpha)\leqq x$). The author proves by elementary methods that if $\nu'(x) \sim C'x^\theta$ ($C' > 0$, $\theta > 0$), then $\nu_G(x) \sim Cx^\theta$ (the constant $C > 0$ is given explicitly), as well as a similar theorem with remainder terms in the asymptotic formulae.

*W. Schwarz* (Freiburg)

## N80-40 (33# 4019)

**Bredihin, B. M.**

**Ordered semigroups with finite and infinite rare systems of generating elements. (Russian)**

*Kuĭbyšev. Gos. Ped. Inst. Učen. Zap. Vyp.* 29 (1959), 3–12.

Let $G$ be a free abelian semigroup with a set $P$ of generators $\omega$ ("primes") and with a norm $N$. The author studies connections between the functions $\nu_G(x) = \sum_{\alpha\in G, N(\alpha)\leqq x} 1$ and $\pi_G(x) = \sum_{\omega\in P, N(\omega)\leqq x} 1$. He proves that $\pi_G(x)$ is bounded if and only if $\nu_G(x) \sim C(\log x)^\theta$ with $C > 0$, $\theta > 0$, and, further, that $\log \nu_G(x) \sim A(\log x)^\rho$ $(0 < \rho < 1)$ if and only if $\pi_G(x) \sim B(\log x)^\beta$ with $\beta = \rho/(1-\rho)$. The last result is analogous to results of Freĭman [Učen. Zap. Kazan. Univ. **115** (1955), no. 14, 109–115; MR **18**, 112; Izv. Akad. Nauk SSSR Ser. Mat. **19** (1955), 275–284; MR **17**, 239].

*W. Schwarz* (Freiburg)

Citations: MR 17, 239c = P72-28; MR 18, 112f = B16-10.

## N80-41 (33# 5583)

**Fogels, E.**

**On the abstract theory of primes. III.**

*Acta Arith.* **11** (1965/66), 293–331.

Abstract analogues of the theory of primes are studied. See Part II [same Acta **10** (1964/65), 333–358; MR **30** #4738] for the specific conditions; the present paper is largely independent of the preceding ones.

Consider classes $\mathfrak{H}$ mod $\mathfrak{f}$ of ideals in a field $K$ of degree $n$ and discriminant $\Delta$. The estimate $\sum_{\mathfrak{a}\in\mathfrak{H}, N\mathfrak{a}\leqq x} 1 = \kappa x + O(D^{17/12}x^{(n-1)/(n+1)})$ is obtained, where $D = |\Delta| N\mathfrak{f}$, $n$ is the number of classes and $\kappa = h^{-1}D^{o(1)}$.

The remainder of the paper deals with the case $n = 2$. In particular, the representation of primes by binary forms $F(x_1, x_2) = ax_1^2 + bx_1x_2 + cx_2^2$ is studied. The following theorem is obtained: For appropriate absolute constants $c'$, $c$, $\theta$ $(0 < \theta < 1)$ and for all $x \geqq |D|^{c'}$ in the region $x < |F(x_1, x_2)| < x + x^\theta$ in the $(x_1, x_2)$-plane between any two straight lines starting from the origin and forming an angle with the non-Euclidean measure $\varphi \geqq x^{-c}$, there is a lattice point $(x_1, x_2)$ at which $|F(x_1, x_2)|$ represents a prime. Here $D = b^2 - 4ac$; an appendix is devoted to the non-Euclidean measure.

The paper concludes with arguments on the production of irreducible polynomials.

*J. D. Swift* (Los Angeles, Calif.)

Citations: MR 30# 4738 = N80-29.

## N80-42 (33# 7315)

**Kalniń, I. M. [Kalniņš, I.]**

**Analogues of elementary theorems on primes in the semigroup of real numbers. (Russian)**

*Rīgas Politehn. Inst. Zinātn. Raksti.* **10** (1963), *vyp.* 1, 151–165.

The object is to extend elementary theorems of Čebyšev and Mertens—essentially Theorems 4 and 7 of the reviewer's tract *The distribution of prime numbers* [Stechert-Hafner, New York, 1964; MR **32** #2391]—to a Beurling system of "generalized primes" $b_r$ [Acta Math. **68** (1937), 255–291], on the assumption that $N(x)=cx+O(x^{\Theta})$ ($c>0$, $\Theta<1$, fixed), where $N(x)$ is the number of "generalized integers" $a=b_1^{\alpha_1}b_2^{\alpha_2}\cdots\leqq x$. By standard methods, the results are made to depend on one basic fact, the analogue of $\pi(x)=O(x/\log x)$, and most of the paper is devoted to a proof of this fact. The author notes that classical methods involving binomial coefficients do not extend in any obvious way to the general system, so that other methods must be used. He chooses a method based on a development of A. Selberg's sieve (a needlessly powerful tool for the purpose).

*A. E. Ingham* (Cambridge, England)

Citations: MR 32# 2391 = N02-11.

## N80-43 (34# 5795)

**Juškis, Z. [Juškys, Z.]**

**An asymptotic decomposition of distribution laws for certain functions defined on ordered semigroups with regular normalization.** (Russian. Lithuanian and German summaries)

*Litovsk. Mat. Sb.* **5** (1965), 167–183.

Let $G$ be a multiplicative semigroup with a countable set of free generators of infinite order. Suppose that there exists a homomorphism $N$ of the semigroup $G$ in the multiplicative semigroup of positive integers. The homomorphic image $N(m)$ is called the norm of the element $m$. Let the number of elements of $G$ with $N(m)\leqq x$ be $Cx^{\theta}+O(x^{\theta_1})$; $C$, $\theta$, $\theta_1$ are constants, $C>0$, $0\leqq\theta_1<\theta$. Denote by $\omega(m)$ the number of different generators dividing $m$. Let $M_x(y)$ be the number of elements $m$ satisfying the inequalities $N(m)\leqq x$, $\omega(m)<\ln\ln x+y(\ln\ln x)^{1/2}$. H. Delange [Acta Arith. **7** (1961/62), 191–215; MR **25** #58] and the reviewer [*Probabilistic methods in the theory of numbers* (Russian), Gos. Izdat. Političesk. i Naučn. Lit. Litovsk. SSR, Vilnius, 1959; MR **23** #A134; second edition, 1962; MR **26** #3691; English translation, Amer. Math. Soc., Providence, R.I., 1964; MR **28** #3956] obtained independently an asymptotic expansion of $M_x(y)/x$ in case $G$ is the multiplicative semigroup of positive integers. The author generalizes this result for any semigroup mentioned above.

*J. Kubilius* (Vilnius)

Citations: MR 23# A134 = N60-37; MR 25# 58 = N60-42; MR 28# 3956 = N60-39.

## N80-44 (36# 122)

**Horadam, E. M.**

**A sum of a certain divisor function for arithmetical semi-groups.**

*Pacific J. Math.* **22** (1967), 407–412.

Let $\{p_i\}$ be an infinite set of real numbers $>1$ such that the finite products $\prod p_i^{\alpha_i}$ ($\alpha_i=0,1,2,\cdots$) are all distinct. Let $S$ be the set of these products, and suppose that $N(x)$, the number of elements $b\in S$ with $b\leqq x$, satisfies $N(x)=x+O(x^{\alpha})$, $\alpha<1$. For any $b\in S$, let $\tau'(b)$ be the number of solutions of the equation $b=d\delta$, with $d$ and $\delta$ square-free, i.e. of the form $\prod p_i^{\varepsilon_i}$ with $\varepsilon_i=0$ or 1. It is shown that if $c\in S$ is fixed, then $T(x)=\sum_{b\leqq x;(b,c)=1}\tau'(b)=Ax\log x+O(x\exp[(\log c)^{1-\alpha}/\log\log c])$, where

$$A=\prod_{p|c}[p^2/(p+1)^2]\prod_p[(p^2-1)^2/p^4].$$

(Here the notions $(b,c)=1$ and $p|c$ have the obvious meanings in the arithmetic based on the generalized primes $\{p_i\}$.) The proof follows the lines of a similar theorem obtained by the reviewer and K. Rogers [Canad. J. Math. **16** (1964), 151–158; MR **28** #1186] in the case where the $p_i$ are the ordinary primes.

*B. Gordon* (Los Angeles, Calif.)

Citations: MR 28# 1186 = N40-51.
Referred to in R02-55.

## N80-45 (36# 1404)

**Horadam, E. M.**

**Unitary divisor functions of a generalised integer.**

*Portugal. Math.* **24** (1965), 131–143.

Let $\{p_n\}$ be a finite or infinite strictly increasing sequence of real numbers with $p_1>1$. Let $L=\{l=p_1^{v_1}p_2^{v_2}\cdots$, where $v_i\geqq0$ are integers and $v_i\neq0$ for at most a finite number of $p$'s$\}$ be the multiplicative semi-group with identity generated by $\{p_n\}$. A. Beurling [Acta Math. **68** (1937), 255–291] called sets $L$ sets of generalized integers. Suppose each $l\in L$ has a unique representation in the form $\prod p_i^{v_i}$ and for all reals $x$, $[x]=\sum_{l\leqq x;l\in L}1=x+O(x^{\alpha})$, with $0<\alpha<1$. The author defines on $L$ various functions analogous to arithmetical functions of rational integers and obtains their average orders by standard methods using the following estimates. $\sum_{l\leqq x;l\in L}l^{-\beta}=(x^{1-\beta})/(1-\beta)+\alpha_\beta+O(x^{\alpha-\beta})$, $\beta\neq1$, $\beta\neq\alpha$, $\alpha_\beta$ a constant and $\sum_{l>x;l\in L}l^{-\beta}=O(1/x^{\beta-1})$ if $\beta>1$.

*R. P. Bambah* (Columbus, Ohio)

## N80-46 (36# 6386)

**Rémond, Paul**

**Étude asymptotique de certaines partitions dans certains semi-groupes.**

*Ann. Sci. École Norm. Sup.* (3) **83** (1966), 343–410.

H. Delange [same Ann. (3) **73** (1956), 15–74; MR **18**, 720; Bull. Soc. Roy. Sci. Liège **30** (1961), 404–415; MR **25** #3910] and E. Wirsing [Arch. Math. **7** (1956), 263–272; MR **18**, 642; Math. Ann. **143** (1961), 75–102; MR **24** #A1241] have investigated asymptotic properties of the domain $\mathscr{E}(E)$, where $E$ denotes a set of primes and $\mathscr{E}(E)$ is the set of integers all of whose prime divisors belong to $E$. It is assumed that the number of elements of $E$ that do not exceed $x$ is asymptotic to $\mu x/\log x$. More generally one can replace $\mathscr{E}(E)$ by a commutative semigroup $(E)$ with unique factorization. This is accomplished by defining a norm on the semigroup, that is, a completely multiplicative function with values greater than 1, and assuming that the number of elements of $E$ with norm $\leqq x$ is asymptotic to $\mu x/\log x$.

In the present paper the author considers normed semigroups $(E)$ in which the number of prime elements of norm $\leqq x$ is asymptotic to $\mu x(\log\log x)^r/\log x$ ($\mu>0$, $r\geqq0$); such a semigroup is called a $\Delta_r$-semigroup. The paper consists of two parts. The first part is concerned with asymptotic properties of $\Delta_r$-semigroups. The first main result is the following: Let $\nu(x)$ denote the number of elements of norm $\leqq x$ of the $\Delta_r$-semigroup $(E)$. Then

$$\nu(x)\sim(\mu x/\log x)(\log\log x)^r\sum_{A\in E:NA\leqq x}1/NA,$$

where $NA$ denotes the norm;

$$\nu(x)=x\exp\{(\mu/(r+1))(\log\log x)^{r+1}[1+o(1)]\}\quad(r>0),$$

$$\nu(x)=x\exp\{(\mu-1+o(1))\log\log x\}\quad(r=0).$$

More precise results are obtained for certain special $\Delta_r$-semigroups but these will not be stated.

In the second part of the paper the author considers a partition of $(E)$ such that the classes form a finite abelian group and the multiplication of classes is compatible with that of the elements of the semigroup. Moreover, it is assumed that the semigroup is a $\Delta_r$-semigroup. Residue classes (mod $k$) of elementary number-theory, the classes of ideals in an algebraic number field and more generally the classes of ideals modulo an ideal furnish examples of such a partition. In Chapter 1 of Part 2 it is shown that the asymptotic distribution of the elements of $(E)$ is the same in each class. The principal class of the partition is itself a semigroup—the factorization is in general not unique. In Chapter 2 an asymptotic formula is obtained for the number of irreducible elements of norm $\leqq x$ in the principal class. Chapter 3 contains an asymptotic formula for the mean value of the number of factorizations into irreducible elements. Finally Chapter 4 is concerned with applications to ideals of an algebraic number field.

*L. Carlitz* (Durham, N.C.)

Citations: MR 18, 642f = N28-35; MR 18, 720a = N24-28; MR 24# A1241 = N36-30; MR 25# 3910 = N24-42.

## N80-47 (37# 1330)

**Horadam, E. M.**

**On the number of pairs of generalized integers with least common multiple not exceeding $x$.**

*Amer. Math. Monthly* **74** (1967), 811–812.

Let $p_1, p_2, \cdots$ be real numbers, with $1 < p_1 < p_2 < \cdots$, and let $\{l\}$ be the multiplicative semigroup generated by these "generalized primes". Suppose that $\{l\}$ has unique factorization, and let $t(l_n)$, $l_n \in \{l\}$, denote the number of (ordered) pairs of "generalized integers" $l_r$ and $l_s \in \{l\}$, with the least common multiple $[l_r, l_s] = l_n$ in the obvious sense. Suppose also $[x] = x + O(x^\alpha)$, $0 < \alpha < 1$, where $[x]$ is the number of $l_n \leqq x$. Put $\zeta(s) = \sum_{n=1}^\infty l_n^{-s}$. The author proves that

$$\sum_{l_n \leqq x} t(l_n) = (\zeta(2))^{-1} x \log x \times \{\tfrac{1}{2} \log x - 2\zeta'(2)/\zeta(2) + 3\gamma_1 - 1\} + O(x),$$

where $\gamma_1$ is the constant in the estimation $\sum_{l_n \leqq x} 1/l_n = \log x + \gamma_1 + O(x^{\alpha-1})$. The proof is based on an earlier result of the author [same Monthly **71** (1964), 893–895; MR **32** #4095].

*T. Hayashida* (Yokohama)

Citations: MR 32# 4095 = N80-32.

## N80-48 (39# 1413)

**Horadam, E. M.**

**Ramanujan's sum and its application to the enumerative functions of certain sets of elements of an arithmetical semi-group.**

*J. Math. Sci.* **3** (1968), 47–70.

Consider a sequence $\{p_i\}$ of real numbers $> 1$ (generalized primes), and suppose that the multiplicative semigroup $S$ generated by the $p_i$ (generalized integers) is free. Suppose further that if $[x]$ denotes the number of generalized integers $\leqq x$, then $[x] = x + O(x^\alpha)$, $\alpha < 1$. Under these conditions the author studies the generalized Ramanujan sum $c_k(m, n) = \sum_{d|n, d^k|m} \mu(n/d)\, d^k$, where $m, n \in S$, $k \in N$, and the symbols are given the natural interpretation in the arithmetic based on $S$. As applications she obtains a number of series expansions and estimates of various arithmetical functions, such as $\sum_{m \leqq x} c_k(m, n)$, $\sum_{m \leqq x} c_k(m, n)/m$, and $Q_k(x)$, the number of $k$th power-free generalized integers $\leqq x$.

*B. Gordon* (Los Angeles, Calif.)

## N80-49 (39# 4105)

**Bateman, Paul T.; Diamond, Harold G.**

**Asymptotic distribution of Beurling's generalized prime numbers.**

*Studies in Number Theory, pp.* 152–210. *Math. Assoc. Amer.* (*distributed by Prentice-Hall, Englewood Cliffs, N.J.*), 1969.

A. Beurling betrachtete 1937 [Acta Math. **68** (1937), 255–291] sogenannte verallgemeinerte Primzahlen und übertrug bekannte Ergebnisse der analytischen Zahlentheorie über die asymptotische Verteilung der gewöhnlichen Primzahlen auf diese. In der vorliegenden Arbeit betrachten Verfasser mit leichten Abänderungen gegenüber Beurling ähnliche Sachverhalte. Sei $P$ eine Folge positiver reeller Zahlen $p_\nu$, welche $1 < p_1 \leqq p_2 \leqq \cdots \leqq p_{\nu-1} \leqq p_\nu$, $p_\nu \to \infty$ erfüllen, so heiße $P$ ein System verallgemeinerter Primzahlen. Es sei $\pi_P(x)$ die Anzahl der $p_\nu \leqq x$. Die Menge $I_P$ sei die Menge der $\prod_{\nu=1}^\infty p_\nu^{\alpha_\nu}$; $\alpha_\nu \geqq 0$, ganz. Es sei $I_P(x)$ die Anzahl dieser Zahlen $\leqq x$.

Als Beispiel für die Ergebnisse diene Satz 7A: Es sei $P$ ein System verallgemeinerter Primzahlen mit der Eigenschaft: Es gibt Zahlen $A > 0$ und $\gamma$ so, daß $I_P(x) = Ax + O(x \log^{-\gamma} x)$. Wenn $\gamma > 3/2$, dann gilt $\pi(x) = x \log^{-1} x + o(x \log^{-1} x)$.

*H. J. Kanold* (Braunschweig)

## N80-50 (39# 4106)

**Diamond, Harold G.**

**The prime number theorem for Beurling's generalized numbers.**

*J. Number Theory* **1** (1969), 200–207.

Let $\mathscr{P} = \{p_j\}_{j=1}^\infty$, where $1 < p_1 \leqq p_2 \leqq \cdots$, and $p_j \to \infty$. Let $\mathscr{N}$ denote the multiplicative semigroup generated by $\mathscr{P}$, and let $N(x) = N_{\mathscr{P}}(x) = \{n \in \mathscr{N} : n \leqq x\}$. [A. Beurling, Acta Math. **68** (1937), 255–291] proved that if $N_{\mathscr{P}}$ satisfies the asymptotic relation (1) $N(x) = Ax + O(x \log^{-\gamma} x)$ with some numbers $A > 0$ and $\gamma > 3/2$, then the conclusion of the prime number theorem (P.N.T.) is valid for the system. He also gave an example of such a system which satisfies (1) with $\gamma = 3/2$, but for which the P.N.T. does not hold. The author proves the following theorem, which lies in the range between the above results. Let $N_{\mathscr{P}}(x) = Ax + O\{x(\log x)^{-3/2} \exp(-[\log\log x]^\alpha)\}$ for some numbers $A > 0$ and $\alpha > \frac{1}{3}$. Then the P.N.T. holds for $\mathscr{P}$.

*R. A. MacLeod* (Victoria, B.C.)

## N80-51 (40# 2621)

**Horadam, E. M.**

**Normal order and the Euler-Φ function for generalised integers.**

*An. Fac. Ci. Univ. Porto* **51** (1968), 211–219.

Given a sequence $\{p_i\}$ of real numbers (generalized primes) such that $1 < p_1 < p_2 < \cdots$, generalized integers are defined as the set $\{l\}$ of all products $p_1^{v_1} p_2^{v_2} \cdots$, where the $v$'s are nonnegative integers, all but a finite number of which are 0. Assume that no two generalized integers are equal if the $v$'s are different. Also assume the $\{l\}$ numbered so that $1 = l_1 < l_2 < \cdots$. Let $[x]$ denote the number of $l_j \leqq x$. Assume that $[x] = x + R(x)$, $R(x) = O(x^\alpha)$, $0 < \alpha < 1$.

Let $f(l_n)$ be defined for all $l_n$. Then $f(l_n)$ has normal order $g(l_n)$ if and only if $|f(l_n) - g(l_n)| < \varepsilon g(l_n)$ for all except possibly $o(x)$ generalized integers $l_n \leqq x$. The notation $d|l_n$ means that $d\delta = l_n$, where both $d$, $\delta \in \{l\}$. The function $\phi_k(l_n)$ is defined as the number of $l_m$ in the set $l, l_2, \cdots, l_n$ for which the g.c.d. $(l_m, l_n)$ is $k$th power free. It is proved that $\phi_k(l_n^k)$ has no normal order.

*L. Carlitz* (Durham, N.C.)

## N80-52 (40# 4198)

**Horadam, E. M.**

**An unsolved problem in number theory.**

*Bull. Soc. Math. Grèce* (*N.S.*) **9** (1968), *fasc.* 1, 143–147.

Let $p_1, p_2, \cdots, l_1, l_2, \cdots$ be real numbers, $1 < p_1 < p_2 < \cdots$, $1 = l_1 < l_2 < l_3 < \cdots$, and assume that every $l_i$ can be uniquely represented as a product of $p_j$'s, with repetitions allowed. The $p$'s and $l$'s are called generalized primes and generalized integers, respectively. If $x > 0$, we define $[x]$ to be the number of $i$'s for which $l_i \leqq x$. The author imposes the extra condition that for all generalized primes $p$ the following is true: if $a > 0$, $b > 0$, $c > 0$, $[c] = [a] + [b]$, then $[c/p] \geqq [a/p] + [b/p]$. This condition is satisfied in the case of the ordinary integers (and also when $l_k = k^\alpha$ with a fixed $\alpha > 0$). The author asks but does not answer the question whether there are other cases. She proves the following: If $n>1$, then $l_n$ and $l_{n+1}$ cannot be both generalized primes. *N. G. de Bruijn* (Eindhoven)

**N80-53** **(40# 5533)**

**Horadam, E. M.**

**Ramanujan's sum and Nagell's totient function for arithmetical semi-groups.**

*Math. Scand.* **22** (1968), 269–281 (1969).

Let $0<1<P_1<P_2<\cdots$ be a given (finite or infinite) sequence of real numbers and let the members (called generalized integers) of the multiplicative semigroup (assumed to be free) generated by these be arranged as an increasing sequence: $1=l_1<l_2<l_3<\cdots$.

In this paper, the author continues the study of an analogue for generalized integers of Ramanujan's sum previously introduced [the author, Duke Math. J. **31** (1964), 697–702; MR **29** #5795], and also studies an analogue of Nagell's totient function. Using a method of the reviewer, the author obtains a Brauer-Rademacher type identity for the case of generalized integers. The paper also contains results relating to $K$-even and $K$-primitive functions of the generalized integers.

*M. V. Subbarao* (Edmonton, Alta.)

Citations: MR 29# 5795 = N80-26.

**N80-54** **(40# 5555)**

**Diamond, Harold G.**

**Asymptotic distribution of Beurling's generalized integers.**

*Illinois J. Math.* **14** (1970), 12–28.

Let $\{p_i\}_{i=1}^{\infty}$ be a sequence of real numbers subject to the following three conditions but otherwise arbitrary: (i) $p_1>1$, (ii) $p_{n+1}\geqq p_n$, (iii) $p_n\to\infty$. Following A. Beurling [Acta Math. **68** (1937), 255–291], such a collection $\{p_i\}$ is called a set of generalized (henceforth $g$-) primes. The multiplicative semigroup generated by the $\{p_i\}$ is countable and may be arranged in a nondecreasing sequence $\{n_i\}_{i=1}^{\infty}$. Taking $n_0=1$, the set $\{n_i\}_{i=0}^{\infty}$ is called the set of $g$-integers associated with $\{p_i\}$. The function $\pi(x)$ is defined to be the number of $g$-primes less than or equal to $x$, and $\Pi(x)$ is defined by $\Pi(x)=\sum_{n=1}^{\infty}(1/n)\pi(x^{1/n})$. And let $N(x)$ be the number of $g$-integers less than or equal to $x$.

The main results of this paper take the following form. Theorem 1: Suppose there exist positive numbers $c$ and $\alpha$ such that for large $x$ the following relation holds:

$$\int_1^x d\Pi(t)/t = \int_1^x (1-t^{-1})\,dt/(t\log t)+\log c+O\{\log^{-\alpha}x\}.$$

Then $N(x)=cx+O\{x\log^{2-\alpha}x\}$. Theorem 2: Suppose there exist numbers $c>0$ and $a\in(0,1)$ such that $\int_1^x d\Pi(t)/t=\int_1^x(1-t^{-1})\,dt/(t\log t)+\log c+O\{\exp(-\log^a x)\}$. Then $N(x)=cx+O\{x\exp(-[\log x\log\log x]^{a'})\}$, where $a'=a/(1+a)$. These theorems sharpen results previously obtained, respectively, by B. Nyman [ibid. **81** (1949), 299–307; MR **11**, 332] and P. Malliavin [ibid. **106** (1961), 281–298; MR **26** #87]. While Nyman and Malliavin use Fourier analysis and Tauberian arguments, the author's approach to the problem is first to show how measures of a certain type may be expressed as "exponentials". Then he applies this formalism to the counting measure of generalized integers and Lebesgue measure, and estimates the one measure by the other. *S. Ikehara* (Tokyo)

Citations: MR 11, 332b = N80-2; MR 26# 87 = N80-12.

Referred to in N20-71.

**N80-55** **(40# 5556)**

**Diamond, Harold G.**

**A set of generalized numbers showing Beurling's theorem to be sharp.**

*Illinois J. Math.* **14** (1970), 29–34.

A Beurling proved [Acta Math. **68** (1937), 255–291] that the prime number theorem holds for generalized (henceforth $g$-) numbers if $N(x)$, the number of $g$-integers not exceeding $x$, satisfies $N(x)=cx+O(x\log^{-\gamma}x)$ for $c$ a positive number and $\gamma$ a number greater than $\frac{3}{2}$. Further, he showed that this result is sharp by giving an example of a "prime measure" and associated "integer measure" for which $\gamma=\frac{3}{2}$, but for which the prime number theorem is false. However, the measures of Beurling's example are continuous and thus differ from the usual (atomic) counting measure of prime number theory.

The author gives an example of $g$-primes and $g$-integers for which the prime number theorem fails, but $N(x)=cx+O\{x(\log x)^{-3/2}\}$. His construction is based on Beurling's example, and the method of approximating measures used in the paper reviewed above [#5555].

*S. Ikehara* (Tokyo)

**N80-56** **(41# 3410)**

**Tuljaganova, M.**

**Distribution of values of Euler's function defined on a normalized semigroup. (Russian. Uzbek summary)**

*Izv. Akad. Nauk UzSSR Ser. Fiz.-Mat. Nauk* **12** (1968), *no.* 5, 33–37.

Verfasser definiert die Eulersche $\varphi$-Funktion auf einer Halbgruppe $S$ mit eindeutiger Faktorzerlegung in Primelemente und mit einer Normfunktion $N:S\to\mathbf{R}^+$. Verfasser beweist für diese verallgemeinerte $\varphi$-Funktion Analoga zu folgenden zwei Sätzen von A. S. Faĭnleĭb [Mat. Zametki **1** (1967), 645–652; MR **35** #6636] für die gewöhnliche $\varphi$-Funktion: Sei $\Phi_N(x)=N^{-1}\sum_{n\leqq N,\varphi(n)/n<x}1$, $\Phi(x)=\lim_{N\to\infty}\Phi_N(x)$. Gleichmäßig für $x\in[0,1]$ gilt dann $\Phi_N(x)=\Phi(x)+O(1/\log\log N)$; für geeignetes $a>0$ ist

$$\operatorname{mes}_{0\leqq x\leqq 1}E\{x;\,|\Phi_N(x)-\Phi(x)|\leqq\exp(-a\sqrt{\log N})\}=1+O\{\exp(-a\sqrt{\log N})\}.$$

*W. Schwarz* (Frankfurt a.M.)

Citations: MR 35# 6636 = N60-66.

**N80-57** **(42# 1757)**

**Subrahmanya Sastri, V. V.**

**On a certain totient function for generalised integers.**

*Math. Student* **37** (1969), 59–66.

**N80-58** **(42# 1784)**

**Horadam, E. M.**

**Normal order for divisor functions of generalized integers.**

*Portugal. Math.* **27** (1968), 201–207.

Suppose there is given an infinite sequence $\{p\}$ of real numbers (generalized primes) such that $1<p_1<p_2<\cdots$. Form the set $\{b\}$ of all possible $p$-products, i.e., products $p_1^{v_1}p_2^{v_2}\cdots$, where $v_1, v_2, \cdots$ are integers $\geqq 0$ of which all but a finite number are 0. Call these numbers generalized integers and suppose that the semi-group consisting of all these products is free. Then assume that $\{b_i\}$ may be arranged as an increasing sequence: $1=b_1<b_2<b_3<\cdots$. A function $f(b_n)$ defined for all generalized integers $b_n$ is said to have normal order $g(b_n)$ if and only if there exists a function $g(x)$ defined for all real $x\geqq 1$ such that for every $\varepsilon>0$, we have $|f(b_n)-g(b_n)|<\varepsilon g(b_n)$ for all except possibly $o(x)$ generalized integers $b_n\leqq x$. Let $b_n=p_1^{v_1}p_2^{v_2}\cdots p_n^{v_n}$. Then $d$ is said to be a divisor of $b_n$ if $d\in\{b\}$ and there is a $\delta\in\{b\}$ such that $d\delta=b_n$. Define $\omega(b_n)$ as the number of different prime factors of $b_n$, $\Omega(b_n)$ as the total number of prime factors of $b_n$, and $\tau(b_n)$ as the number of divisors of $b_n$. In this paper standard methods are employed to show

that the normal orders of $\omega(b_n)$, $\Omega(b_n)$ and $\log \tau(b_n)$ are $\log\log b_n$, $\log\log b_n$ and $\log 2 \log\log b_n$, respectively.
*A. L. Whiteman* (Los Angeles, Calif.)

**N80-59** **(42# 3033 )**

**Spears, Nina**

**A simplified proof of Chebyshev's theorem.**

*Duke Math. J.* **37** (1970), 709–713.

Define $\Psi(x) = \sum_{n \leqq x} \Lambda(n)$; then if it can be shown that $\Psi(x) = O(x)$ $(x \geqq 1)$, Čebyšev's theorem follows. This is done by proving a special case of a theorem partially proved by the reviewer [Nederl. Akad. Wetensch. Proc. Ser. A **66** (1963), 699–704; MR **28** #5048] but originally proved by A. E. Ingham. The theorem is given in the context of generalized integers but is of course true for ordinary integers. Let $F(x) = \sum_{l_m \leqq x} f(x/l_m)$ for all $x \geqq 1$, where $\{l_m\}$ is a set of generalized integers. Then if $F(x) = Ax \log^2 x + Bx \log x + Cx + O(x^\beta)$, $0 \leqq \beta < 1$, then $f(x) = 2Ax \log x + O(x)$. It is understood that $A, B, C, \beta$ are constants and that $[x] = x + R(x)$, where $R(x) = O(x^\alpha)$ and $\alpha$ is a fixed number in $0 \leqq \alpha < 1$. The function $[x]$ is the number of generalized integers $\leqq x$. *E. M. Horadam* (Armidale)

Citations: MR 28# 5048 = N80-23.

# N99 NONE OF THE ABOVE, BUT IN THIS CHAPTER

See also reviews A22-57, A28-21, K15-92, Q15-22, Q20-21, R99-6, Z15-37.

**N99-1** **(37# 2700 )**

**Kalecki, M.**

**On the sum $\sum_{n \leqq x} \{f(x/n)\}$.**

*Prace Mat.* **11** (1968), 189–191.

The author shows that, if $f(y)$ is positive, continuous, and increasing for $y \geqq 1$ and if $\lim_{y \to \infty} f(y) = \infty$, then $\sum_{n \leqq x} \{f(x/n)\} = Cx + O(\phi(x)) = Cx + o(x)$, where $\{y\} = y - [y]$ is the fractional part of $y$, $C$ is a positive constant, and $z = \phi(x)$ satisfies $z = f(x/z)$. In particular, if $f(y) = y$, $\sum_{n \leqq x} \{x/n\} = (1-\gamma)x + O(\sqrt{x})$. The proof is elementary.
*R. A. MacLeod* (Victoria, B.C.)

**N99-2** **(44# 6638 )**

**Erdős, P.; Turán, P.**

**On some problems of a statistical group theory. V.**

*Period. Math. Hungar.* **1** (1971), *no.* 1, 5–13.

Let $O(P)$ denote the order of an element $P$ in the symmetric group $S_n$. In a previous paper in the series [Acta Math. Acad. Sci. Hungar. **18** (1967), 151–163; MR **34** #7624] the authors showed that for all but $o(n!)$ elements $P \in S_n$ the integer $O(P)$ is divisible by each prime $q$ with (1) $q \leqq [\log n/\log\log n][1 + a\{\log\log\log n\}/\{\log\log n\}]$ provided $a > 3$ and not when $a < 3$. They actually proved a more precise result involving a function $\omega(x) \to \infty$ arbitrarily slowly. They also showed that for all but $o(n!)$ elements $P \in S_n$ the largest prime factor $q$ in $O(P)$ satisfies (2) $\omega(n)^{-1} \leqq (\log n)^{-1/2} \log(n/q) \leqq \omega(n)$.

Within each conjugacy class $H$ of $S_n$ the order $O(P)$ is equal to a constant $O(H)$, while in total there are $p(n)$ conjugacy classes. In the present paper it is shown that for all but $o(p(n))$ conjugacy classes $H$ the largest prime factor $\rho(H)$ in $O(H)$ satisfies

(3) $$|\rho(H) - cn^{1/2} \log n + 2cn^{1/2} \log\log n| < n^{1/2}\omega(n),$$

where $c = 6^{1/2}(2\pi)^{-1}$. There is also an announcement of a rather precise result of type (1) for conjugacy classes. This result is much closer to (3) than (1) is to (2).

{Part IV appeared in ibid. **19** (1968), 413–435 [MR **38** #1156].} *J. H. B. Kemperman* (Rochester, N.Y.)

# P. ADDITIVE NUMBER THEORY; LATTICE POINT PROBLEMS

## P02 BOOKS AND SURVEYS

See also reviews D02-12, D02-19, F02-1, F02-23, L02-1, L02-2, L02-5, M02-3, M02-8, N02-9, N02-12, N02-16, P04-39, P08-25, P16-16, P20-16, P20-18, P32-14, P32-34, P60-43, P60-55, P64-43, P80-48, P80-55, P99-6, Z01-58, Z02-1, Z02-30, Z02-31, Z02-39, Z02-63, Z02-71, Z02-75, Z02-77, Z25-17, Z25-29.

**P02-1** **(3, 268b)**

**Griffiths, Lois W. Universal functions of polygonal numbers.** Amer. Math. Monthly **49**, 107–110 (1942).

This is an expository paper on the subject of representing numbers as sums of polygonal numbers beginning with Fermat's problem and its development by Lagrange, Cauchy and recently by Dickson and the author. The reviewer takes exception to the statement that Gauss first proved that $8n+7$ is not the sum of 3 squares. This obvious fact was known to Diophantus. *D. H. Lehmer* (Berkeley, Calif.).

Referred to in E12-13.

**P02-2** **(7, 48d)**

**Brun, Viggo. The study of the prime numbers from antiquity to our time.** Norske Vid. Selsk. Forh. **15**, 16 pp. (1942). (Norwegian)

Contains a bibliography of 71 papers on additive number theory.

**P02-3** **(8, 10g)**

**Kloosterman, H. D. Partitions.** Euclides, Groningen **21**, 67–77 (1946). (Dutch)

An expository lecture.

**P02-4** **(9, 11b)**

**Ricci, Giovanni. Problemi secolari e risposte recenti nel campo dell'aritmetica.** Atti Convegno Mat. Roma 1942, pp. 91–131 (1945).

This lecture discusses the estimation of exponential sums, the distribution of $f(x)$ (mod 1), Waring's problem and Goldbach's problem.

**P02-5** **(10, 597e)**

**Hua, Loo-Keng. The additive prime number theory.** Trav. Inst. Math. Stekloff **22**, 179 pp. (1947). (Russian. English summary)

This is a Russian translation by B. I. Segal and D. A. Vasil'kov of an English manuscript written in 1941. It gives a detailed exposition, starting from scratch, of what was then known on the problem of representing positive integers as sums of a given number of $k$th powers of primes (the so-called Waring-Goldbach problem). The attack on this problem was begun by Vinogradov [C. R. (Doklady) Acad. Sci. URSS (N.S.) **16**, 131–132 (1937); Trav. Inst. Math. Tbilissi [Trudy Tbiliss. Mat. Inst.] **3**, 1–67 (1938)] and continued by the author [C. R. (Doklady) Acad. Sci. URSS (N.S.) **17**, 167–168 (1937); **18**, 4 (1938); Math. Z. **44**, 335–346 (1938)]. However, much of the material in the present memoir is original work. The method used in all this work is an extension of that used by Vinogradov in treating the special case of the Goldbach problem [C. R. (Doklady) Acad. Sci. URSS (N.S.) **15**, 291–294 (1937); Rec. Math. [Mat. Sbornik] N.S. **2(44)**, 179–194 (1937)].

In the first chapter the author proves the following two theorems on trigonometrical sums [cf. Hua, J. Chinese Math. Soc. **2**, 301–312 (1940); these Rev. **2**, 347]. If $f(x)=a_kx^k+\cdots+a_1x$, where $a_1, \cdots, a_k$ are integers such that $(a_1, \cdots, a_k, q)=1$, then

$$\left|\sum_{x=1}^{q} \exp\,(2\pi i f(x)/q)\right| \leqq c(k, \epsilon)q^{1-1/k+\epsilon},$$

where $\epsilon$ is an arbitrary positive number and $c(k, \epsilon)$ denotes a positive constant depending only on $k$ and $\epsilon$. If further $(a_2, \cdots, a_k, q)=1$, then

$$\left|\sum_{x=1}^{m} \exp\,(2\pi i f(x)/q)-mq^{-1}\sum_{x=1}^{q} \exp\,(2\pi i f(x)/q)\right| \leqq c_1(k, \epsilon)q^{1-1/k+\epsilon}$$

for any positive integer $m$. It is to be noted that both in the original paper and in this book the additional hypothesis is not introduced in the second theorem, but unless this is done the estimate must be multiplied by $(a_2, \cdots, a_k, q)^{1/k}$.

In chapter II the results of the first chapter are used to prove the following theorem on the divisors of the values of a polynomial function. If $f(x_1, \cdots, x_n)$ is a polynomial of $k$th degree with integral coefficients having greatest common divisor unity, then

$$\sum_{\substack{x_1=1 \\ f(x_1, \cdots, x_n)\neq 0}}^{P} \cdots \sum_{x_n=1}^{P} d^l(|f(x_1, \cdots, x_n)|) \leqq c_2(k, n, l)A(\log X)^{c_3(k, n, l)},$$

where $d(m)$ denotes the number of divisors of $m$, $X$ is the maximum value of $|f(x_1, \cdots, x_n)|$ for $1\leqq x_1, \cdots, x_n\leqq P$, and $A=\max\,(P^n, X^{n/k})$.

The preceding result is applied in chapter III to prove the following theorem on the mean value of a trigonometrical sum. Let $f(x)$ be an integral-valued polynomial of the $k$th degree and put $T(\alpha)=\sum_{x=1}^{P} \exp\,(2\pi i f(x)\alpha)$; then for $1\leqq \nu\leqq k$ we have

$$\int_0^1 |T(\alpha)|^{2^\nu} d\alpha \leqq c_4(k, \nu)P^{2^\nu-\nu}(\log P)^{c_5(k, \nu)}d^{\nu-1}(u),$$

where $u$ is the greatest common divisor of the numerators of the coefficients of $f(x)$.

Chapter IV is essentially the same as a paper of the author [Quart. J. Math., Oxford Ser. **11**, 161–176 (1940); these Rev. **2**, 150] proving the following theorem. If $2\leqq k\leqq 10$ and $C_k=C_k(\alpha_1, \cdots, \alpha_k)=\sum_{x=1}^{P} \exp\,(2\pi i\{\alpha_kx^k+\cdots+\alpha_1x\})$, then

$$\int_0^1 \cdots \int_0^1 |C_k|^\lambda d\alpha_1 \cdots d\alpha_k \leqq c_6(k, \epsilon)P^{\lambda-\frac{1}{2}k(k+1)+\epsilon},$$

where $\lambda=\lambda(k)$ is an even integer which is tabulated: $\lambda(2)=6, \cdots, \lambda(10)=9190$. This result is a sharpening, for small $k$, of the so-called Vinogradov mean value theorem [cf. Vinogradov, Rec. Math. [Mat. Sbornik] N.S. **3(45)**, 435–470 (1938), lemma 6].

In chapter V is given an original proof of the Vinogradov mean value theorem itself, the statement of which is as follows. Suppose $C_k=\sum_{x=1}^{P}\exp(2\pi i\{\alpha_k x^k+\cdots+\alpha_1 x\})$, $b=b(k)=2[\frac{1}{4}(k+1)(k+2)]$, and $k\leqq n\leqq c_7(k)$; then

$$\int_0^1\cdots\int_0^1 |C_k|^{bn}d\alpha_1\cdots d\alpha_k\leqq c_8(k)P^{bn-\frac{1}{2}k(k+1)+\frac{1}{2}k(k+1)\sigma},$$

where $\sigma=(1-1/k)^n$. This mean value theorem has (among others) the following two consequences. If $f(x)$ is an integral-valued polynomial of degree $k$, then

$$\int_0^1\left|\sum_{x=1}^{P}\exp(2\pi i f(x)\alpha)\right|^{bn}d\alpha\leqq c_9(k)P^{bn-k+\frac{1}{2}k(k+1)\sigma},$$

where $b=2[\frac{1}{4}(k+1)(k+2)]$, $k\leqq n\leqq c_{10}(k)$, $\sigma=(1-1/k)^n$. I₁ $\alpha_1,\cdots,\alpha_k$ are real numbers, $k\geqq 14$, and $|\alpha_k-h/q|\leqq q^{-2}$, where $h$ and $q$ are coprime integers, $q>0$, then for $P^{1-\epsilon}\leqq q\leqq P^{k-1+\epsilon}$ we have

$$\left|\sum_{x=1}^{P}\exp(2\pi i\{\alpha_k x^k+\cdots+\alpha_1 x\})\right|\leqq c_{11}(k,\epsilon)P^{1-\rho+\epsilon},$$

where $\rho>2/\{k^3(\log k^2+2.2\log\log k^2)\}$. An improved version of this chapter is reviewed above.

A theorem of Vinogradov [Trav. Inst. Math. Tbilissi [Trudy Tbiliss. Math. Inst.] **3**, 1–67 (1938), Satz 1] which is basic for the Waring-Goldbach problem is given in chapter VI. However, it is modified here so as to be applicable also to the simultaneous Waring-Goldbach problem. Suppose $0<Q\leqq c_{12}(k)(\log P)^{\sigma_1}$, $\alpha_1,\cdots,\alpha_{k-1}$ are real numbers, $h$ and $q$ are coprime integers, and $(\log P)^{\sigma}<q\leqq P^k(\log P)^{-\sigma}$; then if $\sigma_0$ is a given positive number and $\sigma\geqq 2^{6k}(\sigma_0+\sigma_1+1)$, we have

$$\left|\sum_{p\leqq P;\,p\equiv l\,(\mathrm{mod}\,Q)}\exp(2\pi i\{hq^{-1}x^k+\alpha_{k-1}x^{k-1}+\cdots+\alpha_1 x\})\right|\leqq c_{13}(k)P(\log P)^{-\sigma_0}Q^{-1}.$$

Using the results of the previous chapters and the Hardy-Littlewood-Vinogradov method, the author in chapter VII establishes an asymptotic formula for the number of solutions of the Waring-Goldbach problem. More generally, he proves the following result. Let $f(x)$ be an integral-valued polynomial of $k$th degree with positive first coefficient $A$; suppose there does not exist an integer $q$ such that $f(x)\equiv f(0)$ (mod $q$) for all integers $x$; let $I_s(N)$ denote the number of solutions of the equation $f(p_1)+\cdots+f(p_s)=N$, where the $p$'s are primes; then for $s\geqq 2^k+1$ if $1\leqq k<14$ and $s\geqq k^3(\log k+2.2\log\log k)$ if $k\geqq 14$, we have

$$\left|I_s(N)-A^{-sn}\frac{\Gamma^s(1/k)}{\Gamma(s/k)}\frac{N^{s/k-1}}{(\log N)^s}\mathfrak{S}(N)\right|<c_{14}(k,s,f)\frac{N^{s/k-1}\log\log N}{(\log N)^{s+1}},$$

where $\mathfrak{S}(N)$ is the so-called singular series (which can of course be given explicitly). This is the only point in the memoir at which the treatment is not self-contained, for use is made of a theorem on the number of primes in an arithmetic progression when the difference of the progression grows slowly with the increasing of the number of terms of the progression [cf. Walfisz, Math. Z. **40**, 592–607 (1935), Hilfssatz 3]. This theorem in turn is a consequence of the Siegel lower estimate of the value at $s=1$ of Dirichlet's $L(s,\chi)$ functions with real characters $\chi$ [Acta Arith. **1**, 83–86 (1935)]. However, a simple proof of Siegel's theorem has been given recently by Estermann [J. London Math. Soc. **23**, 275–279 (1948); these Rev. **10**, 356], so that the lemma of Walfisz is not as deep as was formerly supposed.

The singular series for the Waring-Goldbach problem is studied in chapter VIII [cf. Hua, Math. Z. **44**, 335–346 (1938)] and the following result is proved. Suppose $K=2$ for $k$ odd and $K=2\prod_{(p-1)|k}p^{\theta+1}$ for $k$ even, where $\theta=\theta(p)$ is the exact power to which $p$ divides $k$; then for $s\geqq 3k+1$ and $N\equiv s$ (mod $K$) the singular series $\mathfrak{S}(N)$ for $f(x)=x^k$ is greater than a positive constant. In combination with the theorem of the previous chapter this result shows that, if $H(k)$ denotes the smallest natural number $s$ such that every sufficiently large integer $N\equiv s$ (mod $K$) is a sum of $s$ $k$th powers of primes, then $H(k)\leqq 2^k+1$ if $1\leqq k<14$ and $H(k)\leqq k^3(\log k+2.2\log\log k)$ if $k\geqq 14$.

In chapter IX the author improves the result just mentioned to the following: $H(k)\leqq 2k+2m+7\sim 6k\log k$, where $b=k^3(\log k+1.1\log\log k^2)$ if $k\geqq 14$, $b=2^{k-1}$ if $4\leqq k<14$, and $m=[\{\log\frac{1}{2}b+\log(1-2/k)\}/\{-\log(1-1/k)\}]$. He also proves that $H(4)\leqq 15$, $H(5)\leqq 25$ and states that $H(6)\leqq 39$, $H(7)\leqq 55$, $H(8)\leqq 75$.

The next two chapters treat the simultaneous Waring-Goldbach problem, i.e., the problem of finding sufficient conditions for the solvability of the system of Diophantine equations $p_1{}^k+\cdots+p_s{}^k=N_k,\cdots,p_1+\cdots+p_s=N_1$, where the $p$'s are primes. In chapter X an asymptotic formula for the number of solutions is established for $s\geqq s_0\sim 4.14k^3\log k$. In chapter XI the question of the solvability of the system is discussed for $s\geqq s_0\sim 7k^2\log k$.

In chapter XII other problems are mentioned which may be attacked by the method of this memoir. Finally in chapter XIII a corollary of the Vinogradov mean value theorem is derived and some of its important consequences are stated.

Since the writing of this work considerable progress has been made in the Waring-Goldbach problem [see, for example, Vinogradov, C. R. (Doklady) Acad. Sci. URSS (N.S.) **34**, 182–183 (1942); these Rev. **4**, 211]. In particular, with reference to chapter V, the author's paper reviewed above shows that the asymptotic formula in the Waring-Goldbach problem can be established for $s\geqq s_0\sim 4k^2\log k$ and that $H(k)\leqq s_0\sim 4k\log k$; also in the simultaneous problem the asymptotic formula can be established for $s\geqq s_0\sim 6k^2\log k$ and the solvability can be discussed for $s\geqq s_0\sim 3k^2\log k$. In addition one must notice the new proofs by Linnik [Rec. Math. [Mat. Sbornik] N.S. **19**(61), 3–8 (1946); these Rev. **8**, 317] and Tchudakoff [Ann. of Math. (2) **48**, 515–545 (1947); these Rev. **9**, 11] of the Goldbach-Vinogradov theorem; these proofs use rather deep theory of the $L(s,\chi)$ functions instead of the Vinogradov estimations of trigonometrical sums. *P. T. Bateman.*

Citations: MR 2, 150c = L15-3; MR 2, 347h = L05-2; MR 4, 211e = L15-5; MR 8, 317c = P32-9; MR 9, 11d = P32-10; MR 10, 356c = M20-7.

Referred to in D76-21, L15-14, L15-28, P02-6, P02-7, P02-9, P08-11, P44-9, P44-19, R48-33.

**P02-6** **(16, 337d)**

**Hua, Loo-Keng. Tui Lei Su Shu Lun. [Additive prime number theory.]** Chung Kuo Ko Hsueh Yuan [Academia Sinica], Peking, 1953. 206 pp.

This book is a revised translation of the original Russian edition previously reviewed [Trudy Mat. Inst. Steklov. **22** (1947); these Rev. **10**, 597]. Aside from some changes in detail, the principal differences are as follows. Chapter V contains the author's improved version of Vinogradov's mean-value theorem referred to in the preceding review. This improvement leads to sharper results throughout the book.

Thus, in Chap. VII it is shown that the asymptotic formula for the number of representations of an integer as the sum of $s$ $k$th powers of primes is valid for $s\geqq s_0\sim 4k^2\log k$ in place of the earlier result $s\geqq s_1\sim k^3\log k$. In Chap. IX, the author proves that $H(k)\leqq s_2\sim 4k\log k$ in place of the former $H(k) \leqq s_3 \sim 6k \log k$. Chap. X gives the improved result on Tarry's problem quoted in the preceding review.* For the number of solutions of (*) of that review where the unknowns $x_j$ are now taken to be primes, the validity of the asymptotic formula is proved for $s \geqq s_4 \sim 6k^2 \log k$ in place of the earlier $s \geqq s_5 \sim 4.14k^3 \log k$.

Finally, improved results on the singular series are obtained. The addendum and the English summary have been omitted. *L. Schoenfeld* (Princeton, N. J.).

*I.e. MR **16**, 337C = D52-90.

Citations: MR 10, 597e = P02-5.

Referred to in L15-28, P02-7, P02-8, P02-9.

**P02-7** **(23# A1620)**

**Hua, Loo-Keng**

**Additive Primzahltheorie.**

*B. G. Teubner Verlagsgesellschaft, Leipzig*, 1959. vi + 174 *pp.* *DM* 20.50.

This book is an improved translation of the previous Russian [Trudy Mat. Inst. Steklov. **22** (1947); MR **10**, 597; **11**, 870] and Chinese [Acad. Sinica, Peking, 1953; MR **16**, 337] editions. The work deals with the Waring-Goldbach problem and some allied questions. The Vinogradov method of trigonometrical sums is the main tool in the research. Most of the results are original work of the author and several of them have now become classic. In Chaps. I and III some general properties concerning trigonometrical sums are proved. Chap. II deals with sums involving the divisor function $d(n)$. Lemmas of Mordell, van der Corput and H. Weyl are utilized. In Chap. IV the fundamental Vinogradov mean-value theorem is expounded in the form improved by the author. This theorem gives, as known, an upper bound for the integral

$$\int_0^1 \cdots \int_0^1 |C_k(P)|^2 d\alpha_1 \cdots d\alpha_k,$$

where

$$C_k(P) = \sum_{x=1}^{P} \exp(2\pi i(\alpha_k x^k + \cdots + \alpha_1 x)).$$

In Chap. V a sharpened form of the mean-value theorem is obtained in the particular cases $2 \leqq k \leqq 10$, in correspondence to special values of $\lambda = \lambda(k)$. Finally, the following theorem is proved: suppose $|\alpha_r - h/q| < q^{-2}$, for $2 \leqq r \leqq k$; $(h, q) = 1$; $1 \leqq q \leqq P^r$. Then we have for $P \leqq q \leqq P^{r-1}$:

$$\sum_{x=1}^{P} \exp(2\pi i(\alpha_k x^k + \cdots + \alpha_1 x)) = O(P^{1+\varepsilon-1/\sigma})$$

(where $\sigma = \sigma(k)$ is a suitable function such that $\sigma \sim 4k^3 \log k$ when $k \to \infty$), and weaker relations are obtained for $1 \leqq q \leqq P$, $P^{r-1} \leqq q \leqq P^r$. After these preliminary results the trigonometrical sums depending on prime numbers are considered in Chap. VI. The fundamental Vinogradov theorem giving an upper bound of the sum

$$\sum_{\substack{x \leqq P \\ x \text{ prime} = nQ+t}} \exp(2\pi i(hx^k/q + \alpha_1 x^{k-1} + \cdots + \alpha_k))$$

is proved in a form adapted by the author to the particular problems treated in the book. This is an essential step towards the following results strictly concerning the additive prime number theory. The main result of the whole book is proved in Chap. VII. It concerns the asymptotic behaviour of the number $I_s(N)$ of solutions of the equation $f(p_1) + f(p_2) + \cdots + f(p_s) = N$, where $f(x)$ is an integer-valued polynomial, of $k$th degree with positive first coefficient $A$, for which no integer $q$ exists such that $f(x) \equiv f(0) \pmod q$ for every integer $x$. This can be considered as a generalization of the Waring-Goldbach problem, which properly deals, as known, with the particular case $f(x) = x^k$. The fundamental formula proved by the author in the general case is as follows:

$$I_s(N) = A^{-s/k} \mathfrak{S}(N) \Gamma^s(1/k) N^{s/k-1} / (\Gamma(s/k) \log^s N) + O(N^{s/k-1} \log \log N / \log^{s+1} N),$$

where $\mathfrak{S}(N)$ is the so-called singular series; the formula holds for

$$s \geqq s_0 = 2^k + 1 \quad \text{for} \quad 1 \leqq k \leqq 10,$$
$$= 2k^2(2 \log k + \log \log k + 2.5) \quad \text{for} \quad k > 10.$$

In Chap. VIII the singular series are studied in the particular case $f(x) = x^k$, and the following theorem is proved: suppose $s \geqq 3k+1$, and $s \equiv N \pmod K$; then we have $\mathfrak{S}(N) \geqq \eta > 0$ for $f(x) = x^k$ (here we put $K = \prod_{p-1|k} p^\gamma$; $\gamma = \theta + 2$, for $p = 2$, $2 | k$, and $\gamma = \theta + 1$ otherwise; $p^\theta \| k$). Consequently the following theorem is deduced: every sufficiently large integer $N \equiv s \pmod K$ is the sum of $s$ $k$th powers of primes, if $s \geqq s_0$. Several interesting consequences follow immediately; e.g., every sufficiently large odd integer is the sum of three primes (this is the well-known result of Vinogradov); every sufficiently large integer $\equiv 5 \pmod{24}$ is the sum of 5 squares of primes. Considering the problem of finding the least integer $s = H(k)$ having the property that every sufficiently large $N \equiv s \pmod K$ is the sum of $s$ $k$th powers of primes, $H(k) \leqq s_0$ is immediately obtained. In Chap. IX the result concerning $H(k)$ is improved and the formula $H(k) \leqq 2k + 2m + 7$ is shown, where $m \sim 2k \cdot \log k$. For small values of $k$ the following results can also be obtained: $H(4) \leqq 15$, $H(5) \leqq 25$, $H(6) \leqq 37$, $H(7) \leqq 54$, $H(8) \leqq 74$. A lemma of Davenport is utilized. Chap. X deals with the generalized problem of finding the number $I(N_1, \cdots, N_k)$ of solutions of the system (a) $\sum_{i=1}^{s} p_i^h = N_h$, $h = 1, 2, \cdots, k$. A general asymptotic formula is proved, which holds for $s \geqq s_1 \sim 6k^2 \log k$. The conditions of "solvability in integers" and of "solvability as congruence" are also dealt with; when these conditions are simultaneously satisfied, the solvability of (a) is guaranteed. The meaning of these conditions is clarified in Chap. XI, where a deeper result is given concerning the solvability of (a) for $s \geqq s_2 \sim 3k^2 \log k$. In Chap. XII several allied questions are briefly expounded. Some generalized problems and classical conjectures are mentioned and some interesting results are given without proof. *M. Cugiani* (Zbl **88**, 255)

Citations: MR 10, 597e = P02-5; MR 16, 337d = P02-6.

Referred to in L15-25, L15-28, N48-12, P40-10, R48-23.

**P02-8** **(33# 2613)**

**Hua Lo-keng**

**Tui lei su shu lun.** (Chinese) [**Additive prime number theory**]

Revised edition. Edited by the Institute of Mathematics of the Chinese Academy of Science.

*Science Press, Peking*, 1957. viii + 158 *pp.* 2.20 *yuan.*

The first edition of this book has been reviewed [Academia Sinica, Peking, 1953; MR **16**, 337].

{See also #2614 below.}

Citations: MR 16, 337d = P02-6.

**P02-9** **(33# 2614)**

**Hua, L. K. [Hua Lo-keng]**

**Additive theory of prime numbers.**

Translations of Mathematical Monographs, Vol. 13.

*American Mathematical Society, Providence, R.I.*, 1965. xiii + 190 *pp.* $11.00.

This is a translation of the Chinese edition [Academia Sinica, Peking, 1953; MR **16**, 337], which was itself a translation and revision of the Russian edition [Trav. Inst. Mat. Stekloff **22** (1947); MR **10**, 597].

{See also #2613 above.}

Citations: MR 10, 597e = P02-5; MR 16, 337d = P02-6.

Referred to in L15-28.

## P02-10 (11, 501g)

**Ricci, Giovanni. Figure, reticoli e computo di nodi.** Rend. Sem. Mat. Fis. Milano **19** (1948), 165–205 (1949).

This is an expository and historical account of the classical lattice-point problems, including the recent work of D. G. Kendall [Quart. J. Math., Oxford Ser. **19**, 1–26 (1948); these Rev. **9**, 570]. The regions considered include the square, rhombus, circle, hyperbola (divisor problem) and multidimensional ellipsoid. *R. A. Rankin.*

Citations: MR 9, 570b = P20-7.

## P02-11 (13, 326a)

**Rademacher, Hans. Additive algebraic number theory.** Proceedings of the International Congress of Mathematicians, Cambridge, Mass., 1950, vol. 1, pp. 356–362. Amer. Math. Soc., Providence, R. I., 1952.

At the International Congress of Mathematicians, 1950, the author delivered an address on the development of analytic (additive) number theory for algebraic numbers, a branch which was hardly mentioned in his report on analytic number theory in 1941 [Bull. Amer. Math. Soc. **48**, 379–401 (1942); these Rev. **3**, 271]. This is an abstract of that address. The author begins by stating Waring's problem and Goldbach's problem for algebraic numbers. Comparing these with the case of rational integers, he explains how the classical Hardy-Littlewood method can be extended to algebraic number fields, using the equivalent of power series found by Hecke, and states contributions of Siegel and himself to these problems, noting that the formulae thus obtained show complete analogy to the results in rational cases. The author then discusses the problem of partition for algebraic numbers and shows that here the analogy to the rational case breaks down. For instance, the number $P(\nu)$ of partitions of an integer $\nu$ in a real quadratic field satisfies

$$P(\nu)=O(\exp N(\nu)^{2/5}),$$

which differs essentially from the asymptotic formula for the partition function $p(n)$ in the rational field. Showing the different characters of generating functions, the author explains the discrepancy between these two cases and notes that Hecke's "Grössencharaktere" will appear in the presumptive asymptotic formula for $P(\nu)$ in an algebraic number field.

*K. Iwasawa* (Princeton, N. J.).

Citations: MR 3, 271f = Z02-2.

## P02-12 (13, 915b)

**Estermann, T. Introduction to modern prime number theory.** Cambridge Tracts in Mathematics and Mathematical Physics, no. 41. Cambridge, at the University Press, 1952. x+75 pp. $2.50.

The main purpose of this book is to give a complete account of Vinogradoff's famous theorem that every large odd positive integer can be represented as the sum of three primes [Doklady Akad. Nauk SSSR **15**, 291–294 (1937); Mat. Sbornik N.S. **2(44)**, 179–195 (1937)]. It assumes some knowledge of the elementary theory of numbers, for which Hardy-Wright's treatise is quoted, and some of complex function theory. The exposition is very clear and accurate, and also in other respects reminds one of Landau's books. Problems, methods or results which do not directly fit in the author's presentation of Vinogradoff's theorem are completely neglected, and, therefore, the title of the book may be somewhat misleading. Nevertheless it gives a good impression of analytical number theory.

Chapter 1 presents a proof of de la Vallée Poussin's refinement of the prime number theorem

$$\pi(m)=\mathrm{li}\, m+O(m\exp(-c(\log m)^{\frac{1}{2}})).$$

Chapter 2 gives the much deeper analogous result for the primes in an arithmetical progression with emphasis on uniformity in $k$:

$$|\pi(m;k,l)-(\mathrm{li}\, m)/\varphi(k)|<Cm\exp(-(\log m)/200)$$

($(k,l)=1$, $k\leqq\log^u m$, $C$ depending on $u$ only), due to Walfisz. Chapter 3 gives Vinogradoff's theorem.

*N. G. de Bruijn* (Delft).

Referred to in M25-79, P40-27.

## P02-13 (15, 13b)

**Mardžanišvili, K. K. On some additive problems of the theory of numbers.** Acta Math. Acad. Sci. Hungar. **2**, 223–227 (1951). (Russian)

This is a brief expository paper giving the history of the Waring problem, the Goldbach problem and such extensions as the Waring-Goldbach problem and the simultaneous system analogs. No references to the literature are given. The exposition very closely follows that in the author's paper appearing in Uspehi Matem. Nauk (N.S.) **5**, no. 1(35), 236–240 (1950) [these Rev. **11**, 502].

*L. Schoenfeld* (Urbana, Ill.).

Citations: MR 11, 502e = P44-13.

Referred to in P44-19.

## P02-14 (18, 15e)

**Ricci, Giovanni. Aritmetica additiva: aspetti e problemi.** Confer. Sem. Mat. Univ. Bari no. 7 (1954), 31 pp. (1956).

An expository account of classical and modern results of the additive theory of numbers. *H. B. Mann.*

## P02-15 (18, 18a)

**Erdös, P. Problems and results in additive number theory.** Colloque sur la Théorie des Nombres, Bruxelles, 1955, pp. 127–137. Georges Thone, Liège; Masson and Cie, Paris, 1956.

"In this lecture I will discuss several problems in additive number theory. They will not have much in common, except that they are all combinatorial in nature and that probability theory can be applied with advantage to most of them." Much of the paper is devoted to discussing known results and conjectures, but proofs of several new results are outlined. For example, let $a_1<a_2<\cdots$ be an increasing sequence of positive integers and define $f(n)$ by the power-series identity

$$\sum_{n=0}^{\infty} f(n)x^n=\left(\sum_{k=1}^{\infty} x^{a_k}\right)^2.$$

In an earlier paper [Acta Sci. Math. Szeged **15** (1954), 255–259; MR **16**, 336] Erdös proved the existence of a sequence for which (*) $0<f(n)<c\log n$ for large $n$. Here he gives another proof by constructing a suitable probability measure on the space of all increasing sequences of positive integers and then using probability theory to show that (*) is true for almost all sequences relative to this measure. *P. T. Bateman* (Princeton, N.J.).

Citations: MR 16, 336c = B16-8.

## P02-16 (18, 382e)

**Pagni, Plinio. Studio sulle partizioni numeriche. I, II, III.** Period. Mat. (4) **32** (1954), 172–183, 199–211, 294–301.

This is an elementary expository paper on the theory of the partitions of an integer, in which the author's aim is to obtain results using methods which are "direct and of easy access". No use is made of generating functions. The paper is in three parts. Part one gives a classification of the types of partitions and recurrence formulas. Part two gives numerical examples and short tables of values of the various types of partitions. Part three is a study of the number of partitions of an integer $n$ into not more than $k$ positive integers, repetitions allowed. *W. H. Simons.*

**P02-17** **(24# A1244)**

**Davenport, H.**

**Über einige neuere Fortschritte der additiven Zahlentheorie.**

*Jber. Deutsch. Math. Verein.* **63**, *Abt.* 1, 163–169 (1961).

This is an exposition of three recent developments: (I) Roth's proof [J. London. Math. Soc. **28** (1953), 104–109; MR **14**, 536, 1278] of the long-standing conjecture that every sequence of integers of positive density contains three elements in arithmetic progression. (II) The theorem of Cassels [Acta Sci. Math. Szeged **21** (1960), 111–124; MR **24** #A103] giving broad sufficient conditions on a sequence $S$ of natural numbers in order that every sufficiently large integer be the sum of distinct elements of $S$. (III) Theorems of Lewis, Birch and the author concerning the solvability of homogeneous equations $F(x_1, \cdots, x_n)=0$ in a large number of variables [Lewis, Mathematika **4** (1957), 97–101; MR **20** #3827; Birch, ibid. **4** (1957), 102–105; MR **20** #3828; Davenport, Philos. Trans. Roy. Soc. London Ser. A **251** (1959), 193–232; MR **21** #4136].

*W. J. LeVeque* (Ann Arbor, Mich.)

Citations: MR 14, 536g = B24-6; MR 20# 3827 = D72-15; MR 20# 3828 = D72-16; MR 21# 4136 = D72-19; MR 24# A103 = B12-23.

**P02-18** **(25# 3920)**

**Linnik, Ju. V. [Линник, Ю. В.]**

**The dispersion method in binary additive problems [Дисперсионный метод в бинарных аддитивных задачах].**

*Izdat. Leningrad. Univ., Leningrad,* 1961. 208 *pp.* 1.13 *r.*

This book contains an account of a method devised by the author for treating certain types of problems in additive number theory which have previously resisted all attacks. As the title suggests, use is made of certain techniques and concepts from probability theory, but these are quite different both from the limit-distribution theorems of the type discussed, for example, in the monograph of J. Kubilius [*Probability methods in number theory* (Russian), Gosudarstv. Izdat. Politič. i Nauč. Lit. Litovsk. SSR, Vilna, 1959; MR **23** #A134] and from the strong laws occurring in metrical Diophantine approximation [cf. J. F. Koksma, *Diophantische Approximationen*, J. Springer, Berlin, 1936]. There are much closer connections with Turán's proof of the Hardy-Ramanujan theorem on the normal order of $\omega(n)$; both use the concept of dispersion (or variance) and covariance, and Čebyšev's inequality. Indeed, the "dispersion method" is simply the systematic application of these tools in additive problems.

The additive problems which have been successfully treated heretofore could, almost without exception, be formulated so as to be of the following type: find an asymptotic estimate for the number of solutions of the equation $\alpha+\beta+\gamma=N$, where $\alpha$ and $\beta$ run through a set of integers "sufficiently dense" in the interval $[1, N]$ and sufficiently regularly distributed in certain arithmetic progressions, while the range of $\gamma$, although perhaps relatively sparse, is such that the fractional parts $(\vartheta\gamma)$ are sufficiently regularly behaved, for $\vartheta$ on the so-called minor arcs of the unit interval. Problems which fall within the scope of the dispersion method are of more varied nature, but the prototype from which the adjective "binary" arises is the problem of estimating the number of representations of $n$ as $n=\varphi+D'\nu$, in which $\{\varphi\}$ is an arbitrary sequence of positive integers, $D'$ runs without repetition through an arbitrary system of positive integers in an interval $(D)=[D_1, D_1+D_2]$, and $\nu$ independently runs through arbitrary positive integers of an interval $(\nu)=[\nu_0, \nu_0+\nu_0']$. Oversimplifying, the basic technique is to adopt a heuristically-derived estimate $A(n, D)$, then to estimate the dispersion of the number of solutions,

$$\sum_{D'\in(D)} \Big(\sum_{\nu\in(\nu)} U(n-D'\nu)-A(n, D')\Big)^2,$$

where $U(m)=\sum_{\varphi=m} 1$, and finally to use this latter estimate, as in the proof of Čebyšev's inequality, to show that $A(n, D)$ is a valid "asymptotic".

The long introduction, of some 25 pages, is devoted to a qualitative description of the method and several variants; this gives the reader a clear idea of the essential elements of the techniques before plunging into the rather awesome details. Chapters I and II are devoted to necessary lemmas on divisor functions $\tau_k(m)$, prime numbers, trigonometric sums, and quadratic forms. In Chapter III, the problems of estimating the sums

$$\sum_{m\leqq n} \tau_{k_1}(m)\tau_{k_2}(m+a) \quad \text{and} \quad \sum_{m<n} \tau_{k_1}(m)\tau_{k_2}(n-m)$$

are recast as binary problems, and asymptotic estimates are obtained when one of $k_1$ and $k_2$ is 1 or 2. This extends results of C. Hooley [Proc. London Math. Soc. (3) **7** (1957), 396–413; MR **19**, 839].

In Chapter IV the author generalizes results by Kloosterman [Acta Math. **49** (1926), 407–464], Eichler [Arch. Math. **5** (1954), 355–366; MR **16**, 116] and others on representations by quaternary quadratic forms; he obtains an estimate for the number of solutions of $n=\varphi_1(x, y)+\varphi_2(z, t)$, where $\varphi_1$ and $\varphi_2$ are binary quadratic forms.

In Chapter V the author commences the study of the number of solutions of equations of the type $a_1\varphi(x, y)+a_2D'\nu^g=n$, where $a_1$, $a_2$ are fixed integers, $g$ is 1 or a fixed prime, $\varphi$ is a binary quadratic form, $\nu$ runs over the primes such that $\nu^g\leqq n^\gamma$ $(0<\gamma<0.01)$, and $D'$ runs independently over a set of integers having cardinality $n^{1-\gamma}/(\log n)^K$ at least from the interval $[1, n^{1-\gamma}]$. As an example, the function $A(n, D)$ for the equation $\varphi(x, y)+2dD'\nu^2=n$ is obtained (here $d$ is fixed, while $D'$ and $\nu$ range over primes), and the asymptotic estimate for the number of solutions is stated. Details for the proof of the latter are not given. Two more special cases are treated in Chapter VI: the equation $x^2+y^2+p_1p_2$ with $p_i>\exp(\log\log n)^2$ for $i=1, 2$, and the equation $\xi^2+\eta^2+x_1'x_2'\cdots x_k'$, where $k\geqq 6$ and the $x_i'$ run independently over the set $\Omega_P$ of all integers whose prime divisors are all greater than $P=\exp(\log n \log\log\log n/K \log\log n)$, where $K$ is a sufficiently large constant. This second equation is auxiliary to the solution of the Hardy-Littlewood problem in Chapter VII.

The latter, which is perhaps the high point of the book, is the proof of the conjecture that the number of solutions of the equation $n=x^2+y^2+p$ is asymptotic to

$$\pi A_0 \frac{n}{\log n} \prod_{p|n} \frac{(p-1)(p-\chi_4(p))}{(p^2-p+\chi_4(p))},$$

where $A_0=\prod_p (1+\chi_4(p)/p(p-1))$ and $\chi_4$ is the non-principal character (mod 4). This was derived heuristically by Hardy and Littlewood [Acta Math. **44** (1923), 1–70]; the asymptotic estimate was first proved by the author [Mat. Sb. (N.S.) **52 (94)** (1960), 661–700; MR **22** #10963], and later [Izv. Akad. Nauk SSSR Ser. Mat. **24** (1960), 629–706; MR **23** #A130] this was augmented by him with the estimate $O(n/(\log n)^{1.028})$ for the error term. Chapter VII is a new exposition of the contents of these two papers.

Chapter VIII is devoted to the sum $\sum_{p\leq n} \tau(p-l)$. It is not difficult to show that this sum is $O(n)$, and Titchmarsh [Rend. Circ. Mat. Palermo **54** (1930), 414–429] deduced from the extended Riemann hypothesis that it is of the form $E(l)n+O(n \log\log n/\log n)$, where $E(l)$ is independent of $n$. The author now shows, without such hypothesis, that

$$\sum_{p\leq n} \tau(p-1) = \frac{315\zeta(3)}{2\pi^4} n+O(n(\log n)^{-0.999}).$$

In Chapters IX and X, of three or four pages each, some further comments are made about the general Hardy-Littlewood equation $n=\varphi(x, y)+p$, with $\varphi$ a binary quadratic form, and possible variations on the dispersion method. *W. J. LeVeque* (Ann Arbor, Mich.)

Citations: MR 16, 116d = G30-15; MR 19, 839c = N40-30; MR 22# 10963 = P36-24; MR 23# A130 = P36-26; MR 23# A134 = N60-37.

Referred to in N02-12, N36-84, N40-65, P02-19, P36-40, P36-43, P36-45, P36-51, P36-52, P36-56, P48-9, P48-10, P48-12, P48-15, P48-22, P52-11, R48-25.

**P02-19** **(29# 5804 )**

**Linnik, Ju. V.**

**The dispersion method in binary additive problems.**
Translated by S. Schuur.
*American Mathematical Society, Providence, R.I.*, 1963. x+186 *pp.* \$12.30.

The original Russian [Izdat. Leningrad. Univ., Leningrad, 1961] was reviewed earlier [MR **25** #3920].

Citations: MR 25# 3920 = P02-18.

Referred to in N02-12, N36-84, N40-65, P36-43, P36-45, P36-51, P36-52, P36-56, P48-9, P48-12, P48-15, P48-22, P52-11.

**P02-20** **(27# 122 )**

**Grosswald, E.**

**Results, new and old, in the theory of partitions. (Spanish)**
*Rev. Un. Mat. Argentina* **20** (1962), 40–57.

The results in question for the most part are those interesting to the analyst, that is, asymptotic expressions for the numbers of partitions of various kinds. The most famous result of this kind is probably the formula of H. Rademacher, a convergent series for unrestricted partitions; curiously, the author omits the contribution of D. H. Lehmer to its actual use in calculation. The numerous companions to this for partitions with restricted parts (restricted according to analytic convenience, for example, those with residues 1,4 (mod 5)) are given in detail, with emphasis mainly on function-theoretical considerations. A separate section is devoted to the case where the parts are either primes or prime powers. Finally, the quite different results of N. J. Fine [Rep. Inst. Theory of Numbers, Univ. of Colorado, Boulder, Colo., 1959] are given a brief resumé.
*J. Riordan* (Murray Hill, N.J.)

**P02-21** **(28# 3953 )**

**Linnik, Ju. V.**

**Five lectures on some topics in number theory and probability theory. (Russian. Hungarian and English summaries)**
*Magyar Tud. Akad. Mat. Kutató Int. Közl.* **4** (1959), 225–258.

The lectures are on the following topics. (I) The variance method for solving certain binary additive problems; (II) Applications of the variance method, the divisor problem, the Hardy-Littlewood problem, and other problems; (III) Integer points on a sphere and Markov chains, and an analogue of the ergodic theorems for integral matrices; (IV) Some properties of infinitely divisible laws; (V) Contributions to the theory of big deviations for sums of independent random variables, and a problem on Fourier transforms.

**P02-22** **(31# 4775 )**

**Linnik, Ju. V.**

**Additive problems and eigenvalues of the modular operators.**
*Proc. Internat. Congr. Mathematicians (Stockholm,* 1962), *pp.* 270–284. *Inst. Mittag-Leffler, Djursholm,* 1963.

Der Verfasser gibt eine Übersicht (ohne Beweise) über Lösungsmethoden für Probleme der additiven Zahlentheorie, in denen die Anzahl $r(n)$ der Darstellungen einer natürlichen Zahl $n$ als Fourierkoeffizient in der Form

$$r(n) = \int_0^1 f(x) \exp(-2\pi inx)\, dx$$

ausgedrückt ist. Bei Anwendung der Hardy-Littlewood-Methode stellt man $r(n)$ dar als

$$r(n) = \sum I_j, \qquad I_j = \int_{a_j}^{b_j} f(x) \exp(-2\pi inx)\, dx$$

mit einer passenden Aufteilung des Intervalles (0, 1) in Teilintervalle $(a_j, b_j)$, die jedoch verschiedene Längen haben. Der Verfasser schlägt ein Verfahren vor, das er "levelling" nennt, und dessen Kern darin besteht, $r(n)$ in der Form $r(n)=\sum I_j+\gamma(n)$ darzustellen, wobei $\gamma(n)$ ein Restglied ist und die Integrationsintervalle jetzt gleiche Längen haben. Ist $f(x)$ ein trigonometrisches Polynom, so lässt sich dann $r(n)$ bis auf das Restglied als Lösungsanzahl eines Systems von Kongruenzen darstellen. Die Anwendung der Methode auf die Darstellungsanzahlen positiv-definiter quadratischer Formen führt auf das Problem, Summen Kloostermanscher Summen möglichst gut abzuschätzen. Einige Abschätzungen dieser Art ergeben sich über die Thetafunktionen durch den Zusammenhang mit den Hecke-Operatoren. Umgekehrt liefert die Methode durch diesen Zusammenhang gewisse Abschätzungen für Eigenwerte von Hecke-Operatoren. Der Artikel enthält zahlreiche Druckfehler. *K.-B. Gundlach* (Münster)

Referred to in F30-46.

**P02-23** **(34# 4229 )**

**Bredihin, B. M.**

**Dispersion method of Ju. V. Linnik and binary additive problems. (Russian)**
*Studies in Number Theory, No. I (Russian), pp.* 6–11. *Izdat. Saratov. Univ., Saratov,* 1966.

An exposition of the method mentioned in the title and some of the results obtained therewith.
*W. J. LeVeque* (Ann Arbor, Mich.)

**P02-24** **(34# 5739 )**

**Gupta, H.**

**Partitions—a survey.**
*Math. Student* **32** (1964), *appendix in no.* 3–4, 1–19.

This is an expository paper stressing the analytic aspects of the theory of partitions. {No detailed bibliography is given.} *K. Yamamoto* (Boca Raton, Fla.)

**P02-25** **(38# 4431)**

**Klimov, N. I.**

**Šnirel'man's constant and the Goldbach-Euler problem. (Russian)**

*Studies in Number Theory, No. 2 (Russian), pp.* 80–89. *Izdat. Saratov. Univ., Saratov,* 1968.

Sei $S$ [bzw. $s$] die kleinste natürliche Zahl, so daß alle hinreichend großen $N$ [bzw. alle $N \geqq 2$] als Summe von höchstens $S$ [bzw. $s$] Primzahlen darstellbar sind. In dem vorliegenden Übersichtsartikel (mit ausführlichem Literaturverzeichnis) berichtet der Verfasser über Abschätzungen von $S$, besonders über solche, die mit L. T. Šnirel'man's Methode [Uspehi Mat. Nauk **6** (1939), 9–25; ibid. **7** (1940), 7–46] erzielt wurden; er weist auf eine Reihe von Lehrbüchern und Arbeiten hin, in denen derartige Ergebnisse fehlerhaft zitiert wurden. Schließlich erwähnt er Abschätzungen von $s$ ($s \leqq 2 \cdot 10^{10}$ nach A. A. Šanin [Volž. Mat. Sb. Vyp. 2 (1964), 261–265; MR **33** #2617] und T. A. Šeptickaja, $s \leqq 6 \cdot 10^5$ nach V. V. Glazkov).

*W. Schwarz* (Freiburg)

Citations: MR 33# 2617 = P40-20.

**P02-26** **(42# 223)**

**Grasselli, Jože**

**Additive number theory. (Slovenian. English summary)**

*Obzornik Mat. Fiz.* **17** (1970), 49–58.

Introductory expository article.

**P02-27** **(42# 5938)**

**Gupta, Hansraj**

**Partitions—A survey.**

*J. Res. Nat. Bur. Standards Sect. B* **74B** (1970), 1–29.

This survey seems essentially a resumé of the aspects of partitions of integers which have engaged the author's attention over the past half-century. It includes the recurrences used in making his table of unrestricted partitions and also some surprises. For one thing, a formula found by P. A. MacMahon in 1920 [Proc. Cambridge Philos. Soc. **20** (1920/21), 281–283] for the parity of the number of unrestricted partitions retains its singular position to this day; however, there has been active consideration of the following 1960 conjecture of M. Newman [Trans. Amer. Math. Soc. **97** (1960), 225–236; MR **22** #6778]: for every positive integral $m$, $r$, there are infinitely many values of $n$ such that $p(n) \equiv r \pmod{m}$, with $p(n)$ the number of (unrestricted) partitions of $n$. For another, the unimodality of the (asymptotic) distribution of partitions by number of parts, conjectured by F. C. Auluck, S. Chowla and the author in 1942 [J. Indian Math. Soc. (N.S.) **6** (1942), 105–112; MR **4**, 211], according to the author still remains unproved. Also, deserved attention is directed to developments associated with F. J. Dyson's term, rank (largest part less number of parts) [Eureka **8** (1944), 10–15]. There is an extensive bibliography, the use of which is marred by occasional failures to give full identification in the text of the paper in question (dates are omitted or the author in question is ambiguous as in the case of D. J. Newman and M. Newman; indeed in one case, on page 15, a paper cited, by C. B. Haselgrove and H. N. V. Temperley [Proc. Cambridge Philos. Soc. **50** (1954), 225–241; MR **16**, 17], does not appear in the bibliography).

*J. Riordan* (New York)

Citations: MR 4, 211b = P80-5; MR 16, 17f = P72-21; MR 22# 6778 = P76-18.

# P04 WARING'S PROBLEM AND ITS VARIANTS: SPECIFIC EXPONENT

For sums of squares, see **E24**. For square-free or prime arguments, see **P16** or **P44**. For analogous problems over algebraic number fields, see **R48**; over finite fields, **D80** and **T50**.

Many of the papers in **D72** provide Waring-type results for more general forms than a sum of $n$th powers.

See also reviews C05-38, D36-34, D36-38, D36-41, E20-45, P08-4, P08-12, P80-11, P99-5.

**P04-1** **(1, 5c)**

**Davenport, H. On Waring's problem for cubes.** Acta Math. **71**, 123–143 (1939).

There are very few results concerning Waring's problem which may be called best possible. One of these is the main theorem of this paper: If $E_s(N)$ denotes the number of positive integers not greater than $N$ which are not representable as a sum of $s$ positive integral cubes, then $E_4(N)/N \to 0$ as $N \to \infty$. A simple argument shows that the theorem is false if $s < 4$.

The new weapon used here has been explained in detail in several papers by the author [C. R. Acad. Sci. Paris **207**, 1366 (1938); Proc. Roy. Soc. London **170**, 293–299 (1939); Ann. of Math. **40**, 533–536 (1939)]. The remainder of the proof is similar to that given by Landau [Vorlesungen über Zahlentheorie, Bd. 1, 235–303] for the third Hardy-Littlewood theorem [Satz 346] as adapted by Davenport and Heilbronn [Proc. London Math. Soc. (2) **43**, 73–104 (1937)] to the problem of representations by two cubes and one square. Interesting parts of the proof are the use of Poisson's summation formula in Lemma 7 and the handling of the Singular Series.

*R. D. James* (Saskatoon, Sask.).

Referred to in P04-6, P04-17.

**P04-2** **(1, 5e)**

**Dickson, L. E. All integers except 23 and 239 are sums of eight cubes.** Bull. Amer. Math. Soc. **45**, 588–591 (1939).

A method similar to that of W. S. Baer [Dissertation, Göttingen, 1913] shows that every integer beyond a stated limit is a $C_8$. The integers below this limit are treated by several lemmas, proved by the use of tables which are not published here, but are deposited in manuscript in the library of the University of Chicago.

*W. A. Hurwitz.*

**P04-3** **(1, 42a)**

**Davenport, H. On Waring's problem for fourth powers.** Ann. of Math. **40**, 731–747 (1939).

This paper gives a proof of the following theorem: Every sufficiently large integer is representable as a sum of 14 integral fourth powers unless it is congruent to 0 or 15 (mod 16). It follows that every sufficiently large integer is representable as a sum of 16 integral fourth powers. This is a best possible result, since an argument due to Kempner [Math. Ann. **72**, 395–396 (1912)] shows that no integer of the form $16^h 31$ is representable as a sum of less than 16 integral fourth powers. The method of proof is quite similar to that given previously for the case of representation by cubes [Acta Math. **71**, 123–143 (1939)] and the same new idea is used [Proc. Roy. Soc. London **170**, 293–299 (1939)].

*R. D. James* (Saskatoon, Sask.).

Referred to in D76-12, P04-12.

**P04-4** **(1, 69a)**

**Fuchs, W. H. J. and Wright, E. M. The 'easier' Waring problem.** Quart. J. Math., Oxford Ser. **10**, 190–209 (1939).

Let $v(k)$ be the least $s$ such that every integer $n$ can be expressed in the form

$$F=x_1^k+x_2^k+\cdots+x_r^k-x_{r+1}^k-\cdots-x_s^k$$

for some $r$, $0\leqq r\leqq s$. E. M. Wright [J. London Math. Soc. **9**, 267–272 (1934)] proved that $v(2)=3$, $4\leqq v(3)\leqq 5$, $8\leqq v(4)\leqq 12$, $5\leqq v(5)\leqq 10$. Main object of this article is to find bounds for $v(k)$, $6\leqq k\leqq 20$. Define $\Delta(k,m,n)$, $\Gamma(k,m,n)$, $\Lambda(k,m,n)$, respectively, as the least $s$ such that $F\equiv n \pmod m$ is soluble for some $r$, for $r=s$, for every $r$; $\Delta(k,m)=\max\Delta(k,m,n)$ for all $n$, and similarly for $\Gamma(k,m)$ and $\Lambda(k,m)$; $\Delta(k)=\max\Delta(k,m)$, etc. Hence $v(k)\geqq\Delta(k)$; and $v(k)\leqq 2j+\Delta(k,C)$ if we can find an identity

$$(x+a_1)^k+\cdots+(x+a_j)^k-(x+b_1)^k-\cdots-(x+b_j)^k=Cx+D.$$

The investigation of $\Delta(k)$ is in part like that of $\Gamma(k)$ by Hardy and Littlewood [Partitio Numerorum, IV and VIII; Math. Z. **12**, 161–188 (1922); Proc. London Math. Soc. (2) **28**, 518–542 (1928)]. Let $p^\Theta\| k$, $\phi=\phi_p=\Theta+1$ if $p>2$, $\phi_2=\Theta+2$, $\epsilon=(p-1,\,p^{-\Theta}k)$, $d=(p-1)/\epsilon$; let $\delta_p(k)$, $\gamma_p(k)$, $\lambda_p(k)$ be the least $s$ for which $F\equiv n \pmod{p^{\phi_p}}$ is soluble in relative primes $x_1,\cdots,x_s$, for every $n$ and (respectively) some $r$, $r=s$, every $r$. The problem reduces to moduli $p^{\phi_p}$. Theorem 1: If $k$ is odd, $\delta_2(k)=\lambda_2(k)=\gamma_2(k)=2$; if $k$ is even, $\delta_2(k)=2^{\Theta+1}$, $\lambda_2(k)=2^{\Theta+2}$. Theorem 2: If $k$ is odd, $\Delta(k)=\Lambda(k)=\Gamma(k)$. Theorem 3: If $p>2$, $d=1$, then $\lambda_p(k)=\gamma_p(k)=p^\phi$, $\delta_p(k)=\frac{1}{2}(p^\phi-1)$; if $d=2$, $\lambda_p(k)=\gamma_p(k)=\delta_p(k)=\frac{1}{2}(p^\phi-1)$. Theorem 4: If $p>2$, $\Theta=0$, $d>1$, then $\lambda_p(k)\leqq\max(\epsilon,3)\leqq k$. Theorem 5: If $p>2$, $\Theta>0$, $d>2$, then $\lambda_p(k)\leqq p^\Theta\epsilon\leqq k$. Theorem 6: I. If $k=2^\theta$ $(\theta>1)$, $\Delta(k)=2^{\theta+1}$. II. If $k=\frac{1}{2}\pi^\theta(\pi-1)$, $\pi$ an odd prime, $\theta>0$, then $\Delta(k)=\frac{1}{2}(\pi^{\theta+1}-1)\geqq k+1$. III. For $k$ not in classes I or II, $\Delta(k)\leqq k$. IV. If $k=\frac{1}{2}(\pi-1)$, $\pi$ an odd prime, $k$ not in class I or II, $\Delta(k)=k$. Then $\Delta(k)$ is calculated for $k\leqq 36$. Identities from several sources are used to obtain upper bounds for $v(k)\leqq 2j+\Delta(k,C_k)$; for $k=6,\cdots,20$ these bounds are 14, 14, 30, 29, 32, 28, 38, 39, 53, 69, 98, 72, 107, 115, 133. For large $k$ the best upper bound is $v(k)\leqq G(k)+1$, with Vinogradow's result for $G(k)$. *G. Pall.*

Referred to in P04-19, P04-27.

**P04-5** **(2, 35e)**

**Auluck, F. C. On Waring's problem for biquadrates.** Proc. Indian Acad. Sci., Sect. A. **11**, 437–450 (1940).

It was first proved by Hardy and Littlewood that every integer exceeding a certain large number $C$ could be represented as the sum of 19 integral fourth powers. In this paper the numerical values of the constants in the Gelbcke modification of the Hardy-Littlewood method are worked out and it is proved that $\log_{10}\log_{10} C\leqq 88.39$. The introductory remarks lead one to believe that it will be shown that $\log_{10}\log_{10} C\geqq 88.39$. This is not the case.

*R. D. James* (Saskatoon, Sask.).

Referred to in P04-60.

**P04-6** **(2, 35f)**

**Hua, Loo-Keng. Sur le problème de Waring relatif à un polynome du troisième degré.** C. R. Acad. Sci. Paris **210**, 650–652 (1940).

Let $f(x)=a(x^3-x)/6+b(x^2-x)/2+cx+d$, $a>0$, $(a,b,c)=1$, $a, b, c, d$ integers. Two theorems are stated: I. Every large integer is a sum of eight values $f(x)$, $x=0, 1, 2, \cdots$. II. Almost all positive integers are sums of four values (and 4 is best possible); except that 4 must be replaced by 7 if $f(x)\equiv 2(2a'+1)x^3+(2b'+1)x^2+2(2c'+1)x+d' \pmod{16}$, and by 5 if $f(x)$ is not of this form but $f(x)\equiv a''x^3+3b''x^2+3c''x+d'' \pmod 9$ with $b''^2\equiv a''(b''+a'') \pmod 3$. The second theorem requires a lemma analogous to one of Davenport [Acta Math. **71**, 123–143 (1939); these Rev. **1**, 5] and a result by the author [the same C. R. **210**, 520–523 (1940); these Rev. **2**, 40], and the following result which is proved here: the number of solutions of $f(x_1)+f(x_2)+f(x_3)+f(x_4)\equiv n \pmod p$ is $p^3+O(p^2)$. *G. Pall* (Princeton, N. J.).

Citations: MR 1, 5c = P04-1; MR 2, 40d = L05-1.
Referred to in L05-1, P04-10, P04-17.

**P04-7** **(2, 146c)**

**Pillai, S. S. On Waring's problem $g(6)=73$.** Proc. Indian Acad. Sci., Sect. A. **12**, 30–40 (1940).

The main part of this paper is devoted to proving that every integer $N>e^{2400}$ is a sum of at most 73 integral sixth powers. The surprisingly small lower bound is obtained by the use of an inequality due to van der Corput [Nederl. Akad. Wetensch., Proc. **42**, 461–467 (1939)] which does not involve the function $d(n)$, the number of divisors of $n$. Not all the numerical computations are given in detail and in one instance at least (Lemma 4) the result seems to be incorrect. However, the final result will probably not be affected. To show that all integers not greater than $e^{2400}$ are sums of at most 73 integral sixth powers, use is made of R. C. Shook's table of sixth powers and Dickson's method of ascent [Bull. Amer. Math. Soc. **39**, 701–727 (1933)]. Finally the integer 703 requires exactly 73 integral sixth powers in its representation. *R. D. James* (Saskatoon, Sask.).

**P04-8** **(2, 247f)**

**Bang, A. S. On integers representable as a sum of three or four cubes.** Mat. Tidsskr. B. **1940**, 25–42 (1940). (Danish)

**P04-9** **(2, 251b)**

**Sugar, Alvin. On a result of Hua for cubic polynomials.** Bull. Amer. Math. Soc. **47**, 164–165 (1941).

It is proved neatly that every integer is a sum in infinitely many ways of five values of $f(x)=\epsilon(x^3-x)/6+kx+c$ for integers $x$; and a sum of four values of $(x^3-x)/6+kx+c$. Here $\epsilon, c, k$ are given integers, $k$ prime to $\epsilon$. Hua's result [Tôhoku Math. J. **41**, 361–366 (1936)] involved seven summands, $k=1$. The proof: $f(x)\equiv kx+c \pmod\epsilon$, $f(x)\equiv n-4c \pmod\epsilon$ is solvable, $n=m\epsilon+4c+f(t)$, $m\epsilon+4c=f(m+1)+f(m-1)+2f(-m)$ identically; if $\epsilon=1$ take $m=n-4c$. *G. Pall.*

**P04-10** **(2, 348b)**

**Hua, Loo-Keng. On Waring's problem with cubic polynomial summands.** J. Indian Math. Soc. (N.S.) **4**, 127–135 (1940).

It is proved [cf. C. R. Acad. Sci. Paris **210**, 650–652 (1940); these Rev. **2**, 35] that every large $N$ is a sum of eight values of $P(x)=a(x^3-x)/6+\frac{1}{2}b(x^2-x)+cx+d$ for integers $x\geqq 0$. Here $a, b, c$ are integers, $(a,b,c)=1$, $a>0$.
*G. Pall* (Montreal, Que.).

Citations: MR 2, 35f = P04-6.
Referred to in P04-30.

**P04-11** **(3, 162a)**

**Wahlgren, Agne. Numbers which can be represented as a sum of four cubes.** Mat. Tidsskr. B. **1941**, 33–41 (1941). (Swedish)

**P04-12** **(3, 162d)**

**Davenport, H. On Waring's problem for fifth and sixth powers.** Amer. J. Math. **64**, 199–207 (1942).

Let $G(k)$ denote the least value of $s$ for which every sufficiently large positive integer is representable as the sum of $s$ positive integral $k$th powers. Using the lower bounds for $N_s^{(5)}(n)$ and $N_s^{(6)}(n)$ obtained in the paper* reviewed above, the author shows that $G(5)\leqq 23$, $G(6)\leqq 36$, improvements on $G(5)\leqq 28$, $G(6)\leqq 42$. The method of proof is similar to that given for fourth powers [Ann. of Math. (2) **40**, 731–747 (1939); these Rev. **1**, 42].

*R. D. James* (Madison, Wis.).

*MR 3, 162C = P08-80.

Citations: MR 1, 42a = P04-3; MR 3, 162c = P08-4.

**P04-13** **(3, 162e)**

**Davenport, H. Note on sums of fourth powers.** J. London Math. Soc. **16**, 3–4 (1941).

This note contains an elementary proof of the result that every integer $n$ is representable as $n=\pm x_1^4\pm x_2^4\pm\cdots\pm x_{11}^4$ with suitable signs depending on $n$. *R. D. James.*

**P04-14** **(3, 162f)**

**Hunter, W. The representation of numbers by sums of fourth powers.** J. London Math. Soc. **16**, 177–179 (1941).

H. Davenport has recently shown [cf. the preceding review] that, if $V(4)$ is the least value of $s$ for which every integer $n$ is representable in the form $n=\pm x_1^4\pm x_2^4\pm\cdots\pm x_s^4$ (the $x$'s all being integers and a suitable choice of signs being made for each $n$), then $V(4)\leqq 11$. The author proves that $V(4)=9$ or 10 and that $n$ can be represented in an infinity of ways as such a sum with $s=10$. This is done by the use of identities. *B. W. Jones* (Ithaca, N. Y.).

Referred to in P04-27.

**P04-15** **(3, 162g)**

**Sambasiva Rao, K. On Waring's problem for smaller powers.** J. Indian Math. Soc. (N.S.) **5**, 117–121 (1941).

This note contains proofs that $G(5)\leqq 24$, $G(6)\leqq 36$, $G(7)\leqq 52$ using the method of Davenport.

*R. D. James* (Madison, Wis.).

**P04-16** **(3, 162h)**

**Narasimhamurti, V. On Waring's problem for 8th, 9th, and 10th powers.** J. Indian Math. Soc. (N.S.) **5**, 122 (1941).

This note describes a method for establishing the results $G(8)\leqq 73$, $G(9)\leqq 99$, $G(10)\leqq 122$. *R. D. James.*

**P04-17** **(3, 270b)**

**Hua, Loo-keng. On Waring's problem with cubic polynomial summands.** Sci. Rep. Nat. Tsing Hua Univ. (A) **4**, 55–83 (1940).

Hardy and Littlewood [Math. Z. **23**, 1–37 (1925)] proved that almost all positive integers are sums of five positive integer cubes. Davenport [Acta Math. **71**, 123–143 (1939); these Rev. **1**, 5] reduced the number to 4, which is best possible, using a lemma on the number of solutions of $x_1^3+y_1^3+z_1^3=x_2^3+y_2^3+z_2^3$. Hua now proves an extension to all integral-valued polynomials, there being two specific exceptions [cf. previous announcement, C. R. Acad. Sci. Paris **210**, 650–652 (1940); these Rev. **2**, 35]. The second exception $f(x)\equiv ax^3+3bx^2+3cx+d \pmod 9$ with $b^2\equiv a(c+a)$ (mod 3) requires five summands; it was earlier stated incorrectly as $b^2\equiv a(b+a)$. The analytical part is based on Davenport's work. The arithmetical part requires the solvability of $f(x_1)+\cdots+f(x_4)\equiv n \pmod{p^\gamma}$ in integers $x_\nu$ such that not every $f'(x_\nu)/p^k$ is divisible by $p$; here $k$ is the least integer not less than $-1$ such that $f'(x)/p^k$ is prime to $p$ for some $x$, and $\gamma=2+(-1)^p+k$. This fails if $p=3$ and $f(x)=x^3-3x$, giving the above exception. An exception requiring seven summands arises from $p=2$. *G. Pall.*

Citations: MR 1, 5c = P04-1; MR 2, 35f = P04-6.

**P04-18** **(4, 211i)**

**Linnik, U. V. On the representation of large numbers as sums of seven cubes.** C. R. (Doklady) Acad. Sci. URSS (N.S.) **35**, 162 (1942).

A proof that $G(3)\leqq 7$ is announced. The proof is stated to depend on Linnik's result on large numbers represented by certain ternary quadratic forms [Bull. Acad. Sci. URSS. Sér. Math. **4**, 363–402 (1940); these Rev. **2**, 348], an estimate by B. I. Segal of the number of integers containing only two given primes as factors [C. R. (Doklady) Acad. Sci. URSS (N.S.) **1933**, 47–49 (1933)] and theorems on the distribution of primes in arithmetical progressions.

*G. Pall* (Montreal, Que.).

Citations: MR 2, 348f = E20-9.

**P04-19** **(5, 91e)**

**Banerjee, D. P. On the solution of the "easier" Waring problem.** Bull. Calcutta Math. Soc. **34**, 197–199 (1942).

In the "easier" Waring problem, $v(k)$ is defined as the least value of $s$ for which every integer $n$ is representable as $\pm x_1^k\pm\cdots\pm x_s^k$ with integral $x_1, \cdots, x_s$ and with signs which may depend on $n$. Fuchs and Wright [Quart. J. Math., Oxford Ser. **10**, 190–209 (1939); these Rev. **1**, 69] obtained upper and lower bounds for $v(k)$ for $k\leqq 20$, and the present paper extends their results to $21\leqq k\leqq 30$.

*H. Davenport* (Bangor, Wales).

Citations: MR 1, 69a = P04-4.

**P04-20** **(5, 142c)**

**Linnik, U. V. On the representation of large numbers as sums of seven cubes.** Rec. Math. [Mat. Sbornik] N.S. **12(54)**, 218–224 (1943). (English. Russian summary)

In this paper it is shown that every sufficiently large number may be represented as the sum of seven nonnegative cubes. This is an improvement on Landau's result that eight cubes suffice. Landau's proof used results on the representation of integers as the sum of three squares. The present proof uses a theorem on the representation of integers by ternary quadratic forms

$$a^r x^2+b^s y^2+c^t z^2,$$

where $r$ $s$, and $t$ are odd and $a$, $b$, $c$ are primes such that $a\equiv b\equiv c\equiv 1 \pmod 5$, $(ab|c)=(-1|c)$, $(ac|b)=(-1|b)$ and $(bc|a)=(-1|a)$. This theorem is quoted from a previous paper [Bull. Acad. Sci. URSS. Sér. Math. [Izvestia Akad. Nauk SSSR] **4**, 363–402 (1940); these Rev. **2**, 348], which according to the reviewer contained an error. In a footnote in the present paper it is suggested that the reviewer's objections have been met in a paper to appear in C. R. (Doklady) Acad. Sci. URSS. *R. D. James.*

Citations: MR 2, 348f = E20-9.

Referred to in E20-45, P04-29.

**P04-21** **(6, 57f)**

**Richmond, H. W. Notes on a problem of the "Waring" type.** J. London Math. Soc. **19**, 38–41 (1944).

The author describes calculations which have the following results: of the multiples of 5 from 0 to 20,000, more than 70% are the sum of three pyramidal numbers and all the others are the sum of four. This implies that every number less than 20,000 is the sum of six pyramidal numbers. The author found no cases in which six are required. From these and other considerations the author surmises that Dickson's result (that all sufficiently large numbers can be expressed as the sum of eight pyramidal numbers) is not the best possible one. *B. W. Jones* (Ithaca, N. Y.).

**P04-22** **(7, 414d)**

**Streefkerk, Hendrik. Over het Aantal Oplossingen der Diophantische Vergelijking $U=\sum_{i=1}^{s}(Ax_i^2+Bx_i+C)$. [On the Number of Solutions of the Diophantine Equation $U=\sum_{i=1}^{s}(Ax_i^2+Bx_i+C)$].** Thesis, Free University of Amsterdam, 1943. iv+102 pp. (Dutch)

The problem referred to in the title ($A>0$, $B$ and $C$ given integers) is equivalent in an elementary way to the determination of the number $r_s(M)$ of representations of a given number $M$ ($M\equiv b^2s \pmod{4a}$; $(a, b)=1$) as a sum of $s$ squares of integers $y\equiv b \pmod{2a}$. For $s\geqq 3$, the singular series $\rho_s(M)$ belonging to this problem is constructed (for $s=3$ and 4 it is obtained formally by analytic continuation) and summed in finite form. For $s\geqq 3$, the author systematically investigates when $r_s(M)=\rho_s(M)$ holds identically in $M$ [cf. Hardy, Trans. Amer. Math. Soc. **21**, 255–284 (1920)]. The only cases appear to be $a=1$, $3\leqq s\leqq 8$; $a=2$, $3\leqq s\leqq 8$; $a=3$, $s=3$. The last case is new. It furnishes formulas for the number of representations of a given integer as a sum of 3 generalized pentagonal numbers ($\frac{3}{2}x^2-\frac{1}{2}x$ with integral $x$), or of 3 generalized octagonal numbers ($3x^2-2x$ with integral $x$). The other cases lead to known results concerning sums of 3 to 8 squares or 3 to 8 triangular numbers.

*N. G. de Bruijn* (Eindhoven).

Referred to in E12-118, E24-81, E28-19, P04-49.

**P04-23** **(7, 415e)**

**Salzer, Herbert E. On numbers expressible as the sum of four tetrahedral numbers.** J. London Math. Soc. **20**, 3–4 (1945).

The author conjectures two theorems. (a) Every square is the sum of less than 5 tetrahedral numbers $\frac{1}{6}n(n+1)(n+2)$ $(n>0)$. (b) Every tetrahedral is the sum of $d$ tetrahedrals with $2\leqq d\leqq 4$. They have been verified by the author in the first 200 cases. If in (a) "square" is replaced by "triangular" the first 200 cases hold except for the triangular number 153, which requires 5 tetrahedrals.

Pollock's conjecture that every integer is the sum of less than 6 tetrahedrals is verified up to 1000. In fact, 4 tetrahedrals suffice with 45 exceptions: 17, 27, 33, $\cdots$, 953.

*D. H. Lehmer* (Berkeley, Calif.).

**P04-24** **(8, 6g)**

**Mebius, C. A. Zahlentheoretische Untersuchungen. III. Die Diophantische Gleichung $A^3+B^3-C^3-D^3=E$.** Göteborgs Kungl. Vetenskaps- och Vitterhets-Samhälles Handlingar (6) Ser. B. **3**, no. 6, 21 pp. (1945).

By use of the identity $A^3+B^3-C^3-D^3=(12abc)^3E$, where $A, B=6a^3bc\pm b(3c^2+e)$, $C, D=6ab^3c\pm a(3c^2-e)$, $e=4E+b^6-a^6$, the author proves that every integer of the form $3n$ is a sum of 4 integral cubes, positive or negative [a result due to Richmond, Messenger of Math. **51**, 177–186 (1921)], and that any integer expressible as a sum of 4 cubes is so expressible in infinitely many ways. The identity is general in the sense that any integer expressed as a sum of 4 cubes can be treated by appropriate choice of $a, b, c$, not always rational or even real; many of the classical results are thus obtained. Several special cases of the identity are discussed. *I. Niven* (West Lafayette, Ind.).

Referred to in P04-43.

**P04-25** **(12, 393a)**

**Davenport, H. Sums of three positive cubes.** J. London Math. Soc. **25**, 339–343 (1950).

Let $R(N)$ denote the number of positive integers $\leqq N$ that are representable as the sum of three positive cubes. It is proved that $R(N)>N^{\alpha-\epsilon}$ for $\epsilon>0$ and $N>C(\epsilon)$, with $\alpha=47/54$. This is an improvement of a previous result ($\alpha=13/15$) of the author [C. R. Acad. Sci. Paris **207**, 1366–1368 (1938)]. *N. G. de Bruijn* (Delft).

**P04-26** **(12, 481j)**

**Sierpiński, W. Remarques sur la décomposition des nombres en sommes des carrés de nombres impairs.** Colloquium Math. **2**, 52–55 (1949).

The author notes the equivalence of the two theorems: (A) Every integer of the form $8k+3$ is the sum of three squares; and (B) every integer is the sum of at most 10 odd squares, due respectively to Gauss and Turski. If one seeks to base a proof of either (A) or (B) on Lagrange's theorem, (C) every integer is the sum of four squares, using only very elementary reasoning one can prove: (D) Every integer is the sum of at most 11 odd squares. *D. H. Lehmer.*

**P04-27** **(13, 626f)**

**Rai, T. Easier Waring problem.** J. Sci. Res. Benares Hindu Univ. **1** (1950–1951), 5–12 (1951).

Let $v(k)$ denote the least value of $s$ such that every integer $n$ (positive or negative) is represented in the form $n=\sum\epsilon_i m_i^k$, where each $m_i$ is a positive integer or zero, and $\epsilon_i=\pm 1$. The first part of this paper reproduces the work of Wright [J. London Math. Soc. **9**, 267–272 (1934)], Hunter [ibid. **16**, 177–179 (1941); these Rev. **3**, 162] and Fuchs and Wright [Quart. J. Math., Oxford Ser. **10**, 190–209 (1939); these Rev. **1**, 69] for $2\leqq k\leqq 5$. The second part lists new identities which, with the results of Fuchs and Wright, lead to improvements in the bounds of $v(k)$ for $10\leqq k\leqq 20$. [The copy of the paper sent to the reviewer contains a handwritten correction to the entry for $C_k$, $k=13$, in Table 1, which is changed to read $13\cdot 2^4\cdot 3^3\cdot 5^3\cdot 11\cdot 17587125398885771389$.]

*R. D. James* (Vancouver, B. C.).

Citations: MR 1, 69a = P04-4; MR 3, 162f = P04-14.

**P04-28** **(13, 626g)**

**Rai, T. The number of representations of numbers as sums of powers.** Math. Student **19**, 33–36 (1951).

Let $\rho_{s,t,k}(n)$ denote the number of representations of $n$ as the difference of a sum of $s$ $k$th powers and a sum of $t$ $k$th powers. Using special algebraic identities, the author shows that each one of the expressions $\rho_{3,2,6}(n)$, $\rho_{6,5,7}(n)$, $\rho_{4,4,8}(n)$ exceeds $c\log n/\log\log n$ for infinitely many $n$. [It may be remarked that for $\rho_{6,5,7}(n)$ simple density arguments give much sharper results.] Furthermore it is shown that infinitely many $n$ can be represented as a sum of 6 8th powers in two essentially different ways.

*N. G. de Bruijn* (Delft).

**P04-29** **(13, 915a)**

**Watson, G. L. A proof of the seven cube theorem.** J. London Math. Soc. **26**, 153–156 (1951).

Linnik's proof [Mat. Sbornik **12**(**54**), 218–224 (1943); see also Pall, Canadian J. Math. **1**, 344–364 (1949); these Rev. **5**, 142; **11**, 643] that every large positive integer is a sum of seven positive integral cubes, required some deep results on the representation of numbers by ternary quadratic forms. The present simpler proof uses, concerning ternary forms, only the fact that every $8u+3$ is a sum of three squares, but is based on an estimate for the number of primes in an arithmetic progression. This estimate uses (as also did Linnik's proof) Siegel's asymptotic formula for the class-number of binary quadratic forms. Using this estimate, it is shown that if $X$ is sufficiently large, and $k<(\log X)^{100}$ and $(k, l)=1$, then there is a prime $p\equiv l \pmod k$ such that $X<p<1.01\,X$. This makes it possible, with $N=n-t^3$, to choose suitable primes $p$, $q$, $r$ so that

$$8N=(4q^{18}+2r^{18})p^3+6q^6r^6p(8u+3),$$

and hence, putting $8u+3=x^2+y^2+z^2$,

$$8N=(q^6p+r^3x)^3+(q^6p-r^3x)^3+(q^6p+r^3y)^3+(q^6p-r^3y)^3+(r^6p+q^3z)^3+(r^6p-q^3z)^3,$$

with positive even integers in the parentheses. *G. Pall.*

Citations: MR 5, 142c = P04-20; MR 11, 643e = E12-37.

Referred to in E20-45.

## P04-30 (14, 250e)

**Watson, G. L. Sums of eight values of a cubic polynomial.** J. London Math. Soc. **27**, 217–224 (1952).

The author proves that every positive integer is a sum of eight pyramidal numbers and is a sum of eight values of $(x^3+5x)/6$ with integer $x\geqq 0$. These results are improvements of results due to Hua [Math. Ann. **111**, 622–628 (1935); cf. J. Indian Math. Soc. (N.S.) **4**, 127–135 (1940); these Rev. **2**, 348] who proved similar results for sufficiently large integers. *L. K. Hua* (Peking).

Citations: MR 2, 348b = P04-10.

Referred to in P04-56.

## P04-31 (14, 451b)

**Sprague, Roland. Über additive Zerlegungen in lauter verschiedene Glieder einer Teilfolge der natürlichen Zahlenreihe.** Math. Z. **56**, 258–260 (1952).

The author gives a modification of a theorem of Richert [Norsk Mat. Tidsskr. **31**, 120–122 (1949); these Rev. **11**, 646; see also references cited there] about partitioning numbers into distinct parts taken from a given set. The improvement lies in the reduction of the number of early special cases to examine. The author's theorem is as follows: Let $M$ be an infinite set of strictly increasing integers $m_0=0<m_1<m_2<\cdots$ and let $N\geqq -1$ be an integer. Further suppose that there is an integer $k\geqq 0$ such that $2m_k-m_{k+1}\leqq N<m_{k+1}$ whereas $2m_r-m_{r+1}>N$ for all $r>k$. Then, if the numbers $N+1, N+2, \cdots, N+m_k$ may be partitioned into distinct parts taken from $M$, the same is true of all numbers exceeding $N$. With only 9 simple decompositions the author proves Richert's result that every number except 2, 5, 8, 12, 23, 33 is the sum of distinct triangular numbers. The method when applied to $m_k=k(k+1)(k+2)/6$ shows that every integer beyond 558 is a sum of distinct pyramidal numbers. *D. H. Lehmer* (Los Angeles, Calif.).

Citations: MR 11, 646a = A46-8.

## P04-32 (15, 13e)

**Watson, G. L. A simple proof that all large integers are sums of at most eight cubes.** Math. Gaz. **37**, 209–211 (1953).

## P04-33 (15, 103e)

**Parthasarathy, M. On the representation of an integer as the sum of three fourth powers.** Proc. Amer. Math. Soc. **4**, 523–527 (1953).

Let $r_{3,4}(N)$ denote the number of representations of $N$ as the sum of three fourth powers of positive integers. It is proved by S. Chowla [J. Indian Math. Soc. **20**, 121–128 (1934)] that, for infinitely many $N$,

$$r_{3,4}(N)>c_1 \log N/\log\log N.$$

This estimate is improved in the paper under review to

$$r_{3,4}(N)>\exp\,(c_2 \log N/\log\log N)$$

for infinitely many $N$. The argument is elementary and depends on estimates of the number of representations of $N$ in the form $x^2+3y^2$ $(x>7y>0)$ and also in the form $x^2-xy+y^2$ $(x>4y>0)$. The reviewer observes that the term $\xi^2-\eta^2$ in the equation (3.1) should be $(\xi^2-\eta^2)^4$. *L. Mirsky* (Sheffield).

## P04-34 (16, 573g)

**Watson, G. L. Representation of large numbers by cubic forms in seven positive integral variables.** Proc. London Math. Soc. (3) **2**, 311–325 (1952).

Let

$$f(u, u, \cdots, t)=a(u_1^3+u_2^3)+b(v_1^3+v_2^3)+c(w_1^3+w_2^3)+dt^3.$$

The author proves the following results. 1) If $a=b=c=1$ and for any positive integral $d$, the form $f$ represents all sufficiently large positive integers for positive integer values values of the variables. 2) If $a=b=d=1$, the form has the same property provided the positive integer $c$ is not divisible by 3, 7 or 19. 3) Sufficient conditions for $f$ to represent all sufficiently large integers for positive integer values of the variables are: (i) $(3, d)=1$, $(42d, abc)=1$; (ii) if any prime $p$ divides all three of $a, b, c$, then $p^2$ divides none of them; and (iii) no prime $\equiv 1 \pmod 6$ divides more than one of $a, b, c$. *B. W. Jones* (Boulder, Colo.).

## P04-35 (16, 796e)

**Schinzel, A. Sur la décomposition des nombres naturels en sommes de nombres triangulaires distincts.** Bull. Acad. Polon. Sci. Cl. III. **2** (1954), 409–410 (1955).

A recent result of Richert [Norsk Mat. Tidsskr. **31**, 120–122 (1949); MR **11**, 646] states that every integer $>33$ is a sum of distinct triangular numbers. The purpose of the note under review is to show that every integer $>51$ is in fact the sum of four distinct triangular numbers $>0$. This follows from two theorems of Pall [Amer. Math. Monthly **40**, 10–18 (1933), p. 13] about the representation of numbers as sums of four distinct squares. Incidentally, a conjecture of Pall that for $n>0$, $16n+2$ is the sum of three positive squares is shown to fail for $n=8$. *D. H. Lehmer.*

Citations: MR 11, 646a = A46-8.

## P04-36 (17, 827c)

**Scholz, B. Bemerkung zu einem Beweis von Wieferich.** Jber. Deutsch. Math. Verein. **58** (1955), Abt. 1, 45–48.

Wieferich [Math. Ann. **66** (1909), 95–101] proved that every natural integer $S$ is the sum of 9 or fewer positive cubes, with 23 and 239 the only known numbers actually requiring 9. Before Wieferich, 13 cubes were known to be sufficient (Maillet, Fleck). Wieferich left a minor error in his proof (affecting the range $7.4\times 5^{12}<S\leqq 7.4\times 5^{15}$). The proof was completed by Bachmann [Niedere Zahlentheorie, T. II, Teubner, Leipzig, 1910] (with a new error) and Kempner [Math. Ann. **72** (1912), 387–399].

The present paper gives in four pages a sensible simplification of Wieferich's proof, which covers also the exceptional range. *A. J. Kempner* (Boulder, Colo.).

## P04-37 (18, 792a)

**Bini, Umberto. Il teorema di Waring e la rappresentazione per cubi di un numero.** Archimede **8** (1956), 172–176.

## P04-38 (18, 873d)

**Stolt, B. A note on triangular numbers.** Portugal. Math. **15** (1956), 87–88.

An elementary proof of the following theorem: Let $n$ be an integer expressed in the form $n=9k+r$, with $2<r<12$. Then $n$ can be expressed as the sum of $r$ triangular numbers of the form $\Delta_{3s+1}$. *L. Moser.*

Referred to in P04-40.

**P04-39** **(19, 15g)**

**Sierpiński, W. What we know and what we do not know about decomposition of natural numbers into a sum of squares, cubes, and fourth powers.** Prace Mat. 2 (1956), 56–64. (Polish)

Der Artikel behandelt im Wesentlichen verschiedene Fragen über die Existenz und die Anzahl von Zerlegungen der natürlichen Zahlen $n$ in Summen von der Gestalt $n=x_1^r \pm x_2^r \pm \cdots \pm x_s^r$, wo $r$, $s$ einige kleine natürliche Zahlen sind und wo $x_1, \cdots, x_s$ entweder ganze oder natürliche oder verschiedene ganze nichtnegative oder verschiedene natürliche Zahlen sind. Der Verfasser referiert über die älteren, neueren und die neuesten Resultate in diesem Gebiete und gibt einige bis jetzt noch nicht gelöste Probleme aus diesem Ideenkreise an.

*V. Knichal* (Prag).

**P04-40** **(19, 942d)**

**Sierpinski, W. Remarque sur "A note on triangular numbers" de M. B. Stolt.** Portugal. Math. **15** (1956), 123 (1957).

A letter to the editor of Portugaliae Mathematica in which the author disclaims having proved that every positive integer is the sum of at most eleven triangular numbers $\Delta_{3n+1}$, a result attributed to him by B. Stolt [Portugal. Math. **15** (1956), 87–88; MR **18**, 873]. The history of a related result is clarified. *L. Moser.*

Citations: MR 18, 873d = P04-38.

**P04-41** **(19, 942e)**

**Lomadze, G. A. Representation of numbers as sums of generalized polygonal numbers. I.** Akad. Nauk Gruzin. SSR. Trudy Tbiliss. Mat. Inst. Razmadze 22 (1956), 77–102. (Russian)

Referred to in E28-19, P04-49.

**P04-42** **(20# 841 )**

**Lomadze, G. A. Representation of numbers as sums of generalized polygonal numbers. II.** Akad. Nauk Gruzin. SSR. Trudy Tbiliss. Mat. Inst. Razmadze **24** (1957), 3–33. (Russian)

**P04-43** **(20# 1664 )**

**Schinzel, A.; et Sierpiński, W. Sur les sommes de quatre cubes.** Acta Arith. 4 (1958), 20–30.

The second author has conjectured that every integer $g$ can be represented in infinitely many ways in the form $g=x^3+y^3-z^3-t^3$, where $x$, $y$, $z$, $t$ are positive integers. This conjecture is here confirmed for all except integers $g=hn^3$ with $h\equiv\pm2$, $\pm4$, or $\pm5$ (mod 18), $n$ arbitrary. The result is obtained by first proving the conjecture for any integer $g$ having a representation, $g=a^3+b^3-c^3-d^3$, where $a$, $b$, $c$, $d$ are any integers such that $(a+b)(c+d)$ is a positive non-square and $a\neq b$ or $c\neq d$. By applying this theorem in the cases not already covered by the above result, the authors verify the conjecture for $|g|\leqq 100$; and this has been extended by A. Makowski to $|g|\leqq 300$ except for $g=148$, 257, and 284. They also obtain as an easy consequence of their main result the theorem that every positive rational has infinitely many representations in the form, $x^3+y^3-z^3-t^3$, with $x$, $y$, $z$, $t$ positive rationals. They call attention to an error in the proof by C. A. Mebius [Göteborgs Kungl. Vetenskaps- och Vitterhets-Samhälles Handlingar (6) Ser. B 3, no. 6, (1945); MR **8**, 6] that any integer expressible as the (algebraic) sum of 4 integral cubes can be so expressed in infinitely many ways.

*R. J. Levit* (San Francisco, Calif.)

Citations: MR 8, 6g = P04-24.
Referred to in D36-31, P04-45.

**P04-44** **(20# 6391 )**

**Stolt, B. A theorem on triangular numbers.** Portugal. Math. **16** (1957), 3–5.

Let $\Delta_k$ be the $k$th triangular number, $k(k+1)/2$. For a given positive integer $n$, let $k$ be determined by $\Delta_k \leqq n < \Delta_{k+1}$. It is shown that $n$ can be represented in the form

$$n=\Delta_x+\Delta_y+\Delta_u+\Delta_v,$$

where $x+y+u+v=2k-1$, thus establishing a theorem first stated without proof by F. Pollock in 1854.

*L. Moser* (Edmonton, Alta.)

**P04-45** **(21# 5609 )**

**Mąkowski, A. Sur quelques problèmes concernant les sommes de quatre cubes.** Acta Arith. **5** (1959), 121–123.

A conjecture of W. Sierpiński, that every integer $g$ has infinitely many representations in the form $g=x^3+y^3-z^3-t^3$ ($x$, $y$, $z$, $t$ integers $>0$), is verified here for the range $301\leqq|g|\leqq 350$, using the method developed by A. Schinzel and W. Sierpiński [Acta Arith. **4** (1958), 20–30; MR **20** #1664], where the verification is given for $|g|\leqq 300$, omitting the values $|g|=148$, 257, 284. The author corrects some typographical errors in the tables in the paper just cited and gives an affirmative answer to a question raised there, whether the equation, $x^3-y^3-z^3-t^3=2$, has infinitely many solutions in positive integers. He also extends a result of Chao Ko [J. London Math. Soc. **11** (1936), 218–219], that every integer $g$, $|g|\leqq 100$, has a representation in the form $g=x^3+y^3+2z^3$, $x$, $y$, $z$ integers, except possibly for $|g|=76$, 99. The extension is to the range $101\leqq|g|\leqq 220$ with the values $|g|=113$, 148, 183, 190, 195 remaining undecided. *R. J. Levit* (San Francisco, Calif.)

Citations: MR 20# 1664 = P04-43.

**P04-46** **(21# 6353 )**

**Chen, Jing-jun. Waring's problem for $g(5)$.** Sci. Record (N.S.) **3** (1959), 327–330.

If $g(k)$ denotes the least $g$ such that every positive integer is representable as a sum of at most $g$ positive $k$th powers, then using a method similar to that of Hua, it is shown here that $37\leqq g(5)\leqq 40$. Dickson [Bull. Amer. Math. Soc. **39** (1933), 701–727] had shown that $37\leqq g(5)\leqq 54$.

*H. Gupta* (Chandigarh)

**P04-47** **(22# 4700 )**

**Barrucand, Pierre. Sommes de Gauss et séries singulières de Hardy pour les cubes.** C. R. Acad. Sci. Paris **250** (1960), 4249–4251.

The Gauss sum in the title is defined by $S_{h,q}=\sum_{a \bmod q}\exp(2\pi iha^3/q)$. This paper is concerned with the problem of evaluating the singular series $\mathfrak{S}_\nu(n)=\sum_{q=1}^{\infty}B(\nu,q,n)/q^\nu$, where $B(\nu,q,n)=\sum'_{h \bmod q}S_{h,q}^\nu\times\exp(-2\pi inh/q)$ and $h$ runs over a reduced residue system modulo $q$. The principal formula obtained may be stated as follows. Let $p$ be a prime $\equiv 1$ (mod 3) so that $4p=L^2+27M^2$ with $M>0$ and $L\equiv 1$ (mod 3); let $z_a$, $z_b$, $z_c$ denote the three roots of the period equation $z^3-3pz-pL=0$ and put $z_a^\nu+z_b^\nu+z_c^\nu=3\phi_\nu$; let $\varepsilon(n)=\mathrm{Re}\,(n|p)_3$ and $\varepsilon'(n)=3^{-1/2}\,\mathrm{Im}\,(n|p)_3$, where $(n|p)_3$ represents the cubic residue character of $n$ with respect to $p$. (1) If $p\nmid n$, then $B(\nu,p,n)=-\phi_\nu+\varepsilon(n)\phi_{\nu+1}+\varepsilon'(n)3^{-1}M^{-1}(4p\phi_\nu+L\phi_{\nu+1}-2\phi_{\nu+2})$. (2) If $p|n$, then $B(\nu,p,n)=(p-1)\phi_\nu$.

*A. L. Whiteman* (Princeton, N.J.)

**P04-48** **(22# 6754 )**

**Sierpiński, W. On representations by a sum of five cubes.** Wiadom. Mat. (2) **3**, 121–122 (1959). (Polish)

The author proves that every integer can be represented in infinitely many ways by a sum of five cubes of integers.
*S. Knapowski* (Poznań)

## P04-49 (22# 7992 )

**Val′fiš, A. A. Representation of numbers as sums of generalized pentagonal numbers.** Soobšč. Akad. Nauk Gruzin. SSR **22** (1959), 385–392. (Russian)

A generalised pentagonal number $t_5(x)$ is defined, for integral $x$, by the relation $t_5(x)=\frac{3}{2}x^2-\frac{1}{2}x$. Let $r_s(n)$ denote the number of representations of a positive integer $n$ in the form $n=\sum_{k=1}^{s} t_5(x_k)$; in other words, $r_s(n)$ is the number of representations of $M=24n+s$ as the sum of $s$ squares of integers, each integer congruent to $-1 \pmod 6$. Exact formulae for $r_s(n)$ have been computed when $s=3$ by H. Streefkerk [Thesis, Free University of Amsterdam, 1943; MR **7**, 414], and, when $s=4$, 5, 6 and 7, by G. A. Lomadze [Akad. Nauk Gruzin. SSR. Trudy Tbiliss. Mat. Inst. Razmadze **22** (1956), 77–102; MR **19**, 942]. The author now employs a similar analysis to accomplish the same for $s=8$.
*H. Halberstam* (London)

Citations: MR 7, 414d = P04-22; MR 19, 942e = P04-41.

## P04-50 (24# A102 )

**Chowla, S.; Davenport, H.**
**On Weyl's inequality and Waring's problem for cubes.**
*Acta Arith.* **6** (1960/61), 505–521.

In the special case of polynomials of degree 3, Weyl's inequality asserts that $T=\sum_{x=1}^{P} e(\alpha x^3+\varphi(x))$ satisfies $|T|\ll P^{\varepsilon}(P^{3/4}+P^{1/4}q^{1/4}+Pq^{-1/4})$; here $e(u)$ denotes $\exp(2\pi iu)$, $\varphi(x)$ is a polynomial of degree 2 with real coefficients, and $q$ is the denominator of a rational approximation to the real number, such that the error is less than $q^{-2}$. The authors extend this to summation with respect to two variables. Put $f(x,y)=ax^3+bx^2y+cxy^2+dy^3$, where $a$, $b$, $c$, $d$ are integers, and suppose that its determinant is not zero. Let $\varphi(x,y)$ be any polynomial in $x$ and $y$ with real coefficients and degree $\leqq 2$. Let $S$ be the sum $S=\sum_{x=1}^{P}\sum_{y=1}^{Q} e(\alpha f(x,y)+\varphi(x,y))$, where $1\leqq Q\leqq P$. Then we have, for $\varepsilon$ fixed,

$$|S| \ll P^{\varepsilon}(P^{3/2}+P^{1/2}q^{1/2}+P^2q^{-1/2}).$$

The following application is given in detail: Let $a_1$, $a_2$ be integers $\neq 0$, let $f_3$, $f_4$, $f_5$ be binary cubic forms with non-zero discriminants. Then the equation

$$a_1x_1^3+a_2x_2^3+f_3(x_3,y_3)+f_4(x_4,y_4)+f_5(x_5,y_5) = 0$$

has infinitely many solutions in integers, with all the integers arbitrarily large. The non-vanishing of the singular series in the problem is exhibited from the fact that the given equation has, for every prime $p$, a non-singular solution in the $p$-adic field.

Some further applications, connected with representation of an integer $N\neq 0$ by a form of the above type, are indicated.
*N. G. de Bruijn* (Eindhoven)

## P04-51 (27# 5742 )

**Hooley, Christopher**
**On the representations of a number as the sum of two cubes.**
*Math. Z.* **82** (1963), 259–266.

Denote by $r(n)$ the number of solutions of $n=x^3+y^3$. The author proves that

$$(1)\qquad \sum_{n\leqq x}(r(n))^2 = \frac{1}{3}\frac{(\Gamma(\frac{1}{3}))^2}{\Gamma(\frac{2}{3})}x^{2/3}+O\left(\frac{x^{2/3}\log\log x}{(\log x)^{1/2}}\right).$$

The proof is ingenious and difficult. The author easily deduces from (1) that for almost all integers which are the sum of two cubes the representation is unique [see the reviewer, J. London Math. Soc. **14** (1939), 250–254; MR **1**, 42].
*P. Erdős* (Vancouver, B.C.)

Citations: MR 1, 42c = E76-1.
Referred to in E76-27, E76-29, L30-11, P04-54.

## P04-52 (31# 142 )

**Chen Jing-run [Ch′en Ching-run]**
**Waring's problem for $g(5)=37$.**
*Sci. Sinica* **13** (1964), 335.

The author announces that he has a proof, to be published later, that $g(5)=37$, i.e., that every positive integer is a sum of 37 fifth powers, and that 37 is best possible.
*I. Niven* (Eugene, Ore.)

Referred to in P04-53.

## P04-53 (34# 135 )

**Chen, Jing-run [Ch′en Ching-jun]**
**Waring's problem for $g(5)=37$.**
*Sci. Sinica* **13** (1964), 1547–1568.

Details are given of the author's proof that $g(5)=37$, i.e., that every positive integer is a sum of 37 fifth powers, and that 37 is best possible [Sci. Sinica **13** (1964), 335; MR **31** #142]. This paper is a translation of the Chinese version [Acta Math. Sinica **14** (1964), 715–734; translated as Chinese Math.—Acta **6** (1965), 105–127]. The proof uses Vinogradov methods with some improved estimates of the exponential sums involved.
*W. H. Simons* (Corvallis, Ore.)

Citations: MR 31# 142 = P04-52.

## P04-54 (34# 1264 )

**Greaves, George**
**On the representation of a number as a sum of two fourth powers.**
*Math. Z.* **94** (1966), 223–234.

Let $h$ and $n$ be natural numbers, $r_h(n)$ the number of representations of $n$ as a sum of two non-negative $h$th powers. Furthermore, let $N_h(x)$ be the number of all positive integers $\leqq x$ that can be written as a sum of two non-negative $h$th powers. For odd primes $h$, the functions $\sum_{n\leqq x} r_h{}^2(n)$ and $N_h(x)$ were evaluated asymptotically when $x\to\infty$ by C. Hooley [same Z. **82** (1963), 259–266; MR **27** #5742; ibid. **84** (1964), 126–136; MR **29** #71]. When $h$ is composite, new technical difficulties arise in this evaluation. The author shows how to handle the case $h=4$.
*O. H. Körner* (Marburg)

Citations: MR 27# 5742 = P04-51; MR 29# 71 = E76-27.

## P04-55 (36# 1407 )

**Mordell, L. J.**
**Binary cubic forms expressed as a sum of cubes of seven linear forms.**
*J. London Math. Soc.* **42** (1967), 646–651.

Let $f(x,y)=ax^3+3bx^2y+3cxy^2+dy^3$, where $a,b,c,d$ are integral. It was shown by the author [Quart. J. Math. Oxford Ser. **1** (1930), 276–288] that $f(x,y)$ can be expressed as a sum of $N$ cubes of linear forms. Furthermore, $7\leqq N\leqq 8$. In the present paper the following theorem is proved: If $a\equiv\pm 1 \pmod 9$ and $b\equiv d \pmod 3$, then $N\leqq 7$.
*H. Gross* (Zürich)

## P04-56 (37# 177 )

**Salzer, Herbert E.; Levine, Norman**
**Proof that every integer $\leqq 452{,}479{,}659$ is a sum of five numbers of the form $Q_x\equiv(x^3+5x)/6$, $x\geqq 0$.**
*Math. Comp.* **22** (1968), 191–192.

G. L. Watson has proved that every positive integer is a

sum of eight integers of the form $(x^3+5x)/6$, $x \geqq 0$ [J. London Math. Soc. **27** (1952), 217–224; MR **14**, 250]. The authors show that every integer $\leqq 452{,}479{,}659$ is a sum of five integers of this form.

*B. Garrison* (San Diego, Calif.)

Citations: MR 14, 250e = P04-30.

**P04-57** **(38# 1051)**

**Barrucand, Pierre**

**Sur la distribution empirique des sommes de trois cubes ou de quatre bicarrés.**

*C. R. Acad. Sci. Paris Sér. A-B* **267** (1968), A409–A411.

Author's summary: "Désignons par $b_k(n)$ la fonction égale à 1 si et seulement si $n$ est somme de $k$ puissances $k^{\text{ièmes}}$ non négatives; nulle autrement. Des résultats empiriques suggèrent les formules suivantes:

$$\sum_1^n b_3(m) \sim 0.520 \int_c^n (\log x)^{-1} \log\log x\, dx + O(n^{1/2+\varepsilon}),$$

$$\sum_1^n b_4(m) \sim 0.4061 \operatorname{Li}(n) + O(n^{1/2+\varepsilon})."$$

**P04-58** **(42# 230)**

**Mordell, L. J.**

**On sums of four cubes of polynomials.**

*Acta Arith.* **16** (1969/70), 365–369.

Is every integer expressible as a sum of four integer cubes? Identities of the form (*) $P^3+Q^3+R^3+S^3=Mx+N$ with $P, Q, R, S$ polynomials in $x$ and $M, N$ integers have been used to show that every integer not congruent to $\pm 4$ (mod 9) can be expressed as a sum of four integer cubes. Numerical evidence supports the view that integers congruent to $\pm 4$ (mod 9) also have such representations, but so far no proof has been given. The approach used to handle numbers $\not\equiv \pm 4$ (mod 9) suggests that one should seek solutions of (*) in polynomials in $x$ with $N \equiv 4$ (mod 9), but A. Schinzel [J. London Math. Soc. **43** (1968), 143–145; MR **36** #6388] was able to show that this is impossible if $M \neq 0$, and the degree of $P, Q, R$ and $S$ is less than 5. Mordell, in the paper under review, gives a simpler proof of Schinzel's result [loc. cit.]. Also, the author adds in a footnote that J. H. E. Cohn has shown that if $M \neq 0$, (*) has no solution in polynomials $P, Q, R, S$ with degree less than 6.

*D. A. Klarner* (Reading)

Citations: MR 36# 6388 = C05-38.

**P04-59** **(44# 2700)**

**Cohn, J. H. E.**

**Sums of cubes of Gaussian integers.**

*Proc. Amer. Math. Soc.* **29** (1971), 426.

The author shows, by means of seven identities, that every Gaussian integer can be written as a sum of the cubes of four Gaussian integers.

*W. J. Ellison* (Talence)

**P04-60** **(44# 6630)**

**Dress, François**

**Amélioration de la majoration de $g(4)$ dans le problème de Waring: $g(4) \leqq 34$.**

*Séminaire Delange-Pisot-Poitou:* 1969/70, *Théorie des Nombres, Fasc.* 1, *Exp.* 15, 23 *pp. Secrétariat mathématique, Paris*, 1970.

By an elementary but ingenious argument the author shows that every positive integer can be written as the sum of at most 34 fourth powers of positive integers. In a paper to appear in Acta Arithmetica the number 34 has been replaced by 30. Waring conjectured that every positive integer is a sum of at most 19 fourth powers of positive integers and F. C. Auluck [Proc. Indian Acad. Sci. Sect. A **11** (1940), 437–450; MR **2**, 35] proved that every integer greater than $10^{10^{88.39}}$ could be so written.

*W. J. Ellison* (Talence)

Citations: MR 2, 35e = P04-5.

# P08 WARING'S PROBLEM AND ITS VARIANTS: GENERAL EXPONENT

See the comments at the beginning of the preceding section.

See also reviews A66-1, B08-73, B12-7, D02-19, D52-13, D52-40, D52-43, D52-75, D52-90, D52-126, D52-127, D52-130, D72-59, D80-6, D80-30, E76-12, E76-27, J68-19, J68-35, K25-29, L05-1, L15-5, L15-9, P04-4, P12-3, P12-11, P44-18, P99-3, Q05-46, R48-35, S99-11, Z02-3, Z02-8, Z10-10, Z10-20, Z15-70.

**P08-1** **(1, 5d)**

**Davenport, H. and Erdös, P. On sums of positive integral *k*th powers.** Ann. of Math. **40**, 533–536 (1939).

In the application of the Hardy-Littlewood method to Waring's problem [Landau: Vorlesungen über Zahlentheorie, Bd. 1, Teil VI, Kap. 4] use is made of inequalities of the form $N_s^{(k)}(n) > n^{\alpha-\epsilon}$, $\alpha=\alpha(k, s)$. Here $N_s^{(k)}(n)$ denotes the number of integers $m \leqq n$ for which the equation $m=h_1^k+h_2^k+\cdots+h_s^k$ has a solution in integers $h_i \geqq 0$. The larger $\alpha$ can be made the better the final result. In a previous paper, Davenport [Proc. Roy. Soc. London, Ser. A. **170**, 293–299 (1939)] defined admissible exponents as follows: The real numbers $\lambda_1, \lambda_2, \cdots, \lambda_s$ satisfying $\lambda_1 \geqq \lambda_2 \geqq \cdots \geqq \lambda_s > 0$ are called admissible exponents for $k$th powers if the number of solutions of $x_1^k+\cdots+x_s^k=y_1^k+\cdots+y_s^k$ in integers $x_1, \cdots, x_s, y_1, \cdots, y_s$, subject to the conditions $P^{\lambda_i}<x_i<2P^{\lambda_i}$, $P^{\lambda_i}<y_i<2P^{\lambda_i}$, is $O(P^{\lambda_1+\cdots+\lambda_s+\epsilon})$ as $P\to\infty$ for any $\epsilon>0$. He then showed that if $\lambda_1, \cdots, \lambda_s$ are admissible exponents and $\alpha=(\lambda_1+\cdots+\lambda_s)/k\lambda_1$, then $N_s^{(k)}(n)>n^{\alpha-\epsilon}$, for any $\epsilon>0$ and $n>n_0(\epsilon)$. The present paper is concerned with the construction of admissible exponents for $k \geqq 3$ by the method of Erdös, with modifications due to Davenport. The following results are established: Theorem 1. Let $\theta=1-k^{-1}$. Then $1, \lambda, \lambda\theta, \cdots, \lambda\theta^{s-2}$ are admissible exponents for $k$th powers, provided $\lambda$ satisfies $k\lambda-(k-1) \leqq \lambda\theta^{s-2}$. The proof is by induction on $s$. Theorem 2. Admissible exponents for $k$th powers are $1, 1-k^{-2}, 1-k^{-1}-k^{-2}$. The proof employs a device similar to the one used by Davenport for the case $k=4$ [C. R. Acad. Sci. Paris **207**, 1366 (1938)].

*R. D. James* (Saskatoon, Sask.).

**P08-2** **(2, 146a)**

**Hua, Loo-Keng. On a system of Diophantine equations.** C. R. (Doklady) Acad. Sci. URSS (N.S.) **27**, 312–313 (1940).

An improvement is announced of a result of C. Mardjanichvili [C. R. (Doklady) Acad. Sci. URSS (N.S.) **22**, 467 (1939)] on the number of solutions of the system $x_1+\cdots+x_s=N_1, \cdots, x_1^n+\cdots+x_s^n=N_n$ in positive integers $x_i$; this result is said to hold for $s \geqq s_0(n)$, where $s_0(n)$ is an expression asymptotic to $7n^2 \log n$.

*G. Pall.*

**P08-3** **(2, 348a)**

**Hua, Loo-keng. On a generalized Waring problem. II.** J. Chinese Math. Soc. **2**, 175–191 (1940).

In part I [Proc. London Math. Soc. (2) **43**, 161–182 (1937)] and elsewhere [J. Chinese Math. Soc. **1**, 21–61 (1936); Quart. J. Math., Oxford Ser. **9**, 199–202 (1938)], Hua obtained a formula

$$a^{-s/k}(\Gamma(1+1/k)/\Gamma(s/k))\mathfrak{S}(N)N^{s/k-1}+O(N^{s/k-1-\rho})$$

for the number of representations of $N$ as $P(x_1)+\cdots+P(x_s)$ in integers $x_i \geqq 0$. Here $P(x)=ax^k+\cdots$ is an integral-valued

polynomial of degree $k(\geqq 3)$, and $\rho(>0)$ is independent of $N$; and $s \geqq 10k^3 \log k$ if $k>15$, $s \geqq 2^k+1$ if $3 \leqq k \leqq 15$. He now proves that the singular series $\mathfrak{S}(N)$ exceeds a positive constant independent of $N$ if $s \geqq (k-1)2^{k+1}$, whence $G(P) \leqq (k-1)2^{k+1}$, a considerable improvement on his result in I. For the special polynomial $H(x)=2^{k-1}F_k(x)-2^{k-2}F_{k-1}(x)+\cdots+(-)^{k-1}F_1(x)$, where $F_i(x)=x(x-1)\cdots(x-i+1)/i!$, he proves if $k \geqq 5$ that precisely $G(H)=2^k-\frac{1}{2}\{1-(-1)^k\}$.
*G. Pall* (Montreal, Que.).

**P08-4** **(3, 162c)**

**Davenport, H. On sums of positive integral $k$-th powers.** Amer. J. Math. **64**, 189–198 (1942).

In a previous paper with the same title [Proc. Roy. Soc. London. Ser. A. **170**, 293–299 (1939)] the author established certain lower bounds for $N_s^{(k)}(n)$, the number of integers less than $n$ that are representable as a sum of $s$ positive $k$th powers. In the present paper more precise results of the same type are proved. A sample result is the following: If $N_s^{(k)}(n)>n^\alpha$ for all large $n$, where $1/k<\alpha<1$, then $N_{s+1}^{(k)}(n)>n^{\beta-\epsilon}$ for $n>n_0(\epsilon)$, where

$$\beta=\max_{h\leqq k-2}\frac{1}{k}\left\{1+\frac{(2^h-1)(k-1)+h+1}{2^h-1+\alpha}\alpha\right\}.$$

The proof depends on an estimate of the number of solutions of $x^k+u_i=y^k+u_j$ subject to the conditions $P<x$, $y<2P$, $u_i, u_j<P^{k\lambda}$, $\lambda=1-(1-\delta)/k$, $0<\delta<1$. More precise results are obtained for the special cases $k=5$, $k=6$.
*R. D. James* (Madison, Wis.).

Referred to in P04-12.

**P08-5** **(5, 142a)**

**Niven, Ivan. An unsolved case of the Waring problem.** Amer. J. Math. **66**, 137–143 (1944).

The case in which $r=2^n-q-2$, where $3^n=2^nq+r$, $0<r<2^n$, in the determination of $g(n)$ was left untreated by Dickson [Amer. J. Math. **58**, 521–529 (1936)]. This case is considered here and it is shown that $g(n)=I=2^n+q-2$. This completes the determination of $g(n)$ for $n>6$.
*H. S. Zuckerman* (Seattle, Wash.).

Referred to in P08-8.

**P08-6** **(5, 142b)**

**Rubugunday, R. K. On $g(k)$ in Waring's problem.** J. Indian Math. Soc. (N.S.) **6**, 192–198 (1942).

Dickson's [Amer. J. Math. **58**, 521–529, 530–535 (1936)] and Pillai's [J. Indian Math. Soc. (2) **2**, 16–44 (1936)] solutions of the Waring problem are complete for $k>6$, provided (i) $(3/2)^k-[(3/2)^k]\neq 1-2^{-k}[(3/2)^k]$ and (ii) $(3/2)^k-[(3/2)^k]\neq 1-2^{-k}\{[(3/2)]^k+2\}$. Rubugunday proves by elementary arguments that (i) holds for all $k$, and that (ii) is equivalent to $2^k-1 \nmid 3^k+1$ if $k \geqq 3$. Further, (ii) holds in the cases (a) $k$ even, (b) $9|k$, (c) $2^k-1$ a prime not equal to 7, (d) $2^k-1$ has a prime factor not identical to 1 or 7 mod 24, (e) $k$ and $2k+1$ primes, $k\equiv 3$ mod 4, $k>3$, (f) $k$ a multiple of values satisfying (e). The argument depends mainly on the theorem that, for positive odd $k$, $a^k-1$ cannot divide $b^k-1$ unless $b$ is a quadratic residue of all prime factors of $a^k-1$. Finally it is noted that these cases include all $k \leqq n$, excepting at most $s$ values, where $s \leqq O(1)+h \log n$, $1/h=\log\log 4-\log\log 3$. *G. Pall.*

Referred to in P08-8.

**P08-7** **(5, 200b)**

**Linnik, U. V. An elementary solution of the problem of Waring by Schnirelman's method.** Rec. Math. [Mat. Sbornik] N.S. **12(54)**, 225–230 (1943). (Russian. English summary)

The paper gives a purely arithmetical proof of the theorem that for every positive integer $n$ there exists a $k$ such that numbers of the form $x_1^n+\cdots+x_k^n$ have positive density, and therefore the sequence of $n$th powers forms a basis in the sense of Schnirelmann. No estimate is obtained for $k$, and since more precise results are well known from the work of Hardy and Littlewood, and Vinogradow, interest attaches only to the method. It suffices to prove that for suitable $k$ the number of solutions, for fixed $m$, of $x_1^n+\cdots+x_k^n=m$ with $|x_i|\leqq P$ is $O(P^{k-n})$. The proof is by induction, with a polynomial $f(x)$ in place of $x^n$, and the principal weapon is the fact that (briefly) the number of solutions of

$$F(x_1,\cdots,x_s;h_1,\cdots,h_s)=F(x_1',\cdots,x_s';h_1',\cdots,h_s')$$

does not exceed that of

$$F(x_1,\cdots,x_s;h_1,\cdots,h_s)=F(x_1',\cdots,x_s';h_1,\cdots,h_s)$$

multiplied by the number of possibilities for $h_1,\cdots,h_s$. Although the proof is substantially correct, the details in several places are obscure, and there are many misprints.
*H. Davenport* (Bangor).

Referred to in B12-7, P08-23, P08-24, R48-27, R48-31, Z02-8.

**P08-8** **(7, 145b)**

**Chowla, S. On $g(k)$ in Waring's problem.** Proc. Lahore Philos. Soc. **6**, 16–17 (1944).

Continuing work of Rubugunday [J. Indian Math. Soc. (N.S.) **6**, 192–198 (1942); these Rev. **5**, 142] the author proves that $2^k-1$ is not a factor of $3^k+1$ if $k$ is a multiple of 7, or a multiple of 5 but not of 75. He states that "the formulae of Pillai and Dickson determine $g(k)$ exactly except when $2^k-1$ is a factor of $3^k+1$." However, the reviewer has evaluated $g(k)$ in this case [Amer. J. Math. **66**, 137–143 (1944); these Rev. **5**, 142]. *I. Niven.*

Citations: MR 5, 142a = P08-5; MR 5, 142b = P08-6.

**P08-9** **(8, 566e)**

**Hua, Loo-Keng. Some results on additive theory of numbers.** Proc. Nat. Acad. Sci. U. S. A. **33**, 136–137 (1947).

Several statements are made without proof, the most important being that Hardy and Littlewood's asymptotic formula for the number of representations of a number as the sum of $s$ $k$th powers holds for

$$s \geqq 4k^2(\log k+\tfrac{1}{2}(\log k^2)^{\frac{1}{2}}+\tfrac{1}{4}\log\log k+1).$$

*T. Estermann* (London).

**P08-10** **(10, 17f)**

**Anfert'eva, E. A. On the transformation formulas of Vinogradov-Corput.** Doklady Akad. Nauk SSSR (N.S.) **60**, 541–544 (1948). (Russian)

In this paper the author obtains the following approximate transformation formulas:

$$\text{(I)}\quad S(x)=\sum_{n=1}^{\infty}e^{-n^m/N}e^{-2\pi i\alpha n^m}$$
$$=A|\alpha|^{-1/2(m-1)}\sum_{n=1}^{\infty}\frac{1}{n^{\frac{1}{2}-1/2(m-1)}}$$
$$\times\exp\{-n^{m/(m-1)}|\alpha|^{-1/(m-1)}/(2\pi N\alpha(m-1))\}$$
$$\times\exp\{in^{m/(m-1)}|\alpha|^{-1/(m-1)}\}+O(\ln^2|\alpha|N),$$

$$\text{(II)}\quad T(x)=\sum_{n=1}^{\infty}\tau(n)e^{n^m/N}e^{-2\pi i\alpha n^m}$$
$$=B|\alpha|^{-1/(2m-1)}\sum_{n=1}^{\infty}\frac{\tau(n)}{n^{\frac{1}{2}-1/2(2m-1)}}$$
$$\times\exp\{-n^{m/(2m-1)}|\alpha|^{-1(2m-1)}/(2\pi N\alpha(m-1))\}$$
$$\times\exp\{-in^{m/(2m-1)}|\alpha|^{-1/(2m-1)}\}+O(\ln^2|\alpha|N),$$

where $x=(N^{-1}+2\pi\alpha i)^{1/m}$, $m\geqq 2$, $2\pi|\alpha|N>1$, $A$, $B$ are constants, and $\tau(n)$ denotes the number of divisors of $n$. The proof of (I) is sketched and consists roughly of first representing $S(x)$ as

$$S(x)=\frac{1}{2\pi mi}\int_{2-\infty i}^{2+\infty i} x^{-s}\Gamma(s/m)\zeta(s)ds,$$

then shifting the path of integration to the line $\sigma=0$ and expressing $\zeta(it)$ in terms of $\zeta(1-it)$ by using the well-known functional equation for the Riemann zeta function $\zeta(s)$. This, together with standard estimates for $\Gamma(1-it)$, $\Gamma(it/m)$, and $\sin(\frac{1}{2}\pi it)$, leads to (I). It is asserted then that (II) follows in an analogous way if $\zeta^2(s)$ is used instead of $\zeta(s)$.

*H. N. Shapiro* (New York, N. Y.).

Referred to in P08-41.

## P08-11 (10, 597d)

**Hua, Loo-Keng. An improvement of Vinogradov's mean-value theorem and several applications.** Quart. J. Math., Oxford Ser. **20**, 48–61 (1949).

This paper gives a self-contained and clear treatment of the things mentioned in the title. The so-called mean-value theorem states that the number of solutions of the simultaneous Diophantine system of equations $\sum_{i=1}^{s}(x_i^h-y_i^h)=0$ $(1\leqq h\leqq k)$, subject to $T<x_i,\ y_i\leqq T+P$, does not exceed $(7s)^{4sl}(\log P)^{2l}P^{2s-k(k+1)/2+\delta}$ provided $s\geqq k(k+1)/4+lk$, $P\geqq 2$ and $\delta=k(k+1)(1-1/k)^l/2$. (Throughout the paper $k>1$.) This is a considerable improvement over the result in the author's book [review below]*which essentially required that $s$ be larger by a factor of about $2k$. The proof is somewhat similar to that given in the book.

From this result is obtained the following estimate of Weyl's sum $S=\sum_{x=1}^{P}\exp(2\pi i\alpha x^k)$. Let $|\alpha-h/q|\leqq 1/q^2$, $(h,q)=1$ and $P\leqq q\leqq P^{k-1}$. Then $|S|<c(k)P^{1-1/\sigma}$, where $\sigma$ is asymptotic to $4k^2\log k$ as $k\to\infty$. A value of $\sigma$ asymptotic to $6k^2\log k$ is given in Vinogradov's book [see the second following review]** and a value asymptotic to $k^3\log k$ is given in Hua's book. The author mentions that this result can be used to show that the Hardy-Littlewood asymptotic formula for the number of representations of $N$ as the sum of $s$ $k$th powers holds if $s>s_0\sim 4k^2\log k$. This compares with $s>s_1\sim 10k^2\log k$ as given in Vinogradov's book. Thus, the results of this paper and Vinogradov's book are of the same depth; the author remarks that Vinogradov's method seems to have reached a final stage.

A number of obvious misprints were noted. In addition, the following two rather minor corrections, in no way affecting the validity of the main results, may be mentioned: in theorem 4, the estimate for $S$ should have an additional factor of $\log P$, and in theorem 3 the estimate for the integral should have an additional factor of $2^k$.

*L. Schoenfeld* (Urbana, Ill.).

*See MR 10, 597E = P02-20.

**See MR 10, 599A = L02-2.

Citations: MR 10, 597e = P02-5; MR 10, 599a = L02-2.
Referred to in D52-90, D52-120, L15-14, M15-19, M15-20, M25-47, P12-14, P44-10, P44-13.

## P08-12 (10, 684a)

**Nečaev, V. I. The representation of integers by sums of terms of the form $\dfrac{x(x+1)\cdots(x+n-1)}{n!}$.** Doklady Akad. Nauk SSSR (N.S.) **64**, 159–162 (1949). (Russian)

Let $n$ be an integer not less than 2,

$$f(x)=a_nx^n+\cdots+a_1x, \qquad a_n>0,$$

where the $a_i$ are integers, $(a_1,\cdots,a_n)=1$; and denote by $d$ the greatest common divisor of the integers $f(x)$ for all integral $x$. The author defines $G(f)$ to be the least integer $r$ for which there exists an integer $c$ such that all integral $N\geqq c$ can be represented in the form

$$(1)\qquad N=f(x_1)/d+\cdots+f(x_r)/d,$$

with $x_1,\cdots,x_r$ nonnegative integers. If there exists a positive integer $x_0$ for which $f(x_0)=d$ then all integers $N\geqq 1$ can be represented in the form (1) for suitable $r$. In this case the author defines $g(f)$ to be the least $r$ such that all integers can be represented in the form (1) with $r=g(f)$. The case $f(x)=x^n$ is then that of the classical Waring problem. The author proposes to prove analogous results for these generalized $G(f)$, $g(f)$, using the method of Vinogradov; and includes a brief sketch of his proofs.

Let $d'$ denote the greatest common divisor of $f'(x)$ for all integral $x$; and for $p$ a prime dividing $d'$ define $\beta=\beta(p)$ to be such that there exists an integer $b$ having the property that for any integer $m$, and $s\geqq\beta$, the congruence $f(x)/d\equiv b+mp^\beta(\text{mod } p^s)$ has a solution. Then if $p_1,\cdots,p_l$ are the primes dividing $d'$, set

$$r_0=\max(2n+1,\ p_1^{\beta_1},\cdots,p_l^{\beta_l}).$$

The main theorem asserted is that

$$G(f)\leqq\begin{cases}\min\left(r_1,\ r_0+r_2-2n\log\dfrac{r_0}{2n}\right) & \text{for } r_0<r_1;\\ r_0 & \text{for } r_0\geqq r_1,\end{cases}$$

where for $n\geqq 12$, $r_1=[10n^2\log n]$,

$$r_2=4n\log n+2n\log\log n+3.2n;$$

for $4\leqq n\leqq 11$, $r_1=2^n+1$, $r_2=2n(n-2)\log 2+4$.

In the special case $f(x)=\varphi(x)=x(x+1)\cdots(x+n-1)$, as well as in any other case where $d'=1$, the author obtains $G(f)\leqq A(n)$, where $A(n)$ is given by the following table:

| $n=$ | 2 | 3 | 4 | 5 | 6 | 7 | 8 | 9 | 10 | 11 |
|---|---|---|---|---|---|---|---|---|---|---|
| $A(n)=$ | 5 | 8 | 17 | 31 | 45 | 63 | 81 | 103 | 125 | 155 |

and for $n\geqq 12$, $A(n)=4n\log n+2n\log\log n+5.5n$. Also for this special $\varphi(x)$ the author gives the theorem that

$$n+\left[\frac{n}{2}\right]\leqq g(\varphi)\leqq\begin{cases}\frac{1}{2}n^2\log n+8n\log n, & n\geqq 14;\\ n^3\log 2+8n, & 4\leqq n\leqq 13.\end{cases}$$

*H. N. Shapiro* (New York, N. Y.).

## P08-13 (11, 11b)

**Palamà, Giuseppe. Contributo dei recenti risultati delle multigrade al problema di Waring.** Boll. Un. Mat. Ital. (3) **4**, 75–79 (1949).

E. M. Wright published results [J. London Math. Soc. **9**, 267–272 (1934); **10**, 94–99 (1935); Quart. J. Math., Oxford Ser. **7**, 43–45 (1936)] concerning orders and bounds of functions connected with Waring's problem. Combining these results with data from A. Gloden's Mehrgradige Gleichungen [Noordhoff, Groningen, 1944; these Rev. **8**, 441] the author derives some improvements.

*N. G. W. H. Beeger* (Amsterdam).

Citations: MR 8, 441f = D52-13.

## P08-14 (11, 234h)

**Estermann, T. On Waring's problem: A simple proof of a theorem of Hua.** Sci. Rep. Nat. Tsing Hua Univ. Ser. A. **5**, 226–239 (1948).

This paper gives a self-contained proof of a theorem of Hua [Quart. J. Math., Oxford Ser. **9**, 199–202 (1938)] that the Hardy-Littlewood asymptotic formula for the number of representations of an integer as the sum of $s$ $k$th powers is valid if $s\geqq 2^k+1$. For large $k$, this result is, of course, inferior to that obtained by the methods of Vinogradov.

*L. Schoenfeld* (Urbana, Ill.).

Referred to in P08-45, P12-13.

**P08-15** **(13, 321f)**

**Kuipers, L. On the representation of integers by sums of polynomials.** Proc. Amer. Math. Soc. **2**, 750–752 (1951).

Let $\Delta f(x)=f(x+1)-f(x)$, $\Delta^i f=\Delta(\Delta^{i-1}f)$ and

$$F_k(x)=x(x-1)\cdots(x-k+1)/k!.$$

Then $\Delta F_k(x)=F_{k-1}(x)$. Let $f(x)=a_kF_k(x)+\cdots+a_1F_1(x)+a_0$. Then $\Delta^{k-1}f(x)=a_kx+a_{k-1}$. Let $H(f(x))$ be the least integer $s$ such that every integer is a sum or difference of $s$ values of $f(x)$ for integral $x$, and let $\Gamma(f(x))$ be the least integer $t$ such that every integer is congruent to a sum or difference of $t$ values of $f(x)$ mod $a_k$. By the above calculation we have evidently $H(f(x))\leqq 2^k+\Gamma(f(x))$. From this principle the author deduces: (i) Every integer can be expressed in infinitely many ways as a sum of $4^k+1$ values of the $(2k+1)$-th degree polynomial

$$a(x+k)(x+k-1)\cdots(x-k)/(2k+1)!+gx+c,$$

where $(a,g)=1$, and (ii) if $a=1$, we can replace $4^k+1$ by $4^k$ in (i). In the statement of theorems I and II read $2k+1$ for $2^k+1$. *L. K. Hua* (Peking).

**P08-16** **(13, 914e)**

**Nečaev, V. I. Waring's problem for polynomials.** Trudy Mat. Inst. Steklov., v. **38**, pp. 190–243. Izdat. Akad. Nauk SSSR, Moscow, 1951. (Russian) 20 rubles.

In this monograph Vinogradov's methods and results (including his estimate for Weyl sums) are applied to Waring's problem for polynomials. Let $f(x)$ be a polynomial of degree $n$ with integral coefficients. The H.C.F. of such a polynomial is defined to be the greatest integer $d$ which divides all values of $f(x)$ arising from integral $x$. Let $G(f)$ denote the least $r$ with the property that every sufficiently large positive integer $N$ is representable as

$$N=d^{-1}f(x_1)+\cdots+d^{-1}f(x_r)$$

with positive integral $x_1, \cdots, x_r$. The main problem is to determine or estimate $G(f)$; and there is also the same problem for $g(f)$, which is defined in the same way but omitting the words "sufficiently large". The present treatment is concerned primarily with values of $n\geqq 5$. The results are somewhat complicated to formulate, and it may suffice to mention one: if $r_0(f)$, defined below, satisfies $r_0(f)\geqq 10n^2\log n$, then $G(f)$ is either $r_0(f)$ or $r_0(f)+1$. Since there is an example, due to Hua, of a polynomial of degree $n\geqq 5$ for which $G(f)=2^n$ or $2^n-1$ according as $n$ is even or odd, it follows that the upper bound of $G(f)$ for $f$ of degree $n$ can be determined with a possible error of 1. The number $r_0(f)$ is defined by congruential considerations. Let $g(f, p^\beta)$ denote the least $r$ for which the congruence

$$N\equiv d^{-1}f(x_1)+\cdots+d^{-1}f(x_r) \pmod{p^\beta}$$

is soluble for every integer $N$. Let $d'$ be the H.C.F. of $f'(x)$ then $r_0$ is the greatest value of $g(f, p^\beta)$ for all prime factors $p$ of $d'$ and all positive integers $\beta$. Inequalities for $G(f)$ when $r_0(f)<10n^2\log n$ are also given but are less exact than that stated above. The author further proves that $G(f)\leqq 65$ when $n=6$, and in view of Hua's example this upper bound cannot be in error by more than 1.

Chapters 1 and 2 are of an arithmetical character, and are concerned with $g(f, p^\beta)$. It is unfortunate that there is no explicit statement of the relation between the number $g_1(f)$ mentioned in the introduction and the number $g_0(f)$ discussed in chapter 2. Chapter 3 deals with the singular series. Chapter 4 quotes various results from Vinogradov's book [Trudy Mat. Inst. Steklov., v. **23** (1947); these Rev. **10**, 599] and a recent paper [Izvestiya Akad. Nauk SSSR. Ser. Mat. **14**, 199–214 (1950); these Rev. **12**, 161]; also a few older results. Chapters 5 to 7 constitute the main body of the work. The author investigates the number of representations of $Nd$ as

$$f(x_1)+\cdots+f(x_r)+u+u',$$

where $1\leqq x_i\leqq P$ and $u$ and $u'$ run through numbers of the form $f(\xi_1)+\cdots+f(\xi_k)$, where $\xi_1, \cdots, \xi_k$ are in intervals of successively lower orders of magnitude of the kind now usual in Waring's problem. The integral for the number of representations is split into basic and supplementary intervals in the usual way, and various choices of $r$ and $k$ are made according to the ranges of $n$ and of $r_0(f)$. Chapter 8 is concerned with the polynomial $\varphi(x)=x(x+1)\cdots(x+n-1)$, and it is proved by a combination of elementary and analytical methods that $g(\varphi)<\frac{1}{2}n^2\log n+6n\log n$. *H. Davenport* (London).

Citations: MR 10, 599a = L02-2; MR 12, 161a = L15-13.

Referred to in P08-21.

**P08-17** **(15, 202a)**

**Subba Rao, K. Representation of numbers as sums of $k$-th powers.** Math. Student **21**, 49 (1953).

Put $m=2^{[\frac{1}{2}(k+1)]}$, and let $t$ be any rational number. The author proves that there exists an infinity of rational numbers $x_1, x_2, \cdots, x_m$ satisfying $t=\sum_{i=1}^m a_ix_i^k$, $a_i=\pm 1$. *P. Erdös* (South Bend, Ind.).

**P08-18** **(15, 289f)**

**Rieger, G. J. Zur Hilbertschen Lösung des Waringschen Problems: Abschätzung von $g(n)$.** Arch. Math. **4**, 275–281 (1953).

The author shows how Hilbert's method of proof of Waring's conjecture can be used to obtain an upper bound for $g(n)$, the smallest number for which all integers are representable by $g(n)$ $n$th powers. *W. H. Simons.*

Referred to in P08-19, R48-8.

**P08-19** **(15, 603a)**

**Rieger, Georg Johann. Zur Hilbertschen Lösung des Waringschen Problems: Abschätzung von $g(n)$.** Mitt. Math. Sem. Giessen no. **44**, 35 pp. (1953).

The results of this dissertation have been summarized in a note which appeared in Arch. Math. **4**, 275–281 (1953); these Rev. **15**, 289. *R. D. James* (Vancouver, B. V.).

Citations: MR 15, 289f = P08-18.

**P08-20** **(15, 602l)**

**Mardžanišvili, K. K. On some nonlinear systems of equations in integers.** Mat. Sbornik N.S. **33**(**75**), 639–675 (1953). (Russian)

This memoir is concerned with the solubility in positive integers $x_1, \cdots, x_s$ of the system of equations

$$(1)\qquad x_1^k+\cdots+x_s^k=N_k \quad (k=l, m, \cdots, n),$$

where $l, m, \cdots, n$ are $g$ distinct positive integers of which $n$ is the greatest. The treatment represents a generalisation of Vinogradov's work [Trav. Inst. Math. Stekloff **23** (1947); these Rev. **10**, 599] on Waring's problem, which is the case $g=1$. Some condition on the relative magnitudes of $N_l$, $N_m, \cdots, N_n$ is obviously necessary. The author puts $N_k=h_k(N_n)^{k/n}$ for $k=l, m, \cdots, n$, and postulates that the equations $\xi_1^k+\cdots+\xi_g^k=h_k$ $(k=l, m, \cdots, n)$ have a solution in real $\xi_1, \cdots, \xi_g$ for which $\xi_1, \cdots, \xi_g$ and $|\det(\xi_t^{k-1})|$, where $t=1, \cdots, g$, all have a fixed positive lower bound. Suppose $n\geqq 12$ and $f>3ng$, and put

$$r=[2n\log(10ng)+n\log\log(20ng)]+1.$$

In the first part of the paper the author obtains a lower bound for the number of solutions of (1) when $s=f+2gr$. The details of the work are necessarily heavy, as the single integral occurring in the Hardy-Littlewood and Vinogradov work is replaced here by integration over $g$ variables. The significance of the result depends naturally on whether the "singular series" for the problem, which occurs as a factor in the main term of the lower bound, is strictly positive, and this question, which is purely arithmetical, is investigated in the second part of the paper. It is shown that if certain congruences are soluble and if $s$ is greater than a certain number depending on $g$ and on the primes $\leqq n^{n+1}$, then the desired property holds. *H. Davenport.*

Citations: MR 10, 599a = L02-2.

Referred to in D80-30.

## P08-21 (15, 602m)

**Nečaev, V. I. On the representation of natural numbers as a sum of terms of the form**

$$\frac{x(x+1)\cdots(x+n-1)}{n!}.$$

Izvestiya Akad. Nauk SSSR. Ser. Mat. **17**, 485–498 (1953). (Russian)

Let $\varphi_n(x)$ denote the polynomial of the title, and let $g(\varphi_n)$ denote the least $r$ with the property that every positive integer is representable as a sum of at most $r$ values of $\varphi_n(x)$, arising from non-negative integral values of $x$. In his monograph [Trudy Mat. Inst. Steklov. **38**, 190–243 (1951); these Rev. **13**, 914] the author proved that

$$g(\varphi_n) < \tfrac{1}{2}n^2 \log n + 6n \log n$$

for $n \geqq 12$. In the present paper he improves the right-hand side to $6n \log n + 9n \log \log n$. The proof is based on the work of the monograph, but requires improved estimates at many points. The main tool by which these are obtained is the use of the inequality

$$\left| \sum_{x=1}^{p} \exp\,(2\pi i f(x)/p) \right| < np^{1/2}$$

for exponential sums ($p$ prime, $f(x)$ a polynomial of degree $n$), due to A. Weil [Proc. Nat. Acad. Sci. U. S. A. **34**, 204–207 (1948); these Rev. **10**, 234]. Use is also made of some of Tchebychev's estimates for the distribution of primes.

*H. Davenport* (London).

Citations: MR 10, 234e = T25-5; MR 13, 914e = P08-16.

Referred to in P08-34.

## P08-22 (16, 114b)

**Rieger, G. J. Zu Linniks Lösung des Waringschen Problems: Abschätzung von $g(n)$.** Math. Z. **60**, 213–234 (1954).

The author follows Linnik's elementary solution of Waring's Problem, as presented in Chapter 3 of Khintchine's "Three pearls of number theory" [2nd ed., OGIZ, Moscow-Leningrad, 1948; English translation published by Graylock Press, Rochester, N. Y., 1952; these Rev. **11**, 83; **13**, 724]. He obtains an explicit upper bound for $g(n, f, \delta)$, which is defined as the least $g$ such that every positive integer is representable as a sum of at most $g$ numbers, each of which is either 1 or a value of $f(x)$, where $f(x)$ is a given polynomial of degree $n$ with integral coefficients and $x$ runs through any sequence of positive integers of density $\delta$ (in the sense of Schnirelmann). For the classical case when $x$ runs through all positive integers, the upper bound obtained is naturally very poor compared with known results.

*H. Davenport* (London).

Citations: MR 11, 83f = Z02-8; MR 13, 724a = Z02-10.

## P08-23 (17, 1187b)

**Emel'yanov, G. V. On a system of Diophantine equations.** Leningrad. Gos. Univ. Uč. Zap. **137**. Ser. Mat. Nauk **19** (1950), 3–39. (Russian)

Following Kamke [Math. Ann. **83** (1921), 85–112; J. Reine Angew. Math. **152** (1922), 30–22] and Mardžanišvili [C. R. (Dokl.) Acad. Sci. URSS (N.S.) **2** (1936), 263–264; **22** (1939), 467–470; Izv. Akad. Nauk SSSR. Ser. Mat. **1937**, 609–631; **4** (1940), ł93–214; MR **2**, 250] the author considers the set of equations

$$(1) \qquad \sum_{s=1}^{S} x_s^k = N_k \quad (1 \leqq k \leqq n),$$

where $N_j$ are given positive integers and $x_j$ are positive integers to be determined. He writes

$$(2) \qquad N_k = h_k N_n^{k/n} \quad (1 \leqq k < n)$$

and supposes that $S \geqq cn^2 \log n$, $1 < l_k \leqq h_k \leqq i_k S^{1-k/n} (1 \leqq k < n)$ for some constants $c$, $l_k$, $i_k$. In the first two parts he uses the circle method together with the estimates for trigonometrical sums due to Vinogradoff. He shows that the number of solutions of (1) is

$$\frac{B(h_1, \cdots, h_{n-1})}{h_1 \cdots h_{n-1}} N_n^{(S/n)+(n+1)/2} \times \{\mathfrak{S}(N_1, \cdots, N_n) + O(N_n^{-1/c_1 n^3 \log n})\}$$

where $c_1 < 0$ is a constant, $\mathfrak{S}$ is a 'singular series' and $B$ depends only on $h_1, \cdots, h_{n-1}$. If there is an $\varepsilon > 0$ such that the equations

$$\sum_{s=1}^{S} \xi_s^k = h_k' \quad (1 \leqq k \leqq n)$$

have a real positive solution $\xi_1, \cdots, \xi_s$ for all real $h_k'$ in $h_k - \varepsilon \leqq h_k' \leqq h_k$ (with $h_n = 1$), then $B$ is greater than a positive constant depending only on $n$, $S$ (and, presumably, on $\varepsilon$). He shows, further, that the singular series is greater than a constant, and so a solution exists, provided that a further elaborate 'condition of local solubility' is satisfied. In the third part the author adapts Linnik's elementary treatment [Mat. Sb. N.S. **12(54)** (1943), 225–230; MR **5**, 200] of Waring's problem to show that (1) is soluble in positive integers for all $S$ greater than a constant $S_0$ depending only on $n$ provided that the $N_k$ satisfy (2), (4) and provided that the congruences

$$\sum_{i=1}^{n} y_i{}^{ik} \equiv N_k \quad (1 \leqq i,\, k \leqq n)$$

are soluble in integers $y_i$ to every modulus. (This was proved with transcendental methods and an explicit $S_0$ by Mardžanišvili in the second cited work, where the congruence condition was shown to be necessary).

The reviewer was unable to follow the paper in detail as the author presupposes an intimate knowledge of all the preceding literature and seldom makes explicit which parameters depend on others, or which may be chosen arbitrarily. *J. W. S. Cassels* (Cambridge, England).

Citations: MR 2, 250h = P44-7; MR 5, 200b = P08-7.

## P08-24 (18, 466c)

**Kužel', A. V. Elementary solution of Waring's problem for polynomials by the method of Yu. V. Linnik.** Uspehi Mat. Nauk (N.S.) **11** (1956), no. 3(69), 165–168. (Russian)

Kamke [Math. Ann. **83** (1921), 85–112] gave the following generalization to polonymials of Hilbert's theorem on the Waring problem for $n$th powers: Let $f(x)$ be polynomial of degree $n$ with integer coefficients the highest coefficient being positive, then there is a $g$ depending on $f$ such that every positive integer is the sum of not more than $g$ numbers taken from the set

$$1, f(0), f(1), \cdots$$

The present note gives an elementary demonstration of this theorem, using as a lemma a result Linnik [Mat. Sb. N.S. **12(54)** (1943), 225–230; MR **5**, 200] in his elementary proof of Hilbert's theorem by Schnirelmann's method of density. This lemma limits the number of solutions of the diophantine equation $\sum_{i=1}^{k} f(x_i)=m$ subject to the conditions $0 \leqq x_i^n \leqq N$, $1 \leqq m \leqq N$. *D. H. Lehmer.*

Citations: MR 5, 200b = P08-7.

**P08-25** **(19, 251b)**

**Palamà, Giuseppe. Il problema di Waring.** Boll. Un. Mat. Ital. (3) 12 (1957), 83–100.

An expository account, with a bibliography of 38 entries, of the salient points in the history of Waring's problem.

**P08-26** **(19, 391f)**

**Širšov, V. M. On an estimate of a definite integral.** Belorussk. Politehn. Inst. Sb. Nauč. Rabot. **1953**, no. 4, 13–24. (Russian)

Let

$$W_0(N)=\int_{\mathfrak{M}} L_\alpha{}^r \exp(-2\pi i\alpha N)d\alpha,$$

where

$$L_\alpha=\sum_{x=1}^{Q}\sum_{y=1}^{[Px^{-s}]} \exp 2\pi i\alpha x^m y^n,$$

the $m, n, r, N$ being natural numbers and where $\mathfrak{M}$ is the set of points belonging to the union of so-called complementary intervals defined by conditions given in the article.

The author endeavors to prove that $W_0(N) \ll p^{r-n-\nu+\nu\mu}$, which would make it possible to complete the proof of the generalized Waring theorem of the type considered in the article under review.

But the reviewer has been unable to follow all the details of the proof since, for example, there are certain obscurities in the definition of the concept of complementary interval: there is no exact definition of the magnitudes $x, x_1, x_2, \cdots, x_r$ (there is a similar obscurity in an earlier article of the author in no. 2 of the same Sbornik.

*N. G. Čudakov* (RŽMat **1954**, no.1039).

**P08-27** **(20# 23)**

**Hua, Loo-Keng. On the major arcs of Waring problem.** Sci. Record (N.S.) 1 (1957), no 3, 17–18.

Let $T(\alpha)$ denote the exponential sum $\sum_{x=1}^{P} \exp\{2\pi i x^k \alpha\}$ where $P=[N^{1/k}]$. In a previous note **[MR 20 #22]** the author had obtained the estimate

$$T(\alpha)=\frac{1}{q}\sum_{x=1}^{q}\exp\{2\pi i(h/q)x^k\}\int_0^P \exp\{2\pi i\beta y^k\}dy+O(q^{\frac{1}{2}+\varepsilon}),$$

on the major axes $\mathfrak{M}_{h,q}$ of Waring's problem. In the present note the author states that, as a result, the estimate

$$\sum_{\mathfrak{M}_{h,q}}\int_{\mathfrak{M}_{h,q}} T^s(\alpha)e^{-2\pi iN\alpha}d\alpha \sim \mathfrak{S}(N)\frac{\Gamma^s(1+1/k)}{\Gamma(s/k)}N^{(s/k)-1},$$

where $\mathfrak{S}(N)$ denotes the singular series, can be proved for $s \geqq k+1$ (instead of $s \geqq 2k+1$), which is best possible in a certain sense. *E. G. Straus* (Los Angeles, Calif.)

Citations: MR 20# 22 = L05-17.

**P08-28** **(20# 2306)**

**Palamà, G. Sul problema analogo a quello di Waring.** Matematiche, Catania 11 (1956), 117–120 (1957).

By considering the system of multigrade congruences $a_1, a_2, \cdots, a_n \overset{m}{\equiv} b_1, b_2, \cdots, b_n \pmod p$, the author shows that the multiples of infinitely many primes occurring in the arithmetic progression $(m+1)n+1$, $n=1, 2, \cdots$, are representable by means of $2(m+1)$ of the $m$th powers $\pm 1^m, \pm 2^m, \pm 3^m, \cdots$. *W. H. Simons* (Vancouver, B.C.)

**P08-29** **(20# 3838)**

**Tong, Kwang-chang. On Waring's problem.** Advancement in Math. 3 (1957), 602–607. (Chinese. English summary)

The result of this paper is

$$G(n)<n(3\ln n+9), \quad \text{when } n=2^m,$$
$$G(n)<n(3\ln n+7), \quad \text{when } n\neq 2^m.$$

*From the author's summary*

**P08-30** **(20# 3839)**

**Trost, E. Eine Bemerkung zum Waringschen Problem.** Elem. Math. 13 (1958), 73–75.

Regarding the value of $g(k)$ in Waring's problem, it is well known that: For all $k \geqq 6$, for which the inequality 1) $3^k-2^kA_k \leqq 2^k-A_k-2$, $A_k=[(3/2)^k]$, holds, 2) $g(k)=2^k+A_k-2$. The author shows that the above result can be stated in the form: If $k \geqq 6$ and there is a natural number $x_k$ in the interval

$$3) \qquad \frac{3^k}{2^k}+\lambda_k \leqq x_k < \frac{3^k}{2^k}+1, \; \lambda_k=\frac{(3/2)^k+1}{2^k-1},$$

then

$$g(k)=2^k+x_k-3.$$

It is further shown that (3) is true for infinitely many $k$. *H. Gupta* (Chandigarh)

**P08-31** **(20# 4532)**

**Chen, Jun-jing. On Waring's problem for $n$-th powers.** Acta Math. Sinica 8 (1958), 253–257. (Chinese. English summary)

The author proves that the number $G(n)$ in Waring's problem is not greater than $n(3\log n+5.2)$. This slightly improves Vinogradov's estimate with 11 instead of 5.2. *K. Mahler* (Manchester)

Referred to in P08-32.

**P08-32** **(36# 6367)**

**Chen Jing-run [Ch'en Ching-jun]**

**On Waring's problem for $n$th powers.**

*Acta Math. Sinica* 8 (1958), 253–257 (*Chinese*); *translated as Chinese Math.—Acta* 8 (1966), 849–853 (1967).

The original Chinese version has been reviewed [MR **20** #4532]. *B. Garrison* (San Diego, Calif.)

Citations: MR 20# 4532 = P08-31.

**P08-33** **(22# 699)**

**Vinogradov, I. M. On an upper bound for $G(n)$.** Izv. Akad. Nauk SSSR. Ser. Mat. **23** (1959), 637–642. (Russian)

The function $G(n)$ is the least number $s$ such that all but a finite number of integers are sums of $s$ positive $n$th powers. The author proved in 1947 [Trav. Inst. Math. Stekloff **23** (1947); MR **10**, 599] that, for $n>2$, $G(n)/n < 3\log n+11$. By modifying his method of exponential sums the author shows in the present paper that

$$G(n)/n < 2\log n+4\log\log n+2\log\log\log n+13$$

for all sufficiently large $n$. In particular, one of the lemmas requires $n$ to exceed 170,000. *D. H. Lehmer* (Berkeley, Calif.)

Citations: MR 10, 599a = L02-2.

**P08-34** **(22# 4691)**

**Chen, Ching-jun. On the representation of a natural number as a sum of terms of the form** $x(x+1)\cdots(x+k-1)/k!$. Acta Math. Sinica **9** (1959), 264–270. (Chinese. English summary)

Put $\varphi_k(x)=(-1)^k\binom{-x}{k}$ and denote by $g(\varphi_k)$ the smallest $r$ such that every positive integer is the sum of at most $r$ terms $\varphi_k(x)$ with integral $x\geqq 0$. The author improves a previous result by V. I. Nečaev [Izv. Akad. Nauk SSSR. Ser. Mat. **17** (1953), 485–498; MR **15**, 602] and shows that

$$k\log k-k \leqq g(\varphi_k) \leqq 5(k\log k+12) \quad (k \geqq 12).$$

As the author states, the left-hand inequality was also obtained by L. K. Hua. *K. Mahler* (Manchester)

Citations: MR 15, 602m = P08-21.

**P08-35** **(22# 10967)**

**Newman, Donald J. A simplified proof of Waring's conjecture.** Michigan Math. J. **7** (1960), 291–295.

The author gives a simple proof of the well-known theorem that every integer is the sum of a bounded number of $k$th powers of positive integers. He uses the circle method, but only needs crude estimates instead of the usual asymptotic formulae. *P. Erdös* (Budapest)

**P08-36** **(24# A3130)**

**Barrucand, Pierre; Haget, Michel**

**Sur le problème de Waring en particulier pour les cubes.**

*C. R. Acad. Sci. Paris* **253** (1961), 1647–1648.

In their work on Waring's problem, Hardy and Littlewood defined $r_{k,s}(n)$ by

$$(1+2\sum_{n=1}^{\infty} x^{n^k})^s = \sum_{n=0}^{\infty} r_{k,s}(n)x^n.$$

The authors prove a number of congruence properties for the integers $r_{k,s}(n)$. *J. F. Koksma* (Amsterdam)

**P08-37** **(25# 1141)**

**Barrucand, Pierre**

**Propriétés de congruence pour les coefficients de Waring-Hardy.**

*C. R. Acad. Sci. Paris* **253** (1961), 2306–2308.

The coefficient of Waring-Hardy $\tau_{k,s}(n)$ is the number of representations of $n$ as a sum of $s$ integers of the form $|a|^k$, where the order and the sign are taken into account. The author proves by elementary considerations that if $n$ is a non-residue of degree $k$ (mod $p$) and $p$ an odd prime, $s\equiv 1$ (mod $p$), then $\tau_{k,s}(n)\equiv 0$ (mod $p$). Hence he deduces many particular cases. *J. Kubilius* (Vilnius)

**P08-38** **(26# 93)**

**Kothari, D. S.; Auluck, F. C.**

**Symposium on statistical mechanics and the partition theory of number (abstract of paper).**

*Math. Student* **28** (1960), 189–192 (1962).

The authors give a number of striking examples to illustrate the following statement: "The central problem of statistical mechanics is the determination of the number of ways in which a given amount of energy can be shared among the different possible states of an assembly, and this problem is the same as that of determining the number of ways in which a given positive integer can be written as the sum of given summands". For example, they show how to obtain from thermodynamic considerations the Hardy-Ramanujan asymptotic expression for $p(n|s)$, the number of ways of writing $n$ as the sum of the $s$th powers of positive integers.

*A. L. Whiteman* (Los Angeles, Calif.)

**P08-39** **(28# 3019)**

**Stemmler, Rosemarie M.**

**The ideal Waring theorem for exponents** 401–200,000.

*Math. Comp.* **18** (1964), 144–146.

The so-called ideal Waring theorem states that for each integer $k$ every positive integer is the sum of $2^k+[(3/2)^k]-2$ non-negative $k$th powers, provided the fractional part of $(3/2)^k$ is less than $1-(3/4)^k$. Whether there is a $k$ for which this proviso fails is an unsolved problem. The author shows that such a $k$ must exceed 200000. A table gives the distribution of the fractional parts of $(3/2)^n$ into eighths for $n\leqq k$ and for $k=100(100)\ 1000(1000)\ 10000(10000)200000$. The author feels that it is highly unlikely that the above proviso ever fails.

*D. H. Lehmer* (Berkeley, Calif.)

**P08-40** **(31# 2227)**

**Ehlich, Hartmut**

**Zur Pillaischen Vermutung.**

*Arch. Math.* **16** (1965), 223–226.

Let $g(k)$ be the smallest integer so that every integer is the sum of $g(k)$ or fewer $k$th powers. Waring conjectured that (1) $g(k)=2^k+[(3/2)^k]-2$. Put $r_k=3^k-2^k[(3/2)^k]$. It is known that if $k\geqq 35$ and (2) $r_k<2^k-[(3/2)^k]$, then (1) holds. Pillai conjectured that (2) holds for every $k\geqq 2$. With the aid of a computer, the author proves (2) for every $k\leqq 50000$. Mahler proved that (2) holds for all sufficiently large $k$ [Mathematika **4** (1957), 122–124; MR **20** #33]. *P. Erdős* (Budapest)

Citations: MR 20# 33 = J68-19.

**P08-41** **(31# 5852)**

**Anfert'eva, E. A.**

**On certain power series with periodic coefficients. (Russian)**

*Izv. Akad. Nauk SSSR Ser. Mat.* **29** (1965), 137–148.

Let $e(x)$ denote $\exp(2\pi ix)$; $q, k, m$ are fixed natural numbers, $\rho=e(a/q)$ is a fixed primitive $q$th root of unity, and $\{a_n\}$ is a sequence of complex numbers periodic in $n$ with period $k$. Let $k'$ denote the lowest common multiple of $k$ and $q$, so that $\rho a_n$ is then periodic with period $k'$. $N$ is a large positive integer. Following earlier work [Dokl. Akad. Nauk SSSR **60** (1948), 541–544; MR **10**, 17], the author shows that if $z$ is near $\rho$, more precisely, if $z=e^{-1/N}e(-\alpha+a/q)$, then

$$\sum_{n=1}^{\infty} a_n z^{n^m} = \Gamma\left(1+\frac{1}{m}\right)\left(\frac{1}{k'}\sum_{\nu=1}^{k'} a_\nu\rho^{\nu^m}\right)(1-z\rho^{-1})^{-1/m}+O((\log N)^2)$$

provided $|\alpha|<N^{-1+\mu}$, where $\mu$ is an arbitrary number less than $1/m$ (the author's own statement of this result appears to be incorrect). This generalises some well-known results about $\theta$-functions. When $a_n=1$ for all $n$, so that $k=1$ and $k'=q$, one gets an asymptotic formula for the generating function in the original Hardy-Littlewood method for Waring's problem for $m$th powers. However, the dependence of the various implied constants on $q$ is not made explicit, so that in this context the formula as it stands is not applicable. *H. Halberstam* (Nottingham)

Citations: MR 10, 17f = P08-10.

**P08-42** **(32# 7529)**

**Karacuba, A. A.**

**On estimation of the number of solutions of certain equations. (Russian)**

*Dokl. Akad. Nauk SSSR* **165** (1965), 31–32.

The author considers the equation

$$(1)\qquad x_1^n+\cdots+x_k^n = y_1^n+\cdots+y_k^n,$$

where $P > \exp n^6$, $1 \leqq x_i, y_i \leqq P$ $(i = 1, 2, \cdots, k)$, and $I_{k,n}(P)$ is the number of solutions of (1).

An estimate of Vinogradov [*Selected works* (Russian), Izdat. Akad. Nauk SSSR, Moscow, 1952; MR **14**, 610] for $I_{k,n}(P)$ is (2) $I_{k,n}(P) \leqq C(k, n)P^{2k-n}$, where $k \geqq 4n^2 \ln n$ and $C(k, n)$ is a constant depending only on $n$ and $k$.

The author considers the problem of estimates of type 2 for $k$ as small as possible, and proves the following two results: (I) $I_{k,n}(P) \leqq c_1 P^{2k-r}$ if $n \geqq 2$, $2 \leqq r \leqq n$; (II) if $1 \leqq m \leqq n$, then for $k \geqq 6mn \ln n$, $I_{k,n}(P) \leqq c_2 I_{k,m}(P)$, where $c_1$ and $c_2$ denote constants depending only on $n$ and $k$. The author deduces some analogous results for systems of equations of type (1).

{This article has appeared in English translation [Soviet Math. Dokl. **6** (1965), 1402–1404].}

*R. Finkelstein* (Tucson, Ariz.)

## P08-43 (33# 1299)

**Varbanec, P. D.**

**On Waring's theorem. (Russian)**

*First. Republ. Math. Conf. of Young Researchers, Part II (Russian), pp.* 105–112. *Akad. Nauk Ukrain. SSR Inst. Mat., Kiev,* 1965.

An asymptotic formula is given for the number of representations of an integer $N$ as the sum of $r$ terms, each term being a value of a given polynomial $f$ of degree $n$ in two variables, subject to certain identities holding for the coefficients of $f$. *R. A. Rankin* (Glasgow)

## P08-44 (35# 6664)

**Joly, Jean-René**

**Sur le problème de Waring pour un exposant premier dans certains anneaux locaux.**

*C. R. Acad. Sci. Paris Sér. A-B* **262** (1966), A1438–A1441.

Let $d$ be a positive integer. Given a commutative ring $A$, set $A_d = \{a_1{}^d + a_2{}^d + \cdots + a_v{}^d : a_j \in A\}$, and let $\omega(d; A)$ be the smallest integer $m$ such that every element in $A_d$ can be written as $a_1{}^d + \cdots + a_m{}^d$. The author considers the particular case when $d$ is a prime number and shows that, for any complete local ring $A$ with finite residue field, $\omega(p; A) \leqq 10$ if $p = 2$, $\omega(p; A) \leqq 2p - 1$ if $p$ is odd prime. The proof is based on the structure theorem for complete local rings. *D. S. Rim* (Philadelphia, Pa.)

## P08-45 (37# 1332)

**Iseki, Shô**

**A problem on partitions connected with Waring's problem.**

*Proc. Amer. Math. Soc.* **19** (1968), 197–204.

The author proves: Let $P(n)$ denote the number of partitions of a positive integer $n$ into $s$ $k$th powers of positive integers. Then, for $s \geqq 2^k + 1$ $(k \geqq 2)$ or $s \geqq [10k^2 \log k]$ $(k \geqq 12)$, we have $P(n) = (\Gamma^s(1 + 1/k)/s!\Gamma(s/k)) \times \mathfrak{S}(n) n^{s/k - 1} + o(n^{s/k-1})$, $n \to \infty$. The proof uses the Hardy-Littlewood method developed for Waring's problem and closely follows the refinements due to T. Estermann [Sci. Rep. Nat. Tsing Hua Univ. Ser. A **5** (1948), 226–239; MR **11**, 234] and I. M. Vinogradov [*The methods of trigonometric sums in the theory of numbers* (Russian), Trudy Mat. Inst. Steklov. **10** (1937); revision, ibid. **23** (1947); MR **10**, 599; English translation, Interscience, London, 1954; MR **15**, 941]. The original problem is quickly reduced to showing that $Q(n) = o(n^{s/k-1})$, where $Q(n)$ is the number of positive integer solutions of the equation $2x_2^k + x_3^k + \cdots + x_s^k = n$.

*D. J. Lewis* (Ann Arbor, Mich.)

Citations: MR 10, 599a = L02-2; MR 11, 234h = P08-14; MR 15, 941b = L02-3.

## P08-46 (38# 5716)

**Kátai, I.; Mogyoródi, J.**

**On the number of solutions of a diophantine system.**

*Acta Math. Acad. Sci. Hungar.* **20** (1969), 185–191.

Es bezeichne $A_N(v_1, \cdots, v_l)$ die Anzahl der Lösungen des diophantischen Gleichungssystems (1) $\sum_{k=1}^N (\varepsilon_k - \varepsilon_k')k^\nu = v_\nu$ $(\nu = 1, 2, \cdots, l)$ in den Unbekannten $\varepsilon_1, \cdots, \varepsilon_N, \varepsilon_1', \cdots, \varepsilon_N'$, wobei $\varepsilon_j, \varepsilon_j'$ die Werte 0 und 1 annehmen können.

Ferner sei (2) $Q(\beta_1, \cdots, \beta_l) = \sum_{\mu=1}^l \sum_{\nu=1}^l \beta_\nu \beta_\mu/(\nu + \mu + 1)$,

$$(3)\quad \sigma_N(v_1, \cdots, v_l) = \int_{-\infty}^{\infty} \cdots \int_{-\infty}^{\infty} \exp\{-2\pi i(\beta_1 v_1 N^{-3/2} + \cdots + \beta_l v_l N^{-(2l+1)/2})\} \times \exp(-\pi^2 Q(\beta_1, \cdots, \beta_l))\, d\beta_1 \cdots d\beta_l,$$

(4) $\tau_N(v_1, \cdots, v_l) = \sum \exp\{-2\pi i(\sum_{j=1}^l a_j v_j/q_j)\}$, wobei in der letzten Summe über solche $a_j, q_j$ summiert wird, welche die beiden folgenden Bedingungen erfüllen: (1) $(a_j, q_j) = 1$ $(j = 1, \cdots, l)$, (2) $\sum_{j=1}^l a_j x^j/q_j$ nimmt an allen ganzen $x$ ganzzahlige Werte an. Verfasser beweist u.a.

$$A_N(v_1, \cdots, v_l) = 2^{2N} N^{-l(l+2)/2} \{\sigma_N(v_1, \cdots, v_l)\tau_N(v_1, \cdots, v_l) + O(N^{-c})\}$$

mit einer geeigneten positiven Konstanten $C$.

*H. J. Kanold* (Braunschweig)

## P08-47 (38# 5732)

**Ellison, W. J.**

**A 'Waring's problem' for homogeneous forms.**

*Proc. Cambridge Philos. Soc.* **65** (1969), 663–672.

The problem is whether every homogeneous form $f(\mathbf{X})$ of degree $k$ in $n$ variables $\mathbf{X}$ over a field $K$, is representable as $f(\mathbf{X}) = \sum_{i=1}^N L_i{}^k(\mathbf{X})$, where the $L_i$ are linear forms over $K$, and $N$ depends only on $K$, $n$ and $k$. The answer is "yes" if $K = \mathbf{C}$ (complex numbers), and if $k$ is odd and $K = \mathbf{R}$ (reals) or $K = \mathbf{Q}$ (rationals); and it is "no" for all $n \geqq 2$, even for positive definite forms, if $k$ is even and $\geqq 4$ and $K = \mathbf{R}$ or $\mathbf{Q}$. The proofs are quite simple, and give explicit bounds for $N$; as the author points out, the question of the least value of $N$ which is required appears to be very difficult. Corresponding results are given for representations as $f(\mathbf{X}) = \sum_{i=1}^N \varphi_i{}^s(\mathbf{X})$, where the $\varphi_i$ are forms of degree $r$ and $rs = k$. *E. S. Barnes* (Adelaide)

## P08-48 (40# 2626)

**Krätzel, Ekkehard**

**Mittlere Darstellungen natürlicher Zahlen als Differenz zweier $k$-ter Potenzen.**

*Acta Arith.* **16** (1969/70), 111–121.

Let $k$ be an integer $\geqq 3$, and let $t_k(\rho) = 2 \sum'_{m^k - n^k = \rho} 1$, where $m$ and $n$ are nonnegative integers, $m > n \geqq 0$. The prime on the summation signifies that the term for which $n = 0$ receives the value $\frac{1}{2}$. Let $T_k(x) = \sum_{1 \leq \rho \leq x} t_k(\rho)$. It is shown that

$$T_k(x) = (\Gamma(2/k)2k \cos \pi/k)^{-1}\Gamma^2(1/k)x^{2/k} = 2\zeta(k-1)^{-1}(x/k)^{(k-1)^{-1}} + O(x^{(k-1)/k^2}),$$

and that this estimate for the remainder is best possible. The proof involves use of methods developed by J. G. van der Corput [Math. Z. **17** (1923), 250–259; Math. Ann. **89** (1923), 215–254]. *B. Garrison* (San Diego, Calif.)

## P08-49 (41# 166)

**Freĭman, G. A.**

**Waring's problem with an increasing number of terms. (Russian)**

*Elabuž. Gos. Ped. Inst. Učen. Zap.* **3** (1958), 105–119.

By developing the method of A. Ja. Hinčin [*Mathematical foundations of quantum statistics* (Russian), GITTL, Moscow, 1951; MR **13**, 894; German translation, Akademie-Verlag, Berlin, 1956; MR **18**, 443], the author establishes an asymptotic formula for the number of solutions $I_{N,k}$ in positive integers $x_1, \cdots, x_k$ of the equation $x_1^n + x_2^n + \cdots + x_k^n = N$, where $N$, $k$ and $n \neq 2$ are natural numbers, under the condition that $C_1 \ln N < k < \gamma N$, where $C_1$ is a sufficiently large number and $0 < \gamma < 1$. He shows that the validity of the formula obtained under the condition $k \to \infty$ and $k < C_2 \ln N$, where $C_2$ is a sufficiently large integer, is not difficult to prove by means of the usual arguments used in the derivation of the asymptotic formula for the number of solutions $I_{N,k}$ for fixed $N$ and $k$.

{Reviewer's remark: This statement by the author seems questionable. Indeed, $C_2$ cannot be too large. Therefore, the gap between $C_1$ and $C_2$ cannot be considered to be filled.} *V. I. Nečaev* (RŽMat **1960** #84)

## P08-50 (41# 8379)

**Joly, Jean-René**

**Sommes de puissances $d$-ièmes dans un anneau commutatif.**

*Acta Arith.* **17** (1970), 37–114.

Let $A$ be a commutative ring with identity, let $d$ be a positive integer, let $A^d = \{a^d : a \in A\}$, let $A_d{}^+ = \{a_1{}^d + \cdots + a_n{}^d : n \geq 1, a_i \in A\}$, and let $A_d = \{e_1 a_1{}^d + \cdots + e_n a_n{}^d : n \geq 1, e_i = \pm 1, a_i \in A\}$. Relations between $A$ and its subring $A_d$ are discussed in the first five chapters of this paper. It is shown, for example, that if $K$ is an infinite field of characteristic $p$, $A$ is a $K$-algebra, and $d = p^r e$ where $r \geq 0$ and $(e, p) = 1$, then $A_d = A^{p^r}$. In Chapters 6 and 7 constants $u(d; A)$, $v(d; A)$, and $w(d; A)$ are investigated where $w(d; A)$ is the smallest positive integer $n$, if one exists, such that any element of $A_d{}^+$ is a sum of $n$th powers, $v(d; A)$ is the smallest $n$ such that any element of $A_d$ is expressible with the aid of $n$ $d$th powers, and, if $-1 \in A_d{}^+$, $u(d; A)$ is the smallest $n$ such that $-1$ is a sum of $n$ $d$th powers. *B. Garrison* (San Diego, Calif.)

## P08-51 (43# 6177)

**Zuparov, T. M.**

**A multidimensional additive problem with a growing number of terms. (Russian. Uzbek summary)**

*Izv. Akad. Nauk UzSSR Ser. Fiz.-Mat. Nauk* **13** (1969), *no.* 2, 21–27.

The author investigates the asymptotic behaviour of the number of $R_n(P, N)$ of representations of the vector $N = (N_1, N_2)$ in the form $x_1{}^s + x_2{}^s + \cdots + x_n{}^s = N$, where $x_k{}^s = (x_{1k}{}^s, x_{2k}{}^s)$, $k = 1, 2, \cdots, n$, $G = \{(x_{1k}, x_{2k}) | k = 1, 2, \cdots, n\}$ is a set of points in the plane with integral coordinates and $P$ is the number of points in the set $G$. The problem is solved by use of the multidimensional central limit theorem of probability theory. Consider the random vectors $\eta_k = (\xi_{1k}, \xi_{2k})$, $k = 1, 2, 3, \cdots$, with (equal) uniform distributions, such that $\eta_k$ takes the values $(x_{1k}{}^s, x_{2k}{}^s)$ with equal probabilities $1/P$. The set $G$ is now assumed to be in the form $G = \{(i, j) | \alpha_j \leq i \leq \beta_j, \alpha \leq j \leq \beta\}$ and the following notation is introduced: $P = \sum_{j=\alpha}^{\beta} p_j$, where $p_j = \beta_j - \alpha_j + 1$; $a_j = E(\xi_{j1})$; $\sigma_{ij} = E[(\xi_{i1} - a_i)(\xi_{j1} - a_j)]$; $\sigma_j{}^2 = \sigma_{jj}$; $\rho = \sigma_{12}/(\sigma_1 \sigma_2)$; $B_{nj} = \sqrt{(n)}\sigma_j$; $z_{N_j} = (N_j - na_j)/B_{nj}$; $i, j = 1, 2$; and $Q^*(t_1, t_2) = t_1{}^2 - 2\rho t_1 t_2 + t_2{}^2$.

After four lemmas the main result is proved: Let $G$ be the set of points specified above, with the additional property that $p \cdot q = a \cdot P \cdot (1 + o(1))$, where $1 < a < \infty$, $p = \max_\nu p_\nu$ and $q = \beta - \alpha + 1$. Then, for $s \geq 1$ and $n \to \infty$,

$$R_n(P, N) = (P^n/(2\pi\sigma_1\sigma_2 n\sqrt{(1-\rho^2)})) \times \exp\{-(1/(2(1-\rho^2)))Q^*(z_{N_1}, z_{N_2})\} + \Theta_s(P^n/(\sigma_1\sigma_2 n^{3/2})),$$

where $|\Theta_s| < C$, a constant independent of $P$ and $n$.

The assertion is easily generalised to any multidimensional case. *D. Ugrin-Šparac* (Zagreb)

# P12 SUMS OF DIFFERENT POWERS

See also reviews E24-119, P36-4, P36-37.

## P12-1 (2, 35b)

**Pillai, S. S. Waring's problem with indices $\geqq n$.** Proc. Indian Acad. Sci., Sect. A. **12**, 41–45 (1940).

Let $g_2(n)$ denote the least value of $s$ such that the equation $N = u_1 + u_2 + \cdots + u_s$, where each $u_i$ is of the form $x^m$ with $m \geqq n$, has a solution for every positive integer $N$. Miss Haberzetle has proved [Duke Math. J. **5**, 49–57 (1939)] that $g_2(n) = 2^n + k - 1$, where $k = [\log l/\log 2]$ and $l = [3^n/2^n]$, on the assumption that $n \geqq 9$ and $3^n - l2^n \leqq 2^n - k - 3$. Her proof is based on that given by Vinogradov [Ann. of Math. (2) **36**, 395–404 (1935)] for Waring's problem together with Dickson's method of ascent [Amer. J. Math. **58**, 521–529 (1936)]. Pillai notes that the problem under consideration is just made for representation in the scale of $j$ for certain values of $j$. For, if $x = c_0 + c_1 j + \cdots + c_i j^i$, then $xj^n = c_0 j^n + c_1 j^{n+1} + \cdots + c_i j^{n+i}$. With this method instead of Dickson's he proves that $g_2(n) = 2^n + k - 1$ for all $n \geqq 32$ and no other restrictions. *R. D. James* (Saskatoon, Sask.).

## P12-2 (10, 431f)

**Roth, K. F. Proof that almost all positive integers are sums of a square, a positive cube and a fourth power.** J. London Math. Soc. **24**, 4–13 (1949).

The author proves that almost all positive integers $u$ are representable in the form $u = x_1^2 + x_2^3 + x_3^4$, where $x_1$, $x_2$ and $x_3$ are positive integers. The method employs the Hardy-Littlewood technique of Farey dissection and is based on some results of Davenport and Heilbronn [Proc. London Math. Soc. (2) **43**, 73–104 (1937)]. A novel feature of the paper is its simplified treatment of the singular series. This is accomplished by the introduction of a function which excludes unwanted terms from the singular series.

*A. L. Whiteman* (Los Angeles, Calif.).

Referred to in P12-4, P12-12, P44-14.

## P12-3 (11, 162a)

**Freĭman, G. A. Solution of Waring's problem in a new form.** Uspehi Matem. Nauk (N.S.) **4**, no. 1(29), 193 (1949). (Russian)

The author announces the following result. Let $\{n_i\}$ be a sequence of positive integers such that $2 \leqq n_1 \leqq n_2 \leqq \cdots$; then a necessary and sufficient condition that every positive integer be expressible in the form $x_1^{n_i} + \cdots + x_r^{n_{i+r+1}}$, with $x_1, \cdots, x_r$ positive integers and $r$ not greater than some bound depending only on $n_i$, is that $\sum n_i^{-1}$ diverge.

*P. T. Bateman* (Princeton, N. J.).

## P12-4 (12, 80g)

**Halberstam, H. Representation of integers as sums of a square, a positive cube, and a fourth power of a prime.** J. London Math. Soc. **25**, 158–168 (1950).

This paper sharpens a result of K. F. Roth [J. London Math. Soc. **24**, 4–13 (1949); these Rev. **10**, 431]. It is proved that almost all positive integers $n$ are representable in the form $n=x_1^2+x_2^3+p^4$, where $x_1$ and $x_2$ are positive integers and $p$ is a prime. The method employs the technique of Farey dissection and follows the lines of Roth's analysis. Among the new tools required are some results of Hua [Quart. J. Math., Oxford Ser. (1) **9**, 68–80 (1938)] in additive prime number theory. *A. L. Whiteman.*

Citations: MR 10, 431f = P12-2.

## P12-5 (13, 14c)

**Roth, K. F. A problem in additive number theory.** Proc. London Math. Soc. (2) **53**, 381–395 (1951).

It is proved that almost all positive integers $u$ are representable in the form $u=\sum_{s=1}^{4} x_s^{s+1}$, where the $x_s$ are positive integers; the number of exceptions in the range $1 \leqq u \leqq n$ is $O(n^{1-1/10+\epsilon})$. The proof depends on the circle method. Further it is shown elementarily that the number of integers $u$ $(1 \leqq u \leqq n)$ representable in the form $\sum_{s=5}^{50} x_s^{s+1}$ is $> Cn^{46/51}$ $(C>0)$, and it follows that all large numbers $x$ can be written in the form $u=\sum_{s=1}^{50} x_s^{s+1}$. *N. G. de Bruijn* (Delft).

Referred to in P12-8, P12-17, P12-22.

## P12-6 (16, 676d)

**Bambah, R. P. Four squares and a $k$th power.** Quart. J. Math., Oxford Ser. (2) **5**, 191–202 (1954).

The author proves the following theorem: Let $\lambda_1, \cdots, \lambda_4, \mu$ be non-zero real numbers, not all of the same sign and such that at least one ratio $\lambda_r/\lambda_s$ is irrational; let $k$ be a positive integer. Then there exist arbitrarily large $P$ such that the inequalities $1 \leqq x_r \leqq P^k$, $r=1, \cdots, 4$; $1 \leqq x_5 \leqq P^2$; $|F(x)| = |\sum_{r=1}^{4} \lambda_r x_r^2 + \mu x_5^k| < 1$ have more than $\gamma P^{2k+2}$ solutions, where $\gamma$ is a positive number depending only on $\lambda_r$ and $\mu$. Similar results were obtained by Davenport and Heilbronn [J. London Math. Soc. **21**, 185–193 (1946); MR **8**, 565] and by Watson [Proc. London Math. Soc. (3) **3**, 170–181 (1953); MR **15**, 291]. The method of proof is that of Davenport and Heilbronn with some modification due to Watson. It consists of representing the number of solutions of the stated inequalities as integrals involving exponential sums, and then replacing the sums by integrals and estimating the error by the usual Hardy-Littlewood method. *R. D. James* (East Lansing, Mass.).

Citations: MR 8, 565e = D76-1; MR 15, 291g = D76-6.

## P12-7 (17, 827f)

**Sastry, S. On problems allied to the "easier Waring problem".** J. Sci. Res. Banaras Hindu Univ. **6** (1955–56), 87–89.

The author considers the form $u^4-v^4-r^3+s^3$ and shows that every odd number is of this form, even with $u=v+2$, and $s$ restricted to 1, 3, 5, 7. In fact

$$8x+1=(x+1)^4-(x-1)^4-(2x)^3+1^3,$$

$$8x+3=(x-2)^4-(x-4)^4-(2x-6)^3+3^3,$$

$$8x+5=(x-14)^4-(x-16)^4-(2x-30)^3+5^3,$$

$$8x+7=(x-41)^4-(x-43)^4-(2x-84)^3+7^3.$$

There are a few comments about the form $u^4+v^4-r^4-s^4$ and examples of small combinations of fifth powers. *D. H. Lehmer* (Berkeley, Calif.).

Referred to in P12-9.

## P12-8 (18, 793b)

**Sastry, S.; and Singh, Raghuraj. A problem in additive number theory.** J. Sci. Res. Banaras Hindu Univ. **6** (1955–56), 251–265.

The authors prove that almost all positive integers can be expressed as $x_1^2+x_2^3+x_3^3+x_4^6$, and that all large integers can be written as $x_1^2+x_2^3+x_3^3+x_4^6+\sum_{s=5}^{45} x_s^{s+1}$. The proofs closely follow those of K. F. Roth, who proved a similar result [Proc. London Math. Soc. (2) **53** (1951), 381–395; MR **13**, 14]. *N. G. de Bruijn.*

Citations: MR 13, 14c = P12-5.

## P12-9 (19, 15f)

**Sastry, S. Representation of numbers in the form $n=\pm x_1^{k_1} \pm x_2^{k_2} \pm \cdots \pm x_s^{k_s}$.** J. Sci. Res. Banaras Hindu Univ. **6** (1955–56), 214–216.

By purely algebraic methods the author proves that every positive integer is of the form

$$x^4-y^4-z^3+t^3+\varepsilon^3 \quad (\varepsilon=0, 1),$$

and also of the form

$$x^5+y^5-2z^5+w^5-r^3-s^3+t^3.$$

These results continue those of the author's previous paper [same J. **6** (1955–56), 87–89; MR **17**, 827]. *D. H. Lehmer* (Berkeley, Calif.).

Citations: MR 17, 827f = P12-7.

## P12-10 (22# 26)

**Birch, B. J. Note on a problem of Erdös.** Proc. Cambridge Philos. Soc. **55** (1959), 370–373.

The following result is proved: given any positive, coprime integers $p, q$, there exists a number $N(p, q)$ such that every $n > N(p, q)$ is expressible as a sum of the form

$$n = p^{a_1}q^{b_1}+p^{a_2}q^{b_2}+\cdots,$$

where the $(a_i, b_i)$ are distinct pairs of positive integers. The proof is self-contained and elementary, but far from trivial. *L. Mirsky* (Sheffield)

## P12-11 (22# 2591)

**Scourfield, E. J. A generalization of Waring's problem.** J. London Math. Soc. **35** (1960), 98–116.

If $\{n_i\}$ be a sequence of integers with $2 \leqq n_1 \leqq n_2 \leqq \cdots$, then it is here proved that for the existence of an integer $r=r(n_j)$ such that all sufficiently large integers $N$ are representable in the form

$$N = x_1^{n_j}+x_2^{n_{j+1}}+\cdots+x_r^{n_{j+r-1}}, \tag{1}$$

where the $x$'s are positive integers, it is necessary and sufficient that the infinite series

$$\frac{1}{n_1}+\frac{1}{n_2}+\frac{1}{n_3}+\cdots \tag{2}$$

be divergent. In the special case when $\{n_i\}$ is the arithmetic progression $\{n+(i-1)l\}$, with $n \geqq 12$, $l \geqq 1$, it is shown that the least value of $r(n, l)$ is $\leqq C(l)n^{4l+1}(\log n)^{2l}$, $C(l)$ being a certain positive function of $l$. The restriction $n \geqq 12$ has been introduced only for convenience. The necessity of condition (2) is demonstrated in a simple way. For the sufficiency, a variation of the Hardy-Littlewood method is used. *H. Gupta* (Chandigarh)

Referred to in P12-14, P12-22, P44-30.

## P12-12 (32# 4107)

**Schinzel, A.; Sierpiński, W.**

**Sur les puissances propres.**

*Bull. Soc. Roy. Sci. Liège* **34** (1965), 550–554.

A number of the form $a^b$, where $a$ and $b$ are integers $\geqq 2$, is called a proper power. The principal results of the paper are that (1) almost no positive integer is a sum of two or fewer proper powers; (2) almost all positive integers are sums of three proper powers; and (3) every sufficiently large integer is a sum of four proper powers.

The authors begin by noting that there are $[(x+1)/4]$ positive integers $n \leqq x$ of the form $4k+3$; of these, the number of proper powers is $\leqq (\sqrt{x}) \log x/\log 2$, and the number which are sums of two proper powers is $\leqq x^{5/6}(\log x/\log 2)^2$. Therefore, there are at least $f(x) = [(x+1)/4] - x^{5/6}(\log x/\log 2)^2 - (\sqrt{x}) \log x/\log 2$ such numbers which are not sums of two or fewer proper powers. Since $f(x) \to \infty$ as $x \to \infty$, this proves that there exist infinitely many positive integers which are not sums of two or fewer proper powers. A theorem of K. F. Roth [J. London Math. Soc. **24** (1949), 4–13; MR **10**, 431] states that almost all positive integers $n$ are of the form $n = a^2 + b^3 + c^4$, where $a \geqq 0$, $b \geqq 1$, and $c \geqq 0$. The authors show that the number of $n \leqq x$ of the form $a^2 + b^3$, or $a^2 + b^3 + 1$, or $a^2 + c^4 + 1$ is $o(x)$, so Roth's theorem can be sharpened to give statement (2). Since the number of $n \leqq x$ which are the sums of two squares is $o(x)$, these results imply (1). Finally, (3) is proved with the help of a theorem of the first author [Bull. Acad. Polon. Sci. Sér. Sci. Math. Astronom. Phys. **7** (1959), 307–310; MR **22** #2590].

*T. M. Apostol* (Pasadena, Calif.)

Citations: MR 10, 431f = P12-2; MR 22# 2590 = E24-76.

## P12-13 (32# 4108)

**Sinnadurai, J. St.-C. L.**

**Representation of integers as sums of six cubes and one square.**

*Quart. J. Math. Oxford Ser.* (2) **16** (1965), 289–296.

The author obtains, by the well-known circle method as modified by Vinogradov, an asymptotic formula for the number of representations of a positive integer as a sum of six cubes and a square. Results of Davenport and Heilbronn [Proc. London Math. Soc. (2) **43** (1937), 73–104] and Estermann [Sci. Rep. Nat. Tsing Hua Univ. Ser. A **5** (1948), 226–239; MR **11**, 234] are used.

*O. H. Körner* (Marburg)

Citations: MR 11, 234h = P08-14.

## P12-14 (34# 2551)

**Thanigasalam, K.**

**Asymptotic formula in a generalized Waring's problem.**

*Proc. Cambridge Philos. Soc.* **63** (1967), 87–98.

E. J. Scourfield [J. London Math. Soc. **35** (1960), 98–116; MR **22** #2591] proved the following generalization of Waring's problem. Given the sequence of integers $\{n_i\}$ satisfying $2 \leqq n_1 \leqq n_2 \leqq \cdots$, a necessary and sufficient condition for the existence of an integer $s = s(n_j)$ such that all sufficiently large integers $N$ are representable in the form (*) $N = x_1^{n_j} + x_2^{n_{j+1}} + \cdots + x_s^{n_{j+s-1}}$, where the $x$'s are positive integers, is that the infinite series $\sum_{i=1}^{\infty} n_i^{-1}$ be divergent. In deriving an asymptotic formula for the number of representations of $N$ in the form (*), the author overcomes a number of difficulties. Scourfield's method cannot be adopted since it depends on restricting some of the $x$'s to certain intervals. Furthermore, since the sequence $\{n_i\}$ is of a general nature, the methods used by I. M. Vinogradov [*The method of trigonometrical sums in the theory of numbers* (Russian), Trudy Mat. Inst. Steklov. **23** (1947); MR **10**, 599; English translation, Interscience, New York, 1954; MR **15**, 941] and Hua Lo-keng [Quart. J. Math. Oxford Ser. **20** (1949), 48–61; MR **10**, 597] to treat exponential sums in the classical Waring's problem cannot be translated directly. The author relies almost entirely on Weyl's inequality and Vinogradov's estimate for Weyl's sum. His results are analogous to but weaker than the results of Vinogradov and Hua in the classical case. Because of the complicated nature of the asymptotic formula it is not feasible to reproduce it here.

*A. L. Whiteman* (Los Angeles, Calif.)

Citations: MR 10, 597d = P08-11; MR 10, 599a = L02-2; MR 15, 941b = L02-3; MR 22# 2591 = P12-11.

## P12-15 (35# 5406)

**Dianand a, Palahenedi Hewage**

**On integers expressible as a sum of two powers.**

*Proc. Japan Acad.* **42** (1966), 1111–1113.

R. P. Bambah and S. Chowla [Proc. Nat. Inst. Sci. India **13** (1947), 101–103; MR **9**, 273] proved that for every $n \geqq 1$, there exist positive integers $x$ and $y$, such that for a certain fixed $c$, $n < x^2 + y^2 < n + cn^{1/4}$. Recently S. Uchiyama [J. Fac. Sci. Hokkaido Univ. Ser. I **18** (1964/65), 124–127; MR **30** #3071] has shown that this holds with $c = 2^{3/2}$.

Here the author, using methods similar to and as straightforward as those of Bambah and Chowla, and Uchiyama, proves the following theorem: For every $n \geqq 1$, and $f$ and $h \geqq 2$, there exist positive integers $x$ and $y$, such that $n < x^f + y^h < n + g(n)$, where $g(n) = N - (N^{1/h} - 1)^h$, $N = (n^{1/f} + 1)^f - n + 1$. In fact, if $m^f < n < (m+1)^f$, then the theorem holds with $x = m + 1$ or $m$ and $y = 1$ or $[(n - m^f)^{1/h}] + 1$. It is further shown that for large $n$, $g(n) \sim cn^a$, where $a = (1 - 1/f)(1 - 1/h)$, $c = hf^{1-1/h}$.

*H. Gupta* (Allahabad)

Citations: MR 9, 273a = E24-29; MR 30# 3071 = E20-71.

Referred to in P12-16.

## P12-16 (36# 5093)

**Diananda, Palahenedi Hewage**

**On integers expressible as a sum of two powers. II.**

*Proc. Japan Acad.* **43** (1967), 417–419.

The author proves the following theorem: There exists an $n_0$ such that for every $n \geqq n_0$, there are positive integers $x$ and $y$ satisfying $n < x^f + y^h < n + cn^a$, where $f$ and $h$ are integers such that $f \geqq h \geqq 2$, $a = (f-1)(h-1)/fh$ and $c = hf^{(h-1)/h}$. This is a refinement of a theorem proved by the author in an earlier paper [same Proc. **42** (1966), 1111–1113; MR **35** #5406].

*H. Gupta* (Allahabad)

Citations: MR 35# 5406 = P12-15.

Referred to in P12-19.

## P12-17 (36# 5096)

**Thanigasalam, K.**

**On additive number theory.**

*Acta Arith.* **13** (1967/68), 237–258.

The author obtains the following results: (1) Every sufficiently large positive integer $N$ is representable in the form $N = \sum_{s=1}^{35} x_s^{s+1}$, where the $x$'s are positive integers (this improves a result of K. F. Roth [Proc. London Math. Soc. (2) **53** (1951), 381–395; MR **13**, 14] where 50 terms are required). (2) Every sufficiently large positive integer $N$ is representable as the sum of 9 fourth powers and 7 fifth powers (cf. Davenport's well-known result that every sufficiently large positive integer is representable as the sum of 16 fourth powers).

*R. A. MacLeod* (Victoria, B.C.)

Citations: MR 13, 14c = P12-5.

Referred to in P12-22.

## P12-18 (38# 2110)

**Thanigasalam, K.**

**Note on the representation of integers as sums of certain powers.**

*Proc. Cambridge Philos. Soc.* **65** (1969), 445–446.

It is shown that if $N$ is a large natural number, and if $r(N)$ denotes the number of representations of $N$ in the form $N = x_1^2 + x_2^2 + x_3^3 + x_4^3 + x_5^4 + x_6^4$, where the $x$'s are natural numbers, then

$$r(N) = \Gamma^2(3/2)\Gamma^2(4/3)\Gamma^2(5/4)N^{7/6}\mathfrak{S}(N)/\Gamma(13/6) + O(N^{7/6-\eta}),$$

where $\mathfrak{S}(N)$ is the corresponding singular series satisfying $\mathfrak{S}(N) \gg 1$, and $\eta$ is a small positive constant.

*B. Garrison* (San Diego, Calif.)

**P12-19** **(40# 2625 )**

**Diananda, Palahenedi Hewage**

**On numbers expressible as a weighted sum of powers.**
*Proc. Japan Acad.* **44** (1968), 890–894.

The author proves the following theorem: There is $n_0$ such that for every real $n \geqq n_0$, there are positive integers $x_1, \cdots, x_k$ satisfying $n < a_1 x_1^{h_1} + \cdots + a_k x_k^{h_k} < n + cn^p$, where $a$'s are all positive, $h_1, h_2, \cdots, h_k$ each $>1$, $k>1$, and $c$ and $p$ are certain constants explicitly given in terms of $a$'s and $h$'s, and $a_1 h_1^{h_1} \leqq a_2 h_2^{h_2} \leqq \cdots \leqq a_k h_k^{h_k}$. This is a generalization of an earlier theorem of the author [same Proc. **43** (1967), 417–419; MR **36** #5093], and a refinement of a recent theorem of Mordell (to appear in *Abhandlungen aus Zahlentheorie und Analysis*, VEB Deutsch. Verlag Wissensch., Berlin, to appear).
*H. Gupta* (Allahabad)

Citations: MR 36# 5093 = P12-16.

**P12-20** **(41# 8331 )**

**Thanigasalam, K.**

**On sums of positive integral powers.**
*Math. Student* **37** (1969), 87–89.

The author gives an elementary proof of the theorem: Let $k, l$ be natural numbers satisfying $2 \leqq k < l$ and $N$ a large natural number. Then the number $U(N)$ of integers less than $N$ and representable in the form $x^k + y^l$ ($x, y \geqq 0$ and integral) satisfies $U(N) > cN^{1/k+1/l}$, $c = c(k, l)$ a positive constant.
*W. G. H. Schaal* (Marburg)

**P12-21** **(41# 8365 )**

**Mordell, L. J.**

**On numbers which can be expressed as a sum of powers.**
*Number Theory and Analysis (Papers in Honor of Edmund Landau), pp.* 217–221. *Plenum, New York,* 1969.

The author proves the following theorem: Given $n$, $a_i \geqq 1$, $l_i > 1$, $l_1 \leqq l_2 \leqq \cdots \leqq l_n$, the intervals $(r, r + c_n r^{e_n} + O(r^{(l_n-2)e_n/(l_n-1)}))$ contain points of the type $\sum_{i=1}^n a_i x_i^{l_i}$, $x_i$ integers. The constants $c_n, e_n$, which are functions of $a_i, l_i$, are explicitly given and the constant in $O$ depends only on the $a_i, l_i$. The theorem and proof generalise a theorem and its proof by the reviewer and S. Chowla about sums of two squares in the intervals $(r, r + 2\sqrt{2}r^{1/4} + o(r^{1/4}))$ [Proc. Nat. Inst. Sci. India **13** (1947), 101–103; MR **9**, 273].
*R. P. Bambah* (Chandigarh)

Citations: MR 9, 273a = E24-29.

**P12-22** **(42# 7615 )**

**Vaughan, R. C.**

**On the representation of numbers as sums of powers of natural numbers.**
*Proc. London Math. Soc.* (3) **21** (1970), 160–180.

The author proves that every sufficiently large natural number can be represented in the form $\sum_{s=1}^{30} r_s^{s+1}$, where the $r_s$ are natural numbers. The problem derives from an early result of K. F. Roth [same Proc. (2) **53** (1951), 381–395; MR **13**, 14], who showed that almost all positive integers are sums of a square, a cube and a fourth power. Roth pointed out at the time that a result of the above type, but with 50 in place of 30, can be simply derived from his "almost all" theorem. More recently K. Thanigasalam [Acta Arith. **13** (1967/68), 237–258; MR **36** #5096] reduced 50 to 35, and now the author has had to exercise considerable ingenuity with the circle method to achieve this further improvement. The result lies within the orbit of a general theorem of Freiman [see E. J. Scourfield, J. London Math. Soc. **35** (1960), 98–116; MR **22** #2591].
*H. Halberstam* (Nottingham)

Citations: MR 13, 14c = P12-5; MR 22# 2591 = P12-11; MR 36# 5096 = P12-17.

**P12-23** **(43# 6174 )**

**Thanigasalam, K.**

**On sums of positive integral powers.**
*Bull. Calcutta Math. Soc.* **62** (1970), 133–138.

Let $N, k_1, \cdots, k_s$ be positive integers such that $s \geqq 2$ and $k_j^{-1} > k_{j+1}^{-1} + \cdots + k_s^{-1}$ for $1 \leqq j \leqq s-1$. Further let $X_s(k_1, \cdots, k_s; N)$ and $P_s(k_1, \cdots, k_s; N)$ denote respectively the number of distinct positive integers less than $N$ that are expressible in the forms $x_1^{k_1} + \cdots + x_s^{k_s}$ and $p_1^{k_1} + \cdots + p_s^{k_s}$, where the $x$'s are non-negative integers and $p$'s are primes. It is proved that the orders of magnitude of $X_s$ and $P_s$ are respectively $N^{k_1^{-1}+k_2^{-1}+\cdots+k_s^{-1}}$ and $N^{k_1^{-1}+k_2^{-1}+\cdots+k_s^{-1}}(\log N)^{-s}$. For $s=2$, $k_1=k_2$, the same results follow from more general theorems by P. Erdős and K. Mahler [J. London Math. Soc. **13** (1938), 134–139] and by G. J. Rieger [Math. Z. **84** (1964), 137–142; MR **29** #83].
*R. Tijdeman* (Leiden)

Citations: MR 29# 83 = P44-29.

# P16 ADDITIVE QUESTIONS CONCERNING $r$-FREE NUMBERS

For the distribution of $r$-free numbers, see **N24**.

See also reviews N32-5, N32-13, N36-7, P36-2, P36-31, P36-53, P44-2, P44-6, P44-28, P48-2, P48-6, P52-14.

**P16-1** **(9, 80a)**

**Mirsky, L. On the number of representations of an integer as the sum of three $r$-free integers.** Proc. Cambridge Philos. Soc. **43**, 433–441 (1947).

The error term in Evelyn and Linfoot's formula for the number of representations of a number $n$ as the sum of three numbers not divisible by $r$th powers [Math. Z. **34**, 637–644 (1932), p. 638, (1.3), case $s=3$] is reduced from $O(n^{1+2/(r+1)+\epsilon})$ to $O(n^{1+3/(2r+1)+\epsilon})$.
*T. Estermann* (London).

**P16-2** **(9, 80b)**

**Mirsky, L. Note on an asymptotic formula connected with $r$-free integers.** Quart. J. Math., Oxford Ser. **18**, 178–182 (1947).

Let $k_1, \cdots, k_s$ be any integers. Denote by $F(x)$ the number of integers $n \leqq x$ such that all the integers $n+k_1$, $n+k_2$, $\cdots$, $n+k_s$ are $r$-power-free (i.e., not divisible by the $r$th power of any integer). The author proves in an elementary way that $F(x) = cx + O(x^{2/(r+1)+\epsilon})$. The constant $c$ is given by a complicated expression.
*P. Erdös* (Syracuse, N. Y.).

Referred to in P16-6, P16-7, P16-8, P16-9, P16-27.

**P16-3** **(9, 499c)**

**Roth, K. F. A theorem involving squarefree numbers.** J. London Math. Soc. **22** (1947), 231–237 (1948).

The author proves that every large integer $n$ may be represented as the sum of a squarefree number and the square of a squarefree number. He derives the following asymptotic formula for the number $G(n)$ of such representations:

$$G(n) = 6\pi^{-2} n^{1/2} \left\{ \prod_{p^2 | n} \left(1 - \frac{1}{p+1}\right) \right\} \left\{ \prod{}' \left(1 - \frac{v(n, p^2)}{p^2 - 1}\right) \right\} + O(n^{1/3+\epsilon}),$$

where $\prod'$ is over $p$ which do not divide $n$ and

$$v(n, p^2) = \begin{cases} 1 + (n|p), & p > 2, \\ 1 + (-1)^{(n-1)/2}, & p = 2, \end{cases}$$

and where $(n|p)$ denotes the Legendre symbol. A similar theorem, giving an estimation of the number $H(n)$ of square-free numbers not exceeding $n$ that are of the form $z^2+k$, where $k$ is fixed and $z$ squarefree, is stated. The method is elementary and was suggested by some earlier work of Estermann on the representations of an integer as the sum of a square and a squarefree number [Math. Ann. **105**, 653–662 (1931)]. *A. L. Whiteman* (Los Angeles, Calif.).

Referred to in P16-13, P16-14, P16-23.

**P16-4** **(9, 571d)**

**Mirsky, L. The additive properties of integers of a certain class.** Duke Math. J. **15**, 513–533 (1948).

Let **A** be any given class of integers greater than 1 and such that any two integers belonging to **A** are coprime. A number $n$ will be called **A**-free if it is not divisible by any $a$ of **A**. Let $Q(n, \mathbf{A}, s)=Q(n)$ denote the number of representations of $n$ (order being relevant) as the sum of $s$ **A**-free integers. The author obtains an asymptotic formula for $Q(n)$ when $\sum_a 1/a$ is convergent, and gives an upper estimate for $Q(n)$ when $\sum_a 1/a$ is divergent.

*W. H. Simons* (Vancouver, B. C.).

**P16-5** **(10, 105a)**

**Mirsky, L. On a theorem in the additive theory of numbers due to Evelyn and Linfoot.** Proc. Cambridge Philos. Soc. **44**, 305–312 (1948).

The error term $O(n^{s-2+s/[(s-1)r+1]+\epsilon})$ is obtained in place of the $O(n^{s-2+1/r+(r-1)/rs+\epsilon})$ in the result of Evelyn and Linfoot for the number of representations of $n$ as the sum of $s$ $r$-free integers which are congruent to $k(\text{mod } q)$ [Quart. J. Math., Oxford Ser. **4**, 309–314 (1933)]. This is an improvement for $s\geqq 3$. *W. H. Simons* (Vancouver, B. C.).

**P16-6** **(10, 182b)**

**Mirsky, L. On a problem in the theory of numbers.** Simon Stevin **26**, 25–27 (1948).

The following theorem is stated: If $r, s, k_1, \cdots, k_s, q_1, \cdots, q_s$ are given positive integers and $N(x)$ is the number of positive integers $n$ not exceeding $x$ such that all the integers $q_1n+k_1, \cdots, q_sn+k_s$ are $r$th-power-free, then

$$N(x)=Ax+O(x^{2/(r+1)+\epsilon}),$$

where $A$ is a constant depending on the given parameters (which may be given by means of an infinite series or an infinite product). The author has given a proof earlier [Quart. J. Math., Oxford Ser. **18**, 178–182 (1947); these Rev. **9**, 80] of the special case in which $q_1=\cdots=q_s=1$ and remarks in the present paper that the extension of this proof to the general case is quite straightforward. However, the main purpose of this paper is to give a simple direct proof of the fact that lim inf $\{N(x)/x\}>0$ (and thus $A>0$) unless $N(x)$ is zero for all $x$. *P. T. Bateman* (Princeton, N. J.).

Citations: MR 9, 80b = P16-2.

**P16-7** **(10, 431d)**

**Mirsky, L. Arithmetical pattern problems relating to divisibility by $r$th powers.** Proc. London Math. Soc. (2) **50**, 497–508 (1949).

Let $a_1, \cdots, a_l; b_1, \cdots, b_m$ be any distinct positive integers. Denote by $H(x)=H_r(x; a_1, \cdots, a_l; b_1, \cdots, b_m)$ the number of integers $n$ such that $n+a_1, \cdots, n+a_l, n+b_1, \cdots, n+b_m$ are positive and do not exceed $x$, and such that the first $l$ are $r$-free while the remaining $m$ are not. A complicated asymptotic expression, for $x\to\infty$, is obtained for $H(x)$ and applied to the special case of the study of the frequency of systems of consecutive $r$-free numbers and of $r$-numbers. The orders of the error terms in the results of this paper have been reduced by the author in a later paper which has already been published [Quart. J. Math., Oxford Ser. **18**, 178–182 (1947); these Rev. **9**, 80]. *W. H. Simons.*

Citations: MR 9, 80b = P16-2.

**P16-8** **(11, 14f)**

**Mirsky, L. Generalizations of a problem of Pillai.** Proc. Roy. Soc. Edinburgh. Sect. A. **62**, 460–469 (1949).

Pillai [J. Indian Math. Soc. (N.S.) **2**, 116–118 (1936)] gave an asymptotic formula for the number of positive integers $n\leqq x$ such that $n+k_1, \cdots, n+k_s$ are square-free, $k_1, \cdots, k_s$ being fixed distinct positive integers. The corresponding problem for $r$-free integers was considered by Mirsky [Quart. J. Math., Oxford Ser. **18**, 178–182 (1947); these Rev. **9**, 80]. In the present paper the problem of Pillai is generalized as follows. Let **A** be a given set of integers. Numbers of the form $a_1^{t_1}\cdots a_h^{t_h}$, where $a_1, \cdots, a_h \varepsilon \mathbf{A}$, will be called $c$-numbers. Let $C_1, \cdots, C_s$ be given sets of $c$-numbers and denote by $\mathfrak{s}(n)$ the greatest $c$-number dividing $n$. Further, let **M** be the set of integers $n$ for which $\mathfrak{s}(n+k_1)\varepsilon C_1, \cdots, \mathfrak{s}(n+k_s)\varepsilon C_s$ and $M(x)$ be the number of integers $n\leqq x$ belonging to **M**. An asymptotic formula, for $x\to\infty$, is obtained for $M(x)$ and the density of **M** is discussed under various assumptions regarding the integers of $A$. When each $C_i$ consists of the single number 1, **M** consists of the integers $n$ such that $n+k_1, \cdots, n+k_s$ are **A**-free (i.e., not divisible by any integer of **A**). *W. H. Simons.*

Citations: MR 9, 80b = P16-2.

**P16-9** **(11, 161e)**

**Mirsky, L. On the frequency of pairs of square-free numbers with a given difference.** Bull. Amer. Math. Soc. **55**, 936–939 (1949).

Let $f(x)$ denote the number of pairs of square-free integers with fixed difference $k$ such that the smaller of the two does not exceed $x$. The author proves that

$$(*) \qquad f(x)=Kx+O(x^{\frac{2}{3}}\log^{\frac{4}{3}} x),$$

where $K$ is a positive constant which can be given explicitly in terms of $k$. An earlier result of the author [Quart. J. Math., Oxford Ser. **18**, 178–182 (1947); these Rev. **9**, 80] gives (*) only with an error term $O(x^{\frac{2}{3}+\epsilon})$. He remarks that a recent paper of F. V. Atkinson and Cherwell [ibid. **20**, 65–79 (1949); these Rev. **11**, 15] enables him to obtain a generalization of (*) for pairs of $r$th-power-free integers with given difference. *P. T. Bateman* (Princeton, N. J.).

Citations: MR 9, 80b = P16-2; MR 11, 15b = N36-8.

**P16-10** **(11, 234a)**

**Shapiro, Harold N. Powerfree integers represented by linear forms.** Duke Math. J. **16**, 601–607 (1949).

Consider the set $\mathfrak{U}_k$ of $k$-dimensional vectors with integer components. For two such vectors $X_1, X_2$ we write $X_1\equiv X_2$ (mod $\Delta$) if the congruence holds componentwise. A property $P$ of vectors in $\mathfrak{U}_k$ is called periodic if there exists some integer $\Delta>0$ such that $X_1\equiv X_2$ (mod $\Delta$) implies that either both $X_1$ and $X_2$ possess $P$ or that neither does so. The main theorem proved by the author is then as follows. Let $f_1, \cdots, f_k$ be linear polynomials, $P$ a periodic property in $\mathfrak{U}_k$, and $Q_P(N)$ the number of integers $x\leqq N$ for which the vector $(f_1(x), \cdots, f_k(x))$ possesses $P$ and none of $f_1(x), \cdots, f_k(x)$ is divisible by the $r$th power of any prime. Then either $Q_P(N)$ vanishes identically, or else $Q_P(N)=AN+O(N^{2/(r+1)+\epsilon})$, where $A>0$. In addition, necessary and sufficient conditions are obtained in order that $Q_P(N)$ should not vanish identically, and a special case involving products of linear polynomials is considered. *L. Mirsky* (Sheffield).

**P16-11** **(11, 581f)**

**Mirsky, L. Generalization of some results of Evelyn-Linfoot and Page.** Nieuw Arch. Wiskunde (2) **23**, 111–116 (1950).

Let $n, q, k, s, r_1, \cdots, r_s$ be integers such that $n\geqq 1$, $1\leqq k\leqq q$, $s\geqq 2$, $2\leqq r_1\leqq\cdots\leqq r_s$, and let $Q(n)$ denote the number of representations of $n$ in the form $n=n_1+\cdots+n_s$, where the $n_1, \cdots, n_s$ are $r_1$-free, $\cdots$, $r_s$-free respectively, and $n_1 \equiv \cdots \equiv n_s \equiv k \pmod q$. An asymptotic formula, for $n \to \infty$, is obtained for $Q(n)$. Also conditions are given under which $Q(n)=0$. *W. H. Simons* (Kingston, Ont.).

## P16-12 (13, 14b)

**Estermann, T. On sums of squares of square-free numbers.** Proc. London Math. Soc. (2) **53**, 125–137 (1951).

In this paper the author considers the problem of the representation of numbers as sums of squares of square-free numbers, and by an application of the circle-method of Hardy and Littlewood establishes the following results. (1) If $s \geqq 5$ and $n$ is a sufficiently large number for which the congruence $m_1^2+m_2^2+\cdots+m_s^2 \equiv n \pmod{32}$ is soluble in integers $m_1, m_2, \cdots, m_s$ not divisible by 4, then $n$ is representable as a sum of $s$ squares of square-free numbers. (2) If $s \geqq 8$, then any sufficiently large number is representable as a sum of $s$ squares of square-free numbers. Result (2) is best possible in the sense that not all sufficiently large numbers can be represented as sums of 7 squares of square-free numbers. *L. Mirsky* (Bristol).

## P16-13 (13, 914c)

**Cugiani, Marco. Sull'aritmetica additiva dei numeri liberi da potenze.** Rivista Mat. Univ. Parma **2**, 403–416 (1951).

Let $E(N)$ denote the number of representations of an integer $N$ in the form $N=x^g+l_t$, where $x$ is a square-free integer and $l$ is a $t$th power-free integer. In this paper the following extension of a theorem of Roth [J. London Math. Soc. **22**, 231–237 (1948); these Rev. **9**, 499] is proved. If $g \geqq 2$ is fixed and $t=g$, then there exist positive constants $\gamma_1, \gamma_2, \gamma_3$ such that (1) $E(N)>\gamma_1 N^{1/g}(\log\log N)^{-1}$ for $N$ sufficiently large; (2) $E(N)<\gamma_2 N^{1/g}(\log\log N)^{-1}$ for infinitely many values of $N$; (3) $E(N)>\gamma_3 N^{1/g}$ for infinitely many values of $N$. The methods employed are extensions in various directions of methods used by a number of writers among whom the following two may be cited: Ricci [Tôhoku Math. J. **41**, 20–26 (1935)] and Rao [Proc. Indian Acad. Sci., Sect. A. **11**, 429–436 (1940); these Rev. **2**, 42].

*A. L. Whiteman* (Princeton, N. J.).

Citations: MR 2, 42d = P44-6; MR 9, 499c = P16-3.
Referred to in P16-16.

## P16-14 (14, 356c)

**Cugiani, Marco. Sulla rappresentazione degli interi come somme di una potenza e di un numero libero da potenze.** Ann. Mat. Pura Appl. (4) **33**, 135–143 (1952).

Theorem A: If $g \geqq 2$ is a fixed integer and $t=g$, then a number $N_0$ can be determined such that every positive integer $N \geqq N_0$ can be represented in the form $N=x^g+l_t$, where $(x, N)=1$ and $l_t$ is a $t$th power-free integer. Let $E(N)$ denote the number of such representations. Then there exist positive constants $\gamma_1, \gamma_2, \gamma_3$ such that

(a) $$E(N)>\gamma_1 N^{1/g}(\log\log N)^{-1}$$

for $N \geqq N_0$; (b) $E(N)<\gamma_2 N^{1/g}(\log\log N)^{-1}$ for infinitely many values of $N$; (c) $E(N)>\gamma_3 N^{1/g}$ for infinitely many values of $N$. Theorem B: Let $F(x)$ be an integral-valued polynomial of degree $g \geqq 2$ and put $t \geqq g$. Then a number $N_0$ can be determined such that every $N \geqq N_0$ can be represented in the form $N=F(x)+l_t$ with $F(x)>0$. Let $E(N)$ denote the number of such representations. Then there exists a positive constant $\gamma_4$ such that $E(N)>\gamma_4 N^{1/g}(\log\log N)^{1-g}$ for $N \geqq N_0$. Theorems A and B generalize in various directions the theorems of a number of writers among whom the following two may be cited: Rao [Proc. Indian Acad. Sci., Sect. A. **11**, 429–436 (1940); these Rev. **2**, 42] and Roth [J. London Math. Soc. **22**, 231–237 (1947); these Rev. **9**, 499]. The author's methods are related to those used by Ricci [Tôhoku Math. J. **41**, 20–26 (1935)] to treat certain representation problems in additive number theory.

*A. L. Whiteman* (Princeton, N. J.).

Citations: MR 2, 42d = P44-6; MR 9, 499c = P16-3.
Referred to in P16-15, P16-16.

## P16-15 (15, 603c)

**Cugiani, Marco. Sui valori di un polinómio che risultano liberi da potenze.** Ann. Mat. Pura Appl. (4) **35**, 291–298 (1953).

Let $g$ be a fixed integer greater than unity. The author has previously shown [same Ann. (4) **33**, 135–143 (1952); these Rev. **14**, 356] that every sufficiently large integer $N$ can be represented in the form $N=x^g+l_g$, where $x$ is a positive integer and $l_g$ is a $g$th-power-free integer. In the present paper he proves that if $E(N)$ denotes the number of such representations, then

$$E(N) \sim N^{1/g} \prod_{p^g \mid N}\left(1-\frac{1}{p}\right) \prod_{p \nmid N}\left(1-\frac{\nu_N(p^g)}{p^g}\right),$$

where $\nu_N(m)$ is the number of solutions of the congruence $x^g \equiv N \pmod m$. In the case $g=2$ this result reduces to a formula of Estermann [Math. Ann. **105**, 653–662 (1931)]. The author also proves an analogous theorem for the function $E'(N)$ in which the representations involved are subject to the additional restriction that $(x, N)=1$. The main tool employed is the method of Viggo Brun.

*A. L. Whiteman* (Princeton, N. J.).

Citations: MR 14, 356c = P16-14.

## P16-16 (18, 382c)

**Cugiani, Marco. Relazione su un gruppo di ricerche di aritmetica additiva dei numeri liberi da potenze.** Boll. Un. Mat. Ital. (3) **11** (1956), 359–367.

The problem of the number $E(g, t, N)$ of representations of the positive integer $N$ as a sum of a $g$th power and a number free of $t$th powers and generalizations of this problem are given an historical survey. Methods of attack are briefly mentioned. [See also Cugiani, Riv. Mat. Univ. Parma **2** (1951), 403–416; Ann. Mat. Pura Appl. (4) **33** (1952), 135–143; MR **13**, 914; **14**, 356.]

*D. H. Lehmer* (Berkeley, Calif.).

Citations: MR 13, 914c = P16-13; MR 14, 356c = P16-14.

## P16-17 (22# 12086)

**Eda, Yoshikazu. Einige Sätze über $\lambda$-freie Zahlen.** Osaka Math. J. **12** (1960), 39–60.

It is assumed that $\lambda$ and $s$ are integers, $\lambda \geqq 3$, $s \geqq 5$. A $\lambda$-free number is a natural number not divisible by the $\lambda$th power of any integer greater than 1. The author obtains an asymptotic formula for the number of representations of a natural number as a sum of $s$ squares of $\lambda$-free numbers. He also determines which sufficiently large natural numbers have such representations. {Correction: Delete the word 'Professor' before the reviewer's name.} *T. Estermann* (London)

## P16-18 (24# A101)

**Subhankulov, M. A.; Muhtarov, S. N.**

**Representation of a number as a sum of two squarefree numbers. (Russian)**

*Izv. Akad. Nauk UzSSR Ser. Fiz.-Mat.* **1960**, *no.* 4, 3–10.

If $I(N)$ is the number of representations of $N$ as a sum of two square-free numbers, we have for large $N$

$$(1)\quad I(N) = \frac{6N}{\pi^2} \prod_p \left(\frac{p^2-2}{p^2-1}\right) \prod_{p \mid N_2} \left(\frac{p^2-1}{p^2-2}\right) + O(N^{2/3+\varepsilon}).$$

Here $N = N_1N_2$, $(N_1, N_2) = 1$ and $N_1$ is the "square-free part" of $N$. The proof is based on a lemma which gives an estimate for the number of square-free numbers in an arithmetic progression and not exceeding a large number. The method is elementary but gives a sharp result. {In the formula for $I(N)$ on page 7, read $p^2-1$ for $p-1$ in the denominator of the first product, as corrected in (1) above. There are other minor misprints. While the formula (1) is on page 7, $N_2$ is not defined till page 10.}

*S. Chowla* (Boulder, Colo.)

Referred to in P16-25.

## P16-19 (24# A716)

**Subhankulov, M. A.; Moĭšezon, B. G.**

**The representation of a number as a sum of a power and a number free of powers. (Russian. Uzbek summary)**

*Izv. Akad. Nauk UzSSR Ser. Fiz.-Mat.* **1960**, *no.* 6, 3–16.

Given integers $n>1$, $k>1$, $r>1$, let $I(n, r, k)$ denote the number of representations of $n$ in the form $n = x^r + Q_k$, where $Q_k$ is a positive integer not divisible by the $k$th power of any prime. The authors derive the asymptotic formula

$$I(n, r, k) = n^{1/r} \prod_p \left(1 - \frac{\nu(n, p^k, r)}{p^k}\right) + O(n^\alpha)$$

where $\alpha = r^{-1} - \max(1/kr, 1/r^2) + \varepsilon$ and $\nu(n, d, r)$ is the number of solutions of the congruence $x^r \equiv n \pmod d$.

*T. M. Apostol* (Pasadena, Calif.)

## P16-20 (26# 3644)

**Cohen, Eckford**

**Simultaneous binary compositions involving pairs of relatively $k$-free integers.**

*Nederl. Akad. Wetensch. Proc. Ser. A* **66** = *Indag. Math.* **25** (1963), 41–46.

The main result is an asymptotic formula for the number of solutions of the simultaneous equations $m = x_1 + y_1$, $n = x_2 + y_2$ in natural numbers $x_1$, $y_1$, $x_2$, $y_2$ such that neither $(x_1, x_2)$ nor $(y_1, y_2)$ is divisible by the $k$th power of any integer greater than 1. *T. Estermann* (London)

## P16-21 (26# 6140)

**Schwarz, Wolfgang**

**Zur Darstellung einer Zahl als Summe einer $k$-ten Potenz einer potenzfreien Zahl und einer $g$-ten potenzfreien Zahl.**

*Arch. Math.* **14** (1963), 105–115.

Let $h$, $g$ and $k$ be integers, $h \geqq 2$, $g \geqq 2$ and $g \geqq k \geqq 1$. The author proves that every sufficiently large natural number can be represented in the form $q + x^k$, where $q$ and $x$ are natural numbers, $q$ not divisible by $g$th powers, and $x$ not divisible by $h$th powers. He obtains an asymptotic formula for the number of such representations.

*T. Estermann* (London)

## P16-22 (27# 2479)

**Rieger, G. J.**

**Einige Sätze über $k$-freie Zahlen.**

*Math. Nachr.* **25** (1963), 159–168.

Asymptotic formulae for functions called $G(n; \lambda, \alpha, \beta)$ and $Q_{k,l}(n; \lambda, \alpha, \beta)$. The former is the number of representations of $n$ as $q + z^2$, where $q$ and $z$ are natural numbers, $q$ square-free, and $|q - \lambda n| \leqq \beta n^\alpha$. The latter is the number of representations of $n$ as $a + b$, where $a$ and $b$ are natural numbers, not divisible by $k$th and $l$th powers, respectively, and $|a - \lambda n| \leqq \beta n^\alpha$. *T. Estermann* (London)

## P16-23 (27# 3592)

**Rieger, G. J.**

**Einige Ergebnisse mit $k$-freien Zahlen.**

*Arch. Math.* **14** (1963), 289–296.

K. F. Roth [J. London Math. Soc. **22** (1947), 231–237; MR **9**, 499] had obtained an asymptotic formula for the number of representations of a large integer $n$ as the sum of a square-free number and the square of a square-free number. The present paper is concerned with the discussion of this representation in which the summands are restricted to small intervals. More precisely, let $H(n; \lambda, \alpha, \beta)$ denote the number of representations of $n$ in the form $n = q + z^2$, where $q$ and $z$ are square-free and $|q - \lambda n| < \beta n^\alpha$. An asymptotic formula, too long to quote here, is obtained for $H(n; \lambda, \alpha, \beta)$, and as one of several consequences it is shown that, if $0 < \lambda < 1$, $\alpha > \frac{5}{6}$, $\beta > 0$, then the above representation is always possible provided that $n$ exceeds a certain bound depending on $\lambda$, $\alpha$, and $\beta$. An analogous investigation is also undertaken with regard to the number $T(n; \lambda, \alpha, \beta)$ of representations of $n$ in the form $n = p + a$, where $p$ is a prime number, $a$ is a $k$-free number, and $\lambda n < p \leqq \lambda n + \beta n^\alpha$. *L. Mirsky* (Sheffield)

Citations: MR 9, 499c = P16-3.

## P16-24 (28# 3958)

**Sierpiński, W.**

**Sur une propriété des nombres naturels.**

*Elem. Math.* **19** (1964), 27–29.

L'auteur donne une démonstration directe de la proposition suivante; tout nombre naturel est d'une infinité de manières une différence de deux nombres naturels dépourvus de diviseurs premiers carrés. L'auteur remarque que cette proposition est contenue dans le théorème de T. Nagell [Abh. Math. Sem. Hamburg Univ. **1** (1922), 179–194, p. 188]. *A. Schinzel* (Columbus, Ohio)

## P16-25 (31# 143)

**Cohen, Eckford**

**The number of representations of an integer as a sum of two square-free numbers.**

*Duke Math. J.* **32** (1965), 181–185.

It has been proved by Estermann [J. London Math. Soc. **6** (1931), 37–40] and Subhankulov and Muhtarov [Izv. Akad. Nauk UzSSR Ser. Fiz.-Mat. (**1960**), no. 4, 3–10; MR **24** #A101] that the number of representations of an integer $n$ as a sum of two square-free integers is $cn\rho(n) + O(n^{2/3+\varepsilon})$ for each $\varepsilon > 0$, where $c = \prod_p (1 - 2/p^2)$, $\rho(n) = \prod_{p^2 | n} (1 + 1/(p^2 - 2))$. In the present paper the error term is improved to $O(n^{2/3} \log^2 n)$. The method is elementary, and is based on a uniform estimate for the number of square-free integers not exceeding a given bound and contained in a specified residue class.

*W. J. LeVeque* (Ann Arbor, Mich.)

Citations: MR 24# A101 = P16-18.

## P16-26 (31# 5853)

**Lursmanašvili, A. P.**

**On the representation of natural numbers as sums of squares of squarefree numbers and on the number of integral points with squarefree coordinates in a sphere. (Russian. Georgian summary)**

*Akad. Nauk Gruzin. SSR Trudy Tbiliss. Mat. Inst. Razmadze* **29** (1963), 37–46 (1964).

Let $R_{k,s}(n)$ denote the number of representations of the positive integer $n$ as $k$ squares, $n = m_1^2 + m_2^2 + \cdots + m_k^2$, where $m_{k-s+1}, m_{k-s+2}, \cdots, m_k$ are squarefree $(0 \leqq s \leqq k)$.

The author proves that, for $k \geqq 8$,

$$R_{k,s}(n) = \frac{\pi^{k/2}}{\Gamma(k/2)}\left(\frac{6}{\pi^2}\right)^s \sigma(n, k, s)n^{k/2-1} + O(n^{k/2-5/4}),$$

where $\sigma(n, k, s)$ is a certain "singular series" involving Gauss sums, and is positive. The induction argument used in the proof appears to be valid, not for all $s \leqq k$, as stated, but only for $0 \leqq s < k-4$. A corresponding estimate for $\sum_{n \leqq x} R_{k,s}(n)$ is given. *R. A. Rankin* (Glasgow)

## P16-27 (33# 4028 )

**Onishi, H.**

**The number of positive integers $n \leqq N$ such that $n, n+a_2, n+a_3, \ldots, n+a_r$ are all square-free.**

*J. London Math. Soc.* **41** (1966), 138–140.

The result of this paper was anticipated by L. Mirsky [Quart. J. Math. Oxford Ser. **18** (1947), 178–182; MR **9**, 80]. Mirsky had a better error term and a more elementary method. His paper included the analogous problem for $r$-free integers with $r > 2$, a case also indicated (but not treated in detail) by the author.

*N. G. de Bruijn* (Eindhoven)

Citations: MR 9, 80b = P16-2.

## P16-28 (37# 1326 )

**McDonagh, Sean**

**An estimate for trigonometrical sums over square-free integers with a constant number of prime factors.**

*Proc. Edinburgh Math. Soc.* (2) **15** (1966/67), 249–255.

I. M. Vinogradov's estimate for trigonometrical sums of the form $\sum e(\alpha p^k)$ is carried over to sums of the type $\sum e(\alpha \pi_r^{\ k})$, where $\pi_r$ denotes square-free numbers with $r$ prime factors. From this result, following Vinogradov's method and replacing the Siegel-Walfisz theorem by a result of the reviewer's, one can derive asymptotic expressions for the number of representations in the form $N = \pi_{r_1}^{\ k} + \pi_{r_2}^{\ k} + \cdots + \pi_{r_s}^{\ k}$. The author gives an explicit result for the case $k=1$, $s=3$, thus generalizing Vinogradov's theorem ($r_1 = r_2 = r_3 = 1$) and the reviewer's result ($r_3 = 2$) [J. Reine Angew. Math. **192** (1953), 180–203; MR **15**, 603]. *H.-E. Richert* (Marburg)

Citations: MR 15, 603b = N24-19.

## P16-29 (42# 4514 )

**Lursmanašvili, A. P.**

**The representation of numbers by sums of square integers and square-free integers. (Russian. Georgian summary)**

*Thbilis. Sahelmç. Univ. Šrom. Mekh.-Math. Mĕcn. Ser.* **129** (1968), 299–318.

Let $S(h, q) = \sum_{a \bmod q} \exp(2\pi i h a^2/q)$, where $(h/N)$ denotes the Jacobi symbol for $(h, N)=1$, $N>1$. Let $C(h, q) = \sum_{t=1}^{\infty} (\mu(t)/t^2) S(ht^4, q)$ and

$$R_{k,s}(n) = \sum_{a_1^2+\cdots+a_{k-s}^2+r_1^{\ 2}+\cdots+r_s^{\ 2}=n} 1$$

denote the number of representations of a natural number $n$ as the sum of $k-s$ squares of rational integers and $s$ squares of square-free integers. If $n \geqq 6$ then for $0 \leqq s \leqq k$ we have $R_{k,s}(n) = (\pi^{k/2}/\Gamma(k/2))\sigma(n, k, s)n^{k/2-1} + O(n^{\lambda(k)})$, where $\sigma(n, k, s) = \sum_{q=1}^{\infty} A_k(q, n, s)$,

$$A_k = \sum_{h \bmod q} (s(h, q)/q)^{k-s} (C(h, q)/q)^s \exp(-2\pi i n h/q),$$

$\lambda(k) = k/2 - 5/4$ if $k \geqq 7$ and $\lambda(k) = k/2 - 5/4 + \varepsilon$ if $k=6$. If $k \geqq 6$, $0 < s < k$, then $\sigma(n, k, s) > 0$ and $\chi(2) > 0$, where $\chi(2) = (\pi^2/6)^s \cdot \sum_{l=0}^{5} A_k(2^l, n, s)$. If $k \geqq 6$ and $p$ is an odd prime, then for $p > 2$ the infinite product $\prod_{p>2} \chi(2)$ is convergent and $\prod_{p>2} \chi(2) > 0$. Here

$$\chi(p) = (\pi^2/6)^s \sum_{l=0}^{3} A_k(p^l, n, s).$$

*A. Rotkiewicz* (Warsaw)

# P20 LATTICE POINT PROBLEMS: CIRCLE AND SPHERE PROBLEMS

See also reviews E16-12, E44-8, E44-18, H05-52, L99-4, M40-16, M40-49, N36-4, N36-20, N36-32, N36-52, N40-3, N40-21, N40-35, N40-67, N48-28, P02-10, P24-4, P24-9, P28-17, P28-64, P28-72, P28-79, P28-87.

## P20-1 (2, 350f)

**Wintner, Aurel. On the lattice problem of Gauss.** Amer. J. Math. **63**, 619–627 (1941).

Let $r(n)$ be the number of solutions of the equation $x^2+y^2=n$ and let furthermore $R(x) = \sum_{n \leqq x} r(n)$ $(x \geqq 1)$ and $\bar{R}(x) = \frac{1}{2}\{R(x-0)+R(x+0)\}$. It is proved that the function $Q(t) = (\bar{R}(t^2) - \pi t^2)/t^{\frac{1}{2}}$ is almost periodic ($B^2$) for $\infty > t \geqq 1$, having $\pi^{-1}\sum n^{-\frac{3}{4}} r(n) \sin(2\pi n^{\frac{1}{2}} t - \pi/4)$ as its Fourier series. Parseval's relation $M\{Q^2(t)\} = (2\pi)^{-1}\sum r(n)^2/n^{\frac{3}{2}}$ follows at once. The paper ends with some remarks on Waring's problem. *M. Kac* (Ithaca, N. Y.).

Referred to in P20-6.

## P20-2 (4, 190e)

**Hua, Loo-keng. The lattice-points in a circle.** Quart. J. Math., Oxford Ser. **13**, 18–29 (1942).

Let the number $R(x)$ of integer pairs $u, v$ such that $u^2+v^2 \leqq x$ be $\pi x + O(x^\vartheta)$. Titchmarsh [Proc. London Math. Soc. (2) **38**, 96–115 (1934)] obtained $\vartheta \leqq 15/46$. Vinogradow [Bull. Acad. Sci. URSS (7) **1932**, 313–336] erred in proving $\vartheta < 17/53 + \epsilon$. Using some of Titchmarsh's results, and some intricate inequalities, Hua obtains $\vartheta \leqq 13/40 + \epsilon$.

*G. Pall* (Montreal, Que.).

Referred to in N40-22, N40-38, P20-24, P20-28, P20-29.

## P20-3 (4, 191a)

**Delsarte, Jean. Sur le gitter fuchsien.** C. R. Acad. Sci. Paris **214**, 147–149 (1942).

Let $A(x)$ denote the number of points of a Fuchsian lattice on or within a geodesic circle of area $\pi x$ on a surface $S$ of constant negative curvature $1/a$. This function is expanded in a series of hypergeometric functions of the variable $-x/4a^2$, the first two parameters being roots of a quadratic equation $X^2 = X + \lambda_n a^2$ and the third being unity. The quantity $\lambda_n$ is a characteristic value and the coefficient in the series the square of the corresponding characteristic function which satisfies the partial differential equation and the boundary condition that the value is the same at any two congruent points. When $a \to 0$ the series reduces to the well-known formula of Hardy and Littlewood for the number of lattice points in a circle, the hypergeometric function becoming a Bessel function. The behavior of $A(x)$ when $x$ becomes large is discussed briefly. *H. Bateman.*

## P20-4 (5, 256a)

**Hua, Loo-keng. On some problems of the geometrical theory of numbers.** Acad. Sinica Science Record **1**, 19–21 (1942).

Some results are announced, the methods being stated to be refinements of those originated by Van der Corput, Titchmarsh and Vinogradow. The number of lattice points in the circle $u^2+v^2 \leqq x^2$ and in the sphere $u^2+v^2+w^2 \leqq x^2$ are obtained with improved error terms; some results on the order of Epstein's zeta-function are promised. The last uses the following lemma for which an immediate proof is given: a ternary cubic form is factorable into three linearly independent factors if and only if the ratio of the form and its Hessian is a constant. *G. Pall* (Montreal, Que.).

**P20-5** **(7, 312a)**

**Esseen, Carl-Gustav. Fourier analysis of distribution functions. A mathematical study of the Laplace-Gaussian law.** Acta Math. 77, 1–125 (1945).

This is an exhaustive study of the delicate questions concerning the deviation of the distribution function of a sum of independent random variables from the normal distribution. Apart from new and often striking results a thorough review of the whole subject is also given.

The first two chapters review the most important properties of distribution functions and their characteristic functions. We cite the following two results. (1) If $F(x)$ and $G(x)$ are distribution functions and $f(t)$ and $g(t)$ their respective characteristic functions, then $f(t)=g(t)$ for $|t|\leqq L$ implies $\int_{-\infty}^{\infty}|F(x)-G(x)|dx\leqq\pi/L$. (2) If $f(t)=g(t)$ in an interval about 0 and $\alpha_{2k}=\int_{-\infty}^{\infty}x^{2k}dF(x)<\infty$ then the divergence of $\sum\alpha_{2k}^{-1/2k}$ implies $F(x)=G(x)$ at each point of continuity.

The principal result of chapter 3 consists in an estimate for the difference between the distribution function of $(X_1+\cdots+X_n)/S_n^{\frac{1}{2}}$ ($X_i$ independent random variables each with mean 0 and variance $\sigma_i^2$; $S_n=\sigma_1^2+\cdots+\sigma_n^2$) and the normal distribution $\Phi(x)$. The estimate is given in terms of absolute $k$th moments of $X_i$, which are assumed to be finite. For $k=3$ the estimate coincides with that found by Berry [Trans. Amer. Math. Soc. **49**, 122–136 (1941); these Rev. **2**, 228] and independently by the author.

In chapter 4 the author assumes that the $X$'s are identically distributed and proceeds to investigate the asymptotic expansions of the distribution function of $(X_1+\cdots+X_n)/\sigma n^{\frac{1}{2}}$. Cramér's original investigations [Random Variables and Probability Distributions, Cambridge University Press, 1937] were restricted to the case when the characteristic function $f(t)$ of $X_i$ satisfies the condition $\lim\sup_{t\to\pm\infty}|f(t)|<1$. The author obtains results in two more difficult cases, namely (a) $\lim\sup_{t\to\pm\infty}|f(t)|=1$ but $|f(t)|<1$ for $t\neq0$ and (b) $f(t_0)=1$ $(t_0\neq0)$, in which case $|f(t)|$ is known to be periodic.

In chapter 5 the dependence on both $n$ and $x$ of the remainder in the central limit theorem is investigated. Chapters 6, 7 and 8 are devoted to similar questions in the multidimensional case. There are interesting remarks on the connection between the central limit theorem and the problem of lattice points in an $n$-dimensional sphere.

*M. Kac* (Ithaca, N. Y.).

Referred to in N60-31, N60-42, N60-76, P28-12.

**P20-6** **(9, 80c)**

**Guinand, A. P. Discontinuous limits and Fourier-Stieltjes integrals.** Quart. J. Math., Oxford Ser. **18**, 72–84 (1947).

In the first part of the paper it is shown that, if $r(n)$ denotes the number of ways of expressing $n$ as the sum of two squares, then

$$\lim_{T\to\infty} T^{-1}\sum_{n<T^2} n^{-\frac{1}{4}}r(n)\cos\left((2\pi n)^{\frac{1}{2}}y-\pi/4\right)$$

exists and is either $k^{-\frac{1}{4}}r(k)$ or 0 according as $y$ is or is not of the form $(2\pi k)^{\frac{1}{2}}$. The proof depends on asymptotic formulae for the Bessel functions $J_0$, $J_1$ and on known summation formulae involving $r(n)$ and these functions. The author gives examples of other limit relations involving number-theoretic functions and Bessel functions which can be proved in an analogous manner. [It should be pointed out that the above result concerning $r(n)$ can be obtained from an integration by parts of statement (i) of Wintner, Amer. J. Math. **63**, 619–627 (1941), p. 620; these Rev. **2**, 350.]

In the second part of the paper, a general class of similar limit relations obtainable from Fourier-Stieltjes transforms is discussed, viz., if $f(x)$ and its transform $g(x)$, where

$$\int_0^y g(x)dx=(2/\pi)^{\frac{1}{2}}\int_0^\infty x^{-2}(1-\cos xy)df(x),$$

satisfy certain conditions (concerning local smoothness and behavior at $x=0$ and $x=\infty$), then

$$\lim_{T\to\infty}(2\pi)^{\frac{1}{2}}T^{-1}\int_0^T \cos xy\, df(x)$$

exists and equals $g(y+0)-g(y-0)$. *P. Hartman.*

Citations: MR 2, 350f = P20-1.

**P20-7** **(9, 570b)**

**Kendall, David G. On the number of lattice points inside a random oval.** Quart. J. Math., Oxford Ser. **19**, 1–26 (1948).

Let $A(x;\alpha,\beta)$ be the number of lattice points inside or on the circle $(u-\alpha)^2+(v-\beta)^2=x$. Let

$$\sigma^2(x)=\int_0^1\int_0^1(A(x;\alpha,\beta)-\pi x)^2d\alpha d\beta.$$

(1) The author proves, using the expansion of $A(x;\alpha,\beta)$ in a double Fourier series, that $\sigma(x)=O(x^{\frac{1}{4}})$, $\sigma(x)=\Omega(x^{\frac{1}{4}})$ and $\lim_{u\to\infty}u^{-1}\int_1^u x^{-\frac{1}{2}}\sigma^2(x)dx=a^2$, where $a=0.676497\cdots$. (2) Let $\lambda(x)$ be a positive function which increases to $+\infty$ as $x$ tends to $+\infty$ and let the sequence $\{x_\nu\}$ increase so rapidly that $\sum 1/\lambda^2(x_\nu)<\infty$. The author proves that, for almost all $(\alpha,\beta)$ (in the sense of Lebesgue measure),

$$A(x;\alpha,\beta)-\pi x=O(x^{\frac{1}{4}}\lambda(x))$$

when $x$ tends to infinity through the sequence $\{x_\nu\}$. (3) The author then replaces the lattice points $(\mu,\nu)$ by small equal circular spots, say $(u-\mu)^2+(v-\nu)^2\leqq\delta$, where $\delta$ is small and positive, and proves that $B_\delta(x)-\pi x=O(x^{\frac{1}{4}})$ as $x\to+\infty$ for all fixed $\delta>0$. Here $\pi\delta B_\delta(x)$ denotes the total area of the lattice spots included within the circle $u^2+v^2\leqq x$.

(4) If $x$ is not an integer, then

$$A(x)=A(x;0,0)=B_\delta(x)=\pi x+x^{\frac{1}{2}}\sum_{l=1}^{\infty}j_\nu(l\delta)r(l)l^{-\frac{1}{2}}J_1(2\pi(xl)^{\frac{1}{2}})$$

for all $\nu>\frac{1}{2}$ and for all sufficiently small $\delta$. Here $r(l)$ denotes the number of representations of the integer $l$ as the sum of two squares, $j_\nu(u)=\pi^{-\nu}\Gamma(1+\nu)u^{-\frac{1}{2}\nu}J_\nu(2\pi u^{\frac{1}{2}})$ and $J_\nu$ denote the Bessel function. (5) The author says that a series $\sum a_n$ is summable $(j_\nu)$ to the sum $S$ if $\lim_{\delta\to0+}\sum_{n=1}^{\infty}j_\nu(n\delta)a_n=S$ and proves that summability $(j_\nu)$ is regular for $\nu>\frac{1}{2}$, so that, if $\sum a_n$ is convergent in the ordinary sense to the sum $S$, then it is summable $(j_\nu)$ to $S$. Thus Hardy's series $\pi x+x^{\frac{1}{2}}\sum_{l=1}^{\infty}l^{-\frac{1}{2}}r(l)J_1(2\pi(xl)^{\frac{1}{2}})$ is summable $(j_\nu)$ to $A(x)$ for all $\nu>\frac{1}{2}$ if $x$ is not an integer.

(6) The author extends results (1) and (2) to the more general problem in which the circle is replaced by any sufficiently smooth oval curve, free from singularities and points of zero curvature and gives a quantitative assessment of the accuracy of graphical integration, when the area to be measured is bounded by an oval of the type considered.

*V. Knichal* (Prague).

Referred to in P02-10, P28-9.

**P20-8** **(11, 659c)**

**Bochner, S., and Chandrasekharan, K. Lattice points and Fourier expansions.** Acta Sci. Math. Szeged **12**, Leopoldo Fejér et Frederico Riesz LXX annos natis dedicatus, Pars B, 1–15 (1950).

This is a sequel to an earlier paper by the same authors [Quart. J. Math., Oxford Ser. (1) **19**, 238–248 (1948); these Rev. **10**, 431]. Using new theorems on the spherical summability of formally differentiated Fourier series of functions of several variables, the authors shorten the proofs of their previous theorems on the Cesàro summability of the developments, initiated by Voronoi and Hardy and associated with the number of lattice points in $k$-dimensional spheres. *A. Zygmund* (Cambridge, Mass.).

Citations: MR 10, 431h = E44-3.

## P20-9 (13, 919g)

**Val'fiš, A. Z. On lattice points in many-dimensional ellipsoids. X, XI, XII, XIII, XIV, XV.** Akad. Nauk Gruzin. SSR. Trudy Tbiliss. Mat. Inst. Razmadze **15**, 275–296, 297–322 (1947); **16**, 169–213, 215–230 (1948); **17**, 245–258, 259–279 (1949). (Russian. Georgian summary)

[Communication IX (with the author's name spelled Walfisz) appeared in the Trav. Inst. Math. Tbilissi **10**, 111–160 (1941); these Rev. **4**, 132]. The number of lattice points in a $k$-dimensional sphere $z_1^2+\cdots+z_k^2=x$ is given by

$$(1)\qquad A_k(x)=\sum_{j_1^2+\cdots+j_k^2\leqq x}1=\sum_{0\leqq n\leqq x}r_k(x),$$

$j_1,\cdots,j_k$ being integers. This number is approximated by the area of the sphere, $V_k(x)=[\pi^{k/2}/\Gamma(\frac{1}{2}k+1)]x^{k/2}$, with an error $P_k(x)$,

$$(2)\qquad P_k(x)=A_k(x)-V_k(x).$$

In paper X the author establishes the following two results for $P_k(x)$.

$$(\mathrm{A})\qquad P_k(x)=2M_k\{(1-2^{-\frac12 k})\zeta(\tfrac{1}{2}k)\}^{-1}\Psi_k(x)x^{\frac12 k-1}+Bx^{\frac12(k-3)},$$

for $k\equiv 0 \pmod 4$,

$$(\mathrm{B})\qquad P_k(x)=2M_k\{L(\tfrac{1}{2}k)\}^{-1}\Psi_k(x)x^{\frac12 k-1}+Bx^{\frac12(k-3)}$$

for $k\equiv 2 \pmod 4$, where

$$\zeta(x)=\sum_{n=1}^{\infty}n^{-x},\qquad L(x)=\sum_{u=1}^{\infty}(-1)^{\frac12(u-1)}u^{-x},$$

$$M_k=\pi^{\frac12 k}/2\Gamma(\tfrac{1}{2}k),\quad \psi(z)=z-[z]-\tfrac{1}{2},$$

$$(3)\quad \Psi_k(x)=-\sum_{u=1}^{\infty}u^{1-\frac12 k}\psi\left(\frac{x}{u}\right)$$
$$+(-1)^{k/4}\sum_{\substack{n=1\\ n\equiv 0\ (\mathrm{mod}\ 2)}}^{\infty}n^{1-\frac12 k}\left\{\psi\left(\frac{x}{n}\right)-2\psi\left(\frac{x}{2n}\right)\right\},$$

when $k\equiv 0 \pmod 4$, and

$$(4)\quad \Psi_k(x)=-\sum_{u=1}^{\infty}(-1)^{\frac12(u-1)}u^{1-\frac12 k}\psi\left(\frac{x}{u}\right)$$
$$+(-1)^{(k-2)/4}\sum_{n=1}^{\infty}(2n)^{1-\frac12 k}\left\{\psi\left(\frac{x}{n}\right)-\psi\left(\frac{x}{2n}\right)-2\psi\left(\frac{x-n}{4n}\right)\right\},$$

when $k\equiv 2 \pmod 4$. The results are obtained by replacing $r_k(n)$ in the definition of $A_k(x)$ by known expressions due to Hardy [see Proc. Nat. Acad. Sci. U. S. A. **4**, 189–193 (1918); Trans. Amer. Math. Soc. **21**, 255–284 (1920), sects. 3.1 and 5], to give

$$(5)\quad P_k(x)=2M_k\left\{-\psi(x)x^{\frac12 k-1}\right.$$
$$\left.+\sum_{l=2}^{\infty}\sum_{\substack{h=1\\(h,l)=1}}^{l}\left(\frac{S_{h,l}}{l}\right)^k\sum_{n\leqq x}n^{\frac12 k-1}e\left(-\frac{nh}{l}\right)\right\}+Bx^{\frac12(k-3)}.$$

Here the $S_{h,l}$ are Gauss sums and $e(z)=e^{2\pi iz}$. (A) and (B) then follow after lengthy manipulations of the sums in (5). Further, defining

$$\Psi_k=\limsup_{n\to\infty}\Psi_k(n),\qquad \psi_k=\liminf_{n\to\infty}\Psi_k(n),$$

$$P_k=\limsup_{n\to\infty}\frac{P_k(n)}{M_k n^{\frac12 k-1}},\quad \rho_k=\liminf_{n\to\infty}\frac{P_k(n)}{M_k n^{\frac12 k-1}},$$

the author proves that for $k\equiv 0 \pmod 8$

$$(6)\qquad \Psi_k=\tfrac{1}{2}\zeta(\tfrac{1}{2}k-1),$$

$$(7)\qquad \psi_k=-\tfrac{1}{2}\zeta(\tfrac{1}{2}k-1)+(1-2^{-\frac12 k})\zeta(\tfrac{1}{2}k),$$

and hence that

$$(8)\qquad P_k=\frac{\zeta(\frac{1}{2}k-1)}{(1-2^{-\frac12 k})\zeta(\frac{1}{2}k)},\quad \rho_k=2-P_k.$$

Paper XI treats the case $k\equiv 4 \pmod 8$. Here it is only possible to prove that

$$(9)\qquad 0\leqq\Psi_k-\tfrac{1}{2}\zeta(\tfrac{1}{2}k-1)+\theta_k\leqq 1.04(2^{-\frac12 k(k-1)}),$$

$$(10)\qquad -1.04(2^{-\frac12 k(k-1)})\leqq\psi_k-(1-2^{-\frac12 k})\zeta(\tfrac{1}{2}k)$$
$$+\tfrac{1}{2}\zeta(\tfrac{1}{2}k-1)-\theta_k\leqq 0,$$

where $\theta_k$ is given as an infinite series. (9) and (10) are used to obtain analogous results for $P_k$ and $\rho_k$. The still more difficult case $k\equiv 2 \pmod 4$ is discussed in paper XII. Here the results are less precise. In paper XIII a shorter derivation is given for (A) and (B) based upon results of Z. Suetuna [J. Fac. Sci. Univ. Tokyo. Sect. I. **1**, 249–283 (1926)]. A third and still shorter derivation of (A) and (B) is given in paper XIV based upon results of V. Jarnik [Math. Z. **30**, 768–786 (1929)]. Paper XV again treats the cases $k\equiv 0 \pmod 4$ and $k\equiv 2 \pmod 4$ and gives more precise expressions for $P_k(x)$ which contain not only a term in $x^{\frac12 k-1}$ but also a term in $x^{\frac12 k-2}$ and with an error $O(x^{\frac12(k-5)})$. For example, it is shown that for $k\geqq 6$ and $k\equiv 0 \pmod 2$,

$$P_{2k}(x)=\frac{\pi^k}{\Gamma(k)}\{(1-2^{-k})\zeta(k)\}^{-1}$$
$$\times(\Psi_{2k}(x)x^{k-1}+\tfrac{1}{2}(k-1)\Pi_{2k}(x)x^{k-2})+Bx^{k-5/2},$$

where, in this case,

$$\Pi_{2k}(x)=\sum_{u=1}^{\infty}u^{2-k}\psi_1\left(\frac{x}{u}\right)+\sum_{g=2}^{\infty}g^{2-k}\left\{4\psi_1\left(\frac{x}{2g}+\frac{k}{4}\right)-\psi_1\left(\frac{x}{g}\right)\right\},$$

with $\psi_1(z)=(z-[z])^2-(z-[z])+\frac{1}{6}$. A similar expression is given for $P_{2k}(x)$ with $k\equiv 1 \pmod 2$. *W. H. Simons.*

Citations: MR 4, 132b = P24-4.

Referred to in P20-13, P20-14.

## P20-10 (15, 941e)

**Lursmanašvili, A. P. On the number of lattice points in multidimensional spheres of odd dimension.** Soobščeniya Akad. Nauk Gruzin. SSR **14**, 513–520 (1953). (Russian)

Let $A_k(x)$ be the number of lattice points in the $k$-dimensional sphere $z_1^2+z_2^2+\cdots+z_k^2\leqq x$. Write

$$A_k(x)=V_k(x)+\mathrm{P}_k(x),$$

where $V_k(x)$ is the content of the sphere. The author obtains the result

$$\mathrm{P}_{2k+1}(x)=\pi^{k+\frac12}\{\mathrm{Z}(k)\}^{-1}\sum_{s=1}^{m}\Phi_{k,s}(x)x^{k-s+\frac12}+O(x^{k-m}),$$

where $\mathrm{Z}(k)=(1-2^{-k})\zeta(k)$ for even $k$, and $\sum_{n=1}^{\infty}(-1/n)n^{-k}$ for odd $k$. Also

$$\Phi_{k,s}(x)=\sum_{n=1}^{\infty}\left(\frac{-1}{n}\right)^k n^{s-k-1}\vartheta_s(x,n)+\frac{1}{2}\sum_{n=1}^{\infty}(2n)^{s-k-1}G_s(x,n).$$

Here $G_s(x, n)$ is a linear combination of $\vartheta_s(x, l)$ for $l=n$, $2n$, $4n$, and $\vartheta_s(x-n, 4)$ and

$$\vartheta_s(x, l)=\sum_{h=1}^{l}\varphi_s\left(\frac{x-h^2}{l}\right),$$

where $\varphi_s(z)$ is a multiple of the $s$th Bernoullian polynomial (continued as a periodic function outside $0\leqq z<1$). This result is obtained from a similar result for $P_{2k}(x)$ obtained by the author in an earlier paper [Akad. Nauk Gruzin. SSR. Trudy Tbiliss. Mat. Inst. Razmadze **19**, 79–120 (1953)].* *R. A. Rankin* (Birmingham).

*See below.

Referred to in P20-11, P20-20, P20-43.

## P20-11 (16, 451b)

**Lursmanašvili, A. P. On the number of lattice points in multidimensional spheres.** Akad. Nauk Gruzin. SSR. Trudy Tbiliss. Mat. Inst. Razmadze **19**, 79–120 (1953). (Russian. Georgian summary)

Let $A_k(x)$ be the number of lattice points in the $k$-dimensional sphere $z_1^2+z_2^2+\cdots+z_k^2\leqq x$. Write

$$A_k(x)=V_k(z)+P_k(x),$$

where $V_k(x)$ is the content of the sphere. The author obtains the results

$$P_{2k}(x)=\pi^k\{(1-2^{-k})\zeta(k)\Gamma(k)\}^{-1}\sum_{s=1}^{m}\Psi_{k,s}(x)x^{k-s}+O(x^{k-m-\frac{1}{2}}),$$

when $k$ is even, and

$$P_{2k}(x)=\pi^k\{L(k)\Gamma(k)\}^{-1}\sum_{s=1}^{m}\Phi_{k,s}(x)x^{k-s}+O(x^{k-m-\frac{1}{2}}),$$

when $k$ is odd. Here $k\geqq 4$ and $\Psi_{k,s}(x)$ and $\Phi_{k,s}(x)$ are certain complicated combinations of functions such as the Bernoullian polynomials. The proofs, which are too complicated to describe here, follow the methods developed by A. Walfisz. [See also MR **15**, 941 where this paper is referred to.] *R. A. Rankin* (Glasgow).

Citations: MR 15, 941e = P20-10.

Referred to in P20-20, P20-43.

## P20-12 (16, 908b)

**Vinogradov, I. M. Improvement of asymptotic formulas for the number of lattice points in a region of three dimensions.** Izv. Akad. Nauk SSSR. Ser. Mat. **19**, 3–10 (1955). (Russian)

In an earlier paper [same Izv. **13**, 97–110 (1949); MR **11**, 233] the author proved that the error term in the asymptotic formula for $\sum_{n=1}^{N} h(-m)$ is $O(N^\alpha)$, where

$$\alpha=\frac{7}{10}-\frac{1}{405}+\epsilon$$

for any $\epsilon>0$. [$h(-m)$ denotes the number of classes of primitive quadratic forms of discriminant $-m$.] The same applied to the error in the formula for the number of points with integral coordinates in the sphere $x^2+y^2+z^2\leqq N$. The proof of these results required the use of van der Corput's method. The author now gives a proof of a more exact estimate, with

$$\alpha=\frac{11}{16}+\epsilon.$$

This could be further slightly improved by applying van der Corput's method, which is not used in the present paper. The proof, like that of the previous result, depends on skilful subdivisions of regions of summation, and applications of the transformation formula for sums of the type $\sum\varphi(x)e^{2\pi if(x)}$. *H. Davenport* (London).

Citations: MR 11, 233d = E16-12.

Referred to in E16-55, P20-19, P20-22.

## P20-13 (17, 133d)

**Val'fiš, A. Z. On lattice points in multidimensional ellipsoids. XVI.** Akad. Nauk Gruzin. SSR. Trudy Tbiliss. Mat. Inst. Razmadze **20** (1954), 1–20. (Russian)

Let $P_{2k}(x)=A_{2k}(x)-V_{2k}(x)$, where $A_{2k}(x)$ is the number of lattice points in the sphere $z_1^2+\cdots+z_k^2=x$, and $V_{2k}(x)=\pi^k x^k/\Gamma(k+1)$ is its volume. In previous papers of this series [same Trudy **15** (1947), 275–296, 297–322; **16** (1948), 215–230; **17** (1949), 245–258; MR **13**, 919] the author derived properties of the functions $P_{2k}$, $\varrho_{2k}$, defined by

$$P_{2k}=\limsup_{n\to\infty}\frac{P_{2k}(n)}{M_{2k}n^{k-1}}\quad \varrho_{2k}=\liminf_{n\to\infty}\frac{P_{2k}(n)}{M_{2k}n^{k-1}},$$

where $M_{2k}=\pi^k/2\Gamma(k)$. In the present paper he derives analogous results for the functions $P_{2k,a}$, $\varrho_{2k,a}$ defined by

$$P_{2k,a}=\limsup_{\substack{n\to\infty\\ n\equiv a \pmod 2}}\frac{P_{2k}(n)}{M_{2k}n^{k-1}},$$

$$\varrho_{2k,a}=\liminf_{\substack{n\to\infty\\ n\equiv a \pmod 2}}\frac{P_{2k}(n)}{M_{2k}n^{k-1}}.$$

In particular, he shows that (a) $P_{2k,a}+\varrho_{2k,1-a}=2$, (b) $P_{2k,0}=P_{2k}$, (c) $\varrho_{2k,1}=2-P_{2k}=\varrho_{2k}$. *W. H. Simons.*

Citations: MR 13, 919g = P20-9.

Referred to in P20-14, P24-11.

## P20-14 (18, 115a)

**Val'fiš, A. Z. On lattice points in multi-dimensional ellipsoids. XVII.** Akad. Nauk Gruzin. SSR. Trudy Tbiliss. Mat. Inst. Razmadze **21** (1955), 3–64. (Russian)

As in previous papers of this series [see MR **4**, 132; **13**, 919; **17**, 133], $P_k(x)$ denotes the difference between the number of lattice points in the $k$-dimensional sphere $y_1^2+\cdots+y_k^2=x$ and its volume. Moreover, $P_k$ and $\varrho_k$ are defined by

$$\left.\begin{array}{l}P_k=\limsup_{n\to\infty}\\ \rho_k=\liminf_{n\to\infty}\end{array}\right\}\frac{2P_k(n)}{D_k n^{\frac{1}{2}k-1}}$$

where $D_k=\pi^{\frac{1}{2}k}/\Gamma(\frac{1}{2}k)$.

The present paper gives improved estimates for the quantities $P_k$ and $\varrho_k$. The results and methods are of such a detailed nature that they cannot be readily quoted in a review. *W. H. Simons* (Vancouver, B.C.).

Citations: MR 4, 132a = E28-4; MR 4, 132b = P24-4; MR 13, 919g = P20-9; MR 17, 133d = P20-13.

Referred to in P24-11.

## P20-15 (19, 731g)

**Carlitz, L. A formula connected with lattice points in a circle.** Abh. Math. Sem. Univ. Hamburg **21** (1957), 87–89.

An asymptotic formula for $\sum_{n=1}^{N} r(n)(\log n-\log N)$ with error $O(N^{-\frac{1}{4}})$ has been proved by Cl. Müller [same Abh. **19** (1954), no. 1–2, 62–65; MR **15**, 940], by a method connected with partial differential equations. The present author gives a derivation on more classical lines, using partial summation and a summation formula for $r(n)$. The constant term appears as a series involving $r(n)$, in place of Müller's closed form $4\log\Gamma(\frac{1}{4})-\log(4\pi)$. There are a few misprints. *F. V. Atkinson* (Canberra).

Citations: MR 15, 940a = P28-18.

Referred to in N52-45.

## P20-16 (20# 3826)

**Walfisz, Arnold. Gitterpunkte in mehrdimensionalen Kugeln.** Monografie Matematyczne. Vol. 33. Państwowe Wydawnictwo Naukowe, Warsaw, 1957. 471 pp.

This is a beautifully written book by a leading expert in the field. Although of immense value to the specialist, it is addressed to a wider circle of readers. To quote the author's own words, "Das Studium des Buches setzt nur Kenntnisse voraus, wie sie in den üblichen Anfänger-vorlesungen über Analysis, Algebra und Zahlentheorie an den Hochschulen gegeben werden. Auch sind die Rechnungen überall sehr eingehend durchgeführt." Almost a third of the book is devoted to researches of the last ten years.

The book is concerned with the study of $P_k(X)$, which is the difference between the number of lattice-points in the $k$-dimensional hyper-sphere (1) $y_1^2+y_2^2+\cdots+y_k^2\leqq X$ and its volume $V_k(X)$. So (2) $P_k(X)=A_k(X)-V_k(X)$, where $A_k(X)$ is the number of lattice-points satisfying (1). It is well known that we have the asymptotic relation $A_k(X)\sim V_k(X)$.

Gauss observed that $P_2(X)=O(X^{\frac{1}{2}})$. Sierpiński (1909) found $P_2(X)=O(X^{\frac{1}{3}})$, van der Corput proved the sharper result $P_2(X)=O(X^c)$ with $c<1/3$, and there have been petty improvements in the exponent in later years. It is also known (Hardy) that the exponent cannot be lowered below $1/4$; on the other hand it is considered highly probable that an exponent $1/4+\varepsilon$, where $\varepsilon>0$ is arbitrary, represents the truth. We proceed to sketch the contents of the book chapter by chapter.

Chapter 1 contains Estermann's [J. London Math. Soc. **20** (1945), 66–67; MR **7**, 414] well-known short-cut to the determination of the sign in the Gaussian sum. Next, the author obtains Jacobi's formula for the number of representations of a number as a sum of 4 squares. The treatment, involving infinite series, was rediscovered by Ramanujan [Trans. Cambridge Philos. Soc. **22** (1916), 159–184]. The chapter concludes with a formula of Landau for $A_k(X)$ and the well-known "singular series" representation of Hardy for $r_k(n)$, the number of representations of $n$ as a sum of $k$ squares, when $k>4$.

Ch. 2 contains elementary estimates of $P_k(X)$. H. Weyl's method of estimating exponential sums is used to obtain $P_4(X)=O(X\log X/\log\log X)$, which is due to the author [Math. Z. **26** (1927), 66–88]. This chapter concludes with the deep result obtained from L. K. Hua's and Vinogradoff's methods: $P_4(X)=O(X\log^{\frac{3}{4}}X(\log\log X)^{\frac{1}{2}})$.

Ch. 3 contains "Ω-results" (the Ω-notation is due to Littlewood), e.g.

$$P_k(X)=\Omega(X^{k/2-1});\quad P_4(X)=\Omega(X\log\log X).$$

The rest of the chapter studies the function $\rho_k(t)=P_k(t)/t^{k/2-1}$ ($\rho_k(X)$ is bounded for $k>4$ as $X\to\infty$). In particular, we have the result that the sequence of numbers $\rho_k(1)$, $\rho_k(2)$, $\rho_k(3)$, $\cdots$ has infinitely many limit points for $k\geqq 5$.

Chs. 4 and 5 contain results of Petersson [Abh. Math. Sem. Hamburg. Univ. **5** (1926), 116–150] and Lursmanaschwili-Walfisz. These are too complicated to be quoted here.*Chs. 6 and 7 have more on the functions $P_k$ and $\rho_k$ for even $k$ and odd $k$, respectively. Ch. 8: $\int_0^X P_4^2(y)dy=\frac{2}{3}\pi^2X^3+O(X^{5/2})$. This is heavy going — a formidable exercise in analytic number theory! The result is due to Walfisz. Ch. 9: $\int_0^X P_k^2(y)dy$ (Jarnik). Ch. 10: Development of $P_k(t)$ in Bessel function series.

The author remarks that the study of ellipsoids $\alpha_1X_1^2+\alpha_2X_2^2+\cdots+\alpha_kX_k^2\leqq Y$ with irrational coefficients would require a separate monograph. {The reviewer would also like to mention in this connection the striking recent work of Davenport, Heilbronn, and G. L. Watson on irrational indefinite quadratic forms and that of Birch and D. J. Lewis [#3828, #3827 below] on the non-trivial representation of 0 by "mixed" cubic forms (with coefficients in any algebraic number field) with a sufficient number of variables.} *S. Chowla* (Princeton, N.J.)

*See **25** #5038a, b = P20-20.

Citations: MR 7, 414a = A22-5; MR 20# 3827 = D72-15; MR 20# 3828 = D72-16; MR 25# 5038a = P20-20; MR 25# 5038b = P20-20.

Referred to in P20-17, P28-57, Z25-17.

## P20-17 (22# 10982)

**Вальфиш, А. З. [Val′fiš, A. Z.]. Целые точки в многомерных шарах [Integral points in many-dimensional spheres].** Akad. Nauk Gruzin. SSR, Mat. Inst. A. M. Razmadze, Izdat. Akad Nauk Gruzin. SSR, Tbilisi, 1959. 460 pp. 24 r.

This is almost a literal translation into Russian of the author's book *Gitterpunkte in mehrdimensionalen Kügeln*, Państwowe Wydawnictwo Naukowe, Warsaw, 1957 [MR **20** #3826]. Like the German text, this book is written in perfect "Landau style". There are also improvements in the mathematical contents; for example, the theorem $P_4(x)=Bx\log^{3/4}x(\log\log x)^{1/2}$ on page 93 of the German edition appears in the following sharpened form in the Russian edition (also on p. 93): $P_4(x)=Bx\log^{2/3}x$ [note $\frac{2}{3}<\frac{3}{4}$]. *S. Chowla* (Boulder, Colo.)

Citations: MR 20# 3826 = P20-16.

## P20-18 (21# 3401)

**Walfisz, Arnold. Gitterpunkte in mehrdimensionalen Kugeln.** Jber. Deutsch. Math. Verein. **61** (1958), Abt. 1, 11–31.

The author lists the important results in the historical development of the problem of finding the number of lattice points in a many-dimensional sphere. He states these as theorems, thirty-seven in all, without complete proofs, but follows each theorem with brief comments and a reference to where the complete proof can be found.

*W. H. Simons* (Vancouver, B.C.)

Referred to in P20-20.

## P20-19 (23# A860)

**Vinogradov, I. M.**

**On the number of integral points in a given domain. (Russian)**

*Izv. Akad. Nauk SSSR Ser. Mat.* **24** (1960), 777–786.

Let $h(-m)$ denote the number of classes of primitive quadratic forms of discriminant $-m$. The author proved in an earlier paper [same Izv. **19** (1955), 3–10; MR **16**, 908] that the error term in the asymptotic formula for $\sum_{m=1}^n h(-m)$ is $O(n^\alpha)$, where $\alpha=11/16+\varepsilon$, $\varepsilon>0$ arbitrary. In the present paper, the author gives an improved estimate, with $\alpha=19/28+\varepsilon$. The proof depends upon a finer dealing with sums of the form $\sum\varphi(x)e^{2\pi i f(x)}$. Arguments given in this paper apply also to an estimation of the error in the formula for the number of points with integral coordinates in the sphere $x^2+y^2+z^2\leqq n$.

*S. Knapowski* (Poznań)

Citations: MR 16, 908b = P20-12.

Referred to in E16-55, N40-56, P20-22, P20-31, P20-34.

## P20-20 (25# 5038a; 25# 5038b)

**Walfisz, A. [Val′fiš, A. Z.]**

**Über Gitterpunkte in mehrdimensionalen Kugeln. II.**

*Acta Arith.* **6** (1960), 115–136.

**Walfisz, A. [Val′fiš, A. Z.]**

**Über Gitterpunkte in mehrdimensionalen Kugeln. III.**

*Acta Arith.* **6** (1960), 193–215.

Part I appeared in Jber. Deutsch. Math.-Verein. **61** (1958), Abt. 1, 11–31 [MR **21** #3401]. Let $A_q(t)$ denote the number of lattice points in the $q$-dimensional sphere, i.e., $A_q(t)$ is the number of integer solutions of the equation $x_1^2+x_2^2+\cdots+x_q^2\leqq t$. It is known that $A_q(t)\sim V_q(t)$, where $V_q(t)$ is the volume of the sphere $x_1^2+x_2^2+\cdots+x_q^2=t$.

Let $P_q(t)=A_q(t)-V_q(t)$. The papers here reviewed show the relationship between expressions for $P_q(t)$ obtained by Petersson [Abh. Math. Sem. Univ. Hamburg **5** (1926), 116–150] and Lursmanašvili [Soobšč. Akad. Nauk Gruzin. SSR **14** (1953), 513–520; MR **15**, 941; Akad. Nauk Gruzin. SSR Trudy Tbiliss. Mat. Inst. Razmadze **19** (1953), 79–120; MR **16**, 451]. Each paper is in three parts. In section one the notation involved and definitions of the functions appearing in the results of the studies of $P_q(t)$ are developed. In section two a statement of the main result is given. In section three the main result is proved.

Because of their complexity the expressions for $P_q(t)$ are not reproduced here.

*W. H. Simons* (Vancouver, B.C.)

Citations: MR 15, 941e = P20-10; MR 16, 451b = P20-11; MR 21# 3401 = P20-18.

Referred to in P20-16, P20-43.

## P20-21 (26# 108)

**Schaal, Werner**

**Übertragung des Kreisproblems auf reell-quadratische Zahlkörper.**

*Math. Ann.* **145** (1961/62), 273–284.

Let $K$ denote a real quadratic number-field of discriminant $d$. Let $f(\xi)$ be the number of decompositions of an integer $\xi$ of $K$ into the sum of two squares of integers in $K$. If $x$ is a large positive number in $K$, $x'$ its conjugate in $K$, consider the set $G$ of integers of $K$ which satisfy $0\leqq\xi<x$, $0\leqq\xi'<x'$ and put

$$\sum_{\xi\in G} f(\xi) = \frac{\pi^2}{d}xx'+R(x,x').$$

By suitable modifications of the method of C. L. Siegel [Trans. Amer. Math. Soc. **39** (1936), 219–224], it is proved that for each $\delta>0$, $R(x,x')=O[(xx')^{2/3+\delta}]$ as $xx'\to+\infty$. In the opposite direction, the classical work of Hardy for the rational case presents difficulties of adaption, as does the more recent method of P. Erdős and W. H. J. Fuchs [J. London Math. Soc. **31** (1956), 67–73; MR **17**, 586]. That

$$R(x,x')\neq o((xx')^{1/4})$$

follows as a special case of Siegel's earlier work on algebraic number fields [Math. Ann. **87** (1922), 1–35].

*J. H. H. Chalk* (Toronto)

Citations: MR 17, 586d = B16-9.

Referred to in R48-41.

## P20-22 (27# 111)

**Chen, Jing-run**

**Improvement of asymptotic formulas for the number of lattice points in a region of three dimensions.**

*Sci. Sinica* **12** (1963), 151–161.

I. M. Vinogradov [Izv. Akad. Nauk SSSR Ser. Mat. **24** (1960), 777–786; MR **23** #A860; ibid. **19** (1955), 3–10; MR **16**, 908] proved that the error term in the asymptotic formula for $\sum_1^N h(-t)$, where $h(-t)$ denotes the number of classes of primitive quadratic forms with discriminant $-t$, is $O(N^{\alpha+\varepsilon})$ $(\varepsilon>0)$ for $\alpha=19/28$. Using similar methods the author replaces $\alpha$ by $35/52$ and remarks that corresponding improvements can be obtained for the sphere problem.

*J. F. Koksma* (Amsterdam)

Citations: MR 16, 908b = P20-12; MR 23# A860 = P20-19.

Referred to in P20-33.

## P20-23 (27# 3604)

**Maslova, F. G.**

**A problem in the spectral theory of differential operators. (Russian)**

*Dokl. Akad. Nauk SSSR* **152** (1963), 820.

The problem is to estimate for large $T$ the number $\Phi(T)$ of points $(m,n)$ in the first quadrant which have integer coordinates and which lie within a circle of area $T$ with center at the origin. The problem is closely related to the problem of estimating for large $T$ the trigonometric sum, $\sum 4\sin^2 n\pi x\sin^2 m\pi y$, taken over all such $(m,n)$. It is now claimed that this sum is equal to

$$T/(4\pi)+O(T^{1/3}\ln Tl(x,y)^{-1}) + O(l(x,y)^{-2})+O(T^{1/4}l(x,y)^{-3/2}),$$

where $l(x,y)$ is the distance from the point $(x,y)$ in the unit square $[0,1]\times[0,1]$ to the boundary of the square.

*L. de Branges* (Lafayette, Ind.)

## P20-24 (27# 4799)

**Chen, Jing-run**

**The lattice-points in a circle.**

*Sci. Sinica* **12** (1963), 633–649.

Let $R(x)$ denote the number of lattice points inside or on the circle $x^2+y^2=t$. Then $R(t)=\pi t+O(t^\alpha)$. Previously the best-known upper bound for $\alpha$ was $\alpha\leqq 13/40+\varepsilon$ due to Hua [Quart. J. Math. Oxford Ser. **13** (1942), 18–29; MR **4**, 190]. Using methods of Titchmarsh [Proc. London Math. Soc. (2) **38** (1934), 96–115] and Hua [loc. cit.], the author finds the improved bound $\alpha\leqq 12/37+\varepsilon$. Half the paper is devoted to proving intricate inequalities for a certain quadratic form $Q(X,Y,Z,W)$ introduced by Hua.

*S. L. Segal* (Rochester, N.Y.)

Citations: MR 4, 190e = P20-2.

Referred to in P20-25.

## P20-25 (32# 2383)

**Chen Jing-run [Ch'en Ching-jun]**

**The lattice-points in a circle.**

*Acta Math. Sinica* **13** (1963), 299–313 (*Chinese*); *translated as Chinese Math.—Acta* **4** (1963), 322–339.

An English version of this paper has been published in Sci. Sinica **12** (1963), 633–649 [MR **27** #4799].

Citations: MR 27# 4799 = P20-24.

## P20-26 (27# 5722)

**Fraser, W.; Gotlieb, C. C.**

**A calculation of the number of lattice points in the circle and sphere.**

*Math. Comp.* **16** (1962), 282–290.

Put $P_k(x)=A_k(x)-V_k(x)$, where $V_k(x)$ is the volume of the $k$-dimensional hypersphere of radius $x^{1/2}$ with centre at the origin and where $A_k(x)$ is the number of lattice points in that hypersphere. The smallest number $c$ such that $P_2(x)=Ox^{c+\varepsilon}$ for each fixed positive $\varepsilon$, is $<\frac{1}{3}$ and $\geqq\frac{1}{4}$. The smallest number $\gamma$ such that $P_3(x)=Ox^{\gamma+\varepsilon}$ for each fixed positive $\varepsilon$ is $\geqq\frac{1}{2}$ and $\leqq 1$. Applying two independent programs based on different summation formulas, the authors have calculated $A_2(x)$, $|P_2(x)|$, $A_3(x)$, $P_3(x)$ for the following range

$$x^{1/2} = 1(1)50(5)200(100)1000(200)1800.$$

The points of greatest interest in investigating the asymptotic behavior of $P_2(x)$ are those local maxima $M_i$ of $|P_2(M_i)|$ satisfying $|P_2(M_i)|>|P_2(x)|$ for all $x<M_i$. The conjecture $c=\frac{1}{4}$ is not inconsistent with the graph of $|\log P_2(x)|$ for those values $x=M_i$. On the other hand,

according to a remark of the authors, some unpublished computations by H. Mitchell show that for some $x$ between $10^6$ and $10^{10}$ the values of $x^{-1/4}\log|P_2(x)|$ grow very remarkably. The graph of $\log|P_3(x)|$ for those computed values of $x$ where $\log|P_3(x)|$ is larger than any preceding value leads the authors to the conjecture that $0.5 \leqq \gamma \leqq 0.7$.

*J. G. van der Corput* (Berkeley, Calif.)

Referred to in P20-30.

## P20-27 (28# 65 )

**Vinogradov, I. M.**

**On the number of integer points in a sphere. (Russian)**

*Izv. Akad. Nauk SSSR Ser. Mat.* **27** (1963), 957–968.

The author shows that a sphere of radius $a$ contains integral lattice points which differ in number from the volume by $O(a^{4/3}(\ln a)^6)$. The earlier estimate of the author [same Izv. **27** (1963), 3–8; MR **27** #2487] established $O(a^{4/3+\varepsilon})$.

*H. Cohn* (Tucson, Ariz.)

Citations: MR 27# 2487 = E16-55.

## P20-28 (28# 3008 )

**Yin, Wen-lin**

**The lattice-points in a circle.**

*Sci. Sinica* **11** (1962), 10–15.

Let $R(x)$ denote the number of lattice points in and on the circle $u^2+v^2 \leqq x$. It is well known that $R(x)=x+O(x^a)$ for some $a<1$. Let $b$ be the greatest lower bound of $a$. The author outlines an estimation of the trigonometric sums involved to obtain the upper bound $b \leqq 12/37$ thus adding another link to the chain of known upper bounds, namely, $b \leqq 1/2$, $1/3$, $(1/3)-\varepsilon$, $37/112$, $163/494$, $27/82$, $15/46$ and $13/40$, due to Gauss [*Werke*, Bd. II, pp. 269–291, Ges. Wiss., Göttingen, 1863], Sierpiński [Prace Mat.-Fiz. **17** (1906), 77–118], van der Corput [Math. Ann. 87 (1922), 39–65], Littlewood and Walfisz [Proc. Roy. Soc. London Ser. A **106** (1924), 478–488], Walfisz [Math. Z. **26** (1927), 66–88], Nieland [Math. Ann. **98** (1928), 717–736], Titchmarsh [Proc. London Math. Soc. (2) **38** (1934), 96–115] and Hua [Quart. J. Math. Oxford Ser. **13** (1942), 18–29; MR **4**, 190], respectively. The best lower bound known is apparently $b \geqq 1/4$, due to Hardy and Landau [Landau, *Vorlesungen über Zahlentheorie*, Bd. II, Achter Teil, Kap. 6, pp. 233–239, Hirzel, Leipzig, 1927] in 1915.

*A. C. Woods* (Columbus, Ohio)

Citations: MR 4, 190e = P20-2.

Referred to in P20-29.

## P20-29 (29# 2227 )

**Srinivasan, B. R.**

**Lattice points in a circle.**

*Proc. Nat. Inst. Sci. India Part A* **29** (1963), 332–346.

Let $\mathscr{E}(x)$ denote the excess of the number of lattice points inside and on the circle $u^2+v^2=x$ over its area. Hua [Quart. J. Math. Oxford Ser. **13** (1942), 18–29; MR **4**, 190] proved that

$$\mathscr{E}(x) = O(x^{13/40}(\log x)^{9/8}).$$

The author proves that $\mathscr{E}(x)=O(x^{13/40})$. His Lemma 1 is a two-dimensional analogue of a famous lemma of van der Corput. It runs as follows. Suppose $D$ is a finite region in the Euclidean plane subject to some complicated restrictions that we do not repeat. Let $f(u,v)$ possess continuous partial derivatives up to second order in $D$. Let $|f_{uu}| \geqq r_1 > 0$, $|f_{vv}| \geqq r_2 > 0$, $|f_{uu}f_{vv}-f_{uv}{}^2| \geqq r^2 > 0$ throughout $D$, where $r \leqq A\sqrt{(r_1r_2)}$. Then

$$\iint_D e^{2\pi i f(u,v)}\,du dv \ll \frac{1}{r}.$$

The author also states that Yin [Sci. Sinica **11** (1962), 10–15; MR **28** #3008] has claimed a further improvement in the circle-problem, namely,

$$\mathscr{E}(x) = O(x^{12/37+\varepsilon}).$$

*S. Chowla* (University Park, Pa.)

Citations: MR 4, 190e = P20-2; MR 28# 3008 = P20-28.

## P20-30 (29# 3445 )

**Keller, H. B.; Swenson, J. R.**

**Experiments on the lattice problem of Gauss.**

*Math. Comp.* **17** (1963), 223–230.

Where $A(r)$ is the number of lattice points, i.e., points with integer coordinates, in the circle $x^2+y^2 \leqq r^2$, it has been shown by Hua that

$$(1) \qquad E(r) = A(r) - \pi r^2 = O(r^\theta)$$

holds for $\theta = 13/20$ and by Hardy that it does not hold for $\theta=\frac{1}{2}$. It has been conjectured that (1) holds for $\theta > \frac{1}{2}$.

The authors describe a method of calculating $E(r)$ and tabulate sample values of it for $r$ up to 250,002. For some values of $r > 10^5$ there are values of $\ln|E(r)|/\ln r$ greater than Hua's upper bound of 0.65, while for all calculations performed, it was found that $|E(r)|/r^{1/2} < 7$. Thus it appears that the range of values of $r$ considered, though large, is still not large enough to support any conjecture [cf. the reviewer and Gotlieb, Math. Comp. **16** (1962), 282–290; MR **27** #5722].

*W. Fraser* (Toronto, Ont.)

Citations: MR 27# 5722 = P20-26.

Referred to in P20-36.

## P20-31 (30# 60 )

**Chen, Jing-run**

**The number of lattice points in a given region.**

*Acta Math. Sinica* **12** (1962), 408–420 (*Chinese*); *translated as Chinese Math.* **3** (1963), 439–452.

Let $h(-m)$ denote the number of classes of primitive quadratic forms of discriminant $-m$. The author proves that the error term in the asymptotic formula for $\sum_{m=1}^N h(-m)$ is $O(n^{\alpha+\varepsilon})$, where $\alpha = 35/52$. This is of lower order than an estimate due to I. M. Vinogradov [Izv. Akad. Nauk SSSR Ser. Mat. **24** (1960), 777–786; MR **23** #A860], who obtained $\alpha=19/28$. Similar but more powerful methods are used. The author remarks that these methods yield improved estimates in other problems; thus, for the number of lattice points in the sphere $x^2+y^2+z^2 \leqq a^2$, an error term of $O(a^{35/26+\varepsilon})$ can be obtained.

*R. A. Rankin* (Glasgow)

Citations: MR 23# A860 = P20-19.

## P20-32 (30# 1983 )

**Bleicher, M. N.; Knopp, M. I.**

**Lattice points in a sphere.**

*Acta Arith.* **10** (1964/65), 369–376.

In der 3-dimensionalen Kugel um den Nullpunkt mit dem Radius $\sqrt{x}$ mögen $A_3(x)$ Gitterpunkte liegen. Eine erste Näherung an $A_3(x)$ ist das Volumen $\frac{4}{3}\pi x^{3/2}$ der Kugel. Es sei $R_3(x)=A_3(x)-\frac{4}{3}\pi x^{3/2}$. Verfasser zeigen

$$(1) \qquad R_3(x) = O(x^{3/4}\log x), \qquad x \to \infty,$$

$$(2) \qquad R_3(x) = \Omega(x^{1/2}\log\log x), \quad x \to \infty.$$

Für die Abschätzung (1) nach oben gab Vinogradov eine schärfere Schranke, jedoch mit erheblich komplizierteren Methoden. Die Abschätzung (2) nach unten ist neu.

*O.-H. Keller* (Halle)

**P20-33** **(32# 4090)**

**Chen Jing-run [Ch'en Ching-jun]**

**Improvement on the asymptotic formulas for the number of lattice points in a region of the three dimensions. II.**

*Sci. Sinica* **12** (1963), 751–764.

Improving former results by the author and I. M. Vinogradov [cf. Sci. Sinica **12** (1963), 151–161; MR **27** #111], the following is shown: Let $h(-t)$ denote the number of classes of purely radical ternary quadratic forms of discriminant $-t$; then

$$\sum_{t=1}^{n} h(-t) = \frac{4\pi}{21\zeta(3)} n^{3/2} - \frac{2}{\pi^2} n + B(n),$$

where for every positive $\varepsilon$ the remainder term $B(n)$ is in the Landau class $O(n^{2/3+\varepsilon})$. The author remarks that in an analogous way one can prove the number of lattice points in the ball $x^2+y^2+z^2 \leqq a^2$ to be $\frac{4}{3}\pi a^3 + O(a^{4/3+\varepsilon})$.
*L. W. Danzer* (Göttingen)

Citations: MR 27# 111 = P20-22.

**P20-34** **(33# 104)**

**Bleicher, M.; Knopp, M. I.**

**Lattice points in a sphere.**

*J. Res. Nat. Bur. Standards Sect. B* **69B** (1965), 265–270.

Let $A_k(x)$ be the number of lattice points in the $k$-dimensional sphere of radius $\sqrt{x}$ and center at the origin; let $V_k(x)$ denote the volume of this sphere and set $R_k(x) = A_k(x) - V_k(x)$. The authors show that $R_3(x) = O(x^{3/4} \log\log x)$, $x \to \infty$, and $R_3(x) = \Omega(x^{1/2} \log\log x)$, $x \to \infty$. The first result is not as good as the estimate $R_3(x) = O(x^{19/28+\varepsilon})$, $\varepsilon > 0$, of Vinogradov [Izv. Akad. Nauk SSSR Ser. Mat. **24** (1960), 778–786; MR **23** #A860], but the proof, a standard application of the circle method, is much simpler. The second result is new and is obtained by a clever elementary argument from the known estimate $R_4(x) = \Omega(x \log\log x)$, $x \to \infty$. *J. B. Kelly* (Tempe, Ariz.)

Citations: MR 23# A860 = P20-19.

**P20-35** **(33# 2616)**

**Pearson, T. L.**

**Note on the Hardy-Landau summation formula.**

*Canad. Math. Bull.* **8** (1965), 717–720.

The author deduces a form of the Hardy-Landau formula $\sum_{n=0}^{\infty} r(n)f(n) = \sum_{n=0}^{\infty} r(n)g(n)$, where $r(n)$ is the number of integer solutions of $x^2+y^2=n$, and $f$ and $g$ are transforms with respect to the kernel $\pi J_0(2\pi\sqrt{x})$, from results due to A. P. Guinand [Quart. J. Math. Oxford Ser. **9** (1938), 53–67] and C. Fox [Proc. Amer. Math. Soc. **5** (1954), 677–688; MR **16**, 127]. *J. B. Miller* (Canberra)

**P20-36** **(33# 4032)**

**Mitchell, W. C.**

**The number of lattice points in a $k$-dimensional hypersphere.**

*Math. Comp.* **20** (1966), 300–310.

Let $A_k(x)$ be the number of lattice points inside or on the $k$-dimensional hypersphere $\Gamma_k$ of radius $x^{1/2}$ with center at the origin, and let $P_k(x) = A_k(x) - V_k(x)$, where $V_k(x)$ is the volume of $\Gamma_k$.

The calculations described in this paper are for $k = 2(1)6$ and for all integers $x \leqq 250000$, as well as 250 large isolated values of $x \leqq 10^{14}$ for $k=2$, and 20 large values $\leqq 81000000$ for $k=3$. The author's interpretation of the results obtained leads him to the conclusion that the greatest lower bound $\theta_2$ for all $\theta$ for which $P_2(x) = O(x^\theta)$ might as well be the number 12/37 obtained by Chen, although on less evidence Keller and Swensen [Math. Comp. **17** (1963), 223–230; MR **29** #3445] felt that $\theta_2$ could be $\leqq .3$. For $k=3$ the author concludes that the most reasonable conclusion is that $.5 \leqq \theta_3 \leqq .6$. Graphs of extreme points suggest that $\theta_4 = 1.06$, $\theta_5 = 1.52$, $\theta_6 = 2.00$.

There is a table of the first 50 extreme points $(x, P_k(x))$ for $k = 2, 3$ and a table of $A_2(x)$ and $A_3(x)$ for large isolated values of $x$. *D. H. Lehmer* (Berkeley, Calif.)

Citations: MR 29# 3445 = P20-30.

**P20-37** **(33# 5587)**

**Katai, I.**

**The number of lattice points in a circle. (Russian)**

*Ann. Univ. Sci. Budapest. Eötvös Sect. Math.* **8** (1965), 39–60.

Let $U(n)$ denote the number of representations of $n$ as a sum of two integer squares. Writing $P(x) = \sum_{n \leq x} U(n) - \pi x$ and $R(y) = \int_1^y P^2(x)\,dx - \beta y^{3/2}$, with a suitable numerical $\beta$, it has been shown, after the first results due to H. Cramer and E. Landau, that $R(y) = O(y \log^3 y)$ [see A. Z. Val'fiš, Math. Z. **26** (1927), 60–88]. The present author proves that $R(y) = O(y \log^2 y)$. Also, he supplies some results concerning the distribution of those $n$'s for which $U(n) > 0$. *S. Knapowski* (Coral Gables, Fla.)

**P20-38** **(33# 5808)**

**Rodosskiĭ, K. A.**

**On transformation of weighted sums. (Russian)**

*Volž. Mat. Sb. Vyp.* 2 (1964), 111–115.

An absolute value of a function $u$ over a ball in $n$-dimensional space is estimated from above in terms of the radius of the ball and the partial derivatives of $u$ up to order $l$, where $l$ is a natural number. The author finds this kind of estimate to be useful in applications to analytic number theory. *H. Fast* (Detroit, Mich.)

**P20-39** **(35# 2842)**

**Chandrasekharan, K.; Narasimhan, Raghavan**

**On lattice-points in a random sphere.**

*Bull. Amer. Math. Soc.* **73** (1967), 68–71.

The authors show that the following theorem of A. A. Judin (mentioned by I. M. Vinogradov and A. G. Postnikov in their report (in Russian) on "Recent developments in analytic number theory" at the Internat. Congr. Math. (Moscow, 1966) [see *Abstracts of reports on invitation*, pp. 20–21, Internat. Congr. Math., Moscow, 1966*]): If $(\alpha, \beta)$ is an arbitrary point in the plane and $A(x; \alpha, \beta)$ denotes the number of lattice-points inside and on the circumference of a circle with $(\alpha, \beta)$ as center and $x^{1/2}$ as radius, then $\limsup_{x\to\infty} |A(x; \alpha, \beta) - \pi x| \cdot x^{-1/4} > c > 0$—whose proof is reported to make use of arguments of the theory of almost periodic functions—is a direct consequence of their theorem on the average order of arithmetical functions: If $(\alpha_1, \cdots, \alpha_k)$ is an arbitrary point in $k$-space, $k \geqq 2$, and $A(x; \alpha_1, \cdots, \alpha_k)$ denotes the number of lattice-points inside and on a sphere with center $(\alpha_1, \cdots, \alpha_k)$ and radius $x^{1/2}$, then

$$[A(x; \alpha_1, \cdots, \alpha_k) - \pi^{k/2} x^{k/2} / \Gamma(k/2+1)] = \Omega \pm (x^{(k-1)/4})$$

as $x \to \infty$.** *F. Supnick* (New York)

*See MR **39** #138 = Z02-56.

**See MR **25** #3911 = N36-32.

Citations: MR 25# 3911 = N36-32; MR 39# 138 = Z02-56.

**P20-40** **(37# 5175)**

**Yudin, A. A. [Judin, A. A.]**

**On the number of integer points in the displaced circles.**

*Acta Arith.* **14** (1967/68), 141–152.

The author considers the difference $P(\lambda, u, v) = A(\lambda, u, v) -$

$\pi\lambda$, where $0 \leqq u < 1$, $0 \leqq v < 1$ and $A(\lambda, u, v)$ is the number of lattice-points in the circle $(x-u)^2-(y-v)^2 \leqq \lambda$. As a generalization of a well-known inequality of Hardy and Landau [see E. Landau, *Vorlesungen über Zahlentheorie*, Vol. 2, Hirzel, Leipzig, 1927], it is shown that for any positive $\varepsilon$, $\lim\sup P(\lambda, u, v)\lambda^{-1/4}(\log\log \lambda)^{\varepsilon-1/4} > C > 0$ and $\lim\inf P(\lambda, u, v)\lambda^{-1/4}(\log\log \lambda)^{\varepsilon-1/4} < -C$ for some absolute constant $C$.

The proof is based on a representation of $\int_0^x P(\lambda, u, v)\,d\lambda$ by an infinite series, in which, as in the case $u=v=0$, the Bessel function $F_1(z)$ occurs.

*P. Szüsz* (Stony Brook, N.Y.)

**P20-41** **(38# 1064)**

**Smith, R. A.**

**The circle problem in an arithmetic progression.**

*Canad. Math. Bull.* **11** (1968), 175–184.

Let $r(n)$ denote the number of representations of $n$ as a sum of two squares. The object of this note is to obtain a non-trivial estimate on the error term in the asymptotic expansion of the sum $S(x, b, k) = \sum_{n \leqq x; n=b(\mathrm{mod}\, k)} r(n)$. The author bases his proof on a technique used by Estermann. The formula is as follows: $S(x, b, k) = \sum \frac{1}{4}\pi \tilde{H}_k(b)x/k + O(x^{2/3+\beta}k^{-(1+3\beta)/2}(b, k)^{1/2}\, d(k))$, where $k = O(x^{2/3})$ and $0 < \beta < \frac{1}{3}$, $\tilde{H}_k(b)$ is a function depending on $k$ and $b$ which can be explicitly given. As a corollary to his refined estimate, the author gives an improved estimate of the solution of a quadratic congruence initially given by L. J. Mordell [Arch. Math. (Basel) **8** (1957), 153–157; MR **19**, 1039].

*R. Ayoub* (University Park, Pa.)

Citations: MR 19, 1039a = D80-26.

**P20-42** **(40# 5565)**

**Faure, Henri**

**Résultat voisin d'un théorème de Landau sur le nombre de points d'un réseau dans une hypersphère.**

*C. R. Acad. Sci. Paris Sér. A-B* **269** (1969), A383–A386.

A number of results of the following type are stated. Proofs are sketched and will appear later. Let $G$ be a subgroup of rank $n$ of euclidean space of dimension $n$, and let $\phi$ be a spherical harmonic of degree $k$. Put

$$A_\phi(z, G, x) = \sum \phi(u),$$

the summation being extended over all points $s = |s|u$ of $G$ situated in the closed sphere of radius $\sqrt{x}$ centred at $z$. Then $A_\phi(z, G, x) = O(x^{(n-1)n/(2n+2)})$. For $n=2$, $\phi(\theta) = e^{ik\theta}$, this is an unpublished result of A. Blanchard.

*R. A. Rankin* (Glasgow)

**P20-43** **(44# 3968)**

**Walfisz, Arnold [Val'fiš, A. Z.]; Walfisz, Anna [Val'fiš, Anna]**

**Über Gitterpunkte in mehrdimensionalen Kugeln. IV.**

*Number Theory and Analysis (Papers in Honor of Edmund Landau), pp.* 307–333. *Plenum, New York,* 1969.

Es sei $A_q(t)$ die Anzahl der Gitterpunkte in der $q$-dimensionalen Kugel $y_1^2 + \cdots + y_q^2 \leqq t$. Ferner bezeichne $V_q(t)$ das Volumen dieser Kugel und $P_q(t) = A_q(t) - V_q(t)$ den Gitterrest. In den 1960 erschienenen Teilen II und III der hier besprochenen Arbeit [Acta Arith. **6** (1960), 115–136; MR **25** #5038a; ibid. **6** (1960), 193–215; MR **25** #5038b] hat der erste Verfasser Näherungssätze für $P_{2k}(x)$ und $P_{2k+1}(x)$ $(k \geqq 3, x > 0)$ gefunden, wobei als Restglied $Bx^{k/2}\log x$ bzw. $Bx^{k/2+1/4}\log x$ auftritt.

In dieser Arbeit werden die angedeuteten Resultate von neuem und auf eine direktere Weise hergeleitet, und zwar durch Verbesserung einer älteren Methode von A. P. Lursmanašvili [Akad. Nauk Gruzin. SSR Trudy Tbiliss. Mat. Inst. Razmadze **19** (1953), 79–120; MR **16**, 451; Soobšč. Akad. Nauk Gruzin. SSR **14** (1953), 513–520; MR **15**, 941].

*C. G. Lekkerkerker* (Amsterdam)

Citations: MR 15, 941e = P20-10; MR 16, 451b = P20-11; MR 25# 5038a = P20-20; MR 25# 5038b = P20-20.

# P24 LATTICE POINT PROBLEMS: ELLIPSOIDS

See also reviews M15-18, P02-10, P28-55.

**P24-1** **(1, 294e)**

**Jarník, Vojtěch. Eine Bemerkung zur Gitterpunktlehre.** Časopis Pěst. Mat. Fys. **69**, 57–60 (1940). (German. Czech summary)

Let $S_r$ be the set of points $a = (a^{(1)}, \cdots, a^{(r)})$ $(a^{(i)} > 0)$, $A_a(x)$ the number of lattice points in the ellipsoid $a^{(1)}u_1^2 + \cdots + a^{(r)}u_r^2 \leqq x$, $V_a(x)$ the volume of this ellipsoid, and

$$\mathrm{P}_a(x) = A_a(x) - V_a(x), \quad M_a(x) = \int_0^x \mathrm{P}_a^2(y)\,dy.$$

It is known that, when $x \to \infty$,

$$\overline{\lim}\,\frac{\mathrm{P}_a(x)}{x^{\frac{1}{2}r-1}} < +\infty, \quad \underline{\lim}\,\frac{\mathrm{P}_a(x)}{x^{\frac{1}{2}r-1}} > -\infty, \qquad r>4,$$

$$\overline{\lim}\,\frac{M_a(x)}{x^{r-1}} < +\infty, \quad \underline{\lim}\,\frac{M_a(x)}{x^{\frac{1}{2}r+\frac{1}{2}}} > 0, \text{ and}$$

$$\overline{\lim}\,\frac{M_a(x)}{x^{\frac{1}{2}r+\frac{1}{2}}(\log x)^{3r+3}} < +\infty, \qquad r \geqq 4,$$

the last for almost all $a$, the others for all $a$, in $S_r$. It is shown here, with the help of continuity properties of $\mathrm{P}_a(x)$ and $M_a(x)$ in conjunction with known results for rational points $a$, that, given any $f(x) \to \infty$, we have

$$\overline{\lim}\,\frac{\mathrm{P}_a(x)}{x^{\frac{1}{2}r-1}}f(x) = +\infty, \quad \underline{\lim}\,\frac{\mathrm{P}_a(x)}{x^{\frac{1}{2}r-1}}f(x) = -\infty, \qquad r>4,$$

$$\overline{\lim}\,\frac{M_a(x)}{x^{r-1}}f(x) = +\infty, \quad \underline{\lim}\,\frac{M_a(x)}{x^{\frac{1}{2}r+\frac{1}{2}}(\log x)^{3r+3}f(x)} = 0, \quad r \geqq 4,$$

except in a set of the first category in $S_r$.

*A. E. Ingham* (Berkeley, Calif.).

Referred to in P24-11.

**P24-2** **(3, 273c)**

**Jarník, Vojtěch. Zur Gitterpunktlehre der Ellipsoide** $\alpha_1(u_1^2 + \cdots + u_{r_1}^2) + \alpha_2(u_{r_1+1}^2 + \cdots + u_r^2) \leqq x$. **II.** Časopis Pěst. Mat. Fys. **70**, 1–33 (1940). (German. Czech summary)

Let

$$Q(u) = \alpha_1(u_1^2 + u_2^2 + \cdots + u_{r_1}^2) + \alpha_2(u_{r_1+1}^2 + \cdots + u_r^2),$$

$\alpha_1 > 0$, $\alpha_2 > 0$, $\alpha_1/\alpha_2$ irrational, $z = \min(r_1, r_2) \geqq 4$ a positive definite quadratic form. Denote by $A(x)$ the number of lattice points in the ellipsoid $Q(u) \leqq x$, and by $V(x)$ the volume of this ellipsoid. Write $P(x) = A(x) - V(x)$. Let $p_\nu/q_\nu$ be the convergents of $\alpha_1/\alpha_2$. Moreover, let

$$f(Q) = \overline{\lim}\,(\log |P(x)|/\log x),$$

$$\gamma(\alpha_1, \alpha_2) = \overline{\lim}\,(\log q_{\nu+1}/\log q_\nu).$$

It was known that (proved by the author in previous papers) $\lim (P(x)/x^{r/2-1}) = 0$ and $f(Q) = r/2 - 1 - (\gamma(\alpha_1, \alpha_2))^{-1}$. The author proves among others the following results: Assume that $q_{\nu+1}/q_\nu$ is bounded; then for $z > 6$, $\overline{\lim}\,(P(x)/x^{r/2-2}) < \infty$.

Let $z>10$; then, for every $x>c_5$, there exist two numbers $x_1$ and $x_2$ such that $x-c_6/x<x_j<x$ $(j=1, 2)$, $P(x_1)>c_7x_1^{r/2-2}$, $P(x_2)<-c_7x_2^{r/2-2}$. On the other hand, if $x_2>x_1>1$ and $P(x_1)>\epsilon x_1^{r/2-2}$, $P(x_2)<-\epsilon x_2^{r/2-2}$, then $x_2-x_1>c_9\epsilon/x_2$.

*P. Erdös* (Philadelphia, Pa.).

## P24-3 (3, 274a)

**Jarník, Vojtěch. Über die Mittelwertsätze der Gitterpunktlehre. V.** Časopis Pěst. Mat. Fys. **69**, 148–174 (1940). (German. Czech summary)

Let $Q(x)=\sum'_{u,v=1}c_{u,v}x_ux_v$ be a positive definite form with determinant $D$. Denote by $A(y)$ the number of lattice points in the ellipsoid $Q(x)\leqq y$. Write

$$P(y)=A(y)-\pi^{r/2}y^{r/2}/D^{\frac{1}{2}}\Gamma(r/2-1),\quad M(y)=\int_0^y P^2(y)dy.$$

The author proves that for $r>2$, if the $c$'s are integers, there exists an $H>0$ (depending only on $Q$) such that $M(x)=Hx^2\log x-O(x^2\log^{\frac{1}{2}}x)$ for $r=3$ and $M(x)=Hx^{r-1}-O(g(x))$ for $r>3$, where $g(x)=x^{5/2}\log x$ for $r=4$, $g(x)=x^3\log^2 x$ for $r=5$ and $g(x)=x^{r-2}$ for $r>5$. He also shows that the error term is best possible for $r>5$. [This is not difficult.] *P. Erdös* (Philadelphia, Pa.).

Referred to in P24-6.

## P24-4 (4, 132b)

**Walfisz, Arnold. On lattice points in high-dimensional ellipsoids. IX.** Trav. Inst. Math. Tbilissi [Trudy Tbiliss. Mat. Inst.] **10**, 111–160 (1941). (English. Russian summary)

[The last communication appeared in the same Trav. **5**, 181–195 (1938).] This paper is in two parts. The first part deals with the number of lattice points in the closed ellipsoid $Q\leqq x$, where $Q$ is a positive definite quadratic form with integral coefficients. The number of lattice points is approximated by the volume of the ellipsoid with an error denoted by $P_Q(x)$. In papers (V) and (VII) of the same series [Acta Arith. **1**, 222–283 (1936); Trav. Inst. Math. Tbilissi **5**, 1–65 (1938)] the author established for quaternary forms the existence of a positive constant $\mathfrak{S}(Q)$ satisfying

$$\int_0^x P_Q^2(w)dw=\mathfrak{S}(Q)x^3+Bx^{5/2}\log^2 x.$$

In paper (VII) $\mathfrak{S}(Q)$ was evaluated for the forms

$$(1)\qquad n_1^2+n_2^2+d(n_3^2+n_4^2),\qquad d=1, 2, 3, \cdots.$$

Also in (VII) the constant $\mathfrak{T}(Q)$, which appears in the formulas

$$\sum r^2_Q(n)=\mathfrak{T}(Q)x^3+Bx^2\log^3 x\quad\text{(quaternary forms)},$$
$$\sum r^2_Q(n)=\mathfrak{T}(Q)x^2+Bx^{3/2}\log x\quad\text{(ternary forms)},$$

was evaluated for the forms (1) and $n_1^2+d(n_2^2+n_3^2)$, $d=1, 2, 3, \cdots$, respectively. Here $r_Q(n)$ is the number of solutions of $n=Q$.

In the present paper the constants $\mathfrak{S}(Q)$ and $\mathfrak{T}(Q)$ are evaluated for the forms $an_1^2+bn_2^2+cn_3^2+dn_4^2$ and $\mathfrak{T}(Q)$ for the forms $an_1^2+bn_2^2+cn_3^2$. The starting point is the formula

$$\mathfrak{S}(Q)=(\pi^2/6D)\sum_{\substack{h,\,l=1\\(h,\,l)=1}}^{\infty}|T_{h,l}|^2h^{-2}l^{-6},$$

where

$$T_{h,l}=\sum_{n_i=0}^{l-1}\exp\{2\pi i(h/l)Q(n_1,\cdots,n_k)\},$$

with a similar one for $\mathfrak{T}(Q)$.

The second part of the paper deals with lattice points in a $k$-dimensional sphere. Using $P_k(x)$ instead of $P_Q(x)$, the author proved in paper (II) [Math. Z. **19**, 106–124 (1927)] that for $x=n!$, $n\to\infty$,

$$P_k(x)=M_kC_kx^{k/2-1}+o(x^{k/2-1}),$$

where

$$M_k=(\pi^{k/2})/(2\Gamma(k/2)),$$

$$c_k=1+i\sum_{l=2}^{\infty}\sum_{h=1}^{l-1}l^{-k}S_{h,l}{}^ke^{-\pi ih/l}\operatorname{cosec}(\pi h/l),$$

and $S_{h,l}$ is the well-known Gaussian sum. In this paper the series for $C_k$ is summed for $k\equiv 0, 2, 4, 6 \pmod 8$ in terms of the $\zeta$-function and the function $L(s)$ defined by

$$L(s)=\sum_{u=1}^{\infty}(-1|u)u^{-s},\qquad s>1.$$

A typical result is

$$c_k=(L(k/2-1)-2^{1-k/2}\zeta(k/2-1))/L(k/2),\quad k\equiv 2 \pmod 8).$$

Similar results are obtained for $P_k(x+r)$, $r>0$ (fixed), and $x=n!$, $n\to\infty$.

Next, inequalities are obtained which are satisfied by

$$P_k=\overline{\lim_{n\to\infty}}\,(P_k(n)/M_kn^{k/2-1}),\quad \rho_k=\lim_{n\to\infty}(P_k(n)/M_kn^{k/2-1}).$$

They are

$$P_k>1+2^{1-k/2}+2\cdot 3^{-k/2},\quad \rho_k<1-2^{1-k/2}-2\cdot 3^{-k/2}.$$

Similar inequalities are established under the hypotheses $n\equiv a \pmod 4$, $n\equiv b \pmod 3$, $n\equiv c \pmod 8$, $n\equiv d \pmod 5$, $k$ even. A formula is then worked out for

$$\sum_{n=1}^{x}r_k(n)r_{k+q}(n),\quad q\geqq 0;\, q\equiv 0 \pmod 2),$$

analogous to the result obtained in the special case $q=0$. Finally the author points out that his work leads to two curious corollaries, one of which is

$$\sum_{n=1}^{x}r_k{}^2(n)\sim 2\binom{k-2}{k/2-1}P_{2k}(x)$$

for $x=n!$, $n\to\infty$. *R. D. James* (Saskatoon, Sask.).

Referred to in P20-9, P20-14.

## P24-5 (7, 417f)

**Jarník, Vojtěch. Zur Gitterpunktlehre der Ellipsoide**

$$\alpha_1(u_1^2+\cdots+u_{r_1}^2)+\alpha_2(u_{r_1+1}^2+\cdots+u_r^2)\leqq x.$$

Věstník Královské České Společnosti Nauk. Třída Matemat.-Přírodověd. **1940**, no. 3, 63 pp. (1941) (German. Czech and French summaries)

Let $r_1$, $r_2$ be integers, $\alpha_1>0$, $\alpha_2>0$, $\alpha_1/\alpha_2$ irrational, $r=r_1+r_2$, $z=\min(r_1, r_2)\geqq 6$. Put

$$Q(u)=\alpha_1(u_1^2+\cdots+u_{r_1}^2)+\alpha_2(u_{r_1+1}^2+\cdots+u_r^2),$$

and let $A_Q(x)$ be the number of lattice points in the ellipsoid $Q(u)\leqq x$, and $V_Q$ the volume of $Q(u)\leqq 1$. Write

$$\mathbf{P}_Q(x)=A_Q(x)-V_Qx^{\frac{1}{2}r},\quad M_Q(x)=\int_0^x\mathbf{P}_Q^2(y)dy,\quad x\geqq 0.$$

Denote by $p_v/q_v$ $(v=0, 1, \cdots)$ the continued fraction convergents to $\alpha_1/\alpha_2$, and put

$$F_Q(x)=x^{r-1}\sum_{v,m,n}q_v^{-2}n^{2-r_1}m^{2-r_2}\min\{1, (q_{v+1}mnx^{-1})^z\},$$

the summation being carried out over all nonnegative integers $v$, $m$, $n$ satisfying $p_v>0$, $m|p_v$ and $n|q_v$. The greater part of the paper is devoted to the proof of the principal theorem which states that, if $0\leqq\mu<1$, there exist positive numbers $c_1$, $c_2$, $c_3$ depending only on $\mu$, $r_1$, $r_2$, $\alpha_1$, $\alpha_2$ such that $c_1F_Q(x)<M_Q(x)-M_Q(\mu x)<c_2F_Q(x)$ for all $x>c_3$. A considerable amount of information on the range of variation of $M_Q(x)$ for different $\alpha_1$, $\alpha_2$ can be deduced from this result (with $\mu=0$). Let (for $x\to\infty$)

$$f_1(Q)=\overline{\lim}\,\{\log M_Q(x)/\log x\},$$
$$f_2(Q)=\underline{\lim}\,\{\log M_Q(x)/\log x\},$$
$$\gamma=\gamma(\alpha_1,\alpha_2)=\overline{\lim}\,\{\log q_{v+1}/\log q_v\},$$
$$\delta=\delta(\alpha_1,\alpha_2)=\underline{\lim}\,\{\log q_{v+1}/\log q_v\},$$

and let $f_2(r_1, r_2, \gamma)$ be the upper bound of $f_2(Q)$ for given $r_1$, $r_2$, $\gamma$. Clearly $1\leqq\delta\leqq\gamma$ and $f_2(Q)\leqq f_1(Q)$. Write $d=\max\{0, 2-|r_1-r_2|\}$, $\beta=r-1-2z/(z+2)$ and, finally, $\beta'=r-1-2z/(z+2+d/\gamma)$.

Of the various results proved the following are the most important. (i) $f_1(Q)=r-1-2/\gamma\geqq r-3$. (This can also be deduced from a previous paper of the author [Math. Z. **36**, 581–617 (1933)].) (ii) There exist functions $W_1$ and $W_2$ (of forms too complicated to quote here) depending only on $z$, $\gamma$, $d$ such that $W_1<2$ $(\gamma>1)$, $W_1=2$ $(\gamma=1)$, and $r-1-W_1\leqq f_2(r_1, r_2, \gamma)\leqq r-1-W_2$. Furthermore, corresponding to every set $r_1$, $r_2$, $\gamma$ there exists a form $Q$ with $f_2(Q)\geqq r-1-W_1$. From (ii) it follows easily that (a) $f_2(Q)<f_1(Q)$ for $\gamma>1$; (b) $f_2(r_1, r_2, \gamma)=\beta'$ for $\gamma>z+1$; (c) for given $r_1$, $r_2$ a form $Q$ exists with $f_2(Q)\geqq\beta$; and (d) for given $r_1$, $r_2$ with $|r_1-r_2|>1$, $f_2(Q)\leqq\beta$ and there exists a form with $f_2(Q)=\beta$. (iii) If $\delta>z+2$, $f_2(Q)=\beta'$, and if, in addition, $|r_1-r_2|\geqq 2$, then $\underline{\lim}\, x^{-\beta}M_Q(x)>0$. (iv) If $|r_1-r_2|\geqq 4$, $\underline{\lim}\, x^{-\beta}M_Q(x)<\infty$.

*R. A. Rankin* (Cambridge, England).

**P24-6** **(8, 197a)**

**Jarník, Vojtěch. Über die Mittelwertsätze der Gitterpunktlehre. VI.** Časopis Pěst. Mat. Fys. **70**, 89–103 (1941). (Czech. German summary)

Let $Q(u)=\sum_{j=1}^{r}\alpha_j u_j^2$ $(\alpha_j>0)$ and let $V$ be the volume of the ellipsoid $Q(u)\leqq 1$, $A(x)$ the number of lattice points $(u_1, \cdots, u_r)$ satisfying $Q(u)\leqq x$, and

$$M(x)=\int_0^x\{A(y)-Vy^{\frac{1}{2}r}\}^2dy.$$

By methods similar to those used in part V [same Časopis **69**, 148–174 (1940); these Rev. **3**, 274] the author shows that $M(x)=O(x^{\frac{3}{2}})$ $(r=2)$ and $M(x)=O(x^2\log x)$ $(r=3)$, where the $\alpha_j$ are arbitrary positive numbers, rational or irrational. These supplement the known results for $r>3$ and supersede the author's earlier estimates which were $O(x^{\frac{3}{2}}\log^4 x)$ and $O(x^2\log^4 x)$, respectively [Math. Z. **33**, 62–84 (1931)].

*R. A. Rankin* (Cambridge, England).

Citations: MR 3, 274a = P24-3.

**P24-7** **(15, 237g)**

**Kendall, David G., and Rankin, R. A. On the number of points of a given lattice in a random hypersphere.** Quart. J. Math., Oxford Ser. (2) **4**, 178–189 (1953).

In connection with some research on cutaneous sensations of warmth due to G. H. Wright, the authors have undertaken an investigation of the number of points of a given lattice in a random hypersphere, with particular reference to hexagonal lattices. They derive explicit formulae for the expected number of points and for the variance and compare the numerical results obtained in this way with 23,000 random throwings of circles of various sizes on to a hexagonal lattice performed by Wright. The results agree well.

*R. Bellman* (Santa Monica, Calif.).

Referred to in E44-8.

**P24-8** **(15, 687a)**

**Tsuji, Masatsugu. On lattice points in an $n$-dimensional ellipsoid.** J. Math. Soc. Japan **5**, 295–306 (1953).

Let $Q$ denote a positive definite quadratic form in $x_1, \cdots, x_n$ $(n\geqq 2)$, and let $n(r)$ be the number of lattice points inside the $n$-dimensional ellipsoid $Q<r^2$. Then, if $V(r)$ is the volume of the ellipsoid, we write $n(r)=V(r)+\Omega(r)$. Estimates of $\Omega(r)$ are well-known [see Landau, S.-B. Preuss. Akad. Wiss. **1915**, 458–476]. For mean values of $\Omega(r)$ estimates can be obtained which are sharper than those following trivially from estimates for $\Omega(r)$ itself. The author proves that $\int_1^r\Omega(t)t^{1-n}dt=O(1)$. His proof uses $n$-dimensional potential functions and an analogue of methods of Nevanlinna. The reviewer remarks that by classical methods, depending on transformation of the theta series corresponding to $Q$, sharper results can be obtained, e.g. by Landau's method of the paper cited above. It can be shown that the above integral even converges, and estimates can be found for $\int_r^\infty\Omega(t)t^{1-n}dt$. E.g., if $n=2$, Landau's formula (34) (an explicit formula in the form of a series with Bessel coefficients) immediately gives $\int_r^\infty=O(r^{-1/2})$.

*N. G. de Bruijn.*

**P24-9** **(22# 4702 )**

**Walfisz, Arnold. Über Gitterpunkte in vierdimensionalen Ellipsoiden.** Math. Z. **72** (1959/60), 259–278.

With the help of estimates of exponential sums due to Winogradoff the author sharpens the known estimates for the error term in the expression for the number of lattice points in the 4-dimensional sphere $x_1^2+x_2^2+x_3^2+x_4^2\leq x$ to $O(x\log^{2/3}x)$. More generally, he achieves this for a quaternary definite form $Q(x_1, x_2, x_3, x_4)$ with rational coefficients. He has not used recent work of Koroboff which at first seemed necessary to obtain his sharp estimate.

*S. Chowla* (Notre Dame, Ind.)

Referred to in L99-11.

**P24-10** **(24# A93 )**

**Rao, V. Venugopal**

**Lattice point problems and quadratic forms.**

*Math. Student* **27** (1959), 137–152 (1961).

The classical lattice-point problem associated with the circle is concerned with the study of the function $P(x)$ defined by

$$R(x) = \sum_{0\leq n\leq x} r(n) = \pi x+P(x),$$

where $r(n)$ denotes the number of integral representations of the integer $n$ as the sum of squares of two other integers. The following result of Hardy is cited:

$$(1)\qquad R(x)-\delta_x r(x) = \pi x+x^{1/2}\sum_{x=1}^{\infty}\frac{r(n)J_1(2\pi(nx)^{1/2})}{n^{1/2}}.$$

where $J_1(x)$ denotes the Bessel function of the first kind and is $\frac{1}{2}$ or 0, according as $x$ is integral or not.

This paper is devoted to stating and giving references to proofs of known results which generalize (1) to include integral representations of real numbers by definite and indefinite quadratic forms in $m$ variables. For definite forms a transformation formula involving the theta function is mentioned, and an analogue of this function for indefinite forms is dealt with.

*B. W. Jones* (Boulder, Colo.)

**P24-11** **(28# 3009 )**

**Novak, B.**

**Integral points in hyperellipsoids. (Russian)**

*Dokl. Akad. Nauk SSSR* **153** (1963), 762–764.

The author considers exponential sums $A(x)=\sum\exp[2\pi i\sum_{i=1}^{n}\alpha_i\mu_i]$. The summation is extended over the sets $(\mu_1, \cdots, \mu_r)$ satisfying $Q(\mu_1, \cdots, \mu_r)\leq x$, where $Q$ is a positive definite quadratic form with integral coefficients, $r>4$, and in addition, $\mu_i\equiv b_i \pmod{M_i}$ with given $b_i$, $M_i$ for all $i=1, \cdots, r$. For $\alpha_i=b_i=0$ and $M_i=1$ for all $i$,

$A(x)$ reduces to the number of lattice points in the hyperellipsoid ("integral volume"). $A(x)$ is then compared with the "generalized integral volume" and various estimates for the error term are given. The results include and improve earlier results by Val'fiš [Akad. Nauk Gruzin. SSR Trudy Tbiliss. Mat. Inst. Razmadze **20** (1954), 1–20; MR **17**, 133; ibid. **21** (1955), 3–64; MR **18**, 115] and earlier work by Jarník [Časopis Pěst. Mat. Fys. **69** (1940), 57–60; MR **1**, 294]. *V. Linis* (Ottawa, Ont.)

Citations: MR 1, 294e = P24-1; MR 17, 133d = P20-13; MR 18, 115a = P20-14.

**P24-12** **(30# 62)**

**Wu, Fang**

**The lattice-points in an ellipse.**

*Acta Math. Sinica* **13** (1963), 238–253 (*Chinese*); *translated as Chinese Math.* **4** (1963), 260–274.

Let $a, b, c$ be real numbers for which $a>0$, $c>0$ and $D=b^2-4ac<0$, and let $R(x)$ denote the number of lattice-points in the ellipse

$$a\xi^2+b\xi\eta+c\eta^2 \leqq x.$$

Then $R(x)=2\pi x|D|^{-1/2}+O(x^\alpha)$, where $0<\alpha\leqq\frac{1}{2}$. Let $\vartheta$ be the lower bound of numbers $\alpha$ satisfying this equation. For the case when $a, b, c$ are integers, E. C. Titchmarsh [Quart. J. Math. Oxford Ser. **6** (1935), 106–112] proved that $\vartheta\leqq 27/82$. The author replaces this by the improved estimate $\vartheta\leqq 13/40$ (the same index as Hua's estimate in the circle problem), which is valid for real $a, b, c$. For this extension the expression for $\int_0^x R(t)\,dt$ as an infinite series of Bessel functions, which was used by Titchmarsh, is not applicable, and the author replaces this by a lemma of Vinogradov. Titchmarsh's extension of van der Corput's method to two dimensions is also used. *R. A. Rankin* (Glasgow)

**P24-13** **(30# 3068)**

**Jarník, V.**

**Zur Gitterpunktlehre von mehrdimensionalen Ellipsoiden.**

*Acta Arith.* **9** (1964), 321–329.

Let $Q(u)=Q(u_1, u_2, \cdots, u_r)$ be a positive definite quadratic form. Let $A(x)$ denote the number of lattice points in the ellipsoid $Q(u)\leqq x$; we set $P(x)=A(x)-V(x)$, where $V(x)$ stands for the volume of this ellipsoid. It is known that $P(x)=O(x^{r/2-1})$ and that $P(x)=\Omega(x^{r/2-1})$ for $r>4$ and rational $Q$. The author considers a large class of irrational $Q$'s and shows that for almost all of them (in the measure-theoretic sense) the upper bound for $P(x)$ can be reduced to $O(x^{r/2-\lambda})$, where $\lambda>1$ is given explicitly. *S. Knapowski* (Gainesville, Fla.)

**P24-14** **(33# 1297)**

**Leĭbson, K. L.**

**Integral points inside ellipsoids, with regard to the theory of Hecke operators.** **(Russian. English summary)**

*Vestnik Leningrad. Univ.* **20** (1965), *no.* 1, 153–155.

Author's summary: "A commutative ring of operators $\tilde{T}$ consisting of operators of species $\sum c_i T_{m_i}$, where the $T_m$ are the Hecke operators, is considered. For the positive definite quadratic form $Q$ with an even number of variables $(f=2k)$, $\{\vartheta(\tau; Q)\}_{\tilde{T}}$ denotes the totality of functions of species $\vartheta(\tau; Q)|T$, where $T\in\tilde{T}$; $\gamma_Q(d)$ denotes the solution of the $O$—$\Omega$-problem for

$$\sum_{\substack{Q(\varepsilon_1,\cdots,\varepsilon_f)\equiv 0\,(d)\\ 0\leqq\varepsilon_j<d}} P_Q\left(t; \frac{\varepsilon_1}{d}, \cdots, \frac{\varepsilon_f}{d}\right).$$

Let the functions $\vartheta(\tau; Q)|T_{m_i}$ $(i=1, \cdots, s)$ form the basis $\{\vartheta(\tau; Q)\}_{\tilde{T}}$. If $\vartheta(\tau; Q_1)\in\{\vartheta(\tau; Q)\}_{\tilde{T}}$, then $\gamma_{Q_1}(0, \cdots, 0)\leqq \max_{d|m_i}\gamma_Q(d)$ $(i=1, \cdots, s)$."

**P24-15** **(34# 4232)**

**Novák, Břetislav**

**On lattice points in high-dimensional ellipsoids. Preliminary communication.**

*Comment. Math. Univ. Carolinae* **7** (1966), 479–484.

Statements of five theorems whose proofs are to appear in Czechoslovak Math. J. and Acta Arith. *R. P. Bambah* (Columbus, Ohio)

**P24-16** **(35# 4182)**

**Novák, Břetislav**

**A remark on the theory of lattice points in ellipsoids.**

*Comment. Math. Univ. Carolinae* **8** (1967), 219–230.

Let $r$ be an integer $\geqq 2$. Let $Q(\mu_j)=\sum_{j,k=1}^r a_{kj}\mu_k\mu_j$ be a positive definite quadratic form whose discriminant is denoted by $D$. Let $M_j$, $b_j$ and $\alpha_j$ be real numbers, $M_j>0$ $(1\leqq j\leqq r)$.

The author studies the function $A(x)=A(x; \alpha_j)=\sum e^{2\pi i\sum_{j=1}^r \alpha_j\mu_j}$, where the summation runs over all systems $\mu_1, \cdots, \mu_r$ of real numbers satisfying $Q(\mu_j)\leqq x$ and $\mu_j\equiv b_j \bmod M_j$ for $j=1, 2, \cdots, r$. Set

$$V(x) = V(x; \alpha_j) = \delta[\pi^{r/2}x^{r/2}e^{2\pi i\sum_{j=1}^r\alpha_j b_j}/\sqrt{D}\,\textstyle\prod_{j=1}^r M_j\Gamma(r/2+1)]$$

$(\delta=1$ if all $\alpha_j M_j$ are integers, $\delta=0$ otherwise) and $P(x, \alpha_j)=A(x, \alpha_j)-V(x, \alpha_j)$. The author proves (Theorem 1) that $\operatorname{ess\,sup}_{(\alpha_1,\cdots,\alpha_r)\in\mathscr{M}}|P(x; \alpha_j)|\asymp x^{r/2}$. Here $\mathscr{M}=\langle 0, 1/M_1\rangle\times\cdots\times\langle 0, 1/M_r\rangle$, and $A\asymp B$ means that $A\ll B$ and $B\ll A$. *S. Chowla* (University Park, Pa.)

Referred to in P24-24.

**P24-17** **(36# 1408)**

**Novák, Břetislav**

**Über Gitterpunkte mit Gewichten in mehrdimensionalen Ellipsoiden: Mittelwertsätze.** **(Russian summary)**

*Czechoslovak Math. J.* **17** (**92**) (1967), 609–623.

Let $Q(u)=\sum_1^r a_{ij}u_iu_j$ be a positive quadratic form, and for $x>0$ let $A(x)=\sum\exp(2\pi i\sum_{j=1}^r\alpha_j u_j)$, summed over all real $u_1, \cdots, u_r$ satisfying $Q(u)\leqq x$ and $u_j\equiv b_j \pmod{M_j}$ $(j=1, \cdots, r)$. (Here all variables are real, and the $M_j$ are positive.) Set $A(x)=V(x)+P(x)$, where $V(x)$ is the appropriate integral over the ellipsoid $Q(u)\leqq x$, and $P(x)$ is the error term. The author here considers the order of magnitude of the mean value $T(x)=(x^{-1}M(x))^{1/2}$, where $M(x)=\int_0^x P^2(y)\,dy$. V. Jarník, in the years 1931–1941, established many definitive results on this problem, under certain assumptions on the $a_{ij}$, $\alpha_j$, $b_j$ and $M_j$. Here the author, using Jarník's method, establishes formally analogous results, and shows that if the $a_{ij}$, $b_j$ and $M_j$ are all integral, then for almost all (in the sense of Lebesgue measure) systems $\alpha_1, \cdots, \alpha_r$,

$$T(x) = O(x^{(r-1)/4}\log^{(3r+2)/2}x);$$

while always $T(x)=\Omega(x^{(r-1)/4})$ provided that $A(x)\not\equiv 0$. A separate article is promised for the case of rational $\alpha_1, \cdots, \alpha_r$. *E. S. Barnes* (Adelaide)

**P24-18** **(36# 5094)**

**Lursmanašvili, A. P.**

**Integral square-free points in multidimensional ellipsoids.** **(Russian. Georgian summary)**

*Sakharth. SSR Mecn. Akad. Moambe* **49** (1968), 3–8.

Let $A_Q(x)=\sum_{Q(r_1,\cdots,r_k)\leqq x}1$, where $Q$ is a positive definite quadratic form in $k$ variables with integral coefficients, and the $r$'s stand for square-free positive integers (in the classical theorems of Landau, Val′fiš, Jarník, the $r$'s are non-negative integers, and $k \geqq 4$). The author proves the expected estimates for $A_Q(x)$, namely, in Theorem 2 (his Theorem 1 contains the "dominant term" with the "singular series" as a factor), which runs as follows: $A_Q(x) = 6^k \pi^{-3k/2} x^{k/2}/(D^{k/2}\Gamma(k/2+1)) + O(x^{k/2-1})$ for $k \geqq 5$, $A_Q(x) = 648x^2/(D^{1/2}\pi^6) + O(x^{1+\varepsilon})$ for $k=4$. Here $D$ is the determinant of $Q$. The proofs are neatly and elegantly sketched. *S. Chowla* (University Park, Pa.)

## P24-19 (37# 5151 )

**Novák, B.**

**Verallgemeinerung eines Peterssonschen Satzes und Gitterpunkte mit Gewichten.**

*Acta Arith.* **13** (1967/68), 423–454.

Let $r$ be a natural number, $r \geqq 2$, and let (1) $Q(u) = Q(u_j) = \sum_{l,j=1}^r a_{lj}u_l u_j$ be a positive definite quadratic form with determinant $D$. Further, let (2) $M_1, \cdots, M_r, b_1, \cdots, b_r, \alpha_1, \cdots, \alpha_r$ ($M$'s$>0$) be real numbers. We define (3) $A(x) = \sum e^{2\pi i \sum_{j=1}^r \alpha_j u_j}$, where the sum is over the $u$'s for which (4) $Q(u_1, \cdots, u_r) \leqq x$ and (5) $u_j \equiv b_j \pmod{M_j}$ $(1 \leqq j \leqq r)$. We also set

$$V(x) = \pi^{r/2} x^{r/2} e^{2\pi i \sum_{j=1}^r \alpha_j b_j} \delta / (D^{1/2} \textstyle\prod_{j=1}^r M_j \Gamma(\frac{1}{2}r+1))$$

($\delta = 1$ if all $\alpha_t M_t$ are integers, otherwise $\delta = 0$). The author is concerned with the estimation of $P(x) = A(x) - V(x)$. Landau (1915–1924) proved the fundamental $P(x) = O(x^{r/2 - r/(r+1)})$ and (under the hypothesis $A(x) \neq 0$) $P(x) = \Omega(x^{(r-1)/4})$. In the so-called "rational case", Landau and Walfisz proved $P(x) = O(x^{r/2-1})$ for $r \geqq 5$, which is best possible.

The object of the author is the study of the function (3) under the assumption that the coefficients of the form (1) and the numbers $M_j$ and $b_j$ are all integral. However, the $\alpha$'s are allowed to be arbitrary real numbers. He generalizes a well-known theorem of H. Petersson [Abh. Math. Sem. Univ. Hamburg **5** (1926), 116–150, Satz A′] obtained by the circle method. Unfortunately, his theorems are too long to quote here. As an example we merely mention that his Satz 1a (p. 445) bears a close resemblance to the theorem of Petersson mentioned above.

*S. Chowla* (University Park, Pa.)

Referred to in P24-24.

## P24-20 (37# 6243 )

**Novák, B.**

**On lattice points with weight in high-dimensional ellipsoids.**

*Acta Arith.* **14** (1967/68), 371–397.

Let $r \geqq 2$ be an integer, $M_j > 0$, $b_j, \alpha_j$ real numbers $(j = 1, \cdots, r)$, $\Gamma$ the grid $\{b_1 + z_1 M_1, \cdots, b_r + z_r M_r : z_j = 0, \pm 1, \pm 2, \cdots\}$ and $E(x) : Q \leqq x$ the $r$-dimensional ellipsoid corresponding to the positive definite quadratic form $Q = \sum a_{ij}u_i u_j$. Denote the exponential sum $\sum \exp(2\pi i \bar{\alpha} \cdot \bar{u})$ over $\Gamma \cap E$ by $A(x)$ (when $\alpha = 0$ $A(x)$ is then the number of grid points in $E$), and let

$$V(x) = \delta \pi^{r/2} x^{r/2} \exp(2\pi i \bar{\alpha} \cdot \bar{b}) / D^{1/2} \Gamma(\tfrac{1}{2}r+1) \textstyle\prod M_j,$$

where $D$ is the discriminant of $Q$, $\delta = 1$ if all the products $\alpha_j M_j$ are integers, $\delta = 0$ otherwise.

The central problem is to find an $f$ such that $P(x) = A(x) - V(x)$ satisfies $P(x) = O(x^{f+\varepsilon})$, $P(x) \neq o(x^{f-\varepsilon})$ for every $\varepsilon > 0$. It is known that $\frac{1}{4}r - \frac{1}{4} \leqq f \leqq \frac{1}{2}r - r/(r+1)$ [see E. Landau, *Ausgewählte Abhandlungen zur Gitterpunktlehre*, pp. 11–84, VEB Deutsch. Verlag Wissensch., Berlin, 1962; MR **27** #112], and in certain cases $f$ has been found, for example, $f = \frac{1}{2}r - 1$ when $\bar{\alpha} = 0$, the $\alpha_{ij}$ are integers and $\Gamma = \Lambda_0$ the fundamental lattice $(M_j = 1, b_j = 0)$. The author extends this as follows: Let $\Gamma \subset \Lambda_0$ $(M_j \in Z^+, b_j = 0)$, $\alpha_j = \alpha$ $(j = 1, \cdots, r)$ and let the $\alpha_{ij}$ be integers. Then $f = (\frac{1}{2}r - 1)(2\gamma + 1)(2\gamma + 2)^{-1}$, where $\gamma = \gamma(\alpha)$ is the supremum of all numbers $\beta > 0$ for which $q\alpha$ is within $q^{-\beta}$ of $p$ for infinitely many pairs $(p, q)$ of integers $(q > 0)$, and $f = \frac{1}{2}r - 1$ if $\gamma = \infty$. *G. K. White* (Vancouver, B.C.)

Citations: MR 27# 112 = Z25-17.

Referred to in P24-24, P24-29.

## P24-21 (38# 121 )

**Novák, Břetislav**

**Mean value theorems in the theory of lattice points with weight.**

*Comment. Math. Univ. Carolinae* **8** (1967), 711–733.

Let $r$ be a natural number, $r \geqq 2$; let $Q(u_j) = \sum_{l,j=1}^r a_{lj}u_l u_j$ be a positive definite quadratic form with integer coefficients and the determinant $D$. Further, the $M_s$ $(1 \leqq s \leqq r)$ are natural numbers, the $b$'s integers. For arbitrary real $\alpha$'s, define, for $x > 0$, $A(x) = A(x; \alpha_j) = \sum e^{2\pi i \sum_{j=1}^r \alpha_j u_j}$, where the sum is over all systems of $u$'s with $u_j \equiv b_j \pmod{M_j}$ $[1 \leqq j \leqq r]$ and $Q(u_j) \leqq x$. One is interested in estimating $P(x) = A(x) - V(x)$, where

$$V(x) = M x^{r/2} e^{2\pi i \sum \alpha_j b_j} \delta / \Gamma(r/2+1).$$

Here $M = \pi^{r/2} D^{-1/2} (M_1 \cdots M_r)^{-1}$; $\delta = 1$ if all $\alpha_j M_j$ are integers; $\delta = 0$ otherwise. The estimation of $P(x)$ for $r \geqq 2$ (Gauss, Sierpiński, Hardy, Landau, Walfisz, Jarník) is carried still further by the author of the present paper. We shall quote a few of his results. Set $M(x) = \int_0^x |P(y)|^2 \, dy$. The author's main theorem is too long to quote. However, the following are what he calls "two 'exceeding' consequences" (pp. 726 and 727). Theorem 1: Let $r \geqq 4$, and let at least one of the numbers $\alpha_1, \cdots, \alpha_r$ be irrational. Then we have the "little" $o$-result (A) $M(x) = o(x^{r-1})$. Theorem 2: Let $r \geqq 4$ and let $\varphi(x)$ be a non-increasing positive function, $\varphi(x) = o(1)$. Then there exists a system $\alpha_1, \cdots, \alpha_r$ such that (A) holds, and further, $M(x) = \Omega(x^{r-1}\varphi(x))$ (the $\Omega$-notation being that of Littlewood).

*S. Chowla* (University Park, Pa.)

Referred to in P24-26.

## P24-22 (38# 4414 )

**Diviš, Bohuslav**

**On lattice points in high-dimensional ellipsoids.**

*Comment. Math. Univ. Carolinae* **9** (1968), 199–205.

Pour $r$ entier, $r \geqq 5$, soit $Q(u) = \sum_{j=1}^r \alpha_j u_j^2$, $\alpha_j > 0$. $(j = 1, \cdots, r)$. Si $A_Q(x)$ est, pour $x > 0$, le nombre de points à coordonnées entières situés dans l'ellipsoïde $Q(u) \leqq x$, on connait des estimations,. à l'aide de puissances de $x$ dépendant de $r$ et pour $x \to +\infty$, de $P_Q(x) = A_Q(x) - V_Q(x)$, où $V_Q(x)$ est le volume de l'ellipsoïde précédent. On obtient des résultats plus fins quand on particularise la forme $Q$; par exemple, si

$$(*) \qquad Q(u) = \textstyle\sum_{j=1}^{\sigma} \alpha_j (u_{1,j}^2 + u_{2,j}^2 + \cdots + u_{r_j,j}^2)$$

avec $r_j$, $\sigma$ entiers, $\sigma \geqq 2$, $r_j \geqq 4$. Après avoir rappelé des résultats obtenus par V. Jarník, E. Landau et A. Z. Val′fiš entre 1924 et 1934, l'auteur signale, sans démonstration, qu'on peut, dans le cas (*), généraliser à $\sigma > 2$, $r_j \geqq 2\sigma$ ce qu'avait démontré V. Jarník [Tôhoku Math. J. **30** (1929), 354–371] pour $\sigma = 2$. *R. Bantegnie* (Besançon)

## P24-23 (38# 5733 )

**Novák, Břetislav**

**Mittelwertsätze der Gitterpunktlehre.**

*Czechoslovak Math. J.* **19 (94)** (1969), 154–180.

For each integer $r \geqq 2$, let $Q(u) = \sum_{1 \leqq i,j \leqq r} a_{ij}u_i u_j$ be a positive-definite quadratic form with rational integer coefficients and determinant $D$. Further, let $b_1, b_2, \cdots, b_r$

be rational integers, $M_1, M_2, \cdots, M_r$ natural numbers, and $\alpha_1, \cdots, \alpha_r$ reals. For $x>0$, put

$$A(x) = \sum \exp(2\pi i \textstyle\sum_{1\leq j\leq r} \alpha_j u_j),$$

where the sum is over all real $u_j$ for which $Q(u_j)\leq x$ and $u_j\equiv b_j \pmod{M_j}$, $j=1, 2, \cdots, r$. Define

$$M = \pi^{r/2}((\sqrt{D}) \textstyle\prod_{1\leq j\leq r} M_j)^{-1},$$

$V(x)=Mx^{r/2}\exp(2\pi i \sum_{1\leq j\leq r}\alpha_j b_j)/\Gamma((r/2)+1)$, and put $\delta=1$ in the case when $\alpha_1 M_1, \alpha_2 M_2, \cdots, \alpha_r M_r$ are all rational integers, and $\delta=0$ otherwise. If $P(x)=A(x)-V(x)$, the mean-value in the title refers to $M(x)=\int_0^x |P(y)|^2\,dy$. Under the hypothesis that $\alpha_1, \cdots, \alpha_r$ are all rational, an asymptotic formula of the type $M(x)=Kx^{r-1}+O(g(x))$ with, for example, $g(x)=x^{r-2}$ for $r>5$, is presented. The constant $K$ is related to certain general Gaussian sums and is non-zero, when at least one of the sums is non-zero. Other types of estimates for $M(x)$ are also investigated.

*J. H. H. Chalk* (Toronto, Ont.)

## P24-24 (39# 5501)

**Novák, Břetislav**

**A remark on the theory of lattice points in ellipsoids. II.**

*Comment. Math. Univ. Carolinae* **9** (1968), 547–561.

Let $r$ be a natural number $\geqq 2$, $Q$ a positive definite quadratic form in $r$ variables whose determinant is $D$, $\tilde{Q}$ the form conjugate to $Q$. Let $\alpha_1, \cdots, \alpha_r, b_1, \cdots, b_r$ be systems of real numbers and $M_1, \cdots, M_r$ a system of positive real numbers. For $x\geqq 0$ define $A(x)=A(x; Q, \alpha_j, b_j, M_j)=\sum e^{2\pi i \sum_{j=1}^r \alpha_j u_j}$, where the sum runs over all systems $u_1, \cdots, u_r$ of integers which satisfy $Q(u_1, \cdots, u_r)\leqq x$ and $u_j\equiv b_j$ (mod $M_j$), $1\leqq j\leqq r$. Put, as usual,

$$V(x) = \pi^{r/2}x^{r/2}e^{2\pi i \sum_{j=1}^r \alpha_j b_j}\delta/((\sqrt{D})\textstyle\prod_{j=1}^r M_j\cdot\Gamma(r/2+1))$$

($\delta=1$ if all numbers $\alpha$, $M$, etc. are integers, $\delta=0$ otherwise). Similarly, we define $\tilde{A}(x)$, $\tilde{V}(x)$, $\tilde{P}(x)$ for the form $\tilde{Q}$ and systems of real numbers $b_j, -\alpha_j, 1/M_j$ $(1\leqq j\leqq r)$. The author draws attention to a "certain 'dual' relation in the theory of lattice points in ellipsoids", such as is shown by the following interesting Theorem 2 of his paper: Let $\delta=1$, $r\geqq 5$ and (1) $\tilde{P}(x)=O(x^\alpha)$; then (2) $P(x)=O(x^{r/2-1+(r-3-2\alpha)/(r-3-4\alpha)})$ for $\alpha>\frac{1}{4}(r-1)$; and (3) $P(x)=O(x^{r/4+1/4}\log x)$ if $\alpha=\frac{1}{4}(r-1)$. If $O$ in (1) can be replaced by $o$, then the same is true of (2) [see the author, Acta Arith. **13** (1967/68), 423–454; MR **37** #5151; ibid. **14** (1967/68), 371–397; MR **37** #6243; Comment. Math. Univ. Carolinae **8** (1967), 219–230; MR **35** #4182].

*S. Chowla* (University Park, Pa.)

Citations: MR 35# 4182 = P24-16; MR 37# 5151 = P24-19; MR 37# 6243 = P24-20.

## P24-25 (41# 165)

**Diviš, Bohuslav**

**Über Gitterpunkte in mehrdimensionalen Ellipsoiden. I, II. (Loose English summary)**

*Czechoslovak Math. J.* **20 (95)** (1970), 130–139; *ibid.* **20 (95)** (1970), 149–159.

The ellipsoids meant in the title have the form $Q(u)=\sum_{j=1}^\sigma \alpha_j(u_{1,j}^2+\cdots+u_{r_j,j}^2)\leqq x$, where $x>0$, $\sigma\geqq 2$, $\alpha_j>0$ and $r_j\geqq 1$ $(j=1, \cdots, \sigma)$. The classical problem is to estimate the error term $P_Q(x)=A_Q(x)-V_Q(x)$, where $A_Q(x)$ is the number of lattice points in the ellipsoid and $V_Q(x)$ denotes its volume. The result, which depends on the arithmetical nature of the coefficients $\alpha_j$, is as follows. Let $\beta=\beta(\alpha_2/\alpha_1, \cdots, \alpha_\sigma/\alpha_1)$ denote the least upper bound of the numbers $\omega$ such that $|\alpha_j/\alpha_1-p_j/q|<q^{-\omega}$ $(j=2, \cdots, \sigma)$ for infinitely many systems of integers $p_2, \cdots, p_\sigma, q$. Suppose that $r_j\geqq 2\beta/(\beta-1)=1$. Then it is known [V. Jarník, Math. Z. **38** (1934), 217–256] that, for each $\varepsilon>0$, $P_Q(x)=\Omega(x^{f-\varepsilon})$, where $f=\frac{1}{2}(r_1+\cdots+r_\sigma)-\beta/(\beta-1)$. The present author proves that, for each $\varepsilon>0$, $P_Q(x)=O(x^{f+\varepsilon})$; he employs Jarník's expression for $P_Q(x)$, which involves values of theta functions, and uses a Fary dissection of the real line.

In Part II the author improves upon known measure-theoretic results. Theorem. Let $\sigma\geqq 3$ and let $\tau$ be an integer with $3\leqq\tau\leqq\sigma$. Put $\beta=\beta(\alpha_2/\alpha_1, \cdots, \alpha_{\tau-1}/\alpha_1)$. Suppose that $r_j\geqq 2\beta/(\beta-1)$ $(j=1, \cdots, \tau-1)$, $r_j\geqq 4$ $(j=\tau, \cdots, \sigma)$. Then, if $\alpha_1, \cdots, \alpha_{\tau-1}$ are fixed and if $\varepsilon>0$, $P_Q(x)=O(x^{f-(\sigma+1-\tau)+\varepsilon})$ for almost all systems $(\alpha_\tau, \cdots, \alpha_\sigma)$.

*C. G. Lekkerkerker* (Amsterdam)

## P24-26 (41# 6807)

**Novák, Břetislav**

**Mean value theorems in the theory of lattice points with weight. II.**

*Comment. Math. Univ. Carolinae* **11** (1970), 53–81.

Let $r$ be a natural number $\geqq 2$, and let $Q(u)=Q(u_j)=\sum_{j,l=1}^r a_{jl}u_j u_l$ be a positive definite quadratic form with a symmetric matrix of coefficients and determinant $D$, $\bar{Q}$ the form conjugate to $Q$. Further, let $M_j$, $b_j$ and $\alpha_j$ be real numbers, $M_j>0$ $(j=1, 2, \cdots, r)$. Let $0<\lambda_1<\lambda_2<\cdots$ be the sequence of all positive values of $Q(m_j M_j+b_j)$ with integers $m_1, \cdots, m_r$ and, for integral $m\geqq 0$, let $a_m=\sum e^{2\pi i \sum_{j=1}^r \alpha_j u_j}$, where the sum runs over all systems of real numbers $u_1, \cdots, u_r$ such that $Q(u_j)=\lambda_m$ and $u_j\equiv b_j$ mod $M_j$ for $1\leqq j\leqq r$.

For $x\geqq 0$, $\rho\geqq 0$ put $A_\rho(x)=(\Gamma(1+\rho))^{-1}\sum_{\lambda_m\leqq x} a_m(x-\lambda_m)^\rho$, $V_\rho(x)=(Me^{2\pi i\sum_{j=1}^r \alpha_j b_j}\delta/\Gamma(r/2+\rho+1))x^{r/2+\rho}$, where $M=\pi^{r/2}/\sqrt{D}\prod_{j=1}^r M_j$, $\delta=1$ if all $\alpha_j M_j$ are integers, $\delta=0$ otherwise. Further, let (1) $P_\rho(x)=A_\rho(x)-V_\rho(x)$, (2) $M_\rho(x)=\int_0^x |P_\rho(t)|^2\,dt$.

Let $Q$ have integer coefficients, $M_j=1$, $\alpha_j=b_j=0$ for all $j$. For $0\leqq\rho<r/2-2$, we have (3) $P_\rho(x)=O(x^{r/2-1})$, $P_\rho(x)=\Omega(x^{r/2-1})$; for $\rho>r/2-\frac{1}{2}$ we have (4) $P_\rho(x)=O(x^{(r-1)/4+\rho/2})$, $P_\rho(x)=\Omega(x^{(r-1)/4+\rho/2})$. The author says "... we imagine that for $\rho=r/2-\frac{3}{2}$ the estimates (3)" turn into "estimates (4)". Further, he says "certain confirmation of this conjecture is given by the study of the function (2) which is the main object of the present paper". Space considerations prevent us from giving any more details.

{Part I appeared in same Comment. **8** (1967), 711–733 [MR **38** #121].}

*S. Chowla* (State College, Pa.)

Citations: MR 38# 121 = P24-21.

## P24-27 (42# 4495)

**Jarník, V.**

**Bemerkungen zu Landauschen Methoden in der Gitterpunktlehre.**

*Number Theory and Analysis (Papers in Honor of Edmund Landau), pp.* 137–156. *Plenum, New York,* 1969.

Es sei $Q(u)=Q(u_1, \cdots, u_r)=\sum_{i,k=1}^r \alpha_{ik}u_i u_k$, $\alpha_{ik}=\alpha_{ki}$, eine positiv-definite quadratische Form in $r$ Veränderlichen mit der Determinanten $D$. Für $x>0$ sei $A(x)$ die Anzahl der Gitterpunkte im Ellipsoid $Q(u)\leqq x$ und $V(x)$ das Volumen dieses Ellipsoids. Es werde ferner gesetzt $P_0(x)=P(x)=A(x)-V(x)$, $P_\rho(x)=(1/\Gamma(\rho))\int_0^x P(y)(x-y)^{\rho-1}\,dy$ $(\rho>0)$, so daß $P_{\rho+1}(x)=\int_0^x P_\rho(y)\,dy$. Der Verfasser zeigt daß außerhalb des Intervalles $r/2-2\leqq\rho\leqq r/2-\frac{1}{2}$ das $O-\Omega$-Problem für die Funktionen $P_\rho(x)$ vollständig gelöst werden kann: $P_\rho(x)=O(x^{r/2-1})$, $P(x)=\Omega(x^{r/2-1})$ falls $\rho<r/2-2$, $P_\rho(x)=O(x^{\rho/2+(r-1)/4})$, $P(x)=\Omega(x^{\rho/2+(r-1)/4})$ falls $\rho>r/2-\frac{1}{2}$. Für die Werte von $\rho$ innerhalb des genannten Intervalles erhält er Abschätzungen die sich im klassischen Fall $r=2$, $Q(y)=u_1{}^2+u_2{}^2$ auf $O(x^{1/3})$, bzw. $\Omega(x^{1/4})$ reduzieren. Die Beweismethoden schließen sich eng an die aus dem Jahre 1924 stammenden Landauschen Arbeiten [u.a. F. Landau, Math. Z. **21** (1924), 126–132] an; sie beruhen auf Reihenentwicklungen mittels Besselscher Funktionen, geeignete Differenzenbildungen und Integraldarstellungen in denen gewisse Thetareihen auftreten. *C. G. Lekkerkerker* (Amsterdam)

**P24-28** **(43# 3212 )**

**Divis, B.**

**On lattice points in high-dimensional ellipsoids.**

*Number Theory (Colloq., János Bolyai Math. Soc., Debrecen,* 1968), *pp.* 27–30. *North-Holland, Amsterdam,* 1970.

Let $Q(u)=\sum_{j=1}^{\sigma} \alpha_j(u_{1j}^2+u_{2j}^2+\cdots+u_{r_j,j}^2)$, where $\alpha_j>0$. For $x>0$ let $A(x)$ denote the number of integral points $u$ in the ellipsoid $Q(u)\leqq x$ and let $V(x)$ denote the volume of this ellipsoid. Now put $P(x)=A(x)-V(x)$ and denote by $f$ the infimum of those real $w$ for which $P(x)=O(x^w)$.

Denote by $\beta(\alpha_1, \alpha_2, \cdots, \alpha_\sigma)$ the supremum of those real numbers $w$ for which the system of inequalities $|p_j-q\alpha_j|<q^{1-w}$ $(j=1, 2, \cdots, \sigma)$ is satisfied for infinitely many integral points $(p_1, p_2, \cdots, p, q)$ with $q\to\infty$. V. Jarník [Tôhoku Math. J. **30** (1929), 354–371] has shown that, if $\sigma=2$, $r_j\geqq 4$, $r=r_1+r_2$ and $\beta=\beta(\alpha_1/\alpha_2)$, then $f=\frac{1}{2}r-1-1/(\beta-1)$.

The author announces the corresponding result for $\sigma>2$, namely, if $\beta=\beta(\alpha_2/\alpha_1, \alpha_3/\alpha_1, \cdots, \alpha_\sigma/\alpha_1)$, $r_j\geqq 2\beta/(\beta-1)$ and $r=r_1+r_2+\cdots+r_\sigma$, then $f=\frac{1}{2}r-1-1/(\beta-1)$, and he states that Jarník's method was used in the proof.

*A. C. Woods* (Columbus, Ohio)

**P24-29** **(43# 4765 )**

**Novák, B.**

**Über Gitterpunkte mit Gewichten in mehrdimensionalen Ellipsoiden.**

*Number Theory (Colloq., János Bolyai Math. Soc., Debrecen,* 1968), *pp.* 165–179. *North-Holland, Amsterdam,* 1970.

Let $Q(u_1, \cdots, u_r)$, where $r\geqq 2$, be a positive-definite quadratic form in $r$ variables with determinant $D$. Further let the $\alpha_j$, $b_j$, $M_j>0$ be given real numbers. A fundamental question of "lattice point theory" in ellipsoids is the investigation of the function $(x>0)$

$$A(x) = \sum \exp(2\pi i(\alpha_1 u_1+\cdots+\alpha_r u_r)).$$

Here the summation is over all real numbers $u_1, \cdots, u_r$ for which $Q(u_1, \cdots, u_r)\leqq x$ and $u_j\equiv b_j \pmod{M_j}$, for $1\leqq j\leqq r$. In this paper the author discusses the contributions of several authors (e.g., E. Landau, A. P. Lursmanašvili, H. Petersson, A. Walfisz, V. Jarnik and the reviewer, especially the last two) to this topic. See, in particular, the author's paper in Acta Arith. **14** (1967/68), 371–397 [MR **37** #6243]. *S. Chowla* (Princeton, N.J.)

Citations: MR 37# 6243 = P24-20.

# P28 LATTICE POINT PROBLEMS: OTHER REGIONS, GENERAL SUMMATION FORMULAS, ETC.

For the number of nonnegative solutions of linear Diophantine equations, see **D04**. For points in hyperbolic regions (Dirichlet's divisor problem), see **N40**.

See also reviews A54-28, A99-19, B36-134, D04-23, D04-55, D04-58, D16-18, E16-12, F20-6, F20-14, F20-24, F20-33, M05-10, M99-2, N40-62, P02-10, P20-7, P20-29, P24-10, P99-8, R46-3.

**P28-1** **(2, 149g)**

**Lehmer, D. H. The lattice points of an *n*-dimensional tetrahedron.** Duke Math. J. **7**, 341–353 (1940).

The author constructs polynomials which approximate to the number of lattice points lying inside or on the boundary of the $n$-dimensional tetrahedron bounded by the $n$ coördinate hyperplanes $x_1=0$, $x_2=0$, $\cdots$, $x_n=0$ and the hyperplane

$$\omega_1x_1+\omega_2x_2+\cdots+\omega_nx_n=\lambda,$$

where $\omega_i$ are positive and $\lambda$ is a non-negative parameter. Denoting the total number of such points by

$$N_n(\lambda)=N_n(\lambda\,|\,\omega_1, \omega_2, \cdots, \omega_n),$$

he constructs polynomials $P_n(\lambda\,|\,\omega_1, \omega_2, \cdots, \omega_n)$ and $Q_n(\lambda\,|\,\omega_1, \omega_2, \cdots, \omega_n)$ each of degree $n$ in $\lambda$ with coefficients depending on $\omega_1, \omega_2, \cdots, \omega_n$ and such that the inequalities

$$P_n(\lambda\,|\,\omega_1, \cdots, \omega_n)<N_n(\lambda\,|\,\omega_1, \cdots, \omega_n)<Q_n(\lambda\,|\,\omega_1, \cdots, \omega_n)$$

are valid for all $\lambda\geqq 0$. The $P_1(\lambda)$, $P_2(\lambda)$, $\cdots$, $P_n(\lambda)$ are obtained as successive solutions of a sequence of linear difference equations. More precisely, if

$$S_k(x, \omega)=\sum_{1\leqq\mu\leqq x/\omega}(x-\mu\omega)^k,$$

it is shown that

$$(1)\quad \omega^k\{B_{k+1}(x/\omega)-M_{k+1}\}\leqq(k+1)S_k(x, \omega)\leqq\omega^k\{B_{k+1}(x/\omega)-m_{k+1}\},$$

where $B_\nu(x)$ is the $\nu$th Bernoulli polynomial and $M_\nu$, $m_\nu$ are its maximum and minimum, respectively, in the interval $0\leqq x\leqq 1$. Taking $P_1(\lambda/\omega)=\lambda/\omega$, and assuming that $P_{k-1}(\lambda)$ has already been constructed, the formula (which is immediate)

$$N_k(\lambda\,|\,\omega_1, \cdots, \omega_k)=\sum_{0\leqq\mu\leqq\lambda/\omega_k} N_{k-1}(\lambda-\mu\omega_k\,|\,\omega_1, \cdots, \omega_{k-1})$$

yields

$$(2)\quad N_k(\lambda)>\sum_{0\leqq\mu\leqq\lambda/\omega_k} P_{k-1}(\lambda-\mu\omega_k)=P_{k-1}(\lambda)+\sum_{\nu=0}^{k-1} p_\nu^{(k-1)}S_\nu(\lambda, \omega_k).$$

Writing

$$K_n(t)=\begin{cases} tm_n/n \text{ if } t\leqq 0,\\ tM_n/n \text{ if } t\geqq 0,\end{cases}$$

and substituting from (1) into (2), we obtain

$$N_k(\lambda)>P_{k-1}(\lambda)+\sum_{\nu=0}^{k-1} p_\nu^{(k-1)}\frac{\omega_k^\nu}{\nu+1}B_{\nu+1}(\lambda/\omega_k)-\sum_{\nu=0}^{k-1}\omega_k^\nu K_{\nu+1}(p_\nu^{(k-1)}),$$

and the right member, a polynomial in $\lambda$ of degree $k$, is taken for $P_k(\lambda)$. Expanding the Bernoulli polynomials and collecting the coefficients of the various powers of $\lambda$, a recursion formula is obtained for $p_\nu^{(r)}$. The polynomial $Q_n(\lambda)$ is constructed in a similar way.

It is shown among other things that for each $n>0$ infinitely many $n$-dimensional tetrahedra exist for which

$$N_n(\lambda)-P_n(\lambda)=O(\lambda^{n-3}),$$

and the author compares (for $n=5$, $\lambda=1, 2, 3, 5, 8, 10, 10.5$) his polynomials with approximating polynomials of other writers (one of which was used by J. B. Rosser, another by A. E. Western and a third by the reviewer).

*D. C. Spencer* (Cambridge, Mass.).

Referred to in D44-9, P28-3, P28-8, P28-16.

**P28-2** **(2, 347g)**

**Koschliakov, N. Application of Mellin's transformation to the deduction of some summation formulae.** Bull. Acad. Sci. URSS. Sér. Math. [Izvestia Akad. Nauk SSSR] **5**, 43–56 (1941). (Russian. English summary)

Mellin's inversion formulae

$$F(s)=\int_0^\infty f(x)x^{s-1}dx,\quad f(x)=\frac{1}{2\pi i}\int_{\tau-i\infty}^{\tau+i\infty}\frac{F(s)ds}{x^s},\quad x>0,$$

with $F(s)=F(\tau+it)$ suitably restricted, and the calculus of residues are used to give new proofs of three summation formulae (associated with Plana-Abel-Cauchy, Fourier and Voronoi):

$$\tfrac{1}{2}f(0)+\sum_1^\infty f(\nu)=\int_0^\infty f(x)dx-2\int_0^\infty\frac{f(ix)-f(-ix)}{2i}\frac{dx}{e^{2\pi x}-1},$$

$$f(x)=\int_0^1 f(\tau)d\tau+2\sum_{\nu=1}^\infty\int_0^1 f(\tau)\cos 2\nu\pi(\tau-x)d\tau,$$

$$\sum_n^{\alpha<n\leqq\beta} d(n)f(n)$$

$$=\tfrac{1}{2}d(\beta)f(\beta)-\tfrac{1}{2}d(\alpha)f(\alpha)+\int_\alpha^\beta[2C+\log x]f(x)dx$$

$$+2\pi\sum_{n=1}^\infty d(n)\int_\alpha^\beta f(x)\{-Y_0(4\pi(nx)^{\frac{1}{2}})+2\pi^{-1}K_0(4\pi(nx)^{\frac{1}{2}})\}dx,$$

where $d(n)$ denotes the number of divisors of $n$.

*G. Pall* (Montreal, Que.).

**P28-3** **(4, 190d)**

**Spencer, D. C. The lattice points of tetrahedra.** J. Math. Phys. Mass. Inst. Tech. **21**, 189–197 (1942).

This paper is a sequel to a previous paper concerned with the 2-dimensional case [Proc. Cambridge Philos. Soc. **35**, 527–547 (1939); these Rev. **1**, 203] of the right triangle. The tetrahedron considered is the $s$-dimensional one bounded by the hyperplanes

$$\begin{cases} x_i=1, & i=1,2,\cdots,s,\\ \eta=\omega_1x_1+\cdots+\omega_sx_s, \end{cases}$$

where $\eta$ is a positive parameter. The enumerative function of the lattice points of this tetrahedron under discussion is

$$N_r^{(s)}(\eta)=\Sigma(\eta-m_1\omega_1-\cdots-m_s\omega_s)^r,$$

where the summation extends over those sets of integers $m$ for which $\eta\geqq m_1\omega_1+m_2\omega_2+\cdots+m_s\omega_s$, or, in other words, over the lattice points $(m_1, m_2, \cdots, m_s)$ of the tetrahedron. Here $r$ need not be an integer, but the most interesting and useful case is $r=0$. Let $\lambda_1, \lambda_2, \cdots$ be numbers of the form $\lambda_n=m_1\omega_1+m_2\omega_2+\cdots+m_s\omega_s$ and let $a_n$ be the number of such representations. Then

$$P(z)=\prod_{k=1}^s(1-\exp(-\omega_kz))^{-1}=\sum_{n=1}^\infty a_n\exp(-\lambda_nz).$$

Using Perron's formula, we obtain the following contour integral representation of $N_r^{(s)}(\eta)$:

(1) $$N_r^{(s)}(\eta)=(\Gamma(r+1)/2\pi i)$$
$$\times\int_{c-i\infty}^{c+i\infty}P(z)\exp\{z(\eta-\Sigma\,\omega_k)-(1+r)\log z\}dz,$$

where $c>0$. The principal singularity of the integrand is the origin. Deforming the path so that it embraces the negative real axis without enclosing any of the other singularities of $P(z)$, we obtain

$$N_r^{(s)}(\eta)=(-1)^s\zeta_s(-r,\eta|\omega_1,\cdots,\omega_s)+T_r^{(s)}(\eta),$$

where the $\zeta$-function is that of E. W. Barnes [Trans. Cambridge Philos. Soc. **19**, 374–425 (1904)] and the "error term" $T_r^{(s)}(\eta)$ is the contribution to the integral (1) arising from the nonzero singularities of $P(z)$. The paper discusses problems of estimating $T$, whose precise behavior for large $\eta$ is obviously bound up in the arithmetical properties of the real parameters $\omega_k$. Two $\omega$'s are said to belong to the same class if their ratio is rational. According as the number of classes among the given $\omega$'s is one or more, $T_r^{(s)}(\eta)$ is $O(\eta^{s-1})$ or $o(\eta^{s-1})$ as $\eta\to\infty$. In the important case $\omega_k=\log p_k$, where the $p_k$ are distinct primes, there are $s$ classes and we have the slightly better result

$$T_r^{(s)}(\eta)=o(\eta^{s-1}(\log\eta)^{-1-r}).$$

If one considers the $\omega$'s as the coordinates of a point in $s$-dimensional space we have the following result. For almost all points $(\omega_1, \omega_2, \cdots, \omega_s)$,

$$T_r^{(s)}(\eta)=\begin{cases}O(\{\log\eta\}^{s+\epsilon}) & \text{if } r=0,\\ O(1) & \text{if } r>0,\end{cases}$$

so that, on the whole, $T_0^{(s)}(\eta)$ is of very small order as compared with $\zeta_s(0,\eta)$, which is a polynomial in $\eta$ of degree $s$. This polynomial then (except for its constant term) is asymptotically the best approximation to $N_0^{(s)}(\eta)$ [see D. H. Lehmer, Duke Math. J. **7**, 341–353 (1940); these Rev. **2**, 149]. In conclusion the author raises a number of questions of Diophantine approximation suggested by the above problem. One of these is as follows. For $k>1$, can $\theta_1, \theta_2, \cdots, \theta_k$ be found so that

$$\prod_{i=1}^k|\sin m\theta_i|\geqq Km^{-1}$$

holds for some constant $K$ and for all integers $m>0$? If not, what function will best replace $m^{-1}$ so that the inequality is true for at least one set of $\theta$'s? *D. H. Lehmer.*

Citations: MR 1, 203b = K10-1; MR 2, 149g = P28-1.

**P28-4** **(4, 266f)**

**Pillai, S. S. Lattice points in a right-angled triangle. II.** Proc. Indian Acad. Sci., Sect. A. **17**, 58–61 (1943).

Let $\omega$ and $\omega'$ be two positive numbers and denote by $L(\eta)$ the number of lattice points inside and on the boundary of the right triangle whose sides are the coordinate axes and the line $\omega x+\omega'y=\eta>0$. Write $F(\eta)=(\eta+\omega)(\eta+\omega')/2\omega\omega'$ and $\Delta(\eta)=L(\eta)-F(\eta)$. The author, using elementary methods, investigates the asymptotic behavior of $\Delta(\eta)$ as $\eta\to\infty$ obtaining results first proved (also with elementary methods) by Hardy and Littlewood [Abh. Math. Sem. Hansischen Univ. **1**, 212–249 (1922)] and Ostrowski [Abh. Math. Sem. Hansischen Univ. **1**, 77–98 (1922)]. The author's historical remark concerning his theorem IV is erroneous [compare theorem 10 in Hardy and Littlewood's paper cited above].

*D. C. Spencer* (Stanford University, Calif.).

**P28-5** **(4, 266g)**

**Pillai, S. S. Lattice points in a right-angled triangle. III.** Proc. Indian Acad. Sci., Sect. A. **17**, 62–65 (1943).

The author is here concerned with the error term $\Delta(\eta)$ when $\omega$ and $\omega'$ are co-prime positive integers [see the preceding review]. In this case G. H. Hardy [Ramanujan, Cambridge University Press, 1940, p. 73; these Rev. **3**, 71] has shown that $\Delta(\eta)=-(\eta/\omega\omega')(\eta-[\eta]-\frac{1}{2})+E(\eta)$, where $E(\eta)=O(1)$ as $\eta\to\infty$. The author investigates the dependence of $E(\eta)$ on $\omega$ and $\omega'$, and proves that $E(\eta)$ is of the form $O(\omega+\omega')$. *D. C. Spencer* (Stanford University, Calif.).

Citations: MR 3, 71d = Z20-4.

**P28-6** **(9, 335d)**

**Steinhaus, H. Sur un théorème de M. V. Jarník.** Colloquium Math. **1**, 1–5 (1947).

The author gives a proof of the following theorem, stated and proved by V. Jarník in a recent letter to him. Let $J$ be a closed rectifiable Jordan curve of length $l$, enclosing an area $a$. Then, provided $l \geqq 1$, the number $w$ of points with integral coordinates inside $J$ satisfies $|w-a|<l$. The proof is elementary and depends on the following result: if a Jordan arc $S$ joins two points on the boundary of the square $|x|<\frac{1}{2}$, $|y|<\frac{1}{2}$, dividing the square into two regions, and if $\Delta$ is the region which does not contain the origin, then the area of $\Delta$ is less than the length of $S$. This is proved by simple considerations in each of four possible cases.

*H. Davenport* (London).

## P28-7 (11, 13b)

**Nosarzewska, M. Évaluation de la différence entre l'aire d'une région plane convexe et le nombre des points aux coordonnées entières couverts par elle.** Colloquium Math. **1**, 305–311 (1948).

Let $I$ be a plane open convex region of area $a$ which is bounded by a closed curve $J$ of length $l$, and let $w$ be the number of points with integral coordinates covered by $I$. The author proves that $-\frac{1}{4}l-1<a-w<\frac{1}{2}l$. This is done by dividing the plane into a mesh of squares centred at the lattice points. Difficulties arise only for squares which contain points of $J$, and such squares are divided into several different types which are considered separately. The isoperimetric property of the circle and the convexity of $J$ are used to obtain the desired inequalities. The author shows that her inequalities cannot be improved. This follows, for the left-hand inequality, by considering the sequence of squares $I_n$ with a pair of opposite vertices at $(-1/n, -1/n)$, $(m+1/n, m+1/n)$. Here $m$ is a fixed non-negative integer and $n=1, 2, \cdots$. The squares $I_n$ may be taken arbitrarily small or arbitrarily large by suitable choice of $m$. For the right-hand inequality she considers a diminishing sequence of squares of side $1/n$ which do not contain any lattice point ($n=1, 2, \cdots$). It is not known if the right-hand inequality remains the best possible for arbitrarily large regions $I$. *R. A. Rankin* (Cambridge, England).

## P28-8 (12, 82a)

**Lochs, Gustav. Über die Lösungszahl einer linearen, diophantischen Ungleichung.** Jber. Deutsch. Math. Verein. **54**, 41–51 (1950).

Let $\alpha_1, \cdots, \alpha_k$ be linearly independent real numbers, and let the numbers $\sum_{\nu=1}^{k} x_\nu \alpha_\nu$ ($x_1, \cdots, x_n$ nonnegative integers), arranged in increasing order of magnitude, be denoted by $\lambda_1, \lambda_2, \cdots$. It is shown that the number $n(\alpha_1, \cdots, \alpha_k; x)$ of solutions of the inequality $\lambda_n \leqq x$ is

(1) $(k!\alpha_1 \cdots \alpha_k)^{-1}(x^k+\frac{1}{2}k(\alpha_1+\cdots+\alpha_k)x^{k-1}+o(x^{k-2}))$,

which implies that

(2) $\lambda_n=(k!\alpha_1 \cdots \alpha_k \cdot n)^{1/k}-\frac{1}{2}(\alpha_1+\cdots+\alpha_k)+o(1)$.

It is also shown that the term $o(x^{k-2})$ of (1) cannot be replaced by $o(x^{k-1}\zeta(x))$ if $\zeta(x)=o(1)$. A consequence of (2), obtained by taking $\alpha_i=\log p_i$, is that the $n$th positive integer (ordered by size) which is composed exclusively of the primes $p_1, \cdots, p_k$ is asymptotically equal to

$$\exp(k!\log p_1 \cdots \log p_k \cdot n)^{1/k}/(p_1 \cdots p_k)^{\frac{1}{2}}.$$

The method is similar to that used by D. H. Lehmer [Duke Math. J. **7**, 341–353 (1940); these Rev. **2**, 149] to obtain bounds for $n(\alpha_1, \cdots, \alpha_k; x)$. *W. J. LeVeque.*

Citations: MR 2, 149g = P28-1.
Referred to in P28-16.

## P28-9 (12, 197e)

**Hlawka, Edmund. Über Integrale auf konvexen Körpern. I.** Monatsh. Math. **54**, 1–36 (1950).

Let $B$ be a convex body in $R_m$ and let the Gaussian curvature of its surface have a positive lower bound. Suppose the origin is an inner point of $B$ and that $f(x)$ is the distance-function of $B$, where $x=(x_1, \cdots, x_m)$. Write $dx$ for the element of volume and $lx=l_1x_1+\cdots+l_mx_m$, where $l=(l_1, \cdots, l_m)$. The author discusses integrals of the type $\int_B\Phi(f(x))e^{ilx}dx$ subject to differentiability conditions on the surface of $B$ and on the arbitrary function $\Phi(u)$, using the method of stationary phase.

For given unimodular matrix $A$, vector $y$, and real number $u \geqq 0$, denote now by $\Phi(y, u)$ the number of integer vectors $x$ satisfying $f^2(A(x-y)) \leqq u$, i.e., $\Phi(y, u)$ is the number of lattice points in a body, $u$, times $B$ displaced to $Ay$. Then, if $\mathfrak{J}$ is the volume of $B$, we have as $u \to \infty$,

(i) $\Phi(y, u)=\mathfrak{J}u^{m/2}+O(u^{m(m-1)/2(m+1)})$,
(ii) $\Phi(0, u)=\mathfrak{J}u^{m/2}+\Omega(u^{(m-1)/4})$.

Let $\lambda(u)\nearrow\infty$ as $u\nearrow\infty$ and let $0\leqq\delta<2/(m-1)$. Suppose $u_\nu$, $\nu=1, 2, \cdots$, is a sequence such that $\sum\lambda^{-2-\delta}(u_\nu)<\infty$. Then (iii) $\Phi(y, u)=\mathfrak{J}u^{m/2}+O(u^{(m-1)/4}\lambda(u))$ for almost all $y$ as $u$ runs through the sequence $u_\nu$. The proofs depend on the estimates for integrals and are similar to the corresponding known proofs for ellipsoids [for (i) and (ii) see Landau, S.-B. Preuss. Akad. Wiss. **1915**, 458–476; Nachr. Ges. Wiss. Göttingen. Math.-Phys. Kl. **1915**, 161–171 (1916); and for (iii) see D. G. Kendall, Quart. J. Math., Oxford Ser. (1) **19**, 1–26 (1948); these Rev. **9**, 570]. An improvement of Minkowski's convex body theorem is also given for bodies $B$ provided that the dimension-number $m \not\equiv 1 \pmod 4$. Independently of the above, a relation is given between the numbers of lattice points in two polar bodies, generalising one of A. Gelfond [C. R. (Doklady) Acad. Sci. URSS (N.S.) **17**, 447–449 (1937)] for parallelepipeds. The notation $A^*$ for the transpose of $A$ is used. In equation (3), page 21, read $k=A^{*-1}l$. This definition of $k$ is tacitly assumed in §§ 6–10. There are further minor misprints.

*J. W. S. Cassels* (Cambridge, England).

Citations: MR 9, 570b = P20-7.
Referred to in P28-12, P28-53, P28-91.

## P28-10 (12, 198a)

**Hlawka, Edmund. Integrale auf konvexen Körpern. II.** Monatsh. Math. **54**, 81–99 (1950).

In the notation of the review of part I [see the preceding review] let $G(l)=\int_B e^{ilx}dx$ and let $H(l)$ be the function of support (Stützfunktion) of $B$. If $B$ has centre 0 the zeros of $G(l)$ lie with a finite number of exceptions on infinitely many convex surfaces $L_k$, $k=1, 2, \cdots$, with the same centre and asymptotically approaching $H(l)=\frac{1}{4}(m+1)\pi+\frac{1}{2}(2k+1)\pi$. If $B$ has no centre, then a ray through 0 has on it only a finite number of zeros of $G(l)$ except in specified cases. If $m=2$ then $G(l)$ vanishes on infinitely many curves of the type $H(l)=$constant if and only if $B$ is an ellipse. The estimates of part I for some integrals $\int_B\Phi(f(x))e^{ilx}dx$ are improved. *J. W. S. Cassels* (Cambridge, England).

Referred to in P28-12, P28-53.

## P28-11 (12, 198b)

**Hlawka, Edmund. Über die Zetafunktion konvexer Körper.** Monatsh. Math. **54**, 100–107 (1950).

Let a convex body $B$ in $m$-dimensional space be defined by $f(x)\leqq 1$. Let the origin $O$ be an interior point of $B$, and assume that the boundary of $B$ is analytic and that all tangent planes have contact of the first order exactly. Let $A$ be a matrix of determinant 1. The author considers the function $Z(s)=\sum_g'(f(Ag))^{-2s}$, where the summation is over all points $g$ with integral coordinates, excluding 0. This is a special case of $\zeta$-functions considered by Mordell [Quart. J. Math., Oxford Ser. (1) **1**, 77–101 (1930)], but reduces to Epstein's $\zeta$-function when $B$ is a sphere with centre $O$. It is proved that $Z(s)$ is analytic except for a simple pole at $s=\frac{1}{2}m$, with residue $\frac{1}{2}mV(B)$, where $V(B)$ is the volume of $B$. Other results are given which are partial analogues of results known for Epstein's $\zeta$-function, one being a kind of functional equation, and another being an estimate for the difference between $Z(s)$ and an approximating sum. The proofs use results from the two papers reviewed above.

*H. Davenport* (London).

## P28-12 (13, 154a)

**Hlawka, Edmund. Integrale auf konvexen Körpern. III.** Monatsh. Math. **55**, 105–137 (1951).

[For the first two parts see same Monatsh. **54**, 1–36, 81–99 (1950); these Rev. **12**, 197, 198.] In this paper the following integral inversion theorem is obtained. Let $f(x)$, where $x=(x_1, x_2, \cdots, x_m)$, be the distance-function and $H(u)$, where $u=(u_1, \cdots, u_m)$, the support-function (Stützfunktion) of the convex body $K$: $f(x)\leqq 1$ in $m$-dimensional space. It is supposed that $f(x)$, $H(u)$ are analytic except possibly at the origin, and that all tangent planes to $K$ have contact of the first order only. Let $\Phi(t)$ be defined in $0<t<\infty$ such that $\Phi(t)t^{(m-1)/2}$ is absolutely Riemann integrable in $(0, \infty)$ and that $\int_0^\tau|\Phi(t)|t^{(m-1)/2}dt=o(\tau^k)$ for $\tau\rightarrow 0+$ and some $k>0$. Then

$$\mathfrak{F}(x)=\lim_{T\rightarrow\infty}\int_{f(y)\leqq T}\Phi(f(y))e^{ixy}dy$$

(where $xy=x_1y_1+\cdots+x_my_m$) exists for all $x$ and

$$(2\pi)^{-m}\lim_{T\rightarrow\infty}\int_{H(u)\leqq T}\mathfrak{F}(u)e^{ixu}du=\tfrac{1}{2}\{\Phi(f(x)+)+\Phi(f(x)-)\}$$

provided that $\Phi(t)$ is of bounded variation in a neighbourhood of $t=f(x)$. As an application the proof of a theorem of C. G. Esseen on probability distributions is shown to generalize from spheres to bodies of the type $K$ [Acta Math. **77**, 1–125 (1945), chapter VII, theorem 1; these Rev. **7**, 312].

*J. W. S. Cassels* (Cambridge, England).

Citations: MR 7, 312a = P20-5; MR 12, 197e = P28-9; MR 12, 198a = P28-10.

## P28-13 (13, 322c)

**Kruyswijk, D. On the number of lattice-points in a wide convex region.** Nederl. Akad. Wetensch. Proc. Ser. A. **54** = Indagationes Math. **13**, 152–161 (1951).

Let $G$ be a plane, open, convex region with area $I(G)$. Let $A(G)$ be the number of points of the standard lattice (i.e. points with integer coordinates $x, y$) in $G$ and $a(G)$ the number of lattice points on the boundary of $G$. The set $E$ consists of all chords $k$ of $G$ each of which contains at least two lattice points in $G$ and cuts off from $G$ an open region $\omega_k$ which does not contain lattice points. The region $G$ is defined to be wide if each $\omega_k$ of $G$ is contained within an isosceles right angled triangle with hypothenuse $k$. Let $\omega_k$ also denote the area of the region $\omega_k$ and $k$ also the length of the chord $k$. The purpose of the paper is to show that a constant $c$, independent of $G$, exists with the property that a chord $k$ exists with

$$|A(G)-I(G)|<c(k^3/\omega_k)^{2/3},\quad a(G)<c(k^3/\omega_k)^{2/3}$$

for every $G$ which is wide. The author proves by induction that $A(P)=I(P)+\frac{1}{2}a(P)-1$ where $P$ is a simple closed polygon whose vertices are lattice points. From this follows easily that $|A(G)-I(G)|<\sum_E a_k+\sum_E\omega_k$ where $a_k$ is one less than the number of lattice points on the chord $k$. The computations which lead to estimates of these two sums, and hence to the main result, are of an elementary character.

To illustrate the relationship between van der Corput's theorem [Landau, Vorlesungen über Zahlentheorie, v. 2, Hirzel, Leipzig, 1927, pp. 288–289] which connects $I(G)$ and $A(G)$, where $G$ is a region enclosed by the $x$-axis, two ordinates and a curve $y=f(x)$, and his main result the author uses the latter to obtain, by a simple deduction, the following result which is likewise a consequence of the van der Corput theorem. $G$ is a convex region at each of whose boundary points $P$ a radius of curvature $\rho(P)$ is defined. If $r$ is the least upper bound of $\rho(P)$ then $A(G)=I(G)+O(r^{2/3})$, $a(G)=O(r^{2/3})$, for all regions $G$ homothetic to a given region $G_0$, the constant used in the $O$-relationship being independent of $G_0$.

*D. Derry* (Vancouver, B. C.).

## P28-14 (13, 323d)

**Davenport, H. On a principle of Lipschitz.** J. London Math. Soc. **26**, 179–183 (1951).

Let $R$ be a closed and bounded region in $n$-dimensional space. Let $V(R)$ be the volume of $R$, and $N(R)$ the number of points in $R$ with integral coordinates. The object of this paper is to obtain an upper bound for $|N(R)-V(R)|$ under certain mild conditions on $R$. Specifically, suppose that any line parallel to one of the coordinate axes intersects $R$ in at most $h$ intervals. Suppose further that the same is true for any of the $m$-dimensional regions obtained by projecting $R$ on one of the coordinate spaces defined by equating $n-m$ of the coordinates to zero. Let $V_m$ denote the sum of the volumes of these $m$-dimensional regions if $m\geqq 1$, and put $V_0=1$. Then it is shown that

$$|N(R)-V(R)|\leqq\sum_{m=0}^{n-1}h^{n-m}V_m.$$

*W. H. Mills* (New Haven, Conn.).

Referred to in E76-13, G05-71, P28-15.

## P28-15 (29# 3433)

**Davenport, H.**

**Corrigendum: "On a principle of Lipschitz".**

*J. London Math. Soc.* **39** (1964), 580.

A correction to an earlier paper [same J. **26** (1951), 179–183; MR **13**, 323].

Citations: MR 13, 323d = P28-14.

## P28-16 (14, 730d)

**Lochs, Gustav. Über die Anzahl der Gitterpunkte in einem Tetraeder.** Monatsh. Math. **56**, 233–239 (1952).

Denote by $n(x)=n(x; \alpha_1, \alpha_2, \cdots, \alpha_k)$ the number of lattice points inside or on the boundary of the $k$-dimensional "tetrahedron" bounded by the $k$ coordinate hyperplanes $x_1=0, x_2=0, \cdots, x_k=0$ and the hyperplane

$$\alpha_1x_1+\alpha_2x_2+\cdots+\alpha_kx_k=x,$$

where $\alpha_1, \alpha_2, \cdots, \alpha_k$, and $x$ are positive. The reviewer [Duke Math. J. **7**, 341–353 (1940); these Rev. **2**, 149] and the author [Jber. Deutsch. Math. Verein. **54**, 41–51 (1950); these Rev. **12**, 82] have independently considered the problem of obtaining two polynomials, $P$, $Q$, of degree $k$ in $x$, with coefficients depending on the $\alpha$'s, for which $P(x)<n(x)<Q(x)$.

In the present paper the author studies two inequalities, the first of which is

$$n(x)<A^{-1}\left[\left(x+\frac{1}{2}\sum_{i=1}^k\alpha_i\right)^k-\frac{k(k-1)}{24}x^{k-2}\left(\sum_{i=3}^k\alpha_i^2\right)\right]-\Delta,$$

where $A=k!\alpha_1\alpha_2\cdots\alpha_k$ and

$$\Delta=\sum B_1\{\alpha_1^{-1}(x-g_2\alpha_2-\cdots-g_k\alpha_k)\},$$

in which $B_1\{u\}=u-[u]-\frac{1}{2}$ is the first Bernoulli function and the sum extends over all sets of non-negative integers, for which the argument of $B_1$ is non-negative, that is, over the lattice points of a $(k-1)$-dimensional tetrahedron.

The ratio $\alpha_2/\alpha_1$ is considered as expanded in a continued fraction and inequalities for $\Delta$ are obtained in terms of the elements of the continued fraction and $n(x; \alpha_2, \cdots, \alpha_k)$. No very definitive results are obtained. *D. H. Lehmer.*

Citations: MR 2, 149g = P28-1; MR 12, 82a = P28-8.

## P28-17 (15, 939d)

**Müller, Claus. Eine Verallgemeinerung der Eulerschen Summenformel und ihre Anwendung auf Fragen der analytischen Zahlentheorie.** Abh. Math. Sem. Univ. Hamburg **19**, no. 1–2, 41–62 (1954).

Let $\mathfrak{g}_1$, $\mathfrak{g}_2$ be two linearly independent plane vectors. Put $\mathfrak{g}_i\mathfrak{g}_j=g_{ij}$, $g=\det(g_{ij})$, $g^{ij}g_{jk}=\delta^i_k$, and define $\mathfrak{g}^i$ by means of $\mathfrak{g}^i=g^{ij}\mathfrak{g}_j$ so that $\mathfrak{g}^i\mathfrak{g}_k=\delta_k{}^i$. The totality of vectors $\mathfrak{g}=n^1\mathfrak{g}_1+n^2\mathfrak{g}_2$, where the $n$'s are rational integers, define a modul (or lattice) $\Omega$, the vectors $\mathfrak{h}=n_1\mathfrak{g}^1+n_2\mathfrak{g}^2$ define the reciprocal lattice $\Omega^{-1}$. The fundamental domain of $\Omega$ is denoted by $\mathfrak{F}$. If $\mathfrak{x}$ is an arbitrary vector we put $\mathfrak{x}=x^1\mathfrak{g}_1+x^2\mathfrak{g}_2$ and define the operator $\Delta=(\partial/\partial x^1)^2+(\partial/\partial x^2)^2$. Also write $e(x)=e^{2\pi ix}$, $\phi(\mathfrak{h}\mathfrak{x})=g^{-1/4}e(\mathfrak{h}\mathfrak{x})$.

A fundamental function $G(\lambda;\mathfrak{x})$ is defined by means of the following properties: (1) $G(\lambda;\mathfrak{x}+\mathfrak{g})=G(\lambda;\mathfrak{x})$ for $\mathfrak{x}\neq\mathfrak{g}$ and all $\mathfrak{g}\in\Omega$; (2) $G(\lambda;\mathfrak{x})$ is analytic for $\mathfrak{x}\neq\mathfrak{g}$; moreover,

$$\Delta G(\lambda;\mathfrak{x})+\lambda G(\lambda;\mathfrak{x})=g^{-1/2}\sum_{\lambda=4\pi^2\mathfrak{h}^2} e(\mathfrak{h}\mathfrak{x});$$

(3) $G(\lambda;\mathfrak{x})+(2\pi)^{-1}\log|\mathfrak{x}|$ is continuously differentiable in $\mathfrak{F}$; (4) if $\lambda=4\pi^2\mathfrak{h}^2$, then $\int_{\mathfrak{F}}G(\lambda;\mathfrak{x})\overline{\phi(\mathfrak{h}\mathfrak{x})}dF_{\mathfrak{x}}=0$. It is proved that $G(\lambda;\mathfrak{x})$ is uniquely determined by these properties. Also we have the expansion

$$G(\lambda;\mathfrak{x})\sim g^{-1/2}\sum_{4\pi^2\mathfrak{h}^2\neq\lambda}\frac{e(\mathfrak{h}\mathfrak{x})}{4\pi^2\mathfrak{h}^2-\lambda}.$$

For $\lambda=0$, put $G(\mathfrak{x})=G(0;\mathfrak{x})$ and let

$$a_0=a_0(\Omega)=\lim_{\mathfrak{x}\to 0}(G(\mathfrak{x})+(1/2\pi)\log|\mathfrak{x}|);$$

also put $\Theta(\tau)=\prod_{n=1}^{\infty}(1-e^{2\pi i\tau})$, $\tau=(g_{12}+ig^{1/2})/g^{22}$. It is shown that

$$a_0(\Omega^{-1})=a_0(\Omega)-\frac{1}{4\pi}\log g,$$

$$a_0(\Omega)=-\frac{1}{2\pi}\log\frac{2\pi}{\sqrt{g_{22}}}|\Theta(\tau)e^{\pi i\tau/12}|^2.$$

If now $\mathfrak{G}$ is a regular domain with continuously differentiable boundary curve $\mathfrak{C}$ and $f(\mathfrak{x})$ has continuous second derivatives in $\mathfrak{G}$, then the author's extension of the Euler-MacLaurin summation formula is contained in the following:

$$(*)\quad \sum_{\mathfrak{g}\in\mathfrak{G}}{}'f(\mathfrak{g})=g^{-1/2}\int_{\mathfrak{G}}f(\mathfrak{x})dF-\int_{\mathfrak{G}}G(\mathfrak{x})\Delta f\,dF$$
$$-\int_{\mathfrak{C}}\left(f\frac{\partial}{\partial n}G(\mathfrak{x})-G(\mathfrak{x})\frac{\partial}{\partial n}f\right)ds,$$

where $\sum'_{\mathfrak{g}\in\mathfrak{G}}f(\mathfrak{g})=\sum_{\mathfrak{g}\in\mathfrak{G}}f(\mathfrak{g})-\frac{1}{2}\sum_{\mathfrak{g}\in\mathfrak{G}}f(\mathfrak{g})$ and $\partial/\partial n$ denotes the derivative in the direction of the exterior normal.

Application of (*) is made first to the Epstein zeta-function $\zeta(s,\Omega)=\sum_{\mathfrak{g}\neq 0}|g|^{-s}$ (Re $(s)>2$). Proof is given of the analytic continuation and the functional equation of $\zeta(s,\Omega)$, also of the Kronecker formula

$$\lim_{s=2}\left(\zeta(s,\Omega)-\frac{2\pi}{\sqrt{g}}\frac{1}{s-2}\right)=a_0(\Omega).$$

As a second application the author derives the Hardy-Landau identity

$$\sum_{|\mathfrak{g}|\leq R}{}'1=\frac{\pi R^2}{\sqrt{g}}+R\sum_{\substack{\mathfrak{h}\in\Omega^{-1}\\ \mathfrak{h}\neq 0}}\frac{J_1(2\pi R|\mathfrak{h}|)}{|\mathfrak{h}|}.$$

*L. Carlitz* (Durham, N. C.).

Referred to in P28-65.

## P28-18 (15, 940a)

**Müller, Claus. Eine Formel der analytischen Zahlentheorie.** Abh. Math. Sem. Univ. Hamburg **19**, no. 1–2, 62–65 (1954).

As an application of his generalization of the Euler-MacLaurin summation formula (see the preceding review), the author proves the following formula:

$$\prod_{n=1}^{N}\left(\frac{n}{N}\right)^{r(n)}=\frac{\Gamma^4(\frac{1}{4})}{4\pi}Ne^{-\pi N}\{1+O(N^{-1/4})\},$$

where $r(n)$ denotes the number of representations of $n$ as a sum of two squares. *L. Carlitz* (Durham, N. C.).

Referred to in N52-45, P20-15.

## P28-19 (15, 940b)

**Müller, Claus. Eine Erweiterung der Hardyschen Identität.** Abh. Math. Sem. Univ. Hamburg **19**, no. 1–2, 66–76 (1954).

The author first extends his generalization of the Euler-MacLaurin summation formula (see the second preceding review) and then proves the following generalization of the Hardy-Landau identity:

$$\lim_{n\to\infty}{}^{\cdot}R\sum_{|\mathfrak{g}-\mathfrak{n}|\leq N}e^{2\pi i(\mathfrak{a}\mathfrak{g})}\frac{J_1(2\pi R|\mathfrak{g}-\mathfrak{n}|)}{|\mathfrak{g}-\mathfrak{n}|}$$
$$=g^{-1/2}e^{2\pi i(\mathfrak{a}\mathfrak{n})}\sum_{|\mathfrak{h}+\mathfrak{a}|\leq R}{}'e^{2\pi i(\mathfrak{h}\mathfrak{n})}.$$

Here $\mathfrak{g}\in\Omega$, $\mathfrak{h}\in\Omega^{-1}$, the lattice reciprocal to $\Omega$, and

$$\sum_{|\mathfrak{h}+\mathfrak{a}|\leq R}{}'=\sum_{|\mathfrak{h}+\mathfrak{a}|\leq R}-\frac{1}{2}\sum_{|\mathfrak{h}+\mathfrak{a}|=R}.$$

*L. Carlitz* (Durham, N. C.).

Referred to in P28-56.

## P28-20 (17, 948a)

**Ehrhart, Eugène. Sur les polygones et les ovales.** C. R. Acad. Sci. Paris **242** (1956), 332–334.

In an earlier note [same C. R. **241** (1955), 686–689; MR **17**, 350], the author has shown that the area of a convex polygon $\Pi$, whose vertices are situated at points of the lattice with integral coordinates, is simply related to the number of such lattice points in $\Pi$. A similar result is obtained here for more general polygons. The note also contains a theorem giving bounds for the ratio in which the pericentre of an oval divides a chord passing through it. *J. H. H. Chalk* (London).

Citations: MR 17, 350f = H05-45.

## P28-21 (17, 948b)

**Ehrhart, Eugène. Sur les polygones croisés.** C. R. Acad. Sci. Paris **242** (1956), 1570–1573.

This is a continuation of two previous notes [same C. R. **241** (1955), 686–689; MR **17**, 350; see also the paper reviewed above] on the relation between the area of a polygon $\Pi$, with vertices at points of the lattice with integral coordinates, and the number of such lattice points in $\Pi$. It concludes with some remarks on ovals, and contains a revised conjecture for non-central convex bodies (ovoids) [see footnote (4) on p. 484 of Ehrhart, ibid **240** (1955), 483–485; MR **16**, 574]. *J. H. H. Chalk.*

Citations: MR 16, 574b = H05-35; MR 17, 350f = H05-45.

Referred to in P28-22, P28-24, P28-26.

**P28-22** **(18, 383b)**

**Ehrhart, Eugène. Sur les polygones plans dans un réseau de l'espace.** C. R. Acad. Sci. Paris **242** (1956), 1844–1846.

This gives an extension of a result obtained in same C. R. **242** (1956), 1570–1573 [MR **17**, 948]. Here, the polygons are regarded as having vertices at points of a sub-lattice of a lattice in 3-space.

*J. H. H. Chalk* (London).

Citations: MR 17, 948b = P28-21.
Referred to in P28-26.

**P28-23** **(18, 383e)**

**Ehrhart, Eugène. Sur les polyèdres et les ovales.** C. R. Acad. Sci. Paris **242** (1956), 2217–2219.

The results of the paper reviewed above are used to determine a relation between the number of points in 3-space with integral coordinates, lying on the surface of an arbitrary polyhedron whose vertices also have integral coordinates.

It is also shown that if an oval in the plane contains more than 4 points of a lattice, then at least 3 of them are collinear. *J. H. H. Chalk* (London).

Referred to in P28-26.

**P28-24** **(18, 383f)**

**Ehrhart, Eugène. Sur des polygones et des polyèdres particuliers.** C. R. Acad. Sci. Paris **243** (1956), 347–349.

In previous notes [same C. R. **242** (1956), 1570–1573; MR **17**, 948; see also the two papers reviewed above] the problem of determining the number of lattice points in a polygon, or on the surface of a polyhedron, has been considered in the case when the vertices are also lattice points. Here, the corresponding problem for the number of lattice points inside, or on the boundary of, a prism is solved.

A result for polygons, without the restriction that the vertices be lattice points, is also given.

*J. H. H. Chalk* (London).

Citations: MR 17, 948b = P28-21.
Referred to in P28-26.

**P28-25** **(18, 721d)**

**Dupač, Václav. On a stochastic modification of a problem in geometry of numbers.** Czechoslovak Math. J. **5(80)** (1955), 492–502. (Russian. English summary)

Let $J$ be a closed curve in the $u$, $v$ plane defined in polar coordinates by $r=g(\theta)$, where $g(\theta)$ is positive, periodic with period $2\pi$, and satisfies a Lipschitz condition. Suppose further that $J$ contains an arc $v=f(u)$, for some interval of $u$ in which $k_0<|f'(u)|<k_1$ and $|f''(u)|<k_2$ for suitable positive constants. Let $J(x)$ denote the magnification of $J$ given by $r=x^{\frac{1}{2}}g(\theta)$, where $x>0$. Let the unit squares of the plane be enumerated in a fixed order as $Q_1, Q_2, \cdots$, and let $Z_1, Z_2, \cdots$ be independent random points, uniformly distributed in $Q_1, Q_2, \cdots$ respectively. Let $A(x)$ denote the number of those points $Z_1, Z_2, \cdots$ which lie inside $J(x)$ and put $R(x)=A(x)-Px$, where $P$ is the area inside $J$. The main results are (1) the proposition $R(x)\neq o(x^{\frac{1}{4}}\log^{\frac{1}{2}} x)$ has probability 1; (2) if $x_n>n^\delta$ for some fixed $\delta>0$ then the proposition $R(x_n)=O(x_n^{\frac{1}{4}}\log^{\frac{1}{2}}x_n)$ has probability 1. A weaker result for more general regions is also given.

*H. Davenport* (London).

**P28-26** **(19, 19f; 19, 19g)**

**Ehrhart, Eugène. Sur une famille de polyèdres.** C. R. Acad. Sci. Paris **244** (1957), 434–437.

**Ehrhart, Eugène. Sur les polyèdres homothétiques.** C. R. Acad. Sci. Paris **244** (1957), 157–160.

These articles are continuations of previous notes [same C.R. **242** (1956), 1570–1573, 1844–1846, 2217–2219; **243** (1956), 347–349; MR **17**, 948; **18**, 383].

*J. H. H. Chalk* (London).

Citations: MR 17, 948b = P28-21; MR 18, 383b = P28-22; MR 18, 383e = P28-23; MR 18, 383f = P28-24.

**P28-27** **(19, 391g)**

**Širšov, V. M. An asymptotic solution for the number of solutions in positive integers $x_1, y_1, \cdots, x_r, y_r$ of the inequality $x_1^m y_1^n+\cdots+x_r^m y_r^n\leqq N$.** Belorussk. Politehn. Inst. Sb. Naučn. Rabot. **1953**, no. 5, 240–242. (Russian)

Let $K_r(N)$ be the number of solutions of the inequality $x_1^m y_1^n+\cdots+x_r^m y_r^n\leqq N$ in natural numbers with $m>n$. Using induction on the parameter $r$, the author proves that

$$K_r(N)=\Gamma^r\left(1+\frac{1}{n}\right)\Gamma^{-1}\left(1+\frac{r}{n}\right)\zeta^r\left(\frac{m}{n}\right)N^{r/n}+O(N^{r/n-1/n-1/m}).$$

This result is an almost obvious generalization of known facts. *N. G. Čudakov* (RŽMat **1954**, no. 3200).

**P28-28** **(19, 397e)**

**Reeve, John E. Le volume des polyèdres entiers.** C. R. Acad. Sci. Paris **244** (1957), 1990–1992.

Let $l$ denote the lattice of points in the plane $E_2$ with integral coordinates. An $l$-polygon is defined as a non-empty subset of $E_2$ which admits a finite simplicial covering by rectilinear simplices having vertices in $l$ and such that each simplex of dimension 0 or 1 belongs to at least one 2-simplex. The author draws attention to a formula for the area $A(\gamma)$ of an $l$-polygon $\gamma$, with boundary $\bar{\gamma}$:

(*) $$A(\gamma)=\{l(\gamma)+N(\gamma)\}-\tfrac{1}{2}\{l(\bar{\gamma})+N(\bar{\gamma})\},$$

where $l(\gamma)$, $l(\bar{\gamma})$ denote the number of points of $l$ belonging to $\gamma$ and $\bar{\gamma}$, and where $N(\gamma)$, $N(\bar{\gamma})$ are the Euler-Poincaré characteristics of $\gamma$ and $\bar{\gamma}$, respectively. (For an arbitrary finite simplicial complex composed of $\alpha_i$ $i$-simplices, $0\leqq i\leqq n$, the Euler-Poincaré characteristic is defined here as $\sum_{i=1}^n(-1)^{i+1}\alpha_i$.) This is a generalization of the well-known formula $A(\gamma)=l(\gamma)-\frac{1}{2}l(\bar{\gamma})-1$, valid when $\bar{\gamma}$ is a closed Jordan curve. Other generalizations have been published by E. Ehrhart and numerous references are given.

A 3-dimensional analogue of (*) is stated; the proof of this and other results are due to appear later in the Proc. London Math. Soc. *J. H. H. Chalk* (Hamilton, Ont.).

**P28-29** **(19, 1163b)**

**Venugopal Rao, V. The lattice point problem for indefinite quadratic forms with rational coefficients.** J. Indian Math. Soc. (N.S.) **21** (1957), 1–40 (1958).

Let $\mathfrak{x}$ be an $m$-dimensional, integral column vector, $\mathfrak{S}$ a real, rational, symmetric, positive definite, $m\times m$ matrix, $\mathfrak{a}$ and $\mathfrak{h}$ two fixed, real, $m$-dimensional, rational column vectors, denote the transpose by a dash, let $\mathfrak{S}[\mathfrak{x}]=\mathfrak{x}'\mathfrak{S}\mathfrak{x}$, and set

$$A(\mathfrak{S},\mathfrak{a},\mathfrak{h},t)=\sum_{\mathfrak{S}[\mathfrak{x}+\mathfrak{a}]=t} e^{2\pi i\mathfrak{x}'\mathfrak{h}}.$$

For $\mathfrak{a}=\mathfrak{h}=0$, the second member becomes the number of representations of the integer $t$ by the quadratic form $\mathfrak{S}[\mathfrak{x}]$; in particular, if $\mathfrak{S}$ reduces to the unit matrix, this becomes the number of representations of $t$ by a sum of $m$ squares. If $\mathfrak{h}\neq 0$, each representation is weighted by the factor $e^{2\pi i\mathfrak{x}'\mathfrak{h}}$ and the expression is further generalized by taking $\mathfrak{a}\neq 0$. In the case of indefinite forms $\mathfrak{S}[\mathfrak{x}]$, instead of the (no longer finite) number of representations of $t$ by $\mathfrak{S}[\mathfrak{x}]$, one has to consider Siegel's [Ann. of Math. (2) **37** (1936), 230–263] measure of representation. The author generalizes this concept to the present situation with $\mathfrak{h}\neq 0$ (the cases $m=3$, $-t|\mathfrak{S}|$ a square and $m=4$, $t=0$, $|\mathfrak{S}|$ a square excluded; also $m=2$, $-|\mathfrak{S}|$ a square). If $\mu(\mathfrak{S}, \mathfrak{a}, \mathfrak{h}, t)$ is this (properly normalized) generalized measure of representation, one may define the zeta function $\zeta(\mathfrak{S}, \mathfrak{a}, \mathfrak{h}, s)=\sum_{t>0}\mu(\mathfrak{S}, \mathfrak{a}, \mathfrak{h}, t)/t^s$. Let $\lambda$ be a parameter, $0<\lambda<1$, $\mathfrak{X}$ a real matrix of rank $n$, $\mathfrak{S}[\mathfrak{X}]=\mathfrak{T}>0$, and set $\mathfrak{R}=\mathfrak{T}^{-1}[\mathfrak{X}'\mathfrak{S}]$, $\mathfrak{H}=\lambda\mathfrak{S}-\mathfrak{R}$. Furthermore, define the theta series $\vartheta(\xi, \eta, \lambda, \mathfrak{X}, \mathfrak{S}, \mathfrak{a}, \mathfrak{h})=\sum\exp\{\pi i(\xi\mathfrak{S}-i\gamma\eta\mathfrak{H})[\mathfrak{x}+\mathfrak{a}]+2\pi i\mathfrak{x}'\mathfrak{h}\}$ where $\gamma=(\lambda(l-\lambda))^{-\frac{1}{2}}$ and the sum is taken over integral values of $\mathfrak{x}$. Integrating $\vartheta$ over a fundamental domain $F^*(\mathfrak{S})$, using an appropriate measure $dv$ (both too complicated for exact definition here), one obtains

$$g(\xi, \eta, \lambda, \mathfrak{S}, \mathfrak{a}, \mathfrak{h})=\int_{F^*(\mathfrak{S})}\theta(\xi, \eta, \lambda, \mathfrak{X}, \mathfrak{S}, \mathfrak{a}, \mathfrak{h})dv.$$

Using results of Siegel [Abh. Math. Sem. Hansischen Univ. **13** (1940), 209–239; Math. Ann. **124** (1951), 17–54; MR **2**, 148; **16**, 800], the author obtains the Fourier expansion of $g$. From this it follows that $g$ is not an analytic function of $\xi+i\eta$, but satisfies a certain second order elliptic partial differential equation. The Mellin transform of $g(0, \eta, \lambda, \mathfrak{S}, \mathfrak{a}, \mathfrak{h})$ with respect to $\eta$ is shown to be precisely $\zeta(\mathfrak{S}, \mathfrak{a}, \mathfrak{h}, s)$, and use of the transformation formula of the theta function leads to the functional equation of this zeta-function. These results generalize those of Maass (S.-B. Heidelberger Akad. Wiss. Math. Nat. Klasse 1949, no. 1, 42 pp. (1949); MR **11**, 230] and Siegel [Math. Z. **43** (1938), 682–708]. $\zeta$ is in general meromorphic, but is actually an entire function of $s$ if $\mathfrak{h}$ is not integral and either $|\mathfrak{S}|>0$, or $\mathfrak{S}^{-1}[\mathfrak{x}+\mathfrak{h}]$ is not a zero form. In all cases $(s-1)(s-\frac{1}{2}m)\zeta(\mathfrak{S}, \mathfrak{a}, \mathfrak{h}, s)$ is an entire function of finite genus. Finally, using classical theorems and results from the theory of Bessel functions (partly due to the author), the author determines analytic expressions for the Riesz sums $\sum_{0<\lambda_l\leq x}\mu(\mathfrak{S}, \mathfrak{a}, \mathfrak{h}, \lambda_l)(x-\lambda_l)^\alpha$ for $x>0$ and $\alpha>\frac{1}{2}(m-1)$; here $\{\lambda_l\}$ is the sequence of positive values of $\mathfrak{S}[\mathfrak{x}+\mathfrak{a}]$. The formulae are different, according to the sign of $|\mathfrak{S}|$. Furthermore, if $|\mathfrak{S}|>0$, the Riesz summability of $\sum_{l=1}^{\infty}\mu(\mathfrak{S}^{-1}, \mathfrak{h}, -\mathfrak{a}, \mu_l)J_\mu(2\pi(\mu_l x)^{\frac{1}{2}})\mu_l^\alpha$, $\mu>-1$, $\alpha$ real, $x\neq\mu_l$ follows from Theorem 1 of Bochner [Ann. of Math. (2) **53** (1951), 332–363; MR **13**, 920]. Previously mentioned Riesz sums may be considered a generalization of Hardy's representation of $\sum_{0<n\leq x}r(n)(x-n)^\alpha$ ($r(n)$=number of representations of $n$ as sum of two squares, $\alpha\geqq 0$, $x\neq$integer), by a series involving Bessel functions [Quart. J. Math. Oxford Ser. **46** (1915), 263–283; Proc. London Math. Soc. (2) **15** (1916), 192–213]. *E. Grosswald* (Philadelphia, Pa.).

Citations: MR 2, 148b = E12-4; MR 11, 230h = F65-5; MR 13, 920b = M40-7; MR 16, 800a = E12-49.

## P28-30 (20# 2327a; 20# 2327b; 20# 2327c)

**Ehrhart, Eugène. Sur les polygones homothétiques.** C. R. Acad. Sci. Paris **246** (1958), 205–207.

**Ehrhart, Eugène. Polygones homothétiques et inéquations diophantiennes linéaires.** C. R. Acad. Sci. Paris **246** (1958), 354–357.

**Ehrhart, Eugéne. Sur les inéquations diophantiennes linéaires.** C. R. Acad. Sci. Paris **246** (1958), 1147–1149.

Let $S$ denote a plane region and let $i$, $p$ denote the number of points with integral coordinates in the interior and on the boundary of $S$, respectively. Put

$$\Delta(S)=i+\tfrac{1}{2}p-V(S),$$

where $V(S)$ denotes the area of $S$. A polygon $S$ is called "semi-entier" if all the coordinates of the vertices of $S$ are $\equiv\frac{1}{2}$ or 1 (mod 1) and at least one is $\equiv\frac{1}{2}$ (mod 1). Then it is shown that, for a "semi-entier" polygon $S$, the value of $\Delta(S)$ is invariant under homothetic transformations of $S$ (with respect to any fixed integral point), provided that the homothetic ratio is an odd integer.

In the second paper, polygons $S$ with rational vertices are called "$1/n$-entier", if $n$ is the l.c.m. of the denominators of the coordinates of these vertices. An analogue of the above invariance property is established and, in the third paper, application is made to diophantine inequalities of the form

$$\frac{X}{a}+\frac{Y}{b}<C,$$

where $X$, $Y$ are positive integral variables, $a>0$, $b>0$ are coprime integers, and $C$ is any real number.

*J. H. H. Chalk* (Hamilton, Ont.)

## P28-31 (20# 4518 )

**Sierpiński, W. Sur quelques problèmes concernant les points aux coordonnées entières.** Enseignement Math. (2) **4** (1958), 25–31.

It is proved that there are circles and squares in the plane containing in their interior a given number of points with integral coordinates.

*C. G. Lekkerkerker* (Amsterdam)

## P28-32 (20# 5188 )

**Ehrhart, Eugène. Sur les inéquations diophantiennes linéaires à deux inconnues.** C. R. Acad. Sci. Paris **246** (1958), 2987–2989.

Let $a$ and $b$ be relatively prime positive integers. The author studies the number $n_C$ of pairs of positive integers $X$, $Y$ satisfying $aX+bY<C$. In particular, he shows that if $C=abq+r$, where $q$, $r$ are integers with $0<r<q$, then

$$n_C=n_r+\tfrac{1}{2}q(C+r-a-b-1).$$

*C. A. Rogers* (Birmingham)

## P28-33 (20# 5189 )

**Ehrhart, Eugène. Nombre de solutions de l'équation et de l'inéquation diophantiennes linéaires à trois inconnues.** C. R. Acad. Sci. Paris **246** (1958), 3142–3145.

Let $a$, $b$, $c$ be positive integers, relatively prime in pairs. The author studies the numbers $n_D$ and $N_D$ of triples of positive integers $X$, $Y$, $Z$ satisfying $aX+bY+cZ=D$ and $aX+bY+cZ<D$. In particular, he shows that if $D=abcq+r$, where $q$, $r$ are integers with $0<r<q$, then

$$n_D=n_r+\tfrac{1}{2}q(D+r-a-b-c),$$

$$N_D=N_{abcq}+N_r+1+\tfrac{1}{2}qr(D-a-b-c-1),$$

$$N_D=qN_{abc}+N_r+q\{\tfrac{1}{6}(q^2-1)a^2b^2c^2-\tfrac{1}{4}(q-1)abc(a+b+c+1)+\tfrac{1}{2}r(D-a-b-c-1)+1\}.$$

*C. A. Rogers* (Birmingham)

Referred to in P28-38.

## P28-34 (20# 6412 )

**Krupička, Svatopluk. Über die Anzahl der Gitterpunkte in mehrdimensionalen konvexen Körpern.** Czechoslovak Math. J. **7**(82) (1957), 524–552. (Russian. German summary)

For the number of lattice points in $r$-dimensional ellipsoids the formulas $A(x)=x^{r/2}V+P(x)$ are well known, where $V$ denotes the volume of the "fundamental" ellipsoid. If $x$ tends to infinity, then for the remainder $P(x)$ we have the estimate from above $P(x)=O(x^{(r/2)-r/(r+1)})$ and the estimate from below $P(x)=\Omega(x^{(r-1)/4})$. In the present article the author proves the correctness of analogous formulas for the number of lattice points in more general convex $r$-dimensional bodies.

*Author's summary*

## P28-35 (21# 1230)

**Gomory, Ralph E. Outline of an algorithm for integer solutions to linear programs.** Bull. Amer. Math. Soc. **64** (1958), 275–278.

This is a path-breaking contribution which multiplies tenfold the power of linear programming methods. It provides a finite, real field algorithm for solving the discrete problem: Maximize a linear integral form among integer lattice points of a polyhedral convex set. The efficiency of the method where $M$ linear inequalities characterize the polyhedral set is that of linear programming, i.e., the effort involved is that of inverting an $M\times M$ matrix. This is the first method which efficiently solves a reasonably general problem of finding a global maximum where many local maxima are possible. It provides a calculus which straight-forwardly handles problems of combinatorial, diophantine and Boolean analysis constructively, removing them from their heretofore character of intractable curiosities and mathematical recreations. Continuum problems involving disconnected unions of polyhedral convex sets may also be reduced to routine character.

The finiteness of the algorithm, which is the most critical element of novelty, depends on the property of finite increase at each stage, based on regularization ($\varepsilon$-perturbation) techniques first achieved by Charnes, application of the dual (not dual simplex) method of Lemke, and the use of Beale's form of the simplex tableau to obtain the repercussions of integrality. The references cited are inadequate to convey a proper idea of the ubiquitous possibilities for application. The possibility of formulating many important applicational problems as diophantine programming problems has been recognized for years by many other workers in the field of linear programming. However, such a formulation has hitherto been almost exclusively a dead-end.

*A. Charnes* (Evanston, Ill.)

## P28-36 (21# 1298)

**Artyuhov, M. L. A method for counting integral points in $n$-dimensional polyhedrons.** Dokl. Akad. Nauk SSSR (N.S.) **118** (1958), 215–218. (Russian)

Referred to in P28-45.

## P28-37 (22# 708)

**Fast, H.; Świerczkowski, S. On the number of lattice points inside a closed curve.** Colloq. Math. **6** (1958), 211–214.

Let $G$ be a plane region and let its Lebesgue measure $|G|$ be an integer. Under certain conditions it is proved that $G$ can be translated and rotated so as to contain exactly $|G|$ lattice points.

*C. G. Lekkerkerker* (Amsterdam)

## P28-38 (22# 1561a; 22# 1561b; 22# 1561c; 22# 1561d; 22# 1561e; 22# 1561f)

**Ehrhart, Eugène. Nombre de solutions de l'équation et de l'inéquation diophantiennes linéaires à trois inconnues.** C. R. Acad. Sci. Paris **248** (1959), 620–623.

**Ehrhart, Eugène. Nombre de solutions de l'equation diophantienne linéaire à trois inconnues.** C. R. Acad. Sci. Paris **248** (1959), 758–761.

**Ehrhart, Eugene. Sur les équations diophantiennes linéaires à plus de trois inconnues.** C. R. Acad. Sci. Paris **248** (1959), 896–899.

**Ehrhart, Eugène. Nombre de solutions d'un système d'inéquations diophantiennes linéaires à deux ou trois inconnues, à trois ou quatre si on lui adjoint une équation.** C. R. Acad. Sci. Paris **248** (1959), 1096–1099.

**Ehrhart, Eugène. Sur les polyèdres entiers à $n$ dimensions.** C. R. Acad. Sci. Paris **248** (1959), 1281–1284.

**Ehrhart, Eugène. Sur les polyèdres rationnels à $n$ dimensions.** C. R. Acad. Sci. Paris **250** (1960), 272–274.

Further instalments of the author's study "Corps convexes, réseaux entiers, équations et inéquations diophantiennes linéaires" as distilled into Comptes Rendus notes since 1955 [e.g., **246** (1958), 3142–3145; MR **20** #5189]. These give a large number of theorems and conjectures, said to be supported by numerical evidence, about the relations between the numbers of points in and on the surface of homothetic polyhedra in several dimensions. The theorems seem to be pretty straightforward; for example, relating the number of positive integer solutions $(X, Y, Z)$ of $aX+bY+cZ=n$, where $a, b, c$ are given positive integers and two values of $n$ are considered which are congruent modulo each of $a, b, c$. The conjectures may be more interesting but are too circumstantial to quote here.

*J. W. S. Cassels* (Cambridge, England)

Citations: MR 20# 5189 = P28-33.

Referred to in P28-88.

## P28-39 (22# 1562a; 22# 1562b)

**Ehrhart, Eugène. Systèmes diophantiens linéaires.** C. R. Acad. Sci. Paris **250** (1960), 643–645.

**Ehrhart, Eugène. Sur les polyèdres rationnels et les systèmes diophantiens linéaires.** C. R. Acad. Sci. Paris **250** (1960), 959–961.

These are notes 25 and 26 of a sequence [see preceding review] mainly about points in and on the surface of polyhedra in a space of $V$ dimensions. The second enunciates four conjectures all of which have been verified for $V=1$ and two also for $V=2$. They have also been verified in some special cases. The first note contains numerical examples which are stated to be in accordance with these and other conjectures of the author.

*J. W. S. Cassels* (Cambridge, England)

Referred to in P28-82, P28-88.

## P28-40 (22# 1563)

**Ehrhart, Eugène. Sur les polyèdres entiers ou rationnels homothétiques.** C. R. Acad. Sci. Paris **250** (1960), 1428–1430.

This is, according to the author, the last of a series of

nearly thirty notes with the general title "Corps convexes, réseaux entiers, équations et inéquations diophantiennes linéaires" [cf. two preceding reviews]. In this note he tidies up points left from previous instalments and supplies a list of errata.

*J. W. S. Cassels* (Cambridge, England)

Referred to in P28-42.

**P28-41** (22# 3729)

**Wild, R. E. On the number of lattice points in $x^t+y^t=n^{t/2}$.** Pacific J. Math. **8** (1958), 929–940.

Let $t$, $n$ be real numbers with $n>1$, $t>1$ and $t$ of the form $2M/(2N+1)$ where $M$, $N$ are positive integers. Denote by $L(n,t)$ the number of integral points $(x,y)$ which satisfy the inequality $|x|^t+|y|^t\leqq n^{t/2}$. The author derives an expression for the integral $\int_0^n L(w,t)w^{t/2-1}dw$, accurate to within $O(n^{(t-1)/2})$, and states that his method fails to establish a relation when $0<t<1$. In case $t=2$ the result is known [Landau, *Vorlesungen über Zahlentheorie, Vol. 2*, Chelsea, New York, 1947; pp. 221–235]. For other expressions involving $L(n,t)$ see Bachmann [*Zahlentheorie, Vol. 2*, Teubner, Leipzig, 1894; pp. 447–450], Cauer [Dissertation, Gottingen, 1914], and van der Corput [Dissertation, Leyden, Noordhoff, Gröningen, 1919].

*A. C. Woods* (New Orleans, La.)

Referred to in P28-93.

**P28-42** (22# 5624)

**Ehrhart, Eugène. Sur les polygones réticulaires.** C. R. Acad. Sci. Paris **250** (1960), 2986–2988.

**If $P$ is a polygon whose vertices are $1/m$ integral points then the number of lattice points in $(km+r)P$ for fixed integer $r$ is a quadratic function of the integer $k$, the coefficients of $k^2$ and $k$ being determined by the area and** perimeter of the polygon. Numerical examples. Cf. the preceding series of notes culminating in C. R. Acad. Sci. Paris **250** (1960), 1428–1430 [MR **22** #1563].

*J. W. S. Cassels* (Cambridge, England)

Citations: MR 22# 1563 = P28-40.

**P28-43** (22# 5625)

**Ehrhart, Eugène. Polygones et polyèdres réticulaires.** C. R. Acad. Sci. Paris **250** (1960), 3934–3936.

Continuation of #5624; further theorems, numerical examples and conjectures about the number of points with integral coordinates in polyhedra.

*J. W. S. Cassels* (Cambridge, England)

Referred to in P28-46.

**P28-44** (22# 10979)

**Andrews, George E. An asymptotic expression for the number of solutions of a general class of Diophantine equations.** Trans. Amer. Math. Soc. **99** (1961), 272–277.

Let $C$ be a strictly convex body in real Euclidean $n$-space with surface content $S(C)$ and $N$ points with integer coordinates on its boundary. It is shown that a function $K(n)$, independent of $C$, exists such that $S(C)>K(n)N^{(n+1)/n}$. This inequality applied to the case where $C$ is defined as the set of points $(x_1,x_2,\cdots,x_n)$ with $f(x_1,x_2,\cdots,x_n)\leqq R$, $f(x_1,x_2,\cdots,x_n)$ being a homogeneous function, yields the inequality $cR^{(n-1)n/(n+1)}>N$, where $c$ is dependent of $f(x_1,x_2,\cdots,x_n)$. This improves the known result that $cR^{n-1}>N$.

*D. Derry* (Vancouver, B.C.)

Referred to in H05-70.

**P28-45** (22# 10980)

**Artyuhov, M. M. Formulas for the number of solutions of some systems of linear diophantine inequalities.** Mat. Sb. (N.S.) **51 (93)** (1960), 501–514. (Russian).

Using the methods and results of an earlier note [Dokl. Akad. Nauk SSSR **118** (1958), 215–218; MR **21** #1298] the author obtains formulae for the number of integral solutions of the set of inequalities $m_i\leqq f_i\leqq M_i$ $(1\leqq i\leqq n)$, where the $f_i$ are homogeneous linear forms with integral coefficients in $n$ variables and the $m_i$ and $M_i$ are integers. The formulae are rather elaborate and depend on the minors of the matrix of coefficients of the forms $f_i$. The reviewer suspects that everything would have been simplified by applying an integral unimodular transformation of the variables so as to bring the matrix of coefficients to triangular form.

*J. W. S. Cassels* (Cambridge, England)

Citations: MR 21# 1298 = P28-36.

**P28-46** (23# a121a; 23# a121b; 23# a121c; 23# a121d; 23# a121e; 23# a121f)

**Ehrhart, Eugène**
**Fraction génératrice d'un système diophantien linéaire homothétique.**
*C. R. Acad. Sci. Paris* **252** (1961), 651–653.

**Ehrhart, Eugène**
**Systèmes diophantiens homothétiques complémentaires.**
*C. R. Acad. Sci. Paris* **252** (1961), 829–831.

**Ehrnart, Eugène**
**Systèmes diophantiens linéaires en affinité à deux inconnues.**
*C. R. Acad. Sci. Paris* **252** (1961), 971–973.

**Ehrhart, Eugène**
**Systèmes diophantiens linéaires en affinité à $n$ inconnues.**
*C. R. Acad. Sci. Paris* **252** (1961), 1085–1087.

**Ehrhart, Eugène**
**Affinité planaire d'un système diophantien linéaire à domaine rationnel.**
*C. R. Acad. Sci. Paris* **252** (1961), 1261–1263.

**Ehrhart, Eugène**
**Affinité axiale d'un système diophantien linéaire à $n$ inconnues.**
*C. R. Acad. Sci. Paris* **252** (1961), 1544–1546.

These are notes 31–36 of the author's marathon series on "Corps convexes, réseaux entiers, équations et inéquations linéaires" [Note 30 is same C. R. **250** (1960), 3934–3936; MR **22** #5625]. He applies the method of generating functions to his type of problem. As usual, several of the more interesting results enunciated are only conjectures. *J. W. S. Cassels* (Cambridge, England)

Citations: MR 22# 5625 = P28-43.

Referred to in P28-47.

**P28-47** (24# A714)

**Ehrhart, Eugène**
**Sur les polyèdres rationnels homothétiques à $n$ dimensions.**
*C. R. Acad. Sci. Paris* **254** (1962), 616–618.

Author's summary: "On démontre et précise la conjecture de mêmes C. R. **252** (1961), 651–653 [MR **23** #A121a]: les nombres de points entiers intérieurs ou périphériques d'un tel polyèdre ont une fraction génératrice; ils sont donc des polynomes mixtes du rapport d'homothétie et satisfont des relations de récurrence simples."

Citations: MR 23# A121a = P28-46.

**P28-48** (24# A1246)

**Ehrhart, Eugène**
**Affinité d'ordre $r$ d'un système diophantien linéaire rationnal.**
*C. R. Acad. Sci. Paris* **254** (1962), 796–798.

Author's summary: "Le nombre $N$ de solutions d'un tel système est un polynome mixte du rapport d'affinité. Il satisfait une relation de récurrence et a une fraction génératrice. $N$ et $N'$ de deux systèmes strict et large correspondants sont liés simplement."

**P28-49** **(24# A1255)**

**Ehrhart, Eugène**

**Sur les polyèdres homothétiques bordés à $n$ dimensions.**

*C. R. Acad. Sci. Paris* **254** (1962), 988–990.

Author's summary: "Le nombre $i_n$ de points entiers intérieurs au polyèdre $P_n$, fonction du rapport d'homothétie $n$, satisfait la même relation de récurrence que $i_n'$ du polyèdre débarrassé de sa bordure, $i_n$ a donc une fraction génératrice, qui permet de l'exprimer comme polynome mixte en $n$. Résultat analogue pour le nombre de points entiers périphériques de $P_n$."

**P28-50** **(24# A1876)**

**Ehrhart, Eugène**

**Sur les systèmes diophantiens linéaires, qui dépendent linéairement d'un paramètre.**

*C. R. Acad. Sci. Paris* **254** (1962), 1183–1185.

Author's summary: "Si le système est significatif, le nombre $N_n$ de ses solutions vérifie, à partir d'un certain rang, une relation de récurrence linéaire et $N_n$ est donc un polynome mixte du paramètre $n$ (conjecture). Dans beaucoup de cas on sait déterminer effectivement cette fonction."

**P28-51** **(24# A1877)**

**Ehrhart, Eugène**

**Systèmes diophantiens linéaires en dilatation.**

*C. R. Acad. Sci. Paris* **254** (1962), 1367–1369.

Author's summary: "On donne, en fonction des paramètres entiers $n$, $n'$, $n''$, le nombre de solutions de tout système diophantien linéaire, dont le domaine se déduit d'un polygone entier plan par la transformation $X'=nX$, $Y'=n'Y$, $Z'=n''Z$."

**P28-52** **(24# A1878)**

**Ehrhart, Eugène**

**Transformation linéaire d'un système diophantien linéaire.**

*C. R. Acad. Sci. Paris* **254** (1962), 1553–1555.

Author's summary: "On donne le nombre de solutions de tout système diphantien linéaire, dont le domaine se déduit d'un polygone plan, entier dans un réseau de l'espace, par une transformation linéaire à coefficients entiers."

**P28-53** **(25# 3015)**

**Herz, C. S.**

**On the number of lattice points in a convex set.**

*Amer. J. Math.* **84** (1962), 126–133.

Let $C$ be a compact convex subset of $(n+1)$-dimensional euclidean space $E^{n+1}$. Denote by $\Delta(C)$ the difference between the number of points with integral coordinates (lattice points) in $C$ and the volume $V(C)$ of $C$. Further, let $\rho(C)$ be defined by

$$\rho^{\nu}(C) = c_n^{-1} \sup_t |t|^{\nu+1} \left| \int_C \exp(2\pi i t\cdot x)\, dx \right|,$$

where $\nu=n/2$ and $c_n$ is "some convenient normalizing constant". Possibly $\rho(C)=\infty$, but it is known that $\rho(C)$ is finite when the boundary of $C$ has differentiability class $C^{(m)}$ with $m=[\nu+2]$ and strictly positive Gaussian curvature [Herz, Ann. of Math. (2) **75** (1962), 81–92]. Theorem 1: If $V(C)\geqq 1$, then $|\Delta(C)|\leqq k_n\rho^{n\alpha_n}(C)$, where $k_n$ depends only on $n$ and $\alpha_n=(n+1)/(n+2)$. By a result of van der Corput $\rho(C)$ can be taken to be the upper bound of the radius of curvature for $n=1$. As a partial generalization for $n>1$ the author proves the following. Theorem 2: Suppose that $V^2(C)\geqq \delta^{n+2}(C)\geqq 1$, where $\delta(C)$ is the diameter of $C$. Then

$$|\Delta(C)| \leqq k_n' K^{-\alpha_n}(C)+E(C),$$

where $k_n'$ depends only on $n$, $K(C)$ is the minimum Gaussian curvature of $C$ and $\alpha_n$ is as above. Here $E(C)$ is a euclidean invariant which is finite whenever the boundary of $C$ is of differentiability class $C^{(m)}$, $m=[\nu+4]$ and $K(C)>0$. Further, $E(C)$ is homogeneous of degree $(n-1)\alpha_n$ for $n>2$ and $E(hC)=O(\log h)$ as $h\to\infty$ for $n=2$.

In an addendum the author notes that the principal result of his earlier paper and Theorem 1 of this paper are substantially contained in Hlawka's work in Monatsh. Math. **54** (1950), 1–36 [MR **12**, 197]; ibid. **54** (1950), 81–99 [MR **12**, 198]. *J. W. S. Cassels* (Cambridge, England)

Citations: MR 12, 197e = P28-9; MR 12, 198a = P28-10.

Referred to in P28-85.

**P28-54** **(25# 5044)**

**Linnik, Ju. V.; Skubenko, B. F.**

**On the asymptotic behavior of integral matrices of third order. (Russian)**

*Dokl. Akad. Nauk SSSR* **146** (1962), 1007–1008.

The authors consider the $3\times 3$ primitive matrices $X=(x_{ij})$ with $x_{ij}$ integers, $\det(X)=N$, $x_{ij}N^{-1/3}$ restricted to a certain sufficiently regular domain $\Omega$, and supply an asymptotic formula for the number of such matrices as $N\to\infty$.

*S. Knapowski* (New Orleans, La.)

**P28-55** **(26# 83)**

**Val'fiš, A. A.**

**Coefficient sums of some Dirichlet series. (Russian)**

*Soobšč. Akad. Nauk Gruzin. SSR* **26** (1961), 9–16.

Der Verfasser knüpft an den bekannten allgemeinen Gitterpunktsatz von Landau an [Nachr. Ges. Wiss. Göttingen **1915**, 209–243]. Sie beweist unter ähnlich allgemeinen Voraussetzungen über den Landauschen Hauptsatz hinaus die Existenz von Identitäten wie sie in den klassischen Fällen des Teiler- und Kreisproblems von Voronoï und Hardy aufgestellt wurden. Neben diesen wird als Anwendung eine Identität, die gewisse Ellipsoidprobleme umfaßt, angegeben.

*H.-E. Richert* (Syracuse, N.Y.)

Referred to in M40-35, P28-64.

**P28-56** **(26# 3674)**

**Ivanov, V. K.**

**A generalization of the Voronoï-Hardy identity. (Russian)**

*Sibirsk. Mat. Ž.* **3** (1962), 195–212.

Let $D$ be a plane convex region having the origin as an interior point and bounded by a curve $C$ which has nonzero curvature everywhere and which is continuously differentiable with respect to arc length. Denote by $P(D)$ the number of integral points inside and on $C$, counting those on $C$ with coefficient $\frac{1}{2}$. It is the basis of most work on the circle problem and related problems that

$$P(D) = \sum_{m_1,m_2=-\infty}^{\infty} \iint_D e^{2\pi i(m_1x_1+m_2x_2)}\, dx_1\, dx_2 = \sum_{m_1,m_2=-\infty}^{\infty} H(m_1, m_2).$$

This result is extended in the present paper in the following way. Let $\Omega$ be a convex body, symmetric about $O$, the boundary of which has nonzero curvature and is six-times differentiable. Denote by $\Omega(\lambda)$ the body resulting from $\Omega$ by magnifying it by the factor $\lambda$. Then with $D$ as before, $P(D)=\lim_{\lambda\to\infty}\sum_{\Omega(\lambda)} H(m_1, m_2)$, where the summation extends over all lattice points $(m_1, m_2)\in\Omega(\lambda)$. The special case of this, when $\Omega$ is an ellipse, was proved by C. Müller [Abh. Math. Sem. Univ. Hamburg **19** (1954), no. 1–2, 66–76; MR **15**, 940].

*W. J. LeVeque* (Ann Arbor, Mich.)

Citations: MR 15, 940b = P28-19.

## P28-57 (27# 3602)

**Srinivasan, B. R.**

**The lattice point problem of many-dimensional hyperboloids. I.**

*Acta. Arith.* 8 (1962/63), 153–172.

The author studies the sum

$$D_k^{(r,\rho)}(x) = \binom{k}{r} \sum_{n_1\cdots n_{k-r}n_j^r\leq x} (x/n_1\cdots n_{k-r})^{1+\rho}$$

(where $n_j$ are positive integers, $x$ is real, $x\geqq 1$, $\rho>-2$, $0\leqq r<k$) with the object of obtaining asymptotic expressions with error terms "of as small an order as we please". His theorems (e.g., Theorem 5) are too long to state here, but we note the special cases: (1) $r=0$, $\rho=-1$, $k=2$. In this case the error term in the so-called divisor-problem is given by the well-known expression

$$\Delta_2^{(0,-1)}(x) = -2\sum_{n\leqq x^{1/2}} \psi_1(x/n)+O(1);$$

(2) $r=0$, $\rho=-1$, $k=3$. Here

$$\Delta_3^{(0,-1)}(x) = -3\sum_{n_1^2n_2,n_1n_2^2\leqq x} \psi_1(x/n_1n_2)+O(x^{1/3}).$$

For related investigations see E. Landau [Nachr. Ges. Wiss. Göttingen Math.-Phys. Kl. **1920**, 13–32], A. Walfisz [*Gitterpunkte in mehrdimensionalen Kugeln*, Państwowe Wydawn. Naukowe, Warsaw, 1957; MR **20** #3826].

*S. Chowla* (University Park, Pa.)

Citations: MR 20# 3826 = P20-16.

## P28-58 (27# 3603)

**Srinivasan, B. R.**

**The lattice point problem of many-dimensional hyperboloids. II.**

*Acta Arith.* 8 (1962/63), 173–204.

The author studies exponential sums of the type

$$\sum_{n_1,\cdots,n_p} e^{2if(n_1,\cdots,n_p)\pi}$$

for arbitrary positive integer $p$. His results extend the classical results of van der Corput for $p=1$; for $p=2$ his results include and slightly refine those of Titchmarsh.

His theorems (e.g., Theorem 3) are too long to be quoted here.

*S. Chowla* (University Park, Pa.)

Referred to in P28-71.

## P28-59 (27# 4139)

**Macdonald, I. G.**

**The volume of a lattice polyhedron.**

*Proc. Cambridge Philos. Soc.* **59** (1963), 719–726.

In real affine $N$-space, let $\mu(X)$ denote the $N$-dimensional content of a polytope $X$ whose vertices all belong to the lattice $L_1$ consisting of the points whose affine coordinates are integers. Let $L_n$ be the lattice of finer mesh consisting of the points whose coordinates are multiples of $1/n$. Let $L(n, X)$ be the number of points of $L_n$ that lie in $X$, and $L(n, \dot{X})$ the number of points of $L_n$ that lie on the boundary $\dot{X}$ of $X$. Finally, let the meaning of $L(n, X)$ be extended so that $L(0, X)$ is the Euler-Poincaré characteristic of $X$. The author proves that

$$\mu(X) = \frac{2}{(N-1)N!}\sum_{j=0}^{N-1}(-1)^j\binom{N-1}{j} \times\{L(N-1-j, X)-\tfrac{1}{2}L(N-1-j, \dot{X})\}.$$

He thus establishes and extends a conjecture of J. E. Reeve [J. London Math. Soc. **34** (1959), 57–62; MR **20** #7242].

*H. S. M. Coxeter* (Toronto, Ont.)

Referred to in P28-80.

## P28-60 (28# 160)

**Skubenko, B. F.**

**On the asymptotic behaviour of integral matrices of order $n$ and on an integral invariant of the group of unimodular matrices. (Russian)**

*Dokl. Akad. Nauk SSSR* **153** (1963), 290–291.

Given an integer $N$, let $N=\prod_{i=1}^m p_i^{k_i}$, where each $p_i$ is prime. For an $n\times n$ integral matrix $X$ such that det $X=N$, let $X^{\sim}=N^{-1/n}X$. Let $\Omega$ denote a Jordan measurable region in the group of $n\times n$ unimodular matrices, and let $m(\Omega)$ denote its Haar measure. The matrix $X$ is said to be completely primitive if the greatest common divisor of the minors of order $n-1$ is 1. Theorems: Fix $\Omega$. The number of integral points $X$ such that det $X=N$ and $X^{\sim}\in\Omega$ is asymptotic to

$$\frac{m(\Omega)}{\zeta(2)\cdots\zeta(n)}\prod_{i=1}^{m}\prod_{j=1}^{n-1}\frac{(p_i^{k_i+j}-1)}{(p_i^j-1)}$$

as $N\to\infty$. The number of completely primitive points $X$ such that det $X=N$ and $X^{\sim}\in\Omega$ is asymptotic to

$$\frac{m(\Omega)}{\zeta(2)\cdots\zeta(n)}\cdot\frac{N^n}{\phi(N)}\sum_{d|N}\frac{\mu(d)}{d^n}$$

as $N\to\infty$.

*K. A. Ross* (Rochester, N.Y.)

## P28-61 (28# 4431)

**Ehrhart, E.**

**Sur le nombre de points à coordonnées entières d'une région convexe plane ou spatiale.**

*Enseignement Math.* (2) **10** (1964), 138–146.

The author obtains a number of inequalities on the number $j$ of points with integral coordinates contained in a closed convex body in two or three dimensions. Typical results are the following: In two dimensions, let $S$ be the area of a convex body and $l$ its perimeter; then $j\leqq S+\frac{1}{2}l+1$, the equality being obtained only for rectangles with sides parallel to the coordinate axes. In three dimensions, let $V$ be the volume of a convex body, $h$ its width in the $x$-direction, $s$ the maximum area and $l$ the maximum perimeter of plane sections perpendicular to the $x$-axis. Then $j\leqq V+s+(h+1)(\frac{1}{2}l+1)$. The following conjecture is made: Let $a, b, c$, be the widths in the $x$, $y$, and $z$ directions of a convex body of volume $V$ and area $S$. Then $j\leqq V+\frac{1}{2}S+a+b+c+1$.

*John W. Green* (Los Angeles, Calif.)

Referred to in P28-73.

## P28-62 (28# 5026)

**Ehrhart, Eugène**

**Nombre de points entiers d'un tétraèdre.**

*C. R. Acad. Sci. Paris* **258** (1964), 3945–3948.

By using the method of an earlier note [same C. R. **256** (1963), 4566–4569; MR **27** #3596a] the author gives a formula for the number of solutions in integers $X$, $Y$, $Z$ of $X/a+Y/b+Z/c\leqq 1$; here, $a$, $b$, $c$ are integers coprime by pairs.

*B. J. Birch* (Manchester)

Citations: MR 27# 3596a = D04-45.

**P28-63** **(29# 50 )**

**Ehrhart, Eugène**

**Sur les points entiers d'un tétraèdre.**

*C. R. Acad. Sci. Paris* **258** (1964), 4182–4183.

If $a$, $b$, $c$ are integers relatively prime to each other, the author proves a formula for the number of integer points within the domain $X/a+Y/b+Z/c\leqq 1$. His argument is elementary and makes use of Euclid's algorithm.

*S. Knapowski* (Marburg)

**P28-64** **(29# 1187 )**

**Walfisz, Anna [Val'fiš, Anna]**

**Über die summatorischen Funktionen einiger Dirichletscher Reihen. II.**

*Acta Arith.* **10** (1964/65), 71–118.

The author further generalizes her results [Soobšč. Akad. Nauk Gruzin. SSR **27** (1961), 9–16; MR **25** #3017; ibid. **26** (1961), 9–16; MR **26** #83] on identities of the Hardy-Landau type for the sum function of a Dirichlet series satisfying a certain functional equation. The results are too long to be quoted here. It is shown that the main theorem includes the well-known identities of Hardy, Voronoi, Arnold Val'fiš, and Oppenheim.

*H.-E. Richert* (Marburg)

Citations: MR 25# 3017 = E44-18; MR 26# 83 = P28-55.

Referred to in P28-72.

**P28-65** **(29# 2219 )**

**Ivanov, V. K.**

**Higher-dimensional generalizations of the Euler summation formula. (Russian)**

*Izv. Vysš. Učebn. Zaved. Matematika* **1963**, *no.* 6 (37), 72–80.

C. Müller [Abh. Math. Sem. Univ. Hamburg **19** (1954), no. 1–2, 41–62; MR **15**, 939] has generalized the well-known Euler summation formula to the functions of $r$ variables. The role of Bernoulli polynomials is played by the so-called basic functions (Grundfunktionen).

The author shows that the summation formulas of this kind are connected with the differential operators. There exist corresponding summation formulas for many linear differential operators with constant coefficients. The analogues of the Bernoulli polynomials are the distributions, which cannot be expressed by the usual functions.

Let $D$ be an $r$-dimensional space region, which is limited by a smooth surface $S$, not containing integer points. Let $f(x)=f(x_1,\cdots,x_r)$ be a function in $D+S$, having continuous derivatives of order $p$. Denote by $L=L(\partial/\partial x)$ the linear differential operator with constant real coefficients, which is a polynomial in $\partial/\partial x_1,\cdots,\partial/\partial x_r$. Then

$$\sum_{n\in D} f(n)=\int_D f(x)H(x)\,dx+\int_S P(f,G)\,ds+\int_D GM(f)\,dx,$$

where the summation is extended over integer points $n=(n_1,\cdots,n_r)$. Here $M$ is the operator conjugate to $L$; $P(u,v)$ is a polynomial in $u$, $v$ and in their partial derivatives. The polynomial $P(u,v)$ is defined by Green's formula

$$\int_D (uLv-vMv)\,dx=\int_S P(u,v)\,ds.$$

This formula is also true in the case when $v$ or some of its derivatives are distributions if the products under the integral sign make sense, and on the surface $S$ there are no singular points of the distribution $v$ and its derivatives. The function $H(x)$ is equal to

$$\sum_{L(2\pi in)=0} e^{2\pi i(n_1x_1+\cdots+n_rx_r)},$$

where $n$ runs over all integer points such that $L(2\pi in)=0$ and $L(2\pi in)$ is the polynomial which is obtained from $L(\partial/\partial x)$ by replacement of $\partial/\partial x_j$ by $2\pi in_j$. $G(x)$ is a basic function, which is a distribution, having the period 1 and satisfying the equation $LG=\Delta(x)-H(x)$. Here $\Delta(x)$ denotes the distribution $\Delta(x)=\sum_n\delta(x-n)$, where the summation extends over all integer points, and $\delta(x-n)$ is the delta-function having singularity at the point $n$. The basic function $G(x)$ is equal to

$$\sum_{L(2\pi in)\neq 0}\frac{e^{2\pi i(n_1x_1+\cdots+n_rx_r)}}{L(2\pi in)}.$$

The necessary and sufficient condition for the existence of the basic function $G(x)$ is the existence of $k$ such that the Diophantine inequality

$$|L(2\pi in)|<(n_1^2+\cdots+n_r^2)^k$$

has only a finite number of integer solutions $(n_1,\cdots,n_r)$.

The simplest and most complete results are obtained in the case when $L$ is an elliptic operator. If the elliptic operator $L$ is of the type $L=(L_0+(-\lambda)^m)^p$, where $L_0(\omega)$ is a homogeneous positive definite polynomial of degree $2m$ and $\lambda\geqq 0$, then the basic function of the operator $L$ is a usual function.

Some special cases are examined in detail.

*J. Kubilius* (Vilnius)

Citations: MR 15, 939d = P28-17.

**P28-66** **(29# 3442 )**

**Ehrhart, Eugène**

**Calcul de la mesure d'un polyèdre entier par un décompte de points.**

*C. R. Acad. Sci. Paris* **258** (1964), 5131–5133.

In Euclidean $k$-space, let $G_1$ denote the lattice of points with integral coordinates, let $G_n=G_1/n$ and let $\Pi$ be any polyhedron whose vertices are points of $G_1$. The volume and surface area (les mesures réticulaires) of $\Pi$ are expressed in terms of the numbers of points in the sets $G_n\cap\Pi$ $(n=1,2,\cdots,[\frac{1}{2}(k+1)])$.

*J. H. H. Chalk* (Toronto, Ont.)

**P28-67** **(29# 3459 )**

**Linnik, Ju. V.; Skubenko, B. F.**

**Asymptotic distribution of integral matrices of third order. (Russian. English summary)**

*Vestnik Leningrad. Univ. Ser. Mat. Meh. Astronom.* **19** (1964), *no.* 3, 25–36.

The authors give an asymptotic formula for the number of integral matrices $X=(x_{ij})$ of third order with determinant $\det(X)=N$, $N\to\infty$, where the $X$'s are subjected to the following additional restrictions: (1) $X\equiv A\pmod p$ ($p\nmid N$ a given prime, $A$ a given integral matrix of third order with determinant $N\pmod p$); (2) $\tilde X=(N^{-1/3}x_{ij})$ belongs to a prescribed sufficiently regular domain $\Omega$.

*S. Knapowski* (Marburg)

**P28-68** **(29# 4738 )**

**Krätzel, E.**

**Ein Gitterpunktsproblem.**

*Acta Arith.* **10** (1964/65), 215–223.

Denote by $R'_{2k,2}(x)$ the number of integer lattice points $(a,b)$ in the region $a^{2k}+b^{2k}\leqq x$, adjusted if necessary by counting any lattice points on the boundary with multiplicity $\frac{1}{2}$; let $V$ be the volume of the region. Write $F * G$ for the convolution $\int F(\tau)G(t-\tau)d\tau$, and $S(x)$ for $\pi^{-1}\sum(\sin 2\pi nx)/n$. The author shows that

$$R'_{2k,2}(x) = \frac{d}{dx}[S(x^{1/2k}) * S(x^{1/2k})],$$

generalising the classical Hardy identity for $R'_{2,2}$; many details are omitted. He attempts to estimate $|R'_{2k,2}-V|$, but makes an error at the head of page 221. The result he is trying to prove was apparently obtained by D. Cauer [Univ. Göttingen, Göttingen, 1914]; far better results may be deduced from the theorem of van der Corput (see Landau, *Vorlesungen über Zahlentheorie*, Hirzel, Leipzig, 1927, esp. Teil 8, Kap. 11–12). *B. J. Birch* (Manchester)

Referred to in P28-86.

## P28-69 (30# 1263 )

**Krätzel, Ekkehard**

**Höhere Thetafunktionen.**

*Dissertation zur Erlangung des Doktorgrades der Mathematisch-Naturwissenschaftlichen Fakultät der Friedrich-Schiller-Universität Jena, Jena,* 1962. 95 *pp.*

The higher theta functions studied in this Ph.D. thesis are defined by

$$(*)\quad \theta_k(x_1, \cdots, x_k) = \sum_{n=-\infty}^{\infty} \exp 2\pi i\left(x_1 n + \frac{1}{2}x_2 n^2 + \cdots + \frac{1}{k}x_k n^k\right).$$

$\theta_3$ was characterized by W. Maier [Math. Ann. **111** (1935), 183–196] by (A) analyticity properties, (B) periodicity in $x_1$, (C) behaviour under a certain linear transformation of the $x_i$, (D) a partial differential equation in $x_1$ and $x_2$, and (E) behaviour when $x_1=0$ and $\operatorname{Im} y \to \infty$. An alternative characterisation, in which (D) and (E) are replaced by an integral condition, was given by W. Maier and the author [Wiss. Z. Friedrich-Schiller-Univ. Jena **11** (1962/63), 105–107; MR **26** #2642].

In the present thesis, the author characterizes $\theta_3$ by a set of properties in which (D) is replaced by a different partial differential equation. He obtains not only (*) but also an expansion in terms of Airy integrals, and thereby an analytic continuation to complex values of $x_3$.

He then takes up $\theta_4$, gives a similar characterisation and an expansion in terms of integrals $\int_{-\infty}^{\infty}\exp[2\pi i P_4(s)]\,ds$, in which $P_4$ is a biquadratic polynomial. This expansion enables him to investigate the behaviour of $\theta_4(0, 0, 0, \rho+it)$ when $\rho$ is rational and $t\to+0$. A similar characterisation and expansion of $\theta_5$ follows, except that here (D) and (E) are replaced by an integral condition. For general $k$, the alternative expansion to (*) is obtained directly by way of the Poisson summation formula.

In a posthumous paper, van der Pol [Nederl. Akad. Wetensch. Proc. Ser. A **63** (1960), 107–114; MR **22** #1692] discussed series of reciprocals of theta functions; the author extends this to $\theta_4$.

Nearly one-third of the thesis is taken up by an application, in several ways, of the Laplace transformation. This can be used to represent $\theta_4$ in terms of $\theta_2$ to obtain an integral equation (whose kernel is a Bessel function) and other functional equations for $\theta_4$, and to relate $\theta_4$ also to Riemann's zeta function. The extension of this work to higher theta functions is briefly discussed, as are certain relations involving Bessel functions.

Let $R_q(x)$ ($q$ an even integer) be the number of lattice points in the $(\xi, \eta)$-plane inside the curve $\xi^q+\eta^q=x$, if $x$ is not an integer, with an appropriate modification for integer $x$. Using the integral equation satisfied by $\theta_{2^k}$, the author proves

$$\int_0^x R_q(y)\,dy = \int_0^x S(t^{1/q})S((s-t)^{1/q})\,dt,$$

where $S(x)=(1/\pi)\sum_{n=-\infty}^{\infty} n^{-1}\sin 2\pi nx$.

*A. Erdélyi* (Edinburgh)

## P28-70 (31# 5837 )

**Schmidt, Peter Georg**

**Abschätzungen bei unsymmetrischen Gitterpunktproblemen.**

Dissertation zur Erlangung des Doktorgrades der Mathematisch-Naturwissenschaftlichen Fakultät der Georg-August-Universität zu Göttingen.

*Dissertation, Göttingen,* 1964. ii+41 *pp.*

In certain problems in the additive theory of numbers, the size of the error term depends upon the estimation of sums of the type $S(a,b)=\sum_{a<n\le b}\psi(x/n^2)$, where $\psi(u)=u-[u]-\frac{1}{2}$. The author's main theorem is that, for $t\ge 0$, $S(t, x^{1/3})=O(x^{\vartheta})$, where $\vartheta=109556/494419<0.22158534$. This is an improvement on H. E. Richert's value of 2/9 [Math. Z. **56** (1952), 21–32; MR **14**, 349] and of the reviewer's further improvement. The proof relates the sum $S(t, x^{1/3})$ to the two-dimensional trigonometric sum $S_1=\sum_m\sum_n \exp(2\pi ixmn^{-2})$. In a long and complicated proof, occupying nineteen pages, the van der Corput-Phillips theory of exponent pairs is used, with other methods of estimation, to provide an upper bound for $|S_1|$. The author uses his main theorem to obtain corresponding improvements in the error terms in the formulae for $\sum_{mn^2\le x}1$ and $\sum_{n\le x}a(n)$, where $a(n)$ is the number of essentially different abelian groups of order $n$. He also shows that the difference between the $n$th and $(n+1)$st squarefree number is $O(n^{\vartheta})$. *R. A. Rankin* (Glasgow)

Citations: MR 14, 349e = N52-13.

Referred to in N64-35.

## P28-71 (31# 5842 )

**Srinivasan, B. R.**

**The lattice point problem of many dimensional hyperboloids. III.**

*Math. Ann.* **160** (1965), 280–311.

In a previous paper [Acta Arith. **8** (1962/63), 173–204; MR **27** #3603] the author considered exponential sums of the type $S=\sum_{(n_1,\cdots,n_p)\in D} e^{2\pi i f(n_1,\cdots,n_p)}$, where $f(n_1, \cdots, n_p)$ is a real function and the sum is taken over the lattice points of a suitable region $D$ in a $p$-dimensional Euclidean space.

The theory of "exponent systems" introduced by van der Corput [Math. Ann. **87** (1922), 39–65] was further developed by Phillips [Quart. J. Math. Oxford **4** (1933), 209–225] and Rankin [ibid. (2) **6** (1955), 147–153; MR **17**, 240]. The present author extends the theory of exponent pairs to higher dimensions, and obtains further refinements of the estimates already obtained in his previous paper cited above. The sum $S$ above is transformed into another sum of the same type and this is used to obtain a better estimate of the original sum. Theorems 1 and 2 (which we do not quote) give two such transformations, say $A$ and $B$, respectively. The transformation $B$ is "involutory", and so the most general transformation that can be obtained by repeated applications of $A$ and $B$ is of the form: $A^{k_1}BA^{k_2}BA^{k_3}B\cdots$. The trivial inequality $|S|\le$ volume of $D$, gives the result that (0, 0) is an exponent pair. By Definition 2 (p. 294) the author is led to Theorem 4: If $(\lambda_0, \lambda_1)$ is an exponent pair of dimension $p$, so is $(l_0, l_1)$, where $l_0=\frac{1}{2}\lambda_0/(1+p\lambda_0)$, $l_1=\frac{1}{2}(\lambda_1+\lambda_0)/(1+p\lambda_0)$.

Theorems 6 and 7 are similar to Theorem 4. The proofs are heavy and difficult, as one expects in this subject.
*S. Chowla* (University Park, Pa.)

Citations: MR 17, 240a = L99-4; MR 27# 3603 = P28-58.

**P28-72** **(31# 5850)**

**Val'fiš, Anna**

**The Fourier-Poisson formula for a certain class of Dirichlet series. (Russian. Georgian summary)**

*Akad. Nauk Gruzin. SSR Trudy Tbiliss. Mat. Inst. Razmadze* **29** (1963), 1–13 (1964).

Pursuing previous studies [Acta Arith. **10** (1964/65), 71–118; MR **29** #1187], the author obtains a summation formula for $\frac{1}{2}\sum'_{a\leqq l_n\leqq b} c_n\{f(l_n+0)\}$ (the $'$ denotes that if $l_n=a$ [$l_n=b$], the multiplier of $c_n$ is $f(a+0)$ [$f(b-0)$]). It is assumed that $f$ is real and of bounded variation on $[a,b]$, and that the Dirichlet series $\sum_{n=1}^{\infty} c_n l_n^{-s}$ satisfies various conditions, too lengthy to reproduce here. When $l_n=n$ and $c_n=$ the number of representations of $n$ as a sum of two squares [the number of divisors of $n$], the result reduces to a summation formula of E. Landau [G. F. Voronoi]. The method of proof is a generalization of that of Landau [*Vorlesungen über Zahlentheorie*, Band 2, Hirzel, Leipzig, 1927].
*A. Dvoretzky* (Lafayette, Ind.)

Citations: MR 29# 1187 = P28-64.

**P28-73** **(32# 1172)**

**Ehrhart, E.**

**Sur quelques polyèdres en géométrie des nombres.**

*Enseignement Math.* (2) **11** (1965), 199–202.

The author has previously conjectured [Enseignement Math. (2) **10** (1964), 138–146; MR **28** #4431] that if a closed convex body in three dimensions has volume $V$, surface area $S$, and widths $a$, $b$, $c$ in the directions of the three coordinate axes, then the number $j$ of integral points in the body satisfies: $j\leqq V+\frac{1}{2}S+a+b+c+1$. Here he verifies this result for three classes of convex polyhedra: (1) an integral prism (i.e., one whose vertices are lattice points); (2) a truncated integral prism, with one base possessing a centre of symmetry; (3) a restricted family of pyramids.
*E. S. Barnes* (Adelaide)

Citations: MR 28# 4431 = P28-61.

**P28-74** **(33# 5588)**

**Moroz, B. Z.**

**A composition of binary quadratic forms and the scalar product of Hecke series. (Russian)**

*Trudy Mat. Inst. Steklov.* **80** (1965), 102–109.

Consideration of problems related to the topic of the title lead to the problem of estimating the number of integral points in a certain large 4-dimensional region, and the estimation is carried out in this paper. The estimation obtained gives a proof of Theorem 1 of an earlier paper by the author [Dokl. Akad. Nauk SSSR **155** (1964), 1265–1267; MR **29** #2238] with the value $\gamma=0.01$. The integral points problem is to estimate the number of solutions in integers of $x^2+D_1y^2=z^2+D_2t^2\leqq X$, $\tan\varphi_1\leqq yD_1^{1/2}/x\leqq\tan(\varphi_1+\Delta_1)$, $\tan\varphi_2\leqq tD_2^{1/2}/z\leqq\tan(\varphi_2+\Delta_2)$, satisfying a congruence $(x,y,z,t)\equiv(\alpha_1,\alpha_2,\alpha_3,\alpha_4) \pmod d$, where $D_1>0$, $D_2>0$, $\alpha_1,\alpha_2,\alpha_3,\alpha_4,d,\varphi_1,\varphi_2,\Delta_1,\Delta_2$ are given and $X\to\infty$. It is shown that the number is $K\Delta_1\Delta_2X+O(X^{15/16+\varepsilon})$, where the constant $K$ is independent of $\varphi_1,\varphi_2,\Delta_1,\Delta_2$. It is given explicitly as an infinite series not unlike a singular series multiplied by the logarithm of the fundamental unit of the real quadratic field $\mathbf{Q}\{(D_1D_2)^{1/2}\}$.
*J. W. S. Cassels* (Cambridge, England)

Citations: MR 29# 2238 = R42-31.

**P28-75** **(34# 155)**

**Senechalle, Marjorie**

**A summation formula and an identity for a class of Dirichlet series.**

*Acta Arith.* **11** (1966), 443–449.

Let $0<\lambda_n\uparrow\infty$ and $a(n)$ be two given sequences. A number of assumptions are made concerning the function $\varphi(s)=\sum_n a(n)\lambda_n^{-s}$. The author derives a summation formula for $\sum_{x<n\leqq y} a(n)f(\lambda_n)$, where $f(u)$ is a complex-valued function having a number of absolutely continuous derivatives in $\langle x,y\rangle$. The right-hand side of the formula involves $f^{(j)}(u)$ at $u=x$, $u=y$ and $\varphi(s)$. Setting $f(u)=u^{-s}$, an identity for $\varphi(s)$ is provided.
*S. Knapowski* (Coral Gables, Fla.)

**P28-76** **(34# 1291)**

**Randol, Burton**

**A lattice-point problem.**

*Trans. Amer. Math. Soc.* **121** (1966), 257–268.

Let $T(Z)$ be an infinitely differentiable positive function on $E_n\backslash\{0\}$, homogeneous of degree $w$. The problem is to estimate $R(x)$, i.e., the error one makes if one replaces the number of lattice points inside the region $\{Z: T(Z)\leqq x\}$ by its volume. Put $C=\{Z: T(Z)\leqq 1\}$; let $x$ be its boundary.

The author introduces the following postulate, which is satisfied in many applications; there exists a positive integer $h$ and a number $\alpha$ $(0<\alpha\leqq(n-1)/2)$ such that for any function $f(Z)$ which is $C^h$ in a neighbourhood of $\partial C$ there is a positive number $M(f)$, depending only on bounds for $f(Z)$ and its derivatives up to order $h$ in a neighbourhood of $\partial C$, such that for all vectors $Y$ $|\int_{\partial C} f(Z)\exp(2\pi i(Y,Z))\,dS_Z|\leqq M(f)|Y|^{-\alpha}$ ($|Y|$ is the length of $Y$, and $dS_Z$ is the area element on $\partial C$). Under this assumption the author proves that $R(x)=O(x^r)$ with $r=(n^2-n-n\alpha)/w(n-\alpha)$.

The main idea of the proof is to approximate a delta function by a $C^\infty$ function with small support, and to apply Poisson's summation formula. This requires a long and detailed investigation of the properties of the Fourier transform of the characteristic function of $C$.

The author refines his argument in the special case $n=2$, $T(Z)=z_1^{2k}+z_2^{2k}$, $k=2,3,\cdots$. He obtains that $R(x)=O(x^{(2k-1)/4k^2})$ and that $R(x)$ is actually of this order. This result was obtained by different methods in van der Corput's dissertation ["On lattice points in the flat plane" (Dutch), Section 109, Noordhoff, Groningen, 1919].

{See also #1292 below.} *N. G. de Bruijn* (Eindhoven)

Referred to in P28-79, P28-91.

**P28-77** **(34# 1292)**

**Randol, Burton**

**A lattice-point problem. II.**

*Trans. Amer. Math. Soc.* **125** (1966), 101–113.

The author considers the special case $T(Z)=z_1^{2k}+\cdots+z_n^{2k}$ of the problem of Part I [#1291 above], if $k$ is an integer $\geqq 1$. Putting $A=(2k-1)(n-1)(4k^2)^{-1}$, $B=n(n-1)(2kn+2k)^{-1}$, the author proves that $R(x)=O(x^{\max(A,B)})$. If $A>B$ this estimate is the best possible.

In order to prove this, the author requires an estimate for $\int_{\partial C} f(Z)\exp(2\pi i(Y,Z))\,dS_Z$ in terms of the product of the nonzero coordinates of $Y$.
*N. G. de Bruijn* (Eindhoven)

**P28-78** **(35# 136)**

**Niven, Ivan; Zuckerman, Herbert S.**

**Lattice points in regions.**

*Proc. Amer. Math. Soc.* **18** (1967), 364–370.

Let $S$ be a bounded set of points in the Euclidean plane with a unit distance defined. If a rectangular coordinate system is imposed, a certain number of points of $S$ are lattice points. Let $m(S)$ be the minimum number of lattice points of $S$ under all possible choices of the axis system, and $M(S)$ the maximum number. The authors prove the following. (a) If $S$ is a nonempty bounded closed set then $m(S) < M(S)$. (b) If $R$ is a bounded measurable region then $m(R) \leqq \mu(R) \leqq M(R)$, where $\mu(R)$ denotes the measure of $R$; if $\mu(R)$ is not an integer, the inequalities can be made strict. (c) If $R$ is a closed, nonempty, bounded, measurable region, then $m(R) \leqq \mu(R) < M(R)$. It is shown that the inequalities of (b) and (c) can be made strict for a special class of regions. *F. Supnick* (New York)

**P28-79** **(35# 2843 )**

**Krätzel, Ekkehard**

**Eine Verallgemeinerung des Kreisproblems.**

*Arch. Math.* (*Basel*) **18** (1967), 181–187.

Let $k \geqq 3$ be an integer, let $R_{k,2}(x)$ be the number of integral lattice points inside the curve $C: \xi^k + \eta^k = x$, and let $V_{k,2}(x)$ be the area inside $C$. Write $S(x) = (1/\pi) \times \sum_{-\infty}^{\infty} (1/n) \sin 2\pi nx$. Then $R_{k,2}(x) = d[S(x^{1/k}) * S(x^{1/k})]/dx$ if $x$ is not integral ($*$ denotes convolution). The author deduces that $R_{k,2}(x) - V_{k,2}(x) = O(x^{\alpha_k})$ with $\alpha_k = 1/2k - 1/4k^2$. This result was proved earlier by B. Randol [Trans. Amer. Math. Soc. **121** (1966), 257–268; MR **34** #1291]; an elementary method adequate for the 2-dimensional case is presented by A. O. Gel'fond and Ju. V. Linnik in their book *Elementary methods in analytic number theory* [(Russian), Fizmatgiz, Moscow, 1962; MR **32** #5575a; French translation, Gauthier-Villars, Paris, 1965; MR **32** #5576; English translations, Rand McNally, Chicago, Ill., 1965; MR **32** #5575b; Pergamon, Oxford, 1966; MR **34** #1252]. *B. J. Birch* (Oxford)

Citations: MR 32# 5575a = Z02-50; MR 32# 5575b = Z02-50; MR 32# 5576 = Z02-51; MR 34# 1252 = Z02-52; MR 34# 1291 = P28-76.

Referred to in P28-86.

**P28-80** **(35# 4184 )**

**Ehrhart, E.**

**Sur un problème de géométrie diophantienne linéaire. I. Polyèdres et réseaux.**

*J. Reine Angew. Math.* **226** (1967), 1–29.

Let $a_1, \cdots, a_s$ be positive integers. Consider the product $\prod(u) = (1-u)^{a_1}(1-u)^{a_2}\cdots(1-u)^{a_s} = \sum b_i u^i$, say. Write $\{\prod(u)\} = \sum b_i u_{n-i}$. Then $\{\prod(u)\} = 0$ is a homogeneous linear recurrence relation for a numerical sequence $(u_n)$. Each solution $(u_n)$ to the equation $\{\prod(u)\} = 0$ is furnished by some generating fraction $f(t)/\pi(t) = \sum u_n t^n$, where $f$ is a polynomial of lower degree than $\pi$; conversely, each such fraction determines a solution $(u_n)$. Furthermore, each solution $(u_n)$ is of the type $u_n = C_1 n^{s-1} + C_2 n^{s-2} + \cdots + C_s$, where each coefficient $C_j$ is the sum of some terms of the form $\xi \cos(2\pi np/a_i) + \eta \sin(2\pi np/a_i)$, $p$ integral and $1 \leqq i \leqq s$. Such a solution is called by the author a mixed polynomial; it is a true polynomial, i.e., the $C_j$ are constants in case $a_1 = \cdots = a_s = 1$; further, $C_1$ is constant if $a_1, \cdots, a_s$ are coprime.

The author considers what he calls general polyhedra and studies numbers of lattice points contained in them. His basic result is the following elegant theorem (of which a rather special case goes back to Euler): Let $P$ be a general polyhedron in $k'$-space, of dimension $k \leqq k'$ and with vertices $A_1, \cdots, A_s$ all coordinates of which are rational. Further, let $G$ be the lattice of points in $k'$-space with integral coordinates. Denote by $d_n$ the number of points of $P \cap n^{-1}G$ and by $a_i$ the smallest positive integer such that $A_i \in a_i^{-1}G$. Then $(d_n)$ satisfies the recurrence relation $\{\prod(d)\} = 0$, $\prod(t) = \prod_{i=1}^{s}(1-t^{a_i})$. Some consequences of this theorem are as follows. (i) In view of the recurrence relation, the number $d_n$ can be defined for $n \leqq 0$ as well. (ii) If the vertices of $P$ all belong to $G$, then $d_n$ is a true polynomial of degree $k$; so, in this case, $d_n$ is given in terms of the initial values $d_0, d_1, \cdots, d_k$ by the formula

$$d_n = \sum_{r=0}^{k} (-1)^{k-r} \binom{k}{r} \cdot \frac{n(n-1)\cdots(n-k)}{k!(n-r)} d_r \qquad (n > k).$$

(iii) Under the same condition, the volume of $P$ can be expressed as a linear function of $d_0, d_1, \cdots, d_k$ (a result of this type was given earlier by I. G. Macdonald [Proc. Cambridge Philos. Soc. **59** (1963), 719–726; MR **27** #4139]).

The author further discusses the possibility of simplifying the recurrence relation on deleting linear factors of $\prod(t)$, investigates more closely polyhedra of dimension $k \leqq 3$ and enunciates various conjectures for which partial proofs are presented. In particular, he formulates a certain reciprocity law; this law says, inter alia, that the counters $d_n, d_n'$ of a closed normal polyhedron $P$ with vertices in $G$ and of the corresponding open polyhedron $P' = \operatorname{int} P$, respectively, are related by the formula $d_n = (-1)^k d_{-n}'$. (A full proof of the reciprocity law is to be found in a forthcoming paper by C. Chabauty, presented to the Colloque International sur les Tendances Géométriques en Algèbre et Théorie des Nombres (Clermont-Ferrand, 1964) but not published in the Proceedings of the Colloquium [Éditions du Centre National de la Recherche Scientifique, Paris, 1966; MR **34** #2387].)

*C. G. Lekkerkerker* (Amsterdam)

Citations: MR 27# 4139 = P28-59; MR 34# 2387 = Z10-26.

Referred to in P28-81.

**P28-81** **(36# 105 )**

**Ehrhart, E.**

**Sur un problème de géométrie diophantienne linéaire. II. Systèmes diophantiens linéaires.**

*J. Reine Angew. Math.* **227** (1967), 25–49.

Let $k$ be a fixed positive integer and $n$ a variable positive integer. The author investigates the number $C_n$ of sets of integers $x_1, \cdots, x_k$ satisfying a given finite system of linear equations or inequalities with integral coefficients depending linearly on $n$. The following types of systems are considered: (i) eulerian systems $\sum a_i x_i = n$, $x_i \geqq 0$ $(i = 1, \cdots, k)$; (ii) homothetic systems $\sum_{i=1}^{k} a_{ij} x_i = b_j n$ or $\geqq b_j n$ $(j = 1, \cdots, s)$; (iii) so-called bordered systems $\sum_{i=1}^{k} a_{ij} x_i = b_j n$ or $\geqq b_j n + c_j$; (iv) affine systems $\sum_{i=1}^{m} a_{ij} x_i + n \sum_{i=m+1}^{k} a_{ij} x_i = b_j n$ or $\geqq b_j n$, where $n$ is a fixed positive integer $< k$. In all cases, the condition is imposed that the system considered determine a (non-void bounded) polyhedron $P_n$ in $k$-space, at least for sufficiently large $n$.

Applying the results of Part I [same J. **226** (1967), 1–29; MR **35** #4184] the author shows that, at least in the cases (i), (ii) and (iv), the counter $C_n$ satisfies a linear recurrence relation and has the form of a polynomial in $n$, the coefficients of which are constants or periodic functions of $f$. The results are illustrated by a large number of numerical examples. It is an open question whether for the most general system determining a polyhedron, the counter $C_n$ satisfies a linear recurrence relation.

*C. G. Lekkerkerker* (Amsterdam)

Citations: MR 35# 4184 = P28-80.

**P28-82** **(36# 1393 )**

**Ehrhart, Eugène**

**Démonstration de la loi de réciprocité du polyèdre rationnel.**

*C. R. Acad. Sci. Paris Sér. A-B* **265** (1967), A91–A94.

Let $P$ be an open $k$-dimensional polyhedron whose vertices are rational; $\bar{P}$ its closure; $G$ the integral lattice; $n$ a positive integer; $i(n)$ and $j(n)$ the number of points of $(1/n)G$ in $P$ and $\bar{P}$, respectively. Here the author proves one of his conjectures made in 1960 [same C. R. **250** (1960), 959–961; MR **22** #1562b], namely, that $i(n)=(-1)^k j(-n)$. {The notation $j(-n)$ refers to the analytic expression of $j$ in terms of powers and trigonometric functions.}

*E. S. Barnes* (Adelaide)

Citations: MR 22# 1562b = P28-39.

Referred to in P28-83, P28-84.

## P28-83 (37# 5161)

**Ehrhart, Eugène**

**Deux corollaires de la loi de réciprocité du polyèdre rationnel.**

*C. R. Acad. Sci. Paris Sér. A-B* **265** (1967), A160–A162.

With the notation of the review of an earlier paper [same C. R. **265** (1967), A91–A94; MR **36** #1393], the author points out that the recurrence relation satisfied by $i(n)$ and $j(n)$ is also valid if the indices are negative. He indicates, and illustrates with an example, the resulting relation between the generating functions of the two sequences.

*E. S. Barnes* (Adelaide)

Citations: MR 36# 1393 = P28-82.

## P28-84 (38# 3233)

**Ehrhart, Eugène**

**Sur la loi de réciprocité des polyèdres rationnels.**

*C. R. Acad. Sci. Paris Sér. A-B* **266** (1968), A696–A697.

Let $F(t)=\prod(1-t^{a_i})^{-1}=(\sum_1^s \alpha_r t^r)^{-1}=\sum_0^\infty j(n)t^n$. Then $j(n)$ satisfies a recurrence relation (R): $\sum \alpha_r j(n-r)=0$; the author shows that the mixed polynomial extension of $j(n)$ to negative $n$ satisfies (R), and thence deduces $\sum_1^\infty j(-n)t^{-n}=-F(t)$, a formula of Popoviciu which he used previously [the author, same C. R. **265** (1967), A91–A94; MR **36** #1393] to establish the relation $i(n)=(-1)^k j(-n)$ between the number of points of the lattice $G/n$ in an open $G$-rational $k$-dimensional polyhedron and its closure. {There is a misprint in the first footnote: the year should be 1967.} *G. K. White* (Vancouver, B.C.)

Citations: MR 36# 1393 = P28-82.

## P28-85 (38# 1063)

**Abljalimov, S. B.**

**Integral points in perturbed circles.** (Russian)

*Dokl. Akad. Nauk SSSR* **180** (1968), 263–265.

W. Sierpiński showed [Prace Mat.-Fiz. **17** (1906), 77–118] that the number $A(R)$ of integral points in a circle with centre the origin and radius $R$ satisfies the inequality $(A(R)-\pi R^2)\ll R^{2/3}$. The proof was extended to more general convex regions by Vinogradov and van der Corput (see E. Landau [*Vorlesungen über Zahlentheorie*, Vol. 2, Teubner, Leipzig, 1927] and C. S. Herz [Amer. J. Math. **84** (1962), 126–133; MR **25** #3015]). For the circle itself van der Corput showed that the exponent 2/3 could be replaced by a smaller one, but Jarník showed that this cannot be done in the generalized result (see Landau [loc. cit.]). In this note the author sketches a proof of a theorem confirmining a conjecture (unpublished?) of Linnik that the exponent 2/3 can be improved if sufficiently stringent conditions are laid on the behaviour of the boundary. More precisely, let $B$ be the "perturbed circle" whose boundary is given in polar coordinates $(\rho,\varphi)$ by an equation $\rho=R+r(R,\varphi)$, where $\partial^k r(R,\varphi)/\partial\varphi^k=o(R)$, $0\leqq k\leqq 4$, uniformly in $\varphi$. Let $V(B)$ be the area of $B$ and $A(B)$ the number of integral points in $B$. Then

$$|A(B)-V(B)|\ll R^{112/169}\ln^{37/18}R.$$

Note that $112/169<2/3$.

{This article has appeared in English translation [Soviet Math. Dokl. **9** (1968), 599–602].}

*J. W. S. Cassels* (Cambridge, England)

Citations: MR 25# 3015 = P28-53.

## P28-86 (38# 4415)

**Krätzel, Ekkehard**

**Identitäten für die Anzahl der Gitterpunkte in bestimmten Bereichen.**

*Math. Nachr.* **36** (1968), 181–191.

A generalization of a well-known identity of Hardy is proven. Hardy's identity is the following. Let $R(x)=\sum_{u^2+v^2\leqq x}1$. Then we have for non-integer $x$, (*) $R(x)=\pi x+(\sqrt{x})\sum_{n=1}^\infty (r(n)/\sqrt{n})F_1(2\pi\sqrt{(nx)})$, where $r(n)=\sum_{u^2+v^2=n}1$ and $F_1(z)$ is the first Bessel function. The paper considers instead of $R(x)$ more general functions of the form $R_k(x)=\sum_{u^k+v^k\leqq x}1$, where $u,v$ are nonnegative integers and the term corresponding to $u=v=0$ is multiplied by $\frac14$, the terms corresponding to $u=0$, $v\neq0$ and $u\neq0$, $v=0$ are multiplied by $\frac12$. In previous papers the author [Acta Arith. **10** (1964/65), 215–223; MR **29** #4738; Math. Nachr. **30** (1965), 33–46; MR **32** #5931; Wiss. Z. Friedrich-Schiller-Univ. Jena/Thüringen **14** (1965), 369–381; MR **37** #6697; Arch. Math. (Basel) **18** (1967), 181–187; MR **35** #2843] deduced a formula analogous to the integral of (*). Now he gives the analogue for (*) itself. Further, the more general case $R_{m,k}(x)=\sum_{u_1{}^k+u_2{}^k+\cdots+u_m{}^k\leqq x}1$ is considered.

*P. Szüsz* (Stony Brook, N.Y.)

Citations: MR 29# 4738 = P28-68; MR 35# 2843 = P28-79.

## P28-87 (39# 4108)

**Krätzel, Ekkehard**

**Bemerkungen zu einem Gitterpunktsproblem.**

*Math. Ann.* **179** (1969), 90–96.

If $R_{k,2}(x)$ denotes the sum $4\sum_{n^k+m^k\leqq x;n\geqq0,m\geqq0}1$, it is known [full references are supplied in the author's introduction] that (1) $R_{k,2}(x)=(2\Gamma^2(k^{-1})/k\Gamma(2k^{-1}))x^{2/k}+O[x^{1/k-1/k^2}]$ holds for $k\geqq3$ and, moreover, that this estimate cannot be improved upon for $k\geqq4$. In this paper, the remaining case $k=3$ is settled (again, no improvement on (1) is possible) and the author examines the problem anew for arbitrary real $k\geqq2$, using the van der Corput method.

*J. H. H. Chalk* (Toronto, Ont.)

## P28-88 (39# 6826)

**Ehrhart, Eugène**

**Démonstration de la loi de réciprocité pour un polyèdre entier.**

*C. R. Acad. Sci. Paris Sér. A-B* **265** (1967), A5–A7.

Let $P$, $\bar{P}$ denote open and closed, respectively, $k$-dimensional polyhedra whose vertices belong to a lattice $G_k$, and for any integer $n>0$, write $i_n=\text{Card}(P\cap(1/n)G)$, $j_n=\text{Card}(\bar{P}\cap(1/n)G)$. The author proves that $i_n, j_n$ are polynomials in $n$ and that $i(n)=(-1)^k j(-n)$. The latter reciprocity law and another law were conjectured by the author [same C. R. **248** (1959), 1281–1284; MR **22** #1561e; ibid. **250** (1960), 959–961; MR **22** #1562b].

*J. V. Armitage* (London)

Citations: MR 22# 1561e = P28-38; MR 22# 1562b = P28-39.

## P28-89 (40# 110)

**Nasim, C.**

**A summation formula involving $\sigma_k(n)$, $k>1$.**

*Canad. J. Math.* **21** (1969), 951–964.

Let $\sigma_k(n)$ denote the sum of $k$th powers of the divisors of $n$. A. P. Guinand [Quart. J. Math. Oxford Ser. (2) **10** (1939), 104–118] gave summation formulae involving $\sigma_k(n)$ as coefficients for $|k|<1$. The author gives analogous formulae for $|k|>1$.

*K. Thanigasalam* (University Park, Pa.)

**P28-90** **(40# 2617)**

**Chandrasekharan, K.; Narasimhan, Raghavan**

**An approximate reciprocity formula for some exponential sums.**

*Comment. Math. Helv.* **43** (1968), 296–310.

Let $a_n$ denote the number of non-zero integral ideals with norm $n$ of the ideal class $\mathfrak{C}$ in a quadratic field $K=Q(d^{1/2})$, where $d$ is the discriminant of $K$. The main result of the paper is the following theorem: Let $\lambda=|d|^{1/2}$ and $0<x\leqq\lambda$. Then, if $Xx^2\geqq 1/\lambda>0$,

$$\sum_{n\leq X} a_n \exp(2\pi inx/\lambda) = (c_1/x)\sum_{n\leq Xx^2} a_n \exp(-2\pi in/\lambda x)+O(X^{1/2}\log X);$$

if $0<Xx^2<1/\lambda$, then

$$\sum_{n\leq X} a_n \exp(2\pi inx/\lambda) = (c_2/(2\pi ix))(\exp(2\pi ixX/\lambda)-1)+O(X^{1/3}).$$

Here, $c_1$ and $c_2$ are constants depending upon $K$. The error terms are uniform in $x$.

The starting point of the proof is an identity involving an infinite series of Bessel functions for $\sum_{n\leq X} a_n$. This identity was proven by the authors in two earlier papers. However, it should be noted that the identity was first proven by Arnold Walfisz [Math. Z. **22** (1925), 153–188]. The remainder of the proof depends chiefly upon Abel summation and a lemma due to J. R. Wilton [J. Reine Angew. Math. **169** (1932), 219–237] on the estimation of a certain integral involving Bessel functions.

Secondly, the authors establish a Voronoĭ summation formula for $\sum_{\lambda_n\leq X} a_n f(\lambda_n)$, where $\lambda_n=n/\lambda$ and $f$ belongs to a suitable class of functions.

No applications of any of the results are indicated.

*B. Berndt* (Urbana, Ill.)

Referred to in Z02-77.

**P28-91** **(40# 4678a; 40# 4678b)**

**Randol, Burton**

**On the Fourier transform of the indicator function of a planar set.**

*Trans. Amer. Math. Soc.* **139** (1969), 271–278.

**Randol, Burton**

**On the asymptotic behavior of the Fourier transform of the indicator function of a convex set.**

*Trans. Amer. Math. Soc.* **139** (1969), 279–285.

Let $C$ be a compact subset of the plane, with a piecewise smooth boundary $\partial C$. The indicator function of $C$ is defined to be the function that takes the value 1 on $C$ and 0 on the complement of $C$. Let $F(r,\theta)$ be the Fourier transform, in polar coordinates, of the indicator function of $C$. It is known [E. Hlawka, Monatsh. Math. **54** (1950), 1–36; MR **12**, 197] that, if $\partial C$ is sufficiently smooth and has everywhere positive Gaussian curvature, then $\Phi(\theta)=\sup_r r^{3/2}|F(r,\theta)|$ is bounded on $S^1$. It is also known that this need not be true if $\partial C$ has points of zero curvature [the author, Trans. Amer. Math. Soc. **121** (1966), 257–268; MR **34** #1291]. In the first paper under review, the author proves interesting results in the intermediate case. For example, he proves that, if $\partial C$ is of class $C^{n+3}$ for some integer $n\geqq 1$ and the Gaussian curvature of $\partial C$ is non-zero at all points of $\partial C$ except perhaps for a finite set, at each point of which the tangent line has contact of order $\leqq n$, then $\Phi(\theta)$ is bounded on $S^1$ if $n=1$, and of class $L^p$ on $S^1$ for any $p<2n/(n-1)$ if $n>1$. As an application, he proves the following result: Suppose that $A$ is the area of $C$ and that the interior of $C$ contains a point $p_0$ such that no tangent to $\partial C$ intersects $p_0$. Suppose that $\theta\in[0,2\pi]$ and that $L_\theta$ is the image of the integral lattice points under a counter-clockwise rotation of size $\theta$. For $x>0$, let $N(x,\theta)$ be the number of points in $L_\theta$ that intersect the set $xC$. Let $R(x,\theta)=N(x,\theta)-Ax^2$. Then there exists a positive number $M$ such that $\int_0^{2\pi}|R(x,\theta)|\,d\theta\leqq Mx^{2/3}$. The corresponding results when $C$ is a polygon are proved to be of a different nature.

In the second paper under review, the results of the first paper are extended to higher dimensions. Thus if $C$ is a compact convex subset of $R^n$ whose boundary is analytic then, for some $p>2$, $\sup_r r^{(n+1)/2}|F(r,\theta)|$ is of class $L^p$ on $S^{n-1}$. The author raises the question whether the result is true without the convexity hypothesis on $C$, when $n\geqq 3$.

The initial suggestion of the application of the results to the geometry of numbers is credited to Atle Selberg.

*K. Chandrasekharan* (Zürich)

Citations: MR 12, 197e = P28-9; MR 34# 1291 = P28-76.

**P28-92** **(44# 1637)**

**Nasim, C.**

**On the summation formula of Voronoi.**

*Trans. Amer. Math. Soc.* **163** (1971), 35–45.

Voronoĭ's summation formula allows a sum of form $\sum d(n)f(n)$ to be replaced, under certain conditions, by an expression involving integrals $\int f(x)\delta(x)\,dx$ and $\int f(x)\alpha(nx)\,dx$, where $\delta(x)=\log x+2\gamma$ and $\alpha$ is a linear combination of the Bessel functions $K_0$ and $Y_0$. A similar but more symmetric identity is obtained by the author. Although not appearing explicitly in the new formula, the Bessel and Riemann zeta functions weigh heavily in the proof, which rests on the $L^2$-theory of Mellin and Fourier-Watson transforms. An application of the formula leads to a new proof of an identity of N. S. Košljakov [Messenger of Math. **58** (1928), 30–32].

*D. Rearick* (Boulder, Colo.)

**P28-93** **(44# 6607)**

**Abljalimov, S. B.**

**The number of integral points in ovals.** (Russian. Kazakh summary)

*Izv. Akad. Nauk Kazah. SSR Ser. Fiz.-Mat.* **1970**, *no.* 3, 30–37.

Let $k\geqq 2$ be a natural number and denote by $R_{2k}(x)$ the number of lattice points in the region $u^{2k}+v^{2k}\leqq x$. Let $A_{2k}(x)$ be the area of the region $u^{2k}+v^{2k}\leqq x$. The author proves that for $x\to\infty$, $R_{2k}(x)=A_{2k}(x)+B_{2k}(x)x^{1/2k-1/4k^2}+O(x^{\theta(k)})$, where $B_{2k}(x)$ is an explicitly given bounded function, $\theta(2)=71/400$ and $\theta(k)=1/2k-1/4k^2-1/(4k(4k-1))$ for $k\geqq 3$. The method is based on a formula derived by R. E. Wild [Pacific J. Math. **8** (1958), 929–940; MR **22** #3729]; for $k=2$ van der Corput's estimates for trigonometrical sums are also used.

*B. Diviš* (Columbus, Ohio)

Citations: MR 22# 3729 = P28-41.

# P32 GOLDBACH-TYPE THEOREMS

For conjectural and empirical results, see **A46**.
For analogues in algebraic number fields, see **R48**.

See also reviews A36-2, A46-36, B12-52, C05-24, C05-32, L25-21, M02-1, M02-3, M55-37, M55-53, M55-55, N04-14, N12-31, N16-11, N24-19, N32-10, P02-5, P02-12, P02-25, P36-8, P36-12, P36-41, P36-42, P36-44, P40-2, P40-9, P40-11, P40-12, P40-13, P40-17, P40-21, P40-25, P44-13, P48-8, P52-5, P52-10, Q20-14, R48-1, T55-22, T55-28, T55-49, U10-1, U99-4, U99-6, Z02-4, Z15-69, Z30-64.

## P32-1 (2, 348d)

**Buchstab, A. A. Sur la décomposition des nombres pairs en somme de deux composantes dont chacune est formée d'un nombre borné de facteurs premiers.** C. R. (Doklady) Acad. Sci. URSS (N.S.) **29**, 544–548 (1940).

Let $P_\omega(x; x^{1/\alpha})$ denote the number of non-negative integers not exceeding $x$ which do not belong to any of the progressions $a_0+kp_0$, $a_i+kp_i$, $b_i+kp_i$, $i=1, 2, \cdots$, where $p_0=2$, $3\leqq p_i<x^{1/\alpha}$; $a_i$ and $b_i$ are fixed integers such that $0\leqq a_i<p_i$, $0\leqq b_i<p_i$, $a_i\neq b_i$, and $\omega$ is the domain of values of $a_i$ and $b_i$. In the Brun sieve method inequalities such as

$$P_\omega(x; x^{1/\alpha})>\lambda(\alpha)cx/\log^2 x+O(x/\log^3 x)$$

are derived and used to show, for example, that all large even integers are sums of two integers each having not more than a certain number of prime factors. The smaller $\alpha$ can be chosen the better the result. In this paper the author shows how to construct other $\lambda$-functions with smaller $\alpha$ from known ones. The result obtained is that all large even integers are sums of two integers having at most four prime factors. *R. D. James* (Saskatoon, Sask.).

Referred to in M55-13, P32-6, P32-30, P32-35.

## P32-2 (3, 68d; 3, 68e)

**Walfisz, Arnold. Zur additiven Zahlentheorie. VII (1).** Mitt. Akad. Wiss. Georgischen SSR [Soobščenia Akad. Nauk Gruzinskoi SSR] **2**, 7–14 (1941). (German. Russian summary)

**Walfisz, Arnold. Zur additiven Zahlentheorie. VII (2).** Mitt. Akad. Wiss. Georgischen SSR [Soobščenia Akad. Nauk Gruzinskoi SSR] **2**, 221–226 (1941). (German. Russian summary)

The two papers deal with Goldbach's problem and its generalization to the representation of an integer as a sum of $r$ primes, where $r\geqq 3$. The method of proof is a refinement of that of Vinogradoff, but it uses the function

$$\nu_r(n)=\sum \log p_1\cdots\log p_r,\quad p_1+\cdots+p_r=n,$$

instead of the direct number of solutions function

$$N_r(n)=\sum 1,\qquad p_1+\cdots+p_r=n.$$

The first part establishes the result

$$\nu_r(n)=\frac{n^{r-1}}{(r-1)!}S_r(n)+O\left(\frac{n}{\log n}\right)^{r-1},$$

where the constant in the $O$-symbol is independent of $r$ and $S_r(n)$ is the singular series. In the second part the formula

$$N_r(n)=\frac{n^{r-1}}{(r-1)!\log n}S_r(n)+o\left(\frac{n^{r-1}}{\log^r n}\right),$$

assumed true for $r=3$, is proved in general by induction on $r$. [Cf. also the following review.]* *R. D. James* (Saskatoon, Sask.).

*See MR 3, 68F = E28-3.

Citations: MR 3, 68f = E28-3.
Referred to in E28-4.

## P32-3 (3, 165f)

**Mardjanichvili, C. Sur la démonstration du théorème de Goldbach-Vinogradoff.** C. R. (Doklady) Acad. Sci. URSS (N.S.) **30**, 687–689 (1941).

In this variant of Vinogradoff's proof of an asymptotic formula for the number of representations of odd numbers $N$ as a sum of three primes, the approximation to the integrals of $S_\alpha{}^3e^{-2\pi i\alpha N}d\alpha$ on the major arcs ($\alpha=a/q+\theta/(q\tau)$, $q\leqq N/\tau$) is effected by first decomposing

$$S_\alpha=\sum_{P<N} e^{2\pi i\alpha p}$$

into partial sums extended over primes in an arithmetical progression of common difference $q$. A formula due to A. Page [Proc. London Math. Soc. (2) **39**, 116–141 (1935)] for the number of primes $qx+l$ is then applied, and the several terms so obtained are evaluated. For the minor arcs, Vinogradoff's work is used. The resulting error term is $O(N^2/(\log N)^{5-\epsilon})$, and is better than Vinogradoff's $O(N^2\log\log N/(\log N)^4)$. *G. Pall* (Montreal, Que.).

## P32-4 (4, 35b)

**James, R. D. and Weyl, H. Elementary note on prime number problems of Vinogradoff's type.** Amer. J. Math. **64**, 539–552 (1942).

The object of this paper is to indicate how Vinogradoff's method of dealing with the problem of the number of representations of a large number $N$ as a sum of three primes can be applied to the quite general problem described below. An attempt is made to produce actual asymptotic formulas, although these are not very explicit because of the generality of the problem. Let

$$A(N, k)=A_r\left(N, k; \begin{matrix} a_1, \cdots, a_r \\ \beta_1, \cdots, \beta_r\end{matrix}\right)$$

denote the number of representations of an integer $k$ in the form $k=a_1p_1+\cdots+a_rp_r$ by means of primes subject to the inequalities $p_1\leqq\beta_1N, \cdots, p_r\leqq\beta_rN$. Here the $a$'s are nonzero integers, $r\geqq 3$ and the $\beta$'s are positive. The main result of the paper is that

$$A(N, k)=R(N, k)S(k)+(\rho/N)(N/\log N)^r,$$

where $\rho$ tends to zero (uniformly in $k$ as $N\to\infty$) more rapidly than any negative power of $\log N$. The "singular series" $S(k)$ does not depend on the $\beta$'s and is given explicitly by

$$S(k)=S(k; a_1, \cdots, a_r)=\sum_{q=1}^{\infty}\phi(q)\frac{\mu(q/(q, k))}{\phi(q/(q, k))}\prod_{\nu=1}^{r}\frac{\mu(q/(q, a_\nu))}{\phi(q/(q, a_\nu))},$$

where $(t, u)$ denotes the greatest common divisor of $t$ and $u$ and $\phi$ and $\mu$ are the arithmetical functions of Euler and Möbius. The function

$$R(N, x)=R\left(N, x; \begin{matrix} a_1, \cdots, a_r \\ \beta_1, \cdots, \beta_r\end{matrix}\right)$$

is given as the Fourier transform

$$R(N, x)=\int_{-\infty}^{\infty}e^{-2\pi ixz}\prod_{\nu=1}^{r}\int_{N^{\frac{1}{2}}}^{\beta_\nu N}e^{2\pi ia_\nu zt}(\log t)^{-1}dtdz.$$

A probability interpretation of $R(N, x)$ is given as follows. Let

$$\phi_\nu(x)=\begin{cases}1/\log x & N^{\frac{1}{2}}\leqq x\leqq\beta_\nu N,\\ 0 & \text{elsewhere}\end{cases}$$

($1/\log x$ being the density function for primes). Then, if the $r$ primes $p_\nu$ be replaced by $r$ statistically independent continuous variables $x_\nu$ such that the probability of $x_\nu$ lying between $x$ and $x+dx$ is given by $\phi_\nu(x)dx$, then $R(N, x)$ is the probability that $a_1x_1+\cdots+a_rx_r$ lies between $x$ and $x+dx$.

The function $R(N, x)$ is shown to possess an asymptotic expansion

$$R(N, x)\sim\gamma_0(x)+\gamma_1(x)(\log N)^{-1}+\gamma_2(x)(\log N)^{-2}+\cdots.$$

The functions $\gamma_n(x)$ are not determined for $n>0$. For $\gamma_0(x)$ is given the expression

$$\gamma_0(x)=\{(r-1)!a_1a_2\cdots a_r\}^{-1}\Delta_1\Delta_2\cdots\Delta_rx^{r-1},$$

where the operator $\Delta_\nu f(x)=f(x)-f(x-a_\nu\beta_\nu)$. Two simple examples (with $r=3$) of $\gamma_0(x)$ are given. There is finally a brief general discussion of the $l$th power problem of the number of representations of any integer $k$ in the form $k=a_1x_1{}^l+\cdots+a_rx^l$ with $x_\nu{}^l\leqq\beta_\nu N$ ($\nu=1, 2, \cdots, r$).

*D. H. Lehmer* (Berkeley, Calif.).

Referred to in P32-22.

## P32-5 (4, 190a)

**Buchstab, A. On an additive representation of integers.** Rec. Math. [Mat. Sbornik] N.S. **10** (52), 87–91 (1942). (Russian. English summary)

The author considers the problem of representing any even number $2N$ in the form $2N=p+N'$, where $p$ is a prime, and where the prime factors of $N'$ exceed $\psi(N)$, some increasing function of $N$, and proves that for all sufficiently large $N$ such a representation is possible with $\psi(N)=(\log N)^\lambda$, for any $\lambda$, and the number of such representations exceeds $cN/(\log N\log\log N)$ for some $c>0$. The author also proves that there exist infinitely many primes $p$ such that the prime factors of $p+2$ exceed $(\log p)^\lambda$, for any $\lambda$. In the proof use is made of Brun's method, together with estimates by Page and Siegel of the number of primes in certain arithmetical progressions. *D. H. Lehmer* (Berkeley, Calif.).

## P32-6 (4, 265i)

**James, R. D. On the sieve method of Viggo Brun.** Bull. Amer. Math. Soc. **49**, 422–432 (1943).

The object of the present paper is to show that the Eratosthenes sieve methods recently employed by Buchstab [C. R. (Doklady) Acad. Sci. URSS (N.S.) **29**, 544–548 (1940); these Rev. **2**, 348] and which apply to the natural series of primes may, with some modification, be made to apply to infinite subsets of the series of primes, such as primes in arithmetic progression. As a parallel to Buchstab's theorem that every sufficiently large even integer is the sum of two numbers having at most four prime factors, the author proves the following theorem: Let $S$ be the set consisting of all products of at most 6 primes of the form $4n+1$, together with all numbers having two prime factors of the form $4n-1$ and at most three others of the form $4n+1$. Then every sufficiently large even number not divisible by 4 is the sum of two members of $S$.

*D. H. Lehmer* (Berkeley, Calif.).

Citations: MR 2, 348d = P32-1.

## P32-7 (7, 48i)

**Selmer, Ernst S. Eine neue hypothetische Formel für die Anzahl der Goldbachschen Spaltungen einer geraden Zahl, und eine numerische Kontrolle.** Arch. Math. Naturvid. **46**, no. 1, 1–18 (1943).

The author uses $G(2n)$ to denote the number of decompositions (Goldbach decompositions) of $2n$ as the sum of two primes, where $2n=p+q$ and $2n=q+p$ are considered the same decomposition. He derives the following result:

$$H(2x)\sim\tfrac{1}{2}\int_2^{2x-2}\frac{\operatorname{li}(2x-u)}{\log u}\,du,$$

where $H(2x)=\sum_{v=1}^{x}G(2v)$, $\operatorname{li}(x)$ is the Cauchy principal value integral $\int_0^x dz/\log z$ and $f(x)\sim g(x)$ means that $f(x)/g(x)$ approaches 1 as $x$ becomes infinite. A consequence is that

$$dH(2n)/dn\sim 2\int_0^n\frac{dx}{\log(n+x)\cdot\log(n-x)}.$$

Computations are recorded confirming this last result very closely for the 51 even numbers from 1,000,000 to 1,000,100.

*B. W. Jones* (Ithaca, N. Y.).

## P32-8 (7, 507b)

**Linnik, U. V. On the possibility of a unique method in certain problems of "additive" and "distributive" prime number theory.** C. R. (Doklady) Acad. Sci. URSS (N.S.) **49**, 3–7 (1945).

The author outlines a new proof of Vinogradov's theorem on sums of three primes, which will have a more homogeneous structure than the original proof. The "trigonometrical sieve" method of Vinogradov is avoided by using Linnik's deep results on the distribution of the zeros of the $L$-functions. Some of these results are consequences of earlier papers [see the same C. R. (N.S.) **41**, 145–146 (1943); Rec. Math. [Mat. Sbornik] N.S. **15**(**57**), 3–12, 139–178, 347–368 (1944); these Rev. **6**, 58, 260]; others are contained in a paper in course of publication.

*H. Davenport* (London).

Citations: MR 6, 58b = M25-8; MR 6, 260a = N16-4; MR 6, 260b = N16-5.

Referred to in M25-19, P32-9, P40-19.

## P32-9 (8, 317c)

**Linnik, U. V. A new proof of the Goldbach-Vinogradow theorem.** Rec. Math. [Mat. Sbornik] N.S. **19**(**61**), 3–8 (1946). (Russian. English summary)

The author gives a new proof of Vinogradov's theorem that every large odd integer can be expressed as a sum of three odd primes. The author's previous proof of the theorem [C. R. (Doklady) Acad. Sci. URSS (N.S.) **49**, 3–7 (1945); these Rev. **7**, 507] was based on deep results about the zeros of $L$-series in the critical strip, involving an application of the Eratosthenes-Brun method. The present paper derives Vinogradov's theorem by classical arguments from the author's theorem [Bull. Acad. Sci. URSS. Sér. Math. [Izvestia Akad. Nauk SSSR] **10**, 35–46 (1946); these Rev. **8**, 11]: if $\chi$ is an Abelian character mod $q$, $L(s,\chi)$ the corresponding Dirichlet $L$-series, $\frac{1}{2}\leqq\beta<1$, $T\geqq q^{50}$, then $L(s,\chi)$ has in the rectangle $\beta\leqq\sigma\leqq 1$, $|t|\leqq T$, at most

$$O(q^{2\beta-1}T^{4(1-\beta)/(3-2\beta)}\log^{10}T+q^{30})$$

zeros. This theorem is a straightforward generalization of Titchmarsh's theorem on the number of zeros of $\zeta(s)$ [Proc. London Math. Soc. (2) **30**, 319–321 (1929)].

*H. A. Heilbronn* (Bristol).

Citations: MR 7, 507b = P32-8; MR 8, 11g = M25-19.

Referred to in P02-5, P32-10, P32-24, P36-10.

## P32-10 (9, 11d)

**Tchudakoff, N. On Goldbach-Vinogradov's theorem.** Ann. of Math. (2) **48**, 515–545 (1947).

The author proves Vinogradov's theorem that every large odd integer is representable as a sum of three odd primes. The proof is very similar to the latest proof given by Linnik [Rec. Math. [Mat. Sbornik] N.S. **19**(**61**), 3–8 (1946); Bull.

Acad. Sci. URSS. Sér. Math. [Izvestia Akad. Nauk SSSR] **10**, 35–46 (1946); these Rev. **8**, 317, 11].

*H. A. Heilbronn* (Bristol).

Citations: MR 8, 11g = M25-19; MR 8, 317c = P32-9.

Referred to in M02-3, M05-18, M05-38, M15-13, M25-34, M35-6, P02-5, P32-25, P40-19, P44-9.

## P32-11 (9, 136b)

**Ren'i, A. A. On the representation of an even number as the sum of a single prime and a single almost-prime number.** Doklady Akad. Nauk SSSR (N.S.) **56**, 455–458 (1947). (Russian)

A set of integers $S$, with the property that there exists an absolute constant $K$ such that each $x\varepsilon S$ has at most $K$ distinct prime factors, is called an almost-prime set. Each $x\varepsilon S$ is called an almost-prime number. The author indicates the proof, to be given in detail elsewhere, that each even integer is the sum of an almost-prime number (taken from a fixed set $S$) and a prime number. He also states that he can prove that there exist infinitely many primes $p$ such that $p+2$ is almost-prime (being in a fixed set $S^*$).

The first result, regarding the representation of an even number, is an approximation to the unproved Goldbach conjecture and supersedes an earlier proof of the same proposition by Estermann [J. Reine Angew. Math. **168**, 106–116 (1932)] which made use of an unproved generalized Riemann hypothesis for all Dirichlet $L$-series. The second result is an approximation to the conjecture of the existence of infinitely many twin primes and is apparently a new result.

In order to formulate the basic result enabling the author to dispense with the Riemann hypothesis, recall that if $(p, q)=1$ and $D=pq$ then any character $\chi_D(n)$ modulo $D$ can be uniquely decomposed into the product $\chi_p(n)\chi_q(n)$, where the new characters are to the moduli $p$ and $q$, respectively. The author calls $\chi_D(n)$ primitive relative to $p$ if $\chi_p(n)$ is not the principal character modulo $p$. The author's result, for which no proof is indicated, is the following. Let $q$ be a square-free integer and $c_1>0$ an absolute constant. Then there exists a constant $\delta>0$ such that, if $A\geqq c_1$, $k=(\log q)/(\log A)+1\leqq\log^3 A$, $p$ is any prime such that $(p, q)=1$ and $A\leqq p\leqq 2A$ (there being, asymptotically for large $A$, $A/\{\varphi(q)\log A\}$ such $p$) with the possible exception of $A^{3/4}$ values, and if $\chi(n)$ is any character mod $pq$ which is primitive relative to $p$, then $L(\sigma+it,\chi)=\sum_{n=1}^{\infty}\chi(n)n^{-\sigma-it}$ has no zeros in the rectangle $1-\delta/(k+1)\leqq\sigma\leqq 1$, $0\leqq|t|\leqq\log^3 pq$.

To prove his result on the Goldbach conjecture, the author considers $H(2N)=\sum\log p\cdot\exp\{-p(\log 2N)/(2N)\}$, extended over those primes $p<2N$ such that $(2N-p, B)=1$; here $B=\prod p^*$, extended over those primes $p^*$ such that $c_2\leqq p^*\leqq(2N)^{1/R}$, where $R$ is a suitably chosen integer. It is clear that $P=2N-p$ is almost-prime and hence, for the weak Goldbach theorem, it is sufficient to prove that there exists a $c_7>0$ such that if $N\geqq c_7$ then $H(2N)>0$; for then we have that there exists an almost-prime $P$ and a prime $p$ such that $2N=P+p$. The author states that an application of Brun's sieve method [Skrifter Videnskapsselskapets i Kristiania. I. Mat.-Nat. Kl. **1920**, no. 3] gives

$$H(2N)>c_3N/\log^2 N-\sum_{Q\varepsilon E}|R_Q(2N)|,$$

where $E$ is a certain set and

$$R_Q(x)=\sum\log p\cdot\exp(-p\log x/x)-x/\{\varphi(Q)\log x\},$$

where the sum extends over all the primes $p<x$ such that $p\equiv l \bmod Q$, where $(l, Q)=1$. Using the above result on $L(s,\chi)$ and the results of Titchmarsh [Rend. Circ. Mat. Palermo **54**, 414–429 (1930); **57**, 478–479 (1933)], Page [Proc. London Math. Soc. (2) **39**, 116–141 (1935)] and Siegel [Acta Arith. **1**, 83–86 (1935)], the author indicates a proof of the estimate

$$\sum_{Q\varepsilon E}|R_Q(2N)|<4N/\log^3 N$$

from which it follows that $H(2N)>0$ for $N\geqq c_7$.

*L. Schoenfeld* (Cambridge, Mass.).

Referred to in P32-12.

## P32-12 (9, 413g)

**Ren'i, A. On the representation of an even number as the sum of a single prime and a single almost-prime number.** Izvestiya Akad. Nauk SSSR. Ser. Mat. **12**, 57–78 (1948). (Russian)

[The author's name appears in non-Russian publications as Rényi.] In this paper are the details of the proofs sketched in an earlier paper of the same title by the author [Doklady Akad. Nauk SSSR (N.S.) **56**, 455–458 (1947); these Rev. **9**, 136]. In addition to the previously announced result that every even number is the sum of a prime and an almost-prime, the author states that his method yields the results that every odd number is the sum of a prime and twice an almost-prime and that for each fixed integer $m$ (positive or negative) there exists an infinity of primes $p$ such that $p+m$ is almost prime.

In addition to Brun's sieve and the results of Titchmarsh, Page and Siegel on the Dirichlet $L$-series, the author uses a generalization of the "great sieve" due to U. V. Linnik [C. R. (Doklady) Acad. Sci. URSS (N.S.) **30**, 292–294 (1941); Rec. Math. [Mat. Sbornik] N.S. **15(57)**, 3–12 (1944); these Rev. **2**, 349; **6**, 260] to enable him to prove a certain result about the $L$-series. [See the earlier review.]

*L. Schoenfeld* (Urbana, Ill.).

Citations: MR 2, 349a = M55-1; MR 6, 260a = N16-4; MR 9, 136b = P32-11.

Referred to in M25-56, M55-6, M55-42, M55-62, N12-28, N12-31, P32-13, P32-53, P32-62, P32-70, R14-37, R14-47.

## P32-13 (24# A1264)

**Rényi, A.**

**On the representation of an even number as the sum of a prime and of an almost prime.**

*Amer. Math. Soc. Transl.* (2) **19** (1962), 299–321.

The original Russian article appeared in Izv. Akad. Nauk SSSR Ser. Mat. **12** (1948), 57–78 [MR **9**, 413].

Citations: MR 9, 413g = P32-12.

Referred to in M25-56, M55-42, P32-53, P32-70.

## P32-14 (10, 515a)

**James, R. D. Recent progress in the Goldbach problem.** Bull. Amer. Math. Soc. **55**, 246–260 (1949).

This paper, recently delivered as an address before the American Mathematical Society, is an expository article. An account is given of Brun's method and Buchstab's modification of it which has led to the result that every sufficiently large even integer is the sum of two numbers each having no more than four prime factors. Schnirelmann's density method and its subsequent improvements are briefly explained; the best result obtained in this direction is that all sufficiently large integers are expressible as the sum of not more than 67 primes. Finally, an account is given of the analytic method which has come closest to solving the problem. This method, due substantially to Hardy and Littlewood, but only successfully exploited by Vinogradov, yields the result that every sufficiently large odd number is the sum of three primes. The bibliography lists 23 papers.

*L. Schoenfeld* (Urbana, Ill.).

**P32-15** **(12, 244c)**

**Shapiro, Harold N., and Warga, Jack. On the representation of large integers as sums of primes. I.** Comm. Pure Appl. Math. **3**, 153–176 (1950).

Schnirelmann [Izvestiya Donskogo Politehničeskogo Instituta **14**, 3–28 (1930)] proved the existence of a constant $\kappa$ such that every large integer can be expressed as a sum of $\kappa$ or less prime numbers. In the following years various authors gave explicit estimates for $\kappa$, the best one being Ricci's $\kappa \leqq 67$ [Ann. Scuola Norm. Super. Pisa (2) **6**, 71–90, 91–116 (1937)]. These results have been superseded by Vinogradov's theorem that every large odd integer is a sum of three primes and hence $\kappa \leqq 4$ [Rec. Math. [Mat. Sbornik] (N.S.) **2**, 179–194 (1937)]. Vinogradov, however, uses the most powerful tools of analytic number theory while the preceding papers are essentially elementary. The same holds true of the present paper in which $\kappa \leqq 20$ is proved. In fact, except for one point where the prime number theorem for arithmetic progressions is needed, this proof is completely elementary. It may conveniently be divided into three sections.

Let $N_2(y)$ denote the number of decompositions of $y$ into a sum of two primes and put $w(y)$

$$=N_2(y)[\prod_{p>2}(1-(p-1)^{-2})(y/\log^2 y)\prod_{p|y,p>2}(p-1)/(p-2)]^{-1}.$$

The first part leads by means of A. Selberg's modification of the sieve method to (1) $\limsup w(y) \leqq 16$ [theorem 2.1]. Part II consists of the proof of

$$(2)\qquad \lim x^{-1}\sum_{y\leqq x,\, y\equiv 0 \pmod 2} w(y)=1$$

[cf. formula (3.3)]. It is based on ideas of Schnirelmann, Romanov, and Landau which have been used in a similar fashion in other pre-Vinogradov papers [cf. Heilbronn, Landau, and Scherk, Časopis Pěst. Mat. Fys. **65**, 117–140 (1936)]. Finally, comparison between (1) and (2) leads at once to $\liminf \sum_{y\leqq x,\, y\equiv 0 \pmod 2),\, N_2(y)>0} x^{-1} \geqq 1/16$ [cf. theorem 3.1]. A well-known result on the Schnirelmann-sums of sets of integers then yields $\kappa \leqq 20$ [cf. Khintchine, Rec. Math. [Mat. Sbornik] **39**, 27–34 (1932)]. *P. Scherk.*

Referred to in N40-51, P32-31, P32-69, P32-81.

**P32-16** **(12, 805e)**

**Linnik, Yu. V. Some conditional theorems concerning binary problems with prime numbers.** Doklady Akad. Nauk SSSR (N.S.) **77**, 15–18 (1951). (Russian)

Assuming the Riemann hypothesis for $\zeta(s)$ the author shows that for every large integer $N$ and $\epsilon>0$ primes $p$ and $p'$ can be found such that $|N-p-p'|<(\log N)^{3+\epsilon}$. The proof is based on the formula

$$\int_0^{(\log N)^{-3-\epsilon}} (\sum_p \log p e^{-2\pi i p\alpha - p/N})^2 e^{2\pi i N\alpha} d\alpha = \tfrac{1}{2}e^{-1}N + O(N(\log N)^{-\epsilon}).$$

The reviewer is unable to follow the details of the rather sketchy proof. *H. Heilbronn* (Bristol).

Referred to in P52-9.

**P32-17** **(13, 438e)**

**Haselgrove, C. B. Some theorems in the analytic theory of numbers.** J. London Math. Soc. **26**, 273–277 (1951).

The author states four main results and eight others required for their proof; he hopes to publish the proofs in due course. His first main result is that if $63/64<\vartheta<1$ then there exists $n_0$ such that each odd $n>n_0$ is representable as the sum of three primes each of which differs from $n/3$ by no more than $n^\vartheta$. This result is proved by an extension of Linnik's method for proving the Goldbach-Vinogradov three prime theorem and consequently depends on obtaining suitable bounds for the number of zeros of $L(s,\chi)$ in rectangles of the form $\beta<\sigma<1$, $|t-T|<U$. Such an estimate is obtained from an upper bound for $\int_{T-U}^{T+U}|L(\frac{1}{2}+it,\chi)|^4dt$ by following a paper of Ingham. Finally, this integral is estimated by using a method of Carlson and a new estimate for the sum $\sum_{n<\xi} d(n)d(n+k)\chi(n)\bar{\chi}(n+k)$.

The second main result generalizes Hoheisel's result that there is a positive $\varphi<1$ such that for each large $n$ there is a prime $p$ such that $|p-n|<|n|^\varphi$; the author's result deals with Gaussian primes $p$ and complex numbers $n$ and he remarks that this result can be extended to all algebraic number fields. The proof of this result depends on properties of a zeta function studied by Hecke. Zero-free regions for this function similar to those known for $\zeta(s)$ are obtained as well as bounds for the number of zeros in rectangles of the kind previously mentioned. *L. Schoenfeld.*

Referred to in N16-11, P32-42, P32-64, R42-30, R44-3, R44-6, R44-36.

**P32-18** **(14, 356a)**

**Oblàth, R. Sur le problème de Goldbach.** Mathesis **61**, 179–183 (1952).

The author supplements a note by Teghem [Mathesis **61**, 45–47 (1952)] describing recent developments in Goldbach's problem.

**P32-19** **(14, 847a)**

**Ayoub, Raymond. On Rademacher's extension of the Goldbach-Vinogradoff theorem.** Trans. Amer. Math. Soc. **74**, 482–491 (1953).

The author applies Vinogradov's method to the problem of the representation of a large number as the sum of three primes, each of which lies in a given residue-class to a fixed modulus. He obtains the same asymptotic formula as was found by Rademacher on the assumption of the generalized Riemann hypothesis (or something approaching it). No essentially new difficulties are encountered in the work. *H. Davenport* (London).

Referred to in P32-23, P32-25.

**P32-20** **(14, 847b)**

**Linnik, Yu. V. Some conditional theorems concerning the binary Goldbach problem.** Izvestiya Akad. Nauk SSSR. Ser. Mat. **16**, 503–520 (1952). (Russian)

Assuming the Riemann hypothesis for the function $\zeta(s)$, the author proves that

$$\int_{-\chi}^{\chi}\Big(\sum_2^\infty \Lambda(n)e^{-n/N}e^{-2\pi i n\theta}\Big)^2 e^{2\pi i n\theta}d\theta = e^{-1}N + O(N(\log N)^{-\epsilon}),$$

where $\Lambda(n)$ has the usual meaning in prime number theory, $N$ is a large integer, $\epsilon>0$ arbitrary, $\chi=(\log N)^{-3(1+\epsilon)}$. From this it is easily deduced that the interval $(N, N+(\log N)^{3+\epsilon})$ contains a number which is a sum of two odd primes. If the Riemann hypothesis is replaced by the weaker conjecture

$$N(\sigma, T)=O(T^{2(1-\sigma)}\log^2 T),$$

the interval has to be enlarged to $(N, N+(\log N)^7)$. Similar results are formulated for intervals containing a Goldbach number in a given arithmetic progression. In this case the Riemann hypothesis has to be extended to all Dirichlet $L$-series corresponding to the modulus. *H. Heilbronn.*

Referred to in N08-41, P32-72, P32-77, P36-39, P40-23, P52-9.

**P32-21** **(15, 13c)**

**Földes, István. On the Goldbach hypothesis concerning the prime numbers of an arithmetical progression.** Comptes Rendus du Premier Congrès des Mathématiciens Hongrois, 27 Août–2 Septembre 1950, pp. 473–492. Akadémiai Kiadó, Budapest, 1952. (Hungarian. Russian and English summaries)

Using the methods of Vinogradov and Hardy-Littlewood the author proves the following theorems. 1) Let $k \geqq 1$, $(g_j, k)=1$ $(j=1, 2, 3)$. Denote by $N(n)$ the number of representations of $n=p_1+p_2+p_3$, $p_j$ prime, $p_j \equiv g_j \pmod{k}$, $j=1, 2, 3$. Then if $n \equiv g_1+g_2+g_3 \pmod{k}$, $n$ odd,

$$N(n)=\frac{k}{\phi(k)^3}\prod_{p\mid k,\, p\nmid n}\left(1-\frac{1}{p^2-3p+3}\right)$$

$$\times\prod_{p\nmid k}\left(1+\frac{1}{(p-1)^3}\right)\frac{n^2}{2(\log n)^3}+o\left(\frac{n^2}{(\log n)^3}\right).$$

2) Let $k_j \geqq 1$, $(k_j, k_{j'})=1$, $(g_{j'}, k_j)=1$ $(j, j'=1, 2, 3)$. Let $N(n)$ denote the number of solutions of $n=p_1+p_2+p_3$, $p_j \equiv g_j \pmod{k_j}$. Then

$$N(n)=\phi(n)\frac{n^2}{2(\log n)^3}+o\left(\frac{n^2}{(\log n)^3}\right)$$

where $\phi(n)$ is given by a complicated expression.

These results sharpen previous results of Van der Corput [Math. Ann. **116**, 1–50 (1938)]. *P. Erdös.*

Referred to in P32-25.

**P32-22** **(15, 102e)**

**Richert, Hans-Egon. Aus der additiven Primzahltheorie.** J. Reine Angew. Math. **191**, 179–198 (1953).

The first part of this paper is concerned with the number of representations, $R(m; s, n)$, of an integer $m$ in the form $m=\sum a_i p_i$, $1 \leqq i \leqq s$, $s \geqq 3$, where the $a_i$ are integers, positive or negative but not zero, such that $(a_i, a_k)=1$, $i \neq k$, and the $p_i$ are odd primes $\leqq n$. Let $T(m; s, n)$ denote the number of representations of $m$ in the form $m=\sum a_i x_i$, where the $x_i$ are positive integers $\leqq n$. Following the Vinogradov method, the author proves (Satz 1) that

$$R(m; s, n)=(S(m)/\log^s n)T(m; s, n)+O(n^{s-1}/\log^{s+1} n),$$

where $S(m)$, a purely arithmetic function, is the so-called "singular series". A second result (Satz 2) generalizes the Vinogradov result for three primes. It is shown that, if all the $a_i$ are positive, then

$$R(n; s, n)=\frac{S(n)}{(s-1)!a_1\cdots a_s}\cdot\frac{n^{s-1}}{\log^s n}+O\left(\frac{n^{s-1}}{\log^{s+1} n}\right)$$

The author has apparently overlooked a paper by the reviewer and H. Weyl [Amer. J. Math. **64**, 539–552 (1942); these Rev. **4**, 35] in which the first result is implied and the second explicitly stated.

The second part deals with $G(m; n)$, the number of representations of $m$ in the form $m=p_1+p_2$, $3 \leqq p_i \leqq n$. The original Goldbach conjecture was $G(m; m)>0$ for all even $m \geqq 6$. Since the work of Hardy and Littlewood it has been conjectured that, for even $m$, $G(m; m) \sim S(m)m/\log^2 m$, and the author shows, again by the Vinogradov method, that, on the average, this is true. More precisely, he proves (Satz 5) that $(1/2u)\sum G(m; n)$, $n-u \leqq m \leqq n+u$, $u=n/\log^\beta n$, $\beta>0$, and $(1/u)\sum G(m; m)$, $n-u \leqq m \sim n$, are each equal to $n/\log^2 n+O(n \log\log n/\log^3 n)$. A similar result (Satz 6) holds for

$$(k/n)\sum G(m; m),\quad m \leqq n,\quad m \equiv h \pmod{k},$$
$$1 \leqq h \leqq k \leqq \log^\alpha n,\quad \alpha \geqq 25,$$

but with an arithmetic function depending on the primes which divide $k$ and $h$ as a coefficient of $n/\log^2 n$ and an error term which is not quite as good. *R. D. James.*

Citations: MR 4, 35b = P32-4.

**P32-23** **(15, 102f)**

**Iseki, Kanesiroo. A remark on the Goldbach-Vinogradov theorem.** Proc. Japan Acad. **25**, 185–187 (1949).

This paper sketches a proof of the asymptotic formula for the number of solutions in primes $p_1$, $p_2$, $p_3$ of the equation $n=p_1+p_2+p_3$ where $p_m \equiv r_m \pmod{k}$ for $m=1, 2, 3$ and the integers $r_m$ are fixed and such that $(r_m, k)=1$; also, it is required that $n \equiv r_1+r_2+r_3 \pmod{k}$. The result is the same as that obtained in the more detailed later paper of Ayoub [Trans. Amer. Math. Soc. **74**, 482–491 (1953); these Rev. **14**, 847]. *L. Schoenfeld* (Urbana, Ill.).

Citations: MR 14, 847a = P32-19.

Referred to in P32-25.

**P32-24** **(15, 507g)**

**Zulauf, Achim. Über den dritten Hardy-Littlewoodschen Satz zur Goldbachschen Vermutung.** J. Reine Angew. Math. **192**, 117–128 (1953).

The author uses Linnik's modification [Mat. Sbornik **19(61)**, 3–8 (1946); these Rev. **8**, 317] of the Hardy-Littlewood method to obtain a new proof of a generalization of the theorem that almost all even positive integers are sums of two primes. *T. Estermann* (London).

Citations: MR 8, 317c = P32-9.

**P32-25** **(15, 507h)**

**Zulauf, Achim. Beweis einer Erweiterung des Satzes von Goldbach-Vinogradov.** J. Reine Angew. Math. **190**, 169–198 (1952).

Let $m \geqq 3$ and $K \geqq 1$ be given and let $a_1, \cdots, a_m$ be relatively prime to $K$. With fixed $m$, $K$, $a_1, \cdots, a_m$ let $N(n)$ be the number of solutions in odd primes $p_r \equiv a_r \pmod{K}$ of the equation $n=p_1+\cdots+p_m$. Then there is a singular series $S(n)$ such that for all large $n \equiv m \pmod{2}$ such that $n \equiv a_1+\cdots+a_m \pmod{K}$ we have

$$N(n)=\frac{n^{m-1}}{\log^m n}\,\frac{S(n)}{(m-1)!\phi^m(K)}\{1+o(1)\}$$

and $0<c<S(n)/K<c'$ for suitable absolute constants $c$ and $c'$. Actually, by picking $\delta=(m+1)(\log\log n)/\log n$ in the author's proof, the error term $o(1)$ can be replaced by $O(\log\log n/\log n)$. This proof replaces an earlier one by H. Rademacher [Math. Z. **25**, 627–657 (1926)] who, however, assumed a modified Riemann hypothesis. The case $m=3$ has recently been dealt with by a number of authors [K. Iseki, Proc. Japan Acad. **25**, 185–187 (1949); these Rev. **15**, 102; R. Ayoub, Trans. Amer. Math. Soc. **74**, 482–491 (1953); these Rev. **14**, 847; I. Földes, C. R. 1ier Congrès Math. Hongrois, 1950, Akad. Kiadó, Budapest, 1952, pp. 473–492; these Rev. **15**, 13]. Unlike these authors who use Vinogradov's results on exponential sums with prime summation letter, Zulauf uses a method of Linnik and Čudakov. The author closely follows Čudakov [Ann. of Math. (2) **48**, 515–542 (1947); these Rev. **9**, 11]. *L. Schoenfeld.*

Citations: MR 9, 11d = P32-10; MR 14, 847a = P32-19; MR 15, 13c = P32-21; MR 15, 102f = P32-23.

**P32-26** **(15, 508a)**

**Zulauf, Achim. Zur additiven Zerfällung natürlicher Zahlen in Primzahlen und Quadrate.** Arch. Math. **3**, 327–333 (1952).

Let $K_\sigma$, $a_\sigma$, $b_\tau$ be fixed positive integers with $(K_\sigma, a_\sigma)=1$ for $\sigma=1, \cdots, s$ and $\tau=1, \cdots, t$. Let $s \geqq 1$, $t \geqq 0$ and $\omega=s+\frac{1}{2}t \geqq 2$. Let $N_{s,t}(n)$ be the number of solutions in odd primes

$p_\sigma \equiv a_\sigma \pmod{K_\sigma}$ and integers $g_\tau$ of the equation

$$n = p_1 + \cdots + p_s + b_1 g_1^2 + \cdots + b_t g_t^2.$$

The author briefly sketches the proof of three results. The first is that if $\omega > 2$ and $n$ is large then

$$N_{s,t}(n) = \frac{n^{\omega-1}}{\log^s n} \mathfrak{S}_{s,t}(n) + O\left(\frac{n^{\omega-1} \log\log n}{\log^{s+1} n}\right).$$

This result, proved along the lines of the preceding paper, includes the result of the above paper which corresponds to the case $t=0$ and $s=m$; it also includes a result of H. Halberstam [Proc. London Math. Soc. (2) **53**, 363–380 (1951); these Rev. **13**, 112] in which all $K_\sigma$, $a_\sigma$, $b_\tau$ are 1. The second result deals with the case $\omega=2$ for "almost all" $n$. The third result gives lower bounds for the singular series $\mathfrak{S}_{s,t}(n)$ depending on whether $\omega>2$ or $\omega=2$.

*L. Schoenfeld* (Urbana, Ill.).

Citations: MR 13, 112b = P36-4.

## P32-27 (15, 935b)

**Prachar, K. On integers having many representations as a sum of two primes.** J. London Math. Soc. **29**, 347–350 (1954).

Let $f(n)$ denote the number of representations of an even integer $n$ as the sum of two primes. The author proves that, for sufficiently large $x$, there are more than $\exp(c_1\sqrt{(\log x)})$ even integers $n \leqq x$ for which $f(n) > (c_2 x \log\log x)/(\log x)^2$, where $c_1$ and $c_2$ are positive constants. The proof itself is elementary, but uses a formula due to Titchmarsh [Rend. Circ. Mat. Palermo **54**, 414–429 (1930); **57**, 478–479 (1933)] for the number of primes in an arithmetic progression.

*R. D. James* (East Lansing, Mich.).

Referred to in P32-29, P44-26, P44-27.

## P32-28 (16, 14b)

**Cohen, Eckford. A finite analogue of the Goldbach problem.** Proc. Amer. Math. Soc. **5**, 478–483 (1954).

Let $R_m$ denote the ring of residue classes modulo an integer $m>1$. The author considers the Goldbach problem in this ring and proves that every element in $R_m$ is expressible as a sum of $G(m)$ primes in $R_m$ if and only if $m$ has at least two distinct prime factors and that the minimum value of $G(m)$ is 2, if $m$ is odd, 3 if $m$ is even and has at least two distinct odd prime factors or if $m$ is twice an odd prime power, 4 if $m$ is of the form $m=2^\mu p^\lambda$, $\lambda \geqq 1$, $\mu > 1$, $p$ odd. For the proof he uses one of his earlier results about the number of solutions of linear congruences.

*H. Bergström.*

Referred to in R48-11.

## P32-29 (17, 14b)

**Prachar, K. Über die Lösungszahl eines Systems von Gleichungen in Primzahlen.** Monatsh. Math. **59**, 98–103 (1955).

In a previous paper [J. London Math. Soc. **29**, 347–350 (1954); MR **15**, 935] the author proved some inequalities for the number of representations of an even integer as the sum of two primes. He now considers $p_1+p_2=n$, $p_2+p_3=m$, $m\neq n$, where $p_1$, $p_2$, $p_3$ are primes, and obtains similar results for the number of solutions of this system of equations.

*R. D. James* (Vancouver, B.C.).

Citations: MR 15, 935b = P32-27.

## P32-30 (18, 17e)

**Buhštab, A. A. On an additive representation of integers.** Moskov. Gos. Ped. Inst. Uč. Zap. **71** (1953), 45–62. (Russian)

Let $T_{\alpha,\beta}(N)$ denote the number of representations of the positive integer $N$ in the form $n'+n''$, where all prime factors of $n'$ are greater than $N^{1/\alpha}$ and all prime factors of $n''$ are greater than $N^{1/\beta}$. In an earlier paper [C. R. (Dokl.) Acad. Sci. URSS (N.S.) **29** (1940), 544–548; MR **2**, 348] the author has used an improved form of Brun's method to prove that if $N$ is large

$$(*) \qquad T_{5,5}(N) \geqq 0.4N(\ln N)^{-2}$$

(and thus that $N$ is expressible as a sum of two positive integers each containing at most four prime factors). Here he uses results from another paper [Mat. Sb. N.S. **28(70)** (1951), 165–184; MR **13**, 626] to prove that whenever $\beta \geqq \alpha$ we have

$$T_{\alpha,\beta}(N) = CN(\ln N)^{-2}\psi(\alpha,\beta;N)\prod_{p|N}\{1+1/(p-2)\} + O(N(\ln N)^{-3}),$$

where $C$ is a positive absolute constant, $p$ runs over the odd primes, and

$$|\psi(\alpha,\beta;N)/(\alpha\beta)-1| < \exp\{-\alpha(\ln\alpha + \ln\ln\alpha - 1 - \ln 2 + \gamma \ln\ln\alpha/\ln\alpha)\},$$

$\gamma$ being an absolute constant which is unfortunately not calculated. (Even if $\gamma$ were calculated explicitly, the value obtained would probably not be large enough to establish a result analogous to (*) for $T_{4,4}(N)$.)

*P. T. Bateman.*

Citations: MR 2, 348d = P32-1; MR 13, 626h = N28-27.

## P32-31 (19, 16b)

**Yin, Wen-Lin. Note of the representation of large integers as sums of primes.** Bull. Acad. Polon. Sci. Cl. III. **4** (1956), 793–795 (1957).

The author proves by elementary methods that every sufficiently large integer is the sum of at most 18 primes. This improves a previous result of Shapiro and Warga [Comm. Pure Appl. Math. **3** (1950), 153–176; MR **12**, 244] who proved that every sufficiently large integer is the sum of at most 20 primes.

*P. Erdös* (Haifa).

Citations: MR 12, 244c = P32-15.

Referred to in P32-32.

## P32-32 (22# 7990)

**Yin, Wen-lin. Remarks on the representation of large integers as sums of primes.** Acta Sci. Nat. Univ. Pekinensis No. 3 (1956), 323–326. (Chinese. English summary)

This is the original Chinese version of the article reviewed in MR **19**, 16 [Bull. Acad. Polon. Sci. Cl. III **4** (1956), 793–795].

*C.-S. Lin* (Rizal)

Citations: MR 19, 16b = P32-31.

## P32-33 (19, 533a)

**Arkhangelskaya, V. M. Some calculations connected with Goldbach's problem.** Ukrain. Mat. Ž. **9** (1957), 20–29. (Russian. English summary)

Vinogradov proved that every sufficiently large odd integer $n$ ($n>n_0$) can be written as the sum of three odd primes [Trudy Mat. Inst. Steklov. **10** (1937)]. In 1939 K. G. Borozdkin calculated the constant $n_0$ to be equal to $10^{10^{10^{17.86}}}$ [see Čudakov, Introduction to the theory of Dirichlet's $L$-functions, OGIZ, Moscow-Leningrad, 1947, p. 201; MR **11**, 234]. The Goldbach conjecture has been verified for integers $n \leqq 10^7$ by using a table of primes. In the present paper the author discusses the distribution of "Vinogradov" numbers (i.e., numbers representable as a sum of three odd primes) in the interval $10^7 < n < n_0$. He proves: (1) for each $x > x_0 = 10^{10^{8.324}}$ the interval $[x, x+(\ln x)^{14}]$ contains at least one Vinogradov number; (2) assuming the truth of the Riemann hypothesis, for each $x > x_0 = 10^{30}$ the interval $[x, x+(\ln x)^{6.065}]$ contains at least one even integer which is representable as the sum of two odd primes.

*W. H. Simons* (Vancouver, B.C.).

Citations: MR 11, 234b = M02-1.

**P32-34** **(20# 3109)**

**Mirsky, L. Additive prime number theory.** Math. Gaz. 42 (1958), 7–10.

A concise historical discussion of Goldbach's conjecture, delivered at the British Mathematical Colloquium at St. Andrews in September, 1956.

**P32-35** **(20# 3835)**

**Vinogradov, A. I. On the connections between the sieve of Eratosthenes and the Riemann ζ-function.** Vestnik Leningrad. Univ. **11** (1956), no. 13, 142–146. (Russian)

The author sketches a proof, the full details of which are being sent to the Mat. Sbornik [see #3836 below], of the result that every sufficiently large even integer $N$ can be written in the form $N=P_3+P_3'$, where $P_k$, $P_k'$ are numbers having at most $k$ prime factors. In this connection, it should be mentioned that Atle Selberg announced [Proc. Internat. Congress Math. Cambridge, Mass., 1950, v. 1, Amer. Math. Soc., Providence, R.I., 1952, pp. 286–292; MR **13**, 438] the stronger result that $N=P_2+P_3'$. See also the related papers by Y. Wang [Acta Math. Sinica 6 (1956), 500–513, 565–582; MR **20** #4530; Sci. Record (N.S.) **1** (1957), 9–12] which use a combination of the methods of Kuhn [Norske Vid. Selsk. Forh. Trondheim **14** (1941), no. 39, 145–148; MR 8, 503], Buhštab [Mat. Sb. N.S. **4**(**46**) (1938), 375–387; Dokl. Akad. Nauk SSSR **29** (1940), 544–548; MR 2, 348] and Selberg.

The author employs the lower bound sieve method of Selberg given in the above paper and in a later one [11te Skand. Matematikerkongress, Trondheim, 1949, Tanum, Oslo, 1952, pp. 13–22; MR **14**, 726]. He follows a suggestion of Selberg in taking $\lambda_p=1$, $\rho_1=1$ and

$$\rho_d=-\sum_{[d_1,\,d_2]=d/p}\lambda_{pd_1}\lambda_{pd_2},$$

where $p$ is the largest prime divisor of $d>1$ and $[d_1, d_2]$ is the least common multiple of $d_1$ and $d_2$. Let the number of integers among $a_1, \cdots, a_N$ which are divisible by $d$ be given by $N/f(d)+R_d$, where $f(n)$ is multiplicative, and let $f_1(n)$ be the completely multiplicative function which agrees with $f(n)$ at the primes. The author studies the function

$$(*)\qquad \varepsilon(z_p)=1-\sum_{\nu_p}\frac{\mu^2(\nu_p)}{f_1(\nu_p)}\cdot\prod_{p_1<p}\left\{1-\frac{1}{f(p_1)}\right\},$$

where $z_p=(z/p)^{\frac12}$ and $\nu_p\leqq z_p$ has as its largest prime divisor a number less than $p$. For the Goldbach problem in which $a_n=n(N-n)$, we have $f(p)=p/2$ if $p\nmid N$ and $f(p)=p$ if $p|N$. In this case, the author obtains the estimate $\varepsilon(z_p)=O(1/\log^3 z)$ if $p\leqq z^{1/(8\log\log z)}$ and, in the other case, the estimate

$$\varepsilon(z_p)=\frac{1}{2\pi}e^{\omega-u}\int_{-\sqrt{\log z}}^{\sqrt{\log z}}\frac{e^{iut+\Psi(t)}}{(it-1)^3}\,dt+O\left(\frac{(\log\log z)^4}{e^u\sqrt{\log z}}\right),$$

where $u=(\log z_p)/\log p$, $\omega=2\sum_{n=1}^{\infty}1/(n!n)$ and $\Psi(t)=-ie\int_0^t(1-ix)^{-1}e^{-ix}dx$. The proof of this estimate depends on approximating the sum in (*) by

$$\frac{1}{2\pi i}\int_{a-it}^{a+it}\frac{z_p^{\,s}}{s}\prod_{p_1<p}\left\{1+\frac{1}{p_1^{\,s}f_1(p_1)}\right\}ds.$$

On moving the path of integration to the left and altering the product, one finds that $\varepsilon(z_p)$ is given, approximately, by the expression

$$\frac{1}{2\pi i}\int_L\frac{z_p^{\,s}}{s}\prod_{p_1<p}\left\{1+\frac{1}{p_1^{\,s+1}}\right\}^2 ds,$$

since $f_1(p_1)=p_1/2$ with only a finite number of exceptions. Since $\prod_p(1+1/p^s)=\zeta(s)/\zeta(2s)$, the author is able to estimate $\prod_{p<y}(1+1/p^s)$ in terms of $\zeta(s)/\zeta(2s)$ and $y$. This is accomplished with the aid of another integral involving $\log\zeta(s+w)/\zeta(2s+2w)$ by shifting the path to the left again and using the fact that $\zeta(s)$ has no zeros in a region of the type

$$1-\lambda\{\log(|t|+e)\log\log(|t|+e^2)\}^{-3/4};$$

such a region results from the estimation of exponential sums as given by I. M. Vinogradov and his followers. Additional calculations now provide the formula for $\varepsilon(z_p)$.

Selberg's method now enables the author to conclude that for even $N$ the number of integers of the type $n(N-n)$ with $1\leqq n\leqq N$ which are divisible by none of the consecutive primes $p_1, \cdots, p_r\leqq z^{\xi}<p_{r+1}$ with $z=N^{1-\varepsilon}$ and $\xi=1/3.2$ has a lower bound

$$c\frac{N}{\log^2 N}\prod_{p|N}\left\{1+\frac{1}{p-1}\right\}\cdot\prod_{p\nmid N}\left\{1-\frac{1}{(p-1)^2}\right\}$$

for some $c>0$. His final result $N=P_3+P_3'$ follows at once. *L. Schoenfeld* (East Pittsburgh, Pa.)

Citations: MR 2, 348d = P32-1; MR 8, 503c = N24-8; MR 13, 438d = M55-10; MR 14, 726j = M55-11; MR 20# 4530 = P32-38.

Referred to in N16-20, P32-45.

**P32-36** **(20# 3836)**

**Vinogradov, A. I. Application of ζ(s) to the sieve of Eratosthenes.** Mat. Sb. N.S. **41** (**83**) (1957), 49–80; correction, 415–416. (Russian)

This paper is devoted to a proof of the theorem that every sufficiently large even number is representable as $p_1p_2p_3+p_4p_5p_6$, where $p_1, \cdots, p_6$ are primes. The corrigendum makes some substantial changes in the paper; even with these, the exposition does not seem to be altogether clear. *H. Davenport* (Cambridge, England)

Referred to in N16-20, N32-23, N32-29, P32-37, P32-50.

**P32-37** **(22# 3720)**

**Vinogradov, A. I. The application of ζ(s) to the sieve of Eratosthenes.** Amer. Math. Soc. Transl. (2) **13** (1960), 29–60.

The Russian original [Mat. Sb. (N.S.) **41** (**83**) (1957), 49–80, 415–416] has already been reviewed [MR **20** #3836].

Citations: MR 20# 3836 = P32-36.

**P32-38** **(20# 4530)**

**Wang, Yuan. On the representation of large even integer as a sum of a prime and a product of at most 4 primes.** Acta Math. Sinica **6** (1956), 565–582. (Chinese. English summary)

Assume the truth of the Riemann hypothesis in the stronger form that the real parts of all zeros of all Dirichlet $L$-series are $\leqq\frac12$. Then the author can prove the following theorems. (1) Every large even integer is the sum of a prime and of a product of at most 4 primes. (2) There are infinitely many primes $p$ such that $p+2$ is a product of at most 4 primes. (3) If $\varepsilon>0$, then the number of prime pairs $p$, $p+2$ not exceeding $N$ is not greater than

$$(8+\varepsilon)\prod_{p>2}\left(1-\frac{1}{(p-1)^2}\right)\frac{N}{(\log N)^2}+O\left(\frac{N}{(\log N)^3}\right).$$

*K. Mahler* (Manchester)

Referred to in M55-36, P32-35, P32-45, P32-50, P32-51.

**P32-39** **(21# 1957)**

**Vinogradov, A. I. Estimates for binary problems.** Vestnik Leningrad. Univ. **14** (1959), no. 7, 26–31. (Russian. English summary)

This paper is concerned with approximations to Goldbach's conjecture. Let $N$ be a positive integer and $\alpha$ a positive number. The author states that, if $\alpha<\theta$ (where $\theta$ is a certain constant approximately equal to 5/22), then $N$ can be represented as the sum of two integers all of whose prime divisors exceed $N^{\alpha}$. (This is said to follow

Selberg's sieve method.) He then indicates, in bare outline only, how $\theta$ could (in principle) be replaced by a larger constant. The argument is involved, and relies, among other things, on Selberg's method and on complicated estimates for triple contour integrals. The reviewer was not successful in following the details.

*L. Mirsky* (Sheffield)

**P32-40** **(21# 1958)**

**Wang, Yuan. On sieve methods and some of their applications. I.** Acta Math. Sinica **8** (1958), 413–429. (Chinese. English summary)

The author gives fully detailed proofs of the following three theorems. (1) Every sufficiently large even number can be written as a sum $a+b$ where $a \geqq 2$ has at most two and $b \geqq 2$ at most three prime factors. (2) If $k$ is any even number, there exist infinitely many integers $n$ such that $n(n+k)$ has at most five prime factors, while neither $n$ nor $n+k$ has more than three prime factors. (3) Every sufficiently large odd number can be written as a sum $2P+Q$ where $P$, $Q$, and $PQ$ have at most three, three, and five prime factors, respectively. *K. Mahler* (Manchester)

Referred to in P32-41, P32-53.

**P32-41** **(21# 4944)**

**Wang, Yuan. On sieve methods and some of their applications.** Sci. Sinica **8** (1959), 357–381.

The present paper forms the English translation of an earlier one published by the author in Chinese [see Acta Math. Sinica **8** (1958), 413–429; MR **21** #1958].

*K. Mahler* (Manchester)

Citations: MR 21# 1958 = P32-40.

Referred to in M55-34, P32-62, P32-66.

**P32-42** **(22# 3721)**

**Pan, Cheng-tung. Some new results in the additive prime number theory.** Acta Math. Sinica **9** (1959), 315–329. (Chinese. English summary)

Let $N$ be a sufficiently large odd integer. By Vinogradov, there is a representation $N=p_1+p_2+p_3$, where $p_1, p_2, p_3$ are odd primes. The author proves that in this representation either of the following three conditions may be imposed: (1) $p_i=\frac{1}{3}N+O(N^{(5+12c)/(6+12c)+\varepsilon})$ $(i=1, 2, 3)$, where $c=15/19$, $\varepsilon>0$; (2) $p_1 \leqq N$, $p_2 \leqq N$, $p_3 \leqq N^{2c/(1+2c)+\varepsilon}$; (3) $p_1 \leqq N^{2/3+\varepsilon}$, $p_2 \leqq N^{2/3+\varepsilon}$, $N-N^{2/3+\varepsilon}<p_3 \leqq N$. The result (1) improves one by Haselgrove [J. London Math. Soc. **26** (1951), 273–277; MR **13**, 438], and the result (2) implies that there are even numbers between $N$ and $N+N^{2c/(1+2c)+\varepsilon}$ which are the sum of two primes.

*K. Mahler* (Manchester)

Citations: MR 13, 438e = P32-17.

Referred to in P32-64.

**P32-43** **(22# 12083)**

**Statulevičius, V. On the representation of odd numbers as the sum of three almost equal prime numbers.** Vilniaus Valst. Univ. Mokslo Darbai. Mat. Fiz. Chem. Mokslų Ser. **3** (1955), 5–23. (Lithuanian. Russian summary)

Author's summary: "The following theorem is proved. The number $I(N, K)$ of solutions of the equation $N=p_1+p_2+p_3$, where $N$ is an odd positive number, in primes $p_1$, $p_2$, $p_3$ subject to the condition $\frac{1}{3}N-K \leqq p_i \leqq \frac{1}{3}N+K$ $(i=1, 2, 3)$, with $\frac{1}{3}N-2 \geqq K \geqq N^{279/308+\varepsilon}$, and $\varepsilon>0$ an arbitrarily small number, is expressed by the asymptotic formula

$$I(N, K) = \frac{3K^2}{\ln^3 N}S(N)+O\left(\frac{K^2}{\ln^4 N}\right),$$

where

$$S(N) = \prod_p \left(1+\frac{1}{(p-1)^3}\right)\prod_{p|N}\left(1-\frac{1}{p^2-3p+3}\right) > \frac{3}{5},$$

and the constant in the symbol $O$ does not depend on $N$ and $K$ and is effectively calculated.

"Thus, every sufficiently large odd number can be represented as a sum of three primes satisfying the condition $|p-\frac{1}{3}N| \leqq N^{279/308+\varepsilon}$."

**P32-44** **(23# A874)**

**Wang, Yuan**

**On the representation of large even number as a sum of two almost-primes.**

*Sci. Record* (*N.S.*) **1** (1957), 291–295.

The author proves the solvability of the equation $2N=Q_1+Q_2$, where the sum of the numbers of prime divisors of $Q_1$ and $Q_2$ does not exceed 5. The result is achieved by introducing into the method of A. A. Buhštab new estimates obtained by the method of A. Selberg.

*A. I. Vinogradov* (RŽMat **1959** #2289)

**P32-45** **(23# A2400)**

**Wang, Yuan**

**On sieve methods and some of the related problems.**

*Sci. Record* (*N.S.*) **1** (1957), 9–12.

It is a consequence of the generalized Riemann hypothesis that for $\varepsilon>0$, $\pi(x; k, l)=(\varphi(k))^{-1}\operatorname{li} x+O(x^{1/2+\varepsilon})$, the constant depending on $\varepsilon$ only. This equation is the hypothesis of the theorems proved in this paper. Theorem 1: Every sufficiently large even integer is a sum of a prime and a product of at most 3 primes. (The author [Acta Math. Sinica **6** (1956), 500–513, 565–582; MR **20** #4530] and A. I. Vinogradov [Vestnik. Leningrad. Univ. **11** (1956), no. 13, 142–146; MR **20** #3835] had this result with 4 primes.) Theorem 2: There are infinitely many primes $p$ such that $p+2$ is the product of at most 3 primes.

*W. J. LeVeque* (Ann Arbor, Mich.)

Citations: MR 20# 3835 = P32-35; MR 20# 4530 = P32-38.

**P32-46** **(24# A3117)**

**Sierpiński, Wacław**

**Démonstration élémentaire d'un théorème sur les sommes de trois nombres premiers distincts. (Croatian summary)**

*Glasnik Mat.-Fiz. Astronom. Društvo Mat. Fiz. Hrvatske Ser. II* **16** (1961), 87–88.

The author proves that there exists an infinity of odd integers $n$ such that $n$ is the sum of three distinct primes, but is not the sum of fewer than three. The method of proof is to apply the Dirichlet theorem on primes in an arithmetic progression to each of eight residue classes (mod 30). For example, there are infinitely many primes $p=30k+1$, and then $n=7+19+p$, but $n=2+5(6k+5)$.

*R. D. James* (Vancouver, B.C.)

**P32-47** **(25# 1140)**

**Zulauf, A.**

**On the number of representations of an integer as a sum of primes belonging to given arithmetical progressions.**

*Compositio Math.* **15**, 64–69 (1961).

Let $N(n)$ be the number of representations of the positive integer $n$ in the form

$$n = p_1+p_2+\cdots+p_s,\ p_\sigma \equiv a_\sigma (\text{mod } K_\sigma) \quad (1 \leqq \sigma \leqq s),$$

where the $p_\sigma$ are odd prime numbers, $a_\sigma$ and $K_\sigma$ are given integers $(1 \leqq \sigma \leqq s)$, the $K_\sigma$ being positive and having least common multiple $K$. Let $\kappa(n)$ be the number of sets of residues $x_1, x_2, \cdots, x_s \pmod K$ that (i) are relatively prime to $K$, and (ii) satisfy the congruences

$$x_\sigma \equiv a_\sigma (\text{mod } K)\ (1 \leqq \sigma \leqq s), \quad \sum_{\sigma=1}^{s} x_\sigma \equiv n\ (\text{mod } K).$$

In an earlier paper [J. Reine Angew. Math. **192** (1954), 210–229; MR **15**, 778] the author obtained an asymptotic expression for $N(n)$, the main term of which is a singular series with coefficient $\kappa(n)$. In the present paper an explicit formula is obtained for $\kappa(n)$, which is shown to be positive in certain cases for sufficiently large $n$.

*R. A. Rankin* (Glasgow)

Citations: MR 15, 778e = P36-10.

**P32-48** **(26# 88 )**

**Cohen, Eckford**

**A corollary of the Goldbach conjecture.**

*Duke Math. J.* **29** (1962), 625–629.

Let $E(n)$ be the number of pairs of odd primes $p_1, p_2$, both less than $n-1$, such that $n-p_1$ and $n-p_2$ are relatively prime. Let $\beta(n)=\prod\{1-(p-1)^{-2}\}$, the product being taken over those primes $p$ which do not divide $n$. The author proves that, if every sufficiently large even natural number is expressible as a sum of two distinct odd primes, then $E(n)\sim(n/\log n)^2\beta(n)$ as $n\to\infty$ through even numbers.

*T. Estermann* (London)

The last sentence of the review should be replaced by the following sentence: The author proves that $E(n)\sim(n/\log n)^2\beta(n)$ as $n\to\infty$ through even numbers.

Referred to in P32-49.

**P32-49** **(29# 4747 )**

**Cohen, Eckford**

**Errata: "A corollary of the Goldbach conjecture".**

*Duke Math. J.* **30** (1963), 683.

The author deletes the Introduction of an earlier paper [same J. **29** (1962), 625–629; MR **26** #88; errata, MR **26**, p. 1544] and replaces it by another.

Citations: MR 26# 88 = P32-48.

**P32-50** **(27# 1424 )**

**Wang, Yuan**

**On the representation of large integer as a sum of a prime and an almost prime.**

*Sci. Sinica* **11** (1962), 1033–1054.

Assuming the "extended" Riemann hypothesis one easily proves (this has been done, for example, by Titchmarsh and Tchudakoff), in the usual notation, that

$$(\mathrm{R}^*) \qquad \pi(x;k,l) = \frac{\operatorname{li} x}{\varphi(k)} + O(x^{1/2}\log x)$$

when $(k,l)=1$. From (R*) the author deduces the following. Theorem 1: Every sufficiently large even integer is a sum of a prime and a product of at most 3 primes. Theorem 2: There exist infinitely many primes $p$ such that $p+2k$ is a product of at most 3 primes ($k$, a given positive integer). Theorem 3: Every large odd $N=p+2P$, where $p$ is a prime and $P$ an almost prime with at most 3 prime divisors. Theorem 4: Let $Z_k(x)$ denote the number of prime pairs $(p, p+2k)$ not exceeding $x$. Then

$$Z_k(x) \leqq 8 \prod_{\substack{p|2k\\ p>2}} \left(\frac{p-1}{p-2}\right) \prod_{p>2} \left\{1-\frac{1}{(p-1)^2}\right\} \frac{x}{\log^2 x} + O\left(\frac{x}{\log^3 x}\log\log x\right).$$

Theorems 1, 2, 3 improve results obtained independently by A. I. Vinogradov [Mat. Sb. (N.S.) **41** (**83**) (1957), 49–80; correction, 415–416; MR **20** #3836] and the author [Acta Math. Sinica **6** (1956), 565–582; MR **20** #4530]. These results had "4" in place of "3" in the present theorems.

The proofs are based on the sieve method of A. Selberg.

*S. Chowla* (Boulder, Colo.)

Citations: MR 20# 3836 = P32-36; MR 20# 4530 = P32-38.

Referred to in M55-43, N12-31, P32-74.

**P32-51** **(27# 5733 )**

**Wang, Yuan**

**On the representation of large integer as a sum of a prime and an almost prime. (Chinese. English summary)**

*Acta Math. Sinica* **10** (1960), 168–181 (*Chinese*); *translated as Chinese Math.* **1** (1962), 181–195.

Eine Konsequenz der verallgemeinerten Riemannschen Vermutung lautet: $\pi(x;k,l)=(\varphi(x))^{-1}\operatorname{li} x+O(x^{1/2}\log x)$. Diese Gleichung liegt der vorliegenden Arbeit als Hypothese zugrunde. Verfasser zeigt folgende Resultate: (1) Jede genügend grosse gerade Zahl ist Summe einer Primzahl und eines Produktes von höchstens drei Primzahlen. (2) Bei festem natürlichen $k$ gibt es unendlich viele Primzahlen $p$, so dass $p+2k$ Produkt von höchstens drei Primzahlen ist. (3) Jede genügend grosse ungerade Zahl ist von der Gestalt $p+2q$, wo $p$ Primzahl und $q$ Produkt von höchstens drei Primzahlen ist. (4) Für jedes natürliche $k$ ist die Anzahl $Z_k(x)$ der Primzahlpaare $(p, p+2k)$ unterhalb $x$:

$$Z_k(x) \leqq 8 \prod_{\substack{p|2k\\ p>2}} \frac{p-1}{p-2} \prod_{p>2} \left(1-\frac{1}{(p-1)^2}\right) \frac{x}{\log^2 x} + O\left(\frac{x}{\log^3 x}\log\log x\right).$$

Durch diese Sätze werden frühere Resultate des Autors [dieselben Acta **6** (1956), 565–582; MR **20** #4530] verschärft, bei denen obige Sätze mit Produkten von vier statt drei Primzahlen bewiesen wurden.

*H. Klingen* (Freiburg)

Citations: MR 20# 4530 = P32-38.

Referred to in P32-74.

**P32-52** **(27# 1425 )**

**Lavrik, A. F.**

**On the representation of numbers as the sum of primes by Šnirel'man's method. (Russian. Uzbek summary)**

*Izv. Akad. Nauk UzSSR Ser. Fiz.-Mat. Nauk* **1962**, *no.* 3, 5–10.

In 1930 L. G. Šnirel'man [Izv. Donsk. Politeh. Inst. **14** (1930), no. 2–3, 3–28] proved that every positive integer can be represented as a sum of not more than $C$ primes, where $C$ is an absolute constant. Šnirel'man's method is as follows. Let $N(x)$ be the number of positive integers not exceeding $x$ which can be written as a sum of two primes. For $N(x)$, the following estimate holds:

$$N(x) \geqq T(x), \quad T(x) = \Big(\sum_{4\leqq n\leqq x} Q(n)\Big)^2 \Big/ \sum_{4\leqq n\leqq x} Q^2(n),$$

where $Q(n)$ is the number of representations of $n$ by sums of two primes, with the order of summands taken into account. The function $T(x)$ is estimated from below by the sieve method. Then the theorem on the density of sums of sequences is applied. Obviously the value of the constant $C$ depends on the exactness of the estimate of $T(x)$. Šnirel'man has proved that $C$ can be taken to be 80,000. This value of $C$ has been reduced by many authors, and in 1951 Shapiro and Varga proved that $C$ can be less than or equal to 20.

The author deduces the following asymptotic formula

$$T(x) = \frac{3}{4}x\prod_p \frac{(p-1)^3}{p(p^2-3p+3)}(1+O((\ln x)^{\varepsilon-1})),$$

where $p$ runs over all primes and $\varepsilon$ is any positive constant. Hence $T(x) < 0.32637x$ for $x > x_0$.

It follows from this that it is impossible to obtain for $C$ a value less than 8 by Šnirel'man's method.

*J. Kubilius* (Vilnius)

## P32-53 (27# 1427 )

**Pan, Čen-dun [Pan, Cheng-dong]**

**On the representation of even numbers as the sum of a prime and a near prime. (Russian)**

*Sci. Sinica* **11** (1962), 873–888.

Die Arbeit ist auch abgedruckt in Acta Math. Sinica **12** (1962), 95–106. Mit der Selbergschen Siebmethode hat man in Richtung der Goldbachschen Vermutung bewiesen: Jede hinreichend grosse gerade Zahl ist als Summe von zwei Zahlen darstellbar, von denen die eine höchstens $a$, die andere höchstens $b$ Primfaktoren besitzt. Die besten Resultate sind $a=2$, $b=3$ [Wang, ibid. **8** (1958), 413–429; MR **21** #1958] und unter Annahme der Richtigkeit der erweiterten Riemannschen Vermutung: $a=1$, $b=3$ [Wang, ibid. **10** (1960), 168–181]. Der Verfasser beweist die obige Aussage mit $a=1$, $b=5$. Der Beweis benutzt ein Selbergsches Sieb mit Gewichten und Resultate von Rényi [Izv. Akad. Nauk SSSR Ser. Mat. **12** (1948), 57–78; MR **9**, 413; Amer. Math. Soc. Transl. (2) **19** (1962), 299–321; MR **24** #A1264] und Wang (zweites Zitat).

*H.-E. Richert* (Marburg)

Citations: MR 9, 413g = P32-12; MR 21# 1958 = P32-40; MR 24# A1264 = P32-13.

Referred to in P32-54, P32-59.

## P32-54 (29# 4727 )

**Pan, Cheng-dong [Pan, Cheng-Tung]**

**On the representation of an even integer as the sum of a prime and an almost prime.**

*Acta Math. Sinica* **12** (1962), 95–106 (*Chinese*); *translated as Chinese Math.* **3** (1963), 101–112.

Reproduction of an article already published in Sci. Sinica **11** (1962), 873–888 [MR **27** #1427].

Citations: MR 27# 1427 = P32-53.

Referred to in P32-59.

## P32-55 (27# 4805 )

**Lavrik, A. F.**

**The theory of quasi-prime numbers. (Russian)**

*Dokl. Akad. Nauk SSSR* **152** (1963), 544–547.

A positive integer $\leqq N$ is called quasi-prime if its prime factors are greater than $N^{1/\xi}$, where $\xi=\xi(N)$ is a given function of $N$.

The author states some asymptotic formulas for the number of representations of even $N$ as a sum (1) of two coprime quasi-primes; (2) of two quasi-primes, one of which belongs to an arithmetical progression; (3) of one prime and one quasi-prime. He also gives an asymptotic formula for the number of quasi-prime twins. The function $\xi(N)$ is supposed to be an arbitrary slowly increasing function.

The proof is only sketched. It is founded on the method of the sieve of Eratosthenes, the "large sieve" of Linnik, and partly on analytical considerations.

*J. Kubilius* (Vilnius)

## P32-56 (28# 73 )

**Pan, Čen-dun [Pan, Cheng-Tung]**

**On the representation of even numbers as the sum of a prime and a product of not more than 4 primes. (Russian)**

*Sci. Sinica* **12** (1963), 455–473.

The author proves that every sufficiently large positive integer is the sum of a prime and of a positive integer with at most 4 prime factors. The proof is based on the following lemma. Put

$$\sum_{\substack{p\leqq N\\ p\equiv l\,(\mathrm{mod}\,D)}} \log p\cdot e^{-p(\log N)/N} = \frac{N}{\varphi(D)\log N}+R_D(N),$$

where $(l, D)=1$. Then, for every positive constant $\varepsilon$,

$$\sum_{d\leqq N^{3/8-\varepsilon}} |\mu(d)\tau(d)R_D(N)| \leqq \frac{N}{(\log N)^5}.$$

*K. Mahler* (Canberra)

Referred to in N12-31, P32-59.

## P32-57 (28# 3023 )

**Rieger, G. J.**

**Über die Folge der Zahlen der Gestalt $p_1+p_2$.**

*Arch. Math.* **15** (1964), 33–41.

A famous theorem of Schnirelmann (1930) asserts that

$$A(n: n \leqq x,\ n = p_1+p_2) > Cx.$$

Here $p_1, p_2$ are primes, $A(*, \cdots)$ the number of $*$ with the properties $\cdots$, and $n$ is a natural number. The author generalizes the above theorem to Theorem 1: For every $\sigma$ with $0<\sigma\leqq\frac{1}{2}$, every $\alpha$ with $\frac{1}{2}<\alpha<1$ and (recall Hoheisel's theorem)

$$\pi(x+x^\alpha)-\pi(x) > \frac{x^\alpha}{2\log x}\ [x > C_7(\alpha) > 1]$$

and every $x$ such that

$$x > C_{10}(\sigma, \alpha) = \mathrm{Max}[(2/\sigma)^{1/(1-\alpha)}, 8C_7(\alpha)],$$

we have

$$A(n: n \leqq x,\ n = p_1+p_2,\ |p_1-\sigma n| < n^\alpha) \geqq C_{11}\sigma^2 x,$$

where $C_{11}$ is an absolute positive constant.

This is generalized in different ways, in particular, to primes in arithmetic progressions. The author also sharpens a well-known theorem of Rényi, which asserts that every large even number is a sum of a prime and an "almost" prime.

*S. Chowla* (University Park, Pa.)

## P32-58 (29# 85 )

**Rieger, G. J.**

**Über ein lineares Gleichungssystem von Prachar mit Primzahlen.**

*J. Reine Angew. Math.* **213** (1963/64), 103–107.

In this paper the author considers what he calls a Prachar system, viz., the system $p_1+p_2=m$, $p_2+p_3=n$, where $p_1, p_2, p_3$ are primes. Let $A\{\ \}$ denote the number of elements in the set $\{\ \}$. Let $f(m, n) = A\{p_1, p_2, p_3; p_1+p_2 = m, p_2+p_3=n, p_1, p_2, p_3 \text{ primes}\}$. Theorem: There exists an absolute constant $c$ such that, for $x > 8$,

$$A(m, n; n < m < x,\ f(m, n) > 0) > cx^2.$$

Various generalizations are considered.

*R. Ayoub* (University Park, Pa.)

**P32-59** **(29# 2234)**

**Uchiyama, Miyoko; Uchiyama, Saburô**

**On the representation of large even integers as sums of a prime and an almost prime.**

*Proc. Japan Acad.* **40** (1964), 150–154.

It was proved by C. T. Pan [Acta Math. Sinica **12** (1962), 95–106; MR **29** #4727; Sci. Sinica **11** (1962), 873–888; MR **27** #1427] that every sufficiently large even integer is the sum of a prime and a product of at most five prime factors. The authors replace "five" by "four", but seem to be unaware of the fact that this was already achieved meanwhile by Pan [ibid. **12** (1963), 455–473; MR **28** #73]. *N. G. de Bruijn* (Eindhoven)

Citations: MR 27# 1427 = P32-53; MR 28# 73 = P32-56; MR 29# 4727 = P32-54.

Referred to in P32-73.

**P32-60** **(29# 3420)**

**Togashi, Akiyo; Uchiyama, Saburô**

**On the representation of large even integers as sums of two almost primes. I.**

*J. Fac. Sci. Hokkaido Univ. Ser. I* **18** (1964), 60–68.

In connection with Goldbach's famous conjecture the theorem that every sufficiently large even integer is representable as a sum of two integers, each of which has at most three prime factors, was given by A. I. Vinogradov. Here the authors, combining the sieve methods of Viggo Brun and A. Selberg, offer another proof of the theorem. *H. Gupta* (Chandigarh)

**P32-61** **(29# 3421)**

**Uchiyama, Saburô**

**On the representation of large even integers as sums of two almost primes. II.**

*J. Fac. Sci. Hokkaido Univ. Ser. I* **18** (1964), 69–77.

In this paper, the author, refining the method used in the paper reviewed above [#3420], proves that every sufficiently large even integer $N$ can be represented as a sum of two integers $n_1$ and $n_2$ such that $(n_1, n_2)=1$ and $n_1n_2$ is a product of not more than five prime factors. *H. Gupta* (Chandigarh)

**P32-62** **(30# 1991)**

**Levin, B. V.**

**Distribution of "near primes" in polynomial sequences. (Russian)**

*Mat. Sb. (N.S.)* **61 (103)** (1963), 389–407.

According to a well-known theorem of A. Rényi [Izv. Akad. Nauk SSSR Ser. Mat. **12** (1948), 57–78; MR **9**, 413] there exists an absolute constant $R$ such that every sufficiently large even integer $2N$ is the sum of a prime and a number having at most $R$ prime factors. In Rényi's proof $R$ is very large. The author gives a new proof of Rényi's theorem with $R=4$, and thereby provides the closest approach yet to the Goldbach conjecture; his result is all the more remarkable since, as he points out, use of the generalised Riemann hypothesis improves his result only to $R=3$. The author's account is based on the Selberg sieve. Let $1 \leqq a_1 < a_2 < \cdots < a_Z \leqq X$ be the integer sequence to be sifted, let $r, s$ be non-negative integers, and write $A_{r,s}(Z)$ for the number of terms in the sequence $\{a_i\}$ having not more than $r+s$ prime factors, of which not more than $r$ lie between $z^\beta$ and $z$, and not more than $s$ are greater than $z$; here $\beta$ is some number satisfying $0<\beta<1$ and $z=X^{1/(\beta r+s+1)}$. Selberg's method is shown to lead to a lower bound for $A_{r,s}(Z)$, and in any specific application the object is to choose $r, s$ no larger than is necessary to ensure that $A_{r,s}(Z)>0$ for all sufficiently large $Z$. In the special case of Rényi's theorem, $a_i = 2N - p_i$, where $\{p_i\}$ is the sequence of primes. The lower bound for $A_{r,s}(Z)$ is the sum of a complicated "dominant" expression and an error term of relatively simple structure (this last, a characteristic feature of the Selberg method). To deal with the "dominant" expression the author uses the method of differential-difference equations which, in this context, goes back to A. A. Buhštab [e.g., Mat. Sb. (N.S.) **28 (70)** (1951), 165–184; MR **13**, 626; see also N. G. de Bruijn, Nederl. Akad. Wetensch. **53** (1950), 247–256; MR **12**, 11]; and for the error term, which involves the major difficulties when $a_i$ is, as in the case of Rényi's theorem, a polynomial in $p_i$, he uses Barban's mean-value formula described in #1992 below.

The author's result ($R=4$) has previously been given by Yuan Wang [Sci. Sinica **8** (1959), 357–381; MR **21** #4944], but Wang's method is exceedingly complicated; to check it would be a formidable task. The author's approach is much simpler in principle and inspires confidence; unfortunately, it does not appear to be free of errors. For instance, there seems to be an error in the very first stage of the inductive process in the proof of the important Lemma 4 (see the line following equation (13)), and the Laplace transform on p. 397 is incorrectly inverted, thus casting doubt on the relevance of the subsequent numerical calculations. It should be mentioned here that Barban [see #1992 below] also claims the result $R=4$ as a corollary of his main result. The author develops his method in general form so as to yield the corresponding result for prime twins and many other equally striking results; his paper and Barban's contain a full bibliography of the important work done in this area since the appearance in 1947 of Rényi's theorem. *H. Halberstam* (Dublin)

Citations: MR 9, 413g = P32-12; MR 12, 11d = N28-22; MR 13, 626h = N28-27; MR 21# 4944 = P32-41.

Referred to in M55-37, M55-39, N32-44, N32-47, P32-66, P32-70, R46-24, R48-37, Z02-53.

**P32-63** **(30# 1992)**

**Barban, M. B.**

**The "density" of the zeros of Dirichlet $L$-series and the problem of the sum of primes and "near primes". (Russian)**

*Mat. Sb. (N.S.)* **61 (103)** (1963), 418–425.

In a previous paper [#1990 above] (unfortunately not accessible to the reviewer) the author has shown that the mean-value formula

$$(1)\qquad \sum_{D \leq x^{1/a-\varepsilon}} \mu^2(D) \max_{\substack{l (\bmod D) \\ (l,D)=1}} \left| \pi(x, D, l) - \frac{1}{\phi(D)} \operatorname{li} x \right| = O(x \log^{-A} x)$$

for arbitrarily large but fixed $A$, is implied by an inequality of type

$$(2)\qquad N(\alpha, T) \ll T^{c_1} D^{a(1-\alpha)} \log^{c_2} DT$$

($c_1$, $c_2$ are absolute constants),

where $N(\alpha, T)$ is the number of zeros of all $L$-functions mod $D$ in the domain $\alpha<\sigma<1$, $|t| \leqq T$. Tatusawa [see K. Prachar, *Primzahlverteilung*, Springer, Berlin, 1957; MR **19**, 393] proved (2) with $a=6$; in this paper the author proves (2) with $a=3$, and this result suffices for the important application to Rényi's theorem described in #1991 above. A deep result of Linnik [Ju. V. Linnik, Izv. Akad. Nauk SSSR Ser. Mat. **24** (1960), 629–706; MR **23** #A130] on the sixth moment of an $L$-series, implies that (2) holds for almost all $D$, with $a=\frac{8}{3}+\varepsilon$, and the author shows that the exceptional $D$ can be dealt with so as to render (1) true for this value of $a$. If (1) were true with $a=2$, Rényi's theorem would follow with $R=3$ [see #1991 above], and this is as much as would follow from the generalised Riemann hypothesis.

*H. Halberstam* (Dublin)

Citations: MR 19, 393b = N02-7; MR 23# A130 = P36-26; MR 30# 1990 = N12-28.

Referred to in M55-37, M55-43, P32-66, P40-17, R48-37.

## P32-64 (32# 5619)

**Chen Jing-run [Ch'en Ching-jun]**

**On large odd numbers as sum of three almost equal primes.**

*Sci. Sinica* **14** (1965), 1113–1117.

The author sketches a proof of the following theorem: Every sufficiently large odd integer $N$ can be represented in the form $N=p_1+p_2+p_3$, where the $p_i$'s are primes satisfying $p_i=N/3+O(N^t)$, for every fixed $t>\frac{2}{3}$. This is an improvement of results of C. B. Haselgrove [J. London Math. Soc. **26** (1951), 273–277; MR **13**, 438] and of P'an Ch'eng-tung [Acta Math. Sinica **9** (1959), 315–329; MR **22** #3721] on $t$. The author's proof involves Vinogradov's method of trigonometrical sums and uses some previous results (see the second paper cited above) concerning those sums and the zeros of Dirichlet's $L$-functions. As another application of his method, the author announces the following result: Every sufficiently large even integer is the sum of two integers $a>1$ and $b>1$ with $V(a)+V(b)\leqq 4$, where $V(a)$ denotes the number of prime factors of $a$.

*O. H. Körner* (Marburg)

Citations: MR 13, 438e = P32-17; MR 22# 3721 = P32-42.

## P32-65 (33# 4031)

**Klimov, N. I.**

**The local density of certain sequences.** (Russian)

*Proc. First Sci. Conf. Math. Dept. Ped. Inst. Volga Region* (*May*, 1960) (*Russian*), *pp.* 11–15. *Kuĭbyšev. Gos. Ped. Inst., Kuybyshev*, 1961.

The author develops the results of L. G. Šnirel'man [Izv. Donsk. Politeh. Inst. **14** (1930), no. 2–3, 3–28; see also Uspehi Mat. Nauk **6** (1939), 9–25] on the density of a sequence of even numbers representable as a sum of two primes. Let $\nu(H;x)$ be the number of terms of the sequence which are in the interval $(H;H+x)$, and let $\alpha$ and $\theta$ be positive constants, $\theta\leqq 1$. A sequence is called locally dense if there exists a sufficiently large $x_1$ such that for any $H\geqq 0$ and $x>\max(x_1;H^\theta)$, the inequality $\nu(H;x)/x\geqq\alpha$ holds. It is shown that a sequence of numbers representable in the form of a sum of two primes belonging to arithmetic progressions with an increasing difference is locally dense.

*N. V. Gordeev* (RŽMat **1962** #9 A75)

## P32-66 (33# 5579)

**Vinogradov, A. I.**

**The density hypothesis for Dirichlet $L$-series.** (Russian)

*Izv. Akad. Nauk SSSR Ser. Mat.* **29** (1965), 903–934.

The title of the paper is given to the following theorem, which is proved by the author. Theorem 1: Let $N_d(\sigma,t)$ be the number of zeros $\rho$ of all Dirichlet $L$-series of modulus $d$ that lie in the region $\operatorname{Re}\rho\geqq\sigma$, $|\operatorname{Im}\rho|\leqq t$. Then, for all $d$ satisfying $D\leqq d\leqq 2D$, with the exception of at most $D^{1-\varepsilon/2}$ values, we have $N_d(\sigma,t)<(t\log D)^{A\varepsilon^{-4}}D^{2(1+\varepsilon)(1-\sigma)}$ for $\frac{1}{2}\leqq\sigma\leqq 1$ and $t\geqq 1$, where $A$ is a positive constant and $\varepsilon$ is an arbitrarily small positive number. This theorem has a variety of important applications of which only the following two are mentioned here. Theorem 2: In the usual notation,

$$\sum_{d\leqq x^{1/2-\varepsilon}}\max_{(l,d)=1}|\pi(x,d,l)-\operatorname{Li}x/\phi(d)| < x(\log x)^{-B},$$

where $B$ is an arbitrarily large positive constant and $\varepsilon$ is an arbitrarily small positive number. This improves a result of M. B. Barban [Mat. Sb. (N.S.) **61 (103)** (1963), 418–425; MR **30** #1992]. Theorem 3: For any sufficiently large even integer $m$, the equation $m=p+P_3$ is soluble, where $p$ is a prime and $P_3$ has at most three prime factors; the number of solutions of the equation exceeds $C\mathfrak{S}(m)m(\log m)^{-2}$, where $C$ is a positive absolute constant and $\mathfrak{S}(m)$ is a singular series. This theorem had previously been known only under the assumption of the extended Riemann hypothesis and, without the assumption of this hypothesis, was known only in the weaker form where $P_3$ is replaced by $P_4$ (with a similar meaning). See Wang Yuan [Sci. Sinica **8** (1959), 357–381; MR **21** #4944] and B. V. Levin [Mat. Sb. (N.S.) **61 (103)** (1963), 389–407; MR **30** #1991].

The proof of Theorem 1 depends upon the following result. For any integer $n\geqq 2$ and for any $Z$ with $D^{1/n}\leqq Z\leqq D^{1/(n-1)}$,

$$\sum_{d=D}^{2D}\sum_{\chi_d\neq\chi_0}\left|\sum_{m\leqq Z}\chi_d(m)\right|^2\leqq D^2Z^n\exp[(\log D)^\varepsilon].$$

For $n=3$ this is a result of Ju. V. Linnik [Izv. Akad. Nauk SSSR Ser. Mat. **24** (1960), 629–706; MR **23** #A130], and similar methods can be used to establish it for $n=2$. The greater part of the author's paper is taken up with the extension of the result to any $n\geqq 4$.

*R. A. Rankin* (Glasgow)

Citations: MR 21# 4944 = P32-41; MR 23# A130 = P36-26; MR 30# 1991 = P32-62; MR 30# 1992 = P32-63.

Referred to in M55-53, N02-13, P32-67, P32-70.

## P32-67 (33# 2607)

**Vinogradov, A. I.**

**Correction to the paper of A. I. Vinogradov "On the density hypothesis for the Dirichlet $L$-series".** (Russian)

*Izv. Akad. Nauk SSSR Ser. Mat.* **30** (1966), 719–720.

A correction of equality (32) of the author's article [same Izv. **29** (1965), 903–934; MR **33** #5579], where certain hypotheses on the summation indices were left out.

Citations: MR 33# 5579 = P32-66.

Referred to in M55-53, N02-13, P32-70.

## P32-68 (34# 5781)

**Turán, P.**

**Certain function-theoretic sieve methods in the theory of numbers.** (Russian)

*Dokl. Akad. Nauk SSSR* **171** (1966), 1289–1292.

The author outlines a contour integration method for the treatment of binary additive problems, such as the Goldbach or Hardy-Littlewood problem; this method links Goldbach's conjecture with "small" zeros of $L$-functions via the following formula for the number $\nu_2(N)$ of representations of an even integer $N$ as a sum of two primes: $\nu_2(N)=(1+o(1))N(\log N)^{-2}\Pi(N)+(1+o(1))R(N)$, where $\Pi(N)$ is a certain product over the primes and $R(N)=\sum\sum_{k<N,\chi\bmod k}\sum_\rho f(k,\chi,\rho,N)$ is a complicated sum over "small" zeros of all Dirichlet $L$-series $L(s,\chi)$ with moduli $k<N$. A proof of this theorem is to appear in Acta Arithmetica. The author gave another application of this method to prime twins in Proc. London Math. Soc. (3) **14a** (1965), 288–299 [MR **31** #2225]. Of course, the estimation of $R(N)$ is an open problem.

{In the second product in (12) the condition $p/N$ is omitted.}

{This article has appeared in English translation [Soviet Math. Dokl. **7** (1966), 1661–1662].}

*W. Schwarz* (Freiburg)

Citations: MR 31# 2225 = P40-16.

Referred to in P40-21, P40-23.

**P32-69** **(34# 5784)**

**Čudakov, N. G.; Klimov, N. I.**

**Concerning the Šnirel'man constant.** (Russian)
*Uspehi Mat. Nauk* **22** (1967), *no.* 1 (133), 212–213.

The authors list several books on the theory of numbers in which it is alleged that every integer $n \geqq N_0 = 2$ can be represented as a sum of $S = 20$, or less, primes. These books misquote results of H. N. Shapiro and the reviewer [Comm. Pure Appl. Math. **3** (1950), 153–176; MR **12**, 244], who proved by elementary means that every sufficiently large integer $n$ can be so represented. The authors state that the best explicit estimates are, at the present time, those of A. A. Šanin and T. A. Šeptickaja (presented at the Fourth Sci. Conf. Math. Depts. Ped. Inst. Volga Region 1963, apparently unpublished), who proved that $S = 2 \cdot 10^{10}$ for $N_0 = 2$, and those of K. G. Borozdkin [Proc. Third All-Union Math. Conference (Moscow, 1956), Vol. I, p. 3, Izdat. Akad. Nauk SSSR, Moscow, 1956], who proved that $S = 4$ for $N_0 = \exp(\exp(16.038))$.

*J. Warga* (Brookline, Mass.)

Citations: MR 12, 244c = P32-15.

**P32-70** **(34# 7483)**

**Chen Jing-run [Ch'en Ching-jun]**

**On the representation of a large even integer as the sum of a prime and the product of at most two primes.**
*Kexue Tongbao (Foreign Lang. Ed.)* **17** (1966), 385–386.

A. Rényi [Izv. Akad. Nauk SSSR Ser. Mat. **12** (1948), 57–78; MR **9**, 413; translated in Amer. Math. Soc. Transl. (2) **19** (1962), 299–321; MR **24** #A1264] proved that there exists a positive integer $a$ such that every sufficiently large even integer $2N$ is a sum of a prime and a product of at most $a$ primes. In Rényi's proof $a$ is very large. The author announces that he has proved Rényi's theorem with $a = 2$, and gives a very brief sketch of the proof. (The details will be published later.) {Rényi's theorem with $a = 3$ was proved independently by A. A. Buhštab [Dokl. Akad. Nauk SSSR **162** (1965), 735–738; MR **31** #2226] and by A. I. Vinogradov [Izv. Akad. Nauk SSSR Ser. Mat. **29** (1965), 903–934; MR **33** #5579; correction, ibid. **30** (1966), 719–720; MR **33** #2607], employing the sieve method of V. Brun or that of A. Selberg, and some results in the theory of Dirichlet $L$ function. (Cf. also B. V. Levin [Mat. Sb. (N.S.) **61** (**103**) (1963), 389–407; MR **30** #1991].)}

*T. Hayashida* (Yokohama)

Citations: MR 9, 413g = P32-12; MR 24# A1264 = P32-13; MR 30# 1991 = P32-62; MR 31# 2226 = P40-17; MR 33# 2607 = P32-67; MR 33# 5579 = P32-66.

**P32-71** **(34# 7484)**

**Lursmanašvili, A. P.**

**Representation of natural numbers by sums of prime numbers.** (Russian. Georgian summary)
*Thbilis. Sahelmc. Univ. Šrom. Mekh.-Math. Mecn. Ser.* **117** (1966), 63–76.

$N_r(P)$ bezeichne die Anzahl der Darstellungen von $P$ als Summe von $r$ Primzahlen. Der Verfasser beweist in Verschärfung der bekannten Resultate unter der Voraussetzung $P \equiv r \bmod 2$ für jedes $m \geqq r$ eine Entwicklung der Gestalt $N_r(P) =$

$$S_r(P)P^{r-1} \sum_{t=r}^{m} d_t(r)(\log P)^{-t} + O(P^{r-1}(\log P)^{-m-1}).$$

Hierin ist $S_r(P)$ die singuläre Reihe, und die Koeffizienten $d_t(r)$ sind von $P$ unabhängig. Der Beweis verläuft ähnlich wie bei A. Z. Val'fiš [Akad. Nauk Gruzin. SSR Trudy Mat. Inst. Razmadze **22** (1956), 3–31; MR **19**, 943], wo der Fall $r = 3$ der obigen Entwicklung behandelt wurde.

*H.-E. Richert* (Marburg)

Citations: MR 19, 943e = E24-68.

**P32-72** **(35# 5407)**

**Kátai, Imre**

**A comment on a paper of Ju. V. Linnik.** (Hungarian. English summary)
*Magyar Tud. Akad. Mat. Fiz. Oszt. Közl.* **17** (1967), 99–100.

As a refinement of a theorem of Ju. V. Linnik [Izv. Akad. Nauk SSSR Mat. **16** (1952), 503–520; MR **14**, 847], it is shown that, assuming that the Riemann hypothesis is true, the inequality $|x - p - p'| < C_n \log^2 x$ always has solutions; here $p$ and $p'$ are primes. The proof is based on an inequality proved by A. Selberg [Arch. Math. Naturvid. **47** (1943), no. 6, 87–105; MR **7**, 48] assuming the Riemann hypothesis and on the pigeon-hole principle.

*P. Szüsz* (Stony Brook, N.Y.)

Citations: MR 7, 48e = N08-4; MR 14, 847b = P32-20.

**P32-73** **(37# 179)**

**Uchiyama, Saburô**

**On the representation of large even integers as sums of a prime and an almost prime. II.**
*Proc. Japan Acad.* **43** (1967), 567–571.

It was recently proved by A. A. Buhštab [Dokl. Akad. Nauk SSSR **162** (1965), 735–738; MR **31** #2226] that every sufficiently large even integer can be represented as a sum of a prime and an almost prime composed of at most three prime factors.

The author gives a shorter and easier proof for this. In a note added in proof, he points out that a similar proof has been given by H. Halberstam, W. Jurkat and H. E. Richert [C. R. Acad. Sci. Paris Sér. A-B **264** (1967), A920–A923; MR **36** #6374].

{Part I, by the author and M. Uchiyama, appeared in Proc. Japan Acad. **40** (1964), 150–154 [MR **29** #2234].}

*N. G. de Bruijn* (Eindhoven)

Citations: MR 29# 2234 = P32-59; MR 31# 2226 = P40-17; MR 36# 6374 = M55-55.

**P32-74** **(37# 5171)**

**Hsieh Sheng-kang**

**On the representation of a large even number as a sum of a prime and the product of at most three primes.** (Chinese)
*Shuxue Jinzhan* 8 (1965), 209–216.

The author gives a new proof [Wang Yuan, Sci. Sinica **11** (1962), 1033–1054; MR **27** #1424; see also Acta Math. Sinica **10** (1960), 168–181; translated as Chinese Math. Acta **1** (1962), 181–195; MR **27** #5733] that every sufficiently large even number is the sum of a prime and a product of at most three prime factors. His Lemma 2 seems to be incorrectly stated.

*K. Mahler* (Columbus, Ohio)

Citations: MR 27# 1424 = P32-50; MR 27# 5733 = P32-51.

**P32-75** **(38# 2111)**

**Chen Jing-run [Ch'en Ching-jun]**

**On the representation of a large integer as the sum of a prime and of a product of three primes.** (Chinese)
*Shuxue Jinzhan* 8 (1965), 335–337.

**P32-76** **(38# 4432)**

**Miech, R. J.**

**Pseudo-primes and the Goldbach problem.**

*J. Reine Angew. Math.* **233** (1968), 1–27.

For every positive integer $r$, let $n(r)$ be an integer that is the product of $r$ distinct primes, all greater than a certain parameter. Assume that the extended Riemann hypothesis holds, that is, for every integer $k \geqq 1$ and for every character $\chi$ modulo $k$, the associated $L$-series has no zeros in the half-plane $\sigma > \frac{1}{2}$. Then it is shown that the number of solutions of the equation $N = n(r) + n(s)$ satisfies a certain asymptotic relation for nearly every even integer $N$.

*B. Garrison* (San Diego, Calif.)

**P32-77** **(39# 6849)**

**Jutila, Matti**

**On the least Goldbach's number in an arithmetical progression with a prime difference.**

*Ann. Univ. Turku. Ser. A I No.* 118 (1968), 8 *pp.*

Let $G(q, k)$ denote the least natural number $\equiv k \bmod q$ that is the sum of two primes; here $0 \leqq k < q$ and $k$ is even if $q$ is even. Ju. V. Linnik [Izv. Akad. Nauk SSSR Ser. Mat. **16** (1952), 503–520; MR **14**, 847] showed, under the extended Riemann hypothesis, that $G(q, k) \ll q \log^6 q$. The author proves that $G(q, k) \ll q^{1+2c+\varepsilon}$ if $q$ is an odd prime, where $c$ is the lower bound of all numbers $\alpha$ such that, for some $c'$, $L(\frac{1}{2}+it, \chi) \ll q^{\alpha}(T+2)^{c'}$ for $|t| \leqq T$ and all $L$-functions mod $q$. From the work of D. A. Burgess [Proc. London Math. Soc. (3) **13** (1963), 524–536; MR **26** #6133] it follows that, with $c' = 1$, $c$ satisfies $c \leqq 3/16$. As the author remarks, it would be very interesting to show that the restriction of $q$ to prime values can be dropped.

*H. Halberstam* (Nottingham)

Citations: MR 14, 847b = P32-20; MR 26# 6133 = L25-19.

**P32-78** **(42# 4517)**

**Kuzjašev, A. A.; Čečuro, E. F.**

**The representation of large integers by sums of primes. (Russian)**

*Studies in Number Theory, No.* 3 (*Russian*), *pp.* 46–50. *Izdat. Saratov. Univ., Saratov,* 1969.

The Šnirel′man constant is reduced to 10 for even numbers and to 9 for odd numbers. The theorem is valid beginning with a certain $n \geqq n_0$.

*A. I. Vinogradov* (Leningrad)

**P32-79** **(42# 5937)**

**Gandhi, J. M.**

**Two inequalities.**

*Mat. Vesnik* **7 (22)** (1970), 51–52.

It is proved that (1.1) $\pi(n) \geqq (4/\pi) \sum_{2 \leqq u \leqq n, u \equiv 2 (\mathrm{mod}\ 4)} G(u)/u$, where $G(u)$ is the number of solutions of $u = p_1 + p_2$, $p_i$ odd primes.

{The other inequality (1.2) does not appear to be correct. The method makes no use of the $p_i$ being prime and the analogous inequality (1.1) therefore holds for any set of distinct odd numbers. There are numerous inaccuracies and misprints.}

*I. Danicic* (Aberystwyth)

**P32-80** **(44# 6633)**

**Klimov, N. I.**

**Apropos the computations of Šnirel′man's constant. (Russian)**

*Volž. Mat. Sb. Vyp.* 7 (1969), 32–40.

The author finds an improved value of $s$, where $s$ is such that every natural number $\geqq 2$ is the sum of at most $s$ primes. He uses numerical refinements at various stages of the original Šnirelman-Brun approach to arrive at $s \leqq 6 \times 10^9$. For what can be obtained in this way for all sufficiently large natural numbers, see the next review [#6634].

*H. Halberstam* (Nottingham)

**P32-81** **(44# 6634)**

**Kondakova, L. F.; Klimov, N. I.**

**Certain additive problems. (Russian)**

*Volž. Mat. Sb. Vyp.* 7 (1969), 41–44. (*loose errata*)

The authors derive, by means of Selberg's sieve and Bombieri's theorem on primes in arithmetic progressions, an upper bound for the number of prime "twins" $p$, $p + u = p'$, $p \leqq x$; as they note themselves in an addendum, their result is already to be found in a paper by E. Bombieri and H. Davenport [Proc. Roy. Soc. Ser. A **293** (1966), 1–18; MR **33** #7314], where a complete argument is given. The authors also obtain the corresponding bound in the conjugate Goldbach case, and state a similar result for a natural generalization of the prime twin case. They point out that, by the results of H. N. Shapiro and J. Warga [Comm. Pure Appl. Math **3** (1950), 153–176; MR **12**, 244], and their own estimate in the Goldbach case, it follows via the Šnirel′man-Brun approach that every sufficiently large natural number is the sum of almost 12 prime numbers. Of course, since Bombieri's theorem was used on the way, this is no longer an elementary result.

*H. Halberstam* (Nottingham)

Citations: MR 12, 244c = P32-15; MR 33# 7314 = N08-43.

# P36 OTHER ADDITIVE REPRESENTATIONS IN WHICH PRIMES ENTER ONLY LINEARLY

For partitions into primes, see **A46**.

See also reviews A34-39, B16-14, C05-24, M15-24, N40-26, P02-18, P02-20, P02-21, P32-68, P44-22, P48-4, P52-6, P52-7, P56-14, P72-13, P72-21, P72-23, P72-26, Z02-53, Z15-70.

**P36-1** **(7, 49a)**

**Selmer, Ernst S. Eine numerische Untersuchung über die Darstellung der natürlichen Zahlen als Summe einer Primzahl und einer Quadratzahl.** Arch. Math. Naturvid. **47**, no. 2, 21–39 (1943).

The author denotes by $R(n)$ the number of "Romanoff decompositions" of $n$, that is, the number of ways in which it can be expressed as the sum of a prime number and a square. He cites the empirical result of Hardy and Littlewood, $R(n) \sim wn^{\frac{1}{2}}/\log n$, where

$$w = \prod_{p=3}^{\infty} \left\{1 - \frac{1}{p-1}\left(\frac{n}{p}\right)\right\}$$

and $(\frac{n}{p})$ is the Legendre symbol. He proves

$$R_m(n) \sim \int_0^{n^{\frac{1}{2}}} \frac{dx}{\log (n - x^2)},$$

where $R_m(x)$ is the derivative with respect to $x$ of $\sum_{v=1}^{x} R(v)$, and also

$$R_m(n) \approx \frac{n^{\frac{1}{2}}}{\log n - 2(1 - \log 2)} w.$$

He gives a table of the number of Romanoff decompositions of the numbers from 1 to 2000 and from 1,010,000 to 1,010,100, verifying the above results.

*B. W. Jones* (Ithaca, N. Y.).

**P36-2** **(10, 431e)**

**Mirsky, L. The number of representations of an integer as the sum of a prime and a *k*-free integer.** Amer. Math. Monthly **56**, 17–19 (1949).

The author proves that every sufficiently large integer $n$ can be represented as the sum of a prime and a $k$-free integer, and gives an asymptotic formula for the number of such representations. An asymptotic expression is also stated for the number of $k$-free integers not exceeding $n$ having the form $p+l$, where $p$ is a prime, and $l$ is a given nonzero integer. *W. H. Simons* (Vancouver, B. C.).

Referred to in P36-53, P48-2, R24-42.

**P36-3** **(11, 714e)**

**van der Corput, J. G. On de Polignac's conjecture.** Simon Stevin **27**, 99–105 (1950). (Dutch)

Let $N(x)$ denote the number of odd positive integers $n \leqq x$ which are not of the form $n=2^k+p$ ($p$ prime). De Polignac conjectured [Nouv. Ann. Math. Paris (1) **8**, 423–429 (1849)] that $N(x)=0$ for all $x$ (counting 1 as a prime), but Euler already knew the examples $n=127$ and $n=959$. It is proved here that $N(x)/x$ has a positive lower limit, as $x\to\infty$. On the other hand Romanoff proved [Math. Ann. **109**, 668–678 (1934)] that the upper limit is less than 1. *N. G. de Bruijn* (Delft).

**P36-4** **(13, 112b)**

**Halberstam, H. On the representation of large numbers as sums of squares, higher powers, and primes.** Proc. London Math. Soc. (2) **53**, 363–380 (1951).

The author establishes asymptotic formulas for (a) $r_1(n)$, the number of representations of a large positive integer $n$ as a sum of $r$ squares and $s$ primes, where $r+2s>4$; (b) $r_2(n)$, the number of representations as a sum of a $k$th power and two primes; and (c) $r_3(n)$, the number of representations as a sum of a $k$th power, two squares, and a prime. In each case the formula is of the form $R(n)\mathfrak{S}(n)$ plus an error term which contains $(\log n)^{-c}$, where $c$ is an arbitrarily large positive number. The factor $R(n)$ takes the size of $n$ into account and the "singular series" $\mathfrak{S}(n)$ depends only on the arithmetical properties of the integer $n$.

The method is the standard Hardy-Littlewood approach with modifications due to Vinogradov. It is based on the work of Estermann [Proc. London Math. Soc. (2) **42**, 501–516 (1937)], where the result for $r_1(n)$ with $r=1$, $s=2$ is obtained and the problems of $r_2(n)$ and $r_3(n)$ are suggested. The proof uses finite sums and avoids the difficulty of dealing directly with the zeros of the Dirichlet $L$-functions by appealing to the Page-Siegel-Walfisz result on primes in an arithmetical progression [Page, Proc. London Math. Soc. (2) **39**, 116–141 (1935); Walfisz, Math. Z. **40**, 592–607 (1936), p. 598]. *R. D. James* (Vancouver, B. C.).

Referred to in P32-26, P36-10, P36-17.

**P36-5** **(13, 437i)**

**Erdös, P. On integers of the form $2^k+p$ and some related problems.** Summa Brasil. Math. **2**, 113–123 (1950).

Let $c_1, c_2, \cdots$ denote positive absolute constants. Let $f(n)=\sum_{2^k+p=n}1$. Thus $c_1x\leqq\sum_{n\leqq x}f(n)\leqq c_2x$ for $x>2$. Romanoff proved (1) $\limsup x^{-1}\sum_1^x f^k(n)<\infty$ for $k=2$ and hence (2) $\sum_{n\leqq x,\, f(n)>0}1\geqq c_3x$ [cf. Landau, Über einige neuere Fortschritte der additiven Zahlentheorie, Cambridge Univ. Press, 1937]. The author proves (1) for every $k$. He proves the existence of an infinite number of $n$'s such that $f(n)>c_4\ln\ln n$ [thus $\limsup f(n)=\infty$], and constructs on the other hand an arithmetic progression of odd numbers no term of which has the form $2^k+p$. Finally, generalizing (2), he proves: Given an infinite sequence $a_1<a_2<\cdots$ of integers such that $a_k|a_{k+1}$ [$k=1, 2, \cdots$], then $\liminf x^{-1}\sum_{n\leqq x,\, n=p+a_k}1>0$ if and only if both (3) $\limsup \ln a_k/a_k<\infty$ and (4) $\sum_{d|a_k}1/d<c_5$.

Formula (1) is derived from (5) $\sum_1^\infty B^{v(d)}/dl_2(d)<\infty$. Here $B>0$ is constant; $v(d)=\sum_{p|d}1$; $l_2(d)$ is the exponent of 2 (mod $d$). The proof of (5) follows the pattern of the case $B=1$ [cf. Landau, loc. cit., p. 68]. The sufficiency proof of the last theorem is based on the following lemma: (3) and (4) imply $\sum_{l<k}\sum_{d|(a_k-a_l),\,(d,a_k)=1}1/d<c_6k$. *P. Scherk.*

Referred to in P36-30, P36-63.

**P36-6** **(14, 355e)**

**Linnik, Yu. V. Prime numbers and powers of two.** Trudy Mat. Inst. Steklov., v. 38, pp. 152–169. Izdat. Akad. Nauk SSSR, Moscow, 1951. (Russian) 20 rubles.

The author proves that the number of representations of an integer $N$ as a sum of two primes and $k$ powers of 2 is greater than

$$N\left(\frac{\log N}{\log 2}\right)^{k-1}(c_1-c_2(1-\eta)^{k-2})$$

where $c_1$, $c_2$ and $\eta<1$ are absolute constants and $k\geqq3$. It follows at once that there exists a constant $k\geqq3$ such that every large integer $N$ is representable in the form

$$N=p_1+p_2+2^{x_1}+\cdots+2^{x_k},$$

where $p_1$ and $p_2$ are primes and $x_1, \cdots, x_k$ are positive integers.

The proof is based on the investigation of the integral

$$\int_0^1 e(2\pi iN\alpha)S^2(\alpha)T^k(\alpha)d\alpha,$$

where

$$S(\alpha)=\sum_{p<N}e(-pN^{-1}-2\pi ip\alpha),$$

$$T(\alpha)=\sum_{m=1}^{\infty}e(-2^mN^{-1}-2\pi i2^m\alpha).$$

On the "major arcs" one can evaluate the integral

$$\int e(2\pi iN\alpha)S^2(\alpha)d\alpha,$$

whereas on the "minor arcs" one uses the inequality

$$\int_0^1|S(\alpha)|^2|T(\alpha)|^2d\alpha=O(N)$$

by Romanov [Math. Ann. **109**, 668–678 (1934)] and a detailed ingenious study of the set of values of $\alpha$ where $T(\alpha)\geqq(1-\alpha)T(0)$. There is one serious misprint. The last displayed formula in the enunciation of the theorem on p. 154 should read

$$\sum_{(N_1)}>c_3N\left(\frac{\log N}{\log 2}\right)^{k-1}$$

*H. Heilbronn* (Bristol).

Referred to in P36-8.

**P36-7** **(14, 451c)**

**Prachar, K. Über einen Satz der additiven Zahlentheorie.** Monatsh. Math. **56**, 101–104 (1952).

Suppose $k_0, k_1, k_2, \cdots$ is a strictly increasing sequence of non-negative integers, $a$ is a fixed positive integer $>1$, $k(x)$ is the number of $a^{k_i}\leqq x$, and $R(x)$ is the number of distinct integers $\leqq x$ which can be expressed in form $p+a^{k_i}$, where $p$ is a prime number. The author proves the existence of a positive constant $c$ (depending only on $a$) such that $R(x)>cxk(x)/\log x$ for $x>2a^{k_0}$. The proof is a very straightforward adaptation of the method used by Romanoff for the special case $k_i=i$. Cf. Landau, Über einige neuere Fortschritte der additiven Zahlentheorie, Cambridge, 1937, Theorem 106. *P. T. Bateman* (Urbana, Ill.).

**P36-8** **(15, 602j)**

**Linnik, Yu. V. Addition of prime numbers with powers of one and the same number.** Mat. Sbornik N.S. **32**(74), 3–60 (1953). (Russian)

The author proves that every large even integer can be written as a sum of two primes and $k$ powers of 2, where $k$ is an absolute constant. In a previous paper [Trudy Mat. Inst. Steklov. **38**, 152–169 (1951); these Rev. **14**, 355] the author proved this theorem assuming the generalised Riemann hypothesis. If 2 is replaced by an integer $g>2$, the proof also applies, $k$ becoming a function of $g$. The author also states that any large integer, written in the binary scale, can be changed into a Goldbach number by altering a bounded number of digits only. *H. Heilbronn.*

Citations: MR 14, 355e = P36-6.

Referred to in L20-20, P36-14, P36-15, P36-23, P36-41.

**P36-9** **(15, 602k)**

**Linnik, Yu. V. Prime numbers and powers of one and the same number.** Doklady Akad. Nauk SSSR (N.S.) **85**, 953–954 (1952). (Russian)

Preliminary announcement of the results in the paper reviewed above.

**P36-10** **(15, 778e)**

**Zulauf, Achim. Über die Darstellung natürlicher Zahlen als Summen von Primzahlen aus gegebenen Restklassen und Quadraten mit gegebenen Koeffizienten. I. Resultate für genügend grosse Zahlen.** J. Reine Angew. Math. **192**, 210–229 (1953).

The author obtains a generalization of a theorem of Stanley [Proc. London Math. Soc. (2) **29**, 122–144 (1929)] and Halberstam [ibid. **53**, 363–380 (1951); these Rev. **13**, 112] by a method of Linnik [Mat. Sbornik N.S. **19** (61) 3–8 (1946); these Rev. **8**, 317]. The investigation of the singular series involved is to follow in another paper. *T. Estermann* (London).

Citations: MR 8, 317c = P32-9; MR 13, 112b = P36-4.

Referred to in P32-47, P36-11.

**P36-11** **(16, 336e)**

**Zulauf, Achim. Über die Darstellung natürlicher Zahlen als Summen von Primzahlen aus gegebenen Restklassen und Quadraten mit gegebenen Koeffizienten. II. Die singuläre Reihe.** J. Reine Angew. Math. **193**, 39–53 (1954).

The author investigates the singular series which occurs in his Paper I of the same title [J. Reine Angew. Math. **192**, 210–229 (1953); these Rev. **15**, 778]. *T. Estermann* (London).

Citations: MR 15, 778e = P36-10.

**P36-12** **(16, 336f)**

**Zulauf, Achim. Über die Darstellung natürlicher Zahlen als Summen von Primzahlen aus gegebenen Restklassen und Quadraten mit gegebenen Koeffizienten. III. Resultate für "fast alle" Zahlen.** J. Reine Angew. Math. **193**, 54–64 (1954).

The author considers representations of natural numbers in the forms $p_1+p_2$ and $p_1+b_1g_1^2+b_2g_2^2$, where $p_1$ and $p_2$ are odd primes in given classes of residues, $b_1$ and $b_2$ are given natural numbers, and $g_1$ and $g_2$ are integers. He proves that almost all natural numbers which satisfy certain congruences, necessary for trivial reasons, have such representations. ["$b_r$" in the fifth line of the introduction is a misprint for "$g_r$".] *T. Estermann* (London).

**P36-13** **(17, 14d)**

**Erdős, Pál. On a problem concerning congruence systems.** Mat. Lapok **3**, 122–128 (1952). (Hungarian. Russian and English summaries)

The set of congruences $x\equiv a_i \pmod{n_i}$, $1<n_1<n_2<\cdots<n_k$, is called overlapping if every positive integer satisfies at least one of them. Using this concept, the author proves the existence of an arithmetic progression consisting of odd integers none of which is representable as the sum of a prime and a power of two. *P. R. Halmos* (Chicago, Ill.).

Referred to in P36-30.

**P36-14** **(17, 349c)**

**Vinogradov, A. I. On some new theorems of the additive theory of numbers.** Dokl. Akad. Nauk SSSR (N.S.) **102** (1955), 875–876. (Russian)

The author announces the following result, closely related to one of Linnik [Mat. Sb. N.S. **32(74)** (1953), 3–60; MR **15**, 602]. Theorem 1: Let $p>2$ be a given integer, and let any sufficiently large number $N$ be written in the scale of $p$ as

$$N=a_0+a_1p+\cdots+a_Rp^R.$$

Then it is sufficient to diminish by 1 at most $k$ of the coefficients $a_0, \cdots, a_R$ (where $k$ depends only on $p$) in order to obtain a number representable as the sum of two primes. Another more complicated result (Theorem 2), which implies Theorem 1, is enunciated, as is also the main lemma on which the proof of Theorem 2 is said to be based. *H. Davenport* (London).

Citations: MR 15, 602j = P36-8.

Referred to in P36-15.

**P36-15** **(19, 393c)**

**Vinogradov, A. I. On an "almost binary" problem.** Izv. Akad. Nauk SSSR. Ser. Mat. **20** (1956), 713–750. (Russian)

This paper gives the detailed proof of a result already announced [Dokl. Akad. Nauk SSSR (N.S.) **102** (1955), 875–876; MR **17**, 349]. This is that if a sufficiently large number $N$ is expressed in a fixed scale of notation as $N=a_0+a_1p+a_2p^2+\cdots+a_Rp^R$, then by changing an absolutely bounded number of the $a_i$ by $\pm 1$, one can derive a number $N'$ which is a sum of two primes. (It is understood that a digit 0 can be changed only into 1 and a digit $p-1$ only into $p-2$.) A stronger result is proved on the assumption of the generalized Riemann hypothesis, namely, that the changes can be confined to $a_0, \cdots, a_M$, where $M=[(\log N/\log p)^{1/m}]$ and $m$ is any fixed positive integer. The proofs, based on the method of Linnik [Mat. Sb. N.S. **32(74)** (1953), 5–60; MR **15**, 602] are long and intricate. *H. Davenport* (London).

Citations: MR 15, 602j = P36-8; MR 17, 349c = P36-14.

**P36-16** **(18, 564c)**

**Hornfeck, Bernhard. Zur Struktur gewisser Primzahlsätze.** J. Reine Angew. Math. **196** (1956), 156–169.

The author considers what properties of the sequence of prime numbers and other sequences are used in various density theorems, and, in the light of these results, generalizes them. Let $T$ denote the set of all sequences $\mathfrak{A}=\{a_1, a_2, \cdots\}$ of positive integers such that $(a_i, a_j)=1$ for all $i\neq j$. It is shown that, if $\mathfrak{A}\in T$, $d$ is a positive integer and $A(x; 0, d)$ is the number of $a_i\in\mathfrak{A}$ for which $a_i\leq x$ and $a_i+d\in\mathfrak{A}$, then, uniformly in $d$,

$$A(x;0, d)<c_1\frac{x}{\log^2 x}\sum_{q|d}\frac{1}{q}\ (q \text{ square free}).$$

This result is used to show that $\delta^*\{\mathfrak{A}+f(\mathfrak{B})\}>0$, where

$\mathfrak{A} \in T$ and has density lying between positive multiples of $x/\log x$, and where $\mathfrak{B}$ has positive density. Here $\delta^*$ denotes the upper asymptotic density and $f(\mathfrak{B})$ is the sequence $(f(b_1), f(b_2), \cdots)$, where $b_i \in \mathfrak{B}$ and $f$ is a polynomial with integral coefficients and positive highest coefficient. This generalizes a result of Romanov, which is got by taking $\mathfrak{A}$ to be the sequence of primes, $\mathfrak{B}$ to be the sequence of non-negative integers and $f(x)$ to be $x^m$. Other results of Romanov, Prachar and Kai-Lai Chung are generalized. For example, it is shown that if $\mathfrak{A}$ satisfies the conditions just stated, $a$ is an integer greater than unity, $\mathfrak{G}^*$ is a subset of $\{1, a, a^2, a^3, \cdots\}$, and $\mathfrak{H}^*=\mathfrak{A}+\mathfrak{G}^*$, then $H^*(x)>cxG^*(x)/\log x$, for sufficiently large $x$, where $H^*(x)$ is the number of members of $\mathfrak{H}^*$ which do not exceed $x$, and $G^*(x)$ is defined similarly. *R. A. Rankin.*

Referred to in N08-25.

**P36-17** **(19, 532a)**

**Hooley, C. On the representation of a number as the sum of two squares and a prime.** Acta Math. **97** (1957), 189–210.

On the basis of the so-called "extended Riemann hypothesis" the author proves an asymptotic formula, conjectured by Hardy and Littlewood, for the number of representations of a large number as a sum of two squares and a prime. On the same assumption he proves that there are infinitely many primes of the form $x^2+y^2+1$ (a well-known conjecture which had not, so far, been connected with the extended Riemann hypothesis). The Hardy-Littlewood conjecture for the case of 4 squares and a prime was proved (however, without any hypothesis) by the reviewer [Acta Arith. **1** (1935), 115–122] and for a greater number of squares and primes by A. Walfisz [ibid. **1** (1935), 123–160]; Estermann [Proc. London Math. Soc. (2) **42** (1937), 501–516] and Halberstam [ibid. **53** (1951), 363–380; MR **13**, 112] dealt with other cases of $r$ squares and $s$ primes. The author's results are deep, and difficult arguments are necessary to achieve the proofs. *S. Chowla* (Princeton, N.J.).

Citations: MR 13, 112b = P36-4.

Referred to in N02-12, N40-47, P36-25, P36-28, P36-32, P36-50, P36-66, P48-7, P48-17, P52-12.

**P36-18** **(19, 1039g)**

**Zulauf, Achim. On sums and differences of primes and squares.** Compositio Math. **13** (1958), 103–112.

The paper deals with the representations of an integer $q$ as a sum in which each term is either a prime in a given class of residues, or minus such a prime, or a given (positive or negative) integer times a square. The author restricts himself here to the case in which there is at least one positive and one negative term, and the number of prime terms plus half the number of square terms is greater than 2. He obtains an asymptotic formula for the number $N(q, n)$ of such representations in which either the sum of the positive terms or the sum of the negative terms is numerically less than or equal to $n$, and $n\to\infty$. *T. Estermann* (London).

**P36-19** **(19, 1160f)**

**Lavrik, A. F. Representation of numbers as a sum composed of a prime and a power of a given integer.** Dokl. Akad. Nauk SSSR (N.S.) **115** (1957), 445–446. (Russian)

The author states five theorems. The first one is: in the interval $(0, x)$ there exist more than $\alpha x/\log a$ numbers representable in one and only one way as the sum of a prime and a power of the given integer $a>a_0$, where $\alpha$ is an absolute positive constant. The other four theorems are extensions. A proof is sketched for the third one.

**P36-20** **(20# 6400)**

**Linnik, Yu. V. Solution of some binary additive problems by computing dispersion in progressions.** Dokl. Akad. Nauk SSSR **123** (1958), 975–977. (Russian)

The equation $n=p_1p_2+\zeta^2+\eta^2$ is considered; $p_1$, $p_2$ primes; $p_2\leqq n^\alpha$; $\alpha$ a small constant; $\zeta^2+\eta^2$ squarefree. The proof of an asymptotic formula for the solution quantity with a sufficiently good remainder term is sketched. Some other binary problems are considered.

*Summary provided by the author*

Referred to in P36-27.

**P36-21** **(20# 6401)**

**Linnik, Yu. V. Hardy-Littlewood problem on representation as the sum of a prime and two squares.** Dokl. Akad. Nauk SSSR **124** (1959), 29–30. (Russian)

The author claims to prove the Hardy-Littlewood heuristic asymptotic formula for the equation $n=p+\zeta^2+\eta^2$. Yet owing to a gap in his proof, his arguments lead to the weaker result that the Hardy-Littlewood equation is solvable for all sufficiently large $n$ and the representation quantity satisfies the inequality:

$$a(n)>0.7\pi\ \mathrm{Li}(n)\prod_p\left(1+\frac{\chi_4(p)}{p(p-1)}\right)\prod_{p|n}\frac{(p-1)(p-\chi_4(p))}{p^2-p+\chi_4(p)}.$$

Some other binary problems are considered.

*Summary provided by the author*

**P36-22** **(21# 15)**

**Babaev, G. Remark on a paper of Davenport and Heilbronn.** Uspehi Mat. Nauk **13** (1958), no. 6 (84), 63–64. (Russian)

Let $k\geqq 2$ be an integer, and denote by $S_k$ the sequence of numbers $n$ representable in the form $n=p+x^k$, where $p$ is a prime and $x$ is a natural number. It was shown by N. P. Romanoff [Math. Ann. **109**, 668–678 (1934)] that $S_k$ has positive density, and by H. Davenport and H. Heilbronn [Proc. London Math. Soc. (2) **43** (1937), 142–151] that $S_k$ contains almost all integers. In the present note the author uses an easy and elementary argument to establish a result in the opposite direction; he proves, in fact, that there exist infinitely many integers not contained in $S_k$. *L. Mirsky* (Sheffield)

**P36-23** **(21# 31)**

**Lavrik, A. F. On a theorem in the additive theory of numbers.** Uspehi Mat. Nauk **14** (1959), no. 1 (85), 197–198. (Russian)

The problem of representation of integers as sums of primes and of powers of a given integer has been considered, among others, by N. P. Romanoff [Math. Ann. **109** (1934), 668–678] and by Yu. V. Linnik [Mat. Sb. (N.S.) **32** (74) (1953), 3–60; MR **15**, 602]. In the context of these investigations, the following result has been conjectured. Given any integer $g\geqq 2$, there exists an integer $k=k(g)$ such that the density of the sequence of numbers $n$ representable in the form

$$n = p+g^{x_1}+\cdots+g^{x_k}$$

(where $p$ is a prime and the $x_i$ are positive integers) is equal to $\frac{1}{2}$. The author demonstrates that, at any rate for $g>2$, this conjecture is false. Its truth, or otherwise, for $g=2$ remains an open question. *L. Mirsky* (Sheffield)

Citations: MR 15, 602j = P36-8.

**P36-24** **(22# 10963)**

**Linnik, Yu. V. All large numbers are sums of a prime and two squares (A problem of Hardy and Littlewood). I.** Mat. Sb. (N.S.) **52 (94)** (1960), 661–700. (Russian)

If $Q(n)$ is the number of representations of a large number $n$ as a sum of a prime and two squares, the author aims at the inequality (his Theorem 1)

$$(1)\quad Q(n) > .979\pi \frac{n}{\ln n} \prod_p \left(1+\frac{\chi_4(p)}{p(p-1)}\right) \times \prod_{p|n} \frac{(p-1)(p-\chi_4(p))}{p^2-p+\chi_4(p)}$$

(the right-hand side tends to $\infty$ with $n$ since the reciprocal of the second product is less than $c \ln \ln n$, for a certain absolute positive constant $c$).

In this paper the author develops part of the heavy machinery required to prove (1) and

$$(2)\quad 5Q(n)+6S(n) = \pi \prod_p \left(1+\frac{\chi_4(p)}{p(p-1)}\right) \times \prod_{p|n} \frac{(p-1)(p-\chi_4(p))}{p^2-p+\chi_4(p)} \left(\frac{5n}{\ln n}+6L(n)\right)+R(n),$$

where $P=\exp(\ln n \ln \ln \ln n/K \ln \ln n)$, $K$ a sufficiently large constant, $L(n)=\sum_{p_1p_2\leq n;p_i>P} 1$, $S(n)$ is the number of solutions of $n=p_1p_2+\xi^2+\eta^2$ with $p_i>P$ $(i=1, 2)$, $|R(n)| < n/(\ln n)^{1+\tau_0}$ for a certain constant $\tau_0$.

*S. Chowla* (Boulder, Colo.)

Referred to in P02-18, P36-32.

## P36-25 (22# 10964)

**Linnik, Yu. V. All large numbers are sums of a prime and two squares (A problem of Hardy and Littlewood). II.** Mat. Sb. (N.S.) **53 (95)** (1961), 3–38. (Russian)

The author completes the proofs of the results (1) and (2) [#10963]. There is no doubt that the results achieved are of astonishing depth and beauty. It is to be remarked that the Hardy-Littlewood asymptotic formula for the number of representations of a large number as a sum of 4 squares and a prime was first proved (without assuming the Riemann hypothesis) by the reviewer [see Acta Arith. **1** (1935), 115–122]. C. Hooley [Acta Math. **97** (1957), 189–210; MR **19**, 532] first proved the H-L conjecture for the number of representations of a large number as a sum of two squares and a prime, assuming the Riemann hypothesis. (The latter formula is the same as the equation (1) of the preceding review with the "$>$" sign replaced by "$\sim$" (asymptotic equality) and Linnik's .979 by 1.)

*S. Chowla* (Boulder, Colo.)

Citations: MR 19, 532a = P36-17.

Referred to in M15-31, M55-75, N40-64, P36-32, R42-48.

## P36-26 (23# A130)

**Linnik, Ju. V.**

**An asymptotic formula in an additive problem of Hardy-Littlewood. (Russian)**

*Izv. Akad. Nauk SSSR Ser. Mat.* **24** (1960), 629–706.

The author proves that the number $Q(n)$ of representations of a large number $n$ as a sum of a prime and two squares $(n=p+\xi^2+\eta^2)$ is given by

$$(1)\quad Q(n) = \frac{\pi n}{\ln n} \prod_p \left\{1+\frac{\chi_4(p)}{p(p-1)}\right\} \times \prod_{p|n} \frac{(p-1)(p-\chi_4(p))}{p^2-p-\chi_4(p)}+R(n),$$

where $R(n)=O(n/(\ln n)^{1.028})$. Here $\chi_4$ is the non-principal character modulo 4. Noting that on the right side of (1), we have

$$\prod_{p|n} = O(\ln \ln n), \quad (\prod_{p|n})^{-1} = O(\ln \ln n),$$

we see that the first term on the right-side of (1) dominates the second.

The author's proof of a celebrated Hardy-Littlewood conjecture giving the asymptotic formula for $Q(n)$ is a great achievement in analytic number theory. Details of the proof are exceedingly heavy and difficult.

*S. Chowla* (Boulder, Colo.)

Referred to in E16-64, N32-32, P02-18, P32-63, P32-66, P36-27, P36-48, P36-49, P36-50, R14-57, Z10-22.

## P36-27 (24# A1265)

**Linnik, Ju. V.**

**Some additive problems. (Russian)**

*Mat. Sb.* (*N.S.*) **51 (93)** (1960), 129–154; *errata*, **53 (95)** (1961), 38.

In the present paper the author applies his "dispersion" method [Dokl. Akad. Nauk SSSR **120** (1958), 960–962; MR **21** #34; ibid. **123** (1958), 975–977; MR **20** #6400] to several very difficult additive problems which lie outside the scope of the Hardy-Littlewood method, for the most part even when the truth of the Riemann hypothesis is assumed. He obtains asymptotic formulae for the numbers of representations of an integer $n$ in the form (1) $n=x^2+y^2+pq$, where $x$, $y$ are integers, $p\in(\exp(\log\log n)^2, n^{1-\alpha})$ is prime and $q\in[1, n^\alpha]$ takes various forms; for instance, $q$ can be taken as prime ($\alpha$ is some constant satisfying $0<\alpha<\frac{1}{6}$). When $q>\exp(\log\log n)^2$ and is prime (Theorem 1), the author proves that the number of representations is, asymptotically,

$$\pi A_0 n \frac{\log\log n}{\log n} \prod_{p|n} \frac{(p-1)(p-\chi(p))}{p^2-p+\chi(p)},$$

where $A_0=\prod_p(1+\chi(p)/p(p-1))$ ($\chi$ being the non-principal character mod 4). The underlying structure of the argument is, very roughly, as follows: Let $P$ and $Q$ denote two sets of natural numbers containing respectively $L$ primes and $M$ integers; let $p$ run through the primes of $P$ and $q$ through the primes of $Q$. If $U(m)=4\sum_{d|m}\chi(d)$ denotes the number of solutions in $x$, $y$ of $x^2+y^2=m$, the number of solutions of (1) subject to $p\in P$, $q\in Q$ is given by $N(n)=\sum_{q\in Q}\sum_{p\in P} U(n-pq)$. To evaluate $N(n)$ asymptotically, it suffices to obtain a good estimate for $V(n)=\sum_{q\in Q}\{\sum_{p\in P} U(n-pq)-A(n,q)\}^2=\sum_{q\in Q} B_q^2$, say, where $A(n,q)$ denotes an asymptotic estimate of the number of solutions of (1) for fixed $q$ and $p\in P$. To see this, suppose that (2) $V(n)\ll L^2M(\log n)^{-K}$ has been proved, and let $\tau_r$ denote the number of $q\in Q$ such that (3) $rL(\log n)^{-K/10}<|B_q|\leq(r+1)L(\log n)^{-K/10}$; then, as in Tchebycheff's inequality in probability theory, $\tau_r\ll Mr^{-2}(\log n)^{-4K/5}$ and hence

$$|N(n)-\sum_{q\in Q} A(n,q)| \ll \sum_r \tau_r(r+1)L(\log n)^{-K/10} \ll LM(\log n)^{-K/2}\sum_r r^{-1}.$$

For suitable sets $P$, $Q$, this last expression turns out to be a genuine error term. The proof of estimate (2) is too complicated to describe here. To give just a bare indication, the first step is to drop the restriction on $q$ having to be prime (but to retain $2\nmid q$), and the most difficult part of the subsequent argument is the evaluation of

$$\sum_q\{\sum_p U(n-pq)\}^2,$$

readily seen to be the number of solutions in the $p_i$, $x_j$, $y_k$ of the Diophantine equation $p_1(x_1^2+y_1^2)-p_2(x_2^2+y_2^2)=n(p_1-p_2)$ with $p_i\in P$ and $(n-x_i^2-y_i^2)/p_i\in Q$. To find this number requires some intricate analysis and use of deep estimates for various types of trigonometric sums [see also the author, Izv. Akad. Nauk SSSR Ser. Mat. **24** (1960), 629–706; MR **23** #A130].

*H. Halberstam* (London)

Citations: MR 20# 6400 = P36-20; MR 21# 34 = N40-35; MR 23# A130 = P36-26.

Referred to in P52-13.

## P36-28 (24# A2572)

**Bredihin, B. M.**

**Binary additive problems with prime numbers. (Russian)**

*Dokl. Akad. Nauk SSSR* **142** (1962), 766–768.

Using the new "dispersion" method of Linnik (as expounded, for example, in his recent book, *The dispersion method in binary additive problems* (Russian) [Izdat. Leningrad. Univ., Leningrad, 1961]), the author obtains an asymptotic formula for large $n$ of the number of solutions in integers $x$, $y$ and primes $p$ such that (here $a$ is fixed) $p-x^2-y^2=a$ and $x^2+y^2 \leqq n$. In particular, there are infinitely many primes of the form $x^2+y^2+a$. (This striking result was previously proved by C. Hooley in Acta Math. **97** (1957), 189–210 [MR **19**, 532] only under the assumption of the Riemann hypothesis for all Dirichlet $L$-functions.)

*S. Chowla* (Boulder, Colo.)

Citations: MR 19, 532a = P36-17.

Referred to in P36-49.

## P36-29 (27# 121)

**Bredihin, B. M.**

**Binary additive problems of indeterminate type. II. Analogue of the problem of Hardy and Littlewood. (Russian)**

*Izv. Akad. Nauk SSSR Ser. Mat.* **27** (1963), 577–612.

Part I appeared in same Izv. **27** (1963), 439–462 [MR **26** #6149]. Using the "dispersion method" of Linnik the author gives full details for previously announced estimates of $Q(n)$, which represents the number of solutions of the equality $p-\xi^2-\eta^2=a$, where $\xi$, $\eta$ run over integers with $0<\xi^2+\eta^2 \leqq n$, $a$ is a fixed integer, and $p$ runs over primes. We have the following theorem: As $n \to \infty$

$$Q(n) = \pi \frac{n}{\log n} \prod_{p>2}\left(1+\frac{\chi_4(p)}{p^2-p}\right) \prod_{\substack{p \mid a \\ p \equiv 1(4)}} \frac{(p-1)^2}{p^2-p+1} \times \prod_{\substack{p \mid a \\ p \equiv 3(4)}} \frac{p^2-1}{p^2-p-1} + R(n),$$

where $R(n)=O(n(\log n)^{-1.042})$ and $\chi_4$ is the non-principal character (mod 4). A corollary is the long-sought result: There are infinitely many primes of the form $x^2+y^2+1$.

Two of the tools used in the long and difficult proof are the following. (1) Set

$$A(N) = \sum_{\substack{r \leqq N \\ r = xy}} 1,$$

where $1 \leqq x \leqq n_1$, $1 \leqq y \leqq n_2$, $N=n_1 n_2$ $(n_1, n_2 > 2)$. Then (Erdős)

$$A(N) < \frac{cN}{\log n_1 \log n_2} (\log N)(\log N)^{\gamma_0}(\log \log N)^3,$$

where $\gamma_0=(1+\log\log 2)/\log 2=.9141$. (2) The Hardy-Ramanujan estimate

$$\pi_k(x) < c_2 \frac{x}{\log x} \frac{(\log \log x)^{k-1}}{(k-1)!}$$

as long as $k<c_1 \log\log x$. *S. Chowla* (Boulder, Colo.)

Citations: MR 26# 6149 = P48-7.

Referred to in N40-48, P36-52.

## P36-30 (25# 2994)

**Crocker, Roger**

**A theorem concerning prime numbers.**

*Math. Mag.* **34** (1960/61), 316, 344.

Erdős proved the existence of an arithmetic progression consisting of odd numbers, no term of which is representable as the sum of a prime and a power of two [Summa Brasil. Math. **2** (1950), 113–123; MR **13**, 437; Mat. Lapok. **3** (1952), 122–128; MR **17**, 14]. The author gives another infinite sequence of such numbers: $2^{2^n}-5$, $n \geqq 3$. Further, he offers a conjecture concerning the number $P(k)$ which is the least value of $s$ for which it is true that every sufficiently large number can be represented as the sum of a prime and $s$ $k$th powers.

*T. Hayashida* (Yokohama)

Citations: MR 13, 437i = P36-5; MR 17, 14d = P36-13.

## P36-31 (25# 5045)

**Subhankulov, M. A.**

**Additive properties of certain sequences of numbers. (Russian)**

*Issled. po mat. analizu i mehanike v Uzbekistane, pp.* 220–241. *Izdat. Akad. Nauk Uzbek. SSR, Tashkent,* 1960.

The author uses the method of I. M. Vinogradov to obtain asymptotic formulae for the number of representations of a large positive integer $n$ in the forms

$$n = p+x_1^2+x_2^2+x_3^2, \qquad n = p+x^2+Q,$$

$$n = x^2+Q_1+Q_2, \qquad n = p_1+p_2+Q,$$

where $x$, $x_1$, $x_2$, $x_3$ are integers, $p$, $p_1$, $p_2$ are primes, and $Q$, $Q_1$, $Q_2$ are square-free numbers. For example, the number of solutions of the first equation is

$$\frac{2(\pi n)^{3/2}}{3\Gamma(3/2)\log n} \prod_{\substack{p \nmid n \\ p \geqq 3}} \left\{1-\frac{(-n/p)}{p(p-1)}\right\} + O\left(\frac{n^{3/2}\log\log n}{\log^2 n}\right).$$

*R. A. Rankin* (Glasgow)

## P36-32 (26# 1293)

**Bredihin, B. M.**

**Sharpening of the bound for the remainder term in Hardy-Littlewood type problems. (Russian. English summary)**

*Vestnik Leningrad. Univ.* **17** (1962), *no.* 19, 133–137.

G. H. Hardy and J. E. Littlewood conjectured about forty years ago that every large integer $n$ can be represented as the sum of a prime and two squares; they were, moreover, led by heuristic considerations to an asymptotic formula for the number $Q(n)$ of such representations. C. Hooley [Acta Math. **97** (1957), 189–210; MR **19**, 532] was able to establish the conjecture of Hardy and Littlewood on the assumption of the validity of the Riemann hypothesis, and more recently Ju. V. Linnik [Mat. Sb. (N.S.) **52 (94)** (1960), 661–700; MR **22** #10963; ibid. **53 (95)** (1961), 3–38; MR **22** #10964] succeeded in dispensing with this hypothesis. In the present note, the error term in Linnik's asymptotic formula for $Q(n)$, namely $O(n/(\log n)^{1.028})$, is improved to $O(n/(\log n)^{1.042})$. The method is based on a refinement of an argument due to Hooley [loc. cit.] and an idea of P. Erdős [Vestnik Leningrad. Univ. **15** (1960), no. 13, 41–49; MR **23** #A3720].

*L. Mirsky* (Sheffield)

Citations: MR 19, 532a = P36-17; MR 22# 10963 = P36-24; MR 22# 10964 = P36-25; MR 23# A3720 = N28-44.

Referred to in P36-48.

**P36-33** **(26# 2419 )**

**Bredihin, B. M.**

**Applications of the dispersion method in binary additive problems. (Russian)**

*Dokl. Akad. Nauk SSSR* **149** (1963), 9–11.

Let $Q(n)$ denote the number of solutions of $p-\varphi(\xi, \eta)=l$, where $p$ runs through primes, and $l$ is an arbitrary fixed integer different from zero, while $\varphi(\xi, \eta)=a\xi^2+b\xi\eta+c\eta^2$ is a fixed binary quadratic form whose discriminant is different from a square, while $\xi, \eta$ are restricted by $0<\varphi(\xi, \eta)\leqq n$. The author obtains a complicated expression as a lower bound for $Q(n)$, which has the following simple and striking consequence: There are infinitely many primes $p$ of the form

$$p = \varphi(\xi, \eta)+l.$$

His second theorem is concerned with the function $Q_1(n)$ which is the number of solutions of $n=p+xy$, where $p$ is a typical prime, and $x, y$ denote typical natural numbers. In this case his theorem states that

$$Q_1(n) = \frac{315\zeta(3)}{2\pi^4}\prod_{p|n}\frac{(p-1)^2}{p^2-p+1}\,n+O\left(\frac{n}{\log^{1-\varepsilon} n}\right)$$

($\varepsilon>0$, arbitrary). In the form ($\tau$ is the 'divisor' function) $Q_1(n)=\sum_{p<n}\tau(n-p)$, this function was discussed by Titchmarsh [Rend. Circ. Mat. Palermo **54** (1930), 414–429] and an asymptotic formula was obtained by Walfisz [Soobšč. Akad. Nauk Gruzin. SSR **14** (1953), 77–83; MR **15**, 935] under the assumption of the extended Riemann hypothesis. The present author makes no assumptions.

Finally, the author obtains asymptotic formulae for the number of solutions of $n=x_1x_2\cdots x_k+xy$ (where $x_1, \cdots, x_k, x, y$ denote natural numbers) for large $n$ (discussed by Ingham for $k=2$, and by Titchmarsh and Hooley for $k=3$).

The author has used the brilliant and deep methods of Ju. V. Linnik—the so-called "dispersion method". Details are promised. *S. Chowla* (Boulder, Colo.)

Citations: MR 15, 935g = N40-23.

Referred to in P48-9.

**P36-34** **(26# 2427 )**

**Selberg, Sigmund**

**A generalisation of a theorem of Romanoff.**

*Norske Vid. Selsk. Forh. (Trondheim)* **35** (1962), 91–95.

By use of the sieve of A. Selberg (details omitted), the author proves the following theorem. Let $h$ and $a\geqq 2$ be positive integers and $A$ the set $\{a^{1^h}, a^{2^h}, \cdots, a^{n^h}, \cdots\}$. Let $P$ be a set of primes satisfying $\sum_{p\leqq N} 1/p=(1/h)\log\log N+O(1)$, where the summation is over $p\in P$. Suppose $M$ is a set of positive integers, none divisible by any $p\in P$, and satisfying $\sum_{m\leqq N} 1>CN/(\log N)^{1/h}$ for all large $N$, where $C$ is a positive constant, and the summation is over $m\in M$. Then the set $M+A$ has positive density. From this result he derives Romanoff's theorem: The set of integers which can be represented in the form $p+a^i$, where $p$ is a prime, has positive asymptotic density. He proves further, that if $Q(x, y)$ is a positive definite quadratic form with integral coefficients, then the set of integers which can be written in the form $Q(x, y)+a^{i^2}$ ($x, y, i$ integers) has positive asymptotic density.

*D. G. Cantor* (Seattle, Wash.)

**P36-35** **(27# 3593 )**

**Rieger, G. J.**

**On linked binary representations of pairs of integers: some theorems of the Romanov type.**

*Bull. Amer. Math. Soc.* **69** (1963), 558–563.

The object of this paper is to generalize certain theorems due to Romanov. Let $N$ denote the set of natural numbers and $A_1(x, a)$ the number of solutions of the equations $m=p_1+v^a$, $n=p_2+v^a$ with $m<x$, $n<x$, $p_1$ and $p_2$ primes, $a, v\in N$, $a>1$. Then there exist constants $C_1(a)$, $C_2(a)$ such that $x>C_1(a)$ implies that $A_1(x, a)>C_2(a)x^2$. Let $A_2(x, a)$ be the number of solutions of the equations $m=p_1+a^v$, $n=p_2+a^v$, $m<x$, $n<x$, $p_1$ and $p_2$ primes, $a, v\in N$, $a>1$; then there exist constants $D_1(a)$, $D_2(a)$ such that $x>D_1(a)$ implies that $A_2(x, a)>D_2(a)\,x^2/\log x$. Generalizations to algebraic number fields are given.

*R. Ayoub* (University Park, Pa.)

**P36-36** **(29# 84 )**

**Rieger, G. J.**

**Über die Darstellbarkeit quadratfreier Zahlen als Summe einer Primzahl und des Quadrates einer quadratfreien Zahl.**

*Acta Arith.* **10** (1964/65), 1–7.

The author first proves the following generalization of Romanov's theorem: The sequence of square-free numbers which can be represented as a sum of a prime and the square of a natural number has a positive density. He is then able to replace the word "natural number" by "square-free number" in the above generalization. Finally it is shown that the density of the sequence of square-free numbers which can be written as a sum of a prime number from a fixed prime residue class modulo $k$ and the square of a square-free number is bigger than $C/\{\phi(k)\}^2$, where $C$ is a certain absolute positive constant and $\phi$ is Euler's totient function. *H. Gupta* (Chandigarh)

**P36-37** **(29# 86 )**

**Rieger, G. J.**

**Anwendung der Siebmethode auf einige Fragen der additiven Zahlentheorie. I.**

*J. Reine Angew. Math.* **214/215** (1964), 373–385.

In this paper the author applies the sieve method and thereby obtains generalizations of classical results. Let $A\{\ \}$ denote the number of elements in the set $\{\ \}$. Theorems of the following type are proved. Let $F(x)$ be a positive monotone increasing function tending to infinity with $x$, $F(x)\leqq\sqrt{\log x}$. Then there exists a constant $C(F, k)$ depending only on $F$ and $k$ and a positive constant $C(k)$ depending on $k$ such that for $x>C(F, k)$ we have

$$A\{m;\, m\leqq x,\, m = {x_1}^2+{x_2}^2+{x_3}^k,\, x_3\leqq F(x)\} < \frac{C(k)x^{F(x)}}{\sqrt{\log x}}.$$

Let $F(x)$ be a positive monotone increasing function tending to infinity with $x$, $F(x)/\log F(x)\leqq\log x$. Then there exists a constant $C(F)$ depending only on $F$ and an absolute constant $C$ such that for $x>C(F)$

$$A\{n;\, n\leqq x,\, n = p_1+p_2,\, p_1, p_2 \text{ primes},\, p_2\leqq F(x)\} > C\frac{x}{\log x}\frac{F(x)}{\log F(x)}.$$

*R. Ayoub* (University Park, Pa.)

Referred to in N28-54, P36-38, P36-39.

**P36-38** **(31# 131 )**

**Rieger, G. J.**

**Anwendung der Siebmethode auf einige Fragen der additiven Zahlentheorie. II.**

*Math. Nachr.* **28** (1964/65), 207–217.

In this paper the author applies sieve methods to the derivation of certain results in the additive theory of numbers. This is a continuation of the author's previous paper [J. Reine Angew. Math. **214/215** (1964), 373–385; MR **29** #86].

Typical of the kinds of results is the following theorem. Let $D$ be the set of all $n$ which have a prime factor $p \equiv 1 \pmod 4$. Let $F(\tau)$ be a positive and monotone increasing function (at least for large $\tau$) tending to $\infty$ with $\tau$ and satisfying $F(\tau)/\log^{1/2} F(\tau) \leqq \log \tau$. Then there exist constants $C_1$, depending on $F$, and $C_2$, absolute, such that for $x > C_1(F)$

$$A(n; n \leqq x, n = p+v, p \text{ prime}, v \in D, v < F(x)) > C_2 \frac{xF(x)}{\log x \log^{1/2} F(x)}.$$

Here $A(\ )$ denotes the counting function.

*R. Ayoub* (University Park, Pa.)

Citations: MR 29# 86 = P36-37.

## P36-39 (30# 1097 )

**Prachar, K.**

**Über Zahlen, die sich als Summe einer Primzahl und einer "kleinen" Potenz darstellen lassen.**

*Monatsh. Math.* **68** (1964), 409–420.

H. Davenport and H. Heilbronn [Proc. London Math. Soc. (2) **43** (1937), 142–151] proved that the number of positive integers $n \leqq N$ that are expressible as the sum of a prime and a $k$th power is $O(N/(\log N)^\alpha)$, where $\alpha = (1-2\varepsilon)k/(k+2)$, and furthermore if $n = p + m^k$, then $m$ can be chosen $< p/(\log p)^A$ for any positive $A$. The author improves on these results by proving the following results. The number of positive integers $n \leqq N$ expressible as $n = p + m^k$, $m < C \log p$, is greater than $cN$, where $c$ depends only on $C$. (This result was also proved by G. J. Rieger [J. Reine Angew. Math. **214/215** (1964), 373–385; MR **29** #86].) Assuming that the Riemann Hypothesis holds for all Dirichlet $L$-functions, then almost all integers $n$ can be expressed as $n = p + m^k$, $m < (\log p)^{c_1(k)}$, where $c_1(k)$ depends only on $k$, and all sufficiently large integers $n$ are expressible as $n = p_1 + p_2 + m^k$, $m < (\log n)^{c_2(k)}$, where $p_1, p_2$ are primes and $c_2(k)$ depends only on $k$. When $k = 1$, these last results can be found in A. Selberg [Arch. Math. Naturvid. **47** (1943), no. 6, 87–105; MR **7**, 48] and Ju. V. Linnik [Izv. Akad. Nauk SSSR Ser. Mat. **16** (1952), 503–520; MR **14**, 847]. The proofs rely on Linnik's estimates of exponential sums of the form $\sum \exp(2\pi i m^k \theta)$ and on the Davenport-Heilbronn treatment of the singular series.

*D. J. Lewis* (Ann Arbor, Mich.)

Citations: MR 7, 48e = N08-4; MR 14, 847b = P32-20; MR 29# 86 = P36-37.

Referred to in P36-41.

## P36-40 (30# 1099 )

**Bredihin, B. M.**

**Binary additive problems of indeterminate type. IV. The analogue of the generalized Hardy-Littlewood problem. (Russian)**

*Izv. Akad. Nauk SSSR Ser. Mat.* **28** (1964), 1409–1440.

Part III appeared in same Izv. **27** (1963), 777–794 [MR **27** #3611]. Consider the equation

$$(1) \qquad p - \varphi(\xi, \eta) = l,$$

where $l$ is a fixed non-zero integer, $p$ runs over primes and $\varphi(\xi, \eta) = a\xi^2 + b\xi\eta + c\eta^2$ is a fixed binary quadratic form which is not a square. Let $n$ be a large positive integer, while $\xi, \eta$ run over integers such that $0 < \varphi(\xi, \eta) \leqq n$. Let $Q(n)$ be the number of solutions of (1) subject to the above conditions. Generalizing special results previously obtained by the author, he proves (leaning, as before, on previous work of Hooley and Linnik, especially the "dispersion method" of the latter) the following theorem. Let $k = (a, b, c)$ and $(k, l) = 1$. Then, as $n \to \infty$,

$$Q(n) \geqq C(\varphi) \frac{1}{P_l} \prod_{p|2dl} \frac{(p-1)(p-\chi_d(p))}{p^2 - p + \chi_d(p)} \frac{n}{\log n} + R(n),$$

where $R(n) = O(n(\log n)^{-1.043})$,

$$C(\varphi) = \frac{w}{hkr^2} L(1, \chi_d) \prod_p \left(1 + \frac{\chi_d(p)}{p(p-1)}\right),$$

$$L(1, \chi_d) = \sum_{m=1}^{\infty} \frac{\chi_d(m)}{m};$$

$\chi_d(m)$ is Kronecker's symbol; $w = 2$ for $d > 4$, $w = 4$ for $d = 4$, $w = 6$ for $d = 3$ and $w = 1$ for $d < 0$. Also, $P_l$ is defined as follows. Write $\varphi(\xi, \eta) = k\varphi_0(\xi, \eta)$, $\varphi_0(\xi, \eta) = a_0\xi^2 + b_0\xi\eta + c_0\eta^2$, $-d = b_0^2 - 4a_0c_0$, where $-d = \pm 2^{\beta_0} p_1^{\beta_1} \cdots p_s^{\beta_s}$ ($\beta$'s $\geqq 1$). Then $P_l = 2^{2\lambda_0} p_1^{2\lambda_1} \cdots p_s^{2\lambda_s}$, where $\lambda_i = 0$ if $p_i | l$, $\lambda_i = 1$ if $p_i \nmid l$ ($i = 0, 1, \cdots, s$; $p_0 = 2$); $h$ is the number of primitive classes of binary quadratic forms of discriminant $-d$; finally $r = r_1 r_2 \cdots r_t$, where the $r_i$ are defined as in Chapter IX of Linnik's well-known book, *The dispersion method in binary additive problems* (Russian) [Izdat. Leningrad. Univ., Leningrad, 1961; MR **25** #3920].

As might be expected, the proof of this important and deep theorem is long and heavy. The author's style is clear and lucid.

*S. Chowla* (University Park, Pa.)

Citations: MR 25# 3920 = P02-18; MR 27# 3611 = N40-48.

Referred to in P36-43.

## P36-41 (30# 4742 )

**Prachar, K.**

**Über Zahlen, die sich als Summe einer Primzahl und einer "kleinen" Potenz darstellen lassen. II.**

*Monatsh. Math.* **69** (1965), 62–68.

The author proves that given a positive integer $k$, there exists a positive constant $\lambda$ such that almost all positive integers $n$ can be expressed in the form $n = p + m^k$, where $p$ is a prime and $m$ is a positive integer with $m^k < p^{1-\lambda}$. Previously, the author [same Monatsh. **68** (1964), 409–420; MR **30** #1097] proved this same result under the assumption that the Riemann hypothesis for $L$-functions is true. He now dispenses with this assumption. The proof involves exponential sums and is based on ideas and techniques of Linnik [Mat. Sb. (N.S.) **32 (74)** (1953), 3–60; MR **15**, 602], Davenport and Heilbronn [Proc. London Math. Soc. (2) **43** (1937), 142–151] and the author's earlier paper. The author indicates that his methods also imply that almost all positive integers are expressible as $n = p + p_1$, where $p, p_1$ are primes and $p_1 < p^{1-\lambda}$ for some fixed constant $\lambda$. Every sufficiently large integer is expressible as $n = p_1 + p_2 + p_3$ with $p_3 < n^{1-\lambda}$ for some fixed constant $\lambda$.

*D. J. Lewis* (Ann Arbor, Mich.)

Citations: MR 15, 602j = P36-8; MR 30# 1097 = P36-39.

## P36-42 (32# 101 )

**Kalecki, M.**

**On numbers which are sums of prime numbers of a certain type. (Polish. English summary)**

*Prace Mat.* **9** (1965), 193–200.

Denote by $p_i$ the $i$th prime number, by $Q_1$ the set of all $p_{i+1}$, $i = 1, 2, 3, \cdots$, and by $Q_s$ the set of numbers (1) $p_{i+1} + q$, where $q \in Q_{s-1}$ and $q \leqq p_{i+2} - p_{i+1} + 3s - 5$, $i = 1, 2, 3, \cdots$. Theorem 1: Every number $q \in Q_s$ ($s \geqq 2$) can be represented in the form (1) in one way only. Theorem 2: For each $s$ there exists an integer $A_s$ such that all natural numbers $n$ satisfying the conditions $n \equiv s \pmod 2$ and $3s-2<n \leqq A_s$ belong to the set $Q_s$, whereas $A_s+2$ does not. $A_s$ is determined by the relations $A_1=7$, $A_s=p_a+A_{s-1}$, $\delta_{\max}(p_a)+3s-5 \leqq A_{s-1}<p_{a+1}-p_a+3s-5$, where $\delta_{\max}(x)$ denotes the greatest difference of two consecutive primes not exceeding $x$. Corollary 1: $A_1=7$, $A_2=96$, $A_3=370357$, $A_t \geqq (A_3-10)2^{t-3}+3t+1$, $t=3, 4, \cdots$. Corollary 2: All natural numbers $n$ such that $n \equiv s \pmod 2$ and $3s-2<n \leqq A_s$ are sums of $s$ odd prime numbers. Applying to Corollary 2 the well-known theorem of Vinogradov on representation of odd numbers equal to or greater than a certain constant $B$ as a sum of three primes, the author develops Corollary 3: There exists a constant $s_0$ such that the natural numbers $n$ satisfying the conditions $n \equiv s_0 \pmod 2$ and $n>3s_0-2$ are sums of $s_0$ odd primes. Theorem 3: Denote by $\pi^{(s)}(x)$ the number of numbers $q \in Q_s$ not exceeding $x$, and by $\log_s x$ the $s$th iterated logarithm. Then the following relation holds:

$$c^{-1}(N/\log_s N)(1+o(1)) \leqq \pi^{(s)}(N) \leqq (N/\log_s N)(1+o(1)), \quad N \to \infty,$$

where $c$ is a positive constant independent of $s$ and $\leqq 1$. To prove Theorem 3, the author applies a theorem by K. Prachar [Monatsh. Math. **58** (1954), 114–116; MR **16**, 114]. Theorem 4: Denote by $w(n)$ the smallest $s$ for which $n \in Q_s$, and by $v(n)$ the number determined by the relations $v(n) \equiv n \pmod 2$, $A_{v(n)-2}<n \leqq A_{v(n)}$ (assuming $A_{-1}=1$, $A_0=4$). Then it follows that $w(n) \leqq v(n)$ and $\limsup w(N)=\infty$. *J. W. Andrushkiw* (S. Orange, N.J.)

Citations: MR 16, 114d = N08-19.

## P36-43 (32# 5618)

**Bredihin, B. M.**

**The dispersion method and binary additive problems of definite type. (Russian)**

*Uspehi Mat. Nauk* **20** (1965), *no.* 2 (122), 89–130.

Let $k \geqq 2$, $l \neq 0$ be fixed integers; $d_k(m)$ the number of representations of the positive integer $m$ as a product of $k$ factors, so that $d(m)=d_2(m)$ is the number of divisors of $m$. Let $p$ always denote a prime. After a general introduction the author proceeds, in §§ 3 and 4, to the consideration of asymptotic formulae, as $n \to \infty$, for the sums:

(1) $\sum_{p<n} d(n-p)$; (2) $\sum_{0<p-l<n} d(p-l)$;

(3) $\sum_{m<n} d_k(m)\, d(n-m)$; (4) $\sum_{0<m-l<n} d_k(m)\, d(m-l)$.

Early discussions of these sums were heuristic, or based on unproved hypotheses, or confined to special cases. By the use of Linnik's dispersion method, as developed in his book [*The dispersion method in binary additive problems* (Russian), Leningrad. Gos. Univ., Leningrad, 1961; MR **25** #3920; English translation, Amer. Math. Soc., Providence, R.I., 1963; MR **29** #5804], rigorous general solutions of the "indefinite" problems (2) and (4) have been given, in part by Linnik himself and in part by others (including the author) using his method. The author now applies the same method to the "definite" problems (1) and (3). {The classification seems to be based on the interpretation of the relevant sum as the number of solutions of the "definite" equation $\alpha+\beta=n$, or the "indefinite" equation $\alpha-\beta=l$, where $\alpha$ and $\beta$ run through specified sets of (equal or distinct) positive integers.} In § 5 the author turns to problems arising out of the equation $p+x^2+y^2=n$. The Hardy-Littlewood heuristic asymptotic formula for the number $Q(n)$ of solutions was proved by Linnik with the help of his dispersion method (see Chapter VII of the book mentioned above). The author now uses the same method to obtain a lower estimate of $Q(n)$ when $x^2+y^2$ is replaced by a more general binary quadratic form $\varphi(x, y)$; this follows the lines of his previous work on the "indefinite" problem of $p-\varphi(x, y)=l$ [Izv. Akad. Nauk SSSR Ser. Mat. **28** (1964), 1409–1440; MR **30** #1099].

The paper assumes an intimate knowledge of the dispersion method, and of results and methods taken from a large number of papers. Arguments often take the form of instructions to carry out "simple calculations" or to make suitable modifications in methods used elsewhere (largely in the author's own papers). A reader who sets out to present a self-contained account of any of these problems will have to fill in many details.

{The name C. Hooley is misspelt as C. Hooly and unsuitably transliterated as С. Хооли; a better version would be К. (or Х.) Хули.}

{This article has appeared in English translation [Russian Math. Surveys **20** (1965), no. 2, 85–125].}

*A. E. Ingham* (Cambridge, England)

Citations: MR 25# 3920 = P02-18; MR 29# 5804 = P02-19; MR 30# 1099 = P36-40.

Referred to in N48-34, P36-66.

## P36-44 (32# 5620)

**Erdős, P.**

**On a problem of Sierpiński.**

*Acta Arith.* **11** (1965), 189–192.

Let $f_1(s)=\max\{N|N$ is not the sum of $s$ distinct primes$\}$, $f_2(s)=\max\{N|N$ is not the sum of $s$ positive integers which are relatively prime in pairs and are either primes or squares of primes$\}$, $f_3(s)=\max\{N|N$ is not the sum of $s$ integers (each $>1$) which are relatively prime in pairs$\}$. Clearly $f_3(s) \leqq f_2(s) \leqq f_1(s)$. Sierpiński [Enseignement Math. (2) **10** (1964), 229–234; MR **29** #2215] showed $f_3(2)=6$, $f_3(3)=17$, $f_3(4)=30$. Let $A(s)$ be the sum of the first $s$ primes and $B(s)=A(s+1)-2$. The author sketches proofs of the following. (I) There exists a large absolute constant $C_1$ (independent of $s$) such that $f_1(s)<A(s)+C_1 s\log s$; (II) there exists a large absolute constant $C_2$ (independent of $s$) such that $f_2(s)<B(s)+C_2$; (III) $f_3(s) \geqq B(s)-2$.

*D. J. Lewis* (Ann Arbor, Mich.)

Citations: MR 29# 2215 = B28-20.

## P36-45 (33# 4029)

**Bredihin, B. M.; Linnik, Ju. V.**

**Asymptotic behavior in the general Hardy-Littlewood problem. (Russian)**

*Dokl. Akad. Nauk SSSR* **168** (1966), 975–977.

By means of his dispersion method, Linnik solved the Hardy-Littlewood problem concerning the representation of numbers $n$ in the form $n=p+x^2+y^2$. In Chapter IX of his book on the dispersion method [*The dispersion method in binary additive problems* (Russian), Izdat. Leningrad. Univ., Leningrad, 1961; MR **25** #3920; English translation, Amer. Math. Soc., Providence, R.I., 1963; MR **29** #5804] he also gave an outline of the solution for the generalized problem $n=p+\varphi(x, y)$, where $\varphi$ is a binary quadratic form. However, it was pointed out that the method does not lead immediately to an asymptotic formula for the number of solutions. In the present paper, it is shown that by the dispersion method one can actually obtain such a formula for primitive forms with a negative discriminant $-2^\alpha P$, $\alpha=0$, 2 or 3, $P$ odd and square-free.

{This article has appeared in English translation [Soviet Math. Dokl. **7** (1966), 940–943].}

*H.-E. Richert* (Marburg)

Citations: MR 25# 3920 = P02-18; MR 29# 5804 = P02-19.

Referred to in P36-55.

**P36-46** **(33# 5556)**

**Lu Ming-gao [Lu Ming-kao]; Chen Wen-de [Ch'en Wen-te]**

**On the solution of systems of linear equations with prime variables.**

*Acta Math. Sinica* **15** (1965), 731–748 (*Chinese*); *translated as Chinese Math.—Acta* **7** (1965), 461–479.

Let $a_{ik}$ $(i=1, \cdots, n;\ k=1, \cdots, n+1)$ be integers. The authors ask for prime number solutions $p_k$ of the linear system (*) $\sum_{k=1}^{n+1} a_{ik}p_k = b_i$ $(i=1, \cdots, n)$ for almost all sets of positive integers $(b_1, \cdots, b_n)$. There are several restrictions on the matrix of coefficients $(a_{ik})$. One of them is as follows: Let

$$\Delta_n^k = (-1)^{n+1-k}\begin{vmatrix} a_{11}\cdots a_{1,k-1} & a_{1,k+1}\cdots a_{1,n+1} \\ \cdot & \\ \cdot & \\ \cdot & \\ a_{n1}\cdots a_{n,k-1} & a_{n,k+1}\cdots a_{n,n+1}\end{vmatrix}.$$

Then $\Delta_n^k \neq 0$ $(k=1, \cdots, n+1)$ and $(\Delta_n^1, \cdots, \Delta_n^{n+1})=1$.

Let $P$ be a sufficiently large natural number, $c>0$ a constant, and $X=cP$. The set of natural numbers $(b_1, \cdots, b_n)$ with $1 \leqq b_i \leqq X$ $(i=1, \cdots, n)$ is called "nonsingular" if the following conditions are satisfied: (1) the number $S_1(p)$ of systems of solutions of the system of congruences $\sum_{k=1}^{n+1} a_{ik}l_k \equiv b_i \pmod p$ $(i=1, \cdots, n)$ in natural numbers $1 \leqq l_k \leqq p-1$ $(k=1, \cdots, n+1)$ is positive for all primes $p$; (2) $B(a_{ik}, b_i) \neq 0$, where $B$ is a product of determinants and greatest common divisors of determinants, the determinants depending on $a_{ik}$ and $b_i$. Denote the number of nonsingular sets in $[1, X]$ by $Y(X)$. Let $I(b_1, \cdots, b_n; P)$ be the number of systems of solutions of (*) with $2 \leqq p_k \leqq P$ $(k=1, \cdots, n+1)$. Under the assumptions on the matrix of coefficients $(a_{ik})$, the authors prove the following results. Theorem 1: There exists $0<c_1<1$ such that $Y(X)>c_1X^n$. Theorem 2: Let $M>0$ be arbitrarily given. The number $R(P)$ of nonsingular sets in $[1, X]$ with $I(b_1, \cdots, b_n; P)=0$ satisfies $R(P) \ll X^n(\log P)^{-M}$. These theorems generalize results of A. F. Lavrik [Trudy Mat. Inst. Steklov. **64** (1961), 90–125; MR **28** #69]. For the proofs, the authors apply I. M. Vinogradov's method of trigonometric sums. Their work is related to a paper by Wu Fang [Acta Math. Sinica **7** (1957), 102–122]. *Werner G. H. Schaal* (Marburg)

Citations: MR 28# 69 = P40-12.

**P36-47** **(34# 5769)**

**Bredihin, B. M.; Linnik, Ju. V.**

**Asymptotic behavior and ergodic properties of solutions of the generalized Hardy-Littlewood equation.** (Russian)

*Mat. Sb.* (*N.S.*) **71** (**113**) (1966), 145–161.

Let $\varphi(\xi, \eta)$ be a positive primitive quadratic form, with discriminant $D$ not a square. Put $Q(n)$ for the number of solutions of the equation $p+\varphi(\xi, \eta)=n$ in primes $p$ and integers $\xi, \eta$. Denote by $K(\sqrt{d})$ the quadratic field corresponding to $\varphi(\xi, \eta)$. Let $h$ be the class-number of $K(\sqrt{d})$. Let $\varepsilon_0$ be the least positive root of the equation $1/h - 2\varepsilon \ln 2 - \varepsilon + \varepsilon \ln \varepsilon = 0$. Then $Q(n) = C_\varphi(n)A_D(n)n(\ln n)^{-1} + O(n(\ln n)^{-1-\gamma})$, where $\gamma = \min(\varepsilon_1, 0.042)$, $0<\varepsilon_1<\varepsilon_0 \ln 2$. $A_D(n)$ and $C_\varphi(n)$ are two very complicated expressions, $c_0(\ln\ln n)^{-1} < A_D(n) < c_1 \ln\ln n$, $C_\varphi(n) \geqq c_2 > 0$. The constants $c_0, c_1, c_2$ depend only on the quadratic form $\varphi(\xi, \eta)$.

Let $w$ be the number of units in $K(\sqrt{d})$. Denote by $\tilde{Q}(n)/w$ the number of solutions of the equation $p+N(\mathfrak{a})=n$ in primes $p$ and integer ideals $\mathfrak{a}$ belonging to a given genus. Then $\tilde{Q}(n) = t_0C_\varphi(n)A_D(n)n(\ln n)^{-1} + O(n(\ln n)^{-1.042})$, where $t_0$ is the class-number of the genus. *J. Kubilius* (Vilnius)

Referred to in P36-68.

**P36-48** **(34# 5785)**

**Bredihin, B. M.; Linnik, Ju. V.**

**Binary additive problems with ergodic properties of the solutions.** (Russian)

*Dokl. Akad. Nauk SSSR* **166** (1966), 1267–1269.

Denote by $Q(n)$ the number of solutions of the Hardy-Littlewood equation (*) $p+\xi^2+\eta^2=n$ in primes $p$ and integers $\xi, \eta$. The authors have proved [the second author, Izv. Akad. Nauk SSSR Ser. Mat. **24** (1960), 629–706; MR **23** #A130; the first author, Vestnik Leningrad. Univ. **17** (1962), no. 19, 133–137; MR **26** #1293] the asymptotic formula $Q(n) = AB(n)S_K(n)(\ln n)^{-1} + O(n(\ln n)^{-1.042})$, where $A = \prod_{p>2}(1+\chi_4(p)/p(p-1))$,

$$B(n) = \prod_{p\mid n}(p-1)(p-\chi_4(p))/(p^2-p+\chi_4(p)),$$

$\chi_4(n)$ is the non-principal character modulo 4, and $S_K(n)=\pi n$ is the area of the circle $K$ with radius $n^{1/2}$.

In this paper the authors generalize this result. Let $\Omega$ be a region in $K$ of area $S_\Omega(n)$ and let $Q_\Omega(n)$ be the number of solutions of (*) such that $(\xi, \eta) \in \Omega$. Consider a sector $\Delta$ in $K$ with angle $\psi$, where $c_1(\ln\ln n)^{-1/2+\eta_1} \leqq \psi \leqq 2\pi$, $c_1$ a positive constant and $\eta_1$ a small positive constant. Then

$$Q_\Delta(n) = AB(n)S_\Delta(n)(1+O(\psi^{-1}(\ln\ln n)^{-1/2+\eta}))(\ln n)^{-1},$$

$0<\eta<\min(\frac{1}{2}, \eta_1)$.

From this estimate, the authors deduce a similar result in case $\Omega$ is a starlike domain bounded by a smooth contour $r=r(\varphi)$, $0 \leqq \varphi < 2\pi$, $n^{1/2}(\ln n)^{-0.04} \leqq r \leqq n^{1/2}$, $|dr/d\varphi| \leqq c_2n^{1/2}$. Then $Q_\Omega(n) = AB(n)S_\Omega(n)(1+O((\ln\ln n)^{\eta-\eta_1})) \times (\ln n)^{-1}$.

A similar result can be obtained for the generalized Hardy-Littlewood equation $p+\varphi(\xi, \eta)=n$, where $\varphi(\xi, \eta)$ is a positive quadratic form.

{This article has appeared in English translation [Soviet Math. Dokl. **7** (1966), 254–257].}

See also #5786 below. *J. Kubilius* (Vilnius)

Citations: MR 23# A130 = P36-26; MR 26# 1293 = P36-32.

Referred to in P36-54, P36-55, P36-67.

**P36-49** **(34# 5786)**

**Poljanskiĭ, A. A.**

**Solution of the Hardy-Littlewood problem and its indeterminate analogue in sectors and contours.** (Russian)

*Dokl. Akad. Nauk SSSR* **168** (1966), 25–27.

Denote by $Q(n)$ the number of representations of a large integer $n$ as a sum of a prime and two squares: (1) $n = p+\xi^2+\eta^2$. For any fixed integer $l \neq 0$, let $S(n)$ be the number of solutions of the equation (2) $p-\xi^2-\eta^2=l$ in primes $p$ and integers $\xi, \eta$ satisfying the inequality $\xi^2+\eta^2 \leqq n$. Ju. V. Linnik [Izv. Akad. Nauk SSSR Ser. Mat. **24** (1960), 629–706; MR **23** #A130] has proved an asymptotic formula for $Q(n)$. Using Linnik's method, B. M. Bredihin [Dokl. Akad. Nauk SSSR **142** (1962), 766–768; MR **24** #A2572] has done the same for $S(n)$.

The author considers the number of solutions of (1) and (2) with the additional condition that $(\xi, \eta)$ belong to a circular sector. Let $Q_{\Delta\varphi}(n)$ and $S_{\Delta\varphi}(n)$ be the numbers of solutions of (1) and (2) correspondingly satisfying the conditions $\xi^2+\eta^2 \leqq n$, $\varphi_1 \leqq \arg(\xi+i\eta) \leqq \varphi_2$, where $\varphi_2-\varphi_1 = \Delta\varphi \leqq 2\pi$. Let $\varepsilon$ be a positive number, $0<\varepsilon<\Delta\varphi/(2\pi)$, and let $b$ be some integer, $(b, l)=1$, $(b, n)=1$, which depends on $\varepsilon$, $\Delta\varphi$, $n$, and for (2), $b=O(\ln^K n)$, where $K=K(\varepsilon, \Delta\varphi)$ is a positive constant. Then $Q_{\Delta\varphi}(n) \geqq (\Delta\varphi/2\pi - \varepsilon)Q(n)/b$, $S_{\Delta\varphi}(n) \geqq (\Delta\varphi/2\pi - \varepsilon)S(n)/b$.

Asymptotic formulas for $Q_{\Delta\varphi}(n)$ and $S_{\Delta\varphi}(n)$ have been obtained by B. M. Bredihin and Ju. V. Linnik [#5785 above] using another method.

{This article has appeared in English translation [Soviet Math. Dokl. **7** (1966), 588–591].} *J. Kubilius* (Vilnius)

Citations: MR 23# A130 = P36-26; MR 24# A2572 = P36-28.

Referred to in P36-68.

## P36-50 (34# 5788)

**Elliott, P. D. T. A.; Halberstam, H.**

**Some applications of Bombieri's theorem.**

*Mathematika* **13** (1966), 196–203.

The authors show how the remarkable result of E. Bombieri [Mathematika **12** (1965), 201–225; MR **33** #5590],

(*) $\sum_k \max|\pi(y, k, l) - (1/\phi(k)) \operatorname{li} y| \ll n(\log n)^{-\delta}$,

where the max is taken over all $y \leqq n$ and $(l, k) = 1$, the sum over all $k \leqq n^{1/2}(\log n)^{-B}$, $\delta > 0$ is arbitrary and $B = B(\delta)$, can be applied to provide asymptotic formulas for expressions of the type $S = \sum_{p<n} \sum_{d|(n-p)} f(d)$, where $p$ runs through primes and $f(d)$ is some arithmetic function. A classical example of such a problem is that of finding an asymptotic formula for the number of representations of natural $n$ as $n = p + x^2 + y^2$. A complete solution of this problem was given by Ju. V. Linnik [Izv. Akad. Nauk SSSR Ser. Mat. **24** (1960), 629–706; MR **23** #A130] after C. Hooley had solved it [Acta Math. **97** (1957), 189–210; MR **19**, 532] under the generalized Riemann hypothesis. Splitting $S$ into three sums $S_1, S_2, S_3$, according to $d \leqq n^{1/2}(\log n)^{-c}$, $n^{1/2}(\log n)^{-c} < d < n^{1/2}(\log n)^c$, $d \geqq n^{1/2}(\log n)^c$, the authors observe that (*) enables one to evaluate $S_1$ asymptotically, and to estimate $S_3$ satisfactorily, in a great variety of cases. Also, they point out that in some cases the contribution of $S_2$ can be estimated crudely. Although the latter cannot be done in the $n = p + x^2 + y^2$ situation, the authors note that Hooley used the generalized Riemann hypothesis only for the sake of estimation of $S_1$ and $S_3$, whence they conclude that (*) makes his proof free of any hypothesis. *S. Knapowski* (Coral Gables, Fla.)

Citations: MR 19, 532a = P36-17; MR 23# A130 = P36-26; MR 33# 5590 = M55-43.

Referred to in N24-80, P48-14, P48-17, P48-24.

## P36-51 (34# 7485)

**Vinogradov, A. I.**

**General Hardy-Littlewood equation.** (Russian)

*Mat. Zametki* **1** (1967), 189–197.

Mittels der Dispersionsmethode von Ju. V. Linnik [*The dispersion method in binary additive problems* (Russian), Izdat. Leningrad. Univ., Leningrad, 1961; MR **25** #3920; English translation, Amer. Math. Soc., Providence, R.I., 1963; MR **29** #5804] wurde erstmals die Lösbarkeit der Gleichung $n = p + x^2 + y^2$, allgemeiner von $n = p + ax^2 + by^2$ bewiesen; auch wurden asymptotische Formeln für die Lösungsanzahlen gefunden. Hier werden diese Ergebnisse verfeinert. Der Verfasser betrachtet für imaginärquadratische Körper die Gleichung $n = p + N(\alpha)$ in Primzahlen $p$ und idealen Zahlen $\alpha$ der Klasse $C$ mit $\arg \alpha \in S$, ein Sektor der Öffnung $\theta$. Für die zugehörige Lösungsanzahl $Q = Q(n, C, S)$ beweist er $Q(n, C, S) = (\theta/h)\sigma(n, C)\pi(n) + O(\pi(n)/\log^\gamma n)$. Dabei bezeichnen $\pi(n)$, wie üblich, die Anzahl der Primzahlen $\leqq n$, $h$ die Klassenzahl, $\sigma(n, C)$ eine singuläre Reihe und $\gamma$ ($>0$) eine absolute Konstante. *H.-E. Richert* (Marburg)

Citations: MR 25# 3920 = P02-18; MR 29# 5804 = P02-19.

Referred to in E20-88, P36-68.

## P36-52 (35# 1563)

**Poljanskiĭ, A. A.**

**Estimate of the number of solutions in sectors of equations of Hardy-Littlewood type.** (Russian. Lithuanian and German summaries)

*Litovsk. Mat. Sb.* **6** (1966), 257–269.

Seien $n$ und $l$ feste natürliche Zahlen. Untersucht werden die Lösungsanzahlen $Q_{\Delta\varphi}^{(1)}(n)$ und $Q_{\Delta\varphi}^{(2)}(n)$ der Gleichungen (*) $p + \xi^2 + \eta^2 = n$ bzw. (**) $p - \xi^2 - \eta^2 = n$ ($p$ Primzahl; $\xi$, $\eta$ ganz, $\xi^2 + \eta^2 \leqq n$), bei denen der Gitterpunkt $(\xi, \eta)$ in einem gegebenen Sektor mit dem Öffnungswinkel $\Delta\varphi$ liegt. Im klassischen Fall ($\Delta\varphi = 2\pi$) wurden asymptotische Aussagen von Ju. V. Linnik [*The dispersion method in binary additive problems* (Russian), Izdat. Leningrad. Univ., Leningrad, 1961; MR **25** #3920; English translation, Amer. Math. Soc., Providence, R.I., 1963; MR **29** #5804] bzw. von B. M. Bredihin [Izv. Akad. Nauk SSSR Ser. Mat. **27** (1963), 577–612; MR **27** #121] gewonnen. Mit deren Hilfe wird in der vorliegenden Arbeit bewiesen, dass es für gegebenes $\varepsilon > 0$ und $\Delta\varphi$ Zahlen $B_1 > 0$, $B_2 > 0$ (mit gewissen Bedingungen) gibt, so dass für hinreichend grosse $n$ die Ungleichungen $Q_{\Delta\varphi}^{(i)}(n) \geqq (\Delta\varphi/2 - \varepsilon)B_i^{-1}Q_{2\pi}^{(i)}(n)$ ($i = 1, 2$) gelten. Insbesondere folgt daraus, dass (*) für alle hinreichend grossen $n$ Lösungen besitzt und dass (**) bei festem $l$ von unendlich vielen Primzahlen erfüllt wird, beides mit Gitterpunkten $(\xi, \eta)$ aus einem gegebenen Sektor.

Beim Beweis werden zunächst mit Hilfe der Linnikschen Dispersionsmethode untere Schranken für die entsprechenden Lösungsanzahlen der Gleichungen $p \pm B_i(\xi^2 + \eta^2) = n$ ($i = 1, 2$) hergeleitet. *B. Volkmann* (Stuttgart)

Citations: MR 25# 3920 = P02-18; MR 27# 121 = P36-29; MR 29# 5804 = P02-19.

## P36-53 (36# 1409)

**Babaev, G.; Subhankulov, M. A.**

**An asymptotic formula for two additive problems.** (Russian)

*Tadžik. Gos. Univ. Učen. Zap.* **26** (1963), *vyp.* 1, 49–68.

By the well-known Hardy-Littlewood-Vinogradov method, the authors prove asymptotic formulas for the number of solutions of the equations $n = p_1 + p_2 + q$ and $n = p + q_1 + q_2$, with primes $p$ and square-free numbers $q$.

These results, however, may be deduced (with better remainder terms) from the asymptotic formula for the number of solutions of $n = p + q$; A. Z. Val'fiš [Math. Z. **40** (1935), 592–607] and L. Mirsky [Amer. Math. Monthly **56** (1949), 17–19; MR **10**, 431] derived this formula by elementary considerations from the prime number theorem. *W. Schwarz* (Freiburg)

Citations: MR 10, 431e = P36-2.

## P36-54 (37# 178)

**Babaev, G.**

**Further development of the ergodic method.** (Russian. Tajiki summary)

*Dokl. Akad. Nauk Tadžik. SSR* **11** (1968), *no.* 2, 14–15.

Using "ergodicity" results of B. M. Bredihin and Ju. V. Linnik [Dokl. Akad. Nauk SSSR **166** (1966), 1267–1269; MR **34** #5785] as a point of entry upon the Hardy-Littlewood problem concerning asymptotic formulas for the number of solutions to the diophantine equation $n = p + x^2 + y^2$ ($p$ is prime), the author estimates the number of solutions in prescribed sectors for the diophantine equation $n = p + ax^2 + bxy + cy^2$ ($a > 0$ and $p$ is prime) for all sufficiently large $n$. That estimate is expressed in terms of the total number of solutions and the arc tan of a simple function of the discriminant of the binary quadratic form considered. No proof is given.

*A. A. Mullin* (Forest Hill, Md.)

Citations: MR 34# 5785 = P36-48.

**P36-55** **(37# 2709 )**

**Babaev, G.**

**Solution in sectors of a generalized Hardy-Littlewood problem. (Russian)**

*Dokl. Akad. Nauk SSSR* **175** (1967), 263–265.

Let $\varphi(x, y)=Ax^2+Bxy+Cy^2$ be a primitive quadratic form with negative discriminant $-d$ which is free of odd squares and either $-d=-4\mathscr{D}$, $-\mathscr{D}\equiv 2, 3 \bmod 4$ or $-d=-\mathscr{D}$, $-\mathscr{D}\equiv 1 \bmod 4$.

B. M. Bredihin and Ju. V. Linnik [same Dokl. **168** (1966), 975–977; MR **33** #4029] have proved an asymptotic formula for the number $Q(n)$ of solutions of the equation (*) $\varphi(x, y)+p=n$ in primes $p$ and integers $x, y$. The author gives an outline of the proof of an asymptotic formula for the number $Q_\Delta(n)$ of solutions of the equation (*) satisfying the inequalities $0\leqq\psi_1\leqq\arg(x+iy)\leqq\psi_2\leqq 2\pi$, where $\psi_1$ and $\psi_2$ are fixed numbers and the interval $[\psi_1, \psi_2]$ does not contain the points $\pi/2$, $3\pi/2$ and the points $w$ for which $\operatorname{tg} w=-2A/B$ for $B\neq 0$. He proves that for $n\to\infty$,

$$Q_\Delta(n) = Q(n)(\operatorname{arctg} S(\psi_2)-\operatorname{arctg} S(\psi_1))/(2\pi) + O(Q(n)(\log\log n)^{\eta-1/2}),$$

where $S(\psi)=d^{1/2}\operatorname{tg}\psi/(2A+B\operatorname{tg}\psi)$ and $\eta$ is a fixed number, $0<\eta<\frac{1}{2}$.

An asymptotic formula for $Q_\Delta(n)$ has been obtained by B. M. Bredihin and Ju. V. Linnik [ibid. **166** (1966), 1267–1269; MR **34** #5785] in case $\varphi(x, y)=x^2+y^2$.

{This article has appeared in English translation [Soviet Math. Dokl. **8** (1967), 821–823].} *J. Kubilius* (Vilnius)

Citations: MR 33# 4029 = P36-45; MR 34# 5785 = P36-48.

**P36-56** **(37# 5176 )**

**Poljanskiĭ, A. A.**

**An analogue of the Hardy-Littlewood equation. (Russian)**

*Dokl. Akad. Nauk SSSR* **180** (1968), 29–31.

Using his dispersion method, Linnik dealt with the number of representations of a number $n$ in the form (1) $n=x^2+y^2+p_1p_2$, where $p_1$, $p_2$ denote primes, and he proved an asymptotic formula for the number of solutions of equation (1) subject to the conditions $p_i>\exp(\ln\ln n)^2$, $i=1, 2$ [cf. Ju. V. Linnik, *The dispersion method in binary additive problems* (Russian), Izdat. Leningrad. Univ., Leningrad, 1961; MR **25** #3920; English translation, Amer. Math. Soc., Providence, R.I., 1963; MR **29** #5804]. The present author shows that the restrictions on $p_1$, $p_2$ can be removed. He also proves an asymptotic formula for the number of solutions of the equation $n=ap+b(x^2+y^2)$, where $(a, b)=1$, $(ab, 2n)=1$, $a=O(\exp(\ln n)^\alpha)$, $b=O(\ln^c n)$.

{This article has appeared in English translation [Soviet Math. Dokl. **9** (1968), 587–590].}

*H.-E. Richert* (Marburg)

Citations: MR 25# 3920 = P02-18; MR 29# 5804 = P02-19.

Referred to in P36-68.

**P36-57** **(38# 5707 )**

**Crocker, Roger**

**A theorem in additive number theory.**

*Colloq. Math.* **20** (1969), 53–56.

The author proves that for each fixed integer $k\geqq 2$, there is an infinity of positive odd integers neither representable as the sum of a prime and a positive power of 2, nor representable as the sum of a prime and the $k$th power of a positive integer. The elementary method used involves the construction of an appropriate "overlapping" congruence system. *K. S. Williams* (Ottawa, Ont.)

Referred to in P36-58.

**P36-58** **(39# 5499 )**

**Crocker, Roger**

**Correction to the paper "A theorem in additive number theory".**

*Colloq. Math.* **20** (1969), 305.

The original paper appeared in same Colloq. **20** (1969), 53–56 [MR **38** #5707].

Citations: MR 38# 5707 = P36-57.

**P36-59** **(40# 99 )**

**Barban, M. B.; Levin, B. V.**

**Multiplicative functions on "shifted" prime numbers. (Russian)**

*Dokl. Akad. Nauk SSSR* **181** (1968), 778–780.

Let $f(n)$ be a multiplicative function satisfying $f(p^\alpha)=O(\alpha^c)$, where $c$ is a constant. (Here and in what follows, $p$ runs through the primes.) The author proves that

$$(1)\quad \textstyle\sum_{p\leq N} f(N-p) \ll (N/\ln N)\exp\{\sum_{p<N, p\nmid n}(f(p)-1)/p\}.$$

Suppose further that the series $\sum_p \max\{(1-f(p))/p, 0\}$ converges. It is then shown that Vinogradov's sign $\ll$ in (1) can be replaced by Hardy's sign $\asymp$. As an application of (1), estimates are obtained for sums of Hecke characters of imaginary quadratic fields. These estimates imply that if $Q(n)=\#\{(p, x, y)|n=p+x^2+y^2\}$, and if $0<\varphi_1<\varphi_2\leqq 2\pi$, then

$$\#\{(p, x, y)|n=p+x^2+y^2, \varphi_1<\tan^{-1}x/y<\varphi_2\} = \tfrac{1}{2}\pi^{-1}(\varphi_2-\varphi_1)Q(n)\{1+O((\ln\ln n)^c/((\varphi_2-\varphi_1)(\ln n)^{1-2/\pi}))\}$$

for some constant $c$.

{This article has appeared in English translation [Soviet Math. Dokl. **9** (1968), 912–914].}

*B. Gordon* (Los Angeles, Calif.)

**P36-60** **(41# 3421 )**

**Rieger, G. J.**

**Über ein additives Problem mit Primzahlen.**

*Arch. Math.* (*Basel*) **21** (1970), 54–58.

The author establishes six theorems, among which are the following. (1) If $1<\sigma<12/11$ then there exist positive constants $c_1$, $c_2$ depending at most on $\sigma$ such that for any natural number $N>c_1$ there exist at least $c_2N^{1/\sigma}(\log N)^{-1}$ primes of the form $N-[a^\sigma]$, with natural numbers $a$. Thus every sufficiently large $N$ may be written in the form $N=p+[a^\sigma]$ for some prime $p$ and natural number $a$. (2) If $1<\sigma<2$ then the number of natural numbers $a\leqq x$ for which $[a^\sigma]$ and $[a^\sigma]+2$ are primes equals $O(x(\log x)^{-2})$. The number of $a\leqq N^{1/\sigma}$ for which $N-[a^\sigma]$ and $N-[a^\sigma]+2$ are primes equals $O(N^{1/\sigma}(\log N)^{-2})$.

*B. Garrison* (San Diego, Calif.)

**P36-61** **(41# 6806 )**

**Kátai, I.**

**On an algorithm for additive representation of integers by prime numbers.**

*Ann. Univ. Sci. Budapest. Eötvös Sect. Math.* **12** (1969), 23–27.

Letting $P_{i+1}$ denote the $i$th prime ($P_1=1$), every positive integer $n$ can be written uniquely as $P_{i_1}+P_{i_2}+\cdots+P_{i_\nu}$ ($i_1\geqq\cdots\geqq i_\nu$), where $P_{i_1}$ is the largest $P\leqq n$, $P_{i_2}$ is the largest $P \leqq n - P_{i_1}$, etc. Let $\alpha(n) = \nu$. For $x \geqq 1$ let $L(x)$ be that integer $j$ such that $x_j$ (=the $j$th integrated log of $x$) is in the interval $1 \leqq x < e$. The author studies the behavior of $\alpha(n)$ and, in particular, the sums $B_k(x) = \sum_{0 \leqq n \leqq x} \alpha^k(n)$. Assuming the Riemann hypothesis, the formula $B_k(x) = (1 + O(1))xL^k(x)$ $(x \to \infty)$ is shown to hold for all $k$. From this follows $\lim_{m \to \infty} \alpha(n)/L(m) = 1$ (omitting a zero-density set of integers). Used in the proof are the sieve of Brun and Selberg and a result of H. Cramér [Acta Arith. **2** (1936), 23–46]. *A. R. Freedman* (Burnaby, B.C.)

## P36-62 (42# 1775)

**Miech, R. J.**

**On the equation $n = p + x^2$.**

*Trans. Amer. Math. Soc.* **130** (1968), 494–512.

Let $n$ and $x$ be positive integers, $p$ a prime, $(n/p)$ the Legendre symbol. Put $\mathscr{P}(n) = \prod_p [1 - (n/p)/(p-1)]$. Let $\Omega(n)$ denote the number of solutions to $n = p + x^2$. Hardy and Littlewood have conjectured that $\Omega(n) \sim \mathscr{P}(n)n^{1/2} \log n$. The author shows that this is true except for a set of $n$ of density 0. More precisely, he shows that for any $A > 0$ there exists $B > 0$ such that $|\Omega(n) - \mathscr{P}(n)I(n)| < B\surd(n)/(\log n)^A$ for all but $BN/(\log n)^A$ positive integers $n \leqq N$. Here $I(n) = \int_1^{\surd(n-3)} dt/\log(n-t^2)$.

*D. G. Cantor* (Los Angeles, Calif.)

## P36-63 (42# 3015)

**Mientka, Walter E.; Weitzenkamp, Roger C.**

**On $f$-plentiful numbers.**

*J. Combinatorial Theory* **7** (1969), 374–377.

Authors' introduction: "For $f$ an arithmetic function whose range is a subset of the non-negative integers and $x$ a natural number, we say $x$ is $f$-plentiful if $x - f(n)$ is prime for all $n$ such that $x - f(n) > 0$.

"In this paper we determine necessary and sufficient conditions for a number to be $f$-plentiful and investigate the frequency of such numbers, for various functions $f$. The investigation arose from a comment by P. Erdős [Summa Brasil. Math. **2** (1950), 113–123; MR **13**, 437], whose remarks are equivalent to asking whether there exist any $f$-plentiful numbers greater than 105, where $f(n) = 2^n$. He has verified the non-existence of such numbers in the interval (105, 203775]."

Citations: MR 13, 437i = P36-5.

## P36-64 (42# 3042)

**Prachar, K.**

**On sums of primes and $l$-th powers of small integers.**

*J. Number Theory* **2** (1970), 379–385.

The following theorem is proved: Given a natural number $l \geqq 1$, there exist constants $\eta > 1$, $\delta > 0$ depending at most on $l$, such that for large $N$ the number of integers $\leqq N$ that are not representable in the form $p + m^l$, where $p$ is a prime and $m$ is a positive integer satisfying $1 \leqq m \leqq \eta \log N$, is $\geqq \delta N$.

P. Erdős conjectured this in 1964, and proved the result for $l = 1$. In his proof, the author uses the following result of E. Bombieri and H. Davenport [Proc. Roy. Soc. Ser. A **293** (1966), 1–18; MR **33** #7314]. Let $Z(N; 2n) = \sum_{p \leqq N, p' \leqq N, p'-p=2n} (\log p)(\log p')$, $H = \prod_{p>2} \{1 - (p-1)^{-2}\}$, $H(n) = H \prod_{p|n, p>2} (p-1)/(p-2)$ and $k < (\log N)^c$ for some fixed $c$, where $p, p'$ denote primes. Then for every $\varepsilon > 0$, $\sum_{n=1}^k t(n)Z(N; 2n) > 2N \sum_{n=1}^k t(n)H(n) - (\frac{1}{4} + \varepsilon)t(0)N \log N$ if $t(n)$ is real with $t(n) = t(-n)$ and such that

$$\sum_{n=-k}^k t(n)e^{4\pi i n\alpha}$$

is non-negative for real $\alpha$. It is also shown in the paper that for every $\varepsilon > 0$ there exist infinitely many prime pairs $p, p'$ such that $p' - p = m_2^l - m_1^l$ with $0 < m_1 < m_2 < (\frac{1}{2} + \varepsilon) \log p$. *K. Thanigasalam* (Bronx, N.Y.)

Citations: MR 33# 7314 = N08-43.

## P36-65 (43# 3200)

**Crocker, Roger**

**On the sum of a prime and of two powers of two.**

*Pacific J. Math.* **36** (1971), 103–107.

Using elementary methods the author proves that "There is an infinity of distinct, positive odd integers not representable as the sum of a prime and two positive powers of 2". *J. B. Roberts* (Portland, Ore.)

## P36-66 (43# 4785)

**Kondakova, L. F.**

**A generalization of Hooley's lemma.** (Russian)

*Izv. Vysš. Učebn. Zaved. Matematika* **1970**, *no.* 5 (96), 43–46.

The paper deals with representations of the form (*) $n = a_k + \varphi(\xi, \eta)$, where $\{a_k\}$ is a given sequence of primes and $\varphi$ is a given primitive, positive quadratic form. Thus it extends work by B. M. Bredihin [Uspehi Mat. Nauk **20** (1965), no. 2 (122), 89–130; MR **32** #5618], who required the sequence $\{a_k\}$ to contain all primes, and of C. Hooley [Acta Math. **97** (1957), 189–210; MR **19**, 532] who considered representations of integers as sums of squares and a prime. For the purpose of determining the asymptotic number of solutions of (*), a lemma generalizing Bredihin's Lemma 2.3.1 is proved by an extension of his method.

*B. Volkmann* (Stuttgart)

Citations: MR 19, 532a = P36-17; MR 32# 5618 = P36-43.

## P36-67 (43# 4786)

**Poljanskiĭ, A. A.**

**Geometric and ergodic properties of the solutions of an equation of Hardy-Littlewood type.** (Russian)

*Volž. Mat. Sb. Vyp.* 6 (1968), 213–216. (*errata insert*)

The author considers the equation (1) $ap + b(x^2 + y^2) = n$, where $p$ varies over the prime numbers, $x$ and $y$ vary independently over the integers, the parameters $a$ and $b$ have the order $O((\ln n)^C)$. He formulates theorems that supply the asymptotic behavior for a number of such solutions $(p, x, y)$ of equation (1) for which $(x, y)$ belongs to a certain region $D$ that is situated inside a disk of radius $\surd(n/b)$. The proofs, based on the elementary ergodic method of the reviewer and Ju. V. Linnik [Dokl. Akad. Nauk SSSR **166** (1966), 1267–1269; MR **34** #5785], are complete in the case when $D$ is a circular sector of the given angle.

*B. Bredihin* (RŽMat **1969** #4 A103)

Citations: MR 34# 5785 = P36-48.

## P36-68 (44# 3975)

**Poljanskiĭ, A. A.**

**A general equation of Hardy-Littlewood type.** (Russian)

*Volž. Mat. Sb. Vyp.* 7 (1969), 126–127.

An asymptotic evaluation of the number of solutions of the Hardy-Littlewood equation $p + F(x, y) = n$ has been given in previous papers by Ju. V. Linnik [B. M. Bredihin and Linnik, Mat. Sb. (N.S.) **71** (**113**) (1966), 145–161; MR **34** #5769], A. Vinogradov [Mat. Zametki **1** (1967), 189–197; MR **34** #7485] and others. Here $p$ runs over all the rational primes, $n$ is a sufficiently large natural number and $F(x, y)$ is a given positive and primitive quadratic form of discriminant $D$, which is identical with the discriminant of the quadratic field $Q(d^{\frac{1}{2}})$ over the rationals and $0 > d$, $d$ squarefree. The author investigates a generalization of the Hardy-Littlewood equation of the type $ap+bF(x,y)=n$, where $a$ and $b$ are rational integral parameters of the form $a=O(\exp(\log n)^u)$ and $b=O(\log^v n)$, $u$ and $v$ being positive constants, with $u$ small and $v$ large. In terms of the theory of quadratic fields, this generalized Hardy-Littlewood equation can be written in the form $ap+bN(\alpha)=n$, where the $\alpha$ are the ideal numbers of the class $C$ in the field $Q(d^{\frac{1}{2}})$ corresponding to the quadratic form $F$; $(a,b)=1$ is also assumed. The author states (without proof) two formulas concerning the asymptotic number of solutions of $ap+bN(\alpha)=n$ in a fixed spheric sector $S$. He asserts that to prove these formulas he uses methods developed in previous papers by Vinogradov [loc. cit.] and himself [Dokl. Akad. Nauk SSSR **168** (1966), 25–27; MR **34** #5786; ibid. **180** (1968), 29–31; MR **37** #5176]. *L. Bernstein* (Chicago, Ill.)

Citations: MR 34# 5769 = P36-47; MR 34# 5786 = P36-49; MR 34# 7485 = P36-51; MR 37# 5176 = P36-56.

# P40 TWIN PRIMES; SIMULTANEOUS PRIMALITY OF SEVERAL LINEAR FORMS

For conjectural and empirical results, see **A46**.
For the simultaneous primality of higher-degree polynomials, see **N32**.
See also reviews A46-25, M55-33, M55-37, M55-41, M55-66, N02-2, N08-19, N08-34, N12-31, N16-26, N28-43, N32-19, N32-20, N32-22, N32-27, N32-32, N32-33, N32-42, N32-45, N32-51, N32-55, N32-58, N32-59, P32-11, P32-38, P32-40, P32-45, P32-50, P32-55, P32-62, P32-81, P36-46, P36-60, P52-2, P52-5, U10-1, Z30-64.

## P40-1 (9, 11e)

**Ullrich, Egon. Zum Zwillingssatz von Viggo Brun.** Ber. Math.-Tagung Tübingen 1946, pp. 139–143 (1947).

The author states that Brun's theorem on the convergence of $\sum p^{-1}$, summed over the primes $p$ for which $p+2$ is also a prime, can be extended to the case when $p+2$ is replaced by $p+2q$ for any fixed $q$. He also makes some observations on the probable distribution of such primes.

*H. Davenport* (Stanford University, Calif.).

## P40-2 (10, 355g)

**Čulanovskiĭ, I. V. Certain estimates connected with a new method of Selberg in elementary number theory.** Doklady Akad. Nauk SSSR (N.S.) **63**, 491–494 (1948). (Russian)

The author indicates how a result of Selberg [Norske Vid. Selsk. Forh., Trondhjem **19**, no. 18, 64–67 (1947); these Rev. **9**, 271] can be applied to give elementary proofs of the four theorems stated below. These results are somewhat sharper than those obtained by Brun's method.

(I) Let $\pi(x;k,l)$ denote the number of prime numbers not exceeding $x$ which lie in the arithmetic progression $kn+l$, where $(k,l)=1$. Suppose that $k=O(x^\delta)$, where $\delta$ is a fixed number between 0 and 1. Then

$$\pi(x;k,l)\leqq\frac{2x}{\phi(k)\ln(x/k)}\left\{1+O\left(\frac{\ln\ln x}{\ln x}\right)\right\},$$

where $\phi$ is Euler's function.

(II) Let $Z(u;N)$ denote the number of positive integers $n$ not exceeding $N$ such that $n$ and $n+u$ are both primes, where $u$ is an even natural number possibly varying with $N$. Then

$$Z(u;N)\leqq 16\prod_{2<p}\frac{p(p-2)}{(p-1)^2}\times\prod_{2<p|u}\frac{p-1}{p-2}\frac{N}{(\ln N)^2}\left\{1+O\left(\frac{\ln\ln N}{\ln N}\right)+O\left(\frac{(\ln u)^2}{(\ln N)^2(\ln\ln N)^2}\right)\right\}.$$

(III) Let $0, u_1, \cdots, u_{m-1}$ be distinct fixed nonnegative integers not forming a complete system of residues with respect to any prime modulus. Let $Z(u_1,\cdots,u_{m-1};N)$ denote the number of positive integers $n$ not exceeding $N$ such that $n, n+u_1, \cdots, n+u_{m-1}$ are all primes. Then

$$Z(u_1,\cdots,u_{m-1};N)\leqq\frac{2^m m!N}{(\ln N)^m}\prod_p\frac{1-\omega(p)/p}{(1-1/p)^m}\{1+o(1)\},$$

where $\omega(p)$ denotes the number of distinct residue classes modulo $p$ represented by $0, u_1, \cdots, u_{m-1}$.

(IV) If $A(N)$ denotes the number of representations of an even positive integer $N$ as a sum of two primes, then

$$A(N)\leqq 16\prod_{2<p}\frac{p(p-2)}{(p-1)^2}\prod_{2<p|N}\frac{p-1}{p-2}\cdot\frac{N}{(\ln N)^2}\left\{1+O\left(\frac{1}{(\ln\ln N)^2}\right)\right\}.$$

The first of these theorems is proved by using Selberg's method to estimate the number of positive integers not exceeding $x$ which lie in the arithmetic progression $kn+l$ and which are not multiples of any of the primes not dividing $k$ and not exceeding $N^{\frac{1}{2}}/(\ln N)^2$, where $N=[(x-l)/k]+1$. The other theorems are proved similarly.

*P. T. Bateman* (Princeton, N. J.).

Citations: MR 9, 271h = M55-4.
Referred to in P40-7.

## P40-3 (12, 676d)

**Knödel, Walter. Ein Satz über Primzahlen.** Anz. Öster. Akad. Wiss. Math.-Nat. Kl. **1949**, 112–116 (1949).

Let $y$ and $z$ be positive integers, $y$ being fixed and $y\leqq 2\log x$. $A(z)$ is the number of prime factors of $z$ and $B(z)$ the number of different prime factors of $z$. Let $l(x,y,E)$ be the number of primes $p\leqq x$ such that $y$ is the least positive integer for which $p-y=z$ for some $z$ satisfying $\min\{A(z)-1,B(z)\}=E$. The author's result is: (A) There exist values of $y\leqq 2\log x$ such that $l(x,y,E)\geqq c_1x/\log^2 x$ for some constant $c_1$, and the number $Z_1(y)$ of such $y$ satisfies $Z_1(y)\geqq c_2\log x(\log\log x)^{1-E}$ (the last inequality is presumably under the restriction $E\geqq 1$). This is stated to be a particular case of a result of van der Corput published in the Monatshefte für Mathematik in 1938, but the reviewer has not been able to verify this as he cannot find the paper in that journal for 1938. Possibly the paper intended is that in Math. Ann. **116**, 1–50 (1938) in which the representation of numbers $y$ in the form $Kp+K'p'$ is considered. The proof of the second part of (A) depends upon the result (Hilfssatz 3)

$$l(x,y,E)\leqq c_3\frac{x}{\log^2 x}(\log\log x)^E\sum_{q|y}\frac{1}{q},$$

which is stated to be due to Kai-Lai Chung [Sci. Rep. Nat. Tsing Hua Univ. (A) **4**, 249–255 (1940); these Rev. **3**, 68]. The reviewer has been unable to find this result in the paper quoted which contains no mention of a parameter such as $E$; it is possible, however, that it may be an extension of Chung's main lemma in which there is a similar expression with $E$ replaced by 2. Hilfssätze 1 and 2, as stated by the author, are meaningless, although their intended meaning is obvious from the proofs. The author claims that, by taking $z$ to be a prime $p'$ (i.e., $E=0$) in (A), it follows that: (B) There exists an infinity of different values $y_0$ each of which is the difference between infinitely many prime pairs $p, p'$. The reviewer can see no justification for this claim, although (B) is no doubt true. That there exists a $y_0$ which is the difference between infinitely many prime pairs will follow from (A) if it is shown that there exist values of $x$ arbitrarily large for which the least $y$ for which $l(x, y, E) \geqq c_1 x/\log^2 x$ is uniformly bounded. This the author has not done.

*R. A. Rankin* (Cambridge, England).

Citations: MR 3, 68g = P52-1.

Referred to in P40-5.

## P40-4 (12, 676e)

**Knödel, Walter. Sätze über Primzahlen.** Monatsh. Math. **55**, 62–75 (1951).

The following result, which is a generalisation of the result (A) of the preceding review, is proved: Let $k$ be an integer greater than unity. Then there exist at least $c_1(k) \log^{k-1}x(\log\log\log x)^{-k}$ sets $\{y_1, y_2, \cdots, y_k\}$ of non-negative integers such that $y_1=0, y_i<2k\log x\,(1\leqq i\leqq k)$ and with the property that with each such set there are associated at least $c_2(k)x(\log x)^{-k}$ positive integers $z<x$ such that the $k$ numbers $z+y_i$ $(1\leqq i\leqq k)$ are all prime. This is deduced from the theorem that to each set $\{y_1, y_2, \cdots, y_k\}$ there are associated at most $c_3(k; y_1, y_2, \cdots, y_k)x(\log x)^{-k}$ integers $z<x$ for which the numbers $z+y_i$ $(1\leqq i\leqq k)$ are all prime. This latter result is obtained as a straightforward generalisation (from 2 to $k$) of Brun's method as given in chapter 2, §§2 and 3 of E. Landau's book, "Über einige neuere Fortschritte der additiven Zahlentheorie" [Cambridge Univ. Press, 1937]. The paper commences with a repetition of the result (B) claimed to have been proved in the paper reviewed in the preceding review. There are numerous minor printers' errors. *R. A. Rankin* (Cambridge, England).

Referred to in B20-5, B20-6.

## P40-5 (14, 355c)

**Knödel, Walter. Sätze über Primzahlen. II.** Monatsh. Math. **56**, 137–143 (1952).

Let $k$ be a fixed integer greater than unity and $y_1, y_2, \cdots, y_k$ a set of integers satisfying $y_1=0$, $0<y_i<2k\log x$ $(1<i\leqq k)$. Such a set is said to possess the property (E) if the $k$ numbers $z+y_i$ are all prime for more than $c_1(k)x/\log^k x$ values of $z$ less than $x$, where $c_1(k)$ depends only on $k$. The number of sets $(y_i)$ with property (E) is denoted by $Z$. In his first paper under the same title [Monatsh. Math. **55**, 62–75 (1951); these Rev. **12**, 676; in this review the condition $y_i<2\log x$ should be replaced by $y_i<2k\log x$] the author obtained lower and upper bounds for $Z$; in the present paper he obtains a better lower bound which is of the same order of magnitude as his earlier upper bound, namely

$$c_4(k)\log^{k-1}x<Z<c_6(k)\log^{k-1}x.$$

The proof is based on results obtained in the earlier paper and involves an estimate of the number of sets $(y_i)$ for which $\prod_{i>j}(y_i-y_j)$ is divisible by any integer $d$. The proof holds under the assumption $c_{13}>c_1c_6$ which is made without comment or verification. In the proof of Lemma 2 the author's deduction of the inequality (7) is hard to follow because of misprints or minor errors; it is, however, easily verified that (7) holds, and, in fact, remains true if $2k$ is replaced by $k$ in the product. *R. A. Rankin.*

Citations: MR 12, 676d = P40-3.

## P40-6 (19, 251g)

**Klimov, N. I. Upper estimates of some number theoretical functions.** Dokl. Akad. Nauk SSSR (N.S.) **111** (1956), 16–18. (Russian)

Utilizing the sieve method of A. Selberg the author derives various estimates of prime-number-theoretic functions, which represent extensions of previously known results. Typical of these is the following theorem. Let $p$ denote a prime, and $u_1, \cdots, u_{m-1}$ $(m\geqq 2)$, $k$, $l$, integers with $(k, l)=1$. Also, let $h$ and $x$ denote positive reals with $h$ fixed independently of $x$. $Z_h(k; u_1, \cdots, u_{m-1}; x)$ is defined as the number of primes $p$ of the arithmetic progression $kn+l$, such that $h\leqq p\leqq h+x$, and for which $|p+u_i|$ $(i=1, \cdots, m-1)$ are all prime numbers. If (a) $k=O(x^\delta)$ $(\delta<1)$ and (b) $\log u_i=O(\log^c x)$ $(i=1, \cdots, m-1)$, then

$$Z_h(k; u; x)\leqq \frac{m!x}{k\log^m(x/k)}\prod_p \frac{1-\omega(p)/p}{(1-1/p)^m}\left\{1+O\left(\frac{\log\log x}{\log x}\right)\right\}$$

where $\omega(p)$ denotes the number of incongruent solutions modulo $p$ (solutions for $n$) of the congruence

$$(kn+l)\prod_{i=1}^{m-1}(kn+l+u_i)\equiv 0 \pmod p;$$

and the $O$ in the above depends only on $c$, $m$, and $\delta$.

*H. N. Shapiro* (New York, N.Y.,)

## P40-7 (20# 3841)

**Klimov, N. I. Combination of elementary and analytic methods in the theory of numbers.** Uspehi Mat. Nauk (N.S.) **13** (1958), no. 3 (81), 145–164. (Russian)

I. V. Čulanovskiĭ [Dokl. Akad. Nauk SSSR **63** (1948), 491–494; MR **10**, 355] has applied the Selberg sieve method to find an upper bound for various prime-number-theoretic functions, such as the number $Z_{u_1\cdots u_{m-1}}(N)$ of primes $p\leqq N$ such that also $p+u_1, \cdots, p+u_{m-1}$ are prime. His method depended on the estimation of the sum function of a certain multiplicative function; he effected this estimation in an elementary fashion. In the present paper the author generalizes Čulanovskiĭ's results by considering almost primes, in progressions, and lying in more general intervals. His method is similar to that of Čulanovskiĭ, except that the required sum function is now estimated analytically, with the help of the $\zeta$-function; this leads to improved results in the cases considered by Čulanovskiĭ. A generalization and improvement is also obtained of the heretofore best-known upper bound, due to Ricci [Ann. Scuola Norm. Sup. Pisa **6** (1937), 71–116], for the number $\pi^{(2)}(N, D)$ of primes $p\leqq N$ of the form $p=n^2+D$.

*W. J. LeVeque* (Göttingen)

Citations: MR 10, 355g = P40-2.

## P40-8 (24# A1902)

**Lavrik, A. F.**

**The number of $k$-twin primes lying on an interval of a given length.**

*Dokl. Akad. Nauk SSSR* **136** (1961), 281–283 (*Russian*); *translated as Soviet Math. Dokl.* **2** (1961), 52–55.

For integral $k\geqq 1$ let $\pi_k(x)$ denote the number of pairs of primes $p$, $p+2k$ belonging to the interval $(0, x)$. The author uses I. M. Vinogradov's method of trigonometric sums to prove some asymptotic formulas for $\pi_k(x)$ holding for almost all $k$. He gives in particular the formula

$$\pi_k(x) = 2\prod_{p>2}\frac{p(p-2)}{(p-1)^2}\prod_{\substack{p|k\\ p>2}}\frac{p-1}{p-2}\int_2^x\frac{dt}{\log^2 t}+O(x(\log x)^{-c}),$$

valid for all integer $2\leqq 2k\leqq x\,(\log x)^{-c}$, excluding not more than $\ll x(\log x)^{-M-c}$ of them, where $c\geqq 3$ and $M>0$ are arbitrary constants and $p$ runs through primes, with the constants in the symbols $\ll$ and $O$ being independent of $k$. He gives further a similar result for primes $p$, $p+k$ belonging to arithmetical progressions $Dn+l'$, $Dm+l''$, respectively. In conclusion, the possibility of analogous results concerning primes $p$ such that $p+a_1, \cdots, p+a_m$ are also primes, for even integers $a_1, \cdots, a_m$, has been indicated. *S. Knapowski* (Poznań)

## P40-9 (25# 2050)

**Lavrik, A. F.**

**Binary problems of additive prime number theory connected with the method of trigonometric sums of I. M. Vinogradov. (Russian. English summary)**

*Vestnik Leningrad. Univ.* **16** (1961), *no.* 13, 11–27.

Let $\Pi_k(x)$ denote the number of prime pairs $p, p+2k$ in the interval $(0, x)$; let $Q(N)$ denote the number of representations of the even integer $N$ as a sum of two primes. The circle-method of Hardy and Littlewood indicated to them the following conjectures:

$$(1) \qquad \Pi_k(x) \sim 2\prod_{p>2}\frac{p(p-2)}{(p-1)^2}\cdot\frac{x}{\log^2 x}\prod_{\substack{p|k\\p>2}}\left(\frac{p-1}{p-2}\right).$$

$$(2) \qquad Q(N) \sim 2\prod_{p>2}\frac{p(p-2)}{(p-1)^2}\cdot\frac{N}{\log^2 N}\prod_{\substack{p|N\\p>2}}\left(\frac{p-1}{p-2}\right).$$

The author proves that (1) holds for "almost all" integers $k$, and that (2) holds for "almost all" even $N$. This is the essential content of his sharper Theorems 1 and 2 (Theorem 1 for $\Pi_k(x)$; Theorem 2 for $\Pi_k(x, D)$, where the primes are restricted to lie in an arithmetic progression) and 3 for $Q(N, D)$ which is a generalization of the function $Q(N)$ when we restrict the primes in $N=p+p'$ to lie in arithmetic progressions (mod $D$). *S. Chowla* (Boulder, Colo.)

## P40-10 (27# 1428)

**Vinogradov, A. I.**

**On a problem of L. K. Hua. (Russian)**

*Dokl. Akad. Nauk SSSR* **151** (1963), 255–257.

Using the Hardy-Littlewood method, the author estimates the sum

$$S = \sum_{x=-\infty}^{\infty}\sum_{y=1}^{\infty}\sum_{n=1}^{\infty}\sum_{m=1}^{\infty} f(x, y, n, m),$$

where

$$(1) \quad f(x, y, n, m) = \exp\left[-\frac{(|b|+|b'|)y+n+m}{N}\right]\Lambda(n)\Lambda(m)$$

and $x$, $y$ for given $n$, $m$ are subject to $ax+by+c=n$, $a'x+b'y+c'=m$. Also $\Lambda(t)$, as usual, is $\log p$ if $t=p^w$ ($p$ prime) and 0 otherwise. $N$ is a large number. The estimate for $S=S(N)$ is of the form

$$S = \mathfrak{S}\begin{pmatrix} a & b & c\\ a' & b' & c'\end{pmatrix}N^2+O\left(\frac{N^2}{\log^c N}\right)$$

where $c>0$ is independent of $N$, $\mathfrak{S}$ is the "singular" series [see L.-K. Hua, *Additive Primzahltheorie*, Teubner, Leipzig, 1959, Chapter 12, p. 172; MR **23** #A1620].

Thus we have, roughly speaking, a "measure" of the number of times $ax+by+c$ and $a'x+b'y+c'$ are both primes, when $x$ runs over all integers and $y$ runs over the natural numbers [when $y$, $n$, $m$ are large compared to $N$, the "exp" factor in (1) is small].

*S. Chowla* (Boulder, Colo.)

Citations: MR 23# A1620 = P02-7.

## P40-11 (27# 5739)

**Rieger, G. J.**

**Über die Summe beliebiger und die Differenz aufeinanderfolgender Primzahlen.**

*Elem. Math.* **18** (1963), 104–105.

Schnirelmann a démontré que la suite $p_1+p_2$ ($p_1, p_2$ premiers) a une densité asymptotique positive; Prachar, d'un autre côté, a démontré que la suite $p^+-p$, $p^+$ étant le nombre premier immédiatement supérieur à $p$, a une densité asymptotique positive. L'auteur démontre le théorème analogue suivant: Il existe des constantes positives $C_1, C_2, C_3$, telles que $x>C_1$ entraîne la relation $A\{m, n: m<x \wedge n<C_2\log x \wedge m=p_1+p_2 \wedge n=p_2{}^+-p_2 \wedge p_1, p_2 \text{ premiers}\}>C_3 x\log x$, $A$ étant le nombre des $m, n$ définis dans l'accolade, $x$ désignant un nombre naturel, et le symbole $\wedge$ étant celui de la conjonction logique. Il remarque qu'on peut obtenir des généralisations diverses de ce théorème. *A. Gloden* (Luxembourg)

## P40-12 (28# 69)

**Lavrik, A. F.**

**On the theory of distribution of primes based on I. M. Vinogradov's method of trigonometric sums. (Russian)**

*Trudy Mat. Inst. Steklov.* **64** (1961), 90–125.

The author uses the method mentioned in the title to prove several results of 'almost all' type connected with the Goldbach and twin-primes conjectures. If $\pi(x; u_1, u_2, \cdots, u_m)$ denotes the number of primes not exceeding $x$ for which $p+u_1, p+u_2, \cdots, p+u_m$ are also prime, the author obtains an asymptotic formula for $\pi(x; u_1, \cdots, u_m)$ valid for almost all systems $(u_1, \cdots, u_m)$ satisfying $1\leqq m\leqq X$, where $X=x(\ln x)^{-m-c}$ $(c>1)$. He also proves the following theorem: For every even integer $N\equiv l'+l''$ (mod $D$) in the interval $(0, x)$, with at most $\ll x/D(\ln x)^M$ exceptions, $M>0$ being a given constant, the number $I(N; D)$ of solutions of the equation $N=p'+p''$ in primes $p'\equiv l'$ (mod $D$), $p''\equiv l''$ (mod $D$) with $0\leqq l', l''\leqq D$, $(l', D)=(l'', D)=1$, $D\leqq(\log N)^A$ ($A>0$ is an arbitrary constant), satisfies

$$I(N; D) = 2\prod_{p>2}\frac{p(p-2)}{(p-1)^2}\prod_{p|D, p>2}\frac{p-1}{p-2}\cdot\frac{N}{\phi(D)\ln^2 N}\prod_{\substack{p|N, p>2\\ p\nmid D}}\frac{p-1}{p-2}\cdot\left\{1+O\left(\frac{1}{\ln N}\right)\right\};$$

here $p$ denotes a prime number, $\phi$ is Euler's function and the constant implied by the $O$-notation depends only on $A$ and $M$. Proofs are supplied in detail, and a full bibliography is given. *H. Halberstam* (Dublin)

Referred to in P36-46.

## P40-13 (28# 1183)

**Lavrik, A. F.**

**On the twin prime hypothesis of the theory of primes by the method of I. M. Vinogradov.**

*Dokl. Akad. Nauk SSSR* **132** (1960), 1013–1015 (*Russian*); *translated as Soviet Math. Dokl.* **1** (1960), 700–702.

Mit den Vinogradovschen Methoden läßt sich bekanntlich zeigen, daß fast alle geraden natürlichen Zahlen $n$ in der Form $n=p_1+p_2$, $p_1$, $p_2$ Primzahlen, darstellbar sind, d. h. genauer: die Anzahl der nicht darstellbaren, $n\leqq x$ ist $O(x/\log^A x)$, $A$ beliebig groß (Estermann, van der Corput, Čudakov). Verfasser verallgemeinert dies auf den Fall, daß $p_1$ und $p_2$ arithmetischen Reihen mit einer Differenz $D<(\log x)^A$, $A$ beliebig, angehören, und stellt den analogen Satz für Primzahlpaare auf, der für $D=1$ lautet: Sei $\pi_k(x)$ die Anzahl der Paare $p, p+2k$ von Primzahlen mit $p\leqq x$. Für $0<2k\leqq x/\log x$ gilt

$$\pi_k(x) = 2\prod_{p>2}\left(1-\frac{1}{(p-1)^2}\right)\frac{x}{\log^2 x}\prod_{p|k, p>2}\left(1+\frac{1}{p-2}\right)+O\left(\frac{x}{\log^3 x}\right)$$

mit Ausnahme von höchstens $O(x/\log^A x)$ Ausnahmewerten

von $k$. Dieses Resultat (für $D=1$) ist im wesentlichen auch bereits von van der Corput bewiesen worden [Akad. Wetensch. Amsterdam Proc. **40** (1937), 846–851; Acta Arith. **2** (1937), 266–290]. *K. Prachar* (Zbl **97**, 31)

Referred to in N12-49.

## P40-14 (28# 3017)

**Lavrik, A. F.**

**On the distribution of $k$-twin primes. (Russian)**

*Dokl. Akad. Nauk SSSR* **132** (1960), 1258–1260.

Die Arbeit beschäftigt sich mit Primzahl-$k$-Zwillingen, d.h. mit Zahlenpaaren $p$, $q$ für die $p$ und $q$ Primzahlen sind und $p-q=2k$ gilt. Es bezeichne $p_{ki}$ die $i$-te Primzahl, für die $p_{ki}+2k$ auch eine Primzahl ist. Dann wird der Beweis folgender dreier Sätze skizziert. Satz 1. Es sei $f(t)$ eine Funktion, für die die Relation $f(t)\to\infty$ $(t\to\infty)$ gilt und für die $(\log^2 t)/f(t)$ monoton zunimmt. Dann gilt für fast alle $k$ $p_{ki}-p_{k(i-1)}>(\log^2 p_{ik})/f(p_{ik})$. Satz 2. Man setze $\alpha_k=\prod_{p|k,p>5}(p-2)/(p-4)$. Dann gilt $p_{ki}-p_{k(i-1)}>\log^2 p_{ki}/\alpha_k f(p_{ki})$ für alle $k$ mit $1\leqq k\leqq x/2\log x$ bis auf eine Ausnahmemenge mit höchstens $cx/(\log x)^M$ Gliedern, wobei $M>1$, aber sonst beliebig ist und $c$ nur von $M$ abhängt. Satz 3. Man setze $E(x)=(\log^2 x)/f(x)$, $D(x)\ll E(x)$ [d.h. $D(x)=O(E(\varphi))$; es wird vorausgesetzt, daß $E(x)$ monoton gegen unendlich strebt]. Dann existieren für fast alle $k$ im Intervall $1\leqq k\leqq x/2\log x$ Zahlen $N$ und $\alpha'$ mit $N=[\alpha_k'(\log^2 x)/D(x)]$, $\alpha_k'=\beta\prod_{p|k,p>3}(p-4)/(p-2)$ ($\beta$ konst.) derart, daß die Ungleichungen $p_{k(i+s)}-p_{k(i+s-1)}>D(x)$ $(s=1, 2, \cdots, N)$ gelten. Die nur skizzierten Beweise beruhen auf einem ohne Beweis wiedergegebenen Satz des Verfassers, der sich auf die Anzahl der $k$-Prim-Zwillinge unterhalb $x$ bezieht. *P. Szüsz* (Zbl **105**, 33)

## P40-15 (30# 1102)

**Barban, M. B.**

**On the number of divisors of "translations" of the prime number-twins. (Russian. English summary)**

*Acta Math. Acad. Sci. Hungar.* **15** (1964), 285–288.

Let $N(n)$ denote the number of prime twins with first elements $p'\leqq n$ such that

$$|\nu(p'+1)-\log\log n| \geqq (\log\log n)^{1/2+\varepsilon},$$

where $\nu(m)$ is the number of distinct prime factors of $m$. It is shown that for every $\varepsilon>0$, $N(n)=o(n/\log^2 n)$. Hence, by the well-known upper bound for the number of prime twins not exceeding $n$, most such primes do not satisfy the inequality defining $N(n)$. The proof depends on an estimate for the dispersion, $\sum_{p'\leqq n}\{\nu(p'+1)-\log\log n\}^2$, the estimate being obtained by a sieve argument. *W. J. LeVeque* (Ann Arbor, Mich.)

## P40-16 (31# 2225)

**Turán, P.**

**On some conjectures in the theory of numbers.**

*Proc. London Math. Soc.* (3) **14a** (1965), 288–299.

This paper concerns the set $P$ of solutions $\{p, q\}$ of $q=bp+d$ in odd primes $p$, $q$, where $b$, $d$ are given integers with $b>0$, $d\neq 0$, $(b, d)=1$, $b\not\equiv d$ (mod 2). In their famous paper PN3 [Acta Math. **44** (1923), 1–70] Hardy and Littlewood gave (among other things) a heuristic derivation of an asymptotic formula for the number $P(x)$ of solutions with $q\leqq x$ as $x\to\infty$; but no proof of this, or of the weaker assertion that $P$ is infinite, has ever been found, even on the extended Riemann hypothesis. The Hardy-Littlewood method connected $P(x)$ with the non-trivial zeros $\rho=\beta+i\gamma$ of Dirichlet's $L$-functions $L(s,\chi)$. Here the author considers, in place of $P(x)$, a sum

$$S=\sum_{\{p,q\}\in P}\frac{\log p\log q}{p}R_\nu(3\nu-\log p),$$

where $\nu$ is an integer in the range $\frac{1}{5}\log\omega\leqq\nu\leqq\frac{1}{4}\log\omega$ and $R_\nu(u)$ is a specially chosen function vanishing for $|u|\geqq\nu$; and he connects $S$ with the $\rho$ by a "multiplicative" argument quite unlike the Farey-dissection method of PN3. The actual formula is too elaborate to quote in detail, but its general form is $S=U+V+W$, where $U$ corresponds to the Hardy-Littlewood heuristic approximation to $P(x)$, $V$ is a sum over $\rho$'s having $|\gamma|\leqq e^6$ and belonging to $L$-funtions with moduli $k\leqq b\omega+d$, and $|W|$ is small when $\omega$ is large. The sum $V$ presents a serious obstacle to further rigorous development, but the author has prepared the way for a possible application of his well-known method by choosing $R_\nu(u)$ so that $V$ is a generalized power-sum of the type that forms the basis of that method. He intends to return to this question later. *A. E. Ingham* (Cambridge, England)

Referred to in P32-68.

## P40-17 (31# 2226)

**Buhštab, A. A.**

**New results in the investigation of the Goldbach-Euler problem and the problem of prime pairs.**

*Dokl. Akad. Nauk SSSR* **162** (1965), 735–738.

Let $q$ denote numbers which are products of at most three primes. The author proves that (i) there are infinitely many primes $p$ such that $p+2=q$ and (ii) all large even numbers are representable by sums $p+q$. The proof is given merely in outline, and it rests on the sieve method of V. Brun and on a theorem of M. B. Barban [Mat. Sb. (N S.) **61 (103)** (1963), 418–425; MR **30** #1992].

{This article has appeared in English translation [Soviet Math. Dokl. **6** (1965), 729–732].} *E. Fogels* (Riga)

Citations: MR 30# 1992 = P32-63.

Referred to in M55-43, M55-55, P32-70, P32-73.

## P40-18 (32# 4105)

**Lavrik, A. F.**

**On the theory of the distribution of sets of primes with given differences between them. (Russian)**

*Dokl. Akad. Nauk SSSR* **138** (1961), 1287–1290.

Es bezeichne $\pi(x; u_1, \cdots, u_m)$ die Anzahl der Primzahlen unterhalb $x$, für die auch $p+u_1, \cdots, p+u_m$ Primzahlen sind. Es wird eine asymptotische Formel aufgestellt, die jedoch nicht für alle $m$-Tupel $u_1, \cdots, u_m$ gültig ist. Der Satz 1 sei zitiert. Es sei $m\geqq 1$, ferner bezeichne $\gamma_m(p)$ die Anzahl der verschiedenen Restklassen (mod $p$), denen die Zahlen $0, u_1, \cdots, u_m$ angehören, $\beta$ eine reelle Zahl mit $0\leqq\beta\leqq 2$. Dann gilt

$$\pi(x; u_1, \cdots, u_m) = \prod_p\frac{p-\gamma_m(p)}{p(1-1/p)^{m+1}}\left(\int_2^x\frac{dz}{\log^{m+1}z}+O\left(\frac{x}{\log^{m+c}x}\right)\right)+\beta$$

für alle Zahlen $u_1, \cdots, u_m$ in $(1, x/\log^{m+c}x)$, höchstens bis auf eine Ausnahmemenge von $O(y^m/\log^M y)$ Elementen, wobei $y=x/\log^M x$ gesetzt wurde; hier ist $M>1$, aber sonst beliebig. Ein analoger Satz wird auch für die Primzahlen in einer arithmetischen Progression bewiesen. Die Beweise beruhen auf der Vinogradovschen Methode und werden nur skizziert.

{This article has appeared in English translation [Soviet Math. Dokl. **2** (1961), 827–830].} *P. Szüsz* (Zbl **105**, 34)

## P40-19 (33# 2612)

**Turán, P.**

**On the twin-prime problem. I. (Russian summary)**

*Magyar Tud. Akad. Mat. Kutató Int. Közl.* **9** (1964), 247–261 (1965).

The twin-prime problem asks whether or not there exist an infinity of prime pairs $(p, q)$ with $q-p=2$ (or, more generally, with $q-p=2l$, $l$ fixed integer). This problem is as yet unsolved. The classical paper of Hardy and Littlewood [Acta Math. **44** (1923), 1–70] laid down the basis of an analytical treatment of additive number-theoretical problems and made clear the deep connection between them and the distribution of the zeros of Dirichlet's $L$-functions. They studied, among others, the twin-prime problem and the ternary Goldbach problem, and they called these conjugate problems [loc. cit., page 40].

The efforts of Hardy and Littlewood to solve the ternary Goldbach problem—after the first proof by Vinogradov—were completed by Linnik [Dokl. Acad. Nauk SSSR **49** (1945), 3–7; MR **7**, 507] and Čudakov [Ann. of Math. (2) **48** (1947), 515–545; MR **9**, 11], who used density theorems concerning the zeros of $L$-functions. The present author discovers, however, that the solution of the twin-prime problem depends only on the non-trivial $L$-zeros of the Dirichlet $L$-functions with $|\mathrm{Im}\,\rho| \leqq e^4$, i.e., on the "small" $L$-zeros, where $\rho$ denotes non-trivial zeros.

Confining himself to the case that $q-p=2$, the author gives (perhaps for the first time) an explicitly stated relation connecting the twin-primes with finitely many $L$-roots which holds without any unproved conjectures. The critical expression is of power-sum type, which has led to several new results in analytical number theory in a series of papers by S. Knapowski and the author [Acta Math. Acad. Sci. Hungar. **13** (1962), 299–314; MR **26** #3682a; ibid. **13** (1962), 315–342; MR **26** #3682b; ibid. **13** (1962), 343–364; MR **26** #3682c; ibid. **14** (1963), 31–42; MR **26** #3683a; ibid. **14** (1963), 43–63; MR **26** #3683b; ibid. **14** (1963), 65–78; MR **26** #3683c; ibid. **14** (1963), 241–250; MR **28** #70a; ibid. **14** (1963), 251–268; MR **28** #70b]. See also the author's paper [ibid. **11** (1960), 299–316; MR **24** #A1881; erratum, MR **30**, p. 1201].
*S. Ikehara* (Tokyo)

Citations: MR 7, 507b = P32-8; MR 9, 11d = P32-10; MR 24# A1881 = M50-24; MR 26# 3682a = N12-23; MR 26# 3682b = N12-23; MR 26# 3682c = N12-23; MR 26# 3683a = N12-24; MR 26# 3683b = N12-24; MR 26# 3683c = N12-24; MR 28# 70a = N12-25; MR 28# 70b = N12-25.
Referred to in P40-21, P40-27.

## P40-20 (33# 2617)

**Šanin, A. A.**
**Determination of constants in the Brun-Šnirel'man method. (Russian)**
*Volž. Mat. Sb. Vyp.* 2 (1964), 261–265.

Let $A(u, x)$ denote the number of solutions of $p_i - p_j = u$, where $p_i$ denotes the $i$th prime, $p_i \leqq x$, $i \neq j$, and $0 \leqq u \leqq x$. For $A(u, x)$ one has the upper bound $kxS(u)/\log^2 x$, where $S(u) = \prod_{p \geqq 7, p|u} p/(p-2)$ and $k$ is an absolute positive constant independent of $x$. The author gives the following estimate for the Brun-Schnirelmann constant $k$. Theorem: For $x \geqq 2$, $k = 5800$. *S. Chowla* (University Park, Pa.)

Referred to in P02-25.

## P40-21 (36# 3740)

**Turán, P.**
**On the twin-prime problem. II.**
*Acta Arith.* **13** (1967/68), 61–89.

The author continues his study of the twin-prime problem [Magyar Tud. Akad. Mat. Kutató Int. Közl. **9** (1964), 247–261 (1965); MR **33** #2612] and the Goldbach problem [Dokl. Akad. Nauk SSSR **171** (1966), 1289–1292; MR **34** #5781]. An explicit formula is given for the number of prime pairs $(p_1, p_2)$ with $p_1 - p_2 = D$, $p_2 \leqq N$ ($D$ even). The author showed in the first paper of this series that the infiniteness of the twin primes depends only upon small "zeros" of the Dirichlet $L$-functions, and he now asserts that among these zeros only those "near the line $\sigma = \frac{1}{2}$" are significant. A similar formula is given for the number of representations of an even integer $N$ as a sum of two primes, which links Goldbach's conjecture with the assertion about only those zeros near to the line $\sigma = \frac{1}{2}$. This is to be published in a later paper of this series.

It should be mentioned that in both of the above formulas, the main term turns out to be the heuristic Hardy and Littlewood formula [Acta Math. **44** (1923), 1–70, Conjecture B, p. 32]. *S. Ikehara* (Tokyo)

Citations: MR 33# 2612 = P40-19; MR 34# 5781 = P32-68.
Referred to in P40-23, P40-27.

## P40-22 (37# 5170)

**Hsieh Sheng-kang**
**Distribution of the triplet of almost prime numbers. (Chinese)**
*Shuxue Jinzhan* **8** (1965), 71–77.

Assume that the polynomial

$$F(n) = (a_1 n + b_1)(a_2 n + b_2)(a_3 n + b_3)$$

has no fixed prime factor. Then there is a positive $\delta$ such that, for sufficiently large $x$, there are more than $\delta x/(\log x)^3$ positive integers $n \leqq x$ for which each of the factors $a_i n + b_i$ $(i = 1, 2, 3)$ has at most 6 prime factors while $F(n)$ has at most 15 [see M. B. Barban, Dokl. Akad. Nauk UzSSR **1959**, no. 3, 7–8].
*K. Mahler* (Columbus, Ohio)

## P40-23 (38# 127)

**Turán, P.**
**On the twin-prime problem. III.**
*Acta Arith.* **14** (1967/68), 399–407.

Using his new method [Dokl. Akad. Nauk SSSR **171** (1966), 1289–1292; MR **34** #5781], the author worked out in Part II the theorems for the number $P_2(n)$ of Goldbach decompositions of $n$, and for the number $P_d(n)$ of such primes $p \leqq n$ for which $p + d$ is also a prime for fixed even $d$ [Acta Arith. **13** (1967/68), 61–89; MR **36** #3740].

The aim of the present paper is to show that the "large sieve" method of Ju. V. Linnik [Dokl. Akad. Nauk SSSR **30** (1941), 292–294; MR **2**, 349] can considerably narrow the range of nontrivial zeros of the Dirichlet $L(s, k, \chi)$ functions as to its "width", and that thus it is enough to retain zeros "near" to the line $\sigma = \frac{1}{2}$. In the proof an important role is played by the theorem of Bombieri-Davenport-Halberstam-Gallagher [H. Davenport, *Multiplicative number theory*, p. 160, Markham, Chicago, Ill., 1967; MR **36** #117]. And only zeros of $L$-functions belonging to "large" $k$ moduli occur for $R_2(n)$ and $P_d(n)$. This fact was previously pointed out by Linnik in a completely different context [Izv. Akad. Nauk SSSR Ser. Mat. **16** (1952), 503–520 (Russian); MR **14**, 847]. *S. Ikehara* (Tokyo)

Citations: MR 2, 349a = M55-1; MR 14, 847b = P32-20; MR 34# 5781 = P32-68; MR 36# 117 = N02-13; MR 36# 3740 = P40-21.
Referred to in P40-27.

## P40-24 (40# 5557)

**Jutila, Matti**
**A statistical density theorem for $L$-functions with applications.**
*Acta Arith.* **16** (1969/70), 207–216.

The author proves a statistical density theorem on the number of roots of $L$-functions, from which he deduces a theorem concerning the primes in short intervals. Let $X \geqq 1$, $T \geqq \frac{1}{2}$, and $\chi$ be a character mod $q$. Denote by $N(\alpha, T, q, \chi)$ the number of zeros of the function $L(s, \chi)$

in the rectangle $1-\alpha\leqq\sigma\leqq 1$, $|t|\leqq T$. Let

$$A = \sum_{q\leqq X}\sum'_{\chi(\mathrm{mod}\, q)} N(\alpha, T, q, \chi),$$

where the prime denotes summation over primitive characters. Theorem 1: $A\leqq (X^7T^4)^{(1-\alpha)/\alpha}\log^{c_1}(X+T)$, $A\leqq (X^5T^2)^{(1-\alpha)/\alpha}\log^{c_2}(X+T)$. The "large-sieve" is used for the proof.

Let $c$ be a constant, such that $\zeta(\frac{1}{2}+it, w)\ll t^{c+\varepsilon}$ for all $0<w\leqq 1$. (The best result is $c=6/37$ due to W. Haneke [same Acta **8** (1962/63), 357–430; MR **28** #1179].) Theorem 2: Let $x\geqq 2$, $y\geqq 2$, $y=x^\theta$, $\theta$ being a fixed number, $0<\theta<1$. Then $\sum_{q\leqq x^\beta}\max_{z\leqq y}\max_{(a,q)=1}|\psi(x+z, q, a)-\psi(x, q, a)-z/\varphi(q)|\ll y(\log x)^{-A}$, where $\beta=[4c\theta+2\theta-1-4c](6+4c)^{-1}-\varepsilon$, $A$ is an arbitrary positive constant. Theorem 3: For every positive integer $r\geqq 8$ there exists a real number $\theta(r)$ with $0<\theta(r)<1$ such that for $x$ sufficiently large in any interval $(x, x+x^{\theta(r)})$ there exists a pair $(p, p+2)$ such that $p$ prime and $p+2$ has at most $r$ prime factors. Furthermore, $\theta(r)<(1+4c)/(2+4c)+\varepsilon$ if $r\geqq r(\varepsilon)$.

*I. Kátai* (Budapest)

Citations: MR 28# 1179 = M15-29.
Referred to in M25-91.

## P40-25 (40# 5566)

**Faĭziev, R. F.**

**The number of integers, expressible in the form of a sum of two primes, and the number of $k$-twin pairs. (Russian. Tajiki summary)**

*Dokl. Akad. Nauk Tadžik. SSR* **12** (1969), *no.* 2, 12–16.

Using the result due to E. Bombieri [Mathematika **12** (1965), 201–225; MR **33** #5590], the author improves some theorems. Namely, he proves: (1) If $P(N)$ is the number of representation of $N$ as the sum of two primes, then

$$P(N) < (\log^2 N)^{-1}4N\prod_{p|N}(1-p^{-1})^{-1} \times\prod_{p\nmid N, 2<p<N}(1+(p(p-2))^{-1})^{-1} + O((\log^3 N)^{-1}N\log\log N),$$

where $p$ runs over the primes. (2) If $\pi_{2k}(x)$ denotes the number of primes $p\leqq x$ for which $p+2k$ is a prime too, then

$$\pi_{2k}(x)\leqq 4\prod_{p|2k}(p-2)^{-1}(p-1)\prod_{p>2}(1-(p-1)^{-2})N/\log^2 N + O((\log^3 N)^{-1}N\log\log N).$$

This inequality was known previously for 8 in place of 4.

*I. Kátai* (Budapest)

Citations: MR 33# 5590 = M55-43.

## P40-26 (41# 1668)

**Golomb, Solomon W.**

**The lambda method in prime number theory.**

*J. Number Theory* **2** (1970), 193–198.

The author outlines a possible attack on the twin prime problem by a method analogous to Wiener's proof of the prime number theorem. He works with the power series $G(z)=\sum_{\mathrm{even}\, a\geqq 2}\Lambda(a-1)\Lambda(a+1)z^a-(\log^2 3)z^2$, where $\Lambda$ is the Mangoldt function and $|z|<1$. If there are only finitely many twin primes, then $\lim_{z\to 1-}(1-z)G(z)=0$. On the other hand, there is a Lambert type representation

$$(1-z)G(z) = \sum_{\mathrm{odd}\, d\geqq 1}\frac{\mu(d)\log^2 d}{1+z+z^2+\cdots+z^{2d-1}}\sum_{i=1}^{2^{\nu(d)}}z^{a_i},$$

where $\nu(d)$ is the number of distinct prime factors of $d$ and the $a_i$ are the $2^{\nu(d)}$ even roots, between 0 and $2d$, of the congruence $a^2\equiv 1 \pmod d$. If term-by-term limit as $z\to 1-$ could be justified in this last identity, it would imply $\lim_{z\to 1-}(1-z)G(z)=2C>0$, where $C=2\prod_{p\geqq 3}(1-(p-1)^{-2})$ is the twin prime constant. This would prove that there are infinitely many prime pairs $p$, $p+2$ and also, by a known Tauberian theorem, that the number $T(x)$ of such pairs with $p\leqq x$ is asymptotic to $Cx/\log^2 x$. This missing ingredient is an Abelian theorem strong enough to justify passage to the limit term-by-term. The author expresses the hope that an Abelian theorem sufficient for the specific series at hand might be found. The method can be extended to other unsolved problems involving the spacing of two primes or two prime powers.

*T. M. Apostol* (Pasadena, Calif.)

## P40-27 (42# 4505)

**Grosswald, E.**

**On some conjectures of Hardy and Littlewood.**

*Publ. Ramanujan Inst. No.* 1 (1968/69), 75–89.

G. H. Hardy and J. E. Littlewood described a method in their famous paper [Acta Math. **44** (1922), 1–70] which yields heuristic solutions to a large number of problems in additive number theory. Their method is insufficient to prove the validity of the formulae obtained, but these are in rather satisfactory agreement with the available numerical evidence. To be specific, if $N(k', n)$ stands for the number of representations of the integer $k'$ as a difference of two primes $k'=p-p'$, with $p'<p\leqq n$, then Hardy and Littlewood conjectured that for $k'=2k$ and $n\to\infty$, (1) $N(2k, n)\sim N_{2k}(n)$ with

$$N_{2k}(n) = 2C_0 n\log^{-2}\prod_{p|k, p\neq 2}(p-1)(p-2)^{-1},$$

where $C_0=\prod_{p\geqq 2}(1-(p-1)^{-2})$. For $k'=2k+1$, the problem is trivial, because then $N(k', n)=0$, unless there exists a prime $p$ such that $k'=p-2$, in which case $N(k', n)=1$. If $k'=2k$, the prime $p=2$ does not contribute to $N(2k, n)=1$. If $k'=2k$, the prime 2 does not contribute to $N(2k, n)$; therefore, one may exclude $p=2$ from further consideration and define $N(k, n)=\sum_{p-p'=k, 3\leqq p\leqq n}1$. In the particular case $k=2$, the proof of (1) would provide an affirmative answer to the conjecture about the infinity of twin primes.

In the late 1930s J. G. van der Corput published a series of papers proving very general theorems, and in 1960–61 A. F. Lavrik published several papers containing essentially the same results as van der Corput for the number of representations of $2k=p\pm p'$, where the primes $p$ and $p'$ may also be subject to congruence conditions. (The references are listed in the paper under review.) The main purpose of this paper is to produce a streamlined proof of (1) for almost all integers; the results are not as general as those of van der Corput nor are the error terms the best possible. The proof is based on the systematic use of Fourier series and on T. Estermann's version [*Introduction to modern prime number theory*, Cambridge Univ. Press, Cambridge, 1952; MR **13**, 915] of I. M. Vinogradov's theorem [Trudy Mat. Inst. Steklov. **23** (1947); MR **10**, 599]. Some corollaries of the main result seem new, and one of the lemmas has some independent interest.

{Reviewer's remark: In the meantime P. Turán has published three papers based on the study of the complex zeros of the $L$-functions in the critical region [Magyar Tud. Akad. Mat. Kutató Int. Közl. **9** (1964), 247–261 (1965); MR **33** #2612; Acta Arith. **13** (1967/68), 61–89; MR **36** #3740; ibid. **14** (1967/68), 399–407; MR **38** #127].}

*S. Ikehara* (Tokyo)

Citations: MR 10, 599a = L02-2; MR 13, 915b = P02-12; MR 33# 2612 = P40-19; MR 36# 3740 = P40-21; MR 38# 127 = P40-23.

# P44 ADDITIVE REPRESENTATIONS INVOLVING POWERS OF PRIMES (GOLDBACH-WARING, $p_1 + f(p_2)$, ETC.)

See also reviews L15-5, P02-5, P12-23, P16-28, P32-4, P52-1, P52-4.

### P44-1 (1, 69b)

**van der Corput, J. G. et Pisot, Ch. Sur un problème de Waring généralisé. III.** Nederl. Akad. Wetensch., Proc. **42**, 566–572 (1939).

Conditions are stated for the existence of solutions $y_\nu$ of the system

$$t_\mu=\sum_{\nu=1}^{n} b_{\mu\nu}f_\nu(y_\nu), \qquad \mu=1, \cdots, m,$$

$$y_\nu\equiv a_\nu \pmod{A_\nu}, \quad |f_\nu(y_\nu)|\leqq X, \nu=1, \cdots, n,$$

where some or all of the $y_\nu$ are primes. The numbers $t_\mu$, $b_{\mu\nu}$, $a_\nu$, $A_\nu$, and $X$ are given integers satisfying certain conditions and $f_\nu(y_\nu)$ are polynomials of given degree $k$ with integral coefficients. In some cases an approximate formula for the number of representations can be given. The results are said to follow from a general theorem of van der Corput [Acta Arith. **3**, 181–234 (1939)] and recent contributions of Siegel, Walfisz and Vinogradov. *R. D. James.*

### P44-2 (1, 135h)

**Pillai, S. S. On the number of representations of a number as the sum of the square of a prime and a squarefree integer.** Proc. Indian Acad. Sci., Sect. A. **10**, 390–391 (1939).

Let $R(n)$ denote the number of representations of $n$ as the sum of the square of a prime and a squarefree integer; $n\not\equiv 1 \pmod 4$. Following Erdös's proof of $R(n)>\sigma$ [J. London Math. Soc. **10**, 243–245 (1935)], the author proves

$$R(n)=\frac{2\sqrt{n}}{\lg n}\prod_q\left(i-\frac{2}{q(q-1)}\right)+O\left(\frac{\sqrt{n}}{\lg n\lg\lg n}\right),$$

where $q$ runs through all the primes for which $n$ is a quadratic residue. The paper contains inaccuracies.

*P. Scherk* (Waterville, Conn.).

### P44-3 (2, 34h)

**Noguera, Rodrigo. The Goldbach-Waring theorem.** Bol. Mat. **13**, 224–228 (1940). (Spanish)

### P44-4 (2, 35c)

**Pillai, S. S. On Waring's problem with powers of primes.** Proc. Indian Acad. Sci., Sect. A. **12**, 202–204 (1940).

Let $\theta$ be determined so that $p^\theta$ divides $k$ but $p^{\theta+1}$ does not divide $k$; let $\gamma=\theta+2$ for $p=2$ and $k$ even, $\gamma=\theta+1$ otherwise. Let $p_1, p_2, \cdots, p_n$ denote primes for which $p_i-1$ divides $k$, and write $K=p_1^{\gamma_1}\cdots p_n^{\gamma_n}$. In Waring's problem with powers of primes it is necessary to have some upper bound for the least value of $s$ such that the congruence $N\equiv x_1+\cdots+x_s \pmod K$ has a solution for every integer $N$. Here $x_1, \cdots, x_s$ can be 0, $p^k$ or $P^k$, where $p$ is any prime dividing $K$ and $P$ is the least prime which does not divide $K$. Such a bound is determined in this note. *R. D. James.*

Referred to in P44-8.

### P44-5 (2, 35d)

**Gupta, Hansraj. Waring's problem for powers of primes. II.** J. Indian Math. Soc. (N.S.) **4**, 71–79 (1940). [Part I appeared in J. Indian Math. Soc. (2) **3**, 136–145 (1938).] Let $n$ be any integer; write $3^n=2^nq+r$, where $0\leqq r<2^n$, and let $I=2^nq-2$. It is conjectured that for $n\geqq 7$ every integer is the sum of at most $I$ $n$th powers of primes. Numerical evidence is put forward to support this conjecture when $7\leqq n\leqq 19$, a typical result being the following: every integer less than $41^7$ is the sum of at most 143 seventh powers of primes. *R. D. James* (Saskatoon, Sask.).

### P44-6 (2, 42d)

**Sambasiva Rao, K. On the representation of a number as the sum of the $k$th power of a prime and an $l$th power-free integer.** Proc. Indian Acad. Sci., Sect. A. **11**, 429–436 (1940).

The author considers the representation of an integer $n$ in the respective forms $n=p^k+g_t$, $n=\psi(p)+g_t$, where $p$ is a prime, $g_t$ is an integer not divisible by the $t$th power of any integer greater than 1 and $\psi(p)$ is an integral valued polynomial in $p$ of degree $k$ with leading coefficient positive. Asymptotic formulas for the numbers of solutions are obtained for $t\geqq k$ in the first case and $t>k$ in the second. The cases $k=1$, $t=2$ and $k=t$ had been considered by previous writers using similar methods. Their results were less precise because the Page-Walfisz-Siegel theorem on primes in an arithmetical progression was not then known. The present paper makes full use of this. *R. D. James.*

Referred to in P16-13, P16-14.

### P44-7 (2, 250h)

**Mardjanichvili, C. Sur un problème additif de la théorie des nombres.** Bull. Acad. Sci. URSS. Sér. Math. [Izvestia Akad. Nauk SSSR] **4**, 193–214 (1940). (Russian. French summary)

The author considers the problem of the representation of $n$ integers $N_1, \cdots, N_n$ $(N_i<N_{i+1})$ in the form

$$(1) \qquad N_\kappa=\sum_{\nu=1}^{s} p_\nu^\kappa, \qquad \kappa=1, \cdots, n,$$

where $p_1, \cdots, p_s$ are primes. Let $I(N_1, \cdots, N_n; s)$ be the number of ordered sets $(p_1, \cdots, p_s)$ of primes satisfying (1). Then (Theorem I),

$$I(N_1, \cdots, N_n; s)=B(h_1, \cdots, h_{n-1}; s)N_n^{s/n-(n+1)/2}(\lg N_n)^{-s}$$
$$\times\mathfrak{S}(N_1, \cdots, N_n; s)+O(N_n^{s/n-(n+1)/2}(\lg N_n)^{-s-\omega}).$$

Here,

$$\mathfrak{S}=\sum_{q_1, \cdots, q_n=1}^{\infty} A(q_1, \cdots, q_n; s; N_1, \cdots, N_n),$$

$$A(q_1, \cdots, q_n; s; N_1, \cdots, N_n)=\sum_{a_1, \cdots, a_n}' D^s\exp\left(-2\pi i\sum_{i=1}^{n}\frac{a_i}{q_i}N_i\right),$$

$$D(a_1, q_1; \cdots; a_n, q_n)=\frac{1}{\phi(q_1\cdots q_n)}\sum_r{}' \exp\left(2\pi i\left(\frac{a_n}{q_n}r^n+\cdots+\frac{a_1}{q_1}r\right)\right),$$

$$N_\kappa=h_\kappa N_n^{\kappa/n}, \qquad \kappa=1, \cdots, n,$$

$\omega$ is a positive constant, and $0<C_1(n, s)\leqq B(h_1, \cdots, h_{n-1}; s)\leqq C_2(n, s)$. In the last sum the summation is extended over a reduced system of residues mod $q_1\cdots q_n$, whereas in the second sum each $a_i$ runs over the reduced system of residues mod $q_i$. The above estimate for $I$ holds under the assumption that $s\geqq 5n(n+1)(n+2)\lg n$ and that $N_1, \cdots, N_n$ have the following property: there exists $\epsilon>0$ such that for a suitably chosen set of numbers $h_\kappa'$ for which $h_\kappa-\epsilon\leqq h_\kappa'\leqq h_\kappa$, the system $\xi_1^\kappa+\cdots+\xi_s^\kappa=h_\kappa$ $(\kappa=1, \cdots, n)$ has positive solutions $\xi_\nu$. Next (Theorem II) the author proves that, for $n$ integers $M_1, \cdots, M_n$ satisfying a certain system of determinantal congruences, there exists an $s_0 \leqq \beta_0(n)$ (here $\beta_0$ depends on $n$ alone) and such that

$$\mathfrak{S}(M_1, \cdots, M_n; s_0) \geqq C_0(n) > 0.$$

In the proofs use is made of certain estimates of trigonometric sums by Vinogradow [Rec. Math. [Mat. Sbornik] N.S. **2** (**44**), 179–194 (1937); N.S. **3** (**45**), 435–471 (1938), Lemma 6; C. R. (Doklady) Acad. Sci. URSS (N.S.) **17**, no. 4 (1938)] and Mordell [Quart. J. Math., Oxford Ser. **3** (1932)]. Combining the results of the first two theorems the author obtains (Theorem III) conditions on $N_1, \cdots, N_n$ under which (1) would have prime solutions $p_1, \cdots, p_s$ with the bound of $s$ depending only on $n$. *A. E. Ross.*

Referred to in P08-23, P44-12, P44-17.

**P44-8** **(6, 57g)**

**Pillai, S. S. On Waring's problem with powers of primes.** J. Indian Math. Soc. (N.S.) **8**, 18–20 (1944).

An improvement of some of the author's previous results [Proc. Indian Acad. Sci., Sect. A. **9**, 29–34 (1939); **12**, 202–204 (1940); these Rev. **2**, 35]. *H. S. Zuckerman.*

Citations: MR 2, 35c = P44-4.

**P44-9** **(10, 683e)**

**Čudakov, N. G. On some power series containing prime numbers as exponents.** Doklady Akad. Nauk SSSR (N.S.) **65**, 445–448 (1949). (Russian)

The author investigates the behavior of the function $f(x) = \sum_{p \geqq 2} \log p \cdot x^{p^k}$ in the neighborhood of the rational points of the unit circle; the summation letter $p$ runs over all primes. For $k=1$, the author treated this previously [Ann. of Math. (2) **48**, 515–545 (1947); these Rev. **9**, 11]. He now extends his method to the case $k>1$. This result may be stated as follows. Let $x = r \exp i\varphi$, $0 \leqq r < 1$, $M = (1-r)^{-1}$, $(a, q) = 1$, $\rho = \exp 2\pi i a/q$, $\vartheta = \varphi - 2\pi a/q$, $A$ be a fixed positive constant, $\tau_1 = (\log M)^{A_3}$ where $A_3$ (as well as $A_2$ mentioned later) is a certain function of $k$ and $A$, and let $\psi_\rho(x) = \{\varphi(k)(1-x/\rho)^{1/k}\}^{-1}\Gamma(1/k)\sum_n' \rho^{n^k}$, where the prime indicates that $n$ runs through a reduced residue system mod $q$. Then on the Farey arc of order $\tau_1$, $|\vartheta| \leqq \pi/(q\tau_1)$, $q \leqq \tau_1$, we have $f(x) - \psi_\rho(x) = M^{1/k}(\log M)^{1+1/k-A}O(1)$. If $|\vartheta| \leqq 2\pi(\log M)^{A_2}/M$, the treatment is the same as in the paper mentioned above. However, when

$$|\vartheta| > 2\pi(\log M)^{A_2}/M,$$

corresponding to the minor arc in the usual treatment, the author finds it necessary to appeal to known estimates for the exponential sum $\sum_{p \leqq x} \exp(2\pi i a p^k/q)$; in his previous work, exponential sums were avoided.

The author remarks that his theorem implies the known Goldbach-Waring theorem [see L. K. Hua, The additive prime number theory, Trav. Inst. Math. Stekloff **22** (1947); these Rev. **10**, 597] on the number of representations of an integer as the sum of $s$ $k$th powers of primes. He promises further applications later. *L. Schoenfeld.*

Citations: MR 9, 11d = P32-10; MR 10, 597e = P02-5.

**P44-10** **(11, 161g)**

**Mardžanišvili, K. K. On some additive problems with prime numbers.** Uspehi Matem. Nauk (N.S.) **4**, no. 1(29), 183–185 (1949). (Russian)

This note announces results on the simultaneous Waring-Goldbach problem, i.e., the problem of finding sufficient conditions for the solvability of the system of Diophantine equations $p_1 + \cdots + p_r = N_1, \cdots, p_1^n + \cdots + p_r^n = N_n$, where the $p$ are primes. The author is said to have proved earlier that the asymptotic formula for this problem is valid for $r \geqq r_0 \sim 12.5n^2 \log n$. [A slightly sharper statement of this kind can be deduced from results of L. K. Hua, Quart. J. Math., Oxford Ser. **20**, 48–61 (1949); these Rev. **10**, 597.] Here the author gives congruence conditions on $N_1, \cdots, N_n$ which ensure that the singular series is bounded away from zero and thus that the simultaneous Waring-Goldbach problem is solvable if $N_1, \cdots, N_n$ are large and their sizes are properly related, $r$ being again of the order of magnitude of a constant times $n^2 \log n$. *P. T. Bateman.*

Citations: MR 10, 597d = P08-11.

Referred to in P44-12, P44-17.

**P44-11** **(11, 332e)**

**Verdenius, W. On problems analogous to those of Goldbach and Waring.** Nederl. Akad. Wetensch., Proc. **52**, 725–733 = Indagationes Math. **11**, 255–263 (1949).

This paper is a summary of the author's thesis [Over problemen analoog aan die van Goldbach en Waring, Amsterdam, 1948]. It deals with the representation of $m$ integers $t_1, \cdots, t_m$ in the form

$$t_\mu = \sum_{\nu=1}^{n} b_{\mu\nu}\psi_\nu(y_{\nu 1}, \cdots, y_{\nu s_\nu}), \qquad \mu = 1, \cdots, m,$$

where $m$, $n$, $s_1, \cdots, s_n$ are fixed positive integers, the $b_{\mu\nu}$ are fixed integers, the $\psi_\nu$ are fixed integral-valued polynomials, and the $y_{\nu\sigma}$ take on prime values in certain intervals. The theorems stated are too complicated to quote in detail. The author bases his work on van der Corput's version of the Hardy-Littlewood-Vinogradov method [Acta Arith. **3**, 180–234 (1939)]. *P. T. Bateman* (Princeton, N. J.).

**P44-12** **(11, 502d)**

**Mardžanišvili, K. K. On a system of equations in prime numbers.** Doklady Akad. Nauk SSSR (N.S.) **70**, 381–383 (1950). (Russian)

Suppose $l < m < \cdots < n$ are fixed positive integers, $g$ in number, and let $N_l < N_m < \cdots < N_n$ be variable positive integers. For suitable $s$ the author considers the system of equations

$$(*) \quad p_1^l + \cdots + p_s^l = N_l, \; p_1^m + \cdots + p_s^m = N_m, \; \cdots, \; p_1^n + \cdots + p_s^n = N_n$$

Put $N_n = P^n$, $N_k = h_k P^k$ $(k = l, m, \cdots, n)$, and

$$\Delta(z_1, \cdots, z_g) = \begin{vmatrix} z_1^{l-1} & \cdots & z_g^{l-1} \\ \cdots & & \cdots \\ z_1^{n-1} & \cdots & z_g^{n-1} \end{vmatrix}.$$

The author states the following theorem. If $f$ is a whole number not less than $3ng$, if $s = f + 2gr$, where $r = [2n \log 10ng + n \log\log 20ng + 1]$, and if the system of equations $\xi_1^k + \cdots + \xi_f^k = h_k$ $(k = l, m, \cdots, n)$ is solvable in real numbers $\xi_1, \cdots, \xi_f$ satisfying the conditions $\xi_j \geqq \epsilon$ $(j = 1, 2, \cdots, f)$ and $|\Delta(\xi_1, \cdots, \xi_g)| \geqq \epsilon$, where $\epsilon$ is some (fixed) positive number, then the number of solutions, $I = I(N_l, \cdots, N_n; l, \cdots, n; s)$, of the system (*) satisfies the inequality

$$I \geqq P^{f + 2gn\{1-(1-1/n)^r\} - \{l + \cdots + n\}} \{\log P\}^{-f-2gr} \{CS + O(\log P)^{-\omega}\},$$

where $S$ is the singular series and $C$, $\omega$, and the $O$-constant are positive numbers depending only on $l, m, \cdots, n, f, g$, and $\epsilon$. The author also states two theorems giving conditions under which the singular series is bounded away from zero.

In earlier publications [Bull. Acad. Sci. URSS. Sér. Math. [Izvestiya Akad. Nauk SSSR] **4**, 193–214 (1940); Uspehi Matem. Nauk (N.S.) **4**, no. 1(29), 183–185 (1949); these Rev. **2**, 250; **11**, 161] the author has considered the special case in which $l, m, \cdots, n$ are the integers $1, 2, \cdots, n$ (the so-called simultaneous Waring-Goldbach problem). For a general survey of the author's work see the résumé of his doctoral dissertation [see the following review].

*P. T. Bateman* (Urbana, Ill.).

Citations: MR 2, 250h = P44-7; MR 11, 161g = P44-10.

Referred to in P44-17, P44-18.

**P44-13** **(11, 502e)**

**Mardžanišvili, K. K. Investigations on the application of the method of trigonometric sums to additive problems.** Uspehi Matem. Nauk (N.S.) **5**, no. 1(35), 236–240 (1950). (Russian)

This paper is a résumé of the author's doctoral dissertation. Besides the material of the dissertation itself, it includes a brief history of additive number theory, with specific reference to the Waring and Goldbach problems and their generalizations. In the first two chapters of the dissertation the author treats the system of Diophantine equations $x_1^l+\cdots+x_s^l=N_l$, $x_1^m+\cdots+x_s^m=N_m$, $\cdots$, $x_1^n+\cdots+x_s^n=N_n$, where $l<m<\cdots<n$ are fixed positive integers, $g$ in number. He proves that this system is solvable for an $s$ having the order of magnitude $ng\log n$, provided $N_l, \cdots, N_n$ satisfy appropriate order conditions and certain arithmetical requirements. In chapter 3 the author gives a careful estimation of the error term in the Vinogradov formula for the number of representations of a large odd number as a sum of three primes, with a view toward getting a good value for the "Vinogradov constant." In chapter 4 he proves that the asymptotic formula in the simultaneous Waring-Goldbach problem is valid for a number of summands of the order $n^2\log n$ [see the second paragraph of the preceding review and also Hua, Quart. J. Math., Oxford Ser. **20**, 48–61 (1949); these Rev. **10**, 597]. In chapter 5 he discusses the singular series for the system (*) of equations in prime numbers considered in the paper reviewed above, and in chapter 6 he proves the asymptotic inequality for the number of solutions which is stated in the preceding review. Finally in chapter 7 he derives the asymptotic formula and studies the singular series for the system $p_1+\cdots+p_s=N_1$, $p_1^2+\cdots+p_s^2=N_2$, with $s\geqq 7$ (and $p_1, \cdots, p_s$ prime numbers). *P. T. Bateman.*

Citations: MR 10, 597d = P08-11.
Referred to in P02-13, P44-19.

**P44-14** **(12, 805c)**

**Halberstam, H. Representation of integers as sums of a square of a prime, a cube of a prime, and a cube.** Proc. London Math. Soc. (2) **52**, 455–466 (1951).

Davenport and Heilbronn [Proc. London Math. Soc. (2) **43**, 73–104 (1937)] proved that almost all positive integers are the sums of one square and two cubes (of positive integers). It is proved in this paper that almost all positive integers $n$ are representable in the form $n=p_1^2+p_2^3+x^3$, where $p_1$ and $p_2$ are primes, and $x$ is a positive integer. The proof involves the Hardy-Littlewood technique of Farey dissection. The treatment of the singular series is based upon the method of Davenport and Heilbronn as modified by Roth [J. London Math. Soc. **24**, 4–13 (1949); these Rev. **10**, 431]. *A. L. Whiteman* (Los Angeles, Calif.).

Citations: MR 10, 431f = P12-2.

**P44-15** **(13, 112a)**

**Roth, K. F. On Waring's problem for cubes.** Proc. London Math. Soc. (2) **53**, 268–279 (1951).

The author proves that almost all positive integers $u$ are representable in the form $u=p_1^3+p_2^3+p_3^3+x^3$, where $p_1$, $p_2$ and $p_3$ are primes and $x$ is a positive integer, and that all large positive integers $u$ are representable in the form $u=p_1^3+p_2^3+\cdots+p_7^3+x^3$, where $p_1, \cdots, p_7$ are primes and $x$ is a positive integer. *L. K. Hua* (Peking).

**P44-16** **(14, 451d)**

**Šapiro-Pyateckiĭ, I. I. On a variant of the Waring-Goldbach problem.** Mat. Sbornik N.S. **30**(72), 105–120 (1952). (Russian)

This paper is concerned with the number $J(N, r; C, \Delta)$ of solutions $(p_1, \cdots, p_r)$ of the inequality

$$|p_1^C+\cdots+p_r^C-N|<\Delta$$

where $C>1$ is not an integer and the $p$'s are primes. Let $H(C)$ be the least value of $r$ such that for each $\Delta>0$ there is an $N_0(\Delta)$ for which $J(N, r; C, \Delta)>0$ for all integers $N>N_0(\Delta)$. One result proved by the author is that $\limsup_{C\to\infty} H(C)/(C\log C)\leqq 4$; this may be compared with Vinogradov's [Trav. Inst. Math. Stekloff **23** (1947); these Rev. **10**, 599] result that $\limsup_{k\to\infty} G(k)/(k\log k)\leqq 3$ for the Waring problem where $k$ is an integer and the primes $p_m$ are replaced by positive integers $x_m$. Actually, a more general result is proved as are a number of more specialized results dealing with the cases $1<C<3/2$ and $r=2, 3$.

The results obtained considerably improve previous results of B. I. Segal [Ann. of Math. (2) **36**, 507–520 (1935)] who, however, dealt with positive integers $x_m$ instead of primes $p_m$. Segal's results were based on an estimate of exponential sums due to van der Corput and hence were comparable to the older Hardy-Littlewood estimates of $G(k)$. The present author employs the Vinogradov estimates of exponential sums both for the case in which the summation letter runs over consecutive primes and for the case in which the summation letter runs over consecutive integers. In addition, Turán's [Izvestiya Akad. Nauk SSSR. Ser. Mat. **11**, 197–262 (1947); these Rev. **9**, 80] estimate for $\sum_p e^{i\xi p^C}$ is used. As in Segal's work an important part is played in a certain Fourier integral by the kernel $D(\Delta\xi)D^s(\delta\xi)$ where $D(x)=x^{-1}\sin x$ and $\xi$ is the integration variable while $\Delta$, $\delta$ are suitably chosen parameters. *L. Schoenfeld.*

Citations: MR 9, 80e = M30-8; MR 10, 599a = L02-2.

**P44-17** **(15, 12d)**

**Mardžanišvili, K. K. On an asymptotic formula of the additive theory of prime numbers.** Soobščeniya Akad. Nauk Gruzin. SSR. **8**, 597–604 (1947). (Russian)

The author refines a previous paper of his [Izvestiya Akad. Nauk SSSR. Ser. Mat. **4**, 193–214 (1940); these Rev. **2**, 250] concerned with the number $I=I(N_1, \cdots, N_n; s)$ of solutions $(p_1, \cdots, p_s)$ in primes of the system of equations

$$(*)\qquad N_k=p_1^k+\cdots+p_s^k,\quad k=1, \cdots, n$$

for given $s, N_1, \cdots, N_n$. His final result is that the asymptotic formula, for large $n$, which he obtained previously for $s>s_0\sim 5n^3\log n$ also holds if $s>s_1\sim(25/2)n^2\log n$.

This improvement by a factor of about $n$ has been made possible by the work of Vinogradov and others on exponential sums. Thus, with the aid of such work, the author proves the following lemma which is basic for the improved value of $s$. The number of integral solutions $(x_1, \cdots, x_{2l})$ of the system of equations

$$x_1^k+\cdots+x_l^k=x_{l+1}^k+\cdots+x_{2l}^k,\quad k=1, \cdots, n,$$

subject to the conditions $0\leqq x_j\leqq P$ is $O(P^{2l-n(n+1)/2})$ provided $n>11$ and $l>(s_1-3)/2$; this result is almost the same as a later result of Vinogradov [ibid. **15**, 109–130 (1951), Lemma 7; these Rev. **13**, 328]. In the proof of this result, Hua's estimate

$$\sum_{x=1}^{q} e^{2\pi i[f(x)/q]}=O(q^{1-(1/k)+\epsilon}),$$

$f(x)$ a polynomial of degree $k$, is used.

Since the appearance of this paper the author has published two papers in which extensions and improvements are stated [Doklady Akad. Nauk SSSR (N.S.) **70**, 381–383 (1950); Uspehi Matem. Nauk (N.S.) **4**, no. 1(29), 183–185 (1949); these Rev. **11**, 502, 872, 161]. See also the paper reviewed below. *L. Schoenfeld* (Urbana, Ill.).

Citations: MR 2, 250h = P44-7; MR 11, 161g = P44-10; MR 11, 502d = P44-12; MR 13, 328e = L15-14.

**P44-18** **(15, 13a)**

**Mardžanišvili, K. K. On a generalization of Waring's problem.** Soobščeniya Akad. Nauk Gruzin. SSR **11**, 82–84 (1950). (Russian)

In this paper are stated the analogs of the theorems stated by the author in a previous paper [Doklady Akad. Nauk SSSR (N.S.) **70**, 381–383 (1950); these Rev. **11**, 502, 872]. Whereas the former paper restricted the variables (in (*) of the preceding review) to prime numbers, the present paper allows the variables to be any positive numbers.

*L. Schoenfeld* (Urbana, Ill.).

Citations: MR 11, 502d = P44-12.

**P44-19** **(15, 103c)**

**Mardžanišvili, K. K. On the simultaneous representation of pairs of numbers by sums of prime numbers and their squares.** Akad. Nauk Gruzin. SSR. Trudy Mat. Inst. Razmadze **18**, 183–208 (1951). (Russian. Georgian summary)

Suppose $\epsilon$ is a given positive number $<\frac{1}{2}$ and $s$ is a given positive integer $\geqq 7$. The author proves in full that the system of Diophantine equations (*) $p_1+p_2+\cdots+p_s=N_1$, $p_1^2+p_2^2+\cdots+p_s^2=N_2$ is solvable in prime numbers $p_1, p_2, \cdots, p_s$ provided $N_1$ and $N_2$ are sufficiently large positive integers satisfying the requirements $1+\epsilon\leqq N_1N_2^{-\frac{1}{2}}\leqq s^{\frac{1}{2}}-\epsilon$, $N_2\equiv N_1 \pmod 2$, $N_2\equiv s \pmod{24}$. This is done in the usual two steps. First, he proves that if $N_1$ and $N_2$ are any positive integers such that $1+\epsilon\leqq N_1N_2^{-\frac{1}{2}}\leqq s^{\frac{1}{2}}-\epsilon$, then the number of solutions of (*) in prime numbers is given by

$$B(N_1N_2^{-\frac{1}{2}}, s)N_2^{(s-3)/2}(\log N_2)^{-s}\mathfrak{S}_s(N_1, N_2) + O(N_2^{(s-3)/2}(\log N_2)^{-s-\omega}),$$

where $\omega$ is a certain positive constant,

$$0<C_1(s, \epsilon)<B(N_1N_2^{-\frac{1}{2}}, s)<C_2(s, \epsilon),$$

and $\mathfrak{S}_s(N_1, N_2)$ is the singular series. [This first part of the argument, which is based on Vinogradov's method, can also be found in Hua's monograph, The additive theory of prime numbers, Trav. Inst. Math. Stekloff **22** (1947), Chap. 10; these Rev. **10**, 597.] Second, he shows that if $N_2\equiv N_1 \pmod 2$ and $N_2\equiv s \pmod{24}$, then $\mathfrak{S}_s(N_1, N_2)>C(s)>0$. The resumé of the author's doctoral dissertation [Uspehi Matem. Nauk (N.S.) **5**, no. 1(35), 236–240 (1950); these Rev. **11**, 502] seems to indicate that the present paper is essentially the last chapter of that apparently unpublished work. Also the author has asserted in an expository article [Acta Math. Acad. Sci. Hungar. **2**, 223–227 (1951); these Rev. **15**, 13] that he first obtained the above result in 1942.

*P. T. Bateman* (Urbana, Ill.).

Citations: MR 10, 597e = P02-5; MR 11, 502e = P44-13; MR 15, 13b = P02-13.

**P44-20** **(15, 856a; 15, 856b)**

**Prachar, K. Über ein Problem vom Waring-Goldbach'schen Typ.** Monatsh. Math. **57**, 66–74 (1953).

**Prachar, K. Über ein Problem vom Waring-Goldbach'schen Typ. II.** Monatsh. Math. **57**, 113–116 (1953).

In the first paper, the author proves that almost all (in the sense of asymptotic density 1) even numbers can be represented in the form $n=p_2^2+p_3^3+p_4^4+p_5^5$ where the $p_r$ are primes. The proof makes use of a Farey dissection of the unit interval, the asymptotic estimate for the number of primes in a progression, Vinogradov's estimate of exponential sums involving prime summation variable, a number of estimates of Hua, and a result of Cauchy-Davenport-Chowla on the number of residue classes in the sum of two systems of residue classes.

In the second paper, the author shows that all sufficiently large odd numbers are representable in the form

$$n=p_1+p_2^2+p_3^3+p_4^4+p_5^5$$

with primes $p_r$, and that the number of such representations is of the true order of magnitude $N^\gamma/\log^5 N$ where

$$\gamma=1/2+1/3+1/4+1/5.$$

Some of the results of the first paper are used and in addition the major arcs are further divided. *L. Schoenfeld.*

**P44-21** **(20# 842 )**

**Mitsui, Takayoshi. On the partitions of a number into the powers of prime numbers.** J. Math. Soc. Japan **9** (1957), 428–447.

The author develops an asymptotic formula for the number $T(n, m; k)$ of partitions of $n$ into $k$th powers of prime numbers not exceeding $m$, where $m\leqq n^{1/k}$, $k\geqq 1$. He shows that $T(n, m; k)\sim(2\pi A_2)^{-\frac{1}{2}}\exp(n\alpha+A_1)$ as $n, m\to\infty$, where $\alpha$ is the root of the equation $n=\sum_{p\leq m} p^k(e^{\alpha p^k}-1)^{-1}$ and $A_1$, $A_2$ are positive constants defined by similar sums over the primes not exceeding $m$ ($n\alpha\to\infty$ as $m, n\to\infty$). He writes

$$T(n, m; k)=\exp(n\alpha)\int_{-\frac{1}{2}}^{\frac{1}{2}} G(\exp(-\alpha+2\pi i\theta))\exp(-2\pi in\theta)d\theta$$

where $G$ is the generating function $G(w)=\prod_{p\leq m}(1-w^{p^k})^{-1}$ of $T(n, m; k)$. The author then follows a paper of Szekeres [Quart. J. Math. Oxford Ser. (2) **4** (1953), 96–111; MR **15**, 201] and shows that, with the above choice of $\alpha$, the principal contribution to the integral comes from the neighborhood of $\theta=0$. For the difficult estimation of the error term he relies partly on methods and results of Vinogradov and Hua.

Some special cases are discussed in the last section. For example, if $m\leqq n^{1/(k+1)}$, it is shown that $n\alpha\sim(m/\log m)$, $A_1\sim(m/\log m)\log(nm^{-k-1}\log m)$, and $A_2\sim n^2 m^{-1}\log m$.

These results generalize those of Haselgrove and Temperley [Proc. Cambridge Philos. Soc. **50** (1954), 225–241; MR **16**, 17], who, as a special case of their theorems, obtained an asymptotic formula for $T(n, m; 1)$. They used a different method.

*J. Lehner* (East Lansing, Mich.)

Citations: MR 15, 201c = P72-19; MR 16, 17f = P72-21.

**P44-22** **(21# 660 )**

**Wirsing, Eduard. Eine Erweiterung des ersten Romanovschen Satzes.** Arch. Math. **9** (1958), 407–409.

Let $f(x)$ be a polynomial with positive highest coefficient which assumes integral values for integer $x$. The author proves (extending previous results of Romanoff and Wirsing) that the density of integers of the form $p+f(q)$ ($p$, $q$ primes) is positive.

*P. Erdös* (Boulder, Colo.)

**P44-23** **(22# 12087 )**

**Grosswald, E. Partitions into prime powers.** Michigan Math. J. **7** (1960), 97–122.

This paper gives asymptotic formulae for the number of partitions $p(n, m; k)$ of the integer $n$ into $k$th powers of primes $p$ in the range $2\leqq p\leqq m$. These results supersede asymptotic formulae due to Hardy and Ramanujan for the number of partitions of $n$ into powers of primes. Several special ranges of the variables are considered: (i) $m$ fixed; (ii) $m\to\infty$ with $m=O(n^\varepsilon)$; (iii) $m^{k+1}<n\log m$; $m\neq O(n^\varepsilon)$ for all $\varepsilon$; (iv) $n\log m\leqq m^{k+1}<n\log n$; (v) $m^{k+1}>n\log n$. The form and accuracy of the asymptotic formulae depends on the range of the variables. The results may be compared with the more general but less accurate results of Haselgrove and Temperley [Proc. Cambridge Philos. Soc. **50** (1954), 225–241; MR **16**, 17]. These results apply to the number of partitions of $n$ into $m$ parts. *C. B. Haselgrove* (Manchester)

Citations: MR 16, 17f = P72-21.

**P44-24** **(23# A3727)**

**Schwarz, Wolfgang**

**Zur Darstellung von Zahlen durch Summen von Primzahlpotenzen.**

*J. Reine Angew. Math.* **206** (1961), 78–112.

Der Verfasser untersucht additive Zerfällungen in Primzahlen und Primzahlpotenzen, derart, dass fast alle Zahlen in der betrachteten Form darstellbar sind (d.h. die Anzahl der nicht darstellbaren Zahlen $\leqq N$ ist $o(N)$). Eine Reihe bekannter Resultate wird verallgemeinert. Ein typisches Ergebnis ist: Die Anzahl der Zahlen $2n \leqq N$ mit $2n \not\equiv 1 \pmod p$ für jedes $p>2$ mit $(p-1)|k$, die nicht in der Form $2n = p_1 + p_2{}^k$ darstellbar sind, ist, für jedes feste $B=0$, $O(N/\log^B N)$; eine typische Folgerung: Jedes hinreichende grosse ungerade $N$ ist in der Gestalt $N = p_1 + p_2{}^2 + p_3{}^3 + p_4{}^6 + p_5{}^k$ darstellbar.
*H.-E. Richert* (Syracuse, N.Y.)

**P44-25** **(23# A3728)**

**Schwarz, Wolfgang**

**Zur Darstellung von Zahlen durch Summen von Primzahlpotenzen. I. Darstellung hinreichend grosser Zahlen.**

*J. Reine Angew. Math.* **205** (1960/61), 21–47.

Der Verfasser beweist ein allgemeines Resultat der additiven Primzahltheorie, das verschiedene bekannte Einzelergebnisse zusammenfasst und diese teilweise verallgemeinert. Sein Hauptsatz gibt Bedingungen an, unter denen hinreichend grosse Zahlen $N$ in der Form

(1) $$N = b_1p_1 + \cdots + b_sp_s + f_1(p_1') + \cdots + f_r(p_r')$$

darstellbar sind. Hierin sind $p_1, \cdots, p_s, p_1', \cdots, p_r'$ Primzahlen, $b_1, \cdots, b_s$ natürliche Zahlen $(b_1, \cdots, b_s) = 1$, $f_j(x)$ Polynome mit ganzen Koeffizienten vom Grade $k_j \geqq 2$, $j = 1, \cdots, r$, sowie $s \geqq 2$ und $r \geqq 1$ oder $s \geqq 3$ und $r \geqq 0$. Gleichzeitig wird eine asymptotische Formel für die Anzahl der Lösungen von (1) hergeleitet. Der Beweis folgt der Vinogradovschen Methode.
*H.-E. Richert* (Syracuse, N.Y.)

**P44-26** **(25# 3004)**

**Schwarz, Wolfgang**

**Weitere, mit einer Methode von Erdős-Prachar erzielte Ergebnisse.**

*Math. Nachr.* **23** (1961), 327–348.

Let $c, c_1, \cdots$ denote positive constants independent of a sufficiently large integer $N$. Prachar [J. London Math. Soc. **29** (1954), 347–350; MR **15**, 935] proved that there are more than $\exp(c_1\sqrt{\log N})$ integers $n \leqq N$ for which the "prime-diophantine equation" $n = p' + p''$ has more than $(cN \log\log N)/\log^2 N$ solutions in primes $p'$, $p''$. Extending Prachar's methods, the present author derives a number of analogous results. His two main theorems are as follows. (1) Let $f(x) = \sum_{i=0}^k a_ix^{k-i}$ be a polynomial of degree $k \geqq 2$ with integral coefficients $a_i$ and with $a_0 > 0$. Then there are at least $\exp(c_2 \log N/(\log\log N)^2)$ integers $n \leqq N$ for which the equation $n = p' + f(p'')$ has more than $c_3N^{1/k} \log\log N/\log^2 N$ solutions in primes $p'$, $p''$. (2) If $k \geqq 1$, then there are more than $\exp(c_4 \log N/\log\log N)$ integers $n \leqq N$ for which the equation $n = p_1{}^2 + p_2{}^2 + p_3{}^k$ has more than $c_5N^{1/k}(\log\log N)^\eta/\log^3 N$ solutions in primes $p_1, p_2, p_3$. The exponent $\eta$ is here defined as $\frac{3}{2}$ or $\frac{1}{2}$ according as $k$ is even or odd. In the course of the proofs a sequence of fifteen interesting lemmas is developed. One of these lemmas is an application of the prime number theorem of Rodosskii-Tatuzawa [see, e.g., K. Prachar, *Primzahlverteilung*, p. 320, Springer, Berlin, 1957; MR **19**, 393] for primes in an arithmetic progression.
*A. L. Whiteman* (Los Angeles, Calif.)

Citations: MR 15, 935b = P32-27; MR 19, 393b = N02-7.
Referred to in P44-27.

**P44-27** **(28# 1182)**

**Schwarz, Wolfgang**

**Weitere, mit einer methode von Erdős-Prachar erzielte Ergebnisse. II.**

*Monatsh. Math.* **68** (1964), 75–80.

The main objective of the author is to improve Theorem 1 of his earlier paper [Math. Nachr. **23** (1961), 327–348; MR **25** #3004] with the same title. His new result is Theorem 1′: Let $f(x) = a_0x^k + \cdots + a_k$ be a polynomial of degree $k \geqq 1$ with integral coefficients $a_i$ and with $a_0 > 0$. For every $\varepsilon > 0$ there exist positive constants $\delta_j(\varepsilon)$ with the following property: There are more than $\delta_1 N \exp(-\delta_2(\log N)^\varepsilon)$ integers $n \leqq N$ for which the prime-Diophantine equation $n = p' + f(p'')$ has more than $\delta_3 N^{1/k} \log\log N/\log^2 N$ solutions in primes $p'$, $p''$. The author also proves Theorem 2′: Let $s \geqq 4$, and $K = k_1{}^{-1} + \cdots + k_s{}^{-1} > 1$. Then there exist positive constants $\gamma_1$, $\gamma_2$ independent of $N$ such that for at least $\exp(\gamma_1 \log N/\log\log N)$ integers $n \leqq N$ the prime-Diophantine equation $n = c_1p_1{}^{k_1} + \cdots + c_sp_s{}^{k_s}$ has more than $\gamma_2 N^{K-1}(\log N)^{-s}$ solutions in primes $p_1, \cdots, p_s$. The method involves ideas of Prachar [J. London Math. Soc. **29** (1954), 347–350; MR **15**, 935] on integers having many representations as the sum of two primes, and ideas of Hua and Vandiver [Proc. Nat. Acad. Sci. U.S.A. **35** (1949), 94–99; MR **10**, 515] on the number of solutions of certain equations in a finite field.
*A. L. Whiteman* (Los Angeles, Calif.)

Citations: MR 10, 515c = T50-7; MR 15, 935b = P32-27; MR 25# 3004 = P44-26.

**P44-28** **(28# 1184)**

**Rieger, G. J.**

**Über die Anzahl der Darstellungen einer natürlichen Zahl als Summe einer quadratfreien Zahl und eines Primzahlquadrates.**

*Math. Ann.* **152** (1963), 342–350.

Refinements and generalisations of a result of Erdős [J. London Math. Soc. **10** (1935), 243–245], including asymptotic formulae for the number of representations of a number as the sum of a square of a prime and a square-free number, with and without additional restrictions on the size of the prime. *T. Estermann* (London)

**P44-29** **(29# 83)**

**Rieger, G. J.**

**Über die Summe von zwei $n$-ten Primzahlpotenzen.**

*Math. Z.* **84** (1964), 137–142.

Erdős and Mahler [J. London Math. Soc. **13** (1938), 134–139] proved that if $A(u)$ is the number of solutions of

$$x_1{}^n + x_2{}^n = k, \qquad 0 < x_1, x_2 \leqq u^{1/n},$$

then, for $n \geqq 3$,

$$\liminf \frac{A(u)}{u^{2/n}} > 0 \quad \text{as } u \to \infty.$$

They also deduced from a theorem of Siegel that

$$\limsup \frac{A(u)}{u^{2/n}} < \infty.$$

The author proves that if $B(u)$ is the number of solutions of

$$p_1^n + p_2^n = k, \qquad 0 < p_1, p_2 \leq u^{1/n},$$

where $p_1, p_2$ are primes, then

$$\text{(1)} \qquad \liminf \frac{B(u)}{u^{2/n}/\log^2 u} > 0.$$

Since, from the prime number theorem,

$$\limsup \frac{B(u)}{u^{2/n}/\log^2 u} < \infty,$$

it follows that (1) cannot be improved.

*S. Chowla* (University Park, Pa.)

Referred to in P12-23.

**P44-30** **(34# 5790 )**

**Thanigasalam, K.**

**A generalization of Waring's problem for prime powers.**
*Proc. London Math. Soc.* (3) **16** (1966), 193–212.

E. J. Scourfield [J. London Math. Soc. **35** (1960), 98–116; MR **22** #2591] proved the following theorem: Given a sequence $\{n_i\}$ of integers with $2 \leqq n_1 \leqq n_2 \leqq \cdots$, a necessary and sufficient condition that, for any member $n_j$ of the sequence, there exist an integer $r = r(n_j)$ such that all sufficiently large integers $N$ are representable in the form $N = x_1^{n_j} + x_2^{n_{j+1}} + \cdots + x_r^{n_{j+r-1}}$, where $x_1, x_2, \cdots, x_r$ are positive integers, is that (*) $\sum_{i=1}^{\infty} n_i^{-1} = \infty$. The author considers the corresponding problem for prime powers and proves that if the sequence $\{n_i\}$ satisfies (*), then there is a natural number $s_1$, depending on $n_j$ and $\{n_i\}$, such that corresponding to every large integer $N$ there exist a natural number $s \leqq s_1$ and primes $p_1, p_2, \cdots, p_s$ for which $N = p_1^{n_j} + p_2^{n_{j+1}} + \cdots + p_s^{n_{j+s-1}}$. (The necessity of condition (*) is trivial. See Scourfield [loc. cit.].) To prove the theorem, the Hardy-Littlewood method (modified by Vinogradov) is (doubly) used. {In Lemma 7 and its corollary, $L$ must mean $\log P$ instead of $\log N$.}

*T. Hayashida* (Yokohama)

Citations: MR 22# 2591 = P12-11.

**P44-31** **(35# 2847 )**

**Lenskoĭ, D. N.**

**On the theory of prime numbers.** **(Russian)**
*Dokl. Akad. Nauk SSSR* **169** (1966), 266–268.

The author announces and sketches the proofs of two theorems. We quote one. Let $f(X_1, \cdots, X_s)$ be a polynomial in $s \geqq 2$ variables, whose coefficients are natural numbers. Let $d_i$ be the degree of $f$ in $X_i$. Denote by $S_f(n)$ the number of solutions of the equation $p + f(p_1, p_2, \cdots, p_s) = n$ in positive prime numbers $p, p_1, \cdots, p_s$. Then, as $n \to \infty$,

$$S_f(n) \leqq c_f(n^{\sum_{i=1}^{s} d_i^{-1}}/\ln^{s+1} n) \ln \ln n,$$

where $c_f$ is a positive constant depending on $f$ alone.

The references include the papers by S. Lang and A. Weil [Amer. J. Math. **76** (1954), 819–827; MR **16**, 398] and A. Selberg [Eleventh Skandinavian Mathematician's Congress (Trondheim, 1949) (Norwegian), pp. 13–22, J. G. Tanums Forlag, Oslo, 1952; MR **14**, 726].

{This article has appeared in English translation [Soviet Math. Dokl. **7** (1966), 904–906].}

*S. Chowla* (University Park, Pa.)

Citations: MR 14, 726j = M55-11; MR 16, 398d = G25-2.

**P44-32** **(37# 5177 )**

**Rieger, G. J.**

**Über die Summe aus einem Quadrat und einem Primzahlquadrat.**
*J. Reine Angew. Math.* **231** (1968), 89–100.

Verfasser bezeichnet mit $\pi(x)$ die Anzahl der ungeraden Primzahlen $p \leqq x$, mit $E(x)$ $[H(x)]$ die Anzahl der natürlichen Zahlen $n \leqq x$, welche mindestens eine Darstellung $n = p_1^2 + p_2^2$ $[n = b^2 + p^2]$ zulassen, wobei $p, p_1, p_2$ ungerade Primzahlen und $b$ eine ganzrationale Zahl bedeuten. U.a. werden die beiden folgenden Sätze bewiesen: (1) Für $x \geqq 10$ ist $H(x) > cx^{1/2}\pi(x^{1/2})$; $c$ = absolute Konstante. (2) $E(x) = \frac{1}{8}\pi x(\log x)^{-2}(1 + O((\log\log x)^{2/3}(\log x)^{-2/3}))$. (Vgl. P. Erdős [Nederl. Akad. Wetensch. **41** (1938), 37–41] und P. Erdős und K. Mahler [J. London Math. Soc. **13** (1938), 134–139].)

*H. J. Kanold* (Braunschweig)

# P48 PROPERTIES OF THE SHIFTED PRIMES, $\{p + \text{const}\}$

See also reviews A22-47, A30-28, L20-25, M55-79, N12-28, N24-80, N32-68, N40-76, N52-15, N56-33, N60-62, N60-78, N64-12, N64-27, N64-32, N76-6, P02-18, P36-43, P40-15, P40-24.

**P48-1** **(3, 68c)**

**Pillai, S. S. On the sum function connected with primitive roots.** Proc. Indian Acad. Sci., Sect. A. **13**, 526–529 (1941).

Let $P(n)$ denote the number of primitive roots of $n$, $\phi(x)$ and $\mu(x)$ the functions of Euler and Möbius, respectively; let $S(x) = \sum_{p \leq x} \phi(p-1)$, $T(x) = \sum_{n \leq x} P(n)$, $A = \sum_{n=1}^{\infty} \mu(n)/n\phi(n)$, $\text{li}(x) = \int_2^x dt/\log t$. Two theorems are proved in this paper:

(I) $\quad S(x) = A\,\text{li}(x^2) + O\{x^2/(\log x)^m\}$;

(II) $\quad T(x) = A\{\text{li}(x^2) + \text{li}(x^2/4)\} + O\{x^2/(\log x)^m\}$

for any given positive integer $m$. Theorem (II) follows from theorem (I), which depends on an estimate of $S_d = \sum p$ ($p \leqq x$; $p \equiv 1 \pmod d$) for $d \leqq (\log x)^m$. This, in turn, depends on an estimate of the number of primes in an arithmetical progression. It is stated that a similar result holds for $\sum_{p \leq x} \sigma_{-1}(p-1)$, where $\sigma_{-1}(n) = \sum_{d|n}(1/d)$.

*R. D. James* (Saskatoon, Sask.).

**P48-2** **(16, 16d)**

**Knobloch, Hans-Wilhelm. Über Primzahlreihen nebst Anwendung auf ein elementares Dichteproblem.** Abh. Math. Sem. Univ. Hamburg **19**, no. 1–2, 1–13 (1954).

For $s > 1$ let $F(s; m, a)$ denote the Dirichlet series $\sum r^{-1} p^{-rs}$, summed over all prime powers $p^r$, $r \geqq 1$, such that $p^r \equiv a \pmod m$; let $f(s; m, a)$ denote the similar series with the additional condition $p^r > m$. The main result of the paper is that if $s_0 > 1$ is fixed, then for every $\epsilon > 0$, there is a constant $C_\epsilon > 0$, independent of $s$, $m$, $a$, such that $f(s; m, a) - f(s_0; m, a) < C_\epsilon m^{\epsilon - 1} \log\{s/(s-1)\}$ holds uniformly for $1 < s \leqq s_0$. The proof uses Dirichlet $L$-series and only elementary real variable theory.

As an application it follows that, in the infinite series $\sum \mu(m) F(s; m^2, 1)/\log\{s/(s-1)\}$, the limit as $s \to 1+0$ may be taken term by term. This, in turn leads to the result that the set of primes $p$ for which $p-1$ is quadratfrei has Dirichlet density [see, e.g., Hasse, Vorlesungen über Zahlentheorie,

Springer, Berlin, 1950, pp. 223–226; these Rev. **14**, 534] given by $\prod_p\{1-1/p(p-1)\}$. A note added in proof by the referee points out that this last result is contained in a paper by Mirsky [Amer. Math. Monthly **56**, 17–19 (1949); these Rev. **10**, 431], but that the functions $f(s; m, a)$ are not considered there. *R. D. James* (East Lansing, Mich.).

Citations: MR 10, 431e = P36-2; MR 14, 534b = Z02-23.

## P48-3 (17, 461g)

**Erdös, P. Über die Anzahl der Lösungen von $[p-1, q-1]\leq x$. (Aus einem Brief von P. Erdös an K. Prachar.)** Monatsh. Math. **59** (1955), 318–319.

It is proved that the number of solutions of $[p-1, q-1]\leq x$, where $p$, $q$ are primes and the left member denotes the least common multiple, is less than $cx(\log\log x)^3$. [Cf. K. Prachar, Monatsh. Math. **59** (1955), 91–97; MR **16**, 904.] The proof makes use of Brun's sieve method. In a note added in proof it is pointed out that the number of solutions is indeed less than $cx$.

*L. Carlitz* (Durham, N.C.).

Citations: MR 16, 904h = N52-15.

Referred to in P48-11.

## P48-4 (23# A3130)

**Linnik, Ju. V.**

**New versions and new uses of the dispersion method in binary additive problems. (Russian)**

*Dokl. Akad. Nauk SSSR* **137** (1961), 1299–1302.

The author makes fresh applications of the method he so brilliantly used for proving the Hardy-Littlewood conjecture concerning an asymptotic formula for the number of representations of a large number as a sum of two squares and a prime ($N=x^2+y^2+p$). One of the applications he now announces is to a problem of Titchmarsh: To find an asymptotic formula for the number of solutions of (in positive integers $x$, $y$)

$$-1 = xy-p \qquad (p \leq N)$$

for large $N$. He proves in fact that ($\tau(n)$ is the number of divisors of $n$)

$$\sum_{p\leq N}\tau(p-1) = \frac{315\zeta(3)}{2\pi^4}N+R(N),$$

where $R(N)=O(N/(\log N)^\alpha)$ and $\alpha$ is an arbitrary positive constant less than 1. The method also estimates

$$\sum_{m\leq N}\tau(m+1)\tau_k(m) \sim CN(\log N)^k,$$

where $C$ is a constant and $\tau_k(m)$ is the number of solutions of $m$ as a product of $k$ positive integers ($\tau(m)=\tau_2(m)$).

*S. Chowla* (Boulder, Colo.)

## P48-5 (24# A3145)

**Barban, M. B.**

**The normal order of additive arithmetic functions on sets of "shifted" primes. (Russian. English summary)**

*Acta Math. Acad. Sci. Hungar.* **12** (1961), 409–415.

Let $f$ be a non-negative, strongly additive function, so that $f(m)=\sum_{p|m}f(p)$. Put $A_n=\sum_{p|n}f(p)/p$, $\Lambda_n=\max_{p<n}f(p)$, and suppose that $A_n\to\infty$ and $\Lambda_n=o(A_n)$ as $n\to\infty$. It is shown that if $l$ is a fixed positive integer and $\varepsilon>0$, then the number of primes $p\leq n$ for which the inequality $(1-\varepsilon)A_n\leq f(p-l)\leq(1+\varepsilon)A_n$ does not hold is $o(\pi(n))$. *W. J. LeVeque* (Ann Arbor, Mich.)

## P48-6 (26# 6132)

**Rieger, G. J.**

**Über die mittlere Anzahl der Primfaktoren von $p-1$.**

*J. Reine Angew. Math.* **210** (1962), 113–120.

Let $\nu(n)$ denote the number of different prime divisors of $n$. It was shown by Erdős and Kac [Amer. J. Math. **62** (1940), 738–742; MR **2**, 42; see also Rényi and Turán, Acta Arith. **4** (1958), 71–84; MR **20** #3112] that $(\nu(n)-\log\log n)\times(\log\log n)^{-1/2}$ has a normal distribution. The author proves the same result for a number of cases where $n$ does not run through all positive integers but through some subset. (i) In the first place he takes integers $k$, $l$ and $B$ which may depend on $x$, but satisfy $0<k<\exp((\log\log x)^2)$, $(k, l)=1$, $0<|B|<\exp((\log\log x)^2)$; $r$ is a fixed integer $>1$. He considers all integers $m$ which are $r$-free (that is, which are not divisible by $p^r$ for any prime $p$) and satisfy $m\equiv l \pmod k$, $m\leq x$. Then $\nu(m-B)$ has the normal distribution property (if $x\to\infty$). (ii) Let $\mathfrak{M}$ be a set of positive integers, let $\alpha$, $\beta$, $\gamma$, $\delta$, $C$ be positive constants with $\gamma<\beta$. Assume $g(p)>p^\delta$ for all primes $p$, and $f(k)=k\prod_{p|k}(1-(g(p))^{-1})$. Let $M(x)$ be the number of $m\in\mathfrak{M}$, $m\leq x$, and let $M(x; l, k)$ be the number of $m\in\mathfrak{M}$, $m\leq x$, $m\equiv l \pmod k$. Assume that $M(x)>\alpha x^\beta$ for all $x$, and that

$$|M(x, l, k)-M(x)(f(k))^{-1}| < Cx^\gamma$$

for all $x$, $k$, $l$ as long as $(k, l)=1$. Then the $\nu(m-B)$ again have the normal distribution property. (iii) Assuming that there is $\theta$ ($\frac{1}{2}\leq\theta<1$) such that all Dirichlet $L$-series are $\neq 0$ for $\operatorname{Re} s>\theta$, it can be shown that the conditions of (ii) are satisfied if $\mathfrak{M}$ is the set of all primes. This means that $(\nu(p-1)-\log\log p)(\log\log p)^{-1/2}$ is normally distributed. The weaker statement that for almost all primes $p$ the number $p-1$ has about $\log\log p$ prime factors was proved without any hypothesis by Erdős [Quart. J. Math. Oxford Ser. **6** (1935), 205–213]. (iv) The case described under (i) can be completely generalized to the case of the number of different prime ideal factors of the numbers in an algebraic number field.

*N. G. de Bruijn* (Eindhoven)

Citations: MR 2, 42c = N60-4; MR 20# 3112 = N60-31.

## P48-7 (26# 6149)

**Bredihin, B. M.**

**Binary additive problems of indeterminate type. I. (Russian)**

*Izv. Akad. Nauk SSSR Ser. Mat.* **27** (1963), 439–462.

The author gives a detailed account of the proof obtained by Linnik's "dispersion" method of the following. Theorem:

$$(1) \qquad \sum_{0<p-a\leq n} d(p-a) = \frac{315\zeta(3)}{2\pi^4}\prod_{p|a}\frac{(p-1)^2}{p^2-p+1}n+R(n),$$

where $R(n)=O(n(\log n)^{-1+\varepsilon})$. Here $d(n)$ denotes the number of divisors of $n$. The sum in (1) was first considered by Titchmarsh [Rend. Circ. Mat. Palermo **54** (1930), 414–429]. The analogous sum describing the number of solutions of $p=x^2+y^2+a$ (here, as above, $p$ is a typical prime, $a$ an arbitrary fixed integer) was studied by Hooley [Acta Math. **97** (1957), 189–210; MR **19**, 532], who, however, assumed the generalized Riemann hypothesis. The author's theorem is proved without any hypothesis. *S. Chowla* (Boulder, Colo.)

Citations: MR 19, 532a = P36-17.

Referred to in N40-65, P36-29, P48-15.

**P48-8** **(28# 57 )**

**Barban, M. B.**

**Analogues of the divisor problem of Titchmarsh. (Russian. English summary)**

*Vestnik Leningrad. Univ. Ser. Mat. Meh. Astronom.* **18** (1963), *no.* 4, 5–13.

Author's summary: "The following asymptotic formula is proved:

$$\sum_{p_1,p_2\leqq\sqrt{x}} \tau(p_1p_2-1) = \frac{630\zeta(3)}{\pi^4}\frac{x}{\ln x}+O\left(\frac{x(\ln\ln x)^7}{\ln^2 x}\right).$$

The main tool of the proof is a slightly generalized form of 'the large sieve' of Ju. V. Linnik. Among other applications of that form a way is shown by which one can easily prove that the equation

$$2N = p_1p_2+p_3p_4p_5,\quad p_1 \leqq \sqrt{(2N)},\quad p_2 \leqq \sqrt{(2N)}$$

is solvable."

Referred to in N12-40, N24-80, P48-12, Z02-53.

**P48-9** **(33# 5574 )**

**Rodriquez, Gaetano**

**Sul problema dei divisori di Titchmarsh. (English summary)**

*Boll. Un. Mat. Ital.* (3) **20** (1965), 358–366.

The author gives a new proof of the formula (*) $N(z)=E(l)z+O(z\log\log z/\log z)$ as $z\to\infty$, where $N(z)$ is the number of solutions of the equation $xy+l=p$ in integers $x$, $y$, for all primes $p\leqq z$. This result was proved by E. C. Titchmarsh [Rend. Circ. Mat. Palermo **54** (1930), 414–429], assuming that the extended Riemann hypothesis holds. A proof independent of this hypothesis was given by Ju. V. Linnik [*The dispersion method in binary additive problems* (Russian), Izdat. Leningrad. Univ., Leningrad, 1961; MR **25** #3920; English translation, Amer. Math. Soc., Providence, R.I., 1963; MR **29** #5804], with a slightly worse form of the error term (see also B. M. Bredihin [Dokl. Akad. Nauk SSSR **149** (1963), 9–11; MR **26** #2419]). The new proof given here is much simpler and shorter; it is based on a new result, concerning the large sieve of Linnik, due to Bombieri. The author formulates also a conjecture concerning an improved form of the error term. *M. Cugiani* (Milan)

Citations: MR 25# 3920 = P02-18; MR 26# 2419 = P36-33; MR 29# 5804 = P02-19.

Referred to in P48-10, P48-17.

**P48-10** **(34# 4221 )**

**Halberstam, H.**

**Footnote to the Titchmarsh-Linnik divisor problem.**

*Proc. Amer. Math. Soc.* **18** (1967), 187–188.

Ju. V. Linnik's [*The dispersion method in binary additive problems* (Russian), Izdat. Leningrad. Univ., Leningrad, 1961; MR **25** #3920] asymptotic formula for the sum $\sum_{a<p\leqq x} d(p-a)$ is deduced from the theorem of E. Bombieri on the average of the error term in the prime number theorem for arithmetic progression [Mathematika **12** (1965), 201–225; MR **33** #5590]. As the author acknowledges, he has been anticipated by G. Rodriquez [Boll. Un. Mat. Ital. (3) **20** (1965), 358–366; MR **33** #5574]. *A. Schinzel* (Warsaw)

Citations: MR 25# 3920 = P02-18; MR 33# 5574 = P48-9; MR 33# 5590 = M55-43.

**P48-11** **(34# 4222 )**

**Rieger, G. J.**

**Über die Anzahl der Lösungen gewisser Diophantischer Ungleichungen.**

*Math. Nachr.* **32** (1966), 207–216.

Let $N(x)$ denote the number of solutions in natural numbers $a$ and $b$ of the Diophantine inequality (*) $[a, b-1]\leqq x$, where the symbol on the left of (*) denotes least common multiple. The author first proves that $N(x)=O(x\log x)$ if $b$ is restricted to be a prime, thus generalizing a theorem due to P. Erdős [Monatsh. Math. **59** (1955), 318–319; MR **17**, 461]. Among other things, two similar theorems are also proved: The same result is valid if $a+1$ and $b$ both belong to a set $M$ of natural numbers none of which contains a prime factor of the form $4t+3$. If in (*) $b\in M$, then $N(x)=O(x(\log x)^{3/2})$. *W. Ljunggren* (Oslo)

Citations: MR 17, 461g = P48-3.

**P48-12** **(36# 6364 )**

**Karšiev, A. K.**

**The generalized problem of divisors of Titchmarsh. (Russian. Uzbek summary)**

*Izv. Akad. Nauk UzSSR Ser. Fiz.-Mat. Nauk* **11** (1967), *no.* 6, 21–28.

Das Teilerproblem von Titchmarsh, eine asymptotische Entwicklung von $\sum_{p\leqq x}\tau(p-1)$ anzugeben, wurde zuerst von Linnik mittels seiner Dispersionsmethode gelöst [cf. Ju. V. Linnik, *The dispersion method in binary additive problems* (Russian), Izdat. Leningrad. Univ., Leningrad, 1961; MR **25** #3920; English translation, Amer. Math. Soc., Providence, R.I., 1963; MR **29** #5804]. M. B. Barban [Vestnik Leningrad. Univ. Ser. Mat. Meh. Astronom. **18** (1963), no. 4, 5–13; MR **28** #57] bewies mit Hilfe des Linnikschen großen Siebes eine Entwicklung für $\sum_{p_1,p_2\leqq\sqrt{x}}\tau(p_1p_2-1)$ und bestimmte auch [Uspehi Mat. Nauk **21** (1966), no. 1 (127), 51–102; MR **33** #7320] die Größenordnung beim allgemeineren Problem $\sum_{p_i\leqq x^{\alpha_i}}\tau(p_1\cdots p_k-l)$, $i=1,\cdots,k$. In der vorliegenden Arbeit wird die Barbansche Methode benutzt um

$$\sum_{p_i\leqq x^{\alpha_i}}\tau(p_1\cdots p_k-1) = 315\pi^{-4}\zeta(3)(\alpha_1\cdots\alpha_{k-1})^{-1}(x/\log^{k-1}x) + O(x\log\log x/\log^k x)$$

unter den Bedingungen $\alpha_1+\cdots+\alpha_k=1$, $0<\alpha_1<\cdots<\alpha_{k-1}<\alpha_k=\frac{1}{2}$, $\alpha_{k-1}>\frac{1}{4}$ herzuleiten. *H.-E. Richert* (Marburg)

Citations: MR 25# 3920 = P02-18; MR 28# 57 = P48-8; MR 29# 5804 = P02-19; MR 33# 7320 = Z02-53.

Referred to in P48-13.

**P48-13** **(38# 5734 )**

**Karšiev, A. K.; Sokolovskiĭ, A. V.**

**Generalized problem of Titchmarsh divisors. (Russian)**

*Mat. Zametki* **3** (1968), 187–194.

The first author has shown that

$$\sum\tau(p_1p_2\cdots p_k-1) = 315\pi^{-4}\zeta(3)(\alpha_1\alpha_2\cdots\alpha_{k-1})^{-1}(x/\log^{k-1}x) + O(x\log\log x/\log^k x),$$

where the summation is carried out over all primes,

$p_1, p_2, \cdots, p_k$ satisfying $p_i \leqq x^{\alpha_i}$, subject to the conditions that $0 < \alpha_1 < \cdots < \alpha_k$, $\alpha_1 + \alpha_2 + \cdots + \alpha_k = 1$ and (1) $\alpha_k = \frac{1}{2}$, $\alpha_{k-1} > \frac{1}{4}$ [Izv. Akad. Nauk UzSSR Ser. Fiz.-Mat. Nauk **11** (1967), no. 6, 21–28; MR **36** #6364]. The same estimate is obtained in the present paper under the assumptions that (1) is replaced by $\alpha_{k-1} + \alpha_k = \frac{3}{4}$ and that there exist positive integers $i_1, i_2, \cdots, i_l$ not exceeding $k$ for which $\alpha_{i_1} + \alpha_{i_2} + \cdots + \alpha_{i_l} = \frac{1}{2}$. *R. A. Rankin* (Glasgow)

Citations: MR 36# 6364 = P48-12.

**P48-14** **(38# 5738)**

**Kátai, I.**

**A note on a sieve method.**

*Publ. Math. Debrecen* **15** (1968), 69–73.

Let $r(n)$ be the number of representations of $n$ as a sum of two squares. It is proved that $\sum_{p \leqq x} r(p-1)|\mu(p-1)| = A_0 x/\log x + O(x(\log x)^{-1-\delta})$, where $\mu(n)$ is the Möbius function and $A_0$ and $\delta$ are positive constants. From this it is deduced that if $N(x)$ is the number of solutions of $p-1 = 2q$, $p \leqq x$, $p$ prime, $q$ divisible only by primes $\equiv 1 \pmod 4$, then $N(x) \gg x/(\log x)^3$. Some other similar deductions are also stated. The proof is based on Bombieri's theorem and on estimates due to C. Hooley [cf. P. D. T. A. Elliott and H. Halberstam, Mathematika **13** (1966), 196–203; MR **34** #5788].

*I. Danicic* (Aberystwyth)

Citations: MR 34# 5788 = P36-50.

**P48-15** **(39# 147)**

**Kátai, Imre**

**On the local behaviour of the function $d(n)$. (Hungarian. Russian and English summaries)**

*Mat. Lapok* **18** (1967), 297–302.

Author's summary: "Let $d(n)$ denote the number of divisors of $n$. In this paper we prove that

$$\sum_{n \leqq x} \max(d(n), d(n+1)) = 2x \log x + O(x(\log x)^{1-\gamma}),$$

$$\sum_{p \leqq x} \max(d(p-1), d(p+1)) = C(-1, 1)x + O(x(\log x)^{-\gamma_1}),$$

where $\gamma$ and $\gamma_1$ are suitable positive constants, $p$ runs over the primes, and

$$C(-1, 1) = \lim_{x \to \infty} (1/x) \sum_{p \leqq x} \{d(p-1) + d(p+1)\}.$$

The existence of $C(-1, 1)$ was proved earlier [Ju. V. Linnik, *The dispersion method in binary additive problems* (Russian), Izdat. Leningrad. Univ., Leningrad, 1961; MR **25** #3920; English translation, Amer. Math. Soc., Providence, R.I., 1963; MR **29** #5804; B. M. Bredihin, Izv. Akad. Nauk SSSR Ser. Mat. **27** (1963), 439–462; MR **26** #6149]."

Citations: MR 25# 3920 = P02-18; MR 26# 6149 = P48-7; MR 29# 5804 = P02-19.

**P48-16** **(39# 5493)**

**Goldfeld, Morris**

**On the number of primes $p$ for which $p+a$ has a large prime factor.**

*Mathematika* **16** (1969), 23–27.

Let $a$ be any fixed integer and let $N_a(x, y)$ be the number of primes $p \leqq x$ for which $p+a$ has at least one prime factor $\geqq y$. The author proves that $N_a(x, x^{1/2}) \geqq \frac{1}{2}(x/\log x) + O((x \log\log x)/\log^2 x)$. This is obtained as a corollary to the theorem:

$$\sum_{p \leqq x} \sum_{x^{1/2} < q \leqq x, q|p+a} \log q = \tfrac{1}{2}x + O((x \log\log x)/\log x),$$

where the sums are taken over primes $p$ and $q$. The same estimate is also proved when the condition $q|p+a$ is replaced by $q|e_a(p)$, where $e_a(p) = \min\{d \geqq 1 : a^d \equiv 1 \pmod p\}$, and some corollaries are mentioned. The proofs rely heavily on the Brun-Titchmarsh theorem, and, for one crucial estimate, the recent results of E. Bombieri [Mathematika **12** (1965), 201–225; MR **33** #5590] on primes in arithmetic progressions. *S. L. Segal* (Rochester, N.Y.)

Citations: MR 33# 5590 = M55-43.

**P48-17** **(41# 8373)**

**Kátai, I.**

**On an application of the large sieve: Shifted prime numbers, which have no prime divisors from a given arithmetical progression.**

*Acta Math. Acad. Sci. Hungar.* **21** (1970), 151–173.

The author proves an asymptotic formula for (*) $\sum_{p \leqq x} r(p+a)|\mu(p+a)|$, where $r(n) = \sum_{d|n} \chi(d)$ and $\chi$ is a primitive character modulo a prime power. The conjugate problem is also treated. The technique employed is that introduced by C. Hooley [Acta Math. **97** (1957), 189–210; MR **19**, 532]; an appeal to Bombieri's mean value theorem replaces the use of the generalized Riemann hypothesis. The author notes that if $\chi$ and $l$ are such that $\chi(l) = -1$, then $|\mu(n)|r(n) = 0$ when $n$ has a prime factor $\equiv l \pmod D$. From the asymptotic formula for (*) it then follows that there are infinitely many numbers $p+a$ which have no prime divisor $\equiv l \pmod D$, for certain pairs $l, D$. This generalizes a result of Linnik. G. Rodriguez [Boll. Un. Mat. Ital. (3) **20** (1965), 358–366; MR **33** #5574] and P. D. T. A. Elliott and H. Halberstam [Mathematika **13** (1966), 196–203; MR **34** #5788] have previously used these ideas to obtain other generalizations of Linnik's results.

*H. L. Montgomery* (Princeton, N.J.)

Citations: MR 19, 532a = P36-17; MR 33# 5574 = P48-9; MR 34# 5788 = P36-50.

**P48-18** **(42# 1782)**

**Motohashi, Yoichi**

**On a property of $p-1$.**

*Proc. Japan Acad.* **45** (1969), 639–640.

The following theorem is proved: The density, with respect to the sequence of all primes, of the primes $p$ such that $p-1$ has a divisor between $n$ and $n \exp(h^{-1}(n) \log\log n)$ tends to zero as $n \to \infty$, where $h(n)$ is an arbitrary increasing function such that $h(n) \to \infty$ and $h^{-1}(n) \log\log n \to \infty$ as $n \to \infty$. This is similar to a result of P. Erdős [J. London Math. Soc. **10** (1935), 126–128] and uses the same technique plus several lemmas.

*A. R. Freedman* (Burnaby, B.C.)

**P48-19** **(42# 4506)**

**Karacuba, A. A.**

**The distribution of products of shifted prime numbers in arithmetic progressions. (Russian)**

*Dokl. Akad. Nauk SSSR* **192** (1970), 724–727.

Let $D$ be a fixed prime, $(a, D) = (l, D) = 1$; the object of this note is to study the function $\pi_2 = \pi_2(n_1, n_2, a, l) = \sum_{p(p^1+a) \equiv l \pmod D, p \leqq n_1, p^1 \leqq n_2} 1$. Subject to suitable restrictions on $D, n_1, n_2$, the author proves that $\pi_2 = (1/\varphi(D))\pi(n_1)\pi(n_2) + O((n_1 n_2)^{1+\varepsilon} D^{-1-\gamma\omega^2})$ with $0 < \omega \leqq \frac{1}{4}$, $\gamma > 0$, $\varepsilon > 0$. The constant in $O$ depends only on $\omega$. The author uses methods and results of I. M. Vinogradov [see the revised English translation, *The method of trigonometrical sums in the theory of numbers*, Interscience, New York, 1954; MR **15**, 941].

{This article has appeared in English translation [Soviet Math. Dokl. **11** (1970), 707–711].}

*R. Ayoub* (University Park, Pa.)

Citations: MR 15, 941b = L02-3.

**P48-20** **(42# 5928)**

**Deshouillers, Jean-Marc**

**Sur la fonction de répartition de certaines fonctions arithmétiques définies sur l'ensemble des nombres premiers moins un.**

*C. R. Acad. Sci. Paris Sér. A-B* **271** (1970), A1141–A1143.

Let $g(n)$ denote a real-valued multiplicative function: $g(mn)=g(m)g(n)$ for $(m, n)=1$. Let $p$, $p_i$, $p'$ denote primes. The main result of the paper is contained in the following. Theorem 1: Let $g$ be a multiplicative function with values in the interval $[0, 1]$ satisfying the conditions (A) there exist $p_1$ and $\alpha$, $\alpha>0$, such that $1-1/p^\alpha \leqq g(p) \leqq 1$ $(p \geqq p_1)$, (B) there exists $p_2$ such that $g(p') \geqq g(p)$ $(p' \geqq p \geqq p_2)$, (C) $\sum_p (1-g(p))$ is divergent. Then the function $G(x)=\lim_{N=\infty} (\text{li } N)^{-1} \sum_{g(p-1)<x, p \leqq N} 1$ exists, is continuous and strictly increasing on the interval $[0, \sup_{k \geqq 1} g(2^k)]$. Moreover, $G(\sup_{k\geqq 1} g(2^k))=1$.

The following corollaries are stated. Corollary 1: The set of primes satisfying $\phi(p-1)/(p-1)>\frac{1}{3}$, where $\phi$ is the Eulerian function, has positive density with respect to the set of prime numbers. Corollary 2: The set of primes $p$ satisfying $(p-1)/(\sigma(p-1))>\frac{1}{2}$ (or $(p-1)/(\sigma(p-1))<\frac{1}{2}$), has positive density with respect to the set of prime numbers.

The proof of Theorem 1 depends upon the following. Theorem 2: Let $a, b, k$ be positive integers such that (i) $2^k \| a$, (ii) $(a, b)=1$, (iii) $(a+1, b)=1$, (iv) $a/2^k$ and $b$ are squarefree. Let $g$ be a multiplicative function with values in $[0, 1]$ satisfying condition (A) of Theorem 1. Then

$$\lim_{x=\infty} (\phi(a^2b)/(\text{li } x)) \sum_{p \leqq x, p=a+1[a^2b]} g(p-1) = g(a) \prod_{p \nmid ab} \{1+\sum_{k=1}^{\infty} (g(p^k)-g(p^{k-1}))/(p^{k-1}(p-1))\}.$$

*L. Carlitz* (Durham, N.C.)

**P48-21** **(43# 6171 )**

**Deshouillers, Jean-Marc**

**Sur la fonction de répartition de certaines fonctions arithmétiques définies sur l'ensemble des nombres premiers moins un.**

*Séminaire Delange-Pisot-Poitou:* 1969/70, *Théorie des Nombres, Fasc.* 2, *Exp.* 17, 13 *pp. Secrétariat mathématique, Paris*, 1970.

Modifying the qualitative results proved by I. Kátai [Compositio Math. **19**, 278–289 (1968); MR **39** #5498; Acta Math. Acad. Sci. Hungar. **20** (1969), 69–87; MR **38** #5728] the author proves the following theorem.

Let $g$ be a multiplicative function with values in the interval $[0, 1]$ satisfying the following conditions: (A) there exist $p_1$ and $\alpha>0$ such that $1-1/p^\alpha \leqq g(p) \leqq 1$ if $p \geqq p_1$, (B) there exists a $p_2$ such that $g(p) \geqq g(p')$ if $p \geqq p' \geqq p_2$, (C) $\sum_p (1-g(p))$ is divergent, and (D) $g(2^k) \leqq g(2)$ if $k \geqq 1$; then $G(x)=\text{Lim}_{N\to\infty} (1/\text{li } N) \sum_{g(p-1)<x, p \leqq N} 1$ exists and is a continuous strictly increasing function of $x$ in the interval $[0, g(2)]$, moreover $G(g(2))=1$.

*J. M. Gandhi* (Macomb, Ill.)

Citations: MR 38# 5728 = N60-73; MR 39# 5498 = N60-78.

**P48-22** **(43# 6173 )**

**Karšiev, A. K.**

**The generalized problem of Titchmarsh divisors. (Russian)**

*Izv. Akad. Nauk UzSSR Ser. Fiz.-Mat. Nauk* **13** (1969), *no.* 1, 69–70.

Using the dispersion method of Linnik [see Ju. V. Linnik, *The dispersion method in binary additive problems* (Russian), Chapter VIII, Izdat. Leningrad. Univ., Leningrad, 1961; MR **25** #3920; English translation, Amer. Math. Soc., Providence, R.I., 1963; MR **29** #5804] the author obtains the following theorem. Denote by $Q(n)$ the number of solutions of $p_1p_2\cdots p_k-xy=l$, $p_j$ prime, $p_j \leqq n^{\alpha_j}$, $j=1, 2, \cdots, k$, $0<\alpha_1 \leqq \alpha_2 \leqq \cdots \leqq \alpha_k \leqq 1/7$, $\alpha_1+\alpha_2+\cdots+\alpha_k=1$, $xy \leqq n$; then $Q(n)=(315/\pi^4)(1/(\alpha_1\alpha_2\cdots\alpha_k))\xi(3) \times \prod_{p|l} ((p-1)^2/(p^2-p+1))n/\text{lg}^{k-1} n+O(n/\text{lg}^k n)$.

*B. Novák* (Prague)

Citations: MR 25# 3920 = P02-18; MR 29# 5804 = P02-19.

**P48-23** **(44# 163 )**

**Karacuba, A. A.**

**Sums of characters with primes that belong to an arithmetic progression. (Russian)**

*Izv. Akad. Nauk SSSR Ser. Mat.* **35** (1971), 469–484.

Unter Weiterführung seiner Arbeit [dieselben Izv. **34** (1970), 229–321; MR **42** #5923] über die Methode von I. M. Vinogradov betrachtet der Verfasser Primzahlen $p$ in arithmetischen Progressionen und gibt dann für die Anzahlen $p+k$ bei Charakteren, quadratischen Resten und Nichtresten sowie Indizes verschiedene Abschätzungen. Als Beispiel werde hier der folgende Satz wiedergegeben: Sei $0<\omega<\frac{1}{2}$, $\chi$ Nichthauptcharakter modulo der Primzahl $q$ $(\geqq q_0)$, $N, Q, k, l$ natürliche Zahlen mit $(lq, Q)=1$, $k<q$, und mit absoluten Konstanten $A$, $B$ gelte $Q \leqq q^A$ sowie $q^{1/2+\omega} \leqq NQ^{-3} \leqq q^B$; dann gilt mit einer nur von $\omega$ abhängigen $\ll$-Konstanten die Abschätzung $\sum_{p \leqq N, p \equiv l \bmod Q} \chi(p+k) \ll NQ^{-1}q^{-0.0004\omega^2}$.

*H.-E. Richert* (Ulm)

Citations: MR 42# 5923 = L20-25.

**P48-24** **(44# 1638 )**

**Webb, William A.**

**An asymptotic estimate for a class of divisor sums.**

*Duke Math. J.* **38** (1971), 575–582.

P. D. T. A. Elliott and H. Halberstam [Mathematika **13** (1966), 196–203; MR **34** #5788] have obtained an estimate for sums of the form $S=\sum_{a<p\leqq x} \sum_{n|(p-a)} f(n)$, where $p$ is restricted to prime values and $f$ satisfies the condition $f(x) \ll 1$. The present author drops the condition $f(x) \ll 1$ and imposes other, more complicated, conditions on $f$ in order to obtain a new estimate for $S$. As a corollary, he shows that if $r>0$ then $\sum_{a<p\leqq x} \sigma_r(p-a) \sim cx^{r+1}/(r+1) \log x$, where $c=\sum_{n=1,(a,n)=1}^{\infty} 1/n^r\varphi(n)$.

*B. Garrison* (San Diego, Calif.)

Citations: MR 34# 5788 = P36-50.

## P52 OTHER ADDITIVE QUESTIONS INVOLVING PRIMES

See also reviews B20-5, D76-24, N32-31, N40-20, N40-23, N40-35, N68-30, P02-18, P08-28, P32-48, P72-14, P80-70.

**P52-1** **(3, 68g)**

**Chung, Kai-Lai. Two remarks on Viggo Brun's method.** Sci. Rep. Nat. Tsing Hua Univ. (A) **4**, 249–255 (1940).

Romanoff has proved that the set of integers of the form $p+a^i$, where $p$ is a prime and $i\geqq 0$, has positive density. [See, for example, E. Landau, Über einige neuere Fortschritte der additiven Zahlentheorie, Cambridge Tracts, no. 35, London, 1937, pp. 63–70.] In this paper it is shown that the set of integers $\pi p+a^{p_i}$, where $\pi$ and $p$ are different primes and the $p_i$ are also primes, has positive density. The method of proof parallels that given by Landau in the abovementioned reference for the Romanoff result. A generalization of the Viggo Brun result on prime pairs is also indicated. *R. D. James* (Saskatoon, Sask.).

Referred to in P40-3.

**P52-2** **(7, 243l)**

**Chowla, S. There exists an infinity of 3—combinations of primes in A. P.** Proc. Lahore Philos. Soc. **6**, no. 2, 15–16 (1944).

The author proves that there exist infinitely many triplets of primes in arithmetic progression. *P. Erdös.*

Referred to in A18-33.

**P52-3** **(16, 797c)**

**Ricci, Giovanni. Sulla partizione degli interi in addendi primi col procedimento del residuo minimo.** Boll. Un. Mat. Ital. (3) **10**, 1–10 (1955).

By a partition of $n$ into primes proceeding by least remainder is meant a partition $n=q_1+q_2+\cdots+q_k$ in which $q_1$ is chosen as the greatest prime $\leqq n$, $q_2$ as the greatest prime $\leqq n-q_1$, etc. If need be, $q_k$ is chosen to be unity. This leads to an unique representation of $n$. The number $k$ of terms is denoted by $k(n)$ and the first $n$ to require $k$ terms in its partition is denoted by $\mu_k$. Thus $\mu_1=1$, $\mu_2=4$, $\mu_3=27$, $\mu_4=1354$ and $\mu_5$ is unknown but certainly $>10^7$. The author proves two theorems. (I) Let $\epsilon>0$; then for all $k>k_0(\epsilon)$

$$(\theta+\epsilon)^{-1}\log\mu_{k-1}<\log\mu_k<(1-\epsilon)^{-1}\mu_{k-1},$$

where $\theta$ is the lower bound of all $\phi$ for which $p_{n+1}-p_n<p_n^{\phi}$, $p_n$ being the $n$th prime. (II) Let $0<\delta<1$ and $\epsilon>0$; then the number $P=P(\xi,\delta)$ of integers $n$ for which $k(n)=2$ and $(1-\delta)\xi<n\leqq\xi$, satisfies the inequalities

$$(1-\epsilon)K\delta\xi/(\log\log\xi)<P<(1+\epsilon)\delta\xi/(\log\log\xi)$$

for all sufficiently large $\xi$ and for a certain constant $K>1/32$ depending on $\delta$. *D. H. Lehmer* (Berkeley, Calif.).

**P52-4** **(20# 3834)**

**Lavrik, A. F. Addition of a prime to a prime power of a given prime.** Dokl. Akad. Nauk SSSR **119** (1958), 1085–1087. (Russian)

The article discusses questions of the sort: for how many $n$, not greater than a prescribed bound, is the equation

$$n=p+P^q$$

solvable in prime numbers $p$, $P$, $q$, where $P$ is fixed.

**P52-5** **(26# 2413)**

**Uchiyama, Saburô**

**Three primes in arithmetical progression.**

*Proc. Japan Acad.* **37** (1961), 329–330.

Let $a$ be a positive integer, $b$ an arbitrary integer and let $N(x,a,b)$ denote the number of solutions of $p_1+p_3=ap_2+b$ in prime numbers $p_1$, $p_2$, $p_3$, with $2\leqq p_i\leqq x$.

The author sketches the proof of an asymptotic formula for $N(x,a,b)$ when $x\to\infty$, from which, in particular, the existence of infinitely many triplets of primes in arithmetical progression (i.e., such that $p_1+p_3=2p_2$) can be deduced. *M. Cugiani* (Milan)

Referred to in K05-68.

**P52-6** **(28# 75)**

**Moser, L.**

**Notes on number theory. III. On the sum of consecutive primes.**

*Canad. Math. Bull.* **6** (1963), 159–161.

Part II appeared in same Bull. **3** (1960), 23–25 [MR **22** #5619]. Let $A$: $a_1<a_2<\cdots$ be a sequence of positive integers, let $f(n)$ denote the number of representations of $n$ as the sum of one or more consecutive $a$'s, and put $F(x)=x^{-1}\sum_1^x f(n)$. The reviewer showed that if $A$ is an arithmetic progression with difference $d$, then

$$F(x)=\frac{1}{2}\log x+\gamma-\frac{1}{2}\log\frac{d}{2}-\frac{1}{2}+O(x^{-1/2}).$$

In the present note it is shown that when $A$ is the set of primes, $F(x)\to\log 2$. In particular, this shows that $f(n)=0$ for infinitely many $n$. It is stated that the method used, which is elementary except for an application of the prime number theorem, can be modified to show that $F(x)\sim\frac{1}{2}\log x$ for every sequence $A$ of positive asymptotic density. *W. J. LeVeque* (Boulder, Colo.)

Citations: MR 22# 5619 = B24-16.

**P52-7** **(32# 7527)**

**Čuič, A. G.**

**On a recurrence relation for arithmetical functions. (Russian)**

*Ukrain. Mat. Ž.* **17** (1965), *no.* 2, 134–136.

The author considers the problem of the decomposition of a given natural number into distinct prime summands. He defines $A(n)$ to be the number of all possible representations of the natural number $n$ in the form of a sum of distinct prime summands; if $n$ is prime, then one such decomposition will be taken as $n=n$. Now let $r(n)$ be defined as follows: if $n$ is odd, $r(n)$ is the sum of the distinct prime divisors of $n$; if $n\equiv 0 \pmod 4$, $r(n)$ is the negative of the sum of the distinct prime divisors of $n$; if $n\equiv 2 \pmod 4$, then $r(n)$ is the negative of the sum of the distinct prime divisors of $n$ plus 4. The main result of this paper is the following theorem: If $n$ is a natural number greater than unity, then $r(n)+r(n-2)A(2)+\cdots+r(2)A(n-2)=nA(n)$. *R. Finkelstein* (Tucson, Ariz.)

**P52-8** **(33# 5582)**

**Danicic, I.**

**On the integral part of a linear form with prime variables.**

*Canad. J. Math.* **18** (1966), 621–628.

Let $\lambda$, $\mu$ be non-zero real numbers, not both negative, with $\lambda$ irrational. Given any positive integer $k$ there are infinitely many prime triples $p_1$, $p_2$, $p$ such that $[\lambda p_1+\mu p_2]=kp$, where $[x]$ denotes the greatest integer $\leqq x$. In particular, $[\lambda p_1+\mu p_2]$ represents infinitely many primes. The proof of this result is based on the following lemma. Let $\lambda_1$, $\lambda_2$, $\lambda_3$, $\gamma$ be real numbers, the $\lambda$'s being non-zero and not all of the same sign, and with $\lambda_1/\lambda_2$ irrational. Then for each positive $\varepsilon$ there exists a sequence of integers $N\to\infty$ such that the number of solutions of $|\lambda_1p_1+\lambda_2p_2+\lambda_3p_3+\gamma|<\varepsilon$ in primes $p_i<N$ exceeds $CN^2/(\log N)^2$ with $C>0$, $C$ independent of $N$. The theorem is obtained by taking $\lambda_1=\lambda$, $\lambda_2=-k$, $\lambda_3=\mu$, $\varepsilon=-\gamma=\frac{1}{2}$. The proof of the lemma is "based on an adaptation of Vinogradov's method for the Goldbach problem", and so involves deep estimates of integrals. *I. Niven* (Eugene, Ore.)

**P52-9** **(38# 5725)**

**Kátai, Imre**

**Investigation of a number-theoretic function.** (**Hungarian. Russian summary**)

*Magyar Tud. Akad. Mat. Fiz. Oszt. Közl.* **16** (1966), 233–238.

Author's summary: "We denote by $N(\sigma_0,T)$ the number of roots of Riemann's function $\zeta(\sigma+it)$ in the region $\sigma_0\leqq\sigma\leqq 1$, $|t|\leqq T$, and let $S(n)=\sum_{p<n}(n-p)^{-1}$, $p$ prime. The author proves the following conditional statement: Presupposing that the relation $N(\sigma_0,T)=O(T^{2(1-\sigma_0)}\log^2 T)$ is satisfied uniformly on the interval $\frac{1}{2}\leqq\sigma_0\leqq 1$, then the

following estimates are valid:

$$\sum_{n\leqq N}(S(n)-1)^2 = O((N/\log N)(\log\log N)^2),$$

$$\sum_{q\leqq N}|S(q)-1| = O((N/\log^2 N)(\log\log N)^{3/2}),$$

where $q$ runs through the prime numbers. The proofs are based on the method of Ju. V. Linnik [Dokl. Akad. Nauk SSSR **77** (1951), 15–18; MR **12**, 805; erratum, MR **12**, p. 1003; Izv. Akad. Nauk SSSR Ser. Mat. **16** (1952), 503–520; MR **14**, 847]."

Citations: MR 12, 805e = P32-16; MR 14, 847b = P32-20.

### P52-10 (40# 108)

**Kurižev, Ju. A.**

**A binary additive problem.** (Russian)

*Dokl. Akad. Nauk SSSR* **186** (1969), 1010–1011.

Let $L(N; N^{1/\alpha}; N^{1/\beta})$ be the number of solutions of the equation $N=n_1+n_2$, where $n_1, n_2$ runs over the sets of integers all prime factors of which are smaller than $N^{1/\alpha}$, greater than $N^{1/\beta}$, respectively. The following theorem is proved: For any real $\alpha\geqq 1$ and $\beta=\beta(N)\to\infty$, $L(N; N^{1/\alpha}; N^{1/\beta}) = \mathscr{L}(\beta)\omega(\alpha)(N/\log N) + O(N\beta/\log^2 N)$, where $\omega(\alpha)$ satisfies the differential-equation $\alpha\omega'(\alpha)+\omega(\alpha-1)=0$ with the boundary condition $\omega(\alpha)=1$, when $0\leqq\alpha\leqq 1$. Furthermore, $\mathscr{L}(\beta)=e^{-c}\beta[1+\Delta(\beta/2)]$, where $c$ is Euler's constant and $\Delta(u)=O(\exp(-\frac{1}{2}u\log\frac{1}{2}u))$.

The proof is based on the method of A. A. Buhštab [Mat. Sb. **2** (**44**) (1937), 1239–1246].

{This article has appeared in English translation [Soviet Math. Dokl. **10** (1969), 702–704].} *I. Kátai* (Budapest)

### P52-11 (41# 8363)

**Fedulova, T. M.**

**An application of the dispersion method in additive problems with a bounded collection of prime numbers.** (Russian)

*Dokl. Akad. Nauk SSSR* **191** (1970), 290–292.

The author applies Ju. V. Linnik's dispersion method [*The dispersion method in binary additive problems*, Izdat. Leningrad. Univ., Leningrad, 1961; MR **25** #3920; English translation, Amer. Math. Soc., Providence, R.I., 1963; MR **29** #5804] to the solution of various binary additive problems of the form $a+b=n$ and $a-b=c$, where $a$ and $b$ run over prescribed sequences of natural numbers sufficiently well distributed in arithmetic progressions; $c\neq 0$ is a fixed integer; $n$ is a sufficiently large natural number; and $b<n$. Several complex formulas, involving Möbius' function and Euler's totient, are given for the number of solutions to such binary additive problems when $a=p_1\cdot p_2\cdots p_k$, where $p_i$ run independently over the primes and $k$ is fixed.

{This article has appeared in English translation [Soviet Math. Dokl. **11** (1970), 366–369].}

*A. A. Mullin* (Long Binh)

Citations: MR 25# 3920 = P02-18; MR 29# 5804 = P02-19.

### P52-12 (42# 3039)

**Bredihin, B. M.; Linnik, J. V. [Linnik, Ju. V.]; Tschudakoff, N. G. [Čudakov, N. G.]**

**Über binäre additive Probleme gemischter Art.**

*Number Theory and Analysis* (*Papers in Honor of Edmund Landau*), *pp.* 23–37. *Plenum, New York,* 1969.

Let $\phi$ and $\psi$ be two positive definite primitive quadratic forms. Let $n$ be a positive integer. We denote by $Q(n)$ the number of integral quadruples $\xi, \eta, \xi', \eta'$ such that $\psi(\xi', \eta')$ equals a prime number and $n=\phi(\xi,\eta)+\psi(\xi',\eta')$. The authors prove in this note that $Q(n)=A(\phi,\psi,n)n/\log n + O(n(\log n)^{-1-\gamma})$, where $A(\phi,\psi,n)$ is the singular series of the problem; $\gamma$ is a positive number defined in a rather complicated way. The authors use methods of C. Hooley [Acta Math. **97** (1957), 189–210; MR **19**, 532] and results of E. Bombieri [Mathematika **12** (1965), 201–225; MR **33** #5590]. *F. van der Blij* (Bilthoven)

Citations: MR 19, 532a = P36-17; MR 33# 5590 = M55-43.

### P52-13 (43# 4787)

**Poljanskiĭ, A. A.**

**A certain additive problem.** (Russian)

*Volž. Mat. Sb. Vyp.* 6 (1968), 217–219.

By the dispersion method of Ju. V. Linnik the author deduces the asymptotic behavior of the number of solutions of the equation $p_1p_2^a+b(x^2+y^2)=n$ where $p_1$ and $p_2$ vary independently over the prime numbers, $x$ and $y$ vary over the integers, $a$ is a fixed natural number, and the parameter $b>0$ is of the order $O((\ln n)^C)$. An analogous problem in the case when $b=1$, $p_1\in[1, n^{1-\alpha}]$, $p_2\in[1, n^\alpha]$, $0<\alpha<1/6$ was considered earlier by Linnik [Mat. Sb. (N.S.) **51** (**93**) (1960), 129–154; errata, ibid. **53** (**95**) (1961), 38; MR **24** #A1265].

*B. Bredihin* (RŽMat **1969** #4 A102)

Citations: MR 24# A1265 = P36-27.

### P52-14 (43# 7412)

**Uchiyama, Saburô**

**On the number of representations of an integer as the sum of the square of a prime and an $r$-free integer.**

*J. Fac. Sci. Shinshu Univ.* **5** (1970), 141–146.

By means of known techniques the following theorem is proved: Let $r$ be an integer $\geqq 2$ and $Q_r(n)$ the number of representations of an integer $n$ as the sum of the square of a prime and an $r$-free positive integer, let $c_r(n)=1$ or $=2$ for $r=2$, $n\equiv 1 \pmod 4$ or $r\geqq 3$, $n\equiv 1 \pmod 8$, respectively, and put $c_r(n)=0$ otherwise; then, for every positive real number $H$, $Q_r(n)=A_r(n)\,\mathrm{li}\sqrt{n}+O(\sqrt{n}/\log^H n)$ $(n\to\infty)$ with $A_r(n)=(1-c_r(n)/2^{r-2})\prod_{p\nmid 2n}(1-(1+(n/p))/(p^{r-1}(p-1)))$, where the $O$-constant depends only on $r$ and $H$.

*O. H. Körner* (Ulm)

## P56 PARTITIONS: RECURRENCE RELATIONS, TABULATION METHODS

See also reviews A34-25, B36-134, P02-16, P52-7, P64-3, P64-4, P64-7, P64-28, P64-38, P64-40, P64-43, P64-57, P68-5, P76-15, P80-65, P80-67, Z02-29, Z30-2, Z30-8, Z30-27, Z30-52.

### P56-1 (3, 68i)

**Kantz, Georg. Zerfällung einer Zahl in Summanden.** Deutsche Math. 5, 476–481 (1941).

The author considers the number $\{{s \atop r}\}_p$ of partitions of the integer $s$ into $r$ parts each greater than or equal to $p$, and proves a number of simple relations and recursion formulas for this function. Since obviously $\{{s \atop r}\}_p=\{{s-(p-1)r \atop r}\}_1$, it suffices to find a formula for the case $p=1$. The author derives a formula equivalent to (27) on page 128 of Netto's Lehrbuch der Combinatorik [Leipzig and Berlin, 1927]. Netto's table of this function is extended to $s\leqq 25$, $r\leqq 15$.

*D. H. Lehmer* (Berkeley, Calif.).

### P56-2 (6, 198d)

**Hsu, L. Ching-Siur. A combinatorial formula with some applications.** Bull. Amer. Math. Soc. 51, 106–113 (1945).

The author proves a rather complicated combinatorial

formula, which cannot be reproduced because of lack of space. He applies his formula to partitions and to Dirichlet's integral. *P. Erdös* (Ann Arbor, Mich.).

**P56-3** **(8, 137a)**

**Ziaud Din, M. On formulae in partitions and divisors of a number, derived from symmetric functions.** Proc. Nat. Acad. Sci. India. Sect. A. **13**, 221–224 (1943).

The following known formulas are derived:

$$\sigma(n)=p(n-1)+2p(n-2)-5p(n-5)-7p(n-7)+\cdots,$$
$$\sigma(n)=\sigma(n-1)+\sigma(n-2)-\sigma(n-5)-\sigma(n-7)+\cdots,$$
$$np(n)=\sigma(n)+p(1)\sigma(n-1)+p(2)\sigma(n-2)+\cdots+p(n-1)\sigma(1),$$

where $\sigma(k)$ is the sum of the divisors of $k$, $p(k)$ is the number of unrestricted partitions of $k$ and 0, 1, 2, 5, 7, $\cdots$ are the pentagonal numbers. The last formula is not credited to anyone but must be quite old. The reviewer has not succeeded in locating it in 19th century literature. It is proved without reference by Hellund [Amer. Math. Monthly **42**, 91–93 (1935)]. The methods of the present paper are those of the theory of symmetric functions and determinants, as further developed in the author's previous paper [Math. Student **3**, 141–151 (1935)]. *D. H. Lehmer.*

**P56-4** **(13, 13e)**

**Lehmer, D. H. A triangular number formula for the partition function.** Scripta Math. **17**, 17–19 (1951).

Using the elementary theory of formal power series together with Jacobi's formula for $\prod_{n=1}^{\infty}(1-x^n)^3$, the author proves that if $\prod_{n=1}^{\infty}(1-x^n)^{\alpha}=\sum_{m=0}^{\infty}C_{\alpha}(m)x^m$, then

$$\sum_{m=0}^{\infty}(-1)^m(2m+1)\times[n-(3+\alpha)(m+1)m/6]C_{\alpha}(n-\tfrac{1}{2}(m+1)m)=0.$$

The case $\alpha=-1$ yields an apparently new recurrence for the partition function, and $\alpha=24$ recovers one for Ramanujan's $\tau(n)$ [S. Ramanujan, Trans. Cambridge Philos. Soc. **22**, 159–184 (1916)]. *N. J. Fine* (Philadelphia, Pa.).

**P56-5** **(17, 239a)**

**Ostmann, Hans-Heinrich. Über eine Rekursionsformel in der Theorie der Partitionen.** Math. Nachr. **13** (1955), 157–160.

Let $A$ be an arbitrary set of positive integers, and for each $a_i\in A$, let $g_i=g(a_i)$ be a positive integer. Write $G=(g_1, g_2, \cdots)$, and define $q(n)=p(n, A, G)$ to be the number of partitions of $n$ using parts $a_i$ of $g_i$ distinct types. Let $g_v(n)=p_v(n, A, G)$ be the corresponding partition function in which no two parts are of the same value and type. Define

$$\sigma(\nu, A, G)=\sum_{\substack{d|\nu\\ d\in A}} dg(d),\quad \sigma^*(\nu, A, G)=\sum_{\substack{d|\nu\\ d\in A}} dg(d)(-1)^{\nu/d+1}.$$

Then, generalizing results of W. B. Ford [Amer. Math. Monthly **38** (1931), 183–184], the author shows that for $n>0$,

$$q(n)=\frac{1}{n}\sum_{\nu=1}^{n}\sigma(\nu, A, G)q(n-\nu),$$
$$q_v(n)=\frac{1}{n}\sum_{\nu=1}^{n}\sigma^*(\nu, A, G)q_v(n-\nu).$$

The method is the standard one of computing the logarithmic derivative of the generating function in two ways. *N. J. Fine* (Philadelphia, Pa.).

Referred to in P56-6.

**P56-6** **(17, 1187e)**

**Meinardus, Günter. Partitionen und Teilerfunktionen.** Arch. Math. **7** (1956), 52–54.

The author generalizes to $n$-dimensional lattices some results of Ostmann [Math. Nachr. **13** (1955), 157–160; MR **17**, 239] which yield recurrence formulas for partition functions of general type, using divisor functions. A prototype is the well-known $np(n)=\sum_{k=1}^{n}\sigma(k)p(n-k)$. *N. J. Fine* (Philadelphia, Pa.).

Citations: MR 17, 239a = P56-5.

**P56-7** **(24# A719 )**

**Tietze, Heinrich**

**Über eingeschränkte und uneingeschränkte Partitionen.** *Bayer. Akad. Wiss. Math.-Nat. Kl. S.-B.* **1960**, 11–16.

Let $\{g_k\}$ be a strictly increasing sequence of positive integers. The author's aim is to derive a number of easy recurrence relations for partition functions associated with this sequence. We content ourselves with quoting one result. Let $B(m; h)$ denote the number of partitions of $m$ into $g$'s in which no $g$ exceeds $h$, and let $s(h)$ be defined as 1 or 0 according as $h$ belongs or does not belong to the sequence $\{g_k\}$. Then, for $m\geq 1$, $h\geq 1$,

$$B(m; h) = B(m; h-1)+s(h)B(m-h; h).$$

*L. Mirsky* (Sheffield)

**P56-8** **(29# 6204 )**

**Huťa, A.**

**Eine Bemerkung zur Zerlegung der natürlichen Zahlen. (Slovak and Russian summaries)** *Acta Fac. Natur. Univ. Comenian.* **9**, 57–62 (1964).

Author's summary: "Bezeichnen wir mit $R_n(x)$ die Anzahl aller verschiedenen Zerlegungen einer natürlichen Zahl $x$ in $n$ Glieder (Summanden) unter folgenden Voraussetzungen: (1°) die Glieder sind natürliche Zahlen; (2°) die Zerlegungen mit zwar gleichen Gliedern, jedoch in anderer Reihenfolge, werden als gleiche angesehen. Werden also Glieder einer Zerlegung mit $x_j$, $j=1, 2, \cdots, n$ bezeichnet, so kann man im weiteren voraussetzen, daß $x_i\leq x_j$ für $i<j$. Dann gilt die Relation

(1) $$R_n(x+n)-R_n(x) = R_{n-1}(x+n-1)."$$

The author proves this relation. He then solves it recursively, that is, assuming $R_{n-1}(x+n-1)$, he solves for $R_n(x)$ which now is a solution of a linear difference equation. He appends a table completed by equation (1), where $x$ ranges from 1 to 15 and $n$ from 1 to 4.

*T. Fort* (Columbia, S.C.)

**P56-9** **(32# 5622 )**

**Oderfeld, J.; Pleszczyńska, E.**

**On some applications of partitions. (Polish. Russian and English summaries)** *Zastos. Mat.* **6** (1962), 189–198.

Let $p(a, b, c)$ stand for the number of representations of the natural number $a$ in the form $\sum_{j=1}^{b}x_j$, where $0\leq x_1\leq x_2\leq\cdots\leq x_b\leq c$ (restricted partitions of $a$). Generalizing Euler's well-known formula for the number of unrestricted partitions, i.e., for $p(a, b)\overset{\text{def}}{=}p(a, b, a)$, the authors derive a recursive formula for $p(a, b, c)$. They also outline some applications of their formula in statistics and in the theory of mechanisms. *S. Knapowski* (Gainesville, Fla.)

**P56-10** **(32# 5623 )**

**Zubrzycki, S.**

**A recursive formula for the number of restricted partitions. (Polish. Russian and English summaries)** *Zastos. Mat.* **6** (1962), 231–234.

Let $p(a, b, c)$ denote the number of representations of the natural number $a$ in the form $\sum_{j=1}^{b} x_j$, where $0 \leqq x_1 \leqq x_2 \leqq \cdots \leqq x_b \leqq c$. J. Oderfeld and E. Pleszczyńska [see #5622 above] derived a recursive formula for $p(a, b, c)$. The present author gives another recursive formula for $p(a, b, c)$. *S. Knapowski* (Gainesville, Fla.)

**P56-11** **(34# 127)**

**Fielder, Daniel C.**

**Enumeration of partitions subject to limitations on size of members.**

*Fibonacci Quart.* **4** (1966), 209–216.

The author considers how the number of partitions of $n$ into exactly $p$ summands, each $\leqq r$ and/or $\geqq s$, can be computed in practice. *M. S. Cheema* (Tucson, Ariz.)

**P56-12** **(37# 2668)**

**Targhetta, Maria Luisa**

**Costruzione e computo delle partizioni di un numero naturale. (English summary)**

*Rend. Sem. Fac. Sci. Univ. Cagliari* **37** (1967), 1–7.

An elementary inductive method is described for computing the number of partitions of a natural number. *W. G. Brown* (Montreal, Que.)

**P56-13** **(39# 5383)**

**Karpe, Robert**

**Some relations between combinatorial numbers $p(n)$. (Czech)**

*Časopis Pěst. Mat.* **94** (1969), 108–114.

Let $p(n)$ and $q(n)$ be the number of (unrestricted) partitions of $n$, and the number of partitions of $n$ into odd parts, respectively. The author derives the formulae $p(n) = \sum_{i=0} p(i)q(n-2i)$ and $q(n) = \sum_{i=0} (-1)^i q(i)q(2n-i)$, where $p(0) = q(0) = 1$. Several further identities involving $p(n)$ and $q(n)$ are found. *A. Rosa* (Hamilton, Ont.)

**P56-14** **(40# 4227)**

**Chawla, L. M.; Shad, S. A.**

**On a trio-set of partition functions and their tables.**

*J. Natur. Sci. and Math.* **9** (1969), 87–96.

Denoting by $p(n)$ the number of unrestricted partitions of $n$, by $q(n)$ the number of partitions of $n$ into primes, by $r(n)$ the number of partitions of $n$ into non-primes and, finally, by $\lambda(n)$ the number of partitions of $n$ into summands at least one of which is a prime and one a nonprime, the authors prove the obvious relations $p(n) = q(n) + r(n) + \lambda(n)$, $\lambda(n) = q(n-1)r(1) + q(n-2)r(2) + \cdots + q(1)r(n-1)$. Tables are given for each of the four functions for values of $n$ up to 150. Also relevant is the work of the reviewer [Proc. Nat. Inst. Sci. India Part A **21** (1955), 185–187; MR **17**, 1187] and of O. P. Gupta and S. Luthra [ibid. **21** (1955), 181–184; MR **17**, 587] and O. P. Gupta [Res. Bull. Panjab Univ. No. 107 (1957), 283–290; MR **19**, 1159] and of the Royal Society [*Table of partitions*, Cambridge Univ. Press, Cambridge, 1958], where more extensive information about $p(n)$, and $q(n)$ is available. *H. Gupta* (Allahabad)

Citations: MR 17, 587b = A46-14; MR 17, 1187d = A46-16; MR 19, 1159e = A46-19.

**P56-15** **(41# 1669)**

**Arkin, Joseph; Pollack, Richard**

**Recurrence formulas.**

*Fibonacci Quart.* **8** (1970), *no.* 1, 4–5.

The authors show that if $p(n)$ is the number of partitions of $n$, then $p(n) = -\sum_{0 \leqq i \leqq m, m < j \leqq n} p(i)e(j-i)p(n-j)$, where $e(k) = (-1)^k$ if $k = \frac{1}{2}(3h^2 \pm h)$ and $= 0$ otherwise, and $p(0) = 1$. This is derived from a more general formula communicated to the authors by L. Carlitz.

**P56-16** **(41# 6775)**

**Patel, D. M.**

**On the number of solutions of some indeterminate equations in natural numbers.**

*Vidya* **6** (1963), *no.* 1, 126–128.

Let $S(k) = (n-k)^2/12 + (n-k-4)^2/12 + \cdots + (n-k-4j)^2/12$, where $j$ is the largest integer for which $n-k-4j \geqq 0$ and the integer nearest to each fraction being taken; $\sigma(m) = S(m) + S(m+5) + \cdots + S(m+5k) + \cdots$, $m$ being the largest integer for which $n - m - 5k > 0$, and let $S_{n,r}$ denote the number of solutions in natural numbers of the equation $x_1 + x_2 + \cdots + x_r = n$, where $x_1 \geqq x_2 \geqq x_3 \geqq \cdots \geqq x_r$. Then the author infers by actual counting and induction that for $r \geqq 5$, $S_{n,r} = \sigma(r-3) + \sigma(r-3+6) + \sigma(r-3+7) + \sigma(r-3+8) + \cdots + \sigma[r-3+(r-5)(r+6)/2]$.

The cases with $r \leqq 5$ have been treated separately. *J. M. Gandhi* (Macomb, Ill.)

# P60 PARTITIONS: GENERATING FUNCTIONS, IDENTITIES

See also reviews A36-2, F02-23, F35-47, P64-17, P64-32, P64-33, P64-35, P64-36, P64-42, P64-44, P64-45, P64-49, P64-51, P64-52, P64-53, P64-55, P64-56, P68-7, P68-8, P68-10, P68-18, P68-25, P68-26, P68-29, P68-32, P68-33, P68-35, P68-55, P72-37, P80-41, Z02-29, Z02-65, Z02-72.

**P60-1** **(3, 271e)**

**Rademacher, Hans. The Ramanujan identities under modular substitutions.** Trans. Amer. Math. Soc. **51**, 609–636 (1942).

The identities considered are

$$[1] \qquad \sum_{l=0}^{\infty} p(5l+4)x^l = 5\prod_{m=1}^{\infty}(1-x^{5m})^5 / \prod_{m=1}^{\infty}(1-x^m)^6$$

and the similar ones involving the moduli 7, 13, $5^2$ and $7^2$. The author writes these identities in terms of Dedekind's $\eta$-function and then subjects them to modular transformations. Thus [1] can be written in the form

$$[2] \qquad \sum_{\lambda=0}^{4} \eta\left(\frac{\tau+24\lambda}{5}\right)^{-1} = 5^2 \frac{\eta(5\tau)^5}{\eta(\tau)^6}$$

and, under the transformation $\tau \to -\tau^{-1}$, this goes over into a new identity, one form of which expresses certain quadratic relations between the $p(n)$. The author also obtains new proofs of the original identities. For the modulus 5 he multiplies [2] by $\eta(\tau)$ and considers the two members as modular functions belonging to the subgroup $\Gamma_0(5)$. From a knowledge of the transformation equation of $\eta(\tau)$ and a consideration of the behavior of the functions at the parabolic points, he establishes the identity of the two modular functions, and hence proves [1]. The author also shows that the identities with moduli $5^2$ and $7^2$ can be made to yield certain modular equations when subjected to the transformation $\tau \to -\tau^{-1}$. *H. S. Zuckerman.*

Referred to in F10-97, F25-7, F30-8, P76-1, P76-10.

**P60-2** **(6, 118b)**

**Schoenfeld, Lowell. A transformation formula in the theory of partitions.** Duke Math. J. **11**, 873–887 (1944).

The function

$$f_\kappa(x)=\prod_{n=1}^{\infty}(1-x^{m^\kappa})^{-1}$$

is the generating function of the number $p_\kappa(n)$ of partitions of $n$ into $\kappa$th powers. E. M. Wright [Acta Math. **63**, 143–191 (1934)] has obtained the transformation formula for this function, exhibiting its behavior near the rational points on the unit circle, and used it to determine the asymptotic behavior of $p_\kappa(n)$. Here a new and simpler proof of the transformation formula is given. The proof is a generalization of that used by Rademacher [J. Reine Angew. Math. **167**, 312–336 (1932)] for the case $\kappa=1$.

*H. S. Zuckerman* (Seattle, Wash.).

**P60-3** **(7, 243j)**

**Chowla, S. Outline of a new method for proving results of elliptic function theory (such as identities of the Ramanujan-Rademacher-Zuckermann type).** Proc. Lahore Philos. Soc. **7**, 3 pp. (1945).

It is pointed out that Ramanujan's identity

$$\sum p(5n+4)x^n=5\frac{(1-x^5)^5(1-x^{10})^5(1-x^{15})^5\cdots}{(1-x)^6(1-x^2)^6(1-x^3)^6\cdots}$$

and other similar ones could be proved by a consideration of the algebraic differential equation satisfied by each member. *H. S. Zuckerman* (Seattle, Wash.).

**P60-4** **(10, 3k)**

**Chakrabarti, S. Some identities and recurrents.** J. Indian Math. Soc. (N.S.) **11**, 89–94 (1947).

Four sum (identities) and three determinant (recurrents) evaluations, too involved to quote, expressing relations of the elementary symmetric functions of the quantities 1, $a$, $a^2$, $\cdots$, $a^{n-1}$. These functions appear as generating functions in the theory of partitions of numbers [the author's first formula, which he takes from a 1923 paper of his own, appears in MacMahon, Combinatory Analysis, Cambridge University Press, 1916, v. 2, p. 66] but no hint is given of the possible use of the results in this field or elsewhere.

*J. Riordan* (New York, N. Y.).

**P60-5** **(11, 234g)**

**Putter, Joseph. On a modular equation connected with partitions.** Riveon Lematematika **3**, 42–43, 53 (1949). (Hebrew. English summary)

The fact that $\eta(\tau)/\eta(\tau/11)$ and $\eta(11\tau)/\eta(\tau)$ are not connected by a modular equation of degree 11 is proved by considering what the sum of the roots of such an equation would be. Also the nonexistence of an identity of the form $\eta(24\tau)\sum p(11n+6)e^{(24n+13)2\pi i\tau}=R(\eta(11.24\tau)/\eta(24\tau))$, $R$ a rational function, is verified. *H. S. Zuckerman.*

**P60-6** **(11, 246b)**

**Jackson, M. On some formulae in partition theory, and bilateral basic hypergeometric series.** J. London Math. Soc. **24**, 233–237 (1949).

The author shows that a general formula of D. B. Sears for well-poised basic hypergeometric series can be specialized to yield a relation between a well-poised bilateral basic hypergeometric series and two well-poised basic series of the ordinary type. This in turn can be specialized to the following unpublished result of A. O. L. Atkin and H. P. F. Swinnerton-Dyer, as well as generalizations of it:

$$\sum_{n=-\infty}^{\infty}(-1)^n q^{\frac{3}{2}n(n+1)}\left[\frac{\zeta^{-3n}}{1-z\zeta^{-1}q^n}+\frac{\zeta^{3n+3}}{1-z\zeta q^n}\right]$$
$$=\frac{\zeta P(\zeta^2,q)}{P(\zeta,q)}\sum_{n=-\infty}^{\infty}\left\{\frac{(-1)^n q^{\frac{3}{2}n(n+1)}}{1-zq^n}\right\}$$
$$+\frac{P(\zeta,q)P(\zeta^2,q)\prod_{r=1}^{\infty}(1-q^r)^2}{P(z\zeta^{-1},q)P(z,q)P(z\zeta,q)},$$

where $P(z,q)=\prod_{r=0}^{\infty}(1-zq^r)(1-z^{-1}q^{r+1})$. Results of this type can be useful in partition theory. *N. J. Fine.*

**P60-7** **(11, 715g)**

**Kruyswijk, D. On some well-known properties of the partition function $p(n)$ and Euler's infinite product.** Nieuw Arch. Wiskunde (2) **23**, 97–107 (1950).

Let $f(x)=\prod_{n=1}^{\infty}(1-x^n)$ denote Euler's product and let $A_m=A_m(x)=x^m f(x^{24m})$. The author gives proofs, involving only the calculus of formal power series, of the following Ramanujan identities

$$5f^5(x^5)f^{-6}(x)=\sum_{r=0}^{\infty}p(5r+4)x^r,$$

$$7f^3(x^7)f^{-4}(x)+49xf^7(x^7)f^{-8}(x)=\sum_{r=0}^{\infty}p(7r+5)x^r,$$

$$A^4{}_1+5A^3{}_1A_{25}+15A^2{}_1A^2{}_{25}+25A_1A^3{}_{25}+25A^4{}_{25}=A^6{}_5(A_1A_{25})^{-1},$$

$$A^6{}_1+7A^5{}_1A_{49}+21A^4{}_1A^2{}_{49}+49A^3{}_1A^3{}_{49}+7A^2{}_1\{A^4{}_7+21A^4{}_{49}\}$$
$$+7A_1\{5A^4{}_7+49A^4{}_{49}\}A_{49}+49A^4{}_7A^2{}_{49}+343A^6{}_{49}=A^8{}_7(A_1A_{49})^{-1},$$

where $p(n)$ denotes the number of unrestricted partitions of $n$. The paper closes with the author's presentation of Jacobi's proof of the triangular number theorem which he writes in the form $f^3(x)=\sum_{k=0}^{\infty}(-1/k)kx^{(k^2-1)/8}$.

*D. H. Lehmer* (Berkeley, Calif.).

**P60-8** **(13, 321h)**

**Shanks, Daniel. A short proof of an identity of Euler.** Proc. Amer. Math. Soc. **2**, 747–749 (1951).

Let $P_n=\prod_{s=1}^{n}(1-x^s)$, $Q_n=\prod_{s=1}^{n}(1-x^{2s})/(1-x^{2s-1})$. Then

(1) $$\sum_{s=0}^{n}(-1)^s\frac{P_n}{P_s}x^{sn+s(s+1)/2}=1+\sum_{s=1}^{n}(-1)^s[x^{s(3s-1)/2}+x^{s(3s+1)/2}],$$

(2) $$\sum_{s=0}^{n}\frac{Q_n}{Q_s}x^{s(2n+1)}=1+\sum_{s=1}^{n}[x^{s(2s-1)}+x^{s(2s+1)}].$$

These finite identities, discovered by application of a nonlinear transformation to certain sequences, appear to be new. For $n\to\infty$, (1) and (2) yield well-known identities of Euler and Gauss, respectively. *N. J. Fine.*

Referred to in P60-29.

**P60-9** **(13, 327a)**

**Bailey, W. N. On the simplification of some identities of the Rogers-Ramanujan type.** Proc. London Math. Soc. (3) **1**, 217–221 (1951).

In many of the identities discovered by Rogers, and recently by L. J. Slater [same Proc. (2) **53**, 460–475 (1951); these Rev. **13**, 227], the right side involves the sum of two infinite products. An example (due to Rogers) is

$$1+\sum_{n=1}^{\infty}\frac{q^{n(n+1)/2}}{(1-q)(1-q^2)\cdots(1-q^n)(1-q)(1-q^3)\cdots(1-q^{2n-1})}$$
$$=\prod_{n=1}^{\infty}\left(\frac{1+q^n}{1-q^n}\right)\left[\prod_{n=1}^{\infty}(1+q^{21n-10})(1+q^{21n-11})(1-q^{21n})\right.$$
$$\left.-q\prod_{n=1}^{\infty}(1+q^{21n-4})(1+q^{21n-17})(1-q^{21n})\right].$$

The author shows that in many cases the two products can be reduced to one by use of the formula

$$\prod_{n=1}^{\infty}((1+q^nz^{-1})(1+q^{n-1}z)(1-q^{2n-1}z^{-2})(1-q^{2n-1}z^2)(1-q^n)$$
$$=\prod_{n=1}^{\infty}(1-q^{3n-2}z^3)(1-q^{3n-1}z^{-3})(1-q^{3n})$$
$$+z\prod_{n=1}^{\infty}(1-q^{3n-2}z^{-3})(1-q^{3n-1}z^3)(1-q^{3n}),$$

which he proves. This formula is essentially the same as one given by Watson [J. London Math. Soc. 4, 39–48 (1929), pp. 44–45]. The author gives another, simpler formula which is frequently useful. *N. J. Fine.*

Referred to in P60-31.

## P60-10 (13, 327b)

**Gupta, Hansraj. A generalization of the partition function.** Proc. Nat. Inst. Sci. India 17, 231–238 (1951).

Let $v_r(n)$ be defined by

$$nv_r(n)=\sum_{j=1}^{n}\sigma_r(j)v_r(n-j),$$

where $\sigma_r(j)$ is the sum of the $r$th powers of the divisors of $j$ and $v_r(0)=1$. Thus $v_1(n)=p(n)$, the ordinary partition function. It is proved that

$$\sum_{n=0}^{\infty}v_r(n)x^n=\prod_{j=1}^{\infty}(1-x^j)^{-j^{r-1}}.$$

Thus $v_r(n)$ is the number of partitions of $n$ when the part $j$ is of $j^{r-1}$ different types.

Similarly, if $v_r(n, m)$ is defined by

$$nv_r(n, m)=\sum_{j=1}^{n}\sigma_r(j, m)v_r(n-j, m),$$

where $\sigma_r(j, m)$ is the sum of the $r$th powers of those divisors of $j$ which do not exceed $m$, then

$$\sum_{n=0}^{\infty}v_r(n, m)x^n=\prod_{j=1}^{m}(1-x^j)^{-j^{r-1}}.$$

Thus $v_r(n, m)$ is the number of partitions of $n$ into parts not exceeding $m$, each part $j$ being of $j^{r-1}$ different types. If $m=o(n^{1/(2r+1)})$,

$$v_r(n, m)\prod_{j=1}^{m}j^{j^{r-1}}\sim\binom{n-1}{S_{r-1}(m)-1},$$

where $S_k(m)=\sum_{i=1}^{m}i^k$. Also

$$v_2(n)=\exp[\{C+o(1)\}n^{2/3}],$$

where $C^3=(27/4)\zeta(3)$. There is a table of $v_2(n, m)$ for $m\leqq n\leqq 50$. *N. J. Fine* (Philadelphia, Pa.).

## P60-11 (13, 536a)

**Subba Rao, M. V. Ramanujan's trigonometrical sum and relative partitions.** J. Indian Math. Soc. (N.S.) 15, 57–64 (1951).

For $n<m$, a relative partition of $n$ mod $m$ is defined as a partition of $n+tm$, $t\geqq 0$, into positive parts less than $m$. The author develops a method for expressing certain weighted restricted relative partition functions in terms of Ramanujan's $C_m(n)=\sum_\rho \exp(2\pi i\rho n/m)$, where $\rho$ runs over a reduced residue system mod $m$. The restriction on the partitions is that no part is to appear more than $\nu$ times; the weights are of the form $\lambda^k$, where $\lambda$ is real and $k$ is the number of parts, or of forms which can be obtained from this one by differentiation with respect to $\lambda$. The method is valid, but the results are not (for $\nu>1$), since the author uses the generating function

$$\prod_{l=1}^{r}(1+\lambda x^{a_l})^\nu$$

instead of the correct

$$\prod_{l=1}^{r}(1+\lambda x^{a_l}+\lambda^2x^{2a_l}+\cdots+\lambda^\nu x^{\nu a_l})$$

for the absolute weighted partitions of $n$ into parts $a_1$, $a_2, \cdots, a_r$, restricted as above. *N. J. Fine.*

## P60-12 (13, 536c)

**Auluck, F. C. On some new types of partitions associated with generalized Ferrers graphs.** Proc. Cambridge Philos. Soc. 47, 679–686 (1951).

The partitions considered are of the form

$$n=\sum_{k=1}^{r}a_k+\sum_{j=1}^{s}b_j,$$

$$(1)\qquad\begin{cases}0<a_1\leqq a_2\leqq\cdots\leqq a_r, & 0<b_1\leqq b_2\leqq\cdots\leqq b_s,\\ & b_s<a_r.\end{cases}$$

The set "$b$" can be empty. Under Type A, $b_s=a_r-1$, every integer up to $a_r$ is taken at least once in the set "$a$", and every integer up to $b_s$ is taken at least once in the set "$b$". Type B has no restrictions other than (1). In Type C, every integer up to $a_r$ is taken at least once in the set "$a$". The corresponding partition functions are denoted by $P(n)$, $Q(n)$, $R(n)$, and the generating functions are $f(x)$, $g(x)$, $h(x)$, respectively. Then

$$f(x)=\sum_{m=1}^{\infty}\frac{x^{m^2}}{(1-x)^2(1-x^2)^2\cdots(1-x^{m-1})^2(1-x^m)},$$
$$g(x)=\sum_{m=1}^{\infty}\frac{x^m}{(1-x)^2(1-x^2)^2\cdots(1-x^{m-1})^2(1-x^m)},$$
$$h(x)=\sum_{m=1}^{\infty}\frac{x^{\frac{1}{2}(m^2+m)}}{(1-x)^2(1-x^2)^2\cdots(1-x^{m-1})^2(1-x^m)}.$$

The following identities are proved:

$$f(x)=\frac{x-x^3+x^6-x^{10}+\cdots}{(1-x)(1-x^2)(1-x^3)\cdots},$$
$$g(x)=\frac{x-x^3+x^6-x^{10}+\cdots}{[(1-x)(1-x^2)(1-x^3)\cdots]^2},$$
$$h(x)=\prod_{k=1}^{\infty}(1-x^k)^{-1}\sum_{m=0}^{\infty}\frac{x^{(m+1)(2m+1)}}{(1-x^2)(1-x^4)(1-x^6)\cdots(1-x^{2m})}.$$

Using these, the author expresses $P(n)$, $Q(n)$, $R(n)$ in terms of more familiar partition functions, and obtains estimates

$$P(n)\sim\frac{1}{8n\sqrt{3}}\exp\left\{\pi\left(\frac{2n}{3}\right)^{\frac{1}{2}}\right\},$$

$$Q(n)\sim\frac{1}{8\cdot 3^{3/4}n^{5/4}}\exp\left\{2\pi\left(\frac{n}{3}\right)^{\frac{1}{2}}\right\},$$

$$\pi\sqrt{\tfrac{2}{3}}\leqq n^{-\frac{1}{2}}\log R(n)\leqq\pi\sqrt{\tfrac{5}{6}}.$$

*N. J. Fine* (Philadelphia, Pa.).

Referred to in P64-59, P64-62.

## P60-13 (13, 725d)

**Bailey, W. N. A note on two of Ramanujan's formulae.** Quart. J. Math., Oxford Ser. (2) **3**, 29–31 (1952).

In an unpublished manuscript, Ramanujan gave an alternate proof of his famous formula

$$(1)\qquad \sum_{n=0}^{\infty}p(5n+4)x^n=5\prod_{n=1}^{\infty}\frac{(1-x^{5n})^5}{(1-x^n)^6},$$

where $p(n)$ is the number of partitions of $n$. This proof is based on the (unproved) formula

$$(2)\quad x\prod_{n=1}^{\infty}\frac{(1-x^{5n})^5}{(1-x^n)}=\sum_{n=0}^{\infty}\left[\frac{x^{5n+1}}{(1-x^{5n+1})^2}-\frac{x^{5n+2}}{(1-x^{5n+2})^2}-\frac{x^{5n+3}}{(1-x^{5n+3})^2}+\frac{x^{5n+4}}{(1-x^{5n+4})^2}\right].$$

The author supplies a proof of (2), using the known sum of a well-poised basic bilateral hypergeometric series. From this same sum he also deduces another result of Ramanujan's:

$$(3)\quad \prod_{n=1}^{\infty}\frac{(1-x^n)^5}{(1-x^{5n})}=1-5\sum_{m=0}^{\infty}\left[\frac{(5m+1)x^{5m+1}}{1-x^{5m+1}}-\frac{(5m+2)x^{5m+2}}{1-x^{5m+2}}-\frac{(5m+3)x^{5m+3}}{1-x^{5m+3}}+\frac{(5m+4)x^{5m+4}}{1-x^{5m+4}}\right],$$

proofs of which have been given by Darling and by Mordell.

*N. J. Fine* (Philadelphia, Pa.).

Referred to in P60-14.

## P60-14 (14, 138f)

**Bailey, W. N. A further note on two of Ramanujan's formulae.** Quart. J. Math., Oxford Ser. (2) **3**, 158–160 (1952).

In a recent note [same Quart. **3**, 29–31 (1952); these Rev. **13**, 725] the author has supplied a missing link in an alternate proof by Ramanujan of the identity

$$\sum_{n=0}^{\infty}p(5n+4)x^n=5\prod_{n=1}^{\infty}\frac{(1-x^{5n})^5}{(1-x^n)^6}.$$

In that note he used the known sum of a well-poised bilateral basic series ${}_6\Psi_6$. Here he obtains the same result by using a well-known formula in elliptic functions,

$$\wp(v)-\wp(u)=\frac{\sigma(u-v)\sigma(u+v)}{\sigma^2(u)\sigma^2(v)}.$$

[The reviewer remarks that a similar approach has led him to a proof of Ramanujan's congruence $p(7n+5)\equiv 0 \pmod 7$; the corresponding identity differs from Ramanujan's.]

*N. J. Fine* (Philadelphia, Pa.).

Citations: MR 13, 725d = P60-13.
Referred to in P60-18, P60-21.

## P60-15 (14, 139a)

**Iseki, Kanesiroo. A proof of a transformation formula in the theory of partitions.** J. Math. Soc. Japan **4**, 14–26 (1952).

The partition function $p(n)$ is generated by the infinite product $f(x)=\prod_1^\infty(1-x^n)^{-1}=1+\sum_1^\infty p(n)x^n$, whose logarithm, $F(x)$, satisfies the transformation formula (1): $F(x)=F(\bar{x})+\log z^{1/2}+\pi/(12kz)-\pi z/(12k)+\pi is(h,k)$, where $x=\exp(2\pi ih/k-2\pi z/k)$, $\bar{x}=\exp(2\pi iH/k-2\pi/(kz))$, $h, k, H$ are integers with $(h,k)=1$, $hH\equiv -1 \pmod k$, $\Re(z)>0$, and $s(h,k)=\sum_{m=1}^{k-1}(m/k)(hm/k-[hm/k]-\frac{1}{2})$ is a Dedekind sum. Formula (1) is due to Dedekind and is one of the fundamental results in the theory of elliptic modular functions and in the asymptotic theory of partitions. Rademacher [J. Reine Angew. Math. **167**, 312–336 (1932)] gave a proof of (1), basing it on the Mellin transform and the functional equation of the Hurwitz zeta function.

The author gives a longer but somewhat more elementary proof of (1), using theta functions instead of zeta functions. As in Rademacher's proof, the double series expansion $F(x)=\sum_{m,n}m^{-1}x^{mn}$ is used, but the author keeps $z$ real and positive and treats the real and imaginary parts of (1) separately. The restriction $z>0$ is later removed by analytic continuation. The elementary integral

$$\int_0^\infty \exp(-t^2-a^2/t^2)dt=\tfrac{1}{2}\pi^{1/2}e^{-2a}\quad (a>0)$$

plays essentially the same role in this proof that the Mellin integral for $e^{-x}$ played in Rademacher's proof, making possible a definite integral representation for $\Re F(x)$ in terms of theta functions. The transformation theory of theta functions then yields

$$\Re F(x)=\Re F(\bar{x})+\log z^{1/2}+\pi/(12kz)-\pi z/(12k).$$

The author then shows that $\Im F(x)-\Im F(\bar{x})$ is a constant independent of $z$, again via theta functions, and then uses Dedekind's method to show that this constant is $\pi s(h,k)$, and the proof is complete.

The latter part of the paper contains a proof of the reciprocity law for Dedekind sums based on contour integration. This proof has already been given by Rademacher [Mat. Fiz. Lapok, **40**, 24–34 (1933)]. *T. M. Apostol.*

Referred to in F10-98.

## P60-16 (14, 951b)

**Newman, Morris. The coefficients of certain infinite products.** Proc. Amer. Math. Soc. **4**, 435–439 (1953).

Put $\prod_{n=1}^\infty(1-x^n)^r=\sum_{n=0}^\infty p_r(n)x^n$. For $r=1, 3$ we have the familiar identities of Euler and Jacobi, respectively, but as the author remarks, for no other values of $r$ are the coefficients $p_r(n)$ known "explicitly". In the present paper various recursion formulas and identities are set up. The identity

$$(*)\quad \sum p_r(np+\delta)=p_r(\delta)\prod(1-x^n)^r-p^{r/2-1}x^\delta\prod(1-x^{np})^r,$$

where $1\leqq r\leqq 24$, $r(p-1)\equiv 0 \pmod{24}$, $\delta=r(p-1)/24$, is quoted from a previous paper [Trans. Amer. Math. Soc. **73**, 313–320 (1952); these Rev. **14**, 250]. It is then proved that

$$(**)\qquad \sum p_r(np+\Delta)=(-p)^{r/2-1}\prod(1-x^{np})^r,$$

where $r=2$, 4 or 6, $r(p+1)\equiv 0$ (24), $\Delta=r(p^2-1)/24$. By means of (**) results like

$$p_r(r(p^{2t}-1)/24)=(-p)^{(r/2-1)t}$$

are proved; a like result derived from (*) implies that every integer occurs infinitely often as the modulus of the coefficients $p_2(n)$. *L. Carlitz* (Durham, N. C.).

Citations: MR 14, 250a = F10-28.

**P60-17** **(15, 12a)**

**Carlitz, L. Note on some partition identities.** Proc. Amer. Math. Soc. **4**, 530–534 (1953).

Let the numbers $p_k(m)$ be defined by

$$\prod_{n=1}^{\infty}(1-x^n)^k=\sum_{m=0}^{\infty}p_k(m)x^m.$$

The author proves: if $r$ is a prime $>3$ and either $r\equiv 3 \pmod 4$ or $r\equiv 5 \pmod{12}$ then

$$\sum_{m=0}^{\infty}p_2(rm+r_0)x^m=\epsilon\prod_{n=1}^{\infty}(1-x^{rn})^2,$$

where $r_0=(r^2-1)/12$ and $\epsilon=+1$ in the first case, $\epsilon=-1$ in the second case. Similar identities are proved for $p_6(m)$ if $r\equiv 3 \pmod 4$, $r\geqq 3$ and for $p_4(m)$ if $r\equiv 5 \pmod 6$. Special cases of these identities had previously been given by M. Newman [Trans. Amer. Math. Soc. **73**, 313–320 (1952); these Rev. **14**, 250]. The author also derives another formula given by Newman, viz.

$$\sum_{m=0}^{\infty}p_5(5m)x^m=\prod_{n=1}^{\infty}(1-x^n)^6(1-x^{5n})^{-1}$$

from a result of Ramanujan. *H. D. Kloosterman.*

Citations: MR 14, 250a = F10-28.

**P60-18** **(15, 201b)**

**Carlitz, L. Note on some partition formulae.** Quart. J. Math., Oxford Ser. (2) **4**, 168–172 (1953).

Let $p_k(m)$ be the generalized partition function defined by $\prod_{n=1}^{\infty}(1-x^n)^{-k}=\sum_{m=0}^{\infty}p_k(m)x^m$. Employing the method of Bailey [same J. (2) **3**, 158–160 (1952); these Rev. **14**, 138] the author shows that identities such as

$$\sum_{m=0}^{\infty}p_3(3m+2)x^m=9\prod_{n=1}^{\infty}\frac{(1-x^{3n})^9}{(1-x^n)^{12}}$$

can be derived from the familiar formula

$$\wp'(u)=-\sigma(2u)/\sigma^4(u),$$

when the $\wp$-function is replaced by its Fourier series. *A. L. Whiteman* (Princeton, N. J.).

Citations: MR 14, 138f = P60-14.
Referred to in E24-62, P60-21.

**P60-19** **(15, 856c)**

**Alder, Henry L. Generalizations of the Rogers-Ramanujan identities.** Pacific J. Math. **4**, 161–168 (1954).

The first Rogers-Ramanujan identity [Hardy and Wright, Introduction to the theory of numbers, Oxford, 1938, Theorem 362] states that the generating function for the number of partitions into parts of the form $5m\pm 1$ is expressible as

$$\sum_{m=0}^{\infty}x^{m^2}/(1-x)(1-x^2)\cdots(1-x^m).$$

The author considers, for any positive integer $k$, the generating function for the number of partitions into parts that are not congruent to 0, $k$ or $-k$ (mod $2k+1$), and shows that this function is expressible as

$$\sum_{m=0}^{\infty}G_{k,m}(x)/(1-x)(1-x^2)\cdots(1-x^m),$$

where $G_{k,m}(x)$ is a polynomial in $x$. The exact degree of this polynomial is determined in the cases $k=3$ and 4. A similar identity is obtained for the generating function for the number of partitions into parts that are not congruent to 0 or $\pm 1$ (mod $2k+1$), with $G_{k,m}(x)$ replaced by $x^mG_{k,m}(x)$. However, except in the original case of Rogers and Ramanujan, the series obtained are not interpretable as being themselves the generating functions for partitions into parts differing by at least a given amount. *H. Davenport.*

Referred to in B84-15.

**P60-20** **(17, 238h)**

**Carlitz, L. Some partition formulas.** Tôhoku Math. J. (2) **6** (1954), 149–154.

The author derives a number of identities from the elliptic-function formulas for $\wp(u)-\wp(v)$ and $\wp'(u)$ in terms of $\sigma$-functions. A fairly typical one is

$$\frac{1+x}{1-x}-2\sum_{1}^{\infty}\frac{x^{3n}}{1+x^{3n}}(x^n-x^{-n})=\prod_{1}^{\infty}\frac{(1-x^{3n})^6(1-x^{2n})}{(1-x^{6n})^3(1-x^n)^2}.$$

*N. J. Fine* (Philadelphia, Pa.).

**P60-21** **(17, 348e)**

**Dobbie, J. M. A simple proof of some partition formulae of Ramanujan's.** Quart. J. Math. Oxford Ser. (2) **6** (1955), 193–196.

Bailey [same J. (2) **3** (1952), 158–160; MR **14**, 138] showed that certain well-known formulas of Ramanujan can be obtained as special cases of the identity

$$(*)\quad \sum_{-\infty}^{\infty}\left\{\frac{xq^n}{(1-xq^n)^2}-\frac{yq^n}{(1-yq^n)^2}\right\}=\frac{(x-y)(1-xy)}{(1-x^2)(1-y^2)}$$
$$\prod_{1}^{\infty}\frac{(1-xyq^n)(1-x^{-1}yq^n)(1-xy^{-1}q^n)(1-x^{-1}y^{-1}q^n)(1-q^n)^4}{(1-xq^n)^2(1-x^{-1}q^n)^2(1-yq^n)^2(1-y^{-1}q^n)^2},$$

which is itself obtained from

$$\wp(u)-\wp(v)=-\frac{\sigma(u+v)\sigma(u-v)}{\sigma^2(u)\sigma^2(v)}.$$

Similarly, the reviewer [ibid. **4** (1953), 168–172; MR **15**, 201] applied the identity

$$(**)\quad 1+x^{-1}\frac{(1-x)^3}{1+x}\sum_{1}^{\infty}\frac{n^2q^{2n}}{1-q^n}(x^n-x^{-n})$$
$$=\prod_{1}^{\infty}\frac{(1-x^2q^n)(1-x^{-2}q^n)(1-q^n)^6}{(1-xq^n)^4(1-x^{-1}q^n)^4}$$

which is obtained from $\wp'(u)=-\sigma(2u)/\sigma^4(u)$.

In the present paper the identities (*) and (**) are proved by a simple method (frequently employed by Jacobi and Cauchy) that does not presuppose any knowledge of elliptic functions. *L. Carlitz.*

Citations: MR 14, 138f = P60-14; MR 15, 201b = P60-18.

**P60-22** **(17, 1082b)**

**Lenz, H. Eine Bemerkung zur Einführung der Thetafunktionen.** Jber. Deutsch. Math. Verein. **58** (1956), Abt. 2, 57.

This is a short proof of Jacobi's identity

$$\sum_{m=-\infty}^{\infty}q^{m^2}z^{2m}=\prod_{n=1}^{\infty}(1-q^{2n})F(z)\ (|q|<1),$$

where $F(z)=\prod_{n=1}^{\infty}(1+q^{2n-1}z^2)(1+q^{2n-1}z^{-2})$. One shows that in

$$(*)\quad \sum_{m=-\infty}^{\infty}q^{m^2}z^{2m}=C\cdot F(z),\quad (**)\quad C=C(q)=\prod_{n=1}^{\infty}(1-q^{2n})$$

hold. The first equality (**) follows from $F(qz)=q^{-1}z^{-2}F(z)$. Setting in (*) successively $z=i$ and $z=e^{\frac{1}{4}\pi i}$, one obtains after simple manipulations that $C(q^{4^r})\prod_{n=1}^{\infty}(1-q^{4^r\cdot 2n})^{-1}$ is independent of the integral value $r$. As for $r\to\infty$ this constant is clearly one (use $|q|<1$), the last equality follows. *E. Grosswald* (Philadelphia, Pa.).

**P60-23** **(17, 1188a)**

**Nicol, C. A.; and Vandiver, H. S. On generating functions for restricted partitions of rational integers.** Proc. Nat. Acad. Sci. U.S.A. **41** (1955), 37–42; errata, 251.

The authors study the coefficients in the expansion of $\prod_{i=1}^{n}(1-zx^i)^{a_i}$ as a polynomial in $x$, the $a_i$ being non-negative integers not all zero. First, a general recurrence formula is given, and then special results are obtained for $z=1$. Finally, for $a_i=1$ $(1\leqq i\leqq n)$, some arithmetic properties of the coefficients are derived. The von Sterneck number plays an important part. *N. J. Fine.*

**P60-24** **(18, 717d)**

**Carlitz, L. A note on Gauss' "Serierum singularium".** Portugal. Math. **15** (1956), 9–12.

By using an identity of Euler [see Hardy and Wright, Introduction to the theory of numbers, 2nd ed., Oxford, 1945, Th. 349, p. 278] the author deduces in a natural way two formulas of Gauss. One of these, for example, is

$$\sum_{r=0}^{2m}\begin{bmatrix}2m\\ r\end{bmatrix}(-1)^r=(1-x)(1-x^3)\cdots(1-x^{2m-1}),$$

where

$$\begin{bmatrix}m\\ r\end{bmatrix}=(x)_m/\{(x)_r(x)_{m-r}\},$$
$$(a)_m=(1-a)(1-ax)\cdots(1-ax^{m-1}).$$

The use of a more general identity leads to two generalized formulas. *W. H. Gage* (Vancouver, B.C.).

**P60-25** **(19, 543a)**

**Bellman, Richard. The expansions of some infinite products.** Duke Math. J. **24** (1957), 353–356.

The expansion of the double products

$$\prod_{r,s=0}^{\infty}(1-x^ry^st),\quad \prod_{r,s=0}^{\infty}(1-x^ry^st)^{-1}$$

has been discussed (independently) by the reviewer [Proc. Amer. Math. Soc. **7** (1956), 558–564; MR **19**, 29] and E. M. Wright [ibid. **7** (1956), 880–890; MR **18**, 793]. In the present paper it is shown first that

$$\prod_{k=1}^{\infty}\frac{1-x^k}{1-x^kz}=\sum_{r=1}^{\infty}\frac{\prod_{k=1}^{r-1}(1-x^{-k})^{-1}}{1-x^rz},$$

and secondly that

$$(*)\qquad \prod_{k,l=1}^{\infty}\frac{1-x^ky^l}{1-x^ky^lz}=\sum_{r,s=1}^{\infty}\frac{b_{rs}}{1-x^ry^sz},$$

where

$$b_{rs}=\prod_{k,l=1}^{r-1,s-1}(1-x^{-k}y^{-l})^{-1}\prod_{k=1}^{\infty}\prod_{l=0}^{s-1}(1-x^ky^{-l})^{-1}$$
$$\times\prod_{k=0}^{r-1}\prod_{l=1}^{\infty}(1-x^{-k}y^l).$$

The author remarks that a rigorous proof of (*) requires a measure of the irrationality of $\log x/\log y$.

*L. Carlitz* (Durham, N.C.).

Citations: MR 18, 793c = P64-13; MR 19, 29d = P64-17.

**P60-26** **(19, 838e)**

**Kolberg, Oddmund. Some identities involving the partition function.** Math. Scand. **5** (1957), 77–92.

Let $\varphi(x)=\prod_{n=1}^{\infty}(1-x^n)=\sum_{n=-\infty}^{\infty}(-1)^nx^{\frac12n(3n+1)}$, so that $\varphi(x)^{-1}$ generates the partition function $p(n)$. Let $q$ be a prime and define, for $0\leqq s\leqq q-1$,

$$g_s=\sum_{\frac12n(3n+1)\equiv s(\mathrm{mod}\ q)}(-1)^nx^{\frac12n(3n+1)};$$

$$P_s=\sum_{n=0}^{\infty}p(qn+s)x^{qn+s},$$

so that $P_0+P_1+\cdots+P_{q-1}=\varphi(x)^{-1}$; $g_0+g_1+\cdots+g_{q-1}=\varphi(x)$. By elementary methods of great elegance the author derives a number of identities for the functions $P_s$, principally for $q=2, 3, 5, 7$. These include the Ramanujan identities for partitions modulo 5, 7 and many others, such as

$$(1)\quad \sum_{n=0}^{\infty}\{p(5n+1)x^{5n}+p(5n+2)x^{5n+1}\}=$$
$$\varphi(x^5)^{-6}\{\varphi(x)^3\varphi(x^{25})^2+5x\varphi(x)^2\varphi(x^{25})^3+10x^2\varphi(x)\varphi(x^{25})^4$$
$$+10x^3\varphi(x^{25})^5\};$$

$$(2)\quad \sum_{n=0}^{\infty}p(3n)x^n=\varphi(x)^{-4}\varphi(x^3)\varphi(x^9)^2\prod_{n=1}^{\infty}(1-x^{9n-5})^2$$
$$\times(1-x^{9n-4})^2-x\varphi(x)^{-3}\varphi(x^9)^2\prod_{n=1}^{\infty}(1-x^{9n-5})^{-1}(1-x^{9n-4})^{-1}.$$

Formula (1), for example, may certainly be used to obtain information about $p(5n+1)$, $p(5n+2)$ modulo 5 not derivable in any standard way from the theory of the elliptic modular functions (which only yield information about $p(5n+4)$ modulo 5). Unfortunately the new identities for $q=7$ derived by the author do not seem useful for such a purpose, since they all involve products of the $P$'s. *M. Newman* (Washington, D.C.).

Referred to in P60-30, P76-20.

**P60-27** **(20# 1865 )**

**Carlitz, Leonard. A note on the Rogers-Ramanujan identities.** Math. Nachr. **17** (1958), 23–26.

The Rogers-Ramanujan identities [for proof and references, see Hardy, "Ramanujan", Macmillan, New York, 1940; MR 3, 71; chap. 6]:

$$\sum_0^{\infty}\frac{q^{m^2}}{(q)_m}=\prod_0^{\infty}(1-q^{5m+1})^{-1}(1-q^{5m+4})^{-1},$$

$$\sum_0^{\infty}\frac{q^{m^2+m}}{(q)_m}=\prod_0^{\infty}(1-q^{5m+2})^{-1}(1-q^{5m+3})^{-1},$$

where $(q)_m=(1-q)(1-q^2)\cdots(1-q^m)$, $(q)_0=1$, are equivalent to

$$\sum_0^{\infty}\frac{q^{m^2}}{(q)_m}=\sum_{-\infty}^{\infty}(-1)^mq^{\frac12(5m^2+m)}\prod_1^{\infty}(1-q^n)^{-1},$$

$$\sum_0^{\infty}\frac{q^{m^2+m}}{(q)_m}=\sum_{-\infty}^{\infty}(-1)^mq^{\frac12(5m^2+3m)}\prod_1^{\infty}(1-q^n)^{-1},$$

respectively. The author's proof of these identies is a variant of Roger's proof as given by Hardy. His method depends upon the basic analog of the Bessel function first defined by Jackson [Proc. London Math. Soc. (2) **2** (1905), 192–220] and later discussed by Hahn [Math. Nachr. **2** (1949), 340–379; MR **11**, 720]. However, no properties of Jackson's function are assumed. The advantage of the author's procedure is that it eliminates some of the artificial features of previous proofs.

*A. L. Whiteman* (Los Angeles, Calif.)

Citations: MR 3, 71d = Z20-4.

**P60-28** **(20# 2308 )**

**Iseki, Shô. Some transformation equations in the theory of partitions.** Proc. Japan Acad. **34** (1958), 131–135.

The author announces a transformation formula for the

generating function of $p(n; a, M)$, the number of partitions of $n$ into positive summands of the form $Ml \pm a$ ($l=0, 1, 2, \cdots$), where $0<a<M$, $(a, M)=1$, $M \geq 2$. A detailed proof, based on a functional equation derived in an earlier paper [Duke Math. J. **24** (1957), 653–662; MR **19**, 943] is promised in a future paper. The special case $a=1$, $M=4$, which is treated in some detail, leads to a simplification of Hua's results [Trans. Amer. Math. Soc. **51** (1942), 194–201; MR **3**, 270] concerning the generating function for the number of partitions of $n$ into odd (or unequal) parts.

*T. M. Apostol* (Pasadena, Calif.)

Citations: MR 3, 270c = P72-4; MR 19, 943a = F10-50.

**P60-29** **(20# 5994)**

**Shanks, Daniel. Two theorems of Gauss.** Pacific J. Math. **8** (1958), 609–612.

The author obtains the identity

$$\prod_1^\infty \frac{1-x^{2n}}{1-x^{2n-1}} = \sum_1^\infty x^{\frac{1}{2}n(n-1)},$$

as well as the evaluation of Gauss' sum from the identities

$$\sum_{s=0}^{n-1} \frac{P_n}{P_s} x^{s(2n+1)} = \sum_{s=1}^{2n} x^{\frac{1}{2}s(s-1)},$$

$$\sum_{s=1}^{n} \frac{P_n}{P_s} x^{s(2n+1)} = \sum_{s=1}^{2n+1} x^{\frac{1}{2}s(s-1)},$$

where $P_n = \prod_{s=1}^n (1-x^{2s})/(1-x^{2s-1})$, stated in an earlier paper [Proc. Amer. Math. Soc. **2** (1951), 747–749; MR **13**, 321; see p. 749]. The latter identities are proved in the present paper.

*L. Carlitz* (Durham, N.C.)

Citations: MR 13, 321h = P60-8.

**P60-30** **(21# 23)**

**Kolberg, O. Identities involving the partition functions $q(n)$ and $q_0(n)$.** Math. Scand. **6** (1958), 80–86.

Let $q(n)$ denote the number of partitions of $n$ into distinct parts, $q_0(n)$ the number of partitions of $n$ into distinct odd parts. In the same way that he derived identities for $p(n)$, the number of unrestricted partitions of $n$ [Math. Scand. **5** (1957), 77–92; MR **19**, 838], the author proves six identities for $q(n)$, $q_0(n)$, of which the following pair are typical:

$$\sum q(5n)x^n \sum q(5n+2)x^n = (\sum q(5n+1)x^n)^2;$$

$$\sum q_0(5n+1)x^n \sum q_0(5n+7)x^n = (\sum q_0(5n+4)x^n)^2.$$

The methods of proof are elementary and elegant, depending on the dissection of a power series according to the residue class of the exponent modulo a prime.

*M. Newman* (Washington, D.C.)

Citations: MR 19, 838e = P60-26.

**P60-31** **(25# 21)**

**Gordon, B.**

**Some identities in combinatorial analysis.**

*Quart. J. Math. Oxford Ser.* (2) **12** (1961), 285–290.

The author proves the formula

$$(*) \quad \prod_1^\infty (1-x^{2n})(1-x^{2n-1}z)(1-x^{2n-1}z^{-1})(1-x^{4n-4}z^2)$$

$$\times (1-x^{4n-4}z^{-2}) = \sum_{-\infty}^\infty x^{3n^2-2n}(z^{3n}+z^{-3n}-z^{3n-2}-z^{-3n+2}).$$

Various special cases of (*) are cited, in particular,

$$\prod_1^\infty (1-x^n)^3(1-x^{2n-1})^2 = \sum_{-\infty}^\infty (6n+1)x^{n(3n+1)/2}.$$

The author also obtains some congruence properties analogous to those enjoyed by the partition function $p(n)$. For example, if

$$\prod_1^\infty (1-x^n)^{-2}(1-x^{2n})^{-2} = \sum_0^\infty c_n x^n,$$

then $c_n \equiv 0 \pmod 7$ when $n \equiv 2, 3, 4$ or $6 \pmod 7$.

{Reviewer's comment: A formula equivalent to (*) was given by W. N. Bailey [Proc. London Math. Soc. (3) **1** (1951), 217–221; in particular p. 219; MR **13**, 327].}

*L. Carlitz* (Durham, N.C.)

Citations: MR 13, 327a = P60-9.

Referred to in P60-32, P60-34, P60-56.

**P60-32** **(25# 2340)**

**Mordell, L. J.**

**An identity in combinatorial analysis.**

*Proc. Glasgow Math. Assoc.* **5**, 197–200 (1962).

B. Gordon [Quart. J. Math. Oxford Ser. (2) **12** (1961), 285–290; MR **25** #21] proved the formula

$$\prod_1^\infty (1-s^n)(1-s^n t)(1-s^{n+1}t^{-1})(1-s^{2n-1}t^2)(1-s^{2n-1}t^{-2}) =$$

$$\sum_{-\infty}^\infty s^{(3n^2+n)/2}(t^{3n}-t^{-3n-1}).$$

The author gives another proof of the formula that makes uses of properties of theta functions.

*L. Carlitz* (Durham, N.C.)

Citations: MR 25# 21 = P60-31.

**P60-33** **(26# 1298)**

**Banerjee, D. P.**

**On some identities in partition functions.**

*Proc. Nat. Acad. Sci. India Sect. A* **29** (1960), 356–359.

Generating functions are found for the partitions of integers of the form $m=3n+j$ ($j=0, 1, 2$). Let $w$ ($\neq 1$) be a cubic root of unity, set $f(x)=\prod_{n=1}^\infty (1-x^n)$ and $\phi_k(x)=w^{2(k-1)}f(w^2x)+w^{k-1}f(wx)$ ($k=1, 2, 3$). Then, if $F_j(x)=\sum_{n=0}^\infty p(3n+j)x^{3n+j}$ ($j=0, 1, 2$), one has

$$3F_j(x) = \frac{1}{f(x)} + \frac{f(x^9)f(x)}{f^4(x^3)} \phi_{j+1}(x).$$

The method consists of straightforward manipulations of generating functions as formal power series. Among the identities established are the following: $\sum_{k=1}^3 \phi_k(x)=0$ and

$$\sum_{j=0}^2 F_j^3(x) - 3F_0(x)F_1(x)F_2(x) = f(x^9)f^{-4}(x^3) =$$

$$f(x^9)(\sum_{n=0}^\infty p(n)x^{3n})^4.$$

*E. Grosswald* (Philadelphia, Pa.)

**P60-34** **(26# 6072)**

**Djoković, Dragomir Ž. [Đoković, D. Ž.]**

**Quelques identités entre certains produits et séries infinis.**

*Univ. Beograd. Publ. Elektrotehn. Fak. Ser. Mat. Fiz. No.* 92–96 (1963), 1–8.

The principal identity of this paper lies between the identity of Jacobi (in the theory of elliptic functions) and a recent result of B. Gordon [Quart. J. Math. Oxford Ser. (2) **12** (1961), 285–290; MR **25** #21]; it reads, in one form,

$$\prod_{n=1}^\infty (1-s^n)(1-s^{2n-1})(1-s^n t)^2(1-s^{n-1}t^{-1})^2 =$$

$$\prod_{n=1}^\infty (1+s^{2n-1})^2 \sum_{-\infty}^\infty s^{n^2+n}t^{2n} - 2\prod_{n=1}^\infty (1+s^{2n})^2 \sum_{-\infty}^\infty s^{n^2}t^{2n-1}.$$

It is shown to be equivalent to the identity in theta

functions:

$$2\vartheta_0^2(\nu)\vartheta_1^2(\nu) = \vartheta_2^2\vartheta_3\vartheta_3(2\nu)-\vartheta_2\vartheta_3^2\vartheta_2(2\nu).$$

It is used to find other identities, the most interesting of which is

$$\prod_{n=1}^{\infty}(1-s^n)^4(1-s^{2n-1})^4 = 1-8\sum_{n=1}^{\infty}\sigma(2n-1)s^{2n-1} + 24\sum_{k=1}^{\infty}\sum_{n=1}^{\infty}\sigma(2n-1)s^{2^k(2n-1)} = \sum_{n=0}^{\infty}r_4(n)(-s)^n,$$

with $\sigma(n)$ the sum of the divisors of $n$, and $r_4(n)$ the number of representations of $n$ as the sum of four squares (with representations counted as distinct even when they differ only in the ordering or the signs of the numbers squared).
*J. Riordan* (Murray Hill, N.J.)

Citations: MR 25# 21 = P60-31.

## P60-35 (27# 3561)

**Carlitz, L.**
**A note on the Jacobi theta formula.**
*Bull. Amer. Math. Soc.* **68** (1962), 591–592.

The Jacobi theta formula of the title is the identity

$$\prod_{n=1}^{\infty}(1-q^{2n})(1+q^{2n-1}t)(1+q^{2n-1}t^{-1}) = \sum_{n=-\infty}^{\infty}q^{n^2}t^n.$$

The substitutions $q^2=xy$, $t^2=xy^{-1}$ (not $t=xy^{-1}$ as the paper has it) take the identity into a form which shows that the number of bipartite partitions of $(n, m)$ with distinct parts of the forms $(a, a-1)$, $(b-1, b)$, $a, b=1, 2, 3, \cdots$, is equal to the number of unrestricted (one part) partitions of $n-(n-m+1)(n-m)/2$. Replacing $x$, $y$ by $-x$, $-y$ gives a recurrence formula for the number of bipartite partitions with not necessarily distinct parts of the prescribed forms: $(a, a)$, $(b, b-1)$, $(c-1, c)$, $a, b, c=1, 2, \cdots$. Finally, since the form $(a, a)$ is equinumerous with the ordinary partitions, the numbers determined by equation (7) may be expressed in terms of the number of ordinary partitions and bipartite partitions with not necessarily distinct parts of the forms $(b, b-1)$, $(c-1, c)$, $b, c=1, 2, \cdots$.
*J. Riordan* (Murray Hill, N.J.)

Referred to in P80-46.

## P60-36 (28# 74)

**Sudler, Culbreth, Jr.**
**Two algebraic identities and the unboundedness of a restricted partition function.**
*Proc. Amer. Math. Soc.* **15** (1964), 16–20.

Put

$$\prod_{k=1}^{\infty}(1-x^k) = \sum_{k=0}^{\infty}C_kx^k, \quad \prod_{k=1}^{n}(1-x^k) = \sum_{k=0}^{\infty}a_{nk}x^k.$$

The coefficients $C_k$ are given by the pentagonal number theorem of Euler. The author has proved [Quart. J. Math. Oxford Ser. (2) **15** (1964),1–10] *that $\log \max_k |a_{nk}| \sim Kn$, where $K$ is a constant $>0$. In the present paper the following two identities are proved; they yield an unbounded sequence of values of $a_{nk}$:

$$\prod_{k=1}^{n}(1-x^k) = \sum_{r=0}^{\infty}x^{r(n+1)}\prod_{m=r+1}^{\infty}(1-x^m),$$

$$\prod_{m=r+1}^{\infty}(1-x^m) = \sum_{t=0}^{\infty}(-1)^tx^{t(3t+2r-1)/2}(1-x^{2t+r}) \times\prod_{s=1}^{r-1}(1-x^{t+s})\prod_{s=1}^{r}(1-x^s)^{-1} \quad (r\geq 1).$$

*L. Carlitz* (Durham, N.C.)

*See MR **29** #1189 = P60-38.

Citations: MR 29# 1189 = P60-38.
Referred to in P60-37.

## P60-37 (31# 146)

**Sudler, Culbreth, Jr.**
**Errata: "Two algebraic identities and the unboundedness of a restricted partition function".**
*Proc. Amer. Math. Soc.* **15** (1964), 1000.

A typographical error in the paper in same Proc. **15** (1964), 16–20 [MR **28** #74] is noted.

Citations: MR 28# 74 = P60-36.

## P60-38 (29# 1189)

**Sudler, C., Jr.**
**An estimate for a restricted partition function.**
*Quart. J. Math. Oxford Ser.* (2) **15** (1964), 1–10.

According to Euler,

$$\prod_{k=1}^{\infty}(1-x^k) = \sum_{-\infty}^{+\infty}(-1)^mx^{(3m^2+m)/2} = \sum_{h=0}^{\infty}c_hx^h,$$

so $c_h=-1, 0, 1$. Let

$$P_n(x) = \prod_{k=1}^{n}(1-x^k) = \sum_h a_{nh}x^h.$$

The coefficients $a_{nh}$ and $c_h=\lim_{n\to\infty}a_{nh}$ have interpretations in terms of certain partitions of $h$ into distinct parts. Nicol and Vandiver have discussed $a_{nh}$ and Nicol asked whether they are uniformly bounded. Motzkin announced a negative answer. By studying $\Pi_n(\theta)=|P_n(e^{2\pi i\theta})|$, the author proves this result, showing that $M_n =_{\text{def}} \max_h |a_{nh}|$ satisfies $\log M_n=Kn+O(\log n)$, where

$$K = \max_{1/2<w<1} g(w) = g(w_0) = 0.19861\cdots,$$

and $g(w)=w^{-1}\int_0^w \log(2\sin \pi t)\,dt$. He conjectures that $\lim M_{n+1}/M_n=e^K=1.2197\cdots$.
*N. J. Fine* (University Park, Pa.)

Referred to in P60-36.

## P60-39 (29# 1190)

**Wright, E. M.**
**Proof of a conjecture of Sudler's.**
*Quart. J. Math. Oxford Ser.* (2) **15** (1964), 11–15.

This paper is based on the preceding review [#1189]. Let $N=\frac{1}{4}n(n+1)$, $L=(1/n)(N-h)w_0-n/4$, $\varphi_n=Be^{Kn}/n$, $B=2e^K(1-e^{2K}/4)^{-1/4}=2.7424\cdots$. The author proves that $M_n\sim\varphi_n$. Also, if $h=N+o(n^{3/2})$, $a_{nh}=\varphi_n\cos 2\pi L+o(\varphi_n)$. He obtains a good estimate for $\log \Pi_n(\theta)$ in the range $1/2\leq|w|\leq(1+w_0)/2$.
*N. J. Fine* (University Park, Pa.)

## P60-40 (29# 1191)

**Wright, E. M.**
**A closer estimate for a restricted partition function.**
*Quart. J. Math. Oxford Ser.* (2) **15** (1964), 283–287.

See the two preceding reviews [#1189, #1190]. Let $m=h-N$, $S=2\pi mn^{-2}$, $C^2=-g''(w_0)/2$. The author shows that if $m = o(n^2)$, then

$$a_{nh} = Bn^{-1}e^{K_1 n}\{\cos K_2 n + o(1)\},$$

where $K_1$ and $K_2$ are certain power series in $S$:

$$K_1 = K - \frac{S^2}{4C^2} + \cdots, \qquad K_2 = \frac{\pi}{2} + w_0 S + \cdots.$$

*N. J. Fine* (University Park, Pa.)

**P60-41** **(29# 3426 )**

**Carlitz, Leonard**

**Some $q$-identities related to the theta functions.**

*Boll. Un. Mat. Ital.* (3) **17** (1962), 172–178.

Es sei $|q|<1$. Verfasser setzt $(n)! = (1-q^2)\cdots(1-q^{2n})$, $(0)! = 1$ und $1/(-n)! = 0$ für natürliche Zahlen $n$. Er beweist die Formel

$$\sum_{s=0}^{\infty} \frac{q^{2s}}{(s)!(n+s)!} \prod_{r=1}^{\infty} (1-q^{2r})^2 = \sum_{r=0}^{\infty} (-1)^r q^{r(r+1+2n)}$$

für alle ganzen $n$. Zunächst findet er sie unter Benützung einer bekannten Formel, die $\theta_4$ enthält, und einer Reihenentwicklung von $F(x)^{-1}$, wobei

$$F(x) = \prod_{1}^{\infty} (1-q^{2n-1}x)(1-q^{2n-1}x^{-1})$$

ist. Dann leitet er sie noch unter Benützung einer von F. H. Jackson [Proc. London Math. Soc. (2) **2** (1904/05), 192–220; ibid. (2) **3** (1905), 1–23] eingeführten und von W. Hahn [Math. Nachr. **2** (1949), 340–379; MR **11**, 720] diskutierten Funktion her. Schließlich leitet er noch zwei Verallgemeinerungen der obigen Formel her. Bemerkte Druckfehler: In dem Produkt für $F(x)$ sollte $n$ erst bei **1** beginnen. In der Reihe (4) ist das von $x$ unabhängige Glied **nicht 1**, sondern lautet so wie der Koeffizient von $x^n + x^{-n}$ **für** $n=1$. In der ersten Formel unter Punkt 4. fehlt im Nenner ein Index $s$. *G. Lochs* (Zbl **103**, 302)

**P60-42** **(30# 1952 )**

**Andrews, George E.**

**A simple proof of Jacobi's triple product identity.**

*Proc. Amer. Math. Soc.* **16** (1965), 333–334.

The author shows that the Jacobi identity

$$\prod_{0}^{\infty} (1-x^{2n+2})(1+x^{2n+1}z)(1+x^{2n+1}z^{-1}) = \sum_{-\infty}^{\infty} x^{n^2}z^n$$

can be derived in a simple manner from the Euler identities

$$\prod_{0}^{\infty} (1+x^n z) = \sum_{0}^{\infty} \frac{x^{n(n-1)/2}z^n}{(1-x)\cdots(1-x^n)},$$

$$\prod_{0}^{\infty} (1-x^n z)^{-1} = \sum_{0}^{\infty} \frac{z^n}{(1-x)\cdots(1-x^n)}.$$

*L. Carlitz* (Durham, N.C.)

**P60-43** **(31# 72 )**

**Carlitz, L.**

**Generating functions and partition problems.**

*Proc. Sympos. Pure Math., Vol. VIII, pp.* 144–169. *Amer. Math. Soc., Providence, R.I.*, 1965.

The paper is partly expository (especially Sections 1–4), but offers also new results, often with proofs barely sketched, and some only with the indication that proofs are to appear elsewhere. It contains 13 sections. In the first, the author discusses classical material on unrestricted partitions, partitions into distinct parts, etc., as well as Fine's sums over partitions and MacMahon's "plane partitions". In Section 2 he deals with multipartite, especially bipartite numbers (following Wright, Bellman, Gordon). In Section 3 he introduces $\alpha(m,n)$, the number of partitions of the bipartite $(m,n)$ into parts $(a, a-1)$, or $(b-1, b)$. In Section 4 he considers the polynomials $A_n(x)$ defined by $\exp\{x(e^t-1)\} = \sum_{n=0}^{\infty} A_n(x)t^n/n!$, the coefficients $a(n,r)$ of $A_n(x)$, and their congruence properties mod 2. In Sections 5 and 6 he discusses similar problems for an arbitrary prime modulus $p$. Section 7 concerns the Bell polynomials defined by

$$\exp\left\{\sum_{n=1}^{\infty} u_n t^n/n!\right\} = \sum_{n=0}^{\infty} A_n(u_1, u_2, \cdots)t^n/n!,$$

and especially their congruence properties mod $p$. The method involves generating functions and the (obviously finite) $p$-adic expansion of $n$. In Section 8 the author discusses congruence properties of Čebyšev polynomials. In Sections 9–13 he deals mainly with two line arrays. The results here are mostly new, and it is impossible to quote all of them. Here is an example: Let $x_1, x_2, \cdots; y_1, y_2, \cdots$ be indeterminates, set $u_r = x_1y_1x_2y_2\cdots x_ry_r$ $(r = 1, 2, \cdots, k)$ and define $S_k = \sum x_1^{n_1}x_2^{n_2}\cdots x_k^{n_k}y_1^{m_1}y_2^{m_2}\cdots y_k^{m_k}$, where the summation is over all non-negative integers $n_j, m_j$ such that (*) $\min(n_j, m_j) \geqq \max(n_{j+1}, m_{j+1})$ $(j = 1, 2, \cdots, k)$. Then

$$S_{k+1} = \frac{1-u_k u_{k+1}}{(1-xu_k)(1-yu_k)(1-u_{k+1})}\cdot S_k,$$

whence (setting $x_j = x$, $y_j = y$, $j = 1, 2, \cdots, k$)

$$\sum x^{\sum_1^k n_j} y^{\sum_1^k m_j} = \sum \pi_k(N, M)x^N y^M = \frac{\prod_{j=1}^{k} (1-x^{2j-1}y^{2j-1})}{\prod_{j=1}^{k} (1-x^j y^{j-1})(1-x^{j-1}y^j)(1-x^j y^j)},$$

where $\pi_k(N, M)$ is the number of arrays $\begin{matrix} n_1 n_2 \cdots n_k \\ m_1 m_2 \cdots m_k \end{matrix}$ satisfying (*) and $\sum_{j=1}^k n_j = N$, $\sum_{j=1}^k m_j = M$.

*E. Grosswald* (Paris)

**P60-44** **(32# 7532 )**

**Roselle, D. P.**

**Generalized Eulerian functions and a problem in partitions.**

*Duke Math. J.* **33** (1966), 293–304.

Let $n_1, \cdots, n_k$ be nonnegative integers. Let $\pi(n_1, \cdots, n_k)$ denote the number of partitions $n_r = \sum_{s=1}^{\infty} n_{rs}$ $(r = 1, \cdots, k)$, where the $n_{rs}$ are nonnegative integers subject to the conditions

$$\min(n_{1s}, \cdots, n_{ks}) \geqq \max(n_{1,s+1}, \cdots, n_{k,s+1}) \qquad (s = 1, \cdots, k).$$

For $k=1$ the generating function for $\pi(n)$ is the familiar Euler product $\prod_1^{\infty} (1-x^n)^{-1}$; for $k=2$ the reviewer [same J. **30** (1963), 191–201; MR **26** #6063; ibid. **30** (1963), 203–213; MR **26** #6143] proved

$$\sum_{n_1, n_2 = 0}^{\infty} \pi(n_1, n_2)x_1^{n_1}x_2^{n_2} = \prod_{n=1}^{\infty} (1-x_1^n x_2^{n-1})^{-1}(1-x_1^{n-1}x_2^n)^{-1}(1-x_1^{2n}x_2^{2n})^{-1}.$$

In the present paper a generating function for arbitrary $k$ is obtained in terms of a generalized Euler function.

The reviewer [Trans. Amer. Math. Soc. **76** (1954), 332–350; MR **15**, 686] defined the $q$-Eulerian function $H_n(x|q)$ by the recurrence $H_0 = 1$, $xH_n = (1+qH)^n$, $n \geqq 1$.

The author now defines $H_n(x|q_1, \cdots, q_n)$ by means of $H_0 = 1$ and $xH_n = \prod_{j=1}^{n} (1+q_jH)$ $(n \geq 1)$. It is proved that

$$xH_k = \sum_{n_1,\cdots,n_k=0}^{\infty} q_1^{n_1}\cdots q_k^{n_k} x^{-\max(n_1,\cdots,n_k)}.$$

The main result of the paper can now be stated:

$$\sum_{n_1,\cdots,n_k=0}^{\infty} \pi(n_1, \cdots, n_k) x_1^{n_1}\cdots x_k^{n_k} = \frac{1}{\phi}\prod_{n=1}^{\infty} \{(x_1\cdots x_k)^{-n} H_k((x_1\cdots x_k)^{-n}|x_1, \cdots, x_k)\},$$

where $\phi = \prod_{j=1}^{k} (1-x_j)$. As a corollary it follows that

$$\sum_{n=0}^{\infty} x^n \sum_{n_1+\cdots+n_k=n} \pi(n_1, \cdots, n_k) = (1-x)^{-k}\prod_{n=1}^{\infty} \{x^{-kn}H_k(x^{-nk}|x)\}.$$

*L. Carlitz* (Durham, N.C.)

Citations: MR 15, 686a = B68-35; MR 26# 6063 = P64-32; MR 26# 6143 = P64-33.
Referred to in P64-46.

## P60-45 (33# 1502 )

**Andrews, G. E.**

**On basic hypergeometric series, mock theta functions, and partitions. I.**

*Quart. J. Math. Oxford Ser.* (2) **17** (1966), 64–80.

In this paper the fundamental lemma established is the following: If $k, l, r, s$ are integers, $0 \leq l < k$, $0 \leq s < r$, $|t| < 1$, $|x| < 1$, $|q| < 1$, $|b| < |x|^{(ks/r)-l}$, and $\xi$ is a primitive $r$th root of unity, then

$$F(a, b, c; k, l; r, s; q; x; t) = r^{-1}\frac{\prod_\infty(-b, x)}{\prod_\infty(-c, x)} \times \sum_{j=0}^{r-1} \xi^{-js} t^{-s/r} \sum_{m=0}^{\infty} \frac{\prod_m(-c/b, x)\prod_\infty(-a\xi^j t^{1/r} x^{km/r}, q)}{\prod_m(-x, x)\prod_\infty(-\xi^j t^{1/r} x^{km/r}, q)} \times (bx^{l-ks/r})^m,$$

where

$$F(a, b, c; k; l; r, s; q; x; t) = \sum_{n=0}^{\infty} \prod_{\lambda=0}^{rn+s} \frac{(1-aq^\lambda)}{(1-q^{\lambda+1})} \prod_{\nu=0}^{kn+l} \frac{(1-bx^\nu)}{(1-cx^\nu)} t^n,$$

$$\prod_n(-a, q) \equiv \prod_{j=0}^{n-1} (1-aq^j),$$

and $\prod_\infty(-a, q) \equiv \prod_{j=0}^{\infty} (1-aq^j)$.

The special case of the fundamental lemma which is of central importance is Theorem A: Under the conditions of the fundamental lemma,

$$F(a, b, c; k, l; r, s; q^e; q^d; t) = r^{-1}\frac{\prod_\infty(-b, q^d)}{\prod_\infty(-c, q^d)} \sum_{j=0}^{r-1} \xi^{-js} t^{-s/r} \sum_{\mu=0}^{re-1} (bq^{dl-kds/r})^\mu \times \frac{\prod_\infty(-a\xi^j t^{1/r} q^{kd\mu/r}, q^e)}{\prod_\infty(-\xi^j t^{1/r} q^{kd/r}, q^e)} F\Big(\frac{c}{b}, \xi^j t^{1/r} q^{kd\mu/r}, a\xi^j t^{1/r} q^{kd\mu/r}; kd, 0; re, \mu; q^d; q^e; b^{re} q^{de(rl-ks)}\Big).$$

Four specializations of Theorem A are obtained. These theorems are then combined to prove identities which yield the mock theta function identities as special cases. In two cases results are exhibited in terms of the basic hypergeometric series. *B. R. Bhonsle* (Jabalpur)

Referred to in P60-46, P60-52.

## P60-46 (34# 382 )

**Andrews, G. E.**

**On basic hypergeometric series, mock theta functions, and partitions. II.**

*Quart. J. Math. Oxford Ser.* (2) **17** (1966), 132–143.

In this paper the author examines further the consequences of a certain basic hypergeometric series studied in Part I [same J. Ser. (2) **17** (1966), 64–80; MR **33** #1502].

The author establishes two more theorems. In the notation of basic hypergeometric series, the theorems (7 and 8) are as follows:

$${}_3\Phi_2\begin{bmatrix} a, b^{1/2}, -b^{1/2}; t; q \\ (atb)^{1/2}, -(atb)^{1/2} \end{bmatrix} = \frac{\prod_\infty(-at, q^2)\prod_\infty(-bt, q^2)}{\prod_\infty(-t, q^2)\prod_\infty(-atb, q^2)}\,{}_2\Phi_1\begin{bmatrix} a, b; tq; q^2 \\ bt \end{bmatrix},$$

$${}_2\Phi_1\begin{bmatrix} a, b; t; q^2 \\ c \end{bmatrix} = \frac{\prod_\infty(-bt, q^2)\prod_\infty(-c/b, q^2)}{\prod_\infty(-t, q^2)\prod_\infty(-c, q^2)}\,{}_2\Phi_1\begin{bmatrix} b, abt/c; c/b; q^2 \\ bt \end{bmatrix},$$

where $\prod_\infty(-a, q) \equiv \prod_{j=0}^{\infty} (1-aq^j)$.

Further, the author finds some new formulae for the family of third-order mock theta functions of his previous paper, and proves several partition theorems. $q$-series identities for some of the false theta functions studied by L. J. Rogers [Proc. London Math. Soc. (2) **16** (1917), 315–336] are also obtained. Finally, the author proves some results analogous to the Rogers-Ramanujan identities by combining his theory with some formulae due to L. J. Slater [ibid. (2) **54** (1952), 147–167; MR **14**, 138].

*B. R. Bhonsle* (Jabalpur)

Citations: MR 33# 1502 = P60-45.
Referred to in P60-52.

## P60-47 (34# 5740 )

**Koshti, M. E.**

**Partitions and the method of differences.**

*Math. Student* **32** (1964), 83–85.

If $v_m$ is the $m$th term of a series and $v_m - v_{m-1} = u_m$, then $v_m = v_0 + u_1 + u_2 + \cdots + u_m$. Taking $v_m =$

$$(1-ax)(1-ax^2)\cdots(1-ax^m)/(1-bx)(1-bx^2)\cdots(1-bx^m),$$

the author obtains some well-known results concerning generating functions in partition theory.

*H. Gupta* (Allahabad)

## P60-48 (36# 1410 )

**Banerjee, D. P.**

**On some identities in theory of partition.**

*Proc. Nat. Acad. Sci. India Sect. A* **34** (1964), 68–73.

## P60-49 (37# 91 )

**Lloyd, E. K.**

**Pólya's theorem in combinatorial analysis applied to enumerate multiplicative partitions.**

*J. London Math. Soc.* **43** (1968), 224–230.

The well known Pólya theorem in enumerative combinatorial mathematics is stated in terms of formal power series [G. Pólya, Acta Math. **68** (1937), 145–254; N. G. de Bruijn, Nederl. Akad. Wetensch. Proc. Ser. A **62** (1959), 59–69; MR **21** #4112; see also *Applied combinatorial mathematics*, Chapter 5, pp. 144–184, Wiley, New York, 1964; see MR **30** #4687]. In the present paper the author gives an exposition of the theorem using Dirichlet series as generating functions. As an application the generating function $\sum_{n=0}^{\infty} q(n)n^{-s} = \prod_{n=2}^{\infty} (1-n^{-s})^{-1}$, where $q(n)$ denotes the number of unrestricted factorizations of $n$, is obtained.

*L. Carlitz* (Durham, N.C.)

**P60-50** **(38# 4438 )**

**Carlitz, L.**

**A note on the Rogers-Ramanujan identities.**

*Duke Math. J.* **35** (1968), 839–842.

In this note a simple proof of the identities $\sum_0^{\infty} x^{n^2}/(x)_n = \sum_{-\infty}^{\infty} (-1)^n x^{n(5n+1)/2} \prod_1^{\infty} (1-x^m)^{-1}$ and

$$\sum_0^{\infty} x^{n(n+1)}/(x)_n = \sum_{-\infty}^{\infty} (-1)^n x^{n(5n+3)/2} \prod_1^{\infty} (1-x^m)^{-1},$$

which are equivalent to well-known identities by Roger and Ramanujan, is given; here $(x)_n$ stands for $(1-x)\cdots(1-x^n)$ or 1 for $n>0$ or $n=0$, respectively. An appropriate generating function is used. *O. H. Körner* (Marburg)

**P60-51** **(39# 1335 )**

**Eden, Murray**

**A note on a new family of identities.**

*J. Combinatorial Theory* **5** (1968), 210–211.

Let $p_h(m, n)$ be the number of partitions of $n$ into $m$ parts in which the largest part appears exactly $h$ times and all other parts appear at most once. Then if $F_h(b; x) = \sum_{m=1}^{\infty} \sum_{n=1}^{\infty} p_h(m, n) b^m x^n$, the author proves, for $h \geqq 1$,

$$F_h(b; x) = \prod_{j=1}^{h-1} (x^{-j}-1) \prod_{i=1}^{\infty} (1+bx^i) - 1 - \sum_{i=1}^{h-1} b^i \prod_{j=i+1}^{h-1} (x^{-j}-1).$$

*T. V. Narayana* (Edmonton, Alta.)

**P60-52** **(40# 4483 )**

**Agarwal, R. P.**

**Certain basic hypergeometric identities associated with mock theta functions.**

*Quart. J. Math. Oxford Ser.* (2) **20** (1969), 121–128.

Recently the author and A. Verma have developed [Proc. Cambridge Philos. Soc. **63** (1967), 727–734; MR **35** #3090; Quart. J. Math. Oxford Ser. (2) **18** (1967), 181–192; MR **35** #5664] a general theory for transformations of basic hypergeometric series with unconnected bases. Earlier, in a series of three remarkable papers, G. E. Andrews [ibid. (2) **17** (1966), 64–80; MR **33** #1502; ibid. (2) **17** (1966), 132–143; MR **34** #382; Duke Math. J. **33** (1966), 575–581; MR **34** #1254] had deduced a transformation for a particular basic hypergeometric series with two bases that considerably simplified the ideas underlying the numerous transformations involving mock theta functions and identities in the theory of partitions.

The general transformation due to Andrews [in the first paper cited above] has hitherto appeared to be an isolated result that did not fit into any general theory. However, the author has recently found that the fundamental transformation and the various theorems derived by Andrews in the paper cited above do belong to a very general class of identities, and that all his theorems can be extended to more general transformations with many more parameters. In the present paper the author derives a number of general theorems, which extend most of the results due to Andrews. In a subsequent communication the author intends to discuss further consequences of his extensions as applied to mock theta functions and partitions.

There are some interesting theorems that are too technical to state here. *S. D. Bajpai* (Kurukshetra)

Citations: MR 33# 1502 = P60-45; MR 34# 382 = P60-46.

**P60-53** **(40# 5567 )**

**Subrahmanya Sastri, V. V.**

**On some properties of partitions.**

*Math. Student* **35** (1967), 177–192 (1969).

The author derives generating functions for $p(kn+s)$ and $q(kn+s)$, $s=0, 1, 2, \cdots, k-1$, where $p(m)$ is the number of unrestricted partitions of $m$ and $q(m)$ is the number of partitions of $m$ into unequal parts. The special cases $k=2, \cdots, 6$ are examined in more detail and some additional relations between these generating functions are established. *L. D. Baumert* (Pasadena, Calif.)

**P60-54** **(40# 7216 )**

**Onari, Setsuo**

**Formal power series and additive number theory.**

*Hitotsubashi J. Arts Sci.* **10** (1969), 53–73.

Let $S = a_1, a_2, \cdots, a_n, \cdots$ be a set of integers, with $0<a_1<a_2<\cdots<a_n<\cdots$ and let $S(m)$ denote the number of representations of the integer $m$ as a sum of elements of $S$. The author gives an interesting expression of $S(m)$ as a determinant the terms of which are $\sigma_S(k)$ ($\sigma_S(k)$ being the arithmetic function $\sum_{d\in S, d|k} d$). The author distinguishes the cases where $S$ is finite and infinite, and also gives an expression for $S'(m)$, the number of representations of $m$, where each element of $S$ occurs at most once.

The proofs are based on the use of infinite products and logarithmic derivatives on the ring of formal power series.

These theorems give new elementary results in the theory of partitions and new proofs of old results (e.g., that the number of partitions into unequal parts is equal to the number of partitions into odd parts).

*F. Dress* (Talence)

**P60-55** **(41# 8366 )**

**Alder, H. L.**

**Partition identities—from Euler to the present.**

*Amer. Math. Monthly* **76** (1969), 733–746.

This is a very readable and informative expository account of the leading partition identities discovered since the time of Euler. Statements of twenty-four theorems are given together with illuminating remarks. A bibliography of twenty-six items is given. Recent work of some significance due to B. Gordon [Amer. J. Math. **83** (1961), 393–399; MR **23** #A809] and G. E. Andrews [Proc. Amer. Math. Soc. **18** (1967), 945–952; MR **36** #2578; Glasgow Math. J. **8** (1967), 127–132; MR **36** #3744] is discussed. It is not without interest that this paper is one of six to receive the Lester R. Ford Award for Expository Writing for 1969, an award given annually by the Mathematical Association of America. As the author observes, interest in partition identities has revived and new results are being found. The author states an unpublished result (1968) due to one of his students, Elmo Moore. This paper ought to stimulate further interest.

*H. W. Gould* (Morgantown, W. Va.)

Citations: MR 23# A809 = P68-18; MR 36# 2578 = P68-35; MR 36# 3744 = P68-36.

**P60-56** **(41# 8370 )**

**Subbarao, M. V.; Vidyasagar, M.**

**On Watson's quintuple product identity.**

*Proc. Amer. Math. Soc.* **26** (1970), 23–27.

The authors first show that G. N. Watson's quintuple product identity of 1929 [J. London Math. Soc. **4** (1929), 39–48] and Basil Gordon's similar identity of 1961 [Quart. J. Math. Oxford Ser. (2) **12** (1961), 285–290; MR **25** #21] are equivalent. They then give two beautiful identities involving only series, which together with Jacobi's triple product identity imply and are implied by Watson's identity. Their two identities, valid for $|x|<1$ and $a\neq 0$, are $\sum_{n=1}^{\infty}(-1)^{n-1}a^{n-1}x^{n-1}(1+ax)(1+ax^3)(1+ax^5)\cdots(1+ax^{2n-3})=1+\sum_{n=1}^{\infty}a^{3n-1}x^{3n^2}(ax^{2n}-a^{-1}x^{-2n})=\sum_{n=1}^{\infty}(-1)^{n-1}a^{2n-2}x^{n(n-1)}/((1+ax)(1+ax^3)\cdots(1+ax^{2n-1}))$. *H. Gupta* (Allahabad)

Citations: MR 25# 21 = P60-31.

Referred to in P60-59.

**P60-57** **(42# 218 )**

**Hagis, Peter, Jr.**

**A root of unity occurring in partition theory.**

*Proc. Amer. Math. Soc.* **26** (1970), 579–582.

Representations for $w(h, k)$, the 12th root of unity occurring in the well-known transformation equation of the generating function for $p(n)$, the number of partitions of $n$, were given by Hardy and Ramanujan and later also by Rademacher. The author gives here a new representation for $w(h, k)$. *H. Gupta* (Allahabad)

**P60-58** **(43# 4788 )**

**Andrews, George E.**

**A new property of partitions with applications to the Rogers-Ramanujan identities.**

*J. Combinatorial Theory Ser. A* **10** (1971), 266–270.

The author proves the following identity in two variables:

$$(-xq;q)_{2N}=\sum_{n=0}^{N}(-xq;q)_{n-1}x^nq^{n(3n-1)/2}(1+xq^{2n})\begin{bmatrix}N\\n\end{bmatrix}(-xq^{n+N+1};q)_{N-n},$$

where $(x;q)_n=\prod_{j=0}^{n-1}(1-xq^j)$, with $(x,q)_{-1}=(1-x/q)^{-1}$, and $\begin{bmatrix}N\\n\end{bmatrix}=(q^{N-n+1};q)_n/(q;q)_n$ if $0\leqq n\leqq N$ and 0 otherwise. The proof depends on interpreting the expressions in terms of partitions. Using techniques of W. N. Bailey [Proc. London Math. Soc. (2) **50** (1948), 1–10; MR **9**, 585] the author then derives from the above identity an identity in four variables that includes several important identities of partition theory as special cases.

*S. A. Burr* (Whippany, N.J.)

**P60-59** **(44# 6639 )**

**Carlitz, L.**

**Some identities in combinatorial analysis.**

*Duke Math. J.* **39** (1972), 31–37.

The author gives alternative proofs of two identities proved recently by M. V. Subbarao and M. Vidyasagar [Proc. Amer. Math. Soc. **26** (1970), 23–27; MR **41** #8370] observing that his proof is reminiscent of certain proofs of the Rogers-Ramanujan identities.

*D. A. Klarner* (Stanford, Calif.)

Citations: MR 41# 8370 = P60-56.

# P64 PARTITIONS: MULTIPARTITE, MULTIROWED AND MULTIDIMENSIONAL PARTITIONS

See also reviews P60-35, P60-43, P80-33, P80-46, Z30-29, Z30-38.

**P64-1** **(1, 323c)**

**Tietze, Heinrich. Über symmetrische Funktionen von endlich oder abzählbar unendlich vielen Veränderlichen.** Monatsh. Math. Phys. **49**, 1–52 (1940).

This is the sequel to an earlier part by the same author [Monatsh. Math. Phys. **48**, 487–499 (1939); these Rev. **1**, 97]. The whole work is a discussion of the matrix $M$ which arises when the functions $X^{(\kappa)}$ are expressed linearly in terms of $Y^{(\lambda)}$ ($X=MY$, $M=[C_{\kappa\lambda}]$), where $Y^{(\lambda)}=\sum x_1^{b_1}\cdots x_l^{b_l}$ is a symmetric function of $l$ quantities $x_i$, $\sum b_i=p\leqq l$, and the $X^{(\kappa)}$ are monomial products $f_1^{\pi_1}\cdots f_l^{\pi_l}$ of the elementary symmetric functions of the $x_i$. For a given value $p$ the solution $Y=M^{-1}X$ exists and expresses the fundamental theorem of symmetric functions. $M$ has $P$ rows and columns, where $P=P(p)$: it is the Cayley-Perron matrix. The coefficients $C_{\kappa\lambda}$ are integers which depend on the number of ways of constructing a partition, say (3 2 2), from another, say (3 2 1 1), of the same number $p$ of different things. Graphical methods are used, and partitions are arranged in certain orders, such that the matrix $M$ becomes symmetric and triangular in shape, with a base (the secondary diagonal) consisting entirely of $P$ units $+1$. The fundamental theorem is extended to the case when $l\to\infty$ provided that $\sum x_i$ is absolutely convergent. Abundant historical references are given. *H. W. Turnbull* (St. Andrews).

Referred to in P64-3, P64-5.

**P64-2** **(3, 166d)**

**Tietze, Heinrich. Über Tripel konjugierter Partitionen.** Abh. Math. Sem. Hansischen Univ. **14**, 273–284 (1941).

This paper is concerned with the generalization to $n$ dimensions of the notion of conjugate pairs of partitions of a number $m$ arising from a two-dimensional graph. A set $K$ of $m$ lattice points in the $x$, $y$ plane with positive integer coordinates represents a reduced (Ferrers) graph if for each point $(x', y')$ of $K$ the points $(x, y)$ whose coordinates satisfy $0<x\leqq x'$, $0<y\leqq y'$ also belong to $K$. This graph, if read by rows, gives one partition of $m$ and, if read by columns, gives another (possibly the same) partition. These two partitions have been called mutually conjugate. Clearly a given partition of $m$ has one and only one partition conjugate to it.

In three dimensions one may, likewise, have a set $K$ of $m$ lattice points whose coordinates $(x, y, z)$ are positive integers. These points are called reduced if for each point $(x', y', z')$ of $K$ the points $(x, y, z)$ whose coordinates satisfy $0<x\leqq x'$, $0<y\leqq y'$, $0<z\leqq z'$ also belong to $K$. This reduced graph can be read by parallel planes in three ways to produce three conjugate partitions of $m$. This paper shows by means of examples that (contrary to the 2-dimensional case) in general the third conjugate of two arbitrarily chosen partitions of $m$ is not uniquely determined, and, in fact, the number of available third conjugates is an unbounded function of $m$. The $n$-dimensional case ($n>3$) is similar.

*D. H. Lehmer* (Berkeley, Calif.).

Referred to in P64-4.

**P64-3** **(3, 166e)**

**Tietze, Heinrich. Systeme von Partitionen und Gitterpunktfiguren I. Rekursionsformeln.** S.-B. Math.-Nat. Abt. Bayer. Akad. Wiss. **1940**, 23–54 (1940).

The problem under consideration may be described as follows. Let $n$ and $m$ be positive integers. Suppose we have given $n+1$ partitions $\mathfrak{A}^{(0)}, \mathfrak{A}^{(1)}, \cdots, \mathfrak{A}^{(n)}$ of the number $m$ into $m$ non-negative parts so that

$$\mathfrak{A}^{(\nu)}=(a_1^{(\nu)}, a_2^{(\nu)}, \cdots, a_m^{(\nu)}), \quad \nu=0,1,2,\cdots,n.$$

The problem is to determine the number

$$N=N(\mathfrak{A}^{(0)}\,|\,\mathfrak{A}^{(1)}\,|\cdots|\,\mathfrak{A}^{(n)})$$

of ways in which $m^{n+1}$ numbers $g_{\mu_0\mu_1\cdots\mu_n}$ ($\mu_\nu=1, 2, \cdots, m$) may be assigned the values 0 or 1 in such a way that for each $\nu$ ($\nu=0, 1, \cdots, n$) and for each value of $\mu_\nu$ the following equation holds:

$$\sum{}^{(\nu)}g_{\mu_0\mu_1\cdots\mu_n}=a_{\mu_\nu}^{(\nu)},$$

where $\sum^{(\nu)}$ is an $n$-fold multiple sum in which $\mu_\nu$ is fixed. This problem, which is said to be of degree $m$ and dimension $n+1$, is a generalization of the problem for $n=1$ which was considered in a previous paper [Monatsh. Math. Phys. **49**, 1–52 (1940); cf. these Rev. **1**, 323]. In the present paper is derived a complicated recursion formula for $N$ which is illustrated by simple examples. The connection between the problem and the enumeration of certain lattice point figures in $n+1$ dimensional space is discussed in detail.

*D. H. Lehmer* (Berkeley, Calif.).

Citations: MR 1, 323c = P64-1.
Referred to in P64-5, P64-7.

**P64-4** **(4, 36c)**

**Tietze, Heinrich. Über die Anzahl komprimierter Gitterpunktmengen von gegebener Punktezahl.** Math. Z. **47**, 352–356 (1941).

This note is concerned with the generalization to $n$ dimensions of the Ferrers reduced graph of a partition considered also in a recent paper of the author [Abh. Math. Sem. Hansischen Univ. **14**, 273–284 (1941); these Rev. **3**, 166]. A finite set $M$ of lattice points in $n$ dimensional space is called reduced (komprimiert) if first all points have positive integer coordinates and, secondly, if $(x)=(x_1, x_2, \cdots, x_n)$ be any member of $M$ then any point $(x')$ whose coordinates do not exceed the corresponding coordinates of $(x)$ also belongs to $M$. Let $m$ be the number of points of $M$. Clearly if $n$ and $m$ are fixed there are only finitely many such reduced point sets $M$. The number of these is denoted by $P^n(m)$; $P^0(m)$ is taken as unity, which is also the value of $P^1(m)$. The function $P^2(m)$ is, of course, the celebrated partition function $p(m)$, the number of unrestricted partitions of $m$. By a dissection process, it is shown inductively that $P^n(m)$, for $m$ fixed, is a polynomial in $n$ of degree $m-1$. Hence if $P^k(m)$ is known for $k=0, 1, \cdots, m-1$, a formula for $P^n(m)$ for this fixed value of $m$ can be computed. Formulas for $P^n(m)$ for $m=2, 3, 4$ have been given previously [S.-B. Math.-Nat. Abt. Bayer. Akad. Wiss. **1940**, 166]. In the present paper the functions for $m=5$ and 6 are found to be

$$4!P^n(5)=n^4+18n^3-n^2+6n,$$
$$5!P^n(6)=n^5+40n^4-40n^2+24n.$$

*D. H. Lehmer* (Berkeley, Calif.).

Citations: MR 3, 166d = P64-2.
Referred to in P64-7.

**P64-5** **(5, 91g)**

**Tietze, Heinrich. Über die Anzahl der Lösungen gewisser Aufgaben über Gitterpunktfiguren.** Math. Ann. **118**, 290–298 (1942).

This paper is a continuation of the author's series of papers on the $n$-dimensional graphical representation of partitions [Monatsh. Math. Phys. **49**, 1–52 (1940); S.-B. Math.-Nat. Abt. Bayer. Akad. Wiss. **1940**, 23–54 (1940); these Rev. **1**, 323; **3**, 166]. Let $\mathfrak{M}$ be any set of $m$ lattice points in $n$-dimensions $(x_1, x_2, \cdots, x_n)$ with positive integer coordinates. This set of points gives rise to $n$ conjugate partitions $A^{(\nu)}=A^{(\nu)}(\mathfrak{M})$ $(\nu=1, 2, \cdots, n)$ of $m$ in which the $\mu$th part of $A^{(\nu)}$ is the number of lattice points of $\mathfrak{M}$ lying on the $(n-1)$-dimensional hyperplane $x_\nu=\mu$. The converse question considered in this paper is as follows: under what circumstances does a given set $A^{(\nu)}$ of $n$ partitions, all of the same number $m$, determine a lattice point set $\mathfrak{M}$ belonging to it in the above sense? In treating this question the author uses the notion of a reduced (or compressed) lattice point set, defined as a set $\mathfrak{K}$ of lattice points such that if $(x_1', x_2', \cdots, x_n')$ belongs to $\mathfrak{K}$ so also do those points $(x_1, x_2, \cdots, x_n)$ for which $0<x_\nu\leqq x_\nu'$ $(\nu=1, 2, \cdots, n)$. Two partitions $A=(a_1, a_2, \cdots, a_k)$ and $B=(b_1, b_2, \cdots, b_k)$ of the same number (with the parts nonincreasing) being given, we define $A\geqq B$ to mean that, for each $\mu=1, 2, \cdots, k$, $\sum_{\lambda=1}^{\mu}a_\lambda\geqq\sum_{\lambda=1}^{\mu}b_\lambda$. The two results of the paper are then as follows. The $n$ given partitions $A^{(\nu)}$ are the $n$ conjugate partitions of a point set $\mathfrak{M}$ if and only if there exists a reduced lattice point set $\mathfrak{K}$ such that $A^{(\nu)}(\mathfrak{K})\geqq A^{(\nu)}$ $(\nu=1, 2, \cdots, n)$. If this set $\mathfrak{M}$ exists uniquely it is reduced.

*D. H. Lehmer* (Berkeley, Calif.).

Citations: MR 1, 323c = P64-1; MR 3, 166e = P64-3.

**P64-6** **(5, 91h)**

**Tietze, Heinrich. Komprimierte Gitterpunktmengen und eine additiv-zahlentheoretische Aufgabe.** J. Reine Angew. Math. **184**, 49–64 (1942).

This paper is a continuation of the author's investigations of $n$-dimensional lattices and associated partitions [see the preceding review]. The main result of the paper is concerned with the question of the number of different reduced lattices of $n$ dimensions that belong, in the sense of the preceding review, to a given set of $n$ partitions of the same number $m$. The author shows by a general example that even when $n=3$ there exist, for each integer $h$, three partitions of the number $m=4h^3+9h^2$ with which there are associated at least $2^h$ different reduced lattices.

*D. H. Lehmer* (Berkeley, Calif.).

**P64-7** **(8, 196f; 8, 196g, 8, 196h; 8, 196i; 8, 196j; 8, 196k; 8, 196l; 8, 196m)**

**Tietze, Heinrich. Systeme von Partitionen und Gitterpunktfiguren. II. Komprimierte Gitterpunktmengen.** S.-B. Math.-Nat. Abt. Bayer. Akad. Wiss. **1940**, 69–131 (3 plates) (1940).

**Tietze, Heinrich. Systeme von Partitionen und Gitterpunktfiguren. III. Ein Satz über das Verhältnis der Lösungsanzahlen gewisser Partitionsaufgaben.** S.-B. Math.-Nat. Abt. Bayer. Akad. Wiss. **1940**, 133–145 (1940).

**Tietze, Heinrich. Systeme von Partitionen und Gitterpunktfiguren. IV. Formeln und Tabellen.** S.-B. Math.-Nat. Abt. Bayer. Akad. Wiss. **1940**, 147–166 (1940).

**Tietze, Heinrich. Systeme von Partitionen und Gitterpunktfiguren. V. Der Hauptsatz über den Umbau komprimierter Gitterpunktmengen.** S.-B. Math.-Nat. Abt. Bayer. Akad. Wiss. **1941**, 1–37 (1941).

**Tietze, Heinrich. Systeme von Partitionen und Gitterpunktfiguren. VI. Konvexe Polygonzüge und Partitionen nebst deren Ordnungsbeziehungen.** S.-B. Math.-Nat. Abt. Bayer. Akad. Wiss. **1941**, 39–55 (1941).

**Tietze, Heinrich. Systeme von Partitionen und Gitterpunktfiguren. VII. Schrittweise Kompression partiell-komprimierter Mengen.** S.-B. Math.-Nat. Abt. Bayer. Akad. Wiss. **1941**, 165–170 (1941).

**Tietze, Heinrich. Systeme von Partitionen und Gitterpunktfiguren. VIII. Auswirkung der Kompression von Gitterpunktmengen auf die zugehörigen Partitionen.** S.-B. Math.-Nat. Abt. Bayer. Akad. Wiss. **1941**, 171–186 (1941).

**Tietze, Heinrich. Systeme von Partitionen und Gitterpunktfiguren. IX. Beispiele ähnlich geordneter Familien von komprimierten Gitterpunktmengen.** S.-B. Math.-Nat. Abt. Bayer. Akad. Wiss. **1941**, 187–191 (1941).

The first of this series of papers on systems of partitions and their corresponding lattice points appeared in the same S.-B. **1940**, 23–54; these Rev. **3**, 166. It contains a general statement of the problem, which, to put it roughly, is to study the relationships between sets of $n+1$ partitions of $m$

$$a^{(\nu)}=(a_1^{(\nu)},\cdots,a_m^{(\nu)}),\qquad \nu=0,1,\cdots,n,$$

into $m$ nonnegative parts, and geometric realizations of such partitions by "graphs," or lattice point sets in $(n+1)$-dimensional space. Paper I discussed various recursion formulas for the number of such graphs that may be made to correspond with a given set of partitions.

Paper II deals with the $(n+1)$-dimensional analogue of the notion of "regular" or "reduced" Ferrers graph [Tietze, Math. Z. **47**, 352–356 (1941); these Rev. **4**, 36]. Complicated recursion formulas for the number of such graphs are deduced by elementary reasoning.

In paper III the author shows that, if the problem mentioned in paper I is soluble in $N$ ways with a given set of $n+1$ partitions of $m$, then the problem obtained by adjoining another partition to the set is also possible, the number of solutions being at least $(1+1/[\frac{1}{2}m])N$. The number $N$ is at least $(m!)^n$.

Paper IV gives examples, recursion formulas and tables for $m\leqq 5$ and $n=2$, as well as the number $p^{(3)}(m)$ of reduced graphs of $m$ lattice points in three dimensions for $m\leqq 14$.

Paper V defines a class of transformed lattice point sets arising from a reduced lattice point set. This class is built up of elementary transformations in which only two coordinates are changed at a time. Illustrations are given.

Paper VI deals with the problem of ordinary partitions and its connection with certain polygonal lines. To the partition $(a_1, a_2, \cdots, a_m)$ of the integer $m$ into nonnegative parts $a_\nu$ arranged in nonincreasing order one may make correspond a unique polygonal line passing through the points whose coordinates are (0, 0) $(1, a_1)$, $(2, a_1+a_2)$, $(3, a_1+a_2+a_3)$, $\cdots$, $(m, m)$. If one polygonal line $P_1$ lies above another $P_2$ we say that $P_1>P_2$ and the corresponding partitions are ordered in the same way.

Paper VII introduces the notion of a partially reduced set of lattice points. A set $M$ of lattice points in $n$-dimensional space $(x_1, \cdots, x_n)$ is said to be reduced with respect to $x_1, \cdots, x_k$ in case it has the property that if $(x_1', \cdots, x_n')$ is a member of $M$ so also is every point $(x_1, \cdots, x_n)$ for which

$$0<x_\nu<x_\nu',\qquad \nu=1,2,\cdots,k,$$
$$x_\nu=x_\nu',\qquad \nu=k+1,\cdots,n.$$

If $k=n$ we have the case of a completely reduced set of points. A process called "$x$ compression" is defined, the successive application of which transforms a partially reduced set to a totally reduced set. This notion is used in paper VIII, where it is shown that $x$ compression raises the order of the corresponding partition in the sense of paper VI.

Paper IX gives further illustrations of the ideas in paper V.

*D. H. Lehmer* (Berkeley, Calif.).

Citations: MR 3, 166e = P64-3; MR 4, 36c = P64-4.

## P64-8 (11, 710c)

**Fisher, R. A. A class of enumerations of importance in genetics.** Proc. Roy. Soc. London. Ser. B. **136**, 509–520 (1950).

The enumerations given, of isomorphic genotypes, modes of gamete formation, etc., are all of the form $\sum a_k b_k{}^l$, where $l$ is given by the problem, and hence require only a method of determining $a_k$, $b_k$. This is done by a double entry table with rows and columns described by partitions of the same number. The partitions of the rows describe the character (likeness or unlikeness) of objects being distributed, while those of the columns describe the cycle structure of a permutation group. The entries of the tables are of the number of distributions of given character which remain invariant under the permutations of the given group, and their sums by columns are the numbers $b_k$. The $a_k$ are simply the ratios of the numbers of the corresponding permutation groups to the totals of groups. The enumeration of genotypes is said to be of partitions in (on a lattice of) $l$ dimensions, and it is noted that the corresponding $b_k$ are related to the exponential numbers generated by exp $(e^x-1)$ [but it appears that in the statement of this relationship, the word "factor" should be replaced by "divisor"].

*J. Riordan* (New York, N. Y.).

Referred to in P64-15.

## P64-9 (13, 895c)

**Nanda, V. S. Partition theory and thermodynamics of multi-dimensional oscillator assemblies.** Proc. Cambridge Philos. Soc. **47**, 591–601 (1951).

This is a study of partition theory of numbers corresponding to the thermodynamic assemblies of two- and three-dimensional oscillators (quantized according to Bose-Einstein). The "Zustandssumme" of an assembly of a variable number of two-dimensional oscillators is shown to be identical with the generating function of plane partitions, and the two-dimensional oscillator assembly is connected with the partition of bi-partite numbers. These facts are used in obtaining asymptotic forms for the generating functions, these being later generalized to the three-dimensional case. *B. O. Koopman* (New York, N. Y.).

Referred to in P64-11.

## P64-10 (14, 726h)

**Auluck, F. C. On partitions of bipartite numbers.** Proc. Cambridge Philos. Soc. **49**, 72–83 (1953).

Let $p(m, n)$ be the number of partitions of the bipartite number $(m, n)$. The author finds asymptotic expressions for $p(m, n)$ in the two cases: (a) $m$ is fixed; (b) $m$ and $n$ are of the same order. *N. J. Fine* (Philadelphia, Pa.).

Referred to in P64-14, P64-16, P64-22, P64-23.

## P64-11 (14, 1062b)

**Nanda, V. S. Tables of solid partitions.** Proc. Nat. Inst. Sci. India **19**, 313–314 (1953).

In a previous paper [Proc. Cambridge Philos. Soc. **47**, 591–601 (1951); these Rev. **13**, 895] the author considered plane and solid partitions. He denotes by $p^{(3)}(n, m)$ the number of solid partitions of $n$ in which the smallest summand is $m$. Accordingly

$$p^{(3)}(n,n)=n(n+1)/2$$
$$p^{(3)}(n,m)=0\quad\text{for}\quad n/2<m<n.$$

Hence the tabulation of this function is confined to $m\leqq n/2$. The table is for $n=2(1)25$. The entries $p^{(3)}(n, 1)$ give the total number of unrestricted solid partitions of $n-1$. This function is generated by

$$\prod_{r=1}^{\infty}(1-x^r)^{-r(r+1)/2}=1+x+4x^2+10x^3+\cdots.$$

*D. H. Lehmer* (Berkeley, Calif.).

Citations: MR 13, 895c = P64-9.
Referred to in Z30-38.

## P64-12 (16, 786b)

**Robinson, G. de B., and Thrall, R. M. The content of a Young diagram.** Michigan Math. J. **2** (1953–1954), 157–167 (1955).

A partition of $n$, $[\lambda]\equiv[\lambda_1, \cdots, \lambda_r]$, is associated with a graph of $n$ nodes of which $\lambda_i$ are in the $i$th row, in the first $\lambda_i$ columns in this row. If the node in the $i$th row, $j$th column is associated with the number $i-j$, consider the aggregate of $n$ numbers associated with $n$ nodes. If this aggregate includes the integer $h$ repeated $\mu_h$ times, the content of the partition $[\lambda]$ is defined as the expression $C[\lambda]=\prod x_h{}^{\mu_h}$, the number $h$ extending over negative zero and positive integers. The content of a partition defines the partition uniquely.

An operator $S$ is defined, operating from the right, such that $x_h S = x_{h+1}$. An expression $\theta = \prod x_h^{\mu_h}$ will be the content of some partition if

$$m_h = \mu_h - \mu_{h+1} \begin{cases} 0,\ 1 & \text{for } h \geq 0, \\ 0,\ -1 & \text{for } h < 0. \end{cases}$$

Also $\sum m_h = 0$. The expression $\theta/\theta S = \prod x_h^{m_h}$ is called the trace of the partition and is denoted by $D[\lambda]$.

In the modular case the number $i-j$ is replaced by its least positive residue (mod $q$). The content then becomes the $q$-content, $C_q[\lambda] = \prod_{h=0}^{q-1} y_h^{\mu_h}$, and the trace becomes the $q$-trace

$$D_q[\lambda] = C_q[\lambda]/C_q[\lambda]S = \prod y_h^{\mu_h - \mu_{h+1}} = \prod y_h^{m_h}.$$

The $q$-content does not determine the partition uniquely. Two partitions have the same $q$-content if they are partitions of the same numbers and if they have the same $q$-core. Two partitions have the same $q$-trace if and only if they have the same $q$-core. Given an expression

$$y_0^{m_0} y_1^{m_1} \cdots y_{q-1}^{m_{q-1}}$$

such that the $m_i$ are integers and $\sum m_i = 0$, there is exactly one $q$-core of which $t$ is the $q$-trace.

Various connections are obtained between the indices $m_i$ and the properties of the partition of the $q$-core. The following generating function is obtained

$$(1 - Sx_0)^{-1}(1 - Sx_0x_1)^{-1}(1 - Sx_0x_1x_2)^{-1} \cdots = 1 + \sum C[\lambda]$$

summed for all partitions of all integers. The extension to the modular case is immediate. *D. E. Littlewood.*

## P64-13 (18, 793c)

**Wright, E. M. Partitions of multi-partite numbers.** Proc. Amer. Math. Soc. 7 (1956), 880–890.

Let $F_j(Y) = \prod (1 + X_1^{k_1} X_2^{k_2} \cdots X_j^{k_j} Y)$, the product being extended over all non-negative $k_1, \cdots, k_j$. The author studies the coefficients $R_j(n)$ and $Q_j(n)$ defined by $F_j(Y) = \sum_{n \geq 0} R_j(n) Y^n$ and $\{F_j(-Y)\}^{-1} = \sum_{n \geq 0} Q_j(n) Y^n$. The case $j=1$ is well-known, and Bellman [Bull. Amer. Math. Soc. **61** (1955), 92, problem 3] has asked for a formula for $Q_2(n)$. Let $\beta_j(m) = (1 - X_1^m) \cdots (1 - X_j^m)$. Then

$$Q_j(n) = \sum_{(n)} \prod (h_m!)^{-1} \{m\beta_j(m)\}^{-h_m},$$

the sum extending over all partitions of $n$ of the form $n = \sum mh_m$, and the product over all the different parts $m$ in the partition. There is a similar formula for $R_j(n)$. $P_j(n) = \beta_j(1) \cdots \beta_j(n) Q_j(n)$ is a polynomial of degree $n(n-1)/2$ in each $X_i$ (for $j > 1$) with integral coefficients which the author conjectures are non-negative. Results for special values of the $X_i$ and recursion formulas are obtained. The cases $n=2$ and $n=3$ are worked out explicitly, and the case $j=2$ is discussed briefly. Finally, the author obtains an asymptotic formula for $Q_2(n)$, for fixed $X_1$, $X_2$ such that $|X_i| < 1$. *N. J. Fine.*

Referred to in P60-25, P64-27, P64-35.

## P64-14 (19, 16i)

**Nanda, V. S. Bipartite partitions.** Proc. Cambridge Philos. Soc. 53 (1957), 273–277.

Denote by $p(m, n)$ the number of partitions of the bipartite number $(m, n)$. Auluck [same Proc. **49** (1953), 72–83; MR **14**, 726] gave asymptotic formulas for $p(m, n)$ in the cases when $m$ is fixed and $n \to \infty$ and when $m$ and $n$ are of the same order. In this paper the author gives a formula for $m = o(n^{1/4})$. In this case

$$3^{\frac{1}{4}} 4n (m!) p(m, n) \sim (6n\pi^{-2})^{m/2} \exp\{\pi(2n/3)^{\frac{1}{2}}\}.$$

This result follows by splitting the generating function of $p(m, n)$ into various sub-generating functions, of which only one makes an essential contribution when $m = o(n^{\frac{1}{4}})$. Use is then made of the Hardy-Ramanujan asymptotic formula for $p(n)$ with an $m$-fold summation process. One's hope of using the above formula in a special case is not heightened by observing that it gives

$$p(2, 50) \sim 3{\cdot}3070{\cdot}10^6$$

whereas $p(2, 50) = 5569166$. *D. H. Lehmer.*

Citations: MR 14, 726h = P64-10.

## P64-15 (19, 16j)

**Bennett, J. H. Partitions in more than one dimension.** J. Roy. Statist. Soc. Ser. B. 18 (1956), 104–112.

Several important properties are derived for the new partitional functions introduced by Fisher [Proc. Roy. Soc. London. B. **136** (1950), 509–520; MR **11**, 710] in his enumeration of the number of partitions of an integer in an arbitrary number of dimensions. These functions readily lead to the enumeration of the number of partitions of an integer in more than one dimension and with given marginal partitions. This enumeration is given for bi-partitions of the integers 1 to 8 inclusive. (Author's summary.) *N. J. Fine* (Philadelphia, Pa.).

Citations: MR 11, 710c = P64-8.

## P64-16 (19, 16k)

**Wright, E. M. The number of partitions of a large bi-partite number.** Proc. London Math. Soc. (3) 7 (1957), 150–160.

A bi-partite number $(m, n)$ is a two-dimensional vector whose components $m$, $n$ are non-negative rational integers. A partition of $(m, n)$ is a solution of the vector equation

$$\sum_j (m_j, n_j) = (m, n)$$

in bi-partite numbers other than (0, 0), the order being irrelevant. Let $p_1(m, n)$ be the numbers of partitions of $(m, n)$ and $p_2(m, n)$ the number of such partitions in which no part has a zero component. Also let $p_3(m, n)$ be the number of partitions of $(m, n)$ into different parts and $p_4(m, n)$ the number of such partitions without zero components. On the assumption that $A_1 < m/n < A_2$, where $A_1$ and $A_2$ are positive constants, an asymptotic formula for $p_s(m, n)$ is obtained ($s \leq 4$) which is too complicated to quote here. This formula involves rational functions and logarithms of $m$ and $n$ and a definite integral which does not appear to be expressible, in general, in terms of elementary functions. For the case $s=1$ an equivalent result was obtained by F. C. Auluck [Proc. Cambridge Philos. Soc. **49** (1953), 72–83; MR **14**, 726]. *R. A. Rankin* (Glasgow).

Citations: MR 14, 726h = P64-10.

Referred to in P64-21, P64-22.

## P64-17 (19, 29d)

**Carlitz, L. The expansion of certain products.** Proc. Amer. Math. Soc. 7 (1956), 558–564.

Let $G_m(x, y)$, $H_m(x, y)$, $K_m(x, y)$ be defined by

$$\prod_{m,n=0}^{\infty} (1 + x^m y^n t) = \sum_{m=0}^{\infty} \frac{t^m G_m(x, y)}{(x)_m (y)_m},$$

$$\prod_{m,n=0}^{\infty} \frac{1}{(1 - x^m y^n t)} = \sum_{m=0}^{\infty} \frac{t^m H_m(x, y)}{(x)_m (y)_m},$$

$$\prod_{m,n=0}^{\infty} \frac{(1 + x^m y^n t)}{(1 - x^m y^n t)} = \sum_{m=0}^{\infty} \frac{t^m K_m(x, y)}{(x)_m (y)_m},$$

where $(x)_m = \prod_{r=1}^{m} (1 - x^r)$. Recursion formulas for $G_m$, $H_m$, $K_m$ are developed, and it is shown that they are polynomials with integral coefficients, of degree $m(m-1)/2$ in each of $x$ and $y$. Functional equations are also derived;

for example, $H_m(x, y) = y^{m(m-1)/2}G_m(x, y^{-1})$. Special results are obtained for particular values of the arguments. {Reviewer's note: The expression for $K_4$ at the end of § 3 is incorrect, and so are the remarks which follow, concerning the negativity of some coefficients of $G_4$ and $H_4$.}
*N. J. Fine* (Philadelphia, Pa.).

Referred to in P60-25, P64-35.

## P64-18 (20# 3111)

**Wright, E. M. Partitions of large bipartites.** Amer. J. Math. **80** (1958), 643–658.

The author considers partitions of four different kinds of a large bi-partite number $(m, n)$ subject to the condition

$$\tfrac{1}{2}+\varepsilon_1 < \log n/\log m < 2-\varepsilon_2,$$

where $\varepsilon_1$ and $\varepsilon_2$ are any fixed positive numbers. Using a much more precise approximation for the generating function than has been known hitherto, which he has obtained and which will appear in a forthcoming paper, he derives an asymptotic formula for the number of partitions $p(m, n)$, of a rather complicated nature. This formula involves powers of $m$ and $n$ and polynomials in $\log m$ and $\log n$. Numerical estimates and explicit expressions for these polynomials up to the seventh degree are given. The bounds for $\log n/\log m$ represent a considerable improvement over earlier results.
*R. A. Rankin* (Glasgow)

Referred to in P64-29.

## P64-19 (20# 7007)

**Gupta, H. Partition of $j$-partite numbers into $k$ summands.** J. London Math. Soc. 33 (1958), 403–405.

In 1941, Erdös and the reviewer proved that $k!p_k(n) \sim \binom{n-1}{k-1}$ for $k = o(n^{\frac{1}{3}})$, where $p_k(n)$ is the number of partitions of $n$ into exactly $k$ summands [Duke Math. J. **8** (1941), 335–345; MR 3, 69]. A year later the author gave a considerably simpler proof of the same result [Proc. Indian Acad. Sci. **16** (1942), 101–102; MR 4, 190]. In the present paper he makes an analogue of his proof for $j$-partite numbers, i.e., $j$-dimensional vectors with rational integral components. The result is: for $n_1, n_2, \cdots, n_j \to \infty$ and $N_j = (n_1, n_2, \cdots, n_j)$, we have

$$k!p(N_j, k) \sim \prod_{i=1}^{j} \binom{n_i-1}{k-1},$$

where $j$ is fixed, $k$ is fixed, and $p(N_j, k)$ is the number of partitions of $N_j$ into exactly $k$ $j$-partite numbers, each of which has positive components.
*J. Lehner* (East Lansing, Mich.)

Citations: MR 3, 69a = P80-4; MR 4, 190b = P72-6.

Referred to in P64-20.

## P64-20 (21# 2636)

**Gupta, Hansraj. Partitions of $j$-partite numbers.** Res. Bull. Panjab Univ. no. 146, 119–121 (1958).

Another proof of the author's result [J. London Math. Soc. **33** (1958), 403–405; MR **20** #7007] on the partitions of $j$-partite numbers. *J. Lehner* (East Lansing, Mich.)

Citations: MR 20# 7007 = P64-19.

## P64-21 (21# 1286)

**Wright, E. M. A definite integral in the asymptotic theory of partitions.** Proc. London Math. Soc. (3) 8 (1958), 312–320.

In an earlier paper [same Proc. **7** (1957), 150–160; MR **19**, 16], the author found an asymptotic formula for the number of partitions of a bi-partite number $(m, n)$, with $m, n$ large but of the same order of magnitude. In two of his cases, $I(m/n)$ occurs in the asymptotic formula, where

$$I(z) = \int_0^\infty h(u, z)du, \quad \Re(z) \neq 0,$$

$$h(u, z) = \frac{1}{u(e^{zu}-1)(e^u-1)} - \frac{1}{zu^3} + \frac{z+1}{2zu^2} - \frac{2c_2(z)}{e^u-1},$$

$$c_2(z) = \frac{1}{24}\left(z+3+\frac{1}{z}\right).$$

In the present paper, the author finds (i) an asymptotic formula for $I(z)$ for small $z$, (ii) simple expressions giving $I(z)$, for all real, positive $z$, with error $< 10^{-5}$, and (iii) an exact formula for $I(z)$ for rational $z$.
*N. J. Fine* (Princeton, N.J.)

Citations: MR 19, 16k = P64-16.

Referred to in P64-31.

## P64-22 (21# 3386)

**Wright, E. M. The asymptotic behaviour of the generating functions of partitions of multi-partites.** Quart. J. Math. Oxford Ser. (2) **10** (1959), 60–69.

Auluck [Proc. Cambridge Philos. Soc. **49** (1953), 72–83; MR **14**, 726], Meinardus [Math. Ann. **132** (1956), 333–346; MR **18**, 642] and E. M. Wright [Proc. London Math. Soc. (3) **7** (1957), 150–160; MR **19**, 16] have found asymptotic formulae for the number of partitions of a multi-partite number with large components (a multi-partite number is a $j$-dimensional vector with positive integral components). A simple example of a generating function one studies is

$$f(x_1, \cdots, x_j) = \prod_{h_1, \cdots, h_j=1}^{\infty} (1-\exp(-h_1x_1 - \cdots - h_jx_j))^{-1}$$
$$= \sum_{n_1, \cdots, n_j=0}^{\infty} p(n_1, \cdots, n_j) \exp(-n_1x_1 - \cdots - n_jx_j),$$

where $\operatorname{re}(x_l) > 0$ for every $l$ and $p(0, \cdots, 0) = 1$. The author is concerned with approximating to $f$ for small $x_l$, and his results are sharper than those in the previous work mentioned. The author remarks that one cannot expect the same accuracy in an approximation to $f$ as has been achieved in the case $j = 1$ [see G. H. Hardy and S. Ramanujan, Proc. London Math. Soc. (2) **17** (1918), 75–115].
*S. Chowla* (Boulder, Colo.)

Citations: MR 14, 726h = P64-10; MR 18, 642f = N28-35; MR 19, 16k = P64-16.

## P64-23 (21# 4141)

**Luthra, S. M. Partitions of bipartite numbers when the summands are unequal.** Proc. Nat. Inst. Sci. India. Part A **23** (1957), 370–376.

Let $p(m, n)$ be the number of unrestricted partitions of the bipartite number $(m, n)$, and let $q(m, n)$ be the number of partitions of $(m, n)$ into distinct parts. F. C. Auluck found asymptotic expressions for $p(m, n)$ in the two cases: (a) $m$ fixed; (b) $m$ and $n$ of the same order [Proc. Cambridge Philos. Soc. **49** (1953), 72–83; MR **14**, 726], and the author, using Auluck's methods, now obtains asymptotic expressions for $q(m, n)$ in the same two cases.
*H. Halberstam* (London)

Citations: MR 14, 726h = P64-10.

## P64-24 (22# 7993)

**Gupta, Hansraj. Graphic representation of a partition of a $j$-partite number.** Res. Bull. Panjab Univ. (N.S.) **10** (1959), 189–196.

The author begins by giving a method of arranging the partitions of a $j$-partite number (i.e., a $j$-dimensional vector $N_j = (n_1, \cdots, n_j)$ with positive integral components) in "ascending" or "descending" order. For $j=2$ the parts are represented as vectors arranged in order of increasing slope, or increasing magnitude if there are two or more vectors with the same slope. There is an obvious extension to $j$ dimensions, $j>2$. The author then obtains a number of results such as

$$k'\cdot q(N_j,k)\leq\prod_{i=1}^{j}\binom{n_i-1}{k-1}\leq k'\cdot p(N_j,k),$$

where $p(N_j,k)$ denotes the number of partitions of $N_j$ into exactly $k$ parts, and $q(N_j,k)$ the number into exactly $k$ distinct parts.

In spite of the title of the note, very little use is made of the given graphical representation of a $j$-partite number, and the proofs involve only elementary algebra.

*R. D. James* (Vancouver, B.C.)

Referred to in P64-25, P64-27.

## P64-25 (23# A2360)

**Gupta, Om Prakash**

**Partitions of $j$-partite numbers.**

*Proc. Nat. Inst. Sci. India Part A* **26** (1960), 656–660.

This paper gives formulas for $p(N_j,k)$, the number of partitions of a $j$-partite number $N_j$ into exactly $k$ summands, for $k=4$, 5, 6; and for $q(N_j,k)$, the number of partitions of $N_j$ into exactly $k$ parts, for $k=2$, 3, 4, 5, 6. For definitions, and results for $k=1$, 2, 3, see a previous paper by Hansraj Gupta [Res. Bull. Panjab. Univ. (N.S.) **10** (1959), 189–196; MR **22** #7993; in the latter review, $k!$ is misprinted as $k'$]. *R. D. James* (Vancouver, B.C.)

Citations: MR 22# 7993 = P64-24.

Referred to in P64-27.

## P64-26 (23# A2406)

**Robertson, M. M.**

**Asymptotic formulae for the number of partitions of a multi-partite number.**

*Proc. Edinburgh Math. Soc.* (2) **12** (1960/61), 31–40.

Let $p_r(n)=p_r(n_1,n_2,\cdots,n_j)$, $1\leq r\leq 4$, denote the number of partitions of the integral vector $n=(n_1,n_2,\cdots,n_j)$, $n_1\geq n_2\geq\cdots\geq n_j\geq 0$, such that $p_1(n)$ is the total number of partitions of $n$, $p_2(n)$ the number of partitions in which no part has a zero component, $p_3(n)$ the number of partitions into different parts, and $p_4(n)$ the number of partitions into different parts in which no part has a zero component. Put

$$R=\tfrac{1}{2}(n_2+\cdots+n_j),\quad S=\prod_{s=2}^{j}n_s!,$$
$$T=(n_1n_2\cdots n_{j-1})^{n_j-1}((n_j-1)!)^{1-j}(n_j!)^{-1}.$$

The author proves: (1) If $n_s=o(n_1^{1/4})$, $2\leq s\leq j$, then

$$p_1(n)\sim\left\{\frac{6n_1}{\pi^2}\right\}^R(4\cdot 3^{1/2}n_1S)^{-1}\exp\left\{\pi\left(\frac{2n_1}{3}\right)^{1/2}\right\},$$
$$p_3(n)\sim\left\{\frac{12n_1}{\pi^2}\right\}^R(4\cdot 3^{1/4}n_1^{3/4}S)^{-1}\exp\left\{\pi\left(\frac{n_1}{3}\right)^{1/2}\right\},$$

as $n_1\to\infty$. (2) If $n_j=o(n_s^{1/3})$, $1\leq s\leq j-1$, then $p_2(n)\sim p_4(n)\sim T$ as $n_s\to\infty$ for $1\leq s\leq j-1$.

*M. Newman* (Washington, D.C.)

## P64-27 (24# A2573)

**Wright, E. M.**

**Partition of multipartite numbers into a fixed number of parts.**

*Proc. London Math. Soc.* (3) **11** (1961), 499–510.

A semipolynomial of degree $\nu$ in $N$ relative to modulus $m$ is defined as any sum of the form: $\sum_{t=0}^{\nu}\delta_t(N)N^t$ such that $\delta_t(N)=\delta_t(N+m)$. Making use of results obtained by him earlier [Proc. Amer. Math. Soc. **7** (1956), 880–890; MR **18**, 793] and some properties of semipolynomials developed here, the author shows how the dominant terms in the formulae for the number of partitions of $j$-partite numbers into $k$ parts, distinct or otherwise, can be computed. Explicit formulae are given for $k\leq 5$. These are in agreement with those given by the reviewer for $k\leq 3$ [Res. Bull. Panjab Univ. (N.S.) **10** (1959), 189–196; MR **22** #7993], by Cheema, in his Ph.D. dissertation, for $k\leq 4$, and recently by O. P. Gupta [Proc. Nat. Inst. Sci. India Part A **26** (1960), 656–660; MR **23** #A2360] for $k\leq 6$. The reviewer has obtained the author's formulae for $q(n_1,\cdots,n_j)$ and $r(n_1,\cdots,n_j)$ without the use of generating functions [Proc. Nat. Inst. Sci. India (in press)].

*H. Gupta* (Chandigarh)

Citations: MR 18, 793c = P64-13; MR 22# 7993 = P64-24; MR 23# A2360 = P64-25.

Referred to in P64-38.

## P64-28 (25# 2054)

**Gupta, Hansraj**

**On the partition of $J$-partite numbers.**

*Proc. Nat. Inst. Sci. India Part A* **27** (1961), 579–587.

Let $N$ be a $j$-dimensional vector whose components are non-negative integers, and let $p(N,k)$, $q(N,k)$, respectively, denote the number of partitions of $N$ into precisely $k$ parts, and into precisely $k$ distinct parts. Further, let $p(0,0)=q(0,0)=1$, $p(N,0)=q(N,0)=0$ $(N\neq 0)$, and define the operator $\sigma_r$ by $\sigma_rf(N)=\sum f(N-rM)$, where the summation is extended over those vectors $M$ such that $0<rM\leq N$ coordinate-wise. Then the author's principal results are the two recurrence formulas $kp(N,k)=\sum\sigma_sp(N,k-s)$ and $kq(N,k)=\sum(-1)^{s-1}\sigma_sq(N,k-s)$, both summations for $1\leq s\leq k$.

*M. Newman* (Washington, D.C.)

Referred to in P64-37.

## P64-29 (25# 3919)

**Robertson, M. M.**

**Partitions of large multipartites.**

*Amer. J. Math.* **84** (1962), 16–34.

A multipartite number of order $j$ is a $j$-dimensional vector, the components of which are non-negative integers, and a partition of $(n_1,n_2,\cdots,n_j)$ is a solution of the vector equation

$$(*)\qquad \sum_k(n_{1k},n_{2k},\cdots,n_{kj})=(n_1,n_2,\cdots,n_j)$$

in multipartites other than $(0,0,\cdots,0)$. Two partitions, which differ only in the order of the multipartite numbers on the left-hand side of (*), are regarded as identical. Denote by $p_1(n_1,\cdots,n_j)$ the number of different partitions of $(n_1,\cdots,n_j)$ and by $p_2(n_1,\cdots,n_j)$ the number of those partitions in which no part has a zero component. Also, write $p_3(n_1,\cdots,n_j)$ for the number of partitions of $(n_1,\cdots,n_j)$ into different parts and $p_4(n_1,\cdots,n_j)$ for the number of partitions into different parts none of which has a zero component. The author obtains an asymptotic equation for $p_r(n_1,n_2,\cdots,n_j)$ $(r=1,2,3,4)$, which is too complicated to give here, subject to the condition that the components $n_l$ are large and satisfy $n_1n_2\cdots n_j<n_l{}^{j+1-\epsilon}$ $(\varepsilon>0)$. This generalizes work of E. M. Wright [same J. **80** (1958), 643–658; MR **20** #3111].

*R. A. Rankin* (Glasgow)

Citations: MR 20# 3111 = P64-18.

## P64-30 (25# 5005)

**Gordon, Basil**

**Two new representations of the partition function.**

*Proc. Amer. Math. Soc.* **13** (1962), 869–873.

The two-rowed plane partitions of $n$, with the condition

of strict decrease on columns relaxed to non-increase, are proved to be equinumerous with the (ordinary) one-row partitions of $n$, and those with all parts odd with the ordinary partitions of the integral part of $n/2$. {Reviewer's note: The author's equation (1), for which he offers an independent proof, has already been proved on the page preceding it; the coalescence of terms in the first sum on the right in the last equation on page 871 is the sum on the left of equation (1).} *J. Riordan* (Murray Hill, N.J.)

Referred to in P64-41.

**P64-31** **(25# 5046)**

**Robertson, M. M.**

**The evaluation of a definite integral which occurs in asymptotic partition theory.**

*Proc. Roy. Soc. Edinburgh Sect. A* **65**, 283–309 (1960/61).

The integral in question is

$$I = I(x_1, \cdots, x_{j-1}) = \int_0^\infty h(u; z_1, \cdots, z_{j-1})\, du,$$

where

$$h(u, z_1, \cdots, z_{j-1}) = u(e^u - 1)\prod_{s=1}^{j-1}(e^{z_s u} - 1)^{-1} - L^{-1}\left\{\sum_{r=0}^{j-1} V_r u^{r-j-1} + V_j(e^u-1)^{-1}\right\},$$

$$\left\{u(e^u-1)\prod_{s=1}^{j-1}(e^{z_s u}-1)\right\}^{-1} = L^{-1}\sum_{r=0}^{\infty} V_r(u^{r-j-1})$$

for $0 < u < 2\pi \min(1, z_1^{-1}, \cdots, z_{j-1}^{-1})$ and $L = \prod_{s=1}^{j-1} z_s$. In the special case $j=2$ this integral has been investigated by Wright [Proc. London Math. Soc. (3) **8** (1958), 312–320; MR **21** #1286].

In the present paper an asymptotic expansion for $I$ is obtained first when every $z_s$ is small. Then, for $j>2$, when $z_1, \cdots, z_k$ are of a different order from the other $z_s$, an asymptotic formula for $I$ in terms of $z_1, \cdots, z_k$ is obtained in which the coefficients are no longer constants but definite integrals $I_{kr}'(z_{k+1}, \cdots, z_{j-1})$. These integrals are similar to $I$.

In the final part of the paper exact expressions are obtained for both $I$ and $I_{kr}'$ when the $z_s$ are real and rational. The results are too complicated for brief quotation.

The paper closes with some numerical data when $j=2, 3$.

*L. Carlitz* (Durham, N.C.)

Citations: MR 21# 1286 = P64-21.

**P64-32** **(26# 6063)**

**Carlitz, L.**

**Some generating functions.**

*Duke Math. J.* **30** (1963), 191–201.

In the first part of this paper sums of the following type are evaluated:

$$\sum_{n_1,\cdots,n_k=0}^{\infty} x_1^{n_1}\cdots x_k^{n_k} \sum_{m=1}^{M_r(n_1,\cdots,n_k)} z^m,$$

$$\sum_{n_1,\cdots,n_k=0}^{\infty} x_1^{n_1}\cdots x_k^{n_k} z^{M_r(n_1,\cdots,n_k)},$$

$$\sum_{n_1,\cdots,n_k=0}^{\infty} x_1^{n_1}\cdots x_k^{n_k} \sum_{m_1,\cdots,m_t=1}^{M_r(n_1,\cdots,n_k)} z_1^{m_1}\cdots z_t^{m_t},$$

where $M_r(n_1, \cdots, n_k)$ is symmetric in the $n_j$ and is equal to $n_r$ when $n_1 \leqq n_2 \leqq \cdots \leqq n_r$.

In the latter part of the paper it is shown that the sum

$$\sum x_1^{n_1}x_2^{n_2}\cdots x_k^{n_k} y_1^{m_1} y_2^{m_2}\cdots y_k^{m_k},$$

where the summation is over all non-negative $n_j$, $m_j$ such that $\min(n_j, m_j) > \max(n_{j+1}, m_{j+1})$ $(j=1, \cdots, k-1)$ is equal to $N/D$, where

$$N = (1-u_1u_2)(1-u_2u_3)\cdots(1-u_{k-1}u_k),$$

$$D = (1-x_1)(1-y_1)(1-u_1x_2)(1-u_1y_2)(1-u_2) \times (1-u_2x_3)(1-u_2y_3)(1-u_3)\cdots \times (1-u_{k-1})(1-u_{k-1}x_k)(1-u_{k-1}y_k)(1-u_k)$$

and $u_r = x_1y_1x_2y_2\cdots x_ry_r$. The special case $x_1 = \cdots = x_k = x$, $y_1 = \cdots = y_k = y$ (including $k=\infty$) yields an interesting generating function for partitions of bipartite numbers.

*A. L. Whiteman* (Los Angeles, Calif.)

Referred to in P60-44.

**P64-33** **(26# 6143)**

**Carlitz, L.**

**A problem in partitions.**

*Duke Math. J.* **30** (1963), 203–213.

In this paper a generating function is obtained for the number of partitions of the bipartite $(n, m)$: $n = n_1+n_2+n_3+\cdots$, $m = m_1+m_2+m_3+\cdots$, where $n_j$, $m_j$ are non-negative integers that satisfy

$$\min(n_j, m_j) \geqq \max(n_{j+1}, m_{j+1})$$

$(j=1, 2, 3, \cdots)$. Let $\pi(n, m)$ denote this number and put $\xi = \sum_{n,m=0}^{\infty} \pi(n, m)x^n y^m$. Then

$$\xi = \prod_{n=1}^{\infty}(1-x^ny^{n-1})^{-1}(1-x^{n-1}y^n)^{-1}(1-x^{2n}y^{2n})^{-1}.$$

More generally, the power series $\xi_{nm} = \xi_{nm}(x, y)$ which satisfies the recurrence $\xi_{nm} = \sum_{r,s=0}^{\min(n,m)} x^r y^s \xi_{rs}$ is evaluated; in the limit $\xi_{\infty\infty} = \xi$. A generating function is also obtained for the number of partitions such that $\min(n_j, m_j) > \max(n_{j+1}, m_{j+1})$ $(j=1, 2, 3, \cdots)$. Finally, a relationship with theta functions is indicated. With the aid of Jacobi's identity it is shown that

$$\xi^{-1} = \prod_1^{\infty}(1+x^ny^n)\sum_{-\infty}^{\infty}(-1)^r x^{r(r+1)/2} y^{r(r-1)/2};$$

this in turn implies various relations involving partition functions. *A. L. Whiteman* (Los Angeles, Calif.)

Referred to in P60-44.

**P64-34** **(28# 58)**

**Gupta, Hansraj**

**An inequality for $P(N_j, k)$.**

*Res. Bull. Panjab Univ. (N.S.)* **13** (1962), 173–178.

Let $N_j$ denote $(n_1, n_2, \cdots, n_j)$ where each $n_i > 0$, and let $N_{t,j}$ denote $(n_{t1}, \cdots, n_{tj})$ where each $n_{ti} > 0$. Let $p(N_j, k)$ denote the number of solutions of the equation

$$N_j = N_{1j} + N_{2j} + \cdots + N_{kj} \quad (n \geqq k).$$

The author proves the following result:

$$\frac{k!\,p(N_j, k)}{\prod_{i=1}^{j}\binom{n_j-1}{k-1}} = \exp\left(\frac{uk^{j+2}}{2n_1n_2\cdots n_k}\right)$$

for some $u$ between 0 and 1. *L. Carlitz* (Durham, N.C.)

**P64-35** **(28# 1187)**

**Gordon, B.**

**Two theorems on multipartite partitions.**

*J. London Math. Soc.* **38** (1963), 459–464.

Put

$$\prod_{k_j=0}^{\infty}(1-x_1^{k_1}\cdots x_s^{k_s}z)^{-1} = \sum_{r=0}^{\infty}\phi_r(x)z^r,$$

$$\phi_r(x) = \Lambda_r(x)\prod_{k=1}^{r}\prod_{j=1}^{s}(1-x_j^k)^{-1},$$

$$\Lambda_r(x) = \sum_{m_j=0}^{r(r-1)/2}\lambda_r(m_1,\cdots,m_s)x_1^{m_1}\cdots x_s^{m_s}.$$

Wright [Proc. Amer. Math. Soc. **7** (1956), 880–890; MR **18**, 793] conjectured that all the $\lambda_r(m_1,\cdots,m_s)$ are non-negative. The present paper contains a combinatorial proof of this result.

In the case $s=2$ the reviewer [ibid. **7** (1956), 558–564; MR **19**, 29] showed that $\Lambda_r(\omega,\zeta)=0$, where $\omega$ and $\zeta$ are roots of unity, primitive of orders $g$ and $h$, and $g|r$, $h|r$, $g\neq h$. This result is extended to the case $g\leqq r$, $h\leqq r$, $g\neq h$.

*L. Carlitz* (Durham, N.C.)

Citations: MR 18, 793c = P64-13; MR 19, 29d = P64-17.

## P64-36 (28# 3981)

**Cheema, M. S.; Gordon, Basil**

**Some remarks on two- and three-line partitions.**

*Duke Math. J.* **31** (1964), 267–273.

A $k$-line partition of the positive integer $n$ is a representation of $n$ in the form $n=\sum_{i=1}^{k}\sum_{j=1}^{\infty}a_{i,j}$, where $a_{i,j}$ are non-negative integers satisfying $a_{i,j}\geqq a_{i,j+1}$ and $a_{i,j}\geqq a_{i+1,j}$; the number of such partitions of $n$ is denoted by $t_k(n)$. It is known that $\sum_{n=0}^{\infty}t_k(n)x^n=F_k(x)G_k(x)$, where $F_k(x)=\prod_{m=1}^{\infty}(1-x^m)^{-k}$ and $G_k(x)=\prod_{m=1}^{k-1}(1-x^m)^{k-m}$ [P. A. MacMahon, *Combinatory analysis*, Vol. 2, pp. 171–245, Cambridge Univ. Press, London, 1916]. The authors give a purely combinatorial proof of this identity for $k=2$ and use it to derive various identities involving $t_k(n)$ and the coefficients of $F_k(x)$, as well as deriving the congruences $t_2(n)\equiv 0 \pmod 5$ if $n\equiv 3$ or $4 \pmod 5$ and $t_3(n)\equiv 0 \pmod 3$ if $n\equiv 2 \pmod 3$. A table of values of $t_2(n)$ and $t_3(n)$ is given for $n\leqq 50$. *H. W. Brinkmann* (Swarthmore, Pa.)

Referred to in P64-47.

## P64-37 (28# 5049)

**Wright, E. M.**

**Direct proof of the basic theorem on multipartite partitions.**

*Proc. Amer. Math. Soc.* **15** (1964), 469–472.

In 1956, the author used generating functions to obtain formulae for the number of partitions of a $j$-partite number into $k$ parts, distinct or otherwise. In this paper, he gives a direct proof of his results. Use is made of the elementary theory of the symmetric group of permutations on $k$ elements. (For another proof see the reviewer's paper [Proc. Nat. Inst. Sci. India Part A **27** (1961), 579–587; MR **25** #2054].) *H. Gupta* (Chandigarh)

Citations: MR 25# 2054 = P64-28.

## P64-38 (29# 32)

**Blakley, G. R.**

**Combinatorial remarks on partitions of a multipartite number.**

*Duke Math. J.* **31** (1964), 335–340.

A partition of a multipartite number is regarded as specified by listing the number of appearances of each of its permitted parts; thus the set of lists is the set of non-negative integer-valued functions with domain the set of permitted parts. This prescription is used to obtain a recurrence relation for the number of partitions having $r$ parts, zero (multipartite) parts permitted, or what is the same thing, the number with at most $r$ parts. This recurrence, which with all its accompanying definitions is too long to quote, is used to prove E. M. Wright's result [Proc. London Math. Soc. (3) **11** (1961), 499–510; MR **24** #A2573] that for suitably restricted numbers partitioned, the number with at most $r$ parts is a polynomial (in a special sense) in the number partitioned. Recurrences are also found for the total number of partitions with restricted and unrestricted parts. *J. Riordan* (Murray Hill, N.J.)

Citations: MR 24# A2573 = P64-27.

## P64-39 (29# 3453)

**Wright, E. M.**

**Partition of multipartite numbers into $k$ parts.**

*J. Reine Angew. Math.* **216** (1964), 101–112.

Let $q(k;n_1,\cdots,n_j)$ be the number of partitions of the vector $(n_1,\cdots,n_j)$ into $k$ parts $(x_1,\cdots,x_j)$, where the $x_i$ are non-negative integers. The author estimates $q$ for large $n_1,\cdots,n_j$. The problem is first reduced to studying the coefficients $c_n$ of $J(x)=\sum_{n=0}^{\infty}c_nx^n=\prod_{i=1}^{p}(1-x^{a_i})^{-1}$, where $a_1+\cdots+a_p$ is a partition of $k$. If $u\geqq 1$, let $s(u)$ be the number of $a_i\equiv 0 \pmod u$. By partial fractions one gets $J(x)=\sum_{s(u)>0}J_u(x)$, where the poles of $J_u(x)$ are at the primitive $u$th roots of unity. If $J_u(x)=\sum_{n=0}^{\infty}C(u,n)x^n$, then $C(u,n)$ is of the form $\sum_{i=0}^{s(u)-1}\varepsilon_i(u,n)n^i$, where $\varepsilon_i(u,n+u)=\varepsilon_i(u,n)$. Using this to define $C(u,n)$ for $n<0$, one gets $C(u,n)=(-1)^{p-1}C(u,-n-k)$. Putting $N=n+\frac{1}{2}k$, this leads for $u=1$ and 2 to an expansion $C(u,n)=\sum_{0\leqq 2\nu\leqq s(u)-1}\chi_u(\nu)N^{s(u)-1-2\nu}$, where $\chi_1(\nu)$ and $(-1)^n\chi_2(\nu)$ are independent of $n$. Explicit formulas are obtained for $\chi_1$ and $\chi_2$ in terms of Bernoulli numbers. Then $q(k;n_1,\cdots,n_j)$ is expanded in powers of $N_i=n_i+\frac{1}{2}k$, and these formulas are used to evaluate the leading terms. For $k\leqq 4$ this gives explicit formulas for $q$.

*B. Gordon* (Los Angeles, Calif.)

## P64-40 (29# 4697)

**Cheema, M. S.**

**Vector partitions and combinatorial identities.**

*Math. Comp.* **18** (1964), 414–420.

Let $S$ be a given set of vectors $(x,y)$ whose components are non-negative integers. Let $p(m,n|S)$ be the number of partitions $(m,n)=\sum(x_i,y_i)$, where the parts $(x_i,y_i)$ are all in $S$. Let $q_e(m,n|S)$ [$q_0(m,n|S)$] be the number of such partitions into an even [odd] number of distinct parts. Put $A=\{(a,a)|a\in\mathbf{N}\}$, $B=\{(b,b-1)|b\in\mathbf{N}\}$, $C=\{(c-1,c)|c\in\mathbf{N}\}$, $D=\{(2d+1,2d-1)|d\in\mathbf{N}\}$, $E=\{(2e-1,2e+1)|e\in\mathbf{N}\}$. It is shown that $q_e(m,n|A\cup B\cup C)-q_0(m,n|A\cup B\cup C)=(-1)^r$ or 0 according as $(m,n)=(\frac{1}{2}r(r+1),\frac{1}{2}r(r-1))$ (where $r\in\mathbf{Z}$) or not. Recurrence relations are obtained for $p(m,n|D\cup E)$ and $p(m,n|A\cup B\cup C\cup D\cup E)$, but these are incorrect since equations (1.5) [1.8] must be divided by $(1-xy^{-1})$ $[1-x^{-1}y]$ before the reciprocals of their left-hand sides can be interpreted combinatorially. The correct recurrence for $C(m,n)=p(m,n|A\cup B\cup C\cup D\cup E)$, for example, is: $C(0,0)=1$, and if $(m,n)\neq(0,0)$,

$$C(m,n) = \sum_{r=1}^{\infty}\left[\sum_{s=0}^{3r-2}C\left(m-\frac{3r^2+r}{2}+s+1,\, n-\frac{3r^2-5r}{2}-s-1\right)\right.$$
$$\left.-\sum_{s=0}^{3r}C\left(m-\frac{3r^2+5r}{2}+s,\, n-\frac{3r^2-r}{2}-s\right)\right].$$

Next, it is shown that the partitions of $(n_1,\cdots,n_s)$ into vectors with at least one odd component are equinumerous with those into distinct vectors. Putting

$$f(x) = \prod_{n=1}^{\infty}(1-x^n)^{-1},\quad F(x) = f(x^2)f(x^3)f(x)^{-2}f(x^6)^{-1},$$

$$G(x) = f(x^2)f(x^3)f(x^{12})f(x)^{-1}f(x^4)^{-1}f(x^6)^{-2},$$

the author evaluates

$$\int_0^1 x^{-1}(G(x)-1)\,dx \quad\text{and}\quad \int_0^1 x^{-1}(F(x)-1)\,dx.$$

The second of these contains an error; the correct result is $2-2\pi/\sqrt{3}$. The paper concludes with a table of the number of partitions of (49, 49) into at most $r$ parts with non-negative components ($1\leqq r\leqq 98$).

*B. Gordon* (Los Angeles, Calif.)

Referred to in P80-46.

**P64-41** **(31# 74)**

**Sudler, Culbreth, Jr.**

**A direct proof of two theorems on two-line partitions.**

*Proc. Amer. Math. Soc.* **16** (1965), 161–168.

Let $n$ be a positive integer, and consider two-line partitions of $n$ which are strictly decreasing along rows, i.e., representations of the form $n=\sum_{i=1}^r a_i+\sum_{j=1}^s b_j$, where $r\geqq s$, and the $a_i$ and $b_j$ are positive integers satisfying $a_{i-1}>a_i$, $b_{j-1}>b_j$, $a_j\geqq b_j$ (for $i\leqq r$, $j\leqq s$). The reviewer proved [same Proc. **13** (1962), 869–873; MR **25** #5005], using generating functions, that the number of such partitions is $p(n)$, the ordinary partition function, and that if the $a_i$, $b_j$ are all odd, the number is $p([\frac{1}{2}n])$. The author gives a direct proof of these results by establishing one-to-one correspondences between the classes of partitions involved.

*B. Gordon* (Los Angeles, Calif.)

Citations: MR 25# 5005 = P64-30.

**P64-42** **(31# 2231)**

**Wright, E. M.**

**An extension of a theorem of Gordon.**

*Proc. Glasgow Math. Assoc.* **7**, 39–41 (1965).

Let $q(k;n_1,\cdots,n_j)$ be the number of partitions of the vector $(n_1,\cdots,n_j)$ into $k$ parts (where the parts are vectors with non-negative integer components). It is known that

$$\sum_{n_1,\cdots,n_j=0}^{\infty} q(k;n_1,\cdots,n_j)X_1^{n_1}\cdots X_j^{n_j} = P_j(k)\prod_{i=1}^{j}\prod_{s=1}^{k}(1-X_i^s)^{-1},$$

where $P_j(k)=P_j(k;X_1,\cdots,X_j)$ is a polynomial of degree $\frac{1}{2}k(k-1)$ in each $X_i$. The reviewer proved that if $\xi$ and $\eta$ are primitive $u$th and $t$th roots of unity, respectively, where $1\leqq u<t\leqq k$, then $P_j(k;\xi,\eta,X_3,\cdots,X_j)=0$. The author gives a new proof of this result, and extends it as follows. Put

$$\beta(m) = \prod_{i=1}^{j}(1-X_i^m),$$

and

$$\gamma(m) = \prod_{i=1}^{j}\prod_\rho(1-\rho X_i),$$

where $\rho$ runs through the primitive $m$th roots of unity. Suppose $1\leqq u_1<u_2<\cdots<u_a\leqq k$, $v_b=[k/u_b]$, $w_b=k-u_bv_b$. Then

$$P_j(k) = \sum_{b=1}^{a}\frac{P_j(w_b)\prod_{h=w_b+1}^{k}\beta(h)}{v_b!(u_b\beta(u_b))^{v_b}}+T\prod_{b=1}^{a}\gamma(u_b),$$

where $T$ is a polynomial in the $X_i$. When $a=1$, this reduces to

$$P_j(k) = (v!)^{-1}(u\beta(u))^{-v}P_j(w)\prod_{h=w+1}^{k}\beta(h)+T\gamma(u).$$

The reviewer's theorem follows from this, since $\gamma(u)$ and $\beta(t)$ vanish when $X_1=\xi$, $X_2=\eta$.

*B. Gordon* (Los Angeles, Calif.)

**P64-43** **(31# 3372)**

**Gupta, H. [Gupta, Hansraj]**

**Partition of $j$-partite numbers.**

*Math. Student* **31** (1963), 179–186 (1964).

An interesting expository account of the elementary theory of partitions of $j$-partite numbers, in which bounds, recurrence formulas and some exact formulas are developed.

*Morris Newman* (Washington, D.C.)

**P64-44** **(33# 308)**

**Wright, E. M.**

**Coefficients of a reciprocal generating function.**

*Quart. J. Math. Oxford Ser.* (2) **17** (1966), 39–43.

That the coefficients of the reciprocal of the generating function for the number of linear partitions are given by $f(X)=\prod_{k=1}^{\infty}(1-X^k)=1+\sum_{s=1}^{\infty}(-1)^sX^{s(3s\pm1)/2}$ is a classical result due to Euler. If $F(X)$ is the reciprocal of the generating function for the number of plane partitions, then its coefficients $C_n$ are defined by

$$F(X) = \prod_{k=1}^{\infty}(1-X^k)^k = 1+\sum_{n=1}^{\infty}C_nX^n.$$

No simple expressions like Euler's seem to exist for the $C_n$; it is shown that for large $n$,

$$C_n = B(3A/2M)^{23/24}e^M\left[\cos(M\sqrt{3}+5\pi/36)+O\left(\frac{1}{M}\right)\right],$$

where $A=\zeta(3)$,

$$B = \frac{e^{-C}}{\sqrt{(3A\pi)}},\quad C = 2\int_0^\infty\frac{y\log y}{e^{2\pi y}-1}\,dy,\quad M = \tfrac{3}{2}(A/4)^{1/3}n^{2/3}.$$

Another extension is given which is in good agreement with the actual values obtained on a computer. The method of proof involves integration around a circle and application of Cauchy's theorem.

*M. S. Cheema* (Tucson, Ariz.)

**P64-45** **(34# 2549)**

**Carlitz, L.; Roselle, D. P.**

**Restricted bipartite partitions.**

*Pacific J. Math.* **19** (1966), 221–228.

Authors' summary: "Let $\pi_k(n,m)$ denote the number of partitions $n=n_1+n_2+\cdots+n_k$, $m=m_1+m_2+\cdots+m_k$ subject to the conditions $\min(n_j,m_j)\geqq\max(n_{j+1},m_{j+1})$ $(j=1,2,\cdots,k-1)$. Put $\xi^{(k)}(x,y)=\sum_{n,m=0}^{\infty}\pi_k(n,m)x^ny^m$. We show that

$$\xi^{(k)}(x,y) = \prod_{j=1}^{k}\frac{1-x^{2j-1}y^{2j-1}}{(1-x^jy^j)(1-x^jy^{j-1})(1-x^{j-1}y^j)},$$

$$\sum_{n,m=0}^{\infty}\pi(n,m;\lambda)x^ny^m = 1+(1-\lambda)\sum_{k=1}^{\infty}\lambda^k\xi^{(k)}(x,y),$$

$$\sum_{n,m=0}^{\infty}\psi(n,m)x^ny^m = \sum_{n=0}^{\infty}x^ny^n\xi^{(n)}(x^2,y^2),$$

where $\pi(n,m;\lambda)$ denotes the number of 'weighted' partitions of $(n,m)$ and $\psi(n,m)$ is the number of partitions into odd parts ($n_j$, $m_j$ all odd)."

{See also #2550 below.} *J. B. Roberts* (Portland, Ore.)

**P64-46** **(34# 2550)**

**Roselle, D. P.**

**Restricted $k$-partite partitions.**

*Math. Nachr.* **32** (1966), 139–148.

By a $k$-partite number is meant a $k$-tuple $(n_1,\cdots,n_k)$, where the $n_j$ are nonnegative integers. Consider partitions of the type (*) $n_i=\sum_{j=1}^{\infty} n_{ij}$ $(i=1, 2, \cdots, k)$, where the $n_{ij}$ are nonnegative integers such that (**) $\min\{n_{ij}, \cdots, n_{kj}\} \geqq \max\{n_{1,j+1}, \cdots, n_{k,j+1}\}$ $(j=1, 2, 3, \cdots)$. Let $\pi(n_1, \cdots, n_k)$ denote the number of partitions (*) subject to the condition (**). Define the function $H_k(n)=H_k(u|q_1, \cdots, q_k)$ by the recurrence $uH^k=\prod_{j=1}^{k}(1+q_jH)$, $H_0=1$, where it is understood that after expansion of the right member, $q_1\cdots q_rH^r$ is replaced by $q_1\cdots q_rH_r(u|q_1, \cdots, q_r)$. The author has proved [Duke Math. J. **33** (1966), 293–304; MR **32** #7532] that the generating function for $\pi_r(n_1, \cdots, n_k)$ is given by

$$\phi^{-1}\prod_{n=1}^{\infty} X^{-n}H_k(X^{-n}|x_1, \cdots, x_n),$$

where $\phi=\prod_{j=1}^{k}(1-x_j)$, $X=\prod_{j=1}^{k} x_j$.

Let $\xi^{(m)}=\xi^{(m)}(x_1, \cdots, x_m)$ denote the generating function for $k$-partite partitions with at most $m$ parts. In the present paper the author shows that $1+(1-\lambda)\sum_1^{\infty}\lambda^n\xi^{(n)}$, $\sum_1^{\infty} X^{n(n-1)/2}(1-X^n)\xi^{(n)}$, $\sum_0^{\infty} X^n\xi^{(n)}(x_1^2, \cdots, x_k^2)$ are, respectively, the generating functions for partitions with parts weighted by the parameter $\lambda$, partitions with unequal parts and partitions with odd parts; moreover, $\xi^{(m)}=\phi^{-1}X^{-m(m-1)/2}\prod_{j=1}^{m-1} H_k(X^{-j})$. For $k=1$ such results are well known; for $k=2$, see the reviewer and the author [#2549 above]. *L. Carlitz* (Durham, N.C.)

Citations: MR 32# 7532 = P60-44.

## P64-47 (34# 7486 )

**Atkin, A. O. L.**

**Note on a paper of Cheema and Gordon.**

*Duke Math. J.* **34** (1967), 57–58.

In their paper [same J. **31** (1964), 267–273; MR **28** #3981] the reviewer and B. Gordon proved some identities and congruences modulo 5 and 3 for $t_2(n)$ and $t_3(n)$, the number of 2-line and 3-line partitions of $n$, and remarked that these congruences can be interpreted combinatorially in terms of ranks. The author points out that the idea of ranks does not work in all cases, in fact for $t_2(n)$ it works only for $n=3, 4, 8$ and 9, where $n<100$, and for $t_3(n)$ for $n=2, 5, 8, 11, 20, 26$, where $n<60$. Let $\sum_{n=0}^{\infty} p_{-2}(n)y^n=\prod_{v=1}^{\infty}(1-y^v)^{-2}$; formulas for the series $\sum_{n=0}^{\infty} p_{-2}(5n+4)y^n$ and $\sum_{n=0}^{\infty} p_{-2}(5n+2)y^n$ are obtained similar to the one for $\sum_{n=0}^{\infty} p_{-2}(5n+3)y^n$ given in the paper cited above.
*M. S. Cheema* (Tucson, Ariz.)

Citations: MR 28# 3981 = P64-36.

## P64-48 (34# 7487 )

**Gandhi, J. M.**

**Some congruences for $k$ line partitions of a number.**

*Amer. Math. Monthly* **74** (1967), 179–181.

Some congruences are derived, by elementary methods, for the number $t_k(n)$ of $k$ line partitions of $n$. A typical such congruence is $t_3(3n+3)\equiv t_3(3n+4)$ (mod 3).
*M. S. Cheema* (Tucson, Ariz.)

## P64-49 (35# 4114 )

**Wright, E. M.**

**The generating function of solid partitions.**

*Proc. Roy. Soc. Edinburgh Sect. A* **67** (1965/67), 185–195.

Some properties of the generating function $\eta(a, b, c; X)=1+\sum_{n=1}^{\infty} f(a, b, c; n)X^n$ are obtained, where $f(a, b, c; n)$ is the number of solutions in nonnegative integers $m(i, j, k)$ of the equations (1) $n=\sum_{i,j,k\geq 1} m(i, j, k)$, (2) $m(i, j, k)\geqq \max[m(i+1, j, k), m(i, j+1, k), m(i, j, k+1)]$, (3) $m(i, j, k)=0$ unless $(i, j)=(1, 1), (2, 1)$, or $(1, 2)$, (4) $m(1, 1, k)\leqq a$, (5) $m(2, 1, k)\leqq b$, and (6) $m(1, 2, k)\leqq c$.

The results obtained represent a contribution to the problem of "finding" the generating function $1+\sum q(n)X^n$ for solid partitions, where $q(n)$ is the number of solutions to (1) and (2). It is first shown that

$$\eta(a, b, c; X) = \sum_{u=0}^{b}\sum_{v=0}^{c}\beta(u, v; X)X^{u+v}\xi_{a+u+v}\xi_{b-u}\xi_{c-v},$$

where $\beta$ is symmetric in $u$ and $v$ and $\xi_a=\prod_{k=1}^{a}(1-X^k)^{-1}$ is the generating function for linear (ordinary) partitions of $n$ into parts no larger than $a$. It is shown that $\beta(0, 0; X)=1$, $\beta(1, 0; X)=-1$, $\beta(u, 0; X)=0$ if $u\geqq 2$, and $\beta(u, 1; X)=(-1)^{u-1}X^{u(u-1)/2}(1+X^u)$ if $u\geqq 1$. For other values of $u$ and $v$ the function $\beta$ is given by a one-parameter recursion $\beta(u, v; X)=\sum_{r=1}^{v-1}\beta(r, v; X)R(u, v, r; X)$,

$$R(u, v, r; X) = (1-X^{2u+v-1}) \times \sum_{s=r}^{u}(-1)^{u-s}X^{(u-s)(u-s-1)/2}\frac{\xi_{u-s}\xi_{s-r}\xi_{r+v+s+1}}{\xi_{u+v+s-2}}.$$

Finally, it is shown that

$$\eta(\infty, \infty, \infty; X) = (\xi_\infty)^3\sum_{u=0}^{\infty}\sum_{v=0}^{\infty}\beta(u, v; X)X^{u+v}$$

is the generating function for partitions of $n$ satisfying (1), (2), and (3). *D. W. Walkup* (Seattle, Wash.)

## P64-50 (36# 124 )

**Atkin, A. O. L.; Bratley, P.; Macdonald, I. G.; McKay, J. K. S.**

**Some computations for $m$-dimensional partitions.**

*Proc. Cambridge Philos. Soc.* **63** (1967), 1097–1100.

Let $p_m(n)$ be the number of unrestricted $m$-dimensional partitions of $n$, i.e., the number of arrangements of $n$ nodes, with non-negative integral coordinates, such that if a node $(a_1, \cdots, a_m)$ occurs, so do $(x_1, \cdots, x_m)$ for $0\leqq x_i\leqq a_i$ $(i=1, \cdots, m)$. Define also $\pi_m(n)$ by $\sum_{n=0}^{\infty}\pi_m(n)x^n=\prod_{r=1}^{\infty}(1-x^r)^{-(^{r+m-3}C_{m-2})}$. It is known that $E_m(n)=\pi_m(n)-p_m(n)$ is zero for $m=2, 3$, but that this is not always true for $m\geqq 4$. The authors discuss the question of whether $E_m(n)$ is always non-negative and show that for fixed $n$ and sufficiently large $m$, one has $E_m(n)>0$: on the basis of a number of values of $p_m(n)$ and $\pi_m(n)$ which they have calculated and which are given in the paper, they formulate other questions (e.g., is $E_m(n)=O(\pi_m(n))$ valid for fixed $m$ as $n\to\infty$?) but do not find the evidence sufficient to justify any conjecture. There are several interesting problems to be solved here. *H. J. Godwin* (Swansea)

Referred to in P64-55.

## P64-51 (36# 125 )

**Cheema, M. S.; Haskell, C. T.**

**Multirestricted and rowed partitions.**

*Duke Math. J.* **34** (1967), 443–451.

In the first part of the paper the authors define various types of partition functions with restrictions on the size and number of parts, e.g., $p(n, r, m; k)$ is the number of partitions of $n$ into $r$ parts, each $\geqq m$ and $\leqq k$. Theorem 1 states relations between these functions and the functions $q(n, r)$, $v(n, r; m)$ (in the authors' notation), where $q(n, r)$ is the number of partitions of $n$ into at most $r$ parts and $v(n, r; m)$ is the number of partitions of $n$ into at most $r$ distinct parts, each $\leqq m$. These results can be proved through generating functions or combinational arguments. Two results are proved and the reader is referred for the others to the Ph.D. thesis of the second author ["Multirestricted and rowed partitions", Ph.D. thesis, Univ. Arizona, Tucson, Arizona, 1965]. Various relations between formal series and products that arise are stated.

In the second part the authors study the functions $t_r(n)$ and $p_{-r}(n)$ defined by $\sum_{n=0}^{\infty} t_r(n)x^n=\prod_{n=1}^{\infty}(1-x^n)^{-\min(n,r)}$ and $\sum_{n=0}^{\infty} p_{-r}(n)x^n=\{\prod_{n=1}^{\infty}(1-x^n)\}^{-r}$. They sketch a proof of the relation

$$t_r(n) \sim (r-1)!(r-2)!\cdots 2!\, d^{r(r-1)/2}(p_{-r}(n))/dn^{r(r-1)/2}.$$

They then give asymptotic series for $p_{-r}(n)$, $r \leqq 24$. From the sketch of the proof, details of which are available in the above-cited thesis, the proof appears to be similar to the Hardy-Ramanujan-Rademacher proof for the well-known asymptotic series for $p(n) = p_{-1}(n)$.

*R. P. Bambah* (Columbus, Ohio)

## P64-52 (36# 1339)

**Gordon, Basil; Houten, Lorne**

**Notes on plane partitions. I, II.**

*J. Combinatorial Theory* **4** (1968), 72–80; 81–99.

These papers initiate a series of studies on $k$-rowed partitions whose nonzero parts decrease strictly along each row, or along each column, or both. The numbers of such partitions of $n$ are denoted by $b_k(n)$, $c_k(n)$, and $d_k(n)$, respectively.

In Part I the authors discuss the generating function $B_k(x) = \sum_{n=0}^{\infty} b_k(n)x^n$. Given integers $m_1 \geqq m_2 \geqq \cdots \geqq m_k \geqq 0$, let $b(n; m_1, \cdots, m_k)$ denote the number of $k$-rowed partitions of $n$, strictly decreasing along each row, with exactly $m_i$ nonzero parts in the $i$th row. Then $B_k(x) = \sum_{m_i \geqq 0} B(x; m_1, \cdots, m_k)$, where

$$B(x; m_1, \cdots, m_k) = \sum_{n=0}^{\infty} b(n; m_1, \cdots, m_k)x^n.$$

The authors express the sum of this last series in closed form and thereby obtain a multiple series for $B_k(x)$. Their work leads to a new proof of a product formula of MacMahon for the generating function of the total number of $k$-rowed partitions of $n$.

In Part II the multiple series for $B_k(x)$ is transformed to an infinite product,

$$B_k(x) = P^{[k/2]}Q^{2\{k/2\}} \prod_{v=1}^{k-2} (1-x^v)^{[(k-v)/2]},$$

where $P = \prod_{v=1}^{\infty} (1-x^v)^{-1}$, $Q = \prod_{v=1}^{\infty} (1-x^{2v-1})^{-1}$, $[\theta]$ is the greatest integer in $\theta$, and $\{\theta\} = \theta - [\theta]$. The limiting case $k \to \infty$ gives the product formula $\sum_{n=0}^{\infty} b(n)x^n = \prod_{v=1}^{\infty} (1-x^v)^{-[(v+1)/2]}$ for the generating function of the number $b(n)$ of plane partitions of $n$ with strictly decreasing parts on each row. *T. M. Apostol* (Pasadena, Calif.)

Referred to in P64-58, P64-61.

## P64-53 (36# 2512)

**Carlitz, L.**

**Rectangular arrays and plane partitions.**

*Acta Arith.* **13** (1967/68), 29–47.

Let $n_1, n_2, \cdots, n_k$ be nonnegative integers such that $n_1 \geqq n_2 \geqq \cdots \geqq n_k$ and let $\pi_r(n_1, n_2, \cdots, n_k)$ denote the number of $k \times r$ arrays

$$(1.1) \qquad \begin{array}{llll} n_1 & n_{11} & n_{12} \cdots n_{1,r-1} \\ n_2 & n_{21} & n_{22} \cdots n_{2,r-1} \\ \cdot & & \\ \cdot & & \\ \cdot & & \\ n_k & n_{k1} & n_{k2} \cdots n_{k,r-1} \end{array}$$

such that (1.2) $n_i \geqq n_{i1} \geqq \cdots \geqq n_{i,r-1} \geqq 0$ $(i = 1, \cdots, k)$, $n_{1j} \geqq n_{2j} \geqq \cdots \geqq n_{k,j}$ $(j = 1, \cdots, r-1)$. It is shown that

$$(1.3) \qquad \pi_r(n_1, n_2, \cdots, n_k) = \left| \binom{n_j + r - 1}{r - i + j - 1} \right|$$

$(i, j = 1, \cdots, k)$, where the right member is a determinant of order $k$. For $k = 2$ a simple generating function for $\pi_2(n, m)$ is derived. Let (1.4) $\pi_r(n_1, \cdots, n_k; a) = \sum a^{\sigma}$, $\sigma = \sum_{i=1}^{k} \sum_{j=1}^{r-1} n_{ij} + \sum_{i=1}^{k} n_i$, where the first summation is over all $n_{ij}$ satisfying (1.2). It is shown that

$$\pi_r(n_1, \cdots, n_k; a) = a^{n_1 + \cdots + n_k} \left| a^{(i-j)(i-j-1)/2} \begin{bmatrix} n_j + r - 1 \\ r - i + j - 1 \end{bmatrix} \right|,$$

where

$$\begin{bmatrix} n \\ k \end{bmatrix} = (1-a^n)(1-a^{n-1}) \cdots (1-a^{n-k+1}) \times [(1-a)(1-a^2) \cdots (1-a^k)]^{-1}.$$

The generating functions of $k$-line and plane partitions are obtained as applications of the above results.

*M. S. Cheema* (Tucson, Ariz.)

## P64-54 (36# 5097)

**Cheema, M. S.; Gupta, H. [Gupta, Hansraj]**

**The maxima of $P_r(n_1, n_2)$.**

*Math. Comp.* **22** (1968), 199–200.

The expression in the title stands for the number of partitions of the positive integral vector $(n_1, n_2)$ into exactly $r$ positive integral vectors. On the basis of numerical data, there appears to be a unique $s$ such that $P_1(n_1, n_2) < P_2(n_1, n_2) < \cdots < P_s(n_1, n_2) \geqq P_{s+1}(n_1, n_2) \geqq \cdots \geqq P_{n_2}(n_1, n_2)$ when $n_1 \geqq n_2$. Estimates for $s$ are given.

*J. B. Roberts* (Portland, Ore.)

## P64-55 (37# 4043)

**Wright, E. M.**

**Rotatable partitions.**

*J. London Math. Soc.* **43** (1968), 501–505.

A $d$-dimensional $b$-restricted partition $Y$ of $n$ is a solution of $n = \sum_{x_1, x_2, \cdots, x_d \geqq 0} y(x_1, x_2, \cdots, x_d)$, where $y \leqq b$ and $y(x_1, x_2, \cdots, x_d) \geqq y(x_1', x_2', \cdots, x_d')$ whenever $x_i \leqq x_i'$ for all $i$. Let $q(d, b; n)$ be the number of $d$-dimensional $b$ restricted partitions of $n$. A partition $Y$ for which $y(x_1, x_2, \cdots, x_d) = y(x_2, x_3, \cdots, x_d, x_1)$ for all sets $x_1, x_2, \cdots, x_d$ is called a rotatable partition. Let $q'(d, b; n)$ denote the number of $d$-dimensional $b$-restricted partitions of $n$. It has been conjectured that the generating function $Q_d(X) = 1 + \sum_{n=1}^{\infty} q(d, \infty; n)x^n$ is equal to

$$R_d(x) = \prod_{k=1}^{\infty} (1-x^k)^{-\binom{d+k-2}{k-1}} = 1 + \sum_{n=1}^{\infty} r(d, n)x^n.$$

Recently Atkin, Bratley, Macdonald and Mackay ["Some computations for $n$-dimensional partitions", Proc. Camb. Phil. Soc., to appear]* found the conjecture to be false for $d = 3$ by showing $q(3, \infty; 6) \neq r(3, 6)$. The author proves that for $d = p^t$, $q(d, b; n) \equiv q'(d, b, n) \pmod{p}$, and uses this to prove the falsehood of the conjecture for $d = p$ or $d = p - 1$.

*M. S. Cheema* (Tucson, Ariz.)

*See MR 36 #124 = P64-50.

Citations: MR 36# 124 = P64-50.

## P64-56 (37# 5178)

**Wright, E. M.**

**Stacks.**

*Quart. J. Math. Oxford Ser.* (2) **19** (1968), 313–320.

An $n$-stack is a solution of the equation $n = \sum_{x, y \geqq 1} z(x, y)$, in which every $z$ is 0 or 1, $z(1, 1) = 1$, $z(x, y_1) = 1$ implies $z(x, y) = 1 (1 \leqq y \leqq y_1)$, and $z(x_1, y) = z(x_2, y) = 1 (x_1 < x_2)$ implies $z(x, y) = 1 (x_1 \leqq x \leqq x_2)$. The stack may be represented by a figure consisting of $n$ nodes arranged at the points whose coordinates are $x, y$. The number of $n$-stacks is denoted by $s(n)$, and the number of $n$-stacks with just $r$ rows by $s_r(n)$. The author studies $s_r(n)$ and $s(n)$ and a number of related enumerative functions, and develops their generating functions and certain relations between them. The following asymptotic approximations to $s_r(n)$ and $s(n)$ for large $n$ are derived.

$$(1) \quad s_r(n) = (1/r!(r-1)!) \times \sum_{t=1}^{[r/2]} \Omega_t (n+R)^{2r-2t}/(2r-2t)! + O(n^{r-1}),$$

where $r > 1$, $R = \frac{1}{2}r(r-2)$, $\Omega_1 = 1$, and $\Omega_2 = -r(2r^2+1)/72$,

$\Omega_3 = (25r^2(2r^2+1)^2 + 6r(6r^4 + 10r^2 - 1))/259200$. (2) $s(n) = \phi(n)\{1 + O(n^{-1/2})\}$ as $n \to \infty$, where

$$\phi(n) = 8^{-1}(3^3 n^5)^{-1/4} \exp\{2\pi(n/3)^{1/2}\}.$$

*A. L. Whiteman* (Los Angeles, Calif.)

Referred to in P64-62.

**P64-57** **(38# 2036)**

**Houten, Lorne**

**A note on solid partitions.**

*Acta Arith.* **15** (1968), 71–76.

Denoting by $a(n)$, the number of solutions in non-negative integers $n_{i,j,k}$ of the Diophantine equation (1) $n = \sum_{i,j,k=1}^{\infty} n_{i,j,k}$, where (2) $n_{i,j,k} \geqq n_{i+1,j,k}, n_{i,j+1,k}, n_{i,j,k+1}$; and by $b(n)$ the number of solutions of (1), when the first of the three conditions (2) is replaced by $n_{i,j,k} > n_{i+1,j,k}$, the other two conditions remaining unaltered, the author obtains in an elegant way, a recurrence formula for $B(x)$—the generating function for $b(n)$. He then obtains a recurrence formula also for $A(x)$—the generating function for $a(n)$. *H. Gupta* (Allahabad)

**P64-58** **(40# 1358)**

**Gordon, Basil; Houten, Lorne**

**Notes on plane partitions. III.**

*Duke Math. J.* **36** (1969), 801–824.

In an earlier paper [J. Combinatorial Theory **4** (1968), 81–99; MR **36** #1339], the authors obtained infinite product formulas for the generating function for $b_k(n)$, the number of $k$-rowed partitions of $n$ whose nonzero parts decrease strictly along each row, and also for $b(n) = \lim_{k\to\infty} b_k(n)$, the number of plane partitions of $n$ with strictly decreasing parts on each row. In this paper they derive a convergent asymptotic series expansion for $b_k(n)$ using the classic Hardy-Ramanujan-Rademacher method. The method is not applicable to $b(n)$, but in this case an asymptotic series is obtained by the method of E. M. Wright [Quart. J. Math. Oxford Ser. **2** (1931), 177–189], who treated the corresponding problem for the total number of plane partitions of $n$. *T. M. Apostol* (Pasadena, Calif.)

Citations: MR 36# 1339 = P64-52.

**P64-59** **(40# 2628)**

**Gandhi, J. M.**

**Congruences for new types of partitions.**

*Proc. Nat. Inst. Sci. India Part A* **32** (1966), 141–145.

Using the generating functions obtained by F. C. Auluck [Proc. Cambridge Philos. Soc. **47** (1951), 679–686; MR **13**, 536] for certain types of two line partitions of $n$ and the well-known identities of Euler and Jacobi, the author obtains congruences for such partitions modulo 2.

*H. Gupta* (Edmonton, Alta.)

Citations: MR 13, 536c = P60-12.

**P64-60** **(43# 1936)**

**Stolarsky, Kenneth B.**

**Generalizations of the Bellavitis partition identities.**

*J. Number Theory* **3** (1971), 240–246.

The number $c(n_1, n_2, \cdots, n_k)$ of partitions of the $k$-partite number $(n_1, n_2, \cdots, n_k)$ into members of the set $\{(m(1), m(2), \cdots, m(k)); m(j) = (m+1)^j - m^j, m \geqq 0\}$ is shown to be given by $\sum_z f(z; n_1, n_2, \cdots, n_k)$, where $f$ is defined for integral values of $z$ in the paper. In particular, $f(z; x_1, 2x_2 - x_1) = p(x_2 - x_1, z - x_1, x_1)$, where $p(a, b, c)$ is the number of partitions of $a$ into $b$ parts, no part exceeding $c$.

Using simple properties of finitely generated nilpotent groups, the author proves that

$$f(z; x_1, x_2, x_3) = f(z; P_1, P_2, P_3),$$

where $P_1 = x_1$; $P_2 = -2(x_1^2 - zx_1 - z) - x_2$; and $P_3 = x_3 - 3(z\ x_1 + 1)(x_1^2 - zx_1 + x_2 - z)$. He also shows that in general there exist polynomials $P_j = P_j(z; x_1, x_2, \cdots, x_j)$, $1 \leqq j \leqq k$; of degree $j$ such that $f(z; x_1, x_2, \cdots, x_k) = f(z; P_1, P_2, \cdots, P_k)$. *H. Gupta* (Allahabad)

**P64-61** **(43# 6175)**

**Gordon, Basil**

**Notes on plane partitions. V.**

*J. Combinatorial Theory Ser. B* **11** (1971), 157–168.

In an earlier paper [same J. **4** (1968), 81–99; MR **36** #1339] the author and L. Houten showed that $B(x) = \prod_{\nu=1}^{\infty} (1 - x^\nu)^{-[(\nu+1)/2]}$ is the generating function of the number $b(n)$ of plane partitions of $n$ whose parts decrease strictly along each row. This is a planar analog of the generating function for the number of partitions of $n$ into distinct parts. In this paper the author obtains a planar analog of the identity

$$Q_0(x) = \prod_{\nu=1}^{\infty} (1 + x^{2\nu-1}) = \sum_{n=0}^{\infty} q_0(n) x^n$$

which generates the number of partitions of $n$ into distinct odd parts. It is shown that, if $b_0(n)$ is the number of plane partitions of $n$ into odd parts which decrease strictly along each row, then $\sum_{n=0}^{\infty} b_0(n) x^n = Q_0(x) B(x^2)$. This is done by obtaining the generating function $B_{0k}(x)$ for the number $b_{0k}(n)$ of $k$-rowed partitions of $n$ into odd parts, and then letting $k \to \infty$. The proof expresses $B_{0k}(x)$ as a determinant.

{Part IV is as yet unpublished.}

*T. M. Apostol* (Pasadena, Calif.)

Citations: MR 36# 1339 = P64-52.

**P64-62** **(44# 174)**

**Wright, E. M.**

**Stacks. II.**

*Quart. J. Math. Oxford Ser.* (2) **22** (1971), 107–116.

In an earlier paper [same J. (2) **19** (1968), 313–320; MR **37** #5178] the author studied the enumerative properties of a structure known as an $n$-stack with $r$ rows. He now gives an alternative equivalent definition of such a structure and also defines two closely related structures. An $n$-stack with $r$ rows is a set of $2r$ positive integers $x_1(1), \cdots, x_1(r)$, $x_2(1), \cdots, x_2(r)$ such that $n = \sum_{y=1}^{r} \sum_{x=x_1(y)}^{x_2(y)}$ and $1 = x_1(1) \leqq x_1(2) \leqq \cdots \leqq x_1(r) \leqq x_2(r) \leqq x_2(r-1) \leqq \cdots \leqq x_2(1)$. One writes $s_r(n)$ for the number of different $n$-stacks with $r$ rows and $s(n) = \sum_r s_r(n)$ for the number of $n$-stacks with no restriction on the number of rows. The $n$-stack with $r$ rows is said to have strictly receding walls if the preceding chain of inequalities is replaced by the stricter chain $1 = x_1(1) < x_1(2) < \cdots < x_1(r) \leqq x_2(r) < x_2(r-1) < \cdots < x_2(1)$. One writes $g_r(n)$ for the number of such stacks and $g(n) = \sum_r g_r(n)$ for the number of such $n$-stacks with no restriction on the number of rows. A structure known as an $n$-stack with $r$ rows in which the left-hand wall is strictly receding is also defined in the paper. F. C. Auluck [Proc. Cambridge Philos. Soc. **47** (1951), 679–686; MR **13**, 536] studied these three forms of stacks and derived asymptotic approximations to $s(n)$ and $g(n)$ for large $n$. For instance, $g(n) \sim \frac{1}{2}p(n)$, where $p(n)$ is the number of ordinary partitions of $n$. The main object of the present paper is to develop a refinement of Auluck's method that yields asymptotic expansions of $s(n)$ and $g(n)$ for large $n$. The results are somewhat too involved to be reproduced here.

*A. L. Whiteman* (Los Angeles, Calif.)

Citations: MR 13, 536c = P60-12; MR 37# 5178 = P64-56.

# P68 PARTITIONS: RESTRICTED BY CONGRUENCE, INEQUALITY OR REPETITION CONDITIONS

See also reviews P02-16, P56-7, P56-9, P56-11, P56-13, P60-10, P60-11, P60-12, P60-28, P60-30, P60-38, P60-51, P60-53, P60-54, P72-15, P72-20, P72-30, P72-39, P72-44, P72-46, P72-48, P72-49, P72-55, P72-56, P72-57, P76-33, P76-34, P76-35, P80-14.

## P68-1 (1, 201c)

**Niven, Ivan. On a certain partition function.** Amer. J. Math. **62**, 353–364 (1940).

Using the fundamental methods introduced by Hardy and Ramanujan and improved by Rademacher, the author determines the coefficients $a_m$ in the expansion

$$F(x)=\frac{f(x)f(x^6)}{f(x^2)f(x^3)}=\sum_{m=0}^{\infty} a_m x^m,$$

where $f(x)=\prod_{j=1}^{\infty}(1-x^j)^{-1}$. The final result expresses $a_m$ as an infinite series involving Bessel functions with purely imaginary arguments. Since the function $F(x)$ is connected with a modular form of dimension zero it is necessary in the course of the proof to make use of estimates for Kloosterman sums. It is clear from their definition that the $a_m$ are the number of partitions of $m$ into summands of the form $6n\pm1$. This partition function $a_m$ is of particular interest because I. Schur [S.-B. Preuss. Akad. Wiss. **1926**, 448–495] has shown that it also enumerates the number of partitions of $m$ into summands whose differences are at least three, and at least six if both summands are divisible by three.

*H. S. Zuckerman* (Seattle, Wash.).

Referred to in P68-3, P68-19, P72-20.

## P68-2 (2, 248f)

**Wall, H. S. A continued fraction related to some partition formulas of Euler.** Amer. Math. Monthly **48**, 102–108 (1941).

Using continued fractions the author finds a new and ingenious derivation of a number of partition formulas of Euler.

*W. Leighton* (Houston, Tex.).

## P68-3 (3, 69b)

**Haberzetle, Mary. On some partition functions.** Amer. J. Math. **63**, 589–599 (1941).

The coefficient $a_n$ of $x^n$ in

$$F(x)=\frac{f(x)f(x^{pq})}{f(x^p)f(x^q)}=\sum_{n=0}^{\infty} a_n x^n,$$

where $p$ and $q$ are different primes and

$$f(x)=\prod_{m=1}^{\infty}(1-x^m)^{-1},$$

is the number of partitions of $n$ into parts none of which is a multiple of $p$ or of $q$. The author applies the reviewer's variant of the Hardy-Ramanujan method to obtain a convergent infinite series for $a_n$. The resulting expression, which is otherwise of the customary type, depends linearly on those $a_\nu$ with (*) $\nu<\mu=(p-1)(q-1)/24$. This is in accordance with the order of the pole at $\tau=i\infty$ of the modular function corresponding to $F(x)$.

The author assumes that $\mu$ defined in (*) is an integer, which serves to simplify the roots of unity entering into the Kloosterman sums. However, this condition is unessential in the proof. Thus this paper covers also I. Nivens' result for $p=2$, $q=3$ [Amer. J. Math. **62**, 353–364 (1940); cf. these Rev. **1**, 201], although the author disclaims it.

*H. Rademacher* (Philadelphia, Pa.).

Citations: MR 1, 201c = P68-1.
Referred to in P68-19, P72-20.

## P68-4 (3, 166b)

**Lehner, Joseph. A partition function connected with the modulus five.** Duke Math. J. **8**, 631–655 (1941).

In this paper the author derives a convergent series for $p_a(n)$, $a=1$ or 2, the number of partitions of a positive integer into summands of the form $5l\pm a$. The method is that of Hardy and Littlewood in the improved form due to Rademacher [Amer. J. Math. **60**, 501–512 (1938)]. In Part I it is shown that the generating functions

$$F_a(x)=\prod_{m=0}^{\infty}(1-x^{5m+a})^{-1}\prod_{m=1}^{\infty}(1-x^{5m-a})^{-1}$$

transform according to the formula

$$F_a\left\{\exp\left(2\pi i\frac{h}{k}-2\pi\frac{z}{k}\right)\right\}$$
$$=\omega_a(h,k)\exp\left(\frac{\pi}{30k}\left(\frac{B}{z}-Az\right)\right)F_b\left\{\exp\left(2\pi i\frac{h'}{k}-\frac{2\pi}{kz}\right)\right\}$$

if $k\equiv0 \pmod 5$ and in a more complicated way if $k\not\equiv0 \pmod 5$. Here $\Re z>0$, $h$ and $k$ are coprime integers satisfying $0\leqq h<k$, $h'$ is any fixed solution of $hh'\equiv-1 \pmod k$; $b=1$ if $h\equiv\pm a \pmod 5$, $b=2$ if $h\equiv\pm2a \pmod 5$; and $B=6b^2-30b+25$. The functions $\omega_a(h,k)$ are certain roots of unity. Certain sums involving these roots of unity such as

$$\sum_h \omega_a(h,k)\exp(-2\pi ihnk^{-1})$$

have to be estimated more precisely than the trivial $O(k)$. This is done in Part II by reducing them to incomplete Kloosterman sums. Finally in Part III a convergent series and an asymptotic formula for $p_a(n)$ are derived following Rademacher's method. *R. D. James* (Madison, Wis.).

Referred to in P68-6, P68-12, P68-15, P68-21, P72-20, P72-29, P72-44.

## P68-5 (4, 211a)

**Gupta, Hansraj. A formula in partitions.** J. Indian Math. Soc. (N.S.) **6**, 115–117 (1942).

In this paper $P_m(n)$ denotes the number of partitions of $n$ in which the smallest summand is $m$ and $p_m(n)$ denotes the number of partitions in which the largest summand is $m$. The relation

$$P_{m+1}(n+2m+1)=p_1(n)+p_2(n-m)+p_3(n-2m)$$
$$+\cdots+p_{r+1}(n-rm),\quad r=[(n-1)/(m+1)],$$

together with the known inequalities for $p_m(n)$ and similar ones for $P_m(n)$, lead to the asymptotic formula

$$P_m(jm+m+s)\sim\frac{1}{j!}\binom{u}{j-1}+\frac{1}{(j-1)!}\binom{m+u+c_j}{j-2}$$

for $j=o(\log m)$, where $u=s+j(j+1)/2$, $c_j=(j-1)2^{j-3}$.

*R. D. James* (Saskatoon, Sask.).

## P68-6 (6, 259b)

**Livingood, John. A partition function with the prime modulus $P>3$.** Amer. J. Math. **67**, 194–208 (1945).

Convergent series are found for $p_a(n)$, the number of partitions of $n$ into summands of the form $pl\pm a$, where $p$ is a fixed prime greater than 3. The method used is a direct extension of the work of J. Lehner for $p=5$ [Duke Math. J. **8**, 631–655 (1941); these Rev. **3**, 166]. For $p<19$ the resulting series are of the same sort as Lehner's, while new terms of a similar type arise for larger $p$. *H. S. Zuckerman.*

Citations: MR 3, 166b = P68-4.

Referred to in P68-12, P68-15, P68-16, P68-21, P72-20.

## P68-7 (7, 507a)

**Lehmer, D. H. Two nonexistence theorems on partitions.** Bull. Amer. Math. Soc. **52**, 538–544 (1946).

Let $d$ be 0 or a positive integer and let $q_d(n)$ be the number of partitions of $n$ into parts differing by $d$ or more. The author proves:

$$(1)\qquad \sum_{n=0}^{\infty} q_d(n)x^n=\sum_{s=0}^{\infty}\frac{x^{s+ds(s-1)/2}}{(1-x)(1-x^2)\cdots(1-x^s)};$$

(2) corresponding to any $d>2$, there is no set $S$ of positive integers such that, for every $n$, $q_d(n)$ is equal to the number of partitions of $n$ into parts taken from $S$; (3) corresponding to any $d\neq 1$, there is no set $S$ of positive integers such that, for every $n$, $q_d(n)$ is equal to the number of partitions of $n$ into distinct parts taken from $S$. *T. Estermann.*

## P68-8 (9, 571a)

**Tietze, Heinrich. Ein zweiter Beweis eines Satzes über Partitionen.** S.-B. Math.-Nat. Abt. Bayer. Akad. Wiss. **1947**, 45–46 (1947).

The theorem referred to in the title is the following. Let $k$ be a positive integer. Then the number of partitions of $n$ in which no part is divisible by $k$ is the same as the number of partitions of $n$ in which no part is repeated $k$ or more times. For $k=2$ we have a famous theorem of Euler. The author is unaware that this theorem is due to Glaisher [Messenger of Math. **12**, 158–170 (1883)] whose proof is essentially the same as the one presented here. The reviewer has not seen the author's first proof. However, the theorem follows immediately from the identity

$$(1-x^{km})(1-x^m)^{-1}=1+x^m+x^{2m}+\cdots+x^{(k-1)m}.$$

*D. H. Lehmer* (Berkeley, Calif.).

Referred to in P68-9.

## P68-9 (15, 289e)

**Tietze, Heinrich. Über die Glaisher'sche Verallgemeinerung eines Euler'schen Satzes über Partitionen.** J. Reine Angew. Math. **191**, 64–68 (1953).

In a previous note [S.-B. Math.-Nat. Abt. Bayer. Akad. Wiss. **1947**, 45–46; these Rev. **9**, 571] the author has given a proof (not new) of Glaisher's generalization of Euler's theorem on partitions into odd parts and distinct parts. In this paper he gives an earlier proof, which does not use generating functions, together with a generalization of Glaisher's result. There are some remarks about "simplicity" of proofs. *N. J. Fine* (Princeton, N. J.).

Citations: MR 9, 571a = P68-8.

## P68-10 (10, 16c)

**Alder, Henry L. The nonexistence of certain identities in the theory of partitions and compositions.** Bull. Amer. Math. Soc. **54**, 712–722 (1948).

Let $q_{d,m}(n)$ denote the number of partitions of $n$ into parts differing by at least $d$, each part being greater than or equal to $m$. The following theorems are proved. (1) Unless $d=1$ or $d=2$, $m=1, 2$, $q_{d,m}(n)$ is not equal to the number of partitions of $n$ into parts taken from any set of integers. (2) Unless $d=1$, $q_{d,m}(n)$ is not equal to the number of partitions of $n$ into distinct parts taken from any set of integers. (3) The number of partitions of $n$ into parts differing by at least $d$ and where parts divisible by $d$ differ by at least $2d$ is not equal to the number of partitions of $n$ into parts taken from any set of integers if $d>3$. (4) The number of compositions of $n$ into parts differing by at least $d$, each part being greater than or equal to $m$, is not equal to the number of compositions of $n$ into parts taken from any set of integers. *T. Estermann* (London).

## P68-11 (19, 252d)

**Gupta, Hansraj. Partitions in terms of combinatory functions.** Res. Bull. Panjab Univ. no. **94** (1956), 153–159.

The author lists two sets of formulas expressing $p(n, m)$, the number of partitions of $n$ into at most $m$ non-zero summands, in terms of combinatory functions, for values of $m\leq 12$. *W. H. Simons* (Vancouver, B.C.).

Referred to in P68-37, P68-51.

## P68-12 (20# 3840)

**Grosswald, Emil. Some theorems concerning partitions.** Trans. Amer. Math. Soc. **89** (1958), 113–128.

Let $q$ be an odd prime, and let $\{a\}=\{a_1, \cdots, a_m\}$ be a set of $m$ distinct least positive residues mod $q$. Let $F(x)=\prod_{\nu\equiv\{\alpha\}}(1-x^\nu)^{-1}=\sum_{n=0}^{\infty} p_n(q)x^n$, where $\nu\equiv\{a\}$ means that $\nu$ runs only through those integers which are congruent (mod $q$) to some $a_j$ $(j=1, 2, \cdots, m)$; consequently, $p_n(q)$ is the number of partitions of $n$ into summands congruent to elements of $\{a\}$. The author proves that

$$(1)\quad F(x)=(-q\log x)^d\exp\left\{\frac{\Lambda}{-\log x}+K(-\log x)+O(\log^2 x)\right\}$$

as $x\to 1$, and that

$$(2)\quad p_n(q)=\frac{\omega}{q}\left(\frac{q\Lambda^{1/2}}{\lambda_n}\right)^{d+1}\exp\left(\frac{d(d+2)}{4\Lambda^{1/2}\lambda_n}\right)I_1(2\Lambda^{1/2}\lambda_n)(1+O(n^{-1}))$$

as $n\to\infty$, where

$$\omega=\prod_{j=1}^m\{(2\pi)^{-1/2}\Gamma(a_j/q)\},\qquad d=\tfrac{1}{2}\sum_{j=1}^m(a_j-\tfrac{1}{2}q),$$
$$K=(24q)^{-1}\sum_{j=1}^m(q^2-6a_jq+6a_j^2),\quad \Lambda=m\pi^2/(6q),$$
$$\lambda_n=(n-K)^{1/2},$$

and $I_1(x)$ denotes the Bessel function. There are corresponding results about partitions into summands congruent to the elements of $\{a\}$, no summand being repeated more than $l$ times; and several corollaries. The results of this paper generalise theorems of Lehner [Duke Math. J. **8** (1941), 631–655; MR **3**, 166], Livingood [Amer. J. Math. **67** (1945), 194–208; MR **6**, 259], Meinardus [Math. Z. **59** (1954), 388–398; MR **16**, 17] and also, in some respects, theorems of Petersson [Abh. Deutsch. Akad. Wiss. Berlin Kl. Math. Allg. Nat. **1954**, no. 2; Acta Math. **95** (1956), 57–110; MR **17**, 129, 1057]. The author points out that, although he might have used a method based essentially on the theory of modular functions, this would not have proved altogether satisfactory for completely general sets $\{a\}$. Instead, he uses a saddle point method, similar in some respects to that used by Meinardus. To prove (1) the author considers $F(x)$ as a product of $m$ factors, one corresponding to each $a_j$ $(j=1, \cdots, m)$, and to each factor he applies a Mellin transformation. The integrand in the resulting contour integral involves Riemann's and Hurwitz' zeta functions; with the aid of their functional equations the line of integration is moved, and (1) is obtained by means of the calculus of residues. To deduce (2) from (1), the author applies the circle method to $p_n(q)=(2\pi r^n)^{-1}\{\int_0^{2\pi}F(re^{i\theta})e^{-2\pi in\theta}d\theta\}$, $|r|<1$; the range of integration is split up by a certain Farey dissection; and the major contribution is shown to be derived from the arc centred at $\theta=0$. The application of a theorem by Hayman [J. Reine Angew. Math. **196** (1956), 67–95; MR **18**, 293] completes the proof of (2). The details of all of the proofs are complicated, but the method and main steps are clearly described. *H. Halberstam* (London)

Citations: MR 3, 166b = P68-4; MR 6, 259b = P68-6; MR 16, 17e = P72-20; MR 17, 129b = P72-25; MR 17, 1057f = P72-29.

Referred to in P68-13, P68-16, P68-19, P68-21.

## P68-13 (22# 10969)

**Grosswald, Emil. Correction and addition to "Some theorems concerning partitions".** Trans. Amer. Math. Soc. **95** (1960), 190.

The author remarks that Theorem 2 of the above-mentioned paper (that is, formula (2) of the review) [same Trans. **89** (1958), 113–128; MR **20** #3840] is valid only provided that the set $\{\dot{a}\}$ of least positive residues mod $q$ does not consist of the single element $a=q$, and he points out that in this exceptional case his problem reduces trivially to known results. He confirms by a short argument that this is indeed the only case in which the statement of his Theorem 2 needs modification.

*H. Halberstam* (London)

Citations: MR 20# 3840 = P68-12.

Referred to in P68-21.

## P68-14 (21# 661)

**Palamà, Giuseppe. Su di una questione relativa alla partizione di $n$.** Boll. Un. Mat. Ital. (3) **13** (1958), 558–563. (English summary)

Denoting by $(n, >m)$, the number of partitions of $n$ into summands the least of which is greater than $m$, the author evaluates $(n, >[\frac{1}{5}n])$, thus extending some of the reviewer's results [see Proc. London Math. Soc. (2) **39** (1935), 142–149; J. London Math. Soc. **11** (1936), 278–280]. The case $(n, >[\frac{1}{5}n]-2)$ is also considered.

*H. Gupta* (Chandigarh)

## P68-15 (21# 7189)

**Iseki, Shô. A partition function with some congruence condition.** Amer. J. Math. **81** (1959), 939–961.

Let $p(n; a, q)$ be the number of partitions of the integer $n$ into parts congruent to $\pm a$ (mod $q$) ($q$ prime $>3$). Livingood [Amer. J. Math. **67** (1945), 194–208; MR **6**, 259] found a representation of $p(n; a, q)$ by a convergent series, using the Hardy-Ramanujan method of contour integration, with the modifications of Rademacher [Proc. London Math. Soc. (2) **43** (1937), 241–254; Amer. J. Math. **60** (1938), 501–512] and the technique applied by Lehner [Duke Math. J. 8 (1941), 631–655; MR **3**, 166] to the particular case $p=5$. The author now solves this problem for the case of an arbitrary (not necessarily prime) modulus $M$. The method is still that of Hardy-Ramanujan-Rademacher; also some of the techniques of Lehner and Livingood are used, but new difficulties arise, because of the composite modulus. These are overcome, essentially by the following device. For integral $h, k$, $(h, k)=1$, $k\geqq 1$, one sets $k=k_1D$, $M=m_1D$, $(k_1, m_1)=1$, $K=k_1m_1D$, so that $D=(k, M)$, $K=\text{l.c.m.}(k, M)$; one also selects arbitrary integers $\gamma$, $\delta$ satisfying $\gamma k_1-\delta m_1=1$, and denotes by $H$ any fixed solution of $hH\equiv\delta \pmod k$. It turns out that most of the Lehner-Livingood results carry over, provided that one uses $D$ instead of $p$ (if $p|k$) or of 1 (if $p\nmid k$) and $K$ instead of $k$ (if $p|k$) or of $pk$ (if $p\nmid k$). This introduces actually more symmetry into the formulae than can be found in older papers; the essential dichotomy ($D=1$, $D>1$), however, occurs again. Set $x=\exp(2\pi ih/k-2\pi z/k)$, $x'=\exp(2\pi iH/k-2\pi/Kz)$ $(\Re z>0)$, $b=ha-D[ha/D]$, $\rho=\exp(-2\pi i\gamma a/M)$, $A=6a^2-6Ma+M^2$, $B=6b^2-6Db+D^2$ and

$$F(x'; b, D, \rho) = \prod_{m\geqq 0}(1-\rho x'^{mD+b})^{-1}(1-\rho^{-1}x'^{mD+D-b})^{-1};$$

then generating function of $p(n; a, M)$ is

$$F(x; a, M) = \omega(h, k)\exp\{(\pi/6Mk)(B/z-Az)\}F(x'; b, D, \rho),$$

$|\omega(h, k)|=1$, as follows from the author's functional equation [Duke Math. J. **24** (1957), 653–662; MR **19**, 943]. From here on the proof follows the customary lines, with the reduction of exponential sums to generalized Kloosterman sums (evaluated non-trivially following Salié or Weil) and the identification of loop integrals with Bessel functions. The result, of course, is a generalization of Livingood's formula, to which it reduces for $M=p$. [See also Petersson, Abh. Deutsch. Akad. Wiss. Berlin. Kl. Math. Allg. Nat. **1954**, no. 2; MR **17**, 129; thm. 13.] {The reviewer would like to point out a surprising similarity in technique with that used by P. Hagis [Dissertation, Univ. of Pennsylvania, 1959, unpublished] to obtain a generalization of Livingood's result in an entirely different direction, namely the establishment of a convergent series representation for $p(n; a_1, a_2, \cdots, a_r; q)$, the number of partitions of $n$ into parts congruent (mod $q$) to any of the integers $\pm a_1, \pm a_2, \cdots, \pm a_r$ ($r\leqq\frac{1}{2}(q-1)$, $q$ prime).}

*E. Grosswald* (Princeton, N.J.)

Citations: MR 3, 166b = P68-4; MR 6, 259b = P68-6; MR 17, 129b = P72-25; MR 19, 943a = F10-50.

Referred to in P68-16, P68-19.

## P68-16 (22# 4692)

**Iseki, Shô. On some partition functions.** J. Math. Soc. Japan **12** (1960), 81–88.

Let $p_k(n; a, M)$ be the number of partitions of a positive integer $n$ into positive summands of the form $(Ml\pm a)^\kappa$, with integral $M, l, a, \kappa$ satisfying $M\geqq 2$, $0<a<M$, $(a, M)=1$, $\kappa\geqq 1$. Following essentially the method already used in his paper in Amer. J. Math. **81** (1959), 939–961 [MR **21** #7189], the author establishes the transformation formula for

$$F_\kappa(x; a, M) = \prod_{\substack{\nu<0\\ \nu\equiv\pm a(M)}}(1-x^{\nu^\kappa})^{-1} = \sum_{n=0}^{\infty} p_\kappa(n; a, M)x^n.$$

Using a lemma of Hayman [J. Reine Angew. Math. **196** (1956), 67–95; MR **18**, 293] and the reviewer [Trans. Amer. Math. Soc. **89** (1958), 113–128; MR **20** #3840], he then obtains an asymptotic formula for $p_\kappa(n; a, M)$. The particular case $\kappa=1$ is mentioned separately; but in this case, the author's quoted paper gives actually the exact value, as sum of a convergent series. If $n$ is a prime, the asymptotic formula appears also as a particular case of a formula in the reviewer's quoted paper and the exact formula (if $n$ is a prime) is contained in Livingood's result [Amer. J. Math. **67** (1945), 194–208; MR **6**, 259].

*E. Grosswald* (Philadelphia, Pa.)

Citations: MR 6, 259b = P68-6; MR 20# 3840 = P68-12; MR 21# 7189 = P68-15.

## P68-17 (22# 12088)

**Wright, E. M. Partitions into $k$ parts.** Math. Ann. **142** (1960/61), 311–316.

Mit Hilfe von erzeugenden Funktionen wird gezeigt: Die Anzahl $p_k(n)$ der Lösungen der Diophantischen Gleichung $n_1+\cdots+n_k=n$ $(1\leqq n_1\leqq\cdots\leqq n_k)$ erfüllt

$$p_k(n) = \sum_{j=1}^{k}\sum_{t=1}^{[k/j]} a(k, j, t; n)n^{t-1},$$

wobei $a(k, j, t; n)$ nur von $k, j, t$ und der Restklasse von

$n \bmod j$ abhängt. Das verschärft einen einfacher bewiesenen Satz des Referenten [Math. Ann. **138** (1959), 356–362; MR **21** #7188; Satz 2]. *G. J. Rieger* (Munich)

Citations: MR 21# 7188 = P72-38.

**P68-18** **(23# A809 )**

**Gordon, Basil**

**A combinatorial generalization of the Rogers-Ramanujan identities.**

*Amer. J. Math.* **83** (1961), 393–399.

The Rogers-Ramanujan identities [G. H. Hardy and E. M. Wright, *An introduction to the theory of numbers*, Clarendon, Oxford, 1960, p. 290; for review of 3rd ed. of 1954, see MR **16**, 673]:

$$\prod_{n=0}^{\infty}(1-x^{5n+1})^{-1}(1-x^{5n+4})^{-1} = \sum_{n=0}^{\infty}\frac{x^{n^2}}{(1-x)(1-x^2)\cdots(1-x^n)},$$

$$\prod_{0}^{\infty}(1-x^{5n+2})^{-1}(1-x^{5n+3})^{-1} = \sum_{n=0}^{\infty}\frac{x^{n^2+n}}{(1-x)(1-x^2)\cdots(1-x^n)}$$

can be interpreted combinatorially as follows. For the first identity, the number of partitions of any integer $N$ into parts not congruent to 0, $\pm 2$ (mod 5) is equal to the number of partitions of $N=N_1+\cdots+N_k$ with $N_i \geqq N_{i+1}+2$. For the second identity, the number of partitions of $N$ into parts not congruent to 0, $\pm 1$ (mod 5) is equal to the number of partitions $N=N_1+\cdots+N_k$ with $N_i \geqq N_{i+1}+2$, $N_k \geqq 2$. In the present paper the following extension is proved.

The number of partitions of $N$ into parts not congruent to 0, $\pm t$ (mod $2d+1$), where $1 \leqq t \leqq d$, is equal to the number of partitions of the form $N=N_1+\cdots+N_k$ with $N_i \geqq N_{i+1}$, $N_i \geqq N_{i+d-1}+2$ and $N_{k-t+1} \geqq 2$. The method of proof is similar to Schur's proof of the Rogers-Ramanujan identities [I. Schur, S.-B. Deutsch. Akad. Wiss. Berlin **1917**, 302–321]. *L. Carlitz* (Durham, N.C.)

Citations: MR 16, 673b = Z01-28.

Referred to in P60-55, P68-29, P68-33.

**P68-19** **(23# A876 )**

**Iseki, Shô**

**Partitions in certain arithmetic progressions.**

*Amer. J. Math.* **83** (1961), 243–264.

The object of the present paper is to study the growth of the partition function $p_M(n)$, defined as the number of partitions of $n$ into summands which are positive and prime to a square-free number $M$. In the first place, a transformation theory of the generating function

$$F_M(x) = \prod_{\substack{l=1\\(l,M)=1}}^{\infty}(1-x^l)^{-1}$$

has to be developed; this theory enables us to exhibit the behaviour of $F_M(x)$ in the neighbourhood of each rational point of the unit circle. A Farey dissection is then applied to the contour integral $p_M(n)=(2\pi i)^{-1}\int_C x^{-n-1}F_M(x)dx$, where $C$ is a circle with its centre at the origin and radius less than 1, and in the resulting discussion a complicated exponential sum, which is related to a generalized Kloosterman sum, has to be estimated. A method of H. Rademacher [same J. **60** (1938), 501–512] then leads to the representation of $p_M(n)$ as an infinite series involving Bessel functions, and from this an asymptotic formula for $p_M(n)$ (for $M$ fixed and $n\to\infty$) is derived. It is shown, in particular, that

$$p_M(n) \sim \tfrac{1}{2}\tau(M)\left(\frac{\phi(M)}{6M}\right)^{1/4} n^{-3/4}\exp\left\{2\pi\left(\frac{\phi(M)}{6M}\right)^{1/2} n^{1/2}\right\},$$

where $\tau(M)$ is $M^{-1/2}$ or 1 according as $M$ is prime or composite. The argument leans on previous work of the author [ibid. **81** (1959), 939–961; MR **21** #7189], and his conclusions contain as special cases a number of earlier results due to E. Grosswald [Trans. Amer. Math. Soc. **89** (1958), 113–128; MR **20** #3840], M. Haberzetle [Amer. J. Math. **63** (1941), 589–599; MR **3**, 69], L. K. Hua [Trans. Amer. Math. Soc. **51** (1942), 194–201; MR **3**, 270], and I. Niven [Amer. J. Math. **62** (1940), 353–364; MR **1**, 201]. *L. Mirsky* (Sheffield)

Citations: MR 1, 201c = P68-1; MR 3, 69b = P68-3; MR 3, 270c = P72-4; MR 20# 3840 = P68-12; MR 21# 7189 = P68-15.

Referred to in P72-44.

**P68-20** **(23# A3114 )**

**Wright, E. M.**

**A simple proof of a known result in partitions.**

*Amer. Math. Monthly* **68** (1961), 144–145.

Es seien $a_1, \cdots, a_k$ verschiedene natürliche Zahlen mit dem kleinsten gemeinsamen Vielfachen $a$. Fur die Anzahl $p(n)$ der Lösungen der diophantischen Gleichung $n=a_1x_1+\cdots+a_kx_k$ in ganzrationalen Zahlen $x_j \geqq 0$ $(j=1,\cdots,k)$ gilt $p(n)=\sum_{t=1}^{k} c_{kt}(n)n^{k-t}$; dabei besteht die Abhängigkeit der $c_{kt}(n)$ von $n$ nur in der Abhängigkeit von der Restklasse $n \bmod a$. Der Beweis benutzt erzeugende Funktionen. *G. J. Rieger* (München)

**P68-21** **(26# 3688 )**

**Hagis, Peter, Jr.**

**A problem on partitions with a prime modulus $p \geqq 3$.**

*Trans. Amer. Math. Soc.* **102** (1962), 30–62.

Let $p \geqq 3$ be a prime, let $a=\{a_1, a_2, \cdots, a_r\}$ be a set of distinct integers satisfying $1 \leqq a_i \leqq \frac{1}{2}(p-1)$, and let $\bar{a}=\{0, a_1, a_2, \cdots, a_r\}$. The author obtains an exact formula (in the form of a convergent series) for $p_a(n)$, the number of partitions of a positive integer $n$ into summands $\equiv \pm a_i \pmod p$, provided $n$ is large enough. He obtains a corresponding result for $p_{\bar{a}}(n)$, and uses this to derive Rademacher's formula for $p(n)$, the number of unrestricted partitions of $n$. The author's proofs are based on the circle method evolved by Hardy [see G. H. Hardy and S. Ramanujan, Proc. London Math. Soc. (2) **17** (1918), 75–115; Rademacher, Proc. London Math. Soc. (2) **43** (1937), 241–254; Amer. J. Math. **60** (1938), 501–512]; some of his results are included in recent work on partition functions by Petersson [Abh. Deutsch. Akad. Wiss. Berlin. Kl. Math. Allg. Nat. **1954**, no. 2; MR **17**, 129; Acta Math. **95** (1956), 57–110; MR **17**, 1057]. {For related work see J. Lehner [Duke Math. J. **8** (1941), 631–655; MR **3**, 166], J. Livingood [Amer. J. Math. **67** (1945), 194–208; MR **6**, 259], and E. Grosswald [Trans. Amer. Math. Soc. **89** (1958), 113–128; MR **20** #3840; ibid. **95** (1960), 190; MR **22** #10969].} *H. Halberstam* (Dublin)

Citations: MR 3, 166b = P68-4; MR 6, 259b = P68-6; MR 17, 129b = P72-25; MR 17, 1057f = P72-29; MR 20# 3840 = P68-12; MR 22# 10969 = P68-13.

Referred to in P68-23, P68-24, P72-44, P72-49.

**P68-22** **(27# 1430 )**

**Vaidya, A. M.**

**A formula for the partitions of $n$ into four parts.**

*J. Gujarat Univ.* **5** (1962), *no.* 1/2, 172–176.

Let $p(n, r, \geqq m)$ denote the number of partitions of $n$ into $r$ parts, all of which are greater than or equal to $m$, and put $p(n, r, \geqq 1)=p(n, r, *)$. The author evaluates $p(n, 3, \geqq m)$ and $p(n, 4, *)$. In particular, he shows that $p(n, 3, \geqq m)$ is equal to the integer nearest to $(1/12)\times[n-3(m-1)]^2$, while $p(n, 4, *)$ is the integer nearest to $(n^3+3n^2)/144$ or $(3n^3+3n^2-9n)/144$ according as $n$ is even or odd. *L. Carlitz* (Durham, N.C.)

**P68-23** **(29# 3454)**

**Hagis, Peter, Jr.**

**On a class of partitions with distinct summands.**

*Trans. Amer. Math. Soc.* **112** (1964), 401–415.

In an earlier paper [same Trans. **102** (1962), 30–62; MR **26** #3688] the author obtained a convergent series representation and asymptotic formulas for the number $p_a(n)$ of partitions of $n$ into parts each congruent mod $p$ (for a given fixed prime $p$) to one of a fixed set $a$ of $r$ residues mod $p$. In the present paper he deals by means of similar analytic techniques with the corresponding problem for partitions into distinct (i.e., unequal) parts.
*H. Halberstam* (Nottingham)

Citations: MR 26# 3688 = P68-21.

Referred to in P68-24, P72-49.

**P68-24** **(31# 1238)**

**Hagis, Peter, Jr.**

**A correction of some theorems on partitions.**

*Trans. Amer. Math. Soc.* **118** (1965), 550.

The author points out that Theorem 4 of his paper in same Trans. **102** (1962), 30–62 [MR **26** #3688] and Theorem 6 of his paper in ibid. **112** (1964), 401–415 [MR **29** #3454], stated to hold for $n \geqq A/12p$ and $n \geqq -A/12p$, respectively, have been proved only with strict inequality in each case. {The last sentence contains a misprint: for $12r$ read $12/r$.} *H. Halberstam* (Nottingham)

Citations: MR 26# 3688 = P68-21; MR 29# 3454 = P68-23.

**P68-25** **(32# 1179)**

**Göllnitz, Heinz**

**Partitionen mit Differenzenbedingungen.**

Dissertation zur Erlangung des Doktorgrades der Mathematisch-Naturwissenschaftlichen Fakultät der Georg-August-Universität zu Göttingen.

*Dissertation, Göttingen,* 1963. ii + 62 *pp.*

Continuing work of Schur [S.-B. Deutsch. Akad. Wiss. Munich **1926**, 488–495] and Gleißberg [Math. Z. **28** (1928), 372–382], the author states about 15 theorems on partitions; for instance, the number of partitions of $n$ ($n = a_1 + a_2 + \cdots$, $a_1 \geqq a_2 \geqq \cdots$) into positive integers $a_i \equiv 2$, 5 or 11 (mod 12) is equal to the number of partitions of $n$ into different parts $b_i \equiv 2$, 4 or 5 (mod 6), and is equal to the number of partitions of $n$ into parts $c_i \neq 1$, 3, where $c_i - c_{i+1} \geqq 6$ and $c_i - c_{i+1} > 6$, if $c_i \equiv 0$, 1 or 3 and $c_{i+1} \equiv 0$, 1 or 3 (mod 6).

The proofs use algebraic operations with generating functions, yielding identities similar to the Rogers-Ramanujan identities, and induction. Some theorems are given without proof. The formulation of the theorems is often ambiguous. *W. Schwarz* (Freiburg)

Referred to in P68-32.

**P68-26** **(32# 1477)**

**Gordon, Basil**

**Some continued fractions of the Rogers-Ramanujan type.**

*Duke Math. J.* **32** (1965), 741–748.

For each $x$ in $|x| < 1$, the author displays an entire function of $a$, written $P(a, x)$, such that the continued fraction

$$(1) \qquad 1 + ax + \frac{ax^2}{1 + ax^3 +} \cdots \frac{ax^{2n}}{+ 1 + ax^{2n+1} +} \cdots$$

converges to $P(a, x)/P(ax^2, x)$ provided $P(ax^2, x) \neq 0$. From a Rogers-Ramanujan type identity due to Slater [Proc. London Math. Soc. (2) **54** (1952), 147–167; MR **14**, 138], an infinite product representation of $P(1, x)$ and its combinatorial interpretation are derived. Similar results are stated for three analogues of (1). Among the applications is the theorem that the partitions $n = n_1 + n_2 + \cdots + n_k$ satisfying $n_1 > n_2 \geqq n_3 > n_4 \geqq \cdots$ are equinumerous with those whose parts are either odd or $\equiv \pm 4$ (mod 20). *E. P. Merkes* (Cincinnati, Ohio)

Referred to in P68-32, P68-35.

**P68-27** **(32# 1478)**

**Carlitz, L.**

**Note on some continued fractions of the Rogers-Ramanujan type.**

*Duke Math. J.* **32** (1965), 713–720.

The author extends the results of Gordon [see #1477 above] to include the continued fraction

$$F(a, b, x) = 1 + ax + \frac{abx^2}{1 + ax^3 +} \cdots \frac{abx^{2n}}{+ 1 + ax^{2n+1} +} \cdots.$$

Infinite product representations are obtained for $F(x^{-1}, x, x) - 1$, $1 + bx/F(x, b, x)$, and $F(-1, -1, x)$ ($|x| < 1$). *E. P. Merkes* (Cincinnati, Ohio)

**P68-28** **(33# 5561)**

**Vodička, Václav**

**On the decomposition of a natural number as the sum of three natural numbers. (Czech. Russian and French summaries)**

*Časopis Pěst. Mat.* **87** (1962), 305–310.

In der Arbeit wird eine elementare Methode gegeben für die Zahl der Lösungen der Gleichung $n_1 + n_2 + n_3 = n$ ($n$ eine beliebige natürliche Zahl) mit $n_1 < n_2 < n_3$ oder $n_1 \leqq n_2 \leqq n_3$, $n_i$ natürliche Zahlen. *F. Šik* (Brno)

**P68-29** **(34# 2478)**

**Andrews, George E.**

**An analytic proof of the Rogers-Ramanujan-Gordon identities.**

*Amer. J. Math.* **88** (1966), 844–846.

Let $a$ and $k$ be integers with $0 < a \leqq k$. Denote by $A_{k,a}(n)$ the number of partitions of $n$ into parts not of the forms $(2k+1)m$, $(2k+1)m \pm a$. Let $B_{k,a}(n)$ be the number of partitions of the form $n = b_1 + \cdots + b_s$ with $b_i \geqq b_{i+1}$, $b_i - b_{i+k-1} \geqq 2$, and with 1 appearing as a summand at most $a - 1$ times. Using a half analytic, half combinatorial technique first introduced by I. Schur, the reviewer [same J. **83** (1961), 393–399; MR **23** #A809] proved that $A_{k,a}(n) = B_{k,a}(n)$. (The Rogers-Ramanujan identities are the cases $k = 2$, $a = 1$ and $k = 2$, $a = 2$.) The author now gives a much shorter proof which is analytic in character, i.e., establishes directly the equality of the generating functions $\sum_{n=0}^{\infty} A_{k,a}(n)x^n$ and $\sum_{n=0}^{\infty} B_{k,a}(n)x^n$, with combinatorial considerations playing only a small role. The main tool is an identity of A. Selberg [Avh. Norske Vid.-Akad. Oslo **1936**, no. 8, 1–23]. *B. Gordon* (Los Angeles, Calif.)

Citations: MR 23# A809 = P68-18.

**P68-30** **(34# 2479)**

**Andrews, George E.**

**On generalizations of Euler's partition theorem.**

*Michigan Math. J.* **13** (1966), 491–498.

For any positive integer $n$, let $A_k(n)$ be the number of partitions of $n$ into odd parts (allowing repetitions) with exactly $k$ distinct integers among the parts. Let $B_k(n)$ be the number of partitions of $n$ into distinct parts which form exactly $k$ (maximal) sequences of consecutive integers. By using generating functions, the author gives an analytic proof of Sylvester's theorem that $A_k(n) = B_k(n)$. (Sylvester's proof was combinatorial.) Summing over $k$, one obtains Euler's theorem that the partitions of $n$ into odd parts are equinumerous with those into distinct parts. Next, the following generalization of Euler's theorem is proved. For any partition $\pi: n=b_1+\cdots+b_s$ $(b_i \geqq b_{i+1})$, let $g(\pi)$ be the number of subscripts $i$ for which $b_i-b_{i+1} \geqq 2$; here $b_{s+1}=0$ by convention. Let $C_k(n)$ be the number of partitions of $n$ with exactly $k$ distinct even parts appearing (all other parts being odd). Then $C_k(n)=\sum \binom{g(\pi)}{k}$, where the summation is over all $\pi$ in the set $\Pi_d(n)$ of all partitions of $n$ into distinct parts. (Euler's theorem is the case $k=0$.) In the course of the proofs, the identity

$$\begin{vmatrix} 1 & \beta q & 0 & 0 & 0 & \cdots \\ -1 & 1+q & \beta q^2 & 0 & 0 & \cdots \\ 0 & -1 & 1+q^2 & \beta q^3 & 0 & \cdots \\ 0 & 0 & -1 & 1+q^3 & \beta q^4 & \cdots \\ \cdot & & & & & \\ \cdot & & & & & \\ \cdot & & & & & \end{vmatrix} = \prod_{j=0}^{\infty} \frac{1+\beta q^{2j+1}}{1-q^{2j+1}}$$

is obtained. *B. Gordon* (Los Angeles, Calif.)

**P68-31** **(35# 2766 )**

**Andrews, George E.**

**A generalization of a partition theorem of MacMahon.**

*J. Combinatorial Theory* **3** (1967), 100–101.

Using generating functions, the author gives a simple proof of the following theorem (proved in the case $r=1$ by P. A. MacMahon [*Combinatory analysis*, Vol. 2, Cambridge Univ. Press, London, 1916; reprinting, Chelsea, New York, 1960; cf. MR **25** #5003]): Let $A_r(n)$ denote the number of partitions of $n$ of the form $n=b_1+\cdots+b_s$, where $b_i \geqq b_{i+1}$, all odd parts are $\geqq 2r+1$, and if $b_i-b_{i+1}$ is odd then $b_i-b_{i+1} \geqq 2r+1$. Let $B_r(n)$ be the number of partitions of $n$ into parts which are either even or else $\equiv 2r+1 \pmod{4r+2}$. Then $A_r(n)=B_r(n)$.

*D. A. Klarner* (Hamilton, Ont.)

Citations: MR 25# 5003 = Z02-39.

**P68-32** **(35# 2848 )**

**Göllnitz, H.**

**Partitionen mit Differenzenbedingungen.**

*J. Reine Angew. Math.* **225** (1967), 154–190.

This paper is an elaboration of the author's dissertation [*Partitionen mit Differenzenbedingungen*, Dissertation, Univ. Göttingen, Göttingen, 1963; MR **32** #1179]. Theorems are given equating the numbers of partitions of a positive integer into parts restricted to certain residue classes modulo $m$ and into parts whose differences exceed a certain limit, sometimes with additional restrictions. The first examples, extending Euler's assertion that partitions into odd parts and into distinct parts are equally numerous, are the two well-known Rogers-Ramanujan theorems for $m=5$ and a theorem of Schur for $m=6$. The author proves a theorem for $m=8$ discovered independently by B. Gordon [Duke Math. J. **32** (1965), 741–748; MR **32** #1477] and another for $m=12$ quoted in the first review cited above. Complicated generalizations are given for partitions into distinct parts congruent, for example, to $m-1$, $m-2$, $m-4$ modulo $m \geqq 6$. The proofs are all elementary, using generating functions and complete induction, but are sometimes quite lengthy. *D. H. Lehmer* (Berkeley, Calif.)

Citations: MR 32# 1179 = P68-25; MR 32# 1477 = P68-26.

Referred to in P68-35, P68-44.

**P68-33** **(35# 5332 )**

**Andrews, George E.**

**Partition theorems related to the Rogers-Ramanujan identities.**

*J. Combinatorial Theory* **2** (1967), 422–430.

We quote the first of two theorems proved by the author. Let $\lambda>0$, $0<a \leqq k$ be integers. Let $A_{\lambda,k,a}(N)$ denote the number of partitions of $N$ into parts not of the forms $\lambda(2k+1)m$, $\lambda(2k+1)m+\lambda a$, $\lambda(2k+1)m+\lambda(2k+1-a)$. Let $B_{\lambda,k,a}(N)$ denote the number of partitions of $N$ of the form $\sum_1^\infty f_i \cdot i$, where $f_1 \leqq \lambda a-1$ and if $f_i \equiv \alpha \pmod{\lambda}$, $0 \leqq \alpha < \lambda$, then $f_i+f_{i+1} \leqq \lambda k+\alpha-1$. Then $A_{\lambda,k,a}(N)=B_{\lambda,k,a}(N)$.

As corollaries the author obtains Gordon's generalization of the Rogers-Ramanujan identities [B. Gordon, Amer. J. Math. **83** (1961), 393–399; MR **23** #A809] and Glaisher's extension of a theorem of Euler [J. W. L. Glaisher, Messenger of Math. **12** (1883), 158–170].

*L. Carlitz* (Durham, N.C.)

Citations: MR 23# A809 = P68-18.

**P68-34** **(35# 5333 )**

**Andrews, George E.**

**Some new partition theorems.**

*J. Combinatorial Theory* **2** (1967), 431–436.

As pointed out by P. A. MacMahon [*Combinatory analysis*, Vol. 2, Chapter III, Cambridge Univ. Press, London, 1916; reprinting, Chelsea, New York, 1960; MR **25** #5003] the second Rogers-Ramanujan identity is equivalent to the following theorem: The partitions of any positive integer $n$ into parts of the forms $5m+2$, $5m+3$ are equinumerous with those partitions of $n$ into parts $\geqq 2$ which involve neither sequences nor repetitions. MacMahon [op. cit., Chapter IV] proved also that the partitions of any positive integer $n$ into parts of the forms $6m$, $6m+2$, $6m+3$, $6m+4$ are equinumerous with those partitions of $n$ into parts $\geqq 2$ which do not involve sequences. The present author proves that the partitions of any positive integer $n$ into parts of the forms $6m+2$, $6m+3$, $6m+4$ are equinumerous with those partitions of $n$ into parts $\geqq 2$ which neither involve sequences nor allow any part to appear more than twice. Indeed he proves the following more general result: Let $0 \leqq a < k$. Let $A_{k,a}(N)$ denote the number of partitions of $N$ into parts $\not\equiv 0$, $\pm(2a+1) \pmod{4k+2}$. Let $B_{k,a}(N)$ denote the number of partitions of $N$ of the form $\sum_1^\infty f_i \cdot i$, where $f_1 \leqq 2a$ and $[(f_i+1)/2]+[(f_{i+1}+1)/2] \leqq k$. Then $A_{k,a}(N)=B_{k,a}(N)$.

*L. Carlitz* (Durham, N.C.)

Citations: MR 25# 5003 = Z02-39.

Referred to in P68-43.

**P68-35** **(36# 2578 )**

**Andrews, George E.**

**A generalization of the Göllnitz-Gordon partition theorems.**

*Proc. Amer. Math. Soc.* **18** (1967), 945–952.

Let $a$ and $k$ be integers with $0<a \leqq k$. Denote by $C_{k,a}(n)$ the number of partitions of $n$ into parts which are neither $\equiv 2 \pmod 4$ nor $\equiv 0$, $\pm(2a-1) \pmod{4k}$. Let $D_{k,a}(n)$ be the number of partitions of the form $n=\sum_{i \geq 1} f_i i$ with $f_1+f_2 \leqq a-1$, $f_{2i-1} \leqq 1$, and $f_{2i}+f_{2i+1}+f_{2i+2} \leqq k-1$. These will be called $D_{k,a}$-partitions for short. The author proves that $C_{k,a}(n)=D_{k,a}(n)$. (The special cases where $k=2$, $a=1$ or 2 were found by H. Göllnitz [J. Reine Angew. Math. **225** (1967), 154–190; MR **35** #2848] and the reviewer [Duke Math. J. **32** (1965), 741–748; MR **32** #1477].) The idea of the proof is to consider the function $J_{k,a}(x)=E_{k,a}(x) \times \prod_{j=1}^\infty (1+xq^{2j+1})/(1-xq^{2j})$, where

$E_{k,a}(x) = \sum_{n=0}^{\infty} (-1)^n x^{bn} q^{2kn^2+(2k-2a+1)n}$

$$\times \prod_{j=0}^{n-1} \frac{(1+q^{2j+1})(1-xq^{2j+2})}{(1+xq^{2j+1})(1-q^{2j+2})}$$

$$\times \left\{1 + x^a q^{(2n+1)(2a-1)} \frac{1+q^{2n+1}}{1+xq^{2n+1}}\right\}.$$

The author obtains the identities $J_{k,1}(x) = J_{k,k}(xq^2)$ and $J_{k,a}(x) - J_{k,a-1}(x) =$

$$x^{a-1}q^{2a-3}[qJ_{k,k-a+1}(xq^2) + J_{k,k-a+2}(xq^2)],$$

which lead to recurrences for the coefficients $c_{k,a}(n, m)$ in the Laurent expansion $J_{k,a}(x) = \sum c_{k,a}(n, m)x^m q^n$. A combinatorial argument using these recurrences shows that $c_{k,a}(n, m)$ is the number of $D_{k,a}$-partitions of $n$ into $m$ parts. The theorem is then proved by using Jacobi's identity to evaluate $J_{k,a}(1)$. In the final section the author obtains formulas for $E_{1,1}(x)$, $E_{2,2}(x)$, and $E_{3,3}(x)$.

*B. Gordon* (Los Angeles, Calif.)

Citations: MR 32# 1477 = P68-26; MR 35# 2848 = P68-32.

Referred to in P60-55, P68-54.

## P68-36 (36# 3744 )

**Andrews, George E.**

**On Schur's second partition theorem.**

*Glasgow Math. J.* **8** (1967), 127–132.

The author gives a new proof of Schur's theorem which states that the number of partitions of $n$ into parts congruent to $\pm 1$ (mod 6) is equal to the number of partitions of $n$ of the form $b_1 + b_2 + \cdots + b_s = n$, where $b_i - b_{i+1} \geqq 3$ and if $3|b_i$, then $b_i - b_{i+1} > 3$. The proof is based on Appell's comparison theorem. The technique is generalized to obtain a new partition theorem of the same type which states that $P_1(n)$, the number of partitions of $n$ into parts which are either even and not congruent to $4r-2$ (mod $4r$) or odd and congruent to $2r-1$, $4r-1$ (mod $4r$), is equal to $P_2(n)$, the number of partitions of $n$ of the form $n = b_1 + \cdots + b_s$, where $b_i \geqq b_{i+1}$ and for $b_i$ odd, $b_i - b_{i+1} \geqq 2r-1$ $(1 \leqq i \leqq s,\ b_{s+1} = 0)$, where $r \geqq 2$.

*M. S. Cheema* (Tucson, Ariz.)

Referred to in P60-55, P68-41.

## P68-37 (37# 181 )

**Intrator, Jakub**

**Partitions. I.** (Loose Russian summary)

*Czechoslovak Math. J.* **18 (93)** (1968), 16–24.

Using elementary methods and simple congruences, the author proves that the number of partitions of any natural number $n$ into exactly $k$ summands, is given by a polynomial of degree exactly $(k-1)$ in $n$, the first $[(k+1)/2]$ coefficients of which are independent of $n$ and the rest depend on the residue of $n$ modulo the least common multiple of the integers 1, 2, 3, $\cdots$, $k$. In particular, the coefficient of the $[(k+3)/2]$th term depends only on the parity of $n$ and is not the same for $n \equiv 0$ and $n \equiv 1$ (mod 2).

From results given by the reviewer [Res. Bull. Panjab Univ. **94** (1956), 153–159; MR **19**, 252] it appears that the coefficient of $n^j$ in the polynomial depends on the residue of $n$ modulo the least common multiple of integers 1, 2, 3, $\cdots$, $[k/(j+1)]$; $j \leqq (k-1)$. This should not be difficult to prove by elementary methods.

*H. Gupta* (Allahabad)

Citations: MR 19, 252d = P68-11.

## P68-38 (37# 1334 )

**Andrews, George E.**

**On partition functions related to Schur's second partition theorem.**

*Proc. Amer. Math. Soc.* **19** (1968), 441–444.

Let $B_d(n)$ denote the number of partitions of $n$ of the form $n = b_1 + \cdots + b_s$ with $b_{i+1} - b_i \geqq d$ and such that if $d|b_i$ then $b_{i+1} - b_i > d$. Let $C_d(n)$ denote the number of partitions of $n$ as above with the additional condition that $b_s > d$. Then several known results in the theory of partitions can be expressed in terms of $B_d(n)$ and $C_d(n)$. In particular, I. Schur has shown [S.-B. Akad. Deutsch. Wiss. Berlin **1926**, 488–495] that $B_3(n)$ is the number of partitions of $n$ into parts congruent to $\pm 1$ (mod 6). In the present paper the author gives another proof of Schur's theorem and also obtains a generating function for $C_3(n)$.

*W. H. Simons* (Corvallis, Ore.)

## P68-39 (37# 4042 )

**Andrews, George E.**

**A new generalization of Schur's second partition theorem.**

*Acta Arith.* **14** (1967/68), 429–434.

Among the results which the main theorem of this paper implies, the following is typical: Let $H(n)$ denote the number of partitions of $n$ into parts $\equiv 3, 5, 13$ (mod 14); $F(n)$ of those into distinct parts $\equiv 3, 5, 6$ (mod 7) and $G(n)$ the number of partitions of $n$ of the form $n = b_1 + \cdots + b_s$, where $b_i - b_{i+1} \geqq 15$; 10; 7 or 12; according as $b_i \equiv 0$; 1, 2; 3, 5, 6; or 4 (mod 7); and $b_s \neq 1, 2, 4, 7$. Then $F(n) = G(n) = H(n)$.

*H. Gupta* (Allahabad)

Referred to in P68-41.

## P68-40 (38# 2112 )

**Andrews, George E.**

**Two theorems of Euler and a general partition theorem.**

*Proc. Amer. Math. Soc.* **20** (1969), 499–502.

If $S_1$ and $S_2$ be subsets of the set of natural numbers, then $(S_1; S_2)$ is called an Euler-pair, if for all natural numbers $n$, $q(S_1; n) = p(S_2; n)$, where $q(S_1; n)$ is the number of partitions of $n$ into distinct parts taken from $S_1$ and $p(S_2; n)$ the number of partitions of $n$ into parts taken from $S_2$.

The author gives, in this paper, a very simple characterization of Euler-pairs with far reaching consequences. He proves that $(S_1; S_2)$ is an Euler-pair if and only if $2S_1 \subseteq S_1$ and $S_2 = S_1 - 2S_1$, where the symbols $mS$ and $S_i - S_j$ have their usual meaning.

*H. Gupta* (Allahabad)

Referred to in P68-53.

## P68-41 (39# 4109 )

**Andrews, George E.**

**A general theorem on partitions with difference conditions.**

*Amer. J. Math.* **91** (1969), 18–24.

This paper is one of a series by the same author [see, for instance, Glasgow Math. J. **8** (1967), 127–132; MR **36** #3744; Acta Arith. **14** (1967/68), 429–434; MR **37** #4042] concerning theorems which relate the numbers of partitions with various restrictions on the residue classes and differences of the parts. This class of theorems includes the Rogers-Ramanujan identities and Schur's second partition theorem. The latter is essentially the case $a(1) = 1$, $a(2) = 2$, $N = 3$ of the main theorem of the current paper: Let $A = \{a(1), \cdots, a(r)\}$ be a set of $r$ positive integers satisfying $\sum_{i=1}^{k-1} a(i) < a(k)$, $1 < k \leqq r$. Thus the set $A'$ of non-vacuous sums of distinct $a(i)$ consists of $2^r - 1$ distinct elements, designated by $\alpha(1)<\alpha(2)<\cdots<\alpha(2^r-1)$. Let $N$ be an integer with $N\geqq\alpha(2^r-1)$. Let $\beta_N(m)$ denote the least positive residue of $m$ (mod $N$). Let $A_N$ and $A_N'$ be the sets of all positive integers for which $\beta_N(m)\in A$ and $\beta_N(m)\in A'$, respectively. If $m\in A'$, let $w(m)$ be the number of terms appearing in the defining sum of $m$ and let $v(m)$ be the smallest term appearing. Let $D(A_N; n)$ denote the number of partitions of $n$ into distinct parts taken from $A_N$. Let $E(A_N'; n)$ denote the number of partitions of $n$ into parts taken from $A_N'$ of the form $n=b_1+\cdots+b_s$, with $b_i-b_{i+1}\geqq Nw(\beta_N(b_{i+1}))+v(\beta_N(b_{i+1}))-\beta_N(b_{i+1})$. Then $D(A_N; n)=E(A_N'; n)$.

The proof uses Appell's comparison theorem for power series; however, a purely formal argument may be used instead, if desired. *S. A. Burr* (Whippany, N.J.)

Citations: MR 36# 3744 = P68-36; MR 37# 4042 = P68-39.

## P68-42 (39# 5502)

**Alder, Henry L.**

**Proof of Andrews' conjecture on partition identities.**

*Proc. Amer. Math. Soc.* **22** (1969), 688–689.

Let $c_{d,m}(n)$ be the number of partitions of $n$ of the form $n=b_1+b_2+\cdots+b_s$, where (i) $b_i-b_{i+1}\geqq d$, (ii) $b_i-b_{i+1}>d$ whenever $d|b_i$, and (iii) $b_s\geqq m$. For any set $A$ of natural numbers, let $p_A(n)$ denote the number of partitions of $n$ whose parts all lie in $A$. The author proves that if $d\geqq 3$, $m\geqq 2$, then there does not exist any set $A$ such that $c_{d,m}(n)=p_A(n)$ for all $n$. *B. Gordon* (Los Angeles, Calif.)

## P68-43 (40# 49)

**Andrews, George E.**

**Some new partition theorems. II.**

*J. Combinatorial Theory* **7** (1969), 262–263.

Making use of the results of an earlier paper with the same title [same J. **2** (1967), 431–436; MR **35** #5333], the author proves the following theorem.

Let $p_k(n)$ [$q_k(n)$] denote the number of partitions of $n$ in which there are an even [odd] number of parts divisible by $2k+1$ and with no restrictions on parts not divisible by $2k+1$. Let $B_{k,k}(n)$ denote the number of partitions of $n$ of the form $n=\sum_{j=1}^{\infty}f_j\cdot j$ $([\frac{1}{2}(f_j+1)]+[\frac{1}{2}(f_{j+1}+1)]\leqq k)$. Let $Q(n)$ denote the number of partitions of $n$ into distinct odd parts. Then $p_k(n)-q_k(n)=(-1)^nQ(n)$ $(k=0)$, $p_k(n)-q_k(n)=B_{k,k}(n)$ $(k>0)$. Corollary: If $p(n)$ denotes the ordinary partition function, then $p(n)\equiv Q(n)\equiv B_{k,k}(n)$ (mod 2) $(k=0, 1, 2, \cdots)$. *L. Carlitz* (Durham, N.C.)

Citations: MR 35# 5333 = P68-34.

## P68-44 (40# 1355)

**Andrews, George E.**

**On a partition theorem of Göllnitz and related formulae.**

*J. Reine Angew. Math.* **236** (1969), 37–42.

A new proof is given of a theorem of H. Göllnitz [same J. **225** (1967), 154–190; MR **35** #2848], the difficult part of the result being: Let $B(n)$ be the number of partitions of $n$ into distinct parts $\equiv 2, 4, 5$ (mod 6). Let $C(n)$ be the number of partitions of $n$ in the form $n=b_1+\cdots+b_s$, where $b_i-b_{i+1}\geqq 6$ with strict inequality if $b_i\equiv 0, 1, 3$ (mod 6), and where $b_s\neq 1, 3$. Then $B(n)=C(n)$. The author derives a complicated general identity. From this he derives two other identities, ultimately involving $c_m(n)$, which is the number of partitions of $n$ of the type defining $C(n)$, but with the added restriction that all parts are $\leqq m$. From one of these, the theorem of Göllnitz is deduced. The author notes that three other theorems of Göllnitz may also be derived from the results given. The proofs involve elementary, but intricate, manipulation of generating functions. *S. A. Burr* (Whippany, N.J.)

Citations: MR 35# 2848 = P68-32.

## P68-45 (40# 4135)

**Gupta, Hansraj**

**Highly restricted partitions.**

*J. Res. Nat. Bur. Standards Sect. B* **73B** (1969), 329–350.

Author's summary: "The function $g(n, m, h, k)$, which enumerates the number of partitions of $n$ into exactly $k$ summands each less than or equal to $m$ and in which the number of different summands is exactly $h$, is here tabulated and studied."

## P68-46 (40# 4226)

**Andrews, George E.**

**A generalization of the classical partition theorems.**

*Trans. Amer. Math. Soc.* **145** (1969), 205–221.

Let $0\leqq\lambda\leqq a\leqq k$ be integers, with $2\lambda-1\leqq k$. Let $A_{\lambda,k,a}(n)$ be the number of partitions of $n$ into parts $\not\equiv 0, \pm\frac{1}{2}(2a-\lambda)(\lambda+1)$ (mod$(2k-\lambda+1)(\lambda+1)$) and with the following additional restrictions: If $\lambda$ is even, no part $\not\equiv 0$ (mod $\lambda+1$) is repeated; if $\lambda$ is odd, no part $\not\equiv 0$ (mod $\frac{1}{2}(\lambda+1)$) is repeated, and no part is $\equiv\lambda+1$ (mod $2\lambda+2$). Let $B_{\lambda,k,a}(n)$ be the number of partitions of $n$ of the form $n=b_1+\cdots+b_s$ with $b_i\geqq b_{i+1}$, $b_a>\lambda+1$, no parts $\not\equiv 0$ (mod $\lambda+1$) being repeated, and with $b_i-b_{i+k-1}\geqq\lambda+1$, with strict inequality if $\lambda+1|b_i$. Then the author proves that $A_{\lambda,k,a}(n)=B_{\lambda,k,a}(n)$. From this theorem the author derives the following generalization. Let $0\leqq\frac{1}{2}\lambda<a\leqq k$, $2\lambda-1\leqq k$, and let $B^*_{\lambda,k,a}(n)$ be the number of partitions of $n$ of the type enumerated by $B_{\lambda,k,a}(n)$ with the additional restriction that for every integer $j$ in the interval $[1, \frac{1}{2}(\lambda+1)]$, there are at most $a-j$ parts with values in the interval $[j, \lambda-j+1]$. Then $A_{\lambda,k,a}(n)=B^*_{\lambda,k,a}(n)$. (Note that if $a\geqq\lambda$, $B^*_{\lambda,k,a}(n)=B_{\lambda,k,a}(n)$.) The proofs involve intricate manipulations of generating functions. The author conjectures that the theorems remain true if the condition $k\geqq 2\lambda-1$ is relaxed to $k\geqq\lambda$.
*S. A. Burr* (Whippany, N.J.)

## P68-47 (41# 8367)

**Andrews, George E.**

**On a partition problem of J. J. Sylvester.**

*J. London Math. Soc.* (2) **2** (1970), 571–576.

Let $n=\sum_{i=1}^{\infty}f_i\cdot i$ be a partition of $n$. Then, modifying the author's definition slightly, the partition can be said to be 0-flushed or 1-flushed according as the least positive integer $j$ for which $f_j$ is even (including zero) is even or odd.

Let $F(a; S; m, n)$ denote the number of $a$-flushed ($a=0$ or 1) partitions of $n$ into exactly $m$ parts such that no part lying in the set $S$ is repeated. Then, the most important result proved by the author, in this paper, is contained in his Theorem 2: $f_1(S; -1, q)=\prod_{k\in S}(1-q^{2k})$, where $f_a(S; z, q)=\sum_{m=0}^{\infty}\sum_{n=0}^{\infty}F(a; S; m, n)z^mq^n$.
*H. Gupta* (Allahabad)

## P68-48 (42# 2950)

**Metropolis, N.; Stein, P. R.**

**An elementary solution to a problem in restricted partitions.**

*J. Combinatorial Theory* **9** (1970), 365–376.

Let $P(n, r)$ denote the set of partitions of $nr$ into parts less than or equal to $r$, and let $T(n, r)$ denote the subset of $P(n, r)$ consisting of those partitions which can be obtained by partwise addition of $n$ not-necessarily-distinct partitions of $r$. That is, $1^{\mu_1}2^{\mu_2}\cdots r^{\mu_r}\in T(n, r)$ if and only if there exist $n$ partitions of $r$, $1^{\lambda_1^{(1)}}2^{\lambda_2^{(1)}}\cdots r^{\lambda_r^{(1)}}$, $1^{\lambda_1^{(2)}}2^{\lambda_2^{(2)}}\cdots r^{\lambda_r^{(2)}}$, $\cdots$, $1^{\lambda_1^{(n)}}2^{\lambda_2^{(n)}}\cdots r^{\lambda_r^{(n)}}$ (where $\sum_{i=1}^{r}i\lambda_i^{(j)}=r$, $\lambda_i^{(j)}\geqq 0$ all $i, j$) such that $\mu_j=\sum_{k=1}^{n}\lambda_j^{(k)}$ $(j=1, 2, \cdots, r)$. The authors find $|T(n, r)|=\sum_{i=0}^{r-g-1}c_i^{(r)}\binom{n+g}{g+i}$, where $g=$

$[(r+1)/2]$. In general, the nonvanishing $c_i^{(r)}$ must be determined by direct calculation; in this paper they are given for all $r \leqq 11$. Several other interpretations of $|T(n, r)|$ are given, and some additional open questions concerning the interpretation of the results are discussed.

*G. F. Clements* (Boulder, Colo.)

**P68-49** **(42# 4518)**

**Andrews, George E.**

**Note on a partition theorem.**

*Glasgow Math. J.* **11** (1970), 108–109.

Let $r \geqq 2$ be an integer. Let $P_1(n)$ denote the number of partitions of $n$ into parts that are either even and not congruent to $4r-2$ (mod $4r$) or odd and congruent to $2r-1$, $4r-1$ (mod $4r$). Let $P_2(n)$ denote the number of partitions of $n$ of the form $n = b_1 + b_2 + \cdots + b_s$, where $b_i \geqq b_{i+1}$ and for $b_i$ odd, $b_i - b_{i+1} \geqq 2r-1$ $(1 \leqq i \leqq s)$. Let $P_3(n)$ be the number of partitions of $n$ into parts that are either even or else congruent to $2r-1$ (mod $2r$) with the further restriction that only even parts are repeated. It was shown by the author that $P_1(n) = P_2(n)$. It follows easily from their generating functions that $P_1(1) = P_3(n)$. In this note a combinatorial proof is given to show that $P_2(n) = P_3(n)$.

*M. S. Cheema* (Tucson, Ariz.)

**P68-50** **(42# 4519)**

**Andrews, George E.**

**Lambert series, false theta functions, and partitions.**

*Proc. Second Chapel Hill Conf. on Combinatorial Mathematics and its Applications (Univ. North Carolina, Chapel Hill, N.C.,* 1970), *pp.* 1–11. *Univ. North Carolina, Chapel Hill, N.C.*, 1970.

Let $W_{k,i}(n, N)$ denote the number of partitions of $N$ of the form $N = \sum_{t=1}^{n} f_t t$ ($f_t$ is the number of times the summand $t$ appears in the partition), with $f_1 = i$, $f_j \leqq k-1$, $f_j + f_{j+1} = k$ or $k+1$, $1 \leqq j \leqq n-1$; and let $w_{k,i}(n, q)$ be the generating function of $W_{k,i}(n, N)$. Then the author shows how the function $w_{k,i}(n, q)$ is related to a certain Lambert series. A result of L. J. Rogers [Proc. London Math. Soc. (2) **16** (1917), 315–336] is obtained as a special case of the author's result.

*H. Gupta* (Allahabad)

**P68-51** **(42# 5897)**

**Arkin, Joseph**

**Researches on partitions.**

*Duke Math. J.* **37** (1970), 403–409.

The explicit formulas for $p_m(n)$—the number of partitions of $n$ into parts not exceeding $m$, given here for $m \leqq 8$, are already available in the literature for $m \leqq 12$, and in a more compact notation [J. W. L. Glaisher, Quart. J. Pure Appl. Math. **40** (1908/09), 57–143; ibid. **40** (1908/09), 275–348; the reviewer, Res. Bull. Panjab Univ. No. 94 (1956), 153–159; MR **19**, 252; see also *Tables of partitions*, edited by the reviewer, C. E. Gwyther and J. C. P. Miller, Introduction, Cambridge Univ. Press, Cambridge, 1958]. The author derives an interesting congruence property of $p_m(n)$ when $n$ is a multiple of the l.c.m. of $1, 2, 3, \cdots, m$.

*H. Gupta* (Allahabad).

Citations: MR 19, 252d = P68-11.

**P68-52** **(42# 7617)**

**Subbarao, M. V.**

**On a partition theorem of MacMahon-Andrews.**

*Proc. Amer. Math. Soc.* **27** (1971), 449–450.

The two theorems in this paper, like several others already known, specify two sets of conditions such that the number of partitions of any natural number $n$ satisfying one set of conditions equals the number of partitions satisfying the other. The conditions here involve multiplicities of parts on the one hand and congruence relations which the parts satisfy on the other.

*H. Gupta* (Allahabad)

**P68-53** **(43# 175)**

**Subbarao, M. V.**

**Partition theorems for Euler pairs.**

*Proc. Amer. Math. Soc.* **28** (1971), 330–336.

If $S_1$ and $S_2$ are nonempty sets of natural numbers, then $(S_1, S_2)$ is said to be an Euler pair of order $r$ whenever the number of partitions of an arbitrary number $n$ into parts taken from $S_1$, no part repeated more than $(r-1)$ times, $r > 1$; is the same as the number of those into parts taken from $S_2$, with repetitions allowed. Such pairs are completely characterized by the relations: $rS_1 \equiv S_1$, $S_2 = S_1 - rS_1$. Several interesting applications are given. The case $r = 2$ was considered by George E. Andrews [same Proc. **20** (1969), 499–502; MR **38** #2112].

*H. Gupta* (Allahabad)

Citations: MR 38# 2112 = P68-40.

**P68-54** **(44# 1640)**

**Chen, Ming-po**

**A generalization of a partition theorem of Andrews.**

*Studies and Essays (Presented to Yu-why Chen on his 60th Birthday, April* 1, 1970), *pp.* 309–315. *Math. Res. Center, Nat. Taiwan Univ., Taipei,* 1970.

Let $a$, $k$, $\lambda$ and $\mu$ be integers such that $0 < a \leqq k$, $0 \leqq 2\mu < \lambda$ and $4\mu | \lambda$ if $\mu > 0$. Let $A_{\mu,\lambda,k,a}(N)$ be the number of partitions of $N$ into parts that are either congruent to $2\mu$ (mod $4\mu$), or else congruent to 0 (mod $\lambda$) and not congruent to $2\lambda$ (mod $4\lambda$), and not congruent to $0$, $\pm\lambda(2a-1)$ (mod $4\lambda k$). Let $B_{\mu,\lambda,k,a}$ be the number of partitions of $N$ of the form $\sum_{i=1}^{\infty} f_i \cdot i$ with (1) $f_1 + f_2 \leqq \lambda a - 1$, (2) for each $i$, $f_i \equiv 0$ or $\mu$ (mod $\lambda$), (3) for each $i$, $f_{2i-1} = 0$ or $\lambda$, and (4) if $f_{2i} \equiv \alpha$ (mod $\lambda$), where $\alpha$ is either 0 or $\mu$, then $f_{2i} + f_{2i+1} + f_{2i+2} \leqq \lambda k + \alpha - 1$. The author proves that $A_{\mu,\lambda,k,a}(N) = B_{\mu,\lambda,k,a}(N)$. The special case of this theorem with $\lambda = 1$ was proved earlier by G. E. Andrews [Proc. Amer. Math. Soc. **18** (1967), 945–952; MR **36** #2578].

*B. Gordon* (Los Angeles, Calif.)

Citations: MR 36# 2578 = P68-35.

**P68-55** **(44# 3976)**

**Andrews, George E.**

**On a theorem of Schur and Gleissberg.**

*Arch. Math. (Basel)* **22** (1971), 165–167.

An easy analytical proof is given of the following theorem. Let $A(M, N)$ denote the number of partitions of $N$ into $M$ distinct parts not divisible by 3, and let $B(M, N)$ denote the number of partitions of $N$ into $M$ summands (every part divisible by 3 is counted as two summands) where the difference between all parts is at least three and that between parts divisible by 3 at least six; then $A(M, N) = B(M, N)$.

*H. Gupta* (Allahabad)

**P68-56** **(44# 6635)**

**Andrews, George E.**

**On a partition problem of H. L. Alder.**

*Pacific J. Math.* **36** (1971), 279–284.

The author considers the function $\Delta_d(n) = q_d(n) - Q_d(n)$, where $q_d(n)$ is the number of partitions of $n$ into parts differing by at least $d$ and $Q_d(n)$ is the number of partitions of $n$ into parts $\equiv \pm 1$ (mod $d+3$). H. L. Alder [Bull. Amer. Math. Soc. **62** (1956), 76, Res. Problem 4] has asked whether $\Delta_d(n) \geqq 0$ for all positive $d$ and $n$; this is known to be true for $d \leqq 3$. In connection with this question, the author proves that $\lim_{n \to \infty} \Delta_d(n) = \infty$ for $d \geqq 4$, and that $\Delta_d(n) \geqq 0$ for all $n > 0$ if $d = 2^s - 1$, where $s = 1, 2$, or $\geqq 4$.

In addition, the following interesting general result is proved: Let $S=\{a_i\}$ and $T=\{b_i\}$ be strictly increasing sequences of integers such that $b_1=1$ and $a_i \geqq b_i$ for all $i$; let $\rho(S; n)$ denote the number of partitions of $n$ into parts taken from $S$, and similarly for $T$; then $\rho(T; n) \geqq \rho(S; n)$ for all $n$. *S. A. Burr* (Whippany, N.J.)

## P72 PARTITIONS: ASYMPTOTICS, AND CONVERGENT SERIES EXPANSIONS

See also reviews F02-1, F02-23, F10-63, N52-4, P02-20, P02-24, P60-2, P60-10, P60-12, P60-38, P64-9, P64-10, P64-13, P64-14, P64-16, P64-18, P64-19, P64-21, P64-22, P64-23, P64-26, P64-27, P64-29, P64-31, P64-34, P64-39, P64-51, P64-58, P68-1, P68-3, P68-4, P68-5, P68-6, P68-12, P68-15, P68-16, P68-19, P68-21, P68-23, P80-4, P80-13, P80-15, P80-16, P80-19, P80-20, P80-26, P80-50, P80-57, R48-6, R48-12, Z01-70, Z15-74, Z30-2, Z30-8.

**P72-1** **(1, 69c)**

**Lehmer, D. H. On the remainders and convergence of the series for the partition function.** Trans. Amer. Math. Soc. **46**, 362–373 (1939).

The author writes the Hardy-Ramanujan formula and the Rademacher formula for $p(n)$ in the following forms, respectively:

$$(1)\quad p(n)=\frac{12^{1/2}}{24n-1}\sum_{k=1}^{N}A_k^*(n)\left(1-\frac{k}{\mu}\right)e^{\mu/k}+R_1(n, N),$$

$$(2)\quad p(n)=$$

$$\frac{12^{1/2}}{24n-1}\sum_{k=1}^{N}A_k^*(n)\left\{\left(1-\frac{k}{\mu}\right)e^{\mu/k}+\left(1+\frac{k}{\mu}\right)e^{-\mu/k}\right\}+R_2(n, N),$$

with $\mu=\mu(n)=(\pi/6)(24n-1)^{1/2}$. Hardy and Ramanujan proved that, for every fixed $\alpha>0$,

$$(3)\qquad R_1(n, \alpha n^{1/2})=O(n^{-1/4}),$$

whereas Rademacher gave an estimate of $R_2(n, N)$ explicitly depending on $n$ and $N$ which has as consequence on one hand $\lim_{N\to\infty} R_2(n, N)=0$ and on the other hand the relation (3). Of basic importance in the discussion of the remainders $R_1(n, N)$ and $R_2(n, N)$ is an estimate of the "Kloosterman sum" $A_k(n)=k^{1/2}A_k^*(n)$. Trivial is only $|A_k(n)|\leqq k$. In a previous paper the author [Trans. Amer. Math. Soc. **43**, 271–295 (1938)] had completely evaluated the $A_k(n)$ by means of the factorization of $k$ and derived the estimate $|A_k(n)|<2k^{5/6}$. Nevertheless, the question whether for certain fixed $n$ $A_k(n)$ was bounded or not for $k\to\infty$ was not completely settled. This time the author proves (Theorems 5 and 6) that for any given positive or negative $n$ there exist infinitely many primes $p$ such that $|A_p(n)|>3^{1/2}p^{1/2}$. This implies the divergence of the series (1). More precisely, Theorem 7 states that for every positive $n$ the $k$th term in (1) is, for infinitely many values of $k$, greater in absolute value than $13k(24n-1)^{-3/2}$. In numerical applications the convergent Rademacher series seems to show a very rapid approximation of $p(n)$. This is, however, only apparent and is due to the fact that only a limited precision is required since $p(n)$ is known to be an integer. The series as such is not better convergent than $\sum k^{-2}$. In fact the author proves (Theorem 8): For every positive $n$ there exist infinitely many $k$ such that the $k$th term of the series (2) is in absolute value greater than $(43/34)k^{-2}$. Two further questions are treated in this paper. Firstly, the author gives estimates of $R_1(n, N)$ and $R_2(n, N)$ which are better than the previously known ones. These improvements are useful for numerical applications. Secondly, since the Hardy-Ramanujan paper the choice $N=[\alpha n^{1/2}]$ has been of particular interest as far as the order of magnitude of the remainders is concerned. The author improves (3) and obtains here a sort of final result, namely

$$R_i(n, \alpha n^{1/2})=O(n^{-1/2}\log n),\qquad i=1, 2.$$

*H. Rademacher* (Swarthmore, Pa.).

**P72-2** **(2, 41c)**

**Avakumović, Vojislav G. Neuer Beweis eines Satzes von G. H. Hardy und S. Ramanujan über das asymptotische Verhalten der Zerfällungskoeffizienten.** Amer. J. Math. **62**, 877–880 (1940).

Let $p(n)$ denote the number of unrestricted partitions of a positive integer $n$. The asymptotic formula of Hardy and Ramanujan to which reference is made in the title of the paper is

$$p(n)\sim\frac{1}{4n\sqrt{3}}\exp\left\{\pi\sqrt{\frac{2n}{3}}\right\},\qquad n\to\infty.$$

[In the paper $4n\sqrt{3}$ is misprinted as $4\sqrt{3n}$.] Hardy and Ramanujan [Proc. London Math. Soc. (2) **17**, 75–115 (1918)] state that they were unable at that time to obtain, by any method which did not depend on Cauchy's theorem, a result as precise as this. The new short proof by Avakumović does not use Cauchy's theorem, but requires some knowledge of the convergence of infinite integrals and the inversion of repeated infinite integrals. *R. D. James.*

**P72-3** **(3, 166a)**

**Ingham, A. E. A Tauberian theorem for partitions.** Ann. of Math. (2) **42**, 1075–1090 (1941).

The author's principal aim is to deduce the asymptotic formulas

$$p(n)\sim e^{\pi(2n/3)^{\frac12}}/4\sqrt{3}n,\quad q(n)\sim e^{\pi(n/3)^{\frac12}}/4\cdot 3^{\frac14}n^{\frac34},\quad n\to\infty,$$

from reasonably simple properties of the generating functions for $p(n)$ and $q(n)$, the number of unrestricted partitions of $n$ and the number of partitions of $n$ into unequal (or odd) parts, respectively. A Tauberian theorem for the integral $f(s)=\int_0^\infty e^{-us}dA(u)$ is first proved. This can be thought of as an interpolation between the theorems of Hardy-Littlewood type which conclude $A(u)\sim u^a$, and those of Wiener-Ikehara type which conclude $A(u)\sim e^{au}$ as $u\to\infty$. This general theorem is specialized to a theorem which is directly applicable to $p(n)$, $q(n)$ and other types of special partitions. In the application to $p(n)$, for example, the result is obtained from an elementary knowledge of the asymptotic behavior of the generating function $\sum_{n=0}^{\infty}p(n)z^n$, when $z=x+iy$ approaches the principal singularity $z=1$ in an arbitrarily large "Stoltz angle," $|y|\leqq\Delta(1-x)$, $0<\Delta<\infty$.

*H. S. Zuckerman* (Seattle, Wash.).

Referred to in N36-43, P72-14, P72-18, P72-20, P72-24, P72-39, P72-40, P72-50, P80-20.

**P72-4** **(3, 270c)**

**Hua, Loo-keng. On the number of partitions of a number into unequal parts.** Trans. Amer. Math. Soc. **51**, 194–201 (1942).

It is proved that the number $q(n)$ of partitions of $n$ into unequal parts is equal to

$$2^{-\frac{1}{2}} \sum_{k}^{1,3,5,\cdots} A_k(n) dJ_0((i\pi/k)\{\tfrac{1}{3}(n+1/24)\}^{\frac{1}{2}})/dn,$$

where $A_k(n)=\sum_h \omega_{h,k} e^{-2\pi i h n/k}$ ($h$ ranging over $0<h\leqq k$, $(h,k)=1$), and $\omega_{h,k}$ is a certain $24k$th root of unity. The method of Hardy and Ramanujan for $p(n)$ [Proc. London Math. Soc. (2) **17**, 75–115 (1918)] is employed, with modifications due to Rademacher [ibid. (2) **43**, 241–254 (1937)].

*G. Pall* (Montreal, Que.).

Referred to in F10-30, P60-28, P68-19, P72-44.

## P72-5 (4, 36a)

**Erdös, P. On an elementary proof of some asymptotic formulas in the theory of partitions.** Ann. of Math. (2) **43**, 437–450 (1942).

The main purpose of this paper is to give an elementary proof of the result

$$p(n)\sim(a/n)e^{cn^{\frac{1}{2}}},$$

where $p(n)$ is the number of partitions of $n$, $c=\pi(2/3)^{\frac{1}{2}}$ and $a$ is a constant. The author is unable to show by his methods that $a=48^{-\frac{1}{2}}$, the value found by Hardy and Ramanujan [Proc. London Math. Soc. (2) **17**, 75–115 (1918)]. He states that his methods apply to the proof of a similar result for the number of partitions of $n$ into integers congruent to one of a given set of $r$ numbers (mod $m$). Various other applications of his methods are indicated.

*B. W. Jones* (Ithaca, N. Y.).

Referred to in N52-2, P72-16, P72-53, P72-54.

## P72-6 (4, 190b)

**Gupta, Hansraj. On an asymptotic formula in partitions.** Proc. Indian Acad. Sci., Sect. A. **16**, 101–102 (1942).

This paper gives a short elementary proof of the asymptotic formula $p_k(n)\sim\binom{n-1}{k-1}/k!$ due to Erdös and Lehner [Duke Math. J. **8**, 335–345 (1941); these Rev. **3**, 69]. Here $p_k(n)$ is the number of partitions of $n$ into exactly $k$ summands.

*R. D. James* (Saskatoon, Sask.).

Citations: MR 3, 69a = P80-4.

Referred to in P64-19, P72-7, Z30-8.

## P72-7 (4, 211c)

**Auluck, F. C. An asymptotic formula for $p_k(n)$.** J. Indian Math. Soc. (N.S.) **6**, 113–114 (1942).

An elementary proof of the result due to Erdös and Lehner, and also proved by H. Gupta [Proc. Indian Acad. Sci., Sect. A. **16**, 101–102 (1942); these Rev. **4**, 190], that

$$p_k(n)\sim\binom{n-1}{k-1}/k!$$

*R. D. James* (Saskatoon, Sask.).

Citations: MR 4, 190b = P72-6.

## P72-8 (4, 241e)

**Gupta, Hansraj. An inequality in partitions.** J. Univ. Bombay **11**, 16–18 (1942).

Let $p_k(n)$ denote the number of partitions of $n$ into precisely $k$ positive integers. By use of the identity

$$p_k(n)=p_{k-1}(n-1)+p_{k-1}(n-k-1)+p_{k-1}(n-2k-1)+\cdots$$

an inductive proof is given of the inequality

$$\binom{m+a_{k-1}}{k-1}\leqq k!p_k(m+1)\leqq\binom{m+a_k}{k-1},$$

where $a_k=k(k-1)/4$ and where $k\geqq4$ and $m$ is sufficiently large depending on $k$. The argument shows that, as $n\to\infty$,

$$p_k(n)\sim\binom{n-1+a_k}{k-1}\bigg/k!.$$

*D. H. Lehmer* (Berkeley, Calif.).

Referred to in Z30-8.

## P72-9 (5, 35a)

**Rademacher, Hans. On the expansion of the partition function in a series.** Ann. of Math. (2) **44**, 416–422 (1943).

In the usual treatment of the partition function [G. H. Hardy and S. Ramanujan, Proc. London Math. Soc. (2) **17**, 75–115 (1918); H. Rademacher, Proc. London Math. Soc. (2) **43**, 241–254 (1937)] the path of integration used is the circle $|x|=\exp(-2\pi N^{-2})$, which is then broken up by the Farey dissection of order $N$. Here the author replaces the path by that given by $x=\exp(2\pi i\tau)$, where $\tau$ goes from $i$ to $i+1$ along the upper arcs of a series of circles with centers at $h/k+i/2k^2$ and radii $1/2k^2$, where $h/k$ runs through the Farey series of order $N$. That these circles give a suitable connected path follows from a theorem of L. R. Ford [Amer. Math. Monthly **45**, 586–601 (1938)]. The advantage of this new path of integration is that it simplifies considerably the estimates that must be made and it clarifies the manner in which the singularities at the various rational points contribute to the final formula. The author carries out the proof for the evaluation of the partition function but his method will be advantageous in similar problems involving modular functions of nonnegative dimension.

*H. S. Zuckerman* (Seattle, Wash.).

## P72-10 (7, 415c)

**Iseki, Kaneshirō. Ein Theorem der Zahlentheorie.** Tôhoku Math. J. **48**, 60–63 (1941).

The author denotes by $\rho_k(n)$ the number of partitions of $n$ into $k$ positive summands, two summands being counted the same if they differ only in order. He proves that, for each $k$,

$$\rho_k(n)\sim n^{k-1}/k!(k-1)!, \qquad n\to\infty.$$

The proof is elementary and the results closely related to those of Erdös and Lehner [Duke Math. J. **8**, 335–345 (1941); these Rev. **3**, 69].

*B. W. Jones* (Ithaca, N. Y.).

Citations: MR 3, 69a = P80-4.

## P72-11 (8, 567a)

**Whiteman, Albert Leon. A sum connected with the partition function.** Bull. Amer. Math. Soc. **53**, 598–603 (1947).

The $A_k(n)$ appearing in the formula for the partition function $p(n)$ have been evaluated by D. H. Lehmer [Trans. Amer. Math. Soc. **43**, 271–295 (1938)]. Other proofs of the relevant factorization formulas have been given by Rademacher and Whiteman [Amer. J. Math. **63**, 377–407 (1941); these Rev. **2**, 249]. New proofs of the evaluation of the $A_k(n)$ when $k$ is a prime power are given in the present paper.

*H. S. Zuckerman* (Seattle, Wash.).

Citations: MR 2, 249f = F20-1.

Referred to in P72-32.

## P72-12 (9, 271d)

**Gupta, Hansraj. An asymptotic formula in partitions.** J. Indian Math. Soc. (N.S.) **10**, 73–76 (1946).

Let $p(n,m)$ denote the number of partitions of $n$ into exactly $m$ parts and let $p(n)$ denote the number of unrestricted partitions of $n$. The author gives a proof of the following theorem. Let $t>0$ and let $n$ and $m$ tend to infinity in such a way that $\lim_{n,m\to\infty}(6n)^{\frac{1}{2}}\exp(-\pi m(6n)^{-\frac{1}{2}})=t$; then $(6n)^{\frac{1}{2}}p(n,m)/p(n)\sim te^{-t/\pi}$. This is equivalent to a previous result of Auluck, S. Chowla and the author [same J. (N.S.) **6**, 105–112 (1942); these Rev. **4**, 211].

*D. H. Lehmer.*

Citations: MR 4, 211b = P80-5.

**P72-13** **(11, 582b)**

**Brigham, Nelson A. A general asymptotic formula for partition functions.** Proc. Amer. Math. Soc. **1**, 182–191 (1950).

Let $\gamma(n)$ be a nonnegative function and let $g_\gamma(s)$, $a_\gamma(k)$ be defined by the relation

$$g_\gamma(s)=\prod_{n=1}^{\infty}(1-e^{-sn})^{-\gamma(n)}=\sum_{k=0}^{\infty}a_\gamma(k)e^{-sk}\quad(\Re s>0).$$

Then $a_\gamma(k)$ is a weighted partition function of $k$, given by

$$a_\gamma(k)=\sum\prod_{n=1}^{l}\gamma(n)[\gamma(n)+1]\cdots[\gamma(n)+k_n-1]/k_n!,$$

where the sum is extended over all partitions of $k$ having the form $k=k_1+2k_2+\cdots+lk_l$ $(k_1,\cdots,k_l>0)$. Using a method due to G. H. Hardy and S. Ramanujan [Proc. London Math. Soc. (2) **16**, 112–132 (1917)] the author proves that if $\sum_{n\le x}\gamma(n)\sim Kx^u\log^v x$ $(x\to\infty;K>0,u>0)$, then the summatory function $A_\gamma(k)=\sum_{n=0}^{k}a_\gamma(n)$ satisfies, for $k\to\infty$, the relation

(*) $$\log A_\gamma(k)\sim u^{-1}\{Ku\Gamma(u+2)\zeta(u+1)\}^{1/(u+1)}\times(u+1)^{(u-v)/(u+1)}k^{u/(u+1)}(\log k)^{v/(u+1)}.$$

This result is established by showing that

$$\log g_\gamma(s)\sim K\Gamma(u+1)\zeta(u+1)s^{-u}(\log s^{-1})^v$$

$(s\to+0)$ and then appealing to a Tauberian theorem on general Dirichlet series with positive coefficients [Hardy and Ramanujan, loc. cit., theorem A].

The author also shows that under certain conditions the function $A_\gamma(k)$ in (*) may be replaced by $a_\gamma(k)$. Finally, he discusses a number of applications of (*) and points out, in particular, that by appropriate specializations of $\gamma(n)$ we can obtain the Hardy-Ramanujan formulae involving unrestricted partitions, partitions into $r$th powers, and partitions into primes. *L. Mirsky* (Sheffield).

Referred to in P72-50.

**P72-14** **(11, 582c)**

**Brigham, Nelson A. On a certain weighted partition function.** Proc. Amer. Math. Soc. **1**, 192–204 (1950).

The author observes that no asymptotic formula for the number of partitions of a large integer into primes has as yet been found. As a contribution to this problem he obtains, on the assumption of the Riemann hypothesis, an asumptotic formula for $\sum_{n=0}^{k}a(n)$, where $a(k)$ is a weighted partition function involving primes and powers of primes, which is defined by the expansion

$$g(s)=\prod_{n=1}^{\infty}(1-e^{-sn})^{-\Lambda(n)}=\sum_{k=0}^{\infty}a(k)e^{-sk},$$

where $\Lambda(n)$ has its customary meaning. [For the precise arithmetical significance of $a(k)$ see the preceding review.]

The first step in the argument is to apply Mellin's inversion formula; this enables us to show that, as $s\to+0$ in the region $|\arg s|\le\theta_0<\frac{1}{2}\pi$,

(*) $$g(s)=K_2s^{\log 2\pi}\exp\{\tfrac{1}{6}\pi^2/s+Z(s)+O(|s|)\};$$

here

$$K_2=\exp(-1+\pi^2/24+\textstyle\sum_\rho\rho^{-2}),\quad Z(s)=\textstyle\sum_\rho s^{-\rho}\zeta(1+\rho)\Gamma(\rho),$$

and $\rho$ ranges over the complex zeros of $\zeta(s)$, multiple ones being counted according to their multiplicity. A Tauberian theorem due to A. E. Ingham [Ann. of Math. (2) **42**, 1075–1090 (1941), theorem 1; these Rev. **3**, 166] is now made use of; to verify that all its conditions are satisfied it is necessary to assume the full strength of the Riemann hypothesis. Ingham's theorem and relation (*) lead to the conclusion that, for $k\to\infty$,

$$\sum_{n=0}^{k}a(k)\sim K_1\sigma^{\frac{1}{2}+\log 2\pi}\exp\{\sigma^{-1}(\tfrac{1}{3}\pi^2+\sigma Z(\sigma)-\sigma^2Z'(\sigma))\},$$

where $K_1=(3/2\pi)^{\frac{1}{2}}K_2/\pi$ and $\sigma$ is the unique positive solution of the equation $\pi^2/6\sigma^2-Z'(\sigma)=k$. *L. Mirsky* (Sheffield).

Citations: MR 3, 166a = P72-3.

**P72-15** **(12, 392f)**

**Auluck, F. C., Singwi, K. S., and Agarwala, B. K. On a new type of partition.** Proc. Nat. Inst. Sci. India **16**, 147–156 (1950).

Using the standard method of steepest descent, applied to an integral of the generating functions round a suitable contour, asymptotic formulae are derived for the number of partitions of a large integer $n$ into parts satisfying various conditions. A typical result is the following: If $\omega(n)$ is the number of partitions of $n$ into integers, each of which may occur only an odd number of times, then $\omega(n)\sim[\gamma/(2\pi n)]\exp(2\gamma n^{\frac{1}{2}})$, with

$$\gamma^2=(\pi^2/12)+\int_0^1\log(1+y-y^2)(dy/y).$$

*F. J. Dyson* (Birmingham).

**P72-16** **(13, 112c)**

**Newman, D. J. The evaluation of the constant in the formula for the number of partitions of $n$.** Amer. J. Math. **73**, 599–601 (1951).

Hardy and Ramanujan [Proc. London Math. Soc. (2) **17**, 75–115 (1918)] proved using analytical methods that the number of partitions of $n$, $p(n)$, satisfies

$$p(n)=(1+o(1))(1/4\sqrt{3})\exp[\pi(\tfrac{2}{3}n)^{\frac{1}{2}}].$$

The reviewer [Ann. of Math. (2) **43**, 437–450 (1942); these Rev. **4**, 36] proved in an elementary (but complicated) way that $p(n)=(1+o(1))an^{-1}\exp[\pi(\frac{2}{3}n)^{\frac{1}{2}}]$, but did not succeed in showing that $a=1/4\sqrt{3}$. The author proves that $a=1/4\sqrt{3}$; his proof is elementary and simple. *P. Erdös* (Aberdeen).

Citations: MR 4, 36a = P72-5.

Referred to in P72-53.

**P72-17** **(13, 210b)**

**Szekeres, G. An asymptotic formula in the theory of partitions.** Quart. J. Math., Oxford Ser. (2) **2**, 85–108 (1951).

This paper enriches our knowledge of the structure of the partitions of a positive integer by furnishing new results as well as by initiating a new method. Let $p(n,k)$ be the number of partitions of $n$ into exactly $k$ positive integral parts; $P(n,k)$, the number of partitions of $n$ into $k$ or fewer positive parts; $q(n,k)$, the number of partitions of $n$ into exactly $k$ positive unequal parts. An elementary result is (1) $P(n,k)\sim n^{k-1}/k!(k-1)!$ for $k$ fixed, $n\to\infty$. Erdös and Lehner [Duke Math. J. **8**, 335–345 (1941); these Rev. **3**, 69; referred to as I] proved (1) for $k=o(n^{\frac{1}{3}})$, but could not extend it even to $k=O(n^{\frac{1}{3}})$. The author proves

(2) $$P(n,k)\sim[n^{k-1}/k!(k-1)!]\exp(k^3/4n-\cdots)\quad\text{for }k=O(n^{\frac{1}{2}-\delta}),\ \delta>0,$$

also $P(n,k)\sim p(n,k)$ for $k=o(n^{\frac{1}{2}})$; in I this result was conjectured for $k=O(n^{\frac{1}{2}})$ and proved for $k=o(n^{\frac{1}{3}})$.

It was shown in I that $k_0=2^{-1}cn^{\frac{1}{2}}\log n$, $c=6^{\frac{1}{2}}\pi^{-1}$, is the "normal" number of summands in a partition of $n$, i.e.,

(3) $$P(n,k)/p(n)=\{1+o(1)\}\exp(-ce^{-\lambda})\ \text{for}\ k=k_0+c\lambda n^{\frac{1}{2}},$$

where $p(n)=P(n,n)$ is the number of unrestricted partitions of $n$. Erdös [Bull. Amer. Math. Soc. **52**, 185–188 (1946);

these Rev. **7**, 273] proved that $p(n, k)$, for fixed $n$, has a maximum at $k_1=k_0+c\log cn^{1/2}+o(n^{1/2})$, and that $q(n, k)$ has a maximum at $k_2=Acn^{1/2}+dn^{1/4}+o(n^{1/4})$ for a certain constant $d$; $A=2^{1/2}\log 2$. The author improves this to $k_2=Acn^{1/2}+B+O(n^{-1/2})$, with $B$ a specified constant, so that $d=0$. Furthermore, for large $n$, $k_2$ is the nearest integer to $Acn^{1/2}+B$. By his method the author also obtains the first term of the Hardy-Ramanujan asymptotic expansions of $p(n)$, and of $q(n)$ (the number of partitions of $n$ into unequal parts.)

In order to develop these results the author goes back to Sylvester's theory of "waves" [Amer. J. Math. **5**, 251–330 (1882)], which he combines with some complicated theorems of his own which yield asymptotic expansions for the coefficients of certain power series [Acta Sci. Math. Szeged **12B**, 187–198 (1950); these Rev. **13**, 220]. Observing that the residue of $(1-e^{-t})^{-j}$ at $t=0$ is $+1$ for every integer $j\geqq 1$, Sylvester remarks that if $F(x)=N(x)/D(x)$ is a proper rational fraction, $F(x)=\sum_{\mu=-s}^{\infty}c_\mu x^\mu$, then $F(0)=\operatorname{Res}_{t=0}\sum_\nu F(a_\nu e^{-t})$, where $D(a_\nu)=0$. The generating function of $P(n, k)$ being $\prod_{j=1}^{k}(1-x^j)^{-1}$, Sylvester sets

$$(4)\quad P(n, k)=\sum_{q=1}^{k}\sum_{\zeta}P_\zeta(n, k)=P_1(n, k)+\sum_{q=2}^{k}\sum_{\zeta}P_\zeta(n, k),$$

where $P_\zeta(n, k)=\operatorname{Res}_{t=0}\zeta^{-n}e^{nt}\prod_{j=1}^{k}(1-\zeta^j e^{-jt})^{-1}$ and $\zeta$ runs over the primitive roots of unity of order $q\leqq k$. By using the above mentioned theorems, the author proves that $P_1(n, k)$ is the principal term (corresponding in the Hardy-Ramanujan circle method to the "heaviest" singularity at $z=1$) and that it determines the asymptotic behavior of $P(n, k)$. The remaining sum, called the circulatory part, depends on the arithmetic structure of $n$.

The author points out by numerical examples the similarity of the Sylvester terms $P_\zeta(n, n)$ to the terms of the Hardy-Ramanujan-Rademacher infinite series for $p(n)=P(n, n)$. Thus his method of proof opens the attractive possibility that the infinite series for $p(n)$ can be derived without using the theory of the (elliptic) modular functions. To the reviewer this is by far the most interesting aspect of the paper. *J. Lehner* (Philadelphia, Pa.).

Citations: MR 3, 69a = P80-4; MR 7, 273i = P80-10.

Referred to in P72-19.

## P72-18 (14, 138h)

**Auluck, F. C., and Haselgrove, C. B. On Ingham's Tauberian theorem for partitions.** Proc. Cambridge Philos. Soc. **48**, 566–570 (1952).

Under conditions not set forth here, Ingham [Ann. of Math. (2) **42**, 1075–1090 (1941); these Rev. **3**, 166] obtained the asymptotic form of $P_h(u)=[P(u+h)-P(u)]/h$ where $P(u)$ is the number of solutions in integers $n_i\geqq 0$ of the inequality $n_1\lambda_1+n_2\lambda_2+\cdots+n_r\lambda_r<u$. The present paper removes the Ingham condition that $h$ be such that $P_h(u)$ is an increasing function of $u$, and replaces the Ingham condition $0<\lambda_1<\lambda_2<\lambda_3<\cdots$ by the weaker condition $0<\lambda_1\leqq\lambda_2\leqq\lambda_3\leqq\cdots$. Riesz means of second and higher orders enable the authors to overcome difficulties produced by weakening the hypotheses. *R. P. Agnew.*

Citations: MR 3, 166a = P72-3.

Referred to in P72-39.

## P72-19 (15, 201c)

**Szekeres, G. Some asymptotic formulae in the theory of partitions. II.** Quart. J. Math., Oxford Ser. (2) **4**, 96–111 (1953).

The author obtains an asymptotic formula for $P(n, k)$, the number of partitions of $n$ into at most $k$ parts, by applying the method of steepest descents to the integral in

$$P(n, k)=\frac{1}{2\pi i}\int F(w)w^{-n-1}dw,$$

where $F(w)=\prod_{\nu=1}^{k}(1-w^\nu)^{-1}=\sum_{n=0}^{\infty}P(n, k)w^n$. His formula is valid for all ranges of $k$ and $n$ (cf. second paragraph on p. 98) and therefore improves the result obtained in his previous paper [same J. (2) **2**, 85–108 (1951); these Rev. **13**, 210]; the present method is also considerably simpler.

For bounded $n/k^2$ the formula reads

$$(1)\quad P(n, k)=\frac{1}{2\pi}B_0^{-1/2}\beta^{-2}\exp\left\{2\beta\int_0^v\frac{t\,dt}{e^t-1}-(v\beta+\tfrac{1}{2})\times\log(1-e^{-v})+\frac{1}{2}\left(\frac{v}{e^v-1}-1\right)\right\}$$
$$\times[1+B_1(v)\beta^{-1}+\cdots+B_{m-1}(v)\beta^{-m+1}+O(\beta^{-m})],$$

for any $m>0$, where $B_0=\int_0^v t^2e^t(e^t-1)^{-2}dt$, $|B_\mu(v)|\leqq C_\mu$, and $v$, $\beta$ are determined from $v\beta=k$ and a complicated transcendental relation. In particular, $\beta$ is of the exact order of $n^{1/2}$. When $n/k^2$ is not bounded, the formula is slightly different. For $k\geqq\delta n$, $\delta$ fixed and $>0$, the first term of (1) coincides with the first term of the Hardy-Ramanujan formula for $p(n)$, the unrestricted partition function.

The author also investigates $p(n, k)$, the number of partitions of $n$ into exactly $k$ positive parts. Erdös [Bull. Amer. Math. Soc. **52**, 185–188 (1946); these Rev. **7**, 273] proved that the maximum of $p(n, k)$ occurs at $k_1=cn^{1/2}L+o(n^{1/2})$, $L=\log(cn^{1/2})$. In the present paper this is improved to

$$k=cn^{1/2}L+c^2(\tfrac{3}{2}+\tfrac{3}{2}L-\tfrac{1}{4}L^2)-\tfrac{1}{2}+O(n^{-1/2}\log^4 n).$$

Similar results are obtained for $q(n, k)$, the number of partitions of $n$ into exactly $k$ unequal parts.

Presumably, the author's method should be available for a variety of partition problems. *J. Lehner.*

Citations: MR 7, 273i = P80-10; MR 13, 210b = P72-17.

Referred to in N60-35, P44-21, P72-23.

## P72-20 (16, 17e)

**Meinardus, Günter. Asymptotische Aussagen über Partitionen.** Math. Z. **59**, 388–398 (1954).

The author applies a saddle-point method to obtain the asymptotic value of the power-series coefficients $r(n)$ of the function $f(x)=\prod_{n=1}^{\infty}(1-x^n)^{-a_n}$, where $a_n$ are real, non-negative numbers. His formula is

$$(1)\quad r(n)=Cn^\kappa\exp\left\{n^{\alpha/(\alpha+1)}\left(1+\frac{1}{\alpha}\right)\times(A\Gamma(\alpha+1)\zeta(\alpha+1))^{1/(\alpha+1)}\right\}\cdot(1+O(n^{-k_1})),$$

where $\alpha$ is the convergence abscissa of $D(s)=\sum a_n a^{-s}$, $A$ is its residue at $s=1$, and $\kappa$, $C$, $k_1$ are explicitly given in terms of $\alpha$, $D(0)$, $D'(0)$. The validity of (1) requires that $D(s)$ and $\sum_1^\infty a_n x^n$ shall satisfy certain function-theoretic conditions.

The author closes the paper with certain examples, including one in which $r(n)$ is the number of partitions of $n$ into summands $n_1\equiv a \pmod n$, $(a, n)=1$, and so obtains the first terms of the Hardy-Ramanujan-Rademacher series. The reviewer remarks that he could equally well have considered the case in which $n_i\equiv\pm a \pmod n$, and so derived the first terms of the convergent series obtained for special values of $a$ and $n$ by Niven [these Rev. **1**, 201], Haberzetle [these Rev. **3**, 69], the reviewer [these Rev. **3**, 166], and Livingood [these Rev. **6**, 259].

The author points out that his method does not require the

assumption of monotonicity for $r(n)$, which is needed when a Tauberian approach is used [e.g., Ingham, Ann. of Math. (2) **42**, 1075–1090 (1941); these Rev. **3**, 166].

*J. Lehner* (Los Alamos, N. M.).

Citations: MR 1, 201c = P68-1; MR 3, 69b = P68-3; MR 3, 166a = P72-3; MR 3, 166b = P68-4; MR 6, 259b = P68-6.

Referred to in P68-12.

## P72-21 (16, 17f)

**Haselgrove, C. B., and Temperley, H. N. V. Asymptotic formulae in the theory of partitions.** Proc. Cambridge Philos. Soc. **50**, 225–241 (1954).

The authors apply a method of contour integration to obtain asymptotic results about $p_m(n)$, the number of partitions of an integer $n$ into $m$ parts selected from the sequence of integers $0<\lambda_1<\lambda_2<\cdots\to\infty$; the generating function $G(x,z)=\prod_{r=1}^{\infty}(1-xz^{\lambda_r})^{-1}$ is used. Their principal result is that if $\sum\lambda_r^{-2}$ converges and if $\psi(\omega)=\sum e^{-\lambda_r\omega}$, $\mathrm{Re}\,\omega>0$, satisfies certain function-theoretic restrictions, then

$$p_m(n)/p(n)\sim\xi F((m-m_0)\xi),\quad n\to\infty.$$

In this formula, $p(n)$ is the number of unrestricted partitions of $n$, $\xi$ is the root of a transcendental equation involving $n$ and $\psi(\omega)$, $m_0=\sum_r(e^{\lambda_r\xi}-1)^{-1}$, and $F(y)$ has the properties of a probability density function with mean at $y=0$, which is given explicitly as the inverse Laplace transform of the function $\prod_r(1+\alpha/\lambda_r)^{-1}e^{\alpha/\lambda_r}$. By means of this formula and some others involving differences of the $p_m(n)$, the authors are able to verify known results on partitions into $m$ parts, into powers, and into primes, and to prove the conjecture of Auluck, Chowla, and Gupta [J. Indian Math. Soc. (N.S.) **6**, 105–112 (1942), p. 105; these Rev. **4**, 211] that $p_m(n)$ attains its maximum value for at most two consecutive values of $m$ when $n$ is large and fixed.

The method employed appears to be the most powerful of the methods which do not use the Farey dissection of the circle. *J. Lehner* (Los Alamos, N. M.).

Citations: MR 4, 211b = P80-5.

Referred to in P02-27, P44-21, P44-23.

## P72-22 (16, 676f)

**Gupta, Hansraj. On a generating function in partition theory.** Proc. Nat. Inst. Sci. India **20**, 582–586 (1954).

Let

$$f(x,r)=r!/(1-x)(1-x^2)\cdots(1-x^r)=r!\sum p(n,r)x^n,$$

where $p(n,r)$ is the number of partitions of $n$ into at most $r$ parts. Writing $f(x,r)=\sum_{j\geqq 0}A_j(r)(1-x)^{j-r}$, the author shows that $A_j(r)=\sum_{i=1}^{2j}q_{i-2}(j)\binom{r}{i}$, where the $q_i(j)$ are independent of $r$, and are expressible in terms of $A_0(i'),\cdots,A_{j-1}(i')$, $2\leqq i'\leqq i+2$. In this way the functions $A_j(r)$ are computed for $0\leqq j\leqq 5$. Another table gives the values $A_j(r)$ for $0\leqq j\leqq 5$ and $2\leqq r\leqq 12$. It is shown that for fixed $j$ and large $r$, $A_j(r)\sim r!/4^j\cdot j!(r-2j)!$, and an asymptotic formula for $p(n,r)$ is obtained for fixed $r$ and large $n$.

*N. J. Fine* (Philadelphia, Pa.).

## P72-23 (16, 797b)

**Roth, K. F., and Szekeres, G. Some asymptotic formulae in the theory of partitions.** Quart. J. Math., Oxford Ser. (2) **5**, 241–259 (1954).

The authors develop an asymptotic formula for $p_u(n)$, the number of partitions of an integer $n$ into distinct members of an eventually increasing sequence of integers $u_1, u_2, \cdots$, subject only to the conditions:

(1) $$s=\lim_{k\to\infty}\log u_k/\log k$$

exists;

(2) $$\inf_{\alpha}\left\{(\log k)^{-1}\sum_{\nu=1}^{k}\|u_\nu\alpha\|^2\right\}\to\infty\quad\text{with}\quad k\to\infty,$$

where $\|\theta\|$ is the distance of $\theta$ to the nearest integer, and $\frac{1}{2}u_k<\alpha\leqq\frac{1}{2}$. (It is shown that, among others, the choices $u_k=p_k$, as well as $u_k=f(k)$, $f(p_k)$ are allowable, $p_k$ being the $k$th prime, and $f$ being a rather general polynomial.) Their formula is:

$$p_u(n)=\left[2\pi\sum_{\nu=1}^{\infty}u_\nu^2e^{\eta u_\nu}(1+e^{\eta\mu_\nu})^{-2}\right]^{-1/2}$$
$$\times\exp\left[\sum_{\nu=1}^{\infty}\left\{\frac{\eta\mu_\nu}{1+e^{\eta\mu_\nu}}+\log(1+e^{-\eta\mu_\nu})\right\}\right]$$
$$\times\left\{1+\sum_{\rho=1}^{m-2}D_\rho+O(n^{-(m-1)/(s+1)+\delta})\right\},$$

where $\delta>0$, $m$ is a fixed integer $>1$, $\eta$ is determined from $n=\sum_1^\infty u_\nu(1+e^{\eta\mu_\nu})^{-1}$, and the $D$'s are defined by certain complicated summations. This formula is proved by a saddle-point method similar to that used in an earlier paper by Szekeres [same J. (2) **4**, 96–111 (1953); MR **15**, 201]. From this formula the authors deduce:

$$\log p_u(n)=\pi\left(\frac{2}{3}\frac{n}{\log n}\right)^{1/2}\left\{1+O\left(\frac{\log\log n}{\log n}\right)\right\}$$

for the number of partitions into distinct primes, as well as a more complicated formula for partitions into distinct powers. They establish also the result: there exists an $n_0$ and $c>0$, depending only on $\delta$ and the sequence $\{u\}$, such that $p_u(n+1)-p_u(n)>cn^{-s/(s+1)-\delta}p_u(n)$ for $n>n_0$. In the last section the restriction that the summands should be distinct is dropped; an asymptotic formula is obtained.

*J. Lehner* (Los Alamos, N. M.).

Citations: MR 15, 201c = P72-19.

Referred to in B12-23, P72-45.

## P72-24 (16, 905a)

**Meinardus, Günter. Über Partitionen mit Differenzenbedingungen.** Math. Z. **61**, 289–302 (1954).

The author obtains (Theorem 1) the first term in an asymptotic expansion of $r(n)$, where $f(z)=\sum_0^\infty r(n)e^{-nz}$ converges in the right half-plane, $r(n)$ is real, and $f(z)$ satisfies certain function-theoretic conditions similar to those in Ingham's classical theorem [Ann. of Math. (2) **42**, 1075–1090 (1941); MR **3**, 166], except that the monotonicity of $r(n)$ is no longer assumed. The author's result is essentially the same as Ingham's, but the method is different, being a saddle-point method, whereas Ingham used a Tauberian theorem. The author then considers the function

$$F(v)=1+\sum_{\nu=1}^{\infty}\frac{v^{\frac{1}{2}kl\nu(\nu-1)+m\nu}}{(1-v^k)\cdots(1-v^{\nu k})}=1+\sum s(n)v^n,$$

and obtains (Theorem 2) the first term of an asymptotic expansion of $s(n)$ by applying Theorem 1 to the coefficients of the above series. To show that $F(v)$ satisfies the function-theoretic conditions of Theorem 1, use is made of an identity of Euler as well as a saddle-point calculation. By specializing $k$ and $l$ the author obtains in the last section of his paper asymptotic relations for various partition functions.

*J. Lehner* (Los Alamos, N. M.).

Citations: MR 3, 166a = P72-3.

## P72-25 (17, 129b)

**Petersson, Hans. Uber Modulfunktionen und Partitionenprobleme.** Abh. Deutsch. Akad. Wiss. Berlin. Kl. Math. Allg. Nat. **1954**, no. 2, 59 pp.

The author considers a very general partition problem. Let $\mathfrak{S}_b$ be the set of integers congruent to $\pm b \bmod N$, $b=1, 2, \cdots, N/2$, $N$ even. Let $k_{b\nu}$, $0\leqq\nu\leqq f_b$, be even non-negative integers; and $l_{b\nu}$, $1\leqq\nu\leqq f_b$, integers $\geqq 2$. Let $p_n([k], [l], N)$ be the number of partitions of $n$ into positive summands; if a summand lies in $\mathfrak{S}_b$ it is associated with one of the $k_{b\nu}$ "colors", and in the first $k_{b0}$ colors it may occur arbitrarily often, in the next $k_{b1}$ colors it occurs at most $l_{b1}-1$ times, etc. The generating function is

$$\sum_{n=0}^{\infty} p_n([k], [l], N)x^n = \prod_{b=1}^{N/2} \prod_{m=\pm b(N)} \{(1-x^m)^{-k_{b0}} \prod_{j=1}^{f_b} (1+x^m+\cdots+x^{(l_{bj}-1)m})^{k_{bj}}\}, |x|<1.$$

For this partition function the author obtains a convergent series representation of the type of the Rademacher series, as well as an asymptotic formula. The method used is not the Hardy circle method, but the author's own function-theoretic method, which he has expounded in a series of papers.

He treats also cases in which the summands satisfy additional restrictions depending on the Kronecker symbol of a real quadratic field, as well as the asymptotic value of the quotient of two partition functions in which the summands fulfill related conditions. *J. Lehner.*

Referred to in F30-45, F30-50, P68-12, P68-15, P68-21, P72-29, P72-33.

## P72-26 (17, 238i)

**Gupta, Hansraj. Partitions in general.** Res. Bull. Panjab Univ. no. **67** (1955), 31–38.

Let $P_m(n)$ be the number of partitions of $n$ into integers $a_0=1, a_1, a_2, \cdots, a_m$. Then

$$\binom{n+m}{m} \leqq P_m(n) \prod_{t=1}^{m} a_t \leqq \binom{n+\beta_m}{m},$$

where $\beta_m=a_1+a_2+\cdots+a_m$. If $r\beta_r=o(n)$, then

$$P_r(n) \sim \binom{n+r}{r} \prod_{t=1}^{r} a_t^{-1}.$$

In case $a_1, a_2, \cdots, a_r$ are the primes $2, 3, \cdots, p_r$, and $r^3(\log r)^2=O(n)$,

$$P_r(n)=\left\{\binom{n+r}{r}+\tfrac{1}{2}\sum_{i=1}^{r}(p_i-1)(1+o(1))\binom{n+r-1}{r-1}\right\}\prod_{i=1}^{r} p_i^{-1}.$$

*N. J. Fine* (Philadelphia, Pa.).

## P72-27 (17, 239b)

**Freĭman, G. A. An elementary method of solution of problems on the partition of numbers into an unbounded number of summands.** Trudy Moskov. Mat. Obšč. **4** (1955), 113–124. (Russian)

A positive increasing divergent sequence $\{a_r\}$ is given, and the object is to obtain, by elementary methods, asymptotic formulae for

$$p(N)=\frac{q(N)-q(N-h)}{h}, \quad p_r(N)=\frac{q_r(N)-q_r(N-h)}{h},$$

where $q(N)$ is the number of solutions of

$$a_1n_1+a_2n_2+\cdots+a_in_i+\cdots\leqq N$$

in integers $n_i\geqq 0$, $q_r(N)$ is the number of solutions with $n_i=0$ when $i>r$, and $h$ is a fixed member of the sequence $\{a_r\}$. The rate and regularity of growth of $a_r$ are restricted by conditions on a twice differentiable function $a_z$ equal to $a_r$ at $z=r$ $(r=1, 2, \cdots)$. The restrictions correspond roughly to rates of growth between $r^\delta$ and $\exp(r^{\frac{1}{2}-\delta})$ $(\delta>0)$. The formula for $p_r(N)$ is

$$(1) \qquad p_r(N) \sim \frac{e^E}{\sqrt{(2\pi w(1-e^{-wa_r})Y)}} e^T,$$

where

$$E=\lim_{x\to\infty}\left\{\int_1^x \log a_z\,dz-\sum_{r=1}^{x-1}\log a_r-\tfrac{1}{2}\log a_x\right\}$$

and $w$, $Y$, $N$ are functions of $(r, N)$ defined by

$$N=\int_1^r \frac{a_z dz}{e^{wa_z}-1}, \quad Y=\int_1^r \frac{a_z^2 e^{wa_z}dz}{(e^{wa_z}-1)^2},$$

$$T=Nw-\int_1^r \log(1-e^{-wa_z})dz.$$

The formula for $p(N)$ is the formal result of replacing $r$ everywhere by $\infty$. The proof of (1) is by induction from $r$ to $r+1$ based on the recurrence relation

$$p_{r+1}(N)=p_r(N)+p_r(N-a_{r+1})+p_r(N-2a_{r+1})+\cdots.$$

When $r$ is not too large, simple inequalities are derived from this and the assumed properties of $a_z$, but for larger values of $r$ the argument is supplemented by estimates of $p_r(N-\Delta)/p_r(N)$ based on the assumption that suitable inequalities for $p_r(\ )$ are already known. The precise meaning of (1) is not stated explicitly, and the details and logical arrangement of the second stage of the induction argument are obscure. But so far as can be judged from the context, the meaning seems to be that the ratio of the two sides of (1) tends to 1 as a Pringsheim double limit when $r, N\to\infty$. *A. E. Ingham.*

## P72-28 (17, 239c)

**Freĭman, G. A. Inverse problems of the additive theory of numbers.** Izv. Akad. Nauk SSSR. Ser. Mat. **19** (1955), 275–284. (Russian)

Suppose given a positive increasing divergent sequence $\{a_r\}$, and let $n(u)$ be the number of $a_r\leqq u$ and $q(N)$ the number of solutions of

$$a_1n_1+a_2n_2+\cdots\leqq N$$

in integers $n_i\geqq 0$. The author begins by stating the theorem (i) that $\log q(u)\sim Au^\alpha$ implies $n(u)\sim Bu^\beta$ (as $u\to\infty$), where $A, \alpha, B, \beta$ are positive constants connected by

$$(1-\alpha)(1+\beta)=1, \quad B\Gamma(1+\beta)\zeta(1+\beta)=(1-\alpha)(A\alpha)^{1+\beta};$$

and he then raises the question of strengthening hypothesis and conclusion in this theorem. He proves (ii) that, if

$$\log q(u)=Au^\alpha+O(u^{\alpha_1}) \quad (\alpha_1<\alpha),$$

then

$$n(u)=Bu^\beta+O(u^\beta/\log u);$$

and (iii) that this conclusion cannot be improved, even if the hypothesis is replaced by

$$(1) \qquad q(u)\sim A_0u^a \exp(Au^a).$$

The proof of (ii) is based on the formulae

$$g(s)=s\int_0^\infty e^{-su}q(u)du, \quad \log g(s)=\int_0^\infty e^{-su}d\Pi(u) \quad (s>0),$$

where

$$g(s)\equiv\prod_{r=1}^{\infty}\frac{1}{1-e^{-a_rs}}, \quad \Pi(u)\equiv\sum_{k=1}^{\infty}\frac{1}{k}n\left(\frac{u}{k}\right).$$

The main steps are (a) an Abelian inference from $q(u)$ to $g(s)$ $(u\to\infty, s\to 0+)$, (b) a Tauberian inference from $\log g(s)$ to $\Pi(u)$, (c) an application of the Möbius inversion formula. In the corresponding proof of (i) a classical Tauberian theorem of Hardy and Littlewood would be appropriate under (b); in (ii) this is replaced by the known developments of this theorem by Postnikov, Freud, and Korevaar. An example constructed by Korevaar in this connection provides a model for (iii). By a similar construction the sequence $\{r^{1/\beta}\}$ is modified so as to yield a sequence $\{a_r\}$ for which $n(u)=u^\beta+\Omega_\pm(u^\beta/\log u)$ while the asymptotic behaviour (1) of $q(u)$ remains undisturbed;

this last point being established by means of a general theorem of the author [see the paper reviewed above].

*A. E. Ingham* (Cambridge, England).

Referred to in N80-40.

**P72-29** **(17, 1057f)**

**Petersson, Hans. Über die arithmetischen Eigenschaften eines Systems multiplikativer Modulfunktionen von Primzahlstufe.** Acta Math. **95** (1956), 57–110.

The Fourier coefficients of many modular forms may be interpreted as the number of partitions of the corresponding index, with the number, or size (or both) of the summands subjected to specific restrictions. Hence, any progress made concerning the Fourier expansions of such modular forms, can be used, in principle, in order to obtain corresponding information relative to certain partition functions. Using results and methods of his previous papers [Math. Ann. **127** (1954), 33–81; Abh. Deutsch Akad. Wiss. Berlin. Math. Allg. Nat. **1954,** no. 2; see also S. B. Heidelberger Akad. Wiss. Math.-Nat. Kl. **1950,** 417–494; MR **15,** 686; **17,** 129; **12,** 806], the author obtains representations by finite linear combinations of absolutely convergent series for the Fourier coefficients of certain modular functions and forms. Identifying the dominant terms of these expansions, he obtains asymptotic formulae for these Fourier coefficients, i.e. for certain partition functions. Specifically, the following three partition problems are considered: Problem I. Let $q$ be a prime and denote by $k_0$, $k_1$ two non-negative integers, $k=k_0+k_1>0$, by $\eta(\tau)$ the Dedekind $\eta$-function, set $u_m=\exp(2\pi i\tau/m)$ and $\beta_\infty=((q-1)/24)(-k_0+k_1(q-1))$. Then

$$F(\tau)=\eta^{k_0+2k_1}(\tau)\eta^{-k_0-k_1}\left(\frac{\tau}{q}\right)\eta^{-k_1}(q\tau)=\sum_{n=0}^{\infty}r_n(k_0,k_1,q)u_q^{\,n-\beta_\infty}.$$

Here $r_n=r_n(k_0,k_1,q)$ represents the number of partitions of the integer $n$ into summands not divisible by $q$, subject to the following restrictions: the summands occur in the $k$ colors; each summand may appear arbitrarily often in any of the first $k_0$ colors, but only $q-1$ times in any of the last $k_1$ colors and two partitions are considered identical if each summand occurs in both of them the same number of times in each color. The study of the function $F(\tau)$ then leads to the desired expansions and asymptotic formulae for $r_n(k_0,k_1,q)$. Problem II. Let the prime $q>5$ satisfy $q\equiv 1 \pmod 4$, let $k^+$ and $k^-$ be non-negative integers, $k^++k^->0$. Let the integer $m$ occur in any of the $k^+$ colors if $(m/q)=+1$ and in any of the $k^-$ colors, if $(m/q)=-1$. Then $\pi_n(\mathfrak{k},q)$ stands for the number of partitions of $n$ into summands $m$ not divisible by $q$, the colors in which they may occur being restricted only by the value of the Legendre symbol $(m/q)$, and the identity of two partitions being defined as in Problem I. These partitions appear as Fourier coefficients of modular functions, invariant under the transformations of a subgroup $\Gamma^{0+}[q]$ of the modular group, defined as follows:

$$L=\begin{pmatrix}\alpha&\beta\\ \gamma&\delta\end{pmatrix}\in\Gamma^{0+}[q]\subset\Gamma \text{ if } \left(\frac{\alpha}{q}\right)=+1 \text{ and } \beta\equiv 0 \pmod q.$$

Problem III is similar to Problem II, but in addition to summands $m\not\equiv 0 \pmod q$, appearing in $k^++k^-$ colors, as in Problem II, also summands $m\equiv 0 \pmod q$ are admitted in $k^0$ distinct colors. The corresponding numbers $\varrho_n(\mathfrak{l},q)$ of partitions of $n$ appear as Fourier coefficients of modular forms of positive dimension $\frac{1}{2}k^0$, belonging to above defined subgroup $\Gamma^{0+}[q]$ of the modular group. The expressions obtained for $r_n(k_0,k_1,q)$, $\pi_n(\mathfrak{k},q)$ and $\varrho_n(\mathfrak{l},q)$ are too complicated to be reproduced here. Only two remarkable corollaries of Problem II [see, however, also the last paper mentioned above] will be quoted. Let $\pi_n^+(q)$ (and $\pi_n^-(q)$) stand for the number of partitions of $n$ into summands $m$ that are quadratic residues (or non-residues, resp.), mod $q$. Denote by $\pi_n^+(q,\mathfrak{l})$ and $\pi_n^-(q,\mathfrak{l})$ respectively, the corresponding number of partitions, when any summand may appear at most $l-1$ times ($l\geqq 2$). Let $a_5(q)$ stand for the number of representations of the prime $q>5$, $q\equiv 1 \pmod 4$, as a sum of five squares, set $a_5^*(q)=a_5(q)/240$ if $q\equiv 1 \pmod 8$, $a_5^*(q)=a_5(q)/560$ if $q\equiv 5 \pmod 8$. If the quadratic field over the rationals $P(q^{\frac{1}{2}})$ has fundamental unit $\varepsilon>1$ and class-number $h$, then, as $n\to\infty$,

$$\frac{\pi_n^+(q)}{\pi_n^-(q)}=\varepsilon^h\left\{1-\frac{\pi}{6}\sqrt{\left(3\left(1-\frac{1}{q}\right)\right)}a_5^*(q)n^{-\frac{1}{2}}+O(n^{-1})\right\},$$

and

$$\frac{\pi_n^+(\mathfrak{l},q)}{\pi_n^-(\mathfrak{l},q)}=$$

$$1+\frac{\pi}{6}\sqrt{\left(3\left(1-\frac{1}{q}\right)\left(1-\frac{1}{l}\right)\right)}(l-1)a_5^*(q)n^{-\frac{1}{2}}+O(n^{-1}).$$

Hence, if the number of equal summands is restricted ($<l$), then $\lim_{n\to\infty}\pi_n^+(\mathfrak{l},q)/\pi_n^-(\mathfrak{l},q)=1$; while, if no such restriction exists, $\lim_{n\to\infty}\pi_n^+(q)/\pi_n^-(q)=\varepsilon^h>1$. These results, proven here for $q>5$, generalize those obtained by Lehner [Duke Math. J. **8** (1941), 631–655; MR **3,** 166] for $q=5$. *E. Grosswald* (Philadelphia, Pa.).

Citations: MR 3, 166b = P68-4; MR 12, 806e = F10-25; MR 17, 129b = P72-25.

Referred to in P68-12, P68-21, P72-33.

**P72-30** **(18, 194i)**

**Dutta, Mahadeb. On new partition of numbers.** Rend. Sem. Mat. Univ. Padova **25** (1956), 138–143.

Denote by $p_d(n)$ the number of partitions of $n$ so that no summand occurs more than $d$ times. Using a Tauberian theorem of Hardy and Ramanujan [Proc. London Math. Soc. (2) **17** (1918), 75–115] the author proves that

$$\log p_d(n)=(1+o(1))\pi\sqrt{\left(\frac{2dn}{3(d+1)}\right)}.$$

He also obtains some identities for $p_d(n)$. *P. Erdös.*

**P72-31** **(18, 195a)**

**Bateman, P. T.; and Erdös, P. Monotonicity of partition functions.** Mathematika 3 (1956), 1–14.

Let $p(n)$ be the number of partitions of $n$ into parts taken from the set $A$, repetitions being allowed; $A$ is an arbitrary finite or infinite set of positive integers other than the empty set or the set consisting of the single element unity. The authors prove: $p(n)$ is strictly increasing for all large $n$ if and only if the following condition is satisfied: $A$ contains more than one element, and if any element is removed from $A$, the remaining elements have greatest common divisor unity. This result is important in applications of Ingham's Tauberian theorem for partitions.

The authors work with $p^{(k)}(n)$, which is the $k$th difference of $p(n)$ if $k>0$, the $(-k)$th order summatory function of $p(n)$ if $k<0$. In the course of the proof, they develop interesting information on the order of magnitude of $p^{(k)}(n)$. All arguments used are elementary, involving only formal power series and partial fraction decompositions of rational functions. *J. Lehner.*

Referred to in A46-21, P72-65.

**P72-32** **(18, 195b)**

**Whiteman, Albert Leon. A sum connected with the series for the partition function.** Pacific J. Math. **6** (1956), 159–176.

Let $p(n)$ denote the number of unrestricted partitions of $n$ into positive integral parts. H. Rademacher's convergent modification of Hardy and Ramanujan's series for the partition function may be written

$$p(n)=\frac{2\sqrt{3}}{\mu(24n-1)}\sum_{k=-\infty}^{\infty}{}' |k|^{-\frac{1}{2}}A_k(n)(\mu-k)\exp(\mu/k),$$

where $\mu=\pi(24n-1)^{\frac{1}{2}}/6$. The coefficients $A_k(n)$ are the subject of the paper under review. They are defined by

$$A_{-k}(n)=A_k(n)=\sum_{\substack{1\leq h\leq k\\(h,k)=1}}\omega_{hk}\exp(-2\pi ihn/k),$$

whence $\omega_{hk}$ are certain complicated $24k$th roots of unity arising from the theory of Dedekind's modular function $\eta(\tau)$. In 1936 the reviewer discovered that, despite its complicated definition, $A_k(n)$ is a multiplicative function of $k$ and that when $k$ is a power of a prime $k^{-\frac{1}{2}}A_k(n)$ is simply twice the cosine of a rational multiple of $\pi$. The resulting simple formulas for $A_k(n)$ made possible the use of (1) for calculating $p(n)$ for very large isolated values of $n$.

Later Rademacher and Whiteman derived these results from the theory of Dedekind sums $S(h, k)$ [Amer. J. Math. **63** (1941), 377–407; Bull. Amer. Math. Soc. **53** (1947), 598–603; MR **2**, 249, **8**, 567]. In the present paper the results are obtained once more; this time using the following finite Fourier series for $A_k(n)$

$$3^{\frac{1}{2}}k^{-\frac{1}{2}}Ak(n)=\sum(-1)^r\cos(\pi(6r+1)/(6k))$$

the sum extending over all $r$ mod $k$ for which

$$(3r^2+r)/2\equiv -n \pmod{k}.$$

This unpublished result of A. Selberg is shown to be equivalent to the above definition. The author uses a sum due to W. Fisher [Pacific J. Math. **1** (1951), 83–95; MR **13**, 209] to carry out the evaluation of $A_k(n)$ when $k$ is a power of a prime. *D. H. Lehmer* (Berkeley, Calif.).

Citations: MR 2, 249f = F20-1; MR 8, 567a = P72-11; MR 13, 209c = F10-26.

Referred to in P72-34.

## P72-33 (19, 392d)

**Petersson, Hans. Über Partitionenprobleme in Verbindung mit Potenzresten nach einem Primzahlmodul.** Math. Z. **66** (1956), 241–268.

Using the results of previous papers [Abh. Deutsch. Akad. Wiss. Berlin. Kl. Math. Allg. Nat. **1954**, no. 2; Acta Math. **95** (1956), 57–110; MR **17**, 129, 1057], the author discusses a new partition function, $\pi_n(k, q, l)$, defined as follows. Let $l$, $q$ be integers, $l\geqq 2$, $q$ prime, $q\equiv 1 \pmod{2l}$, $q>2l+1$. Let $\mathfrak{R}$ be the multiplicative group of residues modulo $q$ which are prime to $q$, $\mathfrak{P}$ the subgroup of $l$th powers of elements in $\mathfrak{R}$, and $\mathfrak{B}$ a system of representatives of the cosets of $\mathfrak{P}$ in $\mathfrak{R}$. For each $s\in\mathfrak{B}$, let $k_s\geqq 0$, and $k=\sum k_s$ be positive. Then $\pi_n(k, q, l)$ is the number of partitions of the positive integer $n$ into summands not divisible by $q$ in which the summands from $s\mathfrak{P}$ $(s\in\mathfrak{B})$ appear in $k_s$ "colors".

The generating function is essentially a modular function belonging to a subgroup $\Gamma^*[l, q]$ of the modular group which is defined by $b\equiv 0 \pmod{q}$, $a\in\mathfrak{P}$ in $\begin{pmatrix}a & b\\ c & d\end{pmatrix}\in\Gamma^*$. Thus the theorems of the above-mentioned papers enable the author to write the partition function $\pi_n$ as a linear combination of convergent series (of the Rademacher type). He also gives asymptotic formulae; for example,

$$\pi_n=\frac{\omega(-k)}{2\sqrt{2\pi}}\rho_1^{\frac{1}{2}}n^{-3/4}\exp(\rho_1 n^{1/2})$$
$$\times(1+c_1n^{-1/2}+c_2n^{-1}+c_3n^{-3/2}+O(n^{-1})),$$

where $\rho_1=2\pi\sqrt{[k(1-1/q)/6l]}$; $c_1$, $c_2$, $c_3$ are explicitly given rational functions of $\rho_1$ and $\mu$; and $\mu$ and $\omega$ are explicitly given functions of $\{k_s\}$ and $q$.

In the second of the papers quoted above, Petersson proved an asymptotic formula for the quotient

$$\pi_n^+(q)/\pi_n^-(q)$$

of the number of partitions of $n$ into quadratic residues and non-residues modulo $q$, respectively. In the present paper this is generalized. The author defines $\pi_n^{(s)}(q)$ to be the number of partitions of $n$ whose summands lie in the coset $s\mathfrak{P}$, $s\in\mathfrak{B}$; $K$ is the subfield of $R(\exp 2\pi i/q)$ corresponding by the Galois theory to the subgroup $\mathfrak{P}$ of $\mathfrak{R}$. He proves:

$$\left|\log\frac{\pi_n^{(st^{-1})}(q)}{\pi_n^{(t^{-1})}(q)}\right|=Rh(1+C_1(q)n^{-1/2}+O(n^{-1})),$$

where $R$ and $h$ are the regulator and class number, respectively, of $K$, the left member is a determinant in which $s$, $t$ run over $\mathfrak{B}$, $s, t\neq 1$, and $C_1(q)$ depends on $q$, $k$, $l$ and on certain $L$-series. *J. Lehner.*

Citations: MR 17, 129b = P72-25; MR 17, 1057f = P72-29.

## P72-34 (19, 1163a)

**Rademacher, Hans. On the Selberg formula for $A_k(n)$.** J. Indian Math. Soc. (N.S.) **21** (1957), 41–55 (1958).

The arithmetical constants $A_k(n)$ in Rademacher's convergent series for the partition function are defined by

$$A_k(n)=\sum_{\substack{h \bmod k\\(h,k)=1}}\omega_{hk}\exp(-2\pi ihn/k),$$

where $\omega_{hk}$ are certain complicated $24k$th roots of unity arising from the theory of Dedekind's modular function $\eta(\tau)$. Selberg has discovered and the reviewer [Pacific J. Math. **6** (1956), 159–176; MR **18**, 195] has discussed the following much simpler form for $A_k(n)$:

$$3^{\frac{1}{2}}k^{-\frac{1}{2}}A_k(n)=\sum(-1)^j\cos(\pi(6j+1)/6k),$$

the sum extending over all $j$ mod $k$ for which

$$(3j^2+j)/2\equiv -n \pmod{k}.$$

The present author derives the Selberg formula directly from the transformation formula

$$\eta\left(\frac{h+iz}{k}\right)=\frac{\varepsilon}{z^{\frac{1}{2}}}\eta\left(\frac{h'+iz^{-1}}{k}\right),$$

where $hh'+1\equiv 0 \pmod{k}$ and $\varepsilon=\varepsilon(h, k)$ is a root of unity. The method of proof is elegant and does not require any evaluation of Gaussian sums. Lehmer's theorems [Trans. Amer. Math. Soc. **43** (1938), 271–295] for the evaluation and factorization of $A_k(n)$ are also deduced in a form which make the computations more transparent. In particular the author's improved version of the main multiplication theorem avoids any case distinctions with respect to the occurrence of prime factors 2 in $k$. *A. L. Whiteman* (Los Angeles, Calif.).

Citations: MR 18, 195b = P72-32.

## P72-35 (20# 843)

**Gupta, Hansraj. Certain averages connected with partitions.** Res. Bull. Panjab Univ. no. **124** (1957), 427–430.

Let $m$ run over each of the $kp(n, k)$ parts occurring in the $p(n, k)$ partitions of $n$ into exactly $k$ parts, and define

$$S_r(n, k)=\sum_m m^r,$$

$$A_r(n, k)=S_r(n, k)/kp(n, k).$$

It is shown that for large $n$ and a fixed $k$,

$$A_r(n, k)=\binom{r+k-1}{r}^{-1}n^r+O(n^{r-1}).$$

For $k=1, 2, 3$ exact formulas for $A_2(n, k)$ are given; for example, $A_2(n, 2)=\frac{1}{6}n(2n-1)$, $n$ odd. The proofs depend on the facts that, for a fixed $k$ and large $n$, $p(n, k) = n^{k-1}/k!(k-1)!+O(n^{k-2})$; and that

$$S_r(n, k) = \sum_{t=1}^{n} \sum_{i=1}^{j_t} p(n-it, k-i)t^r,$$

where $j_t = \min([n/t], k)$. *M. Newman* (Washington, D.C.)

## P72-36 (20# 2309)

**Kohlbecker, Eugene E. Weak asymptotic properties of partitions.** Trans. Amer. Math. Soc. **88** (1958), 346–365.

The author proves two Abelian-Tauberian theorems, both involving slowly oscillating functions (i.e., continuous positive functions $L(x)$ satisfying $L(cx)/L(x) \to 1$ as $x \to \infty$, for every $c > 0$).

(i) If $n(u)$ is positive and non-decreasing, if $g(s) = s\int_0^\infty e^{-su}/(1-e^{-su})n(u)du$ and if $\alpha > 0$, then the conditions $n(u) \sim u^\alpha L(u)$ $(u \to \infty)$ and $g(s) \sim \Gamma(\alpha+1)\zeta(\alpha+1)s^{-\alpha}L(s^{-1})$ $(s \downarrow 0)$ are equivalent. (If we omit the factors $(1-e^{-su})^{-1}$ and $\zeta(\alpha+1)$ this reduces to a theorem of Karamata [J. Reine Angew. Math. **164** (1931), 27–39].)

(ii) If $P(u)$ is positive and non-decreasing, $f(s) = s\int_0^\infty P(u)e^{-su}du$, and if $\alpha > 0$, $A > 0$, then the conditions

$$\log f(s) \sim A\alpha^{-1}s^{-\alpha}L(s^{-1}) \quad (s \downarrow 0)$$
$$\log P(u) \sim (1+\alpha^{-1})u^{\alpha/(1+\alpha)}L_1(u) \quad (u \to \infty)$$

are equivalent. Here $L_1$ is a slowly oscillating function which has the following property. Let, for large values of $u$, the number $s_u$ satisfy $u = As_u^{-\alpha-1}L(s_u^{-1})$; then $s_u \sim u^{-1/(\alpha+1)}L_1(u)$ $(u \to \infty)$. It is shown that $s_u$ and $L_1$ exist if $L$ is given.

Theorems (i) and (ii) can be combined by taking $g(s) = \log f(s)$, $A = \alpha\Gamma(\alpha+1)\zeta(\alpha+1)$. As a result, asymptotic formulas can be obtained for the logarithm of certain partition functions. For example, if $0 < \lambda_1 < \lambda_2 < \cdots$, and if $n(u)$ is the number of $\lambda_i$ which do not exceed $u$, then $P(u)$ denotes the number of solutions of $m_1\lambda_1 + m_2\lambda_2 + \cdots \leqq u$ in integers $m_i \geqq 0$. The case with $L(u) \equiv 1$ is due to Knopp [Schr. Königsberg. gelehrt. Ges. Naturw. Kl. 2 Heft 3 (1925), 45–74]. {In Theorem 2, $(e^{-su}-1)$ should be $(1-e^{-su})$.} *N. G. de Bruijn* (Amsterdam)

Referred to in M45-35, P72-41, P72-50.

## P72-37 (21# 3385)

**Berg, Lothar. Über eine Differenzengleichung aus der Theorie der Partitionen.** Wiss. Z. Univ. Rostock. Math.-Nat. Reihe **5** (1955/56), 269–278.

The author considers the difference equation $f_r(n) = f_{r-1}(n) + f_r(n-r)$ satisfied when $f_r(n) = p_r(n)$, the number of partitions of $n$ into at most $r$ parts, and obtains particular solutions of this equation of the form $f_r(n) = t^{-n}g_r(t)$. He then derives many known results for the functions $p_r(n)$ and $p(n)$ (the number of unrestricted partitions of $n$), the most striking of which is the inequality $p(n) < (\alpha/n)^{1/2} \exp 2(\alpha n)^{1/2}$, $\alpha = \pi^2/6$, derived in two or three lines.

The author also observes that a knowledge of the behavior of the function $\{(1-x)\cdots(1-x^r)\}^{-1}$ at $x = 1$ would add greatly to our knowledge of the partition function and he gives recurrence formulas for the coefficients of the pole terms at $x = 1$ of this function from which he works out the first few coefficients.

There are numerous other relationships given (well-known) and three short tables of $p_r(n)$.

*M. Newman* (Washington, D.C.)

## P72-38 (21# 7188)

**Rieger, G. J. Über Partitionen.** Math. Ann. **138** (1959), 356–362.

Let $p_k(n)$ denote the number of partitions of $n$ into $k$ positive summands. The author sharpens results of Iseki and of Gupta by proving:

$$p_k(n) = \frac{n^{k-1}}{k!(k-1)!}\left(1+\frac{k(k-1)(k-3)}{4n}+O(n^{-2})\right)$$

for fixed $k \geqq 3$ and $n$ large. Also, for all $k$, $n \geqq 1$,

$$p_k(n) \leqq \frac{1}{k!(k-1)!}\left(n+\frac{k(k-3)}{4}\right)^{k-1}+1.$$

If $n$ runs through a residue class mod $k!$, then $p_k(n)$ is a polynomial of degree $k-1$. The coefficients are given explicitly in terms of Bernoulli numbers.

*N. J. Fine* (Princeton, N.J.)

Referred to in P68-17.

## P72-39 (22# 10968)

**Wetzker, Lothar. Eine asymptotische Partitionenformel für Zerfällungen in Elemente gewisser Multiplamengen.** Arch. Math. **11** (1960), 259–262.

Let $\mathfrak{T} = \{t_1, \cdots, t_k\}$ be a set of pairwise coprime integers greater than 1; $\mathfrak{M}(\mathfrak{T})$ the set of all positive integers not divisible by any $t_i$; and $p(n, \mathfrak{M}(\mathfrak{T}))$ the number of partitions of $n$ into elements of $\mathfrak{M}(\mathfrak{T})$. The author proves that, for $n \to \infty$,

$$p(n, \mathfrak{M}(\mathfrak{T})) \sim 2^{-3/2}\eta^{-1/2}\{\tfrac{2}{3}\psi(\mathfrak{T})\}^{1/4}n^{-3/4}\exp\{\pi(\tfrac{2}{3}\psi(\mathfrak{T})n)^{1/2}\},$$

where $\eta = t_1$ or 1 according as $k = 1$ or $k > 1$ and $\psi(\mathfrak{T}) = \prod_{i=1}^k (1-t_i^{-1})$. This result is shown to be an easy consequence of a theorem on partitions due to A. E. Ingham [Ann. of Math. (2) **42** (1941), 1075–1090; MR **3**, 166]; cf. also F. C. Auluck and C. Haselgrove [Proc. Cambridge Philos. Soc. **48** (1952), 566–570; MR **14**, 138]. A special case of the problem considered in the paper under review had been investigated much earlier by K. Knopp and I. Schur [Math. Z. **24** (1925), 559–574], who obtained an asymptotic formula not for the partition function itself but for its logarithm. *L. Mirsky* (Sheffield)

Citations: MR 3, 166a = P72-3; MR 14, 138h = P72-18.

## P72-40 (24# A3144)

**Tašbaev, V.**

**The remainder term in direct additive problems. (Russian)**

*Izv. Akad. Nauk UzSSR Ser. Fiz.-Mat.* **1960**, *no.* 4, 31–37.

Let $\{\lambda_k\}$ be a non-decreasing sequence of positive integers. Denote by $N(u)$ the number of $\lambda$'s not exceeding $u$, and by $p(n)$ the number of solutions of the equation $n = r_1\lambda_1 + r_2\lambda_2 + \cdots$ in positive integers $r_1, r_2, \cdots$. Assuming that

$$N(u) = Bu^\beta + R(u) \qquad (B > 0, \beta > 0),$$

where

$$(*) \qquad \int_0^u \frac{R(v)}{v}\,dv = b\log u + c + o(1) \qquad (u \to \infty),$$

A. E. Ingham [Ann. Math. (2) **42** (1941), 1075–1090 (Theorem 2); MR **3**, 166] deduced, among other results, an asymptotic formula for $p(n)$. In the present paper, the author replaces (*) by the more exacting requirement

$$\int_0^u \frac{R(v)}{v}\,dv = b\log u + c + O(u^{-\gamma}) \qquad (u \to \infty),$$

where $\gamma > 0$, $\beta > (1+\gamma)^{-1}$, and obtains an estimate of the error term in Ingham's formula. As a particular application of his result, he derives the relation

$$(**) \quad p(n) = \frac{1}{4n\sqrt{3}}\exp\left\{\pi\left(\frac{2n}{3}\right)^{1/2}\right\}\cdot\{1+O(n^{-1/4}\log^2 n)\},$$

where $p(n)$ now denotes the ordinary unrestricted partition function (corresponding to the case $\lambda_1=\lambda_2=\cdots=1$). A result superior to (**) had, of course, been obtained by Hardy and Ramanujan [Proc. London Math. Soc. (2) **17** (1918), 75–115] by means of a much more lengthy and delicate argument. *L. Mirsky* (Sheffield)

Citations: MR 3, 166a = P72-3.

Referred to in Z10-22.

## P72-41 (25# 3918)

**Parameswaran, S.**

**Partition functions whose logarithms are slowly oscillating.**

*Trans. Amer. Math. Soc.* **100** (1961), 217–240.

As it was pointed out by E. E. Kohlbecker [same Trans. **88** (1958), 346–365; MR **20** #2309] we can obtain asymptotic formula for the logarithm of the number of partitions, for several types of partitions, from the study of the relation

$$\exp\{s\int_0^\infty e^{-su}(1-e^{-su})^{-1}n(u)\,du\} = s\int_0^\infty P(u)e^{-su}\,du.$$

Kohlbecker showed that if $\alpha$ is a positive constant, and if $n(u)u^{-\alpha}$ is slowly oscillating (as $u\to\infty$), then $u^{-\alpha/(\alpha+1)}\log P(u)$ is also slowly oscillating, provided that $P(u)$ is non-decreasing, and vice versa if $n(u)$ is non-decreasing.

The present paper carries out the similar program for $\alpha=0$. The author uses the terminology of conjugate pairs of slowly oscillating functions introduced by the reviewer [Nieuw Arch. Wisk. (3) **7** (1959), 20–26; MR **21** #5847]: if $M$ and $M^*$ form a conjugate pair, then the asymptotic relations $xM(x)\sim y$ and $yM^*(y)\sim x$ are equivalent. The author shows (i) if $P(u)$ is non-decreasing and $\int_0^u n(t)t^{-1}dt\sim M(u)$ as $u\to\infty$, then $\log P(u)\sim(M^*(u))^{-1}$ as $u\to\infty$, and (ii) the converse is true if we assume that $n(u)$ (instead of $P(u)$) is non-decreasing.

It requires some extra conditions to translate information about $\int_0^u n(t)t^{-1}dt$ into information about $n(u)$ itself.

*N. G. de Bruijn* (Eindhoven)

Citations: MR 20# 2309 = P72-36; MR 21# 5847 = M45-35.

Referred to in P72-50.

## P72-42 (26# 98)

**Newman, D. J.**

**A simplified proof of the partition formula.**

*Michigan Math. J.* **9** (1962), 283–287.

Another proof of the theorem of Hardy and Ramanujan [Proc. London Math. Soc. (2) **17** (1918), 75–115] that the number of partitions of $n$ is asymptotic to

$$(4n\sqrt{3})^{-1}\exp\{\pi\sqrt{(2n/3)}\}.$$

*T. Estermann* (London)

## P72-43 (26# 6130)

**Grosswald, E.**

**Elementary proofs in the theory of partitions.**

*Math. Z.* **81** (1963), 52–61.

Let $F_p(x)=\prod_{\nu\in A}(1-x^\nu)^{-1}=\sum p_nx^n$, where $A$ is the set of all positive integers congruent mod $k$ to one of the distinct residues $a_1,\cdots,a_s$, with $0<a_i\leqq k$. Similarly, define $F_q(x)$ for the set $B$ corresponding to $b_1,\cdots,b_t$, also mod $k$. The author is concerned with the connection between $L_1=\lim p_n/q_n$ and $L_2=\lim_{x\to1-}F_p(x)/F_q(x)$, if these limits exist. According to an Abelian theorem due to Cesàro, if $L_1$ exists, then so does $L_2$ and $L_2=L_1$. Theorem 1: $L_2$ is finite and non-zero if and only if $s=t$ and $\sum a_j=\sum b_j$, in which case $L_2=\prod\{\Gamma(a_j/k)/\Gamma(b_j/k)\}$; if $s>t$, or $s=t$ and $\sum b_j>\sum a_j$, then $L_2=\infty$; if $s<t$, or $s=t$ and $\sum b_j<\sum a_j$, then $L_2=0$. From an "elementary" result of Erdős on the asymptotic behavior of $p_n$ and $q_n$ when (g.c.d. $A,k$) = (g.c.d. $B,k$) = 1, $L_1$ exists, and then Cesàro's theorem and Theorem 1 yield its value. There are similar results for $A^r$ and $B^r$, the sets of $r$th powers of elements of $A$ and $B$. In this case Erdős' theorem is replaced by more general results of Meinardus. The author conjectures a Tauberian converse of Cesàro's theorem which would eliminate the need for the results of Erdős and Meinardus in obtaining the existence of $L_1$. {Reviewer's note. In the proof of Theorem 1, the author's argument for the case $t\neq s$ is faulty. It seems to say that if $P_N(x)=\prod_{n=0}^N g_n(x)$ is a rational function such that $P_N(1)=0$ for all $N$, and if $P(x)=\lim P_N(x)$, then $\lim_{x\to1-}P(x)=0$. This is clearly false, as the example $g_n(x)=(1-x^{2n+1})(1+x^{n+1})$ shows. The correct argument, taking into account the special form of the $g_n$ in this case, is easy but not trivial.}

*N. J. Fine* (Philadelphia, Pa.)

## P72-44 (27# 3613)

**Hagis, Peter, Jr.**

**Partitions into odd summands.**

*Amer. J. Math.* **85** (1963), 213–222.

The author uses the methods of an earlier paper [Trans. Amer. Math. Soc. **102** (1962), 30–62; MR **26** #3688] to obtain a convergent series and asymptotic formulae for $q(n)$, the number of partitions of $n$ into positive odd summands (or, equivalently, into distinct positive summands). In both his papers the author has followed the procedure of J. Lehner [Duke Math. J. **8** (1941), 631–655; MR **3**, 166]; his results agree with those of L. K. Hua [Trans. Amer. Math. Soc. **51** (1942), 194–201; MR **3**, 270] and S. Iseki [Amer. J. Math. **83** (1961), 243–264; MR **23** #A876], who used different methods.

*H. Halberstam* (Dublin)

Citations: MR 3, 166b = P68-4; MR 3, 270c = P72-4; MR 23# A876 = P68-19; MR 26# 3688 = P68-21.

Referred to in P72-46, P72-47, P72-49.

## P72-45 (28# 3980)

**Hahn, Hwa S.**

**On the relative growth of differences of partition functions.**

*Pacific J. Math.* **14** (1964), 93–106.

Let $A$ be an arbitrary set of positive integers; let $p(n)$ denote the number of partitions of $n$ into parts taken from $A$, repetitions being allowed. If $k>0$, then $p^{(k)}(n)$ denotes the $k$th difference, and if $k\leqq0$ it is the summatory function of order $-k$. Thus, for all integers $k$,

$$f_k(X) = \sum_{n=0}^{\infty} p^{(k)}(n)X^n = (1-X)^k\prod_{a\in A}(1-X^a)^{-1}.$$

It was conjectured by Bateman and Erdős [Mathematika **3** (1956), 1–14; MR **18**, 195] that $p^{(k+1)}(n)/p^{(k)}(n)=O(n^{-1/2})$ (if $k$ is fixed, and if the elements have g.c.d. unity, even if any arbitrary set of $k$ elements is removed from $A$). The author assumes stronger conditions (as introduced by Roth and Szekeres [Quart. J. Math. Oxford Ser. (2) **5** (1954), 241–259; MR **16**, 797]), namely, that $n(u)=u^{\alpha+o(1)}$ ($n(u)$ is the number of $a\in A$ with $a\leqq u$; $\alpha$ is a constant, $0<\alpha\leqq1$), and

$$(\log m)^{-1}\inf\sum_{j=1}^m\|\beta a_j\|^2\to\infty \qquad (m\to\infty).$$

Here $\|x\|$ is the distance of $x$ to the nearest integer, and the infimum is taken over all $\beta$ with $(2a_m)^{-1}<\beta\leqq\frac{1}{2}$.

Under these conditions it is proved that the Bateman-Erdős conjecture holds, and even that $p^{(k+1)}(n)/p^{k(n)}\sim\sigma_n$, where $\sigma_n$ is the solution of $n = \sum_{a \in A} a(e^{\sigma a} - 1)^{-1}$.

Under the further assumption that $n(u) \sim u^{\alpha} L(u)$, where $0 < \alpha \leqq 1$ and $L$ is slowly oscillating in the sense of Karamata, it is proved that

$$p^{(k+1)}(n)/p^{(k)}(n) \sim n^{-1/(1+\alpha)} L_1(n),$$

where $L_1$ is again slowly oscillating.

*N. G. de Bruijn* (Eindhoven)

Citations: MR 16, 797b = P72-23; MR 18, 195a = P72-31.

## P72-46 (29# 3455)

**Hagis, Peter, Jr.**

**Partitions into odd and unequal parts.**

*Amer. J. Math.* **86** (1964), 317–324.

In an earlier paper [same J. **85** (1963), 213–222; MR **27** #3613] the author obtained a convergent series and asymptotic formulas for the number of partitions of $n$ into positive odd summands. In the present paper he uses similar methods to deal with the corresponding problem for partitions into distinct odd parts and, in a concluding section, interprets his results in terms of modular forms.

*H. Halberstam* (Nottingham)

Citations: MR 27# 3613 = P72-44.

Referred to in P72-47, P72-48, P72-49.

## P72-47 (31# 1237)

**Hagis, Peter, Jr.**

**Partitions with odd summands—some comments and corrections.**

*Amer. J. Math.* **87** (1965), 218–220.

The author points out that one case ($k \equiv 2 \pmod 4$) of Theorem 2 of his paper [same J. **85** (1963), 213–222; MR **27** #3613] is not established, contrary to what was asserted in the paper; and proves a weaker result valid for this case which, nevertheless, is good enough to establish the results about partitions with odd parts given in the last section of that paper. Similar remarks are said to apply to Theorem 3 of the author's paper [ibid. **86** (1964), 317–324; MR **29** #3455], and a further misstatement is corrected.

*H. Halberstam* (Nottingham)

Citations: MR 27# 3613 = P72-44; MR 29# 3455 = P72-46.

Referred to in P72-49.

## P72-48 (32# 5621)

**Hagis, Peter, Jr.**

**On the partitions of an integer into distinct odd summands.**

*Amer. J. Math.* **87** (1965), 867–873.

Setting

$$F(x) = \prod (1 - x^{2m+1})^{-1} = \sum_{n=0}^{\infty} q(n) x^n,$$

$$G(x) = \prod (1 + x^{2m+1}) = \sum_{n=0}^{\infty} Q(n) x^n,$$

one sees that $q, Q$ are the number of partitions of $n$ into odd parts, and into odd and unequal parts, respectively. The function $G(x)$, which was discussed by the circle method in an earlier paper [same J. **86** (1964), 317–324; MR **29** #3455], leads to rather complicated formulae for $Q(n)$. Since the number of partitions of $n$ into odd summands is odd or even according as $n$ is odd or even, the author is able to introduce the function $S(n) = (-1)^n Q(n)$ with the much simpler generating function $1/F(x)$. He then applies the circle method and gets simpler formulae (of the well-known Rademacher type) for $Q(n)$. We note, in passing, the identity

$$\sum_{\nu=0}^{n} (-1)^{\nu} Q(\nu) q(n-\nu) = 0,\ n > 0,\ q(0) = Q(0) = 1.$$

*J. Lehner* (College Park, Md.)

Citations: MR 29# 3455 = P72-46.

## P72-49 (34# 159)

**Hagis, Peter, Jr.**

**Some theorems concerning partitions into odd summands.**

*Amer. J. Math.* **88** (1966), 664–681.

In several papers [same J. **85** (1963), 213–222; MR **27** #3613; ibid. **86** (1964), 317–324; MR **29** #3455; ibid. **87** (1965), 218–220; MR **31** #1237; Trans. Amer. Math. Soc. **102** (1962), 30–62; MR **26** #3688; ibid. **112** (1964), 401–415; MR **29** #3454] the author derived convergent series for certain partition functions, using H. Rademacher's method [ibid. **60** (1938), 501–512]. Now the author is concerned with $q(n, t)$, the number of partitions of $n$ into odd summands, no summand appearing more than $t$ times. Having established certain transformation formulae for the generating function $\sum_n q(n, t) x^n = \prod_{0 \leq m < \infty} (\sum_{0 \leq v \leq t} x^{2mv+v})$, the author derives a convergent series for $q(n, t)$, and from it the asymptotic formula $q(n, t) = (\text{main term}) \cdot (1 + O(\exp(-Cn^{1/2})))$, $n \to \infty$.

*W. Schwarz* (Freiburg)

Citations: MR 26# 3688 = P68-21; MR 27# 3613 = P72-44; MR 29# 3454 = P68-23; MR 29# 3455 = P72-46; MR 31# 1237 = P72-47.

## P72-50 (38# 4433)

**Schwarz, Wolfgang**

**Schwache asymptotische Eigenschaften von Partitionen.**

*J. Reine Angew. Math.* **232** (1968), 1–16.

Let $\{\lambda_\nu\}$ be a sequence of increasing real numbers without finite accumulation point and set $N(u) = \sum_{\lambda_\nu < u} 1$. If (*) $N(u) \leq C(\varepsilon) \exp(\varepsilon u)$ holds, then the infinite product $g(s) = \prod_{\nu=1}^{\infty} (1 - \exp(-\lambda_\nu s))^{-1}$ converges for all $s = \sigma + it$ with $\sigma > 0$ and can be expanded into a series $g(s) = \sum_l p(l) e^{-ls}$, convergent for $\sigma > 0$. One observes that the coefficients $p(l)$ are the numbers of partitions of $l$ into summands from $\{\lambda_\nu\}$. The main purpose of the paper is to obtain asymptotic formulae for $\log P(u)$, where $P(u) = \sum_{l < u} p(l)$. Let $\varphi(s) = \log g(s)$ and define $\sigma_u$ by $-\varphi'(\sigma_u) = u$; then (see Theorem 2) (*) and $N(2u) \leq C_2 N(u)$ imply for $u \to \infty$: $\log P(u) = \varphi(\sigma_u) + u\sigma_u + R$; here $R$ depends on $u$, $\sigma_u$, $\varphi'(\sigma_u)$ and $\varphi''(\sigma_u)$ and is of lower order than the first two terms. Furthermore (see Theorem 3), if $\Phi(\sigma)$ is continuously differentiable for $\sigma > 0$, $-\Phi'(\sigma)$ increases monotonically to $+\infty$ as $\sigma$ decreases to zero and also (for $\sigma \to 0^+$) either $\Phi'(\sigma) \sim g'(\sigma)/g(\sigma)$, or $\Phi(\sigma) \sim \log g(\sigma)$ (with some other, rather complicated growth conditions on $\Phi(\sigma)$ satisfied in either case), then $\log P(u) \sim \Phi(t_u) + ut_u$ (for $u \to \infty$), where $t_u$ is defined by $-\Phi'(t_u) = u$ and where the term $ut_u$ may be suppressed if some further conditions are satisfied. The first result follows from a special Tauberian theorem (somewhat similar to that of A. E. Ingham [Ann. of Math. (2) **42** (1941), 1075–1090; MR **3**, 166] and to those of E. Wagner [Math. Nachr. **31** (1966), 153–168; MR **33** #3003] and proven by the method of Hardy and Ramanujan), which may be of some independent interest. Theorem 1: Let $A(u)$ be real, monotonically increasing, with $A(0) = 0$; assume that $\int_0^\infty A(u) e^{-u\sigma}\,du$ converges for $\sigma > 0$ and that, for $\sigma \to 0^+$, $\sigma \int_0^\infty A(u) e^{-u\sigma}\,du = \varphi(\sigma) + O(1)$, with $\varphi''(\sigma)$ and $-\sigma\varphi'(\sigma)$ monotonically increasing for $\sigma \to 0^+$, with $\varphi''(\sigma) > 0$ and $\sigma(\varphi''(\sigma))^{\rho+1}/|\varphi'(\sigma)|^{2\rho+1} \leq C_1$ (for some constants $\rho$ and $C_1$;

observe the printing error in the exponent of the denominator in (3.6)). Then, for $u \to \infty$,

$$\log A(u) = \varphi(\sigma_u) + u\sigma_u + O\left\{u\sigma_u \cdot \left(\frac{\varphi''(\sigma_u)}{|\varphi'(\sigma_u)|^2} \log \frac{|\varphi'(\sigma_u)|^2}{\varphi''(\sigma_u)}\right)^{1/2}\right\}.$$

Results of E. E. Kohlbecker [Trans. Amer. Math. Soc. **88** (1958), 346–365; MR **20** #2309; S. Parameswaran, ibid. **100** (1961), 217–240; MR **25** #3918], as well as some of G. H. Hardy and S. Ramanujan [Proc. London Math. Soc. (2) **16** (1917), 112–132] and N. A. Brigham [Proc. Amer. Math. Soc. **1** (1950), 182–191; MR **11**, 582] can be obtained from the present ones. The author promises asymptotic results on $P(u)$ (rather than on log $P(u)$) by using stronger assumptions on $N(u)$.

*E. Grosswald* (Philadelphia, Pa.)

Citations: MR 3, 166a = P72-3; MR 11, 582b = P72-13; MR 20# 2309 = P72-36; MR 25# 3918 = P72-41; MR 33# 3003 = M45-45.
Referred to in P72-52.

**P72-51** **(43# 174)**

**Schwarz, W.**

**Schwache asymptotische Eigenschaften von Partitionen.**

*Number Theory (Colloq., János Bolyai Math. Soc., Debrecen,* 1968), *pp.* 191–196. *North-Holland, Amsterdam,* 1970.

This is an announcement of results that have already appeared in full (see J. Reine Angew. Math. **234** (1969), 174–178 [MR **40** #7217]; see also a forthcoming paper in the Monatshefte für Mathematik).

*E. Grosswald* (Philadelphia, Pa.)

Citations: MR 40# 7217 = P72-52.

**P72-52** **(40# 7217)**

**Schwarz, Wolfgang**

**Asymptotische Formeln für Partitionen.**

*J. Reine Angew. Math.* **234** (1969), 174–178.

The author fulfills a promise made in his earlier paper [same J. **232** (1968), 1–16; MR **38** #4433] of providing asymptotic formulas for $P(u)$ instead of log $P(u)$, where $P(u) = \sum_{l<u} p(l)$, $g(s) = \prod_{v=1}^{\infty} (1-\exp(-\lambda_v s))^{-1} = \sum_l p(l)e^{-ls}$ converges for Re $s > 0$, and $\lambda_v$ is an increasing sequence of real numbers $\to \infty$. Let $N(u) = \sum_{l<u} 1$. By making stronger assumptions on $N(u)$, the author proves, for example, the following. Let $N(u) \to \infty$, let $N(2u) \leqq C_1 N(u)$, let $N(u) = H(u) + O(1)$, where $H$ is absolutely continuous in every finite interval and $|H'(u)| \leqq C_2 u^{-1}$. Then

$$P(u) \sim \{2\pi\sigma_u^2 \varphi''(\sigma_u)\}^{-1/2} \exp(\varphi(\sigma_u) + u\sigma_u),$$

where $\varphi(\sigma) = \log g(\sigma)$ and $\sigma_u$ is the solution of $-\varphi'(\sigma_u) = u$. Comparison is made with previous asymptotic estimates of Ingham, Mahler, Roth and Szekeres, and Meinardus.

*J. Lehner* (College Park, Md.)

Citations: MR 38# 4433 = P72-50.
Referred to in P72-51.

**P72-53** **(41# 8368)**

**Kerawala, S. M.**

**On an elementary proof of the asymptotic formula for the partition function $p_0(n)$.**

*J. Natur. Sci. and Math.* **9** (1969), 155–159.

J. Uspenskiĭ [Bull. Acad. Sci. Russie (6) **14** (1920), 199–218], using the transformation theory of elliptic modular functions, proved that the number $p_0(n)$ of partitions of $n$ into odd summands satisfies $p_0(n) \sim an^{-\alpha} \exp(cn^{1/2})$, where $a = 3^{1/4}/4$, $\alpha = \frac{3}{4}$, and $c = 3^{-1/2}\pi$. P. Erdős [Ann. of Math. (2) **43** (1942), 437–450; MR **4**, 36] used elementary methods to prove this asymptotic formula with $c = 3^{-1/2}\pi$ and with unspecified values of $a$ and $\alpha$. The author determines by an elementary argument that $p_0(2n)/p(n) \sim p_0(2n-1)/p(n) \sim (3n/8)^{1/4}$, where $p(n)$ is the unrestricted partition function. He then invokes the asymptotic formula for $p(n)$, which was proved in an elementary way by Erdős [loc. cit.] and D. J. Newman [Amer. J. Math. **73** (1951), 599–601; MR **13**, 112], and determines the values of $a$ and $\alpha$. *T. M. Apostol* (Pasadena, Calif.)

Citations: MR 4, 36a = P72-5; MR 13, 112c = P72-16.

**P72-54** **(41# 8369)**

**Kerawala, S. M.**

**On the asymptotic values of ln $p_A(n)$ and ln $p_A^{(d)}(n)$ with $A$ as the set of primes.**

*J. Natur. Sci. and Math.* **9** (1969), 209–216.

If the summands in the partitions of $n$ are restricted to be elements of the set $A$ of positive primes and the superscript $(d)$ denotes the further restriction that the summands be all distinct, write $p_A(n) = q(n)$ and $p_A^{(d)}(n) = q^*(n)$. Then $G(x) = \prod_{p=2}^{\infty} (1-x^p)^{-1}$, where $p$ is a positive prime, and $G^*(x) = G(x)/G(x^2)$ are the generating functions of $q(n)$ and $q^*(n)$. The author proves, using a contradiction technique due to P. Erdős [Ann. of Math. (2) **43** (1942), 437–450; MR **4**, 36] on the size of $G(x)$, that ln $q(n) \sim 2\pi\sqrt{(n/(3 \ln n))}$. Also assuming $q^*(n)$ to be monotonic increasing for $n > n_0$, the author proves that ln $q^*(n) \sim 2\pi\sqrt{(n/(6 \ln n))}$.

*E. M. Horadam* (Armidale)

Citations: MR 4, 36a = P72-5.

**P72-55** **(42# 3044)**

**Hagis, Peter, Jr.**

**Partitions into unequal parts satisfying certain congruence conditions.**

*J. Number Theory* **3** (1971), 115–123.

Using the Hardy-Ramanujan-Rademacher circle dissection method a convergent series representation and asymptotic formulas are obtained for $Q_R(n)$, the number of partitions of a positive integer into distinct summands each of which is congruent mod $p$ to a set $R$ of least positive residues, where $R$ satisfies the property that $p$ belongs to $R$ and if $d$ belongs to $R$ then $p-d$ also belongs to $R$. Convergent series and asymptotic formulas are obtainable in this case as a consequence of the fact that they are related to the Fourier coefficients of modular forms.

*M. S. Cheema* (Tucson, Ariz.)

**P72-56** **(42# 7616)**

**Hagis, Peter, Jr.**

**Partitions with a restriction on the multiplicity of the summands.**

*Trans. Amer. Math. Soc.* **155** (1971), 375–384.

The author derives a convergent infinite series for $p(n, t)$, defined to be the number of partitions of $n$ in which no part is repeated more than $t$ times. The method used is the Hardy-Ramanujan-Rademacher circle method. For certain $t \leqq 24$ the series can be considerably simplified, but even these results are too intricate to state here. From the series, three asymptotic expressions are given for $p(n, t)$ the simplest (and weakest) can be written

$$p(n, t) = 2\sqrt{3}\, t^{1/4}(t+1)^{-3/4}(24n+t)^{-3/4} \times \{\exp(\pi\sqrt{(t(24n+t)/(t+1))/6})\}(1+O(n^{-1/2})).$$

*S. A. Burr* (Whippany, N.J.)

**P72-57** **(44# 2722)**

**Passi, Harsh Anand**

**An asymptotic formula in partition theory.**

*Duke Math. J.* **38** (1971), 327–337.

Let $G$ be a lattice with a sublattice $G'$. Let $\mathbf{r}_1, \mathbf{r}_2, \cdots, \mathbf{r}_l$ be points of $G$ which are pairwise incongruent (mod $G'$) and such that every point of $G$ is congruent modulo $G'$ to an integral linear combination of $\mathbf{r}_1, \mathbf{r}_2, \cdots, \mathbf{r}_l$. Call a vector totally positive if all its coordinates are positive, and for $\mathbf{g}$ a point of $G$ let $P(\mathbf{g})$ be the number of partitions of $\mathbf{g}$ into totally positive summands congruent to some $\mathbf{r}_j$ modulo $G'$. Let $0 < c_0 < c_1$ be arbitrary but fixed. Call a vector $\mathbf{g} = (g_1, g_2, \cdots, g_n)$ "reduced" if $c_0(N\mathbf{g})^{1/n} < g_i < c_1(N\mathbf{g})^{1/n}$ for all $1 \leqq i \leqq n$, where $N\mathbf{g} = \prod_{i=1}^n g_i$. Then the following theorem is proved: For reduced $\mathbf{g}$,

$$\log P(\mathbf{g}) = (n+1)\{(l\zeta(n+1)/\det G')N\mathbf{g}\}^{1/(n+1)} \cdot (1+o(1))$$

as $N\mathbf{g} \to \infty$. This generalizes a result of G. Meinardus [Math. Ann. **132** (1956), 333–346; MR **18**, 642].

*S. A. Burr* (Whippany, N.J.)

Citations: MR 18, 642g = R48-12.

# P76 PARTITIONS: CONGRUENCES FOR PARTITION FUNCTIONS

See also Section F35.

See also reviews F02-23, F10-28, F10-73, F25-7, F30-53, F30-55, F30-62, F35-34, F35-40, P60-14, P60-16, P60-26, P64-36, P64-47, P64-48, P64-59, P80-14, P80-53, P80-61, Z10-47, Z30-2.

## P76-1 (5, 34d)

**Lehner, Joseph. Ramanujan identities involving the partition function for the moduli $11^\alpha$.** Amer. J. Math. **65**, 492–520 (1943).

Rademacher [Trans. Amer. Math. Soc. **51**, 609–636 (1942); these Rev. **3**, 271] has developed a systematic method for the investigation of Ramanujan identities and applied it to the moduli $5^\alpha$, 7, $7^2$, $13^\alpha$. In the present paper the author establishes identities for the moduli $11^\alpha$ in a form involving only modular functions. When expressed in terms of the partition function the identity for the modulus 11, for example, takes the form

$$\sum_{n=0}^{\infty} p(11n+6)x^{n+1} = 11\prod_{m=1}^{\infty}(1-x^{11m})^{-1}\{11AC^2 - 11^2C + 2AC - 32C - 2\}.$$

It follows that the Ramanujan conjecture $p(n) \equiv 0 \pmod{q^\alpha}$ if $24n \equiv 1 \pmod{q^\alpha}$ is true for $q = 11$, $\alpha = 1$.

The general result for powers of 11 is the following theorem: for every integer $\alpha \geqq 1$ there is a "Ramanujan identity" of the form

$$\text{(A)} \qquad L(\tau; 11^\alpha) = P(A, C),$$

where $L$ is defined in terms of the linear operator

$$U_qF(\tau) = q^{-1}\sum_{\lambda=0}^{q-1} F((\tau+\lambda)q^{-1})$$

by means of the equations

$$L(\tau; q^{2\beta+1}) = U_q\{\Phi(\tau; q^2)L(\tau; q^{2\beta})\},$$
$$L(\tau; q^{2\beta+2}) = U_qL(\tau; q^{2\beta+1}),$$
$$\Phi(\tau; q^2) = \eta(q^2\tau)/\eta(\tau),$$
$$\eta(\tau) = e(\tau/24)\prod_{m=1}^{\infty}(1-x^m), \qquad x = e(i\tau);$$

$A = A(\tau)$, $C = C(\tau)$ are certain entire modular functions having power series expansions in $x = e(i\tau)$ with integral coefficients; and $P$ is a polynomial in $A$ and $C$ with rational coefficients.

The author was not able to prove that the coefficients of $P$ were integral except for $\alpha = 1, 2$. Thus for $\alpha > 2$ the identity (A) does not, as yet, yield any information concerning the Ramanujan conjecture for $q = 11^\alpha$.

*R. D. James* (Vancouver, B. C.).

Citations: MR 3, 271e = P60-1.

Referred to in F30-8, P76-9, P76-31.

## P76-2 (6, 118a)

**Simons, William H. Congruences involving the partition function $p(n)$.** Bull. Amer. Math. Soc. **50**, 883–892 (1944).

The congruence properties are for the moduli 13 and 17. They are essentially recursive congruences and they involve either $\sigma_k(m)$ or Ramanujan's $\tau(n)$. The method of proof is similar to that used by Ramanujan for the moduli 5, 7, and 11 and it is based on Ramanujan's identities connecting the functions of the type $\sum_{n=1}^{\infty} n^r\sigma_{s-r}(n)x^n$.

*H. S. Zuckerman* (Seattle, Wash.).

Referred to in F35-37.

## P76-3 (7, 415b)

**Banerjee, D. P. On a theorem in the theory of partition.** Bull. Calcutta Math. Soc. **37**, 113–114 (1945).

The author gives a simple proof of the following theorem due essentially to Sylvester [Collected Mathematical Papers, v. 3, Cambridge University Press, 1909, pp. 680–686]. Let $p(n)$ denote the number of unrestricted partitions of $n$ and $Q(n)$ the number of partitions of $n$ into parts which are both odd and distinct. Then $p(n) - Q(n)$ is even. A small table of $Q(n)$ for $n \leqq 70$ is given. [For a larger table of $Q(n)$ ($n \leqq 400$) see G. N. Watson, Proc. London Math. Soc. (2) **42**, 550–552 (1937).]

*D. H. Lehmer.*

## P76-4 (8, 445d)

**Lahiri, D. B. On a type of series involving the partition function with applications to certain congruence relations.** Bull. Calcutta Math. Soc. **38**, 125–132 (1946).

Let $\delta(m)$ be defined to be $(-1)^s$ in case $m$ is the pentagonal number $(3s \pm 1)s/2$ and zero for nonpentagonal numbers. The author considers the (finite) sum

$$S_r(n) = \sum_{m=1}^{\infty} \delta(m)m^r p(n-m)$$

in which $p(k)$ denotes the number of unrestricted partitions of $k$. For $r = 1, 2, 3, 4$ and 5 the author finds that $S_r(n)$ can be expressed as a linear combination of $\sigma_1(n), \sigma_3(n), \cdots, \sigma_{2r-1}(n)$ with coefficients which are polynomials in $n$. Here $\sigma_k(n)$ denotes the sum of the $k$th powers of the divisors of $n$. For example, $S_1(n) = \sigma_1(n)$ (a fact discovered by Euler), $12S_2(n) = (18n-1)\sigma_1(n) - 5\sigma_3(n)$. These sums are used to obtain congruences (mod $a$) for the sums

$$I_{a,b} = \sum_{m \equiv b \pmod a}^{\infty} \delta(m)p(n-m), \qquad b = 0, 1, \cdots, a-1,$$

for $a = 2, 3, 4, 5, 7, 11$. These are expressed in terms of $\sigma_r(n)$ and used to derive the congruences of Ramanujan,

$$p(5m+4) \equiv 0 \pmod 5, \quad p(7m+5) \equiv 0 \pmod 7,$$
$$p(11m+6) \equiv 0 \pmod{11}.$$

The methods are based on papers 18 and 30 of Ramanujan's Collected Papers. For $r > 5$, it appears necessary to use other functions than $\sigma_r(n)$.

*D. H. Lehmer.*

Referred to in A30-32.

## P76-5 (8, 566g)

**Gupta, Hansraj. A note on the parity of $p(n)$.** J. Indian Math. Soc. (N.S.) **10**, 32–33 (1946).

A short proof is given of the congruence of MacMahon, $p(n) \equiv \sum p(t) \pmod 2$, where $p(m)$ denotes the number of

unrestricted partitions of $m$, $p(0)=1$, and $t$ ranges over all nonnegative integers of the form $(2n-i^2-i)/8$, $i=0, 1, \cdots$. The proof makes use of the fact that Ramanujan's function $\tau(n)$ is odd if and only if $n$ is an odd square.
*D. H. Lehmer* (Berkeley, Calif.).

**P76-6** **(10, 514f)**

**Lahiri, D. B. Some non-Ramanujan congruence properties of the partition function.** Proc. Nat. Inst. Sci. India **14**, 337–338 (1948).

Let $p(n)$ denote the number of unrestricted partitions of $n$. The author has found three new congruences:

$$p(49m+k)=0 \pmod{49}, \qquad k=19, 33, 40.$$

These results follow from the identity of Ramanujan

$$\sum_{n=0}^{\infty} p(7n+5)x^n = 7[f(x^7)]^3[f(x)]^{-4}+49x[f(x^7)]^7[f(x)]^{-8},$$

where $f(x)=(1-x)(1-x^2)(1-x^3)\cdots$, and the use of Jacobi's triangular number theorem concerning $[f(x)]^3$. Similar congruence properties do not hold for the moduli 25 and 121.
*D. H. Lehmer* (Berkeley, Calif.).

**P76-7** **(10, 514g)**

**Lahiri, D. B. Further non-Ramanujan congruence properties of the partition function.** Science and Culture **14**, 336–337 (1949).

Let $p(n)$ denote the number of unrestricted partitions of $n$. The author announces the following theorems. The numbers $p(49m+k)$, $k=19, 33, 40$; $p(125m+r)$, $r=74, 124$ $(m=0, 1, 2, \cdots)$ are respectively divisible by 49 and 125. Proofs are promised in a future paper. *D. H. Lehmer.*

**P76-8** **(11, 13d)**

**Majumdar, Kulendra N. On the parity of the partition function $p(n)$.** J. Indian Math. Soc. (N.S.) **13**, 23–24 (1949).

The function $p(n)$, for $n$ a positive integer, denotes the total number of unrestricted partitions of $n$; $p(0)=1$; and for all other values of $n$, $p(n)$ is taken as zero. No really satisfactory answer has ever been given to the question of whether or not $p(n)$ is odd, given a value of $n$. MacMahon has suggested the use of the congruence

$$p(n) \equiv \sum_{m=0}^{\infty} p\{(2n-m^2-m)/8\} \pmod 2$$

by means of which the parity of $p(n)$ may be determined when those of $p(m)$ are known for $m \leqq n/4$. The author suggests as an alternative the congruence

$$p(n) \equiv \sum_{t} p((8n-t+5)/128) \pmod 2$$

where $t$ ranges over integers of the form $sq^{4\alpha+1}$ where $\alpha$ is a nonnegative integer and $s$ is an odd square, prime to the prime $q=8k+5$. Although this formula involves a knowledge of the parities of $p(m)$ for $m \leqq n/16$ only, it has many more terms than the MacMahon congruence, and is more difficult to apply. *D. H. Lehmer* (Berkeley, Calif.).

**P76-9** **(11, 582a)**

**Lehner, Joseph. Proof of Ramanujan's partition congruence for the modulus** $11^\alpha$. Proc. Amer. Math. Soc. **1**, 172–181 (1950).

The author [Amer. J. Math. **65**, 492–520 (1943); these Rev. **5**, 34] has verified Ramanujan's conjecture $p(11^\alpha l+\rho)\equiv 0 \pmod{11^\alpha}$ if $24\rho \equiv 1 \pmod{11^\alpha}$, for $\alpha=1, 2$. The proof is now extended to include the case $\alpha=3$ by making use of the inductive formulas for $L(\tau, 11^\alpha)$, the modular properties of certain associated functions and the explicit values of a number of the coefficients in their expansions.
*H. S. Zuckerman* (Seattle, Wash.).

Citations: MR 5, 34d = P76-1.

Referred to in P76-28, P76-31.

**P76-10** **(11, 642c)**

**Ramanathan, K. G. Identities and congruences of the Ramanujan type.** Canadian J. Math. **2**, 168–178 (1950).

Let $\{(1-x)(1-x^2)\cdots\}^{-\nu}=\sum_{n=0}^{\infty} P_\nu(n)x^n$, and

$$G_{\nu,p}(x)=\sum_{l=0}^{\infty} P_\nu(p^n l+\rho)x^l, \quad p=5, 7; \quad 24\rho \equiv \nu \pmod{p^n}$$

with $\rho$ minimal positive. (When $\nu=1$, $P_\nu(n)$ reduces to $p(n)$, the number of unrestricted partitions of $n$.) The author, using methods and results of Watson [J. Reine Angew. Math. **179**, 97–128 (1938)] and Rademacher [Trans. Amer. Math. Soc. **51**, 609–636 (1942); these Rev. **3**, 271], establishes identities for $G_{\nu,p}(x)$ and congruences for $P_\nu(n)$ analogous to and including those of Ramanujan and Watson. Examples: (1) if $24m \equiv \nu \pmod{5^\alpha}$ with $\nu \equiv 16$, 21, or 26 (mod 30), then $P_\nu(m)\equiv 0 \pmod{5^u}$ where $u=[(\alpha+1)/2]$;

$$(2) \quad G_{3,5}(x) \equiv \sum_{l=0}^{\infty} P_3(5l+2)x^l = x^{-1}\prod_{1}^{\infty}(1-x^{5m})^{-3} \times\{9\varphi+75.5\varphi^2+125.5^2\varphi^3\},$$

where

$$\varphi = x\prod_{1}^{\infty}(1-x^{5m})^6(1-x^m)^{-6}.$$

He remarks that results for $p=13$ generalizing those of Zuckerman [Duke Math. J. **5**, 88–110 (1939)] can also be obtained by his method. *J. Lehner* (Philadelphia, Pa.).

Citations: MR 3, 271e = P60-1.

**P76-11** **(15, 685d)**

**Atkin, A. O. L., and Swinnerton-Dyer, P. Some properties of partitions.** Proc. London Math. Soc. (3) **4**, 84–106 (1954).

"We denote by $p(n)$ the number of unrestricted partitions of a positive integer $n$. Ramanujan discovered, and later proved, three striking arithmetical properties of $p(n)$, namely:

$$p(5n+4)\equiv 0 \pmod 5, \quad p(7n+5)\equiv 0 \pmod 7, \quad p(11n+6)\equiv 0 \pmod{11}.$$

All existing proofs of these results appeal to the theory of generating functions, and provide no method of actually separating the partitions concerned into $q$ equal classes ($q=5$, 7, or 11). Dyson [Eureka no. **8**, 10–15 (1944)] discovered empirically a remarkable combinatorial method of dividing the partitions of $5n+4$ and $7n+5$ into 5 and 7 equal classes respectively. Defining the rank of a partition as the largest part minus the number of parts, he divided the partitions of any number into 5 classes according to their ranks modulo 5. For numbers of the form $5n+4$, these 5 classes are all equal, while for numbers of other forms some but not all of the classes are equal; similar results hold for 7 but definitely not for 11.

"The main object of the present paper is to prove these conjectures of Dyson. The results form part of Theorems 4 and 5. It is noteworthy that we have to obtain at the same time all the results stated in these theorems—we cannot simplify the working so as merely to obtain Dyson's identities.

"Theorems 1 to 3 give some simple congruence properties of partitions which we obtained in the course of this work. In fact, each series

$$\sum_{n=0}^{\infty} p(qn+b)y^n \quad (q=5, 7, \text{ or } 11; 0\leqq b<q)$$

is congruent modulo $q$ to a simple infinite product. Theorems 1 and 2 follow immediately from Theorems 4 and 5 respectively, but we have given direct proofs also." (From the authors' introduction.)

The authors use a method (which goes back to Ramanujan and Watson) of splitting certain series according to the residue of the exponent (mod $q$). They then identify the components and verify the conjectures of Dyson by means of identities among series and products connected with the theta-functions. *N. J. Fine* (Princeton, N. J.).

Referred to in F10-48, P76-16, P80-53.

## P76-12 (18, 720b)

**Newman, Morris. Some theorems about $p_r(n)$.** Canad. J. Math. **9** (1957), 68–70.

Let $p_r(n)$ be the coefficient of $x^n$ in $\prod_{k=1}^{\infty}(1-x^k)^r$, if $n$ is a non-negative integer, and 0 otherwise. The author proves: A. Let $r=4, 6, 8, 10, 14, 26$, let $p$ be a prime $>3$ such that $r(p+1)\equiv 0 \pmod{24}$, and let $\Delta=r(p^2-1)/24$. Then if $R\equiv r \pmod p$ and $n\equiv\Delta \pmod p$, we have $p_R(n)\equiv 0 \pmod p$. This result generalizes the Ramanujan partition congruences for the moduli 5, 7, 11. B. Let $r=2, 4, 6, 8, 10, 14, 26$. Then $p_r(n)$ vanishes for arbitrarily long strings of consecutive values of $n$, arbitrarily many in number. Both results follow from a congruence relation proved by the author in an earlier paper [J. London Math. Soc. **30** (1955), 488–493; MR **17**, 15]. He states without proof five other relations of which $p_6(3n+2)=9p_6(\frac{1}{3}n)$ is a typical example.

*H. D. Kloosterman* (Leiden).

Citations: MR 17, 15d = F30-16.

## P76-13 (19, 1160b)

**Newman, Morris. Congruences for the coefficients of modular forms and some new congruences for the partition function.** Canad. J. Math. **9** (1957), 549–552.

Let $p_r(n)$ be the coefficient of $x^n$ in $\prod_{n=1}^{\infty}(1-x^n)^r$, so that $p_r(n)=p(n)$, the partition function, when $r=-1$. The author proves the following theorem. Let $r$ be even, $4\leq r\leq 24$ and $p$ a prime greater than 3 such that $\delta=r(p-1)/24$ is an integer. Then if $Q$, $n$ are integers and $R=Qp+r$,

$$p_R(np+\delta)\equiv p_r(\delta)p_{Q+r}(n) \pmod p.$$

From this he deduces that, for $n\equiv 6 \pmod{13}$,

$$p(13^2n-7)\equiv 6p(n) \pmod{13}.$$

A corollary is that $p(a\Delta_n+b)\equiv 0 \pmod{13}$, for a variety of different integers $a$, $b$, where $\Delta_n=13(13^{2n}-1)/24$.

*R. A. Rankin* (Glasgow).

Referred to in F30-53.

## P76-14 (20# 4543)

**Newman, Morris. Further identities and congruences for the coefficients of modular forms.** Canad. J. Math. **10** (1958), 577–586.

The author develops further identities and congruences for $p_r(n)$ defined by $\sum p_r(n)x^n=\prod(1-x^n)^r$, with $p_r(n)=0$ when not covered by the formula. As in his earlier work [J. London Math. Soc. **31** (1956), 350–359; MR **18**, 194], the author deduces his identities by using rational functions on the Riemann surface for $\Gamma_0(p)$ (where $ad-bc=1$ and $p|c$). The main theorem is

$$p_r(np^2+r\nu)-\gamma_n p_r(n)+p^{r-2}p_r\Big(\frac{n-r\nu}{p^2}\Big)=0$$

where $p$ is prime ($>2$), $\gamma_n=c-((r\nu-n)/p)p^{(r-3)/2}a$, $c=p_r(r\nu)+(r\nu/p)p^{(r-3)/2}a$, $a=\alpha_p\exp\{-i\pi r(p-1)/4\}$, and $\alpha_p=1$ or $i$ depending on whether $p\equiv+1$ or $-1 \pmod 4$. Typical results are $p_{-1}(84n^2-(n^2-1)/24)\equiv 0 \bmod 13$ for $p_{-1}(n)$ the partition function if $(n, 6)=1$. Also, $p_{15}(53n^2+5(n^2-1)/8)=0$, $n$ odd; and $p_{-1}(13n^2-7)\equiv 6p_{-1}(n) \bmod 13$. The paper ends with a table of $p_r(r\nu)$ ($\nu=(p^2-1)/24$), for $5\leq r\leq 23$, and a table of values of $c$, found by using the IBM 704 to 15 decimal digit accuracy.

*H. Cohn* (Tucson, Ariz.)

Citations: MR 18, 194g = F30-22.

Referred to in F30-53.

## P76-15 (20# 5177)

**Dutta, Mahadev. On new partitions of numbers.** Bull. Calcutta Math. Soc. **49** (1957), 221–224.

The author obtains various congruence properties and recurrence relations for partitions whose summands are restricted in several ways; e.g., partitions into $m$ parts with at most $d$ repetitions. *P. Erdös* (Haifa)

Referred to in P76-17.

## P76-16 (21# 2635)

**Atkin, A. O. L.; and Hussain, S. M. Some properties of partitions. II.** Trans. Amer. Math. Soc. **89** (1958), 184–200.

This paper is a sequel to one by Atkin and Swinnerton-Dyer [Proc. London Math. Soc. (3) **4** (1954), 84–106; MR **15**, 685]. Its main object is to give a complete account of Dyson's rank function for the case $q=11$. The rank of a partition is defined as the largest part minus the number of parts. For each $q$, the partitions of $n$ are classified according to their rank mod $q$, and the number of partitions of $n$ with rank congruent to $m$ mod $q$ is denoted by $N(m, q, n)$. The authors obtain identities for the series $r_{bc}(d)=r_b(d)-r_c(d)$, where $r_b(d)=\sum N(b, q, qn+d)y^n$, in terms of simpler series and products. The methods, although closely related to the theory of modular functions, are essentially elementary and involve lengthy algebraic manipulations. Among the results obtained is an identity for $\sum p(11n+6)y^n$ which proves the Ramanujan congruence $p(11n+6)\equiv 0 \pmod{11}$. {As pointed out by Atkin in a letter to the reviewer, there is some overlap with a paper by the reviewer [Tôhoku. Math. J. (2) **8** (1956), 149–164; MR **19**, 392]. The authors' functions $\lambda$, $\mu$ are related to the reviewer's $\alpha, \beta$ by $\beta=-\mu+3\lambda-23$, $\alpha=-\lambda-13$, and the authors' equations 8.13, 11.7, 11.9 are, respectively, the reviewer's equations 3.24, 3.22, 3.25. This overlapping is fortunate, since it brought to light an arithmetical error in the reviewer's paper: the last term written in his equation 3.20 for $\alpha$ should be $7x^4$, not $4x^4$; the right side of equation 3.23 should be $\alpha^5$, not $\alpha^5+9(11^2+\alpha)^2$; equation 3.24 should read $\alpha^3+38\alpha^2+3.11^2\alpha=\beta^2+6\alpha\beta+11^2\beta$.} *N. J. Fine* (Princeton, N.J.)

Citations: MR 15, 685d = P76-11; MR 19, 392c = F10-48.

## P76-17 (22# 2593)

**Dutta, Mahadev; Debnath, Lokenath. On new partitions of numbers. II.** Bull. Calcutta Math. Soc. **51** (1959), 77–78.

[For part I see Dutta, same Bull. **49** (1957), 221–224; MR **20** #5177.] Let ${}_dp(n)$ denote the number of partitions of $n$ in which each part occurs at most $d$ times, so that

$$\sum {}_dp(n)x^n = \prod(1-x^{n(d+1)})(1-x^n)^{-1}.$$

Let $p_d(n)$ be defined by

$$\sum p_d(n)x^n = \prod(1-x^n).$$

The authors note that if $d+1$ is prime then ${}_dp(n)\equiv p_d(n) \bmod (d+1)$. This fact and some identities and congruences for $p_d(n)$ due to the reviewer enable the authors to deduce a number of congruence properties of ${}_dp(n)$ of which the following is typical: ${}_4p(np+(p^2-1)/6)\equiv 0 \pmod 5$, $p$ prime, $p\equiv 5 \pmod 6$, $(n, p)=1$.

*M. Newman* (Washington, D.C.)

Citations: MR 20# 5177 = P76-15.

**P76-18** **(22# 6778 )**

**Newman, Morris. Periodicity modulo $m$ and divisibility properties of the partition function.** Trans. Amer. Math. Soc. **97** (1960), 225–236.

The author conjectures that for every pair of natural numbers $m$, $r$, there are infinitely many natural numbers $n$ such that $p(n) \equiv r \pmod{m}$, where $p(n)$ is the number of unrestricted partitions of $n$. He proves particular cases of this conjecture, e.g., all those in which $m=5$ or 13. He also obtains similar results involving arithmetical functions other than $p(n)$. *T. Estermann* (London)

Referred to in P02-27, P76-45.

**P76-19** **(22# 7995 )**

**Kolberg, O. Note on the parity of the partition function.** Math. Scand. **7** (1959), 377–378.

Congruence properties of the partition function $p(n)$ have been the subject of numerous investigations for over forty years; but the knowledge gained in this field, though substantial, is still fragmentary. In the present paper the author uses Euler's identity

$$\sum(-1)^k p\{n-\tfrac{1}{2}k(3k\pm 1)\} = 0$$

to deduce that $p(n)$ takes both even and odd values infinitely often. Although the argument is extremely short and simple, this theorem on the parity of $p(n)$ appears to have been overlooked by earlier writers. A combination of this result with well-known identities of Jacobi and Ramanujan leads to the conclusion that each of the congruences $p(n)\equiv 0 \pmod{10}$, $p(n)\equiv 5 \pmod{10}$, $p(n)\equiv 0 \pmod{14}$, $p(n)\equiv 7 \pmod{14}$ is satisfied for infinitely many values of $n$. *L. Mirsky* (Sheffield)

Referred to in P76-29, P76-45.

**P76-20** **(23# A2394 )**

**Kolberg, O.**

**Congruences involving the partition function for the moduli 17, 19, and 23.**

*Univ. Bergen Årbok Naturvit. Rekke* **1959**, *no.* 15, 10 *pp.* (1960).

Let $p(n)$ denote the number of unrestricted partitions of $n$, and let $p_r(n)$ denote the coefficient of $x^n$ in the infinite product $\prod_{k=1}^{\infty}(1-x^k)^r$, so that $p(n)=p_{-1}(n)$. The author continues his elegant discussion of congruences for $p(n)$ in terms of $p_r(n)$ [Math. Scand. **5** (1957), 77–92; MR **19**, 838], but finds it convenient to employ the modular functions invariant with respect to the substitutions of $\Gamma_0(q)$, $q$ a prime, instead of the $q$-dissection of a power series. Among the more interesting congruences obtained are:

$$\frac{1}{11}p(11n+6) \equiv 6p_{119}(11n+1) \pmod{11};$$

$$p(17n+5) \equiv p_{95}(17n+1) \pmod{17};$$

$$p(19n+4) \equiv p_{71}(19n+1) \pmod{19}.$$

Such congruences are of interest, since, for $r>0$, the associated modular forms are of negative dimension, and recurrence formulas of length independent of $n$ exist for the numbers $p_r(n)$. Thus, congruence properties of $p(n)$ may be deduced from the congruences given above. *M. Newman* (Washington, D.C.)

Citations: MR 19, 838e = P60-26.

**P76-21** **(25# 3892 )**

**Newman, Morris**

**Congruences for the partition function to composite moduli.**

*Illinois J. Math.* **6** (1962), 59–63.

If $p(n)$ denotes the number of unrestricted partitions of the integer $n$, the author had conjectured that for all integers $m\geq 2$ each of the $m$ congruences $p(n)\equiv r \pmod{m}$, $0\leq r\leq m-1$, has infinitely many solutions in positive integers $n$. This conjecture is shown to be true for $m=65$. Similar results are obtained for certain moduli of the form $m=5^\alpha 7^\beta 11^3 13$. He also obtains the result that if $(n, 30)=1$, then $p((167n^2+1)/24)\equiv 0 \pmod{5}$. *R. P. Kelisky* (Yorktown Heights, N.Y.)

**P76-22** **(30# 1084 )**

**Newman, Morris**

**Note on the partition function.**

*Amer. Math. Monthly* **71** (1964), 1022.

Let $p(n)$ denote the number of unrestricted partitions of $n$. The author proves the following result. Let $r$ be a fixed integer. Then neither of the congruences

$$p(13k-7) \equiv r \pmod{13},$$

$$p(13^2k-7) \equiv r \pmod{13}$$

can hold for all sufficiently large $k$. *L. Carlitz* (Durham, N.C.)

**P76-23** **(30# 1086 )**

**Vaidya, A. M.**

**A congruence property of $C_k(n)$.**

*Amer. Math. Monthly* **72** (1965), 38–40.

Put

$$\prod_{n=1}^{\infty}(1-x^n)^r = \sum_{n=0}^{\infty} p_r(n)x^n$$

and let $C_k(n)$ denote the coefficient of $(-x)^n$ in $y^k$, where

$$y = \sum_{j=1}^{\infty}(-1)^j\{x^{j(3j-1)/2}+x^{j(3j+1)/2}\}.$$

The author shows that if $p$ is prime and $k\geq 1$ then

$$C_{p^k}(n) \equiv (-1)^j \pmod{p} \quad (n = \tfrac{1}{2}j(3j\pm 1)p),$$

$$\equiv 0 \quad \text{(otherwise)}.$$

{In the paper $(-1)^{j(j\pm 1)/2}$ appears in place of $(-1)^j$.} *L. Carlitz* (Durham, N.C.)

**P76-24** **(32# 4106 )**

**Gandhi, J. M.**

**Generalization of Ramanujan's congruences $p(5m+4)\equiv 0 \pmod{5}$ and $p(7m+5)\equiv 0 \pmod{7}$.**

*Monatsh. Math.* **69** (1965), 389–392.

Let $\prod_{k=1}^{\infty}(1-x^k)^l=\sum_{n=0}^{\infty}p_l(n)x^n$ and let $l$ be an integer. The author derives in a simple way congruences for $p_l(n)$ which include the well-known congruences for the unrestricted partitions by Ramanujan. *O. H. Körner* (Marburg)

Referred to in P76-39.

**P76-25** **(32# 7531 )**

**Mohammad, Dost**

**A note on some congruences.**

*J. Natur. Sci. and Math.* **5** (1965), *no.* 2, 237–239.

Proof of four congruences in the theory of partitions. *B. Stolt* (Stockholm)

**P76-26** **(34# 1293 )**

**Subbarao, M. V.**

**Some remarks on the partition function.**

*Amer. Math. Monthly* **73** (1966), 851–854.

The author proves by elementary arguments that if $p(n)$ is the unrestricted partition function, then $p(2n+1)$ is odd infinitely often and even infinitely often. The author also remarks that in a private communication to him O.

Kolberg proved the same result for $p(2n)$, and that the author can now do the same for each of $p(4n+r)$, $r=0, 1, 2, 3$. *Morris Newman* (Washington, D.C.)

**P76-27** **(34# 4187)**

**Arkin, Joseph**

**An extension of a theorem of Ramanujan.**

*Amer. Math. Monthly* **73** (1966), 1087–1090.

Congruence relations are established for the coefficients in various formal series related to number-theoretic functions. In particular, let $p_6(n)$ be defined by $\sum_0^\infty p_6(n)x^n = (\prod_1^\infty (1-x^n))^6$; if $P=4m+3$ is a prime and if $n \equiv -(m+1) \bmod P$, then $p_6(n) \equiv 0 \bmod P^2$.

*B. M. Stewart* (E. Lansing, Mich.)

**P76-28** **(34# 5783)**

**Atkin, A. O. L.**

**Proof of a conjecture of Ramanujan.**

*Glasgow Math. J.* **8** (1967), 14–32.

A well-known conjecture of Ramanujan [Proc. Cambridge Philos. Soc. **19** (1919), 207–210] states that if $p(n)$ is the number of unrestricted partitions of $n$, $q=5$, 7 or 11, and $24m \equiv 1 \pmod{q^n}$, then $p(m) \equiv 0 \pmod{q^n}$. As stated, the conjecture is incorrect [see S. Chowla, J. London Math. Soc. **9** (1934), 247]. For $n=1$ and 2, the statement was proved by Ramanujan [loc. cit., Math. Z. **9** (1921), 147–153]; for $q=5$ and $q=7$ (all $n$), the (correct form of the) statement was proved by G. N. Watson [J. Reine Angew. Math. **179** (1938), 97–128], and for $q=11$, $n=3$ by J. Lehner [Proc. Amer. Math. Soc. **1** (1950), 172–181; MR **11**, 582].

The present paper essentially settles the problem, with the proof of the following theorem: Let $24m \equiv 1 \pmod{5^a 7^b 11^c}$ and set $\beta = [(b+2)/2]$; then $p(m) \equiv 0 \pmod{5^a 7^\beta 11^c}$. The method of proof is essentially that of Lehner and depends on the behavior and the Fourier series of entire modular functions on $\Gamma_0(11) = \left\{\begin{pmatrix} a & b \\ c & d\end{pmatrix} : a, b, c, d \in \mathbf{Z}, ad-bc=1, c \equiv 0 \pmod{11}\right\}$. The method requires a fair amount of computation, the most tedious part of which is relegated to three appendices. By similar (but simpler) considerations, the author also shows that if $c(m)$ stands for the Fourer coefficient of the modular invariant $j(\tau)$, then $m \equiv 0 \pmod{11^n}$ implies $c(m) \equiv 0 \pmod{11^n}$. A conjecture, too technical to be quoted, is also stated. {In line 10 of p. 26, "Theorem 1" should read "Theorem 2".} *E. Grosswald* (Philadelphia, Pa.)

Citations: MR 11, 582a = P76-9.

Referred to in P76-31.

**P76-29** **(37# 2711)**

**Parkin, Thomas R.; Shanks, Daniel**

**On the distribution of parity in the partition function.**

*Math. Comp.* **21** (1967), 466–480.

Little is known about the parity of $p(n)$, the number of unrestricted partitions of $n$. O. Kolberg [Math. Scand. **7** (1959), 377–378; MR **22** #7995] has proved that $p(n)$ is infinitely often even and infinitely often odd. The present authors have calculated the parity of $p(n)$ up to $n = 2{,}039{,}999$ and give empirical results and conjectures regarding the distribution of the parity of $p(n)$. Let $m = 1.10111110000111011101\ldots$, where the $k$th bit to the right of the binary point is 0 or 1 according as $p(k)$ is even or odd. Numerical evidence seems to suggest that $m$ is normal with respect to base 2 and that the pairs of bits 00, 01, 10, 11 each have an asymptotic density of $\frac{1}{4}$, so that the ratio of even counts to odd counts has upper bound 1 as $n \to \infty$. *W. H. Simons* (Corvallis, Ore.)

Citations: MR 22# 7995 = P76-19.

**P76-30** **(37# 2712)**

**Newman, Morris**

**Note on partitions modulo 5.**

*Math. Comp.* **21** (1967), 481–482.

In the paper reviewed above [#2711] Parkin and Shanks gave numerical evidence which suggests that there is no apparent preference for the number of times that $p(n)$, the number of unrestricted partitions of $n$, is even or odd. In the paper here reviewed the author considers the analogous question for partitions modulo 5. Define $s(x) = \sum_{n \leq x;\, p(n) \equiv 0 \bmod 5} 1$. Using identities from the theory of elliptic modular functions it is proved that $\liminf_{x\to\infty} s(x)/x \geqq 1/5 + 36/(5.19^4)$ showing that the density (if it exists) of the integers for which $5 | p(n)$ is greater than $1/5$. *W. H. Simons* (Corvallis, Ore.)

**P76-31** **(38# 2098)**

**Atkin, A. O. L.**

**Ramanujan congruences for $p_{-k}(n)$.**

*Canad. J. Math.* **20** (1968), 67–78; *corrigendum, ibid.* **21** (1969), 256.

Let $f(x) = \prod_{r=1}^\infty (1-x^r)$, $f^k(x) = \sum_{n=0}^\infty p_k(n)x^n$ $(|x|<1)$, so that $p_{-1}(n) = p(n)$, the ordinary partition function. S. Ramanujan conjectured [Proc. Cambridge Philos. Soc. **19** (1918/19), 207–210] that if $24m \equiv 1 \pmod{5^a\, 7^b\, 11^c}$, then (*) $p(m) \equiv 0 \pmod{5^a\, 7^b\, 11^c}$, and he proved this for $a, b, c = 0$, 1, or 2. S. Chowla showed [J. London Math. Soc. **9** (1934), 247] that (*) fails for $b=3$ and G. N. Watson [J. Reine Angew. Math. **179** (1938), 97–128], using modular equations, proved (*) for arbitrary non-negative integer $a$ and with $b$ replaced in (*) by $\beta = [(b+2)/2]$ (so far still only with $c=0$, 1 or 2, after Ramanujan). J. Lehner [Amer. J. Math. **65** (1943), 492–520; MR **5**, 34; Proc. Amer. Math. Soc. **1** (1950), 172–181; MR **11**, 582] proved (*) for $c=3$, but it was only quite recently that the author proved [Glasgow Math. J. **8** (1967), 14–32; MR **34** #5783] the (correct form of the) full conjecture (*), i.e., $24m \equiv 1 \pmod{5^a\, 7^b\, 11^c}$ implies $p(m) \equiv 0 \pmod{5^a\, 7^\beta\, 11^c}$. In the present paper the author considers the generalization of these congruences to general $k>0$. The method (a streamlined version of Watson's) limits the author to primes $q$ for which $\Gamma_0(q)$ is of genus zero (in particular, $q \neq 11$). Let $k \equiv k_0 \pmod{24}$, $0 < k_0 \leqq 24$, and let $q$ be one of the primes 2, 3, 5, 7, or 13; then the author computes (and presents in tabular form) an integer $\alpha = \alpha(q, k_0)$ (for $q=2$ and $q=3$, $\alpha$ is defined only if $k \equiv 0 \pmod 8$ and $k \equiv 0 \pmod 3$, respectively) and proves the following Theorem 1: If $24m \equiv k \pmod{q^n}$, then $p_{-k}(m) \equiv 0 \pmod{q^{n\alpha/2+\varepsilon}}$, where $\varepsilon = \varepsilon(k) = O(\log k)$. If $d = d(q, k, n)$ is the highest power of $q$ which divides $p_{-k}(m)$, then Theorem 1 states that $d \geqq \alpha n/2 + O(\log k)$. For $q = 2, 3, 13$, the equality actually holds, and for $q = 5, 7$, there exist in each residue class mod 24 at least some $k$ (conjecture: infinitely many $k$) for which the equality holds; consequently, Theorem 1 is, in this sense, a best possible one. The author conjectures that for $q=5$ and 7, there exists a $\beta = \beta(k_1, q)$ such that $d = \beta n/2 + O(\log k)$ holds for all $n$, where $k \equiv k_1 \pmod{24q^\delta}$ for some $\delta = \delta(q)$. The proofs are given in detail for $q=5$ and the modifications needed for the other primes are sketched very briefly. The author hints at some deep properties of coefficients of forms of non-negative dimension, analogous to those encountered in the theory of the

Hecke operators (for forms of negative dimensions) as the underlying reason for the generalized Ramanujan type congruence properties of $p_{-k}(m)$.

{Misprints: On p. 68, line 2 and p. 71, line 13: read $k$ for 1. On p. 78, line 10, read [6] for (6). In the corrigendum, the author notes that the value of $\alpha(24, 2)$ in Theorem 1 should be 0, not 3.}

*E. Grosswald* (Philadelphia, Pa.)

Citations: MR 5, 34d = P76-1; MR 11, 582a = P76-9; MR 34# 5783 = P76-28.

## P76-32 (38# 4434)

**Winquist, Lasse**

**An elementary proof of $p(11m+6)\equiv 0 \pmod{11}$.**

*J. Combinatorial Theory* **6** (1969), 56–59.

Let $p(n)$ denote the number of unrestricted partitions of $n$. The author gives an elegant proof of the congruence (due to Ramanujan) $p(11m+6)\equiv 0 \pmod{11}$. The proof is reminiscent of Ramanujan's proofs of $p(5m+4)\equiv 0 \pmod 5$ and $p(7m+5)\equiv 0 \pmod 7$, i.e., $\prod_n (1-x^n)^{10}$ is expressed as a double series and congruential conclusions are drawn about certain coefficients of the expansion. In fact, the expansion leads to an explicit formula for the coefficient of $x^m$ in $\prod_n (1-x^n)^{10}$ (first obtained by Rushfort and independently by Atkin) similar to those known for $\prod_n (1-x^n)^k$, $k=8$, 14 and 26.

*R. L. Graham* (Murray Hill, N.J.)

## P76-33 (39# 2717)

**Lahiri, D. B.**

**Some restricted partition functions: Congruences modulo 3.**

*Pacific J. Math.* **28** (1969), 575–581.

Let ${}_r^{\alpha}p(n)$ denote the number of partitions of $n$ with the restriction that no numbers of the forms $\alpha m$, or $\alpha m \pm r$, shall be a part of the partitions. The author proves the following two results. (1) For almost all values of $n$, ${}_3^{27}p(n)\equiv {}_6^{27}p(n)\equiv {}_{12}^{27}p(n)\equiv 0 \pmod 3$. (2) For all values of $n$, ${}_3^{27}p(3n)\equiv {}_6^{27}p(3n+1)\equiv -{}_{12}^{27}p(3n+2) \pmod 3$.

*H. A. Passi* (Denver, Colo.)

## P76-34 (39# 4110)

**Lahiri, D. B.**

**Some restricted partition functions: Congruences modulo 5.**

*J. Austral. Math. Soc.* **9** (1969), 424–432.

Let ${}_r^{75}p(n)$ be the number of partitions of $n$ into parts not of the form $75k$ or $75k\pm r$. Set ${}^{25}p(n)={}_{25}^{75}p(n)$. Then the author proves the following theorems: (1) For almost all $n$, ${}^{25}p(n)\equiv 0$, ${}_{20}^{75}p(n)\equiv {}_5^{75}p(n-5)$ and ${}_{35}^{75}p(n)\equiv -{}_{10}^{75}p(n-5)$ (mod 5). (2) For all $n$, ${}_{5\rho}^{75}p(5n+4)\equiv 0 \pmod 5$ for $\rho=0$, $1, \cdots, 7$. (3) For all $n$, ${}_{20}^{75}p(25n+23)-{}_{20}^{75}p(5n+3)\equiv {}_5^{75}p(25n+18)-{}_5^{75}p(5n-2)$ and

$${}_{35}^{75}p(25n)-{}_{35}^{75}p(5n) \equiv -{}_{10}^{75}p(25n-5)+{}_{10}^{75}p(5n-5) \pmod 5.$$

(4) The three expressions ${}^{25}p(n-1)$, $2\cdot{}_{20}^{75}p(n-2)-2\cdot{}_5^{75}p(n-7)+{}^{25}p(n-1)$, $2\cdot{}_{35}^{75}p(n)+2\cdot{}_{10}^{75}p(n-5)-{}^{25}p(n-1)$ are all multiplicative (mod 5).

The proofs use manipulation of generating functions, starting from Euler's pentagonal number theorem and the Jacobi triple-product theorem.

*S. A. Burr* (Whippany, N.J.)

Referred to in P76-42.

## P76-35 (39# 4111)

**Lahiri, D. B.**

**Some restricted partition functions: Congruences modulo 7.**

*Trans. Amer. Math. Soc.* **140** (1969), 475–484.

Let ${}_r^{\alpha}p(n)$ denote the number of partitions of $n$ into parts that are not of the form $\alpha m$ or $\alpha m\pm r$. The author proves the existence of a variety of congruence relations to the modulus 7 mainly for the seven restricted partition functions ${}_r^{\alpha}p(n)$, $\alpha=147$ and $r=7$, 14, 28, 35, 49, 56 and 70. He also gives a selection of congruence relations for the moduli 2, 3, 5, 7, 11 and 13 without proof. The author intends to publish separate papers on these moduli.

*H. A. Passi* (Denver, Colo.)

Referred to in P76-42.

## P76-36 (40# 1357)

**Gandhi, J. M.**

**On numbers related to partitions of a number.**

*Amer. Math. Monthly* **76** (1969), 1033–1036.

Verfasser behandelt die zahlentheoretische Funktion $G(n)$, welche durch die erzeugende Funktion $\phi(x)/\phi'(x)=\sum_{n=0}^{\infty}(-1)^{n+1}G(n)x^n$ mit $\phi(x)=\prod_{\nu=1}^{\infty}(1-x^{\nu})$ definiert ist. Mit Hilfe des Eulerschen Pentagonalzahlensatzes ist leicht zu sehen, daß die $G(n)$ natürliche Zahlen sind. Das Ergebnis der Untersuchung lautet: $G(n)\equiv 0 \bmod 5$ für $n\not\equiv 0 \bmod 5$, $n>1$. Es wird bewiesen mittels geeigneter Potenzreihenidentitäten unter Verwendung der von K. G. Ramanathan bewiesenen Kongruenzen modulo 5 für die verallgemeinerte Partitionenfunktion $p_{-2}(n)$. Als Folgerung erhält man die bekannten Aussagen $p(n)\equiv 0 \bmod 5$ für $n\equiv -1 \bmod 5$ und $\tau(n)\equiv 0 \bmod 5$ für $n\equiv 0 \bmod 5$ für die Anzahl $p(n)$ der uneingeschränkten Partitionen von $n$ bzw. S. Ramanujans $\tau$-Funktion.

*H. Klingen* (Freiburg)

## P76-37 (40# 2629)

**Herrmann, Oskar**

**Kongruenzeigenschaften der Partitionenfunktion. (English summary)**

*J. Number Theory* **1** (1969), 431–458.

The well-known Euler partition function $p(n)$ is connected with the Dedekind $\eta$-function by $\eta^{-1}(\tau)=\sum_{n=0}^{\infty} p(n)\times \exp[2\pi i(n-1/24)\tau]$. H. B. C. Darling [Proc. London Math. Soc. **19** (1921), 350–372] and L. J. Mordell [ibid. **20** (1922), 408–416] used this connection to prove the following identities stated by Ramanujan without proof: $\sum p(5n+4)\exp[2\pi i(n+19/24)\tau]=5\eta^5(\tau)/\eta^6(\tau)$, $\sum p(7n+5)\times \exp[2\pi i(n+17/24)\tau]=7\eta^3(7\tau)/\eta^4(\tau)+49\eta^7(7\tau)/\eta^8(\tau)$. H. S. Zuckerman [Duke Math. J. **5** (1939), 88–110] showed how to obtain such identities with "13" in place of "7" or "5". The present author uses more powerful methods to obtain similar identities with "17". We quote his result: "Es seien $B_1$ und $B_2$ zwei halbganze symmetrische positivdefinite vierreihige Matrizen mit den Diskriminanten $\det(2B_1)=17$ und $\det(2B_2)=17^3$. Durch diese Angaben sind die Äquivalenzklassen der zugehörigen quadratischen Formen eindeutig bestimmt, so dass auch die Darstellungszahlen $a_n(B_1)$ und $a_n(B_2)$ einer natürlichen zahl $n$ durch diese Formen eindeutig bestimmt sind. Die Funktion

$$\sum_{n=0}^{\infty} p(17n+5)q^n(1+\sum_{n=1}^{\infty} a_n(B_1)q^n) - 112\sum_{n=0}^{\infty} p(n)q^{17n}\sum_{n=1}^{\infty}((a_n(B_2)-a_n(B_1))/8)q^n$$

besitzt eine Potenzreihenentwicklung, wo alle Koeffizienten durch 17 teilbare ganze zahlen sind."

*S. Chowla* (University Park, Pa.)

## P76-38 (40# 5545)

**Kløve, Torleiv**

**Recurrence formulae for the coefficients of modular forms and congruences for the partition function and for the coefficients of $j(\tau)$, $(j(\tau)-1728)^{1/2}$ and $(j(\tau))^{1/3}$.**

*Math. Scand.* **23** (1968), 133–159 (1969).

In this interesting article the author combines methods

of O. Kolberg and the reviewer to derive a number of congruences for the partition function and certain other coefficients of modular forms. Among the most significant of these is the result that $p(n)$ fills all residue classes modulo $p$ infinitely often for $p=7$, 17, 19, 29, 31 (in partial answer to a conjecture of the reviewer's that $p(n)$ fills all residue classes modulo $m$ infinitely often for all positive $m$). Since the result was previously known to be true for $p=2$ (due to O. Kolberg and the reviewer) and for $p=5$, 13 (due to the reviewer) the first unsettled value is $p=3$. This probably will necessitate new techniques, whereas the value $p=11$ should be approachable by the standard methods.

{See the bibliography of the article for the appropriate references.} *Morris Newman* (Washington, D.C.)

Referred to in P76-44, P76-45.

**P76-39** **(41# 167 )**

**Gandhi, J. M.**

**Simple proofs for the Ramanujan congruences** $p(5m+4)\equiv 0 \pmod 5$ **and** $p(7m+5)\equiv 0 \pmod 7$.

*Recent Progress in Combinatorics* (*Proc. Third Waterloo Conf. on Combinatorics*, 1968), *pp.* 221–222. *Academic Press, New York*, 1969.

This contains slightly simpler proofs than in the author's earlier note in the Monatsh. Math. **69** (1965), 389–392 [MR **32** #4106]. *J. H. H. Chalk* (Toronto, Ont.)

Citations: MR 32# 4106 = P76-24.

**P76-40** **(41# 1670 )**

**Gandhi, J. M.**

**Congruences for restricted partitions of a number.**

*Math. Student* **35** (1967), 69–71 (1969).

For $n\geqq m$, let $P_1(n,m)$ be defined by $\prod_{r=1}^{m}(1-t^r)^{-1}=\sum_{n=0}^{\infty}P_1(n,m)t^n$ and $P_2(n,m)$ by

$$\prod_{r=1}^{m}(1-t^r)^{-2}\prod_{r=m+1}^{\infty}(1-t^r)^{-1}=\sum_{n=0}^{\infty}P_2(n,m)t^n.$$

The author establishes criteria for 5, 7 and 25 to divide $P_1(5m+4, 5m-r)$, $P_1(7m+5, 7m-r)$ and $P_1(25m+24, 25m-r)$, respectively, in terms of $P_2(3+r,1)$, $P_2(r+4,1)$ and $P_2(r+23,1)$. He uses well-known criteria that $5|P(5m+4)$, $7|P(7m+5)$ and $25|P(25m+24)$ and recursion relations involving $P_1(n,m)$, $P(n)$ and $P_2(n,m)$.

*J. H. Jordan* (Pullman, Wash.)

**P76-41** **(41# 5289 )**

**Manzur Hussain, S.; Kazi, M. H.**

**On a sum function of functions of partitions.**

*Punjab Univ. J. Math.* (*Lahore*) **2** (1969), 91–95.

Congruences involving $P_r(n)$ and $S(n)$ (mod $p$) are proved, where $P_r(n)=\sum_{k=0}^{n}P(k)P_{r-1}(n-k)$, $P_0(n)=P(n)$, denotes the unrestricted partitions of $n$ ($P_{r+1}(n)$ instead of $P_r(n)$ would be a more suitable notation) and $S(n)=\sum_{r=1}^{p}P_r(n)$. Theorem I states $\sum_{k=1}^{mp+r}P(k)S(mp+r-k)\equiv\sum_{k=1}^{m}P_kP_1((m-k)p+r) \pmod p$ and Theorem II states $S(n)\equiv 0 \pmod p$ for $0\leqq n\leqq p-2$ and for $n=p$ and $S(p-1)\equiv 1 \pmod p$. These results follow easily by considering the generating functions for these numbers (mod $p$). Thus $\sum_{n=0}^{\infty}P_r(n)x^n=1/(r+1)$, where $f(x)=\prod_{n=1}^{\infty}(1-x^n)$ and $\sum_{n=0}^{\infty}S(n)x^n=(f^p(x)-1)f(x)/(f^{p+1}(x)(f(x)-1))$. Lemma 1 follows from $f^{-p-1}(x)\equiv f^{-1}(x)\cdot f^{-1}(x^p) \pmod p$, Theorem I follows from

$$\{-1+f^{-1}(x)\}\sum_{n=0}^{\infty}S(n)x^n\equiv(-1+f^{-1}(x^p))/f^2(x) \pmod p.$$

Theorem II and Lemma 2 also follow from these results.

*M. S. Cheema* (Tucson, Ariz.)

**P76-42** **(41# 5317 )**

**Lahiri, D. B.**

**Some restricted partition functions: Congruences modulo 3.**

*J. Austral. Math. Soc.* **11** (1970), 82–90.

The author studies the restricted partition function ${}_r{}^tp(n)$. In order to determine the value of this function one should count all the unrestricted partitions of $n$ except those which contain a number of the form $tn$, $tn\pm r$, where $t$ and $r$ are fixed integers. The author proves the following theorem: For almost all values of $n$, the following congruences modulo 3 hold: (i) $-{}_{90}{}^{243}p(n)\equiv{}_{72}{}^{243}p(n-3)\equiv{}_{9}{}^{243}p(n-24)$, (ii) $-{}_{90}{}^{243}p(n)\equiv{}_{63}{}^{243}p(n-6)\equiv{}_{18}{}^{243}p(n-21)$, (iii) $-{}_{117}{}^{243}p(n)\equiv{}_{45}{}^{243}p(n-12)\equiv{}_{36}{}^{243}p(n-15)$.

The phrase "for almost all values of $n$" appearing here means the number of integers $n\leqq N$ for which the specified congruence does not hold is $o(N)$.

For similar congruences modulo 5 and modulo 7, reference may be made, respectively, to the author's papers in same J. **9** (1969), 424–432 [MR **39** #4110] and in Trans. Amer. Math. Soc. **140** (1969), 475–483 [MR **39** #4111].

*J. M. Gandhi* (Macomb, Ill.)

Citations: MR 39# 4110 = P76-34; MR 39# 4111 = P76-35.

**P76-43** **(41# 5318 )**

**Lahiri, D. B.**

**Some restricted partition functions: Congruences modulo 2.**

*Trans. Amer. Math. Soc.* **147** (1970), 271–278.

For the restricted partition function ${}_r{}^tp(n)$, defined in the paper reviewed above [#5317], the author proves Theorem 1: For almost all values of $n$, the following congruences modulo 2 hold: (i) ${}_{14}{}^{48}p(n)\equiv{}_{2}{}^{48}p(n-4)$, (ii) ${}_{22}{}^{48}p(n)\equiv{}_{10}{}^{48}p(n-2)$. Theorem 2: For almost all values of $n$, the following congruences modulo 2 hold: (i) ${}_{44}{}^{192}p(n)\equiv{}_{20}{}^{192}p(n-8)$, (ii) ${}_{68}{}^{192}p(n)\equiv{}_{4}{}^{192}p(n-20)$, (iii) ${}_{76}{}^{192}p(n)\equiv{}_{52}{}^{192}p(n-4)$, (iv) ${}_{92}{}^{192}p(n)\equiv{}_{28}{}^{192}p(n-12)$.

From these theorems, the author derives Corollary 1: The members of each of the following pairs have the same parity, unless $n$ is a square or twice a square: (i) ${}_{14}{}^{18}p(n-1)$ and ${}_{2}{}^{48}p(n-5)$, (ii) ${}_{22}{}^{48}p(n)$ and ${}_{10}{}^{48}p(n-2)$; Corollary 2: $\sigma 3(n)\equiv(2n-1)\sigma(n) \pmod{2^3}$; and some other corollaries. *J. M. Gandhi* (Macomb, Ill.)

**P76-44** **(41# 6779 )**

**Hjelle, T.; Kløve, T.**

**Congruence properties and density problems for the Fourier coefficients of modular forms.**

*Math. Scand.* **23** (1968), 160–166 (1969).

Let $p_k(n)$ be defined by $\sum_0^{\infty}p_k(n)x^n=\prod_1^{\infty}(1-x^n)^k$; in particular, $p_{-1}$ is the unrestricted partition function. Let $c(n)$ be the Fourier coefficients of the absolute modular invariant $j(\tau)$. The authors prove a number of congruences for $p_k(n)$ and $c(n)$ that include many of the known congruences and use these results to obtain density theorems.

A typical result: Let $Q$ be a product of different $c$-regular primes. Then for each prime $p\nmid Q$ there is an integer $N$ such that $c(p^{mN-1}Qn)\equiv c(Qn/p) \pmod Q$ for all $n$ and all $m\geqq 0$. In particular, $c(p^{mN-1}Qn)\equiv 0 \pmod Q$ for all $n$ prime to $p$. Moreover, $d(c|Q)>0$. In this theorem the "$c$-regular primes" include, in particular, all primes between 2 and 31, inclusive, and $d(c|Q)=\liminf_{x\to\infty}x^{-1}\sum 1$, where the sum is over those $n\leqq x$ for which $c(n)$ is divisible by $Q$.

The proofs depend heavily on a recurrence formula appearing in an earlier paper of the second author [Math. Scand. **23** (1968), 133–159 (1969); MR **40** #5545].

*J. Lehner* (College Park, Md.)

Citations: MR 40# 5545 = P76-38.

**P76-45** **(42# 219 )**

**Kløve, Torleiv**

**Density problems for $p(n)$.**

*J. London Math. Soc.* (2) **2** (1970), 504–508.

Let $p(n)$ denote the number of unrestricted partitions of $n$. M. Newman [Trans. Amer. Math. Soc. **97** (1960), 225–236; MR **22** #6778] proposed the question: Does the sequence $\{p(n)\}$ fill each residue class modulo $m$ infinitely often? He proves that it does when $m=5$ and 13. O. Kolberg [Math. Scand. **7** (1959), 377–378; MR **22** #7995] proved it for $m=2$, A. O. L. Atkin [Proc. London Math. Soc. (3) **18** (1968), 563–576; MR **37** #2690] for $m=7$ and the author [Math. Scand. **23** (1968), 133–159 (1969); MR **40** #5545] for $m=17$ and some larger primes. In this paper the author proves the theorem: The sequence $\{p(n)\}$ fills each residue class modulo $11^2$ infinitely often. The reviewer would like to mention the following more general problem: Does the sequence $\{p_r(n)\}$ fill each residue class modulo $m$ infinitely often? $p_r(n)$ is defined by $\{(1-x)(1-x^2)\cdots(1-x^n)\cdots\}^r=\sum_{n=0}^{\infty} p_r(n)x^n$, $p_{-1}(n)$ being equal to $p(n)$. In an unpublished paper the reviewer has settled this general problem for $m=2$ and other primes.

*J. M. Gandhi* (Macomb, Ill.)

Citations: MR 22# 6778 = P76-18; MR 22# 7995 = P76-19; MR 37# 2690 = F30-55; MR 40# 5545 = P76-38.

# P80 PARTITIONS: MISCELLANEOUS RESULTS (SUMS OVER PARTITIONS, EXTREMAL PROPERTIES, DISTRIBUTION OF THE NUMBER OF SUMMANDS, PARTITIONS INTO POWERS OF A FIXED INTEGER, SERIES INVOLVING $p(n)$ AND $q(n)$, COMPOSITIONS, ETC.)

For partitions into primes, see **A46**.

See also reviews A34-39, A36-3, B36-133, B72-30, B72-32, F10-65, M05-6, N52-24, P02-11, P02-20, P08-38, P08-45, P44-23, P68-10, Q15-2.

**P80-1** **(1, 40b)**

**Atkinson, F. V. A summation formula for $p(n)$, the partition function.** J. London Math. Soc. **14**, 175–184 (1939).

With $p(n)$ denoting the number of unrestricted partitions of $n$, the author first proves the summation formula:

$$\sum_{n-1/24<x} p(n)\frac{\{2\pi(x-n+1/24)\}^k}{\Gamma(1+k)} = \sum_{n=0}^{\infty} p(n)\left(\frac{x}{n-1/24}\right)^{\frac{1}{2}k-\frac{1}{4}} J_{k-\frac{1}{2}}\{4\pi\sqrt{(x(n-1/24))}\}, \tag{1}$$

valid if $k>-\frac{1}{2}$, $x>1/24$, and $x+1/24$ not an integer. The series on the right-hand side is Abel summable, but not summable by arithmetic means of any order.

The formula (1) appears in the paper as a consequence of the functional equation

$$\sum_{n=0}^{\infty} p(n)e^{-2\pi(n-1/24)z}=\sqrt{z}\sum_{n=0}^{\infty} p(n)e^{-2\pi(n-1/24)/z}, \tag{2}$$

which itself is a special instance of the transformation theory of the modular form $\eta(\tau)^{-1}$. In the same manner as (2) belongs to the point $z=1$, there exist infinitely many other similar functional equations (transformation formulae), each belonging to a root of unity. Each of those, as the author points out, will give rise to a summation formula analogous to (1).

The proof of (1) is a rather direct one and operates with a term by term integration over $1-i\infty$ to $1+i\infty$. The difficulties lie in the justification of certain interchanges of limits. For $k=0$ the formula (1) can be written

$$\sum_{n+1/24<x} p(n)=\lim_{h\to\infty} s(h, x), \tag{3}$$

with

$$s(h, x)= \sum_{n=0}^{\infty} p(n)e^{-2\pi(n-1/24)/h}\frac{1}{\pi(2x)^{1/2}}\cos 4\pi\sqrt{(x(n-1/24))}. \tag{3a}$$

The author proves that, for $x$ in the interval $(a, b)$, $1/24<a<b$, the series $s(h, x)$ remains bounded if $h\to\infty$. Multiplication of (3) by the integrable derivative $f'(x+1/24)$ and termwise integration lead to the result: If $f(x+1/24)$ has an integrable derivative in the closed interval $(a, b)$, where $b>a>1/24$, and neither $a+1/24$ nor $b+1/24$ is an integer, then

$$\sum_{a<n-1/24<b} p(n)f(n)= -\frac{1}{\pi\sqrt{2}}\sum_{n=0}^{\infty} p(n)\int_a^b f(x+1/24)\frac{d}{dx}\{x^{-\frac{1}{4}}\cos 4\pi\sqrt{(x(n-1/24))}\},$$

the series being Abel summable. (The integrability of $f'(x+1/24)$ is not included in the author's own statement of his theorem, but is explicitly mentioned in the course of the proof.)

*H. Rademacher* (Swarthmore, Pa.).

**P80-2** **(1, 201d)**

**Shah, S. M. An inequality for the arithmetical function $g(x)$.** J. Indian Math. Soc. **3**, 316–318 (1939).

Let $f(n)$ be the maximum least common multiple of $a_1, a_2, \cdots, a_\rho$, for all partitions $n=a_1+\cdots+a_\rho$ in positive integers $a_i$. Landau [Primzahlen, vol. 1, 222–229] had proved for $g(x)=\log f(x)$ that $g(x)\sim(x\log x)^{\frac{1}{2}}$. Let $p_r$ denote the $r$th prime, and $y=p_{s+1}-1$, where $p_1+\cdots+p_s\leqq x<p_1+\cdots+p_{s+1}$; set $I(y)=\log p_1+\cdots+\log p_s$; it is known that $I(y)=(x\log x)^{\frac{1}{2}}\{1+(\log\log x)/(2\log x)\}+O(x/\log x)^{\frac{1}{2}}$. It is proved that $I(y)\leqq g(x)\leqq I(y)+O(x\log x)^{\frac{1}{4}}$.

*G. Pall.*

**P80-3** **(2, 133e)**

**Mahler, Kurt. On a special functional equation.** J. London Math. Soc. **15**, 115–123 (1940).

Asymptotic formulae for solutions of the functional equation

$$\frac{f(z+\omega)-f(z)}{\omega}=f(qz), \qquad \omega\neq 0;\ 0<q<1. \tag{1}$$

First a special solution $F(z, \omega, q)$ is constructed with the help of the transformation

$$f(z)=\int_{-\infty}^{+\infty} u(x)e^{zq^{xi}}dx,$$

which transforms (1) into a simple difference equation for $u$.

For $\omega\to 0$ this special solution becomes

$$F(z, q)=\sum_{n=0}^{\infty}\frac{q^{\frac{1}{2}n(n-1)}z^n}{n!}.$$

The author's result is that for every solution $f(z)$ of (1), which is greater than a positive constant, and is bounded in every finite interval, $f(z)=e^{O(1)}F(z)$ for large $z$; in particular

$$\log f(z)\sim(\log z)^2/(2\log(1/q)).$$

From this result, an approximate formula for the number of solutions of $h=h_0+rh_1+r^2h_2+\cdots$, $r\geqq 2$ a constant integer, in nonnegative integers $h_0, h_1, h_2, \cdots$ is derived, when $h$ is large. *F. John* (Lexington, Ky.).

Referred to in P80-13, P80-20, P80-50.

## P80-4 (3, 69a)

**Erdös, Paul and Lehner, Joseph. The distribution of the number of summands in the partitions of a positive integer.** Duke Math. J. **8**, 335–345 (1941).

Denote by $p(n)$ the number of unrestricted partitions of a positive integer $n$ and by $p_k(n)$ the number of partitions of $n$ which have at most $k$ summands. The authors prove that if $k=C^{-1}n^{\frac{1}{2}}\log n+xn^{\frac{1}{2}}$ then

$$\lim_{n\to\infty}\frac{p_k(n)}{p(n)}=\exp(-2C^{-1}e^{-\frac{1}{2}Cx}).$$

Here $C=\pi(\frac{2}{3})^{\frac{1}{2}}$. The proof makes use of the sieve method of Brun and the well-known asymptotic formula for $p(n)$. A similar result is given for $P(n)$, the number of partitions of $n$ into unequal parts. In addition the asymptotic formula

$$p_k(n)\sim\binom{n-1}{k-1}/k!$$

valid uniformly in $k$ in the range $k=o(n^{\frac{1}{3}})$ is established without using the calculus of residues. *R. D. James.*

Referred to in P64-19, P72-6, P72-10, P72-17, P80-5, P80-69, Z30-8.

## P80-5 (4, 211b)

**Auluck, F. C., Chowla, S. and Gupta, H. On the maximum value of the number of partitions of $n$ into $k$ parts.** J. Indian Math. Soc. (N.S.) **6**, 105–112 (1942).

Denote by $P_k(n)$ the number of partitions of $n$ into exactly $k$ parts and by $p_k(n)$ the number of partitions of $n$ which have at most $k$ summands. The latter function has been studied by Erdös and Lehner [Duke Math. J. **8**, 335–345 (1941); these Rev. **3**, 69], who derived an asymptotic formula for $p_k(n)/p(n)$, where $p(n)$ is the number of unrestricted partitions of $n$. Theorem 1 in the present paper is a similar result for $P_k(n)$, namely,

$$\lim_{n\to\infty} n^{\frac{1}{2}}P_k(n)/p(n)=\exp\{-\tfrac{1}{2}Cx-(2/C)e^{-\frac{1}{2}Cx}\},$$

where $k=C^{-1}n^{\frac{1}{2}}\log n+xn^{\frac{1}{2}}$, $C=\pi(\frac{2}{3})^{\frac{1}{2}}$. A proof is given following the method of Erdös and Lehner but without using their explicit results. Theorem 2 concerns a maximum for $P_k(n)$ regarding $n$ as fixed and $k$ variable. The authors present evidence that there exists an integer $k_0$ such that

$$P_k(n)\geqq P_{k-1}(n),\quad k\leqq k_0,$$
$$P_k(n)\leqq P_{k-1}(n),\quad k\geqq k_0.$$

They are, however, able to prove only the following result. If $P_k(n)\leqq P_{k_1}(n)$ if $k\neq k_1$ then, for $n>n_0$,

$$n^{\frac{1}{2}}<k_1<\delta n^{\frac{1}{2}}\log n,$$

where $\delta$ is any fixed number greater than $1/C$. The proof is in two parts and consists of showing by different methods that $n^{\frac{1}{2}}P_k(n)/p(n)=o(1)$ for $k>B^{-1}n^{\frac{1}{2}}\log n$ and for $k\leqq n^{\frac{1}{2}}$, where $B<C$. *R. D. James* (Saskatoon, Sask.).

Citations: MR 3, 69a = P80-4.

Referred to in P02-27, P72-12, P72-21, P80-6, P80-10.

## P80-6 (5, 199i)

**Gupta, Hansraj. On the maximum values of $p_k(n)$ and $\pi_k(n)$.** J. Indian Math. Soc. (N.S.) **7**, 72–75 (1943).

This paper is an informal continuation of the discussion in a previous paper by Auluck, Chowla and Gupta [J. Indian Math. Soc. (N.S.) **6**, 105–112 (1942); these Rev. **4**, 211] of the question: for what value (or values) of $k$ is the number $p_k(n)$ of partitions of $n$ into exactly $k$ parts a maximum; in other words, among all partitions of $n$ what is the most popular number of parts? It was conjectured that such a maximum exists for a value of $k=k_0(n)$ and that, as $n\to\infty$,

$$(1)\qquad k_0\sim(\sqrt{6}/2\pi)n^{\frac{1}{2}}\log n.$$

In the present paper the author discusses the prospects of obtaining upper and lower bounds for $k_0$ by the application of approximate formulas for $p_k(n)$ to the identity

$$p_k(n)-p_{k+1}(n)=p_{k+1}(n+1)-p_{k+1}(n)-p_{k+1}(n-k).$$

However, the general discussion does not take into account the signs of the errors in the two approximate formulas contemplated so that the inequalities obtained are not too reliable. For $n=10{,}000$ the right member of (1) is 359.06, and the author's formulas give $349\leqq k\leqq 353$. [The author gives $349\leqq k\leqq 359$, but this is apparently a miscalculation.] The same argument is applied to the function $\pi_k(n)=p_k(n-k(k-1)/2)$ which enumerates the number of partitions of $n$ into exactly $k$ distinct parts. *D. H. Lehmer.*

Citations: MR 4, 211b = P80-5.

## P80-7 (6, 119g)

**Mian, A. M. and Chowla, S. The differential equations satisfied by certain functions.** J. Indian Math. Soc. (N.S.) **8**, 27–28 (1944).

The authors prove that $\sum_1^\infty p(n)x^n$ satisfies an algebraic differential equation. *P. Erdös* (Ann Arbor, Mich.).

Referred to in P80-8.

## P80-8 (7, 145c)

**Mian, A. M., and Chowla, S. The differential equations satisfied by certain functions.** Proc. Lahore Philos. Soc. **6**, 9–10 (1944).

Identical with a paper in J. Indian Math. Soc. (N.S.) **8**, 27–28 (1944); these Rev. **6**, 119.

Citations: MR 6, 119g = P80-7.

## P80-9 (7, 273h)

**van IJzeren, J. Elementary properties of the partitions of the natural numbers.** Mathematica, Zutphen. B. **12**, 115–118 (1944). (Dutch)

## P80-10 (7, 273i)

**Erdös, Paul. On some asymptotic formulas in the theory of partitions.** Bull. Amer. Math. Soc. **52**, 185–188 (1946).

Let $p_k(n)$ denote the number of partitions of $n$ into exactly $k$ summands and let $k_0$ be that value of $k$ for which $p_k(n)$ is greatest. The formula $k_0=c^{-1}n^{\frac{1}{2}}\log n+an^{\frac{1}{2}}+o(n^{\frac{1}{2}})$, $c=\pi(2/3)^{\frac{1}{2}}$, $c/2=e^{-ca/2}$, is proved. This result includes the conjecture of Auluck, Chowla and Gupta [J. Indian Math. Soc. (N.S.) **6**, 105–112 (1942); these Rev. **4**, 211] that $k_0\sim c^{-1}n^{\frac{1}{2}}\log n$. *H. S. Zuckerman* (Seattle, Wash.).

Citations: MR 4, 211b = P80-5.

Referred to in P72-17, P72-19.

## P80-11 (8, 317e)

**Loria, Gino. Sulla scomposizione di un intero nella somma di numeri poligonali.** Atti Accad. Naz. Lincei. Rend. Cl. Sci. Fis. Mat. Nat. (8) **1**, 7–15 (1946).

The author describes a forthright method of building a table giving the partitions of a number into four or fewer squares. Three tables are given showing the partitions of every number less than 101 into not more than 4 squares,

3 triangular and 5 pentagonal numbers. The tables are quite unreliable as they contain more than thirty errors. This is not due to the method, however. *D. H. Lehmer.*

**P80-12** **(8, 566h)**

**Motzkin, Theodor. Ordered and cyclic partitions.** Riveon Lematematika 1, 61–67 (1947). (Hebrew)

A partition is the representation of a positive integer as a sum of positive integers (elements). If two partitions in which the same elements appear in different order are counted different, we have ordered partitions; if two partitions in which the same elements appear in different order are counted different except when they originate from each other by a cyclic permutation of the elements (when they are regarded as identical), we have cyclic partitions. The inverse of a (cyclic or ordered) partition is the partition which consists of the same elements in reversed order. If a partition and its inverse are considered as identical, we have directionless partitions. The author determines the number of ordered and cyclic partitions of a given positive integer $n$, and investigates restricted partitions whose elements are taken from a given set of positive integers; he also discusses directionless partitions. *A. Erdélyi.*

**P80-13** **(10, 16d)**

**de Bruijn, N. G. On Mahler's partition problem.** Nederl. Akad. Wetensch., Proc. **51**, 659–669 = Indagationes Math. **10**, 210–220 (1948).

By considering the functional equation

$$(f(z+\omega)-f(z))/\omega=f(qz)$$

K. Mahler [J. London Math. Soc. **15**, 115–123 (1940); these Rev. **2**, 133] obtained an approximate formula for the number $p(h)$ of solutions of $h=h_0+h_1r+h_2r^2+\cdots$ in nonnegative integers $h_0, h_1, h_2, \cdots$, where $r\geqq 2$ is a given integer. The author investigates this problem by a different method and sharpens Mahler's result. He proves, in particular, that, for $h\to\infty$,

$$\text{(1)}\quad \log p(rh)=\frac{1}{2\log r}\left(\log\frac{h}{\log h}\right)^2+\left(\frac{1}{2}+\frac{1}{\log r}+\frac{\log\log r}{\log r}\right)\log h-\left(1+\frac{\log\log r}{\log r}\right)\log\log h+\psi\left(\frac{\log h-\log\log h}{\log r}\right)+o(1),$$

where $\psi$ is a periodic function with period 1.

The outline of the argument is as follows. For any real $u$ let $P(u)$ denote the number of solutions of $h_0+h_1r+h_2r^2+\cdots\leqq u$ in nonnegative integers $h_0, h_1, h_2, \cdots$, and write $P_1(u)=\int_{u-1}^{u}P(v)dv$. We introduce the generating function

$$\text{(2)}\qquad F(s)=\prod_{k=0}^{\infty}(1-e^{-sr^k})^{-1}=\int_{-\infty}^{\infty}e^{-su}dP(u),\qquad \Re s>0,$$

and prove without difficulty that

$$\text{(3)}\qquad P_1(u)=r(2\pi i)^{-1}\int_{a-i\infty}^{a+i\infty}s^{-2}F(s)e^{us/r}ds,\qquad a>0.$$

Next, by Mellin's inversion formula and (2), we obtain rather accurate information about the behaviour of $F(s)$ near $s=1$; this enables us to evaluate approximately the integral (3), and so leads to an asymptotic formula for $\log P_1(u)$. A corresponding result for $P(u)$ is now easily deduced, and finally (1) follows by virtue of the relation $p(rh)=P(h)$. *L. Mirsky* (Sheffield).

Citations: MR 2, 133e = P80-3.

Referred to in P80-20, P80-50.

**P80-14** **(10, 356d)**

**Fine, Nathan J. Some new results on partitions.** Proc. Nat. Acad. Sci. U. S. A. **34**, 616–618 (1948).

Five theorems on restricted partitions are announced. Proofs are promised in a later paper. The theorems are as follows. (1) The number of partitions of $n$ into distinct parts, the smallest part being odd, is odd if and only if $n$ is a square. (2) The number of partitions of $n$ into odd parts of which the largest is $r$ is equal to $D_r(n)+D_{r-1}(n)$, where $D_s(n)$ denotes the number of partitions of $n$ into distinct parts in which the maximum part exceeds the number of parts by $s$. (3) The difference between the numbers of unrestricted partitions of $n$ and $n-1$ is equal to the number of partitions of $r+n+1$ in which the largest part exceeds the number of parts by $r$, where $r$ is a positive integer exceeding $n-4$. Denoting the latter number of partitions by $P_r(r+n+1)$ we have (4) $P_{r+1}(n)+P_{r+4}(n-r-3)=P_r(n-1)+P_{r+3}(n-r-2)$. (5) Let $E(n)$ denote the excess of the number of partitions of $n$ into distinct parts in which the largest part is even over the number of partitions into distinct parts the largest part being odd. Then $E(n)=0$ unless $n$ is pentagonal in which case $E(\frac{1}{2}(3k^2+k))=1$ or $-1$ according as $k\geqq 0$ or not. This result parallels a famous theorem of Euler.

*D. H. Lehmer* (Berkeley, Calif.).

**P80-15** **(11, 502a)**

**Mirsky, L. A theorem on sets of coprime integers.** Amer. Math. Monthly **57**, 8–14 (1950).

Let $n, s, r$ be integers such that $n\geqq 1$, $2\leqq r\leqq s$, and let $N_{s,r}(n)$ denote the number of representations (order being relevant) of $n$ as the sum of $s$ positive integers such that the highest common factor of any $r$ of them is equal to 1. A complicated asymptotic formula, as $n\to\infty$, is given for $N_{s,r}(n)$. In the case $r=s$, the result is

$$N_{s,s}(n)=\frac{n^{s-1}}{(s-1)!}\prod_{p\mid n}(1-p^{-s+1})+O(n^{s-2}).$$

The true order of magnitude of $N_{s,r}(n)$ is shown to be $n^{s-1}$.

*W. H. Simons* (Kingston, Ont.).

**P80-16** **(12, 590i)**

**Apostol, T. M. Asymptotic series related to the partition function.** Ann. of Math. (2) **53**, 327–331 (1951).

The author obtains an asymptotic expansion for the coefficients $a_p(n)$ generated by $f_p(x)=1+\sum_1^\infty a_p(n)x^n=\exp G_p(x)$, where $G_p(x)=\sum_1^\infty \sigma_p(n)n^{-p}x^n$ and $\sigma_p(n)=\sum_{d\mid n}d^p$, $p>1$. For $p=1$, the $a_p(n)$ reduce to $p(n)$, the number of unrestricted partitions of $n$. The asymptotic expansion consists of $N$ terms of the usual structure with an error term $O(1)$ as $N\to\infty$. The $a_p(n)$ are rational numbers and represent certain finite sums of divisor functions. The author uses the classical Farey circle method in the form given by Rademacher in his treatment of $p(n)$ [Ann. of Math. (2) **44**, 416–422 (1943); these Rev. **5**, 35]. The behavior of $f_p(x)$ near each "rational" point of $|x|=1$ is obtained from the author's previous paper, which developed a transformation formula for that function [Duke Math. J. **17**, 147–157 (1950); these Rev. **11**, 641]. *J. Lehner* (Philadelphia, Pa.).

Citations: MR 11, 641g = F20-3.

**P80-17** **(13, 536b)**

**Sandham, H. F. Five series of partitions.** J. London Math. Soc. **27**, 107–115 (1952).

Let $p(n)$ denote the number of partitions of $n$. The following series are summed explicitly:

$$\sum_1^\infty \frac{p(n)}{\cosh \pi\sqrt{(6(n-1/24))}},$$

$$\sum_1^\infty \left\{\frac{p(n)}{\cosh \pi\sqrt{(\frac{2}{3}(n-1/24))}} - \frac{1}{2n\sqrt{3}}\right\},$$

$$\sum_0^\infty \frac{p(n)}{\cosh \pi\sqrt{(2(n-1/24))}},$$

$$\sum_0^\infty \frac{p(n)}{\cosh \pi\sqrt{(n-1/24)}},$$

$$\sum_0^\infty \frac{p(n)}{\cosh \pi\sqrt{(4(n-1/24))}}.$$

Three other summations, to be proved in later papers, are also noted. The proofs are based on the Euler and Jacobi expansions of $\prod(1-q^n)$ and $\prod(1-q^n)^3$, termwise integration leading to

$$\int_0^1 q^{x+1/24}\prod(1-q^n)\frac{dq}{q} = \frac{\pi\sqrt{2}}{\sqrt{x}}\cdot\frac{\sinh 2\pi\sqrt{(\frac{2}{3}x)}}{\cosh 3\pi\sqrt{(\frac{2}{3}x)}} \quad (x > -\tfrac{1}{24}),$$

$$\int_0^1 q^{x+1/8}\prod(1-q^n)^3\frac{dq}{q} = \frac{2\pi}{\cosh \pi\sqrt{(2x)}} \quad (x > -\tfrac{1}{8}),$$

application of further identities, and summation of the resulting series by elementary means or by elliptic functions. The method appears to be capable of further application.

*N. J. Fine* (Philadelphia, Pa.).

Referred to in P80-18, P80-40, P80-41.

## P80-18 (14, 356e)

**Sandham, H. F. Two identities due to Ramanujan.** Quart. J. Math., Oxford Ser. (2) **3**, 179–182 (1952).

The author proves two identities stated by Ramanujan and uses them, together with the methods of a previous paper [J. London Math. Soc. **27**, 107–115 (1952); these Rev. **13**, 536], to deduce the partition series

$$(1)\quad \sum_0^\infty \frac{p(n)}{2\cosh \frac{1}{3}\pi\sqrt{(24n-1)}+1} = \frac{\log(\sqrt{2}+1)}{\sqrt{3}},$$

$$(2)\quad \sum_1^\infty \frac{p(n)}{2\cosh \frac{1}{3}\pi\sqrt{(24n-1)}-1} = \frac{\sqrt{3}}{2\pi} - \frac{1}{6} - \frac{\log 2}{\sqrt{3}}.$$

*N. J. Fine* (Philadelphia, Pa.).

Citations: MR 13, 536b = P80-17.

## P80-19 (14, 726g)

**Basu, N. M. A note on partitions.** Bull. Calcutta Math. Soc. **44**, 27–30; corrections, 142 (1952).

Let $B_n^{(s)}$ denote the number of compositions (order of parts taken into account) of $n$ into parts not exceeding $s$. By use of the generating function $(1-z-z^2-\cdots-z^s)^{-1}$, the author shows that there exists a unique $\alpha=\alpha(s)$, $\frac{1}{2}<\alpha<1$, and an explicitly given $K=K(\alpha, s)$ such that $B_n^{(s)}\sim K/\alpha^{n-1}$, as $n\to\infty$. *N. J. Fine* (Philadelphia, Pa.).

## P80-20 (14, 846m)

**Pennington, W. B. On Mahler's partition problem.** Ann. of Math. (2) **57**, 531–546 (1953).

Mahler's problem is to find an asymptotic formula for the number of partitions of $n$ into powers of a fixed integer $r>1$ [J. London Math. Soc. **15**, 115–123 (1940); these Rev. **2**, 133]. Mahler's result had a multiplicative error of the form $e^{O(1)}$; the exact asymptotic behaviour was determined by the reviewer [Nederl. Akad. Wetensch., Proc. **51**, 659–669 = Indagationes Math. **10**, 210–220 (1948); these Rev. **10**, 16].

The present author generalises the problem by considering sequences $\lambda_1<\lambda_2<\lambda_3<\cdots$ of positive numbers which are such that $N(u)$ (i.e., the number of $\lambda$'s which are $\leqq u$) has the form $N(u)=a\log u+b+R(u)$, where $\int_{\lambda_1}^\infty R(v)v^{-1}dv = V(\rho^{-1}\log u)+o(1)$ $(u\to\infty)$; $V(x)$ is integrable, bounded, and periodic mod 1, and $\rho$ is a positive constant. The asymptotic behaviour of $P(u)$ is sought, where $P(u)$ denotes the number of solutions of $r_1\lambda_1+r_2\lambda_2+\cdots<u$ in integers $r_\nu\geqq 0$.

The author applies a general Tauberian theorem of Ingham [Ann. of Math. (2) **42**, 1075–1090 (1941); these Rev. **3**, 166] to the formula

$$\int_0^\infty e^{-us}dP(u) = \exp\left\{\int_0^\infty sN(u)(e^{us}-1)^{-1}ds\right\} = g(s).$$

Ingham's theorem is of the following type: If $P(u)$ is increasing (in the wide sense), and if in every angle $|(\mathrm{Im}\, s)/(\mathrm{Re}\, s)|\leqq\Delta$, $\mathrm{Re}\, s>0$, the behaviour of $g(s)$ for $s\to 0$ is of a certain type, then the asymptotic behaviour of $P(u)$ $(u\to\infty)$ can be determined. The author shows that in every angle of the type just mentioned we have $\log g(s)=\frac{1}{2}a\log^2 s-b\log s+\varphi(-\log s)+o(1)$, where $\varphi(z)$ is periodic mod 1 and analytical in the strip $|\mathrm{Im}\, z|<\frac{1}{2}\pi$, and the Fourier coefficients of $\varphi(z)$ are expressed in terms of those of $V(x)$. All conditions of Ingham's theorem are satisfied. The final result is:

$$\begin{aligned}\log P(u) = \tfrac{1}{2}a(\log u-\log\log u-\log a)^2 + (a-\tfrac{1}{2})\log u \\ +(b+\tfrac{1}{2})(\log u-\log\log u-\log a) \\ +\varphi(\log u-\log\log u-\log a)-\tfrac{1}{2}\log 2\pi+o(1).\end{aligned}$$

At the end of the paper the author shows that his results can be specialized to Mahler's partition problem in the form given by the reviewer ($\lambda_\nu=r^{\nu-1}$, $r$ fixed, $r>1$; $r$ need not be an integer). *N. G. de Bruijn* (Amsterdam).

Citations: MR 2, 133e = P80-3; MR 3, 166a = P72-3; MR 10, 16d = P80-13.

Referred to in P80-57, P80-61.

## P80-21 (14, 1053h)

**Braumann, Peter Bruno Theodor. Partitions in various branches of mathematics.** Univ. Lisboa. Revista Fac. Ci. A. Ci. Mat. (2) **1**, 205–296 (1951). (Portuguese. German summary)

The author considers properties of partitions $I\{i_0,\cdots,i_{t-1}\}$ of an integer $I$ into integral, non-negative components $i_k$ so that $I=i_0+i_1+\cdots+i_{t-1}$ and among these particularly the partitions with $m$ elements where $t=m$ and $0\leqq i_k\leqq m-1$ for all $k$. When $I=mq+r$ the numbers $q$ and $r$ are called the weight and remainder, respectively. Two partitions are congruent if they have the same remainder, complementary if $i_k+i_k'=m-1$ for every $k$. They are concyclic if $i_k'\equiv i_k+l$ (mod $m$). The smallest $l\neq 0$ for which a partition is concylic to itself is called its degree $d$. The partition is ordinary [primitive] if $m=d$, otherwise extraordinary. The author deduces various properties of the numbers $\phi_0(m)$ and $\phi_e(m)$ of primitive and imprimitive partitions of degree $m$ and also the corresponding numbers for partitions of remainder 0.

To every partition of $m$ elements the author associates a sum of roots of unity

$$(1)\quad \sigma(i_0,\cdots,i_{m-1})=\sum\exp\frac{2\pi i}{m}(i_0s_0+\cdots+i_{m-1}s_{m-1})$$

where the sum is extended to all sets of integers $0\leqq s_k\leqq m-1$ with $s_k\neq s_l$. Various properties of these numbers are derived and applications made to combinatorial problems and resultants for polynomials. [The numbers (1) are also the coefficients in the cyclic determinant of order $m$, for which the reviewer has given an explicit expression [Duke Math. J. **18**, 343–354 (1951); these Rev. **13**, 98].] *O. Ore.*

## P80-22 (15, 506j)

**Sandham, H. F. Two series of partitions.** Amer. Math. Monthly **61**, 104–106 (1954).

The series are

$$\sum_0^\infty \frac{p(n)}{(n-1/24+\theta)^{\frac{1}{2}}} \frac{\sinh 2\pi(\frac{2}{3}(n-1/24+\theta))^{\frac{1}{2}}}{\cosh 3\pi(\frac{2}{3}(n-1/24+\theta))^{\frac{1}{2}}} = \frac{1}{2^{\frac{1}{2}}\pi\theta}$$

and

$$\sum_0^\infty \frac{p(n)(n-\theta)}{\cosh \pi(2n-\frac{1}{4}+4\theta)^{\frac{1}{2}}} = 0 \quad (\theta>0),$$

where $p(n)$ is the number of partitions. The formulas are proved by termwise integration of identities of Euler and Jacobi. *L. Carlitz* (Durham, N. C.).

## P80-23 (17, 14a)

**Venkata Narayana, Tadepalli. Sur les treillis formés par les partitions d'un entier et leurs applications à la théorie des probabilités.** C. R. Acad. Sci. Paris **240**, 1188–1189 (1955).

Denote a solution of the equation (1) $t_1+t_2+\cdots+t_r=n$ in integers $t_i\geq 1$ by $n(t_1, t_2, \cdots, t_r)$. A solution $n(t_1, t_2, \cdots, t_r)$ is said to dominate the solution $n(t_1', t_2', \cdots, t_r')$ if and only if $t_1\geq t_1', t_1+t_2\geq t_1'+t_2', \cdots, t_1+\cdots+t_{r-1}\geq t_1'+\cdots+t_{r-1}'$. If $p_1, p_2, \cdots, p_a$, $a=C_{n-1}^{r-1}$, denote the distinct solutions of (1) in some order and $x_i$ the numbers of solutions dominated by $p_i$, then the relation $x_1+\cdots+x_a=C_n{}^rC_n^{r-1}/n$ is stated. It is further shown how this relation can be used when considering a special game of coin-tossing. *H. Bergström* (Göteborg).

Referred to in P80-58.

## P80-24 (18, 3c)

**Sade, Albert. Sur les substitutions dont les cycles sont ordonnés et sur les partitions.** Ann. Fac. Sci. Marseille **24** (1955), 67–81.

The author writes every permutation as a product of cycles without common elements in such a way that the smallest element in each cycle is written first and the cycles are arranged in order according to their first elements. Let $R(n, p)$ be the number of permutations of $n$ digits consisting of $p$ cycles, $g(n, k, c)$ and $F(n, k)$ resp. the number of such permutations where the $k$th cycle has length $c$ and where the $k$th cycle contains the digit $n$. The author computes these three functions by means of difference equations satisfied by them and by means of relations between them. He then studies relations between these functions and others derived from them and applies them to the theory of partitions. *H. B. Mann.*

## P80-25 (19, 531a)

**Čulík, Karel. Über eine Eigenschaft der ganzzahligen nichtnegativen Lösungen der Gleichung $\sum_{i=1}^k r_i=n$.** Časopis Pěst. Mat. **82** (1957), 353–359. (Czech. Russian and German summaries)

Let $n$ and $k$ be natural numbers, and $r_1, r_2, \cdots, r_k$ non-negative integers satisfying $\sum_{i=1}^k r_i=n$ $(r_1\leq r_2\leq\cdots\leq r_k)$. The author has succeeded in picking out from among all such partitions of $n$ into $k$ parts the partition which minimises, for every integer $c\geq 0$, the expression $\sum_{i=1}^k \binom{r_i}{c}$. He was led to this investigation by his own work, and the work of others, on a problem of K. Zarankiewicz [Kövari, Sós, and Turán, Colloq. Math. **3** (1954), 50–57; MR **16**, 456; K. Čulík, Acta Acad. Sci. Čechoslovenicae Basis Brunensis **27** (1955), 341–348; Ann. Polon. Math. **3** (1956), 165–168; MR **18**, 792, 459] concerning matrices with elements equal to 0 or 1, and he describes the application of his new result. He also describes how this result leads him to a conjecture on a problem of Turán [Elem. Math. **11** (1956), 40]. *H. Halberstam.*

Referred to in P80-27.

## P80-26 (19, 1162c)

**Luthra, S. M. On the average number of summands in partition of $n$.** Proc. Nat. Inst. Sci. India. Part A. **23** (1957), 483–498.

Let $p_k(n)$ denote the number of partitions of $n$ into precisely $k$ parts, $p(n)$ the total number of partitions of $n$. By the average number of summands $A$ in a partition of $n$ is meant $A=p(n)^{-1}\sum_{k=1}^n kp_k(n)$. By means of the identity $p(n)A=\sum_{k=1}^n d(k)p(n-k)$ ($d(k)$ the number of divisors of $k$), the asymptotic formula for $p(n)$, and the asymptotic formula of Szekeres for the value of $k$ which maximizes $p_k(n)$, it is shown that

$$A=(CN^{\frac{1}{2}}+\tfrac{1}{2}C^2)(\log(CN^{\frac{1}{2}})+\gamma)+\frac{1+C^2}{4}+O(N^{-\frac{1}{2}}\log N),$$

where $C=6^{\frac{1}{2}}/\pi$, $N=n-1/24$, and $\gamma$ is Euler's constant.

For the average number of summands $B$ in a partition of $n$ into distinct parts (which is similarly defined) it is shown that

$$B=2^{\frac{1}{2}}\log 2CM^{\frac{1}{2}}+\tfrac{1}{2}C^2\log 2-\tfrac{1}{4}+O(M^{-\frac{1}{2}}),$$

where $M=n+1/24$.

In addition asymptotic formulae for certain higher moments are worked out and tables of $A$, $B$ and these moments are given for $1\leq n\leq 100$.

The paper is marred by several minor typographical errors and a disrespect for asymptotic relationships. In several places such relationships are replaced by equalities and in one instance such an equality is differentiated and the result made an asymptotic formula again. Nevertheless the results quoted seem to be correct, at least for the dominant term. *M. Newman* (Washington, D.C.).

## P80-27 (20# 1663)

**Kosmák, Ladislav. Bemerkung über die nichtnegativen ganzzahligen Lösungen der Gleichung $\sum_{i=1}^k r_i=n$.** Časopis Pěst. Mat. **83** (1958), 80–82. (Czech. Russian and German summaries)

The author shows how the proof of a certain theorem of K. Čulik [Časopis Pěst. Mat. **82** (1957), 353–359; MR **19**, 531] may be simplified; thereby he arrives at a slightly sharper form of this theorem, which now reads: If $\sum_{i=1}^k h_i=n$ is a partition of $n$ into non-negative integers which satisfy also the condition $\max_{1\leq i\leq k} h_i-\min_{1\leq i\leq k}h_i\leq 1$, if $\sum_{i=1}^k r_i$ is any partition of $n$ into non-negative integers, and if $c$ is a given positive integer, then

$$\sum_{i=1}^k \binom{h_i}{c} < \sum_{i=1}^k \binom{r_i}{c}$$

if, and only if, $2\leq c\leq\max_{1\leq i\leq k} r_i>1+\min_{1\leq i\leq k} r_i$; otherwise the two expressions are equal.

*H. Halberstam* (London)

Citations: MR 19, 531a = P80-25.

## P80-28 (20# 3110)

**Guy, Richard K. Two theorems on partitions.** Math. Gaz. **42** (1958), 84–86.

It is shown that the numbers of partitions of an integer into (i) odd parts greater than unity, (ii) unequal parts such that the two greatest parts differ by unity, and (iii) unequal parts which are not powers of two, are all equal. Several elementary proofs are given.

*A. C. Woods* (New Orleans, La.)

## P80-29 (21# 2634)

**Narayana, T. V.; and Fulton, G. E. A note on the compositions of an integer.** Canad. Math. Bull. **1** (1958), 169–173.

A composition of an integer is a partition in which the order of the parts is significant (e.g., 1, 2, 3 is not the same as 1, 3, 2). The authors show that the compositions of $n$ into $r$ parts form a distributive lattice with $t_1, \cdots, t_r$ including $t_1', \cdots, t_r'$ if $t_1+\cdots+t_i \geqq t_1'+\cdots+t_i'$ for $i=1, 2, \cdots, r$. They define a natural anti-isomorphism between this lattice and that of the compositions of $n$ into $n-r+1$ parts, and show that it yields a one-one correspondence between the sets of compositions of $n$ with elements $\leqq 2$, and of $n+2$ with elements $\geqq 2$.

*K. Goldberg* (Washington, D.C.)

Referred to in P80-58.

## P80-30 (21# 4252)

**Lehner, Joseph. Partial fraction decompositions and expansions of zero.** Trans. Amer. Math. Soc. **87** (1958), 130–143.

A function $g(z)$ of the complex variable $z$ is said to be of class (1, 0) if it is an entire function and if the maximum of its absolute value on the circle $|z|=r$ is $<e^{\varepsilon r}$ for every $\varepsilon>0$ if $r>r_0(\varepsilon)$. Let $Q$ be the unit circle, $R_1$ its interior and $R_2$ its exterior. The author proves the following. I. Let $g_k(z)$ $(k=1, 2, \cdots)$ be functions of class (1, 0) such that the series $\sum_{k=0}^{\infty} |g_k(n)|$ is convergent for all integral values of $n$ and

$$(1) \qquad \limsup_{n} \left( \sum_{k=0}^{\infty} |g_k(n)| \right)^{1/|n|} \leqq 1.$$

Let further $\{\varepsilon_k\}$ be distinct complex constants of modulus one, and let $\{\alpha_k\}$ be any bounded sequence. Let further

$$(2) \qquad \Phi_k(x) = \sum_{n=0}^{\infty} g_k(n)x^n$$

and let $\Sigma$ be the series

$$\sum_{k=0}^{\infty} \alpha_k \Phi_k(x\varepsilon_k^{-1}).$$

Then the series $\Sigma$ converges uniformly on any set $S$ at a positive distance from $Q$ and defines two regular functions

$$G_1(x) = \sum_{n=0}^{\infty} a_n x^n, \quad x \in R_1,$$

$$G_2(x) = -\sum_{n=1}^{\infty} a_{-n} x^{-n}, \quad x \in R_2,$$

where for all integral values of $n$:

$$(3) \qquad a_n = \sum_{k=0}^{\infty} \alpha_k \varepsilon_k^{-n} g_k(n).$$

II. Conversely, if $\Sigma$ converges uniformly on every set $S$ at a positive distance from $Q$, then functions $\{g_k(z)\}$ exist such that (2), (3), (1) hold.

The author further considers the possibility of continuing the series $\Sigma$ analytically across the unit circle. If the set $\{\varepsilon_k\}$ is not dense in the unit circle, there is an arc on which the function defined by the series will be regular provided a certain condition is satisfied by the $g_k(n)$. He also considers the inverse problem: given a suitably restricted function $G(x)$ regular in the unit circle, is there a series $\Sigma$ which represents $G(x)$?—Theorem I includes the case in which $a_n$ is the partition function

$$p(n) = \sum_{h,k} \alpha_{hk} \varepsilon_{hk}^{-n} g_k(n),$$

$$k = 1, 2, \cdots; h \bmod k, (h, k) = 1,$$

where $\alpha_{hk} = k^{1/2}\omega_{hk}/\pi 2^{1/2}$, $\omega_{hk}$ is a certain $24k$th root of unity, $\varepsilon_{hk} = \exp 2\pi i h/k$ and

$$g_k(z) = \frac{d}{dz}\left\{\frac{\sinh C\lambda(z)/k}{\lambda(z)}\right\}, \quad \lambda(z) = \left(z-\frac{1}{24}\right)^{1/2}.$$

In this case $G_2(z)$ is identically zero.

*H. D. Kloosterman* (Leiden)

## P80-31 (23# A94)

**Sugai, Iwao**

**On unequal partitions of integers.**

*Math. Mag.* **33** (1959/60), 129–138.

It is shown that, under certain special conditions, the total number of unequal partitions of $k^n$ is at least $3 \cdot 2^{n-3}$.

## P80-32 (23# A844)

**Dixon, J. D.**

**A finite analogue of the Goldbach problem.**

*Canad. Math. Bull.* **3** (1960), 121–126.

The author derives an explicit expression for $A(m, n, k)$, the number of ways in which an integer $m$ can be expressed as a sum, modulo $n$, of $k$ of the integers less than and prime to $n$, repetitions being allowed and order of summands taken into account. For $n=q$, a prime, it is first shown that

$$A(m, q, k) = \frac{1}{q}\{(q-1)^k + (-1)^k \lambda\},$$

where $\lambda = q-1$ or $-1$ according as $q$ does or does not divide $m$. The value of $A(m, n, k)$ is made to follow from this result.

*H. Gupta* (Chandigarh)

Referred to in A10-18.

## P80-33 (23# A3124)

**Nanda, V. S.; Pathria, R. K.**

**Theory of numbers and the problem of polymerization.**

*Proc. Nat. Inst. Sci. India Part A* **26** (1960), 700–710.

The problem of polymerization is said to be an inverse to the problem of degradation of polymers; polymers are built up by joining monomers in chains. Hence various problems of probabilistic nature arising in the study of polymerization may be formulated in terms of compositions of integers, the "number theory" approach used by the authors for degradation of polymers. Compositions of multipartite as well as unipartite numbers appear but as asymptotic results are usually in question, the development is more interesting technically than it is mathematically (and also difficult to summarize without detailed technical exposition). However, a suggestion of the content is given by noticing that in the simplest problem treated, "the simplest case of condensation polymerization when there is only one type of monomer present", the compositions in question are those of ordinary numbers; the variable of interest is $n_i$, the ratio of the number of compositions of a given number, with one part of size $i$ to the total number of composition. Asymptotically, this has a geometrical distribution. It may be worth noting that the authors' symbol $Q_j$ is an Eulerian number; indeed, the $s$th ordinary moment of a geometric distribution with parameter $p$ is $(-1)^s$ times the Euler polynomial $H_s(p)$, where $H_0=1$, $(H+1)^n = pH_n$, $H^n \equiv H_n(p)$.

*J. Riordan* (New York)

**P80-34** **(23# A3125)**

**Pathria, R. K.; Nanda, V. S.**

**Theory of numbers and the problem of copolymerization.**
*Proc. Nat. Inst. Sci. India Part A* **26** (1960), *supplement II*, 111–124.

Copolymerization for the authors' purposes is distinguished from polymerization by the presence of more than one type of monomer. In the authors' (additive) number-theory approach to probabilistic problems in the subject, it corresponds to the process of composition of integers from units of different types. The integers composed are ordinary numbers for condensation copolymerization, the simplest case, but may be multipartite otherwise. The treatment begins by considering two types of monomers in a condensation process for the boundary cases, first of strict alternation of types, and then of random arrangement. Expressions for size distributions and various averages are obtained. Then a generalization to more than two types is given in the random case. The further development is too elaborate to be given here.
*J. Riordan* (New York)

**P80-35** **(23# A3126)**

**Nanda, V. S.; Pathria, R. K.**

**Polymers and theory of numbers. I. The single-chain theory of degradation.**
*J. Chem. Phys.* **30** (1959), 27–30.

The process of degradation of linear polymers, which seems to be identified with breaking up of monomer chains, is studied as a problem in compositions (ordered sets of integers having a given sum). The compositions of chief interest are those with $K$ parts, an arbitrary one of which is specified to be of size $i$. Their enumerating generating function is $Kz^i(z+z^2+\cdots)^{K-1}$ (zero parts are excluded), which is used for counting compositions having at least one part $i$, though the generating function for the latter is $(z+z^2+\cdots)^K-(z+z^2+\cdots-z^i)^K$. Properly normalized, it defines a probability distribution, which is taken as applying to the size of fragment in a degraded polymer each of whose chains behaves alike. Moments and their limits for increasing length of chain are given. It is emphasized that the procedure is oversimplified for introductory purposes. *J. Riordan* (New York)

**P80-36** **(23# A3127)**

**Pathria, R. K.; Nanda, V. S.**

**Polymers and theory of numbers. II. The $N$-chain theory of degradation.**
*J. Chem. Phys.* **30** (1959), 31–34.

The analysis of the degradation of linear polymers given in a preceding paper is extended here to chains which do not break down in identical fashion. There are $N$ chains, each of length $P$, and hence with $P-1$ links, each of which may be cut in the degradation process. For $R$ cuts in total, the authors compute in two ways the "size distribution in the degraded material". The second way consists of enumerating compositions of multipartite numbers into a given number of parts, one of which has a specified size; the enumerating generating function is used to determine moments of an associated probability distribution, which seem to be of direct interest.
*J. Riordan* (New York)

**P80-37** **(23# A3128)**

**Nanda, V. S.; Pathria, R. K.**

**Polymers and theory of numbers. III. Some remarks on the theories of random degradation.**
*J. Chem. Phys.* **30** (1959), 35–36.

A generating function $(z+z^2+\cdots+z^P)^{R+N}$ used by R. F. Tuckett in the study of $N$-chain polymers, with each chain of initial length $P$, broken down into $R+N$ fragments, is compared with the generating function developed by the authors in Part II [#A3127]. It is argued that Tuckett's procedure amounts to amalgamating the $N$ chains into a single giant chain. *J. Riordan* (New York)

**P80-38** **(23# A3129)**

**Pathria, R. K.; Nanda, V. S.**

**Polymers and theory of numbers. IV. The problem of weak and strong links in degradation.**
*J. Chem. Phys.* **30** (1959), 1322–1327.

The technique used in earlier papers of this series is extended here to two types (weak, strong) of chain links. Each chain has the same number of each and the size distribution of fragments if found for specified total link cuts of each kind. Further extension to an arbitrary number of link types, the same for each chain, is sketched. An appendix gives a development adapting generating functions for certain compositions of multipartite numbers to the calculation of ordinary moments; a new disguise is given Stirling numbers of the second kind: ${}_0L_\mu=(-1)^{\sigma+\mu}\mu!S(\sigma,\mu)$. *J. Riordan* (New York)

**P80-39** **(24# A3077)**

**Straus, E. G.**

**On a problem in the theory of partitions.**
*Proc. Amer. Math. Soc.* **13** (1962), 192–196.

This paper solves a problem posed by Sherman K. Stein [Bull. Amer. Math. Soc. **66** (1960), 510] by showing that for every positive integer $n$, there exists a set $A(m,n)$ of positive integers such that $n$ has exactly $m$ partitions into elements of $A(m,n)$ for every $m$, $1\leq m\leq p(n)$, where $p(n)$ is the number of partitions of $n$. The result is then generalized to partitions of vectors with non-negative integral components. *S. Lin* (Athens, Ohio)

**P80-40** **(26# 1297)**

**Subrahmanya Sastri, V. V.**

**Three series involving partitions.**
*Math. Student* **29** (1961), 47–51.

Some formulae analogous to those given by H. F. Sandham [J. London Math. Soc. **27** (1952), 107–115; MR **13**, 536] are deduced. *J. F. Koksma* (Amsterdam)

Citations: MR 13, 536b = P80-17.

**P80-41** **(26# 3689)**

**Subrahmanyasastri, V. V.**

**Some results involving partition functions.**
*J. Indian Math. Soc.* (*N.S.*) **26** (1962), 97–113.

The author gives six identities for the partition functions $p(n)$, $q(n)$ and $q_0(n)$ (where $p(n)$ is the number of unrestricted partitions of $n$, $q(n)$ the number of partitions of $n$ into distinct parts and $q_0(n)$ the number of partitions of $n$ into distinct odd parts) involving infinite series of hyperbolic functions, related to those given by H. F. Sandham for $p(n)$ [J. London Math. Soc. **27** (1952), 107–115; MR **13**, 536]. A typical identity is that for $t>0$, $t\neq 1/24$,

$$2\sum_{n=0}^{\infty} q(n)(n+t)^{-1/2}\operatorname{cosech}\{\pi(n+t)^{1/2}\} = \frac{2\cdot 2^{1/2}\left(t-\frac{1}{24}\right)^{-1/2}\sinh\left\{2\pi\left(\frac{2}{3}t-\frac{1}{36}\right)^{1/2}\right\}}{\cosh\left\{3\pi\left(\frac{2}{3}t-\frac{1}{36}\right)^{1/2}\right\}}.$$

*M. Newman* (Washington, D.C.)

Citations: MR 13, 536b = P80-17.

**P80-42** **(28# 1135 )**

**Carlitz, L.**

**A problem in partitions related to the Stirling numbers.**
*Bull. Amer. Math. Soc.* **70** (1964), 275–278.

The variable $\theta_0(n)$, the number of odd $S(n+1, 2r+1)$ with $S(n, r)$ a Stirling number of the second kind, introduced in the author's earlier paper [Collect. Math. **14** (1962), 13–25; MR **26** #3623], is here given further development. The generating function

$$\sum_{n=0}^{\infty} \theta_0(n)x^r = \prod_{n=0}^{\infty} (1+x^{2^n}+x^{2^{n+1}})$$

shows that $\theta_0(n)$ is also the number of partitions into one unit part and one or two parts $2^j$, $j=1, 2, \cdots$, which justifies the title. It is shown, e.g., that $\theta_0(2^r m)=\theta_0(m)+r\theta_0(m-1)$; $\theta_0(2^r m-1)=\theta_0(m-1)$, while if $n=2^{r_0}+2^{r_0+r_1}+\cdots+2^{r_0+r_1+\cdots+r_k}$, $r_0\geqq 0$, $r_j\geqq 1$, $j=1, 2, \cdots, k$ and $n_j=2^{r_j}+2^{r_j+r_{j+1}}+\cdots+2^{r_j+\cdots+r_k}$, $\theta_0(n)=(1+r_0)\theta_0(n_1)-\theta_0(n_2)$. Also the $\theta_0(n)$ are connected with continuants. Finally, the solutions of $\theta_0(n)=t$, $t=1, 2, \cdots$, are examined and upper bounds on $\theta_0(n)$ are given.

*J. Riordan* (Murray Hill, N.J.)

Citations: MR 26# 3623 = B72-22.

Referred to in B72-25, B72-33.

**P80-43** **(29# 64 )**

**Graham, R. L.**

**A theorem on partitions.**
*J. Austral. Math. Soc.* **3** (1963), 435–441.

It is first shown that every integer greater than 77 can be partitioned into distinct positive integers whose reciprocals add to 1. This depends on a table of such partitions for the integers between 78 and 333, together with a pair of transformations by which this table may be extended recursively. Using this result and a further lemma, it is then shown that if $\alpha$ and $\beta$ are positive rational numbers, there is an $r=r(\alpha, \beta)$ such that if $n>r$, there is a partition of $n$ into integers larger than $\beta$ whose reciprocals add to $\alpha$.

*W. J. LeVeque* (Ann Arbor, Mich.)

**P80-44** **(29# 2194 )**

**McAndrew, M. H.**

**A partition problem.**
*Math. Comp.* **17** (1963), 291–295.

From the author's introduction: "The following theorem is proved: Given integers $a, b, c, d$, each $\geqq 2$, then either there exist integers $m, n$ with $|m-n|\leqq 1$, a partition of $a$ into $m$ parts of which each part is coprime to $b$, and a partition of $c$ into $n$ parts, each part coprime to $d$; or the same conclusion holds with the roles of $a$ and $b$ reversed and the roles of $c$ and $d$ reversed. This question arises in the investigation of the minimum length of input strings required to distinguish two partial automata. Elgot and Rutledge [Finite Automata, Switching Circuit Theory and Logical Design Section (Proc. Second Sympos. Switching Circuit Theory and Logical Design, 1961), AIEE—Special Publ. S-134 (1961), 129–132] deduce an upper bound for the length of such strings and by using the theorem quoted above show that this upper bound can be attained. In Section 4 we demonstrate by an example that the restriction $a, b, c, d\geqq 2$ cannot be relaxed."

*C. C. Elgot* (Yorktown Heights, N.Y.)

**P80-45** **(29# 5803 )**

**Kelly, John B.**

**Partitions with equal products.**
*Proc. Amer. Math. Soc.* **15** (1964), 987–990.

The author proves the following theorem: If $k$ is an integer $\geqq 3$, there exists an $N(k)$ such that every $n\geqq N(k)$ can be partitioned into $k$ parts in $(k-1)$ different ways so that the products of the integers in these $(k-1)$ partitions are equal. What is more, the integers which occur in all these partitions are pairwise different.

*S. Knapowski* (Marburg)

**P80-46** **(30# 69 )**

**Wright, E. M.**

**An enumerative proof of an identity of Jacobi.**
*J. London Math. Soc.* **40** (1965), 55–57.

The reviewer [Bull. Amer. Math. Soc. **68** (1962), 591–592; MR **27** #3561] showed that Jacobi's identity

$$(*) \qquad \prod_{n=1}^{\infty} (1-q^{2n})(1+q^{2n+1}t)(1+q^{2n-1}t^{-1}) = \sum_{r=-\infty}^{\infty} q^{r^2}t^r$$

is equivalent to the formula

$$(**) \qquad \alpha(n, m) = p\{n-\tfrac{1}{2}(n-m)(n-m+1)\},$$

where $p(n)$ is the number of unrestricted partitions of $n$, $p(0)=1$, $p(k)=0$ if $k<0$ and $\alpha(n, m)$ is the number of partitions of the bipartite number $(n, m)$ into different parts $(a, a-1)$, $(b-1, b)$ $(b=1, 2, 3, \cdots)$. The present paper contains a direct proof of (**); the author sets up a (1, 1) correspondence between the partitions enumerated by $\alpha(n, m)$ and those enumerated by the right-hand side of (**).

{M. S. Cheema [Math. Comp. **18** (1964), 414–420; MR **29** #4697] has given a combinatorial proof of another equivalent of (*).}

*L. Carlitz* (Durham, N.C.)

Citations: MR 27# 3561 = P60-35; MR 29# 4697 = P64-40.

Referred to in P80-49.

**P80-47** **(30# 1090 )**

**Gould, H. W.**

**Binomial coefficients, the bracket function, and compositions with relatively prime summands.**
*Fibonacci Quart.* **2** (1964), 241–260.

The subjects of the title all appear in the basic result of the paper, namely,

$$\binom{n}{k} = \sum_{j=k}^{n} \left[\frac{n}{j}\right] R_k(j),$$

since $R_k(j)$ is the number of compositions (ordered partitions) of $j$ with $k$ relatively prime parts (but $R_1(j)=\delta_{j1}$, the Kronecker delta). As usual, $[x]$ is the largest integer not greater than $x$. The inverse of this is given as

$$\left[\frac{n}{k}\right] = \sum_{j=k}^{n} \binom{n}{j} A_k(j)$$

with

$$A_k(n) = \sum_{j=k}^{n} (-1)^{n-j}\binom{n}{j}\left[\frac{j}{k}\right] = \sum_{j=1}^{[n/k]} (-1)^{n-kj}\binom{n-1}{jk-1}.$$

It is shown that the congruences $R_k(n)\equiv 0 \pmod k$, $n>k$, and $A_k(n)\equiv 0 \pmod k$, $n>k$ $(R_k(k)=A_k(k)=1)$, are satisfied only when $k$ is a prime. A number of properties of the $R_k(n)$ and $A_k(n)$ are developed, perhaps the most interesting of which are the generating function relations

$$\sum_{j=1}^{\infty} R_k(j)x^j(1-x^j)^{-1} = x^k(1-x)^{-k},$$

$$\sum_{j=1}^{\infty} A_k(j)x^j(1-x)^{-j} = x^k(1-x^k)^{-1}.$$

Tables are given for both $A_k(n)$ and $R_k(n)$ in the range $k, n=1(1)13$.

*J. Riordan* (Murray Hill, N.J.)

Referred to in B72-30, P80-58.

**P80-48** **(31# 2228)**

**Fekete, A. E.**

**Signature of partitions and divisors.**

*Published by the author, Memorial University of Newfoundland, St. John's, Newfoundland*, 1965. i+31 *pp.*

Let $\sum_{k=1}^{n} ki_k = n$ be a partition $\pi$ of the natural integer $n$ into summands $k$ $(1 \leqq k \leqq n)$, with frequencies $i_k$. Motivated by the well-known bijective correspondence between classes of conjugate permutations of the symmetric group of degree $n$ and the partitions of $n$, the author defines the signature of $\pi$ by sgn $\pi = (-1)^s$, where $s = \sum_{m=1}^{[n/2]} i_{2m}$. In particular, to each $d|n$ corresponds the partition with $i_d = n/d$, $i_k = 0$ $(k \neq d)$, of signature $(-1)^{n+i_d}$, called also sgn $d$. Let $(\pi)$ stand for the multinomial coefficient $(i_1+i_2+\cdots+i_n)!/(i_1!i_2!\cdots i_n!)$. Using such classical functions as $p(n)$ (=number of unrestricted partitions of $n$), $q(n)$ (=number of partitions of $n$ into distinct summands), $\sigma_\alpha(n)$ $(=\sum_{d|n} d^\alpha)$, etc., and some new ones, such as $r(n)$ (=excess of partitions with positive signature over those with negative signature), $o(n)$ (=same as $r(n)$, but with partitions selected only among those with distinct summands), etc., some well known, as well as many new formulae are established. It is not possible to mention all of them here, but the following selection should convey the general flavor of the results:

$$p(n) = \sum_\pi \operatorname{sgn} \pi \cdot (\pi) o(1)^{i_1} \cdots o(n)^{i_n} = \sum_\pi \frac{\sigma(1)^{i_1} \cdots \sigma(n)^{i_n}}{1^{i_1} i_1! \cdots n^{i_n} i_n!},$$

$$o(n) = \sum_\pi \operatorname{sgn} \pi \cdot (\pi) p(1)^{i_1} \cdots p(n)^{i_n} = \sum_\pi \operatorname{sgn} \pi \frac{\sigma(1)^{i_1} \cdots \sigma(n)^{i_n}}{1^{i_1} i_1! \cdots n^{i_n} i_n!},$$

$$r(n) = \sum_\pi \operatorname{sgn} \pi \cdot (\pi) \cdot q(1)^{\;1} \cdots q(n)^{i_n},$$

$$q(n) = \sum_\pi \operatorname{sgn} \pi \cdot (\pi) \cdot r(1)^{i_1} \cdots r(n)^{i_n}.$$

These sums are extended over all partitions $\pi$ of $n$. Next, if $n = \frac{1}{2}(3k^2 \pm k)$, then $o(n) = (-1)^{(3k^2 \mp k)/2}$, $o(n) = 0$ otherwise. Applications are made to general and special multiplicative functions, Lambert and Dirichlet series, etc. The proofs make extensive use of generating functions.

The last section consists of historical remarks. These seem to be quite complete up to 1900, but the most recent publications quoted are the classical books by Dickson, Hardy and Wright, and Pólya and Szegö. In particular, it seems that the author is not aware of the work of N. Fine ["Sums over Partitions", Rep. Inst. Theory of Numbers, pp. 86–94, Univ. Colorado (Boulder, Colo., 1959)], where similar sums over partitions occur.

*E. Grosswald* (Paris)

**P80-49** **(33# 5593)**

**Sudler, C., Jr.**

**Two enumerative proofs of an identity of Jacobi.**

*Proc. Edinburgh Math. Soc.* (2) **15** (1966), 67–71.

Following an idea of E. M. Wright [J. London Math. Soc. **40** (1965), 55–57; MR **30** #69], the author gives two quite simple enumerative proofs of the Jacobi identity

$$\prod_{n=1}^{\infty} (1-x^{2n})(1+x^{2n-1}z)(1+x^{2n-1}z^{-1}) = \sum_{r=-\infty}^{\infty} x^{r^2} z^r.$$

To read the paper one needs to have a copy of Wright's paper (cited above) at hand.

*J. B. Roberts* (Dar es Salaam)

Citations: MR 30# 69 = P80-46.

**P80-50** **(33# 7317)**

**Knuth, Donald E.**

**An almost linear recurrence.**

*Fibonacci Quart.* **4** (1966), 117–128.

Consider the sequence $\{\phi_n\}$, where $\phi_0 = 1$ and, for $n \geqq 1$, $\phi_n = \phi_{n-1} + \phi_k$, where $k = [n/2]$. The integer $\phi_n$ is the number of partitions of $2n$ into powers of 2, and it has the generating function $(1-x)^{-1} \prod_{k=0}^{\infty} (1-x^{2^k})^{-1}$. The author proves that $\log \phi_n \sim (\log^2 n)/\log 4$ as $n \to \infty$, using an elementary method similar to that introduced by Knopp and Schur [Math. Z. **24** (1925/26), 559–574] in treating the unrestricted partition function $p(n)$. Much stronger results on the same problem were obtained by K. Mahler [J. London Math. Soc. **15** (1940), 115–123; MR **2**, 133] and later improved by N. G. de Bruijn [Nederl. Akad. Wetensch. Proc. **51** (1948), 659–669; MR **10**, 16].

*T. M. Apostol* (Pasadena, Calif.)

Citations: MR 2, 133e = P80-3; MR 10, 16d = P80-13.

Referred to in P80-51.

**P80-51** **(34# 5741)**

**Knuth, Donald E.**

**Correction: "An almost linear recurrence".**

*Fibonacci Quart.* **4** (1966), 354.

The original article appeared in same Quart. **4** (1966), 117–128 [MR **33** #7317].

Citations: MR 33# 7317 = P80-50.

**P80-52** **(34# 158)**

**Carlitz, Leonard**

**A problem in partitions related to the Stirling numbers.**

*Riv. Mat. Univ. Parma* (2) **5** (1964), 61–75.

Let $\theta_0(n)$ denote the number of odd $C_{n,2r}$ and $\theta_1(n)$ the number of odd $C_{n,2r+1}$, where $C_{n,r} = S(n+1, r+1)$, the $S(n, r)$ being the Stirling numbers of the second kind. It follows that $\theta_0(2n+1) = \theta_0(n)$, $\theta_0(2n) = \theta_0(n) + \theta_0(n-1)$, $\theta_1(n+1) = \theta_0(n)$ and $\sum_{n=0}^{\infty} \theta_0(n) x^n = \prod_{n=0}^{\infty} (1 + x^{2^n} + x^{2^{n+1}})$. Thus $\theta_0(n)$ can be defined as the number of partitions of $n = n_0 + n_1 \cdot 2 + n_2 \cdot 2^2 + \cdots$ $(0 \leqq n_j \leqq 2)$ subject to (i) if $n_0 = 1$ then $n_1 \leqq 1$, (ii) if $n_1 = 2$ then $n_2 \leqq 1$, (iii) if $n_2 = 2$ then $n_3 \leqq 1$, and so on. The author studies the properties of $\theta_0(n)$; in particular, if $n_j = 2^{r_j} + 2^{r_j + r_{j+1}} + \cdots + 2^{r_j + \cdots + r_k}$ $(0 \leqq j \leqq k)$, $r_0 \geqq 0$, $r_1 \geqq 1, \cdots, r_k \geqq 1$, then $\theta_0(n_j) = (1 + r_j)\theta_0(n_{j+1}) - \theta_0(n_{j+2})$. Other results include (1) the explicit evaluation and an asymptotic formula for $\theta_n(n)$ when $r_0 = r_1 = \cdots = r_k$, (2) solutions of $\theta_0(n) = t$, and (3) an upper bound for $\theta_0(n)$.

*M. S. Cheema* (Tucson, Ariz.)

**P80-53** **(34# 2548)**

**Atkin, A. O. L.**

**A note on ranks and conjugacy of partitions.**

*Quart. J. Math. Oxford Ser.* (2) **17** (1966), 335–338.

Defining the rank $d$ of a partition as the largest part minus the number of parts, the author and H. P. F. Swinnerton-Dyer [Proc. London Math. Soc. (3) **4** (1954), 84–106; MR **15**, 685] previously proved that the Ramanujan congruence $p(5n+4) \equiv 0 \pmod 5$ could be extended to the assertion that the number of partitions of $5n+4$ with given $d$ (modulo 5) is independent of $d$. In the present paper the author defines a series of "ranks" for a partition and indicates how $d$ in this result may be replaced by various algebraic expressions involving these new ranks.

*J. B. Roberts* (Portland, Ore.)

Citations: MR 15, 685d = P76-11.

**P80-54** **(35# 145 )**

**Andrews, George E.**

**Enumerative proofs of certain $q$-identities.**

*Glasgow Math. J.* 8 (1967), 33–40.

The author gives ingenious combinatorial proofs of certain $q$-identities. Besides those for less known identities, enumerative proofs of the following identities are given:

$$(1) \quad \sum_{n=0}^{\infty} \frac{(1+a)\cdots(1+aq^{n-1})z^n q^n}{(1-q)\cdots(1-q^n)} = \prod_{j=1}^{\infty} \frac{(1+azq^j)}{(1-zq^j)},$$

$$(2) \quad \sum_{n=0}^{\infty} \prod_{j=0}^{n-1} \left\{\frac{(1-\alpha q^j)(1-\beta q^j)}{(1-q^{j+1})(1-\gamma q^j)}\right\}\tau^n =$$

$$\prod_{j=0}^{\infty} \frac{(1-\beta q^j)(1-\alpha\tau q^j)}{(1-\gamma q^j)(1-\tau q^j)} \cdot \sum_{n=0}^{\infty} \prod_{j=0}^{n-1} \left\{\frac{(1-\gamma\beta^{-1}q^j)(1-\tau q^j)}{(1-q^{j+1})(1-\alpha\tau q^j)}\right\}\beta^n.$$

{There are minor printing errors in Section 4, i.e., $n(2n+1)$ should replace $n(2n-1)$ at a few places.}

*M. S. Cheema* (Tucson, Ariz.)

**P80-55** **(35# 5340 )**

**Lehmer, D. H.**

**Combinatorial types in number-theory calculations.**

*Proc. IBM Sci. Comput. Sympos. Combinatorial Problems (Yorktown Heights, N.Y., 1964), pp.* 23–30. *IBM Data Process. Division, White Plains, N.Y.*, 1966.

The author gives several examples of the use of combinatorial entities in his work on number theory. The first uses weighted (number-theoretic) partitions in establishing properties of the coefficients of a power series. The second resurrects one of the earliest concerns of combinatorialists, that of assigning rank numbers to what may be called combinatorial complexions, in this case the $k$-combinations of $n$ things, and gives a new and interesting answer. The third considers the problem of arranging all the permutations with repetition in a sequence such that consecutive elements are adjacent in the sense that a single interchange of adjacent (permutation) elements sends one into the other. This is a resume of results in the author's paper [Amer. Math. Monthly **72** (1965), no. 2, part II, 36–46; MR **30** #3034]. Finally some remarks are made on computer programs for the exhibition of trees. {The reviewer must demur at the interpretation the author gives the phrase "anything enumerative is combinatorial" in the preface to the reviewer's book on combinatorial analysis. In its context, it is clear that this phrase was intended to limit the scope of the book, not that of combinatorial analysis.} *J. Riordan* (Murray Hill, N.J.)

**P80-56** **(35# 6336a; 35# 6336b)**

**Jack, Henry**

**A matrix analogue of the integral $\int_a^b x^\alpha\, dx$.**

*Proc. Roy. Soc. Edinburgh Sect. A* **67** (1965/67), 205–214.

**Rutherford, D. E.**

**On certain numerical coefficients associated with partitions.**

*Proc. Roy. Soc. Edinburgh Sect. A* **67** (1965/67), 215–219.

In these papers, an expression is obtained for the integral $\int_{\lambda B>X>B} |X|^\alpha\, dX$, where $B$ is a positive definite symmetric matrix, the integration is over the space of positive symmetric matrices, and $Y>X$ means that $Y-X$ is positive definite.

The calculation leads naturally to certain expressions involving partitions. The value of these, which had been correctly conjectured in the first paper, is obtained in the second. *A. M. Macbeath* (Birmingham)

**P80-57** **(36# 126 )**

**Schwarz, Wolfgang**

**Einige Anwendungen Tauberscher Sätze in der Zahlentheorie. C. Mahler's Partitionsproblem.**

*J. Reine Angew. Math.* **228** (1967), 182–188.

Verfasser beweist die folgende Variante eines Satzes von W. B. Pennington [Ann. of Math. (2) **57** (1953), 531–546; MR **14**, 846] zum genannten Partitionenproblem. Sei $0<\lambda_1<\lambda_2<\cdots$ und $\sum_{\lambda_\nu \le u} 1 = B\log^\beta u + 0(1)$, $B>0$, $0<\beta\le 1$. Für $\operatorname{Re} s>0$ sei $\prod_{\nu=1}^{\infty}\{1-\exp(-\lambda_\nu s)\}^{-1} = \exp\{\varphi(s)\}$, und es bezeichne $\sigma_u$ die positive Lösung von $-\varphi'(\sigma_u)=u$ sowie $T(u)=\varphi(\sigma_u)+u\sigma_u$. Dann gilt für die Lösungsanzahl $P(u)$ der Ungleichung $n_1\lambda_1+n_2\lambda_2+\cdots<u$ in ganzen $n_\nu(\ge 0)$ $P(u)\sim\{2\pi B\log^\beta u\}^{-1/2}\exp\{T(u)\}$. Der Beweis beruht wie bei Pennington auf einem Taubersatz von Ingham [vgl. W. B. Pennington, loc. cit.], doch sind Voraussetzungen und Beweis wesentlich vereinfacht; andererseits hat das Ergebnis eine nicht so explizite Gestalt. *H.-E. Richert* (Marburg)

Citations: MR 14, 846m = P80-20.

**P80-58** **(36# 6371 )**

**Mohanty, S. G.**

**Restricted compositions.**

*Fibonacci Quart.* **5** (1967), 223–234.

A $k$-composition $(t_1, \cdots, t_k)$ of an integer $n$ (i.e., $\sum_{i=1}^k t_i = n$, $t_i \ge 1$) dominates another $k$-composition $(t_1', \cdots, t_k')$ of $n$ if and only if (*) $\sum_{i=1}^j t_i \ge \sum_{i=1}^j t_i'$ for $j=1, \cdots, k$. The relation (*) was first studied by the reviewer [C. R. Acad. Sci. Paris **240** (1955), 1188–1189; MR **17**, 14] and an expression for the number $N(t_1, \cdots, t_k)$ of $k$-compositions of $n$ dominated by $(t_1, \cdots, t_k)$ was given by the reviewer and G. E. Fulton [Canad. Math. Bull. **1** (1958), 169–173; MR **21** #2634]. A slightly different recursive expression for $N(t_1, \cdots, t_k)$ was given by P. Switzer [Ann. Math. Statist. **35** (1964), 891–894; MR **29** #5347]. The author gives yet another determinantal expression for $N(t_1, \cdots, t_k)$ and explicitly shows the equivalence of the various expressions; a suitable reinterpretation of $N(t_1, \cdots, t_k)$ as a convolution yields extensions of some results of H. W. Gould [Fibonacci Quart. **2** (1964), 241–260; MR **30** #1090].

*T. V. Narayana* (Edmonton, Alta.)

Citations: MR 17, 14a = P80-23; MR 21# 2634 = P80-29; MR 30# 1090 = P80-47.

Referred to in B44-70.

**P80-59** **(37# 180 )**

**Drago, Antonino**

**Rules to find the partition of $n$ with maximum l.c.m. (Italian summary)**

*Atti Sem. Mat. Fis. Univ. Modena* **16** (1967), 268–280.

This is an attempt to find rules for finding partitions $n_1+n_2+\cdots+n_j=n$ of $n$ such that the l.c.m. $(n_1, n_2, \cdots, n_j)$ is maximum. The last section contains some remarks on the asymptotic behaviour of $\lambda(n)$, the maximum l.c.m. Comparison of results with machine computations for $n\le 300$ show that these rules give exact values of $\lambda(n)$ for most cases. The partition with maximum l.c.m. of the summands yields the maximal state cycle length $(2\lambda(n))$ obtained by connecting in a one-to-one manner the $n$ elements of an autonomous necklace circuit.

*M. S. Cheema* (Tucson, Ariz.)

**P80-60** **(39# 75 )**

**Dyson, Freeman J.**

**A new symmetry of partitions.**

*J. Combinatorial Theory* **7** (1969), 56–61.

Let $p(m, n)$ $(q(m, n))$ denote the number of partitions of $n$ into positive (non-negative) parts $a_1, \cdots, a_j$ with $a_1\le$

$\cdots \leqq a_j$ such that $a_j - j = m$. Thus, for example, $p(m, n) = 0$ if $|m| \geqq n$, and $p(m, n) = p(-m, n)$. Define $p(0) = 1$, and $p(n) = \sum p(m, n)$. Using simple combinatorial arguments, the author proves the following identities: (i) $g(m, n) = g(-m-2, n-m-1)$. (ii) $g(m, n) = p(n)$ for $m \leqq 1-n$, $g(m, n) = 0$ for $m \geqq n$, except when $n = 0$, $m = 0$ or 1. It follows from these observations that (*) $g(m, n) = p(n) - g(m-3, n+m-2)$ except for $n = 0$, $m = 0$ or 1. Iterating (*) leads to $g(m, n) = \sum (-1)^k p(n + km - k(3k+1)/2)$, but the term $(-1)^k p(0)$ is to be omitted in specified circumstances. Using this and a similar result, a new formal proof of Euler's formula for the power series expansion of $(p(0) + p(1)x + \cdots)^{-1}$ is given.

*D. A. Klarner* (Eindhoven)

## P80-61 (40# 1356)

**Churchhouse, R. F.**

**Congruence properties of the binary partition function.**

*Proc. Cambridge Philos. Soc.* **66** (1969), 371–376.

The author studies the title function $b(n)$, the number of ways of writing $n$ as a sum of powers of two, both theoretically and by computer. The function has been analyzed by others, including Euler and de Bruijn. The author establishes that $b(n) \equiv 0 \pmod 2$ for all $n \geqq 2$, characterizes the $n$ for which $b(n) \equiv 0 \pmod 4$, and proves that $b(n) \equiv 0 \pmod 8$ for no $n$. On the basis of numerical evidence, he conjectures that if $k \geqq 1$ and $t$ is odd, then $b(2^{2k+2}t) - b(2^{2k}t) \equiv 0 \pmod{2^{3k+2}}$, $b(2^{2k+1}t) - b(2^{2k-1}t) \equiv 0 \pmod{2^{3k}}$, and further that no higher power of two divides $b(4n) - b(n)$. He gives a counterexample to the analogous conjecture for the $m$-ary partition function. A table of $b(n)$ for $n \leqq 200$ is provided. {Reviewer's note: Comparing the tabulated values of $b(n)$ with de Bruijn's formula for $\log b(n)$ reveals that for $n = 4k$, $2 \leqq k \leqq 50$, the $O(1)$ remainder is monotone decreasing. This suggests the conjecture that de Bruijn's $\psi$ function is a constant $\approx -.4$.}

*W. M. Boyce* (Murray Hill, N.J.)

Referred to in P80-64, P80-66.

## P80-62 (40# 7128)

**Andrews, George E.**

**On a calculus of partition functions.**

*Pacific J. Math.* **31** (1969), 555–562.

In this paper, it is shown that many identities involving basic hypergeometric series and infinite products can be interpreted in terms of arithmetic, and consequently many partition theorems can be given purely combinatorial proofs. The author extends K. T. Vahlen's results [J. Reine Angew. Math. **112** (1893), 1–36] and offers new proofs of Euler's theorem and Jacobi's identity, as examples.

*H. Gupta* (Allahabad)

## P80-63 (41# 5316)

**Gandhi, J. M.**

**Generalization of a certain function related to the partition function.**

*Mathematica (Cluj)* **11 (34)** (1969), 245–251.

Four multiplication theorems for

$$A_k^{(s)}(n) = \sum_\rho (w_{\rho,k})^s e^{-2\pi n\rho i/k}$$

are obtained. These are similar to those for $A_k(n) = \sum_\rho w_{\rho,k} e^{-2\pi n\rho i/k}$ obtained by D. H. Lehmer [Trans. Amer. Math. Soc. **43** (1938), 271–295]. A typical result is the following. Let $k_1, k_2$ be odd coprime integers. Then $A_{k_1}^{(s)}(n_1) A_{k_2}^{(s)}(n_2) = A_{k_1 k_2}^{(s)}(n_3)$, where $n_3 \equiv k_1^2 n_2 + k_2^2 n_1 - s((k_1^2 + k_2^2 - 1)/24) \pmod{k_1 k_2}$. $A_k^{(s)}(n)$ are the coefficients in the asymptotic series for $p_k(n)$, the coefficient of $x^n$ in $\prod_{i=1}^\infty (1 - x^i)^{-k}$.

*M. S. Cheema* (Tucson, Ariz.)

## P80-64 (41# 5319)

**Rödseth, Öystein**

**Some arithmetical properties of $m$-ary partitions.**

*Proc. Cambridge Philos. Soc.* **68** (1970), 447–453.

Let $t_m(n)$ denote the number of partitions of the positive integer $n$ into nondecreasing parts which are nonnegative powers of a fixed integer $m > 1$. The author proves a number of detailed modular results for $t_m(n)$, the simplest being: If $m = 2$, $n$ odd and $r > 0$, then $t_2(2^{r+2}n) - t_2(2^r n) \equiv 2^{\mu(r)} \pmod{2^{\mu(r)+1}}$, where $\mu(r) = [(3r+4)/2]$. This result was first conjectured by R. F. Churchhouse [same Proc. **66** (1969), 371–376; MR **40** #1356]. The techniques used in the proof are elementary and involve careful estimates of the power of a prime which divides certain recursively defined coefficients. *R. L. Graham* (Murray Hill, N.J.)

Citations: MR 40# 1356 = P80-61.

Referred to in P80-66.

## P80-65 (41# 6761)

**Chawla, L. M.; Shad, S. A.**

**On a restricted partition function $t(n)$ and its table.**

*J. Natur. Sci. and Math.* **9** (1969), 217–221.

Let $t(n)$ be the partitions of $n$ into summands, each a product of two distinct primes. A table for $t(n)$ up to $n = 200$ is prepared using the two recursion formulae developed in the paper. *J. M. Gandhi* (Macomb, Ill.)

## P80-66 (42# 3043)

**Andrews, George E.**

**Congruence properties of the $m$-ary partition function.**

*J. Number Theory* **3** (1971), 104–110.

Denote the number of partitions of $n$ into powers of $m$ by $b(m; n)$. R. F. Churchhouse [Proc. Cambridge Philos. Soc. **66** (1969), 371–376; MR **40** #1356] conjectured that for $n$ odd and $k \geqq 1$, $b(2; 2^{2k+2}n) - b(2; 2^{2k}n) \equiv 0 \pmod{2^{3k+2}}$, $b(2; 2^{2k+1}n) - b(2; 2^{2k-1}n) \equiv 0 \pmod{2^{3k}}$, and that these congruences hold for no higher power of 2. This conjecture has been proved by Ö. Rödseth [ibid. **68** (1970), 447–453; MR **41** #5319] and also by the reviewer ("Proof of the Churchhouse conjecture concerning binary partitions", ibid., to appear). In the present paper the author proves that $c(m; r) = b(m; m^{r+1}n) - b(m; m^r n) \equiv 0 \pmod{t^r}$, where $t = m$ or $m/2$ according as $m$ is odd or even. The proof is based on a study of the generating function for $c(m; r)$. For $m$ prime the congruence was proved by Rödseth [loc. cit.].

*H. Gupta* (Allahabad)

Citations: MR 40# 1356 = P80-61; MR 41# 5319 = P80-64.

## P80-67 (43# 173)

**Manzur Hussain, S.**

**On the function $c(n) = q_k^e(n) - q_k^0(n)$ and some inequalities in partition theory.**

*Punjab Univ. J. Math. (Lahore)* **3** (1970), 49–57.

Let $c_k(n) = q_k^e(n) - q_k^0(n)$, where $q_k^e(n)$ and $q_k^0(n)$ are the number of partitions of $n$ into an even and an odd number, respectively, of distinct parts $\leqq k$. In addition to results concerning $c_k(n)$, including recurrence relations, the following inequalities are proved for the standard partition function $p(n)$: (a) $p(n) + p(n-2) \geqq 2p(n-1)$ if $n \geqq 2$, (b) $p(n) \geqq p(n-k) + p(k)$ if $n > k \geqq 1$,

(c) $\sum_{r=0}^{1/2(k+1)} c_k(r) \cdot (p(n-r) - p(n-r-k-1)) \geqq 0$

if $n \geqq \frac{1}{2}(k+1)(k+2)$, $k \geqq 1$. For instance, $k = 2$ in (c) yields $p(n) + p(n-4) + p(n-5) > p(n-1) + p(n-2) + p(n-6)$ if $n \geqq 6$.

*S. A. Burr* (Whippany, N.J.)

**P80-68** **(43# 3134)**

**Knuth, Donald E.**

**A note on solid partitions.**

*Math. Comp.* **24** (1970), 955–961.

Der Verfasser leitet einen allgemeinen Satz her, mit dessen Hilfe die Anzahl der Partitionen von $n$, die einer vorgegebenen Ordnungsrelation genügen, auf einfacher zu bestimmende Anzahlen zurückgeführt werden kann. Als Anwendung bestimmt der Verfasser (mit Hilfe eines Computers) die Anzahl der drei-dimensionalen Partitionen von $n$ für $0 \leqq n \leqq 28$. *W. Schwarz* (Frankfurt a.M.)

**P80-69** **(44# 6636)**

**Erdős, P.; Turán, P.**

**On some general problems in the theory of partitions. I.**

*Acta Arith.* **18** (1971), 53–62.

The authors obtain several results concerning the number of summands in "almost all" solutions of the system (*) $\lambda_{i_1}+\lambda_{i_2}+\cdots \leqq N$, $1 \leqq i_1 \leqq i_2, \cdots$, where $\lambda_{i_k} \in \Lambda$, a sequence of distinct positive numbers. Typical is Theorem II: Let $\Phi_\Lambda(x)$ be the number of $\lambda_\nu \leqq x$, $\lambda_\nu \in \Lambda$, and let $\Phi_\Lambda(x)=(Ax^\alpha/\log^\beta x)\{1+O(1/\log x)\}$, where $0<\alpha \leqq 1$, $\beta$ real; for almost all solutions of (*), the number of summands is $C_1 N^{\alpha/(\alpha+1)} \log^{-\beta/(\alpha+1)} N\{1+O(\log^{-1/4(\alpha+1)} N)\}$. Here $C_1$ is an explicit function of $\alpha$ and $\beta$. There is also a result on partitions into unequal summands when the $\lambda_\nu$ are positive integers. Applications include: for almost all partitions of $n$ into unequal positive integers the number of summands is $(2\pi^{-1}3^{1/2}\log 2)n^{1/2}(1+O(\log^{-1/8} n))$; the first author and the reviewer got the better error term $n^{-1/4}\omega(n)$, where $\omega \to \infty$ arbitrarily slowly [Duke Math. J. **8** (1941), 335–345; MR **3**, 69]. Also: the number of summands in almost all sums $\leqq x$ of different prime powers is asymptotic to an explicit constant times $x^{1/2}\log^{-1/2} x$ [the authors, Acta Math. Acad. Sci. Hungar. **19** (1968), 413–435; MR **38** #1156]. *J. Lehner* (College Park, Md.)

Citations: MR 3, 69a = P80-4.

**P80-70** **(44# 6637)**

**Kerawala, S. M.**

**On the asymptotic value of $\ln p_{A_k}(n)$, where each element of $A_k$ is a quadratfrei product of $k$ primes.**

*J. Natur. Sci. and Math.* **10** (1970), 71–74.

The author studies the number $p_{A_k}(n)$ of partitions of a natural number $n$ into summands each of which is a product of exactly $k$ distinct primes. The proof of the asymptotic formula for $\ln p_{A_k}$ is barely outlined. *H. Gupta* (Allahabad)

## P99 NONE OF THE ABOVE, BUT IN THIS CHAPTER

See also reviews P04-31, Z10-10, Z15-74.

**P99-1** **(1, 200c)**

**James, R. D. Integers which are not represented by certain ternary quadratic forms.** Duke Math. J. **5**, 948–962 (1939).

This paper contains the proof of the following theorem: Let any negative integer $d$ be written as $-2^b S^2 h$, where $S$ and $h$ are odd, and $h$ is quadratfrei. Then every sufficiently large integer $N$ can be represented in the form

$$N=u^2+epH^2M,$$

where $u$ is a positive integer, $p$ is a prime such that $(d|p)=-1$, every prime dividing $H$ also divides $d$, every prime $q$ dividing $M$ satisfies $(d|q)=1$, and $e$ is 1 except in the three following cases: (1) $b$ odd, $h|N$, $h\equiv 3 \pmod 4$, $N\equiv 6 \pmod 8$; (2) $b$ even, $h|N$, $h\equiv 1 \pmod 4$, $N\equiv 2 \pmod 4$; (3) $b$ odd, $h|N$, $h\equiv 1 \pmod 4$, $N\equiv 2 \pmod 8$, in all of which $e=2$.

The proof is accomplished by an application of the Viggo Brun method, which the author quotes in Estermann's presentation [J. Reine Angew. Math. **168**, 106–116 (1932)]. The multiplicative function which regulates the sieving in this case is

$$w(q)=\prod_{\substack{p|q\\(d|p)=1}}\left\{\frac{1+(D|p)}{p}\right\},$$

where $(d|p)$ is the Kronecker symbol. The author gives in his Lemma 5 a slight improvement of the numerical constants included in Estermann's principal lemma. The crucial step of the proof is about as follows: It has been shown by Viggo Brun's sieve method that to every sufficiently large integer $N$ there exists an integer $u<N^{\frac{1}{2}}$ of the following properties: (1) setting $N-u^2=K\cdot Q$ with $(K,Q)=1$, where $K$ contains only prime factors of $d$ and $Q$ is prime to $d$, then we have (*) $(d|Q)=-1$; (2) every prime $p$ with $(d|p)=-1$ dividing $N-u^2$ is greater than $N^{\frac{1}{4}}$. Then, because of (2), at most 2 primes $p_1$ and $p_2$ with $(d|p_1)=(d|p_2)=-1$ can divide $N-u^2$. But since the product of these primes divides $Q$, and since (*) holds, only one prime of such a sort can exist. Therefore $Q=p\cdot M$, with $(d|p)=-1$, and where $(d|q)=1$ for all primes $q$ dividing $M$.

The introductory remarks of the paper, which connect the main theorem with the problem mentioned in the title of the paper, are incomplete and not conclusive. (The author, in a letter to the reviewer, explains that those remarks refer only to sufficiently large integers "of a certain form," as, for example, in the case $d=-3$ to the integers of the form $9^k(9l+6)$.) *H. Rademacher* (Swarthmore, Pa.).

**P99-2** **(11, 161f)**

**Selberg, Sigmund. Note on the distribution of the integers $ax^2+by^2+c^{z^2}$.** Arch. Math. Naturvid. **50**, no. 2, 65–69 (1949).

The author proves that if $a$ and $b$ are given positive integers and $c$ is a given positive integer greater than 1, then the sequence of positive integers representable in the form $ax^2+by^2+c^{z^2}$, with integral $x$, $y$, and $z$, has positive density. The method is similar to that which has been used in proving that the sequence of positive integers representable in the form $p+c^z$, with $p$ a prime and $z$ a nonnegative integer, has positive (asymptotic) density [Romanoff, Math. Ann. **109**, 668–678 (1934); Erdös and Turán, Bull. [Izvestiya] Inst. Math. Mech. Univ. Tomsk. **1**, 101–103 (1935); Landau, Über einige neuere Fortschritte der additiven Zahlentheorie, Cambridge University Press, 1937, pp. 63–70]. *P. T. Bateman* (Princeton, N. J.).

**P99-3** **(15, 403h)**

**Krubeck, Eleonore. Über Zerfällungen in paarweis ungleiche Polynomwerte.** Math. Z. **59**, 255–257 (1953).

The author proves the following result. To every polynomial

$$f(x)=a_0+a_1x+\cdots+a_nx^n \quad (a_n>0)$$

there exists a positive integer $s$ such that every integer $N\geqq 0$ is represented by $N=r+f(x_1)+f(x_2)+\cdots$, where $0\leqq r<s$, and where $x_i$ are positive integers such that $0<x_1<x_2<\cdots$, and $0<f(x_1)<f(x_2)<\cdots$. The method of proof is based upon that of R. Sprague [see Math. Z. **51**, 289–290, 466–468 (1948); these Rev. **10**, 283, 514; also H. Richert, Norsk Mat. Tidsskr. **31**, 120–122 (1949); these Rev. **11**, 646] and depends on a solution of the Tarry-Escott problem. *D. H. Lehmer* (Berkeley, Calif.).

Citations: MR 10, 283d = E24-31; MR 10, 514h = D52-40; MR 11, 646a = A46-8.

**P99-4** **(15, 685a)**

**Johnson, S. M. On the representations of an integer as the sum of products of integers.** Trans. Amer. Math. Soc. **76**, 177–189 (1954).

Let $d_n(\nu)$ denote the number of representations of $\nu$ in the form $\nu=a_1\cdots a_n$, where $a_1, \cdots, a_n$ are positive integers, and let $R(N; n, k)$ denote the sum $\sum d_n(\nu_1)\cdots d_n(\nu_k)$ extended over all sets of positive integers $\nu_1, \cdots, \nu_k$ satisfying $\nu_1+\cdots+\nu_k=N$. Making use of the circle-method of Hardy and Littlewood, the author obtains an asymptotic formula, with estimation of remainder, for $R(N; n, k)$ when $N\to\infty$ and $n$, $k$ are fixed and subject to the conditions $n\geqq 2$, $k\geqq 3$. The case $n=3$, $k=3$ is discussed in detail while the general case and a still further generalization are considered more briefly. The case $n=2$, $k=2$ had been previously investigated by A. E. Ingham [J. London Math. Soc. **2**, 202–208 (1927), pp. 207–208] and T. Estermann [Proc. London Math. Soc. (2) **31**, 123–133 (1930)] and the case $n=2$, $k=3$ by Estermann [ibid. **29**, 453–478 (1929)]. *L. Mirsky.*

**P99-5** **(19, 252b)**

**Postnikov, A. G. Additive problems with a growing number of terms.** Izv. Akad. Nauk SSSR. Ser. Mat **20** (1956), 751–764. (Russian)

Let $f(x)$ be a function which assumes integral values for integral $x$. The author considers the number of representations of an integer $N$ in the form $f(x_1)+\cdots+f(x_n)=N$ when $0\leqq x_i\leqq P$, $P$ fixed, $i=1, 2, \cdots, n$, and $n\to\infty$. An asymptotic formula is obtained for each of the cases $f(x)=x$ and $f(x)=x^2$. For example, in the case $f(x)=x$, the author shows that there exists a constant $k>1$ such that the number of solutions of the equation $x_1+x_2+\cdots+x_n=N$ in integers $0\leqq x_i\leqq P\leqq k^n/n$, $i=1, 2, \cdots, n$, is given by

$$r_{n,P}(N)=\frac{(P+1)^n}{\sqrt{(\pi n(P^2+2P)/6)}}\exp\left(-\frac{(N-nP/2)^2}{n(P^2+2P)/6}\right)O\left(\frac{(P+1)^{n-1}}{n}\right)$$

uniformly with respect to $N$. The proof of the result makes use of the local limit theorem of probability theory and estimates of the trigonometric sum $\sum_{0\leq x\leq P}\exp(2\pi i\alpha x)$. *W. Simons* (Vancouver, B.C.).

Referred to in P99-7.

**P99-6** **(24# A720 )**

**Postnikov, A. G.**

**Über additive Aufgaben mit wachsender Summandenanzahl. (Russian. Bulgarian and German summaries)**

*Bŭlgar. Akad. Nauk Izv. Mat. Inst.* **4**, *no.* 1, 73–79 (1959).

An expository article on recent applications of the limit laws of probability, in conjunction with the method of trigonometric sums, to additive problems.

*H. Halberstam* (London)

**P99-7** **(28# 3020 )**

**Siraždinov, S. H.; Azlarov, T. A.**

**On a uniform local theorem. (Russian. Uzbek summary)**

*Izv. Akad. Nauk UzSSR Ser. Fiz.-Mat. Nauk* **1963**, *no.* 2, 32–37.

Let $s$ be a positive integer and let $R$ denote the number of representations of the integer $N$ in the form $N=x_1{}^s+x_2{}^s+\cdots+x_n{}^s$, where $x_k=0, 1, 2, \cdots, p_k$. It is proved that there is an $n_0(s)$ such that as $n\geqq n_0(s)$ uniformly with respect to $N$

$$R=\frac{\prod_{k=1}^{n}(p_k+1)}{B_n}\left[\varphi\left(\frac{N-A_n}{B_n}\right)+\theta(s)\frac{1}{\lambda_n}\right].$$

Here, $A_n=a_1+\cdots+a_n$, $a_k=\sum_{m=0}^{p_k}m^s/p_k+1$, $B_n{}^2=\sigma_1{}^2+\cdots+\sigma_n{}^2$,

$$\sigma_k{}^2=\sum_{m=0}^{p_k}(m^s-a_k)^2/p_k+1,\quad \varphi(x)=(2\pi)^{-1/2}\exp\{-\tfrac{1}{2}x^2\},$$

$\lambda_n=B_n\cdot\min_{1\leqq k\leqq n}(1/p_k{}^s)$ and $|\theta(s)|\leqq c(s)$, a constant depending on $s$ only.

This generalizes and improves former results of A. G. Postnikov [Izv. Akad. Nauk SSSR Ser. Mat. **20** (1956), 751–764; MR **19**, 252] where the cases $s=1$, and $s=2$, $p_1=p_2=\cdots=p_k=\cdots$ had been considered.

*H.-E. Richert* (Syracuse, N.Y.)

Citations: MR 19, 252b = P99-5.

**P99-8** **(29# 281 )**

**Krätzel, Ekkehard**

**Umformung mehrfach-unendlicher Reihen mit Anwendungen insbesondere auf die Thetareihen. (Romanian and Russian summaries)**

*An. Şti. Univ. "Al. I. Cuza" Iaşi Secţ. I (N.S.)* **8** (1962), 57–64.

Gegenstand dieser Abhandlung ist die Umformung mehrfachunendlicher Reihen

$$(1)\qquad \sum_{n_i}^{+\infty}{}_{-\infty} f(n_1, n_2, \cdots, n_r)\quad (r\geqq 2).$$

Hierzu denke man sich in einem $r$-dimensionalen Raum ein rechtwinkliches Koordinatensystem gegeben, auf dessen Achsen die ganzen Zahlen $n_1, n_2, \cdots, n_r$ abgetragen sind. Durch Drehung dieses Koordinatensystems wird bei gewissen Voraussetzungen eine Umformung von (1) erreicht. Die Menge der Gitterpunkte zerfällt in eine endlich Anzahl von Teilmengen, über die dann einzeln summiert wird, wodurch eine Zerlegung von (1) in endlich viele Teilsummen erreicht wird. Von van der Pol wurde der Spezialfall zweifach-unendlicher Reihen mit einer Drehung des Koordinatensystems um $\frac{1}{4}\pi$ betrachtet [B. van der Pol, Enseignement Math. (2) **1** (1956), 258–261; MR **17**, 1082; *Selected scientific papers*, Vol. 2, North-Holland, Amsterdam, 1960; MR **22** #10898]. Das allgemeine Ergebnis ist:

$$(2)\qquad \sum_{m=-\infty}^{+\infty}\sum_{n=-\infty}^{+\infty} f(m, n) = \sum_{\beta_i}\sum_{k=-\infty}^{+\infty}\sum_{l=-\infty}^{+\infty} f(ak-bl+\beta_1, bk+al+\beta_2).$$

Hier sind $a$ und $b$ ganze Zahlen, $(a, b)=1$. In der ersten Summe auf der rechten Seite von (2) ist über diejenigen $\beta_1$, $\beta_2$ zu summieren, die sich aus den Beziehungen $\beta_1=-(a\alpha_1-b\alpha_2)/(a^2+b^2)$, $\beta_2=-(b\alpha_1+a\alpha_2)/(a^2+b^2)$ ergeben, wenn $\alpha_1$ und $\alpha_2$ alle Lösungen der Kongruenz $a\alpha_1-b\alpha_2\equiv 0$ [mod $(a^2+b^2)$] durchlaufen. Spezialfall $a=b=1$:

$$(2')\qquad \sum_{m=-\infty}^{+\infty}\sum_{n=-\infty}^{+\infty} f(m, n) = \sum_{k=-\infty}^{+\infty}\sum_{l=-\infty}^{+\infty} f(k-l, k+l)+\sum_{k=-\infty}^{+\infty}\sum_{l=-\infty}^{+\infty} f(k-l, k+l-1).$$

Anwendungen: (I)

$$\sum_{n^2>m^2} q^{n^2-m^2} = 2\sum_{k=1}^{\infty}\sum_{l=1}^{\infty}\{q^{4kl}+q^{(2k-1)(2l-1)}\}$$

(Zahlentheoretisches Resultat). (II) Jacobische Thetafunktionen. Völlig elementare Herleitung der Differentialgleichung $\theta_1' = \pi\theta_0\theta_2\theta_3$ (abgesehen vom letzten Schritt, bei dem noch eine Integration notwendig wird). (III) Beweis der Beziehung $\pi^2\theta_3^4 = \theta_0''/\theta_0 - \theta_2''/\theta_2$ woraus bekanntlich eine Aussage über die Anzahl der Darstellungen von natürlichen Zahlen als Summe von vier Quadraten gefunden wird. Diese Betrachtungen werden vom Verfasser auf beliebigen Drehungen des $r$-dimensionalen Raumes ausgedehnt, und angewendet auf der Ableitung der Jacobischen Fundamentalformel der Thetafunktionen

$$\prod_{k=1}^{4} \theta_3(v_k, \tau) + \prod_{k=1}^{4} \theta_2(v_k, \tau) = \prod_{k=1}^{4} \theta_3(w_k, \tau) + \prod_{k=1}^{4} \theta_2(w_k, \tau),$$

$$2w_1 = v_1 + v_2 + v_3 + v_4,$$

$$2w_2 = v_1 + v_2 - v_3 - v_4,$$

$$2w_3 = v_1 - v_2 + v_3 - v_4,$$

$$2w_4 = v_1 - v_2 - v_3 + v_4.$$

*S. C. van Veen* (Delft)

## P99-9 (32# 7484)

**Tinsley, M. F.**

**A combinatorial theorem in number theory.**

*Duke Math. J.* **33** (1966), 75–79.

Let $G$ be an additive abelian group of order $n$; denote its zero by $\theta$. Suppose that $G$ is generated by $d_1, \cdots, d_r$, where $d_1, \cdots, d_r$ are distinct and $r > 1$. The author considers the solution of the equation $\sum x_i d_i = \theta$ in integers $x$. Write $(x_1, \cdots, x_r) < (y_1, \cdots, y_r)$ if $x_i \leqq y_i$ for all $i$, but $x_i \neq y_i$ for some $i$. Theorem: If $\sum x_i d_i = \theta$ with at least two of the integers $x$ non-zero and $\sum x_i \geqq n$, then there are $y_1, \cdots, y_r$ with $\sum y_i d_i = \theta$ and $(0, \cdots, 0) < (y_1, \cdots, y_r) < (x_1, \cdots, x_r)$. The theorem with $\sum x_i > n$ is a triviality; the critical case with $\sum x_i = n$ takes a bit longer.

*B. J. Birch* (Oxford)

Referred to in T35-58.

## P99-10 (44# 170)

**Tkačev, M. I.**

**A formula for the number of decompositions of numbers into sums of a definite form.** (Russian)

*Kabardino-Balkarsk. Gos. Univ. Učen. Zap. No.* 3 (1959), 231–235.

## P99-11 (44# 6591)

**Goodstein, R. L.**

**On sums of progressions of positive integers.**

*Math. Gaz.* **54** (1970), 113–115.

The author gives necessary and sufficient conditions for a positive integer to be the sum of an arithmetical progression of positive integers (with a given common difference and even number of terms, etc.). Further, using Čebyšev's result (conjectured by Bertrand) that there is a prime $p$ such that $x < p \leqq 2x$, if $x \geqq 1$ [*Collected papers of Ramanujan*, pp. 208–209, Chelsea, New York, 1962], the author proves that there are integers $n$ as large as we please such that $n$ has an odd factor and $n$ is not the sum of an arithmetical progression of positive integers with common difference an odd number greater than unity.

*T. Hayashida* (Yokohama)

# Q. MISCELLANEOUS ARITHMETIC-ANALYTIC QUESTIONS

See also Sections B80, K45.

## Q05 ANALYTIC FUNCTIONS

See also reviews A22-64, A54-29, B44-64, B44-76, C15-23, J64-5, J72-57, J76-4, J76-13, J76-15, J76-20, J76-27, J76-47, J76-53, J76-58, J76-61, J76-68, K05-58, K15-79, M05-12, M40-9, N32-38, N40-13, N48-19, P80-30, Q10-5, Q20-55, Q25-33, Q99-7, R06-3, R06-7, R06-23, R06-26, R06-33, R06-38, T25-23, Z10-6, Z10-8, Z10-20, Z10-30, Z10-32.

**Q05-1** **(2, 356e)**

**Selberg, Atle. Über ganzwertige ganze transzendente Funktionen.** Arch. Math. Naturvid. **44**, 45–52 (1941).

Let $f(z)$ be an entire function and call $M(r)$ the maximum of $f(z)$ in the circle $|z| \leqq r$. If $f(z)$ takes rational integral values for $z=0, 1, 2, \cdots$ and $\limsup_{r\to\infty} r^{-1}\log M(r) \leqq a$, where $a=\log 2+(1/1500)$, then $f(z)$ is necessarily of the form $P(z)2^z+Q(z)$, where $P(z)$ and $Q(z)$ are polynomials. This remarkable result of the author cannot be found in the foregoing papers on the subject written by the reviewer, G. H. Hardy, E. Landau and F. Carlson. The author's proof follows an essentially new line; it is based on the consideration of the successive differences of the series of successive differences $f(0)$, $\Delta f(0)$, $\Delta^2 f(0)$, $\cdots$.

It may be observed that the result, except for the numerical value of $a$, can also be obtained by a different proof. It follows from the hypothesis concerning $M(r)$ that the power series $\sum f(n)z^{-n}$ is regular outside the domain $(\log r)^2 + \phi^2 \leqq a^2$ (we put $z=re^{i\phi}$). But, if $a>\log 2$ and $a$ is sufficiently near to log 2, the transfinite diameter of this domain is less than 1, and therefore the power series, having integral coefficients, represents a rational function whose poles are at $z=1$ and $z=2$; hence the result. Even the best value of $a$ could be discussed. *G. Pólya* (Providence, R. I.).

Referred to in Q05-3, Q05-4, Q05-9.

**Q05-2** **(4, 6f)**

**Selberg, Atle. Über einen Satz von A. Gelfond.** Arch. Math. Naturvid. **44**, 159–170 (1941).

Gelfond has shown that, if $g(z)$ is an entire function such that $g(n)$, $g'(n)$, $\cdots$, $g^{p-1}(n)$ are all integers when $n$ is any nonnegative integer, then

$$|g(z)| < Ae^{\Theta|z|}, \quad \Theta < p\log(1+e^{(1-p)/p}),$$

implies that $g(z)$ is a polynomial. In case $p=1$, the example $g(z)=2^z$ shows that this theorem is "best possible." The author shows that, for $p>1$, the bound on $\Theta$, $p\log(1+e^{(1-p)/p})$, can be increased. In particular, as $p\to\infty$ the Gelfond bound behaves like $p\log(1+1/e)$, whereas the author's behaves like $p\log\omega$, where $\omega>1+1/e$. The author uses a more general interpolation polynomial than did Gelfond in carrying out the proof. *N. Levinson.*

**Q05-3** **(4, 6g)**

**Selberg, Atle. Über ganzwertige ganze transzendente Funktionen. II.** Arch. Math. Naturvid. **44**, 171–181 (1941).

[Part I appeared in Arch. Math. Naturvid. **44**, 45–52 (1941); cf. these Rev. **2**, 356.] The author proves the following theorem: Let $f(z)$ be an entire function and let $M(r)$ be the max $|f(z)|$ on $|z|=r$. Let $f(n)$ be an integer for every integer value of $n$, $-\infty<n<\infty$. Then if

$$(*) \qquad \overline{\lim}\,\frac{\log M(r)}{r} \leqq \log\frac{3+\sqrt{5}}{2}+2\cdot 10^{-6},$$

$f(z)$ must be of the form

$$P_1(z)\left(\frac{3+\sqrt{5}}{2}\right)^z + P_2(z)\left(\frac{3+\sqrt{5}}{2}\right)^{-z} + P_3(z),$$

where $P_1$, $P_2$ and $P_3$ are polynomials. This generalizes the result of Carlson which in place of (*) requires that

$$\overline{\lim}\,\frac{\log M(r)}{r} \leqq \log\frac{3+\sqrt{5}}{2}.$$

The author uses difference and interpolation methods. *N. Levinson* (Cambridge, Mass.).

Citations: MR 2, 356e = Q05-1.

**Q05-4** **(4, 270c)**

**Pisot, C. Über ganzwertige ganze Funktionen.** Jber. Deutsch. Math. Verein. **52**, 95–102 (1942).

Let $g(z)$ be an entire function having the property that $g(z)$ is an integer whenever $z$ is a nonnegative integer. Let $M(r)$ be the maximum of $|g(z)|$ for $|z|=r$ and let

$$\overline{\lim_{r\to\infty}}\,\frac{\log M(r)}{r} \leqq \alpha.$$

Pólya proved in 1915 that, if $\alpha<\log 2$, $g(z)$ is a polynomial. Later Hardy, Pólya and Carlson proved that, if $\alpha=\log 2$, $g(z)$ is of the form $P_1(z)+2^zP_2(z)$, $P_1(z)$ and $P_2(z)$ being polynomials. Recently Selberg proved that this result is also true if only $\alpha\leqq\log 2+(1/1500)$ [see Arch. Math. Naturvid. **44**, 45–52 (1941); these Rev. **2**, 356, where Pólya suggests an alternative proof for Selberg's theorem].

The purpose of the present paper is to prove that, if $\alpha\leqq 0.8$, $g(z)$ is of the form

$$P_1(z)+2^zP_2(z)+\gamma^zP_3(z)+\bar{\gamma}^zP_4(z),$$

where the $P_k(z)$ are polynomials and $\gamma$, $\bar{\gamma}$ are the roots of $z^2-3z+3=0$. This result is itself a consequence of the following interesting theorem: there exists a constant $\alpha_0$ $(0.825<\alpha_0<0.850)$ such that, if $\alpha\leqq\alpha_0$, $g(z)$ is of the form $\sum_1^3\beta_k^zP_k(z)$, the $P_k(z)$ being polynomials and the $\beta_k$ certain algebraic numbers such that $|\log\beta_k|\leqq\alpha$. The idea of the proof is essentially the same as the idea of the alternative proof of Selberg's theorem sketched by Pólya [loc. cit. above]. *R. Salem* (Cambridge, Mass.).

Citations: MR 2, 356e = Q05-1.

Referred to in Q05-7, Q05-9, Q05-85.

**Q05-5** **(6, 263a)**

**Walker, A. G. Note on integral functions.** J. London Math. Soc. **19**, 106–107 (1944).

By an elementary proof the author shows that every real number is a zero of an integral function $f(x)$ whose power series $\sum_0^\infty a_n x^n$ has rational coefficients. *M. S. Robertson.*

Referred to in Q05-8, Q05-10.

## Q05-6 (7, 200e; 7, 200f)

**Teissier du Cros, F. Sur la convergence d'une série entière dont le terme général à sa partie réelle bornée en deux points de la circonférence-unité.** C. R. Acad. Sci. Paris **219**, 44–45 (1944).

**Valiron, Georges. Sur l'approximation des nombres réels et un théorème de M. Teissier du Cros.** C. R. Acad. Sci. Paris **219**, 45–47 (1944).

Let $S=\sum\gamma_n z^n$. If the general term of the real part of $S$ is bounded for $z=e^{i\theta_1}$ and $z=e^{i\theta_2}$ and if $(\theta_2-\theta_1)/\pi=\omega$ is algebraic and irrational, then the series $S$ converges for $|z|<1$. This result of the first paper is extended to a larger class of numbers $\omega$ in the second paper, which also contains a related result on the zeros of certain entire functions.
*R. Salem* (Cambridge, Mass.).

## Q05-7 (8, 23d; 8, 23e)

**Pisot, Charles. Sur les fonctions arithmétiques analytiques à croissance exponentielle.** C. R. Acad. Sci. Paris **222**, 988–990 (1946).

**Pisot, Charles. Sur les fonctions analytiques arithmétiques et presque arithmétiques.** C. R. Acad. Sci. Paris **222**, 1027–1028 (1946).

An "arithmetical function" is a function $f(x)$ such that $f(x)$ is a rational integer when $x=0, 1, 2, \cdots, n, \cdots$. Generalizing results obtained by Pólya, Hardy, Carlson, and Selberg, the author has previously proved the following theorem: there exists a real number $\gamma_0=0.843\cdots$ such that, if $f(x)$ is an entire function satisfying the inequality $|f(x)|<e^{\gamma|x|}$ with $\gamma<\gamma_0$ for large $|x|$, then $f(x)=\alpha_1^x P_1(x)+\cdots+\alpha_k^x P_k(x)$, where the $\alpha_i$ are algebraic integers and the $P_i(x)$ are polynomials. [In particular, if $\gamma<\log 2$, $f(x)=P_1(x)$, which is Pólya's result; if $\gamma<|\log(3+i\sqrt{3})/2|=0.7588\cdots$, then $f(x)=P_1(x)+2^x P_2(x)$, which is an improvement of Selberg's result, and the best possible one; if $\gamma<0.8$, then

$$f(x)=P_1(x)+2^x P_2(x)+\alpha^x P_3(x)+\bar{\alpha}^x P_4(x),$$

where $\alpha=(3+i\sqrt{3})/2$ and $\bar{\alpha}$ is its conjugate. Cf. these Rev. **4**, 270.]

The new results of the first paper are (1) the generalization of this theorem to functions not supposed to be entire under the conditions of the regularity of $f(re^{i\phi})$ in an angle $|\phi|<\delta$ $(\delta\geqq\pi/2)$ and the regularity of a Laplace transform of $f$ outside a strip parallel to the real axis and of width less than $2\pi$; (2) the application of this result to functions of the form $\sum_0^\infty A_\nu(x)e^{-\lambda_\nu x}$ $(x\geqq 0)$, where the $A_\nu$ are polynomials of bounded degree. In particular, if $a, b$ are real, $|b|>1$, the function $(a^x-1)/(b^x-1)$ is "arithmetical" if and only if $a, b$ are rational integers and $a=b^m$, $m$ being a positive rational integer.

The main result of the second paper is the establishment of a theorem, analogous to the one stated above, concerning entire functions $f(x)$ taking integral rational values whenever $x$ is a positive or negative integer. *R. Salem.*

Citations: MR 4, 270c = Q05-4.

## Q05-8 (9, 179d)

**Graetzer, H. Note on power series.** J. London Math. Soc. **22**, 90–92 (1947).

The author extends the result of A. G. Walker [same J. **19**, 106–107 (1944); these Rev. **6**, 263] that any real number $z_0$ is a zero of an integral function represented by a power series with real rational coefficients. He shows that the theorem still holds when $z_0$ is complex and furthermore that if $z$ is complex with $|z|<1$ then $z$ is a zero of a function whose power series representation has real integral coefficients and is convergent for $|z|<1$. *M. S. Robertson.*

Citations: MR 6, 263a = Q05-5.
Referred to in Q05-10, Q05-13.

## Q05-9 (10, 693c)

**Buck, R. Creighton. Integral valued entire functions.** Duke Math. J. **15**, 879–891 (1948).

Verf. stellt sich die Aufgabe, jene ganzwertigen Funktionen zu bestimmen, die in gewissen Klassen ganzer Funktionen vom Exponentialtypus enthalten sind. Mit Hilfe einer allgemeinen Methode, welche von G. Pólya [vgl. sein Referat zur Arbeit von A. Selberg, Arch. Math. Naturvid. **44**, 45–52 (1941); diese Rev. **2**, 356] angeregt und von C. Pisot [Jber. Deutsch. Math. Verein. **52**, 95–102 (1942); diese Rev. **4**, 270; **6**, 334] verwertet wurde, werden mannigfache Spezialfälle diskutiert, welche die frühern in diesem Problemkreis erzielten Resultate von G. Pólya, F. Carlson, A. Selberg und C. Pisot enthalten. *A. Pfluger* (Zürich).

Citations: MR 2, 356e = Q05-1; MR 4, 270c = Q05-4.
Referred to in Q05-79, Q05-85.

## Q05-10 (11, 338b)

**Lekkerkerker, C. G. On power series with integral coefficients. I.** Nederl. Akad. Wetensch., Proc. **52**, 740–746 = Indagationes Math. **11**, 270–276 (1949).

The author extends results of A. G. Walker [J. London Math. Soc. **19**, 106–107 (1944); these Rev. **6**, 263] and of H. Graetzer [ibid. **22**, 90–92 (1947); these Rev. **9**, 179]. His extension is that if $r$ is a positive integer, if $p_1, p_2, \cdots, p_r$ are different from zero with $-1<p_1<p_2<\cdots<p_r<1$ and if $\eta_1, \eta_2, \cdots, \eta_r$ are arbitrary real numbers, then there exists a power series $f(x)=\sum_0^\infty a_n x^n$ with bounded integral coefficients $a_n$, such that $f(p_m)=\eta_m$, $m=1, 2, \cdots, r$. In the particular case $r=1$, it is shown also that

(1) $$|a_n|<\tfrac{1}{2}|p_1|^{-1}+\tfrac{1}{2}, \qquad n=1, 2, 3, \cdots.$$

Furthermore (1) is sharp in the following sense. All numbers which can be represented by a power series $\sum_0^\infty a_n p_1^n$ with integral coefficients $a_n$ so that

$$|a_n|<\tfrac{1}{2}|p_1|^{-1}-\tfrac{1}{2}, \qquad n\geqq 1,$$

form a set of measure zero. [For an extension in another direction the reviewer calls attention to a result of J. Lehner, Bull. Amer. Math. Soc. **55**, 1060 (1949).]
*M. S. Robertson* (New Brunswick, N. J.).

Citations: MR 6, 263a = Q05-5; MR 9, 179d = Q05-8.
Referred to in Q05-11.

## Q05-11 (11, 425e)

**Lekkerkerker, C. G. On power series with integral coefficients. II.** Nederl. Akad. Wetensch., Proc. **52**, 1164–1174 = Indagationes Math. **11**, 438–448 (1949).

This paper is a continuation of another by the same author [same Proc. **52**, 740–746 = Indagationes Math. **11**, 270–276 (1949); these Rev. **11**, 338] who now obtains the following generalizations of an earlier theorem. Let $p_1, \cdots, p_s$ be different complex numbers in the domain $0<|p_\sigma|<1$, $\Re p_\sigma\geqq 0$ $(\sigma=1, 2, \cdots, s)$ and let $r_1, \cdots, r_s$ be $s$ positive integers. Given the complex numbers $\eta_{\sigma\rho}$ $(\rho=1, \cdots, r_\sigma; \sigma=1, \cdots, s)$ there exists a power series $f(z)=\sum_{n=0}^\infty a_n z^n$ with bounded integral coefficients $a_n$, so that $f^{(\rho-1)}(p_\sigma)=\eta_{\sigma\rho}$ for every pair $\sigma, \rho$. Let $\{A_n\}$ be a sequence of sets of real numbers and $\{g_n\}$ a sequence of positive numbers so that each closed interval of length $g_n$ contains at least one number of $A_n$ for every $n$. Let $h_m$ denote $\max(g_{(m-1)r+1}, g_{(m-1)r+2}, \cdots, g_{mr})$. Let $G=\liminf_{n\to\infty}(g_n)^{-1/n}$ be positive or infinite. If $p_1, \cdots, p_r$; $\eta_1, \cdots, \eta_r$ are complex numbers such that (1) $p_1, \cdots, p_r$ are different, (2) for each $\rho$ the complex conjugate of $p_\rho$ is $p_{r'}$, a member of the set (1) and then $\bar{\eta}_\rho=\eta_r$, (3) $0<|p_\rho|<G$, $\rho=1, 2, \cdots, r$, then there exist a power series $f(z)$ and a positive number $Q$, which depends only on $p_1, \cdots, p_r$, so that (a) $a_n$ belongs to $A_n$ for every $n$, (b) $|a_{mr+\rho}|\leqq Qh_m+\frac{1}{2}h_{m+1}$ $(\rho=1, \cdots, r;\ m=1, 2, \cdots)$, (c) $f(p_\rho)=\eta_\rho$ $(\rho=1, \cdots, r)$. These results were obtained by a study of determinants whose elements are of the form $(a+r)_{r_\sigma-1}\cdot p_\sigma^r$, where $(a+r)_t$ denotes $(a+r)(a+r-1)\cdots(a+r-t+1)$.

*M. S. Robertson* (New Brunswick, N. J.).

Citations: MR 11, 338b = Q05-10.

## Q05-12 (12, 15k)

**Straus, E. G. On entire functions with algebraic derivatives at certain algebraic points.** Ann. of Math. (2) **52**, 188–198 (1950).

Let $f$ be an entire function, and suppose that $f^{(n)}(z)$ is integral for each $z$ in a finite set $S$, and for all $n=0, 1, 2, \cdots$. The problem posed by the author is that of finding $\rho$ and $\sigma$ such that if $f$ is of growth less than order $\rho$ type $\sigma$, $f$ must be a polynomial. For $S=\{0, 1, 2, \cdots, k\}$ he finds $\rho=k+1$, $\sigma=(k!)^{-2}$. For $S=\{0, p_1/q, p_2/q, \cdots, p_k/q\}$ with $(p_1, p_2, \cdots, p_k/q)=1$, $\rho=k+1$ and $\sigma=q^k/m^2$ where $m$ depends upon the numbers $p_1, \cdots, p_k$. For $S=\{0, r\}$ with $r$ rational, he obtains the sharper estimate $\rho=2$, $\sigma=r^{-1}$. These are generalized as follows. Let $K$ be an algebraic field of degree $r$, and suppose that $S=\{0, \alpha_1, \cdots, \alpha_{k-1}\}$ where the $\alpha_i$ are chosen from $K$ and obey certain conditions. Suppose that (rational) integers $q_n$ exist such that $q_nf^{(n)}(z)$ is an integer in $K$ for each $z\varepsilon S$ and for $n=0, 1, 2, \cdots$. Let $\overline{|f^{(n)}(z)|}=O((A+\epsilon)^nn^{sn})$ and $q_n=O((B+\epsilon)^nn^{tn})$, where $\overline{|\alpha|}$ denotes the maximum of the absolute values of the conjugates of $\alpha$. Then, there exist $\rho_0$ and $\sigma_0$ (explicitly determined by $A$, $B$, $s$, and $t$) such that if $f$ is of growth less than order $\rho_0$ type $\sigma_0$, $f$ must be a polynomial. The proof is based on a lemma which asserts that if the entire function $g(z)=\sum\alpha_nz^n/n!$ is of sufficiently slow growth, and if the $\alpha_n$ are in $K$, and also limited in growth, then $g$ must be a polynomial. The author's main theorem may be applied to give transcendence proofs. That of $\pi$ and that of $e^\alpha$ for algebraic $\alpha$ result from the choice of $f(z)$ as in $\sin z$, and $e^z$. Additional examples may be obtained by choosing $f$ to satisfy specified differential equations or difference equations, having algebraic coefficients.

*R. C. Buck* (Madison, Wis.).

Referred to in Q05-64, Q05-69, Q05-79.

## Q05-13 (12, 325e)

**Lehner, Joseph. Note on power series with integral coefficients.** J. London Math. Soc. **25**, 279–282 (1950).

This note contains a generalization of a result due to Graetzer [same J. **22**, 90–92 (1947); these Rev. **9**, 179] who proved that any complex number of absolute value less than unity is a zero of a power series with rational integral coefficients and radius of convergence unity. The generalization states that, if $E$ is a countable set of complex numbers lying within the unit circle, then there is a power series, with rational integral coefficients and radius of convergence unity, which vanishes on the set $E$ and on the set $\bar{E}$ of complex conjugates, but nowhere else in $|z|<1$. The author observes that no transcendental number of modulus greater than unity is the zero of a function represented by a power series (about $z=0$) with integral coefficients.

*M. S. Robertson* (New Brunswick, N. J.).

Citations: MR 9, 179d = Q05-8.

## Q05-14 (12, 688h)

**Dörge, Karl. Entscheidung des algebraischen Charakters von Potenzreihen mit algebraischen Koeffizienten auf Grund ihres Wertevorrates.** Math. Ann. **122**, 259–275 (1950).

Let the Puiseux series

$$\varphi(z)=a_kz^{k/q}+a_{k-1}z^{(k-1)/q}+\cdots+a_0+a_{-1}z^{-1/q}+\cdots$$

be given, where $q$ is a positive integer, $k$ any integer, and $z^{1/q}$ is that $q$th root of $z$ the absolute value of whose amplitude is least. The author investigates conditions under which $\varphi(z)$ is an algebraic or transcendental function. The notion of the degree of transcendentality of a complex number $z$ plays an important part here and is defined as follows. If $z$ is an algebraic number and $P(x)$ that irreducible polynomial which vanishes at $z$, possesses relatively prime integral coefficients, and has a positive leading coefficient, the height $\omega(z)$ of $z$ is defined to be the maximum of the moduli of the coefficients of $P(x)$. By the exponent $\eta(z)$ of $z$ is meant the expression $(\log\omega(z))|\log|z||^{-1}$, provided $z\neq0$ and $|z|\neq1$. The excluded numbers $z$ are called singular. If $z$ is nonsingular, its degree of transcendentality $\tau(z)$ is defined by $\max(\gamma(z), \eta(z))$, where $\gamma(z)$ is the order of $z$; if $z$ is singular, any real number $\geqq1$ may be assigned to it as its degree of transcendentality; finally, if $z$ is transcendental, $\tau(z)=\infty$. The conditions under which $\varphi(z)$ is an algebraic or transcendental function when the $a_\nu$ $(\nu=k, k-1, \cdots)$ are algebraic numbers are too complicated to be stated here in detail. Under additional restrictions on the Puiseux series, however, the algebraic or transcendental character of $\varphi(z)$ may be inferred from the boundedness or unboundedness, respectively, of the set of degrees of transcendentality of the values assumed by $\varphi(z)$ on certain sequences of points which tend to infinity.

*W. Seidel* (Rochester, N. Y.).

Referred to in Q05-18.

## Q05-15 (13, 335a)

**Evgrafov, M. A. Power series with integral coefficients. I.** Mat. Sbornik N.S. **28(70)**, 715–722 (1951). (Russian)

The author generalizes a theorem of Szegö on power series with integer coefficients. It is shown that if $f(z)=\sum_{n=0}^\infty a_nz^n$, $a_n$ integral, is single valued in $|z|<1$ and with the exception of a finite number of points is regular there, and if, in addition, $f(z)$ can be continued analytically across some arc of the unit circle, then it is a rational function.

*P. Davis.*

## Q05-16 (13, 335b)

**Evgrafov, M. A. Power series with integer coefficients. II.** Mat. Sbornik N.S. **29(71)**, 121–132 (1951). (Russian)

The following result is established, again generalizing a theorem of Szegö on power series with integer coefficients. Let $f(z)=\sum_{n=0}^\infty a_nz^n$, $a_n$ integral. Let $P(z)$ be a polynomial and $f(z)P(z)=\sum_{n=0}^\infty a_n'z^n$, $F_1(z)=\sum_{n=0}^\infty a_n'z^n/n!$. The following conditions now suffice to insure the rationality of $f(z)$:

$$1)\quad |F_1(re^{i\theta})|<Me^{r(1+\delta(r))},\qquad 2)\quad |F_1(re^{i\theta})|<Me^{r(1-\epsilon(r))}$$

for $|\theta-\theta_0|\leqq\eta$, 3) $\epsilon(r)\to0$ for $r\to\infty$, 4) $\delta(r)/\epsilon(r)\to0$ for $r\to\infty$, 5) $r\epsilon(r)/\ln r\to\infty$ for $r\to\infty$. By way of showing the exactness of his conditions, the author has constructed a counterexample $f(z)=\sum_{n=0}^\infty a_nz^n$, $a_n$ integral, $f(z)$ not rational, such that if $F(z)=\sum_{n=0}^\infty a_nz^n/n!$, then $|F(re^{i\theta})|<Me^{r(1+\delta(r))}$, and for arbitrary $\alpha>0$, an $r_0=r_0(\alpha)$ and an $\eta=\eta(\alpha)$ may be found such that $|F(re^{i\theta})|<Me^{r(1-\alpha^{-1}\delta(r))}$ for $|\theta|<\eta$ and $r>r_0$. Moreover, such a counterexample may be found for all $\delta(r)$ satisfying the above conditions.

*P. Davis.*

## Q05-17 (13, 439b)

**Gel'fond, A. O. On integral valuedness of analytic functions.** Doklady Akad. Nauk SSSR (N.S.) **81**, 341–344 (1951). (Russian)

Let $E$, $E_1=\{\alpha_1, \alpha_2, \cdots\}$, and $E_2=\{\beta_1, \beta_2, \cdots\}$ be three enumerable sets of complex numbers with $\infty$ as only limit

point and such that $E$ consists of all sums $\alpha_i+\beta_j$. Write
$$N_1(r)=\sum_{|\alpha_i|\leqq r}1,\quad N_2(r)=\sum_{|\beta_j|\leqq r}1,\quad N(r)=\min(N_1(r), N_2(r)).$$
Denote by $f(z)$ an integral function, by $M(r)$ the maximum of $|f(z)|$ on $|z|=r$, and by $K$ an algebraic field of finite degree $\nu$. Assume that $f(\gamma)$, for all $\gamma\varepsilon E$, is an integer in $K$ with the following property: There exists to every $\delta>0$ a $C_0(\delta)>0$ independent of $\gamma$ such that $f(\gamma)$ and all its conjugates with respect to $K$ are $<C_0M(|\gamma|)^{1+\delta}$ in absolute value. The author proves that then two constants $\theta$ and $\lambda$ can be given such that, if
$$\log M(\theta r)<\lambda N(r),$$
then $f(z)$ satisfies a functional equation
$$\sum_{k=1}^{m}A_kf(z+\beta_k)=0,\qquad m>1,$$
where $A_1, \cdots, A_m$ are non-zero rational integers. (It suffices to take $\theta>4$, $\lambda>4(\nu+1)\log(\frac{1}{2}\theta-1)$.) *K. Mahler.*

## Q05-18 (13, 735i)

**Schneider, Theodor. Zur Charakterisierung der algebraischen und der rationalen Funktionen durch ihre Funktionswerte.** Acta Math. **86**, 57–70 (1951).

In a recent paper [K. Dörge, Math. Ann. **122**, 259–275 (1950); these Rev. **12**, 688] criteria were established that a Puiseux series represent an algebraic function of a complex variable. These criteria involved the algebraic character both of the values assumed by the function on a set of points and of the coefficients of the Puiseux series. The present author obtains criteria for the algebraic or rational character of a function solely in terms of the values assumed by the function on a sequence of points. More specifically, let $g(z)$ be regular at $z=0$ (it may be multiple-valued). Then, $g(z)$ is an algebraic function of $z$ if, and only if, a) the values assumed by $g(z)$ on a sheet of its Riemann surface over those points $z=1/\nu$, $\nu=1, 2, \cdots$, which lie in a fixed neighborhood of $z=0$, are algebraic numbers of at most degree $s$, where $s$ is a fixed natural number, and

b) $$\limsup_{\nu\to\infty}\frac{\log\log H(g(1/\nu))}{\log\nu}<1,$$

where $H(g(1/\nu))$ denotes the "height" of $g(1/\nu)$, i.e., the maximum of the moduli of the relatively prime integral coefficients of the irreducible equation for $g(1/\nu)$.

Similarly, $g(z)$ is a rational function of $z$ if, and only if, a) the values assumed by $g(z)$ on a sheet of its Riemann surface over those points $z=1/\nu$, $\nu=1, 2, \cdots$, which lie in a fixed neighborhood of $z=0$, belong to a fixed algebraic number field, and

b) $$\limsup_{\nu\to\infty}\frac{\log\log H(g(1/\nu))}{\log\nu}<1.$$

It turns out that in both criteria conditions a) and b) together imply the sharper condition
$$\limsup_{\nu\to\infty}\frac{\log H(g(1/\nu))}{\log\nu}<t,$$
$t$ a fixed number. Analogous criteria are established which involve this sharper condition, but on the other hand, less stringent conditions on the algebraic character of the numbers $g(1/\nu)$. *W. Seidel* (Rochester, N. Y.).

Citations: MR 12, 688h = Q05-14.
Referred to in Q05-29, Q05-61.

## Q05-19 (13, 834a)

**Lelong, P. Sur les séries de Taylor $F(x, y)$ ayant des coefficients entiers.** Publ. Math. Debrecen **1**, 209–221 (1950).

The author considers questions relating to the rationality of analytic functions of two complex variables whose Taylor coefficients are integers. For Taylor series in one variable such questions were previously considered by Borel and by Pólya [Math. Ann. **99**, 687–706 (1928)]. Let $D$ be a domain in the space of two complex variables $x$ and $y$ and containing the origin 0. Let $E(D)$ designate the class of functions $F(x, y)$ which are analytic and single-valued in $D$ and all of whose Taylor coefficients $a_{pq}=(p!q!)^{-1}(\partial^{p+q}F/\partial x^p\partial y^q)_0$ are integers. The author gives certain sufficient conditions on $D$ in order that $E(D)$ contain only rational functions. This result is applied to the case in which $D$ is a Hartogs domain of regularity $H$ defined by $H$: $[y\varepsilon d, |x|<R(y)]$. Here $d$ designates a domain lying in the complex $y$-plane and $-\log R(y)$ is subharmonic or $-\infty$. It is shown that a necessary and sufficient condition that $E(H)$ contain only rational functions is that (a) there exists an open set $e$ containing the origin and contained in $[x=0, y\varepsilon d]$ on which $R(y)>\rho>1$, (b) under the transformation $y'=y^{-1}$, the component $e_0$ of $e$ which contains the origin goes into a region whose closed bounded complement $\sigma$ possesses a transfinite diameter $c(\sigma)<1$.

*P. Davis* (Washington, D. C.).

## Q05-20 (14, 359e)

**Gel'fond, A. O. The distribution of fractional parts and convergence of functional series with gaps.** Moskov. Gos. Univ. Učenye Zapiski **148**, Matematika **4**, 60–68 (1951). (Russian)

Let $L$ be an increasing sequence of real numbers $y_1, y_2, \cdots$ and $M$ a sequence of points $\tau_k=(\beta_{1k}, \beta_{2k}, \cdots, \beta_{\nu k})$ in the unit cube in $\nu$-dimensional space, so that $0\leqq\beta_{ik}<1$ for $1\leqq i\leqq\nu$, $k=1, 2, \cdots$. The fractional parts $\{f_i(y)\}$ of $\nu$ functions $f_i(y)$ are said to be $(\varphi, M)$ distributed in $\nu$-dimensional space if the set of inequalities
$$|\{f_i(y)\}-\beta_{ik}|\leqq\varphi(y)\quad(i=1, 2, \cdots, \nu)$$
[in the paper the braces { } are omitted] possess for every $\tau_k$ of $M$ an infinity of solutions in values of $y$ belonging to $L$. Here $\varphi(y)$ is any given decreasing function satisfying $0\leqq\varphi(y)\leqq1$ for $y>0$ and $\lim_{y\to\infty}\varphi(y)=0$. Two theorems which are similar to the two theorems of an earlier paper of the author [Doklady Akad. Nauk SSSR (N.S.) **64**, 437–440 (1949); these Rev. **10**, 682] are proved and from them results concerning gap-series and the construction of analytic functions with prescribed fractional parts at the points $z=1, 2, 3, \cdots$ are proved. The final result concerns the Dirichlet series $f(z)=\sum_0^\infty C_ne^{-\lambda_nz}$ where $\{\lambda_n\}$ is an increasing sequence such that $\lim_{n\to\infty}n/\lambda_n=0$, and $U(z)$ is defined by $U(z)=\prod_1^\infty(1-z^2/\lambda_n^2)$. The author proves that if the series for $f(z)$ converges in the half-plane $\Re z>0$ and if $\limsup_{n\to\infty}|C_nU'(\lambda_n)|^{1/\lambda_n}=1$, then $f(z)$ cannot be continued analytically onto the imaginary axis.

The proof of the first theorem needs slight modification since, in contrast to the earlier paper, $|z_{ik}|\geqq1$, so that the inequality (8) need not be true. *R. A. Rankin.*

Citations: MR 10, 682e = J24-10.

## Q05-21 (14, 759d)

**Gel'fond, A. O. Isčislenie konečnyh raznosteĭ. [The calculus of finite differences.]** Gosudarstv. Izdat. Tehn.-Teor. Lit., Moscow-Leningrad, 1952. 479 pp. 10.20 rubles.

This book is based on the author's book of the same title [ONTI, Moscow-Leningrad, 1936], which he has revised and supplemented with material on calculus of finite differences for complex variables. All of the material presented has been previously published. Chapter I, after disposing of elementary questions, treats the general interpolation process for a triangular table, devoting considerable attention to representation and approximation problems. (A minor error—formula (83), used in the proof of the theorem on p. 67, is "unfounded"—is corrected in the paper reviewed below.) Chapter II is an extensive treatment of convergence and regularity properties for the Newton series with interpolation points 1, 2, ⋯; the chapter concludes with a treatment, largely based on previous published work of the author, of general interpolation points. Chapter III is concerned with the general problem of determining an entire function having given elements. A typical problem of this type is: find all entire functions $F(z)$ satisfying $F^{(n)}(n)=0$, $n=1, 2, \cdots$. A number of such problems are treated in detail. There is a discussion of the connection of problems of this type with certain moment problems in the complex domain, and finally applications of the theory of infinite linear differential equations to problems escaping the moment technique. The fourth chapter is an elementary discussion of summation problems, Bernoulli numbers and polynomials, Euler's formula, etc. Most of Chapter V is concerned with a fairly standard treatment of finite difference equations. The last section of Chapter V, on differential equations of finite order, is based on Gelfond's paper in Trudy Mat. Inst. Steklov. **38**, 42–67 (1951) [these Rev. **13**, 929]. This book is very much in the spirit of the modern Russian school concerned with the so-called constructive theory of functions, approximative methods for the solution of differential equations, and so forth. The book is a valuable collection of results in these directions. The exposition is excellent. *J. M. Danskin* (Washington, D. C.).

Citations: MR 13, 929a = J76-27.

## Q05-22 (14, 1074d)

**Bieberbach, Ludwig. Über einen Satz Pólyascher Art.** Arch. Math. 4, 23–27 (1953).

We denote the order of an entire function $f(z)$ by $\rho$ and its type by $\sigma$. Assuming that $f(z)$ and all its derivatives are integral at the points $z=0, 1, \cdots, m-1$, one must have either $\rho>m$ or $\rho=m$ and $\sigma\geqq 1$. The example

$$f(z)=\exp\{z(z-1)\cdots(z-m+1)\}$$

has this property and illustrates that the assertion is sharp. The author indicates the connection of this theorem with that of Carlson and Pólya. The proof is given in the author's "Theorie der geometrischen Konstruktionen" [Birkhäuser, Basel, 1952; these Rev. **14**, 677]. *G. Szegö.*

Referred to in Q05-42, Q05-70, Q05-86.

## Q05-23 (15, 939b)

**Schneider, Theodor. Zur Charakterisierung algebraischer Funktionen mit Hilfe des Eisensteinschen Satzes.** Math. Z. **60**, 98–108 (1954).

The author proves the following converse to Eisenstein's theorem: "Let $f(z)$ be an analytic function regular for $|z|<\rho$; let $s$ and $\gamma$ be given positive integers; and let $\nu_0=2[\rho^{-1}+1]$. If $|z_0|<\rho$, denote by

$$f(z)=\sum_{\kappa=0}^{\infty}a_\kappa(z_0)(z-z_0)^\kappa$$

the Taylor series of $f(z)$ in the neighborhood of $z_0$. Assume that, for

$$n\geqq 6(s+1)\gamma(\nu_0+1)^2,\quad \tau=n+1, n+2, \cdots, 2n,$$

(i) the algebraic field $\mathfrak{K}_{\nu_0+\tau}$ generated by $a_0(1/(\nu_0+\tau))$ is at most of degree $s$; (ii) this field contains also all the coefficients $a_\kappa=a_\kappa(1/(\nu_0+\tau))$ where $\kappa=1, 2, \cdots$; (iii) there exists a positive integer $T=T(1/(\nu_0+\tau))$ such that the products $T^{\kappa+1}a_\kappa$ ($\kappa=0, 1, 2, \cdots; \tau=n+1, n+2, \cdots, 2n$) are algebraic integers; (iv) for all these $\kappa$ and $\tau$

$$\max(T^{\kappa+1}, |\overline{T^{\kappa+1}a_\kappa}|)<(\nu_0+\tau)^{\gamma(\kappa+1)}.$$

Then $f(z)$ is a branch of an algebraic function." If, in particular, $\mathfrak{K}_{\nu_0+\tau}$ is independent of $\tau$ and if $n$ satisfies the stronger inequality

$$n\geqq 10^4(s+1)^3\gamma^2(\nu_0+1)^2,$$

then $f(z)$ is a rational function of $z$. For the proof, polynomials

$$\Phi(z)=\sum_{\lambda=0}^{l}\sum_{\mu=0}^{m}c_{\lambda\mu}z^\lambda f(z)^\mu$$

with rational integral coefficients $c_{\lambda\mu}$ not all zero are constructed that vanish to a high order at the places $1/(\nu_0+\tau)$, and it is shown that these vanish there identically. The paper is unfortunately not free of misprints; thus, in the statement of the theorem, the condition for $\tau$ is wrongly given as $\tau=1, 2, \cdots, n$. *K. Mahler* (Manchester).

Referred to in Q05-61.

## Q05-24 (16, 25e)

**Evgrafov, M. A. On the construction and uniqueness of an entire function $F(z)$ for given values $F^{(n)}(n^2)$.** Izvestiya Akad. Nauk SSSR. Ser. Mat. **18**, 201–206 (1954). (Russian)

By applying the theory developed in a previous paper [same Izvestiya **17**, 421–460 (1953); these Rev. **15**, 515] the author proves the following theorems. (1) If

$$F(z)=\sum_{n=0}^{\infty}\frac{a_n}{(2n)!}z^n,\quad f(z)=\sum_{n=0}^{\infty}a_nz^{-n-1}$$

and if all singular parts of $f(z)$ lie in a domain $\Delta$ of univalence of $g(z)=((1+z)^{1/2}-1)\exp((1+z)^{1/2}-1)$ containing $z=0$, then $F^{(n)}(n^2)=0$ ($n=0, 1, \cdots$) implies $F(z)\equiv 0$. (2) If the singular points of $f(z)$ lie in a domain $D$ such that $0\in D$, $|g(z)|<1$ in $D$, then $F(z)=\sum_{n=0}^{\infty}F^{(n)}(n^2)p_n(z)$, where the $p_n$ are interpolation polynomials. (3) The domains $D$ and $\Delta$ in these results cannot be replaced by larger ones. Similar results can be obtained for $F^{(n)}(n^k)$ in place of $F^{(n)}(n^2)$ ($k$ positive integer). *W. H. J. Fuchs* (Ithaca, N. Y.).

## Q05-25 (17, 597c)

**Mahler, K. On the Taylor coefficients of rational functions.** Proc. Cambridge Philos. Soc. **52** (1956), 39–48.

The author proves: If $F(z)=\sum_{h=0}^{\infty}f_hz^h$ is a rational function of $z$ and infinitely many $f_h$ vanish, then there exist integers $L$, $L_1$ ($0\leqq L_1<L$) such that $f_h=0$ for all sufficiently large $h\equiv L_1 \pmod L$. This theorem is contained in a theorem of C. Lech [Ark. Mat. **2** (1953), 417–421; MR **15**, 104] which discusses power series $\sum f_hz^h$ for which $f_h$ satisfies a recurrence relation $f_h=\alpha_1f_{h-1}+\cdots+\alpha_nf_{h-n}$, $h=n, n+1, \cdots$. Lech's result is slightly stronger. *J. Lehner* (Los Alamos, N.M.).

Citations: MR 15, 104e = B44-14.
Referred to in Q05-26, Q05-33, Q05-34.

## Q05-26 (19, 641d)

**Mahler, K. Addendum to the paper "On the Taylor coefficients of rational functions".** Proc. Cambridge Philos. Soc. **53** (1957), 544.

Observation that the main results of the paper [same Proc. **52** (1956), 39–48; MR **17**, 597] were already obtained by C. Lech [Ark. Mat. **2** (1953), 417–421; MR **15**, 104]; this was pointed out in the review cited.

Citations: MR 15, 104e = B44-14; MR 17, 597c = Q05-25.

## Q05-27 (18, 724c)

**Grau, A. A.; and Goldbeck, B. T., Jr. Algebraic properties of classes of functions.** Amer. Math. Monthly **63** (1956), 636–638.

The authors generalize the notions of odd and even functions in the following manner: Let $\omega$ be a primitive $n$th root of unity. A function $f(z)$ of a complex variable $z$ is called to be of type $(n, k)$ with $0 \leqq k < n$ if $f(\omega z) = \omega^k f(z)$. Then the following theorem is proved: Every complex valued function $f(z)$ may be expressed uniquely as

$$f(z) = f_0(z) + f_1(z) + f_2(z) + \cdots + f_{n-1}(z),$$

where $f_k(z)$ is of type $(n, k)$. Moreover, it is proved that (with suitable definitions of the operations) the ring of classes, ${}_n\mathfrak{F}_k$, of the functions of type $(n, k)$ is isomorphic to the ring of residue classes of integers modulo $n$.

*A. Rosenthal* (Lafayette, Ind.).

## Q05-28 (20# 2437)

**Bertrandias, Françoise. Sur les fonctions analytiques possédant une certaine propriété arithmétique.** C. R. Acad. Sci. Paris **247** (1958), 22–24.

The principal results stated in this note are as follows. Let $f$ be analytic and of exponential type in the angle $|\arg z| < \delta$, where $\delta > \pi/2$. The Laplace transform of $f$ is regular outside a set $S$ in the $s$-plane; let $T$ be the image of $S$ under $z = se^s$. Then if $f^{(n)}(n)$ is an integer when $n$ is a nonnegative integer, and if the transfinite diameter of $T$ is less than 1, it follows that $f^{(n)}(n) = P_1(n)\alpha_1{}^n + \cdots + P_k(n)\alpha_k{}^n$, where $P_j$ are polynomials and $\alpha_j$ are algebraic integers which, with their conjugates, are in $T$. If $S$ is in the domain with polar equation $\rho < (\pi - \theta)\csc\theta$, then $f(z) = Q_1(z)\exp(z\sigma(\alpha_1)) + \cdots + Q_k(z)\exp(z\sigma(\alpha_k))$, where $\sigma(z)$ is the inverse of $se^s$. In particular, if $f$ is an entire function of exponential type $\gamma$ and $f^{(n)}(n)$ is an integer, then for $\gamma \leqq .678\cdots$, $f$ is of the above form; if $\gamma < .567\cdots$, $f$ is a polynomial.

*R. P. Boas, Jr.* (Evanston, Ill.)

## Q05-29 (20# 3849)

**İçen, Orhan Ş. Eine Verallgemeinerung und Übertragung der Schneiderschen Algebraizitätskriterien ins $p$-adische mit Anwendung auf einen Transzendenzbeweis im $p$-adischen.** J. Reine Angew. Math. **198** (1957), 28–55.

Let $f(z)$ be an analytic function in the usual or in the $p$-adic sense [F. Loonstra, Thesis, Univ. of Amsterdam, 1941; MR **7**, 111]. $f(z)$ is said to be algebraic in the arithmetic sense if $f(z)$ satisfies an algebraic equation $\sum_{r=0}^{a}\sum_{s=0}^{b} a_{rs}z^r f(z)^s = 0$ with coefficients $a_{rs}$ algebraic over the rationals. Let $\{z_n\}$ be a sequence of distinct algebraic numbers, $z_n$ of height $h_n$. $\{z_n\}$ is said to be a permissible sequence if: (1) the $z_n$'s are of uniformly bounded degree; (2) there is a $\zeta$ (not necessarily algebraic) and a $c > 0$ such that for sufficiently large $n$, $|z_n - \zeta| \leqq h_n^{-c}$, where "$|\ |$" is the $p$-adic valuation or the usual absolute value; and (3) if for some $A > 0$ and for sufficiently large $n$, the sequence $\{\log h_n\}$ satisfies

$$\sum_{r=1}^{n} \underline{\log h_r} > nA\,\overline{\log h_{r+1}},$$

where

$$\underline{\log h_n} = \min_{1 \leq r \leq n} \log h_r, \quad \overline{\log h_n} = \max_{r \geq n} \log h_r.$$

The author's principal result is the following generalization of a theorem of Schneider [Acta Math. **86** (1951), 57–70; MR **13**, 735]. Let $f(z)$ be an analytic function which is regular at $z = \zeta$. Let $\{z_n\}$ be a permissible sequence converging to $\zeta$ such that the points $f(z_n)$ are in the domain of definition of $f(z)$, and: (a) the $f(z_n)$'s are algebraic numbers of uniformly bounded degree; (b) $\log H_n = o(n \log h_n)$ for $n \to \infty$, where $H_n$ is the height of the algebraic number $f(z_n)$. Then $f(z)$ is algebraic in the arithmetic sense.

Conversely, if $f(z)$ is algebraic in the arithmetic sense and if $\{z_n\}$ is a sequence of algebraic numbers of uniformly bounded degree converging to a regular point $\zeta$ of $f(z)$ such that the points $f(z_n)$ are in the domain of definition of $f(z)$, then the sequence $\{f(z_n)\}$ satisfies (a) and (b) above.

Further theorems of this type are proved and an application is given to the proof of the Mahler-Veldkamp theorem on the $p$-adic transcendence of $\alpha^\beta$ [K. Mahler, Compositio Math. **2** (1935), 259–275; G. R. Veldkamp, J. London Math. Soc. **15** (1940), 183–192; MR **2**, 149].

*Morris Newman* (Washington, D.C.)

Citations: MR 2, 149d = J76-2; MR 13, 735i = Q05-18.
Referred to in Q05-61.

## Q05-30 (20# 3850)

**İçen, Orhan Ş. Eine weitere Verallgemeinerung eines Schneiderschen Algebraizitätskriteriums.** Rev. Fac. Sci. Univ. Istanbul. Sér. A. **21** (1956), 155–187 (1957); Fehlerverzeichnis zur Arbeit, 261. (Turkish summary)

The author generalises a result of his thesis [reviewed above], using the same method and notation. Let $\{z_n\}$ be an infinite sequence of distinct (complex or $p$-adic) algebraic numbers of bounded degrees and heights $h_n$. Let there be a (complex or $p$-adic) $\zeta$ and a $c > 0$ such that $|z_n - \zeta| \leqq h_n^{-c}$ for $n \geqq n_0$. Let $\{j_n\}$ be a sequence of positive integers such that

$$J_{n+1} = O(J_n) \text{ where } J_n = \sum_{\nu=1}^{n} j_\nu,$$

ring $S$, $S^n = 0$, while $R^n \neq 0$, $n$ a fixed natural number and let

$$\log \bar{h}_{n+1} = O(J_n{}^{-1} \sum_{\nu=1}^{n} j_\nu \log \underline{h}_\nu).$$

Let $f(z)$ be an analytic function of the (complex or $p$-adic) variable $z$ regular in a neighbourhood of $z = \zeta$. Let all numbers

$$a_{nj} = \frac{1}{j!} f^{(j)}(z_n) \quad (j = 0, 1, \cdots, j_n - 1)$$

for each $n$ be algebraic and lie in an extension of the rational field of bounded degree. Denote by $B_n$ a positive integer such that all $B_n \cdot a_{nj}$ are algebraic integers, by $H_{nj}$ the height of $a_{nj}$. Finally let

$$\log B_n = O(J_n \log h_n), \quad \log H_{nj} = O(J_n \log h_n).$$

Then $f(z)$ is an algebraic function. A converse theorem also holds. This result leads to a new proof of the transcendency of the $p$-adic exponential function [K. Mahler, J. Reine Angew. Math. **169** (1931), 61–66; A. Günther, ibid. **192** (1953), 155–166; MR **15**, 604]. — The paper unfortunately is full of bad misprints.

*K. Mahler* (Manchester)

Citations: MR 15, 604f = J76-31.
Referred to in Q05-61.

## Q05-31 (21# 6433)

**Chamfy, Christiane. Fonctions méromorphes dans le cercle-unité et leurs séries de Taylor.** Ann. Inst. Fourier. Grenoble **8** (1958), 211–262.

Es sei $\sum_0^\infty u_n z^n$ die Nullpunktsentwicklung der meromorphen Funktion $f(z)$. Verf. beweist: Es gibt rationale Ungleichungen in den Koeffizienten $u_n$, die notwendig und hinreichend dafür sind, dass $|f(z)| \leq 1$ ist für $|z|=1$ und genau $p$ von 0 verschiedene Pole in $|z|<1$ hat. Ist überdies $f(z)$ reell für reelles $z$, so sei der Rang $s$ von $f(z)$ endlich, wenn $f(z)=d(z)/e(z)$ und $d(z)=\pm z^s e(1/z)$ ein Polynom vom Grad $s$ ist, sonst sei $s=\infty$. Über die rationalen Ungleichungen gilt der Satz: (1) Für jedes $n$ mit $n_0 \leq n \leq s$ ($n_0$ abhängig von $f$) gibt es eindeutig bestimmte teilerfremde Polynome $d_n^+(z)$ und $e_n^+(z)$ und teilerfremde Polynome $d_n^-(z)$ und $e_n^-(z)$ vom Grad $n$ mit folgenden Eigenschaften: (i) $e_n^+(0)=1$, $e_n^-(0)=-1$, $d_n^+(z)=z^n e_n^+(1/z)$, $d_n^-(z)=-z^n e_n^-(1/z)$; (ii) $e_n^+(z)$ und $e_n^-(z)$ haben genau $p$ Nullstellen in $|z|<1$; (iii) $d_n^+(z)/e_n^+(z)=u_0+\cdots+u_{n-1}z^{n-1}+v_n^+z^n+\cdots$, $d_n^-(z)/e_n^-(z)=u_0+\cdots+u_{n-1}z^{n-1}+v_n^-z^n+\cdots$. (2) Es gilt $v_n^-<u_n<v_n^+$ für $n_0 \leq n<s$, $v_n^-<u_s=v_s^+$ wenn $f(1)=+1$, $v_n^-=u_s<v_s^+$ wenn $f(1)=-1$.

Es folgen Sätze über im Einheitskreis meromorphe Funktionen $f(z)$, deren Reihenentwicklung im Nullpunkt nur ganzzahlige Koeffizienten hat: $f(z)$ ist rational, wenn $f(z)-a$ für irgendeine komplexe Zahl $a$ in einem verallgemeinerten Sinn nur endlich viele Nullstellen im Einheitskreis hat. Hat $f(z)$ höchstens zwei Pole in $|z|<1$, so ist $f(z)$ nicht beschränkt in der Umgebung von $|z|=1$, wenn diese Pole einen grösseren Betrag als $\theta_1$ haben, wobei $\theta_1^3-\theta_1-1=0$ und $0<\theta_1<1$ ist; dies Ergebnis ist scharf. *F. Huckemann* (Giessen)

Referred to in Q05-44, Z10-31.

## Q05-32 (22# 9483)

**Newman, Morris. Irrational power series.** Proc. Amer. Math. Soc. **11** (1960), 699–702.

The author proves the following theorem. Let $\alpha$ be a real number. Let $g$ denote a polynomial of degree $\geq 1$. Then the power series $\sum_{n=0}^{\infty} g([n\alpha])x^n$ defines a rational function of $x$ if and only if $\alpha$ is a rational number.

The proof uses the fact that if $\alpha$ is irrational the fractional parts of $n\alpha$ $(n=1, 2, 3, \cdots)$ are everywhere dense in the unit interval.

As a special case it easily follows that, when $\alpha>0$, the power series $\sum_{n=0}^{\infty} x^{[n\alpha]}$ represents a rational function if and only if $\alpha$ is rational. *J. Popken* (Amstelveen)

Referred to in Q05-36, Q05-37, Q05-49, Q05-52, Q05-56.

## Q05-33 (22# 12078)

**Shapiro, Harold N. On a theorem concerning exponential polynomials.** Comm. Pure Appl. Math. **12** (1959), 487–500.

Basing his work on previous results by Skolem [Skr. Norske Vid. Akad. Oslo no. 6 (1933)], Mahler [Akad. Wetensch. Amsterdam Proc. **38** (1935), 50–60], and Lech [Ark. Mat. **2** (1953), 417–421; MR **15**, 104], the author studies in more detail the set of integers in which a function

$$F(x) = \sum_{j=1}^{m} A_j^x P_j(x)$$

can vanish; here $A_1, \cdots, A_m$ are distinct numbers, and $P_1(x), \cdots, P_m(x)$ are polynomials with coefficients in a field of characteristic 0. His most interesting result is that $F(x)$ can be written as a product of two functions of the same kind where the first puts the zeros of $F(x)$ in evidence. [See also J. F. Ritt, Trans. Amer. Math. Soc. **31** (1929), 654–679, 680–686; and K. Mahler, Proc. Cambridge Philos. Soc. **52** (1956), 39–48; MR **17**, 597.] *K. Mahler* (Manchester)

Citations: MR 15, 104e = B44-14; MR 17, 597c = Q05-25.

## Q05-34 (23# A851)

**Popken, J.**

**Arithmetical properties of the Taylor coefficients of algebraic functions.**

*Nederl. Akad. Wetensch. Proc. Ser. A* **62** = *Indag. Math.* **21** (1959), 202–210.

By the familiar Eisenstein criterion, if the power series $\sum a_n x^n$ with rational coefficients represents a branch of an algebraic function, then there exists a positive integer $N$ such that all the numbers $N^n a_n$ are integers. As the author points out, this theorem gives no information about the numerators of the $a_n$. In the present paper, the author considers a power series $f(z)=\sum_{n=0}^{\infty} a_n z^n$ with rational coefficients $a_n$, convergent for $|z|<R$, that represents a branch of an algebraic function. The case $f(z)$ a polynomial is excluded. Let $b$ be a rational number such that $0<|b|<R$, and put $S_n=\sum_{r=0}^{n} a_r b^r$ $(n=0, 1, 2, \cdots)$. The following theorems are proved. (1) Assume $f(b)\neq 0$. Then if $p_n$ is the largest prime divisor of the numerator of $S_n$, $\limsup_{n=\infty} p_n=\infty$. (The condition $f(b)\neq 0$ is necessary, as is seen from the example $f(z)=1-\sum_1^{\infty} 2^{-n}z^n$, $b=1$, $S_n=2^{-n}$.) (2) If $f(b)$ is irrational, then $p_n\to\infty$ $(n\to\infty)$. (3) Let $f(z)$ be the Taylor series of a rational function. Let its poles $\omega_1, \cdots, \omega_r$ be such that none of the quotients $\omega_j/\omega_k$ $(j<k)$ is a root of unity. Also assume $f(b)\neq 0$. Then $p_n\to\infty$ $(n\to\infty)$.

The proofs of Theorems 1 and 2 make use of a special case of Ridout's recent generalization [Mathematika **4** (1957), 125–131; MR **20** #32] of the Thue-Siegel-Roth theorem. The proof of Theorem 3 depends on the theorem of Mahler [Proc. Cambridge Philos. Soc. **52** (1956), 39–48, p. 40; MR **17**, 597] that if $f(z)$ is a rational function, not a polynomial, with poles $\omega_1, \cdots, \omega_n$ such that none of the quotients $\omega_j/\omega_k$ $(j<k)$ is a root of unity, then at most a finite number of the Taylor coefficients can vanish.

As an application of the above, the following result may be quoted. Let $a$, $b$, $c$, $d$ be non-vanishing integers, $|b|>|d|$. Then the largest prime divisor of $ab^n+cd^n$ tends to infinity with $n$. *L. Carlitz* (Durham, N.C.)

Citations: MR 17, 597c = Q05-25; MR 20# 32 = J68-18.

## Q05-35 (23# A2527)

**Liu, H. C.; Macintyre, A. J.**

**Cartwright's theorem on functions bounded at the integers.**

*Proc. Amer. Math. Soc.* **12** (1961), 460–462.

Let $f(z)$ be an entire function of exponential type $\tau \leq k<\pi$ which is bounded at the integers. A theorem of Cartwright's states that $\sup_{-\infty<x<\infty} |f(x)| \leq A(k)M$, $M=\sup|f(n)|$, $n=0, \pm 1, \cdots$. Many estimates of the value of the smallest $A(k)$ have been made. It is shown that known estimates can be improved so that $A(k) \leq (1-\frac{1}{8}k^2)^{-1}$, $0<k<2^{3/2}$, and $A(k) \leq 2(3-k)^{-1}$, $2<k<3$. These inequalities are accomplished by employing arguments based upon inequalities arising from a theorem of Bernstein which states that if $f(z)$ is of exponential type $\tau$ and $|f(x)|<M$ for real $x$, then $|f'(x)| \leq M\tau$.

*W. C. Royster* (Lexington, Ky.)

## Q05-36 (23# A3244)

**Mordell, L. J.**

**Irrational power series.**

*Proc. Amer. Math. Soc.* **12** (1961), 522–526.

The author proves the following result. Let $\alpha$ be a real number, $f(u, v)$ a polynomial in $u$ and $v$ of degree $\geq 1$ in $v$.

Then, if $\{n\alpha\}$ denotes the fractional part of $n\alpha$, $F(x)=\sum_{n=0}^{\infty}f(n, \{n\alpha\})x^n$ represents a rational function of $x$ if and only if $\alpha$ is rational.

This is a generalization of a theorem due to M. Newman [Proc. Amer. Math. Soc. **11** (1960), 699–702; MR **22** #9483], with the same assertion for the more special function $F_1(x)=\sum_{n=0}^{\infty}f([n\alpha])x^n$, where $f(u)$ stands for a polynomial of degree $\geqq 1$ and $[n\alpha]$ for the integral part of $n\alpha$. However, the proofs of both authors differ essentially. In the case that $\alpha$ is irrational, the present author shows not only that $F(x)$ cannot be a rational function, but even that $|x|=1$ is a curve of essential singularities for $F(x)$. To this end the author investigates the asymptotic behaviour of $F(x)$ when $x$ tends radially to the points $\exp(2m\pi i\alpha)$ $(m=0, 1, 2, \cdots)$. *J. Popken* (Amsterdam)

Citations: MR 22# 9483 = Q05-32.

Referred to in Q05-40, Q05-52, Q05-56.

## Q05-37 (25# 4084)

**Schwarz, Wolfgang**

**Irrationale Potenzreihen.**

*Arch. Math.* **13** (1962), 228–240.

The author generalizes theorems of E. Hecke [Abh. Math. Sem. Univ. Hamburg **1** (1921), 54–76], M. Newman [Proc. Amer. Math. Soc. **11** (1960), 699–702; MR **22** #9483] and R. Salem [Duke Math. J. **12** (1945), 153–172; MR **6**, 206] concerned with continuability and irrationality of a power series, by a combination of methods of each author. Many results are given, among which the three that follow are typical. (1) Let $[x]$ denote the largest integer not exceeding $x$, and $\{x\}=x-[x]$ the fractional part of $x$. Let $t\geqq 1$ be an integer, and $\alpha$ a real irrational number. Then if $f(x)$ is a real function defined for $0\leqq x\leqq 1$ which is at least $(t+1)$-times differentiable and such that there is at least one integer $\tau$, $0\leqq\tau\leqq t-1$ for which $f^{(\tau)}(0)\neq f^{(\tau)}(1)$, then the power series $\sum_{n=0}^{\infty}f(\{\alpha n\})Z^n$ is not continuable over the unit circle. (2) Let $g(x)$ be a non-constant polynomial. Let $\tau$, $\rho$ be rational numbers, $0<\tau<1$. Then the power series $\sum_{n=0}^{\infty}g([\rho n^{\tau}])Z^n$ is irrational. (3) Let $h(x)$ be a real non-constant polynomial. Then $\sum_{n=0}^{\infty}[h(n)]Z^n$, $\sum_{n=0}^{\infty}\{h(n)\}Z^n$ are rational functions only when all the coefficients of $h(x)$ (apart from the constant term) are rational, and are not continuable over the unit circle if at least one coefficient of $h(x)$ (apart from the constant term) is irrational. *M. Newman* (Washington, D.C.)

Citations: MR 6, 206b = R06-3; MR 22# 9483 = Q05-32.

Referred to in Q05-49, Q05-52, Q05-56, Q05-60.

## Q05-38 (25# 5167)

**Argirova, Tatjana; Genčev, Todor**

**Über die Taylorsche Reihenentwicklungen der rationalen Funktionen.**

*Annuaire Univ. Sofia Fac. Sci. Phys. Math. Livre* 1 *Math.* **54** (1959/60), 111–114.

Authors' summary: "In dieser Arbeit wird folgendes Theorem bewiesen: Es sei $\sum_{\nu=0}^{\infty}a_\nu z^\nu$ eine Potenzreihe mit ganzzahligen Koeffizienten, die im Kreise $|z|<1$ konvergent und in einer Teilmenge von $|z|=1$ mit positivem Lebesgueschem Mass überkonvergent ist. Hat die Funktion $f(z)=\sum_{\nu=0}^{\infty}a_\nu z^\nu$ wenigstens einen Regulärpunkt auf $|z|=1$, so ist $f(z)$ ein Polynom."

## Q05-39 (26# 3903)

**Sato, Daihachiro**

**On the rate of growth of entire functions of fast growth.**

*Bull. Amer. Math. Soc.* **69** (1963), 411–414.

Let $f(z)$ be an entire function, $a_n$ its Taylor coefficients, and $M(r)$ its maximum modulus; let $\log^{[n]}$ be the $n$th iterate of the logarithm. Define

$$\lambda = \lambda_{(q)} = \limsup \log^{[q]}M(r)/\log r,$$

$$k = k_{(q)} = \limsup \log^{[q-1]}M(r)/r^{\lambda}.$$

If $\lambda_{(q-1)}=\infty$ and $\lambda_{(q)}<\infty$, then $f(z)$ is said to be of index $q$; in particular, $\lambda_{(2)}$ and $k_{(2)}$ are the ordinary order and type for functions of finite order; $\lambda_{(3)}$ is called the rank. The author shows that if $f(z)$ is of index $q$, then

$$\lambda = \limsup n \log^{[q-1]}n/\{-\log|a_n|\},$$

$$k = \limsup |a_n|^{\lambda/n}\log^{[q-2]}n \qquad (q>2).$$

He states that a transcendental entire function which, together with all its derivatives, assumes integral values at all integral points must have index $q\geqq 3$, and if of index 3 must have rank at least 1; this is best possible. {These results were first found by E. Lindelöf [Bull. Sci. Math. (2) **27** (1903), 213–232].}

*R. P. Boas, Jr.* (Evanston, Ill.)

Referred to in Q05-71.

## Q05-40 (26# 4984)

**Mordell, L. J.**

**The series $\sum a_n/(1-xe^{2n\pi i\alpha})$.**

*J. London Math. Soc.* **38** (1963), 111–116.

Let $\alpha$ be an irrational number and let $\{n\alpha\}$ denote the fractional part of $n\alpha$ $(n=0, \pm 1, \pm 2, \cdots)$. The main purpose of this paper is to study the convergence of the series

$$\sum_{n=-\infty}^{\infty} a_n/(1-xe^{2n\pi i\alpha})$$

for $|x|<1$ when $\sum a_n$ is only conditionally convergent. The author solves this problem for the special case $a_n=e^{2\pi i\beta n}/n$, where $\beta$ denotes a real number. In this case he obtains, when $\alpha m+\beta$ is not an integer for any integer $m$,

$$\frac{1}{2\pi i}H(x) = \frac{1}{2\pi i}\sum_{-\infty}^{\infty}{}' a_n/(1-xe^{2n\pi i\alpha})$$

$$= \frac{1}{2(1-x)}-\sum_{m=0}^{\infty}\{\alpha m+\beta\}x^m,$$

the dash denoting that $n=0$ has been omitted from the summation. If $\alpha m+\beta$ is an integer for $m=k$, then $-\frac{1}{2}x^k$ has to be added to the right-hand side.

The result given above is used to study the behaviour of $H(x)$ if $x$ tends radially to a point on the unit circle:

$$H(x) = e^{2l\pi i\beta}/l(1-xe^{2l\pi i\alpha})+o(1/|1-xe^{2l\pi i\alpha}|)$$

$$\text{as } x\to e^{-2l\pi i\alpha} \ (l \text{ any integer}).$$

The problem discussed here is closely connected with the study of power series of the form $\sum_{n=0}^{\infty}f(\{n\alpha\}, n)x^n$, $f$ denoting a polynomial in two variables, considered by the author before [Proc. Amer. Math. Soc. **12** (1961), 522–526; MR **23** #A3244].

{The last formula $\theta=m\alpha+n$ in the present paper should read $l\theta=m\alpha+n$.} *J. Popken* (Berkeley, Calif.)

Citations: MR 23# A3244 = Q05-36.

Referred to in Q05-54, Q05-55.

## Q05-41 (26# 6155)

**Narkiewicz, W.**

**Remark on rational transformations.**

*Colloq. Math.* **10** (1963), 139–142.

Denote by $R_\infty$ the field of rational numbers to which an ideal element $\infty$ is adjoined. Let $F(\infty)=\lim_{|t|\to\infty}|F(t)|$, $t$ rational, and $F(z)=\infty$ if $z$ is a pole of the rational function $F(t)$. The author shows that $X\subset F(X)$ for an infinite subset $X\subset R_\infty$ implies $F(t)=(at+b)/(ct+d)$ with rational constants $a, \cdots, d$. The method of proof is an extension of that in earlier work of the author [Acta Arith. **7** (1961/62), 241–249; MR **26** #110; ibid. **8** (1962), 11–19; MR **26** #4987].

*O. F. G. Schilling* (Lafayette, Ind.)

Citations: MR 26# 110 = R08-32; MR 26# 4987 = R08-33.

Referred to in R08-40.

## Q05-42 (27# 303)

**Sato, Daihachiro**

**Two counterexamples and some remarks on integer-valued functions. (Japanese)**

*Sûgaku* **14** (1962/63), 95–98.

Let $f(z)$ be an entire function. Straus [Proc. Amer. Math. Soc. **2** (1951), 24–27; MR **12**, 700; errata, MR **12**, 1003] conjectured that if $f(z)$ and all its derivatives $f^{(n)}(z)$ $(n=1, 2, \cdots)$ assume integral values at all the integers, then $f(z)$ will be a polynomial. The author gives a counterexample for this conjecture by constructing a transcendental entire function $F(z)$ of the form

$$F(z) = f_1(\sin(\pi z)) + \cos(\pi z) \cdot f_2(\sin(\pi z)),$$

where $f_1(\omega)$ and $f_2(\omega)$ are two suitable entire functions. Bieberbach [Arch. Math. **4** (1953), 23–27; MR **14**, 1074] states a theorem: If $f(z)$ is an entire function of order $\rho$ and of type $\sigma$, and if $f(z)$ and all its derivatives $f^{(n)}(z)$ $(n=1, 2, \cdots)$ assume integral values at $k$ points $z=0, 1, \cdots, k-1$, then either $\rho > k$ or $\rho = k$, $\sigma \geqq 1$. For this theorem, the author gives a simple counter-example $h(z) = \exp(\frac{1}{2}z(z-1)(z-2)(z-3))$ in the case $k=4$ (clearly, the order of $h(z)$ is 4 and the type is $\frac{1}{2}$). Furthermore, the author obtains a deep result as follows. Let $V(x_1, x_2, \cdots, x_n) = \prod_{i<j}(x_j - x_i)$ and put $\sigma_c = [V(1, 2, \cdots, k)]^{-2/k}$. Denote by $E$ the set of transcendental entire functions of order $\rho$ and of type $\sigma$ which satisfy the conditions of the Bieberbach theorem. The author proves that given any order $\rho > k$ and any type $\sigma \geqq 0$, the set $E$ has the power of continuum; for $\rho = k$ and any type $\sigma \geqq \sigma_c$, the set $E$ is also of the power of continuum; on the contrary, for order $\rho = k$ and type $\sigma < \sigma_c$, $E$ is at most countable; for order $\rho < k$, $E$ is empty.

*K. Noshiro* (Nagoya)

Citations: MR 12, 700c = C05-7; MR 14, 1074d = Q05-22.

## Q05-43 (27# 304)

**Sato, Daihachiro**

**On integer-valued functions and transcendental numbers. (Japanese)**

*Sûgaku* **14** (1962/63), 99–108.

This is an interesting expository paper on integer-valued entire functions [see the preceding review #303] and transcendental numbers. Historical background, generalized Taylor expansions of entire functions and relations among coefficients and order and type, and some results on integer-valued entire functions and integer-valued polynomials are stated. The bibliography contains 48 papers.

*K. Noshiro* (Nagoya)

## Q05-44 (27# 1565)

**Cantor, David G.**

**Power series with integral coefficients.**

*Bull. Amer. Math. Soc.* **69** (1963), 362–366.

The author proves the following theorem. Let $f(z)$ be a function of bounded characteristic in $|z|<1$, whose Laurent series around the origin has integral coefficients. Then $f(z)$ is rational. This result includes results of Salem [Duke Math. J. **12** (1945), 153–172; MR **6**, 206] and Chamfy [Ann. Inst. Fourier (Grenoble) **8** (1958), 211–262; MR **21** #6433]. If $g(z) = \sum_{i=0}^{\infty} a_i z^i$, set $A_r$ = the matrix $\|a_{i+j}\|$, $0 \leqq i, j \leqq r$. The theorem follows from a theorem of Kronecker and the following lemma. Suppose $g(z)$ is of bounded characteristic in $|z|<1$. Then $\lim_{r\to\infty} |\det(A_r)|^{1/r} = 0$. The author proves an analogous theorem for power series whose coefficients are algebraic integers in a given algebraic number field.

*G. R. MacLane* (Houston, Tex.)

Citations: MR 6, 206b = R06-3; MR 21# 6433 = Q05-31.

## Q05-45 (27# 5908)

**Sato, Daihachiro**

**A simple example of a transcendental entire function that together with all its derivatives assumes algebraic values at all algebraic points.**

*Proc. Amer. Math. Soc.* **14** (1963), 996.

The title of this paper describes accurately and concisely its contents. The example is set up in a straightforward manner by the use of infinite products.

*John W. Green* (Los Angeles, Calif.)

## Q05-46 (28# 3003)

**Heilbronn, H.**

**On the representation of a rational as a sum of four squares by means of regular functions.**

*J. London Math. Soc.* **39** (1964), 72–76.

It has been known since Lagrange, if not Diophantus, that every positive rational can be expressed as a sum of four squares of rational numbers. The author obtains the following beautiful extension. Theorem 1: There exist four integral functions $f_j(x)$ which are positive for $x>0$, satisfy $\sum_{j=1}^{4} f_j^2(x) = 1$, and have the property that $x^{1/2} f_j(x)$ is rational for positive rational $x$.

Next, let $k \geqq 2$ be a rational integer, and let $s = s(k)$ be the smallest integer such that for each rational $x>0$ the rational points are everywhere dense on the surface $\sum_{\sigma=1}^{s} y_\sigma^k = x$ $(y_\sigma > 0)$. Also let $L$ denote the complex plane exclusive of the negative real axis $x \leqq 0$. The author sketches a proof of Theorem 2: There exist $s$ functions $g_\sigma(x)$, $1 \leqq \sigma \leqq s$, regular in $L$, such that (1) $g_\sigma(x)$ is rational for rational $x>0$ and (2) $\sum_{\sigma=1}^{s} g_\sigma^k(x) = x$ in $L$.

He also remarks that $s = s(k)$ satisfies $s = O(k \log k)$, by the methods of Vinogradoff. On the other hand, it seems hard to prove that $s>3$ for a single odd $k$.

*S. Chowla* (University Park, Pa.)

## Q05-47 (28# 3161)

**Sato, Daihachiro; Straus, Ernst G.**

**Rate of growth of Hurwitz entire functions and integer valued entire functions.**

*Bull. Amer. Math. Soc.* **70** (1964), 303–307.

Let $g(z)$ and $f(z)$ be entire functions. The function $g(z)$ is integer-valued if $g(n)$ is an integer for $n=0, 1, 2, 3, \cdots$. Similarly, $f(z)$ is a Hurwitz function if $f^{(n)}(0)$ is an integer for $n=0, 1, 2, 3, \cdots$ $(f^{(0)}(z) \equiv f(z))$. The authors also consider two-point Hurwitz functions, which are Hurwitz entire functions at two consecutive integers, say $z=0$ and $z=1$. The authors state seven theorems concerning the above functions. Their purpose is to find, as accurately as possible, a dividing line for the growth of such functions such that, below this line, one finds only polynomials. Two of the simplest results of the authors may be stated as follows. Let $\phi(r) = \max_n \{r^n/\Gamma(n+1)\}$ $(r \geqq 0)$. (I) A Hurwitz entire function is a polynomial if $M(r) = \max_{|z|=r} |f(z)| < \phi(r) + r^N$ for some $N$ and all $r > r_0$. (II) There exists a denumerable infinite set of transcendental, integer-valued entire functions which satisfy

$M(r) < 2^r - r^N$ for any fixed $N$ and all $r > r_0$.

The authors give brief sketches of their proofs.

*A. Edrei* (London)

## Q05-48 (29# 220)

**Bertrandias, Françoise**

**Séries de Taylor à coefficients rationnels.**

*C. R. Acad. Sci. Paris* **257** (1963), 3793–3795.

Let $f(z)$, which is given by $\sum_0^\infty a_n z^{-n-1}$ in the neighborhood of $z = \infty$, be holomorphic and uniform in the complement of a compact set $K_f$ of transfinite diameter $\tau_f$ and be meromorphic with a finite number of poles in $|z| > \rho_f$. It is well known that if the $a_n$ are rational and $\tau_f < 1$, then $f(z)$ is rational. Now let $a_n \in Q$, the rational field. Denote by $Q_p$ the field of $p$-adic numbers, by $K_p$ a finite algebraic extension of $Q_p$ and by $|\alpha|_p$ the $p$-adic absolute value on $K_p$. Then the author states without proof a number of theorems that generalize the above result. A typical theorem follows. Suppose there exists a positive constant $A$ such that for all primes $p$ and for all $n > n_0$, $|a_n|_p \leqq An$. Then if $\rho_f < \exp(-A)$, $f(z)$ is rational. With the same hypothesis if $\tau_f < \exp((-3/2)A)$, then $f(z)$ is rational.

*V. F. Cowling* (New Brunswick, N.J.)

## Q05-49 (29# 1184)

**Meijer, H. G.**

**Irrational power series.**

*Nederl. Akad. Wetensch. Proc. Ser. A* **66** = *Indag. Math.* **25** (1963), 682–690.

The author generalizes a theorem of the reviewer [Proc. Amer. Math. Soc. **11** (1960), 699–702; MR **22** #9483] and proves that if $\alpha$ is a real number, $k$ a positive integer and $g(x)$ a polynomial of degree $\geqq 1$, then the power series

$$\sum_{n=0}^{\infty} g([\alpha n^k])x^n$$

represents a rational function of $x$ if and only if $\alpha$ is a rational number. Essentially the same result is proved by W. Schwarz [Arch. Math. **13** (1962), 228–240; MR **25** #4084].

*Morris Newman* (Washington, D.C.)

Citations: MR 22# 9483 = Q05-32; MR 25# 4084 = Q05-37.

Referred to in Q05-52, Q05-56.

## Q05-50 (29# 1185)

**Popken, J.**

**Irrational power series.**

*Nederl. Akad. Wetensch. Proc. Ser. A* **66** = *Indag. Math.* **25** (1963), 691–694.

The author generalizes the work of H. G. Meijer described in the preceding review [#1184] and proves some very general results, among which the following is both elegant and beautiful: Let $g(u)$ denote a polynomial with algebraic coefficients. Let $\varphi(n)$ be an integer-valued function, and suppose that the power series $G = \sum_{n=1}^\infty g(\varphi(n))x^{-n}$ converges for $|x| > 1$. Then $G$ is either a rational function of $x$ or a function having the unit circle as a natural boundary. The proof makes use of a generalization of Liouville's theorem on approximation of algebraic numbers and on a result of Pólya relating transfinite diameter to a certain limit involving Hankel determinants.

*Morris Newman* (Washington, D.C.)

Referred to in Q05-52, Q05-60.

## Q05-51 (30# 1999)

**Baker, A.**

**Power series representing algebraic functions.**

*J. London Math. Soc.* **40** (1965), 108–110.

A classical theorem of Eisenstein states that if the series $a_0 + a_1x + a_2x^2 + \cdots$ has rational coefficients and represents an algebraic function, regular at the origin, then there is an integer $q$ such that $q^n a_n$ is an integer for each $n$ [E. Heine, *Handbuch der Kugelfunctionen. Theorie und Anwendungen*, zweite Auflage, G. Reimer, Berlin, 1878/81]. The author of the present article shows that this theorem can be supplemented by the following result. There exists a wide class of algebraic functions for which an integer $q$ can be chosen such that, for all $n$, $q^n a_n$ is an integer and $q^{n-1}a_n$ is not. Such functions can be obtained from an equation of the form

$$P_N(x)w^N + P_{N-1}(x)w^{N-1} + \cdots + P_1(x)w + P_0(x) = 0,$$

where the $P_i(x)$, $i = 0, 1, \cdots, N$, are polynomials in $x$ satisfying the following two conditions: (1) The constant terms of the $P_i(x)$ are equal to one for $i = 0, 1$ and equal to zero for $i = 2, \cdots, N$; (2) All the other coefficients are integers, except for the coefficient of $x$ in $P_1(x)$, which is rational but not an integer.

*E. Inaba* (Tokyo)

## Q05-52 (30# 3964)

**Carroll, F. W.; Kemperman, J. H. B.**

**Noncontinuable analytic functions.**

*Duke Math. J.* **32** (1965), 65–83.

A well-known theorem of Hecke states that the power series $\sum_{n=0}^\infty [n\alpha]z^n$ represents an analytic function with $|z| = 1$ as a natural boundary whenever the real constant $\alpha$ is irrational. This result has been generalized by R. Salem, M. Newman, L. J. Mordell, W. Schwarz, H. G. Meijer and the reviewer [R. Salem, same J. **12** (1945), 153–172; MR **6**, 206; M. Newman, Proc. Amer. Math. Soc. **11** (1960), 699–702; MR **22** #9483; L. J. Mordell, ibid. **12** (1961), 522–526; MR **23** #A3244; W. Schwarz, Arch. Math. **13** (1962), 228–240; MR **25** #4084; H. G. Meijer, Nederl. Akad. Wetensch. Proc. Ser. A **66** (1963), 682–690; MR **29** #1184; the reviewer, ibid. **66** (1963), 691–694; MR **29** #1185]. The present authors generalize most of these results in turn.

In the first part of the paper the power of Hecke's method is exhibited and it is used in conjunction with Hadamard's multiplication theorem for singularities of an analytic function. A sequence $(a_n)$ is said to be of type (H) if $\lim |a_n|^{1/n} = 1$ and if, moreover, the series $\sum_{n=n_0}^\infty a_n^{-1}z^n$ ($|z| < 1$), for sufficiently large $n_0$, represents a function analytic at each point $z_0 \neq 1$ on the unit circle. Example: $a_n = c(\log n)^\rho n^\sigma \exp(dn^\tau)$, where $n \geqq 2$ and $\rho, \sigma, d$ and $\tau$ are real constants, $\tau < 1$ and $c \neq 0$. As a corollary of a more general theorem, the following is proved. Let $\varphi(x)$ be complex-valued and Riemann integrable on $[0, 1)$; let it be extended periodically mod 1. Let its Fourier transform $\int_0^1 \varphi(x)\exp(2\pi ipx)\,dx$ be nonzero for all sufficiently large integers $p$. Moreover, let $(a_n)$ be a sequence of type (H) and let $\alpha$ be irrational. Then a power series $\sum_{n=0}^\infty (a_n\varphi(\alpha n) + o(a_n))z^n$ has $|z| = 1$ as a natural boundary. This result is applied in some special cases, e.g., by taking $\varphi(x) = \{x\} = x - [x]$ and $(a_n)$ related to the example given above.

Hecke's method is connected with Riemann integrability of the function $\varphi(x)$. In the second part of the paper the authors consider also Lebesgue integrable functions, and then they are led to "almost all" results. For instance, they find the following as a special case of a more general theorem. Let $\varphi(x)$ be any (Lebesgue) integrable function on $[0, 1)$. Then the power series $f_\alpha(z) = \sum_{n=0}^\infty \varphi(\{n\alpha\})z^n$ has, for almost all real $\alpha$, a radius of convergence $\geqq 1$. Moreover, $f_\alpha(z)$ has, for almost all $\alpha$, the circle $|z| = 1$ as a natural boundary if and only if $\varphi(x)$ is not equivalent to a trigonometric polynomial of period 1.

In the last part of the paper, power series of the form (1) $f(z)=\sum_{n=0}^{\infty} P([g_n])z^n$, $|z|<1$, are studied. Here $P(u)$ denotes a polynomial of degree $\geqq 1$ with algebraic coefficients and the $g_n$ are real numbers with $|g_n|\to\infty$ and $\lim\sup_{n\to\infty}|g_n|^{1/n}=1$. The reviewer has already shown that unless $f(z)$ is a rational function it has $|z|=1$ as a natural boundary [the reviewer, loc. cit.]. The authors introduce a large class of sequences, which they call $U$-sequences. The actual definition is too intricate to reproduce here, but it involves the notion of $L$-functions contained in Hardy's book *Orders of Infinity; the 'infinitärcalcül' of Paul Du Bois-Reymond* [Cambridge Univ. Press, Cambridge, England, 1910; second edition, 1924]. The authors prove that if $(g_n)$ is a $U$-sequence, then $f(z)$, given by (1), cannot be a rational function and therefore has $|z|=1$ as a natural boundary. As special cases they find that the functions $\sum P([\log n])z^n$, $\Sigma P([bn^\gamma])z^n$, $\Sigma P([n/\log n])z^n$ have $|z|=1$ as a natural boundary if $b\neq 0$, $0<\gamma<1$. *J. Popken* (Amstelveen)

Citations: MR 6, 206b = R06-3; MR 22# 9483 = Q05-32; MR 23# A3244 = Q05-36; MR 25# 4084 = Q05-37; MR 29# 1184 = Q05-49; MR 29# 1185 = Q05-50.

Referred to in Q05-54.

## Q05-53 (31# 1245 )

**Cantor, David G.**

**On arithmetic properties of coefficients of rational functions.**

*Pacific J. Math.* **15** (1965), 55–58.

A theorem of Pólya [J. Reine Angew. Math. **150** (1921), 1–31] asserts that if $\sum_{n=0}^{\infty} na_nz^n$ is a rational function*, then so is $\sum_{n=0}^{\infty} a_nz^n$. The same deduction can be made if $\sum_{n=0}^{\infty}(n-k)a_nz^n$ is a rational function, where $k$ is a rational integer, and so also, by induction, if $\sum_{n=0}^{\infty} f(n)a_nz^n$ is rational, where $f$ is a polynomial with complex coefficients all of whose roots are rational integers. The author generalizes Pólya's result as follows. Let $\{a_n\}$ be a sequence of algebraic integers and let $f$ be a non-zero polynomial with complex coefficients. Then if $\sum_{n=0}^{\infty} f(n)a_nz^n$ is a rational function, so is $\sum_{n=0}^{\infty} a_nz^n$. For $f$ may be taken to have algebraic integer coefficients and so, by an induction argument, the theorem is a consequence of the result that if $\sum_{n=0}^{\infty}(n-\alpha)a_nz^n$ is a rational function, so is $\sum_{n=0}^{\infty} a_nz^n$, where $\alpha$ is an algebraic number. The proofs of these results depend on the fact that a power series $\sum_{n=0}^{\infty} c_nz^n$, where the $c_n$ are algebraic numbers, is a rational function if and only if there exist distinct non-zero algebraic numbers $\theta_1,\cdots,\theta_m$ and polynomials $\lambda_1,\cdots,\lambda_m$ with algebraic coefficients such that $c_n=\sum_{i=1}^{m}\lambda_i(n)\theta_i^n$, and on the extension theorem for the existence of places. *J. V. Armitage* (Durham)

Referred to in B44-76, Q05-76.

## Q05-54 (32# 1186 )

**Mordell, L. J.**

**Irrational power series. II.**

*Acta Arith.* **11** (1965), 181–188.

**Mordell, L. J.**

**Irrational power series. III.**

*Proc. Amer. Math. Soc.* **16** (1965), 819–821.

Let $\alpha$ be irrational and $\beta$ real; further, let $\phi(y)$ be uniformly bounded for $0\leqq y\leqq 1$. The author considers in both papers the function $f(x)$ defined by $f(x)=\sum_{n=0}^{\infty}\phi(\{\alpha n+\beta\})x^n$, $|x|<1$, where $\{\alpha n+\beta\}$ denotes the fractional part of $\alpha n+\beta$. In the first paper, a meromorphic expansion is sought for $f(x)$. Suppose that $\alpha n+\beta$ is not an integer for any integer $n\geqq 0$. Let $\phi(y)$ be continuous for $0\leqq y\leqq 1$, and let $\phi(y)$, for $0<y<1$, have the Fourier expansion $\phi(y)=\sum_{r=-\infty}^{\infty} a_r\exp(2r\pi iy)$. If $\sum|a_r|$ converges, then it is easily shown that

$$f(x)=\sum_{r=-\infty}^{\infty} a_r\exp(2r\pi i\beta)/(1-x\exp(2r\pi i\alpha)).$$

However, if $\sum a_r$ converges conditionally, then the author points out that one has here a delicate and difficult problem, which is solved in this paper only in a special case. [See also an earlier paper by the author, J. London Math. Soc. **38** (1963), 111–116; MR **26** #4984].

In the second paper reviewed here, the author proves the following theorem: "Let $\phi(x)$ be Riemann integrable in $0\leqq x\leqq 1$, and let $l$ be any integer. Then as $x\to\exp(2l\pi i\alpha)$ along a radius from $x=0$, $f(x)(1-x\exp(-2l\pi i\alpha))\to\exp(-2l\pi i\beta)\int_0^1\phi(t)\exp(2l\pi it)\,dt$. Further, if $\phi(x)$ is continuous for $0\leqq x<1$, except for a finite number of finite discontinuities, then $f(x)$ is a rational function of $x$ if and only if $\phi(y)$ is a finite Fourier series:

$$\phi(y)=\sum_{r=-L}^{L} a_r\exp(2r\pi iy);$$

and then $f(x)=\sum_{r=-L}^{L} a_r\exp(2r\pi i\beta)/(1-x\exp(2r\pi i\alpha))$. If $\phi(x)$ is not a finite Fourier series, then $f(x)$ cannot be continued outside of the circle $|x|=1$."

In both papers the author also considers the extension where $\phi$ is a function of more than one variable; e.g., $\phi(y,z)$, and

$$f(x)=\sum_{n=0}^{\infty}\phi(\{\alpha_1n+\beta_1\},\{\alpha_2n+\beta_2\})x^n,$$

with appropriate conditions for $\phi$, $\alpha_1$, $\alpha_2$, $\beta_1$, $\beta_2$.

In the second paper, the author uses the method first applied by Hecke, some 45 years ago, in his well-known treatment of the series $\sum_{n=1}^{\infty}\{n\alpha\}x^n$. The same method has been employed for a similar purpose, but in a much more general setting, by F. W. Carroll and J. H. B. Kemperman [Duke Math. J. **32** (1965), 65–83; MR **30** #3964].

There are a few misprints in the second paper. *J. Popken* (Amstelveen)

Citations: MR 26# 4984 = Q05-40; MR 30# 3964 = Q05-52.

## Q05-55 (32# 7501 )

**Davenport, H.**

**Note on an irrational power series.**

*Proc. Amer. Math. Soc.* **17** (1966), 1–5.

Mordell investigated several times [e.g., J. London Math. Soc. **38** (1963), 111–116; MR **26** #4984] the series (1) $f(x)=\sum_{n=-\infty}^{\infty} a_ne(n\gamma)/(1-xe(n\alpha))$, where $|x|<1$ and $\alpha$, $\gamma$ are real. As usual, $e(x)$ denotes here $e^{2\pi ix}$. If $\sum|a_n|$ converges, then also (1) converges and has the alternative expression (2) $f(x)=\sum_{\nu=0}^{\infty} g(\nu\alpha+\gamma)x^\nu$, where (3) $g(t)=\sum_{-\infty}^{\infty} a_ne(nt)$. Further, if $\alpha$ is irrational, $k$ a fixed integer and $x=re(k\alpha)$, then it easily follows that (4) $f(x)\sim a_{-k}e(-k\gamma)/(1-r)$ as $r\uparrow 1$. The problem becomes much more complicated if one supposes only relative convergence of $\sum a_n$. Generalising a result of Mordell, the author proves: Suppose that $a_n\to 0$ as $n\to\pm\infty$, and that both series $\sum_{-\infty}^{\infty} a_n$ and $\sum_{-\infty}^{\infty}|a_n-a_{n+1}|$ converge. Suppose, moreover, that the partial sums of (3) are uniformly bounded for all real $t$. Then for any real irrational $\alpha$, the two series for $f(x)$ in (1) and (2) converge and have the same sum, and the asymptotic relation (4) holds.

The convergence of (1) and (2) is shown by means of partial summation. For the proof of (4), rational approximations of $\alpha$ in the form $\alpha=a/q+\theta/q^2$ are introduced.

Also, the proof of a similar theorem for double series is indicated. *J. Popken* (Amstelveen)

Citations: MR 26# 4984 = Q05-40.

Referred to in Q05-62.

## Q05-56 (32# 7715)

**Cantor, David G.**

**Irrational power series.**

*Nederl. Akad. Wetensch. Proc. Ser. A* **68** = *Indag. Math.* **27** (1965), 777–786.

Let $f$ be a non-constant polynomial with complex coefficients and let $(a_n)$ be a sequence of complex numbers. Several authors (for example, M. Newman [Proc. Amer. Math. Soc. **11** (1960), 699–702; MR **22** #9483]; L. J. Mordell [ibid. **12** (1961), 522–526; MR **23** #A3244]; W. Schwarz [Arch. Math. **13** (1962), 228–240; MR **25** #4084]; H. G. Meijer [Nederl. Akad. Wetensch. Proc. Ser. A **66** (1963), 682–690; MR **29** #1184]) have investigated the questions of the continuability or irrationality of the power series $\sum_{n=0}^{\infty} f(a_n)z^n$ in terms of properties of the polynomial $f$ and the sequence $(a_n)$. The present author considers problems of this type for sequences of rational or Gaussian integers which are close to the coefficients of rational functions. He begins by showing that $\sum_{n=0}^{\infty} a_n z^n$ rational implies $\sum_{n=0}^{\infty} f(a_n)z^n$ rational, and then uses this result to prove several theorems, of which the following is a typical example. Let $a_n = p(n)\theta^n + \delta_n$ be a sequence of Gaussian integers, where $p$ is a non-zero polynomial, $|\theta| > 1$, and $\delta_n$ is such that $\sum_{n=0}^{\infty} \delta_n z^n$ has radius of convergence $> |\theta|^{-1}$ and defines a function meromorphic in the unit disc. Then, if $f$ is a polynomial of degree $d \geqq 1$, the function $h(z) = \sum_{n=0}^{\infty} f(a_n)z^n$ is meromorphic in $|z| < |\theta|^{1-d}$. Moreover, if $h(z)$ can be analytically extended across an arc of the circle $|z| = |\theta|^{1-d}$, then both $h(z)$ and $\sum_{n=0}^{\infty} a_n z^n$ are rational functions. *J. V. Armitage* (Durham)

Citations: MR 22# 9483 = Q05-32; MR 23# A3244 = Q05-36; MR 25# 4084 = Q05-37; MR 29# 1184 = Q05-49.

## Q05-57 (32# 7744)

**Balakrishnan, P.**

**A uniqueness theorem for integral functions.**

*J. Indian Math. Soc.* (*N.S.*) **29** (1965), 63–66.

The typical theorem which the author proves in this paper states that an entire function with certain growth properties must vanish identically. The precise statement of the theorem is as follows. Let $f(z)$ be an entire function of order less than or equal to 1, and let

$$(*)\qquad \limsup_{r\to\infty} \frac{\log M(r)}{r \log r} = 0,$$

where $M(r)$ is the maximum modulus of $f(z)$ on $|z| \leqq r$, $\mathrm{Re}(z) \leqq 0$,

$$(**)\qquad \limsup_{x\to\infty} \frac{\log|f(x)|}{x \log x} = -d < 0,$$

and

$$(***)\qquad \limsup_{n\to\infty} \frac{|f(-n)|}{n \log n} = a < 1.$$

Then $f(z)$ vanishes identically.

It is pointed out that a similar result holds when (*) is satisfied for $\mathrm{Re}(z) \geqq 0$ and (**), (***) hold. It is worthwhile to compare the theorem of the author to the uniqueness theorems of Pólya and that of Carlson. Pólya asserted that an entire function of zero exponential type (i.e., $f(z) = O\{\exp(\varepsilon|z|)\}$), bounded at positive and negative integers, reduces to a constant. Carlson proved that if $f(z)$ is regular and of exponential type $k < \pi$ in the right half plane, then $f(z)$ vanishes identically provided it vanishes at positive integers. Observe that (*) holds if the function is of zero type in the left hand plane; (***) holds if $\{f(-n)\}$ is bounded for each positive integer $n$. {There are a few minor misprints in the paper which can easily be corrected.} *Hari Shankar* (Athens, Ohio)

## Q05-58 (33# 257)

**Sato, Daihachiro; Straus, Ernst G.**

**On the rate of growth of Hurwitz functions of a complex or $p$-adic variable.**

*J. Math. Soc. Japan* **17** (1965), 17–29.

A Hurwitz function is a function of one variable $z$ whose derivatives of all orders at $z = 0$ are integral. The authors are interested in establishing a precise dividing line for the growth of a Hurwitz function below which one finds only polynomials.

Let $\varphi(r) = \max_n r^n/\Gamma(n+1)$ $(r \geqq 0)$ and let $\psi(r)$ be any increasing function such that for every $N$, there exists an $r_N$ so that $\psi(r) > r^N$ for all $r > r_N$. Let $f(z)$ be a Hurwitz function and let $M(r) = \max_{|z|=r}|f(z)|$.

With these conventions, two typical results of the paper may be stated as follows. (I) There exists a non-denumerable set of Hurwitz functions satisfying $M(r) < \varphi(r) + \psi(r)$ for all $r \geqq R$, where $R$ is a suitable positive number depending only on $\psi$. (II) If $M(r) < \varphi(r) + r^n$ for some $n$ and all $r > r_0$, then $f(z)$ is a polynomial.

The authors extend their results to two-point Hurwitz functions, the two points being consecutive integers, say 0 and 1. (An entire Hurwitz function at 0 and 1 is an entire function whose derivatives of all orders assume integral values at both 0 and 1.)

The authors generalize their results by considering the $p$-adic behavior of Hurwitz functions. They conclude by posing the following unsolved problem: Does there exist a transcendental entire function which (together with all its derivatives) has algebraic values at every algebraic point and has transcendental values at every transcendental point? *A. Edrei* (Syracuse, N.Y.)

## Q05-59 (34# 1309)

**Uchiyama, Saburô**

**On a theorem of G. Pólya.**

*Proc. Japan Acad.* **41** (1965), 517–520.

The author, generalizing a theorem of G. Pólya [J. Reine Angew. Math. **151** (1920/21), 1–31], proves the following theorem. Let $M$ be a finitely generated submodule of the complex numbers and suppose $a_0, a_1, a_2, \cdots$ is a sequence of elements of $M$. Then, if $\sum_{n=0}^{\infty} n a_n z^n$ is a rational function, so is $\sum_{n=0}^{\infty} a_n z^n$. *D. G. Cantor* (Los Angeles, Calif.)

Referred to in Q05-76.

## Q05-60 (34# 1502)

**Schwarz, Wolfgang**

**Irrationale Potenzreihen. II.**

*Arch. Math.* (*Basel*) **17** (1966), 435–437.

The author uses known results of G. Pólya and H. Petersson to prove a refinement of a theorem of J. Popken [Nederl. Akad. Wetensch. Proc. Ser. A **66** (1963), 691–694; MR **29** #1185]. The result is now as follows. Let $g$ be a polynomial of degree $m$ with coefficients from some algebraic number field of degree $r$ over the rationals, and let $\psi$ be an integer valued arithmetic function. Set $F(Z) = \sum_{n=1}^{\infty} g(\psi(n))Z^{-n}$. Then (a) if $F(Z)$ converges for $|Z| > 1$, then it is either a rational function or cannot be continued past the unit circle; and (b) if $F(Z)$ converges for $|Z| > \rho$ and is single valued and holomorphic in the complement of some compact set $B$ of transfinite diameter $\tau$, then it is either a rational function or else $\tau \geqq \rho^{-(r-1)}$.

{Part I appeared in Arch. Math. **13** (1962), 228–240 [MR **25** #4084].} *Morris Newman* (Washington, D.C.)

Citations: MR 25# 4084 = Q05-37; MR 29# 1185 = Q05-50.

**Q05-61** **(34# 4207)**

**Hilliker, D. L.**

**On analytic functions which have algebraic values at a convergent sequence of points.**

*Trans. Amer. Math. Soc.* **126** (1967), 534–550.

Let $g(z)$ be analytic at $z=0$. The function is said to be algebraic in the arithmetic sense (for short, an $A$-function) if it satisfies an equation $p_0g^m+p_1g^{m-1}+\cdots+p_m=0$, where $p_0\neq 0$, $p_1, \cdots, p_m$ are polynomials with algebraic coefficients. If $\theta$ is an algebraic number, $H(\theta)$ denotes the maximum of the absolute values of the coefficients of the minimum polynomial of $\theta$. Assume, firstly, that the function values $g(1/\nu)$, where $\nu$ runs over all integers $\geqq \nu_0$, are algebraic, say of the degrees $\delta_\nu$, and put $d_\nu = \max_{\nu_0\leqq k\leqq \nu} \delta_k$,

$$y = \limsup_{\nu\to\infty}[\log H(g(1/\nu))]/[\nu \log \nu],$$

$$\eta = \limsup_{\nu\to\infty}[d^3 \log 3H(g(1/\nu))]/[\nu \log \nu].$$

The author proves that if $g(z)$ is an $A$-function, then $d_\nu$ is bounded and $y=0$; conversely, if $d_\nu$ is bounded, say $d_\nu\leqq d$, and if $y<(20d^3+12d^2-13d+2)^{-1}$, then $g(z)$ is an $A$-function. More generally, $g(z)$ is an $A$-function if and only if $\eta=0$.

These results are extended to systems of more than one function analytic at $z=0$. For the work of this paper, compare, in particular, O. Ş. Içen [J. Reine Angew. Math. **198** (1957), 28–55; MR **20** #3849; Rev. Fac. Sci. Univ. Istanbul. Sér. A **21** (1956), 155–187 (1957); MR **20** #3850] and Th. Schneider [Acta Math. **86** (1951), 57–70; MR **13**, 735; Math. Z. **60** (1954), 98–108; MR **15**, 939; *Einführung in die transzendenten Zahlen*, Springer, Berlin, 1957; MR **19**, 252]. *K. Mahler* (Canberra)

Citations: MR 13, 735i = Q05-18; MR 15, 939b = Q05-23; MR 19, 252f = J02-9; MR 20# 3849 = Q05-29; MR 20# 3850 = Q05-30.

Referred to in Q05-74.

**Q05-62** **(34# 4747)**

**Henniger, J.**

**Power series with almost periodic coefficients.**

*Proc. Amer. Math. Soc.* **18** (1967), 53–56.

The author generalizes some results of Mordell and Davenport [see H. Davenport, same Proc. **17** (1966), 1–5; MR **32** #7501] about the representability of (*) $f(x)=\sum_{n=-\infty}^{\infty} a_ne^{in\gamma}(1-xe^{in\alpha})^{-1}$ ($\gamma$ real, $\alpha$ real and $\alpha/2\pi$ irrational, $|x|<1$) as a power series. It is shown that one can obtain the power series expansion of (*) by taking the power series of the summands under milder conditions than previously proved. Further, instead of (*), series of more general form (**) $g(z)=\sum_{n=-\infty}^{\infty} a_n/(1-xe^{i\alpha_n})$ are considered, where $\alpha_1, \alpha_2, \cdots$ denotes a sequence of real numbers.

*P. Szüsz* (Stony Brook, N.Y.)

Citations: MR 32# 7501 = Q05-55.

**Q05-63** **(34# 5760)**

**Mahler, K.**

**On a class of entire functions.**

*Acta Math. Acad. Sci. Hungar.* **18** (1967), 83–96.

Let $E(z)=\sum_{\nu=0}^{n-1}\sum_{\mu=0}^{m_\nu-1} A_{\mu\nu}z^\mu e^{\alpha_\nu z}$ ($A_{\mu\nu}$, $\alpha_\nu$ arbitrary complex numbers, $\alpha_\mu\neq\alpha_\nu$ if $\mu\neq\nu$). These functions were considered by A. O. Gel'fond [*Transcendental and algebraic numbers* (Russian), GITTL, Moscow, 1952; MR **15**, 292; English translation, Dover, New York, 1960; MR **22** #2598], who proved that if all $A_{\mu\nu}\neq 0$ and if the $\alpha_\nu$ satisfy certain conditions, then $\max_{0\leqq s\leqq r_1-1}|E^{(s)}(\beta_\sigma)|>0$, where $\{\beta_\sigma\}$ is an arbitrary finite point set and $r_1$ is a computable constant, depending on the $\alpha_\nu$, $\beta_\sigma$. In the present paper the theorem is strengthened as follows. Let $A=\max_{\mu,\nu}|A_{\mu\nu}|$ and assume that the set $\{\beta_\sigma\}$ $(0\leqq\sigma\leqq s-1)$ consists of $s$ points, with $s$ not too small and with an integer $r_\sigma$ attached to each point $\beta_\sigma$; let also $r=\sum_{\sigma=0}^{s-1} r_\sigma$. Then an explicit formula is obtained for a constant $c$ (depending on the $\alpha_\nu$, $m_\nu$, $\beta_\sigma$, $r_\sigma$ and $s$) such that

$$\max\{|E^{(\rho)}(\beta_\sigma)| : 0 \leqq \rho \leqq r_\sigma-1,\ 0\leqq\sigma\leqq s-1\} \geqq cA.$$

In particular, if the $r$ values $E^{(\rho)}(\beta_\sigma)$ vanish, then $A=0$ and $E(z)$ vanishes identically. The proof is too long (over 12 pages) even to be sketched in full, but its main tool (somewhat like in Gel'fond's proof) is the following sequence of steps. A function $f(z)$ is represented by a Cauchy integral around a simple closed curve; this contour is replaced by a finite number of circles, and the corresponding integrals are evaluated using residues. Next, having obtained bounds on $|f(z)|$, these are used to evaluate $f^{(k)}(z)=(k!/2\pi i)\int[f(\zeta)/(\zeta-z)^{k+1}]\,d\zeta$.

*E. Grosswald* (Philadelphia, Pa.)

Citations: MR 15, 292e = J02-6; MR 22# 2598 = J02-7.

**Q05-64** **(35# 4168)**

**Baker, A. [Baker, Alan]**

**A note on integral integer-valued functions of several variables.**

*Proc. Cambridge Philos. Soc.* **63** (1967), 715–720.

The type of problem considered in this note was first proposed by E. G. Straus [Ann. of Math. (2) **52** (1950), 188–198; MR **12**, 15] and considered independently by T. Schneider [Math. Ann. **121** (1949), 131–140; MR **11**, 160], and an extension of such results was given by S. Lang [Topology **3** (1965), 183–191; MR **32** #7506].

The results of the author are as follows. (i) If $h$ denotes a positive integer for which all the partial derivatives

$$f_{m_1,\cdots,m_n}(z_1,\cdots,z_n) = \partial^{m_1+\cdots+m_n}f(z_1,\cdots,z_n)/\partial z_1^{m_1}\cdots\partial z_n^{m_n}$$

with $0\leqq m_k<h$ $(1\leqq k\leqq n)$ assume integer values for all nonnegative integers $z_1,\cdots,z_n$ and if further

$$\limsup_{\|r\|\to\infty}\|r\|^{-1}\log M(r) < h\log(1+e^{-(h-1)/h}),$$

where $\|r\|=r_1+\cdots+r_n$ and $M(r)=\max_{|z_t|\leqq r_t}|f(z_1,\cdots,z_n)|$, $t=1, 2, \cdots, n$, then $f(z_1,\cdots,z_n)$ is a polynomial. (ii) If $h$ denotes a positive integer for which all the partial derivatives $f_{m_1,\cdots,m_n}(z_1,\cdots,z_n)$ assume integer values for all integers $z_1,\cdots,z_n$ with $0\leqq z_k<h$ $(1\leqq k\leqq n)$ and if further $\lim_{\|r^{h'}\|\to\infty}\|r^{h'}\|^{-1}\log M(r)<\infty$ for some positive $h'<h$, where $\|r^{h'}\|=r_1^{h'}+\cdots+r_n^{h'}$, then $f(z_1,\cdots,z_n)$ is a polynomial. *S. K. Bose* (Calcutta)

Citations: MR 11, 160a = J76-17; MR 12, 15k = Q05-12; MR 32# 7506 = J76-51.

**Q05-65** **(35# 6630)**

**Gel'fond, A. O.**

**On functions assuming integral values.** **(Russian)**

*Mat. Zametki* **1** (1967), 509–513.

The author proves that, if an entire function $f$ and its first $s-1$ derivatives take integral values at the points $\beta^k$ $(k=0, 1, 2, \cdots)$, for some fixed integer $\beta\geqq 1$, and if $|f(z)|<\exp\{\gamma\log^2 z/\log\beta\}$, where $\gamma<\frac{1}{4}s\{1+3(s-1)/s\pi^2\}^{-1}$, then $f$ is a polynomial. This is a generalization of an earlier theorem of the author obtained for the case $s=1$ [Mat. Sb. **40** (1933), 42–47]. *R. A. Rankin* (Glasgow)

**Q05-66** **(36# 2582)**

**Gerig, Stephen**

**Sequences of integers satisfying congruence relations and Pisot-Vijayaraghavan numbers.**

*J. Austral. Math. Soc.* **7** (1967), 508–512.

Let $\{f_n\}_1^\infty$ be an infinite sequence of positive integers and

$M$ a finite set of pairwise relatively prime positive integers. Then if (i) $f_{n+1}/f_n \to a > 1$, (ii) the sequence becomes ultimately periodic modulo $m^k$ for each $m \in M$ and each positive integer $k$, and (iii) the growth and periodicities of the sequence satisfy certain stated conditions; the author proves that $\sum_1^\infty f_n z^n = P(z)/Q(z)$, where $P$, $Q$ are polynomials over the rational integers, $P/Q$ is irreducible, $Q(0)=1$ and $Q(a^{-1})=0$. *H. Gupta* (Allahabad)

## Q05-67 (36# 2785)

**Robinson, Raphael M.**

**An extension of Pólya's theorem on power series with integer coefficients.**

*Trans. Amer. Math. Soc.* **130** (1968), 532–543.

Let $E$ be a bounded closed set symmetric in the real axis. $G$, the complement of $E$, is a region. Denote by $p_1, p_2, \cdots, p_l, q_1, q_2, \cdots, q_l$ integers such that $q_k \neq 0$, $(p_j - p_k) | q_k$, $j \neq k$, $p_k \notin E$ $(k=1, 2, \cdots, l)$. Suppose that $f(z)$ is regular in $G$ and has expansions near $\infty$, respectively, near $p_k$, $f(z) = \sum_{v=0}^\infty a_v z^{-v}$, $f(z) = \sum_{v=0}^\infty b_{kv}((z-p_k)/q_k)^v$ with integral $a_v$ and $b_{kv}$. If there is a function (*) $h(z) = \sum_{v=0}^r A_v z^v + \sum_{k=1}^l \sum_{v=1}^{s_k} B_{kv}(q_k/(z-p_k))^v$, where $r>0$, $|A_r| \geqq 1$, $s_k > 0$, $|B_{ks_k}| \geqq 1$ $(k=1, 2, \cdots, l)$ such that $|h(z)| < 1$ on $E$, then $f(z)$ is rational. If such an $h(z)$ exists, then there is one with integer coefficients too and in this latter case the poles of $f(z)$ are the zeros of $h(z)$. If there is no $h(z)$ of the form (*) with $|h(z)| < 1$ on $E$, then there exist nondenumerably many nonrational functions $f(z)$ regular in $G$ with expansion of the required sort. For $l=0$, that is, if $f(z)$ has only a single pole at infinity, the result reduces to Pólya's original theorem, however, with a new proof. In Pólya's theorem the function $h(z)$ does not occur, but as corresponding condition it is required that $d$, the transfinite diameter of $E$, should be less than 1. On the other hand M. Fekete proved [Math. Z. **17** (1923), 228–249] that $d<1$ if and only if there exists a polynomial $h_0(z) = z^r + A_{r-1}z^{r-1} + \cdots + A_0$ such that $|h_0(z)| < 1$ on $E$. The basic ideas of the present paper are to point out in Pólya's theorem the equivalence of the conditions "$d<1$ and $h_0(z)$ exists" and to replace, as an extension of this theorem, the polynomial $h_0(z)$ by the rational function $h(z)$ which has no pole in $E$ and satisfies the inequality $|h(z)| < 1$ on $E$. Thus $\infty$ as a pole of $h(z)$ plays the same role as $p_1, \cdots, p_l$. It can be omitted by dropping the polynomial part of $h(z)$ and the condition of boundedness of $E$ as well as the assumption concerning the form of $f(z)$ near $\infty$. In addition, it is established that if $G$ is a union of disjoint regions and $E$ separates any of the points $p_k$ from $\infty$, then there is no function $h(z)$ of the form (*) with $|h(z)| < 1$ on $E$. *L. Alpár* (Budapest)

## Q05-68 (36# 5104)

**Rauzy, Gérard**

**Ensembles arithmétiquement denses.**

*C. R. Acad. Sci. Paris Sér. A-B* **265** (1967), A37–A38.

Nous dirons qu'un ensemble $J \subset N$ est arithmétiquement dense s'il contient au moins un élément de toute progression arithmétique. On a alors le théorème suivant, généralisation d'un théorème de Fatou: Soient $A$ en $B$ deux polynômes non nuls de $Q[X]$ premiers entre eux, $B$ étant à coefficients entiers primitifs et tel que $B(0) \neq 0$. Posons $A(x)/B(X) = \sum_{n=0}^\infty u(n)X^n$. Si $u(n)$ est entier pour $n \in J$, où $J$ est un ensemble arithmétiquement dense, alors $|B(0)| = 1$. *J. E. Cigler* (Groningen)

## Q05-69 (36# 5346)

**Osgood, Charles F.**

**Theorems about the derivatives of certain entire functions at algebraic points. I, II.**

*Nederl. Akad. Wetensch. Proc. Ser. A* **70** = *Indag. Math.* **29** (1967), 431–443; 547–555.

This paper generalizes results of E. G. Straus [Ann. of Math. (2) **52** (1950), 188–198; MR **12**, 15]. Let $Q$ denote the rationals, $K$ be a finite extension of $Q$, and let $l = [K(i):Q(i)]$. Let $f(z)$ be a transcendental entire function of order no greater than $0 \leqq \rho < \infty$, satisfying the differential equation $g(z)f^{(n)}(z) = P(z, f(z), \cdots, f^{(n-1)}(z))$, where $g(z) \not\equiv 0$ belongs to $K[z]$ and $P$ belongs to $K[z, f(z), \cdots, f^{(n-1)}(z)]$. A point $z$ for which $g(z) \neq 0$ is called a regular point. Let $\beta_i \in K$ $(i=1, 2, \cdots, m)$ be linearly independent over $Q$, set $\Delta_j f(z) = f(z+\beta_j) - f(z)$, $\Delta f(z) = f(z+1) - f(z)$ and $Df(z) = f^{(1)}(z)$. The maximum of the absolute value of the conjugates, over $Q$, of any algebraic number $\beta$ is denoted by $\overline{|\beta|}$. This paper consists of the following three theorems, a corollary and their proofs, which are divided into several lemmas. (1) There are at most $l\rho$ regular points of the differential equation in $K$ at which $f(z)$ and all of its derivatives take values in $K$. (2) If the differential equation is linear homogeneous, then (a) for each $\varepsilon > 0$ there exists $c(\varepsilon) > 0$ such that

$$\max_{i,j}\{|f^{(i)}(w_j) - \alpha_{i,j}/\alpha|\} \geqq$$

$$c(\varepsilon) \min_{i,j}\{((1+\overline{|\alpha|})(1+\overline{|\alpha_{i,j}|})^{l-1})^{-\theta}\},$$

where $\theta = 1 + (1+\varepsilon) \times (t/l\rho - 1)^{-1}$, for all $(\alpha, \alpha_{0,1}, \cdots, \alpha_{n-1,t})$, and (b) the $f^{(i)}(w_j)$ $(0 \leqq i \leqq n-1$ and $1 \leqq j \leqq t)$ and 1 span a vector space over $K$ of dimension at least $t/l\rho$. (3) If the differential equation is linear, then $f(z)$ cannot satisfy a generalized linear difference equation of the form $\Delta_m{}^p f(z) = \gamma(z) + \sum \gamma_{i_1,\cdots,i_m}(z)\Delta_1{}^{i_1} \cdots \Delta_m{}^{i_m} f(z)$, $0 \leqq i_m < p$, with $p \geqq 1$, where $\gamma(z)$ and each of the $\gamma_{i_1,\cdots,i_m}(z)$ belongs to $K(z)$. (4) A transcendental entire function $f(z)$ of finite order cannot satisfy simultaneously a pair of linear difference-differential equations with coefficients $\delta_{i,j}(z)$ in $K(z)$ of the form $D^r f(z) = \sum_{0 \leqq i+j < r} \delta_{i,j}(z)\Delta^j D^i f(z)$ and $\Delta^p f(z) = \sum_{0 \leqq i+j < p} \gamma_{i,j}(z)\Delta^j D^i f(z)$ with $r \geqq 1$ and $p > 1$. *D. Sato* (Regina, Sask.)

Citations: MR 12, 15k = Q05-12.

## Q05-70 (36# 6619)

**Fridman, G. A.**

**Entire integer-valued functions.** (Russian)

*Mat. Sb.* (*N.S.*) **75** (**117**) (1968), 417–431.

Let $f(z)$ be an entire function such that $f^{(\nu)}(k)$, $\nu = 0, 1, \cdots, s-1$ $(\leqq \infty)$, $k = 0, 1, \cdots, m-1$ $(\leqq \infty)$ are all integers. Further, let

$$M(r, f) = \max_{|z|=r} |f(z)|,$$

$$\sigma(\rho, f) = \limsup_{r\to\infty} [\log M(r)]/r^\rho.$$

Gel'fond's generalization of Pólya's theorem states that for $s$ finite, $m$ infinite $\sigma(1, f) \geqq s \log\{1 + \exp[(1-s)/s]\}$. Conversely, if $s$ is infinite and $m$ is finite, then L. Bieberbach* [*Theorie der geometrischen Konstruktionen*, Birkhäuser, Basel, 1952; MR **14**, 677; *Analytische Fortsetzung*, Ergeb. Math. Grenzgeb. (N.F.), Heft 3, Springer, Berlin, 1955; MR **16**, 913; Russian translation, Izdat. "Nauka", Moscow, 1967; MR **35** #5585] stated without proof that $\sigma(m, f) \geqq 1$. The author disproves this by a counterexample and remarks that Bieberbach's estimations give

only $\sigma(m,f) \geqq [(m-1)!]^{-2}$. By more careful estimations, the author replaces this constant by a larger constant $\gamma_m$. He then investigates the case when both $s$ and $m$ are infinite and finds that $A(f) = \lim \sup_{r\to\infty}[\log\log M(r)]/r \geqq \log(1+1/e)$, while $A(f) \leqq \pi$ is possible. He also reproduces the proof of Gel'fond's theorem mentioned above.
*G. Halász* (Budapest)

Citations: MR 14, 1074d = Q05-22.

## Q05-71 (37# 414)

**Gelfond, Alexandre**

**Sur quelques questions concernant les fonctions entières à valeurs entières.**

*C. R. Acad. Sci. Paris Sér. A-B* **264** (1967), A932–A934.

The author constructs a function as a uniformly convergent series of polynomials in order to prove that a necessary and sufficient condition for there to exist an entire function, not a polynomial, which together with all its derivatives assumes integral values at the distinct points $z_k$ ($k \geqq 1$), is that $z_k \to \infty$ as $k \to \infty$. In the case when $z_k = k$, a similar theorem, due to E. Lindelöf, has been stated by D. Sato [Bull. Amer. Math. Soc. **69** (1963), 411–414; MR **26** #3903; errata, MR **28**, p. 1246]. The author also states a number of other theorems of a similar type.
*R. A. Rankin* (Glasgow)

Citations: MR 26# 3903 = Q05-39.

## Q05-72 (37# 2699)

**Van der Poorten, A. J.**

**Transcendental entire functions mapping every algebraic number field into itself.**

*J. Austral. Math. Soc.* **8** (1968), 192–193.

The author constructs a transcendental entire function which maps every algebraic number field into itself. Further, the example has the property that all its derivatives also assume algebraic values at every point in every algebraic number field.
*N. Toda* (Sendai)

## Q05-73 (37# 6263)

**Berstel, Jean**

**Une application d'un théorème de Mahler aux propriétés arithmétiques des coefficients des séries rationnelles.**

*C. R. Acad. Sci. Paris Sér. A-B* **266** (1968), A693–A695.

The purpose of the present paper is to characterize those power series $f(x) = \sum_{n=0}^{\infty} a_n z^n$, with $a_n \in \mathbf{Z}$ and $\sup_n \tau(a_n) < \infty$, that represent rational functions. Here $\tau(a_n)$ stands for the number of positive divisors of the integer $a_n$ ($\tau(0) = 0$). Denoting that class of power series by $\mathscr{F}$, the main result is the theorem that $f \in \mathscr{F}$ if and only if $\sup_n |a_n| < \infty$. This shows that $\mathscr{F}$ is a subclass of the power series of rational functions studied by G. Pólya [J. Reine Angew. Math. **151** (1920/21), 1–31] and characterized by the fact that there exists a finite set of prime numbers, say $\mathbf{P}$, such that every coefficient $a_n$ of $f(x)$ is divisible only by primes of $\mathbf{P}$. The proof of the theorem is based on: (1) the remark that if $\sup|a_n| < \infty$ and $f(x)$ is not a polynomial, then all the poles of $f(x)$ are simple and are roots of unity; (2) the lemma (of some independent interest) that if $f(x)$ is rational, but not a polynomial and $\sup_n \tau(a_n) < \infty$, then there exist infinitely many $n_j$ such that $0 \neq a_{n_1} = a_{n_2} = \cdots$; (3) Mahler's theorem of the title [K. Mahler, Nederl. Akad. Wetensch. Proc. Ser. A **38** (1935), 50–60].
*E. Grosswald* (Philadelphia, Pa.)

Referred to in B44-76.

## Q05-74 (38# 135)

**Hilliker, D. L.**

**Algebraically dependent functions of a complex and $p$-adic variable.**

*Proc. Amer. Math. Soc.* **19** (1968), 1052–1056.

Let $K$ be a subfield of the complexes $C$ such that $K$ contains a field $Q_p$ isomorphic to the field of $p$-adic numbers, and let $|\ |_p$ denote a rank 1 valuation of $K$ which extends the $p$-adic valuation of $Q_p$. Assume that $f_1, \cdots, f_m \in K[[Z]]$, the ring of formal power series in one indeterminate $Z$, have positive radius of convergence in the usual complex sense and also with respect to the valuation $|\ |_p$. The author then outlines how most of the results of his previous paper [Trans. Amer. Math. Soc. **126** (1967), 534–550; MR **34** #4207], which gives conditions for $f_1, \cdots, f_m$ to be algebraically dependent over $C$, can be carried over to this setting.
*J. Ohm* (Baton Rouge, La.)

Citations: MR 34# 4207 = Q05-61.

## Q05-75 (38# 2113)

**Carlitz, Leonard**

**A note on products of sequences.** (Italian summary)

*Boll. Un. Mat. Ital.* (4) **1** (1968), 362–365.

The reviewer [Amer. Math. Monthly **74** (1967), 813–816; MR **36** #2612] showed that the sequences of complex numbers that satisfy linear, homogeneous difference equations with constant coefficients form a ring under term-by-term addition and multiplication of sequences. Showing that term-by-term multiplication is a closed operation in this set of sequences is equivalent to proving the following: If $a_0 + a_1 z + \cdots$ and $b_0 + b_1 z + \cdots$ represent rational functions of $z$, then $a_0 b_0 + a_1 b_1 z + \cdots$ also represents a rational function of $z$. Actually, this result is implied by results proved in R. Vaidyanathaswamy's classic paper [Trans. Amer. Math. Soc. **33** (1931), 579–662]. In the paper under review, the author proves this theorem by observing that $a_0 + a_1 z + \cdots$ represents a rational function of $z$ if and only if there exist polynomials $p_1(n), \cdots, p_k(n)$ and constants $c_1, \cdots, c_k$ such that $a_n = p_1(n)c_1^n + \cdots + p_k(n)c_k^n$.

Suppose $f(z)$ and $g(z)$ are functions analytic in a neighborhood of $z=0$, and let $f(z) = f_0 + f_1 z + \cdots$, $g(z) = g_0 + g_1 z + \cdots$ denote the series representations of $f(z)$ and $g(z)$ at $z=0$; now define $(f * g)(z) = f_0 g_0 + f_1 g_1 z + \cdots$, and note that $(f * g)(z)$ represents a function analytic at $z=0$. The author observes that there exist algebraic functions $f$ and $g$ such that $f * g$ is not algebraic; the same thing is true if we replace "algebraic" with "elementary" in this statement. If $f$ is algebraic and $g$ is rational, then $f * g$ is algebraic. If $a_0 + a_1 z + \cdots$ represents a rational function, then there exist polynomials $p_1(z), \cdots, p_k(z)$ and constants $c_1, \cdots, c_k$ such that $(a_0/0!) + (a_1/1!)z + \cdots = p_1(z)e^{c_1 z} + \cdots + p_k(z)e^{c_k z}$; thus, if $f$ and $g$ have this form, then so does $f * g$.
*D. A. Klarner* (Eindhoven)

Citations: MR 36# 2612 = B44-50.

## Q05-76 (39# 422)

**Cantor, David G.**

**On arithmetic properties of the Taylor series of rational functions.**

*Canad. J. Math.* **21** (1969), 378–382.

G. Pólya has shown that if $b_n$ is a sequence of algebraic integers and $\sum_{n=0}^{\infty} n b_n z^n$ is a rational function, then so is $\sum_{n=0}^{\infty} b_n z^n$ [J. Reine Angew. Math. **151** (1921), 1–31]. This result was generalized by S. Uchiyama, who showed that the assumption that the $b_n$ are algebraic integers can be replaced by the assumption that the $b_n$ lie in a finitely generated submodule of the complex numbers [Proc. Japan Acad. **41** (1965), 517–520; MR **34** #1309]. Pólya's result was also generalized in another direction by the present author; he showed that if $p(x)$ is a non-zero polynomial with complex coefficients and if $b_n$ is a sequence of algebraic integers such that $\sum_{n=0}^{\infty} p(n) b_n z^n$ is a rational function, then so is $\sum_{n=0}^{\infty} b_n z^n$ [Pacific J. Math. **15** (1965), 55–58; MR **31** #1245]. In the present paper there is given a theorem which combines all of these results. Let $R$ be the integral closure of a finitely generated subring of the field of the complex numbers. Suppose that $b_n$ is a sequence of elements of $R$ and that $p(x)$ is a non-zero polynomial with complex coefficients. It is proved that if $\sum_{n=0}^{\infty} p(n)b_n z^n$ is a rational function, then so is $\sum_{n=0}^{\infty} b_n z^n$.

*E. Inaba* (Tokyo)

Citations: MR 31# 1245 = Q05-53; MR 34# 1309 = Q05-59.

## Q05-77 (39# 2722)

**Rauzy, Gérard**

**Algébricité des fonctions méromorphes prenant certaines valeurs algébriques.**

*Bull. Soc. Math. France* **96** (1968), 197–208.

The author discusses the problem of finding sets of algebraic numbers $S$ such that a function $f$ meromorphic at $\infty$, having the property that $f(n) \in S$ for large enough integers $n$, is an algebraic function, even a member of some preassigned set of algebraic functions. He remarks that this is the converse of the result whereby algebraic functions take on algebraic numbers at large enough integer values of the argument.

To be more precise, one starts with a commutative ring $A$ together with an absolute value $|\ |$, and one assumes that the pair $(A, |\ |)$ satisfies the following three conditions: (1) $(\forall \alpha \in A)(\alpha \neq 0 \Rightarrow |\alpha| \geqq 1)$; (2) $|\ |$ is not the trivial absolute value; (3) $A$ satisfies Fatou's lemma: If the formal series $\sum_{n=0}^{\infty} u_n X^n \in A[[X]]$ is the Taylor series of the rational function $P(X)/Q(X)$ (where $P, Q \in K_0[X]$, $K_0$ is the fraction field of $A$, and $(P, Q) = 1$), then $(1/Q(0))Q(X) \in A[X]$. The author remarks that conditions (1), (2), (3) show that the ring $A$ has a unity; hence, is an integral domain, has infinitely many elements, has elements of arbitrarily large value, is integrally closed, and even is a U.F.D. He then introduces the sets $S(A, |\ |, \gamma)$ for a given real number $\gamma > 0$. To do this, let $K$ be the completion of $K_0$, let $\hat{K}$ be the algebraic closure of $K$. Then $S(A, |\ |, \gamma)$ is the set of all $\xi \in K$ such that (a) $\xi$ is integral over $A$, (b) $|\xi| > 1$, and (c) every conjugate of $\xi$ over $K_0$ in $\hat{K}$ (not $\xi$ itself) has absolute value in $\hat{K}$ less than or equal to $|\xi|^{-\gamma}$. If one sets $S(A, |\ |)$ equal to $\bigcup_\gamma S(A, |\ |, \gamma)$ one obtains a generalization of the P.-V. numbers (which is the case: $A = \mathbf{Z}$, $|\ |$ = ordinary absolute value). The author shows, à la Pisot, that $\xi \in S(A, |\ |, \gamma)$ if and only if $(\exists c > 0)(\forall n \in \mathbf{N})(\inf\{|\xi^n - \alpha| \mid \alpha \in A\} < c|\xi|^{-n\gamma})$. He shows, moreover, that the sets $S(A, |\ |, \gamma)$ are discrete in their natural topology.

Now let $K'$ be the field $K((X^{-1}))$ of formal Laurent series ("bounded above") with the usual exponential valuation at $\infty$. Let $|f|_\infty$ be $2^{-\nu(f)}$, where $\nu$ is this valuation. Given $A$, we look at the subring $A'$ of $K'$ formed from those elements $\eta$ of $K[X]$ such that $(\forall \alpha \in A)(\eta(\alpha) \in A)$. The author proves that if $A$ satisfies conditions (1), (2), (3) for the absolute value $|\ |$, then $A'$ satisfies these conditions for the absolute value $|\ |_\infty$. He may thus manufacture the set $S(A', |\ |_\infty, \gamma)$, and this is the preassigned set of algebraic functions mentioned in the first paragraph.

A function $f \in K'$ is said to be meromorphic at $\infty$ if $\rho(f) = \lim \sup |u_n|^{1/n} < \infty$. If $R > \rho(f)$, then for all $z \in D(R; K) = \{z \in K : |z| > R\}$, the series $\sum_n u_n z^n = f(z)$ converges absolutely in $K$. The author can now prove his main theorem: If $\gamma$ is irrational then $f \in S(A', |\ |_\infty, \gamma)$ if and only if $f$ is meromorphic at $\infty$, non-constant, and for $\alpha \in A$ sufficiently large, $f(\alpha) \in S(A, |\ |, \gamma)$.

*S. S. Shatz* (Philadelphia, Pa.)

## Q05-78 (39# 5508)

**Pathiaux, Geneviève**

**Algèbre de Hadamard de fractions rationnelles.**

*C. R. Acad. Sci. Paris Sér. A-B* **267** (1968), A977–A979.

The following theorem is proved: Let $A(z) = \sum_{n=0}^{\infty} a_n z^n$ and $B(z) = \sum_{n=0}^{\infty} b_n z^n$ be rational functions whose coefficients are in one and the same algebraic number field; if the number of poles of $B(z)$ is $\leqq 2$ and if $c_n = a_n/b_n$ are algebraic integers, then $c(z) = \sum_{n=0}^{\infty} c_n z^n$ is a rational fraction.

*T. Kubota* (Nagoya)

Referred to in B44-76.

## Q05-79 (39# 5800)

**Cayford, Afton H.**

**A class of integer valued entire functions.**

*Trans. Amer. Math. Soc.* **141** (1969), 415–432.

Let $Q$ be the Gaussian integers $\{m + ni\}$ and let $A$ be an arbitrary finite set in the plane. The object of this paper is to determine bounds on the minimal growth of entire functions $f$ in the class $\mathscr{F}_A$ characterized by the property that $f^{(n)}(z) \in Q$ for all $z \in A$ and all $n = 0, 1, 2, \cdots$. Note that $\mathscr{F}_A$ is a ring closed under differentiation. When $A$ is a single point, an easy argument [G. Pólya, Tôhoku Math. J. **19** (1921), 65–68] shows that if $f \in \mathscr{F}_A$ and is not a polynomial, then $f$ must be at least of order 1, type 1. With $A = \{0, 1, 2, \cdots, s-1\}$, results of E. G. Straus [Ann. of Math. (2) **52** (1950), 188–198; MR **12**, 15] give the lower bounds order $\rho = s$, type $\tau = \{(s-1)!\}^{-2}$. This paper is directed to the conjecture that the bound $\rho = s$ holds and is best possible for every set $A$ with $s$ points. (It is asserted in a footnote that this conjecture has now been verified.) The main results in the present paper are as follows. Theorem 1: There are at most a countable number of functions in $\mathscr{F}_A$ with order $\rho < s$, and noncountably many of any assigned order $\rho \geqq s$. Theorem 2: If $f_1, \cdots, f_N$ are functions in $\mathscr{F}_A$ each with order less than $s - (s-1)\{s/(s+N)\}^{1/2}$, then the $f_i$ must satisfy a differential identity of the form $\sum_{i=0}^{N} \sum_{j=0}^{M} C_{ij} b_i^{(j)} = 0$, where the $C_{ij}$ are in $Q$. Theorem 3: If $f_1, \cdots, f_N$ are in $\mathscr{F}_A$ and have order less than $s(1 - 1/N)$, then the $f_i$ are algebraically dependent over $Q$. In special cases, one may hope to characterize members of $\mathscr{F}_A$ explicitly as in other studies of integral-valued entire functions [e.g., the reviewer, Duke Math. J. **15** (1948), 879–891; MR **10**, 693]. For example, the author obtains the following result. If $A = \{0, \alpha\}$ and if $\mathscr{F}_A$ contains functions of order less than $2 - (1/3)\sqrt{6}$, then either $\alpha$ is rational and $f$ a polynomial, or $\alpha = \log(n/m)$ and $f$ has the form $ae^z + be^{-z}$, or $f$ has the form $a\cosh(uz) + bu\sinh(uz)$, where $u^2$ is square free and $\alpha$ is such that $\cosh(\alpha u)$ is rational.

*R. C. Buck* (Madison, Wis.)

Citations: MR 10, 693c = Q05-9; MR 12, 15k = Q05-12.

## Q05-80 (41# 1690)

**Benzaghou, Benali**

**Sur le quotient de Hadamard de deux fractions rationnelles.**

*Séminaire Delange-Pisot-Poitou:* 1968/69, *Théorie des Nombres, Fasc.* 1, *Exp.* 1, 14 *pp. Secrétariat mathématique, Paris,* 1969.

Let $(c_n)$ be a sequence of elements in an algebraic number field $k$. A prime ideal $P$ of the ring of integers of $k$ is called a prime divisor of $(c_n)$ if there is a non-zero $c_n$ in the sequence, having a non-zero $p$-adic valuation. If $(c_n)$ has a finite number of prime divisors it is called a Pólya sequence. $\mathscr{R}(K)$ denotes the algebra of formal power series $\sum_{n=0}^{\infty} a_n x^n$ representing rational fractions, with coefficients in a field $K$ of characteristic 0 (the product in $\mathscr{R}(K)$ is the Hadamard product). The set $\mathscr{P}(K)$ of Pólya functions is defined by $\mathscr{P}(K) = \{\sum_{n=0} a_n X^n \in \mathscr{R}(K) | \text{there exists } m \geqq 1, \alpha_0, \alpha_1, \cdots, \alpha_m \in K \text{ such that } \alpha_{\mu+rm} = a_\mu \alpha_\mu{}^r \text{ for every } \mu = 0, 1, \cdots, m-1 \text{ and for every } r\}$.

$\mathscr{P}(k)$ is the group of units in the ring $\mathscr{R}(K)$. The main result of the paper is the following theorem: If $\sum_{n=0}^{\infty} a_n X^n \in \mathscr{R}(K)$, $\sum_{n=0}^{\infty} b_n X^n \in \mathscr{R}(K)$ with $a_n = b_n c_n$ (in case $b_n = 0$, assume $a_n = 0$ and $c_n = 1$), and if $(c_n)$ is a Pólya sequence of rationals, then $\sum_{n=0}^{\infty} c_n X^n$ is a Pólya function in $\mathscr{R}(Q)$. The proof of this theorem (in case $K = Q$) is by induction on the number of prime divisors of the sequence $(c_n)$, and uses the fact that for every non-archimedean valuation $v$ of an algebraic number field $k$ (and, in particular, $Q$), one can extract from every sequence $(a_n)$ such that $\sum_{n=0}^{\infty} a_n X^n \in k(X)$ a subsequence $(a_{\mu+rm})$ with the property that $r \to v(a_{\mu+rm})$ is affine for $r \geqq r_0$.

As an application (among others) the author proves that for $\sum a_n X^n$, $\sum b_n X^n \in \mathscr{R}(Q)$, $a_n, b_n, c_n \in Z$, $a_n = b_n c_n$, then $(c_n)$ is a Pólya sequence if $(c_n)$ and $(b_n)$ have a finite number of common prime divisors and if the number of positive divisors of the $c_n$'s is bounded.

*G. J. Lallement* (University Park, Pa.)

## Q05-81 (41# 3404)

**Bundschuh, Peter**

**Ein Satz über ganze Funktionen und Irrationalitätsaussagen.**

*Invent. Math.* **9** (1969/70), 175–184.

There are various ways to insure that a number be irrational. For example, as is found in A. O. Gel'fond's works [Rec. Math. Moscov **40** (1933), 42–47], an entire transcendental function which takes rational values at all powers of a natural number bigger than one cannot increase very slowly. In the present work, an analogous theorem with its various corollaries is proved for an entire transcendental function whose coefficients lie in an imaginary quadratic field.

*T. Kubota* (College Park, Md.)

## Q05-82 (41# 3799)

**Gross, Fred**

**Entire functions of several variables with algebraic derivatives at certain algebraic points.**

*Pacific J. Math.* **31** (1969), 693–701.

The author generalizes earlier theorems on entire functions with integral values at integral points to the case of several variables. Theorem 2: Let $f(z, w)$ be entire and all the values $\partial^{n+m} f(z, w)/\partial z^n \partial w^m$, $(z, w) = (a_i, b_j)$, be integers, where the $a_i$'s and $b_j$'s are $k$ and $l$ distinct integers, respectively. If $f(z, w)$ is of order less than $(k, l)$ or of type less than $(|V(a_i)^{-2}|, |V(b_j)^{-2}|)$, then $f(z, w)$ is a polynomial. Suitable definitions of order and type are given. $V(a_i)$ and $V(b_j)$ are the Vandermonde determinants. In other results integers are replaced by algebraic integers under additional hypotheses on the magnitude of the algebraic conjugates.

*G. Halász* (Budapest)

## Q05-83 (41# 5616)

**Rauch, Harry E.**

**Theta constants on a Riemann surface with many automorphisms.**

*Symposia Mathematica, Vol. III (INDAM, Rome, 1968/69), pp.* 305–323. *Academic Press, London,* 1970.

From the author's introduction and summary: "The purpose of this paper is to treat some examples which have led me to formulate the following conjecture: On a compact Riemann surface with many automorphisms the ratios of the theta constants to any nonvanishing one of them are algebraic numbers, which arise from the theta transformation formula and the theta identities.

"The examples to be described indicate that, in general, to obtain a number field in which the ratios of the conjecture lie, it will be necessary first to adjoin to the rationals the eighth roots of unity and certain other roots of unity determined by the orders of the generators of the automorphism group of the surface. To this field one will then have to adjoin certain roots of certain quartic equations with coefficients in the field. In the examples, in fact, one simply adjoins fourth roots."

*H. H. Martens* (Trondheim)

## Q05-84 (41# 8378)

**Gerig, Stephen**

**Analytic continuation of power series whose coefficients belong to an algebraic number field.**

*Mathematika* **16** (1969), 167–169.

The author proves the following theorem which is an extension of a result of Pólya and Carlson [see F. Carlson, Math. Z. **9** (1921), 1–13]: Let $a$ be a non-zero algebraic number. Let $P_n(x)$ be a polynomial over the integers for each $n = 0, 1, \cdots$. (i) Let $B > 0$, $0 < \delta < 1$ be such that $h(P_n) \leqq \exp(n^{1-\delta} B)$ for each $n = 0, 1, \cdots$, where $h(P_n)$ is the sum of the absolute values of the coefficients of $P_n$. (ii) Suppose the degree $P_n = o(n)$. Then $\sum_{n=0}^{\infty} P_n(a) z^n$ converges for $|z| < 1$ and, if it can be continued analytically across the unit circle, then $\sum_{n=0}^{\infty} P_n(a) z^n = S(a, z)$, where $S$ is a rational function in two variables over the integers.

The author shows that hypothesis (ii) is the best possible and he discusses a modification of hypothesis (ii) which will make (i) best possible. *J. P. King* (Bethlehem, Pa.)

## Q05-85 (43# 522)

**Robinson, Raphael M.**

**Integer-valued entire functions.**

*Trans. Amer. Math. Soc.* **153** (1971), 451–468.

Der Verfasser beschäftigt sich mit ganzen Funktionen $f$ vom Exponentialtyp, die für alle natürlichen Zahlen (bzw. für alle ganzen Zahlen) ganzzahlige Werte annehmen. Wie man seit G. Pólya [Rend. Circ. Mat. Palermo **40** (1915), 1–16], C. Pisot [Jber. Deutsch. Math. Verein. **52** (1942), 95–102; MR **4**, 270] und R. C. Buck [Duke Math. J. **15** (1948), 879–891; MR **10**, 693] weiß, wird bei genügend kleinem Typ durch die arithmetische Bedingung der Ganzwertigkeit die Gestalt der Funktion $f$ weitgehend bestimmt: $f$ ist ein Exponentialpolynom (mit algebraischen Zahlen als Basen).

In der vorliegenden Arbeit skizziert der Verfasser kurz die benötigten Hilfsmittel und die bekannten Methoden zur Behandlung der Problemstellung; er gibt verschiedene neue Methoden an und skizziert die Herleitung der bisher bekannten Ergebnisse. Auf seine früheren Untersuchungen über ganzalgebraische Zahlen [*Studies in mathematical analysis and related topics*, pp. 305–315, Stanford Univ. Press, Stanford, Calif., 1962; MR **26** #2433; Math. Comp. **18** (1964), 547–559; MR **29** #6624; Ann. of Math. (2) **80** (1964), 411–428; MR **31** #157; Math. Z. **110** (1969), 41–51; MR **40** #95] gestützt, leitet der Verfasser eine Reihe neuer Ergebnisse her über ganzwertige ganze Funktionen, deren Indikatorfunktion $h(\theta) = \lim\sup_{r\to\infty} r^{-1} \log|f(re^{i\theta})|$ die Bedingungen $h(\pm\frac{1}{2}\pi) = 0$, $h(0) \leqq \lambda$, $h(\pi) \leqq \mu$ bzw. $-h(\pi) = h(0) \geqq 0$, $h(\pm\frac{1}{2}\pi) < \pi$ erfüllt [das Indikatordiagramm wird dann eine horizontale bzw. vertikale Strecke]; der Verfasser gibt mögliche Gestalten der Funktion $f$, solange der Typ unterhalb des kritischen liegt, und zeigt, was oberhalb des kritischen Typs eintreten kann. Wegen der Formulierung der Ergebnisse muß auf die Arbeit verwiesen werden.

{R. Wallisser [J. Reine Angew. Math. **235** (1969), 189–206; MR **39** #5797] hat ebenfalls die bekannten Methoden zusammenfassend dargestellt und eine Fülle von Ergebnissen über ganze Funktionen erhalten, deren Werte arithmetischen Bedingungen genügen (z. B. $f^{(n)}(0)$ ganz für $n=1, 2, \cdots$ bzw. $f^{(n)}(n)$ ganz für $n=1, 2, \cdots$ bzw. $\Delta^n f(n)$ ganz für $n=1, 2, \cdots$); in dieser Arbeit finden sich auch weitere Literaturhinweise.}

*W. Schwarz* (Frankfurt a.M.)

Citations: MR 4, 270c = Q05-4; MR 10, 693c = Q05-9; MR 26# 2433 = R04-18; MR 29# 6624 = R04-22; MR 31# 157 = R04-23; MR 40# 95 = R04-36.

## Q05-86 (43# 6434)

**Sato, Daihachiro**

**On the type of highly integer valued entire functions.**

*J. Reine Angew. Math.* **248** (1971), 1–11.

An entire function which together with all its derivatives assumes integer values at the integers $z=0, 1, \cdots, k-1$ is a $k$-point highly integer valued entire function (or a $k$-point Hurwitz entire function). The author offers the function $h(z)=\exp[z(z-1)(z-2)(z-3)/2]$ as a 4-point Hurwitz transcendental entire function of order $\rho=4$ and type $\sigma=\frac{1}{2}$, which serves as a counter-example to the statement of L. Bieberbach [Arch. Math. (Basel) **4** (1953), 23–27; MR **14**, 1074] that if a transcendental entire function of order $\rho$ and type $\sigma$ is a $k$-point Hurwitz entire function then either $\rho>k$, or $\rho=k$ and $\sigma\geqq 1$.

Subsequent developments concern the quantities $\sigma_p(k)$, the type of $k$-point Hurwitz entire functions of order $\rho=k$ below which one finds only polynomials, and $\sigma_c(k)$, below which one finds only countably many $k$-point Hurwitz entire functions. It is shown that $\sigma_p(1)=\sigma_p(2)=1$, and upper and lower bounds for all $\sigma_p(k)$ are obtained (with these bounds tabulated for $3\leqq k\leqq 9$). The bounds involve the values $\sigma_c(k)$, which in turn are defined in terms of Vandermonde determinants.

A final section poses several unsolved problems. Care must be taken to recognize some misprints; e.g., in Equation (5). *C. R. Deeter* (Ft. Worth, Tex.)

Citations: MR 14, 1074d = Q05-22.

## Q05-87 (43# 7409)

**Baker, A. [Baker, Alan]**

**An estimate for the ℘-function at an algebraic point.**

*Amer. J. Math.* **92** (1970), 619–622.

Let $\wp(z)$ be a Weierstrass function with algebraic invariants $g_2$ and $g_3$. It is easily verified that there exist arbitrarily large integers $n$ with $|\wp(n)|>Cn$ for some constant $C$. The purpose of this paper is to get an opposite estimate: For any algebraic number $\alpha\neq 0$ one has $|\wp(\alpha)|<C\exp(\log H(\alpha))^\kappa$, where $\kappa$ is an absolute constant, $C$ a constant depending on $g_2$, $g_3$ and the degree of $\alpha$, and $H(\alpha)$ denotes the height of $\alpha$. The proof is based on an earlier paper of the author [*Symposia Mathematica*, Vol. IV (INDAM, Rome, 1968/69), pp. 155–174, Academic Press, London, 1970; MR **43** #4768], refining the following result: Let $\alpha_1$, $\alpha_2$ be algebraic numbers, $w_1$, $w_2$ any pair of fundamental periods of $\wp(z)$; then $\alpha_1 w_1+\alpha_2 w_2$ is either transcendental or zero.

It does not seem easy to obtain improvements with the present techniques, e.g., to get an upper bound of the form $C(H(\alpha))^\kappa$. *W.-D. Geyer* (Heidelberg)

Citations: MR 43# 4768 = J76-75.

## Q05-88 (44# 2739)

**Berstel, Jean**

**Sur les pôles et le quotient de Hadamard de séries N-rationnelles.**

*C. R. Acad. Sci. Paris Sér. A-B* **272** (1971), A1079–A1081.

Parmi les séries rationnelles en $z$ et à coefficients entiers non négatifs, on définit le semi-anneau $\mathscr{A}$ des séries **N**-rationnelles comme le plus petit semi-anneau $\mathscr{S}$ de séries en $z$ qui contienne les polynômes à coefficients entiers non négatifs et tel que $a(z)\in\mathscr{S}$ implique $(1-za(z))^{-1}\in\mathscr{S}$. L'auteur démontre que pour toute série $a(z)$ **N**-rationnelle (non polynôme), développement de Taylor autour de l'origine de la fraction rationnelle $f(z)$, on a la propriété suivante: Pour tout pôle $\alpha$ de $f(z)$ situé sur le cercle de convergence de $a(z)$, $\alpha/|\alpha|$ est une racine de l'unité. En reprenant un exemple dû à S. Eilenberg, l'auteur montre que cette propriété n'est pas caractéristique.

Ce résultat permet enfin de montrer que, si le quotient de Hadamard de deux séries **N**-rationnelles est à coefficients entiers, il est rationnel (cf. à ce sujet B. Benzaghou [Bull. Soc. Math. France **98** (1970), 209–252; MR **44** #1658]).

*F. Dress* (Talence)

Citations: MR 44# 1658 = B44-76.

## Q05-89 (44# 4193)

**Tijdeman, R.**

**On the number of zeros of general exponential polynomials.**

*Nederl. Akad. Wetensch. Proc. Ser. A* **74** = *Indag. Math.* **33** (1971), 1–7.

Für die Anzahl der Nullstellen $N(z_0, R, f)$ des allgemeinen Exponentialpolynoms $f(z)=\sum_{k=1}^{l} P_k(z)e^{\omega_k z}$ ($f\not\equiv 0$, $\omega_k$ komplex, $P_k$ Polynom vom Grad $\rho_k-1$, $n=\sum_{k=1}^{l}\rho_k$, $\Delta=\max_k|\omega_k|$) in einem Kreis mit Mittelpunkt $z_0$ und Radius $R$ wird die bemerkenswert einfache Abschätzung $N(z_0, R, f)\leqq 3(n-1)+4R\Delta$ angegeben. Die Arbeit verbessert ein Resultat von S. Dancs und P. Turán [Publ. Math. Debrecen **11** (1964), 257–265; MR **30** #3217; ibid. **11** (1964), 266–272; MR **30** #3218], indem sie vor allem zeigt, daß die Anzahl der Nullstellen nicht von $\delta=\min_{k\neq j}|\omega_k-\omega_j|$ abhängt. Dies hat insbesondere Konsequenzen in der Theorie der transzendenten Zahlen [vgl. A. O. Gel'fond, Englische Übersetzung, *Transcendental and algebraic numbers*, pp. 140–141, Dover, New York, 1960; MR **22** #2598]. Der Beweis gelingt mit Hilfe einer vom Verfasser ebenfalls bewiesenen Verallgemeinerung des ersten Turánschen Hauptsatzes [A. A. Balkema und der Verfasser, "Some theorems in the theory of exponential sums", Rep. No. 70–74, Math. Inst., Univ. Amsterdam, Amsterdam, 1970] und einer geschickten Anwendung der Jensenschen Formel. Schließlich werden in den Fällen $R\cdot\Delta$ klein bzw. groß bezüglich $n$ die Abschätzungen für $N(z_0, R, f)$ mit klassischen asymptotischen Resultaten verglichen.

*R. Wallisser* (Freiburg)

Citations: MR 22# 2598 = J02-7; MR 30# 3217 = M50-30.

# Q10 DIFFERENTIAL EQUATIONS

See also Section J88.

See also reviews A22-56, A32-32, D44-113, J02-16, J12-63, J88-47, P80-7, Q05-12, Q05-69, Q25-21, Z10-35.

## Q10-1 (7, 417c)

**Popken, J. An arithmetical property of a class of Dirichlet's series.** Nederl. Akad. Wetensch., Proc. **48**, 517–534 = Indagationes Math. 7, 105–122 (1945).

The purpose of the paper is to prove the following theorem. Let the convergent Dirichlet series $\sum_{h=1}^{\infty} a_h e^{-\lambda_h s}$ ($\lambda_1 < \lambda_2 < \cdots$; $\lim \lambda_h = \infty$) represent an analytic function $f(s)$ satisfying an algebraic differential equation

$$P(s, f(s), f'(s), \cdots, f^{(n)}(s)) = 0,$$

$P$ being a polynomial in $s, f', \cdots, f^{(n)}$. Let the coefficients $a_h$ be rational and let $p_h$ denote the largest prime divisor of the denominator of $a_h$ written in its irreducible form. Then there exists a positive number $c$ such that $p_h < \lambda_h^c$ except for a finite number of values of $h$. Transforming the power series with rational coefficients $\sum a_h x^h$ into a Dirichlet series by the substitution $x = e^{-s}$, the author obtains as a special case of his theorem the well-known result of Hurwitz that $p_h < h^{c_1}$ ($h > 1$), where $c_1$ is a constant. *R. Salem.*

## Q10-2 (10, 432f)

**Morduhaĭ-Boltovskoĭ, D. On hypertranscendental functions and hypertranscendental numbers.** Doklady Akad. Nauk SSSR (N.S.) **64**, 21–24 (1949). (Russian)

The author designates a function as hyperalgebraic or hypertranscendental according as it does or does not satisfy an algebraic differential equation (1) $f(x, y, y', \cdots, y^{(n)}) = 0$. If (1) has algebraic numbers for coefficients, a solution $y$ of (1) is called algebraically-hyperalgebraic if $y$ and its first $n-1$ derivatives assume algebraic values for some algebraic value of $x$. A value of such a function for any algebraic value of $x$ is called a hyperalgebraic number. Such numbers are seen to form a countable set. It is shown that if a power series represents an algebraically-hyperalgebraic function, the coefficients all lie in a field generated by an algebraic number. *J. F. Ritt* (New York, N. Y.).

## Q10-3 (10, 682b)

**Postnikov, A. G. On the differential independence of Dirichlet series.** Doklady Akad. Nauk SSSR (N.S.) **66**, 561–564 (1949). (Russian)

Let $m$ be a positive integer and $\chi$ any character modulo $m$. It is shown that the $\varphi(m)$ Dirichlet series $L(s, \chi)$ are differentially independent. By this is meant that no nonzero polynomial in $s$, the series and their derivatives of arbitrary orders, with constant coefficients, vanishes for every $s$. The author proves first that if several Dirichlet series of the type $\sum a_n n^{-s}$ are differentially dependent, then the series obtained from them by suppressing all terms except those in which $n$ is prime, and sufficiently large, satisfy together a linear differential equation. *J. F. Ritt.*

## Q10-4 (11, 86g)

**Popken, J. A property of a Dirichlet series, representing a function satisfying an algebraic difference-differential equation.** Nederl. Akad. Wetensch., Proc. **52**, 499–504 = Indagationes Math. **11**, 159–164 (1949).

Unter Verwendung von Gedanken einer Arbeit von Ostrowski [Math. Z. **8**, 241–298 (1920)] wird eine neue notwendige Bedingung für Dirichletsche Reihen, die einer algebraischen Differenzen-Differentialgleichung der Form

$$F(s, f^{(n_1)}(s+u_1), \cdots, f^{(n_t)}(s+u_t)) = 0$$

genügen, bewiesen, wobei $F(x_0, x_1, \cdots, x_t) \not\equiv 0$ ein Polynom bedeutet, $u_1, \cdots, u_t$ reelle Zahlen und $n_1, \cdots, n_t$ nichtnegative ganze Zahlen, dass die $t$ Systeme $(u_1, n_1), \cdots, (u_t, n_t)$ voneinander verschieden sind. Die Bedingung lautet: Die konvergente Dirichletsche Reihe $\sum_{h=1}^{\infty} a_h e^{-\lambda_h s}$ mit nichtverschwindenden Koeffizienten $a_h$ stelle eine Funktion $f(s)$ dar, die einer algebraischen Differenzen-Differentialgleichung genügt. Dann gibt es eine positive Zahl $c$ derart, dass $\lambda_h > h^c$ für alle $h$, ausser einer endlichen Anzahl, gilt. Daraus folgt sofort speziell, dass $\zeta(s)$ transzendental-transzendent ist. *T. Schneider* (Göttingen).

## Q10-5 (12, 600g)

**Popken, J. An arithmetical theorem concerning linear differential equations of infinite order.** Nederl. Akad. Wetensch., Proc. **53**, 1645–1656 = Indagationes Math. **12**, 522–533 (1950).

The number $\zeta$ is called an exceptional point of the integral function $y(z)$ if $\zeta$ and $y(\zeta)$ are both algebraic numbers; and if $\zeta, y^{(j)}(\zeta), j = 0, 1, \cdots, \mu-1$ are algebraic but $y^{(\mu)}(\zeta)$ is not, then $\zeta$ is an exceptional point of multiplicity $\mu$ ($\mu = \infty$ if $\zeta$ and all derivatives at $z = \zeta$ are algebraic). The principal result is theorem 1: Let the integral function $y(z) = \sum_0^{\infty} c_n z^n / n!$, with $\lim \sup |c_n|^{1/n} \leqq q$ ($q > 0$), satisfy the linear differential equation of infinite order $\sum_0^{\infty} a_n y^{(n)}(z) = 0$, where $\{a_n\}$ are constants not all zero. Let the function $F(t) = \sum_0^{\infty} a_n t^n$ be regular in $|t| \leqq q$ and let $\nu$ be the maximum of the multiplicities of the zeros of $F(t)$ in $0 < |t| \leqq q$. Then: (i) If $y(z)$ has $\nu$ or more exceptional points $\zeta$ ($\neq 0$), where an exceptional point of multiplicity $\mu$ is counted $\mu$ times, then $y(z)$ is a polynomial with algebraic coefficients. (ii) If $a_0 \neq 0$, and $\zeta \neq 0$ is an exceptional point with multiplicity $\mu$, then $\zeta$ is a zero of $y(z)$ of order $\mu$. A corollary is theorem 2: Let the entire transcendental function $y(z) = \sum_0^{\infty} c_n z^n / n!$ with $c_n = O(q^n)$ and $c_n$ algebraic, satisfy the linear differential-difference equation $\sum_{\mu=0}^{m} \sum_{\nu=0}^{n} A_{\mu\nu} y^{(\mu)}(z + \omega_\nu) = 0$, where the $A_{\mu\nu}$ are constants not all zero, and the constants $\omega_\nu$ are distinct. Then $y(z)$ is a transcendental number for all but a finite number of algebraic values of $z$. Moreover, if $\sum_{\nu=0}^{n} A_{0\nu} \neq 0$, then each exceptional point $\zeta$ ($\neq 0$) is a zero of $y(z)$. *I. M. Sheffer* (State College, Pa.).

Referred to in J76-39.

## Q10-6 (18, 563d)

**Postnikov, A. G. On the generalization of one of the Hilbert problems.** Dokl. Akad. Nauk SSSR (N.S.) **107** (1956), 512–515. (Russian)

Soit $\chi$ un caractère modulo $m$, et posons $L(x, s, \chi) = L_x = \sum \chi(n) x^n n^{-s}$. L'auteur démontre le théorème suivant: Entre differentes fonctions $L_x$ (modulo $m$) aucune relation de la forme

$$\Phi\left(x, s, \frac{\partial^{p+q} L(x, s, \chi)}{\partial x^p \partial s^q}\right) \equiv 0,$$

où $\Phi$ est un polynome, n'est possible. Ce théorème généralise un theorème d'Ostrowski correspondant aux fonctions du type $\xi$, et qui est une réponse à un des problèmes posés par Hilbert au Congrès de Paris [voir Ostrowski, Math. Z. **8** (1920), 241–298]. L'auteur utilise plusieurs faits étables par Ostrowski dans le travail cité, ainsi que le lemme suivant: En posant $L = L(s, \chi) = \sum \chi(n) n^{-s}$, la rélation $\Phi(s, f_k^{(\nu)}(s + h_{k,\nu,\tau})) \equiv 0$, où $f_k$ sont differentes fonctions $L$ (modulo $m$) et où $h_{k,\nu,\tau}$ sont des constantes, est impossible. *S. Mandelbrojt* (Paris).

**Q10-7** **(18, 792f)**

**Postnikov, A. G. Generalization of one of the Hilbert problems.** J. Indian Math. Soc. (N.S.) **20** (1956), 207–216.

Let $m$ be a fixed positive integer. The author proves that the $\varphi(m)$ Dirichlet $L$-series $L(s, \chi_1), \cdots, L(s, \chi_{\varphi(m)})$ are difference-differentially independent. That is, if $k_1, \cdots, k_q$ are distinct real numbers, and if $N$ is an integer $\geqq 0$, there does not exist any algebraic identity between the $(N+1)q\varphi(m)$ functions $L^{(j)}(s+k_i, \chi_h)$ $(j=0, \cdots, N;$ $i=1, \cdots, q;$ $h=1, \cdots, \varphi(m))$. As an application it is shown that there is no algebraic relation between the various partial derivatives (with respect to $x$ and $s$) of the $\varphi(m)$ functions

$$L(x, s, \chi_h)=\sum_{n=1}^{\infty} \chi(n)n^{-s}x^n \quad (h=1, \cdots, \varphi(m)).$$

The case $m=1$ was one of Hilbert's problems (Paris 1901); it was solved by D. D. Morduchai-Boltovskoy [Izvestiya Warsawskovo Polytechnicheskovo Instituta 1914; Tôhoku Math. J. **35** (1932), 19–34] and by A. Ostrowski [Math. Z. **8** (1920), 241–298]. The present author follows Ostrowski's method. *N. G. de Bruijn* (Amsterdam).

**Q10-8** **(21# 6366)**

**Kolchin, E. R. Rational approximation to solutions of algebraic differential equations.** Proc. Amer. Math. Soc. **10** (1959), 238–244.

The author formulates and proves an interesting differential-algebraic generalization of Liouville's classical result about a limit to the accuracy with which algebraic numbers can be approximated by rational numbers and, thereby, opens the way for new types of investigations in differential algebra.

First, he generalizes the notion of the degree of an algebraic number as follows: If $s$ is a natural number, then $\sum_{j=1}^{k}(j+s)e_j$ is called the $s$-denomination of the $D$-(differential-) monomial $\prod_{j=1}^{k}(D^jy)^{e_j}$ in a $D$-indeterminate $y$. The $s$-denomination of a non-zero $D$-polynomial is then defined to be the maximum of the $s$-denominations of the $D$-monomials of which it is a linear combination with non-zero coefficients. Now an element $u$ which is $D$-algebraic over a commutative $D$-ring $Z$ is said to have $s$-denomination $d$ over $Z$ if $d$ is the smallest natural number such that there exists a non-zero $D$-polynomial $P$ in $Z\{y\}$ of $s$-denomination $d$ vanishing at $u$.

Theorem: Let $F$ be a field with a derivation $D$ and a non-trivial valuation $a \to |a|$ for which there exist elements $\alpha$, $\beta$ of the value group such that $\alpha|a| \leqq |Da| \leqq \beta|a|$ holds for all $a \in F$ with $|a|<1$. Let $Z$ be a non-zero $D$-subring of $F$ with $|a| \geqq 1$ for all its non-zero elements $a$. Then for any $u \in F$ which is $D$-algebraic over $Z$ and any natural number $s$ there exists an element $\gamma$ of the value group such that $|u-a/b^s| \geqq \gamma/|b|^{d_s}$ for all $a, b \in Z$ with $b \neq 0$ and $u \neq a/b^s$. The main part of the proof consists in showing that there exists an element $\gamma_0$ of the value group such that $|v-u| \geqq \gamma_0$ for every $v(\neq u) \in F$ which is a zero of a polynomial $P$ of minimal $s$-denomination vanishing at $u$. For this purpose some properties of Wronskian determinants are established and applied. From the theorem it follows that a power series $\sum_{k=0}^{\infty} c_k x^{s_k}$ with non-zero coefficients $c_k$ in a field $K$ of characteristic 0, and with strictly increasing integral exponents $s_k>0$ such that the sequence of ratios $s_{k+1}/s_k$ is unbounded, is $D$-transcendental over $K(x)$.

*A. Jaeger* (Cincinnati, Ohio)

Referred to in J68-60.

**Q10-9** **(26# 5756)**

**Bellman, R.; Kotkin, B.**

**On the numerical solution of a differential-difference equation arising in analytic number theory.**

*Math. Comp.* **16** (1962), 473–475.

Authors' summary: "The computational solution of a certain class of differential-difference equations requires numerical procedures involving an extremely high degree of precision to obtain accurate results over a large range of the independent variable. One method of solution uses an iterative procedure which relates the differential-difference equation over a large range to a system of ordinary differential equations over a limited range. When the characteristic roots of the related system indicate borderline stability, it is evident that small perturbations in obtaining successive initial values eventually grow out of control as the system increases. To investigate this phenomenon, we examine the equation $u'(x)=-u(x-1)/x$, arising in analytic number theory."*

[*See, for example, MR **13**, 724E = N28-28. Ed.]

Citations: MR 13, 724e = N28-28.

**Q10-10** **(31# 3394)**

**Popken, J.**

**Note on a generalization of a problem of Hilbert.**

*Nederl. Akad. Wetensch. Proc. Ser. A* **68** = *Indag. Math.* **27** (1965), 178–181.

Let $\chi_\mu(n)$, $1 \leqq \mu \leqq \varphi(m)$, denote the characters modulo $m$ and set $L(x, s, \chi_\mu)=\sum_{n=1}^{\infty} \chi_\mu(n)x^n n^{-s}$. The author generalizes results of Ostrowski and Postnikov to prove the following theorem. Let $k$, $l$ be the non-negative integers, and let $c_1, c_2, \cdots, c_r$ denote different real numbers such that $c_i-c_j \neq 1, 2, \cdots, k$ for all choices of $i$ and $j$. Then the $(k+1)(l+1)r\varphi(m)$ functions $\partial^{\alpha+\beta}L(x, s+c_\gamma, \chi_\mu)/\partial x^\alpha \partial s^\beta$, $0 \leqq \alpha \leqq k$, $0 \leqq \beta \leqq l$, $1 \leqq \gamma \leqq r$, $1 \leqq \mu \leqq \varphi(m)$, are algebraically independent over the ring of polynomials $C[x, s]$; $C$, the complex numbers. The proof is made to depend on the following elegant lemma. Let $f_\tau(n)$, $1 \leqq \tau \leqq t$, be arithmetical functions with values in a torsion-free ring $R$, which are algebraically dependent over $R$ in the sense of arithmetic convolution. Then there exist elements $A_\tau \in R$, $1 \leqq \tau \leqq t$, not all zero, such that the linear relation $\sum_{\tau=1}^{t} A_\tau f_\tau(p)=0$ holds for all sufficiently large primes $p$.

*Morris Newman* (Washington, D.C.)

**Q10-11** **(33# 1293)**

**Popken, J.**

**Algebraic independence of certain zêta functions.**

*Nederl. Akad. Wetensch. Proc. Ser. A* **69** = *Indag. Math.* **28** (1966), 1–5.

Let $Q_\tau$ be a quadratic extension of the rationals of discriminant $d_\tau$, $1 \leqq \tau \leqq t$, and suppose that $d_1^{u_1} \cdots d_t^{u_t}$ is a square if and only if each exponent $u_\tau$ is even. Let $\zeta_\tau(s)$ be the zeta-function of $Q_\tau$, $1 \leqq \tau \leqq t$, and let $\zeta_0(s)$ be the ordinary zeta-function. The author proves the elegant result that any finite number of different functions taken from the set $d^\lambda \zeta_\tau(s+r)/ds^\lambda$ $(0 \leqq \tau \leqq t;$ $\lambda=0, 1, \cdots;$ $r$ real) are algebraically independent over the ring of polynomials $C[s]$ ($C$ the complex field). The author also proves, with the aid of a theorem of Ostrowski, that the zeta-function $\zeta_F(s)$ of an arbitrary algebraic number field $F$ of finite degree over the rationals does not satisfy any algebraic differential-difference equation. *Morris Newman* (Washington, D.C.)

**Q10-12** **(41# 3415)**

**Popken, J.**

**A measure for the differential-transcendence of the zeta-function of Riemann.**

*Number Theory and Analysis (Papers in Honor of Edmund Landau), pp.* 245–255. *Plenum, New York,* 1969.

The author refines the well-known result of Hilbert that the Riemann $\zeta$-function does not satisfy an algebraic differential equation in the following way. Let $R$ denote the differential ring of formal Dirichlet series $D=\sum a_n n^{-s}$ $(1\leqq n<\infty)$ with complex coefficients. Define a valuation on $R$ by $|D|=N^{-1}$, where $a_N$ is the first non-zero coefficient of $D$. Then for any non-zero polynomial $f(x_0, x_1, \cdots, x_r)$ with complex coefficients of total degree $g$, we have $|f(\zeta, \zeta^1, \cdots, \zeta^{(r)})|\geqq(r+2)^{-1}$ (if $g=1$), $|f(\zeta, \zeta^1, \cdots, \zeta^{(r)})|\geqq(cg\log g(r+2)\log^2(r+2))^{-g}$ (if $g>1$), where $c$ is an absolute effectively computable constant.

*W. W. Adams* (College Park, Md.)

**Q10-13** **(43# 7419)**

**Oleĭnikov, V. A.**

**The differential irreducibility of linear equations. (Russian. English summary)**

*Vestnik Moskov. Univ. Ser. I Mat. Meh.* **26** (1971), *no.* 1, 44–51.

A differential equation $P(z, y, y', \cdots, y^{(n)})=0$ is said to be algebraic if $P$ is a non-zero polynomial in $n+1$ variables $y, y', \cdots, y^{(n)}$ with coefficients from the field of algebraic functions of the complex variable $z$. The equation is said to be differentially reducible if there exists a transcendental (over the field of algebraic functions) solution satisfying an algebraic differential equation of order less than the order of the equation $P=0$. The main result is that if the linear homogeneous algebraic differential equation $y^{(n)}+p_1y^{(n-1)}+\cdots+p_ny=0$ is differentially reducible then there exists a solution $y(z)\neq 0$ satisfying a homogeneous differential equation of order $m<n$.

*Andrzej Białynicki-Birula* (Warsaw)

**Q10-14** **(43# 7420)**

**Oleĭnikov, V. A.**

**A sufficient criterion for differential irreducibility of a linear equation. (Russian. English summary)**

*Vestnik Moskov. Univ. Ser. I Mat. Meh.* **26** (1971), *no.* 3, 45–52.

The author continues his study of reducible algebraic differential equations [see #7419 above] in the special case of an ordinary linear homogeneous algebraic equation (1) $y+p_1y^{(n)}+\cdots+p_{n-1}y'+p_ny=0$. The equation is said to be normal if, for some (and hence any) fundamental system $y_1, \cdots, y_n$ of solutions of this equation and for any integer $s>0$, the system of functions $\{y_1^{s_1}\cdots y_n^{s_n};\ s_1+\cdots+s_n=s, s_1>0, \cdots, s_n>0\}$ is linearly independent. Let (1) be a normal equation and let $y_1, \cdots, y_n$ be its fundamental system of solutions. Then an algebraic differential equation (2) $y^{(N)}+a_1y^{(N-1)}+\cdots+a_Ny=0$ is said to be the $s$-th power of (1) if the set of solutions of (2) coincides with the space of linear combinations of functions $y_1^{s_1}\cdots y_n^{s_n}$, where $s_1+\cdots+s_n=s$ and $s_1>0, \cdots, s_n>0$. The $s$-th power of the normal equation (1) is uniquely determined. The main result of the paper says that if (1) is normal and differentially reducible then an $s$-th power of (1), for some integer $s>0$, is linearly reducible (a linear algebraic homogeneous differential equation of order $n$ is said to be linearly reducible if it has a solution $y\neq 0$ which satisfies a linear homogeneous algebraic differential equation of order $m<n$).

*Andrzej Białynicki-Birula* (Warsaw)

# Q15 PROBABILITY THEORY AND ERGODIC THEORY

Many heuristic arguments of a probabilistic nature are to be found in **A46** and **N32**. Many results in **N24** and **N28** have probabilistic interpretations.

See also Sections J24, J60, K15, K40, K45, K50, K55, N60.

See also reviews A38-26, A38-58, A62-84, B08-76, B16-14, B16-20, B20-13, B28-29, B44-49, B99-12, D44-163, D60-73, E16-27, E16-31, E16-77, E16-82, E24-54, E24-65, E28-29, E76-2, J68-69, K02-2, K02-5, K02-6, K05-3, K05-6, K05-21, K05-23, K05-55, K05-57, K15-50, K20-5, K20-16, K25-1, K25-2, K30-23, K30-25, K40-20, K40-26, K40-27, K40-30, K40-39, K40-62, L15-32, L99-6, M30-5, M30-31, M30-39, M30-47, M30-51, M50-8, N02-2, N04-29, N04-49, N08-34, N12-5, N28-53, N28-55, N36-37, N56-19, N56-26, N64-16, N76-13, N76-14, P02-15, P02-18, P02-21, P08-51, P20-5, P24-7, P28-12, P28-25, P32-4, P36-48, P36-54, P36-67, P48-6, P52-13, P80-4, P80-33, P99-5, P99-6, P99-7, R14-104, R52-20, R52-21, Z02-55, Z02-60, Z02-76.

**Q15-1** **(3, 165g)**

**Wintner, Aurel. On a statistics of the Ramanujan sums.** Amer. J. Math. **64**, 106–114 (1942).

Denote by $c_m(n)$ the Ramanujan sums. We have

$$c_m(n)=\sum_{\substack{0<r\leq m\\(r,m)=1}}\cos(2\pi nr/m).$$

It is easy to see that the $c_m(n)$ are integers. For $n=1$ we have $c_m(n)=\mu(m)$. The author proves by using Tauberian theorems that the distribution function of $c_m(n)$ (with respect to $m$) exists for every $n$. For $n=1$ this is equivalent to the prime number theorem.

*P. Erdös.*

**Q15-2** **(5, 124c)**

**Hadwiger, H. Über gleichwahrscheinliche Aufteilungen.** Z. Angew. Math. Mech. **22**, 226–232 (1943).

Despite its title, this paper is actually concerned with the following two questions on geometric probability considered by Laplace. Let $n-1$ points, taken at random from the unit interval $[0, 1]$, divide it into $n$ subintervals. What is the probability that no subinterval exceed a given number $\xi<1$? What is the expected value of the largest subinterval? The answer to the first question is simply

$$\sum_{\lambda=0}^{[\xi^{-1}]}(-1)^\lambda\binom{n}{\lambda}(1-\lambda\xi)^{n-1},$$

but is given in the present paper in a nearly unrecognizable form by means of an infinite integral. The answer to the second question is

$$(1+\tfrac{1}{2}+\cdots+1/n)/n.$$

This is a special case of Laplace's rule [see, for example, Encyclopaedia Britannica, 13th ed., v. 22, p. 384 a] which asserts that the expected value of the $r$th largest interval is

$$(1/r+1/(r+1)+\cdots+1/n)/n.$$

The questions are stated in terms of combinatorial Diophantine analysis as follows. Out of all the $\binom{n+s-1}{s}$ compositions of the integer $s$ into $n$ parts not less than 0, how many have no part exceeding $\xi s$? What is the average size of the largest part? These questions have answers which are numerical functions of the integer $s$. The above results are, of course, only the leading, or "volume," terms in the asymptotic formulas for these two lattice point problems.

*D. H. Lehmer* (Berkeley, Calif.).

## Q15-3 (16, 1002a)

**Postnikov, A. G. On an application of the central-limit theorem of the theory of probability.** Uspehi Mat. Nauk (N.S.) **10**, no. 1(63), 147–149 (1955). (Russian)

Let $r_1, \cdots, r_k$ be positive integers and $J_k(t)$ the number of integer solutions of $\sum_{i=1}^{k} x_i r_i^{-1} \leqq t$ in $|x_i| \leqq \frac{1}{2} r_i$ $(i=1, \cdots, k)$. Then $J_k(t)$, properly normalised, is asymptotically normal with error $O(k^{-1/2} \log k)$ according to Lyapunov's theorem. A lemma of T. Schneider [J. Reine Angew. Math. **175**, 182–192 (1936)] follows.

*K. L. Chung.*

## Q15-4 (18, 17d)

**Kubilyus, I. P. Probabilistic methods in the theory of numbers.** Uspehi Mat. Nauk (N.S.) **11** (1956), no. 2(68), 31–66. (Russian)

This is an enlarged version of a report delivered before a Conference on the Theory of Probability and its Applications, held in Leningrad in 1955. It is divided into three main sections; the first is a full account of strongly additive arithmetic functions, the second of Linnik's "Large Sieve" and its generalisations, and the third of the Arithmetic of Quaternions. Appended is an exhaustive bibliography. [For an earlier and less comprehensive account of this subject see Kac, Bull. Amer. Math. Soc. **55** (1949), 641–665; MR **11**, 161.]

*H. Halberstam* (Exeter).

Citations: MR 11, 161b = N60-10.

Referred to in N56-26, N60-23, N60-31, N60-37, N60-63, N60-65, Q15-5.

## Q15-5 (24# A1266 )

**Kubilyus, I. P.**

**Probabilistic methods in the theory of numbers.**

*Amer. Math. Soc. Transl.* (2) **19** (1962), 47–85.

The original Russian article appeared in Uspehi Mat. Nauk **11** (1956), no. 2 (68), 31–66 [MR **18**, 17].

Citations: MR 18, 17d = Q15-4.

Referred to in N56-26, N60-63, N60-65.

## Q15-6 (20# 4535 )

**Rényi, Alfréd. Probability methods in number theory.** Advancement in Math. **4** (1958), 465–510. (Chinese)

Expository paper. *K. L. Chung* (Syracuse, N.Y.)

## Q15-7 (22# 996 )

**Kac, Mark. Statistical independence in probability, analysis and number theory.** The Carus Mathematical Monographs, No. 12. Published by the Mathematical Association of America. Distributed by John Wiley and Sons, Inc., New York, 1959. xiv+93 pp. $3.00.

The author states in the preface that his aim is to show that "(a) extremely simple observations are often the starting point of rich and fruitful theories and (b) many seemingly unrelated developments are in reality variations on the same simple theme." This aim is achieved in the most instructive way.

The central theme is the concept of statistical independence, to which are devoted four chapters out of five; viz.: Chapter 1 "From Vieta to the notion of statistical independence", Chapter 2 "Borel and after", Chapter 3 "The normal law" and Chapter 4 "Primes play a game of chance". A large number of propositions in analysis and number theory are thus closely related by means of the notion of statistical independence. Chapter 5, entitled "From kinetic theory to continued fractions", is centered about the ergodic problem. The discussion in physical terms leads to the ergodic theorem and its application to continued fractions.

Many problems throughout the book provide other applications to analysis and number theory. Bibliographical indications allow the reader to pursue further the study of the ideas and methods. The book is written in the inimitable style of the author. It ought to be put in the hands of every graduate student in mathematics.

*M. Loève* (Berkeley, Calif.)

Referred to in N24-56, N36-38, N48-23.

## Q15-8 (22# 9478 )

**Rényi, A. Probabilistic methods in number theory.** Proc. Internat. Congress Math. 1958, pp. 529–539. Cambridge Univ. Press, New York, 1960.

This is an exposition of recent work in probabilistic number theory. Topics mentioned include the proof by P. Turán and the author [Acta Arith. **4** (1958), 71–84; MR **20** #3112] of a conjecture of the reviewer, Linnik's large sieve, statistical properties of digits in various expansions of real numbers, and the additive theory of random sequences of integers.

*W. J. LeVeque* (Ann Arbor, Mich.)

Citations: MR 20# 3112 = N60-31.

## Q15-9 (22# 12079 )

**McKean, H. P., Jr. A problem about prime numbers and the random walk. I.** Illinois J. Math. **5** (1961), 351.

It is shown that with probability one the 3-dimensional random walk hits the $x$-axis in a point the abscissa of which is a prime number infinitely often.

*A. Rényi* (Budapest)

## Q15-10 (22# 12080 )

**Erdös, P. A problem about prime numbers and the random walk. II.** Illinois J. Math. **5** (1961), 352–353.

Let $e(n)$ be equal to the number of primes $p \leqq n$ such that the 3-dimensional random walk passes through the point with abscissa $p$ on the $x$-axis. It is shown that $e(n) \cdot (\log \log n)^{-1}$ tends in probability to a positive constant $c$. This implies that with probability one the random walk hits an infinity of points on the $x$-axis the abscissa of which is a prime. It is indicated that by the same method it can also be proved that $e(n) \cdot (\log \log n)^{-1}$ tends to $c$ with probability one. *A. Rényi* (Budapest)

## Q15-11 (25# 57 )

**Kubiljus, I. P.; Linnik, Ju. V.**

**An arithmetic analogue of Brownian motion. (Russian)**

*Izv. Vysš. Učebn. Zaved. Matematika* **1959**, *no.* 6 (13), 88–95.

Let $p$ be a prime, $p>2$, let $\left(\frac{n}{p}\right)$ denote the Legendre symbol and let $h>0$, $t>s\geqq 0$. Put

$$S_p(m, s, t, h) = \frac{1}{\sqrt{h}} \sum_{hs<n\leqq ht} \left(\frac{m+n}{p}\right).$$

Generalizing a previous result of H. Davenport and P. Erdős [Publ. Math. Debrecen **2** (1952), 252–265; MR

**14**, 1063] the authors prove that the joint distribution of the quantities $S_p(m, s_j, t_j, h)$ $(j=1, 2, \cdots, k)$, where $m$ runs over a complete system of residues mod $p$, is normal in the limit if $p$ and $h$ both tend to $+\infty$ in such a way that $(\log h)/(\log p) \to 0$, and the mentioned quantities are independent in the limit if the intervals $(s_j, t_j)$ are disjoint. This result is further generalized for the Jacobi symbol and for complex-valued characters with respect to a composite modulus. These results are proved by the method of moments, using the estimates of A. Weil [Proc. Nat. Acad. Sci. U.S.A. **34** (1948), 204–207; MR **10**, 234].

The above results show that when, in applying Monte Carlo methods, a Brownian motion process is needed, this can be modelled by character sums.

*A. Rényi* (Budapest)

Citations: MR 10, 234e = T25-5.

## Q15-12 (26# 4385 )

**Paul, E. M.**

**Density in the light of probability theory.**

*Sankhyā Ser. A* **24** (1962), 103–114.

Let $p_k$ be the $k$th prime, and let $X_1, X_2, \cdots$ be independent random variables with $\Pr\{X_k=n\}=(1-1/p_k)p_k^{-n}$, $n=0, 1, \cdots$. Let $Y_n$ be the random variable $\prod_1^n p_k^{X_k}$ regarded as a mapping of the space of sequences of integers into the integers. Denoting by $D_l(A)$, $D_u(A)$ the lower and upper logarithmic densities of an arbitrary set of integers $A$, the author proves that

$$P(\liminf Y_n^{-1}(A)) \leqq D_l(A) \leqq D_u(A) \leqq P(\limsup Y_n^{-1}(A)).$$

If $Q$ is a probability measure on the reals, a function $f$ from the integers to the reals is said to have a logarithmic measure $Q$ if $Q(c)=0$ implies that the logarithmic density of $\{n \mid f(n)<c\}$ is $Q(-\infty, c)$. If $f$ is such that $f(Y_n)$ converges with probability one to $G$, then $f$ has a logarithmic measure, which corresponds to the distribution of $G$.

The above results are false in general if the logarithmic densities and measures are replaced by the ordinary ones.

*D. A. Darling* (Ann Arbor, Mich.)

Referred to in Q15-14, Q15-16, Q15-21.

## Q15-13 (29# 5805 )

**Novoselov, E. V.**

**A new method in probabilistic number theory. (Russian)**

*Izv. Akad. Nauk SSSR Ser. Mat.* **28** (1964), 307–364.

This paper is a continuation of the author's previous investigations on topological methods in number theory [Učen. Zap. Elabužsk. Gos. Ped. Inst. **8** (1960), 3–23; Izv. Vysš. Učebn. Zaved. Matematika **1961**, no. 1 (20), 119–129; MR **27** #6249; ibid. **1961**, no. 3 (22), 66–79; MR **28** #77; ibid. **1963**, no. 5 (36), 71–88; MR **28** #78].

The ring $S$ of integer rational numbers may be topologized by means of the topology for which the principal ideals constitute a neighbourhood base of 0. By completion of $S$ we get a compact topological ring $\mathfrak{S}$; the elements of $\mathfrak{S}$ are called polyadic numbers. The set $\mathfrak{S}$ is also a bicompact topological group; accordingly, there exists a normed Haar measure $\mu$ on $\mathfrak{S}$. The completion of $\mu$ is a probabilistic measure $P$.

The author gives a number of applications of the theory of measure $P$ and the corresponding integral calculus to the value distribution theory of the arithmetical functions and to the calculation of their means.

In particular, the author obtains some results on the almost periodicity of the arithmetical functions due to Erdős, Hartman, Kac, van Kampen and Wintner [Kac, van Kampen and Wintner, Amer. J. Math. **62** (1940), 107–114; MR **1**, 203; van Kampen and Wintner, ibid. **62** (1940), 613–626; MR **2**, 41; van Kampen, ibid. **62** (1940), 627–634; MR **2**, 41; Erdős and Wintner, ibid. **62** (1940), 635–645; MR **2**, 41; Hartman and Wintner, ibid. **62** (1940), 753–758; MR **2**, 41; Wintner, ibid. **67** (1945), 173–193; MR **6**, 260; Wintner, ibid. **67** (1945), 481–485; MR **7**, 147]. From Kolmogorov's three series criterion on the convergence of the series of the independent random variables he deduces the Erdős theorem [J. London Math. Soc. **13** (1938), 119–127] on the sufficient condition for the existence of the asymptotic distribution law of additive number-theoretic functions. He also proves a theorem of Rényi [Acad. Serbe Sci. Publ. Inst. Math. **8** (1955), 157–162; MR **17**, 944], a theorem of Hardy and Ramanujan [Quart. J. Pure Appl. Math. **48** (1917), 76–92], and some results of the reviewer [*Probabilistic methods in the theory of numbers* (Russian), Gosudarstv. Izdat. Politič. i Naučn. Lit. Litovsk. SSR, Vilna, 1959; MR **23** #A134; second enlarged edition, 1962; MR **26** #3691].

*J. Kubilius* (Vilnius)

Citations: MR 1, 203c = Q20-2; MR 2, 41d = Q20-3; MR 2, 41e = Q20-4; MR 6, 260f = Q20-16; MR 7, 147a = N36-3; MR 17, 944f = N24-23; MR 23# A134 = N60-37; MR 26# 3691 = N60-38; MR 27# 6249 = Q25-16; MR 28# 77 = Q25-17; MR 28# 78 = Q25-18.

## Q15-14 (30# 595 )

**Paul, E. M.**

**Density in the light of probability theory. II.**

*Sankhyā Ser. A* **24** (1962), 209–212.

Part I appeared in Sankhyā Ser. A **24** (1962), 103–114 [MR **26** #4385]. Author's summary: "Let $\{X_n\}$ be a sequence of abstract spaces, each $X_n$ consisting of the points $0, 1, 2, \cdots$. At the point $r$ in $X_n$, we place the probability $1/q_n^r(1-1/q_n)$, $q_n$ being the $n$th prime number. Let $X$ be the product space $X_1X_2\cdots$ and let $P$ be the product measure. Let $J$ be a sequence $\{j_m\}$ of positive integers. Let $S$ be any set of positive integers. $M_J^U(S)$ is the set of vectors $(x_1, x_2, \cdots) \in X$ such that $2^{x_1}\cdots q_n^{x_n} \in S$ for infinitely many $n \in J$. $M_J^L(S)$ is the set of vectors $(x_1, x_2, \cdots) \in X$ such that $2^{x_1}\cdots q_n^{x_n} \in S$ for all sufficiently large $n \in J$. We prove that $P[M_J^L(S)] \leqq \delta_L(S) \leqq \delta^U(S) \leqq P[M_J^U(S)]$ for all sets $S$ if and only if $\log j_{m+1}/\log j_m$ is bounded as $m \to \infty$. $\delta_L$ and $\delta^U$ stand for lower and upper logarithmic densities, respectively. Let $f$ be a finite function defined on the set of positive integers. Suppose for a $J$ satisfying the condition above, $\lim_{m\to\infty} f(2^{x_1}\cdots q_{j_m}^{x_{j_m}})=g(x)$ exists with probability 1. Then $f$ has a distribution and this is the same as that of $g(x)$; we employ logarithmic density."

*D. A. Darling* (Ann Arbor, Mich.)

Citations: MR 26# 4385 = Q15-12.

## Q15-15 (30# 596 )

**Paul, E. M.**

**Density in the light of probability theory. III.**

*Sankhyā Ser. A* **25** (1963), 273–280.

For Part II, see #595 above. Author's summary: "Using magnification methods, we prove the Erdős-Wintner theorem on additive arithmetical functions having distributions, and obtain some generalizations of it. It is also shown that if each of a finite collection of additive functions has a distribution, they have a joint distribution in the sense of logarithmic density."

*D. A. Darling* (Ann Arbor, Mich.)

Referred to in Q15-21.

**Q15-16** **(30# 1996)**

**Billingsley, Patrick**

**An application of Prohorov's theorem to probabilistic number theory.**

*Illinois J. Math.* **8** (1964), 697–704.

For a fixed sequence $\lambda=(\lambda_1, \lambda_2, \cdots)$ of positive constants, let $X_\lambda$ consist of those sequences $x=(x_1, x_2, \cdots)$ of nonnegative integers for which each of the sums $\sum_i \lambda_i x_i'$ and $\sum_i x_i''$ is finite, where $x_i'$ is $x_i$ or 0 according as $x_i \leqq 1$ or $x_i>1$, and $x_i''$ is $x_i$ or 0 according as $x_i>1$ or $x_i \leqq 1$. Under the metric

$$d(x, y) = \sum_i \lambda_i|x_i'-y_i'|+\sum_i |x_i''-y_i''|,$$

$X_\lambda$ is a complete, separable metric space. Denote by $\mathscr{X}_\lambda$ the $\sigma$-field generated by the open sets.

Let $p_i$ be the $i$th prime. For each positive integer $n$ let $\alpha(n)=(\alpha_1(n), \alpha_2(n), \cdots)$, where $\alpha_i(n)$ is the exponent of the prime $p_i$ in the factorization $n=\prod_i p_i^{\alpha_i(n)}$. Let now $\mu_N$ be the probability measure on $\mathscr{X}_\lambda$ corresponding to a mass $1/N$ at each of the points $\alpha(1), \alpha(2), \cdots, \alpha(N)$. By means of Prohorov's theorem on the weak compactness of probability measures [Teor. Verojatnost. i Primenen. **1** (1956), 177–238; MR **18**, 943] the author proves the following theorem: If $\sum_i \lambda_i'/p_i<\infty$, where $\lambda_i'=\lambda_i$ if $\lambda_i \leqq 1$ and $\lambda_i'=1$ if $\lambda_i>1$, then $\mu_N$ converges weakly to some probability measure $\mu$, where the measure $\mu$ on $\mathscr{X}_\lambda$ is uniquely determined by the relation

$$\mu\{x: x_i = v_i, i = 1, \cdots, k\} = \prod_{i=1}^{k} \left(\frac{1}{p_i}\right)^{v_i},$$

valid for any finite sequence $(v_1, \cdots, v_k)$ of nonnegative integers.

If $\mu_N$ converges weakly to $\mu$ and if $A$ is a $\mu$-continuity set, then the natural density $D\{n: \alpha(n) \in A\}=\mu(A)$.

Some results on the distribution of additive arithmetic functions, due to Erdős [J. London Math. Soc. **12** (1937), 7–11], are obtained. A comparison with Paul's results [Sankhyā, Ser. A **24** (1962), 103–114; MR **26** #4385] is given. *J. Kubilius* (Vilnius)

Citations: MR 26# 4385 = Q15-12.

**Q15-17** **(31# 144)**

**Galambos, J.**

**On the distribution of number-theoretical functions.**

*Ann. Univ. Sci. Budapest. Eötvös Sect. Math.* **7** (1964), 25–31.

Let $a(n)$ be the number of essentially distinct Abelian groups of order $n$. The density of the sequence of those numbers $n$, for which $a(n)=k$ $(k=1, 2, \cdots)$, exists. If $S_k$ denotes this density and $P(k)$ is the number of partitions of $k$ into positive parts, then $\sum_{k=1}^{\infty} S_k=1$ and

$$A(s) = \sum_{k=1}^{\infty} S_k k^{-s} = \prod_p \left(1-\frac{1}{p}\right)\left(1+\sum_{k=1}^{\infty} p^{-k}P^{-s}(k)\right)$$

is an entire function. For any $\varepsilon>0$, the number of those positive integers $k \leqq x$ for which $S_k=0$ equals $x+O(x^\varepsilon)$.

The author gives also simple proofs of Schoenberg's theorem on the asymptotic distribution of additive number-theoretical functions [Trans. Amer. Math. Soc. **39** (1936), 315–330] and the theorem of Rényi [Acad. Serbe Sci. Publ. Inst. Math. (Beograd) **8** (1955), 157–162; MR **17**, 944]. *J. Kubilius* (Vilnius)

Citations: MR 17, 944f = N24-23.

**Q15-18** **(33# 5596)**

**Paul, E. M.**

**Density as probability.**

*Math. Student* **32** (1964), 23–24.

Let $p_1, p_2, \cdots$ be the prime numbers in increasing order. Let $x_k$ $(k=1, 2, \cdots)$ be independent random variables such that $P(x_k=r) = p_k^{-r}(1-1/p_k)$ $(r=0, 1, \cdots)$. Let $f(n)$ be a real-valued function on the set of positive integers and put $y_N=f(\prod_{k=1}^{N} p_k^{x_k})$. Let $j_s$ $(s=1, 2, \cdots)$ be a sequence of positive integers such that $\log j_{s+1}/\log j_s$ is bounded. The following theorem is announced without proof: If the sequence $y_{j_s}$ $(s=1, 2, \cdots)$ of random variables tends with probability 1 to a random variable $y$ having the distribution function $F(z)$, then the arithmetic function $f(n)$ has $F(z)$ as its limit distribution in the sense of logarithmic density, i.e.,

$$\lim_{X\to+\infty} (1/\log X) \sum_{f(n)<z, n\leqq X} 1/n = F(z)$$

for every real $z$ which is a point of continuity of $F(z)$.

*A. Rényi* (Budapest)

**Q15-19** **(35# 5409)**

**Postnikov, A. G.**

**Ergodic problems in the theory of congruences and of Diophantine approximations.**

Proceedings of the Steklov Institute of Mathematics, No. 82 (1966). Translated from the Russian by B. Volkmann.

*American Mathematical Society, Providence, R.I.*, 1967. iv+128 *pp*. $5.80.

The Russian original is reviewed below [#5410].

**Q15-20** **(35# 5410)**

**Postnikov, A. G.**

**Ergodic aspects of the theory of congruences and of the theory of Diophantine approximations. (Russian)**

*Trudy Mat. Inst. Steklov.* **82** (1966), 3–112.

This monograph deals with the problems mentioned in the title and summarizes the work done by the author, N. M. Akuliničev, I. I. Pjateckiĭ-Šapiro, R. H. Muhutdinov, A. M. Polosuev and others. Much of the detail of the proofs and several of the results are published here for the first time.

The book consists of an introduction, three chapters and a bibliography containing 59 references. The introduction contains a brief survey of the contents of the book.

Chapter I concerns the distribution of residues, modulo a prime $p$, of a polynomial with integer coefficients and of a matrix exponential function. The main tool of investigation is the well-known estimate of A. Weil for rational exponential sums. The author deduces it comparatively simply from the estimate of the number of solutions of the Diophantine equation $y^p-y=f(x)$ in the finite field of $p^r$ elements, where $f(x)$ is a polynomial with integer coefficients. The main results are the two following theorems. (1) For any fixed non-zero residue class $a_{n+1}$ and any $n$-tuple $(a_1, a_2, \cdots, a_n)$ of residue classes mod $p$, denote by $T^x(a_1, a_2, \cdots, a_n)$ $(x=0, 1, \cdots, p-1)$ the $n$-tuple of residue classes $(f_1^{(x)}, f_2^{(x)}, \cdots, f_n^{(x)})$, where (*) $f_l^{(x)}=\sum_{k=0}^{n-l+1}\binom{n-l+1}{k}a_{n-k+1}x^{n-k-l+1}$. For any positive integers $u_l \leqq p$ $(l=1, \cdots, n)$ let $N(u_1, u_2, \cdots, u_n)$ be the number of $n$-tuples of residue classes $(b_1, b_2, \cdots, b_n)$ among $T^x(a_1, a_2, \cdots, a_n)$ $(x=0, 1, \cdots, p-1)$ satisfying the inequalities $0 \leqq b_l \leqq u_l-1$ $(l=1, 2, \cdots, n)$. Then $|N(u_1, u_2, \cdots, u_n)-u_1u_2\cdots u_n p^{-n+1}| \leqq \frac{1}{2}n(n-1)p^{1/2}\ln^n p$. (2) Let $A$ be an integral $n\times n$ matrix, $\det A \not\equiv 0 \bmod p$, such that its characteristic equation is not reducible in the field $k_p$. Let $\tau$ be the least positive integer satisfying the equality $A^\tau Y=Y$ for every $n$-tuple $Y$ of residue classes mod $p$. For any positive integers $u_l \leqq p$ $(l=1, 2, \cdots, n)$ let $N_1(u_1, u_2, \cdots, u_n)$ be the number of the $n$-tuples of residue classes $(b_1, b_2, \cdots, b_n)$ among $A^xY$ $(x=0, 1, \cdots, \tau-1)$ satisfying the inequalities $0 \leqq b_l \leqq u_l-1$ $(l=1, 2, \cdots, n)$. Then for any non-zero $n$-tuple $Y$ of residue classes,

$|N_1(u_1, u_2, \cdots, u_n) - \tau u_1 u_2 \cdots u_n p^{-n}| \leqq 2p^{n/2} \ln^n p$.

Chapter II begins with some information on the metric theory of dynamical systems. Then the author considers a dynamical system connected with the distribution of the fractional parts of a polynomial. Let $\Omega$ be the unit $n$-dimensional hypercube. For any irrational $a_{n+1}$ and every $(a_1, a_2, \cdots, a_n) \in \Omega$ let $T^x(a_1, a_2, \cdots, a_n) = (\{f_1^{(x)}\}, \{f_2^{(x)}\}, \cdots, \{f_n^{(x)}\})$, where $f_l^{(x)}$ is defined by (*) and $\{v\}$ denotes the fractional part of $v$. The set $\Omega$, the Lebesgue measure and the sequence of transformations $T^x$ ($x = 0, 1, \cdots$) form a dynamical system which is ergodic. The cases $n=1, 2$ are discussed in detail.

In Chapter III the author gives the construction of J. Ville [*Étude critique de la notion de collectif*, Gauthier-Villars, Paris, 1939] of a number $\alpha$ with a given law of distribution of the fractional parts of $\alpha g^x$ ($x=0, 1, \cdots$), where $g \geqq 2$ is a given integer.

Let $A$ be an integral $n \times n$ matrix, det $A \neq 0$, such that no eigenvalue of $A$ is a root of unity. Then the transformation $Y \to AY$ mod 1 of the $n$-dimensional hypercube $\Omega$ unto itself is ergodic with respect to Lebesgue measure. It satisfies the mixing condition.

The criterion of I. I. Pjateckiĭ-Šapiro [Izv. Akad. Nauk SSSR Ser. Mat. **15** (1951), 47–52; MR **13**, 213] and its generalizations on the uniform distribution of the fractional parts of the exponential function $\alpha g^x$ as well as of the matrix exponential function $A^x Y$ are proved.

Finally, the author states an estimate of the rate of convergence in the central limit theorem of R. M. Fortet [Studia Math. **9** (1940), 54–70; MR **3**, 169] and I. S. Kac [Ann. of Math. (2) **47** (1946); MR **7**, 436] for sums $n^{-1/2} \sum_{x=0}^{n-1} \varphi(\alpha g^x)$, where $\varphi(u)$ is a real-valued periodic function with period 1.

{For an English translation, see #5409 above.}

*J. Kubilius* (Vilnius)

Citations: MR 3, 169e = K15-4; MR 7, 436f = K15-7; MR 13, 213d = K15-14.

## Q15-21 (38# 2114 )

**Paul, E. M.**

**Some properties of additive arithmetical functions.**

*Sankhyā Ser. A* **29** (1967), 279–282.

The author shows that if an additive arithmetic function $f$ has a distribution, every value assumed by $f$ is in the spectrum of the distribution; roughly speaking, this means that if $f$ assumes a value once, it assumes that value or a value near to it fairly frequently. He shows also that if $f$ has a non-uniform distribution (in the sense of logarithmic or natural density) on an open interval, it has distribution on $(-\infty, \infty)$. He conjectures that the same result holds for uniform distribution [see H. Delange, Ann. Sci. École Norm. Sup. (3) **78** (1961), 1–29; MR **30** #71]. Finally, the author studies the joint distribution of infinitely many additive functions. He uses measure-theoretic methods established by himself [Sankhyā Ser. A **24** (1962), 103–114; MR **26** #4385; ibid. **25** (1963), 273–280; MR **30** #596].

*H. Halberstam* (Nottingham)

Citations: MR 26# 4385 = Q15-12; MR 30# 71 = N36-37; MR 30# 596 = Q15-15.

## Q15-22 (41# 3425 )

**Kogan, I. A.**

**A certain problem of Itô and McKean on the massivity of the set of prime numbers. (Russian)**

*Mat. Zametki* **7** (1970), 211–215.

K. Itô and H. P. McKean [Illinois J. Math. **4** (1960), 119–132; MR **22** #12317] raised the following problem. Given a symmetric random walk on the lattice of integral points in $R^3$, is the set of points on the axes whose coordinates are prime numbers a massive set? The author answers the question affirmatively. He shows the following theorem: The set $A = \{(p_n, 0, 0)\}$, $p_n$ denotes the $n$th prime, is massive (that means: the hitting probability is one). He uses the theory of capacity and some deeper result concerning the prime number function $\pi(x)$. Furthermore, he shows (exhibiting an example): If the two sets $B = \{(b_n, 0, 0)\}$ and $D = \{(d_n, 0, 0)\}$ are massive, a set $C = \{(c_n, 0, 0)\}$ with $b_n < c_n < d_n$ need not be massive. This seems to forbid an easier proof of the foregoing theorem with help of the inequality $n \log n < p_n < 2n \log n$.

*F. Schweiger* (Salzburg)

## Q15-23 (43# 4161 )

**Linnik, Ju. V.**

**A certain application of number theory to mathematical statistics. (Russian)**

*Mat. Zametki* **7** (1970), 383–388.

Let $k \geqq 5$ be a square-free integer (if $k$ is even we suppose that it is not of the form $2(2^s+1)$), let $x_1, \cdots, x_n$ be a sample with replacement and let $P_{k-1}(\ )$ be a polynomial of, degree $\leqq k-1$.

The following result is proved. If $n^{-1} \sum_{i=1}^n (x_i - \bar{x})^k + P_{k-1}(x_1 - \bar{x}, \cdots, x_n - \bar{x})$ and $\bar{x}$ are stochastically independent and the sample size $n \geqq 2(2^k k! + 1)^{k+1}$, then the sample is normal.

The proof depends on the theory of divisibility of rational integers.

{This article has appeared in English translation [Math. Notes **7** (1970), 230–233].}

*J. Kubilius* (Vilnius)

# Q20 FOURIER ANALYSIS, APPROXIMATION THEORY AND FUNCTIONAL ANALYSIS

See also Section A36, Chapter F (especially Sections F25, F30, F60), and Sections K25, K40.

See also reviews A34-4, A66-15, C15-23, F10-6, F10-67, F70-7, F70-15, J12-3, J20-10, J20-13, J20-30, J76-64, K05-15, K05-22, K10-10, K10-11, K10-12, K10-44, K10-47, K15-28, K15-73, K20-6, K20-10, K20-11, K35-23, K40-32, K40-43, K40-64, K45-1, K45-23, M15-1, M15-4, M15-7, M15-14, M30-2, M30-3, M30-13, M30-21, M30-36, M40-22, M45-9, M50-2, M55-42, M55-82, N04-3, N20-41, N36-1, N36-12, N36-29, N60-1, N60-3, N64-23, P20-1, P20-8, P28-65, Q05-62, Q25-15, Q25-34, R06-1, R06-13, R06-24, R06-38, R42-36, R56-12, T40-7, Z02-4.

## Q20-1 (1, 136a)

**Kac, M.** **Almost periodicity and the representation of integers as sums of squares.** Amer. J. Math. **62**, 122–126 (1940).

The author discusses almost periodic properties of the sequence $f_s(n) = n^{1-\frac{1}{2}s} r_s(n)$, where $r_s(n)$ is the number of representations of $n$ as a sum of $s$ squares, in relation to the Hardy-Littlewood singular series

$$\rho_s(n) = \frac{\Pi^{\frac{1}{2}s}}{\Gamma(\frac{1}{2}s)} \sum_{\substack{h,k \\ 0 \leqq h < k;\ (h,k)=1}} k^{-s} S_{hk}^s e\left(-\frac{hn}{k}\right),$$

where

$$S_{hk}=\sum_{j=0}^{k-1} e\left(\frac{hj^2}{k}\right), \quad e(x)=e^{2\pi ix},$$

regarded as a formal Fourier series $\sum_\lambda a_s(\lambda)e(-\lambda n)$ with

$$a_s(\lambda)=\lim_{N\to\infty} N^{-1}\sum_{n=1}^{N} f_s(n)e(\lambda n), \qquad 0\leqq\lambda<1.$$

For $5\leqq s\leqq 8$ it is inferred from Hardy's identity $f_s(n)=\rho_s(n)$ and the absolute convergence of $\rho_s(n)$ that $f_s(n)$ is a uniformly a.p. sequence. For $s=4$ it is proved (from Jacobi's formula for $r_4(n)$), and for $s=3$ it is stated, that $f_s(n)$ is a.p. ($B^2$). It is suggested that the same should be true for $s>8$. [This is so since $f_s(n)=\rho_s(n)+o(1)$ as $n\to\infty$.] It is shown that $f_2(n)=r_2(n)$ is not even a.p. ($B^1$).

*A. E. Ingham* (Berkeley, Calif.).

## Q20-2 (1, 203c)

**Kac, M., van Kampen, E. R. and Wintner, Aurel. Ramanujan sums and almost periodic functions.** Amer. J. Math. **62**, 107–114 (1940).

Ramanujan has [Trans. Cambridge Philos. Soc. **22**, 259–276 (1918); Collected Papers, 179–199] obtained expressions of a variety of arithmetical functions $f(n)$ in the form of a series $\sum_{r=1}^{\infty} a_r c_r(n)$, where $c_r(n)$ denotes the sum $\sum_m \cos(2\pi(m/r)n)$ extended over all $m$ in the interval $0<m\leqq r$ which are prime to $r$. In the present paper it is shown that for a certain class of functions $f(n)$ the trigonometrical series in question are almost periodic Fourier series of the functions in the sense of Besicovitch. The main result is that, if $f(n)$ is a strongly multiplicative function (that is, $f(n)=\Pi_{p|n} f(p)$) for which

$$\sum_p \frac{|f(p)-1|}{p}$$

is convergent, then $f(n)$ is almost periodic in the sense of Besicovitch and has the Fourier series $f(n)\sim\sum_{n=1}^{\infty} a_r c_r(n)$, where

$$a_r=\prod_p\left(1+\frac{f(p)-1}{p}\right)\prod_{p|r}\frac{f(p)-1}{f(p)-1+p}$$

or 0 according as $r$ is or is not squarefree. *B. Jessen.*

Referred to in Q15-13.

## Q20-3 (2, 41d)

**van Kampen, E. R. and Wintner, Aurel. On the almost periodic behavior of multiplicative number-theoretical functions.** Amer. J. Math. **62**, 613–626 (1940).

A function $f(n)$ is multiplicative if $f(n_1n_2)=f(n_1)f(n_2)$ whenever $(n_1, n_2)=1$ and $f(1)=1$. If $p$ is a fixed prime number, a function $g(n)=g_p(n)$ is "prime" if $g(np^k)=g(p^k)$ whenever $(n, p)=1$. Any $f(n)$ is a product $\Pi_p g_p(n)$. The authors prove theorems of the following type. A prime function $g(n)$ is almost periodic ($B$) if and only if $\sum p^{-k}|g(p^k)|<\infty$. Also, the product of a finite number of such functions $g(n)$ which belong to distinct prime numbers, and for which $g(1)=1$, is almost periodic ($B$) if each factor is. A multiplicative function $f(n)\geqq 0$ is almost periodic ($B$) if $\sum_{n=1}^{\infty}|h(n)|<\infty$, where $h(n)$ is the multiplicative function for which $h(p^k)=p^{-k}\{f(p^k)-f(p^{k-1})\}$. Also the Fourier series of $f(n)$ is $\sum_{m=1}^{\infty} a_m c_m(n)$, where $a_m=\sum_{l=1}^{\infty} h(ml)$ and

$$c_m(n)=\sum_s \exp\left(2\pi i\frac{s}{m}n\right), \quad 1\leqq s\leqq m;\ (s, m)=1.$$

For instance,

$$\frac{\sigma_\alpha(n)}{n^\alpha}\sim J(\alpha+1)\sum_{m=1}^{\infty}\frac{c_m(n)}{m^{\alpha+1}}, \qquad \alpha>0.$$

*S. Bochner* (Princeton, N. J.).

Referred to in Q15-13.

## Q20-4 (2, 41e)

**van Kampen, E. R. On uniformly almost periodic multiplicative and additive functions.** Amer. J. Math. **62**, 627–634 (1940).

The author discusses uniform almost periodicity (Bohr) of a function $f(n)$ which is multiplicative [see the preceding review] or of a function $g(n)$ which is additive, that is, $g(n_1n_2)=g(n_1)+g(n_2)$ if $(n_1, n_2)=1$ and $g(1)=0$. Purely formally, just as $f(n)$ is an infinite product of factors belonging to different primes, so $g(n)$ is an infinite sum of such terms. The author's main result is that $f(n)$ is u.a.p. if and only if the infinite product is uniformly convergent and that $g(n)$ is u.a.p. if and only if the infinite sum is uniformly convergent. Furthermore, in the case of additive functions the result also holds for functions which are complex-valued.

*S. Bochner* (Princeton, N. J.).

Referred to in Q15-13.

## Q20-5 (2, 41f)

**Erdös, Paul and Wintner, Aurel. Additive functions and almost periodicity ($B^2$).** Amer. J. Math. **62**, 635–645 (1940).

For additive functions [see the preceding review] the authors prove a clear-cut criterion of almost periodicity (valid also for complex-valued functions) which apparently has no analogue for the more difficult type of multiplicative functions [see the second review above]. The theorem states that an additive function $f(n)$ is almost periodic ($B^2$) if and only if both series

$$\sum_p\frac{f(p)}{p}, \quad \sum_{p,l}\frac{|f(p^l)|^2}{p^l}$$

are convergent (the letter $p$ to run over all primes, and the exponent $l$ over all positive integers). The proof includes interesting points. *S. Bochner* (Princeton, N. J.).

## Q20-6 (2, 41g)

**Hartman, Philip and Wintner, Aurel. On the almost periodicity of additive number-theoretical functions.** Amer. J. Math. **62**, 753–758 (1940).

It was known [cf. the preceding review] that an additive function $f(n)$, $n=1, 2, \cdots$, is almost periodic ($B$) if and only if the two series

$$\sum_p p^{-1}f(p), \quad \sum_{l=1}^{\infty}\sum_p p^{-l}|f(p^l)|^2$$

are convergent, $p$=prime number. The authors obtain the same conclusion replacing those two series by the four series

$$\sum_p p^{-1}f(p), \quad \sum_p p^{-1}|f^+(p)|^2,$$

$$\sum_{l=2}^{\infty}\sum_p p^{-l}|f(p^l)|, \quad \sum_{|f(p)|\geqq 1} p^{-1}|f(p)|.$$

In this connection, $f^+(p)=f(p)$ if $|f(p)|<1$ and $=1$ if $|f(p)|\geqq 1$. *S. Bochner* (Princeton, N. J.).

## Q20-7 (2, 249a)

**Wintner, Aurel. On Dirichlet's divisor problem.** Proc. Nat. Acad. Sci. U. S. A. **27**, 135–137 (1941).

Let $D(x)=d(1)+d(2)+\cdots+d([x])$, where $d(n)$ is the number of divisors of $n$; and $F(x)=x(\log x+2C-1)$. Let $\bar{D}(x)$ be the limit of $\frac{1}{2}\{D(x+h)+D(x-h)\}$ as $h\to 0$. The function $Q(t)=\{\bar{D}(t^2)-F(t^2)\}/t^{\frac{1}{2}}$ is said to be almost periodic ($B^2$), $1\leqq t<\infty$, and to have the Fourier series

$$Q(t)\sim\frac{1}{2^{\frac{1}{2}}\pi}\sum_{n=1}^{\infty}\frac{d(n)}{n^{\frac{3}{4}}}\cos(4\pi n^{\frac{1}{2}}t-\pi/4).$$

The proof is to be published elsewhere. *G. Pall.*

## Q20-8 (3, 69f)

**Erdös, P., Kac, M., van Kampen, E. R. and Wintner, A. Ramanujan sums and almost periodic functions.** Studia Math. **9**, 43–53 (1940). (English. Ukrainian summary)

If $f(n)$ has the property $f(n_1n_2)=f(n_1)f(n_2)$ and $f(p)=f(p^2)=f(p^3)=\cdots$ ($p$=prime), and if $\sum|f(p)-1|/p$ is finite, then the sequence $\{f(n)\}$ is almost periodic $(B)$ and the familiar Ramanujan expansion

$$c+c\sum_{q>1}\sum_{m}\sum_{p|q}\frac{f(p)-1}{f(p)-1+p}\cos\left(2\pi\frac{m}{q}p\right)$$

(with the familiar restrictions on $p$, $q$, $m$) is its formal Fourier expansion. The sequence is almost periodic $(B^2)$ if $\sum|f(p)^2-1|/p$ is also finite and it is uniformly almost periodic if $\sum|f(p)-1|$ is finite. *S. Bochner.*

## Q20-9 (3, 270f)

**Hartman, Philip and Wintner, Aurel. Additive functions and almost periodicity.** Duke Math. J. **9**, 112–119 (1942).

An additive function $f(n)$ (in the number-theoretic sense of this paper) is one which has the property that $f(mn)=f(m)+f(n)$ whenever $m$ and $n$ are relatively prime. Such functions have been shown to have certain almost periodic properties when suitably restricted, and the authors now show that an additive function is almost periodic in the sense of Weyl ($W^2$ a.p.) if and only if it is bounded. It is also shown that an additive function has a uniform mean value if and only if it is bounded, and a number of illustrations are given to show the difference between the ordinary mean value and the more restrictive uniform mean value which exists only when $[f(m+1)+\cdots+f(m+n)]/n$ approaches a constant limit uniformly for positive $m$ as $n\to\infty$. *R. H. Cameron* (Cambridge, Mass.).

## Q20-10 (3, 270g)

**Wintner, Aurel. Prime divisors and almost periodicity.** J. Math. Phys. Mass. Inst. Tech. **21**, 52–56 (1942).

Using a representation by Ramanujan sums the author shows that the function

$$\delta(n)=\sum_{p|n}1-\sum_{p^k|n}1$$

is almost periodic $(B^\lambda)$ for every $\lambda>0$ no matter how large. However, since it is unbounded, it is not almost periodic Bohr, and, in fact, its asymptotic distribution has arbitrarily large jumps. *S. Bochner* (Princeton, N. J.).

## Q20-11 (5, 3c)

**Salem, R. Sets of uniqueness and sets of multiplicity.** Trans. Amer. Math. Soc. **54**, 218–228 (1943).

Let $0<\xi<\frac{1}{2}$ be a fixed number and let $P$ denote the perfect and nondense set constructed as follows. The interval $0\leqq\theta\leqq2\pi$ is divided into three parts, of lengths proportional to $\xi$, $1-2\xi$, $\xi$, respectively, and the interior of the middle part is removed. With each of the two remaining intervals we proceed similarly, and so on. What is finally left is the set $P$. It is of measure 0, and the problem is to determine the values of $\xi$ for which $P$ is a set of uniqueness for trigonometric series.

Let $\theta=1/\xi>2$. For the case of rational $\xi$ the problem has been solved: the set $P$ is one of uniqueness if and only if $\theta$ is an integer [cf. N. Bary, Rec. Math. [Mat. Sbornik] N.S. **2**(44), 699–722 (1937); R. Kershner, Amer. J. Math. **58**, 450–452 (1936)]. In particular, Cantor's well-known ternary set ($\theta=3$) is a set of uniqueness, a result known for a long time [Rajchman, Fund. Math. **3**, 287–302 (1922)]. The present paper presents the solution of the problem for general $\xi$: a necessary and sufficient condition that $P$ be a set of uniqueness is that $\theta$ be an algebraic integer all of whose conjugates are inside the circle $|z|=1$. Basic for the (very interesting) argument are certain results of Pisot [Ann. Scuola Norm. Super. Pisa (2) **7**, 205–248 (1938)] and Vijayaraghavan [Proc. Cambridge Philos. Soc. **37**, 349–357 (1941); these Rev. **3**, 274]. It also turns out that, if $P$ is a set of uniqueness, then it is a sum of a finite number of sets of type $H$, first considered by Rajchman [loc. cit.]. By choosing appropriate $\xi$'s, we obtain sets of uniqueness whose Hausdorff dimension is as close to 1 as we wish.

*A. Zygmund* (South Hadley, Mass.).

Citations: MR 3, 274c = K25-5.

Referred to in Q20-12, Q20-13.

## Q20-12 (6, 47c)

**Salem, R. Sets of uniqueness and sets of multiplicity. II.** Trans. Amer. Math. Soc. **56**, 32–49 (1944).

The author investigates the "uniqueness" and "multiplicity" character of certain "unsymmetric" perfect sets on $(0, 2\pi)$ [for the terminology, see the first part of the paper [same Trans. **54**, 218–228 (1943); these Rev. **5**, 3], where the "symmetric" case is solved completely]. We quote the main result of the paper which clearly shows that the general situation in the theory of uniqueness of trigonometric series is rather complex, and that a proper key will not be easy to find. Given an interval $I=(a, b)$ of length $L=b-a$, let us consider $d+1$ "white" subintervals, each of length $L\xi$, $0<\xi<1/(d+1)$. The origin of the first and the end-point of the last coincide with $a$ and $b$, respectively. The distances of the origins of the "white" intervals from $a$ will be denoted by $L\alpha_0=0, L\alpha_1, \cdots, L\alpha_d$. The numbers $d, \xi, \alpha_1, \alpha_2, \cdots, \alpha_d$ are fixed once and for all, and we consider the operation $D$ of removing from $I$ the interiors of the $d$ "black" intervals that separate the "white" ones. We first apply $D$ to the interval $(0, 2\pi)$, then to each of the remaining "white" intervals, and so on. What is left is a perfect set $P$ of measure 0. It turns out that $P$ is a set of uniqueness if and only if the following conditions are satisfied: (i) $\theta=1/\xi$ is a "Pisot-Vijayaraghavan" number, that is, an algebraic integer whose conjugates are all inside the unit circle, (ii) $\alpha_1, \alpha_2, \cdots, \alpha_d$ are algebraic numbers of the field $K(\theta)$. *A. Zygmund* (South Hadley, Mass.).

Citations: MR 5, 3c = Q20-11.

Referred to in Q20-13.

## Q20-13 (10, 34a)

**Salem, R. Rectifications to the papers: Sets of uniqueness and sets of multiplicity, I and II.** Trans. Amer. Math. Soc. **63**, 595–598 (1948).

In the papers cited in the title [same Trans. **54**, 218–228 (1943); **56**, 32–49 (1944); these Rev. **5**, 3; **6**, 47] the author gives the theorem that a necessary and sufficient condition for a perfect set $P$ of constant ratio $\xi$ to be a set of uniqueness for trigonometric series is that $\theta=1/\xi$ be an algebraic integer all of whose conjugates are inside the unit circle. The author has now found that the proof of the sufficiency of the condition is not conclusive and that this part of the problem remains open. [The proof of the necessity is not affected.] Some new partial results are obtained for the sufficiency condition from which it follows in particular that the old result remains valid if $\theta=1/\xi$ is a quadratic integer whose conjugate is inside the unit circle.

*A. Zygmund* (Chicago, Ill.).

Citations: MR 5, 3c = Q20-11; MR 6, 47c = Q20-12.

**Q20-14** **(5, 173c)**

**Wintner, Aurel. On an harmonic analysis of the irregularities in Goldbach's problem.** Revista Ci., Lima **45**, 175–182 (1943).

Supplementing Goldbach's conjecture, Sylvester has surmised that the number of decompositions of an even integer $n$ into a sum of two primes is asymptotically $(An/\log^2 n)f(n)$, where

$$f(n)=\prod_{q|n}((q-1)/(q-2)).$$

The author finds that $f(n)$ is substantially a multiplicative function and he points out that by previous results of his and others it is almost periodic $B^\lambda$ for arbitrary large $\lambda$. There is a similar result for decomposition in $r$ primes, $r>2$. *S. Bochner* (Princeton, N. J.).

**Q20-15** **(6, 172g)**

**Wintner, Aurel. Diophantine approximations and Hilbert's space.** Amer. J. Math. **66**, 564–578 (1944).

This paper deals with the completeness in Hilbert space of certain sequences of functions of importance in number theory and with transformations in Hilbert space based on the sieve of Eratosthenes. The sequence $\{1, \varphi(nt)\}$ is shown to be $L^2$-complete (closed) on the interval $0\leqq t\leqq\frac{1}{2}$ if

$$\phi(t)\sim\sum_{k=1}^{\infty} k^{-\lambda}\cos 2\pi kt, \qquad \Re(\lambda)>\tfrac{1}{2};$$

in particular, this is true for $\phi(t)=t-[t]$. For more general functions whose Fourier coefficients are $O(k^{-\frac{1}{2}-\epsilon})$, it is shown that $\sum c_n\phi(nt)$ converges in the $L^2$ sense whenever $c_k=O(k^{-\frac{1}{2}-\epsilon})$.

It is shown from the theory of bounded infinite matrices that the transformation

$$y_k=\sum_{d|k}\lambda_{k/d}x_d$$

takes each point $(x_1, x_2, \cdots)$ in Hilbert space into a point $(y_1, y_2, \cdots)$ of Hilbert space if and only if $\sum\lambda_k k^{-s}$ is regular and bounded in $\Re(s)>0$; this implies that $c_k=O(k^{-\frac{1}{2}-\epsilon})$ in the above theorem cannot be weakened to $\sum|c_k|^2<\infty$ unless $\sum a_k k^{-s}$ and $\sum b_k k^{-s}$ are regular and bounded in $\Re(s)>0$.

Finally, let $\sum_p$ denote summation over all primes and $(k; l)=kl(\text{g.c.d. of } k \text{ and } l)^{-2}$. Then it is stated (among other related theorems) that, if $\lambda_1, \lambda_2, \cdots$ is a real nontrivial sequence satisfying $\lambda_{mn}=\lambda_m\lambda_n$ and $\sum_p\lambda_p{}^2<\infty$, then $\{\lambda_{(k;\, l)}\}$ is a bounded matrix if and only if $\prod_p[1+(p^s-1)^{-1}\lambda_p]$ is regular and bounded in $\Re(s)>0$. [It appears to the reviewer that the product should be $\prod_p[1+(p^s-\lambda_p)^{-1}\lambda_p]$. We note also that $b=n^{-\frac{1}{2}}\log(n+1)$ on line 3 of page 570 should be $b_n=n^{-\frac{1}{2}}/\log(n+1)$.] *R. H. Cameron.*

**Q20-16** **(6, 260f)**

**Wintner, Aurel. Number-theoretical almost-periodicities.** Amer. J. Math. **67**, 173–193 (1945).

The author proves, among others, the following results. Let $f(n)$ be a function. Consider the unique $f'(n)$ which satisfies $f(n)=\sum_{d|n}f'(d)$. Assume that $\sum|f'(k)|/k<\infty$. Then $f(n)$ is almost periodic $B$, and it has the Fourier series $f(n)\sim\sum_{r=1}^{\infty}a_r c_r(n)$, where

$$c_r(n)=\sum_{\substack{(s,r)=1\\ 1\leqq s\leqq r}}\epsilon(ns/\pi), \qquad \epsilon(x)=e^{2\pi ix},$$

and $a_r=\sum_{r|k}f'(k)/k$. An analogous theorem is proved for the representation $f(n)=\sum f^*(l)$, where the sum is over $1\leqq l<n$, $(l, n)=1$, if $\sum_{k=1}^{\infty}|f^*(k)|\varphi(k)/k$ converges. Another interesting result is that, if $f(n)$ is almost periodic $B$ (or even if $f(n)$ and $|f(n)|$ have mean values), then $\sum f'(\kappa)/k$ converges. *P. Erdös* (Stanford University, Calif.).

Referred to in Q15-13.

**Q20-17** **(7, 365i)**

**Romanoff, N. P. On a special orthonormal system and its connection with theory of primes.** Rec. Math. [Mat. Sbornik] N.S. **16**(58), 353–364 (1945). (Russian. English summary).

Let $B_k(z)$ be the $k$th Bernoullian polynomial (for example, $B_1(z)=z-\frac{1}{2}$) and let $B_k=B_k(0)$. For each $k$ the author considers the system of functions $\theta_{n,k}(x)$ $(n=1, 2, \cdots)$ defined by $\theta_{n,k}(x)=B_k(nx-[nx])$ in the interval $0\leqq x\leqq 1$ and obtains from them a normal orthogonal set $S_k$ of functions

$$\psi_{n,k}(x)=\left\{\frac{k!^2}{(2k)!}|B_{2k}|\varphi_{2k}(n)\right\}^{-\frac{1}{2}}\sum_{d|n}\mu(n/d)d^k\theta_{d,k}(x)$$

of $L^2(0, 1)$. Here $\mu(n)$ is the Möbius function and

$$\varphi_{2k}(n)=\sum_{d|n}\mu(n/d)d^{2k}.$$

[The right hand sides of formulae (22) and (23) on page 361 should be multiplied by $\sqrt{2}$ and by $1/\sqrt{2}$, respectively.] The system $S_k$ is not, as it stands, complete. However, it is shown (in detail for the case $k=1$) that the modified system consisting of unity, $S_k$ and $S_{k+1}$ forms a complete orthonormal system for $L^2(0, 1)$. Parseval's theorem then leads to a number of identities which may have applications to the study of the order of $\sum_{n\leqq x}\mu(n)$ and to other similar problems of Diophantine approximation of the type considered by Hecke, Behnke, Hardy and Littlewood. [Cf., for example, Koksma, Diophantische Approximationen, Ergebnisse der Math., vol. 4, no. 4, Springer, Berlin, 1936, chap. 9.] *R. A. Rankin* (Cambridge, England).

Referred to in Q20-23.

**Q20-18** **(7, 508a)**

**Wintner, Aurel. The values of the norms in algebraic number fields.** Amer. J. Math. **68**, 223–229 (1946).

A nonartificial example is given of a multiplicative function $F(n)$, whose mean value $M(F)=\lim_{m\to\infty}\sum_1^m F(n)/m$ exists, but which is not almost periodic $(B)$. Let $\mathfrak{K}$ be an algebraic number field of degree greater than 1 and let $F(n)$ denote the number of integral ideals of $\mathfrak{K}$ whose norm is $n$. It is proved that $F(n)=0$ for almost all natural numbers $n$. Since, on the other hand, $M(F)\neq 0$ ($M(F)$ being the residue at $s=1$ of Dedekind's $\zeta$-function $\zeta(s, \mathfrak{K})$), $F(n)$ cannot be almost-periodic $(B)$. [The assertion (12) is derived from the erroneous formula (11): $F(p^i)\leqq C$, $C$ independent of $i$ and $p$. However, (12) can easily be proved otherwise.]

*N. G. de Bruijn* (Eindhoven).

**Q20-19** **(8, 9a)**

**de Bruijn, N. G. Almost periodic multiplicative functions.** Nieuw Arch. Wiskunde (2) **22**, 81–95 (1943). (Dutch)

The author establishes necessary and sufficient conditions for an arithmetic multiplicative function to be almost periodic in the sense of Bohr. *M. Kac* (Ithaca, N. Y.).

**Q20-20** **(8, 9c)**

**Romanoff, N. P. Hilbert space and the theory of numbers.** Bull. Acad. Sci. URSS. Sér. Math. [Izvestia Akad. Nauk SSSR] **10**, 3–34 (1946). (Russian. English summary)

A sequence $\{f_r\}$ $(r=1, 2, \cdots)$ of elements of a Hilbert space $H$ is called a $D_\varrho$-sequence if the scalar product

$(f_m, f_n) = g\{(m, n)\}$ for all $m, n$, where $g(r)$ is a given function of the positive integral variable $r$, and $(m, n)$ denotes the highest common factor of $m$ and $n$. The author shows how $D_g$-sequences can be constructed from any given orthonormal sequence in $H$. Thus, if $\{\alpha_r\}$ is an orthonormal sequence, and $\omega(n)$ is any complex-valued function satisfying $\omega(ab) = \omega(a)\omega(b)$, $\omega(a) \neq 0$ for all positive integral $a, b$, and $\sigma = \sum_{k=1}^{\infty} |\omega(k)|^2 < \infty$, then $\{f_n\} = \{\overline{\omega(n)}^{-1} \sum_{k=1}^{\infty} \omega(k) \alpha_{kn}\}$ is a $D_g$-sequence for $g(n) = \sigma |\omega(n)|^{-2}$, and a second orthonormal sequence $\{\psi_n\}$ is given by

$$\psi_n = \{\sigma\Omega(n)\}^{-\frac{1}{2}} \sum_{d|n} \mu(n/d) f_d,$$

where $\Omega(n) = \sum_{d|n} \mu(n/d) |\omega(d)|^{-2}$ and $\mu(n)$ is the Möbius function. Furthermore, if $\{\alpha_n\}$ is complete in a subspace $H'$ of $H$ then so is $\{\psi_n\}$. The transition from $\{\alpha_n\}$ to $\{\psi_n\}$ defines a transformation of matrix $C_\omega = \|c_{ik}\|$, where

$$c_{ik} = (\psi_i, \alpha_k) = \frac{\omega(k)}{\{\sigma\Omega(i)\}^{\frac{1}{2}}} \sum_{d|(i,k)} \mu(i/d) |\omega(d)|^{-2}.$$

From the known properties of orthonormal sequences in Hilbert space it can be concluded that $C_\omega$ is unitary, but the author gives, in addition, two direct proofs, the second of which arises as a particular case of a discussion of the form of the matrix $T = \|t_{ik}\| = C_{\omega_1}^* C_\omega$, where $\omega(n)$ and $\omega_1(n)$ are multiplicative functions of the type mentioned above. Complicated expressions for $t_{ik}$ are derived in terms of infinite products over the primes. Similar results are also derived for biorthogonal sequences and for functions $\omega(n)$ which may vanish for certain values of $n$.

The two alternative representations $(F, G) = \sum_{k=1}^{\infty} a_k \bar{b}_k = \sum_{k=1}^{\infty} (F, \psi_n)\overline{(G, \psi_n)}$ of the scalar product of two elements $F = \sum a_k \alpha_k$ and $G = \sum b_k \alpha_k$ ($\sum |a_k|^2 < \infty$, $\sum |b_k|^2 < \infty$) in the space lead, for the choice $\omega(n) = n^{-\frac{1}{2}s}$ ($s > 1$), to the identity

$$(*) \qquad \zeta(s) \sum_{k=1}^{\infty} a_k \bar{b}_k = \sum_{n=1}^{\infty} \{\Omega(n)\}^{-1} A_n \bar{B}_n,$$

where

$$A_n = \sum_{d|n} \mu(n/d) d^{\frac{1}{2}s} \sum_{k=1}^{\infty} k^{-\frac{1}{2}s} a_{kd}$$

and $B_n$ is defined similarly. Several particular cases of (*) are given for different choices of $a_k$, $b_k$. A second paper is to be devoted to the application of the methods developed to the theory of the distribution of primes and to other questions. *R. A. Rankin* (Cambridge, England).

Referred to in A34-14, N04-14, Q20-21, Q20-22, Q20-27, Q20-46, Q20-51.

## Q20-21 (13, 208g)

**Romanov, N. P. Hilbert space and the theory of numbers. II.** Izvestiya Akad. Nauk SSSR. Ser. Mat. **15**, 131–152 (1951). (Russian)

In the first part of this paper [same Izvestiya Ser. Mat. **10**, 3–34 (1946); these Rev. **8**, 9] the author defined and considered the properties of $D_g$-sequences. The present paper contains applications of the results obtained there to different spaces of functions. Two methods are used. In the first any function $F(x)$ of $L^2(0, 1)$ with the property

$$F(mx) = m^{s-1} \sum_{k=0}^{m-1} F\left(x + \frac{k}{m}\right) \quad \text{(all integers } m > 0)$$

is taken, and from it is constructed a sequence of functions $f_n(x) = C^{-\frac{1}{2}} n^s F(nx - [nx])$ possessing the $D_g$-property. Here $C = \int_0^1 F^2 dx$. Orthonormal sequences can be constructed from such sequences $\{f_n\}$ by the methods described in the first part. In the second method a given orthonormal sequence $\{\alpha_n\}$ and multiplicative function $\omega(n)$ are taken, and from them a sequence possessing the $D_g$-property is constructed (see review referred to above). This method has the advantage that if $\{\alpha_n\}$ is complete in a subspace $H'$ of the space $H$ so is the derived sequence. Non-trivial examples, which are too numerous and complicated to quote, are given for different choices of the space and involving, among other functions, the Bernouilli and Legendre polynomials, Laguerre functions as well as number-theoretical functions such as $\Lambda(n)$ and Dirichlet characters $\chi(n)$.

*R. A. Rankin* (Birmingham).

Citations: MR 8, 9c = Q20-20.
Referred to in Q20-30.

## Q20-22 (8, 137c)

**Romanov, N. P. On a special family of infinite unitary matrices.** C. R. (Doklady) Acad. Sci. URSS (N.S.) **52**, 295–297 (1946).

The author restates the main properties of the family of infinite unitary matrices which he derived in an earlier paper [Bull. Acad. Sci. URSS. Sér. Math. [Izvestia Akad. Nauk SSSR] **10**, 3–34 (1946); these Rev. **8**, 9] in terms of an arbitrary sequence of differentiable functions satisfying certain conditions. Orthogonality relations and other properties are deduced from the differential equations satisfied by the matrices. *R. A. Rankin* (Cambridge, England).

Citations: MR 8, 9c = Q20-20.

## Q20-23 (8, 137d)

**Chagleev, P. On a certain orthonormalized sequence.** Bull. Acad. Sci. URSS. Sér. Math. [Izvestia Akad. Nauk SSSR] **10**, 271–276 (1946). (Russian. English summary)

The author shows that the system

$$\rho_n(x) = \{\varphi_2(n)\}^{-\frac{1}{2}} \sum_{d|n} \mu(n/d) dF(dx), \qquad n \text{ odd},$$

is orthonormal in $L^2(0, 1)$. Here $F(x) = 1$ $(0 \leqq x < \frac{1}{2})$, $F(x) = -1$ $(\frac{1}{2} < x \leqq 1)$, $\mu(n)$ is the Möbius function and $\varphi_2(n) = \sum_{d|n} \mu(n/d) d^2$. The system is shown to be complete for the class of functions $\lambda(x)$ (of period 1) belonging to $L^2(0, 1)$ for which $\lambda(1-x) = -\lambda(x)$ and $\lambda(\frac{1}{2}-x) = \lambda(x)$. The method employed is similar to one used by N. P. Romanoff [Rec. Math. [Mat. Sbornik] N.S. **16(58)**, 353–364 (1946); these Rev. **7**, 365] whose orthonormal system $\{\psi_n(x)\}$ is connected with $\{\rho_n(x)\}$ by a simple relation. There are several misprints. *R. A. Rankin* (Cambridge, England).

Citations: MR 7, 365i = Q20-17.

## Q20-24 (8, 316a)

**Delsarte, J. Essai sur l'application de la théorie des fonctions presque périodiques à l'arithmétique.** Ann. Sci. École Norm. Sup. (3) **62**, 185–204 (1945).

The author investigates almost periodic properties and Fourier developments of number theoretic functions. He proves among others the following theorem. Let $f(n)$ be an arbitrary number theoretic function. There exists a mapping $I(n)$ ($n|m$ if and only if $I(n)|I(m)$) so that $f(n) = F(I(n))$, where $F(n)$ is a Besicovitch almost periodic function.

*P. Erdös* (Syracuse, N. Y.).

Referred to in Q20-35.

## Q20-25 (8, 446b)

**Romanov, N. P. The application of functional analysis to questions of the distribution of prime numbers.** Bull. [Izvestiya] Math. Mech. Inst. Univ. Tomsk **3**, 145–173 (1946). (Russian)

The author considers a set of distributive functional operators $L_u$ ($u > 0$) which map a family of functions onto itself and which possess the multiplicative property $L_m L_n = L_{mn}$ for all $m, n$. This property is possessed, for example, by the operator

$$L_u = u^{-\lambda} = \sum_{r=0}^{\infty} \frac{(-\log u)^r}{r!} \lambda^r,$$

where $\lambda$ is an arbitrary linear operator. It is shown that many of the properties of the Riemann zeta-function hold also for the operator $\zeta(s+\lambda)=\sum_{n=1}^{\infty} n^{-s}n^{-\lambda}$ when certain convergence conditions are satisfied and when the expressions obtained are interpreted in a suitable and natural manner. Thus $\zeta(s+\lambda)$ can be continued to the left of its region of absolute convergence and satisfies a functional relation connecting it with $\zeta(1-s-\lambda)$. This relation only differs from that which holds for the ordinary zeta-function in the presence of certain simple operators which vanish when $\lambda$ is a pure number. The occurrence of these extra operators can be attributed to the fact that, in the theory of the Riemann zeta-function, the term $1/(s-1)$ due to the pole at $s=1$ appears first, for $\Re s>1$, as an integral $\frac{1}{2}\int_0^1 t^{\frac{1}{2}(s-1)-1}dt$ and is later identified with the integral $-\frac{1}{2}\int_0^1 t^{\frac{1}{2}(1-s)-1}dt$ when $\Re s<1$. This identification between the two integrals is not always possible in the case of integrals which are operators. *R. A. Rankin.*

## Q20-26 (10, 433g)

**Dinghas, Alexander. Verallgemeinerung eines Hilbertschen Satzes über das Verhalten einer mit den Legendreschen Polynomen zusammenhängenden quadratischen Form.** S.-B. Deutsch. Akad. Wiss. Berlin. Math.-Nat. Kl. **1948**, no. 2, 12 pp. (1948).

It is proved that if $P_n(x)$ is a polynomial of degree $n$ with integer coefficients and $|b-a|<4$, then for sufficiently large $n$ these coefficients can be so chosen as to make $\int_a^b x^{\gamma-1}(1-x)^{\alpha-\gamma}P_n^2(x)dx$ $(\gamma>0, \alpha-\gamma>-1)$ arbitrarily small.

*H. S. A. Potter* (Aberdeen).

## Q20-27 (16, 676g)

**Romanov, N. P. On asymptotic theorems of the theory of numbers.** Akad. Nauk Uzbek. SSR. Trudy Inst. Mat. Meh. **5**, 54–60 (1949). (Russian)

By taking special values in his identity

$$\zeta(s)\sum_{n=1}^{\infty} a_n b_n = \sum_{n=1}^{\infty} \frac{A_n B_n}{\varphi_s(n)}$$

[Izv. Akad. Nauk SSSR. Ser. Mat. **10**, 3–34 (1946); MR **8**, 9] the author obtains a variety of identities such as

$$\sum_{n=1}^{\infty} \lambda(n,s)x^n = -x\zeta(s) - \sum_{n=1}^{\infty} \frac{\mu(n)}{\varphi_s(n)} \sum_{i=1}^{\varphi(n)} \frac{x}{x-\rho_i^{(n)}},$$

where $\rho_i^{(n)}$ runs through the primitive $n$th roots of unity, $|x|<1$, and

$$\lambda(n,s)=\zeta(s)\frac{\varphi_{s-1}(n)}{n^{s-1}} \quad (n>1);\ \lambda(1,s)=0.$$

From this he deduces

$$\lim_{x\to\exp(2\pi il/k)} (1-|x|)\sum_{n=1}^{\infty}\lambda(n,s)x^n = \frac{\mu(k)}{\varphi_s(k)},$$

where $(k,l)=1$, and a similar relation involving a function $\Lambda(n,s)$. This is obtained by letting $x\to\exp(2\pi il/k)$ in each term of an infinite series, without anything being said to justify the inversion of limiting operations involved.

Since $\lambda(n,s)\to\Lambda(n)$ as $s\to1$, we should have, if the order of limiting operations $x\to\exp(2\pi il/k)$, $s\to1$, can be inverted, that

$$\lim_{x\to\exp(2\pi il/k)} (1-|x|)\sum_{n=1}^{\infty}\Lambda(n)x^n = \frac{\mu(k)}{\varphi(k)}$$

a result equivalent to the Prime Number Theorem. By using a theorem of Hardy and Littlewood and by means of some rather complicated analysis which is only briefly sketched, it is shown that this inversion can be justified, and that the corresponding result for primes in arithmetic progression can be deduced. It is of interest that while this involves a knowledge of the order of magnitude of Dirichlet $L$-series and their derivatives and reciprocals it does not require the property $L(1+iy)\neq0$ $(y\neq0)$.

There are numerous misprints. *R. A. Rankin.*

Citations: MR 8, 9c = Q20-20.

## Q20-28 (16, 694i; 16, 694j)

**Fekete, Michel. Approximations par polynomes avec conditions diophantiennes.** C. R. Acad. Sci. Paris **239**, 1337–1339 (1954).

**Fekete, Michel. Approximation par des polynomes avec conditions diophantiennes. II.** C. R. Acad. Sci. Paris **239**, 1455–1457 (1954).

Soit $E$ un ensemble borné et fermé de points $z$ dans le plan complexe, et $T(E)$ son diamètre transfini. Soit $K$ un corps quadratique imaginaire. Par noyau de $E_1$ relatif à $K$ on désigne le sous-ensemble $N$ de $E$ formé par les racines de chaque equation $z^m+a_1z^{m-1}+\cdots+a_m=0$, où les coefficients $a_j$ sont des entiers de $K$, irréductible dans $K$, et dont les racines appartiennent toutes à $E$. L'auteur montre d'abord que si $T(E)<1$, alors $N$ est vide, ou bien contient un nombre fini de points de $E$. Il démontre ensuite que les conditions nécessaires et suffisantes pour qu'une fonction $f(z)$ continu dans $E$ admette des polynomes d'approximation uniforme dont les coefficients soient des entiers de $K$ sont 1°) que $T(E)<1$ et 2°) que $f(z)$ prenne aux points $z_\nu$ $(\nu=1,2,\cdots,n)$ du noyau des valeurs $f(z_\nu)$ telles que le polynome d'interpolation de Lagrange de $f$ relatif aux points $z_\nu$ n'ait comme coefficients que des entiers de $K$. *R. Salem* (Paris).

Referred to in Q20-29, Q20-49.

## Q20-29 (17, 30e)

**Gel'fond, A. O. On uniform approximations by polynomials with integral rational coefficients.** Uspehi Mat. Nauk (N.S.) **10**, no. 1(63), 41–65 (1955). (Russian)

Dans l'introduction sont exposés les principaux résultats concernant la possibilité d'approcher les fonctions définies sur un segment par des polynômes à coefficients entiers: l'approximation uniforme d'une fonction $f$ continue sur un segment de longueur $l$ est toujours possible si $l<1$, impossible si $l>4$ (à part les cas triviaux), et elle nécessite certaines conditions ârithmétiques si $1<l<4$ [pour des conditions nécessaires et suffisantes, cf. Fekete, C. R. Acad. Sci. Paris **239,** 1337–1339, 1455–1457 (1954); MR **16**, 694]; l'approximation dans $L_\lambda$ $(\lambda>0)$ est possible, sans conditions arithmétiques, si $l<4$ [pour $\lambda=2$, l'auteur cite E. Aparisio, Dissertation, Moscow, 1954]. Les paragraphes suivants sont consacrés à des théorèmes liant la rapidité de l'approximation uniforme sur le segment [0, 1] aux propriétés locales de la fonction $f$ approchie: divisabilité d'ordre $m$, analyticité, etc.; moyennant les hypothèses naturelles sur $f$ aux points 0 et 1, l'auteur montre que les énoncés de Jackson et S. Bernstein (relatifs à l'approximation par des polynômes quelconques) valent encore, quand il s'agit d'approximation par des polynômes à coefficients entiers.

*J. P. Kahane* (Montpellier).

Citations: MR 16, 694i = Q20-28; MR 16, 694j = Q20-28.

Referred to in Q20-36.

## Q20-30 (17, 1059b)

**Tomaševič, V. F. On a family of arithmetic normed systems of functions.** Akad. Nauk Uzbek. SSR. Trudy Inst. Mat. Meh. **13** (1954), 159–161. (Russian)

One of the examples given by N. P. Romanov [Izv.

Akad. Nauk SSSR. Ser. Mat. **15** (1951), 131–152, p. 146, formula (30); MR **13**, 208] of a complete orthonormal system of functions over $L^2(0, \infty)$ concerned a one-parameter family $\psi_n(x)$, here called $\Psi_n(s, x)$, where the parameter $s$ satisfies $\operatorname{Re} s > \frac{1}{2}$. This is generalized by the author to a two-parameter family $\Psi_n(\alpha, s; x)$ periodic in the new parameter $\alpha$ with period $2\pi$. This new family is also a complete orthonormal system and reduces to $\Psi_n(s, x)$ for $\alpha=0$. Detailed results are too complicated to quote here. There are several misprints. *R. A. Rankin.*

Citations: MR 13, 208g = Q20-21.

## Q20-31 (18, 304b)

**Goldberg, Richard R.; and Varga, Richard S. Moebius inversion of Fourier transforms.** Duke Math. J. 23 (1956), 553–559.

Let

$$F(t)=\int_0^\infty \phi(u)\cos tu\,du,\ \phi(t)=(2/\pi)\int_0^\infty F(u)\cos tu\,du.$$

Let $\mu(n)$ be the Möbius function of number theory. Then if $\phi(u)$ is of bounded variation in every finite interval and $\phi(u)\log u \in L(1, \infty)$, the authors show that

$$G(t)=t^{-1}\{\tfrac{1}{2}F(0)+\sum_1^\infty (-1)^k F(k\pi/t)\}$$

is finite almost everywhere and

$$\phi(t)=\sum_{n=1}^\infty \mu(2n-1)G\{(2n-1)t\}$$

almost everywhere. Under mild additional hypotheses, for example $\phi(t)=O(t^{-\alpha})$, $\alpha=1$, the conclusions hold everywhere. The proof depends on the Möbius inversion formula, two lemmas on sums, and a form of the Poisson summation formula. The latter are as follows. (1) If $\phi(t)\in L(R, \infty)$ for every positive $R$ then $\sum|\phi(kt)|$ converges almost everywhere. (2) If also $\phi(t)\log t\in L(1,\infty)$, then $\sum\sum|\phi(knt)|$ converges almost everywhere. (3) If $\phi$ is of bounded variation on every $(0, R)$ and $\phi\in L(R,\infty)$ for some $R$, then $G(t)$ (defined above) exists almost everywhere and $G(t)=\sum \phi\{(2k-1)t\}$ almost everywhere. [The functions of bounded variation are supposed to be normalised, although this condition was inadvertently omitted in the paper.] *R. P. Boas, Jr.* (Evanston, Ill.).

**See also:** Teghem, p. 286; Schwartz, p. 288; Mandelbrojt, p. 305; Levitan and Sargeyan, p. 310; Lipschutz, p. 340; Kovalenko, p. 349; Prem, p. 352; Kovtun, p. 359.

## Q20-32 (21# 791)

**Salem, Raphaël. Recherches récentes sur l'unicité du developpement trigonométrique.** Enseignement Math. (2) **4** (1958), 284–291.

A set $E\subset(0, 2\pi)$ is a set of uniqueness ($U$) if the only trigonometric series $\sum_0^\infty a_n\cos nx+b_n\sin nx$ that converges to zero everywhere outside $E$ is the trivial series $a_n\equiv b_n\equiv 0$. Otherwise, $E$ is a set of multiplicity ($M$). In this expository article, a survey is made of progress on the problem of classifying sets $E$ as $U$ or $M$. Many intrinsically interesting questions in Diophantine approximation arise. The completely solved case where $E$ is a Cantor set with constant ratio of dissection illustrates the strong role that arithmetic properties can play.

*L. A. Rubel* (Princeton, N.J.)

## Q20-33 (22# 12236)

**Håstad, Matts. Uniform approximation with Diophantine side-conditions of continuous functions.** Ark. Mat. **3** (1958), 487–493.

Let $P$ be a set situated on a line segment, the extension of which does not intersect $I=[-1, 1]$ perpendicularly, having a subset which is dense in itself. Let $\bar{P}$ be the image of $P$ under reflection in the real axis. Each continuous function admits uniform approximation in $I$ by the quotient of two polynomials, the zeros of the numerator belonging to $I$, $P$ and $\bar{P}$, and those of the denominator to $P$ and $\bar{P}$.

A polynomial whose coefficients are rational integers is called an $I$-polynomial. A necessary and sufficient condition that each continuous function in several real variables admit uniform approximation on a compact set $A$ by an $I$-polynomial is the existence of an $I$-polynomial $u$ so that $u\neq 0$ and $|u|<1$ holds in $A$. Let $M$ denote the class of compact sets $B$ for which there exist an $I$-polynomial $u(x, y)$ with $u\not\equiv 0$ and (*) $|u|<1$ in $B$. Let $N(B)$ be the subset of $B$ such that $(\bar{x}, \bar{y})\in N(B)$ implies $u(\bar{x}, \bar{y})=0$ for every $I$-polynomial satisfying (*). If $B\in M$, those and only those continuous functions $f$ admit uniform approximation by polynomials for which there exists an $I$-polynomial $p$ such that $f(x, y)=p(x, y)$ for $(x, y)\in N(B)$. Finally, some special results are discussed.

*K. Tandori* (Szeged)

## Q20-34 (24# A2803)

**Duffin, R. J.**

**Orthogonal saw-tooth functions.**

*Duke Math. J.* **28** (1961), 559–561.

Let $r(x)$ be a function with period 1 such that $r(x)=\frac{1}{2}-x$, $0<x<1$; $r(0)=0$. Define

$$r_n(x) = \sum_{k|n} \frac{\mu(k)}{k} r\left(\frac{nx}{k}\right),$$

where $\mu(k)$ is the Möbius function. The author proves that the functions $r_n(x)$ are orthogonal on the interval $0\leq x\leq 1$ and that

$$\int_0^1 r_n^2(x)\,dx = \frac{1}{12}\sum_{k|n}\frac{\mu(k)}{k^2}.$$

The sequence $\{r_n(x)\}$ is complete in the space of continuous periodic functions of period 1.

The functions $r_n(x)$ are related to the square-wave functions $S_n(x)$ defined by Harrington and Cell [same J. **28** (1961), 393–407]:

$$S_n(2x) = 4r_n(x)-2r_n(2x) = 3r_n(x)-2r_{2n}(x),$$

where $n$ is odd. *L. Carlitz* (Durham, N.C.)

## Q20-35 (25# 3031)

**Cohen, E.**

**Almost even functions of finite abelian groups.**

*Acta Arith.* **7** (1961/62), 311–323.

A Fourier theory of almost periodic arithmetical functions was developed by Wintner [*Eratosthenian averages*, Baltimore, Md., 1943; MR **7**, 366] and independently by Delsarte [Ann. Sci. École Norm. Sup. (3) **62** (1945), 185–204; MR **8**, 316]. Both investigations were based on the Besicovitch theory of almost periodic functions and made use of the additive properties of the integers, although the functions treated were all defined on the multiplicative semigroup of the positive integers. The present author outlines a Fourier theory of arithmetical functions which makes no use of additivity properties or of the notion of almost periodicity. The positive integers are replaced by the multiplicative semigroup $X$ of the finite abelian groups, and the class of almost periodic functions is replaced by a class of functions which the author calls "almost even". This is an extension of the class of even functions (mod $H$), characterized by the property that $f(G, H)=f((G, H), H)$, where $(G, H)$ denotes the greatest common direct factor of groups $G$ and $H$ in $X$. (The functions are complex-valued.) A function $f_k$ is then defined to be even of order not exceeding $k$ if $f_k$ is representable as a sum of even functions (mod $H$) where each group $H$ has order $\rho(H)\leqq k$. Finally, a function $f$ is called almost even if there exists a sequence of even functions $f_k$, where $f_k$ is of order $\leqq k$, such that

$$\lim_{k\to\infty} \limsup_{x\to\infty} \frac{1}{A(x)} \sum_{\rho(G)\leqq x} |f(G)-f_k(G)| = 0,$$

where $A(x)$ is the number of groups in $X$ of order $\leqq x$. Fourier expansions of the form $f(G)\sim\sum_{H\in X} a_H c(G, H)$ are defined in terms of generalized Ramanujan sums $c(G, H)$, characterized by the relation

$$\sum_{D|H} c(G, H) = \rho(H) \text{ if } H|G, \quad = 0 \text{ if } H\nmid G,$$

where the sum is over all direct factors $D$ of $H$ (in $X$). The author shows that a large number of almost even functions have Fourier expansions whose coefficients can be determined explicitly. He also gives sufficient conditions for convergence of some of these expansions. Most of the convergence criteria are analogues of criteria in Wintner's theory, and some of them seem to be of a new type.

*T. M. Apostol* (Pasadena, Calif.)

Citations: MR 7, 366a = Z02-4; MR 8, 315a = Q20-24.

## Q20-36 (25# 3917)

**Aparisio Bernardo, È. [Aparicio Bernardo, E.]**

**On least deviation from zero of quasi-polynomials with integral algebraic coefficients. (Russian. English summary)**

*Vestnik Moskov. Univ. Ser. I Mat. Meh.* **1962**, *no.* 2, 21–32.

The paper gives an upper bound of the least mean deviation from zero in the interval (0, 1) with the weight $x^\tau$ of quasi-polynomials of the form $p_n(x)=\sum_{k=0}^n \alpha_k x^{\lambda_k}$ with integral algebraic coefficients from an imaginary quadratic field and complex exponents. An asymptotic order of this estimate is also established for $R\to\infty$ when the exponents $\lambda_k$ $(k=0, \cdots, n)$ form a sequence of all algebraic integers of the above field lying in a semicircle $|z|<R$, Re $z\geqq 0$.

There is related work by A. O. Gel'fond [Uspehi Mat. Nauk **10** (1955), no. 1 (63), 41–65; MR **17**, 30] and M. Fekete [Math. Z. **17** (1923), 228–249].

*S. Chowla* (Boulder, Colo.)

Citations: MR 17, 30e = Q20-29.

## Q20-37 (26# 1690)

**Harrington, Walter J.; Cell, John W.**

**A set of square-wave functions orthogonal and complete in $L_2(0, 2)$.**

*Duke Math. J.* **28** (1961), 393–407.

This paper and the one following [#1691] are likely to appeal to those interested in number theory, as well as to analysts. Let $S(x)=\operatorname{sgn}(\sin \pi x)$, $C(x)=\operatorname{sgn}(\cos \pi x)$. Theorems 2–4 assert the completeness of $\{S(nx)\}$, $\{C(nx)\}$ and $\{S(nx), C(nx)\}$ in the appropriate spaces of functions. The authors then introduce $S_n(x)=\sum d^{-1}\mu(d)S(d^{-1}nx)$, where $\mu$ is the Möbius function and the summation is for $d$ odd, $d|n$. It is shown that $\int_0^1 S_n^2 dx=\prod(1-p^{-2})$, the product being over all odd primes $p|n$. The sequence $\{S_n(x)\}$ is orthogonal and complete in $L^2(0, 1)$. Approximation by linear combinations is uniform for continuous functions. Similar results apply to a corresponding sequence $\{C_n(x)\}$ and to $\{S_n, C_n\}$. The paper concludes with several interesting special expansions.

*R. M. Redheffer* (Hamburg)

Referred to in Q20-46.

## Q20-38 (26# 1691)

**Cell, John W.; Harrington, Walter J.**

**Repeated integrals of the square-wave functions and related sets of orthogonal functions.**

*Duke Math. J.* **28** (1961), 409–419.

A sequence of functions $S(m, x)$, $C(m, x)$ for $n=1, 2, 3, \cdots$ is defined as follows. With suitable normalization, $S(m, x)$ is obtained by integrating $C(m-1, x)$, and $C(m, x)$ by integrating $S(m-1, x)$. In the notation of the preceding review [#1690], $S(1, x)=S(x)$, $C(1, x)=C(x)$. The paper obtains results like those detailed above, for each integral $m$.

*R. M. Redheffer* (Hamburg)

Referred to in Q20-46.

## Q20-39 (26# 6656)

**Hewitt, Edwin; Zuckerman, Herbert S.**

**Approximation by polynomials with integral coefficients, a reformulation of the Stone-Weierstrass theorem.**

*Duke Math. J.* **26** (1959), 305–324.

J. Pál (1914), S. Kakeya (1915), Y. Okada (1923) e successivamente M. Fekete (1923, 1930, 1933), S. Bernstein (1930, 1936), L. Kantorovič (1931) hanno studiato il problema dell'approssimazione di una funzione continua con polinomi a coefficienti interi. Nella loro ricerca gli AA. hanno esteso i risultati di J. Pál, S. Kakeya e Y. Okada. — Sia $\mathfrak{C}(\alpha, \beta)$ l'insieme di tutte le funzioni continue in $[\alpha, \beta]$, $\alpha<\beta$, $Q$ indichi un polinomio della variabile reale $x$ a coefficienti interi. Si dirà che $f\in\mathfrak{C}(\alpha, \beta)$ è approssimabile in $[\alpha, \beta]$ se per ogni $\varepsilon$ esiste un polinomio $Q$ tale che $|f(x)-Q(x)|<\varepsilon$, per tutti gli $x\in[\alpha, \beta]$, e che $f\in\mathfrak{C}(\alpha, \beta)$ è associabile a un insieme $S\in[\alpha, \beta]$ se esiste un polinomio $Q$ tale che $Q(x)=f(x)$ per tutti gli $x\in S$. Sia $\mathfrak{U}(\alpha, \beta)$ l'insieme di tutti i $Q$ non identicamente nulli tali che $0\leqq Q(x)<1$ per tutti gli $x\in[\alpha, \beta]$ e se $\mathfrak{U}(\alpha, \beta)$ non è vuoto, sia $J(\alpha, \beta)$ l'insieme $\{x: x\in[\alpha, \beta],\ Q(x)=0$ per tutti i polinomi $Q\in\mathfrak{U}(\alpha, \beta)\}$. Sia $R$ un polinomio della variabile reale $x$ a coefficienti interi e col primo coefficiente uguale ad 1, e indichi $J'(\alpha, \beta)$ l'insieme delle radici di tutti i polinomi $R$ aventi la proprietà che le loro radici sono tutte reali e appartenenti all'intervallo $[\alpha, \beta]$. Ciò premesso gli AA. dimostrano il seguente teorema che estende i risultati di Pál, S. Kakeya, Y. Okada: Sia $f(x)\in\mathfrak{C}(\alpha, \beta)$. Se $\beta-\alpha\geqq 4$ la $f(x)$ è appossimabile se e soltanto se $f(z)$ stessa è un polinomio $Q$. Se $\beta-\alpha<4$, allora $\mathfrak{U}(\alpha, \beta)$ esiste e $J(\alpha, \beta)=J'(\alpha, \beta)=\{x_1, \cdots, x_n\}$ è finito; la funzione $f(x)$ è approssimabile se e soltanto se il polinomio di grado $n-1$ che assume nei punti $x_1, \cdots, x_n$ rispettivamente i valori $f(x_i)$ ha coefficienti interi. I risultati sono estesi alle funzioni continue di uno spazio compatto di Hausdorff.

*G. Sansone* (Zbl **87**, 58)

Referred to in Q20-49.

## Q20-40 (27# 3601)

**Bateman, P. T.; Chowla, S.**

**Some special trigonometrical series related to the distribution of prime numbers.**

*J. London Math. Soc.* **38** (1963), 372–374.

Construction of two non-trivial real functions $f$, continuous on the set of real numbers, with period 1, and having the property $\sum_{h=1}^k f(h/k)=0$ for every positive integer $k$. The functions are given by $f_1(\theta)=\sum \lambda(n)n^{-1}\cos 2\pi n\theta$ and $f_2(\theta)=\sum \mu(n)n^{-1}\cos 2\pi n\theta$, where $\lambda$ and $\mu$ are Liouville's and Möbius's functions.

*T. Estermann* (London)

## Q20-41 (32# 4100)

**Mustafin, D. S.**

**On the classification of arithmetic functions. (Russian)**

*Izv. Akad. Nauk SSSR Ser. Mat.* **29** (1965), 877–886.

The author defines three classes $W$, $A$, $T$ of (complex-valued) arithmetical functions: $f \in W$ if and only if $\sum |f'(d)|/d$ converges, where $f'(d) = \sum_{t|d} \mu(t) f(d/t)$; $f \in A$ if and only if $\sum_{d \leq x} |f'(d)| = O(x)$ and $\sum f'(d)/d$ converges; $f \in T$ if $f$ is (in a certain sense) well approximable by periodic functions. Theorems of Wintner and Axer [Wintner, *Eratosthenian averages*, Baltimore, 1943; MR **7**, 366] show that $f$ has a mean-value if $f \in W$ or $f \in A$; the same is true for $f \in T$.

The author proves that $W \subset A \cap T$, $W \neq A$, $A \not\subset T$, and $T \not\subset A$ ($\chi_3 \in T$, but $\chi_3 \notin A$ if $\chi_3$ is a complex character).

*W. Schwarz* (Freiburg)

Citations: MR 7, 366a = Z02-4.

## Q20-42 (32# 4452)

**Kiselev, A. A.; Onufrieva, L. A.**

**Application of the biorthogonal Čebyšev and Markov systems for the approximation of functions. (Russian)**

*Studies of Modern Problems of Constructive Theory of Functions (Russian)*, *pp.* 183–189. *Fizmatgiz, Moscow,* 1961.

Le système biorthogonal est défini par

$$\varphi_n(x) = \frac{2}{\pi} \sum_{d|n} \frac{\mu(d)}{d} \sin \frac{2\pi n x}{d},$$

$$\psi_n(x) = \frac{\pi}{2} \sum_{d|n} \frac{\mu(d)\chi(d)}{d} \cos \frac{2\pi n x}{d},$$

$$\psi_0(x) = 1, \qquad \chi(d) = \begin{cases} (-1)^{(d-1)/2}, & d = 2k+1, \\ 0, & d = 2k, \end{cases}$$

où $\mu(d)$ désigne la fonction de Möbius. On associe à $f \in L[0, 1]$ la série (*) $\sum [A_n \psi_n(x) + B_n \varphi_n(x)]$ avec $B_n = \int_0^1 f(x) \operatorname{sign} \sin 2\pi n x \, dx$, $A_n = \int_0^1 f(x) \operatorname{sign} \cos 2\pi n x \, dx$. Alors, si $f$ est à variation bornée et appartient à Lip $\alpha$, $\alpha > 0$, (*) converge dans $[0, 1]$ absolument et uniformément vers $f(x)$; la même conclusion a lieu si $f \in \mathrm{Lip}\, \alpha$, $\alpha > \frac{1}{2}$. On donne des résultats semblables pour $f \in L^2[0, 1]$ et pour le système $4n^{-1} \int_0^x \psi_n(t) \, dt$, $4n^{-1} \int_0^x \varphi_n(t) \, dt$.

*M. Tomić* (Belgrade)

Referred to in Q20-47, Q20-48.

## Q20-43 (36# 3736)

**Romanov, N. P.**

**Operator methods in number theory. (Russian)**

*Proc. Fourth All-Union Math. Congr. (Leningrad, 1961) (Russian), Vol. II, pp.* 135–136. *Izdat. "Nauka", Leningrad,* 1964.

One considers operator methods in number theory, based on the isomorphism $\sum_{n=1}^\infty a_n/n^s \leftrightarrow \sum_{n=1}^\infty a_n L_n/n^s$, where there is an ordinary Dirichlet series on the left and an operator Dirichlet series on the right, and where the $L_n$ ($n = 1, 2, 3, \cdots$) form a sequence of operators which possess the M-property (multiplicative property) $L_n L_m = L_{nm}$.

One can obtain sequences possessing the M-property as particular values of a one-parameter operator group $\mathfrak{C}_u$, $u \geq 0$, $\mathfrak{C}_u \mathfrak{C}_v = \mathfrak{C}_{uv}$, for integral values of the parameter (see E. Hille and R. S. Phillips [*Functional analysis and semi-groups*, Amer. Math. Soc., Providence, R.I., 1957; MR **19**, 664] and N. P. Romanov [Ann. of Math. (2) **48** (1947), 216–233; MR **8**, 520]). In the article there are also considered sequences of elements $f_n$ of a Hilbert space which possess the D-property (division property) $(f_n, f_m) = g((n, m))$. The orthogonalization of this sequence takes place in accordance with the formula $\gamma_n = \sum_{d|n} \mu(n/d) f_d$, where $\mu$ is the Möbius function. A consideration of the sequence $f_n$ leads to new arithmetical identities, cited in the article.

*N. Romanov* (RŽMat **1965** #8 A95)

## Q20-44 (37# 6665)

**Meyer, Yves**

**Une caractérisation des nombres de Pisot.**

*C. R. Acad. Sci. Paris Sér. A-B* **266** (1968), A63–A64.

If $R$ denotes the reals and $\Lambda \subset R$, then any expression of the form $\sum_{\lambda \in \Lambda} a_\lambda e^{i\lambda x}$, where $x \in R$ and all but a finite number of the complex numbers $a_\lambda$ are zero, is called a trigonometric polynomial with spectrum in $\Lambda$. $\Lambda$ is said to have an associated compact set if there exists a compact set $K \subset R$ and an $\varepsilon > 0$ such that, for any trigonometric polynomial $P(x)$ with spectrum in $\Lambda$, $\sup_{x \in K} |P(x)| \geq \varepsilon \sup_{x \in R} |P(x)|$. Let $I$ be the set of sequences $\sigma = \{\varepsilon_k\}_{k \geq 0}$ such that $\varepsilon_k \in [0, 1]$ and the $\varepsilon_k$ are zero for sufficiently large $k$, and, if $\xi \in R$, $\xi > 2$, let $\Lambda$ be the set of finite sums $\sum_{\sigma \in I} \varepsilon_k \xi^k$. The author presents the theorem: $\Lambda$ has an associated compact set if and only if $\xi$ is a Pisot number. The proof of sufficiency is given only in a (typical) special case.

*J. Burlak* (Ann Arbor, Mich.)

Referred to in Q20-45, R06-40.

## Q20-45 (39# 6000)

**Meyer, Yves**

**Caractérisation des nombres de Pisot-Vijayaraghavan (P.-V.).**

*Séminaire Delange-Pisot-Poitou: 1967/68, Théorie des Nombres, Fasc. 1, Exp. 8, 4 pp. Secrétariat mathématique, Paris,* 1969.

This paper is in essentials the same as an earlier paper of the author [C. R. Acad. Sci. Paris Sér. A-B **266** (1968), A63–A64; MR **37** #6665].

Citations: MR 37# 6665 = Q20-44.

## Q20-46 (38# 4897)

**Israilov, M. I.**

**On some special orthonormal systems. (Russian)**

*Voprosy Kibernet. Vyčisl. Mat. Vyp.* 10 (1967), 105–118.

Let $\{\alpha_n\}$ be a complete orthonormal system in the complex Hilbert space $H$ and let $\omega(n)$ be a complex-valued multiplicative function on the natural numbers such that $\omega(n) \neq 0$ for $(n, N) = 1$ and $C = \sum_{(n,N)=1} |\omega(n)|^2 < \infty$, where $N$ is a fixed natural number. The author shows that the series $\sum_{(k,N)=1} \omega(k) \alpha_{kn}$ converge in $H$ to elements $f_n \in H$, $n = 1, 2, \cdots$, and he deduces (Theorem 1) that the sequence $\{\beta_n\}$ is also a complete orthonormal system in $H$, where $\beta_n(x) = \{G(n)\}^{-1/2} \sum_{d|n;(d,N)=1} \mu(d) \bar{\omega}(d) f_{n/d}(x)$, $G(n) = C \sum_{d|n;(d,N)=1} \mu(d) |\omega(d)|^2$, $\mu$ is the Möbius function and the bar denotes the complex conjugate. This modification of the work of N. P. Romanoff [Izv. Akad. Nauk SSSR Ser. Mat. **10** (1946), 3–34; MR **8**, 9] allows the author to consider various special cases (such as that discussed by W. J. Harrington and J. W. Cell [Duke Math. J. **28** (1961), 393–407; MR **26** #1690; ibid. **28** (1961), 409–419; MR **26** #1691]), to extend his results to $C[0, 1]$ (under additional conditions on $\{\alpha_n\}$), and to discuss the absolute and uniform convergence of Fourier series with respect to the above orthonormal systems. {Cf. also the article reviewed below [#4898].}

*J. Burlak* (Ann Arbor, Mich.)

Citations: MR 8, 9c = Q20-20; MR 26# 1690 = Q20-37; MR 26# 1691 = Q20-38.

## Q20-47 (38# 4898)

**Israilov, M. I.**

**Some special biorthonormal systems and their applications. (Russian)**

*Voprosy Kibernet. Vyčisl. Mat. Vyp.* 11 (1967), 93–110.

Using the notation and hypotheses of the article reviewed

above [#4897], the author proves (Theorem 1) that the systems $\{X_n\}$, where $X_n=\sum_{(k,N)=1}\omega(k)\alpha_{kn}$ $(n=1, 2, \cdots)$, and $\{Y_n\}$, where $Y_n=\sum_{d\mid n;(d,N)=1}\mu(d)\bar{\omega}(d)\alpha_{n/d}$ $(n=1, 2, \cdots)$, form a complete biorthogonal system in $H$. He then extends the results to $C[0, 1]$, considers some special cases, discusses the absolute and uniform convergence of Fourier series with respect to the systems mentioned above, and indicates some connections with the theory of trigonometric Fourier series. These results extend those of the author's earlier article [Voprosy Vyčisl. Mat. Tehn. Vyp. 7 (1965), 3–19] and those of A. A. Kiselev and L. A. Onufrieva [*Studies of modern problems of constructive theory of functions* (Russian), pp. 183–189, Fizmatgiz, Moscow, 1961; MR **32** #4452]. {Cf. also the article reviewed below [#4899].} *J. Burlak* (Ann Arbor, Mich.)

Citations: MR 32# 4452 = Q20-42.

## Q20-48 (38# 4899)

**Kiselev, A. A.; Nagmetžanov, K. K.**

**On series of signs of sines and cosines. (Russian)**

*Voprosy Kibernet. Vyčisl. Mat. Vyp.* 13 (1967), 118–123.

The authors consider the biorthogonal systems $\{\varphi(nx)\}$, $\{\varphi_n(x)\}$ and $\{\psi(nx)\}$, $\{\psi_n(x)\}$, which are similar to those used earlier by the first author and L. A. Onufrieva [*Studies of modern problems of constructive theory of functions* (Russian), pp. 183–189, Fizmatgiz, Moscow, 1961; MR **32** #4452]. Here $\varphi(nx)=\text{sign}\sin 2\pi nx$,

$$\varphi_n(x) = (\pi/2)\sum_{d\mid n} d^{-1}\mu(d)\chi^2(d)\ \text{sign}\ 2\pi nx/d,$$

$\psi(x)=1$, $\psi(nx)=\text{sign}\cos 2\pi nx$, $\psi_0(x)=1$,

$$\psi_n(x) = (\pi/2)\sum_{d\mid n} d^{-1}\mu(d)\chi(d)\cos 2\pi nx/d,$$

$\mu$ is the Möbius function and $\chi(k)=0$ if $k$ is even while $\chi(k)=(-1)^{(k-1)/2}$ if $k$ is odd. Let $f(x)\in L[0, 1]$, let $a_0+\sum_{n=1}^{\infty}(a_n\cos 2\pi nx+b_n\sin 2\pi nx)$ be its trigonometric Fourier series, let $A_0+\sum_{n=1}^{\infty}(A_n\psi(nx)+B_n\varphi(nx))$ be the series in which $A_0=\int_0^1 f(x)\,dx$, $A_n=\int_0^1 f(x)\psi_n(x)\,dx$, $B_n=\int_0^1 f(x)\varphi_n(x)\,dx$, and let $g(n)$ be a real-valued function on the positive integers satisfying $0\le g(mn)\le g(m)g(n)$ and $\sum_{n=1}^{\infty}g(n)/n<\infty$. Then the authors prove (Theorem 1) that $\sum_{n=1}^{\infty}g(n)(|A_n|+|B_n|)$ and $\sum_{n=1}^{\infty}g(n)(|a_n|+|b_n|)$ converge or diverge together and (Theorem 2) that a similar result holds for the absolute convergence of the series $\sum_{n=1}^{\infty}g(n)(a_n\cos 2\pi nx+b_n\sin 2\pi nx)$ and

$$\sum_{n=1}^{\infty}g(n)(A_n\psi(nx)+B_n\varphi(nx)).$$

*J. Burlak* (Ann Arbor, Mich.)

Citations: MR 32# 4452 = Q20-42.

## Q20-49 (41# 1680)

**Cantor, David G.**

**On approximation by polynomials with algebraic integer coefficients.**

Number Theory (Proc. Sympos. Pure Math., Vol. XII, Houston, Tex., 1967), pp. 1–13.

*Amer. Math. Soc., Providence, R.I.*, 1969.

Let $K$ be an algebraic number field and $\Omega$ a complete set of inequivalent valuations $|\ |_v$ of $K$, with corresponding completions $K_v$. Take a finite subset $T$ of $\Omega$ containing the Archimedean valuations in $\Omega$. Put $K^T=\{k\in K: |k|_v\le 1$ if $v\in\Omega\backslash T\}$; this is a subring of $K$ containing the algebraic integers of $K$. For $v\in T$, let $X_v$ be a compact subset of $K_v$ (nowhere dense and with connected complement if $K_v$ is the field of real or complex numbers) and $f_v$ a $K_v$-valued continuous function on $X_v$. Then the $f_v$ are approximable by polynomials over $K^T$. The problem is to find conditions ensuring the existence of polynomials $f\in K^T[x]$ such that $f-f_v$ is uniformly small on $X_v$ for all $v\in T$. It is shown that if the product of the transfinite diameters of the $X_v$ is $\ge 1$, then such approximation is possible if and only if there exists a polynomial $p\in K^T[x]$ such that $p(x)=f_v(x)$ for all $x\in X_v$ and $v\in T$; while if the product of the transfinite diameters of the $X_v$ is $<1$, then there exist finite subsets $J_v$ of the $X_v$ such that approximation is possible if and only if there exists a polynomial $f\in K^T[x]$ such that $f(x)=f_v(x)$ for all $x\in J_v$ and $v\in T$. Several characterizations of the sets $J_v$ are given. In particular, if one or more of the $X_v$ are empty, then all $J_v$ are empty.

This generalizes results of M. Fekete [C. R. Acad. Sci. Paris **239** (1954), 1337–1339; MR **16**, 694; ibid. **239** (1954), 1455–1457; MR **16**, 694], E. Hewitt and H. S. Zuckerman [Duke Math. J. **26** (1959), 305–324; MR **26** #6656] and L. B. O. Ferguson ["Uniform approximations by polynomials with coefficients in discrete subrings of $C$", Ph.D. Thesis, Univ. of Washington, Seattle, Wash., 1965], who investigate approximation by polynomials with integer coefficients or algebraic integer coefficients from a quadratic imaginary field.

The results are extended to the case where $X_v$ is a subset of $\tilde{K}_v$, the algebraic closure of $K_v$, and $f_v$ is a $\tilde{K}_v$-valued continuous function on $X_v$.

*C. G. Lekkerkerker* (Amsterdam)

Citations: MR 16, 694i = Q20-28; MR 16, 694j = Q20-28; MR 26# 6656 = Q20-39.

## Q20-50 (41# 8885)

**Ferguson, L. B. O.**

**Some remarks on approximation by polynomials with integral coefficients.**

*Approximation Theory (Proc. Sympos., Lancaster*, 1969), *pp.* 59–62. *Academic Press, London*, 1970.

An expository paper.

## Q20-51 (42# 3547)

**Nagmetžanov, K. K.**

**A generalized biorthogonal system. (Russian. Uzbek summary)**

*Dokl. Akad. Nauk UzSSR* **1966**, *no.* 6, 3–5.

N. P. Romanov [Izv. Akad. Nauk SSSR Ser. Mat. **10** (1946), 3–34; MR **8**, 9] made some number-theoretical use of sequences $(f_i, i=1, 2, \cdots)$ in Hilbert space for which $(f_i, f_j)=g(k)$, where $g$ is a real-valued function on the integers and $k$ is the greatest common divisor of $i$ and $j$. He constructed such sequences from orthonormal sequences by using the Möbius-function inversion for $g$. The present author uses a well-ordered Weisner hierarchy [L. Weisner, Trans. Amer. Math. Soc. **38** (1935), 474–485; see also L. C. Hsu, Duke Math. J. **14** (1947), 465–473; MR **9**, 17] and the inversion formulas in it to adapt Romanov's ideas to a pair of sequences in Hilbert space. No applications are suggested. *M. M. Day* (Edinburgh)

Citations: MR 8, 9c = Q20-20.

## Q20-52 (42# 6532)

**Lohoué, Noël**

**Nombres de Pisot et synthèse harmonique dans les algèbres $A_p(\mathbf{R})$.**

*C. R. Acad. Sci. Paris Sér. A-B* **270** (1970), A1676–A1678.

The author studies the algebra $A_p(\mathbf{R})$, $1<p<\infty$ (for definitions, etc., see P. Eymard [Séminaire Bourbaki, Vol. 1969/70, Exp. 367, Springer, Berlin, 1971; see MR **42** #7461]). Let $E_\theta$ be the Cantor set in [0, 1] with constant ratio of dissection $1/\theta$, where $\theta>2$ is a Pisot number. He shows that, for every multiplier $S$ on $L^p(\mathbf{R})$, supported on $E_\theta$, there exists an operator-norm bounded sequence of discrete measures $\{\mu_m\}_{m=1}^{\infty}$ converging weakly to $S$, and $\mu_m$ is supported on $\Lambda_m$ for each $m$. The class $\{\Lambda_m\}$ is a collection of finite subsets of $E_\theta$, independent of $S$. The techniques involve the idea of a "modèle" [see Y. Meyer, *Nombres de Pisot, nombres de Salem, et analyse harmonique*, Springer, Berlin, 1970]. *C. F. Dunkl* (Charlottesville, Va.)

Citations: MR 42# 7461 = Z10-67.

## Q20-53 (42# 6533)

**Meyer, Yves**

**Nombres algébriques et analyse harmonique.**

*Ann. Sci. École Norm. Sup.* (4) **3** (1970), 75–110.

A compact subset $E \subseteq \mathbf{R}$ is said to be a set of multiplicity if there is a distribution concentrated on $E$ whose Fourier transform goes to 0 at $\infty$. If $E \subseteq [-\pi, \pi)$, then this is equivalent to saying that there is a trigonometric series $\sum_{n=-\infty}^{\infty} \alpha_n e^{inx}$ that converges to 0 off $E$. Compact sets that are not sets of multiplicity are called sets of uniqueness.

A Pisot number is a real positive algebraic integer all of whose conjugates (over $\mathbf{Q}$) have absolute value less than 1. Pisot (or Pisot-Vijayaraghavan) numbers are closely connected with sets of uniqueness in the following way: suppose that one constructs a set like the Cantor set, but cutting out the middle $\xi$th each time (where $\xi < 1$); the result will be a set of multiplicity when $\xi^{-1}$ is a Pisot number (and, in fact, only then).

The author begins his paper with a new proof of the fact that Pisot numbers do yield sets of uniqueness in this way. One advantage of his new proof is that it leads to a more general theorem: Let $K$ be a real algebraic field of degree $n$ over $\mathbf{Q}$, and suppose that $0 < \alpha < 1$, and $\beta > 2$; if $\{\omega_k\}$ is a sequence of algebraic integers in $K$ with $\omega_k \geqq b$ and all other conjugates of $\omega_k$ less than $\alpha$ in absolute value, then the Cantor-type set that is formed by extracting the middle $(\omega_k{}^{-1})$th at the $k$th step is a set of uniqueness.

The second section of the paper is concerned with Pisot numbers and almost periodic functions. If $\theta$ is a real number, let $\Lambda$ be the set of all finite sums $\sum_{k=0} \varepsilon_k \theta^k$, with $\varepsilon_k = 0$ or 1. If $\theta$ is also an algebraic integer, we say that $t = \sum_{k=0}^{\infty} \varepsilon_k \theta^k$. Let $\Lambda'$ be the set of all such $t$. The author's main theorem is the following: If $\theta$ is greater than 1 and is not a Pisot number, then every almost periodic function that vanishes on $\Lambda$ is 0; if $\theta$ is a Pisot number, then every almost periodic function vanishing on $\Lambda$ also vanishes on $\Lambda'$, and $\Lambda'$ is the largest subset of $R$ with this property. In Section 3, he obtains necessary and sufficient conditions for the statement $\Lambda' = \Lambda$ to hold.

The set $\Lambda$ is called a coherent set of frequencies if there exist an interval $I$ and a constant $C$ such that, for every finite trigonometric sum $P(t) = \sum_{\lambda \in \Lambda} a_\lambda e^{2\pi i \lambda t} (a_\lambda \in C)$, one has $\sup_{t \in R} |P(t)| \leqq C \sup_{t \in I} |P(t)|$; one consequence of this condition is that the points of $\Lambda$ must be some minimum distance apart from one another. The main result of Section 4 is that $\Lambda$ is a coherent set of frequencies if and only if $\theta$ is a Pisot number; in that case, one can choose $C$ to be an arbitrary number $> 1$ for appropriate $I$.

Sections 5 and 6 deal with Pisot numbers and spectral synthesis. A typical result is the following: Let $\theta$ be a Pisot number, let $E = \{\sum_{k=1}^{\infty} \varepsilon_k \theta^{-k}, \varepsilon_k = 0 \text{ or } 1\}$, and let $E_0 = \{\sum_{k=1}^{\infty} \varepsilon_k \theta^{-k}, \varepsilon_k = 0$ or 1, almost all $\varepsilon_k = 0\}$; if $f$ is continuous on $E$, the following three properties are equivalent: (1) $|\int_E f(t)\, d\mu(t)| \leqq A \|\hat{\mu}\|_\infty$, for some constant $A$ and for all measures $\mu$ of finite support in $E_0$; (2) there exists a complex Radon measure $\nu$ on $R$ of norm at most $A$ whose Fourier transform agrees with $f(t)$ on $E$; and (3) for all $\varepsilon > 0$, there exists a function $g \in L^1(R)$ whose norm is at most $A + \varepsilon$ and whose Fourier transform on $E$ agrees with $f$.

The results in this section lead the author to define a property called "perfect synthesis"; again, Pisot numbers are related to this property. *L. Corwin* (New York)

## Q20-54 (43# 529)

**Al'per, S. Ja.; Vinogradova, I. Ju.**

**Approximation in the mean by polynomials with entire coefficients on curves in the complex plane.** (Russian)

*Izv. Akad. Nauk SSSR Ser. Mat.* **34** (1970), 547–563.

Es sei $C$ eine rektifizierbare Jordankurve in der komplexen Ebene, deren (kürzeste) Bogenlänge die Ungleichung $s(z_1, z_2) \leqq A|z_1 - z_2|$ erfüllt. Betrachtet wird die Approximation von Funktionen im Sinne der Norm $\int_C |f(z)|^p |dz|$ mit $p > 0$ durch Polynome, deren Koeffizienten ganze Zahlen aus einem quadratischen, imaginären Zahlkörper sind. Für diese Approximierbarkeit werden in folgenden beiden Fällen notwendige und hinreichende Bedingungen angegeben: (1) $C$ ist geschlossen, die Funktion $f(z)$ ist im Innern von $C$ analytisch und besitzt auf $\dot{C}$ bei Annäherung aus einem Winkelraum Randwerte aus $L_p$. (2) $C$ ist offen und $p \geqq 1$. *L. Berg* (Rostock)

## Q20-55 (44# 2720)

**Belgy, Jean Nöel**

**Fonctions arithmétiques.**

Thèse présentée à la Faculté des Sciences de l'Université de Clermont-Ferrand pour obtenir le grade de Docteur ès-Sciences Mathématiques. Série E, No. d'Ordre 121. *Université de Clermont-Ferrand, Clermont-Ferrand*, 1970. viii + 92 *pp.*

The author initiates a study of the algebra of complex-valued arithmetic functions under Dirichlet convolution (and pointwise addition) primarily from a functional-analytic viewpoint. Because this algebra $A$ is isomorphic to the algebra of complex formal power series in countably many variables, the last chapter of this thesis is devoted to an examination of some relevant results obtained for such functions (see below). There follows a chapter by chapter summary.

Chapter I looks at the algebra $A$ and various natural topologies on $A$, examined briefly for their relative strength. If $f \in A$, the support of $f$, denoted $S(f)$, is defined as $\{x: f(x) \neq 0\}$, and the prime support $S_1(f)$ as $\{p$ prime; $p$ divides some member of $S(f)\}$. The set of functions with finite prime support is shown to be an algebraically closed subalgebra of $A$. A logarithm $L$ and exponential exp are defined by the corresponding power series expansions (with convolution as the multiplication); $L$ being defined only if $f(1) \neq 0$. Multiplicative, completely multiplicative, additive, and completely additive functions are then examined. In particular, it is observed that $\alpha$ is completely multiplicative if and only if the map $f \to \alpha f$ is an endomorphism of $A$ and $\beta$ is completely additive if and only if the map $f \to \beta f$ is a derivation on $A$. A proof is also given that $\beta$ is additive if and only if it has the form $\beta = e * L(m)$, where $L$ is the logarithm, $m$ is a non-zero multiplicative function, $*$ is Dirichlet convolution and $e$ is the function defined by $e(x) \equiv 1$ for all $x$. Both $A$ and $\Phi_1$ (the ring of functions with finite prime support) turn out to be factorial rings.

Let $\alpha$ be a real-valued positive completely multiplicative arithmetic function. The arithmetic function $f$ is called "$\alpha$-convergent" if $\sum_{n=1}^{\infty} |f(n)|\alpha(n)$ converges. The set of all $\alpha$-convergent $f$ is denoted $A_\alpha$ and it is easily seen that $A_\alpha$ is a Banach algebra with norm $\|f\|_\alpha = \sum_{n=1}^{\infty} |f(n)|\alpha(n)$. Chapter II is devoted to these $A_\alpha$, particularly $A_e$, that is the set of all arithmetic functions $f$ such that $\sum_{n=1}^{\infty} |f(n)|$ converges. Any two $A_\alpha$ are isometrically isomorphic and $A_\alpha \subseteq A_\beta$ if and only if $\alpha \geqq \beta$ (i.e., $\alpha(n) \geqq \beta(n) > 0$ for all $n$). It turns out that the intersection of all $A_\sigma$ which properly contain $A_e \neq A_e$, and a description is given of the elements of $\bigcap A_\sigma - A_e$, $A_\sigma \supset A_e$.

The functions $u_n(x)$ defined by $u_n(n)=1$; $u_n(x)=0$ for $x \neq n$, clearly form a Schauder basis for $A_e$; other Schauder bases are considered in Appendix I. Multiplicative and completely multiplicative functions are studied in this context; in particular, it is shown that $f \in A_e$ if and only if $\sup_\sigma \sum |f(n)\sigma(n)| < \infty$, where $\sigma$ denotes a completely multiplicative function in $A_e$ with finite prime support. It turns out that the maximal ideals of $A_e$ are those of the form $m=\{f\colon \sum_{n=1}^\infty f(n)\alpha(n)=0\}$, where $\alpha$ is completely multiplicative and $|\alpha| \leqq e$. It is easy to see that if $\alpha \neq \beta$, $m_\alpha \neq m_\beta$, and one easily deduces using Mertens theorem that if $f \in A_e$, and its "Dirichlet inverse" $f^{*^{-1}}$ has the property that $\sum f^{*^{-1}}(n)\alpha(n)$ converges for all completely multiplicative $\alpha$ with $|\alpha| \leqq e$, then $f^{*^{-1}} \in A_e$. $A_e$ is also shown to be semisimple.

The spectrum $S_p(f)$ of an element $f \in A_e$ is discussed and it is shown, among other results, that $S_p(f)$ is arcwise connected, but need not be simply connected. Let $\mathfrak{M}$ be the set of all maximal ideas of $A_e$. As observed above, the elements of $\mathfrak{M}$ may be identified with completely multiplicative functions $\alpha$, $|\alpha| \leqq e$. $\mathfrak{M}$ is equipped with the metric topology defined by $d(\alpha,\beta)=\sum_{n=1}^\infty (\alpha(n)-\beta(n))/2^n$, $\alpha, \beta$ completely multiplicative. Let $\mathfrak{M}^1$ be the subset of completely multiplicative functions with $|\alpha|=e$. It is shown that $\mathfrak{M}^1$ is the Silov boundary of $\mathfrak{M}$.

Let $G$ consist of all invertible elements of $A_e$ (i.e., those for which $f(1) \neq 0$). Then $G$ is arcwise connected; the group of multiplicative invertible elements is also arcwise connected. Weak and strong topological divisors of zero are defined and investigated. Completely multiplicative, additive, and completely additive functions as well as the previously defined exponential and logarithm are also looked at in this functional-analytic context.

One of the most interesting results in this monograph concerns zero-sets. For $f \in A_e$, a $\sigma \in \mathfrak{M}$ is called a "zero" of $f$ if $\sum f(n)\sigma(n)=0$. (Note that the only functions under consideration as "zeros" are completely multiplicative and with $|\sigma| \leqq e$.) Let $Z(f)$ be the set of zeros of $f$. Various easy properties of $Z(f)$ are listed, and it is proved that if $\sum f(n)\sigma(n)$ is zero for all $\sigma$ belonging to some non-empty open set of $\mathfrak{M}$, then $f$ is identically zero. In connection with zero-sets, domains of invertibility and annihilators are also defined and studied. The former, denoted $I(f)$, is the set of all $\sigma \in \mathfrak{M}$ such that $f\sigma$ is invertible; the latter, denoted $A(f)$, is the set of all $\alpha \in \mathfrak{M}$ such that $f\alpha=0$. For example, $I(f)=\bigcap_\alpha [Z(\alpha f)]'$, where denotes complement, and various equivalent conditions are given for $A(f)=Z(f)$. The notions of zero-set, annihilator, and domain of invertibility are also extended to ideals in $A_e$ and examined.

Chapter III is concerned with $A_e$ equipped with the norm $\sup_\alpha \sum_n |f(n)\alpha(n)|$, $\alpha$ completely multiplicative, and, more exactly, with the completion of this space, $\hat{A}_e$, as well as the set $S$ of all arithmetic functions $f$ such that $\sum f(n)\alpha(n)$ converges for some completely multiplicative $\alpha$. In particular it is shown that if $f \in S$, $f$ not identically zero, and $f*g \in S$, then $g \in S$ ($*$ is Dirichlet convolution). The set $E$ of "entire functions" defined as those $f \in S$ such that $\sum f(n)\alpha(n)$ converges for all positive completely multiplicative functions is also examined. A typical result is that if $f \in E$, then $f$ has finite prime support.

Chapter IV is concerned with an appropriate definition for an analytic function of countably many complex variables for the preceding context. Suppose $\alpha$ is a completely multiplicative arithmetic function and we associate with $\alpha$ the point $(\alpha(p_1), \cdots, \alpha(p_i), \cdots) \doteq (\alpha_1 \cdots)$, in $\mathbf{C}^{\mathbf{N}}$, the space of countably many complex variables, where the $p_i$ are the primes. To say that a function $\hat{f}$ is analytic at the origin in $\mathbf{C}^{\mathbf{N}}$ is equivalent to saying that there is a sequence $f(n)$ of complex coefficients such that for all $\alpha$ (identified with $(\alpha_1 \cdots \alpha_i \cdots)$) in some "neighborhood" of the origin, the series $\hat{f}(\alpha')=\sum_{n=1}^\infty f(n)\alpha(n)$ converges. If we wish to allow exactly those $f \subseteq S$ as coefficients, it appears appropriate to give $\mathbf{C}^{\mathbf{N}}$ the box-topology; and neighborhoods are defined in this sense. With this topology $\mathbf{C}^{\mathbf{N}}$ is a topological group, but not a topological vector space. The problem of defining when $f$ is analytic on an open set $\Omega$ arises; it is insufficient to say $f$ is analytic in $\Omega$ if $f$ analytic at each $\omega \in \Omega$, at least if we wish to preserve one notion of analytic continuation. Therefore $f$ is defined to be analytic in $\Omega$ if for each open polydisc in $\Omega$ with center $\omega$, there is a sequence of complex coefficients $f_\omega(n)$ such that $\hat{f}(\omega+\alpha)=\sum f_\omega(n)\alpha(n)$ converges absolutely for all $\alpha$ in the polydisc. To study analytic continuation, the author uses the notion of a $\Delta$-connected set where $\Delta$ is the family of open polydiscs. This notion is actually introduced and examined in the more general situation, denominated $\Lambda$-connectivity, where $X$ is an arbitrary topological space, and $\Lambda$ a non-empty family of subsets of $X$. Then an open set $A \subset X$ is called $\Lambda$-connected if it is: (1) connected, and (2) for every partition of $A$ into two open non-empty subsets, there is some non-empty subset of $\Lambda$ contained in $A$ which has non-void intersection with both subsets of the partition. The principal theorem proved in this chapter is: Suppose $\hat{f}$ is analytic on an open $\Delta$-connected set $\Omega$. If $\hat{f}$ is identically zero on some open subset of $\Omega$, then $\hat{f}$ is identically zero on $\Omega$.

{There are many trivial typographical errors.}

*S. L. Segal* (Rochester, N.Y.)

**Q20-56** **(44# 3055)**

**Andria, George D.**

**Approximation of continuous functions by polynomials with integral coefficients.**

*J. Approximation Theory* **4** (1971), 357–362.

The author considers an old problem (papers on it date back at least to 1914) in approximation theory: Let $Q(Z)$ be the space of polynomials with integral coefficients and let $f \in C[a,b]$; what can be said about the approximation of $f$ by elements of $Q(Z)$?

The best-known result on this question states that if $b-a \geqq 4$, then the only $f$ which is approximable arbitrarily closely by $Q(Z)$ is an $f \in Q(Z)$.

Among the theorems proved in this paper are the following. (1) If $f$ is approximable arbitrarily closely by $Q(Z)$ on $[a,b]$, then either $f \in Q(Z)$ or else there does not exist a polynomial of best approximation from $Q(Z)$. (2) There is an $f \in C[0,1]$ whose polynomial of best approximation (from $Q(Z)$) is not unique. (3) There is an $[a,b]$ with $b-a<4$ and an $f \in C[a,b]$ such that $f$ is not approximable (arbitrarily closely) on $[a,b]$ by $Q(Z)$ and such that there does not exist a polynomial of best approximation to $f$ from $Q(Z)$. *R. Feinerman* (Bronx, N.Y.)

# Q25 $p$-ADIC ANALYSIS

See also Chapter S.

See also reviews A54-44, D04-65, E64-2, E64-3, E64-10, E64-17, F70-14, F70-20, G25-57, G25-58, H05-75, J02-14, J20-13, J64-8, J64-9, J64-14, Q05-48, Q05-58, Q05-74, Q15-13, R06-26, S30-21, S30-24, S40-2, Z02-69, Z10-9, Z10-10, Z10-30, Z10-31, Z10-33, Z10-35, Z10-47.

**Q25-1** **(5, 256b)**

**Monna, A. F. Zur Geometrie der *P*-adischen Zahlen.** Nederl. Akad. Wetensch., Proc. **45**, 981–986 (1942).

The author shows that Blichfeldt's method in the geometry of numbers, in the form given by C. Visser [Nederl. Akad. Wetensch., Proc. **42**, 487–490 (1939)], has an analogue in the $n$-dimensional space of all points $(x_1, \cdots, x_n)$ with $P$-adic coordinates $x_1, \cdots, x_n$. For this space, measure and upper densities of sets and an integral analogous to Lebesgue's are defined. *K. Mahler* (Manchester).

## Q25-2 (5, 256c)

**Monna, A. F. Zur Theorie des Maszes im Körper der *P*-adischen Zahlen.** Nederl. Akad. Wetensch., Proc. **45**, 978–980 (1942).

A simple one-to-one mapping of the real interval $R$: $0 \leqq x \leqq 1$ onto the set $R_P$ of all $P$-adic integers ($P$ a prime number) is defined which changes open real sets $O$ in $R$ into (both open and closed) $P$-adic sets $\bar{O}$ in $R_P$, such that the Lebesgue measure of $O$ is equal to the $P$-adic measure of $\bar{O}$ as defined by H. Turkstra [Metrische bijdragen tot de theorie der diophantische approximaties in het lichaam der $P$-adische getallen, Dissertation, Amsterdam, 1938].

*K. Mahler* (Manchester).

## Q25-3 (7, 429e; 7, 429f; 7, 429g; 7, 429h)

**Krasner, Marc. Essai d'une théorie des fonctions analytiques dans les corps valués complets: séries de Taylor et de Laurent issues de ces corps.** C. R. Acad. Sci. Paris **222**, 37–40 (1946).

**Krasner, Marc. Essai d'une théorie des fonctions analytiques dans les corps valués complets: fonctions holomorphes et méromorphes.** C. R. Acad. Sci. Paris **222**, 165–167 (1946).

**Krasner, Marc. Essai d'une théorie des fonctions analytiques dans les corps valués complets: théorèmes de Nevanlinna; transformations holomorphes.** C. R. Acad. Sci. Paris **222**, 363–365 (1946).

**Krasner, Marc. Essai d'une théorie des fonctions analytiques dans les corps valués complets; transformations holomorphes et leurs applications algébriques; fonctions holomorphes de plusieurs variables et fonctions implicites; familles normales; prolongement analytique.** C. R. Acad. Sci. Paris **222**, 581–583 (1946).

In these notes the author develops the theory of analytic functions in a complete valuation field and makes algebraic applications of this theory and of his previous results.

Let $n$ run through all integral values and let $M$ be any set of points $Q_n$ in the real plane $O\xi\eta$ with coordinates $\xi(Q_n)=n$ and $\eta(Q_n)$. The lower convex envelope of $M$ is the Newton polygon $\Pi$ of $M$. Let $P_0$ be the intersection of $\Pi$ with $O\eta$ if this exists; let $P_1, P_2, \cdots, P_{s^*}$ be the vertices of $\Pi$ for $\xi$ positive and $P_{-1}, P_{-2}, \cdots, P_{-s'+1}$ be those for $\xi$ negative; let $L_i = P_iP_{i+1}$, and $-\nu_i$ the slope of $L_i$. Let $\bar{\nu}'$ be the upper bound of $\nu_{-i}$ $(0<i\leqq s')$ and $\bar{\nu}^*$ be the lower bound of $\nu_i$ $(0\leqq i\leqq s^*)$, these bounds being taken on the semi-real number system [Krasner, same C. R. **219**, 433–435 (1944); these Rev. **7**, 364]. A $\nu$-tangent to $M$ is a straight line of slope $-\nu$, where $\bar{\nu}^* \leqq \nu \leqq \bar{\nu}'$, which is tangent to $\Pi$ in the sense that it either coincides with a side or passes through a vertex of $\Pi$ in such a way that the two sides meeting in the vertex are on the same side of the $\nu$-tangent. A $\nu$-tangent is unique. If $\varphi(\Pi;\nu)$ is the $\eta$-intercept of the $\nu$-tangent to $\Pi$ then $\varphi(\Pi;\nu)$ is a continuous function of $\nu$, linear by segments, and convex increasing, constant or decreasing according as $\nu\leqq\nu_0$, $\nu_0\leqq\nu\leqq\nu_{-1}$, or $\nu_{-1}\leqq\nu$.

Let $k$ be a field complete with respect to a valuation $|\cdots|$ and $K$ an extension of $k$, the valuation $|\cdots|$ also being extended to $K$. Assume that $K$ is not locally compact and that it contains the completion of every simple subextension of $K/k$. An element $\infty_K$ with neighborhoods $|x|>r$, $r$ any real number, is adjoined to $K$. A function defined in $K$ and having values in $K$ is called a Laurent $k$-series in $x-\alpha$ if it has the form $\sum_{-\infty}^{+\infty} a_n(x-\alpha)^n$, $\alpha \varepsilon K$ and $a_n \varepsilon k$. It is a Taylor series if $a_n=0$ for $n<0$. A function $f(x)$ is holomorphic in an open set $\mathfrak{D}$ of $K$ if there exists a Laurent series which converges to $f(x)$ everywhere in $\mathfrak{D}$.

Let $f(x)=\sum a_n(x-\alpha)^n$ be a Laurent $k$-series and let $|\cdots|$ and $\omega(\cdots) = -\log|\cdots|$ denote the valuation and order in $K$. Let $M(f)$ be the set of points $Q_n$ with coordinates $\xi(Q_n)=n$, $\eta(Q_n)=\omega(a_n)$. The Newton polygon $\Pi$ of $M(f)$ is called the Newton polygon of $f(x)$. The domain of convergence of $f(x)$ is then $r'<|x-\alpha|<r^*$, where $\log r' = -\nu'$ and $\log r^* = -\nu^*$ except in certain stated circumstances when $f(x)$ converges also for $|x-\alpha|=r'$ and/or $|x-\alpha|=r^*$. Also $-\log|f(x)| = \omega[f(x)] \geqq \min \omega[a_n(x-\alpha)^n] = \varphi(\Pi;\nu)$, where $\nu=\omega(x-\alpha)$. The sign of equality holds if the minimum is attained for one term only, which occurs if $\nu$ is not among the $\nu_i$. If $\nu=\nu_i$ all terms $T_n$ for which $\omega(T_n)$ obtains its minimum correspond to points on the side $L_i$ of $\Pi$. Letting $\bar{\beta}$ represent the element of the skeleton $S$ of $K$ [see Krasner, same C. R. **219**, 345–347 (1944); these Rev. **7**, 363] to which $\beta$ belongs, and writing $\xi=\overline{x-\alpha}$ and $\xi^{\lambda_i}f_i(\xi)=\sum \bar{a}_n(\overline{x-\alpha})^n$, where the summation extends over all terms $T_n$ for which $\omega(T_n)$ attains its minimum, the function $\Phi_\alpha(\xi)$ is defined to be $\xi^{\lambda_i}f_i(\xi)$ or $\bar{a}_{\lambda_i}\xi^{\lambda_i}$ according as $|\xi|=r_i$ or $r_{i-1}<|\xi|<r_i$. This function is of importance in later applications.

Let $M(r)$ and $M_\epsilon(r)$ be the upper bounds of $|f(x)|$ for $x\varepsilon K$, on the circle $|x-\alpha|=r$ and in the ring $r-\epsilon<|x-\alpha|<r+\epsilon$, respectively. The possible points of discontinuity of $M(r)$ are $r_i=\exp(-\nu_i)$, which form a discrete set on the open interval $(r', r^*)$. At all points of continuity $\log M(r) = -\varphi(\Pi; -\log r)$. At all points of $(r', r^*)$, however, $M^*(r) = \lim_{\epsilon\to 0+} M(r)$ exists and is equal to $-\varphi(\Pi; -\log r)$. Replacing $M(r)$ by $M^*(r)$, the Hadamard three circle theorem follows as does the Cauchy inequality $|a_n|r^n \leqq M^*(r)$ and the Weierstrass theorem that the limit of a sequence of functions holomorphic in a circle $C$ is a holomorphic function in $C$. There follows a discussion of meromorphic functions, position of zeros, and integral functions. In the case that $K$ is algebraically closed analogues of several well-known results are obtained, including the theorems of Weierstrass and Picard on integral functions and the first and second theorems of Nevanlinna.

Let $\psi(\xi)$ be a polynomial in $S$ and $Z_\psi$ the set of all elements $\xi$ of $S$ for which $\psi(\xi)$ has a meaning (that is, all its terms are addible). If $Z\subseteq Z_\psi$ is a ring $\bar{\rho}\leqq|\xi|\leqq\rho$ in $S$, the set of values of $\psi(\xi)$, $\xi\varepsilon Z$, is denoted by $(Z;\psi)$ and is called a polynomial retract of $S$. The union $\Lambda$ of polynomial retracts is called a retractive set of $S$. If $\psi(\xi)$ and $S$ are such that there exists a subcorpoid $S'$ of $S$ containing the coefficients of $\psi(\xi)$ and such that the field $R$ of $S$ is a pure transcendental extension of the field $R'$ of $S'$, then the retract $(Z;\psi)$ is said to be decomposable by means of $S'$. A retractive set $\Lambda$ is decomposable if it is the union of retracts all decomposable by means of the same corpoid $S'$. A decomposable retract $(Z;\psi(\xi))$ defines $\psi(\xi)$ up to a linear transformation $\xi'=\alpha\xi+\beta$ $(\alpha, \beta\varepsilon S')$ and a decomposable retractive set completely defines its minimal retracts.

There follows a discussion of holomorphic transformations of the form $T: x\to F(x)$, where $F(x)$ is a Taylor series with circle of convergence $C^*$. If $A\subseteq K$ the set $S(A)$ consists of all elements $\bar{\alpha}$ of $S$, where $\alpha\varepsilon A$. Then $S(TC^*-F(\alpha))$, denoted by $S_\alpha(T;K)$, is a retractive set of $S$ and its decomposition is discussed. It is decomposable if there exists a field $K'$ between $k$ and $K$ such that $R$ is a pure transcendental extension of its field of residues $R'$.

Algebraic applications are then considered. If $\alpha$ is a simple zero of an irreducible polynomial $F(x)$ in a field $k^*$, and $k=k^*(\alpha)$, the Newton polygon $\Pi$ and skeleton function $\Phi_\alpha(\xi)$ are constructed for $F(x)$. These determine the structural properties of $S_\alpha(T;K)$, where $K$ is the union of $k$ and a field in which $F(x)$ remains irreducible. These are in turn linked with the ramification properties of $k/k^*$. The manner in which $S_\alpha(T;K)$ decomposes also indicates whether or not $k/k^*$ is a Galois extension.

Finally, there are some remarks on Taylor and Laurent expansions of functions of several variables, corresponding Newton polytopes, implicit functions and analytic continuation. *D. C. Murdoch* (Vancouver, B. C.).

Citations: MR 7, 363j = S20-2; MR 7, 364a = S20-3.

Referred to in Q25-10, R02-8, R36-14, S15-6, S15-7, S15-11.

## Q25-4 (10, 16a)

**Krasner, Marc. Certaines propriétés des séries de Taylor d'un ensemble au plus dénombrable de variables dans les corps valués complets et une démonstration structurale des formules de M. Pollaczek.** Bull. Sci. Math. (2) **71**, 123–152, 180–200 (1947).

For the formulas of Pollaczek [same Bull. (2) **70**, 199–218 (1946); these Rev. **9**, 273] see (4) below. The author develops at some length a theory of Taylor series with coefficients and variables in an ultrametric field $K$, that is, a field which is closed with respect to a non-Archimedean valuation $|\alpha|$, $\alpha\varepsilon K$, $|\alpha+\beta|\leqq\max\{|\alpha|,|\beta|\}$. He considers derangement, substitution, uniqueness, inversion, sequences of series, continuity and differentiability, as far as these are needed for his primary purpose. Since a series $\sum\alpha_n$ converges in $K$ if and only if $|\alpha_n|\to0$ as $n\to\infty$, derangement, for example, is unrestricted, and the theory also differs in other ways from that for the complex field. The notion of majorant plays an important rôle in the theory as developed, where $\sum A_i$ is said to majorize $\sum\alpha_i$ if $|\alpha_n|\leqq|A_n|$, for all $n$, and a number $A$ of $K$ majorizes $\sum\alpha_n$ if $|\alpha_n|\leqq|A|$, for all $n$. Henceforth assume further that $K$ has characteristic zero, that its residue class field has characteristic $p\neq0$, and that it is algebraically closed. The series $\log(1+x)\equiv x-\frac{1}{2}x^2+\cdots$, $e^x=1+x/1!+x^2/2!+\cdots$ converge in $K$ if and only if $|x|<1$, and $|x|<\lambda=|p^{1/(p-1)}|$, respectively, and define functions having the usual properties with the restrictions on $x\varepsilon K$. The author applies his lemmas on series to prove the following:

$$(1)\qquad l_j(\alpha)=\left[\frac{\partial^j\log\left[1+\sum_{i=0}^{\infty}\alpha_i(e^v-1)^i\right]}{\partial v^j}\right]_{v=0},\qquad j=1,2,\cdots,$$

is a convergent series in the denumerably infinite set of variables $(\alpha)$, at least inside the parallelotope $|\alpha_i|<\lambda^{-i}$, $i=0,1,\cdots$; this extends the definition of the Kummer logarithmic derivatives;

$$(2)\qquad L_j(\alpha)=\lim_{n\to\infty} l_{jp^n}(\alpha),\qquad j=1,2,\cdots,$$

is a convergent series in $(\alpha)$ for $|\alpha_i|<d^{-i}$, $i=0,1,\cdots$, for any positive $d>\lambda$, and $L_{j_1}(\alpha)=L_{j_2}(\alpha)$, if $j_1\equiv j_2 \pmod{p-1}$; the $L_j$ are called the logarithmic limits of Pollaczek;

$$(3)\qquad \log_m(\alpha)=\log\Big(1+\sum_{i=0}^{\infty}\alpha_i(\xi^m-1)^i\Big),\qquad m=0,1,\cdots,p-1,$$

where $\xi$ is a primitive $p$th root of unity in $K$, is a convergent series in $(\alpha)$ for $|\alpha_i|<d^{-i}$, $d>\lambda$; these are the so-called $p$-adic logarithms;

$$(4)\qquad \begin{gathered} L_0(\alpha)+\sum_{m=0}^{p-1}(\log_0(\alpha)-\log_m(\alpha)),\\ L_j(\alpha)=\frac{(-1)^j}{p}\Big(\sum_{m=1}^{p-1}\epsilon_m^j\xi^m\Big)\sum_{m=1}^{p-1}\epsilon_m^{-j}\log_m(\alpha),\\ j=1,\cdots,p-1,\end{gathered}$$

where $\epsilon_m\ (=\lim_{s\to\infty}m^{p^s})$ is a $(p-1)$th root of unity in $K$. In the proof of (4), use is made of the property of $K$ that it contains subfields isomorphic to the $p$-adic extension $k_p$ of the rational field $k$ and to $k_p(\xi)$, respectively. If $\alpha_0,\alpha_1,\cdots$ are in $k_p$ so are the $L_j$, while $\log_m(\alpha)$ is in $k_p(\xi)$. Then (4) is valid in $k_p(\xi)$, and hence includes Pollaczek's relations. [The section of the paper beginning on p. 180 apparently should be numbered 4, not 9.] *R. Hull* (Lafayette, Ind.).

Citations: MR 9, 273e = R18-4.

## Q25-5 (12, 319b)

**Mahler, Kurt. A correction.** Compositio Math. **8**, 112 (1950).

The author corrects a minor error in a previous paper [same journal **2**, 259–275 (1935)] and shows that the only zeros of the dyadic logarithm function are $\pm1$.
*L. Schoenfeld* (Urbana, Ill.).

## Q25-6 (12, 676f)

**Monna, A. F. *P*-adic numbers.** Simon Stevin **28**, 40–54 (1951). (Dutch)

An expository talk presented at the University of Leiden.
*W. J. LeVeque* (Manchester).

## Q25-7 (16, 799a; 16, 799b; 16, 799c)

**Krasner, Marc. Prolongement analytique dans les corps valués complets: domaines quasi connexes.** C. R. Acad. Sci. Paris **238**, 2385–2387 (1954).

**Krasner, Marc. Prolongement analytique dans les corps valués complets: éléments analytiques, préliminaires du théorème d'unicité.** C. R. Acad. Sci. Paris **239**, 468–470 (1954).

**Krasner, Marc. Prolongement analytique dans les corps valués complets: démonstration de la loi d'unicité: fonctions analytiques uniformes.** C. R. Acad. Sci. Paris **239**, 745–747 (1954).

Let $K$ be a valuated field whose value group is dense in the group of reals. The author calls a subset $D\subset K$ quasi-connected if, for each pair of points $\alpha,\xi\varepsilon D$, the distance $|x-\alpha|$ from $\alpha$ to a variable point $x$ not in $D$ takes only a finite number of values less than $|\xi-\alpha|$. Extending the notion of quasi-connectivity to subsets of the projective line $K'=K\cup\{\infty\}$, he shows it is invariant under homographies $x\to(ax+b)(cx+d)^{-1}$. Finite intersections and arbitrary unions of non-disjoint quasi-connected sets are quasi-connected.

Assuming $K$ algebraically closed, the author defines an analytic element to be a $K$-valued function on a quasi-connected set $D$ which is a uniform limit of rational functions without poles on $D$. He then proves the uniqueness theorem: two analytic elements which coincide on a set having a limit point within their common domain of definition coincide whenever they are both defined. *J. Tate.*

Referred to in Q25-8, Q25-10.

**Q25-8** **(19, 395b; 19, 395c; 19, 395d; 19, 395e; 19, 395f)**

**Krasner, Marc. Prolongement analytique dans les corps valués complets: préservation de l'analycité par les opérations rationnelles.** C. R. Acad. Sci. Paris **244** (1957), 1304–1306.

**Krasner, Marc. Prolongement analytique dans les corps valués complets: préservation de l'analyticité par les opérations rationnelles; quasi-connexité et éléments analytiques réguliers.** C. R. Acad. Sci. Paris **244** (1957), 1599–1602.

**Krasner, Marc. Prolongement analytique dans les corps valués complets: uniformité des fonctions analytiques; l'analyticité des fonctions méromorphes.** C. R. Acad. Sci. Paris **244** (1957), 1996–1999.

**Krasner, Marc. Prolongement analytique dans les corps valués complets: préservation de l'analyticité par la convergence uniforme et par la dérivation; théorème de Mittag-Löffler généralisé pour les éléments analytiques.** C. R. Acad. Sci. Paris **244** (1957), 2570–2573.

**Krasner, Marc. Prolongement analytique dans les corps valués complets: démonstration du théorème de Mittag-Löffler; singularités au bord.** C. R. Acad. Sci. **245** (1957), 270–274.

Continuing earlier notes [same C. R. **238** (1954), 2385–2387; **239** (1954), 468–470, 745–747; MR **16**, 799], and using the definitions in the review cited, the author defines two analytic elements to be equivalent if they can be connected by a chain of analytic elements in which adjacent elements coincide on a set containing a limit point. He defines an analytic function to be an equivalence class of analytic elements, and proves: Two equivalent analytic elements always take the same value at every point where both are defined (consequence of the ultrametric geometry). Analyticity is preserved by the rational operations. If the field $k$ is not algebraically closed, analytic functions can be defined on $k$ by embedding it in a $K$ for which this is so, and the result is independent of $K$. Analytic functions have analytic derivatives, and a theorem on preservation of differential relations holds. The "Mittag-Löffler Theorem" states sufficient conditions (depending on the region of definition $D$) that an analytic element $f$ be expressible as $f_1+f_2$, with $f_1$ defined by the principal parts of the poles of rational approximates to $f$ and $f_2$ an analytic element with a larger region of definition; under further conditions, $f_2$ is a constant. *G. Whaples.*

Citations: MR 16, 799a = Q25-7; MR 16, 799b = Q25-7; MR 16, 799c = Q25-7.

Referred to in Q25-10.

**Q25-9** **(19, 395g)**

**Krasner, Marc. Prolongement analytique dans les corps valués complets: démonstration du théorème de Mittag-Löffler; singularités au bord.** C. R. Acad. Sci. Paris **245** (1957), 1285–1288.

Remarque de l'auteur: Le présente texte remplace celui de C.R. Acad. Sci Paris **245** (1957), 270–274 [analysé ci-dessus], rendu incompréhensible par une erreur dans l'ordre des pages.

*G. Whaples* (Bloomington, Ind.).

To the second review, add "If an analytic function is given by a Taylor series, then either it cannot be prolonged outside its circle of convergence or the circle of convergence does not include its circumference, and (in a suitable extension field) there is a singularity (i.e., a point to which the function cannot be prolonged) on the circumference".

**Q25-10** **(34# 4246)**

**Krasner, Marc**

**Prolongement analytique uniforme et multiforme dans les corps valués complets.**

*Les Tendances Géom. en Algèbre et Théorie des Nombres, pp.* 97–141. *Éditions du Centre National de la Recherche Scientifique, Paris,* 1966.

This is essentially a more comprehensive exposition of results already announced by the author [see, e.g., MR **7**, 429; MR **16**, 799; MR **19**, 395; errata, MR **28**, p. 1246].

*G. Whaples* (Amherst, Mass.)

Citations: MR 7, 429e = Q25-3; MR 7, 429f = Q25-3; MR 7, 429g = Q25-3; MR 7, 429h = Q25-3; MR 16, 799a = Q25-7; MR 16, 799b = Q25-7; MR 16, 799c = Q25-7; MR 19, 395b = Q25-8; MR 19, 395c = Q25-8; MR 19, 395d = Q25-8; MR 19, 395e = Q25-8; MR 19, 395f = Q25-8.

Referred to in Z10-38.

**Q25-11** **(20# 2321)**

**Mahler, K. An interpolation series for continuous functions of a $p$-adic variable.** J. Reine Angew. Math. **199** (1958), 23–34.

L'auteur donne une nouvelle et très intéressante démonstration du théorème d'approximation de Weierstrass pour une fonction continue à valeurs $p$-adiques, définie dans l'espace $\mathfrak{Z}_p$ des entiers $p$-adiques. Cette démonstration a l'intérêt de prouver que le processus d'approximation peut être pris linéaire par rapport à la fonction approché $f$: de façon précise, si on pose $a_n=\sum_{k=0}^{n}(-1)^k\binom{n}{k}f(n-k)$, la suite des nombres $p$-adiques $a_n$ tend vers 0, et la série $\sum_{n=0}^{\infty}a_n\binom{x}{n}$ converge uniformément vers $f(x)$. L'auteur montre en outre que si $f$ est continûment dérivable, alors toutes les séries $a_n'=\sum_{k=1}^{\infty}(-1)^{k-1}a_{k+n}/k$ sont convergentes, la suite $(a_n')$ tend vers 0 et on a $f'(x)=\sum_{n=0}^{\infty}a_n'\binom{x}{n}$.

*J. Dieudonné* (Evanston, Ill.)

Referred to in Q25-12, Q25-23, Q25-25, Q25-39, Z10-30.

**Q25-12** **(25# 3035)**

**Mahler, K.**

**A correction to the paper "An interpolation series for continuous functions of a $p$-adic variable".**

*J. Reine Angew. Math.* **208** (1961), 70–72.

L'auteur rectifie une démonstration erronée d'un travail antérieur [même **J. 199** (1958), 23–34; MR **20** #2321]. Il s'agit du théorème suivant. Soit $f(x)=\sum_{n=1}^{\infty}a_n\binom{x}{n}$ pour tout $x$ dans l'anneau des entiers $p$-adiques $Z_p$, avec $\lim_{n\to\infty}a_n=0$ dans $Z_p$; si $\lim_{x\to 0}f(x)/x=0$ dans $Z_p$ pour la topologie $p$-adique, alors on a $\lim_{n\to\infty}(a_n/n)=0$ dans $Z_p$.

*J. Dieudonné* (Paris)

Citations: MR 20# 2321 = Q25-11.

Referred to in Q25-20.

**Q25-13** **(23# A3135)**

**Leopoldt, Heinrich-Wolfgang**

**Zur Approximation des $p$-adischen Logarithmus.**

*Abh. Math. Sem. Univ. Hamburg* **25** (1961), 77–81.

Es ist allgemein üblich, den $p$-adischen Logarithmus durch die Logarithmusreihe zu definieren. Wenn es sich dann darum handelt, den Logarithmus durch vernünftige Ausdrücke zu approximieren, so ergeben sich die bekannten Schwierigkeiten. Der Verfasser zeigt in dieser Note, daß man diesen Schwierigkeiten auf eine recht einfache Weise entgehen kann. Von der Approximationsaufgabe hergesehen erweist es sich als vernünftig, den $p$-adischen

Logarithmus nicht durch die schwierig zu behandelnde Potenzreihe zu definieren, sondern durch das $p$-adische Analogon der im reellen für positive $x$ gültigen Formel:

$$\log x = \lim_{h\to 0} \frac{x^h-1}{h}.$$

Der Verfasser übernimmt diese Formel zur Definition des Logarithmus auch in einem $p$-adischen Zahlkörper, wobei $h$ durch $p^n$ zu ersetzen ist, und der Grenzwert für $n\to\infty$ zu bilden ist. Der Verfasser zeigt, daß dieser Grenzwert für alle Einseinheiten konvergiert. Die Funktionalgleichung des Logarithmus ergibt sich nach dieser Definition fast unmittelbar. Der Beweis der Konvergenz liefert bereits die gewünschten Approximationsformeln, deren erste ($n=1$) sich übrigens mit einem etwas schwächeren Restglied schon in einer Arbeit von Ankeny, Artin und Chowla findet [Ann. of Math. (2) **56** (1952), 479–493; MR **14**, 251]. Eine dieser Approximationsformeln lautet:

$$w_p\left(\log H - \frac{H^{p^n}-1}{p^n}\right) > n+\omega$$

dabei bedeutet $w_p$ die durch $w_p(p)=1$ normierte Exponentenbewertung des zugrunde liegenden $p$-adischen Zahlkörpers, und $H$ ist ein Element dieses Zahlkörpers mit $\omega = w_p(H-1) > 1/(p-1)$. Der Verfasser zeigt abschließend, wie man aus der angegebenen Definition des Logarithmus seine Reihenentwicklung herleiten kann. Dabei werden die bekannten $p$-adischen Abschätzungen der Binomialkoeffizienten benutzt und hergeleitet.

*P. Roquette* (Tübingen)

Citations: MR 14, 251h = R14-19.

## Q25-14 (25# 30)

**Novoselov, E. V.**

**Topological-metrical properties of the multiplicative lattice of integers. (Russian)**

*Dokl. Akad. Nauk SSSR* **142** (1962), 1255–1257.

Die Menge $N$ aller natürlichen Zahlen ist ein Verband, wenn das kleinste gemeinsame Vielfache und der grösste gemeinsame Teiler von zwei Zahlen als Verbandsoperationen genommen werden. Dieser Verband kann topologisiert werden, indem man als Umgebung der Zahl $n$ jede Restklasse modulo $m$ betrachtet, in der $n$ liegt ($m=1, 2, \cdots$). Bei dieser Topologie ist $N$ ein topologischer Verband, der metrisierbar ist. Bei der betreffenden Metrik ist $N$ kein vollständiger metrischer Raum; die vollständige metrische Hülle von $N$ ist einer perfekten nirgendsdichten Menge der Geraden homöomorph.

Die vorliegende Arbeit ist die vierte in der Reihe von Arbeiten des Verfassers, in welchen topologische Methoden in gewisse zahlentheoretische Probleme eingeführt werden [vgl. z. B., Novoselov, Uč. Zap. Elabužsk. Gos. Ped. Inst. **8** (1960), 3–23].

*M. Novotný* (Brno)

## Q25-15 (26# 1733)

**Serre, Jean-Pierre**

**Endomorphismes complètement continus des espaces de Banach $p$-adiques.**

*Inst. Hautes Études Sci. Publ. Math. No.* 12 (1962), 69–85.

In his papers on the zeta functions of algebraic varieties, Dwork studied the $p$-adic analytic function $\det(1-tA)$ defined for a certain infinite matrix $A$, and developed an analogue of the spectral theory of F. Riesz for such $A$ [cf. Amer. J. Math. **82** (1960), 631–648; MR **25** #3914; Inst. Hautes Études Sci. Publ. Math. No. 12 (1962), 5–68]. In the present paper, the author exploits the same theory from a more general point of view, considering completely continuous endomorphisms of certain Banach spaces.

Let $K$ be a complete field with respect to a non-trivial non-archimedean valuation. A Banach space $E$ over $K$ is a complete normed linear space over $K$ such that $|x+y| \leqq \operatorname{Max}(|x|, |y|)$ for any $x$, $y$ in $E$. Let $F$ be also a Banach space over $K$, and let $L(E, F)$ denote the Banach space of all continuous linear maps of $E$ into $F$. A map $A$ in $L(E, F)$ is called completely continuous if $A$ is a limit of linear maps with finite rank in $L(E, F)$.

Let $I$ be any set, and let $c(I)$ be the family of all sets $\{x_i\}$, $x_i \in K$, indexed by $i \in I$, such that $x_i$ tends to 0 with respect to the filter of the complements of finite subsets in $I$. Put $|x| = \operatorname{Max}|x_i|$. With the structure of a linear space defined in the obvious manner, $c(I)$ then becomes a Banach space over $K$. The author defines the Fredholm determinant $\det(1-tA)$ of a completely continuous endomorphism $A$ of such a space $E=c(I)$, and proves various properties of the determinant, e.g., that $\det(1-tA)$ is an entire function of $t$. He then also defines the resolvent of $A$, and obtains the following theorem: if $a$, in $K$, is a zero of order $h$ of the function $\det(1-tA)$, then $E$ is uniquely decomposed into the direct sum of closed $A$-invariant subspaces $N$ and $F$ such that $1-aA$ is nilpotent on $N$, and is invertible on $F$; furthermore, dim $N=h$. Finally, the author briefly explains the application to Dwork's theory.

*K. Iwasawa* (Cambridge, Mass.)

Citations: MR 25# 3914 = G25-20.

Referred to in G25-24, G25-50, G25-57, Z10-55.

## Q25-16 (27# 6249)

**Novoselov, E. V.**

**Some topological properties of the natural numbers. (Russian)**

*Izv. Vysš. Učebn. Zaved. Matematika* **1961**, *no.* 1 (20), 119–129.

This paper is the continuation of the author's previous investigations on topological methods in number theory [Učen. Zap. Elabužsk. Gos. Ped. Inst. **8** (1960), 3–23]. Let $S$ be the topological ring of the rational integers with the topology for which the sets $U_m=\{km: k\in S\}$ ($m=1, 2, \cdots$) constitute a neighbourhood base of 0. By completion of $S$ we get a compact topological ring $\mathfrak{S}$; the elements of $\mathfrak{S}$ are called polyadic numbers. For $x\in\mathfrak{S}$ there is a unique representation of the form $x=\sum_{n=1}^{\infty}\psi_n(x)n!$, $\psi_n(x)\in S$, $0\leqq\psi_n(x)\leqq n$. The map $\lambda(x)=\sum_{n=1}^{\infty}\psi_n(x)/(2n+1)!!$ is a homeomorphism of $\mathfrak{S}$ onto a perfect nondense subset $\phi$ of the real line; the points of $S$ are carried over by $\lambda$ into the unilaterally isolated points of $\phi$. Moreover, $h(x)=\sum_{n=1}^{\infty}\psi_n(x)/(n+1)!$ is a continuous map of $\mathfrak{S}$ onto the interval [0, 1] and $h|\mathfrak{S}\setminus S$ is a homeomorphism onto the set of the irrational numbers lying in (0, 1). For $n, m\in S$, put $n\succ m$ if and only if $n$ is a multiple of $m$ and, for $n\succ m$, denote by $\pi_m{}^n$ the natural homomorphism of $\mathfrak{S}_n$ onto $\mathfrak{S}_m$ where $\mathfrak{S}_n=S/U_n$. Then $\mathfrak{S}$ is isomorphic to the projective limit of the system $\{\mathfrak{S}_n, \pi_m{}^n\}$. The character group of the additive group of $\mathfrak{S}$ is isomorphic to the additive group of the rational numbers mod 1 with the discrete topology. If $\{x_k\}\subset S$, $x_k\to x\in\mathfrak{S}$, then $\{x_k\}$ converges for any prime number $p$ with respect to the $p$-adic topology to a $p$-adic integer $f_p(x)$ depending only on $x$. $f_p$ is a homomorphism of $\mathfrak{S}$ onto the ring of the $p$-adic integers; denoting by $\mathfrak{J}_p$ the corresponding closed ideal, $\mathfrak{S}$ is the direct sum of these ideals $\mathfrak{J}_p$. For $x\in\mathfrak{S}$, $n=1, 2, \cdots$, put $\varphi_n(x)=0$ or 1 according to whether $x\equiv 0$ ($n$) or $x\not\equiv 0$ ($n$) in $\mathfrak{S}$, and $\|x\|=\sum_{n=1}^{\infty}\varphi_n(x)/2^n$. Then $\rho(x, y)=\|x-y\|$ is a metric for $\mathfrak{S}$ and $\psi(x)=\|x\|$ is a continuous map of $\mathfrak{S}$ onto a perfect nondense subset $\Psi$ of the real line; the points $\|m\|$ ($m\in S$) constitute the left end-points of the contiguous intervals.

*Á. Császár* (Budapest)

Referred to in Q15-13.

**Q25-17** **(28# 77)**

**Novoselov, E. V.**

**Integration on a bicompact ring and its applications to number theory. (Russian)**

*Izv. Vysš. Učebn. Zaved. Matematika* **1961**, *no.* 3 (22), 66–79.

Es sei $Z$ der Ring aller ganzen rationalen Zahlen; $Z$ kann topologisiert werden, indem man jedes von Null verschiedene Hauptideal als Umgebung der Zahl Null betrachtet. Die Menge $Z$ kann man metrisieren; die vollständige Hülle $\mathfrak{S}$ von $Z$ ist der Ring von polyadischen Zahlen. Die Menge $\mathfrak{S}$ ist gleichzeitig eine bikompakte topologische Gruppe; also gibt es ein reguläres normiertes invariantes Mass $\mu$, welches auf offenen Borelschen Teilmengen von $\mathfrak{S}$ positiv ist. In bezug auf dieses Mass kann man das invariante Integral konstruieren. Für jede begrenzte fast überall stetige Funktion $f(x)$ auf $\mathfrak{S}$ gilt

$$\int f(x)\,dx = \lim_{n\to\infty} n^{-1}\sum_{i=1}^{n} f(i).$$

Für einige Funktionen auf $\mathfrak{S}$ hat der Verfasser das Integral berechnet. Auf Grund der oben angeführten Formel werden die Limites gewisser Funktionen abgeleitet.

Es sei $N$ die Menge aller natürlichen Zahlen. Für jede Menge $M \subseteq N$ werden die äussere und innere Dichte durch die Formeln

$$\pi^*(M) = \mu(\bar{M}), \qquad \pi_*(M) = 1-\mu(\overline{N-M})$$

erklärt, wo $\bar{P}$ die abgeschlossene Hülle der Menge $P \subseteq \mathfrak{S}$ bedeutet. Es wird gezeigt, dass die Funktionen $\pi_*$, $\pi^*$ ähnliche Eigenschaften wie das innere und äussere Mass haben; die Menge $M \subseteq N$, für welche $\pi_*(M) = \pi^*(N)$ gilt, heisst bi-messbar. Es sei $n \in N$, $M \subseteq N$; mit $M(n)$ wollen wir die Mächtigkeit der Menge $\{m \mid m \in M, m \leqq n\}$ bezeichnen. Die obere und untere asymptotische Dichte der Menge $M \subseteq N$ werden durch die Formeln

$$\tilde{\pi}(M) = \limsup n^{-1}M(n), \quad \underset{\sim}{\pi}(M) = \liminf n^{-1}M(n)$$

erklärt. Für jede Menge $M \subseteq N$ ist $\pi_*(M) \leqq \underset{\sim}{\pi}(M) \leqq \tilde{\pi}(M) \leqq \pi^*(M)$. Eine Bedingung wird angegeben, unter welcher die asymptotische Dichte der Menge $M$ gleich Null ist. Aus dieser wird eine Reihe von Folgerungen abgeleitet.

*M. Novotný* (Brno)

Referred to in Q15-13, Q25-24.

**Q25-18** **(28# 78)**

**Novoselov, E. V.**

**Foundations of classical analysis and of the theory of analytic functions in a polyadic region. (Russian)**

*Izv. Vysš. Učebn. Zaved. Matematika* **1963**, *no.* 5 (36), 71–88.

Mit $\mathfrak{S}$ werden wir den vollständigen metrischen Ring von polyadischen Zahlen bezeichnen (vgl. das oben stehende Referat #77). Es ist möglich die Theorie von unendlichen Folgen und Reihen in $\mathfrak{S}$ zu konstruieren. Ausser Sätzen, welche den Sätzen der klassischen Analysis analog sind, enthält diese Theorie auch Sätze, zu welchen es keine Analogien gibt; z.B. notwendig und hinreichend für die Konvergenz der Reihe $\sum_{n=1}^{\infty}\alpha_n$ ist die Bedingung $\lim \alpha_n = 0$. Die Menge aller Punkte in $\mathfrak{S}$, in welchen eine Potenzreihe konvergiert, ist ein Hauptideal des Ringes $\mathfrak{S}$; dabei ist die Konvergenz gleichmässig, also ist die Summe der Reihe auf dem Hauptideal stetig. Eine Potenzreihe $\sum_{k=0}^{\infty}\alpha_k x^k$, für welche $\alpha_k \in \mathfrak{S}$ und $\lim \alpha_k = 0$ gilt, konvergiert in $\mathfrak{S}$ und ihre Summe heisst analytische Funktion. Die Struktur einer auf $\mathfrak{S}$ analytischen Funktion wird mit Hilfe von gewissen analytischen Funktionen einer reellen Veränderlichen beschrieben. Ist $f(x)$ eine analytische Funktion, so ist unter gewissen Bedingungen auch die Funktion $f^{-1}(x)$ analytisch. Die Übersicht einiger analytischen Funktionen wird angegeben. Mit Hilfe dieser Funktionen wird die Struktur der multiplikativen Gruppe von Einheiten des Ringes $\mathfrak{S}$ studiert.

*M. Novotný* (Brno)

Referred to in Q15-13.

**Q25-19** **(28# 1193)**

**Amice, Yvette**

**Séries d'interpolation sur un corps valué complet.**

*C. R. Acad. Sci. Paris* **256** (1963), 1650–1651.

Let $K$ be a field of characteristic 0, complete relative to a valuation $|x|$, $A$ the valuation ring of $K$, $E$ a Banach space over $K$, and $N$ the set of all integers $\geqq 0$. The family $(e_n)_{n\in N}$ is called a basis of $E$ if every $x \in E$ has a unique representation $x = \sum x_n e_n$, where $|x_n| \to 0$ as $n \to \infty$. The basis is called orthonormal if in addition $\|x\| = \sup |x_n|$. (I) Let $L(A)$ be the Banach space of all analytic functions $f(x) = \sum w_n x^n$ for $x \in A$, with norm $\|f\| = \sup |w_n|$; further, let $(u_n)_{n\in N}$ be a sequence of distinct points of $A$. Then the polynomials $p_0 = 1$, $p_n = (x-u_0)(x-u_1)\cdots(x-u_{n-1})$ for $n \geqq 1$, form a basis of $L(A)$. (II) Let $C$ be the Banach space of continuous functions on the $p$-adic integers with values in a finite algebraic extension of the $p$-adic field, and let $\|f\| = \max |f(x)|$. Any sequence of polynomials $q_n$ of degrees $\deg q_n = n$ forms a basis of $C$ if and only if $0 < \liminf \|q_n\| \leqq \limsup \|q_n\| < \infty$. The sequence is orthonormal if and only if $\|q_n\| = 1$ for $n \in N$. The special sequence where $q_0 = 1$, $q_n(x) = p_n(x)/p_n(u_n)$ is orthonormal if and only if $|p_n(u_n)| = n!$ for $n \in N$.

*K. Mahler* (Canberra)

**Q25-20** **(28# 1194)**

**Amice, Yvette**

**Interpolation des fonctions continues sur la boule unité d'un corps valué complet localement compact.**

*C. R. Acad. Sci. Paris* **256** (1963), 2742–2744.

Let the notation be as in the preceding review [#1193], and let $C(A, L)$ be the Banach space of all functions continuous on $A$ and with values in a finite extension $L$ of $K$, with the norm $\|f\| = \sup |f(x)|$. Let $(u_n)$ be a sequence of distinct elements of $A$, and let $f_n$ be that polynomial of degree $\leqq n$ for which $f(u_j) = f_n(u_j)$ $(j = 0, 1, 2, \cdots, n)$. If, for all $f \in C(A, L)$, $\|f_n - f\| \to 0$ as $n \to \infty$, $(u_n)$ is said to be a sequence of interpolation. The author states necessary and sufficient conditions for this to be the case. Her result includes the reviewer's [J. Reine Angew. Math. **208** (1961), 70–72; MR **25** #3035]. *K. Mahler* (Canberra)

Citations: MR 25# 3035 = Q25-12.

Referred to in K40-45.

**Q25-21** **(32# 4350)**

**Clark, D. N.**

**A note on the $p$-adic convergence of solutions of linear differential equations.**

*Proc. Amer. Math. Soc.* **17** (1966), 262–269.

Consider the $p$-adic differential equation in one variable

$$A_n(x)y^{(n)} + \cdots + A_0(x)y = C(x),$$

where the $A_i(x)$ are $p$-adic power series with non-zero radius of convergence in the $p$-adic sense, and suppose the coefficients of the $A_i$ are algebraic over the rationals $\mathbf{Q}$, while the coefficients of $C$ satisfy a mild growth condition. Then it is proved that any formal power series solution (even around a non-regular singular point) has a non-zero radius of convergence. The essential step is to estimate $\mathrm{ord}_p(\alpha+s)!$, where $\alpha$ is algebraic and $s$ is a positive integer, by using Newton polygons.

*A. Mattuck* (Cambridge, Mass.)

**Q25-22** **(32# 4645 )**

**Kurepa, Đuro**

**On $p$-adic spaces of Hensel.**

*Publ. Inst. Math. (Beograd) (N.S.)* **5 (19)** (1965), 133–135.

The space of rationals $Q$ with the $p$-adic norm given by $\|0\|=0$, $\|r\|=\theta^{-r'}$, where $r'$ denotes the index of $p$ in $r$ (reduced to lowest terms), is the space $Q(\theta, p)$. The principal result is that the spaces $Q(\theta, p)$ and $Q(\theta, q)$ are isometric for any two primes $p$, $q$, while $Q(\theta, p)$ is $C$-homeomorphic to $Q(p^{-1}, p)$, that is, connected by a homeomorphism which preserves Cauchy sequences.

Consequently, the Hensel spaces, obtained by completing the $Q(p^{-1}, p)$, are homeomorphic.

*V. S. Krishnan* (Buffalo, N.Y.)

**Q25-23** **(32# 5638 )**

**Amice, Yvette**

**Interpolation $p$-adique.**

*Bull. Soc. Math. France* **92** (1964), 117–180.

The author begins with a long discussion of "very well distributed sequences" in a "compact, regular valued set $M$" in a "regular projective system". (The latter two concepts are straightforward generalizations of the concept of a compact subset of the ring of $p$-adic integers $Z_p$. "Well distributed" means that for each $n$, the set $\{u_1, \cdots, u_n\}$ is equally distributed among the neighborhoods of the same size; e.g., the sequence of positive integers is well distributed in $Z_p$.) With each sequence $\{u_n\}$ in a compact regular valued set $M$ of a local field $K$ and each function $f$ from $M$ to $K$ is associated a sequence of interpolation polynomials, namely, $f_n=\sum_{k=0}^{n-1} a_kQ_k$, where $Q_k=\prod_{j=0}^{k}(x-u_j)/(u_k-u_j)$ and the $a_k$ depend on $f$. A sequence $\{u_n\}$ in $M$ is said to be an interpolation series if for each $f$ in $C(M, K)$, the ring of continuous functions from $M$ to $K$, one has (1) $\lim_{n\to\infty}|f-f_n|=0$ and (2) $|f|\leq 1$ implies $|f_n|\leq 1$ for all $n$. The author proves that the following are equivalent: (a) $\{u_n\}$ is an interpolation series for $C(M, K)$; (b) $|Q_n|=1$ for all $n$; (c) $\{u_n\}$ is very well distributed in $M$; (d) $\{Q_n\}$ is a normal basis for $C(M, K)$. This result generalizes a theorem of K. Mahler [J. Reine Angew. Math. **199** (1958), 23–34; MR **20** #2321] which states that a $p$-adic valued function continuous on $Z_p$ is the sum of the uniformly convergent series $\sum_0^\infty a_n\binom{x}{n}$, where

$$a_n = \sum_{k=0}^{n} (-1)^{n-k}\binom{n}{k}f(k).$$

The author also proves some very general results regarding locally analytic functions on $M$. Typical is the following specialized result: Let

$$f(x) = \sum a_n n!\binom{x}{n}, \qquad a_n \in Q_p;$$

then (a) $f$ is continuous on $Z_p$ if and only if $\lim_n \operatorname{ord}(a_n n!)\to\infty$; (b) $f$ is locally analytic on $Z_p$ if and only if

$$\lim \frac{\operatorname{ord}(a_n)}{n} > -\frac{1}{p-1};$$

(c) there are conditions giving the radius of convergence of $f$ at any $x\in Z_p$.

The author also discusses continuous and locally analytic functions of several variables. The paper abounds with misprints. *D. J. Lewis* (Ann Arbor, Mich.)

Citations: MR 20# 2321 = Q25-11.

Referred to in Q25-32, Q25-34, Z10-30, Z10-55.

**Q25-24** **(35# 2863 )**

**Čudakov, N. G.**

**Periodic number-theoretic functions.** **(Russian)**

*Certain Problems in the Theory of Fields (Russian), pp.* 3–5. *Izdat. Saratov. Univ., Saratov,* 1964.

The author proves that each periodic finite-valued function defined on the ring $Z$ of integers has a continuous extension to the ring $\gamma$ of polyadic numbers, previously studied by E. V. Novoselov [Izv. Vysš. Učebn. Zaved. Matematika **1961**, no. 3 (22), 66–79; MR **28** #77]. Conversely, each continuous function on $\gamma$ is periodic on $Z$. Moreover, the primitive Dirichlet characters form an orthogonal system over $\gamma$. *Á. Császár* (Budapest)

Citations: MR 28# 77 = Q25-17.

**Q25-25** **(37# 6261 )**

**Amice, Yvette**

**Interpolation $p$-adique.**

*Les Tendances Géom. en Algèbre et Théorie des Nombres, pp.* 15–25. *Éditions du Centre National de la Recherche Scientifique, Paris,* 1966.

K. Mahler [J. Reine Angew. Math. **199** (1958), 23–34; MR **20** #2321] proved that a continuous function from the ring of $p$-adic integers into the $p$-adic numbers was the uniform limit of series $\sum_{n=0}^{\infty} a_n\binom{x}{n}$, where

$$a_n = \sum_{j=0}^{n}(-1)^{n-j}\binom{n}{j}f(j).$$

The author extends this result to valued fields which are complete and locally compact, where the functions $f$ have as domain a compact "regular" subset of the field, a set $M$ being "regular" if it is the projective limit of sets $M_n$ with surjective mappings $\phi_{n,k}: M_n\to M_k$, card $M_0=1$, and for each $q$ there is an integer $q_k$ such that for each $\alpha$ in $M_{k-1}$, $\operatorname{card}[\phi_{k,k-1}^{-1}(\alpha)]=q_k$. The functions $\binom{x}{n}$ are replaced by polynomials defined in terms of a dense sequence $\{u_n\}$ in $M$. Properties of locally analytic functions are studied.

*D. J. Lewis* (Ann Arbor, Mich.)

Citations: MR 20# 2321 = Q25-11.

**Q25-26** **(38# 114 )**

**Durix, Marie-Claude**

**Prolongement de la fonction exponentielle en dehors de son disque de convergence.**

*Séminaire Delange-Pisot-Poitou:* 1966/67, *Théorie des Nombres, Fasc.* 1, *Exp.* 1, 12 *pp. Secrétariat mathématique, Paris,* 1968.

The author shows that the exponential function over a $p$-adic field can be extended from its domain of convergence to the entire $p$-adic field in such a way that the functional equation is preserved. There are many ways of doing this. *W. W. Adams* (Berkeley, Calif.)

**Q25-27** **(39# 5529)**

**Helsmoortel, Ève**

**Module de continuité de polynômes d'interpolation. Application à l'étude du comportement local des fonctions continues sur un compact régulier d'un corps local.**

*C. R. Acad. Sci. Paris Sér. A-B* **268** (1969), A1168–A1171.

The author announces the following result: Let $A$ be the valuation ring of a local field and let $M$ be a compact, regular set of $A$. Let $\{u_n\}$ be a partition of $M$ and $\{Q_n(x)\}$ be the associated sequence of interpolation polynomials for $M$. If $f(x)=\sum a_nQ_n(x)$ is continuous in $M$ and if $|a_n|$ tends to 0 at an appropriate rate, then $f$ satisfies a Lipschitz condition. *D. J. Lewis* (Ann Arbor, Mich.)

Referred to in Q25-32.

**Q25-28** **(39# 6860)**

**Sarmant, Marie-Claude**

**Prolongement de la fonction exponentielle en dehors de son cercle de convergence.**

*C. R. Acad. Sci. Paris Sér. A-B* **269** (1969), A123–A125.

Suppose that $K_p$ is a finite extension of ramification degree $e$ over the field of $p$-adic numbers $Q_p$. Let $A_k=\{a|a\in K_p;\ |a|_p<p^{k/e}\}$. Then there exists on each $A_k$ a function which is a prolongation of the usual exponential function of $K_p$. For the proof one notes that, if $f$ is the residue class degree of $K_p$, there exist $f$ independent elements $\omega_1{}^k, \cdots, \omega_f{}^k$ of $A_k$ such that each coset of $A_k/A_{k-1}$ is a linear combination of the $\omega_i{}^k$ with coefficients $c$ satisfying $0\leqq c\leqq p-1$. If one selects for each $\omega_i{}^k=\omega_i{}^{-m-r}/p^q$, $k=-m+eq+r$, $r<e$, $\exp \omega_i{}^k$ such that

$$[\exp(\omega_i{}^{-m+r}p^{-q})]^p = \exp(\omega_i{}^{-m+r}p^{q-1}),$$

one obtains on each $A_k$ a function which is a prolongation of the exponential function.

*O. F. G. Schilling* (Lafayette, Ind.)

**Q25-29** **(41# 3435)**

**Monna, A. F.**

**Real and $p$-adic numbers considered from a topological standpoint. (Dutch)**

*Euclides (Groningen)* **41** (1965/66), 169–176.

The author discusses the elementary properties of the field of $p$-adic numbers and points out that, by virtue of Pontrjagin's characterization of locally compact connected topological fields, it is distinguished from the real field in an essential way through not being connected.

**Q25-30** **(41# 6792)**

**Decomps-Guilloux, Annette; Motzkin-Elhanan**

**Fonctions analytiques univalentes dans un corps ultramétrique complet algébriquement clos.**

*C. R. Acad. Sci. Paris Sér. A-B* **268** (1969), A1531–A1533.

Let $\Omega$ be the completion of the algebraic closure of the rational $p$-adic field $\mathbf{Q}_p$. The authors study analytic functions $f$ defined in a disk or an annulus of $\Omega$. Using the Newton and Straus polygons, they give the number of zeros of $f(x)-a$ for suitable $a$ when $x$ ranges over an open disk interior to the disk of convergence and when $x$ lies on the circumference of such a disk. Their main theorem is one which gives necessary and sufficient conditions for a power series [a Laurent series] to define a univalent function in a disk [an annulus]. As a consequence of this theorem, they show that the image of an open disk [a closed disk] is open [closed] under a univalent $f$. If the disk of univalence is the unit disk, they prove that the function induced on the residue field is linear. Finally, they give the following criterion for $f$ to be a bijection from the open [closed] unit disk to itself: If $f(x)=\sum_{n=0}^{\infty} u_nx^n$, then $f$ is a bijection from the open [closed] unit disk to itself if and only if $|u_0|<1$, $|u_n|\leqq|u_1|=1$ [$|u_n|<|u_1|=1$] for every $n$.

*S. S. Shatz* (Philadelphia, Pa.)

**Q25-31** **(42# 5918)**

**Gout, Gérard**

**Sur les fonctions exponentielles des corps locaux.**

*C. R. Acad. Sci. Paris Sér. A-B* **271** (1970), A984–A986.

A continuous homomorphism of an open subgroup $D$ of a local field $K$ into the multiplicative group $K^*$ is called exponential function. The set of all exponential functions of a fixed $D$ is denoted by $E(D)$. For $K$ of characteristic zero and of finite degree $d$ over $\mathbf{Q}_p$, let $R$ be the maximal compact subring of $K$ and $P$ the maximal ideal of $R$. With these notations, numerous results are stated, among which are the following: For $0\leqq n\in Z$, $(1+P)^{p^n}\subset 1+P^{n+1}$. $e\in E(D)$ implies $e(D)\subset 1+P$. If $a\in 1+P$, then there exists a unique, continuous homomorphism of $\mathbf{Z}_p$ into $1+P$, which is a continuation of the mapping $n\mapsto a^n$ defined on $\mathbf{Z}$. Every closed subgroup of $K$ is a $\mathbf{Z}_p$-module. Let $\nu_i$ $(1\leqq i\leqq d)$ be a base of $K$ over $\mathbf{Q}_p$ and let $D$ be an open subgroup of $K$; then $D=\sum_{i=1}^r \mathbf{Z}_p\nu_i+\sum_{i=r+1}^d \mathbf{Q}_p\nu_i$ ($r=$ rank of $D$ as a $\mathbf{Z}_p$-module). Every exponential of $E(D)$ is of the form $x\mapsto\prod_{i=1}^r a_i^{x_i}$, with $a_i\in 1+P$ $(1\leqq i\leqq r)$ and $x=\sum_{i=1}^d x_i\nu_i\in D$, and $E(D)$ is isomorphic to the direct product of $r$ groups isomorphic to $1+P$. $E(D)$ contains injective exponentials if and only if $D$ is a $\mathbf{Q}_p$-lattice. If $e\in E(D)$ is injective, then the exact sequence $0\to \mathrm{Im}(e)\to 1+P\to\Gamma\to 0$ splits ($\Gamma=$ group of roots of unity, whose order is a power of $p$). If $e\in E(D)$, $D\subset D'$ ($D$, $D'$ open subgroups of $K$), then necessary and sufficient conditions are indicated for the existence of a continuation of $e(D)$ to $e(D')$. Specifically, the existence of such a continuation to a $\mathbf{Q}_p$-lattice containing $D$ depends on the existence in $1+P$ of roots of unity of order $p^n$. If $\overline{\mathbf{Q}}_p$ is an algebraic closure of $\mathbf{Q}_p$ and $D$ is a $\mathbf{Q}_p$-lattice of $K$, then the set of homomorphisms of $K$ into $\overline{\mathbf{Q}}_p{}^x$ that are continuations of the exponentials $E(D)$ form a group isomorphic to $E(D)\times(1+P)^d\times\mathbf{Z}_p{}^d$. *E. Grosswald* (Philadelphia, Pa.)

**Q25-32** **(42# 5953)**

**Helsmoortel, Ève**

**Comportement local des fonctions continues sur un compact régulier d'un corps local.**

*C. R. Acad. Sci. Paris Sér. A-B* **271** (1970), A546–A548.

Let $K$ be a local field, $A$ the valuation ring of the valuation $v$, $\pi$ a uniformizing parameter, $M$ a regular compact set (for its definition see the paper by Y. Amice [Bull. Soc. Math. France **92** (1964), 117–180, especially p. 134; MR **32** #5638]), where $M=\varprojlim M_k$, $k\in\mathbf{N}$, Card $M_0=1$, Card $M_k\in N_k$, $k\geqq 1$, $N_k=q_1\cdots q_k$, $\mathbf{N}$ being the set of natural numbers. For $n\in N$, $h(n)$ is defined by $N_{h(n)-1}\leqq n<N_{h(n)}$. Let $f\in\mathscr{C}(M,A)$, the ring of continuous functions from $M$ to $A$. The interpolation coefficients of $f$ over the so-called TBRBO sequence $u$ [see the author, C. R. Acad. Sci. Paris Sér. A-B **268** (1969), A1168–A1171; MR **39** #5529] are denoted by $a_n$. By means of the above mentioned TBRBO sequences over $M$ (defined in the paper of the author [loc. cit.], using a concept of Amice [loc. cit.]), one gives some characterizations for $f$ to be lipschitzian, differentiable and continuously and uniformly differentiable in a point of $M$ or in $M$. Among these characterizations one finds the following: (i) there exists $C$ such that

$v(a_n)-h(n)v(\pi)\geqq C$ if and only if $f$ is lipschitzian in $M$. (ii) $v(a_n)-h(n)v(\pi)\to\infty$ when $n\to\infty$ implies $f$ is continuously and uniformly differentiable in $M$. (iii) $v(a_n)-mh(n)v(\pi)\to\infty$ when $n\to\infty$ implies $f$ is $m$ times uniformly continuously differentiable in $M$. *P. Abellanas* (Madrid)

Citations: MR 32# 5638 = Q25-23; MR 39# 5529 = Q25-27.

## Q25-33 (43# 184 )

**Lenskoĭ, D. N.**

**Integral functions that are bounded on a locally compact nonarchimedean normed field.** (Russian)

*Studies in Number Theory, No. 3 (Russian), pp.* 51–56. *Izdat. Saratov. Univ., Saratov*, 1969.

Let $\Omega$ be an algebraically closed field complete with respect to a non-archimedean norm and let $K$ be a locally compact subfield of $K$. It is known that some entire functions defined over $\Omega$ are bounded on $K$. In the present paper a condition is given which is sufficient for an entire function defined over $\Omega$ to be bounded on $K$. *E. Inaba* (Tokyo)

## Q25-34 (43# 3218 )

**Levron, François**

**Polynômes de Tchebycheff en analyse $p$-adique.**

*C. R. Acad. Sci. Paris Sér. A-B* **271** (1970), A1052–A1053.

Soient $K$ un corps valué non archimédien complet, $M$ un compact de $K$, et soit $\mathscr{C}(M,K)$ l'espace de Banach des fonctions continues de $M$ dans $K$ muni de la norme de la convergence uniforme. On dit qu'une famille $(e_i)_{i\in I}$ d'éléments de $\mathscr{C}(M,K)$ est une base pseudo-normale de $\mathscr{C}(M,K)$ si tout $f\in\mathscr{C}(M,K)$ admet une décomposition unique $f=\sum_{i\in I}x_ie_i$ avec $\|f\|=\sup_{i\in I}\|x_ie_i\|$, où $x_i\in K$ pour tout $i\in I$. On appelle polynôme de Čebyšev de $M$ de degré $n$ tout polynôme de $M$ de norme minimale parmi les polynômes unitaires de $M$ de degré $n$ [F. Bertrandias, Séminaire Delange-Pisot, 5<sup>e</sup> année (1963–64): *Théorie des nombres*, Exp. 3, Secrétariat mathématique, Paris, 1967; see MR **35** #6503]. L'auteur énonce le résultat suivant: Soit $(Q_n)_{n\in\mathbf{N}}$ une suite de polynômes unitaires de $M$ à coefficients dans $K$ et à degrés croissants; pour que $(Q_n)$ soit une base pseudo-normale de $\mathscr{C}(M,K)$, il faut et il suffit que $(Q_n)$ soit une suite de polynômes de Čebyšev de $M$. Soit maintenant $(u_n)_{n\in\mathbf{N}}$ une suite injective d'éléments de $M$, et soit $(P_n)_{n\in\mathbf{N}}$ la suite de polynômes unitaires de $M$ définie par $P_0(x)=1$, $P_n(x)=\prod_{1\leq k\leq n}(x-u_{k-1})$ pour tout $n\geqq 1$. Étendant une définition antérieure, qui s'appliquait seulement au cas d'un compact $M$ régulier [Y. Amice, Bull. Soc. Math. France **92** (1964), 117–180; MR **32** #5638], on dit que la suite $(u_n)$ est très bien répartie (t.b.r.) dans $M$ si, pour tout couple d'entiers $(k,n)$ tel que $k\leqq n$, on a $\|P_n\|\leqq|P'_{n+1}(u_k)|$, où $P'_{n+1}$ désigne le polynôme dérivé de $P_{n+1}$. Enfin, à tout $f\in\mathscr{C}(M,K)$, on associe la suite $(f_n)_{n\in\mathbf{N}}$ des polynômes d'interpolation de $f$ sur la suite $(u_n)$. L'auteur énonce alors le résultat constitué par l'équivalence des quatre propriétés suivantes: (a) on a $\|P_n\|=|P_n(u_n)|$ pour tout $n\in\mathbf{N}$; (b) on a $\sup_{n\in\mathbf{N}}\|f_n\|\leqq\|f\|$ pour tout $f\in\mathscr{C}(M,K)$; (c) la suite $(u_n)_{n\in\mathbf{N}}$ est t.b.r. dans $M$; (d) la suite $(P_n)_{n\in\mathbf{N}}$ est une suite de polynômes de Čebyšev de $M$. *J. Chauvineau* (Paris)

Citations: MR 32# 5638 = Q25-23; MR 35# 6503 = Z10-31.

## Q25-35 (43# 3504 )

**Adams, W. W.; Straus, E. G.**

**Non-archimedian analytic functions taking the same values at the same points.**

*Illinois J. Math.* **15** (1971), 418–424.

The authors study the theory of analytic functions in which the variable ranges over a non-archimedean valued complete algebraically closed field with characteristic zero, proving theorems that are analogous to the following theorem of Nevanlinna in complex function theory: "Suppose that $f_1$ and $f_2$ are meromorphic in the plane and let $E_j(a)=\{z|f_j(z)=a\}$ $(j=1,2)$; then if $E_1(a)=E_2(a)$ for five distinct values of $a$, $f_1(z)\equiv f_2(z)$ or $f_1$ and $f_2$ are both constant". Among their results are the following theorems. (A) Let $f$ and $g$ be two non-constant entire functions of a non-archimedean variable such that for two distinct (finite) values $a$ and $b$ we have $f(x)=a$ if and only if $g(x)=a$ and $f(x)=b$ if and only if $g(x)=b$; then $f\equiv g$. (B) Let $f$ and $g$ be two non-constant meromorphic functions of a non-archimedean variable such that for four distinct values $a_1,a_2,a_3,a_4$ we have $f(x)=a_i$ if and only if $g(x)=a_i$; $i=1,2,3,4$; then $f\equiv g$. There are analogous theorems for functions defined in an annulus.

Proofs are given by means of the maximum-modulus principle in non-archimedean function theory and some other general results in the theory of non-archimedean analytic functions. *A. F. Monna* (Utrecht)

## Q25-36 (43# 4803 )

**Lenskoĭ, D. N.**

**A note on Strassman's theorem.** (Russian)

*Studies in Number Theory, No. 3 (Russian), pp.* 57–63. *Izdat. Saratov. Univ., Saratov*, 1969.

Let $K$ be an algebraically closed field complete with respect to a non-archimedean norm and consider the function $f(x)$ defined by a power series $\sum_{n=0}^{\infty}a_n(x-x_0)^n$, $a_n\in K$. Denote by $D_f$ the set of real numbers $r$ such that the series converges for $|x-x_0|=r$. From Strassman's theorem one can infer that the set $\{x\in K\,|\,|x-x_0|=r\}$, where $r\in D_f$, contains a zero of $f(x)$ if and only if $\mathrm{Max}(|a_n|r^n)$ is attained by at least two terms in the sequence $\{|a_n|r^n\}$. Such an $r$ is called a critical point of $f(x)$ [R. Strassmann, J. Reine Angew. Math. **159** (1929), 13–28]. It is known that the set of critical points is finite or countable and that in the latter case the radius of convergence is the single accumulation point of the set [the author, *Functions in non-Archimedean normed fields* (Russian), Izdat. Saratov. Univ., Saratov, 1962; MR **27** #2498]. In the present paper he shows how the critical points can be expressed in terms of the coefficients of the series. *E. Inaba* (Tokyo)

## Q25-37 (44# 213 )

**Sarmant, Marie-Claude**

**Fonctions automorphes dans un corps valué non archimédien.**

*Séminaire Delange-Pisot-Poitou:* 1969/70, *Théorie des Nombres, Fasc.* 1, *Exp.* 11, 8 *pp. Secrétariat mathématique, Paris*, 1970.

The author gives some theorems concerning automorphic functions defined over a non-archimedean complete and algebraically closed field. The theorems are of the following type: An automorphic function that has only one pole and one zero in a set $r\leqq|x|\leqq|\lambda|r$ is a constant, and if the function $f$ has only a finite number of poles and zeros in this set then there are two polynomials $g$ and $h$ such that $f(x)=k\prod_{n\in Z}g(\lambda^nx)h^{-1}(\lambda^nx)$. Theorems concerning the algebraic dependence of automorphic functions are also given. One has to compare this note with the results of M. Lazard [Inst. Hautes Études Sci. Publ. Math. No. 14 (1962), 47–75; MR **27** #2497], P. Roquette [*Analytic theory of elliptic functions over local fields*, Vandenhoeck & Ruprecht, Göttingen, 1970; MR **41** #5376] and A. F.

Monna [*Analyse non-archimédienne*, Chapitre II, Ergeb. Math. Grenzgeb., Band 56, Springer, Berlin, 1970].
*F. van der Blij* (Bilthoven)

Citations: MR 41# 5376 = G20-44.

## Q25-38 (44# 6650)

**Barsky, Daniel**
**Formes linéaires $p$-adiques.**
*Séminaire Delange-Pisot-Poitou:* 1969/70, *Théorie des Nombres, Fasc.* 1, *Exp.* 2, 8 *pp. Secrétariat mathématique, Paris,* 1970.

The author describes a formula for $p$-adic functions that is an analogue of the Cauchy integral formula from complex analysis. *D. G. Cantor* (Los Angeles, Calif.)

## Q25-39 (44# 6658)

**Wagner, Carl G.**
**Linear operators in local fields of prime characteristic.**
*J. Reine Angew. Math.* **251** (1971), 153–160.

K. Mahler gave a new and very interesting proof of Weierstrass' approximation theorem for a continuous $p$-adic function defined on the ring of $p$-adic integers [same J. **199** (1958), 23–34; MR **20** #2321]. In this paper the author gives an analogue of Mahler's theorem for local fields for finite characteristic. The main theorem is the following. Let $f$ be a continuous linear operator on the vector space $K[[x]]$ of formal power series in one variable over the finite field $K$. Then the series $\sum_0^\infty \Delta^i f(1)\cdot\psi_i(t)/F_i$, where $\Delta^i$'s are defined recursively, $F_i$ is the product of all monic polynomials over GF($q$) of degree $i$ and $\psi_i(t)=\prod_{\deg m<n}(t-m)$, $m$ in $K[x]$, converge uniformly to $f$ on $K[[x]]$. Moreover the coefficients are uniquely determined by $f$. The author also shows that if $f$ is as above and $L=(x^{q^i}-x)(x^{q^{i-1}}-x)\cdots(x^q-x)$, $L_0=1$, is a null sequence then $f$ is everywhere differentiable in $K[[x]]$ and $f'(t)=\sum_0^\infty(-1)^i\,{}^if(1)/L_i$. In case $f$ is differentiable at 0 then the above sequence is a null sequence.
*N. Sankaran* (Chandigarh)

The next to the last sentence should read as follows. The author also shows that if $f$ is as above, $L_i=(x^{q^i}-x)(x^{q^{i-1}}-x)\cdots(x^q-x)$, $L_0=1$ and $(\Delta^i f(1)/L_i)$ is a null sequence, then $f$ is everywhere differentiable in $K[[x]]$ and $f'(t)=\sum_0^\infty(-1)^i\Delta^i f(1)/L_i$.

Citations: MR 20# 2321 = Q25-11.

# Q99 NONE OF THE ABOVE, BUT IN THIS CHAPTER

See also reviews A22-10, A22-41, A26-45, B36-98, B80-40, D99-3, J76-17, K25-16.

## Q99-1 (17, 128a)

**de Bruijn, N. G. Some classes of integer-valued functions.** Nederl. Akad. Wetensch. Proc. Ser. A. **58**= Indag. Math. **17** (1955), 363–367.

An integer-valued function $f(x)$ is called universal if it has the property that

$$(*)\qquad f(x+m)-f(x)\equiv 0 \pmod m$$

for all $x=0, 1, 2, \cdots$ and $m=1, 2, 3, \cdots$. It is proved that $f(x)$ is universal if and only if it has the form

$$f(x)=c_0+s_1c_1\binom{x}{1}+s_2c_2\binom{x}{2}+\cdots,$$

where the $c$'s are integers and $s_k$ is the least common multiple of $1, 2, \cdots, k$. Call $f(x)$ modular if (*) holds for all $m$ without the restriction $x\geqq 0$. It is shown by an example that modular extension of a universal function is not always possible. Also it is proved that $f(x)$ is modular if and only if

$$f(x)=c_0+\sum_1^\infty s_kc_k\binom{x+[k/2]}{k},$$

where the $c$'s are integers. Finally it is proved that a function $f(x_1, \cdots, x_n)$ is universal if and only if in the representation

$$f(x_1, \cdots, x_n)=\sum_0^\infty b(k_1, \cdots, k_n)\binom{x_1}{k_1}\cdots\binom{x_n}{k_n},$$

each $b(k_1, \cdots, k_n)$ is a multiple of $s_t$, where

$$t=\max(k_1, \cdots, k_n).$$

The author wishes to point out that the results of the present paper are closely related to Theorems 1 and 2 of E. G. Straus, Duke Math. J. **19** (1952), 379–395 [MR **14**, 21]. In this connection see also L. Rédei and T. Szele, Acta Math. **79** (1947), 291–320 [MR **9**, 407]. *L. Carlitz.*

Citations: MR 9, 407e = T30-1; MR 14, 21d = B48-3.
Referred to in A22-120, C05-21.

## Q99-2 (20# 6488)

**Mordell, L. J. Integral formulae of arithmetical character.** J. London Math. Soc. **33** (1958), 371–375.

Let $f_i(x)$ be definedfor $x\geqq 0$. Assume that $f_i(x)$ satisfies the functional relation

$$f_i(x)+f_i\left(x+\frac{1}{k}\right)+\cdots+f_i\left(x+\frac{k-1}{k}\right)=f_i^{(k)}f(kx),$$

where $f_i^{(k)}$ is a constant independent of $x$. Let $a_1, \cdots, a_n$ be a set of relatively prime integers; put $A=a_1a_2\cdots a_n$, $\{x\}=x-[x]$. The author proves that, if the integrals exist, then

$$\int_0^A f_1\left(\left\{\frac{x}{a_1}\right\}\right)f_2\left(\left\{\frac{x}{a_2}\right\}\right)\cdots f_n\left(\left\{\frac{x}{a_n}\right\}\right)dx=$$
$$f_1^{(a_1)}f_2^{(a_2)}\cdots f_n^{(a_n)}\int_0^1 f_1(x)f_2(x)\cdots f_n(x)dx.$$

A special case of this theorem has been proved by Mikolás [Publ. Math. Debrecen **5** (1957), 44–53; MR **19**, 731].
*P. Erdös* (Birmingham)

Citations: MR 19, 731f = M35-10.
Referred to in Q99-3.

## Q99-3 (22# 1549)

**Carlitz, L. Some finite summation formulas of arithmetic character.** Publ. Math. Debrecen **6** (1959), 262–268.

Let $f_1(x), f_2(x), \cdots, f_n(x)$ be functions of $x$ such that for any positive integer $k$ there exists the relation

$$(*)\qquad \sum_{r=0}^{k-1} f_i(x+r/k) = C_i^{(k)}f_i(kx)\quad (i=1, \cdots, n),$$

where $C_i^{(k)}$ is independent of $x$. Three theorems are proved in this paper of which the following is theorem 1. Let $n\geqq 1$ and let $a_1, \cdots, a_n$ be positive integers that are relatively prime in pairs and put $A=a_1a_2\cdots a_n$. Let $f_1(x), \cdots, f_n(x)$ be functions of $x$ of period 1 that satisfy (*). Then if $k$ is an arbitrary positive integer, we have

$$\sum_{r=0}^{kA-1} f_1\left(\frac{r}{a_1k}\right)f_2\left(\frac{r}{a_2k}\right)\cdots f_n\left(\frac{r}{a_nk}\right)=$$
$$C_1^{(a_1)}C_2^{(a_2)}\cdots C_n^{(a_n)}\sum_{r=0}^{k-1} f_1\left(\frac{r}{k}\right)f_2\left(\frac{r}{k}\right)\cdots f_n\left(\frac{r}{k}\right).$$

The proof is very similar to the proof of a related theorem

by Mordell [J. London Math. Soc. **33** (1958), 371–375; **MR 20** #6488] which involves integrals in place of finite sums. Let $B_m(x)$ be the Bernoulli polynomial of degree $m$, and let $\bar{B}_m(x)$ be the corresponding Bernoulli function; let $\zeta(s, x)$ denote the Hurwitz zeta-function. Both $B_m(x)$ and $\zeta(s, x)$ satisfy relations of the form (*). Theorems 2 and 3 are applications of theorem 1 and are derived by putting $n=2$, $f(x)=\bar{B}_m(x)$ and $n=2$, $f(x)=\zeta(s, x)$ respectively. *A. L. Whiteman* (Princeton, N.J.)

Citations: MR 20# 6488 = Q99-2.
Referred to in Q99-4.

## Q99-4 (22# 2579)

**Carlitz, L. Some finite summation formulas of arithmetic character. II.** Acta Math. Acad. Sci. Hungar. **11** (1960), 15–22. (Russian summary, unbound insert)

Extending results of his earlier paper [Publ. Math. Debrecen **6** (1959), 262–268; MR **22** #1549] the author derives a number of arithmetical summation theorems of which the following is representative. Let $n \geqq 1$; $e_1, \cdots, e_n \geqq 1$; let $\zeta_i$ denote a primitive $e_i$th root of unity. Let $f_i(x, \zeta_i)$ be functions that satisfy:

$$(1) \qquad f_i(x+1, \zeta_i) = \zeta_i^{-1} f_i(x, \zeta_i) \quad (i = 1, \cdots, n),$$

$$(2) \qquad \sum_{r=0}^{k-1} \zeta_i^r f_i(x+r/k, \zeta_i) = C_i^{(k)} f_i(kx, \zeta_i),$$

where $C_i^{(k)}$ is independent of $x$ and $k \equiv 1 \pmod{e}$, where $e$ is the least common multiple of $e_1, \cdots, e_n$. Also let $a_1, \cdots, a_n$ be positive integers that are relatively prime in pairs and such that $a_i \equiv 1 \pmod{e}$ $(i=1, \cdots, n)$; put $A = a_1 a_2 \cdots a_n$. Then we have

$$\sum_{r=0}^{kA-1} \zeta_1^r \zeta_2^r \cdots \zeta_n^r f_1(x_1 + r/a_1 k, \zeta_1) \cdots f_n(x_n + r/a_n k, \zeta_n) =$$
$$C \sum_{r=0}^{k-1} \zeta_1^r \zeta_2^r \cdots \zeta_n^r f_1(a_1 x_1 + r/k, \zeta_1) \cdots f_n(a_n x_n + r/k, \zeta_n),$$

where $C = C_1^{(a_1)} C_2^{(a_2)} \cdots C_n^{(a_n)}$. Relations (1) and (2) are suggested by certain functional equations for the Euler polynomials and functions.

*A. L. Whiteman* (Princeton, N.J.)

Citations: MR 22# 1549 = Q99-3.

## Q99-5 (22# 2599)

**Melzak, Z. A. A countable interpolation problem.** Proc. Amer. Math. Soc. **11** (1960), 304–306.

Let $\mathscr{K}$ be the metric space of all order-preserving homeomorphisms $f$ of $I=[0, 1]$ onto itself, the metric being $\rho(f_1, f_2) = \max_I |f_1(x) - f_2(x)|$. Let $\mathscr{K}_\alpha$ $(\alpha > 2)$ be the subset of $\mathscr{K}$ consisting of all functions $f \in \mathscr{K}$ whose values, for algebraic $x \in I$, are either rational or transcendental and approximable to degree $> \alpha$. (I.e., the inequality $|x - p/q| < q^{-d}$ has infinitely many rational integral solutions $p$, $q$, for some $d > \alpha$.) Then it is shown that $\mathscr{K}_\alpha$ is a dense $G_\delta$-set of second category in $\mathscr{K}$. The theorem remains true if "approximable to degree $>\alpha$" is replaced by "a Liouville number".

*W. J. LeVeque* (Ann Arbor, Mich.)

## Q99-6 (22# 6763)

**Sierpiński, W. A general formula on integer-valued functions of an integral variable.** Wiadom. Mat. (2) **2**, 245–248 (1959). (Polish)

The author proves the following: all integer-valued functions $f(x)$ of an integral variable and only such functions are given by the formula

$$(1) \qquad f(x) = c_0 + \sum_{k=1}^{\infty} c_k \binom{x+[\frac{1}{2}k]}{k},$$

where $c_0, c_1, \cdots$ are integers. Furthermore, the representation (1) is unique. *S. Knapowski* (Poznań)

## Q99-7 (27# 3752)

**Neumann, B. H.; Rado, R.**

**Monotone functions mapping the set of rational numbers on itself.**

*J. Austral. Math. Soc.* **3** (1963), 282–287.

The authors produce, by two different constructions, examples of differentiable, strictly monotone, real-valued functions of a real variable which map the set of all rational numbers one-to-one onto itself, and which are not linear. A quite simple construction yields a once-differentiable example; a more elaborate construction produces an example which is the restriction to the real axis of an entire function.

*John W. Green* (Los Angeles, Calif.)

## Q99-8 (31# 3550)

**Heuer, G. A.**

**Functions continuous at the irrationals and discontinuous at the rationals.**

*Amer. Math. Monthly* **72** (1965), 370–373.

Let $f(x)=0$ for irrational $x$, $f(p/q)=|1/q|$ if $p$ and $q$ are relatively prime integers, $f(0)=1$. The author investigates the powers of $f$. For example, he shows that $f^\alpha$ is nowhere Lipschitzian if $0<\alpha<2$, discontinuous at the rational numbers if $\alpha>0$, continuous but not Lipschitzian at the Liouville numbers if $\alpha>0$, and differentiable at every algebraic irrational number if $\alpha>2$ and at none if $0<\alpha\leqq 2$.

*T. M. Apostol* (Pasadena, Calif.)

## Q99-9 (39# 4331)

**Kristensen, Erik**

**Functions which are discontinuous at every rational point.** (**Danish. English summary**)

*Nordisk Mat. Tidskr.* **16** (1968), 150–156, 174–175.

As a consequence of the Thue-Siegel-Roth theorem, the author gives an example of a function which is defined on the real line, discontinuous at all rational points, and differentiable at all algebraic irrationals. He proves further that for every function which is defined on the real line and discontinuous at all rational points, there exists a dense set of irrational points of non-differentiability.

*L. C. Young* (Madison, Wis.)

## Q99-10 (39# 4335)

**Nymann, J. E.**

**An application of Diophantine approximation.**

*Amer. Math. Monthly* **76** (1969), 668–671.

For real positive numbers $a$ define $f^a$ by $f^a(x)=1/n^a$ if $x=m/n$, $\gcd(n, m)=1$ and $n>0$, and $f^a(x)=0$ if $x$ is irrational. It is shown, by easy applications of standard results in diophantine approximation, that if $a\leqq 2$, then $f^a$ is nowhere differentiable, and if $a>2$, then $f$ is differentiable at algebraic irrational points (and also almost everywhere) but that there still exist uncountably many points where $f$ is not differentiable. This last result also holds if $n^a$ is replaced by any positive function of $n$.

*W. W. Adams* (College Park, Md.)